⊘3321651

D1107623

⊘3321651

PIERCE COLLEGE LIBRARY
PUYALLUP WA 98374
LAKEWOOD WA 98498

Hoover's Handbook of

Emerging Companies

2019

HOOVERS™

A D&B COMPANY

Austin, Texas

Hoover's Handbook of Emerging Companies 2019 is intended to provide readers with accurate and authoritative information about the enterprises covered in it. Hoover's researched all companies and organizations profiled, and in many cases contacted them directly so that companies represented could provide information. The information contained herein is as accurate as we could reasonably make it. In many cases we have relied on third-party material that we believe to be trustworthy, but were unable to independently verify. We do not warrant that the book is absolutely accurate or without error. Readers should not rely on any information contained herein in instances where such reliance might cause financial loss. The publisher, the editors, and their data suppliers specifically disclaim all warranties, including the implied warranties of merchantability and fitness for a specific purpose. This book is sold with the understanding that neither the publisher, the editors, nor any content contributors are engaged in providing investment, financial, accounting, legal, or other professional advice.

The financial data (Historical Financials sections) in this book are from a variety of sources. Mergent Inc., provided selected data for the Historical Financials sections of publicly traded companies. For private companies and for historical information on public companies prior to their becoming public, we obtained information directly from the companies or from trade sources deemed to be reliable. Hoover's, Inc., is solely responsible for the presentation of all data.

Many of the names of products and services mentioned in this book are the trademarks or service marks of the companies manufacturing or selling them and are subject to protection under US law. Space has not permitted us to indicate which names are subject to such protection, and readers are advised to consult with the owners of such marks regarding their use. Hoover's is a trademark of Hoover's, Inc.

A D&B COMPANY

Copyright © 2019 by Dun & Bradstreet. All rights reserved. No part of this book may be reproduced or transmitted in any form or by any means, electronic or mechanical, including by photocopying, facsimile transmission, recording, rekeying, or using any information storage and retrieval system, without permission in writing from Hoover's, except that brief passages may be quoted by a reviewer in a magazine, in a newspaper, online, or in a broadcast review.

10 9 8 7 6 5 4 3 2 1

Publishers Cataloging-in-Publication Data
Hoover's Handbook of Emerging Companies 2019
    Includes indexes.
    ISBN: 978-1-64141-144-8
    ISSN 1073-6433
    1. Business enterprises — Directories. 2. Corporations — Directories.
HF3010 338.7

U.S. AND WORLD BOOK SALES

Mergent Inc.

580 Kingsley Park Drive
Fort Mill, SC 29715
Phone: 800-342-5647
e-mail: orders@mergent.com
Web: www.mergentbusinesspress.com

Mergent Inc.

Executive Managing Director: John Pedernales

Publisher and Managing Director of Print Products : Thomas Wecera

Director of Print Products: Charlot Volny

Quality Assurance Editor: Wayne Arnold

Production Research Assistant: Davie Christna

Data Manager: Jason Horvat

MERGENT CUSTOMER SERVICE

Support and Fulfillment Manager: Melanie Horvat

ABOUT MERGENT INC.

For over 100 years, Mergent, Inc. has been a leading provider of business and financial information on public and private companies globally. Mergent is known to be a trusted partner to corporate and financial institutions, as well as to academic and public libraries. Today we continue to build on a century of experience by transforming data into knowledge and combining our expertise with the latest technology to create new global data and analytical solutions for our clients. With advanced data collection services, cloud-based applications, desktop analytics and print products, Mergent and its subsidiaries provide solutions from top down economic and demographic information, to detailed equity and debt fundamental analysis. We incorporate value added tools such as quantitative Smart Beta equity research and tools for portfolio building and measurement. Based in the U.S., Mergent maintains a strong global presence, with offices in New York, Charlotte, San Diego, London, Tokyo, Kuching and Melbourne. Mergent, Inc. is a member of the London Stock Exchange plc group of companies. The Mergent business forms part of LSEG's Information Services Division, which includes FTSE Russell, a global leader in indexes.

Abbreviations

AFL-CIO – American Federation of Labor and Congress of Industrial Organizations
AMA – American Medical Association
AMEX – American Stock Exchange
ARM – adjustable-rate mortgage
ASP – application services provider
ATM – asynchronous transfer mode
ATM – automated teller machine
CAD/CAM – computer-aided design/computer-aided manufacturing
CD-ROM – compact disc – read-only memory
CD-R – CD-recordable
CEO – chief executive officer
CFO – chief financial officer
CMOS – complementary metal oxide silicon
COO – chief operating officer
DAT – digital audiotape
DOD – Department of Defense
DOE – Department of Energy
DOS – disk operating system
DOT – Department of Transportation
DRAM – dynamic random-access memory
DSL – digital subscriber line
DVD – digital versatile disc/digital video disc
DVD-R – DVD-recordable
EPA – Environmental Protection Agency
EPS – earnings per share
ESOP – employee stock ownership plan
EU – European Union
EVP – executive vice president
FCC – Federal Communications Commission
FDA – Food and Drug Administration
FDIC – Federal Deposit Insurance Corporation

FTC – Federal Trade Commission
GATT – General Agreement on Tariffs and Trade
GDP – gross domestic product
HMO – health maintenance organization
HR – human resources
HTML – hypertext markup language
ICC – Interstate Commerce Commission
IPO – initial public offering
IRS – Internal Revenue Service
ISP – Internet service provider
kWh – kilowatt-hour
LAN – local-area network
LBO – leveraged buyout
LCD – liquid crystal display
LNG – liquefied natural gas
LP – limited partnership
Ltd. – limited
mips – millions of instructions per second
MW – megawatt
NAFTA – North American Free Trade Agreement
NASA – National Aeronautics and Space Administration
NASDAQ – National Association of Securities Dealers Automated Quotations
NATO – North Atlantic Treaty Organization
NYSE – New York Stock Exchange
OCR – optical character recognition
OECD – Organization for Economic Cooperation and Development
OEM – original equipment manufacturer
OPEC – Organization of Petroleum Exporting Countries
OS – operating system

OSHA – Occupational Safety and Health Administration
OTC – over-the-counter
PBX – private branch exchange
PCMCIA – Personal Computer Memory Card International Association
P/E – price to earnings ratio
RAID – redundant array of independent disks
RAM – random-access memory
R&D – research and development
RBOC – regional Bell operating company
RISC – reduced instruction set computer
REIT – real estate investment trust
ROA – return on assets
ROE – return on equity
ROI – return on investment
ROM – read-only memory
S&L – savings and loan
SEC – Securities and Exchange Commission
SEVP – senior executive vice president
SIC – Standard Industrial Classification
SOC – system on a chip
SVP – senior vice president
USB – universal serial bus
VAR – value-added reseller
VAT – value-added tax
VC – venture capitalist
VoIP – Voice over Internet Protocol
VP – vice president
WAN – wide-area network

Contents

Companies Profiled vi

About *Hoover's Handbook of Emerging Companies 2019* x

Using Hoover's Handbooks xi

A List-Lover's Compendium xiii

    The 300 Largest Companies by Sales in *In Mergents Data Base for 2019* xiv

    The 300 Largest Employers in *In Mergents Data Base for 2019* xvi

    Top 200 Companies by Net Income in *In Mergents Dulu Base for 2019* xviii

The Companies 1

The Indexes 451

    Index of Companies by Headquarters Location 453

    Index of Company Executives 481

Companies Profiled

1-800 Flowers.com, Inc. 1
1ST Constitution Bancorp 2
ABIOMED, Inc. 2
Acacia Communications Inc 3
Acadia Realty Trust 4
Addus HomeCare Corp. 4
Advanced Emissions Solutions Inc 5
AG Mortgage Investment Trust Inc 6
Agree Realty Corp. 6
Air Lease Corp. 7
Air Transport Services Group, Inc. 8
Alarm.com Holdings Inc 9
Alerus Financial Corp 9
Alexandria Real Estate Equities Inc 9
Align Technology Inc 10
Allegiance Bancshares Inc 11
Allegiant Travel Company 11
Allete Inc. 11
Allied Motion Technologies Inc 13
Ambarella, Inc. 13
America First Multifamily Investors LP 14
American Homes 4 Rent 14
American Woodmark Corp. 15
Ameris Bancorp 15
AMN Healthcare Services Inc 17
Anika Therapeutics Inc. 17
Antero Midstream Partners LP 18
Apogee Enterprises Inc 18
Apollo Commercial Real Estate Finance
    Inc. 19
Apollo Medical Holdings Inc 20
AppFolio Inc 20
Apple Hospitality REIT Inc 20
Applied Optoelectronics Inc 20
Aptevo Therapeutics Inc 21
Arbor Realty Trust Inc 22
Ares Commercial Real Estate Corp 22
Ares Management Corp 22
Argan Inc 22
Arista Networks Inc 23
Arlington Asset Investment Corp 24
Armada Hoffler Properties Inc 24
Astronics Corp. 24
At Home Group Inc 25
ATN International Inc 25
AvalonBay Communities, Inc. 26
Axcelis Technologies Inc 27
Axos Financial Inc 27
B Riley Financial Inc 28
B&G Foods Inc 29
Balchem Corp. 30
Banc Of California Inc 31
BancFirst Corp. (Oklahoma City, Okla) 32
Bank First National Corp 34
Bank OZK 34
BankUnited Inc. 35
Bankwell Financial Group Inc 36
Banner Corp. 36
Bar Harbor Bankshares 37
Barrett Business Services, Inc. 38
BBX Capital Corp (New) 39
BCB Bancorp Inc 39
Beasley Broadcast Group Inc 40

Berkshire Hills Bancorp Inc 40
BG Staffing Inc 41
Bio-Techne Corp 41
Biospecifics Technologies Corp. 42
Black Knight Inc 43
Blackbaud, Inc. 43
Blackstone Mortgage Trust Inc 44
Blue Hills Bancorp Inc 45
Boot Barn Holdings Inc 45
Braemar Hotels & Resorts Inc 45
Bridge Bancorp, Inc. (Bridgehampton,
    NY) 46
Bright Horizons Family Solutions, Inc 46
Brown & Brown Inc 46
BRT Apartments Corp 47
Bryn Mawr Bank Corp 48
BSB Bancorp Inc. (MD) 49
Cabot Microelectronics Corp 49
Cadence Bancorporation 50
CAI International Inc 50
CalAmp Corp 51
Calavo Growers, Inc. 52
Callon Petroleum Co. (DE) 53
Cambrex Corp 54
Camden National Corp. (ME) 54
Cantel Medical Corp 55
Capital Southwest Corp. 56
Care.com Inc 57
CareTrust REIT Inc 58
Carolina Financial Corp (New) 58
Carrizo Oil & Gas, Inc. 58
Carrols Restaurant Group Inc 59
Cars.com Inc 60
Carter Validus Mission Critical REIT Inc ...60
Casa Systems Inc 60
Cavco Industries Inc (DE) 60
CB Financial Services Inc 61
Cboe Global Markets Inc 62
CenterState Bank Corp 63
Central Garden & Pet Co 64
Central Valley Community Bancorp 66
Century Casinos, Inc. 66
Century Communities Inc 67
Ceva Inc 67
Charles River Laboratories International
    Inc. 68
Chatham Lodging Trust 69
Chefs' Warehouse Inc (The) 70
Chemical Financial Corp 71
ChemoCentryx, Inc. 72
Cherry Hill Mortgage Investment Corp 72
Chesapeake Lodging Trust 73
Chesapeake Utilities Corp. 74
Chimera Investment Corp 75
Choice Hotels International, Inc. 75
Chuy's Holdings Inc. 76
CIB Marine Bancshares Inc 76
CIM Commercial Trust Corp 77
Cirrus Logic Inc 77
CNB Community Bancorp Inc 79
CNB Financial Corp. (Clearfield, PA) 79
CNX Midstream Partners LP 80
Codorus Valley Bancorp, Inc. 80

Cogent Communications Holdings, Inc 80
Cognex Corp 81
Coherent Inc 82
Cohu Inc 83
Cole Credit Property Trust IV Inc 84
Columbia Banking System Inc 84
Columbia Sportswear Co. 85
Columbus McKinnon Corp. (NY) 86
Community Bank System Inc 87
Comtech Telecommunications Corp 88
Concert Pharmaceuticals Inc 89
ConnectOne Bancorp Inc (New) 90
Consolidated Communications Holdings
    Inc 90
Consolidated-Tomoka Land Co. 91
Continental Building Products Inc 92
Control4 Corp 92
Copart Inc 93
Corcept Therapeutics Inc 94
CoreLogic Inc. 95
CorEnergy Infrastructure Trust Inc 95
CoreSite Realty Corp 96
Corporate Property Associates 18 Global
    Inc 97
CoStar Group, Inc. 97
County Bancorp, Inc. 98
Cousins Properties Inc 98
Credit Acceptance Corp (MI) 99
Croghan Bancshares, Inc. 100
Cross Country Healthcare Inc 100
CubeSmart 101
Customers Bancorp Inc 102
Cutera Inc 103
Dave & Busters Entertainment Inc 104
Deckers Outdoor Corp. 105
Diamond Hill Investment Group Inc. 106
Diamondback Energy, Inc. 107
Digital Realty Trust Inc 107
Diversified Gas & Oil PLC 108
DNB Financial Corp. 108
Dolphin Entertainment Inc 108
Douglas Dynamics, Inc. 109
Douglas Emmett Inc 109
Duluth Holdings Inc 110
e.l.f. Beauty Inc 110
EACO Corp 110
Eagle Bancorp Inc (MD) 111
Eagle Materials Inc. 112
Eagle Pharmaceuticals, Inc. 113
East West Bancorp, Inc 113
Eastman Kodak Co. 114
Ebix Inc 115
Echo Global Logistics Inc 116
Eclipse Resources Corp 117
Eldorado Resorts Inc. 118
Ellie Mae Inc. 118
Ellington Residential Mortgaging Real
    Estate Investment Trust 119
Embassy Bancorp Inc. 120
Emerald Expositions Events Inc 120
Emergent BioSolutions Inc 120
Empire State Realty OP LP 121
Empire State Realty Trust Inc 121

Companies Profiled (continued)

Enanta Pharmaceuticals Inc....122
Encore Capital Group Inc....123
Energy Recovery Inc....124
Ensign Group Inc....124
Entegris Inc....125
Entercom Communications Corp....126
Enterprise Bancorp, Inc. (MA)....127
Enterprise Financial Services Corp....128
Entravision Communications Corp....129
Enviva Partners LP....129
Epam Systems, Inc....130
EPR Properties....130
EQM Midstream Partners LP....131
Equity Bancshares Inc....131
ESCO Technologies, Inc....131
Essex Property Trust Inc....133
Etsy Inc....134
Euronet Worldwide Inc....134
Evans Bancorp, Inc....135
Evercore Inc....135
Evolution Petroleum Corp....136
Evoqua Water Technologies Corp....137
Exelixis Inc....137
ExlService Holdings Inc....138
Extra Space Storage Inc....139
F & M Bank Corp....139
FactSet Research Systems Inc....140
Farmers & Merchants Bancorp (Lodi, CA)....141
Farmers National Banc Corp. (Canfield,OH)....141
Farmland Partners Inc....142
FB Financial Corp....142
Federal Agricultural Mortgage Corp....142
Federal Home Loan Bank Boston....143
Federal Home Loan Bank Indianapolis....144
Federal Home Loan Bank New York....144
Federal Home Loan Bank Of Cincinnati....145
Federal Home Loan Bank Of Dallas....145
Federal Home Loan Bank Of Des Moines....145
Federal Home Loan Bank of Pittsburgh....145
Federal Home Loan Bank Of San Francisco....146
Federal Home Loan Bank Topeka....146
FedNat Holding Co....146
Fentura Financial Inc....147
Fidelity Southern Corp....147
Finjan Holdings Inc....148
First Bancshares Inc (MS)....149
First Bank (Williamstown, NJ)....149
First Busey Corp....150
First Business Financial Services, Inc....151
First Capital Inc....151
First Choice Bancorp....152
First Citizens BancShares Inc (NC)....152
First Community Corp (SC)....153
First Defiance Financial Corp....153
First Financial Bankshares, Inc....154
First Foundation Inc....155
First Internet Bancorp....155
First Interstate BancSystem Inc....155
First Merchants Corp....156
First Mid-Illinois Bancshares Inc....157
First Midwest Bancorp, Inc. (Naperville, IL)....158
First of Long Island Corp....159
First Savings Financial Group Inc....160
FirstCash Inc....160
Five Below Inc....161
FleetCor Technologies Inc....162
Floor & Decor Holdings Inc....163
FNB Corp....164
FormFactor Inc....165
Fortinet Inc....165
Forward Air Corp....166
Foundation Building Materials Inc....167
Four Corners Property Trust Inc....167
Fox Factory Holding Corp....168
Francesca's Holdings Corp....168
Franklin Financial Network Inc....168
FRMO Corp....169
FS Bancorp Inc (Washington)....169
FS Energy & Power Fund....169
FVCBankcorp Inc....170
Gaming & Leisure Properties, Inc....170
Gencor Industries Inc....170
Genesee & Wyoming Inc....171
Gentex Corp....172
Gentherm Inc....173
GEO Group Inc (The) (New)....174
German American Bancorp Inc....175
Glacier Bancorp, Inc....176
Gladstone Commercial Corp....177
Global Net Lease Inc....178
Globus Medical Inc....178
GoDaddy Inc....179
Goldman Sachs BDC Inc....179
Grand Canyon Education Inc....179
Gray Television Inc....180
Great Ajax Corp....181
Great Western Bancorp Inc....181
Green Dot Corp....181
Green Plains Partners LP....183
Greene County Bancorp Inc....183
GrubHub Inc....183
Guaranty Bancshares Inc....184
Gulfport Energy Corp....184
Hallador Energy Co....185
Halozyme Therapeutics Inc....185
Hamilton Lane Inc....186
Hanmi Financial Corp....186
Hannon Armstrong Sustainable Infrastructure Capital Inc....187
HarborOne Bancorp Inc....188
Health Insurance Innovations Inc....188
Healthcare Services Group, Inc....189
Healthcare Trust Of America Inc....189
HealthEquity Inc....190
Healthstream Inc....190
Heartland BancCorp....191
Heartland Financial USA, Inc. (Dubuque, IA)....191
HEICO Corp....192
Hennessy Advisors Inc....193
Heritage Commerce Corp....194
Heritage Financial Corp (WA)....194
Hersha Hospitality Trust....195
Heska Corp....196
HFF Inc....196
Hi-Crush Partners LP....197
Hilltop Holdings, Inc....197
Hilton Grand Vacations Inc....198
Hingham Institution for Savings....198
Holly Energy Partners LP....199
Home Bancorp Inc....199
Home BancShares Inc....200
Homefed Corp....201
HomeStreet Inc....201
HomeTrust Bancshares Inc....202
Hooker Furniture Corp....203
Hope Bancorp Inc....204
Horizon Bancorp Inc....204
Hospitality Properties Trust....205
Houlihan Lokey Inc....206
Howard Bancorp Inc....206
Howard Hughes Corp....207
Hudson Pacific Properties Inc....208
Hudson Technologies Inc....209
IBERIABANK Corp....209
Ichor Holdings Ltd....211
ICU Medical Inc....211
Idexx Laboratories, Inc....212
II-VI Inc....213
Independence Realty Trust Inc....214
Independent Bank Group Inc....214
InfraREIT Inc....215
Innospec Inc....215
Innoviva Inc....216
Inogen, Inc....217
Inovalon Holdings Inc....218
Installed Building Products Inc....218
Integer Holdings Corp....218
Integra LifeSciences Holdings Corp....219
Interactive Brokers Group Inc....220
Interdigital Inc (PA)....221
Investar Holding Corp....222
Investors Bancorp Inc (New)....222
IPG Photonics Corp....223
iRobot Corp....224
iStar Inc....225
J.Jill Inc....226
j2 Global Inc (New)....226
John Bean Technologies Corp....227
Kaanapali Land LLC....228
Kadant Inc....228
KBS Strategic Opportunity REIT Inc....229
Kearny Financial Corp (MD)....229
KEMET Corp....230
Kennedy-Wilson Holdings Inc....230
Kentucky Bancshares Inc....231
Kilroy Realty Corp....232
Kilroy Realty L.P....232
Kimball Electronics Inc....232
Kingstone Companies Inc....233
Kinsale Capital Group Inc....233
Kite Realty Group Trust....233
Knight-Swift Transportation Holdings Inc....234
Korn Ferry....234
Kraton Corp....235
Ladenburg Thalmann Financial Services Inc....236
Lakeland Bancorp, Inc....237
Lakeland Financial Corp....238
Landmark Infrastructure Partners LP....239
Lannett Co., Inc....239
LCI Industries....240
LegacyTexas Financial Group Inc....241
LeMaitre Vascular Inc....241
LendingTree Inc (New)....242
LGI Homes, Inc....243
LHC Group Inc....244
Life Storage Inc....245
Ligand Pharmaceuticals Inc....245
Littelfuse Inc....246
Live Oak Bancshares Inc....247
Live Ventures Inc....247
LogMeIn Inc....248
LTC Properties, Inc....249
Lumentum Holdings Inc....249
Luminex Corp....250
Luna Innovations Inc....251
Lydall, Inc....251
Lyon (William) Homes....252
M/I Homes Inc....253
Macquarie Infrastructure Corp....254
Madison Square Garden Co (The) (New)....254
Main Street Capital Corp....255
Malibu Boats Inc....255
Malvern Bancorp Inc....255
Mammoth Energy Services Inc....255
Manhattan Associates, Inc....256
Marcus & Millichap Inc....256
Marcus Corp. (The)....257
Marine Products Corp....258
MarineMax Inc....258
MarketAxess Holdings Inc....259
Marlin Business Services Corp....260
Masimo Corp....261
MasterCraft Boat Holdings Inc....262
Matador Resources Co....262
Match Group Inc....262
Matthews International Corp....262
Maui Land & Pineapple Co., Inc....264
MAXIMUS Inc....264
MB Financial Inc....265
MedEquities Realty Trust Inc....267
Medical Properties Trust Inc....267
Medidata Solutions, Inc....268
Medpace Holdings Inc....269

Companies Profiled (continued)

Mercantile Bank Corp. 269
Mercury Systems Inc 270
Meredith Corp 271
Meridian Bancorp Inc 272
Merit Medical Systems, Inc. 273
Meritage Hospitality Group Inc 274
Merrill Lynch Life Insurance Co - Insurance Products 274
Mesabi Trust 275
Meta Financial Group Inc 275
Mid Penn Bancorp Inc 276
Mid-America Apartment Communities Inc 276
Middleby Corp 277
Middlefield Banc Corp. 278
Midland States Bancorp Inc 278
MidWestOne Financial Group, Inc. 279
Miller Industries Inc. (TN) 280
Minerals Technologies, Inc. 280
MKS Instruments Inc 281
Modine Manufacturing Co 282
Moelis & Co 283
Monmouth Real Estate Investment Corp 283
Monolithic Power Systems Inc 284
Monotype Imaging Holdings Inc 285
Motorcar Parts of America Inc. 286
MTS Systems Corp 287
Multi-Color Corp. 288
MVB Financial Corp 288
MYR Group Inc. 289
Nanometrics, Inc. 290
National Beverage Corp. 291
National Commerce Corp 292
National Health Investors, Inc. 292
National Retail Properties Inc 293
National Rural Utilities Cooperative Finance Corp 293
National Vision Holdings Inc 294
Natural Grocers By Vitamin Cottage Inc 294
Natural Health Trends Corp. 295
Nautilus Inc 296
Navigators Group Inc (The) 296
NCI Building Systems, Inc. 297
Neogen Corp 299
NetScout Systems Inc 300
New England Realty Associates L.P. 301
New Mountain Finance Corp 301
New Residential Investment Corp 302
New Senior Investment Group Inc 302
New York Mortgage Trust Inc 302
NexPoint Residential Trust Inc 303
Nexstar Media Group Inc 303
NI Holdings Inc 304
Nicolet Bankshares Inc 304
NMI Holdings Inc 304
NN, Inc 305
Noble Midstream Partners LP 305
Northeast Bancorp (ME) 306
Northeast Community Bancorp Inc 306
Northern Technologies International Corp. 306
Northfield Bancorp Inc (DE) 307
Northrim BancCorp Inc 307
Novanta Inc 308
NutriSystem Inc 309
Nuvasive Inc 310
NV5 Global Inc 310
Oak Valley Bancorp (Oakdale, CA) 311
Oaktree Capital Group LLC 311
OceanFirst Financial Corp 312
Office Properties Income Trust 313
Old Line Bancshares Inc 314
Ollie's Bargain Outlet Holdings Inc 315
Omega Healthcare Investors, Inc. 315
Omnicell Inc 315
One Liberty Properties, Inc. 316
OP Bancorp 317
Opus Bank (Irvine, CA) 317
OraSure Technologies Inc. 318
Orchids Paper Products Co. (DE) 318
Osiris Therapeutics Inc 319
OTC Markets Group Inc 320
Pacific City Financial Corp 320
Pacific Mercantile Bancorp 320
Pacific Premier Bancorp Inc 321
PacWest Bancorp 321
Par Pacific Holdings Inc 322
Parade Technologies Ltd. 323
Paramount Group Inc 323
Parsley Energy Inc 323
Patrick Industries Inc 323
Paycom Software Inc 324
Paylocity Holding Corp 325
PCSB Financial Corp 325
Peapack-Gladstone Financial Corp. 325
Pebblebrook Hotel Trust 326
Pegasystems Inc 327
Pendrell Corp 327
PennyMac Financial Services Inc (New) 328
People's Utah Bancorp 329
Peoples Bancorp Inc (Marietta, OH) 329
Peoples Financial Services Corp 330
PGT Innovations Inc 330
Phillips 66 Partners LP 331
Physicians Realty Trust 332
Pinnacle Financial Partners Inc 332
Planet Fitness Inc 334
Plumas Bancorp Inc 334
Pope Resources LP 334
PQ Group Holdings Inc 335
PRA Health Sciences Inc 335
Preferred Apartment Communities Inc. 335
Preferred Bank (Los Angeles, CA) 336
Premier Inc 336
Prestige Consumer Healthcare Inc 337
Proto Labs Inc 338
Providence Service Corp 339
Provident Bancorp Inc 340
Prudential Bancorp Inc (New) 340
Psychemedics Corp. 340
Pzena Investment Management Inc 341
QCR Holdings Inc 341
Qualys, Inc. 342
Quanex Building Products Corp 343
Quantenna Communications Inc 344
QuinStreet, Inc. 344
Radian Group, Inc. 345
Radiant Logistics, Inc. 346
RBB Bancorp 346
RBC Bearings Inc 346
Ready Capital Corp 347
Realty Income Corp 348
Regency Centers Corp 348
Regional Management Corp 349
Reliant Bancorp Inc 350
Renasant Corp 350
Repligen Corp 351
Republic Bancorp, Inc. (KY) 352
Republic First Bancorp, Inc. 353
ResMed Inc. 354
Retail Opportunity Investments Corp 355
REV Group Inc 356
Rexford Industrial Realty Inc 356
RF Industries Ltd. 356
River Financial Corp 357
Riverview Bancorp, Inc. 357
RLJ Lodging Trust 358
RMR Group Inc (The) 358
Rogers Corp. 358
RPT Realty 359
RTI Surgical, Inc. 360
Rudolph Technologies, Inc. 361
S & T Bancorp Inc (Indiana, PA) 362
Sabra Health Care REIT Inc 363
Salisbury Bancorp, Inc. 363
Sanchez Energy Corp 364
Santa Cruz County Bank (CA) 365
Seacoast Banking Corp. of Florida 365
Senior Housing Properties Trust 366
ServisFirst Bancshares Inc 366
Shell Midstream Partners LP 367
Shenandoah Telecommunications Co 367
Shutterfly Inc 368
Shutterstock Inc 368
Sierra Bancorp 369
Signature Bank (New York, NY) 370
Silicon Laboratories Inc 371
Simmons First National Corp 372
Simply Good Foods Company (The) 373
Simpson Manufacturing Co., Inc. (DE) 373
Simulations Plus Inc 374
SiteOne Landscape Supply Inc 374
SJW Group 375
Sleep Number Corp 376
Smart Sand Inc 376
Somero Enterprises Inc 376
Sorrento Therapeutics Inc 377
South State Corp 377
Southern First Bancshares, Inc. 378
Southern Missouri Bancorp, Inc. 378
Southern Power Co 379
Southside Bancshares, Inc. 379
Spark Energy Inc 380
Spartan Motors, Inc. 380
Spirit Realty Capital Inc (New) 381
SRC Energy Inc 381
SS&C Technologies Holdings Inc 382
STAG Industrial Inc 383
Stamps.com Inc. 384
Starwood Property Trust Inc. 385
Sterling Bancorp (DE) 386
Sterling Construction Inc 386
STORE Capital Corp 387
Summit Financial Group Inc 387
Summit Hotel Properties Inc 387
Summit Materials Inc 388
Summit Midstream Partners LP 388
Sun Communities Inc 389
Sun Hydraulics Corp 390
Sunrun Inc 390
Superior Group of Companies Inc 390
Supernus Pharmaceuticals Inc 391
SVB Financial Group 392
Tabula Rasa HealthCare Inc 393
Tactile Systems Technology Inc 393
Teradyne, Inc. 394
Terreno Realty Corp 395
Texas Capital Bancshares Inc 395
Texas Pacific Land Trust 396
Texas Roadhouse Inc 397
The New Home Company Inc 397
The Trade Desk Inc 398
Thomasville Bancshares, Inc. 398
Tile Shop Holdings Inc 399
Timberland Bancorp, Inc. 399
TowneBank 399
TPG RE Finance Trust Inc 399
TPG Specialty Lending Inc 400
TPI Composites Inc 400
TransUnion 400
Trex Co Inc 400
Tribune Media Co 401
TriCo Bancshares (Chico, CA) 402
TriState Capital Holdings Inc 403
Triumph Bancorp Inc 404
Turning Point Brands Inc 404
Tyler Technologies, Inc. 404
U.S. Physical Therapy, Inc. 405
Ubiquiti Networks Inc 406
Ultimate Software Group, Inc. 406
Ultra Clean Holdings Inc 407
UMH Properties Inc 408
Umpqua Holdings Corp 408
Union Bankshares Corp (New) 410
Unique Fabricating Inc 410
United American Healthcare Corp. 410
United Bankshares Inc 411
United Community Banks Inc (Blairsville, GA) 412
United Community Financial Corp. (OH) 413

Companies Profiled (continued)

United Financial Bancorp Inc (New) 414
United Insurance Holdings Corp.............414
United Security Bancshares (CA) 414
United States Brent Oil Fund L.P. 415
United Therapeutics Corp.....................415
Unity Bancorp, Inc. 416
Universal Display Corp.........................416
Universal Insurance Holdings Inc 417
Univest Financial Corp.........................418
US Concrete Inc 419
US Ecology, Inc. 420
US Silica Holdings, Inc. 421
USA Compression Partners LP 422
USANA Health Sciences Inc...................422
USD Partners LP 423
Vail Resorts Inc 423
Vector Group Ltd 424
Veeva Systems Inc..............................425
VEREIT Inc...426

Veritex Holdings Inc 427
Versum Materials Inc 427
Vertex Pharmaceuticals, Inc. 427
VICI Properties Inc...................................428
Viper Energy Partners LP 429
Vivint Solar Inc 429
VSE Corp. 429
W.P. Carey Inc..430
Walker & Dunlop Inc 431
Warrior Met Coal Inc 432
Wells Fargo Real Estate Investment Corp432
WesBanco Inc...433
Western Alliance Bancorporation.............434
Western Asset Mortgage Capital Corp......435
Western Capital Resources Inc 435
Western Gas Equity Partners LP 435
Western Gas Partners LP 435
Western New England Bancorp Inc..........436
Westwood Holdings Group, Inc................436

Wex Inc..437
Whitestone REIT.......................................438
Willdan Group Inc.....................................439
Willis Lease Finance Corp...........................439
Wingstop Inc 440
Winnebago Industries, Inc...........................440
Wintrust Financial Corp (IL)........................441
WisdomTree Investments, Inc. 443
World Wrestling Entertainment Inc 444
WSFS Financial Corp.................................445
Xenia Hotels & Resorts Inc.......................446
XOMA Corp...446
Yelp Inc..447
ZAGG Inc 448

About Hoover's Handbook of Emerging Companies 2019

Hoover's Handbook of Emerging Companies enters its 26th year as one of America's premier sources of business information on younger, growth-oriented enterprises. Given our current economic realities, finding value in the marketplace becomes ever more difficult, and so we are particularly pleased to present this edition of Hoover's Handbook of Emerging Companies 2019 — the result of a search of our extensive database of business information for companies with demonstrated growth and the potential for future gains.

The 600 companies in this book were chosen from the universe of public US companies with sales between $10 million and $2.5 billion. Their selection was based primarily on sales growth and profitability, although in a few cases we made some rather subjective decisions about which companies we chose to include. They all have reported at least three years of sales and have sustained annualized sales growth of at least 7% during that time. Also, they are profitable (through year-end September 2016).

In addition to the companies featured in our handbooks, comprehensive coverage of more than 40,000 business enterprises is available in electronic format on our website, Hoover's Online (www.hoovers.com). Our goal is to provide one site that offers authoritative, updated intelligence on US and global companies, industries, and the people who shape them. Hoover's has partnered with other prestigious business information and service providers to bring you all the right business information, services, and links in one place.

Hoover's Handbook of Emerging Companies is one of our four-title series of handbooks that covers, literally, the world of business. The series is available as an indexed set, and also includes Hoover's Handbook of American Business, Hoover's Handbook of World Business, and Hoover's Handbook of Private Companies. This series brings you information on the biggest, fastest-growing, and most influential enterprises in the world.

We believe that anyone who buys from, sells to, invests in, lends to, competes with, interviews with, or works for a company should know as much as possible about that enterprise. Taken together, Hoover's Handbook of Emerging Companies 2016 and the other Hoover's products represent the most complete source of basic corporate information readily available to the general public.

How to use this book

This book has four sections:

1. "Using Hoover's Handbooks" describes the contents of our profiles.

2. "A List-Lover's Compendium" contains lists of the fastest-growing and most profitable companies. The lists are based on the information in our profiles, or compiled from well-known sources.

3. The company profiles section makes up the largest and most important part of the book — 600 profiles arranged alphabetically. Each profile features an overview of the company; some larger and more visible companies have an additional History section. All companies have up to five years of financial information, product information where available, and a list of company executives and key competitors.

4. At the end of this volume are the combined indexes from our 2019 editions of all Hoover's Handbooks. The information is organized into three separate sections. The first sorts companies by industry groups, the second by headquarters location. The third index is a list of all the executives found in the Executives section of each company profile. For a more thorough description of our indexing style, see page xii.

Using Hoover's Handbooks

ORGANIZATION

The profiles in this volume are presented in alphabetical order. This alphabetization is generally word by word, which means that Bridge Bancorp precedes Bridgepoint Education. You will find the commonly used name of the enterprise at the beginning of the profile; the full, legal name is found in the Locations section. If a company name starts with initials, such as BJ's Restaurants or U.S. Physical Therapy, look for it under the combined initials (in the above example, BJ or US, respectively).

Basic financial data is listed under the heading Historical Financials; also included is the exchange on which the company's stock is traded, the ticker symbol used by the stock exchange, and the company's fiscal year-end. The annual financial information contained in the profiles is current through fiscal year-ends occurring as late as January 2017. We have included certain nonfinancial developments, such as officer changes, through January 2019.

OVERVIEW

In the first section of the profile, we have tried to give a thumbnail description of the company and what it does. The description will usually include information on the company's strategy, reputation, and ownership. We recommend that you read this section first.

HISTORY

This extended section, which is available for some of the larger and more well-known companies, reflects our belief that every enterprise is the sum of its history and that you have to know where you came from in order to know where you are going. While some companies have limited historical awareness, we think the vast majority of the enterprises in this book have colorful backgrounds. We have tried to focus on the people who made the enterprises what they are today. We have found these histories to be full of twists and ironies; they make fascinating reading.

EXECUTIVES

Here we list the names of the people who run the company, insofar as space allows. In the case of public companies, we have shown the ages and pay of key officers. The published data is for the previous fiscal year, although the company may have announced promotions or retirements since year-end. The pay represents cash compensation, including bonuses, but excludes stock option programs.

Although companies are free to structure their management titles any way they please, most modern corporations follow standard practices. The ultimate power in any corporation lies with the shareholders, who elect a board of directors, usually including officers or "insiders," as well as individuals from outside the company. The chief officer, the person on whose desk the buck stops, is usually called the chief executive officer (CEO). Often, he or she is also the chairman of the board.

As corporate management has become more complex, it is common for the CEO to have a "right-hand person" who oversees the day-to-day operations of the company, allowing the CEO plenty of time to focus on strategy and long-term issues. This right-hand person is usually designated the chief operating officer (COO) and is often the president of the company. In other cases one person is both chairman and president.

A multitude of other titles exists, including chief financial officer (CFO), chief administrative officer, and vice chairman. We have always tried to include the CFO, the chief legal officer, and the chief human resources or personnel officer. Our best advice is that officers' pay levels are clear indicators of who the board of directors thinks are the most important members of the management team.

The people named in the Executives section are indexed at the back of the book.

The Executives section also includes the name of the company's auditing (accounting) firm, where available.

LOCATIONS

Here we include the company's full legal name and its headquarters, street address, telephone and fax numbers, and website, as available. The back of the book includes an index of companies by headquarters locations.

In some cases we have also included information on the geographic distribution of the company's business, including sales and profit data. Note that these profit numbers, like those in the Products/Operations section below, are usually operating or pretax profits rather than net profits. Operating profits are generally those before financing costs (interest income and payments) and before taxes, which are considered costs attributable to the whole company rather than to one division or part of the world. For this reason the net income figures (in the Historical Financials section) are usually much lower, since they are after interest and taxes. Pretax profits are after interest but before taxes.

PRODUCTS/OPERATIONS

This section lists as many of the company's products, services, brand names, divisions, subsidiaries, and joint ventures as we could fit. We have tried to include all its major lines and all familiar brand names. The nature of this section varies by company and the amount of information available. If the company publishes sales and profit information by type of business, we have included it.

COMPETITORS

In this section we have listed companies that compete with the profiled company. This feature is included as a quick way to locate similar companies and compare them. The universe of competitors includes all public companies and all private companies with sales in excess of $500 million. In a few instances we have identified smaller private companies as key competitors.

HISTORICAL FINANCIALS

Here we have tried to present as much data about each enterprise's financial performance as we could compile in the allocated space. Although the information varies somewhat from industry to industry, the following is generally present.

A five-year table, with relevant annualized compound growth rates, covers:

- Sales — fiscal year sales (year-end assets for most financial companies)
- Net income — fiscal year net income (before accounting changes)
- Net profit margin — fiscal year net income as a percent of sales (as a percent of assets for most financial firms)
- Employees — fiscal year-end or average number of employees
- Stock price — the fiscal year closing price
- P/E — high and low price/earnings ratio
- Earnings per share — fiscal year earnings per share (EPS)
- Dividends per share — fiscal year dividends per share
- Book value per share — fiscal year-end book value (common shareholders' equity per share)

The information on the number of employees is intended to aid the reader interested in knowing whether a company has a long-term trend of increasing or decreasing employment. As far as we know, we are the only company that publishes this information in print format.

The numbers on the left in each row of the Historical Financials section give the month and the year in which the company's fiscal year actually ends. Thus, a company with a September 30, 2018, year-end is shown as 9/18.

In addition, we have provided in graph form a stock price history for each company. The graphs, covering up to five years, show the range of trading between the high and the low price, as well as the closing price for each fiscal year.

Key year-end statistics in this section generally show the financial strength of the enterprise, including:

- Debt ratio (long-term debt as a percent of shareholders' equity)
- Return on equity (net income divided by the average of beginning and ending common shareholders' equity)
- Cash and cash equivalents
- Current ratio (ratio of current assets to current liabilities)
- Total long-term debt (including capital lease obligations)
- Number of shares of common stock outstanding
- Dividend yield (fiscal year dividends per share divided by the fiscal year-end closing stock price)
- Dividend payout (fiscal year dividends divided by fiscal year EPS)
- Market value at fiscal year-end (fiscal year-end closing stock price multiplied by fiscal year-end number of shares outstanding)

Per-share data has been adjusted for stock splits. The data for public companies has been provided to us by Morningstar, Inc. Other public company information was compiled by Hoover's, which takes full responsibility for the content of this section.

Hoover's Handbook of

Emerging Companies

A List-Lover's Compendium

The 300 Largest Companies by Sales in Mergent's Database

Rank	Company	Sales ($ mil.)	Rank	Company	Sales ($ mil.)	Rank	Company	Sales ($ mil.)
1	Walmart Inc	$485,873	62	Coca-Cola Co (The)	$41,863	123	Qualcomm Inc	$22,291
2	Apple Inc	$229,234	63	Charter Communications Inc (	$41,581	124	Sears Holdings Corp	$22,138
3	Exxon Mobil Corp	$226,094	64	HCA Healthcare Inc	$41,490	125	Dollar General Corp	$21,987
4	Berkshire Hathaway Inc	$223,604	65	Facebook Inc	$40,653	126	AutoNation, Inc.	$21,535
5	UnitedHealth Group Inc	$201,159	66	Centene Corp	$40,607	127	Whirlpool Corp	$21,253
6	McKesson Corp	$198,533	67	T-Mobile US Inc	$40,604	128	Union Pacific Corp	$21,240
7	CVS Health Corp	$184,765	68	Honeywell International Inc	$40,534	129	Eli Lilly & Co	$21,222
8	Amazon.com Inc	$177,866	69	American Airlines Group Inc	$40,180	130	Southwest Airlines Co	$21,171
9	AT&T Inc	$163,786	70	Merck & Co Inc	$39,807	131	International Paper Co	$21,079
10	Ford Motor Co. (DE)	$156,776	71	Cigna Corp	$39,668	132	Bristol-Myers Squibb Co.	$20,776
11	AmerisourceBergen Corp.	$153,144	72	Delta Air Lines Inc (DE)	$39,639	133	Dollar Tree Inc	$20,719
12	General Motors Co	$145,588	73	Best Buy Inc	$39,403	134	Halliburton Company	$20,620
13	Cardinal Health, Inc.	$129,976	74	Tyson Foods Inc	$38,260	135	Lear Corp.	$20,467
14	Costco Wholesale Corp	$129,025	75	Morgan Stanley	$37,949	136	Cummins, Inc.	$20,428
15	Verizon Communications Inc	$125,980	76	Oracle Corp	$37,728	137	Micron Technology Inc.	$20,322
16	General Electric Co	$123,693	77	Goldman Sachs Group Inc	$37,712	138	Plains GP Holdings LP	$20,182
17	Walgreens Boots Alliance Inc	$118,214	78	Energy Transfer Equity LP	$37,504	139	Plains All American Pipeline	$20,182
18	Kroger Co (The)	$115,337	79	United Continental Holdings	$36,556	140	Penske Automotive Group Inc	$20,119
19	Chevron Corporation	$114,472	80	Allstate Corp.	$36,534	141	ManpowerGroup	$19,654
20	Alphabet Inc	$110,855	81	American Express Co.	$35,583	142	Tenet Healthcare Corp.	$19,621
21	Fannie Mae	$107,162	82	NIKE Inc	$34,350	143	Burlington Northern & Santa F	$19,278
22	JPMorgan Chase & Co	$105,486	83	Publix Super Markets, Inc.	$34,274	144	Western Digital Corp	$19,093
23	Express Scripts Holding Co	$100,288	84	Exelon Corp	$33,531	145	Jabil Inc	$19,063
24	Home Depot Inc	$94,595	85	Sprint Corp (New)	$33,347	146	Fluor Corp.	$19,037
25	Wells Fargo & Co.	$94,176	86	TJX Companies, Inc.	$33,184	147	Kohl's Corp.	$18,686
26	Bank of America Corp.	$93,662	87	Rite Aid Corp.	$32,845	148	Community Health Systems, In	$18,438
27	Boeing Co.	$93,392	88	CHS Inc	$31,935	149	Visa Inc	$18,358
28	Microsoft Corporation	$89,950	89	3M Co	$31,657	150	Hartford Financial Services	$18,300
29	Phillips 66	$85,777	90	General Dynamics Corp	$30,973	151	Thermo Fisher Scientific Inc	$18,274
30	Anthem Inc	$84,863	91	Gilead Sciences Inc	$30,390	152	Kimberly-Clark Corp.	$18,259
31	Comcast Corp	$84,526	92	Deere & Co.	$29,738	153	AECOM	$18,203
32	Citigroup Inc	$82,386	93	INTL FCStone Inc.	$29,382	154	DXC Technology Co	$18,112
33	International Business Machi	$79,919	94	Time Warner Inc	$29,318	155	Molina Healthcare Inc	$17,782
34	Philip Morris International	$78,098	95	Travelers Companies Inc (The	$28,902	156	Exelon Generation Co LLC	$17,751
35	Valero Energy Corp	$75,659	96	Hewlett Packard Enterprise C	$28,871	157	CenturyLink Inc	$17,470
36	Johnson & Johnson	$71,390	97	21st Century Fox Inc	$28,500	158	Avnet Inc	$17,440
37	Target Corp	$69,195	98	AbbVie Inc	$28,216	159	NextEra Energy Inc	$17,195
38	Freddie Mac	$65,565	99	Capital One Financial Corp	$27,519	160	PG&E Corp (Holding Co)	$17,135
39	Procter & Gamble Co (The)	$65,058	100	Abbott Laboratories	$27,390	161	Synnex Corp	$17,046
40	Lowe's Companies Inc	$65,017	101	World Fuel Services Corp.	$27,016	162	Paccar Inc.	$17,033
41	PepsiCo Inc	$63,525	102	Arrow Electronics, Inc.	$26,813	163	Danaher Corp	$16,882
42	MetLife Inc	$63,476	103	Tech Data Corp.	$26,235	164	Performance Food Group Co	$16,762
43	Marathon Petroleum Corp.	$63,364	104	Kraft Heinz Co (The)	$26,232	165	PNC Financial Services Group	$16,423
44	Aetna Inc.	$63,155	105	Mondelez International Inc	$25,896	166	American Electric Power Co.,	$16,380
45	Intel Corp	$62,761	106	Northrop Grumman Corp	$25,803	167	Icahn Enterprises LP	$16,348
46	DowDuPont Inc	$62,484	107	Macy's Inc	$25,778	168	Nucor Corp.	$16,208
47	Dell Technologies Inc	$61,642	108	Altria Group Inc	$25,744	169	PBF Energy Inc	$15,920
48	United Parcel Service Inc	$60,906	109	Raytheon Co.	$25,348	170	Carmax Inc.	$15,875
49	Archer Daniels Midland Co.	$60,828	110	McDonald's Corp	$24,622	171	Sunoco LP	$15,698
50	FedEx Corp	$60,319	111	Andeavor	$24,582	172	Bank of New York Mellon Corp	$15,674
51	United Technologies Corp	$59,837	112	ConocoPhillips	$24,360	173	General Mills, Inc.	$15,620
52	Prudential Financial, Inc.	$59,689	113	Progressive Corp. (OH)	$23,441	174	Gap Inc	$15,516
53	Sysco Corp	$55,371	114	Enterprise Products Partners	$23,022	175	Colgate-Palmolive Co.	$15,454
54	Disney (Walt) Co. (The)	$55,137	115	Southern Co.	$19,896	176	XPO Logistics, Inc.	$15,381
55	Humana, Inc.	$54,379	116	US Foods Holding Corp	$22,919	177	Goodyear Tire & Rubber Co.	$15,377
56	Pfizer Inc	$52,824	117	Marriott International, Inc.	$22,894	178	Genuine Parts Co.	$15,340
57	HP Inc	$52,056	118	Amgen Inc	$22,849	179	Omnicom Group, Inc.	$15,274
58	Lockheed Martin Corp	$51,048	119	U.S. Bancorp (DE)	$22,744	180	Emerson Electric Co.	$15,264
59	American International Group	$49,520	120	Duke Energy Corp	$22,743	181	Synchrony Financial	$15,122
60	Cisco Systems Inc	$48,005	121	AFLAC Inc.	$22,559	182	Dish Network Corp	$15,095
61	Caterpillar Inc.	$45,462	122	Starbucks Corp.	$22,387	183	WestRock Co	$14,860

SOURCE: MERGENT INC., DATABASE, JANUARY 2018

Rank	Company	Sales ($ mil.)	Rank	Company	Sales ($ mil.)	Rank	Company	Sales ($ mil.)
184	Freeport-McMoRan Inc	$14,830	223	Penney (J.C.) Co.,Inc. (Hold	$12,547	262	Xerox Corp	$10,771
185	Nordstrom, Inc.	$14,757	224	Mastercard Inc	$12,497	263	Santander Holdings USA Inc.	$10,745
186	PPG Industries Inc	$14,750	225	Supervalu Inc	$12,480	264	Priceline Group Inc (The)	$10,743
187	DaVita Inc	$14,745	226	Stryker Corp	$12,444	265	Tennessee Valley Authority	$10,739
188	Monsanto Co	$14,640	227	Arconic Inc	$12,394	266	Ally Financial Inc	$9,835
189	Aramark	$14,604	228	Automatic Data Processing In	$12,380	267	BorgWarner Inc	$9,799
190	FirstEnergy Corp	$14,562	229	NRG Energy Inc	$12,351	268	Liberty Interactive Corp	$10,647
191	Applied Materials, Inc.	$14,537	230	Biogen Inc	$12,274	269	State Street Corp.	$10,635
192	Core Mark Holding Co Inc	$14,529	231	Bed, Bath & Beyond, Inc.	$12,216	270	Norfolk Southern Corp.	$10,551
193	Waste Management, Inc. (DE)	$14,485	232	Devon Energy Corp.	$12,197	271	HollyFrontier Corp	$10,536
194	Illinois Tool Works, Inc.	$14,314	233	Becton Dickinson And Co	$12,093	272	Praxair Inc	$10,534
195	WellCare Health Plans Inc	$14,237	234	Consolidated Edison Inc	$12,075	273	L3 Technologies Inc	$10,511
196	Principal Financial Group In	$14,093	235	VF Corp.	$12,019	274	Discover Financial Services	$10,497
197	DR Horton Inc	$14,091	236	Anadarko Petroleum Corp	$11,908	275	Occidental Petroleum Corp	$10,398
198	CDW Corp	$13,982	237	Edison International	$11,869	276	United States Steel Corp.	$10,261
199	Textron Inc	$13,788	238	Sherwin-Williams Co (The)	$11,856	277	Liberty Interactive Corp – Q	$10,219
200	Loews Corp.	$13,735	239	Southern California Edison C	$11,830	278	Liberty Interactive Corp – Q	$10,219
201	Kinder Morgan Inc.	$13,705	240	Lauder (Estee) Cos., Inc. (T	$11,824	279	Sempra Energy	$10,183
202	AES Corp.	$13,586	241	Dominion Energy Inc (New)	$11,737	280	Consolidated Edison Co. of N	$10,165
203	Cognizant Technology Solutio	$13,487	242	Ameriprise Financial Inc	$11,696	281	Baxter International Inc	$10,163
204	Texas Instruments, Inc.	$13,370	243	Netflix Inc	$11,693	282	Grainger (W.W.), Inc.	$10,137
205	Lincoln National Corp.	$13,330	244	Murphy USA Inc	$11,595	283	Autoliv Inc.	$10,074
206	Baker Hughes A GE Co	$13,269	245	First Data Corp (New)	$11,584	284	Leucadia National Corp.	$10,063
207	Newell Brands Inc	$13,264	246	Henry Schein Inc	$11,572	285	Expedia Inc	$10,060
208	Viacom Inc	$13,263	247	BB&T Corp.	$11,538	286	Jacobs Engineering Group, In	$10,023
209	Parker-Hannifin Corp	$12,029	248	Reinsurance Group of America	$11,522	287	Universal Health Services, I	$9,766
210	Marsh & McLennan Companies I	$13,211	249	Las Vegas Sands Corp	$11,410	288	Sonic Automotive, Inc.	$9,732
211	CBS Corp	$13,166	250	CSX Corp	$11,408	289	Owens & Minor, Inc. (New)	$9,723
212	Ecolab Inc	$13,153	251	Stanley Black & Decker Inc	$11,407	290	Huntsman Corp	$9,657
213	Robinson (C.H.) Worldwide, I	$13,144	252	BlackRock Inc	$11,155	291	LabCorp	$9,642
214	PayPal Holdings Inc	$13,094	253	Xcel Energy Inc	$11,107	292	Advance Auto Parts Inc	$9,568
215	CBRE Group Inc	$13,072	254	Unum Group	$11,047	293	eBay Inc.	$9,567
216	NGL Energy Partners LP	$13,022	255	Office Depot, Inc.	$11,021	294	Fidelity National Financial	$9,554
217	Kellogg Co	$13,014	256	Toyota Motor Credit Corp.	$11,020	295	MGM Resorts International	$9,455
218	Celgene Corp	$13,003	257	Florida Power & Light Co.	$10,895	296	Corning Inc	$9,390
219	Ross Stores, Inc.	$12,867	258	AutoZone, Inc.	$10,889	297	Republic Services Inc	$9,388
220	Lennar Corp	$12,646	259	Group 1 Automotive, Inc.	$10,888	298	CNA Financial Corp	$9,366
221	DTE Energy Co	$12,607	260	Entergy Corp. (New)	$10,846	299	Alcoa Corporation	$9,318
222	L Brands, Inc	$12,574	261	Voya Financial Inc	$10,782	300	United Natural Foods Inc.	$9,274

The 300 Largest Companies by Employees in Mergent's Database

Rank	Company	Employees	Rank	Company	Employees	Rank	Company	Employees
1	Walmart Inc	2,300,000	61	Dollar General Corp	121,000	121	Hewlett Packard Enterprise C	66,000
2	Amazon.com Inc	566,000	62	Community Health Systems, In	120,000	122	Envision Healthcare Corp	65,200
3	Kelly Services, Inc.	507,500	63	Barrett Business Services, I	115,746	123	Bed, Bath & Beyond, Inc.	65,000
4	Kroger Co (The)	443,000	64	Synnex Corp	113,600	124	Laureate Education Inc	65,000
5	United Parcel Service Inc	434,000	65	DXC Technology Co	112,900	125	Raytheon Co.	64,000
6	Yum China Holdings Inc	420,000	66	Penney (J.C.) Co.,Inc. (Hold	106,000	126	Goodyear Tire & Rubber Co.	64,000
7	Home Depot Inc	406,000	67	Intel Corp	102,700	127	Ascena Retail Group Inc	64,000
8	International Business Machi	380,300	68	Coca-Cola Co (The)	100,300	128	Danaher Corp	62,000
9	McDonald's Corp	375,000	69	Kindred Healthcare Inc	100,100	129	Amphenol Corp.	62,000
10	Berkshire Hathaway Inc	367,700	70	Lockheed Martin Corp	100,000	130	Fluor Corp.	61,551
11	Walgreens Boots Alliance Inc	345,000	71	Abbott Laboratories	99,000	131	Brinks Co (The)	60,700
12	Target Corp	323,000	72	General Dynamics Corp	98,600	132	Deere & Co.	60,476
13	General Electric Co	295,000	73	Caterpillar Inc.	98,400	133	Marsh & McLennan Companies I	60,000
14	Lowe's Companies Inc	290,000	74	DowDuPont Inc	98,000	134	Cummins, Inc.	58,600
15	Starbucks Corp.	277,000	75	Pfizer Inc	96,500	135	MetLife Inc	58,000
16	Wells Fargo & Co.	269,100	76	Conduent Inc	96,000	136	Automatic Data Processing In	58,000
17	AT&T Inc	268,000	77	Procter & Gamble Co (The)	95,000	137	Brinker International, Inc.	57,906
18	PepsiCo Inc	263,000	78	XPO Logistics, Inc.	95,000	138	Parker–Hannifin Corp	56,690
19	UnitedHealth Group Inc	260,800	79	Charter Communications Inc (	94,800	139	Southwest Airlines Co	56,100
20	Aramark	260,500	80	L Brands, Inc	93,600	140	On Assignment, Inc.	55,880
21	Cognizant Technology Solutio	260,200	81	Whirlpool Corp	92,000	141	Sykes Enterprises, Inc.	55,525
22	CVS Health Corp	246,000	82	3M Co	91,536	142	Morgan Stanley	55,311
23	JPMorgan Chase & Co	243,355	83	Icahn Enterprises LP	90,960	143	Fidelity National Financial	55,219
24	HCA Healthcare Inc	241,000	84	Mondelez International Inc	90,000	144	Chevron Corporation	55,200
25	TJX Companies, Inc.	235,000	85	Yum! Brands Inc	90,000	145	American Express Co.	55,000
26	Half Robert International In	231,100	86	United Continental Holdings	88,000	146	International Paper Co	55,000
27	Costco Wholesale Corp	231,000	87	Rite Aid Corp.	87,000	147	Halliburton Company	55,000
28	Citigroup Inc	219,000	88	AECOM	87,000	148	Thermo Fisher Scientific Inc	55,000
29	Bank of America Corp.	208,000	89	AutoZone, Inc.	87,000	149	Fidelity National Informatio	55,000
30	United Technologies Corp	205,000	90	Delta Air Lines Inc (DE)	84,000	150	Jacobs Engineering Group, In	54,700
31	Ford Motor Co. (DE)	202,000	91	Genesis Healthcare Inc	82,000	151	Humana, Inc.	54,200
32	Disney (Walt) Co. (The)	199,000	92	Philip Morris International	80,600	152	Stanley Black & Decker Inc	54,023
33	Publix Super Markets, Inc.	191,000	93	Alphabet Inc	80,110	153	RMR Group Inc (The)	53,475
34	General Motors Co	180,000	94	Ross Stores, Inc.	78,600	154	Newell Brands Inc	53,400
35	Darden Restaurants, Inc. (Un	178,729	95	McKesson Corp	78,000	155	Anthem Inc	53,000
36	Marriott International, Inc.	177,000	96	Brookdale Senior Living Inc	77,600	156	Texas Roadhouse Inc	52,500
37	Dollar Tree Inc	176,300	97	Omnicom Group, Inc.	77,300	157	PNC Financial Services Group	52,006
38	Jabil Inc	170,000	98	Jones Lang LaSalle Inc	77,300	158	Bank of New York Mellon Corp	52,000
39	FedEx Corp	169,000	99	Emerson Electric Co.	76,500	159	LabCorp	52,000
40	Lear Corp.	165,000	100	Universal Health Services, I	75,325	160	T–Mobile US Inc	51,000
41	Comcast Corp	164,000	101	CBRE Group Inc	75,000	161	Foot Locker, Inc.	50,168
42	Hilton Worldwide Holdings In	163,000	102	O'Reilly Automotive, Inc.	74,715	162	Illinois Tool Works, Inc.	50,000
43	Verizon Communications Inc	160,900	103	NIKE Inc	74,400	163	IQVIA Holdings Inc	50,000
44	Macy's Inc	148,300	104	Advance Auto Parts Inc	74,000	164	Michaels Companies Inc	50,000
45	Boeing Co.	140,800	105	Cracker Barrel Old Country S	73,000	165	American International Group	49,800
46	Sears Holdings Corp	140,000	106	Cisco Systems Inc	72,900	166	Interpublic Group of Compani	49,800
47	ABM Industries, Inc.	140,000	107	Nordstrom, Inc.	72,500	167	Prudential Financial, Inc.	49,705
48	Dell Technologies Inc	138,000	108	U.S. Bancorp (DE)	71,191	168	Aetna Inc.	49,500
49	Oracle Corp	138,000	109	Exxon Mobil Corp	71,100	169	HP Inc	49,000
50	Kohl's Corp.	138,000	110	DaVita Inc	70,300	170	Las Vegas Sands Corp	49,000
51	Gap Inc	135,000	111	Autoliv Inc.	70,300	171	Healthcare Services Group In	48,900
52	Honeywell International Inc	131,000	112	Northrop Grumman Corp	70,000	172	Baxter International Inc	48,000
53	Tenet Healthcare Corp.	130,000	113	VF Corp.	69,000	173	TTEC Holdings Inc	48,000
54	Convergys Corp	130,000	114	MGM Resorts International	69,000	174	Ecolab Inc.	47,565
55	Johnson & Johnson	126,400	115	Chipotle Mexican Grill Inc	68,890	175	Capital One Financial Corp	47,300
56	Best Buy Inc	125,000	116	Merck & Co Inc	68,000	176	PPG Industries Inc	47,200
57	Microsoft Corporation	124,000	117	Western Digital Corp	68,000	177	Sanmina Corp	47,000
58	Apple Inc	123,000	118	GameStop Corp	68,000	178	LifePoint Health Inc	47,000
59	American Airlines Group Inc	122,300	119	HanesBrands Inc	67,200	179	Six Flags Entertainment Corp	47,000
60	Tyson Foods Inc	122,000	120	Sysco Corp	66,500	180	Lauder (Estee) Cos., Inc. (T	46,000

SOURCE: HOOVER'S, INC., DATABASE, JANUARY 2018

Rank	Company	Employees	Rank	Company	Employees	Rank	Company	Employees
181	Cedar Fair LP	45,600	221	Wyndham Worldwide Corp	37,800	261	Freeport–McMoRan Inc	30,000
182	Hyatt Hotels Corp	45,000	222	Xerox Corp	37,600	262	Avis Budget Group Inc	30,000
183	WestRock Co	44,800	223	BB&T Corp.	37,500	263	Cooper–Standard Holdings Inc	30,000
184	PVH Corp	44,500	224	Kellogg Co	37,369	264	Texas Instruments, Inc.	29,865
185	Marathon Petroleum Corp.	44,460	225	Huntington Ingalls Industrie	37,000	265	United States Steel Corp.	29,800
186	RR Donnelley & Sons Company	44,360	226	Textron Inc	36,000	266	Sally Beauty Holdings Inc	29,475
187	Allstate Corp.	43,500	227	Hertz Global Holdings Inc (N	36,000	267	Red Robin Gourmet Burgers In	29,293
188	Quest Diagnostics, Inc.	43,000	228	Colgate–Palmolive Co.	35,900	268	BG Staffing Inc	29,291
189	Jones Financial Companies LL	43,000	229	Big Lots, Inc.	35,100	269	AbbVie Inc	29,000
190	Abercrombie & Fitch Co	43,000	230	Casey's General Stores, Inc.	35,014	270	Supervalu Inc	29,000
191	Sherwin–Williams Co (The)	42,550	231	Exelon Corp	34,621	271	BorgWarner Inc	29,000
192	LKQ Corp	42,500	232	Ryder System, Inc.	34,500	272	Boston Scientific Corp.	29,000
193	Waste Management, Inc. (DE)	42,300	233	Goldman Sachs Group Inc	34,400	273	Dover Corp	29,000
194	Kimberly–Clark Corp.	42,000	234	Command Center Inc	34,219	274	Rockwell Collins Inc	29,000
195	Cintas Corp	42,000	235	Micron Technology Inc.	34,100	275	Duke Energy Corp	28,798
196	Union Pacific Corp	41,992	236	Baker Hughes A GE Co	34,000	276	TTM Technologies Inc	28,360
197	Eli Lilly & Co	41,975	237	Qualcomm Inc	33,800	277	Frontier Communications Corp	28,300
198	Becton Dickinson And Co	41,933	238	State Street Corp.	33,783	278	Williams Sonoma Inc	28,300
199	Arconic Inc	41,500	239	NCR Corp.	33,500	279	AMERCO	28,300
200	Select Medical Holdings Corp	41,500	240	Vail Resorts Inc	33,500	280	Quanta Services, Inc.	28,100
201	AMC Entertainment Holdings I	41,373	241	Stryker Corp	33,000	281	Sprint Corp (New)	28,000
202	Cigna Corp	41,000	242	Republic Services Inc	33,000	282	ManpowerGroup	28,000
203	Burlington Northern & Santa F	41,000	243	Southern Co.	32,020	283	Encompass Health Corp	27,908
204	Regis Corp.	41,000	244	Leidos Holdings Inc	32,000	284	Amkor Technology Inc.	27,900
205	Corning Inc	40,700	245	Mattel Inc	32,000	285	KBR Inc	27,500
206	Dick's Sporting Goods, Inc	40,500	246	YRC Worldwide Inc	32,000	286	Genesco Inc.	27,200
207	Cardinal Health, Inc.	40,400	247	ON Semiconductor Corp	32,000	287	Norfolk Southern Corp.	27,110
208	Acadia Healthcare Company In	40,400	248	National Oilwell Varco Inc	31,889	288	Gallagher (Arthur J.) & Co.	26,800
209	CenturyLink Inc	40,000	249	Ulta Beauty Inc	31,800	289	Civitas Solutions Inc	26,700
210	Genuine Parts Co.	40,000	250	Progressive Corp. (OH)	31,721	290	Owens–Illinois, Inc.	26,500
211	Dillard's Inc.	40,000	251	Archer Daniels Midland Co.	31,300	291	Praxair Inc	26,498
212	Burlington Stores Inc	40,000	252	Bright Horizons Family Solut	31,200	292	Avon Products, Inc.	26,400
213	Pilgrims Pride Corp.	39,600	253	Tenneco Inc	31,000	293	AutoNation, Inc.	26,000
214	Kraft Heinz Co (The)	39,000	254	EMCOR Group, Inc.	31,000	294	News Corp (New)	26,000
215	Cheesecake Factory Inc. (The	38,800	255	Caesars Entertainment Corp	31,000	295	Masco Corp.	26,000
216	American Eagle Outfitters, I	38,700	256	Energy Transfer Equity LP	30,992	296	Tractor Supply Co.	26,000
217	General Mills, Inc.	38,000	257	Travelers Companies Inc (The	30,800	297	Cerner Corp.	26,000
218	Office Depot, Inc.	38,000	258	Contene Corp	30,500	298	Barnes & Noble Inc	26,000
219	L3 Technologies Inc	38,000	259	Dana Inc	30,100	299	ExlService Holdings Inc	26,000
220	Mohawk Industries, Inc.	37,800	260	Tesla Inc	30,025	300	Express Scripts Holding Co	25,600

The 300 Largest Companies by Net Income in Mergent's Database

Rank	Company	Net Income ($ mil.)	Rank	Company	Net Income ($ mil.)	Rank	Company	Net Income ($ mil.)
1	Apple Inc	$48,351	62	Merck & Co Inc	$3,920	123	Northrop Grumman Corp	$2,015
2	JPMorgan Chase & Co	$24,733	63	Mastercard Inc	$3,915	124	Lockheed Martin Corp	$2,002
3	Berkshire Hathaway Inc	$24,074	64	PNC Financial Services Group	$3,903	125	Amgen Inc	$1,979
4	Comcast Corp	$22,714	65	Exelon Corp	$3,770	126	Molson Coors Brewing Co.	$1,976
5	Wells Fargo & Co.	$21,938	66	Capital One Financial Corp	$3,751	127	Kroger Co (The)	$1,975
6	Microsoft Corporation	$21,204	67	Corning Inc	$3,695	128	Waste Management, Inc. (DE)	$1,949
7	Bank of America Corp.	$17,906	68	Texas Instruments, Inc.	$3,595	129	PPL Corp	$1,902
8	Johnson & Johnson	$16,540	69	Bank of New York Mellon Corp	$3,547	130	Charles Schwab Corp	$1,889
9	Facebook Inc	$15,934	70	Southwest Airlines Co	$3,488	131	SunTrust Banks Inc	$1,878
10	Procter & Gamble Co (The)	$15,326	71	Applied Materials, Inc.	$3,434	132	Allstate Corp.	$1,877
11	Citigroup Inc	$14,912	72	United Parcel Service Inc	$3,431	133	Viacom Inc	$1,874
12	Altria Group Inc	$14,239	73	Express Scripts Holding Co	$3,404	134	Cigna Corp	$1,867
13	Walmart Inc	$13,643	74	BlackRock Inc	$3,172	135	Simon Property Group, Inc.	$1,839
14	Gilead Sciences Inc	$13,501	75	Lowe's Companies Inc	$3,093	136	PayPal Holdings Inc	$1,795
15	Verizon Communications Inc	$13,127	76	Amazon.com Inc	$3,033	137	Tyson Foods Inc	$1,774
16	AT&T Inc	$12,976	77	Ford Motor Credit Company LL	$3,007	138	Marsh & McLennan Companies I	$1,768
17	Alphabet Inc	$12,662	78	Air Products & Chemicals Inc	$3,000	139	Automatic Data Processing In	$1,733
18	Fannie Mae	$12,313	79	FedEx Corp	$2,997	140	Florida Power & Light Co.	$1,727
19	International Business Machi	$11,872	80	21st Century Fox Inc	$2,952	141	Lam Research Corp	$1,698
20	Kraft Heinz Co (The)	$10,999	81	Celgene Corp	$2,940	142	Franklin Resources, Inc.	$1,697
21	Union Pacific Corp	$10,712	82	Mondelez International Inc	$2,922	143	Adobe Systems Inc	$1,694
22	UnitedHealth Group Inc	$10,558	83	General Dynamics Corp	$2,912	144	Illinois Tool Works, Inc.	$1,687
23	Charter Communications Inc (	$9,895	84	HCA Healthcare Inc	$2,890	145	Las Vegas Sands Corp	$1,670
24	Cisco Systems Inc	$9,609	85	Starbucks Corp.	$2,885	146	NVIDIA Corp	$1,666
25	Intel Corp	$9,601	86	Eli Lilly & Co	$2,738	147	PG&E Corp (Holding Co)	$1,660
26	Oracle Corp	$9,335	87	Target Corp	$2,737	148	General Mills, Inc.	$1,658
27	Disney (Walt) Co. (The)	$8,980	88	American Express Co.	$2,736	149	Honeywell International Inc	$1,655
28	General Electric Co	$8,831	89	Costco Wholesale Corp	$2,679	150	Duke Realty Corp	$1,634
29	Boeing Co.	$8,197	90	American Airlines Group Inc	$2,676	151	Yum! Brands Inc	$1,619
30	Home Depot Inc	$7,957	91	AFLAC Inc.	$2,659	152	Archer Daniels Midland Co.	$1,595
31	Prudential Financial, Inc.	$7,863	92	Danaher Corp	$2,554	153	PPG Industries Inc	$1,591
32	Exxon Mobil Corp	$7,840	93	Biogen Inc	$2,539	154	Fifth Third Bancorp (Cincinn	$1,564
33	Freddie Mac	$7,815	94	HP Inc	$2,526	155	Phillips 66	$1,555
34	Ford Motor Co. (DE)	$7,602	95	Intercontinental Exchange In	$2,514	156	Cognizant Technology Solutio	$1,553
35	Goldman Sachs Group Inc	$7,398	96	Enterprise Products Partners	$2,513	157	Constellation Brands Inc	$1,535
36	Pfizer Inc	$7,215	97	Southern Co.	$2,493	158	CME Group Inc	$1,534
37	Visa Inc	$6,699	98	Anthem Inc	$2,470	159	Emerson Electric Co.	$1,518
38	CVS Health Corp	$6,622	99	Qualcomm Inc	$2,466	160	EQT Corp	$1,509
39	Coca-Cola Co (The)	$6,527	100	BB&T Corp.	$2,426	161	Praxair Inc	$1,500
40	Philip Morris International	$6,035	101	Discover Financial Services	$2,393	162	Southern California Edison C	$1,499
41	Morgan Stanley	$5,979	102	Principal Financial Group In	$2,310	163	T Rowe Price Group, Inc.	$1,498
42	U.S. Bancorp (DE)	$5,888	103	TJX Companies, Inc.	$2,298	164	S&P Global Inc	$1,496
43	CSX Corp	$5,471	104	Liberty Expedia Holdings Inc	$2,292	165	DowDuPont Inc	$1,460
44	Norfolk Southern Corp.	$5,404	105	Valero Energy Corp	$2,289	166	Public Storage	$1,454
45	NextEra Energy Inc	$5,378	106	Kimberly-Clark Corp.	$2,278	167	Dish Network Corp	$1,450
46	AbbVie Inc	$5,309	107	Aetna Inc.	$2,271	168	Annaly Capital Management In	$1,434
47	Micron Technology Inc.	$5,089	108	United Continental Holdings	$2,263	169	Marriott International, Inc.	$1,372
48	McKesson Corp	$5,070	109	Monsanto Co	$2,260	170	Sempra Energy	$1,371
49	Baxter International Inc	$4,965	110	Synchrony Financial	$2,251	171	Ventas Inc	$1,356
50	3M Co	$4,858	111	Energy XXI Gulf Coast Inc	$2,248	172	Georgia Power Co	$1,347
51	PepsiCo Inc	$4,857	112	Deere & Co.	$2,159	173	United Rentals Inc	$1,346
52	McDonald's Corp	$4,687	113	Duke Energy Corp	$2,152	174	M & T Bank Corp	$1,315
53	United Technologies Corp	$4,552	114	State Street Corp.	$2,143	175	Ameriprise Financial Inc	$1,314
54	T-Mobile US Inc	$4,536	115	Priceline Group Inc (The)	$2,135	176	Lear Corp.	$1,313
55	ERP Operating L.P.	$4,464	116	Dominion Energy Inc (New)	$2,123	177	Edison International	$1,311
56	Delta Air Lines Inc (DE)	$4,373	117	Travelers Companies Inc (The	$2,056	178	GGP Inc	$1,288
57	Equity Residential	$4,292	118	Liberty Broadband Corp	$2,034	179	Cardinal Health, Inc.	$1,288
58	Burlington Northern & Santa F	$4,260	119	Publix Super Markets, Inc.	$2,026	180	AutoZone, Inc.	$1,281
59	NIKE Inc	$4,240	120	Raytheon Co.	$2,024	181	CBS Corp	$1,261
60	Walgreens Boots Alliance Inc	$4,078	121	Colgate-Palmolive Co.	$2,024	182	L Brands, Inc.	$1,253
61	Time Warner Inc	$3,926	122	Thermo Fisher Scientific Inc	$2,022	183	CME Group Inc	$1,247

SOURCE: MERGENT INC., JANUARY 2018

Rank	Company	Net Income ($ mil.)	Rank	Company	Net Income ($ mil.)	Rank	Company	Net Income ($ mil.)
184	Consolidated Edison Inc	$1,245	223	Lear Corp.	$975	262	Eastman Chemical Co	$848
185	AutoZone, Inc.	$1,241	224	Northern Trust Corp.	$974	263	Alaska Air Group, Inc.	$848
186	Tennessee Valley Authority	$1,233	225	Baxter International Inc.	$968	264	Dr Pepper Snapple Group Inc	$847
187	VF Corp.	$1,232	226	Stanley Black & Decker Inc	$965	265	TD Ameritrade Holding Corp	$842
188	Spectra Energy Partners LP	$1,225	227	Sysco Corp	$950	266	Bed, Bath & Beyond, Inc.	$841
189	T Rowe Price Group, Inc.	$1,215	228	Antero Resources Corp	$941	267	Citizens Financial Group Inc	$840
190	Prologis Inc	$1,210	229	Moody's Corp.	$941	268	MetLife Insurance Company of	$839
191	Exelon Corp	$1,204	230	International Paper Co	$938	269	Camden Property Trust	$838
192	Discovery Communications, In	$1,194	231	Toyota Motor Credit Corp.	$932	270	Jones Financial Companies LL	$838
193	Energy Transfer Equity LP	$1,189	232	O'Reilly Automotive, Inc.	$931	271	Western Union Co	$838
194	Energy Transfer Corp LP	$1,189	233	Gap Inc	$920	272	Santander Consumer USA Holdi	$827
195	Waste Management, Inc. (DE)	$1,182	234	KeyCorp	$916	273	Amphenol Corp.	$823
196	MGIC Investment Corp. (WI)	$1,172	235	Lam Research Corp	$914	274	Zoetis Inc	$821
197	Adobe Systems Inc	$1,169	236	Lennar Corp	$912	275	Magellan Midstream Partners	$819
198	Dollar General Corp	$1,165	237	Equity Residential	$908	276	Alabama Power Co.	$811
199	Electronic Arts	$1,156	238	Vornado Realty Trust	$907	277	Boston Properties L.P.	$809
200	Lincoln National Corp.	$1,154	239	ERP Operating L.P.	$904	278	Parker-Hannifin Corp	$807
201	Omnicom Group, Inc.	$1,149	240	Plains All American Pipeline	$903	279	Vornado Realty L.P.	$804
202	Lauder (Estee) Cos., Inc. (T	$1,115	241	Celanese Corp (DE)	$900	280	CA Inc	$783
203	Southern California Edison C	$1,111	242	Best Buy Inc	$897	281	Marriott International, Inc.	$780
204	Virginia Electric & Power Co	$1,087	243	Regeneron Pharmaceuticals, I	$896	282	Grainger (W.W.), Inc.	$769
205	Consolidated Edison Co. of N	$1,084	244	Popular Inc.	$895	283	Paychex Inc	$757
206	Duke Energy Carolinas LLC	$1,081	245	RiverSource Life Insurance C	$895	284	Dish Network Corp	$747
207	M & T Bank Corp	$1,080	246	Kimco Realty Corp.	$894	285	SCANA Corp	$746
208	Qwest Corp	$1,074	247	Activision Blizzard, Inc.	$892	286	Sirius XM Holdings Inc	$746
209	Macy's Inc	$1,072	248	Hormel Foods Corp.	$890	287	AvalonBay Communities, Inc.	$742
210	Brown-Forman Corp.	$1,067	249	Welltower Inc	$889	288	HollyFrontier Corp.	$740
211	Regions Financial Corp	$1,062	250	Whirlpool Corp	$888	289	Southern Copper Corp	$736
212	CIT Group, Inc.	$1,057	251	Horton (D.R.) Inc.	$886	290	Intuitive Surgical Inc	$736
213	Constellation Brands Inc	$1,055	252	Eversource Energy	$886	291	Tesoro Corporation	$734
214	Sherwin-Williams Co (The)	$1,054	253	Prologis LP	$881	292	T-Mobile US Inc	$733
215	Ross Stores, Inc.	$1,021	254	CenturyLink, Inc.	$878	293	Rockwell Automation, Inc.	$730
216	Ecolab Inc	$1,002	255	PPG Industries Inc	$877	294	Rockwell Collins, Inc.	$728
217	VMware Inc	$997	256	Liberty Interactive Corp	$869	295	Fiserv Inc	$712
218	Navient Corp	$997	257	DTE Energy Co	$868	296	Blackstone Group LP	$710
219	Skyworks Solutions, Inc.	$995	258	Unum Group	$867	297	Quest Diagnostics, Inc.	$709
220	Xcel Energy, Inc.	$984	259	Fortive Corp	$864	298	Kinder Morgan Inc.	$708
221	Intuit Inc	$979	260	Analog Devices Inc	$862	299	Genuine Parts Co.	$706
222	Becton, Dickinson & Co.	$976	261	PSEG Power LLC	$856	300	KLA-Tencor Corp.	$704

Hoover's Handbook of

Emerging Companies

2019

1-800 Flowers.com, Inc.

Some say it's all in the name but 1-800-FLOW-ERS.COM does more than deliver the daisies. The company sells fresh-cut flowers floral arrangements and plants through its toll-free number and websites; it also markets gifts for every occasion via catalog TV and radio ads and third-party online affiliates. Through subsidiaries 1-800-FLOWERS.COM offers gift baskets gourmet foods chocolates and candies cookies and popcorn. Its BloomNet service provides products and services to florists too. Inspired by the emergence of toll-free calling founder and CEO James McCann launched the flower business in 1976 and over time established a national brand that was further fueled by the evolution of the Internet.

Geographic Reach
Aside from its online business 1-800-FLOWERS operates a retail store in New York and eight retail shops across the Midwest. Its nearly 200 franchised floral stores operate in some of the country's top retail markets such as New York Los Angeles Chicago San Francisco San Diego and Phoenix among others.

Sales and Marketing
1-800-FLOWERS works to make its business synonymous with "sending smiles." To this end the retailer aims to reach customers through online and offline media direct marketing public relations and strategic Internet partnerships. In fiscal 2014 the firm's advertising expenses reached $83 million up steadily from $77.9 million in 2013 and $75.1 million in 2012.

Financial Performance
1-800-FLOWERS rang up $756.3 million in revenue in fiscal 2014 (ended June) — representing a $20.8 million increase from 2013's $735.5 million — following several years of steady gains. Driving growth were an $9.8 million increase in its 1-800-FLOWERS consumer floral business combined with both BloomNet Wire Service revenue (a 3% gain) and Gourmet Food & Gift Baskets revenue (4% rise). The retailer's net income has fluctuated during the past five years. In 2014 1-800-FLOWERS posted a profit of $15.4 million a 25% increase from 2013. Increased sales in 2014 were dragged down by rising operating expenses from marketing and sales technology and development and general and administrative expenses.

Strategy
Going forward 1-800-FLOWERS.COM is adopting a strategy that focuses on controlling costs while merchandising original new products across all business categories that ring up a higher average order. (Formerly the company used promotional pricing and markdowns and free shipping to woo demand.)

The shift in strategy is likely to most impact its consumer floral sales business. During 2011 1-800-FLOWERS.COM added to the business' offerings by acquiring Fine Stationery an online retailer of personalized stationery invitation and announcements. More significant in reversing an unfavorable trend in the consumer floral business the company cites its marketing efforts led by its 2010 launch of a mobile shopping app Mobile Flower & Gift Center. Quick turnaround is further facilitated by BloomNet 1-800-FLOWERS.COM's network of independent local florists.

Mergers and Acquisitions

The online flower giant expanded its menu to include gift baskets and gourmet foods with its purchase of Oregon-based Harry & David Holdings (HDH) known for its Royal Riviera Pears and Moose Munch popcorn snacks. The company offered $142.5 million in cash for HDH whose sales are approaching $400 million. The deal which includes HDH's brands and websites as well as its manufacturing and distribution facilities and orchards in Medford Oregon and 47 retail stores throughout the country among other assets closed in September 2014. The acquisition is consistent with 1-800-FLOWERS.COM's strategy of pursuing a competitive position in the gourmet food and gift basket marketplace.

HISTORY

Social worker Jim McCann bought a New York City florist shop in 1976 to supplement his income from St. John's Home for Boys. By 1986 he had expanded his Flora Plenty chain to 14 shops in the New York metropolitan area and made the floral business his full-time job.

The next year McCann paid $9 million for 1-800-FLOWERS a young struggling Dallas-based floral-delivery company that had been founded by John Davis and Jim Poage. McCann's shops had worked with 1-800-FLOWERS but he had to sell most of his Flora Plenty stores to keep the telemarketing business from wilting altogether. By 1990 however business was blossoming and 1-800-FLOWERS was profitable.

In 1992 the company began selling flowers online through Compuserve. 1-800-FLOWERS launched its own website three years later and teamed with online providers such as America Online (now Time Warner Inc.) and Microsoft Network.

1-800-FLOWERS added home and garden merchandise to its offerings — and picked up catalog expertise — when it bought an 80% stake in Plow & Hearth in 1998 (it acquired the remainder in 1999). In May 1999 the company received more than $100 million from Benchmark Capital Japanese technology firm SOFTBANK and luxury goods kingpin LVMH. 1-800-FLOWERS then added ".COM" to its name and went public in August 1999.

In late 1999 the company bought online gourmet foods retailer GreatFood.com for $18.5 million. It added jewelry to its offerings by teaming up with retailer Finlay Enterprises in 2000. It also launched its Spanish language Web site — 1-800-LASFLORES.COM. New additions in 2001 included a partnership with Touchpoint allowing customers to create personalized cards and photos and the addition of children's gifts dolls crafts and other toys and games with the acquisition of The Children's Group.

1-800-FLOWERS.COM continued its acquisitive ways in 2002 by acquiring The Popcorn Factory (direct marketing of premium popcorn chocolates and other food gift products packaged in decorative tins and baskets). That year the firm agreed to cross-promote its goods with American Greetings; under the agreement 1-800-FLOWERS.COM became the exclusive provider of flowers on several American Greetings Web sites. And in 2004 it got into the wine distribution business with its purchase of The Winetasting Network which is now a subsidiary.

In March 2005 the company acquired cookie-and-baked-gifts-maker Cheryl & Co. for an undis-

closed price. The company moved its corporate headquarters to Carle Place New York the next year. In mid-2006 the Internet flower company acquired candy maker Fannie May Confections Brands for $85 million.

1-800-FLOWERS.COM bought gourmet gift basket maker DesignPac Gifts in May 2008 for about $36 million. It also purchased Napco Marketing which wholesales and markets products for the floral industry for $9 million.

In March 2009 the company acquired certain assets of online wine seller Geerlings & Wade Inc. for about $2 million to complement its Winetasting Network business. It also launched 1-800-BASKETS.com that year.

To focus on its core floral and food units 1-800-FLOWERS.COM sold its home décor and children's gift brands to PH International a Virginia-based home décor distributor in January 2010. The deal which was worth $17 million included the brands of HearthSong Magic Cabin Plow & Hearth Problem Solvers and Wind & Weather.

EXECUTIVES

SVP Finance and Administration Treasurer and CFO, William E. Shea, age 59, $721,002 total compensation

SVP Retail and Fulfillment and COO Consumer Floral Brand, Thomas G. Hartnett, age 55

President and CEO, Christopher G. (Chris) McCann, age 57, $721,002 total compensation

President BloomNet, Mark Nance, age 68

President Gourmet Foods and Gift Baskets, David L. (Dave) Taiclet, age 55, $439,409 total compensation

CIO, Arnold P. (Arnie) Leap

Vice President Ecommerce Product Management, Chris Barca

Vice President Multi Brand Customer: Enterprise Marketing, Jon Mandell

Vice President Merchandising Consumer Floral, Alfred Palomares

Vice President, Brian Mcgee

Vice President Quality Assurance and Delivery Manager, Robert Schumann

Senior Vice President, Ted Nelson

Vice President of Financial Reporting and Taxation, Scott Archila

Senior Vice President Information Technology and Chief Technology Officer, Harriet Harriet Wolpin Wolpin

National Sales Manager, Earl Hurd

Vice President, Joseph Pititto

Vice President Operations, David French

Senior Vice President Business Development And Strategy, Ed Slezak

Vice President Technology, Marc Grzeskowiak

Vice President Creative, Mark Lefkin

Vice President Information Technology Operations, Angel Rivera

Vice President of Corporate Systems, Phil Disanto

Vice President Retail and Franchising, Ted Marlowe

Senior Vice President and Chief Financial Officer, Bill Shea

SVP BloomNet, Vincent McVeigh

Executive Chairman, James F. (Jim) McCann, age 67

Board Member, Celia Brown

Auditors: BDO USA, LLP

LOCATIONS

HQ: 1-800 Flowers.com, Inc.
One Old Country Road, Carle Place, NY 11514
Phone: 516 237-6000
Web: www.1800flowers.com

PRODUCTS/OPERATIONS

2016 sales

	$ mil.	% of total
1-800-Flowers.com consumer floral	418.5	36
Gourmet food & gift baskets	670.5	57
BloomNet Wire Service	85.5	7
Corporate	1.0	-
Adjustments	(2.5)	-
Total	**1,173.0**	**100**

2016 sales

	$ mil.	% of total
E-commerce	882.8	75
Other	290.2	25
Total	**1,173.0**	**100**

Selected Brands

The BloomNet Wire Service
  BloomNet
  BloomNet Technologies
  Napco
Consumer floral
  1-800-Flowers.com
  Celebrations
  FineStationery.com
Gourmet Food and Gift Baskets
  1-800-Baskets
  Cheryl's
  Mrs. Beasley's
  DesignPac
  Fannie May Confections Brands
  Fannie May
  Harry London
  Harry & David
  The Popcorn Factory
  Wintasting.com

Selected Products and Services

BloomNet products and services
  Advertising
  Member directories
  On-line directory
  Clearinghouse services
  Communications services
  Bloomlink
  Other services
  Point of sale
  Web hosting
  Wholesale products
  Branded and non-branded floral supplies
Flowers and plants
  Floral arrangements
  Fresh-cut flowers
  Plants
Gourmet foods and gift baskets
  Chocolate and candy
  Cookies and baked gift items
  Gourmet gift baskets
  Popcorn and specialty snack products
  Wine

Selected Domain Names

www.1800flowers.com
www.800flowers.com
www.1800baskets.com
www.ambrosiawine.com
www.celebrations.com
www.cheryls.com
www.designpac.com
www.fanniemay.com
www.finestationery.com
www.flowers.com
www.geerwade.com
www.greatfood.com
www.harrylondon.com
www.mybloomnet.net
www.napcoimports.com
www.thepopcornfactory.com

COMPETITORS

AMES International	Hickory Farms
Dean & DeLuca	KaBloom
Edible Arrangements	Martha Stewart Living
FTD	Provide Commerce
Godiva Chocolatier	Teleflora
Hallmark	Vermont Teddy Bear

HISTORICAL FINANCIALS

Company Type: Public

Income Statement
FYE: July 1

	REVENUE ($ mil.)	NET INCOME ($ mil.)	NET PROFIT MARGIN	EMPLOYEES
07/18	1,151.9	40.7	3.5%	4,785
07/17	1,193.6	44.0	3.7%	4,633
07/16*	1,173.0	36.8	3.1%	4,490
06/15	1,121.5	20.2	1.8%	4,524
06/14	756.3	15.3	2.0%	2,034
Annual Growth	**11.1%**	**27.6%**		**23.8%**

*Fiscal year change

2018 Year-End Financials

Debt ratio: 17.9%
Return on equity: 13.7%
Cash ($ mil.): 147.2
Current ratio: 2.19
Long-term debt ($ mil.): 92.2
No. of shares (mil.): 64.6
Dividends
  Yield: —
  Payout: —
Market value ($ mil.): 811.0

	STOCK PRICE ($) FY Close	P/E High/Low	Earnings	Dividends	Book Value
07/18	12.55	21 13	0.61	0.00	4.87
07/17	9.75	16 13	0.65	0.00	4.33
07/16*	8.99	19 11	0.55	0.00	3.72
06/15	10.38	42 16	0.30	0.00	3.21
06/14	5.74	30 19	0.23	0.00	2.86
Annual Growth	**21.6%**	**— —**	**27.6%**	**—**	**14.3%**

*Fiscal year change

1ST Constitution Bancorp

In order to "secure the blessings of liberty" the founding fathers established the US Constitution. As for promoting the general welfare some banks share the same dedication to "We the people." 1st Constitution Bancorp is the parent of 1st Constitution Bank which serves consumers small businesses and not-for-profits through more than a dozen branches in Middlesex Mercer and Somerset counties in New Jersey. Services and products include demand savings and time deposits as well as loans and mortgages. Commercial mortgages business loans and construction loans make up more than half of the bank's lending portfolio.

In 2011 1st Constitution acquired three branch locations from another New Jersey company Amboy Bank. The acquisition added some $110 million in deposits and boosted the company's presence in Mercer and Somerset counties.

EXECUTIVES

Vice President, Tom Berger
Vice President Commercial Loans, Steve Landau
Auditors: BDO USA, LLP

LOCATIONS

HQ: 1ST Constitution Bancorp
2650 Route 130, P.O. Box 634, Cranbury, NJ 08512
Phone: 609 655-4500
Web: www.1stconstitution.com

COMPETITORS

Amboy Bancorp	Provident Financial
Bank of America	Services
Brunswick Bancorp	Sovereign Bank
Hudson City Bancorp	Sun Bancorp (NJ)
OceanFirst Financial	Wells Fargo
PNC Financial	

HISTORICAL FINANCIALS

Company Type: Public

Income Statement
FYE: December 31

	ASSETS ($ mil.)	NET INCOME ($ mil.)	INCOME AS % OF ASSETS	EMPLOYEES
12/17	1,079.2	6.9	0.6%	185
12/16	1,038.2	9.2	0.9%	206
12/15	967.9	8.6	0.9%	183
12/14	956.7	4.3	0.5%	187
12/13	742.3	5.7	0.8%	173
Annual Growth	**9.8%**	**4.6%**	**—**	**1.7%**

2017 Year-End Financials

Return on assets: 0.6%
Return on equity: 6.4%
Long-term debt ($ mil.): —
No. of shares (mil.): 8.0
Sales ($ mil): 49.9
Dividends
  Yield: 0.0%
  Payout: 19.2%
Market value ($ mil.): 148.0

	STOCK PRICE ($) FY Close	P/E High/Low	Earnings	Dividends	Book Value
12/17	18.30	23 19	0.83	0.16	13.81
12/16	18.70	16 10	1.14	0.10	13.11
12/15	12.87	12 10	1.07	0.00	12.72
12/14	10.89	19 17	0.58	0.00	11.63
12/13	11.00	13 10	0.86	0.00	10.30
Annual Growth	**13.6%**	**— —**	**(0.9%)**	**—**	**7.6%**

ABIOMED, Inc.

ABIOMED gives weary hearts a rest. The medical device maker has developed a range of cardiac assist devices and is developing a self-contained artificial heart. Its Impella micro heart pumps can temporarily take over blood circulation during surgery or catheterization. Its AB5000 ventricular assist device temporarily takes over the heart's pumping function and improves circulatory flow in patients with acute heart failure thus allowing their hearts to rest and recover. ABIOMED markets its products through both a direct sales force and distributors.

Operations

ABIOMED has also developed a battery-powered implantable replacement heart system called AbioCor which can be used to extend life for dying patients who aren't eligible for a heart transplant. ABIOMED developed the AbioCor system based on technology developed at Pennsylvania State University. However due to the limited number of patients that qualify for use of the AbioCor the company places little emphasis on marketing efforts for this product line.

Geographic Reach

While many of ABIOMED's products are approved for use in other countries international sales to Canada parts of Europe Asia South America and the Middle East only make up some 10% of its revenue. The company intends to improve its international results with more sales and support teams in Europe. It manufactures its Impella products at a facility in Germany while the rest of its products are made in Massachusetts.

In addition to its locations in Massachusetts and Aachen Germany the company has a sales and marketing office in Paris and another office in Tokyo where it is preparing for a commercial launch of products.

Financial Performance

After years of steady sales growth ABIOMED made its first profit in 2012. Sales have continued to rise and in fiscal 2015 (ended March) revenue rose 25% to $230.3 million on higher sales of the Impella system. This was largely due to disposable catheter sales in the US and growing business in Europe primarily Germany.

Net income jumped more than 1000% in fiscal 2015 to $113.7 million. That sharp increase was driven both by the higher revenues and changes in income tax benefit provisions. Operating cash flow increased 84% to $43.3 million that year.

Strategy

The company's research efforts are focused on developing new products for acute heart failure patients as well as next-generation versions and support systems for its existing products. The company has shifted more of its development and sales efforts onto the Impella product line in order to expand its uses and variations while gradually discontinuing its other products.

In addition to expanding its product portfolio and approvals the company also dedicates personnel and financial resources to raising awareness of its products in the medical community. ABIOMED also continuously evaluates opportunities for strategic acquisitions. To that end it acquired a German heart catheter pump maker in 2014 ex panding its product line and German sales efforts.

Mergers and Acquisitions

In 2014 as part of its plan to expand it product line and its German sales force ABIOMED purchased Berlin-based ECP Entwicklungsgesellschaft for $14 million. ECP produces heart catheter pumps that use an external drive shaft to increase circulation.

HISTORY

David Lederman founded ABIOMED in 1981 to make products he had designed (such as artificial heart pumps and valves) as well as dental diagnostic products. ABIOMED went public in 1987. In 1988 it got about $1 million from the National Institutes of Health for heart replacement device (HRD) research and development. In 1990 it began working with Canada's World Heart on HRD technology. In 1992 ABIOMED launched BVS-5000.

In 1990 the company formed ABIODENT to consolidate its dental operations. It received FDA clearance to market the PerioTemp device in 1994. In 1996 it voluntarily recalled some of its BVS-5000 blood pumps citing component irregularities (it said no patients were affected).

To fund product development ABIOMED accepted government funding to finish testing its battery-powered HRD (1996) and to develop a laser-based tissue-welding system (1998). Biotech firm Genzyme invested about $15 million in ABIOMED that year acquiring 14% of the firm.

In 1998 ABIOMED again recalled some lots of BVS-5000 this time for electrical problems. The company attributed 1998's losses to an increase in self-funding on the HRD project as well as to red ink in its now-discontinued dental business.

ABIOMED received funding from the National Heart Lung and Blood Institutes in 2000 to support the testing of its AbioCor product an implantable heart replacement device. The following year AbioCor became the first artificial heart implanted in a patient.

The FDA approved the use of the artificial hearts in five patients in 2001 all of whom were considered too sick to receive heart transplants. The first patient died the same year but the cause of death was not attributed to AbioCor.

The fifth patient to receive the device died early in 2002. By late 2002 seven patients had been fitted with the device but only one was living. A moratorium on recruiting new patients was imposed. ABIOMED wanted patients that were healthy enough to live long past the time of implantation but only patients that were extremely ill would be considered candidates for the device.

By January of 2003 the moratorium had been lifted and three more patients had received implants by March. Because of the troubles with finding qualified recipients for its AbioCor product the company began focusing on other products to sustain revenues. It got good news on that front that same year when the FDA approved ABIOMED's AB5000 Circulatory Support System Console a device that temporarily pumps the patient's blood when the heart has failed.

EXECUTIVES

President CEO and Director, Michael R. Minogue, age 51, $519,663 total compensation
Chief Medical Officer, Karim Benali, age 52, $171,200 total compensation
VP Healthcare Solutions, Andrew J. Greenfield, age 46, $211,592 total compensation
CTO, Thorsten Siess
COO, David M. Weber, age 57, $341,844 total compensation
VP and General Manager Global Sales and Marketing, Michael G. Howley, age 54, $296,970 total compensation
VP and CFO, Michael Tomsicek, age 52
Vice President Human Resources, Franky Leblanc
Medical Director, Daniel Raess
Vice President Asia Pacific, Geoffrey Christanday
Vice President Solutions Engineering, Mahoney Karen
Auditors: DELOITTE & TOUCHE LLP

LOCATIONS

HQ: ABIOMED, Inc.
22 Cherry Hill Drive, Danvers, MA 01923
Phone: 978 646-1400   **Fax:** 978 777-8411
Web: www.abiomed.com

PRODUCTS/OPERATIONS

2015 Revenues

	$ mil.	% of total
Impella products	212.7	92
Service & other revenue	13.8	6
Other products	3.5	2
Funded research & development	0.3	-
Total	**230.3**	**100**

COMPETITORS

CardiacAssist	St. Jude Medical
Edwards Lifesciences	Teleflex
Getinge	Terumo
HeartWare	Thoratec Corp
Medtronic	

HISTORICAL FINANCIALS

Company Type: Public

Income Statement

FYE: March 31

	REVENUE ($ mil.)	NET INCOME ($ mil.)	NET PROFIT MARGIN	EMPLOYEES
03/18	593.7	112.1	18.9%	1,143
03/17	445.3	52.1	11.7%	908
03/16	329.5	38.1	11.6%	747
03/15	230.3	113.6	49.4%	589
03/14	183.6	7.3	4.0%	511
Annual Growth	**34.1%**	**97.6%**	**—**	**22.3%**

2018 Year-End Financials

Debt ratio: —	No. of shares (mil.): 44.3
Return on equity: 79.7%	Dividends
Cash ($ mil.): 42.9	Yield: —
Current ratio: 5.84	Payout: —
Long-term debt ($ mil.): —	Market value ($ mil.): 12,913.0

	STOCK PRICE ($) FY Close	P/E High/Low		Earnings	PER SHARE ($) Dividends	Book Value
03/18	290.99	116	76	2.45	0.00	15.54
03/17	125.20	109	78	1.17	0.00	10.35
03/16	94.81	118	66	0.85	0.00	8.66
03/15	71.58	26	7	2.65	0.00	7.05
03/14	26.04	158	86	0.18	0.00	4.22
Annual Growth	**82.8%**	**—**	**—**	**92.1%**	**—**	**38.5%**

Acacia Communications Inc

Auditors: DELOITTE & TOUCHE LLP

LOCATIONS

HQ: Acacia Communications Inc
Three Mill and Main Place, Suite 400, Maynard, MA 01754
Phone: 978 938-4896
Web: www.acacia-inc.com

HISTORICAL FINANCIALS

Company Type: Public

Income Statement

FYE: December 31

	REVENUE ($ mil.)	NET INCOME ($ mil.)	NET PROFIT MARGIN	EMPLOYEES
12/17	385.1	38.5	10.0%	354
12/16	478.4	131.5	27.5%	290
12/15	239.0	40.5	17.0%	228
12/14	146.2	13.5	9.2%	0
Annual Growth	**38.1%**	**41.8%**	**—**	**—**

2017 Year-End Financials

Debt ratio: —
Return on equity: 8.2%
Cash ($ mil.): 279.4
Current ratio: 5.22
Long-term debt ($ mil.): —

No. of shares (mil.): 39.6
Dividends
Yield: —
Payout: —
Market value ($ mil.): 1,435.0

	STOCK PRICE ($)	P/E		PER SHARE ($)		
	FY Close	High/Low	Earnings	Dividends	Book Value
12/17	36.23	68 36	0.92	0.00	12.68
12/16	61.75	33 7	3.22	0.00	11.44
12/15	0.00	— —	0.91	0.00	11.82
Annual Growth	—	— —	0.5%	—	3.6%

Acadia Realty Trust

Acadia Realty acquires redevelops and manages retail properties in the Northeast Mid-Atlantic and Midwest. The self-managed real estate investment trust (REIT) specializes in community shopping centers and mixed-use properties in urban areas. It owns 90 properties — mostly shopping centers anchored by a grocery store drug store or big box store — sporting more than 5.5 million sq. ft. of leasable space. The REIT's largest tenants include SUPERVALU Best Buy Stop & Shop Target and LA Fitness. Acadia Realty owns joint venture interests in another 60 similar properties with investments in self-storage units mortgage loans and other real estate investments.

Operations
Acadia Realty operates three business segments. Its Core Portfolio segment which generated 69% of the REIT's total revenue during 2015 counts its high-quality street retail and urban properties as well as suburban properties in densely-populated trade areas with high-barriers-to-entry. Acadia's Funds segment (23% of revenue) invests through joint ventures while the Structured Financing segment (8% of revenue) offers specialized loans.

Geographic Reach
The Rye New York-based REIT has 90 properties in California Delaware Indiana Massachusetts Pennsylvania New York Virginia and the District of Columbia.

Sales and Marketing
The company's top five largest tenants in 2015 included: Stop & Shop SUPERVALU Best Buy Target and LA Fitness. No individual tenant accounted for more than 3.1% of Acadia's rental revenue which represents a wide tenant base.

Financial Performance
Acadia Realty's annual revenues have risen 45% since 2011 as the REIT has expanded its property portfolio through acquisitions and has charged higher rental rates as the real estate market has strengthened. Its annual profits have also grown over 25% over the same period as a result.

The REIT's revenue climbed 11% to $217.26 million during 2015 mostly as new Core property acquisitions in 2015 and 2014 spurred additional rental income.

Despite double-digit revenue growth in 2015 Acadia Realty's net income tumbled nearly 8% to $65.71 million for the year as Core portfolio acquisition-related operating costs and associated income taxes increased. The REIT's operating cash levels jumped 38% to $113.5 million as its newly acquired Core and Fund properties increased cash-based rental revenue during the year.

Strategy
Since its founding in 1998 Acadia has focused on growing its portfolio in densely-populated high barrier-to-entry markets. Most of its properties also are anchored by discount and necessity stores (such as grocery stores and pharmacies) that rely less on discretionary consumer spending. Acadia also carefully culls low-growth and non-core properties. That strategy (along with a healthy balance sheet and access to fresh capital) helped Acadia weather the economic recession which was marked by high unemployment low consumer confidence and retailer bankruptcies.

Toward its core portfolio acquisition-growth strategy Acadia in late 2014 purchased an 88.4% interest in an 87000 square foot four-story street-retail property in Chicago for $144.3 million — an amount equal to more than half its 2015 revenues. This property located on Michigan Avenue was 100% occupied by Verizon and H&M which both maintained their long-term lease contracts.

Beyond its direct investment Acadia prefers to engage in discretionary fund joint ventures through which it can conduct its acquisition redevelopment and leasing activities. One such fund carries out its New York Urban Infill Redevelopment Initiative which is dedicated to retail and mixed-use redevelopment projects in dense urban areas of the New York metropolitan region. Another fund invests in properties owned by retailers.

EXECUTIVES

Senior Vice President Chief Accounting Officer, Richard Hartmann
SVP General Counsel Chief Compliance Officer and Corporate Secretary, Robert Masters, age 73, $327,500 total compensation
President and CEO, Kenneth F. Bernstein, age 56, $582,700 total compensation
EVP and CIO, Joel Braun, age 66, $404,000 total compensation
EVP and COO, Christopher Conlon, age 58, $381,900 total compensation
CFO, John Gottfried
Vice President Technology, David Rodriguez
Vice President Acquisitions, Reggie Livingston
Senior Vice President, Herb Eilberg
Vice President Chief Accounting Officer, Jon Grisham
Vice President Leasing, Michael Oliverio
Auditors: BDO USA, LLP

LOCATIONS

HQ: Acadia Realty Trust
411 Theodore Fremd Avenue, Suite 300, Rye, NY 10580
Phone: 914 288-8100
Web: www.acadiarealty.com

PRODUCTS/OPERATIONS

2015 Sales

	$ mil.	% of total
Rental income	158.6	73
Expense reimbursements	36.3	17
Interest income	16.6	8
Other	5.7	2
Total	217.2	100

2015 sales

	% of total
Core Portfolio	69
Funds	23
Structured Financing	8
Total	100

Selected Major Tenants
A&P (Waldbaum's Pathmark)
Ahold (Stop & Shop)
Barnes & Noble
Best Buy
BJ's Wholesale Club
CVS
Home Depot
JP Morgan Chase
LA Fitness
Pier 1 Imports
Restoration Hardware
Sleepy's
Stage Deli
Supervalu (Shaw's)
TJX Companies (T.J. Maxx Marshalls Homegoods)
Walgreens
Wal-Mart

COMPETITORS

Brixmor	Kimco Realty
CBL & Associates Properties	National Retail Properties
DDR	Pennsylvania Real Estate
Federal Realty Investment	Ramco-Gershenson Realty Income
GGP	

HISTORICAL FINANCIALS

Company Type: Public

Income Statement — FYE: December 31

	REVENUE ($ mil.)	NET INCOME ($ mil.)	NET PROFIT MARGIN	EMPLOYEES
12/17	250.2	61.4	24.6%	118
12/16	189.9	72.7	38.3%	122
12/15	217.2	65.7	30.2%	116
12/14	195.0	71.0	36.4%	114
12/13	168.2	40.1	23.8%	120
Annual Growth	10.4%	11.3%	—	(0.4%)

2017 Year-End Financials

Debt ratio: 37.7%
Return on equity: 3.9%
Cash ($ mil.): 74.8
Current ratio: 3.00
Long-term debt ($ mil.): 1,495.0

No. of shares (mil.): 83.7
Dividends
Yield: 0.0%
Payout: 143.8%
Market value ($ mil.): 2,290.0

	STOCK PRICE ($)	P/E		PER SHARE ($)		
	FY Close	High/Low	Earnings	Dividends	Book Value
12/17	27.36	46 37	0.73	1.05	18.72
12/16	32.68	40 33	0.94	1.16	19.00
12/15	33.15	39 30	0.94	1.22	15.66
12/14	32.03	28 21	1.18	1.23	15.50
12/13	24.83	41 32	0.72	0.86	12.66
Annual Growth	2.5%	— —	0.3%	5.1%	10.3%

Addus HomeCare Corp

Addus HomeCare is there for those who need in-home personal and medical care services. Doing business through subsidiary Addus HealthCare it serves the elderly and disabled. Its home and community unit provides long-term non-medical social services such as bathing grooming housekeeping meal preparation and transportation. State and county government payors generate most of its revenues. Operating from more than 100 locations Addus provides its services in about 25 states primarily in the midwestern and western US with its largest markets in Illinois California Nevada and Washington.

Operations

The company employs home care aides to cover a range of patient needs. In its home and community segment it also operates a handful of community adult day care centers in Illinois that offer social activities transportation exercise and cognitive therapy in a group setting.

Sales and Marketing

Addus provides personal and home support services that are reimbursed by state and county elder care programs. The Illinois Department of Aging is its largest customer (40% of revenues). Medicare is its second-largest payer group (12% of revenues) with Addus providing services to Medicare-eligible patients recovering from acute medical conditions. Other payer clients include the Veterans Health Administration commercial insurers and private individuals.

Strategy

Addus' ability to keep its net revenues growing is dependent on maintaining current payer client relationships winning new payers and increasing its referrals through coordinated care. It is also dependent on state agencies continuing to authorize home health care services to consumers. The company is focused on serving dual eligibility customers (patients that qualify for elderly and disability Medicare/Medicaid benefits). Addus is working widen the breadth of its service offerings open new offices and make strategic acquisitions of smaller providers in existing and new markets.

Mergers and Acquisitions

Addus regularly buys small to midsized home care companies to expand its operations. With the aging US population it expects demand for its offerings will continue to grow. In 2017 it bought Options Home Care which provides home care services in New Mexico. The following year it acquired another New Mexico firm Ambercare Corporation for some $40 million.

EXECUTIVES

EVP and Chief Human Resources Officer, Brenda A. Belger, age 63
President CEO and Director, R. Dirk Allison, age 62
EVP and COO, W. Bradley Bickham, age 55
Chief Business Development and Strategy Officer, Darby Anderson, age 52, $293,170 total compensation
CIO, James G. (Zeke) Zoccoli
EVP and CFO, Brian W. Poff
Auditors: Ernst & Young LLP

LOCATIONS

HQ: Addus HomeCare Corp
6801 Gaylord Parkway, Suite 110, Frisco, TX 75034
Phone: 469 535-8200
Web: www.addus.com

COMPETITORS

Active Day	Home Instead
Amedisys	LHC Group
American HomePatient	Lincare Holdings
Apria Healthcare	LivHOME
Critical Homecare Solutions	National Home Health
	Personal-Touch Home
Gentiva	Care
Girling Health Care	Star Multi Care
Guardian Home Care Holdings	Trinity HomeCare

HISTORICAL FINANCIALS

Company Type: Public

Income Statement

FYE: December 31

	REVENUE ($ mil.)	NET INCOME ($ mil.)	NET PROFIT MARGIN	EMPLOYEES
12/17	425.7	13.6	3.2%	26,097
12/16	400.6	12.0	3.0%	23,070
12/15	336.8	11.6	3.5%	21,395
12/14	312.9	12.2	3.9%	18,054
12/13	265.9	19.1	7.2%	16,585
Annual Growth	12.5%	(8.2%)	—	12.0%

2017 Year-End Financials

Debt ratio: 16.0%
Return on equity: 8.1%
Cash ($ mil.): 53.7
Current ratio: 2.90
Long-term debt ($ mil.): 39.8

No. of shares (mil.): 11.6
Dividends
Yield: —
Payout: —
Market value ($ mil.): 405.0

	STOCK PRICE ($) FY Close	P/E High/Low		PER SHARE ($) Earnings	Dividends	Book Value
12/17	34.80	34	25	1.17	0.00	15.05
12/16	35.05	34	15	1.06	0.00	13.79
12/15	23.28	34	18	1.04	0.00	12.76
12/14	24.27	26	15	1.10	0.00	11.62
12/13	22.45	18	4	1.73	0.00	10.43
Annual Growth	11.6%	—	—	(9.3%)	—	9.6%

Advanced Emissions Solutions Inc

Advanced Emissions Solutions wants to make "clean coal" more than just a marketing term. The company makes environmental technology systems and specialty chemicals to reduce emissions at coal-burning power plants. It offers integrated mercury control systems as well as flue gas conditioning and combustion aid chemicals. Advanced Emissions Solutions provides consulting and testing services and mercury measurement equipment. It also has a joint venture with NexGen Refined Coal to market technology that reduces emissions of nitrogen oxides and mercury from some treated coals. The company has three reportable segments: Refined Coal Emission Control and CO2 Capture.

Change in Company Type
Advanced Emissions Solutions took itself private in 2103.

Operations

The Refined Coal segment (92% of Advanced Emissions Solutions' 2012 revenues) includes revenues from coal facilities and sales.

The Emission Control segment includes revenues from the supply of emissions control systems including powdered activated carbon injection systems and dry sorbent injection systems to reduce emissions of pollutants (including particulate matter SO2 NOx mercury and acid gases) and from the licensing of technology and its consulting services.

The CO2 Capture segment generates revenues from the CO2 capture and control market including projects co-funded by the Department of Energy (DOE) and private industry.

Advanced Emissions Solutions' four subsidiaries are Advanced Emissions Solutions and ADA Intellectual Property LLC (neither of which had operations in 2012); BCSI; and ADA Environmental Solutions.

Advanced Emissions Solutions also holds 42.5% of Clean Coal Solutions a Colorado limited liability company. The joint venture's partners include an affiliate of NexGen Resources and an affiliate of Goldman Sachs.

Financial Performance

The company's revenues grew by almost 300% in 2012 primarily due to the increased rental income from leased Refined Coal facilities and higher Refined Coal sales from raw coal purchases that Clean Coal Solutions operated on its own account.

Emission Control revenues increased due to increased systems and equipment sales and flue gas chemicals and services. This was partially offset by lower consulting revenues as a result of potential clients deferring compliance work until 2013.

Advanced Emissions Solutions' net loss decreased by 34% in 2012 thanks to higher revenues a decrease in legal and settlement costs associated with its arbitration and litigation and higher net income from unconsolidated entities as a result of the relinquishment of its interest in ADA Carbon Solutions in late 2011. This was partially offset by the absence of a deferred income tax benefit.

Strategy

Advanced Emissions Solutions sees the activated carbon market growing rapidly as coal-fired power plants in 19 states and four Canadian provinces move to meet mercury mitigation regulations and as other governments promulgate new rules.

In 2012 it had several consulting R&D contracts funded by the DOE industry groups and Advanced Emissions Solutions aimed at controlling mercury emissions through dry sorbent injection systems providing CO2 capture and supporting other Refined Coal and Emission Control activities.

That year the Clean Coal Solutions joint venture finalized a contract for a fifth Refined Coal facility with a new investor with a value for Advanced Emissions Solutions of $10 million. The JV subsequently leased two additional Refined Coal facilities to an existing coal investor for $14 million.

Mergers and Acquisitions

In 2012 the company spent $2 million in cash and $3 million (in payouts over time) to acquire the assets of Bulk Conveyor Specialist a maker of systems coal-fired power plants use to reduce acid gas emissions. The acquisition includes a manufacturing facility and Bulk Conveyor Services which provides testing and related services. The purchase positions Advanced Emissions Solutions to take advantage of upcoming EPA mandates to reduce the level of acid gas emissions from coal-fired plants. The assets are held in a wholly-owned subsidiary BCSI.

The acquisition increases the company's market leading position in commercial acid gas control and allows the company to vertically-integrate its Emissions Control business operations including expanding its capacity to supply Activated Carbon Injection systems.

Auditors: Moss Adams LLP

LOCATIONS

HQ: Advanced Emissions Solutions Inc
  640 Plaza Drive, Suite 270, Highlands Ranch, CO 80129
Phone: 720 598-3500
Web: www.advancedemissionssolutions.com

PRODUCTS/OPERATIONS

2012 Sales

	$ mil.	% of total
Refined Coal		
Coal sales		**157.9**
75		
Rental income	36.9	17
Other	0.1	-
Emission Control		
Systems & equipment	9.6	5
Consulting & development	4.2	2
Chemicals	0.8	
COS Capture 3.0 1		
Total	**212.5**	**100**

COMPETITORS

ALSTOM	Nalco
BWX Technologies	Wahlco
Calgon Carbon	Wheelabrator
Clyde Bergemann EEC	Woodward Governor
Donaldson Company	

HISTORICAL FINANCIALS

Company Type: Public

Income Statement
FYE: December 31

	REVENUE ($ mil.)	NET INCOME ($ mil.)	NET PROFIT MARGIN	EMPLOYEES
12/17	35.6	27.8	78.1%	29
12/16	50.6	97.6	193.0%	25
12/15	62.7	(30.1)	—	69
12/14	16.9	1.3	8.2%	231
12/13	13.2	(15.9)	—	0
Annual Growth	**28.0%**	—	—	—

2017 Year-End Financials

Debt ratio: —
Return on equity: 37.2%
Cash ($ mil.): 30.6
Current ratio: 5.36
Long-term debt ($ mil.): —

No. of shares (mil.): 20.7
Dividends
  Yield: 0.0%
  Payout: 58.1%
Market value ($ mil.): 200.0

	STOCK PRICE ($) FY Close	P/E High/Low		Earnings	PER SHARE ($) Dividends	Book Value
12/17	9.66	9	6	1.29	0.75	3.54
12/16	9.24	2	1	4.34	0.00	3.46
12/15	9.40	—	—	(1.37)	0.00	(1.15)
12/14	22.79	930302		0.06	0.00	(0.03)
12/13	54.23	—	—	(0.78)	0.00	(0.28)
Annual Growth	**(35.0%)**	—	—	—	—	—

AG Mortgage Investment Trust Inc

AG Mortgage Investment Trust invests in acquires and manages a diverse portfolio of residential mortgage assets as well as other real estate-related securities and financial assets. Residential mortgage-backed securities backed by US government agencies including Fannie Mae Freddie Mac and Ginnie Mae known as "Agency RMBS" make up about 70% of the mortgage real estate investment trust's (REIT) portfolio. Credit assets including RMBS not issued or backed by the government account for most of the rest. Formed in 2011 by executives of investment adviser Angelo Gorden looking to profit from a recovery in the US mortgage bond market the mortgage REIT is managed by a subsidiary of Angelo Gordon.

IPO
The REIT went public in June 2011 with an offering worth $110 million far less than the $300 million it initially planned on raising.

Financial Performance
AG Mortgage reported net interest income of $125.4 million in 2013 up from $81.4 million and $17.1 million in 2012 and 2011 respectively. However substantial losses on other income sources and rising expenses led to a loss of $31.6 million in 2013 versus a profit of $135 million in 2012. Cash flow from operations has risen steeply since the REIT's inception from $15.4 million in 2011 to $130.8 million in 2013.

The REIT's portfolio was valued at $3.4 billion at the end of 2013.

Strategy
In the months after its IPO the REIT primarily focused on investing in Agency RMBS. However as market conditions and US monetary policy evolved the firm has focused more on credit assets of late. Indeed the REIT has gradually shifted its deployment of capital to its credit portfolio increasing its allocation as a percentage of assets from 9% to 22% to nearly 35% as of December 31 2011 2012 and 2013 respectively.

In January 2014 the mortgage REIT closed on a $10 million commercial real estate investment secured by a hotel property.

EXECUTIVES

CFO Principal Accounting Officer and Treasurer, Brian C. Sigman, age 40, $150,000 total compensation
Chairman and CEO, David N. Roberts, age 56
President and Chief Investment Officer, Jonathan Lieberman, age 55
General Counsel and Secretary, Raul E. Moreno, age 37, $28,493 total compensation
Auditors: PricewaterhouseCoopers LLP

LOCATIONS

HQ: AG Mortgage Investment Trust Inc
  245 Park Avenue, 26th Floor, New York, NY 10167
Phone: 212 692-2000
Web: www.agmit.com

COMPETITORS

ARMOUR Residential REIT	Hatteras Financial
	MFA Financial

Annaly Capital Management	MFResidential
Bimini Capital Management	PIMCO REIT
Capstead Mortgage	PennyMac Mortgage
Galiot Capital	Provident Mortgage Capital

HISTORICAL FINANCIALS

Company Type: Public

Income Statement
FYE: December 31

	REVENUE ($ mil.)	NET INCOME ($ mil.)	NET PROFIT MARGIN	EMPLOYEES
12/17	172.4	118.5	68.7%	0
12/16	118.2	63.6	53.8%	0
12/15	66.2	13.8	20.9%	0
12/14	156.6	109.4	69.8%	0
12/13	18.0	(31.5)	—	0
Annual Growth	**75.9%**	—	—	—

2017 Year-End Financials

Debt ratio: 1.0%
Return on equity: 17.3%
Cash ($ mil.): 15.2
Current ratio: 0.03
Long-term debt ($ mil.): 16.4

No. of shares (mil.): 28.1
Dividends
  Yield: 0.1%
  Payout: 53.0%
Market value ($ mil.): 536.0

	STOCK PRICE ($) FY Close	P/E High/Low		Earnings	PER SHARE ($) Dividends	Book Value
12/17	19.01	5	5	3.77	2.00	25.34
12/16	17.11	10	6	1.80	1.90	23.68
12/15	12.84	19521258		0.01	2.28	23.58
12/14	18.57	6	5	3.37	2.40	25.81
12/13	15.64	—	—	(1.61)	2.80	24.83
Annual Growth	**5.0%**	—	—	— (8.1%)	0.5%

Agree Realty Corp.

Shopping sprees really agree with Agree Realty. The self-managed real estate investment trust (REIT) owns develops and manages retail real estate primarily freestanding big-box properties. It owns around 280 retail properties spanning 5.5 million square feet of leasable space across 40-plus states. Most of its tenants are national retailers with its largest tenants being Wal-Mart Wawa and Walgreens. The REIT typically acquires either property portfolios or single-asset net lease retail properties (worth between $2 million and $30 million per asset) with creditworthy tenants. It was founded in 1979 by CEO Richard Agree.

Operations
The REIT's portfolio was made up of 278 properties in 41 states at the end of 2015 which spanned 5.2 million square feet of gross leasable space. All but three of these properties were net lease properties that contributed 97.6% to the REIT's rental income. The three others were community shopping centers.

Geographic Reach
While Agree Realty had properties in 41 US states during 2015 about 20% of its rental revenue came from properties in Michigan while another 20% came from properties based in Florida Ohio and Texas. All other regions each accounted for less than 6% of its revenue.

Sales and Marketing
The REIT mostly leases properties to retailers such as pharmacies restaurants general merchan-

disers apparel retailers grocery stores warehouse clubs sporting goods stores health & fitness centers convenience stores and dollar stores among others.

Agree Realty's largest tenant by revenue continues to be Walgreens which leased 32 properties and contributed 17.2% to the REIT's total rental income during 2015. Its four next largest tenants that year were Wal-Mart (5.5% of rental income) Wawa (3.4%) CVS (3.4%) and Academy Sports (2.8%).

Financial Performance

Agree Realty's annual revenues have more than doubled since 2011 mostly as rent-boosting acquisitions have increased its gross leasable square footage by 46% while nearly tripling its property count from 87 to 278 at the end of 2015. The REIT's net income has nearly quadrupled over the period as it's managed to keep a lid on rising operating expenses.

The REIT's revenue climbed 31% to almost $70 million during 2015 mostly as its 150 property acquisitions made from 2014 through 2015 boosted minimum rental revenues. Its existing property rental income increased by 13% thanks to better tenant performance and higher rental rates.

Strong revenue growth combined with $12.1 million in property sale gains in 2015 caused Agree Realty's net income to more than double to $39 million for the year. The company's operating cash levels jumped 28% to $44.7 million in 2015 mostly thanks to a spike in cash-denominated earnings from higher rental income.

Strategy

The REIT typically acquires either property portfolios or single-asset net lease retail properties (worth between $2 million and $30 million per asset) with creditworthy tenants to diversify its portfolio of "industry-leading" retailers.

Agree Realty normally holds onto its properties for long-term investment which is why it prefers to establish long-term leases and invest in capital improvements. Indeed at the end of 2015 the REIT's property portfolio boasted a 99.5% occupancy rate and a weighted average remaining lease term of 11.4 years.

EXECUTIVES

Interim CFO, Kenneth R. Howe, age 70, $42,325 total compensation
President CEO and Director, Joey Agree, age 40, $414,064 total compensation
EVP and COO, Laith M. Hermiz, age 47, $269,259 total compensation
Vice President Transactions, Danielle Spehar
Chairman, Richard Agree, age 75
Auditors: GRANT THORNTON LLP

LOCATIONS

HQ: Agree Realty Corp.
70 E. Long Lake Road, Bloomfield Hills, MI 48304
Phone: 248 737-4190   **Fax:** 248 737-9110
Web: www.agreerealty.com

PRODUCTS/OPERATIONS

2015 sales

	in mil.	%of total
Minimum rents	64.3	92
operating cost reimbursement	5.3	8
Percentage rents	0.2	-
other income	0.2	-
Total	**70.0**	**100**

COMPETITORS

CBL & Associates Properties	Pennsylvania Real Estate
DDR	Ramco-Gershenson
GGP	Simon Property Group
Kimco Realty	Taubman Centers

HISTORICAL FINANCIALS

Company Type: Public

Income Statement

FYE: December 31

	REVENUE ($ mil.)	NET INCOME ($ mil.)	NET PROFIT MARGIN	EMPLOYEES
12/17	116.5	58.1	49.9%	32
12/16	91.5	45.1	49.3%	24
12/15	69.9	39.0	55.8%	20
12/14	53.5	18.4	34.5%	14
12/13	43.5	19.6	45.2%	14
Annual Growth	**27.9%**	**31.1%**	**—**	**23.0%**

2017 Year-End Financials

Debt ratio: 34.7%	No. of shares (mil.): 31.0
Return on equity: 7.3%	Dividends
Cash ($ mil.): 58.7	Yield: 0.0%
Current ratio: 2.26	Payout: 97.3%
Long-term debt ($ mil.): 519.5	Market value ($ mil.): 1,595.0

	STOCK PRICE ($) FY Close	P/E High/Low		PER SHARE ($) Earnings	Dividends	Book Value
12/17	51.44	25	21	2.08	2.03	29.31
12/16	46.05	26	16	1.97	1.92	26.10
12/15	33.99	16	13	2.16	1.85	21.86
12/14	31.09	26	22	1.24	1.74	20.16
12/13	29.02	22	18	1.50	1.64	19.46
Annual Growth	**15.4%**	**—**	**—**	**8.5%**	**5.4%**	**10.8%**

Air Lease Corp

Air Lease doesn't really lease air unless of course you include the air inside the cabins of its fleet of airplanes. An aircraft leasing company Air Lease buys new and used commercial aircraft from manufacturers and airlines and then leases to airline carriers in Europe the Asia-Pacific region and the Americas. It owns a fleet of almost 240 aircraft comprised of 181 single-aisle narrowbody jet aircraft 40 twin-aisle widebody jet aircraft and 19 turboprop aircraft. In addition to leasing Air Lease also offers fleet management services such as lease management and sales.

Geographic Reach

Air Lease is based in Los Angeles and has airline customers throughout the world. Europe accounted for 32% of its net sales in 2015. Other markets included China (22%); Asia excluding China (19%); Central America South America and Mexico (10%); the Middle East and Africa (8%); the US and Canada (5%); and the Pacific Australia and New Zealand (4%).

Sales and Marketing

Its customers have included Air Canada; Sunwing Airlines; WestJet; AeroMexico; Aeromar; Interjet; Volaris; Hawaiian Airlines; Southwest Airlines; Spirit Airlines; Sun Country; United Continental Holdings; Liat Airline; and Caribbean-Airlines.

Financial Performance

Air Lease has experienced explosive growth over the years with revenues reaching a record-setting $1.22 billion in 2015. Profits also remained consistent hovering around the $255 million mark for both 2014 and 2015. The static profits for 2015 was attributed to about $72 million it paid in litigation settlement expenses. The company's cash from operating activities has gradually increased the last five years climbing by 9% from 2014 to 2015.

The historic growth for 2015 was fueled by an 18% spike in the rental of flight equipment. This was aided by the delivery of 51 additional aircraft all of which were leased at the time of delivery. Air Lease also enjoyed major growth in the key markets of the Middle East and Africa (89%); the Pacific Australia and New Zealand (52%) and China (21%).

Strategy

Although the largest portion of its fleet is leased to customers in Western Europe Air Lease is setting its sights on markets in the Asia-Pacific region Eastern Europe South America and the Middle East where it predicts the travel industry will grow the fastest in coming years. It has also targeted carriers in stable but slower-growing travel markets such as North America.

One way Air Lease has achieved impressive revenue growth over the years is by adding to its fleet size. In 2015 it purchased and took delivery of 51 aircraft and sold 24 aircraft ending the year with a total of 240 owned aircraft. During 2015 it increased its managed fleet by 12 aircraft ending the year with 29 aircraft in its managed fleet portfolio. (The company typically sells aircraft that are currently operated by an airline with multiple years of lease term remaining on the contract.)

Company Background

Air Lease went public in 2011. Udvar-Hózy and other Air Lease used a significant portion of the proceeds raised to acquire additional aircraft and for general corporate purposes. With sufficient capital and financing already in place Air Lease has placed orders for some 150 new aircraft to be delivered by 2017. While most of its fleet will consist of Boeing and Airbus passenger airplanes the company has ordered similar aircraft manufactured by Embraer and turboprops from Avions de Transport Régional (ATR).

Udvar-Hózy had co-founded ILFC now one of the largest aircraft leasing companies in the industry in the 1970s. He stayed on after AIG bought ILFC in the 1990s and continued to head the company until 2010 when he retired in the wake of the ongoing financial trouble that hit AIG in 2008. Udvar-Hózy subsequently founded Air Lease with the help of institutional investors including some that were large shareholders prior to the IPO's filing (Ares Management which held an 11% stake; Leonard Green & Partners 11%; and Commonwealth Bank of Australia 10%). Udvar-Hózy maintained a 7% stake in Air Lease in 2013.

EXECUTIVES

Executive Vice President, Jie Chen
Executive Vice President, John Poerschke
Vice President Marketing, Michael Bai
Assistant Vice President and Assistant Controller, Sabrina Lemmens
Executive Vice President, Grant Levy
Executive Vice President, Marc Baer

Assistant Vice President and Corporate Counsel,
  Heidi Hyun
Assistant Vice President, Stephanie Brimmer
Assistant Vice President, Czar Vigil
Vice President Technical Asset Management,
  Pierce Chang
Executive Vice President and General Counsel
  Corporate Secretary and Chief Compliance
  Officer, Carol Forsyte
Assistant Vice President, Sara Evans
Vice President Technical Asset Management, Eric
  Hoogenkamp
Executive Vice President, Alex Khatibi
Assistant Vice President Information Technology,
  Pablo Chavez
Assistant Vice President Technical Asset
  Management, Kenneth Coursey
Auditors: KPMG LLP

LOCATIONS

HQ: Air Lease Corp
  2000 Avenue of the Stars, Suite 1000N, Los Angeles, CA
  90067
Phone: 310 553-0555
Web: www.airleasecorp.com

PRODUCTS/OPERATIONS

2015 Sales

	$ mil.	% of total
Rental of flight equipment	1,174.5	96
Aircraft sales trading and other	48.3	4
Total	**1,222.8**	**100**

COMPETITORS

AerCap	Fly Leasing
Aircastle	GE Capital Aviation
Aviation Capital Group	Services
Boeing Capital	ICON Capital
CIT Transportation	ILFC
Finance	

HISTORICAL FINANCIALS

Company Type: Public

Income Statement   FYE: December 31

	REVENUE ($ mil.)	NET INCOME ($ mil.)	NET PROFIT MARGIN	EMPLOYEES
12/17	1,516.3	756.1	49.9%	87
12/16	1,419.0	374.9	26.4%	76
12/15	1,222.8	253.3	20.7%	74
12/14	1,050.4	256.0	24.4%	65
12/13	858.6	190.4	22.2%	63
Annual Growth	**15.3%**	**41.2%**	**—**	**8.4%**

2017 Year-End Financials

Debt ratio: 62.1%	No. of shares (mil.): 103.6
Return on equity: 20.1%	Dividends
Cash ($ mil.): 292.2	Yield: 0.0%
Current ratio: 1.61	Payout: 4.7%
Long-term debt ($ mil.): 9,698.7	Market value ($ mil.): 4,983.0

	STOCK PRICE ($) FY Close	P/E High/Low		Earnings	PER SHARE ($) Dividends	Book Value
12/17	48.09	7	5	6.82	0.33	39.83
12/16	34.33	10	6	3.44	0.23	32.89
12/15	33.48	16	12	2.34	0.17	29.44
12/14	34.31	17	12	2.38	0.13	27.07
12/13	31.08	18	11	1.80	0.11	24.78
Annual Growth	**11.5%**		**—**	**39.5%**	**32.6%**	**12.6%**

Air Transport Services Group, Inc.

Air Transport Services Group (ATSG) has a lease on (aircraft) life. Through its subsidiaries the company provides aircraft leases maintenance operations and other support services to the cargo transportation and package delivery industries. The company's largest segment ACMI Services provides aircraft crew maintenance and insurance operations to the company's largest customers DHL and the US military through airline subsidiaries Ohio-based ABX Air Inc. and Arkansas-based ATI. ATSG's Cargo Aircraft Management (CAM) subsidiary leases converted cargo Boeing 767 and 757 aircraft internally to ATSG airlines and to external customers through multiyear agreements.

Operations

Under its support services business ATSG provides aircraft maintenance repair and overhaul (MRO) through Airborne Maintenance and Engineering Services Inc.; flight crew training and flight simulator rental through ABX; aircraft parts and brokerage through AMES Material Services Inc.; facility maintenance and ground equipment rentals for aircraft support through LGSTX Services Inc.; and aircraft dispatch and flight tracking services through Global Flight Source. The support services business also operates five mail sorting centers for the US Postal Service through LGSTX Distribution Services Inc.

Sales and Marketing

Another subsidiary Airborne Global Solutions Inc. (AGS) provides sales leads to ATSG businesses and develops customized air cargo plans to meet customer needs. ATSG's largest customers DHL Network Operations (USA) and the US military accounted for 55% and 16% of revenue respectively in fiscal 2014.

Financial Performance

ATSG experienced revenue declines and a net loss of $20 million for 2013; however revenues improved marginally by 2% to reach $590 million in 2014. The slight growth was driven by a 4% bump in sales from its cargo aircraft management segment. The company also posted $30 million of positive net income in 2014 mostly due to the absence of impairment of goodwill charges that were present the previous year.

Strategy

To extend its European reach in 2014 ATSG acquired a 25% interest in West Atlantic AB of Gothenburg Sweden. West Atlantic AB through its two airlines — Atlantic Airlines Ltd. and West Air Sweden AB — operates a fleet of 40 aircraft and is Europe's largest regional cargo aircraft operator. West Atlantic AB operates its aircraft on behalf of European regional mail carriers and express logistics providers.

Mergers and Acquisitions

In 2018 Air Transport Services agreed to acquire Omni Air International LLC for $845 million. Omni Air provides passenger aircraft crew maintenance and insurance (ACMI) and charter services with significant sales to US and allied foreign governments and commercial customers. With the acquisition Air Transport anticipates expanding its customer base and increasing its presence in the growing government passenger charter services market.

Company Background

ATSG was formed as a holding company in late 2007 from the reorganization of ABX.

EXECUTIVES

President CEO and Director, Joseph C. (Joe) Hete,
  age 64, $535,000 total compensation
CFO, Quint O. Turner, age 55, $302,500 total
  compensation
Chief Commercial Officer and President Cargo
  Aircraft Management, Richard F. (Rich) Corrado,
  age 58, $259,077 total compensation
Vice President Human Resources, John Starkovich
Vice President General Counsel, George Golder
Director, James H. Carey, age 85
Board Member, Richard Baudouin
Auditors: DELOITTE & TOUCHE LLP

LOCATIONS

HQ: Air Transport Services Group, Inc.
  145 Hunter Drive, Wilmington, OH 45177
Phone: 937 382-5591
Web: www.atsginc.com

PRODUCTS/OPERATIONS

2014 Sales

	$ mil.	% of total
ACMI Services	439.9	59
CAM	166.3	22
Other	142.3	19
Adjustments	(158.9)	-
Total	**589.6**	**100**
Services		
Aircraft leasing		
ACMI services		
Support services		

COMPETITORS

ASTAR USA	Atlas Air Worldwide
American Airlines	Delta Air Lines
Group	Evergreen Holdings
Amerijet	Kalitta Air
Arrow Air	United Continental

HISTORICAL FINANCIALS

Company Type: Public

Income Statement   FYE: December 31

	REVENUE ($ mil.)	NET INCOME ($ mil.)	NET PROFIT MARGIN	EMPLOYEES
12/17	1,068.2	18.5	1.7%	3,010
12/16	768.8	23.4	3.1%	3,230
12/15	619.2	41.2	6.7%	2,170
12/14	589.5	29.8	5.1%	1,810
12/13	580.0	(19.6)	—	1,800
Annual Growth	**16.5%**	**—**		**13.7%**

2017 Year-End Financials

Debt ratio: 33.3%	No. of shares (mil.): 59.0
Return on equity: 5.0%	Dividends
Cash ($ mil.): 32.7	Yield: —
Current ratio: 1.00	Payout: —
Long-term debt ($ mil.): 497.2	Market value ($ mil.): 1,367.0

	STOCK PRICE ($)	P/E	PER SHARE ($)		
	FY Close	High/Low	Earnings	Dividends	Book Value
12/17	23.14	82 48	0.31	0.00	6.69
12/16	15.96	45 24	0.37	0.00	5.58
12/15	10.08	17 12	0.63	0.00	5.68
12/14	8.56	20 13	0.46	0.00	5.36
12/13	8.09	— —	(0.31)	0.00	5.71
Annual Growth	30.0%	— —	—	—	4.1%

Alarm.com Holdings Inc

Auditors: PricewaterhouseCoopers LLP

LOCATIONS

HQ: Alarm.com Holdings Inc
8281 Greensboro Drive, Suite 100, Tysons, VA 22102
Phone: 877 389-4033
Web: www.alarm.com

HISTORICAL FINANCIALS

Company Type: Public

Income Statement   FYE: December 31

	REVENUE ($ mil.)	NET INCOME ($ mil.)	NET PROFIT MARGIN	EMPLOYEES
12/17	338.9	29.2	8.6%	784
12/16	261.1	10.1	3.9%	607
12/15	208.8	11.7	5.6%	507
12/14	167.3	13.5	8.1%	400
12/13	130.2	4.5	3.5%	253
Annual Growth	27.0%	59.5%	—	32.7%

2017 Year-End Financials

Debt ratio: 19.1%
Return on equity: 13.8%
Cash ($ mil.): 96.3
Current ratio: 3.68
Long-term debt ($ mil.): 71.0
No. of shares (mil.): 47.2
Dividends
 Yield: —
 Payout: —
Market value ($ mil.): 1,782.0

	STOCK PRICE ($)	P/E	PER SHARE ($)		
	FY Close	High/Low	Earnings	Dividends	Book Value
12/17	37.75	78 43	0.59	0.00	4.93
12/16	27.83	150 65	0.21	0.00	4.14
12/15	16.68	— —	(0.30)	0.00	3.74
Annual Growth	50.4%	— —	—	—	14.8%

Alerus Financial Corp

EXECUTIVES

Senior Vice President, Mike Winkel
President; Chief Executive Officer Chairman Director, Randy Newman
Vice President Purchasing, Scott Harter

Vice President Commercial Relationship Manager, Robert Hartzell
Auditors: CliftonLarsonAllen LLP

LOCATIONS

HQ: Alerus Financial Corp
401 Demers Avenue, Grand Forks, ND 58021
Phone: 701 795-3200   **Fax:** 701 795-3378
Web: www.alerusfinancial.com

HISTORICAL FINANCIALS

Company Type: Public

Income Statement   FYE: December 31

	ASSETS ($ mil.)	NET INCOME ($ mil.)	INCOME AS % OF ASSETS	EMPLOYEES
12/17	2,137.0	15.4	0.7%	0
12/16	2,050.5	14.0	0.7%	0
12/15	1,744.8	16.5	0.9%	0
12/14	1,488.3	20.2	1.4%	0
12/13	1,380.7	20.2	1.5%	584
Annual Growth	11.5%	(6.6%)	—	—

2017 Year-End Financials

Return on assets: 0.7%
Return on equity: 8.8%
Long-term debt ($ mil.): —
No. of shares (mil.): 13.7
Sales ($ mil): 179.1
Dividends
 Yield: 0.0%
 Payout: 43.6%
Market value ($ mil.): 280.0

	STOCK PRICE ($)	P/E	PER SHARE ($)		
	FY Close	High/Low	Earnings	Dividends	Book Value
12/17	20.45	18 15	1.10	0.48	13.18
12/16	17.00	19 16	1.00	0.44	12.47
12/15	18.90	17 15	1.17	0.42	13.61
12/14	19.75	42 14	1.44	0.38	(0.00)
12/13	51.00	35 21	1.46	0.34	11.21
Annual Growth	(20.4%)	— —	(6.8%)	9.0%	4.1%

Alexandria Real Estate Equities Inc

The pearl of the Mediterranean might be found in Egypt but the pearls of science are typically found in the lab. Alexandria Real Estate Equities owns develops and operates offices and labs to life science tenants including biotech and pharmaceutical companies universities research institutions medical office developers and government agencies. A real estate investment trust (REIT) Alexandria owns approximately 170 specialized properties with more than 15 million sq. ft. of rentable space in the US and Canada. Its portfolio is largely located in high-tech hotbeds such as Boston greater New York City the San Francisco Bay area San Diego Seattle and suburban Washington DC.

EXECUTIVES

Chairman and CEO, Joel S. Marcus, age 70, $895,000 total compensation
EVP CFO and Treasurer, Dean A. Shigenaga, age 51, $450,000 total compensation

EVP and Regional Market Director San Diego, Daniel J. Ryan, $375,000 total compensation
SVP and Regional Market Director Seattle, John J. Cox
SVP and Regional Market Director Maryland, Larry J. Diamond
EVP and Regional Market Director Greater Boston, Thomas J. Andrews, $475,000 total compensation
COO and Regional Market Director San Francisco Bay Area, Stephen A. Richardson, $450,000 total compensation
Chief Investment Officer, Peter M. Moglia, $450,000 total compensation
SVP and Regional Market Director New York City, John H. Cunningham
EVP; General Counsel and Corporate Secretary, Jennifer J. Banks
Vice President San Francisco Bay Area, Todd Miller
Vice President Risk Management, Vahe Simitian
Vice President Talent Management, Madeleine Thorp
Assistant Vice President Life Sciences, Amanda Cashin
Executive Vice President Regional Market Director, Tom Andrews
Vice President Financial Reporting, Jonathan Dapeer
Vice President Strategic Operations, Hart Cole
Vice President Accounting, Andrew Houghton
Senior Vice President Construction Development, Greg Gehlen
Assistant Vice President Financial Reporting, Eric Chin
ASSISTANT VICE PRESIDENT, Howard Yao
Senior Vice President Chief Technology Officer, Mehran Khordodi
Auditors: Ernst & Young LLP

LOCATIONS

HQ: Alexandria Real Estate Equities Inc
385 East Colorado Boulevard, Suite 299, Pasadena, CA 91101
Phone: 626 578-0777
Web: www.are.com

PRODUCTS/OPERATIONS

2015 Sales

	$ mil.	% of total
Rental	608.8	72
Tenant recoveries	209.1	25
Other	25.6	3
Total	**843.5**	**100**

2015 Client Tenant Mix by ABR

	% of total
Public Biotechnology	26
Multinational Pharmaceutical	22
Life Science Product Service and Device	22
Institutional	20
Private Biotechnology	7
Office & Tech Office	3
Total	**100**

COMPETITORS

Beacon Capital Partners	First Industrial Realty
BioMed Realty	Liberty Property Trust
Boston Properties	PS Business Parks
Brandywine Realty	Shorenstein
Equity Commonwealth	

HISTORICAL FINANCIALS

Company Type: Public

Income Statement

FYE: December 31

	REVENUE ($ mil.)	NET INCOME ($ mil.)	NET PROFIT MARGIN	EMPLOYEES
12/18	1,327.4	379.3	28.6%	386
12/17	1,128.1	169.0	15.0%	323
12/16	921.7	(65.9)	—	285
12/15	843.4	144.2	17.1%	278
12/14	726.8	101.5	14.0%	243
Annual Growth	16.2%	39.0%	—	12.3%

2018 Year-End Financials

Debt ratio: 37.8%
Return on equity: 5.7%
Cash ($ mil.): 272.1
Current ratio: 0.26
Long-term debt ($ mil.): 5,478.2

No. of shares (mil.): 111.0
Dividends
  Yield: 3.2%
  Payout: 88.8%
Market value ($ mil.): 12,793.0

	STOCK PRICE ($) FY Close	P/E High/Low	PER SHARE ($) Earnings	Dividends	Book Value
12/18	115.24	37 31	3.52	3.73	66.14
12/17	130.59	84 68	1.58	3.45	59.63
12/16	111.13	— —	(1.99)	3.23	55.85
12/15	90.36	63 51	1.63	3.05	54.79
12/14	88.74	89 63	1.01	2.88	53.57
Annual Growth	6.8%	— —	36.6%	6.7%	5.4%

Align Technology Inc

Brace-face begone! Align Technology produces and sells the Invisalign system which corrects malocclusion or crooked teeth. Instead of using metal or ceramic mounts that are cemented on the teeth and connected by wires (traditional braces) the system uses an array of clear and removable dental aligners to move a patient's teeth into a desired alignment. The company markets its products to orthodontists and dentists worldwide. Align also provides training for practitioners to model treatment schemes using its online ClinCheck application which simulates tooth movement and suggests the appropriate aligner. Additionally it makes and sells orthodontic scanning and CAD (computer-assisted design) devices.

Operations

Align Technology operates through two segments: Clear Aligner and Scanners and Services (Scanner). Clear Aligner is the Invisalign product lines and it accounts for about 90% of revenue. The Invisalign system is offered in more than 80 countries by more than 43000 doctors to teenage and adult patients.

The Scanner segment offers the iTero intra-oral 3D scanning system for orthodontic and restorative dentistry as well as CAD services.

Geographic Reach

Align Technology has administrative and manufacturing locations in the US Mexico Costa Rica Israel the Netherlands and China; it also has R&D locations in the US Israel and Russia. Its products are primarily marketed in the US (accounting for nearly 60% of sales) and the Netherlands (another 30%).

Sales and Marketing

Align Technology sells its Invisalign System through a direct sales force in North America the Asia/Pacific region Europe the Middle East Africa and Latin America. The company primarily markets its products to orthodontist and dental practices who then commit to sell the products to consumers. It is targeting general practice dentists as a primary sales growth channel since general dentists have larger patient populations than orthodontists who traditionally treat malocclusion. The company also distributes its products to restorative and aesthetic dentists including prosthodontists periodontists and oral surgeons.

Align sells its iTero Scanner and CAD services through its direct sales force and through distributors in North America parts of Europe and parts of the Asia/Pacific region. It sells them through distributors in Thailand Russia and Scandinavia.

Financial Performance

Align Technology has seen several years of strong revenue growth and 2074 was no exception. That year the company had a 36% revenue increase to $1.5 billion as both the Clear Aligner and Scanner segments saw significant gains. The Clear Aligner segment sold a higher volume of cases both domestically and abroad. Training fees and ancillary product sales also increased. This was partially offset by a decrease in the average US selling price. The smaller Scanner segment had higher revenues due to an increase in the number of scanners recognized.

The higher revenues helped boost net income which rose 22% to $231.4 million. However an increase in operating expenses and a larger provision for income taxes cut into Align's bottom line. Cash flow from operations grew 77% to $438.5 million that year thanks largely to positive adjustments to long-term income tax payable.

Strategy

To stay ahead of potential competitors looking to enter the clear alignment market Align Technology continuously tries to expand sales of its Invisalign system by increasing the number of dentists and orthodontists that are committed to selling the products. It also increases brand awareness through consumer marketing programs. Geographically the firm is looking to expand into new markets as well as building up business in existing markets. It has transitioned to a direct sales model in most of its smaller international markets. The company is also investing in its infrastructure abroad to further grow operations. It opened new treatment planning facilities in China and Germany during 2017.

To widen usage of its products Align Technology develops new versions and variations of the Invisalign system as well as tools that make it easier for dentists to adopt use of the Invisalign offerings. It has recently launched Invisalign G6 and Invisalign G7 and in 2017 it launched the first system designed for tweens and teens (whose jaws are still growing). It also introduced its TimeLapse technology for practitioners to track orthodontic movement. Some of the company's distribution efforts are conducted through partnerships with other firms such as Patterson Dental and Glidewell Dental.

Additionally Align advertises to consumers directly so that they will proactively seek Invisalign treatment from providers.

EXECUTIVES

VP Legal Affairs and General Counsel, Roger E. George, age 53, $382,368 total compensation
President and CEO, Joseph M. (Joe) Hogan, age 60, $548,077 total compensation
VP; Managing Director Americas, Lynn S. Pendergrass
VP Operations, Emory M. Wright, age 49, $349,543 total compensation
VP; Managing Director North America, Christopher C. Puco, age 57
VP Research and Development, Zelko Relic, age 53, $366,231 total compensation
VP iTero Scanner and Services Chief Marketing Portfolio and Business Development Officer, Raphael S. Pascaud, age 46, $374,317 total compensation
VP; Managing Director EMEA, Simon Beard, age 51
VP; Managing Director Asia/Pacific, Julie Tay, age 51
VP; Managing Director Doctor-Directed Consumer Channel, Jennifer Olson-Wilk
CFO, John F. Morici
VP Information Technology, Sreelakshmi Kolli
Managing Director Latin America, Ritesh Sharma
Vice President Product Innovation, Srini Kaza
Chairman, C. Raymond Larkin, age 69
Auditors: PricewaterhouseCoopers LLP

LOCATIONS

HQ: Align Technology Inc
2820 Orchard Parkway, San Jose, CA 95134
Phone: 408 470-1000
Web: www.aligntech.com

PRODUCTS/OPERATIONS

2017 Sales by Segment

	$ mil.	% of total
Clear Align	1,309.3	89
Scanner	164.1	11
Total	**1,473.4**	**100**

COMPETITORS

3M	Patterson Companies
Dentsply Sirona	Straumann
Henry Schein	Sybron Dental

HISTORICAL FINANCIALS

Company Type: Public

Income Statement

FYE: December 31

	REVENUE ($ mil.)	NET INCOME ($ mil.)	NET PROFIT MARGIN	EMPLOYEES
12/17	1,473.4	231.4	15.7%	8,715
12/16	1,079.8	189.6	17.6%	6,060
12/15	845.4	144.0	17.0%	4,375
12/14	761.6	145.8	19.1%	3,580
12/13	660.2	64.3	9.7%	3,420
Annual Growth	22.2%	37.7%	—	26.3%

2017 Year-End Financials

Debt ratio: —
Return on equity: 21.5%
Cash ($ mil.): 449.5
Current ratio: 2.32
Long-term debt ($ mil.): —

No. of shares (mil.): 80.0
Dividends
  Yield: —
  Payout: —
Market value ($ mil.): 17,784.0

	STOCK PRICE ($) FY Close	P/E High/Low	PER SHARE ($) Earnings	Dividends	Book Value
12/17	222.19	91 31	2.83	0.00	14.37
12/16	96.13	42 25	2.33	0.00	12.51
12/15	65.85	38 29	1.77	0.00	10.67
12/14	55.91	35 25	1.77	0.00	9.39
12/13	57.14	73 32	0.78	0.00	7.87
Annual Growth	40.4%	— —	38.0%	—	16.3%

Allegiance Bancshares Inc

Auditors: Crowe Horwath LLP

LOCATIONS

HQ: Allegiance Bancshares Inc
8847 West Sam Houston Parkway N., Suite 200, Houston, TX 77040
Phone: 281 894-3200
Web: www.allegiancebank.com

HISTORICAL FINANCIALS

Company Type: Public

Income Statement   FYE: December 31

	ASSETS ($ mil.)	NET INCOME ($ mil.)	INCOME AS % OF ASSETS	EMPLOYEES
12/17	2,860.2	17.6	0.6%	375
12/16	2,450.9	22.8	0.9%	327
12/15	2,084.5	15.7	0.8%	310
12/14	1,280.0	9.0	0.7%	304
12/13	1,164.7	6.8	0.6%	0
Annual Growth	26.2%	26.7%	—	—

2017 Year-End Financials

Return on assets: 0.6%	Dividends
Return on equity: 6.0%	Yield: —
Long-term debt ($ mil.): —	Payout: —
No. of shares (mil.): 13.2	Market value ($ mil.): 498.0
Sales ($ mil): 125.3	

	STOCK PRICE ($) FY Close	P/E High/Low	PER SHARE ($) Earnings	Dividends	Book Value
12/17	37.65	30 23	1.31	0.00	23.20
12/16	36.15	21 9	1.75	0.00	21.59
12/15	23.65	18 15	1.43	0.00	20.17
Annual Growth	26.2%	— —	(4.3%)	—	7.2%

Allegiant Travel Company

Allegiant Travel pledges to serve the vacation needs of residents of more than 100 small US cities in 41 states. Through Allegiant Air the company provides nonstop service to tourist destinations such as Las Vegas Los Angeles and Orlando Florida from places such as Cedar Rapids Iowa; Fargo North Dakota; and Toledo Ohio. It maintains a fleet of about 50 MD-80 series aircraft. Besides scheduled service Allegiant Air offers charter flights for casino operators Caesars Entertainment (formerly Harrah's Entertainment) and MGM MIRAGE in addition to other customers. Sister company Allegiant Vacations works with partners to allow customers to book hotel rooms and rental cars along with their airline tickets.

Operations

Allegiant Travel's operating fleet consists of 51 MD-80 aircraft 26 A320 series aircraft and five Boeing 757-200 aircraft providing service on 294 routes to 104 cities. The company is also expecting that the services would expand to 322 routes and 111 cities by late 2016.

Geographic Reach

The company has a route network providing service on 294 routes between 87 cities and 17 leisure destinations. It serves 41 US states.

Financial Performance

Allegiant Travel has achieved extraordinary growth over the last five years with revenues surging 11% from $1.14 billion in 2014 to peak at $1.26 billion in 2015 a company milestone. Profits also more than doubled from $87 million in 2014 to reach a record-setting $220 million in 2015 mostly due to the lower price of fuel. Cash flow has also followed the same upward trend climbing by 35% in 2015.

The historic growth for 2015 was attributed to a spike in ancillary air-related revenue fueled by an increase in scheduled service passengers as well as continued revenue optimization efforts. In addition increased customer convenience fees and the effective yield management of other existing products drove an increase in its average ancillary air-related fare per passenger.

Strategy

Allegiant Travel's business strategy includes expanding its ancillary products and services and adding new destinations to its flight network. During 2015 the company added service to four leisure destinations commenced service on 69 new routes and discontinued service on under-performing routes. Based on its currently published schedule through August 2016 the company plans to increase total routes to 322 increase the number of leisure destinations served to 19 and increase the number of cities served to 92.

In 2016 the company entered into forward purchase agreements for 11 Airbus A320 series aircraft. It expects delivery of seven aircraft in 2016 and the remaining four in the first half of 2017.

EXECUTIVES

President, John T. Redmond, age 60
President CEO and Director, Maurice J. (Maury) Gallagher, age 68
EVP and Chief Marketing Officer, M. Ponder Harrison, age 56, $185,000 total compensation
SVP and CIO, Scott M. Allard, age 50, $195,000 total compensation
SVP CFO and Interim COO, D. Scott Sheldon, age 40, $195,000 total compensation
VP and Principal Accounting Officer, Gregory C. Anderson, $147,500 total compensation
Auditors: KPMG LLP

LOCATIONS

HQ: Allegiant Travel Company
1201 North Town Center Drive, Las Vegas, NV 89144
Phone: 702 851-7300
Web: www.allegiant.com

PRODUCTS/OPERATIONS

Selected Products and Services
Air-related ancillary products and services.
Fixed fee contract air transportation.
Scheduled service air transportation.
Third party ancillary products and services

2015 Sales

	$ mil.	% of total
Scheduled service	735.6	58
Ancillary revenues		
Air-related charges	434.3	34
Third party products	40.2	3
Fixed fee contract revenues	19.7	2
Other	32.4	3
Total	**1,262.2**	**100**

COMPETITORS

AirTran Airways	Frontier Airlines
Alaska Air	Horizon Air
American Airlines Group	JetBlue
	Southwest Airlines
Delta Air Lines	United Continental

HISTORICAL FINANCIALS

Company Type: Public

Income Statement   FYE: December 31

	REVENUE ($ mil.)	NET INCOME ($ mil.)	NET PROFIT MARGIN	EMPLOYEES
12/17	1,503.7	194.9	13.0%	3,951
12/16	1,362.8	219.5	16.1%	3,589
12/15	1,262.1	220.3	17.5%	3,018
12/14	1,137.0	86.6	7.6%	2,564
12/13	996.1	92.2	9.3%	2,235
Annual Growth	10.8%	20.6%	—	15.3%

2017 Year-End Financials

Debt ratio: 53.4%	No. of shares (mil.): 16.0
Return on equity: 38.1%	Dividends
Cash ($ mil.): 59.4	Yield: 0.0%
Current ratio: 0.98	Payout: 23.4%
Long-term debt ($ mil.): 950.1	Market value ($ mil.): 2,486.0

	STOCK PRICE ($) FY Close	P/E High/Low	PER SHARE ($) Earnings	Dividends	Book Value
12/17	154.75	15 10	11.93	2.80	34.11
12/16	166.40	14 9	13.21	2.40	28.47
12/15	167.83	18 11	12.94	2.75	20.83
12/14	150.33	30 18	4.86	2.50	16.82
12/13	105.44	23 15	4.82	2.25	20.26
Annual Growth	10.1%	— —	25.4%	5.6%	13.9%

Allete Inc.

ALLETE provides light to the northern climes. Most of its business is classified within its regulated operations which include electric gas and water utilities located in northeastern Minnesota and northwestern Wisconsin. Those operations are conducted through subsidiaries Minnesota Power (about 144000 customers) and Superior Water Light and Power (37000 electric gas and water customers). ALLETE's other segment includes coal mining operations emerging technologies related to electric utilities and a real estate business (large land tracts in Florida). Subsidiary BNI Coal operates a mine in North Dakota that supplies primarily two generating co-ops Minnkota Power and Square Butte.

Operations

The company's regulated operations include utilities Minnesota Power and Superior Water Light and Power as well Rainy River Energy which holds an 8% stake in American Transmission Company (ATC) a Wisconsin-based regulated utility that owns and maintains electric transmission assets in parts of Illinois Michigan Minnesota and Wisconsin.

Minnesota Power holds franchises to construct and maintain an electric distribution and transmission system in 91 cities. The remaining cities villages and towns served do not require a franchise to operate. Superior Water Light and Power serves customers with electric natural gas and/or water systems in 1 city and 16 villages or towns.

In 2014 industrial customers represented 54% of the company's total regulated utility kilowatt-hour sales.

Non-regulated assets included BNI Coal (coal mining operations in North Dakota) ALLETE Properties (10000 acres of Florida real estate investments) ALLETE Clean Energy (wind solar biomass hydro natural gas/liquids shale resources clean coal and other clean energy projects). Other activities include business development and corporate expenditures unallocated interest expense a small amount of non-rate base generation approximately 5000 acres of land in Minnesota and earnings on cash and investments.

BNI Coal owns and operates a surface lignite mine in Center North Dakota producing about 4 million tons annually.

ALLETE Clean Energy operates independently of Minnesota Power to develop or acquire capital projects aimed at creating energy solutions via wind solar biomass midstream gas and oil infrastructure among other energy-related projects. It intends to market to electric utilities cooperatives municipalities independent power marketers and large end-users across North America through long-term contracts or other sale arrangements.

Geographic Reach

ALLETE has operations in Florida Illinois Michigan Minnesota North Dakota and Wisconsin.

Sales and Marketing

Minnesota Power has 10 Large Power Customer contracts each serving requirements of 10 MW or more of customer load. The customers consist of five taconite producing facilities (two of which are owned by one company and are served under a single contract) one iron nugget plant one concentrate reclamation facility and four paper and pulp mills.

Large industrial power customers includes ArcelorMittal Blandin Paper Mill Boise White Paper Hibbing Taconite Co. NewPage Corporation United Taconite LLC and USS Corporation.

That year the company's residential and commercial customers represented 20% of total regulated utility kilowatt-hour sales.

ALLETE's power marketing activities consist of purchasing energy in the wholesale market to serve its regulated service territory when energy requirements exceed generation output; and selling excess available energy and purchased power. From time to time its utility operations may have excess energy that is temporarily not required by retail and municipal customers in its regulated service territory. It actively sells any excess energy to the wholesale market to optimize the value of its generating facilities.

Financial Performance

ALLETE's revenues have consistently increased since 2010.

In 2014 net sales grew by 12% due to higher revenues from regulated operations and investment and other.

Operating revenues increased by 8% in 2014 primarily due to a 5% increase in kilowatt-hour sales higher cost recovery rider revenues transmission revenues gas sales and fuel adjustment clause recoveries.

Revenue from Investments and Other increased by 43% primarily due to higher revenues from ALLETE Clean Energy due to the 2014 wind facility acquisitions and higher BNI Coal sales resulting from increased coal deliveries and higher expenses in 2014.

ALLETE's net income has followed the similar trend to that of the company's revenues.

In 2014 net income increased by 19% due to higher revenues partially offset by a growth in operating and maintenance expenses (up by 7%). (An expense was recorded to reflect a liability associated with environmental mitigation projects required as part of an EPA Consent Decree settlement. It was also higher due to a rise in transmission expense purchased gas and property taxes partially offset by lower benefit expense).

The company's net cash provided by the operating activities increased by 13%.

Strategy

To meet the growing demand for electricity and comply with Minnesota's carbon emission regulations the company anticipates adding up to 500 MW of renewable energy capacity (primarily through building hydropower and wind facilities) by 2025. It also plans to increase the use of biomass as a cleaner-burning fuel at its fossil-fueled plants.

The company's current strategy for its assets is to complete and maintain key entitlements and infrastructure improvements without requiring significant additional investment sell the portfolio when opportunities arise and reinvest the proceeds in our growth initiatives. ALLETE does not intend to acquire additional Florida real estate.

Minnesota Power will continue to pursue customer growth opportunities and cost recovery rider approval for environmental renewable and transmission investments as well as work with regulators to earn a fair rate of return. The company believes that ATC is poised for future growth both organically and through its partnership with Duke Energy. The company also plans to make investments in transmission opportunities that strengthen or enhance the transmission grid or take advantage of its geographical location between sources of renewable energy and end users. These include the GNTL and the CapX2020 initiative as well as investments to enhance its own transmission facilities and investments in other

transmission assets (individually or in combination with others).

In 2015 Minnesota Power completed latest phase of its Bison Wind Energy Center. The 205-megawatt expansion makes it the largest wind farm in North Dakota and ranks Minnesota Power as one of America's top-10 wind power-owning electric utilities.

In 2014 BNI Coal signed an agreement with Minnkota Power Cooperative to continue supplying lignite coal to the North Dakota electric generating cooperative through 2037. The agreement extends the current contract which would have ended in 2027 by 10 years.

Mergers and Acquisitions

In 2015 ALLETE acquired US Water Services consistent with ALLETE's stated strategy of investing in energy infrastructure and related services to complement its core regulated utility balance exposure to business cycles and changing demand and provide potential long-term earnings growth. ALLETE initially purchased 87% of U.S. Water for $168 million based on a total implied enterprise value of $194 million. US Water has a national footprint and serves a growing and diverse mix of over 3600 industrial customers including a significant number of Fortune 500 companies. Water and energy are intricately linked and attention to that nexus was increasing.

In 2015 ALLETE Clean Energy acquired a handful of wind facilities including AES Armenia Mountain Wind LLC a 100.5 MW wind facility in Pennsylvania and a 97.5 MW wind generation facility in Minnesota for $47.5 million from a subsidiary of EDF Renewable Energy. In 2014 ALLETE Clean Energy acquired wind energy facilities located in Lake Benton Minnesota Storm Lake Iowa and Condon Oregon for $26.9 million.

Company Background

In 2013 Minnesota Power began construction on a 200-MW expansion of its Bison wind project that will deliver more economical carbon-free energy to customers while substantially meeting Minnesota's renewable energy standard of 25% renewable energy by 2025. The project will be the single largest wind addition to the company's fleet.

Growing its long-term power supply arrangements in 2012 Minnesota Power entered into a long-term deal with Minnkota Power through which Minnkota Power will by 50MW of capacity and the energy associated with that capacity from 2016 to 2020.

In 2011 the company launched ALLETE Clean Energy to leverage industry knowledge and innovation to bring clean energy to customers across North America.

Expanding its transmission capacity in 2011 American Transmission Company and Duke Energy formed the Duke-American Transmission Co. joint venture (DATC) to build own and operate a new electric transmission infrastructure in the US and Canada.

ALLETE's primary unit Minnesota Power was founded in 1906.

EXECUTIVES

SVP Regulated Operations and Chief Strategy Officer; President Superior Water Light and Power, Deborah A. (Deb) Amberg, age 52, $338,731 total compensation

SVP External Affairs; EVP Minnesota Power, David J. McMillan, age 55, $289,907 total compensation

SVP, Steven Q. (Steve) DeVinck, age 58, $356,876 total compensation
Chairman President and CEO, Alan R. Hodnik, age 58, $613,584 total compensation
SVP and CFO, Robert J. Adams, age 55, $258,021 total compensation
President and General Manager BNI Energy, Wade W. Boeshans
President ALLETE Clean Energy, Al Rudeck
SVP; President Regulated Operations, Bradley W. Oachs, $292,780 total compensation
CEO U.S. Water Services, Allan Bly
Board Member, Sidney W Emery
Treasurer, Donald Stellmaker
Auditors: PricewaterhouseCoopers LLP

LOCATIONS

HQ: Allete Inc.
30 West Superior Street, Duluth, MN 55802-2093
Phone: 218 279-5000
Web: www.allete.com

PRODUCTS/OPERATIONS

2014 Sales

	$ mil.	% of total
Regulated operations	1,003.5	88
Investments & other	133.3	12
Total	**1,136.8**	**100**

COMPETITORS

Alliant Energy	United Road Services
Coteau Properties	United Utilities
Florida Public	Utilities Inc.
Utilities	WEC Energy
MGE Energy	Xcel Energy
Otter Tail	
Pittsburgh Independent	
Auto Auction	

HISTORICAL FINANCIALS

Company Type: Public

Income Statement				FYE: December 31
	REVENUE ($ mil.)	NET INCOME ($ mil.)	NET PROFIT MARGIN	EMPLOYEES
12/17	1,419.3	172.2	12.1%	2,017
12/16	1,339.7	155.3	11.6%	1,963
12/15	1,486.4	141.1	9.5%	1,945
12/14	1,136.8	124.8	11.0%	1,625
12/13	1,018.4	104.7	10.3%	1,560
Annual Growth	**8.7%**	**13.2%**	**—**	**6.6%**

2017 Year-End Financials

Debt ratio: 29.5%	No. of shares (mil.): 51.1
Return on equity: 8.6%	Dividends
Cash ($ mil.): 98.9	Yield: 0.0%
Current ratio: 1.05	Payout: 63.3%
Long-term debt ($ mil.): 1,439.2	Market value ($ mil.): 3,801.0

	STOCK PRICE ($) FY Close	P/E High/Low		Earnings	PER SHARE ($) Dividends	Book Value
12/17	74.36	24	18	3.38	2.14	40.46
12/16	64.19	21	15	3.14	2.08	38.20
12/15	50.83	20	16	2.92	2.02	37.09
12/14	55.14	20	15	2.90	1.96	35.04
12/13	49.88	20	16	2.63	1.90	32.44
Annual Growth	**10.5%**	—	—	**6.5%**	**3.0%**	**5.7%**

Allied Motion Technologies Inc

Allied Motion Technologies has the motor to control your drive. The company makes specialized motors optical encoders and brushless drives used in mechanical motion control applications. Its products are incorporated into a number of end products including high-definition printers barcode scanners surgical tools robotic systems wheelchairs and satellite tracking systems. Allied Motion targets applications in the alternative energy automotive aerospace and defense industrial automation medical printing and imaging and semiconductor equipment markets.

Operations

Allied Motion is organized around six technology units: Allied Motion Controls Emoteq Corporation Motor Products Corporation Precision Motor Technology B.V. (Premotec) Stature Electric and A–stergrens Elmotor.

Geographic Reach

The company manufactures its products in the US Canada China the Netherlands and Sweden. Products are sold through the company's direct sales force and through distributors. It has 15 direct sales offices. The US accounts for nearly 60% sales.

Financial Performance

Allied Motion enjoyed unprecedented growth for the year as revenues jumped 23% from $102 million in 2012 to a record-high of $126 million in 2013. The growth for 2013 was due to the acquisition of Globe in addition to increases in its vehicle and aerospace and defense markets.

However its profits have been falling over the last three years with earnings declining from $7 million in 2011 to $4 million in 2013. The erosion of profits was due to expenses incurred as a result of acquisitions which included a rise in business development and interest expenses.

Allied Motion's cash flow from operations steadily grew from $2.8 million in 2009 to $8.9 million in 2011. After decreasing to $4.6 million in 2012 cash flow shot up again to almost $11 million in 2013 due to changes in working capital.

Mergers and Acquisitions

The company makes acquisitions in order to add to its customer base product lines and market reach. In 2013 Allied Motion acquired Globe Motors from Safran USA for about $90 million. Globe Motors is stationed in Dayton Ohio with additional operations in Dothan Alabama; Reynosa Mexico; and Oporto Portugal. The deal expanded its global reach and fortified its sales marketing and manufacturing capabilities.

EXECUTIVES

Chairman President and CEO, Richard S. (Dick) Warzala, age 64
VP Marketing and CTO, Kenneth R. Wyman, age 76
VP Operational Excellence, Robert P. (Rob) Maida
CFO, Michael R. (Mike) Leach
Auditors: Deloitte & Touche, LLP

LOCATIONS

HQ: Allied Motion Technologies Inc
495 Commerce Drive, Amherst, NY 14228
Phone: 716 242-8634
Web: www.alliedmotion.com

PRODUCTS/OPERATIONS

Selected Products

Brushless DC motors
Brushless drives
Encoders
Gearmotors
Permanent magnet DC motors
Servo motors
Small precision motors
Torque motors
Transaxles

COMPETITORS

ACS Motion Control	Danaher
Applied Industrial	Galil Motion Control
Technologies	Moog
Custom Sensors &	Newport Corp.
Technologies	UQM Technologies

HISTORICAL FINANCIALS

Company Type: Public

Income Statement				FYE: December 31
	REVENUE ($ mil.)	NET INCOME ($ mil.)	NET PROFIT MARGIN	EMPLOYEES
12/17	252.0	8.0	3.2%	1,250
12/16	245.8	9.0	3.7%	1,220
12/15	232.4	11.0	4.8%	1,046
12/14	249.6	13.8	5.6%	977
12/13	125.5	3.9	3.1%	942
Annual Growth	**19.0%**	**19.4%**	**—**	**7.3%**

2017 Year-End Financials

Debt ratio: 28.2%	No. of shares (mil.): 9.4
Return on equity: 10.0%	Dividends
Cash ($ mil.): 15.5	Yield: 0.0%
Current ratio: 2.77	Payout: 11.4%
Long-term debt ($ mil.): 52.6	Market value ($ mil.): 312.0

	STOCK PRICE ($) FY Close	P/E High/Low		Earnings	PER SHARE ($) Dividends	Book Value
12/17	33.09	38	22	0.87	0.10	9.27
12/16	21.39	26	16	1.00	0.10	7.71
12/15	26.18	34	14	1.20	0.10	6.96
12/14	23.69	16	7	1.51	0.10	6.07
12/13	12.45	28	15	0.45	0.10	5.28
Annual Growth	**27.7%**	—	—	**17.9%**	**(0.0%)**	**15.1%**

Ambarella, Inc.

Ambarella's technology helps capture crisp clear digital images in cameras designed for sports autos drones and security. The company designs and markets video processing semiconductors for taking high-definition video and still images. It combines its system-on-a-chip semiconductor designs with proprietary software to create both industry and consumer products. The hardware/software combo helps cameras compensate for motion as a skier swoops downhill or a drone sweeps over a mountain. In security applications Amabarella's video chips can gather high-def images in low light. The company designs its chips which are made by contractors for small form factors and to run on low power.

Operations

Ambarella's chips and software allow for greater compression of the HD video signal which translates to broadcasters being able to offer more channels in fixed bandwidths and consumer products that capture higher quality video in smaller devices.

Samsung Electronics handles most of Ambarella's contract manufacturing chores. Ambarella also works with contractors Global UniChip Corp. and Taiwan Semiconductor Manufacturing Co.

Geographic Reach

Ambarella has offices and design centers in China Hong Kong Italy Japan South Korea and Taiwan. Hong Kong accounts for 90% of sales with the remainder split between the rest of Asia the US other North American countries and Europe.

Sales and Marketing

Ambarella's chips are used by GoPro Inc. Hikvision Digital Technology Co. Robert Bosch Garmin Ltd. Motorola Mobility Inc. and Asia Optical Co. While Ambarella has a number of end users most of its sales go through two companies. About two-thirds of sales are made via logistic services provider Wintech Microelectronics Co. and another 20% are through Chicony Electronics an original design manufacturer.

Financial Performance

A snapshot of Ambarella's financials for 2016 (ended January) shows revenue profit and cash flow headed up. The company's revenue shot up 55% in 2016 to $316 million. The increase came from strong demand for its A9 A7L S2L and A12 SoCs for the IP security drone automotive aftermarket and wearable sports camera markets. In the second half of the year however Ambarella saw a decline in wearables because of high inventory levels at GoPro a major end customer.

The revenue increase helped Ambarella post a 51% increase in net income to $77 million in 2016 despite spending more for research and development and other expenses. The company has been profitable since 2012. Cash flow from operations increased to $124 million in 2016 from $52 million in 2015 on higher net income decreased accounts receivable and decreased inventory.

Strategy

In 2011 Ambarella lost a good chunk of its business when Kodak stopped making cameras. Ambarella rebounded finding new customers in wearable sports cameras security cameras and aerial drones. But once again it ran into problems when sales stalled at one its major customers GoPro. Ambarella had to work through a load of inventory of its chips held by GoPro which held up new sales to the camera company.

But Ambarella increased its supply of chips for drones and security and added automotive applications to its arsenal with virtual reality applications on the horizon. To maintain the pipeline of new products Ambarella increased R&D spending to $83 million in 2016 from $58 million in 2015. The company has concentrated more technology on its systems-on-a-chip which has enables camera manufacturers to reduce the size of their products. A new automotive application is cameras for side-

view mirrors which provide wider views for tasks such as parking.

Camera makers like Ambarella's chips for their capability of capturing high resolution video. Nikon became a first time customer using the A9AC SOC for 4K ultra-HD video in a new underwater camera. Home security customer Bosch incorporated Ambarella's HD chip into cameras that capture a 360-degree view. For virtual reality headsets Ambarella released a line of SoCs that capture HD video at high rates of speed at 360 degrees.

Mergers and Acquisitions

In 2015 Ambarella acquired VisLab a privately held company based in Italy for $30 million. VisLab is a pioneer in perception systems and autonomous vehicle research. The acquisition provides expertise for research into computer vision for the automotive IP security wearable and drone markets.

EXECUTIVES

CFO, George W. Laplante, age 66
CTO and Director, Les Kohn, age 61, $226,250 total compensation
EVP, Didier LeGall, age 63, $217,500 total compensation
Auditors: PricewaterhouseCoopers LLP

LOCATIONS

HQ: Ambarella, Inc.
  3101 Jay Street, Santa Clara, CA 95054
Phone: 408 734-8888
Web: www.ambarella.com

COMPETITORS

Canon	Panasonic Corp
Fujitsu	Samsung Electronics
Intel	Sony
NVIDIA	Texas Instruments

HISTORICAL FINANCIALS
Company Type: Public

Income Statement — FYE: January 31

	REVENUE ($ mil.)	NET INCOME ($ mil.)	NET PROFIT MARGIN	EMPLOYEES
01/18	295.4	18.8	6.4%	706
01/17	310.3	57.8	18.6%	669
01/16	316.3	76.5	24.2%	640
01/15	218.2	50.5	23.2%	524
01/14	157.6	25.6	16.3%	495
Annual Growth	17.0%	(7.4%)	—	9.3%

2018 Year-End Financials

Debt ratio: —	No. of shares (mil.): 33.4
Return on equity: 4.0%	Dividends
Cash ($ mil.): 434.5	Yield: —
Current ratio: 9.27	Payout: —
Long-term debt ($ mil.): —	Market value ($ mil.): —

America First Multifamily Investors LP

Auditors: DELOITTE & TOUCHE LLP

LOCATIONS

HQ: America First Multifamily Investors LP
  1004 Farnam Street, Suite 400, Omaha, NE 68102
Phone: 402 444-1630
Web: www.ataxfund.com

HISTORICAL FINANCIALS
Company Type: Public

Income Statement — FYE: December 31

	ASSETS ($ mil.)	NET INCOME ($ mil.)	INCOME AS % OF ASSETS	EMPLOYEES
12/17	1,069.7	30.5	2.9%	0
12/16	944.1	23.7	2.5%	0
12/15	872.5	26.6	3.0%	0
12/14	744.2	15.0	2.0%	0
12/13	534.2	17.7	3.3%	0
Annual Growth	19.0%	14.6%	—	—

	STOCK PRICE ($) FY Close	P/E High/Low	PER SHARE ($) Earnings	Dividends	Book Value
12/17	6.05	14 12	0.44	0.50	6.76
12/16	5.40	18 13	0.34	0.50	5.33
12/15	5.06	17 15	0.34	0.50	5.20
12/14	5.26	26 21	0.25	0.50	5.14
12/13	6.29	18 16	0.40	0.50	3.98
Annual Growth	(1.0%)	— —	2.4%	(0.0%)	14.2%

American Homes 4 Rent

Auditors: Ernst & Young LLP

LOCATIONS

HQ: American Homes 4 Rent
  30601 Agoura Road, Suite 200, Agoura Hills, CA 91301
Phone: 805 413-5300
Web: www.americanhomes4rent.com

HISTORICAL FINANCIALS
Company Type: Public

Income Statement — FYE: December 31

	REVENUE ($ mil.)	NET INCOME ($ mil.)	NET PROFIT MARGIN	EMPLOYEES
12/17	960.4	81.0	8.4%	1,135
12/16	878.8	6.7	0.8%	953
12/15	630.5	(62.3)	—	781
12/14	398.8	(48.0)	—	752
12/13	139.0	(32.3)	—	430
Annual Growth	62.1%	—	—	27.5%

Debt ratio: 28.7%
No. of shares (mil.): 286.7
Return on equity: 1.7%
Dividends
Cash ($ mil.): 46.1
Yield: 0.0%
Current ratio: 0.31
Payout: —
Long-term debt ($ mil.): 2,137.8
Market value ($ mil.): 6,263.0

	STOCK PRICE ($) FY Close	P/E High/Low	PER SHARE ($) Earnings	Dividends	Book Value
12/17	21.84	— —	(0.08)	0.20	17.96
12/16	20.98	— —	(0.14)	0.20	17.23
12/15	16.66	— —	(0.40)	0.20	15.68
12/14	17.03	— —	(0.34)	0.20	16.31
12/13	16.20	— —	(0.36)	0.05	15.82
Annual Growth	**7.8%**	**— —**	**—**	**41.4%**	**3.2%**

American Woodmark Corp.

American Woodmark has more cabinet selections than the prime minister of Russia. A top maker of home cabinets in the US the company makes and distributes about 500 styles of low- to mid-priced kitchen cabinets and vanities. Styles vary by finish (oak cherry hickory maple as well as laminate) and door design. Brands include American Woodmark Shenandoah Cabinetry Timberlake and Waypoint. Targeting the remodeling and new home construction markets American Woodmark sells its lineup through home centers and independent dealers and distributors; it also sells directly to major builders. American Woodmark was established through a leveraged buyout of Boise Cascade's cabinet division.

Operations

Business is divided between two markets — remodeling and new home construction. Products are distributed through four assembly plants and a third-party logistics network.

Through its seven service centers nationwide American Woodmark offers complete turnkey installation services to its direct builder customers.

The company keeps in stock about 85 door designs in more than 20 colors.

Geographic Reach

Virginia-based American Woodmark operates nine manufacturing facilities in Arizona Georgia Indiana Kentucky Maryland Tennessee Virginia and West Virginia. Its coast-to-coast service centers expand its customer reach beyond the Sun Belt construction market.

Sales and Marketing

Together Lowe's and The Home Depot accounted for 45% of the company's fiscal 2015 (ended April) sales.

Through three primary channels — home centers builders and independent dealers and distributors — American Woodmark services the remodeling and new home construction markets. Its brand names include American Woodmark Timberlake (sold to major home builders) Shenandoah Cabinetry (Lowe's) Potomac (Lowe's) and Waypoint Living Spaces.

In fiscal 2015 advertising expenses totaled $34.3 million up from $30.4 million in fiscal 2014 but down from $36.5 million in fiscal 2013.

Financial Performance

American Woodmark has enjoyed rising revenue since 2009. In fiscal 2014 (ended April) the cabinet maker reported sales of $825.5 million a 14% increase versus the prior year. The double-digit growth was largely driven by increased sales in the new construction market as well as higher per-unit revenue.

After experiencing losses in 2011 and 2012 the company's profits have rebounded. Higher revenues helped net income rise 73% to $35.5 million in fiscal 2015 (although increased income tax expense partially offset those gains). Cash flow from operations also rose growing 45% to $58.7 million that year.

HISTORY

Alvin Goldhush in 1951 started cabinet company Form Laminates which lumber giant Boise Cascade acquired two decades later. Four senior managers of Boise Cascade's cabinet division — William Brandt Jeff Holcomb Al Graber and Donald Mathias — engineered an LBO of the unit in 1980 and named it American Woodmark after a popular line of cabinets. The company started selling cabinets nationwide through distribution centers and went public in 1986.

American Woodmark spent the first half of the 1990s diversifying its product and brands. In 1990 it introduced Timberlake a cabinet line for the construction industry. Other brands including Coventry and Case Crestwood and Scots Pine were added and quintupled its product line.

President and COO Jake Gosa became CEO in 1996. The sales cupboard was rather bare that year from a downturn in the closely linked home centers industry. The market surged in 1997 causing American Woodmark's profits to nearly triple and new equipment and manufacturing techniques boosted output. In 1998 the company began offering hickory cabinets (its first new wood species in a decade) kitchen accessories and high-quality ready-to-assemble framed cabinets (Flat Pack).

In 1999 American Woodmark expanded its hickory cabinet offerings (adding the Newport and Charleston brands). The company began operations at its new assembly facility in Gas City Indiana in 2000. To both preserve and increase market share in a slow-growth economy in 2001 American Woodmark initiated plans to expand two plants and open two more in Kentucky and Oklahoma.

EXECUTIVES

Vice President Builder Direct, Steve Heafner
SVP and General Manager New Construction, R. Perry Campbell, age 52, $240,623 total compensation
President and CEO, S. Cary Dunston, age 52, $396,218 total compensation
SVP Remodel Sales and Marketing, Bradley S. (Brad) Boyer, age 58, $267,984 total compensation
CFO, M. Scott Culbreth, age 46
Vice President, Gary Wolf
National Account Manager, Jason Bryan
Vice President and Chief Human Resources Officer, Heather Banks
Chairman, Kent B. Guichard, age 61
Auditors: KPMG LLP

LOCATIONS

HQ: American Woodmark Corp.
561 Shady Elm Road, Winchester, VA 22602
Phone: 540 665-9100
Web: www.americanwoodmark.com

PRODUCTS/OPERATIONS

Selected Brands
American Woodmark
Potomac
Shenandoah Cabinetry
Timberlake
Waypoint Living Spaces

COMPETITORS

Armstrong World Industries	MasterBrand Cabinets
Elkay Manufacturing	Norcraft Companies Inc.
Masco	US Home Systems

HISTORICAL FINANCIALS

Company Type: Public

Income Statement — FYE: April 30

	REVENUE ($ mil.)	NET INCOME ($ mil.)	NET PROFIT MARGIN	EMPLOYEES
04/18	1,250.2	63.1	5.1%	9,400
04/17	1,030.2	71.2	6.9%	5,808
04/16	947.0	58.7	6.2%	5,600
04/15	825.4	35.5	4.3%	5,070
04/14	726.5	20.4	2.8%	4,916
Annual Growth	**14.5%**	**32.5%**	**—**	**17.6%**

2018 Year-End Financials

Debt ratio: 49.4%
No. of shares (mil.): 17.5
Return on equity: 13.5%
Dividends
Cash ($ mil.): 86.4
Yield: —
Current ratio: 2.14
Payout: —
Long-term debt ($ mil.): 809.9
Market value ($ mil.): 1,439.0

	STOCK PRICE ($) FY Close	P/E High/Low	PER SHARE ($) Earnings	Dividends	Book Value
04/18	82.20	37 21	3.77	0.00	33.23
04/17	91.90	21 14	4.34	0.00	21.71
04/16	72.84	25 13	3.57	0.00	17.28
04/15	50.70	25 12	2.21	0.00	14.29
04/14	30.01	30 23	1.31	0.00	12.31
Annual Growth	**28.6%**	**— —**	**30.2%**	**—**	**28.2%**

Ameris Bancorp

Ameris Bancorp enjoys the financial climate of the Deep South. It is the holding company of Ameris Bank which holds roughly $3.6 billion in assets and serves retail and consumer customers through more than 75 full-service and mortgage branches in Alabama Georgia South Carolina and northern Florida. In addition to its standard banking products and services the bank also provides treasury services mortgage and refinancing solutions and investment services through an agreement with Raymond James Financial. Loans secured by commercial real estate accounted for approximately 45% of the company's loan portfolio while 1-4 family residential and construction &

land development mortgages accounted for nearly a quarter and about 10% respectively.

Operations

Like most banks Ameris earns the vast majority of its recurring revenue (71.5%) from interest income from loans. Nearly 80% of these loans are made up of commercial real estate 1-4 family residential and construction & land development loans. The remaining 20% are from a mix of commercial multi-family residential and consumer loans (home improvement home equity personal lines of credit auto loans and student loans).

Traditional banking products (deposit accounts) and services along with investment products and services (which primarily earn income from fees and commissions) made up about 28% of the bank's annual sales in fiscal 2013.

Sales and Marketing

Through an acquisition-oriented growth strategy Ameris seeks to grow its brand and presence in the markets it currently serves in Georgia Alabama Florida and South Carolina as well as in neighboring communities. In addition the bank expects its community-oriented philosophy will help strengthen existing customer relations and attract new customers.

The company spent $1.62 million on advertising and public relations in Fiscal Year 2013 just under the $1.622 million it spent in 2012 and more than double the $722000 it spent in 2011. The company increased its advertising spending by $900000 during 2012 to support its revenue and growth- strategies during the year.

Financial Performance

Ameris carried $3.67 billion in total assets as of December 31 2013. Loans made up $2.5 billion (approximately 68.9% of total assets). The bank also reported carrying $3 billion in deposits.

Ameris' net revenue dipped in fiscal 2013 declining 5% to $163 million from its high of $172 million in 2012 mostly from an $11.3 million dip in non-interest revenue. But this dip in non-interest revenue is primarily because the bank recorded a large gain of $20 million from acquisitions in 2012. When excluding this acquisition gain from 2012's revenues and thanks to $6.1 million revenue increase in mortgage banking activity management reports that total non-interest income actually increased $8.7 million in 2013 compared to 2012. A decline in interest-earning loan assets from $2.47 billion in 2013 compared to $2.5 billion in 2012 also played a role in the dip in net revenues.

Thanks to aggressive acquisitions and despite revenue decreasing net income jumped a whopping 43% to $20 million in 2013 from $14 million in 2012. This is only slightly below the bank's net income high of $21 million in 2011. It's most notable acquisition of Prosperity Bank increased Ameris' total assets by $744.9 million and added $449.7 million in loans to its interest-earning loan portfolio. Adding to the extra income from new loans Ameris collected higher net interest margins on all of its loans which increased to 4.74% in 2013 from 4.60% in 2012.

Strategy

Ameris plans to continue using its community banking philosophy to lessen its risk and identify prime local lending markets. Management reports that by encouraging a personalized service experience and building deeper customer relationships the bank has already grown a "substantial" base of low-cost core deposits (which pad the bank's reserves and lessen financial risk). And between

its bench of experienced decision makers and lenders operating in a "decentralized" structure (which differentiates Ameris from mega banks) and its deep familiarity with local markets management believes the bank can better identify prime growth markets (for lending and bank services) with managed risk in the years ahead.

Mergers and Acquisitions

Integral to the bank's growth strategy Ameris has aggressively acquired banks to broaden its reach into its primary southern markets.

Ameris Bancorp purchased Jacksonville Bancorp and its eight branches more than doubling its branch network in Jacksonville Illinois to 14 branches.

Company Background

In addition to acquiring several troubled and failing banks with help from the FDIC Ameris merged with Prosperity Bank in 2013 which broadened its reach into Florida through Prosperity's branches in St. Augustine Jacksonville Panama City Lynn Haven Palatka and Ormand Beach.

Georgia's economy was one of the hardest hit in the US during the recession and Ameris has taken advantage of the plethora of banks seized by regulators in the state. Since 2009 the company has acquired about 10 failed banks in Georgia though FDIC-assisted transactions adding some 20 branches to its network. Ameris also snagged the failed First Bank of Jacksonville in Florida which had two locations.

EXECUTIVES

Chief Banking Executive Ameris Bancorp and Ameris Bank, Andrew B. (Andy) Cheney, age 68, $400,000 total compensation
EVP and Chief Credit Officer, Jon S. Edwards, age 56, $260,000 total compensation
SVP and Director of Human Resources, Cindi H. Lewis, age 64, $90,333 total compensation
President and CEO, Edwin W. (Ed) Hortman, age 64, $625,000 total compensation
EVP and Banking Group President Ameris Bancorp and President Ameris Bank, Lawton E. Bassett
EVP CFO and COO, Dennis J. Zember, age 48, $320,000 total compensation
EVP and Chief Risk Officer, Stephen A. Melton, $275,000 total compensation
EVP and Chief Banking Officer, James A. LaHaise
Assistant Vice President, Ann Dunn
Vice President And Business Banker, Charles Hudgens
Senior Vice President, Rob Kowkabany
Vice President Special Assets Division, Leo Story
Vice President of Residential Mortgage, Greg Seabaugh
Senior Vice President, Karen Cross
Senior Vice President, Jw Dukes
Vice President Mortgage Sales Manager, Jason Fralix
Senior Vice President Special Assets Division, David Aldridge
Vice President Senior Treasury Services Advisor, Lori Putnam
Vice President Accounting Manager P. O. Box 3668, Marsha Dotson
Vice President, Connie Romay
Vice President Regional Area Manager, Candace Adkins
Senior Vice President Commercial Banker, Brian Samson
Senior Vice President, Jayson Griffin

Senior Vice President Branch Manager, Vicki Blanton
Chairman, Daniel B. Jeter, age 66
Auditors: Crowe Horwath LLP

LOCATIONS

HQ: Ameris Bancorp
310 First Street S.E., Moultrie, GA 31768
Phone: 229 890-1111
Web: www.amerisbank.com

PRODUCTS/OPERATIONS

2016 sales chart

	$ mil.	% of total
Interest income:		
Interest and fees on loans	218.7	64
Interest on taxable securities	17.9	5
Interest on nontaxable securities	1.8	-
Interest on deposits in other banks	0.9	-
Interest on federal funds sold - -		
Non Interest income:		
Service charges on deposit accounts	42.8	13
Mortgage banking activity	48.2	14
Other service charges commissions and fees	3.5	1
Net gains on sales of securities - -		
Gain on sale of SBA loans	3.9	1
Other noninterest income	7.1	2
Total	**344.8**	**100**

2016 sales chart

	% of total
Banking Division	91
Retail Mortgage Division	5
Warehouse Lending Division	3
SBA Division	1
Total	**100**

Selected Acquisitions

American United Bank
Central Bank of Georgia
Darby Bank & Trust
First Bank of Jacksonville
High Trust Bank
Montgomery Bank & Trust
One Georgia Bank
Satilla Community Bank
Tifton Banking Company
United Security Bank

COMPETITORS

BBVA Compass Bancshares	First South Bancorp (NC)
Bank of America	Regions Financial
Capital City Bank	Southwest Georgia Financial
Colony Bankcorp	SunTrust
Community Capital Bancshares	Thomasville Bancshares

HISTORICAL FINANCIALS

Company Type: Public

Income Statement				FYE: December 31
	ASSETS ($ mil.)	NET INCOME ($ mil.)	INCOME AS % OF ASSETS	EMPLOYEES
12/17	7,856.2	73.5	0.9%	1,460
12/16	6,892.0	72.1	1.0%	1,298
12/15	5,588.9	40.8	0.7%	1,304
12/14	4,037.0	38.7	1.0%	1,027
12/13	3,667.6	20.0	0.5%	984
Annual Growth	21.0%	38.4%	—	10.4%

2017 Year-End Financials

Return on assets: 1.0%
Return on equity: 10.1%
Long-term debt ($ mil.): —
No. of shares (mil.): 37.2
Sales ($ mil): 398.8

Dividends
Yield: 0.0%
Payout: 20.2%
Market value ($ mil.): 1,796.0

	STOCK PRICE ($) FY Close	P/E High/Low	PER SHARE ($) Earnings	Dividends	Book Value
12/17	48.20	26 21	1.98	0.40	21.59
12/16	43.60	23 12	2.08	0.30	18.51
12/15	33.99	27 18	1.27	0.20	15.98
12/14	25.64	18 13	1.46	0.15	13.67
12/13	21.11	28 16	0.75	0.00	12.62
Annual Growth	22.9%	— —	27.5%	—	14.4%

AMN Healthcare Services Inc

Understaffed hospitals say "amen" for AMN Healthcare Services. Operating under such brands as American Mobile Healthcare Medical Express NurseChoice NursesRx Medfinders Med Travelers Staff Care and O'Grady-Peyton International the firm is one of the leading temporary health care staffing companies in the world. It places nurses technicians and therapists for 13-week stints at hospitals clinics and schools nationwide. With professionals recruited from Australia Canada South Africa the UK and the US AMN provides travel reimbursement and housing for its nurse and health care workers on assignment. The majority of temporary assignments for its clients are at acute-care hospitals in the US.

Geographic Reach

The company has offices in California Illinois North Carolina Oregon Colorado Indiana New Jersey Pennsylvania Florida Massachusetts New Mexico South Carolina Georgia Maryland New York Tennessee Hawaii Minnesota Ohio Texas Iowa Missouri Oklahoma and Virginia.

Financial Performance

AMN reported revenue of a little more than $1 billion for fiscal 2014. That was an increase of about $24 million compared to the prior fiscal period.

The company's net income was $33 million in fiscal 2014. That was a slight increase compared to fiscal 2013.

AMN's cash from operations decreased by about $32 million during fiscal 2014 compared to fiscal 2013 levels but the company still had more than $27 million in cash on hand at the end of the fiscal year.

Strategy

AMN's growth strategy consists of increasing its network of temporary health care workers and making strategic acquisitions that complement its core offerings.

EXECUTIVES

CEO President and Director, Susan R. Salka, age 54, $788,077 total compensation

Chief Clinical Officer and SVP Operations, Marcia R. Faller
President Healthcare Staffing, Ralph S. Henderson, age 57, $448,846 total compensation
President Merritt Hawkins & Associates, Mark Smith
CFO Chief Accounting Officer and Treasurer, Brian M. Scott, age 48, $448,846 total compensation
Division President Travel Nursing, Landry Seedig
CIO, Jeanette Sanchez
President Locums Tenens Division, Jeff Decker
SVP Candidate Sourcing and Digital Marketing, Brian McCloskey
President Strategic Workforce Solutions, Dan White
Chairman, Douglas D. (Doug) Wheat, age 67
Auditors: KPMG LLP

LOCATIONS

HQ: AMN Healthcare Services Inc
12400 High Bluff Drive, Suite 100, San Diego, CA 92130
Phone: 866 871-8519
Web: www.amnhealthcare.com

PRODUCTS/OPERATIONS

2017 Sales

	$ mil.	% of total
Nurse & allied solutions	1,238.5	62
Locum tenens solutions	430.6	22
Other workforce solutions	319.3	16
Total	**1,988.5**	**100**

COMPETITORS

ATC Healthcare
CHG Healthcare
CompHealth
Cross Country Healthcare
Gentiva

Kelly Services
Maxim Healthcare Services Inc.
On Assignment
TeamStaff

HISTORICAL FINANCIALS

Company Type: Public

Income Statement   FYE: December 31

	REVENUE ($ mil.)	NET INCOME ($ mil.)	NET PROFIT MARGIN	EMPLOYEES
12/17	1,988.4	132.5	6.7%	2,980
12/16	1,902.2	105.8	5.6%	2,990
12/15	1,463.0	81.8	5.6%	2,550
12/14	1,036.0	33.2	3.2%	1,800
12/13	1,011.8	32.9	3.3%	1,900
Annual Growth	18.4%	41.6%	—	11.9%

2017 Year-End Financials

Debt ratio: 25.5%
Return on equity: 26.2%
Cash ($ mil.): 15.1
Current ratio: 1.79
Long-term debt ($ mil.): 319.8

No. of shares (mil.): 47.4
Dividends
Yield: —
Payout: —
Market value ($ mil.): 2,338.0

	STOCK PRICE ($) FY Close	P/E High/Low	PER SHARE ($) Earnings	Dividends	Book Value
12/17	49.25	18 13	2.68	0.00	11.85
12/16	38.45	20 10	2.15	0.00	9.44
12/15	31.05	22 11	1.68	0.00	7.29
12/14	19.60	28 15	0.69	0.00	5.50
12/13	14.70	22 15	0.69	0.00	4.73
Annual Growth	35.3%	— —	40.4%	—	25.8%

Anika Therapeutics Inc.

Anika Therapeutics uses hyaluronic acid (HA) a natural polymer extracted from rooster combs and other sources to make more than 20 products that treat bone cartilage and soft tissue. Anika's Orthovisc treats osteoarthritis of the knee and other joints and is available in the US and overseas. (DePuy Mitek sells the product in the US.) The company also makes and sells products that maintain eye shape and protect tissue during eye surgery. Other items include surgical anti-adhesive products veterinary osteoarthritis therapies and dermatology products. The US accounts for about four-fifths of sales.

Operations

Orthobiologics products make up about 85% of the company's annual revenues. In addition to Orthovisc Anika markets osteoarthritis drugs in international markets: Orthovisc mini (for treatment in small joints); Monovisc a next-generation single-injection therapy; and Cingal an HA formulation plus steroid. Anika received Canadian approval for Monovisc in 2009 and FDA approval for Monovisc in 2014. It received Canadian approval for Cingal in 2015 followed by European approval for the product in 2016. It has additional osteoarthritis and joint health treatments under development.

The company is seeking FDA approval for Cingal and Hyalofast a biodegradable support for bone marrow stem cells used in cartilage regeneration.

Geographic Reach

Headquartered in Massachusetts Anika has an international office in Italy. The US accounts for more than 80% of revenue followed by Europe which accounts for about 10% of revenue.

Sales and Marketing

The company uses a contract sales organization to market Cingal in the US but it ultimately hopes to bring those functions in-house.

While Anika markets some products on its own a number are sold through additional partnering firms and distribution representatives. DePuy Mitek is Anika's largest customer accounting for 72% of product sales.

Dermal products are sold through a network of distributors in Europe Latin America and the Middle East; surgical products are sold through a similar network in Europe the Middle East and in certain Asian markets.

Anika also has partnerships to distribute products with such firms as Medtronic Boehringer Ingelheim Vetmedica and Medline Industries.

Financial Performance

Anika has seen strong revenue growth over the past several years including a 41% jump to $105.6 million in 2014. However revenue declined 12% to $93 million in 2015 in the absence of certain milestone payments (despite growth of sales that year).

Net income has also risen and like revenue dropped in 2015. It fell 20% to $31 million that year due to the lower revenue and an increase in R&D costs. Cash flow from operations slipped 2% to $39 million over the same period.

Strategy

The company's growth efforts stem from adding new products adding new indications for existing products and expanding its geographic reach. Its orthobiologics products are seeing the fastest growth now accounting for some 85% of sales. Additionally Anika seeks more partnerships with others to commercialize its products. In 2016 the company gained European approval for Cingal as a medical device to treat knee pain.

R&D spending is largely dedicated to developing products for tissue protection repair and regeneration. In 2015 R&D spend totaled $9 million up from $8.1 million in 2014 and $7.1 million in 2013.

Anika is taking on the manufacturing of its HYAFF (HA-based) products which have been made by an Italian third party. By doing so it can bring additional products to the markets more quickly.

EXECUTIVES

CEO, Charles H. Sherwood, $505,447 total compensation
President, Joseph G. Darling
Chief Scientific Officer, John W. Sheets
CFO, Sylvia Cheung
Chief Medical Officer, Stephen R. Mascioli
COO, Dana M. Alexander
Svp- Mktg & Bus Dev't, Elizabeth C Chen
Vice President of Human Resour, Steven Cyr
Auditors: DELOITTE & TOUCHE LLP

LOCATIONS

HQ: Anika Therapeutics Inc.
  32 Wiggins Avenue, Bedford, MA 01730
Phone: 781 457-9000
Web: www.anikatherapeutics.com

PRODUCTS/OPERATIONS

2015 Sales

	$ mil.	% of total
Product sales		
Orthobiologics	73.2	79
Surgical	5.8	6
Dermal	2.3	2
Other	6.4	7
Licensing milestone & contract revenue	5.3	6
Total	**93.0**	**100**

Selected Products

Orthobiologics
  Hyalofast (bone marrow support)
  Hyaloglide (tenolysis)
  Hyalograft C (autograft for cartilage regeneration)
  Hyalonect (graft gauze wrap)
  Hyaloss (bone regeneration)
  Monovisc (osteoarthritis)
  OrthoVisc (osteoarthritis marketed by DePuy Mitek)
  OrthoVisc mini (osteoarthritis in small joints)
Dermal
  Elevess/Hydrelle (aesthetic dermatology products)
  Hyalograft 3D (skin regeneration)
  Hyalomatrix (burn and ulcer treatment)
Ophthalmic
  Amvisc (eye surgery product sold by Bausch & Lomb)
  Amvisc Plus (eye surgery product sold by Bausch & Lomb)
  AnikaVisc (eye surgery product)
  Optivisc (formerly ShellGel ophthalmic product)
  STAARVISC II (ophthalmic product sold by STAAR Surgical)
Surgical
  Hyalobarrier (post-operative adhesion barrier)
  Incert (post-surgical adhesion prevention product)
Veterinary
  Hyvisc (equine osteoarthritis treatment distributed by Boehringer Ingelheim)

COMPETITORS

Exactech
Fibrocell Science
Pathfinder Cell Therapy
Genzyme Biosurgery
Harvard Bioscience
ImmunoGen
Integra LifeSciences
Lifecore Biomedical
Medicis Pharmaceutical
Merz Aesthetics
Obagi Medical
OrthoLogic
Pfizer
Quidel
RTI Surgical
Smith & Nephew
Solta Medical
Stryker
XOMA
Zimmer Biomet

HISTORICAL FINANCIALS
Company Type: Public

Income Statement
FYE: December 31

	REVENUE ($ mil.)	NET INCOME ($ mil.)	NET PROFIT MARGIN	EMPLOYEES
12/17	113.4	31.8	28.1%	123
12/16	103.3	32.5	31.5%	122
12/15	93.0	30.7	33.1%	107
12/14	105.5	38.3	36.3%	102
12/13	75.0	20.5	27.4%	102
Annual Growth	**10.9%**	**11.5%**	**—**	**4.8%**

2017 Year-End Financials

Debt ratio: —
Return on equity: 13.0%
Cash ($ mil.): 133.2
Current ratio: 15.78
Long-term debt ($ mil.): —
No. of shares (mil.): 14.6
Dividends
  Yield: —
  Payout: —
Market value ($ mil.): 792.0

	STOCK PRICE ($) FY Close	P/E High/Low	Earnings	PER SHARE ($) Dividends	Book Value
12/17	53.91	27 19	2.11	0.00	17.94
12/16	48.96	24 16	2.15	0.00	15.23
12/15	38.16	22 15	2.01	0.00	14.02
12/14	40.74	19 11	2.51	0.00	11.99
12/13	38.16	26 7	1.39	0.00	9.49
Annual Growth	**9.0%**	**—**	**11.0%**	**—**	**17.2%**

Antero Midstream Partners LP

Auditors: KPMG LLP

LOCATIONS

HQ: Antero Midstream Partners LP
  1615 Wynkoop Street, Denver, CO 80202
Phone: 303 357-7310
Web: www.anteromidstream.com

HISTORICAL FINANCIALS
Company Type: Public

Income Statement
FYE: December 31

	REVENUE ($ mil.)	NET INCOME ($ mil.)	NET PROFIT MARGIN	EMPLOYEES
12/17	772.5	237.6	30.8%	593
12/16	590.2	219.7	37.2%	480
12/15	387.3	117.6	30.4%	0
12/14	95.7	7.4	7.8%	0
12/13	22.3	(14.3)	—	0
Annual Growth	**142.4%**	**—**	**—**	**—**

2017 Year-End Financials

Debt ratio: 39.3%
Return on equity: —
Cash ($ mil.): 8.3
Current ratio: 0.99
Long-term debt ($ mil.): 1,196.0
No. of shares (mil.): 186.9
Dividends
  Yield: 0.0%
  Payout: 96.8%
Market value ($ mil.): 5,428.0

	STOCK PRICE ($) FY Close	P/E High/Low	Earnings	PER SHARE ($) Dividends	Book Value
12/17	29.04	28 20	1.28	1.24	8.11
12/16	30.88	25 14	1.24	0.97	6.84
12/15	22.82	39 22	0.76	0.67	6.15
12/14	27.50	580463	0.05	0.00	8.84
Annual Growth	**1.8%**	**—**	**—194.7%**	**—**	**(2.8%)**

Apogee Enterprises Inc

Apogee Enterprises goes to great panes for its glass customers. The company designs and develops value-added glass products primarily for the US market. Its architectural products and services segment fabricates and installs glass that features specialized colors or coatings and aluminum framing systems for commercial and institutional buildings. Customers include architects general contractors glazing subcontractors and building owners. Its large-scale optical (LSO) technologies segment manufactures anti-reflective UV-protected glass and acrylic under the Tru Vue brand for custom picture framing. Tru Vue products are sold through independent distributors and mass merchandisers.

Operations
Apogee divides its operations across four segments with three of the segments serving the commercial construction market: architectural glass (more than 35% of total sales) architectural framing systems (roughly 30%) architectural services (almost 25%) and large-scale optical products (LSO; 10%). Its LSO segment caters to the custom picture framing market.

High-performance glass made by its architectural glass segments allows for specific light transmission levels and features solar options. High-performance glass is typically fabricated into custom insulating units or laminated units to allow for installation into window frames curtain walls storefronts or entrances. The architectural framing segments also offer thermally-enhanced aluminum framing systems as well as ones with recycled content and energy-efficient glass coatings to target architects and contractors demanding specialty glass for constructing green commercial buildings.

Geographic Reach
Within the installation services market Apogee is one of only a few companies to have a national presence with offices in seven locations serving multiple US markets. It also has an office each in Canada and Brazil but the US continues to be Apogee's main market representing about 95% of sales.

Sales and Marketing
LSO glass and acrylic products are distributed primarily in North America through mass merchandisers and independent distributors which supply national and regional chains and local picture framing shops. Apogee occasionally supplies products directly to museums and public and pri-

vate galleries. It also has limited distribution in global markets through independent distributors.

Financial Performance

Apogee has enjoyed unprecedented growth over the years with revenues peaking at a record-setting $981 million in 2016. Mostly due to the additional revenue profits also peaked at $65 million in 2016 another company milestone. In addition cash flow from operating activities soared from $69 million in 2015 to $124 million in 2016 mostly due to tax refunds and additional billings from uncompleted contracts.

The historic growth for 2016 was driven by surges in sales from its architectural glass and architectural services segments and higher demand form its architectural framing systems segment. These increases were mainly due to pricing and volume growth resulting from strong commercial construction activity in the US partially offset by declines in the Canadian and Brazilian commercial construction markets.

Strategy

Apogee has identified several opportunities for growth in the coming years. It has recorded increased interest from the non-residential and high-end multi-family building sectors in upgrading the front of buildings and improving buildings' energy efficiency.

Its strategy pertaining to its LSO segment involves continuing to convert the custom picture framing and fine art markets from clear uncoated glass and acrylic products to value-added products that protect art from UV damage and minimize reflection both within the US and international markets. Apogee has also identified new display markets that desire the value-added properties its glass and acrylic products provide.

Mergers and Acquisitions

Apogee in late 2016 acquired Sotawall a North America-based designer and fabricator of high-performance unitized curtain wall systems for commercial construction projects for $135 million. The deal extended Apogee's geographic presence and enhanced its product offerings.

EXECUTIVES

SVP Technology and Strategy, Donald C. Pyatt
General Counsel; Secretary, Patricia A. Beithon, age 62, $277,070 total compensation
CFO, James S. Porter, age 55, $334,750 total compensation
President CEO and Director, Russell Huffer, age 65, $700,000 total compensation
VP Human Resources, Warren Planitzer
Chairman, Bernard P. (Bernie) Aldrich, age 66
VP and Treasurer, Gary R. Johnson, age 54, $192,679 total compensation
President, Rick A. Marshall
Director Investor Relations, Mary Ann Jackson
President Tru Vue, Jane Boyce
Senior Vice President Operations and Supply Chain Management, John A. Klein
President; Chief Executive Officer; Director, Joseph Puishys
Vice President - Finance; Corporate Controller, Mark Augdahl
President CEO and Director, Russell Huffer, age 65
Director, Jerome L. Davis Sr., age 61
Director, John T. (Terry) Manning, age 67
Director, Robert J. Marzec, age 71
Director, David E. Weiss, age 72
Director, Stephen C. Mitchell, age 72
Director, Sara L. Hays, age 51

Director, Richard V. Reynolds, age 67
Auditors: DELOITTE & TOUCHE LLP

LOCATIONS

HQ: Apogee Enterprises Inc
4400 West 78th Street - Suite 520, Minneapolis, MN 55435
Phone: 952 835-1874
Web: www.apog.com

COMPETITORS

AGC North America	Pilkington Group
Asahi Glass	Pilkington North
Cardinal Glass	America
Guardian Glass	Saint-Gobain
Nippon Sheet Glass	Schott Corporation
PPG Industries	Vitro

HISTORICAL FINANCIALS

Company Type: Public

Income Statement
FYE: March 3

	REVENUE ($ mil.)	NET INCOME ($ mil.)	NET PROFIT MARGIN	EMPLOYEES
03/18	1,326.1	79.4	6.0%	6,700
03/17*	1,114.5	85.7	7.7%	5,511
02/16	981.1	65.3	6.7%	4,614
02/15	933.9	50.5	5.4%	4,802
03/14	771.4	27.9	3.6%	4,266
Annual Growth	14.5%	29.8%	—	11.9%

*Fiscal year change

2018 Year-End Financials

Debt ratio: 21.1%	No. of shares (mil.): 28.1
Return on equity: 16.2%	Dividends
Cash ($ mil.): 19.3	Yield: 0.0%
Current ratio: 1.62	Payout: 20.9%
Long-term debt ($ mil.): 215.8	Market value ($ mil.): 1,238.0

	STOCK PRICE ($) FY Close	P/E High/Low		PER SHARE ($) Earnings	Dividends	Book Value
03/18	43.97	21	15	2.76	0.58	18.16
03/17*	58.19	20	13	2.97	0.52	16.41
02/16	39.41	27	15	2.22	0.46	14.16
02/15	45.85	27	16	1.72	0.41	13.17
03/14	34.23	38	23	0.95	0.37	12.18
Annual Growth	6.5%	—	—	30.6%	11.8%	10.5%

*Fiscal year change

Apollo Commercial Real Estate Finance Inc.

Apollo Commercial Real Estate Finance thinks the sky is the limit for commercial property loans. The New York-based mortgage real estate investment trust (REIT) originates buys and manages performing US commercial real estate loans subordinate loans commercial mortgage-backed securities (CMBS) and other commercial real estate debt investments. About 40% of its $2.6 billion investment portfolio is made up of commercial mortgage loans while another 35% is made up of subordinate loans. Formed in 2009 by Apollo Global Management the REIT is externally managed by

ACREFI Management (an indirect subsidiary of Apollo Global Management).

Operations

About 39% of the REIT's $2.57 billion investment portfolio was made up of commercial mortgage loans at the end of 2015 while another 36% was made up of subordinate loans. The rest was made up of CMBS (19% of portfolio assets) and CMBS held-to-maturity (6%).

Apollo Commercial Real Estate Finance (which is abbreviated as ARI) generates all of its revenue from interest income from its portfolio. Around 48% of its revenue came from subordinate loan interest during 2015 while interest income from commercial mortgage loans and securities made up 29% and 23% of annual revenues respectively.

Financial Performance

ARI's annual revenues and profits have quadrupled since 2011 as its interest-earning loan assets have swelled.

The REIT's revenue spiked 52% to $192.16 million during 2015 as it continued to earn higher interest from acquired loans. Strong revenue growth drove ARI's net income up 25% to $103.26 million while the REIT's operating cash levels jumped 31% to $88.12 million on higher cash earnings.

Strategy

While Apollo's priority is to invest in senior performing commercial mortgage loans CMBS and commercial real estate debt and loans it's expanding into other asset types. Its 2016 acquisition of Apollo Residential Mortgage for example more than doubled its loan portfolio while also diversifying its investments into residential mortgage loans.

Mergers and Acquisitions

In February 2016 ARI would enter the residential mortgage market and double its loan portfolio after agreeing to buy Apollo Residential Mortgage Inc. along with its $3.4 billion worth of Agency and non-Agency residential mortgage backed securities (RMBS) residential mortgage loans and other investments.

Company Background

The REIT raised $200 million from its initial public offering in 2009.

EXECUTIVES

President and CEO, Stuart A. Rothstein, age 52
Secretary Treasurer and CFO, Jai Agarwal
Chief Investment Officer, Scott Weiner
Chairman, Jeffrey M. (Jeff) Gault, age 73
Auditors: DELOITTE & TOUCHE LLP

LOCATIONS

HQ: Apollo Commercial Real Estate Finance Inc.
c/o Apollo Global Management, LLC, 9 West 57th Street, 43rd Floor, New York, NY 10019
Phone: 212 515-3200
Web: www.apolloreit.com

PRODUCTS/OPERATIONS

2015 Sales

	$ mil.	% of total
Interest income from subordinate loans	90.8	48
Interest income from commercial mortgage loans	56.1	29
Interest income from securities	33.2	17
Interest income from securities held-to-maturity	12.1	6
Total	**192.2**	**100**

COMPETITORS

Capital Trust
Petra Real Estate
Resource Capital
iStar Financial Inc

HISTORICAL FINANCIALS

Company Type: Public

Income Statement

FYE: December 31

	REVENUE ($ mil.)	NET INCOME ($ mil.)	NET PROFIT MARGIN	EMPLOYEES
12/17	338.5	193.0	57.0%	0
12/16	264.3	157.8	59.7%	0
12/15	192.1	103.2	53.7%	0
12/14	123.3	82.7	67.1%	0
12/13	77.4	52.4	67.8%	0
Annual Growth	44.6%	38.5%	—	—

2017 Year-End Financials

Debt ratio: 46.8%
Return on equity: 9.6%
Cash ($ mil.): 77.6
Current ratio: 0.98
Long-term debt ($ mil.): 1,915.7

No. of shares (mil.): 107.1
Dividends
  Yield: 0.1%
  Payout: 119.4%
Market value ($ mil.): 1,976.0

	STOCK PRICE ($) FY Close	P/E High/Low	Earnings	PER SHARE ($) Dividends	Book Value
12/17	18.45	13 11	1.54	1.84	19.49
12/16	16.62	10 9	1.74	1.84	21.14
12/15	17.23	12 10	1.54	1.78	20.47
12/14	16.36	10 9	1.72	1.60	18.23
12/13	16.25	15 12	1.26	1.60	18.51
Annual Growth	3.2%	— —	5.1%	3.6%	1.3%

Apollo Medical Holdings Inc

EXECUTIVES

Chb, Edward Schreck
Vice President Operations Corporate Secretary, Nidia Flores
Medical Director, Diane Pham
Board Member, TED SCHRECK
Auditors: BDO USA, LLP

LOCATIONS

HQ: Apollo Medical Holdings Inc
  1668 S. Garfield Avenue, 2nd Floor, Alhambra, CA 91801
Phone: 626 282-0288
Web: www.apollomed.net

HISTORICAL FINANCIALS

Company Type: Public

Income Statement

FYE: December 31

	REVENUE ($ mil.)	NET INCOME ($ mil.)	NET PROFIT MARGIN	EMPLOYEES
12/17*	357.7	25.8	7.2%	613
03/17	57.4	(8.9)	—	1,149
03/16	44.0	(9.3)	—	1,235
03/15	32.9	(1.8)	—	1,190
03/14	2.3	(0.7)	—	0
Annual Growth	251.8%	—	—	—

*Fiscal year change

2017 Year-End Financials

Debt ratio: 1.2%
Return on equity: 31.1%
Cash ($ mil.): 101.7
Current ratio: 1.32
Long-term debt ($ mil.): 0.6

No. of shares (mil.): 32.3
Dividends
  Yield: —
  Payout: —
Market value ($ mil.): 775.0

	STOCK PRICE ($) FY Close	P/E High/Low	Earnings	PER SHARE ($) Dividends	Book Value
12/17*	24.00	24 6	0.90	0.00	4.95
03/17	9.00	— —	(1.49)	0.00	(0.06)
03/16	5.93	— —	(1.79)	0.00	0.99
03/15	0.50	— —	(0.37)	0.00	(0.58)
03/14	0.55	— —	(0.16)	0.00	(0.49)
Annual Growth	157.0%	— —	—	—	—

*Fiscal year change

AppFolio Inc

Auditors: PricewaterhouseCoopers LLP

LOCATIONS

HQ: AppFolio Inc
  50 Castilian Drive, Santa Barbara, CA 93117
Phone: 805 364-6093
Web: www.appfolioinc.com

HISTORICAL FINANCIALS

Company Type: Public

Income Statement

FYE: December 31

	REVENUE ($ mil.)	NET INCOME ($ mil.)	NET PROFIT MARGIN	EMPLOYEES
12/17	143.8	9.7	6.8%	672
12/16	105.5	(8.2)	—	626
12/15	74.9	(15.6)	—	573
12/14	47.6	(8.6)	—	430
12/13	26.5	(7.3)	—	0
Annual Growth	52.6%	—	—	—

2017 Year-End Financials

Debt ratio: —
Return on equity: 12.5%
Cash ($ mil.): 16.1
Current ratio: 2.25
Long-term debt ($ mil.): —

No. of shares (mil.): 33.9
Dividends
  Yield: —
  Payout: —
Market value ($ mil.): 1,410.0

	STOCK PRICE ($) FY Close	P/E High/Low	Earnings	PER SHARE ($) Dividends	Book Value
12/17	41.50	178 76	0.28	0.00	2.50
12/16	23.85	— —	(0.25)	0.00	2.07
12/15	14.60	— —	(0.73)	0.00	2.17
Annual Growth	68.6%	— —	—	—	7.5%

Apple Hospitality REIT Inc

Auditors: Ernst & Young LLP

LOCATIONS

HQ: Apple Hospitality REIT Inc
  814 East Main Street, Richmond, VA 23219
Phone: 804 344-8121
Web: www.applehospitalityreit.com

HISTORICAL FINANCIALS

Company Type: Public

Income Statement

FYE: December 31

	REVENUE ($ mil.)	NET INCOME ($ mil.)	NET PROFIT MARGIN	EMPLOYEES
12/17	1,238.6	182.4	14.7%	56
12/16	1,041.0	144.6	13.9%	56
12/15	898.3	117.2	13.1%	54
12/14	803.9	6.8	0.9%	51
12/13	387.9	115.2	29.7%	52
Annual Growth	33.7%	12.2%	—	1.9%

2017 Year-End Financials

Debt ratio: 24.9%
Return on equity: 5.1%
Cash ($ mil.): 29.7
Current ratio: 0.27
Long-term debt ($ mil.): 1,222.2

No. of shares (mil.): 229.9
Dividends
  Yield: 0.0%
  Payout: 134.1%
Market value ($ mil.): 4,510.0

	STOCK PRICE ($) FY Close	P/E High/Low	Earnings	PER SHARE ($) Dividends	Book Value
12/17	19.61	25 21	0.82	1.10	15.53
12/16	19.98	27 23	0.76	1.20	15.78
12/15	19.97	32 25	0.65	0.80	15.18
Annual Growth	(0.9%)	— —	12.3%	17.3%	1.1%

Applied Optoelectronics Inc

When it comes to making lasers Applied Optoelectronics stays on the beam. The company designs and makes fiber-optic networking components that go into communications equipment used by data centers cable-TV providers telecommunications providers and fiber-to-the-home applications to allow for faster connections. Applied Optoelectronics makes laser chips components subassemblies and modules using its proprietary Molecular Beam Epitaxy (MBE) fabrication process. Customers include Arris Group Cisco Systems Amazon Facebook and Microsoft. About 95% of sales are to customers in Taiwan and China.

Operations

Applied Optoelectronics serves three end-markets: data centers cable television or CATV telecommunications and fiber-to-the-home or FTTH.

Data centers are the Applied Optoelectronics? biggest end market accounting for 80% of sales. CATV accounts for about 15% of revenue and telecom providers supply about 5%. Sales for the FTTH market are negligible.

Geographic Reach

Applied Optoelectronics is based in Sugar Land Texas and it operates manufacturing plants in Sugar Land China and Taiwan. Its Texas plant handles research and development and manufactures laser chips sub-assemblies and components. In Taiwan it makes transceivers and optical components such as butterfly lasers which incorporate the US-made laser chips sub-assemblies and components. In China the company takes advantage of lower labor costs and makes the more labor-intensive components and optical equipment systems such as CATV transmitters and CATV outdoor equipment.

Applied Optoelectronics sales are concentrated in three geographic markets that are centers of electronics manufacturing. Customers in Taiwan account for more than 60% of revenue with Chinese customers supplying more than 30% and US customers accounting for the rest.

Sales and Marketing

Applied Optoelectronics has three data center customers that account for a significant portion of its revenue. The biggest is Amazon.com which accounts for about 35% of revenue followed by Facebook with nearly 30% and Microsoft with about 14%. Its biggest CATV equipment customers are Cisco Systems about 5% of sales a China-based customer and ARRIS Group each less than 5% of sales.

While it primarily uses a direct sales force the company also uses third-party sales representatives and distributors.

Financial Performance

Applied Optoelectronics has posted annual revenue gains of about 35% for nine years as its products have caught on in data centers. It exceeded that rate in 2017 when sales jumped 46% from 2016 to reach $382 million. Sales of its data center products leaped more than 50% in 2017 from 2016 driven primarily by customers buying 40 Gbps and 100 Gbps chips to upgrade their technology infrastructure. Upgrades in CATV networks propelled a 40% increase in the company?s CATV products. Sales of products for FTTH applications dropped about 68% as sales of older products continued to wane. Telecom sales slipped slightly because reduced orders from customers in China.

Applied Optoelectronics? costs rose in 2017 from 2016 mostly driven by adding some 280 employees year-to-year. Even with the rising costs the company?s profit increased about 140% to $74 million in 2017 from 2016.

The company?s profits helped drive its cash holdings to about $84 million in 2017 from $52 million in 2016. It spent $67 million on capital improvements that included production equipment and machinery and construction and building improvements.

Strategy

As long as end-users want their devices to be faster Applied Optoelectronics sees a strong demand for its products across its markets. Its transceiver products are a key element in driving better performance in data centers telecommunications networks CATV and fiber-to-the-home applications. It also predicts a transition to its faster 100 GB products from 40 GB products as more

providers upgrade their infrastructures. The company also expects demand from the transition to 5G telecom networks which is getting underway.

Applied Optoelectronics is to continue spending more on research and development to produce more efficient manufacturing processes as well as develop 200 GB and 400 GB products. The company increased capital spending in 2018 to build a new factory in China which is expected to be completed in 2020.

With tensions rising in international trade relations Applied Optoelectronics? sales to China could be caught in a tariff war. About 30% of its sales are to customers in China which has been one of the main targets for US trade threats.

EXECUTIVES

Chairman President and CEO, Lin (Thompson) Chih-Hsiang, age 55, $336,533 total compensation
SVP Optical Component Business Unit, Chang (Fred) Hung-Lun, age 54, $196,788 total compensation
SVP Network Equipment Module Business Unit, Yeh (Joshua) Shu-Hua, age 52
CFO and Chief Strategy Officer, Stefan J. Murry, age 46, $218,575 total compensation
SVP and General Manager Asia, Li (Ford) Chung-Yao
Auditors: Grant Thornton LLP

LOCATIONS

HQ: Applied Optoelectronics Inc
13139 Jess Pirtle Blvd., Sugar Land, TX 77478
Phone: 281 295-1800
Web: www.ao-inc.com

PRODUCTS/OPERATIONS

2017 Sales by End Market

	% of total
Data center	80
Cable TV	16
Fiber-to-the-home	4
Other	-
Total	**100**

COMPETITORS

ANADIGICS	NeoPhotonics
Broadcom	Oclaro
EMCORE	Optek Technology
Finisar	Source Photonics
Foxconn Technology	Sumitomo Electric
Lumentum	Viavi Solutions

HISTORICAL FINANCIALS
Company Type: Public

Income Statement   FYE: December 31

	REVENUE ($ mil.)	NET INCOME ($ mil.)	NET PROFIT MARGIN	EMPLOYEES
12/17	382.3	73.9	19.3%	3,054
12/16	260.7	31.2	12.0%	2,776
12/15	189.9	10.7	5.7%	2,513
12/14	130.4	4.2	3.3%	1,447
12/13	78.4	(1.4)	—	1,146
Annual Growth	**48.6%**	—	—	**27.8%**

2017 Year-End Financials

Debt ratio: 10.9%	No. of shares (mil.): 19.4
Return on equity: 26.3%	Dividends
Cash ($ mil.): 82.9	Yield: —
Current ratio: 3.25	Payout: —
Long-term debt ($ mil.): 49.0	Market value ($ mil.): 736.0

	STOCK PRICE ($) FY Close	P/E High/Low		PER SHARE ($) Earnings	Dividends	Book Value
12/17	37.82	26	6	3.67	0.00	17.13
12/16	23.44	15	5	1.76	0.00	12.36
12/15	17.16	32	12	0.65	0.00	9.82
12/14	11.22	91	32	0.28	0.00	7.76
12/13	15.01	—	—	(0.14)	0.00	4.99
Annual Growth	**26.0%**	—	—	—	—	**36.1%**

Aptevo Therapeutics Inc

Auditors: Ernst & Young LLP

LOCATIONS

HQ: Aptevo Therapeutics Inc
2401 4th Avenue, Suite 1050, Seattle, WA 98121
Phone: 206 838-0500
Web: www.AptevoTherapeutics.com

HISTORICAL FINANCIALS
Company Type: Public

Income Statement   FYE: December 31

	REVENUE ($ mil.)	NET INCOME ($ mil.)	NET PROFIT MARGIN	EMPLOYEES
12/17	14.6	6.9	47.6%	121
12/16	36.4	(112.4)	—	118
12/15	33.6	(59.3)	—	140
12/14	45.6	(51.1)	—	0
12/13	0.1	(53.3)	—	0
Annual Growth	**204.7%**	—	—	—

2017 Year-End Financials

Debt ratio: 16.2%	No. of shares (mil.): 21.6
Return on equity: 10.5%	Dividends
Cash ($ mil.): 7.1	Yield: —
Current ratio: 5.14	Payout: —
Long-term debt ($ mil.): 15.7	Market value ($ mil.): 92.0

	STOCK PRICE ($) FY Close	P/E High/Low		PER SHARE ($) Earnings	Dividends	Book Value
12/17	4.24	13	4	0.33	0.00	3.80
12/16	2.44	—	—	(5.55)	0.00	2.49
Annual Growth	**73.8%**	—	—	—	—	**52.2%**

Arbor Realty Trust Inc

Money doesn't grow on trees so Arbor Realty Trust invests in real estate-related assets. The real estate investment trust (REIT) buys structured finance assets in the commercial and multifamily real estate markets. It primarily invests in bridge loans (short-term financing) and mezzanine loans (large and usually unsecured loans) but also invests in discounted mortgage notes and other assets. The REIT targets lending and investment opportunities where borrowers seek interim financing until permanent financing is attained. Arbor Realty Trust is managed by financing firm Arbor Commercial Mortgage though in early 2016 the REIT agreed to buy Arbor Commercial Mortgage for $250 million to expand into the government-sponsored multi-family real estate loan origination business.

EXECUTIVES

Secretary and Director, Walter K. Horn, age 73, $225,000 total compensation

Chairman President and CEO; Chairman and CEO Arbor Commercial Mortgage, Ivan Kaufman, age 55, $800,000 total compensation

EVP Structured Finance, Fred Weber, age 55, $500,000 total compensation

EVP Structured Securitization, Gene Kilgore, age 49, $500,000 total compensation

CFO and Treasurer; CFO Arbor Commercial Mortgage, Paul Elenio, age 48, $270,000 total compensation

Chief Credit Officer, Andrew Guziewicz

SVP Asset Management, John Felletter, $225,000 total compensation

Senior Vice President Structured Finance, Gianni Ottaviano

Secretary and Director, Walter K. Horn, age 73

Director, Archie R. Dykes, age 85

Director, C. Michael Kojaian, age 54

Director, Melvin F. (Mel) Lazar, age 77

Director, John J. Bishar Jr., age 66

Director, William Helmreich, age 70

Director, Joseph Martello, age 60

Director, Karen K. Edwards, age 59

Independent Director, William Green

Auditors: Ernst & Young LLP

LOCATIONS

HQ: Arbor Realty Trust Inc
333 Earle Ovington Boulevard, Suite 900, Uniondale, NY 11553
Phone: 516 506-4200
Web: www.arbor.com

COMPETITORS

Annaly Capital Management	Institutional Financial Markets
Anworth Mortgage Asset	RAIT Financial Trust
Capital Trust	Redwood Trust
Drive Shack	Starwood Property
Impac Mortgage Holdings	iStar Financial Inc

HISTORICAL FINANCIALS
Company Type: Public

Income Statement				FYE: December 31
	REVENUE ($ mil.)	NET INCOME ($ mil.)	NET PROFIT MARGIN	EMPLOYEES
12/17	346.6	121.6	35.1%	445
12/16	213.2	74.6	35.0%	288
12/15	142.5	53.4	37.5%	39
12/14	141.0	93.0	66.0%	37
12/13	129.1	21.1	16.4%	37
Annual Growth	28.0%	54.8%	—	86.2%

2017 Year-End Financials

Debt ratio: 69.8% No. of shares (mil.): 61.7
Return on equity: 18.9% Dividends
Cash ($ mil.): 104.3 Yield: 0.0%
Current ratio: 0.39 Payout: 64.2%
Long-term debt ($ mil.): 2,002.6 Market value ($ mil.): 533.0

	STOCK PRICE ($) FY Close	P/E High/Low		PER SHARE ($) Earnings	Dividends	Book Value
12/17	8.64	8	6	1.12	0.72	11.27
12/16	7.46	10	7	0.83	0.62	11.42
12/15	7.15	8	7	0.90	0.58	11.09
12/14	6.77	4	4	1.70	0.52	10.61
12/13	6.66	21	15	0.39	0.50	8.91
Annual Growth	6.7%	—		30.2%	9.5%	6.1%

Ares Commercial Real Estate Corp

Auditors: Ernst & Young LLP

LOCATIONS

HQ: Ares Commercial Real Estate Corp
245 Park Avenue, 42nd Floor, New York, NY 10167
Phone: 212 750-7300
Web: www.arescre.com

HISTORICAL FINANCIALS
Company Type: Public

Income Statement				FYE: December 31
	REVENUE ($ mil.)	NET INCOME ($ mil.)	NET PROFIT MARGIN	EMPLOYEES
12/17	97.5	30.4	31.2%	0
12/16	81.9	40.3	49.2%	930
12/15	121.7	34.2	28.2%	870
12/14	98.7	24.4	24.7%	750
12/13	47.3	13.7	29.1%	790
Annual Growth	19.8%	21.9%	—	—

2017 Year-End Financials

Debt ratio: 75.5% No. of shares (mil.): 28.6
Return on equity: 7.2% Dividends
Cash ($ mil.): 28.3 Yield: 0.0%
Current ratio: 2.78 Payout: 100.9%
Long-term debt ($ mil.): 1,336.7 Market value ($ mil.): 369.0

	STOCK PRICE ($) FY Close	P/E High/Low		PER SHARE ($) Earnings	Dividends	Book Value
12/17	12.90	13	12	1.07	1.08	14.66
12/16	13.73	10	6	1.41	1.04	14.71
12/15	11.44	11	9	1.20	1.00	14.31
12/14	11.48	16	13	0.85	1.00	14.10
12/13	13.10	24	17	0.72	1.00	14.25
Annual Growth	(0.4%)	—		10.4%	1.9%	0.7%

Ares Management Corp

Auditors: Ernst & Young LLP

LOCATIONS

HQ: Ares Management Corp
2000 Avenue of the Stars, 12th Floor, Los Angeles, CA 90067
Phone: 310 201-4100
Web: www.aresmgmt.com

HISTORICAL FINANCIALS
Company Type: Public

Income Statement				FYE: December 31
	REVENUE ($ mil.)	NET INCOME ($ mil.)	NET PROFIT MARGIN	EMPLOYEES
12/17	1,415.5	76.1	5.4%	1,000
12/16	1,199.2	111.8	9.3%	925
12/15	814.4	19.3	2.4%	870
12/14	603.8	34.9	5.8%	800
12/13	478.6	180.4	37.7%	700
Annual Growth	31.1%	(19.4%)	—	9.3%

2017 Year-End Financials

Debt ratio: 66.7% No. of shares (mil.): 82.2
Return on equity: 25.5% Dividends
Cash ($ mil.): 675.4 Yield: 0.0%
Current ratio: 5.97 Payout: 182.2%
Long-term debt ($ mil.): 5,717.5 Market value ($ mil.): 1,646.0

	STOCK PRICE ($) FY Close	P/E High/Low		PER SHARE ($) Earnings	Dividends	Book Value
12/17	20.00	38	28	0.62	1.13	6.97
12/16	19.20	16	9	1.20	0.83	7.32
12/15	12.93	90	54	0.23	0.88	3.35
12/14	17.14	46	36	0.43	0.42	16.67
Annual Growth	5.3% (25.2%)	—	—	13.0%	39.1%	

Argan Inc

Argan makes sure its customers stay all juiced up. The holding company owns subsidiaries that provide power services and products for the government telecommunications power and personal health care industries. Its main subsidiary Gemma Power Systems designs builds and maintains power plants including traditional and alternate fuel plants. The company's Southern Maryland Cable unit provides inside-premise wiring and also performs splicing and underground and aerial telecom infrastructure construction services to carriers government entities service providers and electric utilities. Argan's power industry segment accounts for more than 95% of its total revenues.

Operations

Argan operates two main segments: Power Industry Services which generated 98% of its total revenue in fiscal 2015 (ended January 2015) and operates through Gemma Power Systems and Atlantic Projects Company; and Telecom Infrastructure Services which operates through Southern Maryland Cable.

Main subsidiary Gemma Power Systems (GPS) has completed projects at more than 76 power-generating facilities (representing some 11000 megawatts of capacity). It has expertise working with combined-cycle cogeneration facilities simple-cycle peaking plants emergency peaking plants and boiler plants. The firm also completes renovation work for utilities.

Subsidiary Atlantic Projects Company (acquired in mid-2015) installs turbines boilers and large rotating equipment. It also provides commissioning and outage services to original equipment manufacturers global construction firms and plant owners around the globe.

Geographic Reach

Argan operates in the US as well as internationally in Hong Kong and Singapore.

Sales and Marketing

GPS serves a variety of customers including public utilities independent power project owners municipalities public institutions and private companies. Southern Maryland Cable serves the federal government local governments telecommunications and broadband service providers and electric utilities. Atlantic Projects Company serves customers in the power generation oil & gas industrial and process industries.

Argan's major customers in fiscal 2015 (ended January 2015) included: Howard County and the state of Maryland Verizon EDS and the Southern Maryland Electric Cooperative (SMECO). About 25% of SMC's revenues that year came from outside plant services provided under its contract with SMECO.

Financial Performance

Argan's annual revenues while volatile have been trending higher over the past few years as demand for energy continues to grow in the US. Its profits have been rising steadily over the past few years as well.

The company's revenue spiked 68% to $383.11 million in fiscal 2015 (ended January 2015) thanks to higher construction activity on two natural gas-fired combined cycle power plant projects (the Panda Liberty and Panda Patriot power plants).

Despite revenue growth in FY2015 Argan's net income fell 24% to $30 million for the year due to higher operating costs and overhead expenses all resulting from more activities going toward the Panda Liberty and Panda Patriot projects. The company's operating cash levels dipped 5% to $93 million as the company's cash earnings fell during the year.

Strategy

Argan's main subsidiary GPS continued in 2015 to work on high-profile power projects (usually extending up to three years) recently expanding into alternative energy generation to cover EPC contracting services for alternative energy facility owners including biomass plants wind farms and solar fields.

Some of GPS's projects completed between FY2013 through FY2015 included: an 800 MW simple-cycle quick start peaking power plant in Desert Hot Springs California; wind-energy farms with 150 turbines powering 230 MW in the states of Illinois and Pennsylvania; and two large solar energy fields in Massachusetts with 40000 photovoltaic panels. Its past projects include biodiesel production plants in Texas and a natural gas-fired power plant in California.

Mergers and Acquisitions

In May 2015 Argan bought Ireland-based Atlantic Projects Company Limited a private company that provides turbine boiler and large rotating equipment installation commissioning and outage services. The deal expanded Argan's service lines and extended its operations internationally thanks to office acquisitions in Hong Kong Singapore and New York.

EXECUTIVES

SVP CFO and Secretary, Arthur F. Trudel Jr., age 63, $200,000 total compensation
Chairman President and CEO, Rainer H. Bosselmann, age 72, $200,000 total compensation
Vice Chairman and CEO Gemma Power Systems, William F. (Bill) Griffin Jr., age 59, $365,000 total compensation
President Gemma Power Systems, Daniel L. (Dan) Martin
Director, William F. Leimkuhler, age 63
Director, DeSoto S. Jordan, age 70
Director, James W. (Jim) Quinn, age 57
Director, Daniel A. (Dan) Levinson, age 54
Director, W.G. Champion (Champ) Mitchell, age 67
Director, Henry A. Crumpton, age 58
Director, Cynthia Flanders, age 60
Independent Director, Brian Sherras
Auditors: Grant Thornton LLP

LOCATIONS

HQ: Argan Inc
One Church Street, Suite 201, Rockville, MD 20850
Phone: 301 315-0027
Web: www.arganinc.com

PRODUCTS/OPERATIONS

2015 Sales

	$ mil.	% of total
Power industry services	376.7	98
Telecommunications infrastructure services	6.4	2
Total	**383.1**	**100**

COMPETITORS

Bechtel	John Wood Group
CH2M HILL	Kiewit Power
Chicago Bridge & Iron	Constructors
EMCOR	Quanta Services
Fagen Inc.	SNC-Lavalin
Fluor	Skanska
IES Holdings	

HISTORICAL FINANCIALS

Company Type: Public

Income Statement				FYE: January 31
	REVENUE ($ mil.)	NET INCOME ($ mil.)	NET PROFIT MARGIN	EMPLOYEES
01/18	892.8	72.0	8.1%	1,552
01/17	675.0	70.3	10.4%	1,286
01/16	413.2	36.3	8.8%	1,188
01/15	383.1	30.4	7.9%	862
01/14	227.4	40.1	17.6%	359
Annual Growth	**40.8%**	**15.7%**	**—**	**44.2%**

2018 Year-End Financials

Debt ratio: —
Return on equity: 22.1%
Cash ($ mil.): 122.1
Current ratio: 2.24
Long-term debt ($ mil.): —
No. of shares (mil.): 15.5
Dividends
Yield: 2.2%
Payout: 21.9%
Market value ($ mil.): 679.0

	STOCK PRICE ($) FY Close	P/E High/Low		PER SHARE ($) Earnings	Dividends	Book Value
01/18	43.60	16	9	4.56	1.00	23.00
01/17	73.75	16	6	4.50	1.00	18.87
01/16	30.12	17	12	2.42	0.70	14.73
01/15	30.41	19	13	2.05	0.70	12.68
01/14	28.41	11	5	2.78	0.75	10.94
Annual Growth	**11.3%**		**— —**	**13.2%**	**7.5%**	**20.4%**

Arista Networks Inc

Auditors: Ernst & Young LLP

LOCATIONS

HQ: Arista Networks Inc
5453 Great America Parkway, Santa Clara, CA 95054
Phone: 408 547-5500
Web: www.arista.com

HISTORICAL FINANCIALS

Company Type: Public

Income Statement				FYE: December 31
	REVENUE ($ mil.)	NET INCOME ($ mil.)	NET PROFIT MARGIN	EMPLOYEES
12/17	1,646.1	423.2	25.7%	1,800
12/16	1,129.1	184.1	16.3%	1,500
12/15	837.5	121.1	14.5%	1,200
12/14	584.1	86.8	14.9%	1,000
12/13	361.2	42.4	11.8%	850
Annual Growth	**46.1%**	**77.7%**	**—**	**20.6%**

2017 Year-End Financials

Debt ratio: 1.5%
Return on equity: 30.5%
Cash ($ mil.): 859.1
Current ratio: 4.28
Long-term debt ($ mil.): 37.6
No. of shares (mil.): 73.7
Dividends
Yield: —
Payout: —
Market value ($ mil.): 17,364.0

	STOCK PRICE ($) FY Close	P/E High/Low		PER SHARE ($) Earnings	Dividends	Book Value
12/17	235.58	42	15	5.35	0.00	22.55
12/16	96.77	37	20	2.50	0.00	15.64
12/15	77.84	48	31	1.67	0.00	11.57
12/14	60.76	66	39	1.29	0.00	8.48
Annual Growth	**57.1%**		**— —**	**60.7%**	**—**	**38.5%**

Arlington Asset Investment Corp

Arlington Asset Investment invests mostly in residential mortgage-backed securities (MBS) to provide funds in the mortgage market for institutions such as commercial banks savings and loans associations mortgage banking companies seller/servicers securities dealers and other investors. More than 85% of the securities in the financial firm's $4 billion-plus MBS portfolio are backed by the US government through agencies such as Freddie Mac and Fannie Mae. The remainder of Arlington's MBS portfolio consists of private-label funds issued by private organizations. Arlington Asset Investment was founded as Friedman Billings Ramsey in 1989.

Operations

Arlington Asset Investment's portfolio was worth $4.385 billion at the end of 2015 with 88% of the assets being tied to agency MBS guaranteed by US government agencies and most of the rest being made up of private-label MBS.

The firm makes most of its money in the form of interest on its securities though it also trades investments held-for-sale. About 80% of its revenue came from interest income on agency MBS during 2015 while 9% came from interest on the private label MBS and 10% of revenue came from realized gains on available-for-sale investment sales.

Geographic Reach

The Washington DC-based firm has an administrative office in Virginia.

Financial Performance

The investment firm's annual revenue and profits have been volatile over the last few years as bond yield fluctuations and investment trades have affected its performance.

Arlington Asset Investments' revenue plunged 97% to $2.21 million during 2015 despite a 42% rise in interest income on its agency MBS mostly as the firm took a $148.5 million loss on trading investments (it suffered $38.7 million in trading losses in 2014). The trading losses were caused by the widening of MBS spread which resulted in net losses on interest rate derivative instruments (used by the firm to hedge against interest rate risk).

Steep revenue declines combined with steady overhead costs in 2015 led the firm to a net loss of $69.4 million (compared to a profit of $7.75 million in 2014). Arlington's operating cash levels jumped 59% to $111 million during 2015 after adjusting its earnings for trading losses which were not cash based.

Strategy

Arlington's primary investment strategy is to acquire and hold fixed-rate agency-backed mortgage-backed securities. The firm's risk for losses may increase as the threat of rising interest rates in 2016 and beyond may cause its longer-term holdings to lose value.

Company Background

Arlington went through a transformation in 2009. In addition to changing its name the company divested its remaining stake in former subsidiary FBR Capital Markets through which it had provided investment banking institutional brokerage and fee-based asset management services to corporations institutions and wealthy individuals. To this end Arlington no longer offers those services. Arlington also revoked its status as a real estate investment trust. The change allowed the company more financial flexibility and gave it the opportunity to acquire other types of assets besides those related to real estate.

EXECUTIVES

Chairman and CEO, Eric F. Billings, age 65, $800,000 total compensation
President and COO, J. Rock Tonkel, age 56, $750,000 total compensation
EVP CFO and Treasurer, Richard E. (Rich) Konzmann, age 49
Chief Investment Officer and Portfolio Manager, Brian J. Bowers
Vice President and Corporate Controller, Benjamin Strickler
Board Member, Daniel E Berce
Auditors: PricewaterhouseCoopers LLP

LOCATIONS

HQ: Arlington Asset Investment Corp
 1001 Nineteenth Street North, Arlington, VA 22209
Phone: 703 373-0200
Web: www.arlingtonasset.com

PRODUCTS/OPERATIONS

2015 Sales

	% of total
Interest income	
Agency mortgage-backed securities	80
Private-label mortgage-backed securities	9
Investment loss net	
Realized gain on sale of available-for-sale investments net	10
Other	1
Eliminations	-
Total	**100**

COMPETITORS

AG Mortgage Investment Trust	MFA Financial
Ares Capital	Merrill Lynch
Bimini Capital Management	Morgan Stanley
	Oppenheimer Holdings
Citigroup Global Markets	Putnam Mortgage
	RBC Wealth Management
Goldman Sachs	ROTH Capital Partners
KKR Financial	UBS Financial Services

HISTORICAL FINANCIALS
Company Type: Public

Income Statement				FYE: December 31
	REVENUE ($ mil.)	NET INCOME ($ mil.)	NET PROFIT MARGIN	EMPLOYEES
12/17	127.1	17.4	13.7%	12
12/16	36.0	(41.3)	—	11
12/15	2.2	(69.4)	—	11
12/14	84.8	5.9	7.0%	11
12/13	39.2	49.4	126.0%	11
Annual Growth	**34.1%**	**(22.9%)**	**—**	**2.2%**

2017 Year-End Financials

Debt ratio: 1.7%	No. of shares (mil.): 28.1
Return on equity: 4.5%	Dividends
Cash ($ mil.): 21.6	Yield: 0.1%
Current ratio: 0.01	Payout: 344.7%
Long-term debt ($ mil.): 73.8	Market value ($ mil.): 331.0

	STOCK PRICE ($) FY Close	P/E High/Low	PER SHARE ($) Earnings	Dividends	Book Value
12/17	11.78	23 16	0.66	2.28	13.73
12/16	14.82	— —	(1.79)	2.50	16.23
12/15	13.23	— —	(3.02)	3.00	21.07
12/14	26.61	95 83	0.29	3.50	27.95
12/13	26.39	9 7	3.06	3.50	33.24
Annual Growth	**(18.3%) (19.8%)**		**—**	**(31.9%) (10.2%)**	

Armada Hoffler Properties Inc

Auditors: Ernst & Young LLP

LOCATIONS

HQ: Armada Hoffler Properties Inc
 222 Central Park Avenue, Suite 2100, Virginia Beach, VA 23462
Phone: 757 366-4000
Web: www.armadahoffler.com

HISTORICAL FINANCIALS
Company Type: Public

Income Statement				FYE: December 31
	REVENUE ($ mil.)	NET INCOME ($ mil.)	NET PROFIT MARGIN	EMPLOYEES
12/17	302.7	21.0	7.0%	160
12/16	258.3	28.0	10.9%	151
12/15	252.4	19.6	7.8%	139
12/14	168.0	7.6	4.6%	137
12/13	140.0	7.3	5.2%	120
Annual Growth	**21.3%**	**30.1%**	**—**	**7.5%**

2017 Year-End Financials

Debt ratio: 49.5%	No. of shares (mil.): 44.9
Return on equity: 11.2%	Dividends
Cash ($ mil.): 19.9	Yield: 0.0%
Current ratio: 1.87	Payout: 152.0%
Long-term debt ($ mil.): 517.2	Market value ($ mil.): 698.0

	STOCK PRICE ($) FY Close	P/E High/Low	PER SHARE ($) Earnings	Dividends	Book Value
12/17	15.53	32 25	0.50	0.76	5.04
12/16	14.57	18 12	0.85	0.72	3.95
12/15	10.48	15 13	0.75	0.68	1.65
12/14	9.49	29 24	0.37	0.64	(0.11)
12/13	9.28	30 23	0.39	0.40	(2.43)
Annual Growth	**13.7%**		**—**	**— 6.4% 17.4%**	

Astronics Corp

In the glare of its own lights but without histrionics Astronics Corporation displays its talents daily to a specialized audience. Astronics makes external and internal lighting systems as well as power generation and distribution technology for commercial general aviation and military defense aircraft. Products include cabin emergency lighting systems (escape path markers and exit locators) cockpit lighting systems (avionics keyboards ambient light sensors annunciator panels and electronic dimmers) external lights and military test equipment. Astronics operates subsidiaries include Astronics Advanced Electronic Systems Corp. Ballard Luminescent Systems and DME Corporation.

Operations

The company operates in two segments: Aerospace (almost 80% of net sales) and Test Systems (20%). The Aerospace segment designs and makes a range of products for the global aerospace industry. Its products include aircraft lighting airframe power avionics airfield lighting and cabin electronics. The Test Systems segment designs develops and manufactures communications and weapons test systems and training and simulation devices for military clients.

Geographic Reach
The company's Aerospace segment has 11 principal operating facilities located in New York Florida Illinois New Hampshire Oregon and Washington; international resides in Canada and Montierchaume France. Its Test Systems segment has facilities located in Florida and California.

Sales and Marketing
Astronics' customers include the Department of Defense (DOD) Federal Aviation Administration and airport operators US military forces foreign military agencies and makers of military communication systems.

Financial Performance
The company has achieved explosive growth the last two years mostly due to a surge in Aerospace sales and additional revenue from acquisitions. Revenues grew 5% to peak at a record-setting $692 million in 2015. Profits also jumped 19% to reach $67 million in 2015 another company milestone.

The historic growth for 2015 was fueled by an 11% spike in Aerospace sales and a 15% rise in sales from North America. This growth was driven by a spike in electrical power and motion sales particularly in-seat power products. Its lighting and safety product line increased due to growth passenger service unit sales. Systems certification sales also received a boost from acquisitions.

Astronics' unprecedented profit total for 2015 was due to the higher net sales coupled with a decrease in interest expenses due to decreased debt levels. The company's operating cash flow has trended upwards until 2015 when it decreased by 21%.

Strategy
The company continues to invest in new technologies and aircraft programs for each of its markets even while the aerospace industry as a whole is experiencing a slowdown along with the economy in general. In particular Astronics is developing an electrical power distribution system for the Learjet 85 that shows promise of becoming a standard component of business jets. Its products and technologies are also used in the F-35 Joint Strike Fighter the Airbus A380 XWB and the Boeing 787 to name a few.

Mergers and Acquisitions
Growing its Aerospace portfolio in 2015 Astronics paid $52 million to purchase Armstrong Aerospace located in Itasca Illinois. Armstrong is a provider of engineering design and certification products and services for commercial aircraft specializing in connectivity in-flight entertainment and electrical power systems.

Company Background
Founded in 1968 Astronics was originally involved in electroluminescent products until it began to diversify into the packaging and printing industries. The company acquired MOD-PAC a maker of paperboard packaging in 1972 and Krepe-Kraft a specialized printing company in 1987.

EXECUTIVES
Executive Vice President Luminescent Systems, James S. (Jim) Kramer, $242,000 total compensation
President and Chief Executive Officer, Peter J. Gundermann, age 56, $430,000 total compensation
VP and CFO, David C. Burney, age 56, $270,000 total compensation
Executive Vice President Astronics Advanced Electronic Systems, Mark Peabody, $310,000 total compensation
Chairman of the Board, Kevin T. Keane, age 85
Auditors: Ernst & Young LLP

LOCATIONS
HQ: Astronics Corp
130 Commerce Way, East Aurora, NY 14052
Phone: 716 805-1599
Web: www.astronics.com

PRODUCTS/OPERATIONS

2015 Sales

	$ mil.	% of total
Aerospace	549.7	79
Test systems	142.5	21
Total	692.2	100

Aircraft lighting
Astronics Advanced Electronic Systems Corp
Ballard Technology Inc
DME Corporation
Luminescent Systems Canada Inc
Luminescent Systems Inc
Max-Viz Inc

COMPETITORS

AIM Altitude	L-3/IS
C&D Zodiac	TransDigm Group
Ducommun	Ultra Electronics
Honeywell Aerospace	Zodiac Aerospace
Indel	

HISTORICAL FINANCIALS
Company Type: Public

Income Statement				FYE: December 31
	REVENUE ($ mil.)	NET INCOME ($ mil.)	NET PROFIT MARGIN	EMPLOYEES
12/17	624.4	19.6	3.2%	2,500
12/16	633.1	48.4	7.6%	2,300
12/15	692.2	66.9	9.7%	2,300
12/14	661.0	56.1	8.5%	2,000
12/13	339.9	27.2	8.0%	1,715
Annual Growth	16.4%	(7.8%)	—	9.9%

2017 Year-End Financials
Debt ratio: 36.9%
Return on equity: 5.9%
Cash ($ mil.): 17.9
Current ratio: 3.06
Long-term debt ($ mil.): 269.0

No. of shares (mil.): 32.2
Dividends
Yield: —
Payout: —
Market value ($ mil.): 1,337.0

	STOCK PRICE ($) FY Close	P/E High/Low	PER SHARE ($) Earnings	Dividends	Book Value
12/17	41.47	73 42	0.58	0.00	10.23
12/16	33.84	32 17	1.40	0.00	10.08
12/15	40.71	39 18	1.93	0.00	8.88
12/14	55.31	42 25	1.63	0.00	6.84
12/13	51.00	62 27	0.82	0.00	5.26
Annual Growth	(5.0%)	— —	(8.1%)	—	18.1%

At Home Group Inc

Auditors: Ernst & Young LLP

LOCATIONS
HQ: At Home Group Inc
1600 East Plano Parkway, Plano, TX 75074
Phone: 972 265-6227
Web: www.athome.com

HISTORICAL FINANCIALS
Company Type: Public

Income Statement				FYE: January 27
	REVENUE ($ mil.)	NET INCOME ($ mil.)	NET PROFIT MARGIN	EMPLOYEES
01/18	950.5	31.8	3.3%	4,400
01/17	765.6	27.0	3.5%	3,172
01/16	622.1	3.5	0.6%	2,941
01/15	497.7	(0.4)	—	0
01/14	403.9	(22.2)	—	0
Annual Growth	23.9%	—	—	—

2018 Year-End Financials
Debt ratio: 34.5%
Return on equity: 5.6%
Cash ($ mil.): 8.5
Current ratio: 0.88
Long-term debt ($ mil.): 309.5

No. of shares (mil.): 61.4
Dividends
Yield: —
Payout: —
Market value ($ mil.): 2,072.0

	STOCK PRICE ($) FY Close	P/E High/Low	PER SHARE ($) Earnings	Dividends	Book Value
01/18	33.73	64 27	0.50	0.00	9.62
01/17	15.14	33 21	0.48	0.00	8.86
Annual Growth	122.8%	— —	4.2%	—	8.6%

ATN International Inc

ATN International makes connections from the maple groves of Vermont to the rain forests of Guyana. In the US the company provides wholesale wireless voice and data roaming services to local and national communications carriers through subsidiary Commnet Wireless. ATN voice and broadband Internet services New England particularly Vermont through its SoVerNet subsidiary. SoVerNet subsidiary ION offers fiber-optic transport services in New York State on a wholesale basis.

Operations
The company operates in five segments with the US wireless segment accounting for about 44% of revenue followed by international wireless 23% wireline 24% renewable energy 6% and equipment 4%.

Geographic Reach
ATN gets about 23% of its revenue from its internationally designated segments while US segments account for the rest. Besides the US and Guyana ATN provides service in Bermuda the U.S. Virgin Islandsthe Cayman Islands and Aruba. Its Caribbean customers are served by its subsidiaries including Choice Communications which offers In-

ternet access in the US Virgin Islands under the ClearChoice brand.

Sales and Marketing
ATN's two biggest customers are Verizon 19% of revenue and AT&T 17% of revenue.

Financial Performance
ATN's revenue rose to $55.4 million in 2015 6% higher than 2014's $336 million. The company reported higher revenue in its US wireless wireline and equipment segments. The increase in the number of base stations from 760 to approximately 800 helped drive traffic levels higher. However the traffic volume increase was offset by reduced rates that cut wholesale revenue.

The telecom's net income dropped to about $17 million in 2015 a 65% tumble from 2014. It had a loss on deconsolidation of its subsidiary in selling operations in Turks and Caicos. The costs associated with its renewable energy acquisition also shaved off profit.

Cash flow from operations strengthened to $140 million from $78 million the previous year.

Strategy
ATN is building and strengthening its network through acquisitions and construction of more cell towers. It also is branching out beyond telecom into renewable energy with the purchase of a solar power concern.

After selling its Turks and Caicos operations (for some $0 million) ATN bought into the telecom market in Bermuda. In its telecom infrastructure ATN added about 100 base stations and upgraded a number to advanced wireless technologies (especially in the American wireless market).

Perhaps most interesting is ATN's foray into renewable energy. It acquired Ahana Renewables a provider of distributed generation solar power services in the US in 2014. It followed with the purchase of the development business of Armstrong Energy Global a developer builder and owner of solar farms in India. ATN believes distributed solar energy operations offer solid investment returns.

Mergers and Acquisitions
In 2015 ATN acquired controlling interest in Keytech Ltd. a company that provides broadband cable TV and other telecommunications services to residential and business customers under the 'Logic' name in Bermuda and the Cayman Islands.

EXECUTIVES

CFO, Justin D. Benincasa, age 56, $333,000 total compensation
President and CEO, Michael T. Prior, age 53, $565,000 total compensation
SVP Business Operations, Barry C. Fougere
Vice President Carrier Services, Richard Bosler
Chairman, Cornelius B. Prior, age 84
Auditors: PricewaterhouseCoopers LLP

LOCATIONS

HQ: ATN International Inc
500 Cummings Center, Beverly, MA 01915
Phone: 978 619-1300
Web: www.atni.com

PRODUCTS/OPERATIONS

2015 Sales

	$ mil.	% of total
U.S Wireless	155.4	44
International Wireless	81.7	23
Wireline	86.5	24
Renewable Energy	21.0	6
Equipment and other	10.8	3
Total	**355.4**	**100**

COMPETITORS

AT&T Mobility	Sprint Communications
América M vil	Telephone & Data
Digicel Jamaica	Systems
FairPoint	Verizon
Communications Inc.	

HISTORICAL FINANCIALS
Company Type: Public

Income Statement				FYE: December 31
	REVENUE ($ mil.)	NET INCOME ($ mil.)	NET PROFIT MARGIN	EMPLOYEES
12/17	481.1	31.4	6.5%	1,800
12/16	457.0	12.1	2.6%	1,800
12/15	355.3	16.9	4.8%	1,200
12/14	336.3	48.1	14.3%	1,000
12/13	292.8	311.7	106.4%	1,000
Annual Growth	13.2%	(43.6%)	—	15.8%

2017 Year-End Financials

Debt ratio: 12.9%	No. of shares (mil.): 16.0
Return on equity: 4.6%	Dividends
Cash ($ mil.): 207.9	Yield: 0.0%
Current ratio: 2.12	Payout: 52.5%
Long-term debt ($ mil.): 144.8	Market value ($ mil.): 886.0

	STOCK PRICE ($) FY Close	P/E High/Low		PER SHARE ($) Earnings	Dividends	Book Value
12/17	55.26	44	26	1.94	1.02	42.98
12/16	80.13	111	85	0.75	1.32	41.95
12/15	78.23	79	59	1.05	1.22	42.34
12/14	67.59	24	18	3.01	1.12	42.52
12/13	56.57	3	2	19.71	1.04	40.68
Annual Growth	(0.6%)	—	—	(44.0%)	(0.5%)	1.4%

AvalonBay Communities, Inc.

AvalonBay Communities has it down in the apartment department. The real estate investment trust (REIT) buys develops renovates and operatesA multifamily properties in the US. It specializes in upscale properties in high barrier-to-entry marketsA such asA Boston Los Angeles New York City San Francisco Seattle and Washington DC. By providing luxury living in high-demand areas where apartment-zoned landA is in low supply AvalonBay can also charge premium rent. The REIT ownsA about 180 apartment communities with more than 53000A units. It also has more than 30 properties under construction or redevelopment and owns rights to develop more than 30 additional ones.

EXECUTIVES

Regional VP Development, Matthew H. (Matt) Birenbaum, age 52, $490,385 total compensation
Chief Administrative Officer, Leo S. Horey, age 55, $420,192 total compensation
EVP Development, William M. (Bill) McLaughlin, age 53, $390,000 total compensation
Chairman President and CEO, Timothy J. (Tim) Naughton, age 56, $950,000 total compensation
EVP General Counsel and Secretary, Edward M. (Ted) Schulman, age 55, $319,282 total compensation
EVP Development, Stephen W. (Steve) Wilson, age 61, $425,000 total compensation
COO, Sean J. Breslin, age 51, $490,385 total compensation
SVP Investment Management, Kevin P. O'Shea, age 52, $480,769 total compensation
Chief Construction Officer, Michael M. Feigin, age 57
Senior Vice President Development, Frederick Harris
Executive Vice President Corporate Strategy, Matthew Fry
Auditors: Ernst & Young LLP

LOCATIONS

HQ: AvalonBay Communities, Inc.
Ballston Tower, 671 N. Glebe Road, Suite 800, Arlington, VA 22203
Phone: 703 329-6300   **Fax:** 703 329-9130
Web: www.avalonbay.com

COMPETITORS

AMLI Residential	Essex Property Trust
Apartment Investment	Gables Residential
and Management	Services
Camden Property	Home Properties
Equity Residential	UDR

HISTORICAL FINANCIALS
Company Type: Public

Income Statement				FYE: December 31
	REVENUE ($ mil.)	NET INCOME ($ mil.)	NET PROFIT MARGIN	EMPLOYEES
12/17	2,158.6	876.9	40.6%	3,112
12/16	2,045.2	1,034.0	50.6%	3,071
12/15	1,856.0	742.0	40.0%	2,981
12/14	1,685.0	683.5	40.6%	3,006
12/13	1,462.9	353.1	24.1%	0
Annual Growth	10.2%	25.5%	—	—

2017 Year-End Financials

Debt ratio: 39.8%	No. of shares (mil.): 138.0
Return on equity: 8.5%	Dividends
Cash ($ mil.): 67.0	Yield: 0.0%
Current ratio: 0.79	Payout: 89.4%
Long-term debt ($ mil.): 7,329.4	Market value ($ mil.): 24,637.0

	STOCK PRICE ($) FY Close	P/E High/Low		PER SHARE ($) Earnings	Dividends	Book Value
12/17	178.41	31	27	6.35	5.68	75.22
12/16	177.15	25	21	7.52	5.40	74.07
12/15	184.13	33	29	5.51	5.00	71.83
12/14	163.39	32	23	5.21	4.64	68.51
12/13	118.23	51	42	2.78	4.28	66.42
Annual Growth	10.8%	—	—	22.9%	7.3%	3.2%

Axcelis Technologies Inc

Ions are iconic at Axcelis Technologies. The company develops and makes ion implanters that semiconductor manufacturers use to insert ions into silicon wafers to change their conductive properties. Axcelis Technologies manufactures its ion implantation devices in house at its plant in Beverly Massachusetts. In addition to equipment it offers aftermarket service and support including spare parts equipment upgrades maintenance and training. While the company sells its products around the world the US accounts for about two-thirds of sales.

Operations

Ion implantation devices (sold under the Purion brand name) and services and royalties surrounding them account for 90% of Axcelis Technologies' revenue. The other 10% comes from its legacy processing systems. The company works with customers and industry experts to design applications and processes at its Advanced Technology Center in Beverly Massachusetts.

Geographic Reach

The company has 30 field offices serving customers in a dozen countries. Its primary operations are in China France Germany Italy Japan Korea Malaysia Singapore Taiwan and the US.

Sales and Marketing

Axcelis Technologies sells equipment and services through a direct sales force from offices in China Germany Italy Singapore South Korea and Taiwan. The US is its largest market while sales to customers in Asia make up 23% of revenues and Europe accounts for about 14%.

The company also has a limited customer base; two customers accounted for 17% of revenue and its top 10 customers accounted for about 70% of revenue.

Financial Performance

After two years of declining revenue Axcelis Technologies recorded a 4% increase in 2014 to reach to $203.1 million. The increase came from better product sales as chip makers loosened their purse strings to buy new systems spare parts product upgrades and used systems from Axcelis Technologies.

The company recorded a net loss for the third straight in 2014 but the loss was less. The 2014 loss was $11.2 million compared to $17 million in 2013 and $35 million in 2012. The company spent less in 2014 to reduce the loss.

The company had a negative cash flow of $16 million in 2014 compared to a negative $15 million in 2013.

Strategy

To address the challenges facing the semiconductor equipment industry the company restructures its operations just about every year. For the past two years restructuring has cost about $5 million overall. In 2015 the company sold its corporate headquarters facility to Beverly Property Owner LLC an affiliate of Middleton Partners a real estate investment firm for about $50 million in a sale-leaseback arrangement.

Axcelis Technologies aims to push its sales of its Purion systems into the Korean semiconductor market. The common Purion platform combines a high-speed state-of-the-art single wafer end station that has throughput of 500 wafers per hour.

EXECUTIVES

Chairman and CEO, Mary G. Puma, age 60, $400,481 total compensation
EVP Engineering and Marketing, William (Bill) Bintz, age 61, $271,385 total compensation
EVP Corporate Marketing and Strategy, Douglas A. (Doug) Lawson, age 58
EVP Human Resources Legal and General Counsel, Lynnette C. Fallon, age 58, $301,538 total compensation
EVP Customer Operations, John E. Aldeborgh, age 62, $271,154 total compensation
EVP and CFO, Kevin J. Brewer, age 59, $310,962 total compensation
Auditors: Ernst & Young LLP

LOCATIONS

HQ: Axcelis Technologies Inc
108 Cherry Hill Drive, Beverly, MA 01915
Phone: 978 787-4000   **Fax:** 978 787-3000
Web: www.axcelis.com

PRODUCTS/OPERATIONS

2014 Sales

	$ mil.	% of total
Ion implantation systems services & royalties	183.2	90
Other products services & royalties	19.9	10
Total	**203.1**	**100**

2014 Sales

	% of total
Product	88
Services	12
Total	**100**

COMPETITORS

Applied Materials	Tokyo Electron
BTU International	ULVAC
Mattson Technology	USHIO
Nissin Electric	Ultratech
Sumitomo Heavy Industries	

HISTORICAL FINANCIALS

Company Type: Public

Income Statement

FYE: December 31

	REVENUE ($ mil.)	NET INCOME ($ mil.)	NET PROFIT MARGIN	EMPLOYEES
12/17	410.5	126.9	30.9%	985
12/16	266.9	11.0	4.1%	845
12/15	301.5	14.6	4.9%	808
12/14	203.0	(11.2)	—	765
12/13	195.6	(17.1)	—	863
Annual Growth	**20.4%**	—		**3.4%**

2017 Year-End Financials

Debt ratio: 9.7%	No. of shares (mil.): 32.0
Return on equity: 45.7%	Dividends
Cash ($ mil.): 133.4	Yield: —
Current ratio: 4.29	Payout: —
Long-term debt ($ mil.): 47.7	Market value ($ mil.): 920.0

	STOCK PRICE ($) FY Close	P/E High/Low		PER SHARE ($) Earnings	Dividends	Book Value
12/17	28.70	9	3	3.80	0.00	11.03
12/16	14.55	38	6	0.36	0.00	6.82
12/15	2.59	7	5	0.48	0.00	6.56
12/14	2.56	—	—	(0.40)	0.00	5.97
12/13	2.44	—	—	(0.64)	0.00	6.39
Annual Growth	**85.2%**	—	—	—	—	**14.6%**

Axos Financial Inc

Skip the teller lines by banking with a branchless online-only bank BofI Holding Inc. It is the holding company for BofI Federal Bank which provides consumers and businesses a variety of banking choices for both deposits and loans. It conducts its business without any physical bank branches preferring to support its customers through a comprehensive online banking platform supported occasionally by physical retail locations of its partners. The majority of its business originates in its headquarter state of California though its online operations attract customers from every US state.

Operations

BofI operates a single financial reporting segment. Its operations are generally divided into attracting money (deposits) and then lending it out (loans).

The lending business originates purchases and sometimes sells loans. The bank issues loans for single family homes commercial real estate (for example multi-family units) commercial & industrial needs small business operations and consumer purchases (such as for automobiles). Single family residential and multi-family mortgages make up more than 70% of its loan portfolio. About 85% of its loan and lease holdings are adjustable rate loans.

The bank?s deposit operations attract money from consumers and businesses with about 50% held in checking and other demand deposit accounts roughly 35% in savings accounts and the rest in time deposits (CDs) and IRA accounts. The bank?s deposits have grown dramatically between 2013 and 2017 from $2.1 billion to $6.8 billion because of significant growth in business deposits (10X increase over the same time).

Behind the scenes BofI operates a robust software platform that enables secure responsive banking interactions with nationwide customers who use smartphones and computers to access their accounts.

Geographic Reach

San Diego-based BofI holds deposits from customers in every US state with large sources of balances in Florida the Mid-Atlantic states and the California coast. Nearly 70% of its loans are secured by real estate in California.

Sales and Marketing

Because the bank is branchless the traditional means of attracting customers ? such as local advertising a physical bank presence community charity sponsorship ? are not used. Rather the bank creates brand awareness through digital marketing ensures a productive and intuitive user experience and gathers analytical data about their customers to help cross-sell other products and generate ideas for product/service enhancements.

Financial Performance

In recent years BofI experienced strong annual increases in revenue composed mainly of interest and non-interest income and in net income. Interest income jumped from $63 million in FY2009 (ending June 30) to more than $380 million in FY2017. Non-interest income typically fees and gains from loan sales rose from $1.4 million to more than $68 million in the same time. Net income experienced a similar rise swelling from $3.9 million in 2009 to almost $135 million in 2017.

For the fiscal year 2017 BofI generated $387 million of interest income a 22% increase from FY2016. An increase in the bank?s net interest margin to 3.95% in FY2017 (versus 3.91% in the prior year) as well as a larger loan portfolio ($7.4 billion vs $6.4 billion) produced most of the increase. The bank also saw its non-interest income rise 3% to $68 million.

Net income rose 13% in FY2017 to $134 million compared to the prior year. The rise in interest income as the result of a larger loan portfolio was the primary reason for increased net income.

Cash and cash equivalents rose $156 million in FY2017 to $644 million. The cash buildup was the result of $753 million from financing activities (mainly from an increase in bank deposits) and $224 million from operations both offset by an $821 million use by investing activities (due to loan origination amounts higher than repayment amounts).

Strategy

BofI?s strategy is simply to grow its loan portfolio ? and therefore its interest income ? through new products expanded distribution channels leveraged data mining and occasional acquisitions.

In FY2017 the bank introduced two new products: retail auto loans and unsecured lending offerings. It also established a US tax refund advance through H&R Block. It?s partnership with H&R Block began in 2015 when it acquired $419 million in deposits from tax preparer?s owned bank. From there the H&R Block distribution channel has blossomed to include several BofI services made available to the tax preparer?s nearly 20 million customers including coordinating the US government?s electronically delivered tax refund and an offer made by H&R Block tax preparers to open a BofI-originated IRA account.

The amount of customer data gathered by BofI through its own customer base and through the H&R Block customers that choose to use BofI?s tax refund services is a significant data mining asset. The bank analyzes this information to help cross-sell other products & services and even anticipates deploying artificial intelligence to assist with the effort.

From time to time the bank purchases loans and leases from other entities. It did so in early 2016 with the acquisition of $140 million of equipment leases from Pacific Western Equipment Finance and with the 2015 acquisition of H&R Block Bank deposits.

EXECUTIVES

EVP and CFO BofI Holding Inc. and BofI Federal Bank, Andrew J. Micheletti, age 61, $231,000 total compensation

President and CEO BofI Holding Inc. and BofI Federal Bank, Gregory Garrabrants, age 47, $375,000 total compensation

EVP Specialty Finance and Chief Legal Officer BofI Federal Bank, Eshel Bar-Adon, age 63, $250,000 total compensation

EVP and Chief Credit Officer BofI Federal Bank, Thomas Constantine, age 56, $235,000 total compensation

EVP and Chief Lending Officer BofI Federal Bank, Brian Swanson, age 38, $235,000 total compensation

EVP Chief of Staff and Chief Performance Officer BofI Federal Bank, Jan Durrans

EVP Chief Deposit Officer and Chief Marketing Officer BofI Federal Bank, Eduardo Urdapilleta

SENIOR VICE PRESIDENT WAREHOUSE LENDING AND LOAN OPERATIONS, Darin Sullivan

Vice President Wholesale Banking, Johnson Raymond

Chairman, Paul J. Grinberg, age 57

Vice Chairman, Nicholas A. Mosich

Member Board of Directors, Edward Ratinoff

Auditors: BDO USA, LLP

LOCATIONS

HQ: Axos Financial Inc
4350 La Jolla Village Drive, Suite 140, San Diego, CA 92122
Phone: 858 350-6200
Web: www.bofiholding.com

PRODUCTS/OPERATIONS

2016 Sales

	$ mil.	% of total
Interest and dividend income:		
Loans and leases including fees	358.8	79
Investments	28.4	6
Non-interest income	68.1	14
Total	**455.3**	**100**

COMPETITORS

Ally Bank	ISN Bank
California Bank & Trust	MUFG Americas Holdings
Discover	PacWest Bancorp
E*TRADE Bank	San Diego County
First IB	Credit Union
HSBC USA	Scottrade

HISTORICAL FINANCIALS

Company Type: Public

Income Statement

FYE: June 30

	ASSETS ($ mil.)	NET INCOME ($ mil.)	INCOME AS % OF ASSETS	EMPLOYEES
06/18	9,539.5	152.4	1.6%	801
06/17	8,501.6	134.7	1.6%	681
06/16	7,601.3	119.2	1.6%	647
06/15	5,823.7	82.6	1.4%	467
06/14	4,403.0	55.9	1.3%	366
Annual Growth	**21.3%**	**28.5%**	**—**	**21.6%**

2018 Year-End Financials

Return on assets: 1.6%	Dividends
Return on equity: 16.9%	Yield: —
Long-term debt ($ mil.): —	Payout: —
No. of shares (mil.): 62.6	Market value ($ mil.): 2,565.0
Sales ($ mil): 546.0	

	STOCK PRICE ($) FY Close	P/E High/Low		PER SHARE ($) Earnings	Dividends	Book Value
06/18	40.91	19	10	2.37	0.00	15.32
06/17	23.72	16	7	2.07	0.00	13.13
06/16	17.71	77	7	1.85	0.00	10.81
06/15	105.71	79	49	1.34	0.00	8.59
06/14	73.47	109	48	0.96	0.00	6.41
Annual Growth	**(13.6%)**	**—**		**25.3%**	**—**	**24.3%**

B Riley Financial Inc

EXECUTIVES

Chb-ceo, Andy Gumaer

Vice President Business Development, Michael Presto

Vice President Financial Planning and Analysis, Dario Lucciola

Auditors: Marcum LLP

LOCATIONS

HQ: B Riley Financial Inc
21255 Burbank Boulevard, Suite 400, Woodland Hills, CA 91367
Phone: 818 884-3737
Web: www.brileyfin.com

HISTORICAL FINANCIALS

Company Type: Public

Income Statement

FYE: December 31

	REVENUE ($ mil.)	NET INCOME ($ mil.)	NET PROFIT MARGIN	EMPLOYEES
12/17	322.1	11.5	3.6%	833
12/16	190.3	21.5	11.3%	388
12/15	112.5	11.8	10.5%	220
12/14	77.1	(5.8)	—	225
12/13	76.1	1.0	1.4%	176
Annual Growth	**43.4%**	**81.8%**	**—**	**47.5%**

2017 Year-End Financials

Debt ratio: 72.7%	No. of shares (mil.): 26.5
Return on equity: 5.5%	Dividends
Cash ($ mil.): 132.8	Yield: 0.0%
Current ratio: 1.38	Payout: 139.5%
Long-term debt ($ mil.): 203.6	Market value ($ mil.): 481.0

	STOCK PRICE ($) FY Close	P/E High/Low		PER SHARE ($) Earnings	Dividends	Book Value
12/17	18.10	43	27	0.48	0.67	10.01
12/16	18.45	16	7	1.17	0.28	7.80
12/15	9.90	19	13	0.73	0.32	6.65
12/14	9.90	—		(0.60)	0.03	6.08
12/13	0.28	1	0	0.80	0.00	(2.78)
Annual Growth	**183.6%**	**—**		**(12.0%)**	**—**	**—**

B&G Foods Inc

Peter Piper picks more than a peck of peppers from B&G Foods. The company makes markets and distributes jalapeA±os beans maple syrup fruit spreads and other shelf-stable foods and household goods. B&G's products are sold under brand names many of which are regional or national best-sellers including B&G and Trappey (beans) Green Giant (frozen and canned foods) Ac'cent (meat flavoring) Spice Islands (seasonings) Ortega (Mexican condiments) Grandma's and Brer Rabbit (molasses) and Underwood (meat spread). They're sold through B&G's subsidiaries to supermarkets mass merchants warehouse clubs and drug store chains as well as institutional and food service operators in the US Canada and Puerto Rico.

Operations

B&G Foods serves a single industry segment. The company balances its branded-product retail sales business with sales to institutions and food service customers as well as making products under private labels for others. Many of its branded items boast leading regional or national market shares.

The food company operates three distribution centers located in Texas Tennessee and Pennsylvania. It has 10 manufacturing and warehouse locations in the US. B&G Foods stores products in facilities in Quebec and Maryland and houses its major sales offices in Arkansas and Illinois.

The company distributes certain brands — such as Cream of Wheat Ac'cent Underwood Polaner Static Guard Mrs. Dash New York Style and Sugar Twin — to similar food channels in Canada.

Geographic Reach

Based in Parsippany New Jersey B&G Foods makes sells and distributes a diverse portfolio of shelf-stable foods nationwide and in Canada and Puerto Rico.

Sales and Marketing

B&G Foods has a unique sales strategy for each of its brands. To this end the food company allocates brand-specific promotional spending. Its regional sales managers coordinate promotions with customers. The company's marketing department partners with the sales department to coordinate special account activities and marketing support the likes of public relations media advertising and couponing. Marketing executives typically use the radio Internet social media and limited television advertising. B&G Foods spent about $5.9 million in advertising in fiscal 2012 as compared to $4.3 million in 2011.

The 120-year-old company sells markets and distributes its products through a multichannel system. It serves all major US food channels selling and shipping to mass merchants supermarkets warehouse clubs food service distributors and direct accounts specialty food distributors military commissaries and non-food outlets the likes of drug store chains and dollar stores. To better serve Wal-Mart which accounts for nearly 20% of sales B&G Foods operates a sales office in Wal-Mart's hometown of Bentonville Arkansas.

The company sells its products primarily through broker sales networks to supermarket chains mass merchants food service outlets warehouse clubs non-food outlets and specialty distributors. This network incidentally handles B&G Foods' sales at the retail level. Regional sales managers sell its food items nationwide through national and regional brokers with separate organizations concentrating on food service grocery chain accounts and special markets.

Financial Performance

The company has seen its sales rise during the past five years. Due to several recent acquisitions B&G Foods logged its highest net sales in 2016. Acquisitions of Green Giant and LeSueur brands helped raise revenue about 44% to $1.4 billion in 2016 from $966 million in 2015. B&G Foods' net income leaped nearly 60% for the same reporting period thanks to the Green Giant acquisition and lower prices for commodities packaging and distribution. The company's syrup business led a sales decline in its base businesses in 2016. B&G Food's syrup brands have faced maple syrup price deflation due to the strength of the US dollar relative to the Canadian dollar which has resulted attracted more competition in maple syrup. The company also had to meet contractually mandated price reductions with some foodservice customers.

Profit was about $110 million in 2016 compared to about $69 million in 2015.

The increase in net income helped raise cash from operating activities to about $290 million in 2016 from about $128 million in 2015.

Strategy

Acquisitions have been key to B&G's recent growth as it extends its reach throughout the grocery story. It acquired the Green Giant frozen foods and Le Sueur canned foods businesses from General Mills in 2015 and in 2017 it agreed to buy the Snackwell and Back to Nature Foods lines. In late 2016 the company bought the spices and seasonings business of ACH and Victoria Fine Foods. B&G remains on the lookout for more deals although in late 2018 it agreed to sell its Pirate Brands business — which includes Pirate's Booty cheese puffs — to Hershey for $420 million.

Other growth strategies are continuing to develop new products and getting them on shelves leveraging the company's channel sales and distribution system and maintaining focus on higher growth customers and distribution channels.

Mergers and Acquisitions

In 2017 B&G Foods acquired the Snackwell cookie and Back to Nature granola bars businesses from Brynwood Partners and Mondelez International for more than $162 million in cash. The deal gives B&G a stronger lineup to approach natural food grocery chains like Whole Foods Markets and Sprouts. Back to Nature's products include cookies crackers nuts and trail mixes granola juices soups and cereal. B&G expects the acquisition to add about $80 million in revenue.

In line with its growth goals in 2016 the company acquired ACH Food Companies' spice and seasonings business for $365 million in cash. Through the deal the company added Spice Islands Tone's Durkee and Weber brands to its product line up. The acquisition significantly expands the company's existing flavor enhancing products which include Ms. Dash Ac'cent and Emeril's seasonings.

B&G in mid-2015 bought the Green Giant and Le Sueuer frozen and canned vegetables brands from General Mills for about $765 million. Green Giant became the company's largest product line and boost its revenue to about $1.4 billion. The deal fulfilled B&G's long-term goal of moving into the frozen foods business.

EXECUTIVES

EVP Finance and CFO, Thomas P. Crimmins, age 49, $307,692 total compensation
President and CEO, Robert C. (Bob) Cantwell, age 61, $700,000 total compensation
EVP General Counsel Secretary and Chief Compliance Officer, Scott E. Lerner, age 45, $412,000 total compensation
EVP Sales and Marketing, Vanessa E. Maskal, age 61, $400,000 total compensation
EVP Operations, William F. (Bill) Herbes, age 63, $291,500 total compensation
EVP Quality Assurance and Research and Development, William H. (Bill) Wright, age 73
EVP Human Resources and Chief Human Resources Officer, Eric H. Hart, age 51
Vice President Sales, Steve Fortunato
Vice President Export Sales, Greg Price
Vice President Trade Marketing, Anthony Pacelli
Executive Vice President of Operations, Bill Herbes
Vice President Marketing Advertising and Brand Management, Jordan Greenberg
Vice President Information Technology and CIO, Chris Colla
National Account Manager, Ben Baugh
Vice President Marketing, Marc Simon
VICE PRESIDENT, Clay Wiedemann
Chairman, Stephen C. Sherrill, age 65
Auditors: KPMG LLP

LOCATIONS

HQ: B&G Foods Inc
Four Gatehall Drive, Parsippany, NJ 07054
Phone: 973 401-6500
Web: www.bgfoods.com

PRODUCTS/OPERATIONS

2016 Sales

	$ mil.	% of total
Green Giant	506.7	36
Ortega	142.0	10
Pirate Brands	84.9	6
Maple Grove Farms of Vermont	72.8	5
Cream of Wheat	62.2	4
Mrs. Dash	60.6	4
Bear Creek Country Kitchens	52.9	4
Las Palmas	39.1	3
Mama Mary's	35.8	2
Polaner	34.3	2
New York Style	33.1	2
Spices & Seasonings	28.2	2
All other brands	238.6	17
Total	**1,391.3**	**100**

Selected Products

Bagel chips
Canned meats and beans
Dry soups
Frozen and canned vegetables
Fruit spreads
Hot cereals
Hot sauces
Maple syrup
Mexican-style sauces
Molasses
Nut clusters
Peppers
Pickles
Pizza crusts
Puffed corn
Rice snacks
Salad dressings
Salsas
Seasonings
Spices
Taco shells and kits
Wine vinegar

Selected Brands

Ac'cent
B&G
B&M
Baker's Joy
Brer Rabbit
Cream of Rice
Cream of Wheat
Devonsheer
Don Pepino
Emeril's (licensed)
Grandma's Molasses
JJ Flats
Joan of Arc
Kleen Guard (sells and distributes)
Las Palmas
Maple Grove Farms of Vermont
Molly McButter
Mrs. Dash
New York Style
Old London
Ortega
Polaner
Red Devil
Regina
Sa-son
Sclafani
Static Guard (sells and distributes)
Sugar Twin
Trappey's
TrueNorth
Underwood
Vermont Maid
Wright's

COMPETITORS

ACH Food Companies	Kikkoman
Adams Extract & Spice	Kraft Heinz
Best Maid Products	La Flor
Big Heart Pet Brands	MOM Brands
Bolner's Fiesta	McCormick & Company
Products	McIlhenny
Bruce Foods	MegaMex Foods
Bush Brothers	Mondelez International
Campbell Soup	Nestlé
ConAgra	PepsiCo
Frito-Lay	Pinnacle Foods
General Mills	Renée's Gourmet Foods
Goya	Smucker
Heinz	Snyder's-Lance
Herdez	Spectrum Organic
Homestat Farm	Products
Hormel	

HISTORICAL FINANCIALS

Company Type: Public

Income Statement   FYE: December 30

	REVENUE ($ mil.)	NET INCOME ($ mil.)	NET PROFIT MARGIN	EMPLOYEES
12/17	1,668.0	217.4	13.0%	2,680
12/16*	1,391.2	109.4	7.9%	2,590
01/16	966.3	69.0	7.1%	2,003
01/15	848.0	40.9	4.8%	956
12/13	724.9	52.3	7.2%	984
Annual Growth	23.2%	42.8%	—	28.5%

*Fiscal year change

2017 Year-End Financials

Debt ratio: 62.2%
Return on equity: 26.1%
Cash ($ mil.): 206.5
Current ratio: 4.40
Long-term debt ($ mil.): 2,217.5

No. of shares (mil.): 66.5
Dividends
Yield: 0.0%
Payout: 57.0%
Market value ($ mil.): 2,337.0

	STOCK PRICE ($) FY Close	P/E High/Low		PER SHARE ($) Earnings	Dividends	Book Value
12/17	35.15	15	9	3.26	1.86	13.25
12/16*	43.80	30	19	1.73	1.73	11.83
01/16	35.02	31	23	1.22	1.38	7.89
01/15	29.68	46	36	0.76	1.36	6.30
12/13	33.93	38	28	0.98	1.23	7.08
Annual Growth	0.9%	—	—	35.1%	10.9%	17.0%

*Fiscal year change

Balchem Corp.

Believe Balchem when they say they have it covered. The company has developed a technology that covers or encapsulates ingredients used in food and animal health products; the encapsulation improves nutritional value and shelf life and allows for controlled time release. Balchem also provides specialty gases such as ethylene oxide (used to sterilize medical instruments) propylene oxide (used to reduce bacteria in spice treating and chemical processing) and methyl chloride (a refrigerant). It also provides SensoryEffects provide microencapsulation solutions to a variety of applications in food pharmaceutical and nutritional ingredients.

Operations

Balchem's operations are divided into four main business segments: SensoryEffects; Animal Nutrition and Health; Specialty Products; and Industrial Products.

Its ARC Specialty Products segment offers repackaging and distribution of select chemicals (including ethylene oxide and propylene oxide) to healthcare and other markets. The Animal Nutrition and Health segment makes and supplies products (including choline chloride) to several animal health markets and also certain derivative chemical products for industrial use. Balchem's SensoryEffects segment provides human-grade choline and microencapsulation products for a range of applications in human food pharmaceutical and nutrition markets.

The company's unencapsulated feed ingredients unit (BCP Ingredients) supplies the nutrient choline chloride to poultry and swine farmers. Reashure an encapsulated choline product increases milk production in dairy cows.

SensoryEffects the largest segment accounts for 50% of total sales; Animal Nutrition & Health 30%; Specialty Products 10%; and Industrial Products 10%.

Geographic Reach

Balchem operates two four subsidiaries in the US: BCP Ingredients SensoryEffects Inc. SensoryEffects Cereal Systems Inc. and Aberco. It also has two subsidiaries in Europe: Balchem BV and Balchem Italia which has a manufacturing facility in Italy that makes and distributes methylamines (a building block for choline products) and choline.

The company operates repackaging facilities in South Carolina and Missouri and uses distribution points in New York California and Puerto Rico. It also has manufacturing facilities in Utah Virginia Louisiana Minnesota Wisconsin Pennsylvania Ohio and Nebraska as well as in Canada.

Sales and Marketing

The company sells its products through its own sales force independent distributors and sales agents.

Financial Performance

Balchem has recorded rising net revenues over the last five years.

In 2015 it had net revenue of $552.5 million up 2% on 2014 due to an increase in SensoryEffects results.

Net sales for the SensoryEffects segment increased by 35% due to the acquired SensoryEffects business that contributed $69.8 million to the overall increase. The Powder & Flavor Systems and Cereal Systems product lines comprised $56.5 million and $10.2 million of the increase respectively. Also contributing to the higher sales was an 11.1% rise in encapsulated ingredients used for baking and food preservation primarily due to greater volume.

Specialty Products segment sales were flat compared to the prior year and revenue from the Animal Nutrition & Health and Industrial Products segments decreased.

Balchem's net income has also risen over the last five years.

In 2015 net income was $59.7 million up 13% due to higher net sales outpacing an increase in operating expenses.

Cash from operating activities was $103.8 million up 22% compared to 2014.

Strategy

The company is continuing to focus on leveraging its plant capabilities driving efficiencies from core volume growth broadening product applications of human and animal health specialty products as well as capitalizing on its varied choline production capabilities. It invested $41.3 million in capital expenditures in 2015 up from $13.2 million in 2014.

In 2015 Balchem integrated SensoryEffects and made significant investments in new production capacity and technology. Looking forward growth for this segment will be fueled by its investment in agglomeration technology Curemark and the RDI and EFSA first-ever intake recommendations for choline. The company will continue to drive strategic growth initiatives through both organic investments in new manufacturing capabilities and new product development as well as acquisitions.

In 2015 the company expanded its Verona Missouri facility by adding another ReaShure manufacturing unit.

In 2014 Taminco and Balchem built and operated a choline chloride facility in St. Gabriel Louisiana where both companies operate production facilities.

Mergers and Acquisitions

In 2016 Balchem acquired Utah-based Albion International (a privately held manufacturer of mineral amino acid chelates specialized mineral salts and mineral complexes) for $116.4 million. The acquisition of Albion continues to expand Balchem's science-based human health and wellness products and increases its product offerings in the nutritional ingredient market. Additionally the company also benefits from a broader geographic footprint and a stronger position as a technological leader in spray-drying and ingredient delivery products.

To accelerate the growth of its food and nutrition platforms with new product offerings in 2014 Balchem spent $567 million to acquire Missouri-based Performance Chemicals & Ingredients Company (aka SensoryEffects) a privately held supplier of customized food and beverage ingredient systems.

HISTORY

Herbert Weiss Leslie Balassa three ex-officers of the Alcolac company and a group of Baltimore-based investors founded Balchem in 1967 in New York City. The company focused on the development of encapsulated specialty ingredients (the coating of individual particles that allow precise control of nutrient delivery). Initially Balchem developed food ingredients used in meat processing flavor enhancement and dough leavening as well as in nutritional supplements. In 1971 the company won its first big order: encapsulating the ingredients in pudding mix for General Foods. Balchem later applied the same technology to foaming agents for plastics aquaculture supplements and animal feeds. It also developed a line of specialty gases.

In 1994 Balchem boosted its gas business with the purchase of AlliedSignal's sterilant gas business (used to sterilize medical devices). Weiss retired as CEO in 1996 and was succeeded by EVP Raymond Reber. Reber left the company a few months later and chemical industry veteran Dino Rossi replaced him. The next year Balchem developed a rumen-protected choline chloride for the animal nutrition market.

Balchem restructured its operations in 1998 away from aquaculture and towards animal nutrition and other growth markets. After successful university and field trials the company introduced Reashure its encapsulated choline product for dairy cows.

In 2000 Balchem was granted a patent for its technology that increases milk production in dairy cows. In 2001 the company acquired the choline and encapsulated product lines of DCV Inc. and its DuCoa L.P. affiliate which contributed to the company's increase in net sales by about 30% in 2002. In 2002 sales continued to build as the encapsulated/nutritional products segment introduced several new products and product applications for the enhancement of shelf-life and fortification of products in certain markets of the food industry.

Balchem's unencapsulated feed ingredients segment also referred to as BCP Ingredients got larger in 2007 when the company acquired two choline-related businesses. The first was in Italy from Akzo Nobel and the other deal was for a company called Chinook Global Limited whose operations were integrated into Balchem's business. Those deals nearly tripled the size of BCP Ingredients making it Balchem's largest unit.

In 2010 the company's growth increased again with the acquisition of Maryland-based Aberco a marketer and distributor of propylene oxide.

In 2013 Balchem's capital expenditures were about $8.2 million out of which $3.3 million was invested in its new manufacturing facility in Covington Virginia. Balchem expanded production capacities to meet growing demand by opening the Covington plant in 2012 which doubled the output capacity for the Animal Nutrition and Health ruminant sector.

EXECUTIVES

Chief Financial Officer; Treasurer; Assistant Secretary, Francis J. (Frank) Fitzpatrick, age 55, $215,400 total compensation
Chairman of the Board; President; Chief Executive Officer, Dino A. Rossi, age 61, $467,500 total compensation
Executive Vice President Arsenal Capital Partners, John Y. Televantos, age 63
Vice President General Manager, David R. Ludwig, age 58, $220,000 total compensation
President of Nestles Research & Development Center, Elaine R. Wedral, age 72
VP Research and Development, Paul H. Richardson, age 45, $191,000 total compensation
General Counsel; Secretary, Matthew D. Houston, age 52, $177,000 total compensation
Vice President General Manager Animal Nutrition, Dana Putnam
Vice President Human Resources, Bob Miniger
Vice President of Operations, John E. Kuehner
Chief Accounting Officer Treasurer, William A. Backus
IR Contact, Karin McCaffery
Chief Operating Officer, Richard Bendure
Member of the Executive Board; Chief Risk Officer, Hassan Basri
Chairman of the Board and Chief Executive Officer, Mohamed Benchaaboun
Director, Paul D. Coombs, age 60
Director, Perry W. Premdas, age 63
Director, Edward L. McMillan, age 70
Director, Elaine R. Wedral, age 72
Director, David B. Fischer
Director, John Y. Televantos
Auditors: RSM US LLP

LOCATIONS

HQ: Balchem Corp.
52 Sunrise Park Road, New Hampton, NY 10958
Phone: 845 326-5600
Web: www.balchem.com

COMPETITORS

ABCO Laboratories	Coating Place
Air Products	Dow Chemical
Airgas	IGENE
BASF Corporation	Mitsubishi Chemical
BioDelivery Sciences International	Praxair
	Sigma-Aldrich
Clariant	

HISTORICAL FINANCIALS

Company Type: Public

Income Statement

FYE: December 31

	REVENUE ($ mil.)	NET INCOME ($ mil.)	NET PROFIT MARGIN	EMPLOYEES
12/17	594.7	90.0	15.1%	1,165
12/16	553.2	55.9	10.1%	1,060
12/15	552.4	59.7	10.8%	875
12/14	541.3	52.8	9.8%	845
12/13	337.1	44.8	13.3%	387
Annual Growth	15.2%	19.0%	—	31.7%

2017 Year-End Financials

Debt ratio: 22.7%	No. of shares (mil.): 32.0
Return on equity: 15.8%	Dividends
Cash ($ mil.): 40.4	Yield: 0.0%
Current ratio: 1.84	Payout: 15.0%
Long-term debt ($ mil.): 183.9	Market value ($ mil.): 2,581.0

	STOCK PRICE ($) FY Close	P/E High/Low	PER SHARE ($) Earnings	Dividends	Book Value
12/17	80.60	32 26	2.79	0.42	19.27
12/16	83.92	49 30	1.75	0.38	16.41
12/15	60.80	36 27	1.89	0.34	14.71
12/14	66.64	39 28	1.69	0.30	12.71
12/13	58.70	39 24	1.45	0.26	10.96
Annual Growth	8.2%	— —	17.8%	12.7%	15.1%

Banc Of California Inc

Banc of California offers deposit and loan services at 35 branches in Southern California's Los Angeles Orange County and San Diego. Customers enjoy checking savings and money market accounts as well as mobile online and card payment services telephone banking automated bill payment safe deposit boxes direct deposit and wire transfers. Customers can also access their accounts through a nationwide network of 55000 surcharge-free ATMs. In addition to its branches the $9 billion-asset Banc of California operates around 70 mortgage loan production offices in California Arizona Oregon Indiana Idaho Nevada and Virginia.

Operations

Banc of California operates three core segments: Commercial Banking which offers commercial consumer and real estate secured loans as well as deposit accounts; Mortgage Banking which originates conforming SFR loans and sells the loans in the secondary market; and the Financial Advisory segment which purchases sells and manages SFR mortgage loans.

Unlike most retail banks Banc of California's income streams are less dependent on interest rates. The bank made 50% of its revenue from loan interest (including fees) during 2015 and another 5% from interest on investments. But it also made 29% of its revenue from its mortgage banking business while the rest came from other non-interest income sources.

Geographic Reach

The Irvine California-based bank has 90-plus banking locations in California including 35 branches in San Diego Orange Santa Barbara and Los Angeles Counties (as of mid-2016). It has 68 loan production offices in California Arizona Oregon Virginia Indiana Maryland Colorado Idaho and Nevada.

Sales and Marketing

The bank spent $6.2 million on advertising during 2015 or 23% more than in the prior year due to higher overall marketing costs tied to the bank's continued expansion.

Financial Performance

Banc of California's revenue has risen sevenfold since 2011 as a slew of bank acquisitions and organic growth have driven its loan and deposit business as well as its mortgage banking business.

The bank's revenue jumped 46% to $486.5 million during 2015 thanks to a 34% spike in loan interest income on more loan origination and loan and lease purchase activity; and thanks to a 52% rise in mortgage banking income as the bank originated and sold nearly twice as many mortgage loans on the secondary market than in 2014.

Strong revenue growth in 2015 caused Banc of California's net income to double to $62 million despite an uptick in salary and benefits cost that stemmed from additional hiring and commercial banking and mortgage banking expansion. The bank's operations used $45.24 million during the year or less than one-tenth as much cash as in 2014 mostly after adjusting its earnings for non-cash items related to proceeds of mortgage banking loans held-for-sale and proceeds from other loans held-for-sale.

Strategy

With its eye on becoming "California's Bank" Banc of California sometimes acquires smaller banks or bank branch networks to boost its loan and deposit business while expanding its branch network (mostly around California).

From 2010 through 2015 the bank has made seven acquisitions including three bank acquisitions (Gateway Bancorp Beach Business Bank and The Private Bank of California) and three other specialty financial firm acquisitions (Palisades Group which it divested in 2016; CS Financial; and Renovation Ready.)

Mergers and Acquisitions

In November 2014 the bank bought 20 branches in Southern California from Banco Popular North America (BPNA) along with $1.07 billion in loans and $1.08 billion in deposits for a total price of $24 million.

In January 2014 Banc of California purchased service contracts and intellectual property of RenovationReady a specialized loan services provider that served financial institutions and mortgage bankers that originated agency-eligible residential renovation and construction loan products.

Company Background

In 2012 it paid $15.5 million for Gateway Business Bank and $37 million for Beach Business Bank. The next year it took over The Private Bank of California for $25 million and bought The Palisades Group a residential mortgage investment advisory firm and specialty finance company CS Financial. In 2014 it announced plans to buy 20 branches of Banco Popular North America to reach California's Hispanic community.

In 2013 it sold eight branches to AmericanWest Bank in order to reshape its retail branch network to focus on servicing small - to midsized businesses and high net worth families.

EXECUTIVES

EVP Division General Counsel Lending, John F. Madden, age 57
EVP Enterprise Risk Analytics, Gilda Youdeem
Managing Director Institutional Banking and Fiduciary Services, Steven C. (Steve) Canup
EVP and CFO Banc of California Inc. and Banc of California N.A., John A. Bogler
EVP and General Counsel Banking, Angelee J. Harris, age 48
Chief Investment Officer, Brian P. Kuelbs, age 55
Managing Director Community Banking, Gaylin D. Anderson
Vice Chairman and EVP, Jeffrey T. Seabold, age 51, $750,000 total compensation
President and CEO, Douglas H. (Doug) Bowers, age 60
Chief Risk Officer, Hugh F. Boyle, age 58, $599,679 total compensation
Managing Director Warehouse Lending, Zoila Price

EVP and Chief Compliance Officer, Diane M. Summers
EVP Community Development, Gary S. Dunn
EVP and CIO, Ken Plummer
EVP Division General Counsel Banking, Manisha K. Merchant
Managing Director Construction Lending, Jim Fraser
Chief Credit Officer, Paul Simmons
Managing Director Portfolio Lending, Julie Duong
SVP Operations, Robert Villaneda
SVP Marketing, Samantha Haugh
Managing Director Payment Solutions, Ben Kessler
EVP General Counsel and Secretary, John C. Grosvenor, age 68, $501,378 total compensation
EVP Private Banking, Jay D. Sanders
Assistant Vice President Senior Financial Analyst, Marianna Helton
Vice President Relationship Manager, Kristin Koptyra
Vice President Credit Administration, Edward Massey
Executive Vice President, Chang Liu
Vice President Loan Accounting, Barbara Curtis
Vice President Branch Manager, Rena Alekperova
Senior Vice President Residential Lending, Jon Irvine
Vice President Information Technology Infrastructure, Len Tateyama
Assistant Vice President Credit Portfolio Manager, Aida Rodriguez
Senior Vice President Treasury Management Sales Director, Gary Tackoor
Chairman, Robert D. Sznewajs, age 71
Board Member, Jonah Schnel
Auditors: KPMG LLP

LOCATIONS

HQ: Banc Of California Inc
3 MacArthur Place, Santa Ana, CA 92707
Phone: 855 361-2262
Web: www.bancofcal.com

PRODUCTS/OPERATIONS

2013 Sales

	% of total
Interest and dividend income	
Loans including fees	53
Securities and others	2
Noninterest income	
Net gain on mortgage banking activities	31
Gain on sale of branches	6
Net gain on sale of loans	4
Loan servicing income	1
Customer service fees	1
Others	2
Total	**100**

COMPETITORS

American Business Bank	East West Bancorp
Bank of America	JPMorgan Chase
Bank of the West	MUFG Americas Holdings
BofI	PacWest Bancorp
California Bank & Trust	Pacific Mercantile
	Pacific Premier
City National	Simplicity Bancorp
Comerica	U.S. Bancorp

HISTORICAL FINANCIALS
Company Type: Public

Income Statement   FYE: December 31

	ASSETS ($ mil.)	NET INCOME ($ mil.)	INCOME AS % OF ASSETS	EMPLOYEES
12/17	10,327.8	57.7	0.6%	738
12/16	11,029.8	115.4	1.0%	1,797
12/15	8,235.5	62.0	0.8%	1,710
12/14	5,971.5	30.3	0.5%	1,470
12/13	3,628.0	0.0	0.0%	1,384
Annual Growth	**29.9%**	**419.9%**	**—**	**(14.5%)**

2017 Year-End Financials

Return on assets: 0.5%   Dividends
Return on equity: 5.7%   Yield: 0.0%
Long-term debt ($ mil.): —   Payout: 73.2%
No. of shares (mil.): 50.5   Market value ($ mil.): 1,045.0
Sales ($ mil): 433.8

	STOCK PRICE ($) FY Close	P/E High/Low		PER SHARE ($) Earnings	Dividends	Book Value
12/17	20.65	32	20	0.71	0.52	20.01
12/16	17.35	12	6	1.94	0.49	19.65
12/15	14.62	11	8	1.34	0.48	17.15
12/14	11.47	15	11	0.91	0.48	14.47
12/13	13.41	—	—	(0.14)	0.48	16.13
Annual Growth	**11.4%**	**—**	**—**	**—**	**2.0%**	**5.5%**

BancFirst Corp. (Oklahoma City, Okla)

This Oklahoma bank wants to be more than OK. It wants to be super . BancFirst Corporation is the holding company for BancFirst a super-community bank that emphasizes decentralized management and centralized support. BancFirst operates more than 100 branches in more than 50 Oklahoma communities. It serves individuals and small to midsized businesses offering traditional deposit products such as checking and savings accounts CDs and IRAs. Commercial real estate lending (including farmland and multifamily residential loans) makes up more than a third of the bank's loan portfolio while one-to-four family residential mortgages represent about 20%. The bank also issues business construction and consumer loans.

Operations

The company operates three core units: metropolitan banks community banks and other financial service. Metropolitan and community banks offer traditional banking products such as commercial and retail lending and a full line of deposit accounts in the metropolitan Oklahoma City and Tulsa areas. Community banks consist of banking locations in communities throughout Oklahoma. Other financial services are specialty product business units including guaranteed small business lending residential mortgage lending trust services securities brokerage electronic banking and insurance.

The company's BancFirst Insurance Services arm sells property/casualty coverage while the bank's trust and investment management division oversees some $1.21 billion of assets on behalf of clients. Bank subsidiaries Council Oak Investment Corporation and Council Oak Real Estate focus on small business and property investments respectively.

Like other retail banks BancFirst makes the bulk of its money from interest income. More than 60% of its total revenue came from loan interest (including fees) during 2015 while another 2% came from interest on taxable securities. The rest of its revenue came from service charges on deposits (19% of revenue) insurance commissions (5%) trust revenue (3%) securities transactions (3%) and loan sales (1%).

Geographic Reach

BancFirst has 95 banking locations serving more than 52 communities across Oklahoma.

Sales and Marketing

The bank customers are generally small to medium-sized businesses engaged in light manufacturing local wholesale and retail trade commercial and residential real estate development and construction services agriculture and the energy industry.

BancFirst spent about $6.9 million for advertising and promotion during 2015 compared to $6.6 million in each of 2014 and 2013.

Financial Performance

BancFirst's annual revenues have risen 20% since 2011 thanks to continued loan asset and deposit growth (partly thanks to branch expansion). The company's annual profits have grown more than 40% over the same period as it's kept a lid on operating expenses and loan loss provisions.

BancFirst's revenue climbed 6% to $306.85 million during 2015 thanks to a combination of loan asset growth and gains on the sales of some of its securities.

Revenue growth in 2015 drove the company's net income up nearly 4% to $66.17 million. The bank's operating cash levels increased by almost 2% to $78.1 million with the rise in cash-based earnings.

Strategy

BancFirst's strategy focuses on providing a full range of commercial banking services to retail customers and small to medium-sized businesses in both the non-metropolitan trade centers and cities in the metropolitan statistical areas of Oklahoma. It operates as a 'super community bank' managing its community banking offices on a decentralized basis which permits them to be responsive to local customer needs. Underwriting funding customer service and pricing decisions are made by presidents in each market within the company's strategic parameters.

Mergers and Acquisitions

In October 2015 BancFirst purchased $196 million-asset CSB Banchsares and its Bank of Commerce branches in Yukon Mustang and El Reno in Oklahoma. The deal also added $148 million in new loan business and $170 million in deposits.

Company Background

The company has been buying smaller banks to expand in Oklahoma. In 2011 it acquired FBC Financial Corporation and its subsidiary bank 1st Bank Oklahoma with about five branches throughout the state. In 2010 BancFirst acquired Union Bank of Chandler Okemah National Bank and Exchange National Bank of Moore adding about another five branches. It acquired First State Bank Jones in 2009 to expand in eastern Oklahoma.

President and CEO David Rainbolt owns some 40% of BancFirst .

EXECUTIVES

EVP Investments BancFirst, Robert M. Neville, age 62

EVP Financial Services BancFirst, D. Jay Hannah, age 62

EVP and Chief Risk Officer, Randy P. Foraker, age 62, $174,423 total compensation

EVP Human Resources BancFirst, J. Michael Rogers, age 74

EVP and CIO BancFirst, Scott Copeland, age 53

SEVP and Chairman Executive Committee, Dennis L. Brand, age 70, $525,000 total compensation

Vice Chairman and CEO Council Oak Investment Corporation and Council Oak Real Estate Inc., William O. Johnstone, age 70, $200,000 total compensation

EVP and Chief Credit Officer BancFirst, Roy C. Ferguson, age 71

Regional Executive BancFirst, Karen James, age 62

President and CEO BancFirst, Darryl Schmidt, age 56, $350,000 total compensation

Regional Executive BancFirst, David M. Seat, age 67

EVP and CTO BancFirst, David Westman, age 62

CEO, David R. Harlow, age 55, $325,000 total compensation

Regional Executive BancFirst, Harvey G. Robinson, age 59

EVP CFO and Treasurer, Kevin Lawrence, age 39, $214,231 total compensation

President BancFirst Frederick, Jason McQueen

EVP and Chief Internal Auditor, Paul Fleming, age 67

Regional Executive BancFirst, John Anderson, age 62

Senior Vice President, Gail Norman

Senior Vice President, Patrick A Lippmann

Senior Vice President General Manager, Michael Kernan

Senior Vice President, Blane Allen

Senior Vice President Chief In, Scott Lewis

Vice President Treasury Management Sales, Ashlea Briggs

Senior Vice President, Denise Duffle

Vice President Mortgage Production Manager, Billy Parsley

Senior Vice President, Brian Renz

Vice President Mortgage Lending, Shelly Matthews

Assistant Vice President Network Services, Dian Joysizemore

Senior Vice President, Bill Miller

Vice President Marketing, Ben Harrington

Executive Vice President, Sean Shadid

EXECUTIVE VICE PRESIDENT, Janet W Gotwals

SENIOR VICE PRESIDENT, Kevin J Calabrese

Vice President, Alan Geiger

Assistant Vice President and Consumer Loan Officer, Jenny Gifford

Assistant Vice President, Dauna Dines

Senior Vice President Asset Quality Loan Compliance, Frances Peterson

Assistant Vice President Commercial Loan Officer, Mary Johnston

Vice Chairman, James R. Daniel, age 78

Vice Chairman, K. Gordon Greer, age 81

Chairman, David E. Rainbolt, age 62

Board Member, Ronald Norick

Auditors: BKD, LLP

LOCATIONS

HQ: BancFirst Corp. (Oklahoma City, Okla)
101 North Broadway, Oklahoma City, OK 73102-8405
Phone: 405 270-1086   **Fax:** 405 270-1089
Web: www.bancfirst.com

PRODUCTS/OPERATIONS

2015 Sales

	$ mil.	% of total
Interest		
Loans including fees	190.3	63
Securities	6.5	2
Interest-bearing deposit	4.2	1
Noninterest		
Service charges on deposits	57.7	18
Insurance commissions	14.8	5
Security transactions	9.3	3
Trust revenue	9.1	3
Income from sale of loans	2.0	1
Cash management	7.5	2
Other	5.5	2
Total	**306.9**	**100**

Selected Subsidiaries

BancFirst
  BancFirst Agency Inc. (credit life insurance)
  BancFirst Community Development Corporation
  Council Oak Investment Corporation (small business investments)
  Council Oak Real Estate Inc. (real estate investments)
Council Oak Partners LLC
BancFirst Insurance Services Inc.

COMPETITORS

Arvest Bank	Midland Financial
BOK Financial	Southwest Bancorp
Bank of America	UMB Financial
International	Wells Fargo
Bancshares	

HISTORICAL FINANCIALS

Company Type: Public

Income Statement				FYE: December 31
	ASSETS ($ mil.)	NET INCOME ($ mil.)	INCOME AS % OF ASSETS	EMPLOYEES
12/17	7,253.1	86.4	1.2%	1,782
12/16	7,018.9	70.6	1.0%	1,773
12/15	6,692.8	66.1	1.0%	1,744
12/14	6,574.9	63.8	1.0%	1,688
12/13	6,038.9	54.3	0.9%	1,653
Annual Growth	4.7%	12.3%	—	1.9%

2017 Year-End Financials

Return on assets: 1.2%	Dividends
Return on equity: 11.6%	Yield: 0.0%
Long-term debt ($ mil.): —	Payout: 30.1%
No. of shares (mil.): 31.8	Market value ($ mil.): 1,631.0
Sales ($ mil): 366.1	

	STOCK PRICE ($) FY Close	P/E High/Low	PER SHARE ($) Earnings	Dividends	Book Value
12/17	51.15	40 18	2.65	0.80	24.32
12/16	93.05	42 23	2.22	0.74	22.49
12/15	58.62	32 26	2.09	0.70	21.01
12/14	63.39	33 25	2.02	0.65	19.65
12/13	56.06	32 22	1.75	0.60	18.16
Annual Growth	(2.3%)	— —	11.0%	7.5%	7.6%

Bank First National Corp

EXECUTIVES

Chb, Robert S Weinert
Vice President business Banking, Meghann Kasper
Vice President Marketing, Debbie Weyker
Vice President Business Banking, Christopher Stream
Auditors: Porter Keadle Moore, LLC

LOCATIONS

HQ: Bank First National Corp
402 North Eighth Street, P.O. Box 10, Manitowoc, WI 54220-0010
Phone: 920 652-3100   **Fax:** 920 652-3182
Web: www.bankfirstnational.com

HISTORICAL FINANCIALS

Company Type: Public

Income Statement

FYE: December 31

	ASSETS ($ mil.)	NET INCOME ($ mil.)	INCOME AS % OF ASSETS	EMPLOYEES
12/17	1,753.4	15.3	0.9%	0
12/16	1,316.0	14.9	1.1%	0
12/15	1,237.6	13.4	1.1%	0
12/14	1,105.0	12.6	1.1%	0
12/13	1,060.8	11.5	1.1%	0
Annual Growth 13.4%		7.3%	—	—

2017 Year-End Financials

Return on assets: 1.0%	Dividends
Return on equity: 10.5%	Yield: 0.0%
Long-term debt ($ mil.): —	Payout: 26.2%
No. of shares (mil.): 6.8	Market value ($ mil.): 304.0
Sales ($ mil): 60.9	

	STOCK PRICE ($) FY Close	P/E High/Low	PER SHARE ($) Earnings	Dividends	Book Value
12/17	44.70	18 14	2.44	0.64	23.76
12/16	33.33	14 11	2.40	0.59	20.53
12/15	28.25	13 10	2.13	0.51	18.97
12/14	22.65	12 9	1.99	0.34	17.42
12/13	19.00	11 8	1.79	0.22	15.91
Annual Growth 23.8%		— —	8.1%	30.6%	10.6%

Bank OZK

Bank of the Ozarks is the holding company for the bank of the same name which has about 260 branches in Alabama Arkansas California the Carolinas Florida Georgia New York and Texas. Focusing on individuals and small to midsized businesses the $12-billion bank offers traditional deposit and loan services in addition to personal and commercial trust services retirement and financial planning and investment management. Commercial real estate and construction and land development loans make up the largest portion of Bank of the Ozarks' loan portfolio followed by res-

idential mortgage business and agricultural loans. Bank of the Ozarks grows its loan and deposit business by acquiring smaller banks and opening branches across the US.

Operations

The bank makes three-fourths of its total revenue from interest income while the rest comes from fee-based sources. About 43% of Bank of the Ozark's total revenue came from non-purchased loan interest in 2014 while another 26% came from interest on purchased loans and a further 8% came from interest on its investment securities. The rest of its revenue came from service charges on deposit accounts (8% of revenue) mortgage lending income (1%) trust income (1%) and other non-recurring sources.

Geographic Reach

Bank of the Ozarks had 174 branches in eight states at the end of 2014 with 81 of them in Alabama and another 75 branches split among Georgia North Carolina and Texas. It has two loan offices in Houston and Manhattan that serve as an extension of the bank's Dallas-based Real Estate Specialties Group.

Sales and Marketing

The bank spent $3.03 million on advertising and public relations expenses in 2014 compared to $2.2 million and $4.09 million in 2013 and 2012 respectively.

Financial Performance

Bank of the Ozarks' annual revenues and profits have doubled since 2010 mostly as its loan assets have doubled from recent bank acquisitions spawning higher interest income.

The bank's revenue jumped 31% to $376 million during 2014 mostly thanks to strong purchased and non-purchased loan asset growth during the year from recent bank acquisitions. Its non-interest income grew 12% thanks to a 20% increase in deposit account service charges stemming from newly acquired deposit customers.

Strong revenue growth in 2014 boosted Bank of the Ozarks' net income by 30% to $119 million for the year. Its operating cash levels jumped 22% to $61 million during the year mostly thanks to higher cash earnings.

Strategy

Bank of the Ozarks continues its strategy of loan and deposit volume growth by acquiring smaller banks in new and existing geographic markets. It has also opened new branches and loan offices sparingly. During 2014 for example the bank opened retail branches in Bradenton Florida; Cornelius North Carolina; and Hilton Head Island South Carolina along with a new loan production office in Asheville North Carolina.

Mergers and Acquisitions

In July 2016 Bank of the Ozarks acquired Georgia-based Community & Southern Holdings and its Community & Southern Bank subsidiary. Adding some 45 branch locations in Georgia plus another in Florida it was the company's largest acquisition to-date.

Also in July 2016 the bank purchased C1 Financial along with its 32 CI Bank branches on the west coast of Florida and in Miami-Dade and Orange Counties. The deal added $1.7 billion in total assets $1.4 billion in loans and $1.3 billion in deposits. This transaction was the bank's fifteenth acquisition in the past six years.

In August 2015 the bank purchased Bank of the Carolinas Corporation (BCAR) — and its eight Bank of the Carolinas branches in North Carolina

$345 million in total assets $277 million in loans and $296 million in deposits — for a total price of $65.4 million.

In February 2015 Bank of the Ozarks bought Intervest Bancshares Corporation and its seven Intervest National Bank branches in (five in Clearwater Florida and two more in New York City and Pasadena Florida) for $238.5 million. The deal added $1.5 billion in assets including $1.1 billion in loans and $1.2 billion in deposits.

In May 2014 it bought Arkansas-based Summit Bancorp Inc. and its 23 Summit Bank branches across Arkansas for $42.5 million though it closed more than a handful of them later in the year.

In March 2014 the company acquired Houston-based Bancshares Inc. and its subsidiary Omnibank N.A. for $21.5 million adding three branches in Houston Texas and a branch each in Austin Cedar Park Lockhart and San Antonio.

Company Background

The expansion strategy of Bank of the Ozarks - which had a mere five branches in Arkansas 20 years ago — centered on opening new locations in smaller communities in Arkansas. But with the financial crash the bank was able to expand to more states through a series of FDIC-assisted transactions to take over failed banks. It bought Chestatee State Bank First Choice Community Bank Horizon Bank Oglethorpe Bank Park Avenue Bank Unity National and Woodlands Bank.

Chairman and CEO George Gleason initially bought the bank more than three decades ago at age 25.

EXECUTIVES

Chief Credit Officer Bank of the Ozarks, Darrel Russell, age 64, $252,308 total compensation
Chairman; Chief Executive Officer of the Company and the Bank, George G. Gleason, age 64, $1,730,769 total compensation
President Leasing Division Bank of the Ozarks, Scott Hastings, age 60, $181,925 total compensation
President Mortgage Division Bank of the Ozarks, Gene Holman, age 70, $150,042 total compensation
President Trust and Wealth Management Division Bank of the Ozarks, Rex Kyle, age 61, $241,674 total compensation
President Real Estate Specialties Group Bank of the Ozarks, Dan Thomas, age 55, $1,242,308 total compensation
CFO and Chief Accounting Officer Bank of the Ozarks Inc. and Bank of the Ozarks, Greg McKinney, age 50, $368,077 total compensation
Chief Operating Officer and Chief Banking Officer of the Company and the Bank, Tyler Vance, age 43, $366,923 total compensation
President Western Division, Don Keesee
Senior Vice President Market Leader, Russell Hewatt
Senior Vice President of Information Systems, Malcolm Hicks
Vice President Payment Systems, Paula Shaw
Senior Vice President, Chris Bragg
Senior Vice President Retail Banking Manager, Bob Moore
Vice President Regional Manager, Lisa Amato
Vice President Commercial Loan Officer, Austin Simpson
Vice President Lending, Erik Larson
Assistant Vice President Community Development Officer, Kimberly L Marshall
Vice President Marketing, Mark Greenhaw
Senior Vice President Treasury Management, Steve Woodruff

Assistant Vice President Branch Operations Manager, Fabian Garantiva

Senior Vice President Commercial Lender, Jeni Chokron

Vice President, Eric Teague

Senior Vice President, Ryan Tanner

Assistant Vice President Branch Manager, Pam Toney

Assistant Vice President Branch Manager, Derek Labrosse

Assistant Vice President Community Development Officer, Joann Smith

Executive Vice President, David Sarner

Executive Vice President, Martin Ball

Senior Vice President, Aram Zakian

Vice President Loan Officer, Dawn Speas

Vice President Treasury Management Wire Manager, Mona Kalchik

Auditors: PricewaterhouseCoopers LLP

LOCATIONS

HQ: Bank OZK
17901 Chenal Parkway, Little Rock, AR 72223
Phone: 501 978-2265   Fax: 501 978-2224
Web: www.bankozarks.com

PRODUCTS/OPERATIONS

2014 Sales

	$ mil.	% of total
Interest income		
Non-purchased loans and leases	162.5	43
Purchased loans	98.2	26
Investment securities	30.7	8
Non-interest income		
Service charges on deposit accounts	26.6	8
Other income from purchased loans net	14.8	4
Others	43.5	11
Total	**376.3**	**100**

Selected Services

Personal Banking

Apple PayChecking AccountsCredit CardsFree Bill PayFREE Debit CardsCustom Debit CardsEMV Chip CardsMobile BankingMortgage LoansMy Change KeeperOnline BankingOverdraft ProtectionPersonal LoansReloadable Spending CardsRetirement PlanningReorder ChecksSafe

Business Banking

Business ProductsApple Pay for BusinessDebit CardEMV Chip CardsBusiness Credit CardsChecking & Money MarketCommercial LoansExpress DepositMerchant ProcessingOnline BankingOverdraft ProtectionReorder ChecksTreasury Management Services

Online & Mobile Banking

Online BankingMobile BankingMobile DepositOnline Bill Pay

Wealth Management Services

Investment ProgramsFinancial PlanningCustomer Service

COMPETITORS

Arvest Bank	IBERIABANK
BOK Financial	JPMorgan Chase
BancorpSouth	Regions Financial
Bank of America	Simmons First
Bear State Financial	SunTrust
Cullen/Frost Bankers	Wells Fargo
Home BancShares	

HISTORICAL FINANCIALS

Company Type: Public

Income Statement   FYE: December 31

	ASSETS ($ mil.)	NET INCOME ($ mil.)	INCOME AS % OF ASSETS	EMPLOYEES
12/17	21,275.6	421.8	2.0%	2,400
12/16	18,890.1	269.9	1.4%	2,315
12/15	9,879.4	182.2	1.8%	1,642
12/14	6,766.5	118.6	1.8%	1,479
12/13	4,787.0	87.1	1.8%	1,223
Annual Growth	**45.2%**	**48.3%**	**—**	**18.4%**

2017 Year-End Financials

Return on assets: 2.1%	Dividends
Return on equity: 13.5%	Yield: 0.0%
Long-term debt ($ mil.): —	Payout: 10.9%
No. of shares (mil.): 128.2	Market value ($ mil.): 6,216.0
Sales ($ mil): 1,056.4	

	STOCK PRICE ($) FY Close	P/E High/Low	PER SHARE ($) Earnings	Dividends	Book Value
12/17	48.45	17 12	3.35	0.37	26.98
12/16	52.59	21 13	2.58	0.63	23.02
12/15	49.46	26 15	2.09	0.55	16.19
12/14	37.92	46 20	1.52	0.47	11.37
12/13	56.59	48 28	1.21	0.36	8.48
Annual Growth	**(3.8%)**	**— —**	**29.1%**	**0.3%**	**33.6%**

BankUnited Inc.

BankUnited is uniting the north and south again. It's the bank holding company for BankUnited N.A. which provides standard banking services to individuals and businesses through nearly 90 banking centers in about 15 Florida counties and five banking centers in the New York metro area. Deposit offerings include checking and savings accounts treasury management services and certificates of deposit. Commercial loans including multi-family residential mortgages account for some 80% of the bank's lending portfolio. In 2018 the company launched BankUnitedDirect an online division offering money market and CD accounts nationwide. BankUnited does not offer investment banking or wealth management services.

Sales and Marketing

BankUnited serves individuals growing companies and established middle-market companies. It markets its products through local television and radio ads digital and print ads and direct mail campaigns.

Financial Performance

BankUnited's revenue has been growing steadily for the last five years. Profits were relatively static until 2017 when they more than doubled. Cash flow has been somewhat volatile.

In 2017 revenue increased 14% to $1.1 billion as both interest and non-interest income grew. Interest on loans and securities rose while gains of sales of loans boosted non-interest income.

Net income rose 172% to $591 million that year. Part of that gain was due to a $327.9 million income tax benefit received.

The company ended 2017 with some $195 million in cash versus $448 million held at the end of 2016. Financing activities provided $1.9 billion in cash and operating activities provided $319 million. Investing activities used $2.5 billion in 2017 (the fifth straight year investments have used more than $2 billion).

Strategy

BankUnited has placed its bets on two large and growing markets — the Miami metro area and the Tri-State area of New York New Jersey and Connecticut. Because those geographic markets are so attractive though competition is fierce.

The company is also open to making strategic acquisitions of other financial firms or companies in complementary businesses.

Company Background

BankUnited was formed in 2009 following the demise of the former BankUnited FSB which collapsed under the weight of bad mortgages. A team of private investors bought BankUnited from the FDIC injected $900 million in fresh capital and in 2011 took the company public via an initial public offering (IPO); it was the first IPO of a rescued bank during the economic crisis.

In February 2012 BankUnited acquired Herald National Bank for $65 million in cash and stock. At the time of the purchase BankUnited converted to a bank holding company. It also converted the charter of subsidiary BankUnited from a thrift to a national commercial bank. Herald National was merged into BankUnited in mid-2012.

EXECUTIVES

President New York Region, Joseph (Joe) Roberto, age 61, $300,000 total compensation

Chief Risk Officer, Mark P. Bagnoli, age 66

President and CEO, Rajinder P. (Raj) Singh, age 47, $500,000 total compensation

CFO, Leslie N. Lunak, age 61, $400,000 total compensation

COO, Thomas M. Cornish, age 60, $500,000 total compensation

CIO, Julio Jogaib

Senior Vice President Commercial Real Estate, Robert Hummel

Vice President Hub Manager, Amy Ouellette

Assistant Vice President Portfolio Manager, Tracey Snow

Vice President, Kenneth Lipke

Senior Vice President Treasury Management, Nicholas Schiralli

Senior Vice President Commercial Private Banking, Corey Prinz

Vice President, Bill Williams

Vice President, Peter Dumelle

Senior Vice President Associate General Counsel, Alina Pastiu

Vice President Treasury Management Relationship Manager Treasury Management, Mark Stevens

Vice President, Carol Hammond

Assistant Vice President Design and Development, Sonya Moro

Vice President Portfolio Manager For Commercial Real Estate, Sabine SE Bouchereau

Vice President, Frank Puccio

Senior Vice President Community Development Offic, Claire Raley

Vice President Banking Center Assistant Manager, Theresa Schuman

Vice President Accounting Department, Dorrett Boothe

Senior Vice President Bsa Officer, Scott Nathan

Senior Vice President NYC Business Banking Team Leader, Gene Sullivan

Vice President Busines Banker, Nicholas Marrone

Senior Vice President Enterprise Stress Testing, Filippo Ghia

Vice President Financial Center Manager, John Hernandez

Senior Vice President, Stephen Hartigan

Senior Vice President Corporate Banking, Joseph Disanti

Vice President Corporate Banking, Justin Allbright

Vice President And Business Banking, Jose Alonso

Senior Vice President Relationship Manager Commercial Real Estate, Patricia Lubian

Vice President, Mireya Foster

Senior Vice President Associate General Counsel, Nancy Elia

Senior Vice President, Percy R Aguila

Vice President Commercial Banking, Ted Kunkel

Vice President, Carlos X Ramos

Vice President Commercial Real Estate, Jeremy Romine

Vice President Business Development Officer, Amy Rice

Senior Vice President Senior Business Development Officer, Scott Gilman

Senior Vice President, Michael Del Rocco

Senior Vice President Commercial Private Banking, Meghan Sheehan

Senior Vice President Senior Credit Officer Commercial Real Estate, John Kenyon

Senior Vice President, Jose Valdes

Assistant Vice President Regulatory Compliance Analyst II, Paula Gagnon

Assistant Vice President, Gloria Persaud

Senior Vice President Environmental Risk Manager, Michael Tartanella

Senior Vice President Business Banking Sales Manager, Gregory Milford

Vice President Branch Sales Leader, Milton Price

Vice President Commercial Real Estate, Chris Nielsen

Vice President Corporate Banking Division, Milciades Herrera

Executive Vice President, Gardner Semet

Senior Vice President, John Wamboldt

Senior Vice President, Larry Crowley

Vice President Operations Manager, Jose Alvarado

Vice President Corporate Banking, Jennifer Garcia-Barbon

Vice President Business Development Officer, Marissa Ames

Vice President Private Client Team Lead, Thomas Pla

Vice President Business Banking Lead Underwriter, Alexanders Saenz

Senior Vice President Corporate Team Leader, Christine Gerula

Assistant Vice President Project Administrator and Executive Assistant, Natalia Valenti

Vice President Commercial Real Estate, Chris Demeter

AVP Corporate Banking Portfolio Manager, Anthony Fulchi

Assistant Vice President, Shannie DeFreitas

Executive Vice President Mortgage Services, Ray Barbone

Vice President Branch Sales Leader, Monica Ribeiro

Vice President Business Development Officer, Stephen Speer

Vice President, Sul Hemani

Senior Vice President, Steve Markowski

Vice President Senior Analyst Business Development Officer, Tom Francis

Vice President Branch Sales Leader Downtown Delray Branch, Glenn Milspaugh

AVP SBA Loan Closer, Muni Chum

Senior Vice President, Brett Shulick

Vice President Business Banking Relationship Manager, Marshall Fulton

Vice President Business Development Officer Franchise Lending Specialist, Turner Gaw

AVP SBA Loan Closer, Leslie Giannantoni

AVP Recruiter III HR Generalist, Tsahai Green

SVP Credit Review Group Manager, Nancy Lanzoni

Vice President Commercial Credit Review Officer III, Elizabeth Nader

Senior Vice President Senior CRE Credit Officer Florida Region, Raul Llanes

VP Electronic Banking Manager, Daniel Cox

Senior Vice President, Candy Dugan

Senior Vice President Commercial Private Banking, Kelly Sleece

Avp Business Banking Portfolio Manager, Fredy Calderon

Vice President, Peter Anderson

Senior Vice President Corporate Banking, Jackson Young

Vice President Business Banking, Richard Rippy

Vice President Business Development Officer, Jared Johnson

Vice President Branch Sales Manager, Kathy Nemeth

Assistant Vice President Mortgage Warehouse Lending, Rosemarie Loparrino

Chairman: John A. Kanas, age 71

Auditors: KPMG LLP

LOCATIONS

HQ: BankUnited Inc.
14817 Oak Lane, Miami Lakes, FL 33016
Phone: 305 569-2000
Web: www.bankunited.com

COMPETITORS

BB&T	Ocean Bankshares
Bank of America	PNC Financial
Capital One	Regions Financial
Citibank	Signature Bank
Great Florida Bank	SunTrust
JPMorgan Chase	TD Bank USA
M&T Bank	Valley National
New York Community Bancorp	Bancorp
	Wells Fargo

HISTORICAL FINANCIALS

Company Type: Public

Income Statement   FYE: December 31

	ASSETS ($ mil.)	NET INCOME ($ mil.)	INCOME AS % OF ASSETS	EMPLOYEES
12/17	30,346.9	614.2	2.0%	1,763
12/16	27,880.1	225.7	0.8%	1,706
12/15	23,883.4	251.6	1.1%	1,741
12/14	19,210.5	204.2	1.1%	1,647
12/13	15,046.6	208.9	1.4%	1,623
Annual Growth	19.2%	30.9%	—	2.1%

2017 Year-End Financials

Return on assets: 2.1%	Dividends
Return on equity: 22.5%	Yield: 0.0%
Long-term debt ($ mil.): —	Payout: 15.0%
No. of shares (mil.): 106.8	Market value ($ mil.): 4,351.0
Sales ($ mil): 1,362.3	

	STOCK PRICE ($) FY Close	P/E High/Low	PER SHARE ($) Earnings	Dividends	Book Value
12/17	40.72	7 5	5.58	0.84	28.32
12/16	37.69	18 13	2.09	0.84	23.22
12/15	36.06	17 11	2.35	0.84	21.65
12/14	28.97	18 14	1.95	0.84	20.19
12/13	32.92	16 12	2.01	0.84	19.09
Annual Growth	5.5%	— —	29.1%	(0.0%)	10.4%

Bankwell Financial Group Inc

Auditors: RSM US LLP

LOCATIONS

HQ: Bankwell Financial Group Inc
220 Elm Street, New Canaan, CT 06840
Phone: 203 652-0166
Web: www.mybankwell.com

HISTORICAL FINANCIALS

Company Type: Public

Income Statement   FYE: December 31

	ASSETS ($ mil.)	NET INCOME ($ mil.)	INCOME AS % OF ASSETS	EMPLOYEES
12/17	1,796.6	13.8	0.8%	141
12/16	1,628.9	12.3	0.8%	127
12/15	1,330.3	9.0	0.7%	125
12/14	1,099.5	4.5	0.4%	130
12/13	779.6	5.1	0.7%	0
Annual Growth	23.2%	27.9%	—	—

2017 Year-End Financials

Return on assets: 0.8%	Dividends
Return on equity: 9.0%	Yield: 0.0%
Long-term debt ($ mil.): —	Payout: 15.7%
No. of shares (mil.): 7.7	Market value ($ mil.): 266.0
Sales ($ mil): 75.8	

	STOCK PRICE ($) FY Close	P/E High/Low	PER SHARE ($) Earnings	Dividends	Book Value
12/17	34.34	21 16	1.78	0.28	20.77
12/16	32.50	21 12	1.62	0.22	19.14
12/15	19.85	17 14	1.21	0.05	17.53
12/14	21.00	28 21	0.78	0.00	17.98
12/13	20.90	16 9	1.44	0.00	17.93
Annual Growth	13.2%	— —	5.4%	—	3.8%

Banner Corp.

Flagging bank accounts? See Banner Corporation. Banner is the holding company for Banner Bank which serves the Pacific Northwest through about 100 branches and 10 loan production offices in Washington Oregon and Idaho. The company also owns Islanders Bank which operates three branches in Washington's San Juan Islands. The banks offer standard products such as deposit accounts credit cards and business and consumer loans. Commercial loans including business agriculture construction and multifamily mortgage loans account for about 90% of the company's portfolio. Bank subsidiary Community Financial writes residential mortgage and construction loans.

Geographic Reach

Washington-based Banner Bank is focused on five primary markets in the Northwest: the Puget Sound region of Washington; the greater Portland Oregon market; Boise Idaho; and Spokane Washington. The fifth is the bank's historical base in the agricultural communities in the Columbia Basin region of Washington and Oregon.

Sales and Marketing

Banner Corp. reported advertising and marketing expenses of $6.9 million in 2013 versus $7.2 million in 2012. Banner Bank launched a redesigned website and new ad campaign in Boise Seattle and Portland and on social media in fall 2014.

Financial Performance

The regional bank holding company reported revenue of $223 million in 2013 an increase of 4% versus 2012. The rise in revenue was due to increased operating income as a result of gains on the sale of securities and a fee received from the termination of the bank's proposed acquisition of Home Federal Bancorp. The bank's growing customer base led to increased income from deposit fees and other service charges of $1.3 billion (5%) in 2013 versus the prior year. Net income declined 28% in 2013 versus 2012 to $46.6 million primarily due to higher provision for income tax expenses. After three consecutive years of losses (2008 thru 2010) the bank returned to profitability in 2011 and has remained profitable.

Banner Corp. has total consolidated assets of about $4.5 billion.

Strategy

Historically Banner Corp. has grown by acquisition. Since going public (in 1995) Banner has acquired about 10 commercial banks. Islanders Bank was acquired in 2007 the same year Banner acquired F&M Bank and NCW Community Bank of Wenatchee both also based in Washington. After the spate of acquisitions the company focused on opening branches. The company continues to look for acquisition opportunities with an eye on banks shut down by regulators.

In 2013 however a plan to merge with Home Federal Bancorp was terminated when that bank received a better offer from Cascade Bancorp. Also the company abandoned plans to buy Idaho Banking Company out of bankruptcy after being outbid.

Mergers and Acquisitions

In August 2014 Banner Bank acquired Siuslaw Financial Group the holding company for Siuslaw Bank the operator of 10 branches along the coast of Oregon. In June 2014 Banner Bank purchased six branches in Oregon from Sterling Savings Bank.

EXECUTIVES

EVP and CFO Banner Corporation, Lloyd W. Baker, age 69, $260,724 total compensation
EVP Retail Banking and Administration, Cynthia D. (Cindy) Purcell, age 60, $289,038 total compensation
EVP and Chief Lending Officer Banner Corporation and Banner Bank, Richard B. Barton, age 74, $264,895 total compensation
President and CEO, Mark J. Grescovich, age 53, $716,415 total compensation
EVP and Real Estate Lending Manager Banner Bank, Douglas M. Bennett, age 65, $236,174 total compensation
EVP and CIO, Steven W. (Steve) Rust, age 70
EVP Retail Products and Services, Gary W. Wagers, age 57
EVP and Commercial Executive East Region, M. Kirk Quillin, age 55
EVP and Commercial Executive West Region, James T. (Jim) Reed, age 55

EVP and CFO Banner Bank, Peter J. Conner, age 52
EVP Human Resources, Kayleen Kohler
EVP and Mortgage Banking Director, Kenneth A. (Ken) Larsen, age 48
EVP and General Counsel Banner Bank, Craig Miller
EVP and Chief Risk Officer Banner Bank, Judy Steiner
EVP and Commercial Executive (South Region), Keith A. Western, age 62
Senior Vice President SBA Manager, Walter Mclaughlin
Senior Vice President, Mark Brandon
Assistant Vice President And Senior Underwriter, Nancy Piestrack
Vice President And Portfolio Manager, Michael Thomas
Vice President Senior Commercial Relationship Manager, Jeanne Walker
Assistant Vice President Training Manager, Terri Anderson
Vice Chairman Banner Corporation and Banner Bank, Jesse G. Foster, age 80
Chairman Banner Corporation and Banner Bank, Gary L. Sirmon, age 75
Auditors: Moss Adams LLP

LOCATIONS

HQ: Banner Corp.
10 South First Avenue, Walla Walla, WA 99362
Phone: 509 527-3636
Web: www.bannerbank.com

PRODUCTS/OPERATIONS

2016 Sales

	% of total
INTEREST INCOME:	
Loans receivable	75
Mortgage-backed securities	4
Securities and cash equivalents	3
NON-INTEREST INCOME:	
Deposit fees and other service charges	10
Mortgage banking operations	6
BOLI	1
Miscellaneous	1
Total	**100**

COMPETITORS

Bank of America	Sound Financial
Cascade Bancorp	U.S. Bancorp
Columbia Banking	Umpqua Holdings
FCA	Washington Federal
Glacier Bancorp	Wells Fargo
KeyCorp	

HISTORICAL FINANCIALS

Company Type: Public

Income Statement

FYE: December 31

	ASSETS ($ mil.)	NET INCOME ($ mil.)	INCOME AS % OF ASSETS	EMPLOYEES
12/17	9,763.2	60.7	0.6%	2,128
12/16	9,793.6	85.3	0.9%	2,137
12/15	9,796.3	45.2	0.5%	2,143
12/14	4,723.9	54.1	1.1%	1,193
12/13	4,388.1	46.5	1.1%	1,131
Annual Growth	**22.1%**	**6.9%**	**—**	**17.1%**

2017 Year-End Financials

Return on assets: 0.6%	Dividends
Return on equity: 4.7%	Yield: 0.0%
Long-term debt ($ mil.): —	Payout: 107.6%
No. of shares (mil.): 32.7	Market value ($ mil.): 1,804.0
Sales ($ mil): 523.2	

	STOCK PRICE ($) FY Close	P/E High/Low		PER SHARE ($) Earnings	Dividends	Book Value
12/17	55.12	34	28	1.84	1.98	38.89
12/16	55.81	22	15	2.52	0.65	39.34
12/15	45.86	28	21	1.89	0.72	37.97
12/14	43.02	16	13	2.79	0.72	29.82
12/13	44.82	19	12	2.40	0.54	27.63
Annual Growth	**5.3%**	**—**	**—**	**(6.4%)**	**38.4%**	**8.9%**

Bar Harbor Bankshares

Bar Harbor Bankshares which holds Bar Harbor Bank & Trust is a Maine -stay. Boasting $1.6 billion in assets the bank offers traditional deposit and retirement products trust services and a variety of loans to individuals and businesses through 15 branches in the state's Hancock Knox and Washington counties. Commercial real estate and residential mortgages loans make up nearly 80% of the bank's loan portfolio though it also originates business construction agricultural home equity and other consumer loans. About 10% of its loans are to the tourist industry which is associated with nearby Acadia National Park. Subsidiary Bar Harbor Trust Services offers trust and estate planning services.

Operations

Around 80% of the bank's loan assets are tied to real estate. About 41% of its loan portfolio was made up of residential real estate mortgages at the end of 2015 while another 37% was made up of commercial real estate mortgages. The rest of the portfolio was tied to commercial and industrial loans (8% of loan assets) home equity loans (5%) agricultural and farming loans (3%) commercial construction (3%) and other consumer loans (1%).

More than 80% of Bar Harbor's revenue comes from interest income. About 61% of its total revenue came from loan interest (including fees) during 2015 while another 25% came from interest income on investment securities. The remainder of its revenue came from trust and other financial services (6% of revenue) debit card service charges and fees (3%) deposit account service charges (1%) and other miscellaneous income sources.

Geographic Reach

The Bar Harbor Maine-based group operates 15 branches across the downeast midcoast and central regions of Maine more specifically in Bar Harbor Northeast Harbor Southwest Harbor Somesville Deer Isle Blue Hill Ellsworth Rockland Topsham South China Augusta Winter Harbor Milbridge Machias and Lubec.

Sales and Marketing

Bar Harbor serves individuals and retirees nonprofits municipalities as well as businesses that are vital to Maine's coastal economy including retailers restaurants seasonal lodging bio research laboratories.

Financial Performance

The group's annual revenues have risen more than 10% since 2013 as its loan assets have swelled over 35% to $990 million. Its profits have grown more than 30% over the same period as Bar Harbor has kept a lid on rising operating costs and as it's enjoyed low interest rates.

Bar Harbor's revenue climbed 4% to $64.2 million during 2015 mostly as its loan and other interest earning assets grew by more than 7%.

Revenue growth in 2015 drove the bank's net income up 4% to $15.15 million. Bar Harbor's operating cash levels spiked 31% to $20.33 million for the year mainly thanks to favorable working capital changes related to changes in other assets.

Strategy

Bar Harbor Bankshares looks to grow its loan and deposit business organically and through strategic bank acquisitions targeting the downeast midcoast and central Maine markets. It also continued in 2016 to focus on managing its operating expenses building upon its strong efficient ratio of 56.3% in 2015.

EXECUTIVES

EVP Business Banking Bar Harbor Bank & Trust, Gregory W. Dalton, age 58, $203,000 total compensation

EVP Retail Banking, Stephen M. Leackfeldt, age 61, $225,000 total compensation

EVP and Chief Risk Officer, Richard B. Maltz, $255,000 total compensation

EVP CFO and Treasurer, Josephine Iannelli, age 46

President and CEO Bar Harbor Bankshares and Bar Harbor Bank & Trust, Curtis C. Simard, age 47, $438,000 total compensation

Assistant Vice President and Senior Risk Management Analyst, John Williams

Vice President Regional Relationship Manager, Larissa Darcy

Senior Vice President Internal Audit, Johanne Lapointe

Vice President Regional Market Manager, Michelle Curtis

Chairman, David B. Woodside, age 66

Board Member, Matthew Caras

Auditors: RSM US LLP

LOCATIONS

HQ: Bar Harbor Bankshares
P.O. Box 400, 82 Main Street, Bar Harbor, ME 04609-0400
Phone: 207 288-3314   **Fax:** 207 288-4560
Web: www.bhbt.com

PRODUCTS/OPERATIONS

2015 sales

	$ mil.	% of total
Interest and dividend income		
Interest and fees on loans	39.3	61
Interest on securities	15.3	24
Dividends on FHLB stock	0.6	1
Non-interest income		
Trust and other financial services	3.9	6
Debit card service charges and fees	1.7	3
Net securities gains	1.3	2
Other operating income	1.2	2
Service charges on deposit accounts	0.9	1
Total	**64.2**	**100**

Selected Services

Retail Products and Services
Retail Brokerage Services
Electronic Banking Services
Commercial Products and Services

COMPETITORS

Bangor Savings Bank	TD Bank USA
Bank of America	The First Bancorp
Camden National	
People's United	
Financial	

Income Statement   FYE: December 31

	ASSETS ($ mil.)	NET INCOME ($ mil.)	INCOME AS % OF ASSETS	EMPLOYEES
12/17	3,565.1	25.9	0.7%	423
12/16	1,755.3	14.9	0.9%	186
12/15	1,580.0	15.1	1.0%	221
12/14	1,459.3	14.6	1.0%	223
12/13	1,373.8	13.1	1.0%	185
Annual Growth	**26.9%**	**18.5%**	**—**	**23.0%**

2017 Year-End Financials

Return on assets: 0.9%   Dividends
Return on equity: 10.1%   Yield: 0.0%
Long-term debt ($ mil.): —   Payout: 43.9%
No. of shares (mil.): 15.4   Market value ($ mil.): 417.0
Sales ($ mil): 142.0

	STOCK PRICE ($) FY Close	P/E High/Low	PER SHARE ($) Earnings	Dividends	Book Value
12/17	27.01	28 15	1.70	0.75	22.96
12/16	47.33	30 18	1.63	0.73	17.19
12/15	34.42	22 18	1.67	0.67	17.10
12/14	32.00	24 15	1.63	0.60	16.40
12/13	39.99	27 23	1.48	0.56	13.70
Annual Growth	**(9.3%)**	**— —**	**3.4%**	**7.7%**	**13.8%**

Barrett Business Services, Inc.

Barrett Business Services (BBSI) is employed in helping businesses. BBSI offers professional employment organization (PEO) services to some 5600 small and mid-sized businesses and their nearly 200000 employees. Its PEO services business provides outsourced human resource services such as payroll management benefits administration risk management recruiting and placement. The company also offers temporary and long-term staffing services such as on-demand or short term staffing on-site management contract staffing master-vendor programs. Established in 1965 BBSI operates through about 60 branch offices across 10 US states. More than three-quarters of its PEO revenue comes from clients in California.

Operations

BBSI operates through two categories of services: Professional Employer Services (PEO) and Staffing.

Accounting for more than 80% of company revenue the company's PEO services provide employee payroll payroll taxes workers' compensation coverage and certain other administrative functions to small and mid-sized businesses.

Staffing services bringing in the remaining 20% of revenue includes on-demand or short-term staffing assignments contract staffing direct placement and long-term or indefinite-term on-site management.

Geographic Reach

BBSI operates through about 60 branch offices in 10 states many of which are located throughout

California and Oregon as well as Utah and Washington. The company supports clients' employees in two dozen states but company does 80% of its business in California which leaves the company's financial performance largely dependent on a single state's economy.

Sales and Marketing

BBSI relies on referrals from existing clients as well as B2B sales initiatives managed by area managers and a referral network to growth its client base. It serves small to mid-sized businesses operating in an array of industries including electronics manufacturers light-manufacturing industries agriculture companies transportation and shipping enterprises food processors telecommunications companies public utilities construction general contractors and professional services firms.

Financial Performance

BBSI's revenue has been trending upwards in recent years nearly doubling from $537 million to $920 million between 2013 and 2017. During the same 5-year span net income fluctuated between $15 million and $25 million but has failed to pace the company's revenue trend.

Year-over-year BBSI reported a 9% increase in its 2017 revenue over 2016 up to $920 million from $840.6 million. The increase was driven by a 12% jump in revenue in its PEO services business and offset slightly by a 3% decrease in its smaller Staffing business. That year the company's new client numbers outpaced its contractual losses resulting in its PEO business serving 5600 clients in 2017 up from 4900 clients in 2016.

Net income jumped 34% from $18 million to $25 million an uptick attributed to the company's revenue increase and a lack of other net expenses that had been recorded the previous year.

Cash on hand at the end of the year was $59 million compared to $50.7 million at the beginning of the year. Cash from operations contributed $112.8 million while investing activities used $94.7 million and financing activities used $9 million.

Strategy

BBSI's growth strategy centers on building its client numbers through organic means. It relies on existing client referrals sales mangers recruiting clients through direct B2B sales and a sales referral network. Its referral network is composed of business professionals like lawyers financial advisors and insurance brokers that refer their small to mid-sized business clients to BBSI in exchange for a fee.

The company also looks for opportunities to expand geographically within and outside of its core California market. BBSI will either expand its staff at existing locations to facilitate client number increases or when necessary open a new branch office to reach clients in a new geographic area.

EXECUTIVES

VP and COO Corporate Operations, Gregory R. (Greg) Vaughn, age 62, $400,000 total compensation
President and CEO, Michael L. (Mike) Elich, age 53, $650,000 total compensation
VP and COO Field Operations, Gerald R. Blotz, age 48, $400,000 total compensation
CFO, Gary Kramer, age 38
Board Member, Roger Johnson
Chairman, Anthony Meeker, age 79
Auditors: DELOITTE & TOUCHE LLP

LOCATIONS

HQ: Barrett Business Services, Inc.
8100 NE Parkway Drive, Suite 200, Vancouver, WA 98662
Phone: 360 828-0700   **Fax:** 360 828-0701
Web: www.barrettbusiness.com

PRODUCTS/OPERATIONS

2017 Sales

	$ mil.	% of total
Professional employer service fees	758.0	82
Staffing services	162.4	18
Total	**920.4**	**100**

Selected Services

PEO services
  Employee benefits
  Health insurance
  Human resource administration
  Drug testing
  Hiring
  Interviewing
  Placement
  Recruiting
  Regulatory compliance
  Payroll
  Workers' compensation coverage
  Workplace safety programs
Staffing services
  Contract
  Long-term
  Short term

COMPETITORS

ADP TotalSource	Paychex
Adecco	Robert Half
Insperity	TeamStaff
Kelly Services	TriNet Group
ManpowerGroup	

HISTORICAL FINANCIALS

Company Type: Public

Income Statement				FYE: December 31
	REVENUE ($ mil.)	NET INCOME ($ mil.)	NET PROFIT MARGIN	EMPLOYEES
12/17	920.4	25.1	2.7%	124,212
12/16	840.5	18.8	2.2%	115,746
12/15	740.8	25.4	3.4%	103,250
12/14	636.1	(27.0)	—	93,040
12/13	532.8	17.8	3.4%	79,315
Annual Growth	14.6%	8.9%	—	11.9%

2017 Year-End Financials

Debt ratio: 0.6%
Return on equity: 31.7%
Cash ($ mil.): 59.8
Current ratio: 0.96
Long-term debt ($ mil.): 4.1

No. of shares (mil.): 7.3
Dividends
Yield: 0.0%
Payout: 30.0%
Market value ($ mil.): 471.0

	STOCK PRICE ($) FY Close	P/E High/Low		PER SHARE ($) Earnings	Dividends	Book Value
12/17	64.49	20	14	3.33	1.00	12.17
12/16	64.10	25	9	2.55	0.88	9.62
12/15	43.54	15	7	3.47	0.88	7.57
12/14	27.40	—	—	(3.78)	0.76	5.42
12/13	92.74	38	15	2.42	0.57	10.13
Annual Growth	(8.7%)	—	—	8.3%	15.1%	4.7%

BBX Capital Corp (New)

Holding company BFC Financial controls Florida-based investment firm Woodbridge Holdings which has holdings in real estate companies Core Communities and Bluegreen Corporation and restaurant franchise Pizza Fusion. BFC also owns a minority stake in Asian-themed restaurant chain Benihana. Chairman president and CEO Alan Levan and vice chairman Jack Abdo control BFC Financial. In 2016 the company agreed to merge with BBX Capital Corporation which owns the remaining 46% of Woodbridge Holdings that BFC doesn't own. The merger will create a simplified corporate structure.

EXECUTIVES

Vice Chairman BFC Financial and BankAtlantic, John E. (Jack) Abdo, age 73, $660,739 total compensation
Chairman of the Board; President; Chief Executive Officer, Alan B. Levan, age 71, $677,375 total compensation
EVP and CFO, John K. Grelle, age 72, $192,166 total compensation
SVP Investor Relations, Leo Hinkley Jr.
Executive Vice President; Director, Seth M. Wise, age 46
VP and Investor Relations Officer, Sharon Lyn
Senior Vice President; Chief Accounting Officer, Maria R. Scheker, age 59, $215,000 total compensation
Executive Vice President; Director, Jarett S. Levan, age 42
Vice Chairman BFC Financial and BankAtlantic, John E. (Jack) Abdo, age 72
Director, Darwin C. Dornbush, age 86
Director, D. Keith Cobb, age 75
EVP and Director, Seth M. Wise, age 46
Director, Oscar J. Holzmann, age 73
Director, Neil Sterling, age 64
EVP and Director, Jarett S. Levan, age 41
Director, Joel Levy, age 76
Director, Alan J. Levy, age 76
Director, William R. Nicholson, age 70
Auditors: GRANT THORNTON LLP

LOCATIONS

HQ: BBX Capital Corp (New)
401 East Las Olas Boulevard, Suite 800, Fort Lauderdale, FL 33301
Phone: 954 940-4900
Web: www.bbxcapital.com

COMPETITORS

BKF Capital Group	Huizenga Holdings
Bank of America	St. Joe
H.I.G. Capital	Sun Capital

HISTORICAL FINANCIALS

Company Type: Public

Income Statement				FYE: December 31
	REVENUE ($ mil.)	NET INCOME ($ mil.)	NET PROFIT MARGIN	EMPLOYEES
12/17	815.7	82.2	10.1%	6,914
12/16	764.0	28.3	3.7%	6,141
12/15	740.2	122.4	16.5%	6,108
12/14	672.1	13.8	2.1%	5,364
12/13	563.7	29.0	5.2%	5,050
Annual Growth	9.7%	29.7%	—	8.2%

2017 Year-End Financials

Debt ratio: 43.6%
Return on equity: 15.9%
Cash ($ mil.): 362.5
Current ratio: 21.85
Long-term debt ($ mil.): 700.6

No. of shares (mil.): 99.6
Dividends
Yield: 0.0%
Payout: 3.8%
Market value ($ mil.): 794.0

	STOCK PRICE ($) FY Close	P/E High/Low		PER SHARE ($) Earnings	Dividends	Book Value
12/17	7.97	11	6	0.79	0.03	5.75
12/16	4.88	15	8	0.32	0.02	4.64
12/15	3.39	3	2	1.40	0.00	4.46
12/14	3.20	26	17	0.16	0.00	3.03
12/13	2.89	8	4	0.35	0.00	3.05
Annual Growth	28.9%	—	—	22.6%	—	17.2%

BCB Bancorp Inc

BCB Bancorp be the holding company for BCB Community Bank which opened its doors in late 2000. The independent bank serves Hudson County and the surrounding area from about 15 offices in New Jersey's Bayonne Hoboken Jersey City and Monroe. The bank offers traditional deposit products and services including savings accounts money market accounts CDs and IRAs. Funds from deposits are used to originate mortgages and loans primarily commercial real estate and multi-family property loans (which together account for more than half of the bank's loan portfolio). BCB Bancorp's branch network tripled in size when it added 10 locations through its 2010 acquisition of Pamrapo Bancorp.

EXECUTIVES

COO and Director; COO and CFO BCB Community Bank, Thomas M. Coughlin, age 56, $128,544 total compensation
Chairman, Mark D. Hogan, age 50
Director; Senior Lending Officer BCB Community Bank, James E. Collins, age 67, $131,222 total compensation
VP Commercial Lending BCB Community Bank, Amer Saleem, age 61, $94,500 total compensation
Independent Vice Chairman of the Board, Joseph Brogan, age 77
Chief Financial Officer of BCB Community Bank and BCB Bancorp, Kenneth Walter
COO and Director; COO and CFO BCB Community Bank, Thomas M. Coughlin, age 56
Director; Senior Lending Officer BCB Community Bank, James E. Collins, age 67
Independent Director, Robert Ballance, age 57

Independent Director, Judith Q. Bielan, age 51
Independent Director, Alexander Pasiechnik, age 54
Independent Director, Joseph Lyga, age 56
Independent Director, Gary Stetz
Independent Director, Robert Hughes
Independent Director, Spencer Robbins
Auditors: Wolf & Company, P.C.

LOCATIONS

HQ: BCB Bancorp Inc
  104-110 Avenue C, Bayonne, NJ 07002
Phone: 201 823-0700
Web: www.bcbcommunitybank.com

COMPETITORS

Bank of America	PNC Financial
City National	Provident Financial
Bancshares	Services
Hudson City Bancorp	Sterling Bank
Meridian Capital Group	Stewardship Financial
New York Community	
Bancorp	

HISTORICAL FINANCIALS

Company Type: Public

Income Statement | | | FYE: December 31

	ASSETS ($ mil.)	NET INCOME ($ mil.)	INCOME AS % OF ASSETS	EMPLOYEES
12/17	1,942.8	9.9	0.5%	314
12/16	1,708.2	8.0	0.5%	353
12/15	1,618.4	7.0	0.4%	331
12/14	1,301.9	7.5	0.6%	327
12/13	1,207.9	9.4	0.8%	249
Annual Growth	12.6%	1.5%	—	6.0%

2017 Year-End Financials

Return on assets: 0.5%	Dividends
Return on equity: 6.4%	Yield: 0.0%
Long-term debt ($ mil.): —	Payout: 74.6%
No. of shares (mil.): 15.0	Market value ($ mil.): 218.0
Sales ($ mil): 85.0	

	STOCK PRICE ($) FY Close	P/E High/Low		Earnings	PER SHARE ($) Dividends	Book Value
12/17	14.50	22	16	0.75	0.56	11.73
12/16	13.00	21	16	0.63	0.56	11.63
12/15	10.40	18	14	0.69	0.56	11.91
12/14	11.73	17	14	0.81	0.54	12.18
12/13	13.45	14	8	1.06	0.48	12.01
Annual Growth	1.9%	—	—	(8.3%)	3.9%	(0.6%)

Beasley Broadcast Group Inc

Beasley Broadcast Group is a leading radio broadcaster with some 52 stations operating in about a dozen large and mid-sized markets in seven states primarily Florida Georgia and North Carolina. The company's stations (serving 7.7 million listeners per week) broadcast a variety of formats including news sports and talk radio as well as Top 40 Urban Oldies and other music formats. Most of its stations operate as part of a cluster within a specific market allowing the company to combine certain business functions between those stations and achieve greater operating efficiencies. Beasley Broadcast Group was founded by George Beasley in 1961.

Geographic Reach

The company's market include Atlanta and Augusta GA; Boston MA; Fayetteville and Greenville-New Bern-Jacksonville NC; Fort Myers-Naples Miami-Fort Lauderdale and West Palm Beach-Boca Raton FL; Las Vegas NV; Philadelphia PA; and Wilmington DE.

Financial Performance

Beasley reported revenue of about $105 million in 2013 up 5% from the prior year as it saw significant increases in advertising revenue in the Philadelphia and Las Vegas markets. Net income which has been rising every year since 2009 was also up 5% to $11.5 million.

Cash from operations has been following a similar trajectory as net income although it was down slightly in 2013 to $19.9 million on increases in cash paid for station operating expenses income tax payments and cash receipts from the sale of advertising airtime.

EXECUTIVES

Vice President Of Communications, Denyse Mesnik
Vice President Corporate Communications, Soni Dimond
Vice President Of Strategic Planning, Kathryn Cook
National Sales Manager, Matthew Cowper
Vice President of Corporate Communications, Heidi Raphael
Vice President Market Manager, Mac Edwards
Vice President Market Manager, Bill Schoening
Auditors: Crowe Horwath LLP

LOCATIONS

HQ: Beasley Broadcast Group Inc
  3033 Riviera Drive, Suite 200, Naples, FL 34103
Phone: 239 263-5000   Fax: 239 263-8191
Web: www.bbgi.com

COMPETITORS

CBS Radio	Radio One Inc.
Cox Radio	SIRIUS XM
Cumulus Media	Univision Radio
Entravision	iHeartCommunications
Lincoln Financial	
Media	

HISTORICAL FINANCIALS

Company Type: Public

Income Statement | | | FYE: December 31

	REVENUE ($ mil.)	NET INCOME ($ mil.)	NET PROFIT MARGIN	EMPLOYEES
12/17	232.1	87.1	37.5%	1,484
12/16	136.6	47.4	34.7%	1,406
12/15	105.9	6.3	6.0%	809
12/14	58.7	40.0	68.1%	807
12/13	104.9	11.5	11.0%	660
Annual Growth	22.0%	65.7%	—	22.5%

2017 Year-End Financials

Debt ratio: 32.8%	No. of shares (mil.): 28.8
Return on equity: 35.6%	Dividends
Cash ($ mil.): 13.9	Yield: 0.0%
Current ratio: 2.92	Payout: 5.7%
Long-term debt ($ mil.): 212.4	Market value ($ mil.): 387.0

	STOCK PRICE ($) FY Close	P/E High/Low		Earnings	PER SHARE ($) Dividends	Book Value
12/17	13.40	5	2	3.14	0.18	9.92
12/16	6.15	4	2	1.98	0.18	7.02
12/15	3.59	20	11	0.28	0.18	5.75
12/14	5.11	5	3	1.74	0.18	5.65
12/13	8.73	19	9	0.51	0.05	4.08
Annual Growth	11.3%	—	—	57.5%	41.4%	24.9%

Berkshire Hills Bancorp Inc

Berkshire Hills Bancorp is the holding company for Berkshire Bank which serves individuals and small businesses through some 90 branches in Massachusetts New York Connecticut and Vermont. Established in 1846 the bank provides standard deposit products such as savings checking and money market accounts CDs and IRAs in addition to credit cards investments private banking wealth management and lending services. Real estate mortgages make up nearly three-quarters of Berkshire Hills Bancorp's loan portfolio which also includes business and consumer loans. In addition to its banking activities the company also owns insurance agency Berkshire Insurance Group.

Geographic Reach

Berkshire Hills Bancorp also is eyeing further expansion into Connecticut and other parts of New England and New York by opening new branches and through acquisitions.

Financial Performance

Berkshire Hills Bancorp's revenue increased in fiscal 2013 compared to the prior year. It reported $262 million in revenue for fiscal 2013 up from $230 million in fiscal 2012. Net income also went up to $58 million in fiscal 2013 compared to the $47 million Berkshire Hills Bancorp reported for net income in fiscal 2012.

The company's cash on hand increased by more than $100 million in fiscal 2013 compared to fiscal 2012 levels.

Strategy

Berkshire Hills Bancorp which was established in 1846 believes one of its competitive advantages is the regional niche it serves which has been relatively unscathed by the recession compared to other parts of the country.

The bank's performance has been boosted by an increase in business development in the company's market area in addition to growth in its asset-based lending and private banking businesses. The bank also has grown its loans and deposits and has plans to grow its insurance and wealth management operations as well.

In 2016 the company completed the $150 million acquisition of New Jersey-based First Choice Bank. That deal which add eight bank branches and introduce Berkshire Hills to the greater Philadelphia area will bring the bank's network to more than 100 branches.

EXECUTIVES

President Chief Executive Officer, Michael P. Daly, age 54, $450,000 total compensation
Chairman, Lawrence A. (Larry) Bossidy, age 81
Executive Vice President of Human Resources, Linda A. Johnston
SVP Commercial Lending, Michael J. Ferry
EVP, Michael J. (Mike) Oleksak, age 57, $225,000 total compensation
Executive Vice President of Retail Banking, Sean A. Gray
Executive Vice President Chief Financial Officer Treasurer, Kevin P. Riley, age 56, $250,000 total compensation
Executive Vice President Chief Risk Officer, Richard M. Marotta
Chief Compliance Officer and Anti Money Laundering Officer, Brian Kindelan
Chief Investment Officer, Charles N. Leach
Executive Vice President of Commercial Banking and Wealth Management, Patrick Sullivan
Vice President Manager, Paul Lesukoski
Vice President Personal Lines, James Herrick
Director, Rodney C. Dimock, age 69
Director, Cornelius D. Mahoney, age 70
President CEO and Director Berkshire Hills Bancorp and Berkshire Bank, Michael P. Daly, age 54
Director, Catherine B. Miller, age 73
Director, Corydon L. Thurston, age 62
Director, D. Jeffrey Templeton, age 74
Director, David E. Phelps, age 63
Director, Robert M. Curley
Director, John B. Davis, age 66
Director, Wallace W. Altes, age 73
Director, Susan M. Hill, age 66
Independent Director, John Davies
Independent Director, Williar Dunlaevy
Auditors: Crowe Horwath LLP

LOCATIONS

HQ: Berkshire Hills Bancorp Inc
60 State Street, Boston, MA 02109
Phone: 800 773-5601
Web: www.berkshirebank.com

COMPETITORS

Bank of America
Hudson City Bancorp
KeyCorp
Pathfinder Bancorp
RBS Citizens Financial Group
Sovereign Bank
TD Bank USA

HISTORICAL FINANCIALS

Company Type: Public

Income Statement   FYE: December 31

	ASSETS ($ mil.)	NET INCOME ($ mil.)	INCOME AS % OF ASSETS	EMPLOYEES
12/17	11,570.7	55.2	0.5%	1,992
12/16	9,162.5	58.6	0.6%	1,731
12/15	7,831.9	49.5	0.6%	1,221
12/14	6,502.0	33.7	0.5%	1,091
12/13	5,672.8	41.1	0.7%	939
Annual Growth	19.5%	7.6%	—	20.7%

2017 Year-End Financials

Return on assets: 0.5%	Dividends
Return on equity: 4.2%	Yield: 0.0%
Long-term debt ($ mil.): —	Payout: 60.4%
No. of shares (mil.): 45.2	Market value ($ mil.): 1,658.0
Sales ($ mil): 485.9	

	STOCK PRICE ($) FY Close	P/E High/Low	Earnings	PER SHARE ($) Dividends	Book Value
12/17	36.60	28 24	1.39	0.84	33.04
12/16	36.85	20 13	1.88	0.80	30.65
12/15	29.11	17 14	1.73	0.76	28.64
12/14	26.66	20 16	1.36	0.72	28.17
12/13	27.27	18 14	1.65	0.72	27.08
Annual Growth	7.6%	— —	(4.2%)	3.9%	5.1%

BG Staffing Inc

Auditors: Whitley Penn LLP

LOCATIONS

HQ: BG Staffing Inc
5850 Granite Parkway, Suite 730, Plano, TX 75024
Phone: 972 692-2400
Web: www.bgstaffing.com

HISTORICAL FINANCIALS

Company Type: Public

Income Statement   FYE: December 31

	REVENUE ($ mil.)	NET INCOME ($ mil.)	NET PROFIT MARGIN	EMPLOYEES
12/17	272.6	5.8	2.1%	29,349
12/16	253.8	6.8	2.7%	29,291
12/15	217.5	5.3	2.5%	26,840
12/14	172.8	(0.4)	—	24,170
12/13	151.6	8.3	5.5%	21,222
Annual Growth	15.8%	(8.4%)	—	8.4%

2017 Year-End Financials

Debt ratio: 42.1%	No. of shares (mil.): 8.7
Return on equity: 14.4%	Dividends
Cash ($ mil.): —	Yield: 0.0%
Current ratio: 1.75	Payout: 153.8%
Long-term debt ($ mil.): 41.2	Market value ($ mil.): 140.0

	STOCK PRICE ($) FY Close	P/E High/Low	Earnings	PER SHARE ($) Dividends	Book Value
12/17	15.94	28 19	0.65	1.00	4.47
12/16	15.55	25 14	0.82	1.00	4.67
12/15	13.72	19 14	0.73	0.90	3.51
12/14	11.99	— —	(0.08)	0.15	2.48
Annual Growth	10.0%	— —	—	88.2%	21.7%

Bio-Techne Corp

Bio-Techne is a biotechnology research specialist. Through subsidiaries including Research and Diagnostic Systems (R&D Systems) Boston Biochem BiosPacific and Tocris the firm makes and distributes biological research supplies used by researchers around the globe to study cellular and immune system responses. Bio-Techne's products include cytokines (purified proteins that affect cell behavior) and diagnostic reagents (including antibodies and enzymes) as well as its Quantikine assay kits that determine the amount of cytokine in a given sample. R&D Systems also makes hematology controls and calibrators for blood analysis systems and sells them to equipment makers.

Operations

Bio-Techne operates through three reportable segments: Biotechnology Clinical Controls and Protein Platforms.

Bio-Techne's Biotechnology segment which makes products used by laboratories for both drug discovery research and clinical diagnostic purposes accounts for more than 70% of sales. Cytokines are a key product offering as commercial and institutional researchers are increasingly using the proteins as a swift and effective means of impacting the processes of cells and tissues. Subsidiary R&D Systems and its BiosPacific Boston Biochem and R&D Systems China as well as the R&D Systems Europe (UK) unit and its Tocris and R&D Systems (Germany) units are all included in the Biotechnology segment.

The newest segment established in 2014 is Protein Platforms (15% of sales). It develops and commercializes systems for protein analysis. The smallest Clinical Controls segment (13% of sales) develops and manufactures controls and calibrators for the global clinical market.

Altogether Bio-Techne sells more than 275000 products under such brands as Novus Biologicals Tocris Bioscience ProteinSimple R&D Systems BiosPacific CLINIQA and RNA Medical.

Geographic Reach

The US market accounts for more than half of Bio-Techne's annual revenues. Europe is the second-largest region accounting for about 30% of sales; the firm also conducts sales in Asia and other regions.

The company has operations in the US Europe and China.

Sales and Marketing

Bio-Techne sells its products through subsidiaries and third-party distributors worldwide. Its R&D Systems Europe and Tocris subsidiaries handle distribution efforts abroad and have a direct presence in France Germany and the UK. The company is growing its Asian distribution network which includes the R&D Systems China subsidiary. Thermo Fisher Scientific distributes Bio-Techne's R&D Systems Tocris and Boston Biochem products in the US and Canada.

Customers of the Biotechnology segment include researchers employed by pharma and biotech drug companies as well as universities and government agencies.

Bio-Techne has been increasing its advertising expenditures which totaled $4.1 million in fiscal 2015 (ended June). It spent $3.4 million in fiscal 2014 and $3.2 million in fiscal 2013.

Financial Performance

Bio-Techne's revenue which has been trending upward over the past five years increased 26% to $452.2 million in fiscal 2015 (ended June). Both the Biotechnology and Clinical Controls segment saw growth that year thanks to the recent acquisitions of Novus Biologicals and Bionostics as well as through continuing organic growth. (The newly formed Protein Platforms segment was no slouch either contributing 15% of the company's total earnings that year.)

After years of remaining relatively flat net income slipped a marginal 3% to $107.7 million in fiscal 2015. Despite the revenue growth higher operating expenses related to acquisitions as well as investments in resources and infrastructure ended up cutting into profits.

Cash flow from operations rose 2% to $139.4 million that year as cash inflows from accounts payable more than offset the decline in net income.

Strategy

Bio-Techne works to expand its product offerings through internal R&D efforts. The firm develops hundreds of new biological proteins antibodies and immunoassays each year. It also develops new hematology control technologies to keep up with changing technologies and markets as well as to provide efficient and high-quality offerings. In addition Bio-Techne grows its offerings through acquisitions partnerships and joint ventures.

The company has expanded the scope of its operations over the years by building up a collection of minority stakes in a number of drug developers and biotech companies working in complementary areas. It owns about 15% of drug developer ChemoCentryx which is researching chemokines a type of cytokine involved in immune response. Other investments have included blood filtration technology firm Hemerus Medical diagnostics developer Nephromics and biotechnology firm ACTGen.

In 2015 the company launched its first Simple Plex platform member Ella through its new Proteins Platform segment. It rebranded the CyPlex immunoassay platform acquired from CyVek under the name ProteinSimple.

Mergers and Acquisitions

In early 2018 Bio-Techne acquired Atlanta Biologicals and its Scientific Ventures affiliate. Atlanta Biologicals supplies cell culture cera media and reagents for life science research customers. The purchase helped Bio-Techne expand its cell culture and tissue regeneration capabilities.

Later that year the company bought Massachusetts-based Exosome Diagnostics which makes non-invasive liquid biopsy tests. The $250 million deal positions Bio-Techne for growth in that market as it expands its offerings for scientific researchers.

HISTORY

David Mundschenk founded biological products maker Research and Diagnostics Systems in 1976. In 1983 Mundschenk made a disastrous move buying heavily indebted French hematology instrument maker Hycel. R&D System's disgruntled board named Thomas Oland (at the time a consultant) CEO.

Enter TECHNE. Founded in 1981 by George Kline and Peter Peterson to pursue profitable acquisitions it went public in 1983 and in 1985 bought R&D Systems (which became an operating subsidiary of TECHNE) a sign of their confidence in Oland. TECHNE formed a biotechnology division in 1986 to produce and market human cytokines. In 1988 Kline resigned following a failed acquisition attempt by medical test kit maker Incstar.

In 1991 TECHNE bought Amgen's research reagent and diagnostic assay kit business and began selling Quantikine cytokine diagnostic kits. In 1993 it acquired what would become the company's R&D Europe unit. In 1995 the company debuted 10 new Quantikine immunoassay kits. TECHNE restructured its European research operation in 1997 pulling underperforming molecular biology products from

the market and refocusing on TECHNE's core cytokine-related products. The next year TECHNE bought Genzyme's research products business (antibodies proteins and research kits) for about $65 million.

As drug and biotechnology research became growth markets in the late 1990s and early 21st century TECHNE expanded through purchases. In 1999 it bought the reagent business and immunoassay patents of partner Cistron. The next year the firm increased its ownership in drug developer ChemoCentryx to almost 50% (reduced in 2001 to about 25% and then again in 2004 to 20%). TECHNE also acquired research and diagnostic market rights to all products developed by the firm. A similar deal was made in 2001 with functional genomics firm Discovery Genomics; that investment was not realized to TECHNE's satisfaction so it wrote off the investment in 2004.

It didn't wait long to fill the gap when it acquired the operations of Fortron Bio Science and Biospacific in 2005. The makers of antibodies and reagents had been partners since 1992 before they were integrated into TECHNE's R&D Systems division.

In 2007 the company set up a sales and distribution subsidiary in Shanghai to capitalize on the growing Chinese market. In 2007 TECHNE acquired minority stakes in two additional companies: diagnostics developer Nephromics and biotechnology firm ACTGen.

EXECUTIVES

SVP Clinical Controls, Marcel Veronneau, age 64, $210,000 total compensation
CFO and Vice President - Finance and Treasurer, Gregory J. (Greg) Melsen, age 67, $384,375 total compensation
President and CEO, Charles R. (Chuck) Kummeth, age 58
CIO, Fernando Bazan
Vice Chairman, Roger C. Lucas, age 75
Chairman, Robert V. Baumgartner, age 62
Auditors: KPMG LLP

LOCATIONS

HQ: Bio-Techne Corp
 614 McKinley Place N.E., Minneapolis, MN 55413
Phone: 612 379-8854
Web: www.bio-techne.com

PRODUCTS/OPERATIONS

2015 Sales by Segment

	$ mil.	% of total
Biotechnology	325.9	72
Protein Platforms	66.2	15
Clinical Controls	60.4	13
Adjustments	(0.3)	-
Total	**452.2**	**100**

Selected Products and Services

R&D Systems
 Activity assays and reagents
 Antibodies
 Biomarker testing service
 ELISAs
 ELISpot kits & FluoroSpot kits
 Flow cytometry and cell selection/detection
 General laboratory reagents
 Multiplex assays/arrays
 Proteins
 Stem cell and cell culture products
Tocris
 Caged compounds

Controlled substances
 Fluorescent probes
 Ligand sets
 Peptides
 Screening libraries
 Small molecules
 Toxins
Boston Biochem
 Affinity matrices/proteins
 Antibodies
 Buffers solutions and standards
 Fractions
 Inhibitors
 Kits
 Proteasome
 Substrate Proteins
 Ubiquitin

COMPETITORS

ABCAM PLC	Merck KGaA
Abbott Labs	Ortho-Clinical
BD Biosciences	Diagnostics
Beckman Coulter	Santa Cruz
Bio-Rad Labs	Biotechnology
Enzo Biochem	Sigma-Aldrich
GE Healthcare Medical	Streck
Diagnostics	Thermo Fisher
Life Technologies	Scientific
Corporation	
Marker Gene	
Technologies	

HISTORICAL FINANCIALS

Company Type: Public

Income Statement

FYE: June 30

	REVENUE ($ mil.)	NET INCOME ($ mil.)	NET PROFIT MARGIN	EMPLOYEES
06/18	642.9	126.1	19.6%	2,000
06/17	563.0	76.0	13.5%	1,800
06/16	499.0	104.4	20.9%	1,560
06/15	452.2	107.7	23.8%	1,356
06/14	357.7	110.9	31.0%	1,021
Annual Growth	**15.8%**	**3.3%**	**—**	**18.3%**

2018 Year-End Financials

Debt ratio: 21.2%	No. of shares (mil.): 37.6
Return on equity: 12.4%	Dividends
Cash ($ mil.): 121.9	Yield: 0.0%
Current ratio: 5.01	Payout: 38.6%
Long-term debt ($ mil.): 339.0	Market value ($ mil.): 5,564.0

	STOCK PRICE ($) FY Close	P/E High/Low	PER SHARE ($) Earnings	Dividends	Book Value
06/18	147.95	49 34	3.31	1.28	28.69
06/17	117.50	58 48	2.03	1.28	25.42
06/16	112.77	41 29	2.80	1.28	23.60
06/15	98.47	35 30	2.89	1.27	22.80
06/14	92.57	32 23	3.00	1.23	21.49
Annual Growth	**12.4%**	**— —**	**2.5%**	**1.0%**	**7.5%**

Biospecifics Technologies Corp.

BioSpecifics Technologies specifically uses collagenase (an enzyme that breaks the bonds of collagen) to treat a variety of skin-thickening diseases and conditions. Its current product named Xiaflex

(Xiapex in Europe) is an injectable collagenase that treats Dupuytren's disease and Peyronie's disease. It partners with Endo International to market Xiaflex in the US and with Swedish Orphan Biovitrum to market Xiapex in Europe and Eurasia. BioSpecifics is also testing collagenase treatments for human and canine lipoma (benign fatty tumor) frozen shoulder cellulite plantar fibromatosis and lateral hip fat.

Operations

Most of BioSpecific's revenues come from royalties and other payments it receives related to the development manufacturing and commercialization of its drug candidate.

Sales and Marketing

BioSpecifics partners with Endo International to sell Xiaflex in the US and Canada. Endo partners with Swedish Orphan Biovitrum to market Xiapex in the European Union; it partners with Asahi Kasei Pharma to sell Xiaflex in Japan and with Actelion Pharmaceuticals to commercialize the drug in Australia and New Zealand.

Financial Performance

BioSpecifics' revenue has been rising over the past few years. That revenue comes primarily from the company's licensing agreement with Endo International which markets Xiaflex in various markets around the world. Its net income has generally been on the rise as well.

In 2017 revenue increased 4% to $17.7 million. Royalties increased that year thanks to higher product sales and a slight price increase but that was partially offset by the absence of licensing fees and milestone payments.

Net income slipped 1% to $11.3 million in 2017. Primary factors of that decline were an increase in general and administrative expenses and a $7 million income tax provision made.

The company ended 2017 with $7.3 million in net cash $2.6 million more than it had at the end of 2016. Operating activities provided the company with $13.2 million in cash while investing activities used $10.4 million and financing activities used $0.2 million.

Strategy

BioSpecifics will continue to develop Xiaflex for Peyronie's disease frozen shoulder cellulite and lipomas while looking for additional indications where the drug would be useful. It sees potential for double-digit growth in Xiaflex sales as the vast majority of patients with Peyronie's disease and Dupuytren's contracture are currently not being treated. To reach those potential customers it has awareness educational and advertising campaigns in place.

BioSpecifics also sees promise in its drug to treat uterine fibroids which could help cut the number of hysterectomies performed.

The company relies heavily on the activities of Endo International which holds the right to develop manufacture market and sell its products worldwide. If Endo is not successful in these activities or if it decides to terminate the companies' agreement that would have a dramatic impact on BioSpecifics' revenue. Additionally Endo has faced some struggles lately and it cut its workforce by 18% in 2017.

EXECUTIVES

President, Thomas L. Wegman, age 63, $350,000
 total compensation
Auditors: EisnerAmper LLP

LOCATIONS

HQ: Biospecifics Technologies Corp.
 35 Wilbur Street, Lynbrook, NY 11563
Phone: 516 593-7000
Web: www.biospecifics.com

COMPETITORS

Cynosure   Pfizer
Genzyme

HISTORICAL FINANCIALS

Company Type: Public

Income Statement				FYE: December 31
	REVENUE ($ mil.)	NET INCOME ($ mil.)	NET PROFIT MARGIN	EMPLOYEES
12/17	27.4	11.3	41.3%	5
12/16	26.2	11.3	43.3%	5
12/15	22.7	9.6	42.3%	5
12/14	14.0	4.6	33.0%	5
12/13	14.4	5.2	36.5%	5
Annual Growth	17.4%	21.0%	—	0.0%

2017 Year-End Financials

Debt ratio: —
Return on equity: 18.3%
Cash ($ mil.): 7.3
Current ratio: 31.04
Long-term debt ($ mil.): —

No. of shares (mil.): 7.1
Dividends
 Yield: —
 Payout: —
Market value ($ mil.): 312.0

	STOCK PRICE ($) FY Close	P/E High/Low	PER SHARE ($) Earnings	Dividends	Book Value
12/17	43.33	37 27	1.55	0.00	9.39
12/16	55.70	35 19	1.56	0.00	7.86
12/15	42.97	49 26	1.32	0.00	6.48
12/14	38.62	57 29	0.66	0.00	4.50
12/13	21.67	28 18	0.76	0.00	3.51
Annual Growth	18.9%	— —	19.5%	—	27.9%

Black Knight Inc

Auditors: KPMG LLP

LOCATIONS

HQ: Black Knight Inc
 601 Riverside Avenue, Jacksonville, FL 32204
Phone: 904 854-5100
Web: www.bkfs.com

HISTORICAL FINANCIALS

Company Type: Public

Income Statement				FYE: December 31
	REVENUE ($ mil.)	NET INCOME ($ mil.)	NET PROFIT MARGIN	EMPLOYEES
12/17	1,051.6	182.3	17.3%	4,640
12/16	1,026.0	45.8	4.5%	4,480
12/15	930.7	20.0	2.1%	4,450
12/14	852.1	(107.1)	—	4,600
12/13	15.0	(3.0)	—	0
Annual Growth	189.4%	—	—	—

2017 Year-End Financials

Debt ratio: 39.2%
Return on equity: 14.1%
Cash ($ mil.): 16.2
Current ratio: 1.21
Long-term debt ($ mil.): 1,379.0

No. of shares (mil.): 151.4
Dividends
 Yield: —
 Payout: —
Market value ($ mil.): 6,686.0

	STOCK PRICE ($) FY Close	P/E High/Low	PER SHARE ($) Earnings	Dividends	Book Value
12/17	44.15	23 20	1.47	0.00	11.28
Annual Growth	—	— —	—	—	—

Blackbaud, Inc.

Blackbaud wants to make it easy to give. The company provides financial fundraising and administrative software for not-for-profit organizations and educational institutions. Software offerings include The Raiser's Edge for fundraising management Blackbaud Enterprise CRM for customer relationship management The Financial Edge for accounting and The Education Edge for managing school admissions registration and billing. Blackbaud has about 35000 customers in more than 60 countries including colleges environmental groups health and human services providers churches and animal welfare groups. The company generates most of its sales in the US.

Operations

Blackbaud generates 52% of its revenue from subscriptions to its cloud-based services to which the company has transitioned over the past few years. Maintenance and services revenue account for 24% and 21% respectively. Licensing and fee revenue for its on-premise software packages generated just 3% of revenue in 2015 and that was down 23% from 2014.

Geographic Reach

The US is its largest market accounting for 89% of sales. Canada and Europe each account for 4% of sales while the Australia generates 3%. Blackbaud has roughly 10 offices spanning the US and a handful of international offices in Australia Canada the Netherlands New Zealand and the UK.

Sales and Marketing

Blackbaud sells into three markets. The General Markets Business is the biggest generating 49% of revenue. It focuses on marketing sales delivery and support to emerging and mid-sized prospects and customers in North America.

The Enterprise Customer Business unit sells to and works wit large and strategic prospects and customers in North America. It accounts for 44% of sales.

The self-explanatory International Business unit delivered 7% of sales.

Financial Performance

Blackbaud has experienced strong revenue growth over the past decade with 2015 sales up 13% to reach $638 million. Subscriptions for its cloud-based software offerings rose 26%. The company also had double digit growth in its general markets and enterprise businesses. International sales fell 11%.

Increased spending on sales and marketing reduced profit 9% to $25.6 million in 2015 from 2014. It was the second straight year of declining profit as Blackbaud invests in sales and marketing to drive customers to its cloud products and increase market share.

Cash flow from operations rose to $114 million in 2015 from $102 million in 2014.

Strategy

Blackbaud is looking to expand its product offerings for the Internet. Online donations account for a growing percentage of charitable donations and marketing membership newsletters event management and volunteer recruitment can often be done over the Internet at a lower cost and a higher success rate. Its Sphere eMarketing Suite which facilitates online giving can be integrated into its most popular product The Raiser's Edge.

The latest product Blackbaud SKY is part of the company's cloud strategy. It combines infrastructure processes and integrated services (payments analytics email and online donations) to help customers achieve their goals.

The company's strategy also includes expanding geographically. Over the years it has established a Hong Kong office and a Mexico City office which joined other international offices in Canada the UK and Australia.

Mergers and Acquisitions

In 2017 Blackbaud acquired YourCause a developer of software for corporate philanthropy corporate social responsibility and employee engagement for about $157 million. The deal expands Blackbaud's offerings to software that helps companies address social causes. YourCause's customers include Fortune 500 companies and small businesses.

Blackbaud acquired JustGiving a crowd-source funding provider for charities for £95 million in 2017. The acquisition added a peer-to-peer fundraising source to Blackbaud's offerings. Peer-to-peer fundraising is a growing force in social and mobile arenas. Blackbaud rolled out a personal crowdfunding capability in the US. UK-based JustGiving also expanded Blackbaud's reach in that market.

EXECUTIVES

Senior Vice President New Business Development, Charlie Cumbaa

EVP and President General Markets, Kevin W. Mooney, age 60, $433,914 total compensation

EVP Human Resources, John J. Mistretta, age 63, $310,277 total compensation

CTO, Mary Beth Westmoreland

SVP and Chief Scientist, Charles L. (Chuck) Longfield, age 61, $226,667 total compensation

EVP Finance and Administration and CFO, Anthony W. (Tony) Boor, age 55, $447,615 total compensation

President and CEO, Michael P. (Mike) Gianoni, age 57, $679,526 total compensation

President and General Manager everydayhero, Jerry Needel

EVP and President Enterprise Business, Brian E. Boruff, age 58, $419,241 total compensation

EVP and Chief Products Officer, Kevin McDearis

President Higher Education Solutions Group, Tim Hill

President Healthcare Solutions Group, Russ Cobb

CIO, Todd Lant

SVP and President International Markets Group, Jerome Moisan

VICE PRESIDENT OF CUSTOMER SUCCESS, Kevin Knight

Vice President of Sales, Patrick Hodges

Vice President Sales, Kathy Gallagher

National Account Manager, Kim Blake

Vice President of Enterprise Sales, Doug Schaafsma

Senior Vice President Services and Development, Charles Cumbaa

Vice President Service Delivery Operations (Product), Stacy Williams

Vice President Distinguished Engineer, Michael Andrews

Vice President Cyber Security, Terence Runge

Vice President Corporate Communications and Branding, Amy Lucia

Vice President Strategic Consulting, June CFRE

Steve Served AS Senior Vice President, Steve Halleck

Chairman, Andrew M. Leitch, age 74

Board Member, Joyce Nelson

Treasurer Pay Services, Jim Cunningham

Auditors: PricewaterhouseCoopers LLP

LOCATIONS

HQ: Blackbaud, Inc.
65 Fairchild Street, Charleston, SC 29492
Phone: 843 216-6200 **Fax:** 843 216-6100
Web: www.blackbaud.com

PRODUCTS/OPERATIONS

2015 Sales

	$ mil.	% of total
General Markets Business Unit (GMBU)	313.9	49
Enterprise Customer Business Unit (ECBU)	279.9	44
International Business Unit (IBU)	42.0	7
Other	2.1	-
Total	**637.9**	**100**

2015 Sales

	$ mil.	% of total
Subscriptions	331.8	52
Maintenance	153.8	24
Services	132.9	21
Licenses	19.4	3
Total	**637.9**	**100**

Selected Products

Accounting software
 Blackbaud Forms (wealth identification)
 The Financial Edge (not-for-profit accounting)
Analytical services
 Prospect Management (prospect management and research)
 Wealth & Affluence Indicators (wealth identification and information)
Business intelligence software
 Altru (general admissions management)
 The Patron Edge (ticketing management for admissions)
Customer relationship management
 Blackbaud Enterprise CRM
 eTapestry
Education administration software
 The Education Edge (admissions registrar business office and development office software)
 Small Colleges (suite for colleges under 300 students)
 Student Billing
 Total Campus Solution (suite for colleges under 2000 students)
Fundraising management software
 The Raiser's Edge (fundraising management system)

COMPETITORS

Acorn Systems	Microsoft
Advanced Solutions	Oracle
Auctionpay	Sage Software
Campus Management Corp	SunGard
Intuit	salesforce.com

MicroEdge

HISTORICAL FINANCIALS
Company Type: Public

Income Statement   FYE: December 31

	REVENUE ($ mil.)	NET INCOME ($ mil.)	NET PROFIT MARGIN	EMPLOYEES
12/17	788.3	65.9	8.4%	3,182
12/16	730.8	41.5	5.7%	3,156
12/15	637.9	25.6	4.0%	3,095
12/14	564.4	28.2	5.0%	3,033
12/13	503.8	30.4	6.0%	2,666
Annual Growth	**11.8%**	**21.3%**	**—**	**4.5%**

2017 Year-End Financials

Debt ratio: 24.9%	No. of shares (mil.): 48.0
Return on equity: 23.7%	Dividends
Cash ($ mil.): 29.8	Yield: 0.0%
Current ratio: 0.81	Payout: 34.7%
Long-term debt ($ mil.): 429.6	Market value ($ mil.): 4,543.0

	STOCK PRICE ($) FY Close	P/E High/Low	PER SHARE ($) Earnings	Dividends	Book Value
12/17	94.49	74 44	1.38	0.48	6.38
12/16	64.00	79 57	0.88	0.48	5.21
12/15	65.86	121 75	0.55	0.48	4.48
12/14	43.26	72 47	0.62	0.48	4.01
12/13	37.65	62 34	0.67	0.48	3.50
Annual Growth	**25.9%**	**— —**	**19.8%**	**(0.0%)**	**16.2%**

Blackstone Mortgage Trust Inc

Capital Trust thinks investing in commercial mortgages is a capital idea. The self-managed real estate investment trust (REIT) originates underwrites and invests in commercial real estate assets on its own behalf and for other investors. Its portfolio includes first mortgage and bridge loans mezzanine loans and collateralized mortgage-backed securities. Subsidiary CT Investment Management which the company is selling manages five private equity funds and a separate account for third parties. Most Capital Trust's assets are related to US properties but the REIT does make occasional investments in international instruments.

In the aftermath of the subprime mortgage crisis wherein the credit markets slowed and property values fell Capital Trust cut back on its own origination and investment activities. In 2011 the REIT restructured its recourse debt obligations a move that included the transfer of a substantial portion of its assets to a newly formed subsidiary CT Legacy REIT. Investment firm Five Mile Capital Partners acquired nearly a quarter of the unit and ownership of almost another quarter was transferred to lenders; Capital Trust holds a majority. In 2012 Capital Trust agreed to sell CT Investment Management to Blackstone for $20 million; Blackstone will also purchase an 18% stake in Capital Trust.

Co-founder John Klopp retired as the company's CEO in late 2009. He was succeeded by longtime COO Stephen Plavin. Billionaire property mogul Samuel Zell has served as the company's chairman since 1997. He serves in the same capacity at several other firms as well including Equity Group Investments Equity LifeStyle Properties and Equity Residential.

W. R. Berkley a holding company involved mainly in insurance owns around 17% of Capital Trust.

EXECUTIVES

Vice President, Robert Holder
Auditors: DELOITTE & TOUCHE LLP

LOCATIONS

HQ: Blackstone Mortgage Trust Inc
345 Park Avenue, 42nd Floor, New York, NY 10154
Phone: 212 655-0220
Web: www.bxmt.com

COMPETITORS

Annaly Capital Management	MFA Financial
Arbor Realty Trust	RAIT Financial Trust
Drive Shack	Redwood Trust
Institutional Financial Markets	iStar Financial Inc

HISTORICAL FINANCIALS

Company Type: Public

Income Statement   FYE: December 31

	REVENUE ($ mil.)	NET INCOME ($ mil.)	NET PROFIT MARGIN	EMPLOYEES
12/17	537.9	217.6	40.5%	0
12/16	497.9	238.3	47.9%	0
12/15	410.6	196.8	47.9%	0
12/14	184.7	90.0	48.7%	0
12/13	53.1	15.0	28.3%	0
Annual Growth	78.4%	95.1%	—	—

2017 Year-End Financials

Debt ratio: 69.4%
Return on equity: 8.0%
Cash ($ mil.): 69.6
Current ratio: 1.39
Long-term debt ($ mil.): 7,120.1
No. of shares (mil.): 107.8
Dividends
  Yield: 0.0%
  Payout: 109.2%
Market value ($ mil.): 3,472.0

	STOCK PRICE ($) FY Close	P/E High/Low	Earnings	PER SHARE ($) Dividends	Book Value
12/17	32.18	14 13	2.27	2.48	26.98
12/16	30.07	12 9	2.53	2.48	26.38
12/15	26.76	13 11	2.41	2.28	26.60
12/14	29.14	16 14	1.86	1.98	25.15
12/13	27.13	4 0	8.10	0.72	24.33
Annual Growth	4.4%	— —	(27.2%)	36.2%	2.6%

Blue Hills Bancorp Inc

Auditors: Wolf & Company, P.C.

LOCATIONS

HQ: Blue Hills Bancorp Inc
500 River Ridge Drive, Norwood, MA 02062
Phone: 617 360-6520
Web: www.bluehillsbancorp.com

HISTORICAL FINANCIALS

Company Type: Public

Income Statement   FYE: December 31

	ASSETS ($ mil.)	NET INCOME ($ mil.)	INCOME AS % OF ASSETS	EMPLOYEES
12/17	2,668.5	16.4	0.6%	237
12/16	2,469.6	8.6	0.4%	228
12/15	2,114.3	7.2	0.3%	209
12/14	1,728.1	(0.1)	—	202
12/13	1,314.2	2.6	0.2%	147
Annual Growth	19.4%	57.7%	—	12.7%

2017 Year-End Financials

Return on assets: 0.6%
Return on equity: 4.2%
Long-term debt ($ mil.): —
No. of shares (mil.): 26.8
Sales ($ mil): 101.8
Dividends
  Yield: 0.0%
  Payout: 89.5%
Market value ($ mil.): 539.0

	STOCK PRICE ($) FY Close	P/E High/Low	Earnings	PER SHARE ($) Dividends	Book Value
12/17	20.10	32 24	0.67	0.60	14.83
12/16	18.75	54 38	0.35	0.11	14.46
12/15	15.31	59 46	0.28	0.04	14.00
12/14	13.58	— —	(0.00)	0.00	14.46
Annual Growth	14.0%	— —	—	—	0.8%

Boot Barn Holdings Inc

Auditors: DELOITTE & TOUCHE LLP

LOCATIONS

HQ: Boot Barn Holdings Inc
15345 Barranca Pkwy., Irvine, CA 92618
Phone: 949 453-4400
Web: www.bootbarn.com

HISTORICAL FINANCIALS

Company Type: Public

Income Statement   FYE: March 31

	REVENUE ($ mil.)	NET INCOME ($ mil.)	NET PROFIT MARGIN	EMPLOYEES
03/18*	677.9	28.8	4.3%	3,500
04/17	629.8	14.2	2.3%	3,000
03/16	569.0	9.8	1.7%	2,900
03/15	402.6	13.7	3.4%	1,700
03/14	345.8	5.3	1.6%	1,800
Annual Growth	18.3%	52.2%	—	18.1%

*Fiscal year change

2018 Year-End Financials

Debt ratio: 36.7%
Return on equity: 14.6%
Cash ($ mil.): 9.0
Current ratio: 1.60
Long-term debt ($ mil.): 194.4
No. of shares (mil.): 27.3
Dividends
  Yield: —
  Payout: —
Market value ($ mil.): 484.0

	STOCK PRICE ($) FY Close	P/E High/Low	Earnings	PER SHARE ($) Dividends	Book Value
03/18*	17.73	18 6	1.05	0.00	7.86
04/17	9.89	31 11	0.53	0.00	6.77
03/16	9.34	89 15	0.37	0.00	6.13
03/15	23.21	46 30	0.54	0.00	5.51
Annual Growth	(8.6%)	— —	24.8%	—	12.5%

*Fiscal year change

Braemar Hotels & Resorts Inc

Hotels and motels nsk

EXECUTIVES

Attorney, David A Brooks
Auditors: BDO USA, LLP

LOCATIONS

HQ: Braemar Hotels & Resorts Inc
14185 Dallas Parkway, Suite 1100, Dallas, TX 75254
Phone: 972 490-9600
Web: www.ahpreit.com

HISTORICAL FINANCIALS

Company Type: Public

Income Statement   FYE: December 31

	REVENUE ($ mil.)	NET INCOME ($ mil.)	NET PROFIT MARGIN	EMPLOYEES
12/17	414.0	23.0	5.6%	0
12/16	405.8	19.3	4.8%	0
12/15	349.5	(6.7)	—	0
12/14	307.3	1.9	0.6%	0
12/13	233.5	(11.7)	—	0
Annual Growth	15.4%			

2017 Year-End Financials

Debt ratio: 57.6%
Return on equity: 5.3%
Cash ($ mil.): 137.5
Current ratio: 3.24
Long-term debt ($ mil.): 820.9
No. of shares (mil.): 32.1
Dividends
  Yield: 0.0%
  Payout: 125.4%
Market value ($ mil.): 313.0

	STOCK PRICE ($) FY Close	P/E High/Low	Earnings	PER SHARE ($) Dividends	Book Value
12/17	9.73	28 17	0.51	0.64	15.18
12/16	13.65	28 17	0.55	0.46	14.40
12/15	14.50	— —	(0.34)	0.35	14.09
12/14	17.16	233 185	0.07	0.20	11.40
12/13	18.20	— —	(0.73)	0.05	9.05
Annual Growth	(14.5%)	— —	—	89.1%	13.8%

Bridge Bancorp, Inc. (Bridgehampton, NY)

Bridge Bancorp wants you to cross over to its subsidiary The Bridgehampton National Bank which operates about 25 branches on eastern Long Island New York. Founded in 1910 the bank offers traditional deposit services to area individuals small businesses and municipalities including checking savings and money market accounts and CDs. Deposits are invested primarily in mortgages which account for some 80% of the bank's loan portfolio. Title insurance services are available through bank subsidiary Bridge Abstract; wealth management services include financial planning estate administration and trustee services. Bridge Bancorp bought Hamptons State Bank in 2011 to fortify its presence on Long Island.

Geographic Reach

Bridgehampton New York-based Bridge Bancorp's market area is Suffolk County in eastern Long Island. The bank serves customers in the towns of East Hampton Southampton Southold and Riverhead. It also has branches in Brookhaven Babylon and Islip.

Financial Performance

The bank reported net income of $13.1 million in 2013 versus $12.8 million in 2012. Revenue increased 3% to $67.3 million on rising net interest income. Bridge Bancorp had total assets of $1.9 billion in 2013 an increase of 17% versus the prior year. Total deposits rose 9% in 2013 versus 2012 to $1.5 billion.

Mergers and Acquisitions

In February 2014 Bridge Bancorp acquired FNBNY Bancorp and its wholly-owned subsidiary the First National Bank of New York and converted its three branches to Bridgehampton National Bank (BNB) branches. The purchase expanded BNB's reach into Nassau County. Following the acquisition Bridge Bancorp's assets totaled approximately $2.1 billion with loans of approximately $1.1 billion and deposits of $1.7 billion with 26 branches throughout Long Island and one loan production office in Manhattan.

EXECUTIVES

President and CEO, Kevin M. O'Connor, age 55, $300,000 total compensation
EVP and Chief Lending Officer, Kevin L. Santacroce, $180,000 total compensation
SVP and CIO Bridgehampton National Bank, Thomas H. Simson, $175,000 total compensation
President CEO and Director, Kevin OConnor
Chief Financial Officer, Adam Hall
EVP and Chief Retail Banking Officer, James J. Manseau, $235,000 total compensation
Vice Chairman, Dennis A. Suskind, age 75
Chairman, Marcia Z. Hefter, age 74
Auditors: Crowe Horwath LLP

LOCATIONS

HQ: Bridge Bancorp, Inc. (Bridgehampton, NY)
2200 Montauk Highway, Bridgehampton, NY 11932
Phone: 631 537-1000
Web: www.bridgenb.com

COMPETITORS

Bank of America	JPMorgan Chase
Bank of New York Mellon	Suffolk Bancorp

HISTORICAL FINANCIALS

Company Type: Public

Income Statement — FYE: December 31

	ASSETS ($ mil.)	NET INCOME ($ mil.)	INCOME AS % OF ASSETS	EMPLOYEES
12/17	4,430.0	20.5	0.5%	480
12/16	4,054.5	35.4	0.9%	477
12/15	3,781.9	21.1	0.6%	433
12/14	2,288.6	13.7	0.6%	348
12/13	1,896.7	13.0	0.7%	271
Annual Growth	23.6%	11.9%	—	15.4%

2017 Year-End Financials

Return on assets: 0.4%	Dividends
Return on equity: 4.9%	Yield: 0.0%
Long-term debt ($ mil.): —	Payout: 88.4%
No. of shares (mil.): 19.7	Market value ($ mil.): 690.0
Sales ($ mil): 167.9	

	STOCK PRICE ($) FY Close	P/E High/Low	Earnings	PER SHARE ($) Dividends	Book Value
12/17	35.00	37 29	1.04	0.92	21.78
12/16	37.90	19 13	2.00	0.92	21.36
12/15	30.43	22 17	1.43	0.92	19.62
12/14	26.75	23 20	1.18	0.92	15.03
12/13	26.00	19 14	1.36	0.92	14.10
Annual Growth	7.7%	— —	(6.5%)	(0.0%)	11.5%

Bright Horizons Family Solutions, Inc

Child day care services nsk

EXECUTIVES

Senior Vice President of Operations, Jackie Legg
Senior Vice President of Strategic Planning, Ann Pickens
Senior Vice President of Business Operations, Dave Shaby
Chief Executive Officer Director; Executive Chairman, Roger H Brown
Vice President Education and Training, Linda Whitehead
Vice President Client Relations, Yvonne Lynch
Vice President Information Technology, Anya Anderson
Division Vice President Of Operations, Cynthia Hartzel
Vice President, Alan Robins
Senior Vice President Back Up Care Services, Mandy Berman
Vice President Information Security and Risk Manager, Javed Ikbal
Vice President Client Solutions Back up Centers, Kevin Brown
Vice President Customer Acquisition, Christine Healy
Vice President Sales, Audrey Elisha

Vice President Client Services, Bruce Karten
Division Vice President, Sheila Niehaus
Vice President, Joanne Urso
Auditors: DELOITTE & TOUCHE LLP

LOCATIONS

HQ: Bright Horizons Family Solutions, Inc
200 Talcott Avenue South, Watertown, MA 02472
Phone: 617 673-8000
Web: www.brighthorizons.com

HISTORICAL FINANCIALS

Company Type: Public

Income Statement — FYE: December 31

	REVENUE ($ mil.)	NET INCOME ($ mil.)	NET PROFIT MARGIN	EMPLOYEES
12/17	1,740.9	156.9	9.0%	31,600
12/16	1,569.8	94.7	6.0%	31,200
12/15	1,458.4	93.9	6.4%	26,000
12/14	1,353.0	72.0	5.3%	25,400
12/13	1,218.7	12.6	1.0%	25,000
Annual Growth	9.3%	87.8%	—	6.0%

2017 Year-End Financials

Debt ratio: 47.9%	No. of shares (mil.): 58.0
Return on equity: 21.8%	Dividends
Cash ($ mil.): 23.2	Yield: —
Current ratio: 0.42	Payout: —
Long-term debt ($ mil.): 1,046.0	Market value ($ mil.): 5,453.0

	STOCK PRICE ($) FY Close	P/E High/Low	Earnings	PER SHARE ($) Dividends	Book Value
12/17	94.00	36 26	2.59	0.00	12.91
12/16	70.02	45 38	1.55	0.00	11.68
12/15	66.80	45 29	1.50	0.00	12.13
12/14	47.01	43 33	1.07	0.00	12.20
12/13	36.74	191138	0.20	0.00	13.62
Annual Growth	26.5%	— —	89.7%	—	(1.3%)

Brown & Brown Inc

Insurance agency Brown & Brown (B&B) provides property/casualty life and health insurance and risk management services through its retail division mainly to commercial clients. Its national programs division designs customized programs for such niche clients as dentists lawyers optometrists and towing operators. Its wholesale brokerage unit distributes excess and surplus commercial insurance as well as reinsurance to retail agents. B&B's services segment provides self-insured and third-party administrator services. The company has 240 offices in about 40 states as well as offices in London the Cayman Islands and Bermuda.

Operations

B&B's retail segment accounts for about half of revenue while its national programs segment accounts for about a quarter of sales. The wholesale brokerage and service segments round out the firm's earnings.

Geographic Reach

B&B's largest market is Florida where it operates more than 40 agency or brokerage locations. The firm also has significant operations in California Georgia Illinois Indiana Kansas Kentucky Massachusetts Michigan New Jersey New York North Carolina Oregon Pennsylvania Texas Virginia and Washington. Although B&B has expanded its operations to serve the UK market the US still accounts for nearly all of its revenues.

Sales and Marketing

B&B's network of agency offices sells insurance policies that are underwritten by third-party carriers. B&B's retail division employs more than 3900 agents and receives commission fees on policy sales to customers including commercial businesses government agencies trade groups and individual consumers. The national programs division sells niche policies to businesses and professionals through independent agents and through B&B's retail offices. The wholesale brokerage division sells commercial policies to independent brokers and agents (as well as some B&B retail offices).

Financial Performance

B&B's revenues have grown steadily over the past decade (with the exception of 2009 when the insurance industry experienced a downturn due to economic conditions). In 2015 revenue rose 5% to $1.7 billion as all segments saw growth — primarily from higher commissions and fees new business and new client advocacy services. Net income has also been on the rise with the exception of 2014 when B&B acquired flood insurance carrier Wright. Profits resumed their climb in 2015 growing 18% to $243 million thanks to the higher revenue plus gains from disposals. This was partially offset by higher operating expenses such as salaries and benefits.

Cash flow from operations increased 7% to $412 million in 2015.

Strategy

B&B has a long-term growth strategy that is focused on acquisitions — it has acquired the assets or operations of more than 470 firms since 1993. Acquisitions target a range of growth areas including retail and wholesale brokerage and employee benefit plan development. In 2015 the company acquired 13 smaller firms for a combined cost of $136 million; in 2014 it completed 10 acquisitions for a combined $721.9 million.

The company prefers to acquire agencies whose principal executives intend to stay after the sale and whose corporate cultures are a good fit. Following its acquisitions B&B tends to leave things in place but lifts some administrative duties off of an agency freeing up its agents to sell more.

Mergers and Acquisitions

B&B is a highly acquisitive firm using purchases of other businesses to expand into new markets. For example it acquired 19 companies in 2018 before announcing its largest-ever deal to buy Hays Companies' insurance operations. That purchase will add some 700 team members and more than 30 locations to its retail network.

EXECUTIVES

COO and Regional President, Linda S. Downs, age 68, $475,000 total compensation
Regional President and Chief Acquisitions Officer, J. Scott Penny, age 51, $308,844 total compensation
EVP and People Officer, Richard Freebourn, age 70
Regional EVP, Sam R. Boone, age 64
President Peachtree Special Risk Brokers, Anthony T. (Tony) Strianese, age 56, $450,000 total compensation

Retail Division President, Charles H. (Charlie) Lydecker, $450,000 total compensation
EVP CFO and Treasurer, R. Andrew Watts
Chief Information Officer, B. Carl Owen
President and CEO, J. Powell Brown, $565,000 total compensation
National Programs Division President, Chris Walker
Vice President New Business Marketing Manager, Julie Aai
Executive Vice President National Benefits Leader, Pattysue Rauh
Vice President, Nancy Scott
Vice President Claims P And C, Janice Alexander
Executive Vice President, Aaron Phillips
Vice President Account Executive, Martin Michelle
Regional Vice President, P Brown
Vice President, Gayle Donaldson-reitz
Vice President, Matthew Seese
Senior Vice President, Vince Castro
Chairman, J. Hyatt Brown, age 80
Auditors: DELOITTE & TOUCHE LLP

LOCATIONS

HQ: Brown & Brown Inc
220 South Ridgewood Avenue, Daytona Beach, FL 32114
Phone: 386 252-9601
Web: www.bbinsurance.com

PRODUCTS/OPERATIONS

2015 Sales

	% of total
Core commissions and fees	96
Profit-sharing contingent commissions	3
Guaranteed supplemental commissions	1
Investment income	-
Other income net	-
Total	**100**

2015 Sales

% of total	$ mil
Retail	52
National Programs	26
Wholesale Brokerage	13
Services	9
Other	-
Total	**100**

Selected Products and Services
Personal Insurance
Business Insurance
Employee Benefits
Wholesale Brokerage
Services Division
Financial Services
Trade Credit
Surety Bonds
Risk Management

COMPETITORS

Alexander Forbes	Gallagher
All Risks	Hub International
Alliant	IMA Financial Group
Aon	Marsh & McLennan
Barney & Barney	NIA group
Bollinger Inc.	Rutherfoord
Bolton & Company	Sedgwick Claims
Burns & Wilcox	Management Services
CRC Insurance	The Lockton Companies
Campbell Group	USI
Crawford & Company	Willis Towers Watson

HISTORICAL FINANCIALS

Company Type: Public

Income Statement   FYE: December 31

	REVENUE ($ mil.)	NET INCOME ($ mil.)	NET PROFIT MARGIN	EMPLOYEES
12/17	1,881.3	399.6	21.2%	8,491
12/16	1,766.6	257.4	14.6%	3,981
12/15	1,660.5	243.3	14.7%	7,807
12/14	1,575.8	206.9	13.1%	7,591
12/13	1,363.2	217.1	15.9%	6,992
Annual Growth	8.4%	16.5%	—	5.0%

2017 Year-End Financials

Debt ratio: 16.9%	No. of shares (mil.): 276.2
Return on equity: 16.1%	Dividends
Cash ($ mil.): 573.3	Yield: 0.0%
Current ratio: 1.13	Payout: 19.7%
Long-term debt ($ mil.): 856.1	Market value ($ mil.): 14,214.0

	STOCK PRICE ($) FY Close	P/E High/Low	PER SHARE ($) Earnings	Dividends	Book Value
12/17	51.46	36 29	1.41	0.28	9.35
12/16	44.86	49 31	0.91	0.25	8.42
12/15	32.10	40 36	0.85	0.23	7.73
12/14	32.91	47 40	0.71	0.21	7.37
12/13	31.39	45 34	0.74	0.19	6.90
Annual Growth	13.2%	— —	17.4%	10.7%	7.9%

BRT Apartments Corp

EXECUTIVES

SVP, Israel Rosenzweig, age 64
SVP, Matthew J. Gould, age 52
VP and CFO, George E. Zweier, age 46, $175,134 total compensation
SVP and General Counsel, Mark H. Lundy, age 49, $181,020 total compensation
SVP and Secretary, Simeon Brinberg, age 75, $133,934 total compensation
President CEO and Trustee, Jeffrey A. Gould, age 46, $442,890 total compensation
Chairman, Fredric H. Gould, age 76
SVP Finance, David W. Kalish, age 69
EVP, Mitchell K. Gould, $247,360 total compensation
Director Marketing, Dana Canavan
Senior Underwriter, William O'Hagen
VP, Lonnie Halpern
President CEO and Trustee, Jeffrey A. Gould, age 46
Trustee, Kenneth F. Bernstein, age 50
Trustee, Jeffrey G. Rubin, age 44
Trustee, Gary Hurand, age 65
Trustee, Louis C. (Lou) Grassi, age 56
Trustee, Alan H. Ginsburg, age 73
Trustee, Jonathan H. (Jon) Simon, age 46
Trustee, Elie Weiss, age 39
Auditors: BDO USA LLP

LOCATIONS

HQ: BRT Apartments Corp
60 Cutter Mill Road, Great Neck, NY 11021
Phone: 516 466-3100
Web: www.brtrealty.com

COMPETITORS

COMPETITORS

CIFC	Drive Shack
CapLease	RAIT Financial Trust
Capital Trust	iStar Financial Inc

HISTORICAL FINANCIALS

Company Type: Public

Income Statement   FYE: September 30

	REVENUE ($ mil.)	NET INCOME ($ mil.)	NET PROFIT MARGIN	EMPLOYEES
09/18	119.6	23.7	19.9%	13
09/17	105.7	13.6	12.9%	12
09/16	94.2	31.2	33.2%	12
09/15	82.5	(2.3)	—	13
09/14	66.4	(9.4)	—	0
Annual Growth	15.9%	—	—	—

2018 Year-End Financials

Debt ratio: 71.9%	No. of shares (mil.): 15.0
Return on equity: 13.0%	Dividends
Cash ($ mil.): 27.3	Yield: 0.0%
Current ratio: 2.13	Payout: 48.4%
Long-term debt ($ mil.): 829.4	Market value ($ mil.): 181.0

	STOCK PRICE ($) FY Close	P/E High/Low		PER SHARE ($) Earnings	Dividends	Book Value
09/18	12.04	9	6	1.61	0.78	13.16
09/17	10.72	11	8	0.97	0.18	12.45
09/16	8.00	4	2	2.23	0.00	11.43
09/15	7.09	—	—	(0.17)	0.00	9.13
09/14	7.50	—	—	(0.66)	0.00	9.53
Annual Growth	12.6%	—	—	—	—	8.4%

Bryn Mawr Bank Corp

Bryn Mawr Bank Corporation stands atop a "big hill" in Pennsylvania. Bryn Mawr (which in Welsh translates as "big hill") is the bank holding company for Bryn Mawr Trust operates some 20 offices in Pennsylvania and Delaware. The bank offers traditional services as checking and savings accounts CDs mortgages and business and consumer loans in addition to insurance products equipment leasing investment management retirement planning tax planning and preparation and trust services. Founded in 1889 Bryn Mawr boasts more than $5 billion of assets under administration and management.

Operations

Bryn Mawr operates two business segments. Its Banking segment which makes up two-thirds of overall business provides commercial and retail banking services. The Wealth Management division which includes the Bryn Mawr Trust of Delaware and Lau Associates businesses makes up about one-third of the bank's overall revenue and provides a variety of custody investment management tax and brokerage services.

Broadly speaking the company generated 60% of its total revenue from interest and fees on loans and leases in 2014 while another 30% of its total revenue came from fees for wealth management services.

Bryn Mawr operated 19 full-service branches seven Life Care Community Offices five wealth offices and a full-service insurance agency in 2014.

Geographic Reach

The bank corporation has branches and offices across Montgomery Delaware Chester and Dauphin counties in Pennsylvania and New Castle county in Delaware.

Financial Performance

Bryn Mawr has enjoyed rising revenues and profits over the past several years reflecting strong growth in its loan business and wealth management business.

The bank's revenue rose by 4% to a record $131.23 million in 2014 mostly thanks to higher interest income from loans as it grew its loan assets by $153.9 million during the year. The company's Wealth Management services fees also grew by 5% thanks to new business acquisitions and solid market appreciation during the year which resulted in higher assets under management.

Higher revenue and a strong grip on costs in 2014 also boosted Bryn Mawr's net income by 14% to a record $27.84 million. Despite higher earnings the bank's operating cash declined by 6% to $37.68 million for the year as it made less in net proceeds from the sales of its loans held for resale.

Strategy

Bryn Mawr Bank Corporation continued to push its acquisition strategy in 2015 designed to broaden its service offerings boost its loan and deposit business and expand its branch network. The bank looks to strategically acquire smaller insurance businesses small to mid-sized banks and community banks wealth management companies and advisory and planning services firm that complement its existing businesses.

Besides acquisitions the company has been growing its wealth management business through marketing campaigns to raise brand awareness.

Mergers and Acquisitions

In April 2015 to grow its wealth management business the bank purchased Robert J. McAllister Agency which provides insurance and risk management solutions to individuals and businesses in the Philadelphia region.

In January 2015 Bryn Mawr acquired the Continental Bank Holdings and its Plymouth Meeting-based flagship Continental Bank adding some $433 million in loans and $480 million in deposits along with 10 full-service branches located in key markets in Montgomery Chester and Philadelphia counties.

In October 2014 Bryn Mawr bought the Rosemont Pennsylvania-based insurance agency Powers Craft Parker & Beard Inc. (PCPB) for $7 million to enhance its own insurance business among individuals and commercial clients.

In 2012 as part of a strategy to build its wealth management division the company acquired Davidson Trust adding some $1 billion in assets under management.

Company Background

In 2011 the company bought the private wealth management business of Hershey Trust Company for more than $14.5 million; that deal brought in approximately $1 billion of assets under management. In 2010 the company purchased First Keystone Financial adding about 10 bank branches in Pennsylvania and some $2.7 billion in trust and investment assets.

EXECUTIVES

EVP and COO, Alison E. Gers, age 60, $250,000 total compensation

EVP and Chief Lending Officer Bryn Mawr Trust, Joseph G. (Joe) Keefer, age 59, $238,500 total compensation

President and CEO, Francis J. Leto, age 58, $310,000 total compensation

EVP Secretary and Chief Risk Officer, Geoffrey L. Halberstadt

CFO and Treasurer Bryn Mawr Bank Corporation; EVP CFO and Treasurer Bryn Mawr Bank, Michael W. (Mike) Harrington, age 55

EVP Wealth Management Division, Harry R. Madeira

Senior Vice President of Wealth Management Division, Rande Whitham

Vice President, John Metz

Senior Vice President, Richard Gentile

Vice President Construction Real Estate, Michelle Wilson

Vice President, Martha Hilty

Vice President, John Roman

Senior Vice President Market Leader, Tony Poluch

Vice President Real Estate Lending, Kristin Reese

Vice President Wealth Management Division, J Keefer-Hugill

VICE PRESIDENT, Brian Snyder

Vice President Small Business Account Lending Division, Douglas Whalen

Vice President, Drew Smith

Vice President Relationship Manager, Shawn Williams

Vice President Director of Investment Services, Bryan Andersen

Vice President Mortgage Division, Anne Stulpin

VICE PRESIDENT COMPTROLLERS AND FINANCE, Maral Kaloustian

Vice President Mortgage Division, Patrick McGowan

Senior Vice President Managing Partner, Robert McLaughlin

Assistant Vice President Service Manager Chadds Ford Branch, Leslie Paynter

Chairman, Britton H. Murdoch

Assistant Treasurer, Linda McLaughlin

Auditors: KPMG LLP

LOCATIONS

HQ: Bryn Mawr Bank Corp
801 Lancaster Avenue, Bryn Mawr, PA 19010
Phone: 610 525-1700
Web: www.bmtc.com

PRODUCTS/OPERATIONS

2014 Sales

	$ mil.	% of total
Interest		
Interest & fees on loans & leases	78.5	60
Investment securities	4.2	3
Cash & cash equivalents	0.2	-
Noninterest		
Fees for wealth management services	36.7	30
Service charges on deposits	2.6	2
Net gain on sale of residential mortgages	1.8	1
Loan Servicing and other fees	1.8	1
Other	5.4	3
Total	131.2	100

Selected Subsidiaries

Bryn Mawr Advisors Inc.
Bryn Mawr Asset Management Inc.
Bryn Mawr Brokerage Co. Inc.
Bryn Mawr Financial Services Inc.
Bryn Mawr Trust Company of Delaware
Joseph W. Roskos Co. Inc.
Lau Associates LLC
The Bryn Mawr Trust Company

BMT Leasing Inc.
BMT Mortgage Services Inc.
BMT Settlement Services Inc.
Insurance Counsellors of Bryn Mawr Inc.

COMPETITORS

Alliance Bancorp of	Royal Bancshares
Pennsylvania	Sovereign Bank
Firstrust Savings Bank	Wells Fargo
PNC Financial	

HISTORICAL FINANCIALS

Company Type: Public

Income Statement   FYE: December 31

	ASSETS ($ mil.)	NET INCOME ($ mil.)	INCOME AS % OF ASSETS	EMPLOYEES
12/17	4,449.7	23.0	0.5%	680
12/16	3,421.5	36.0	1.1%	544
12/15	3,031.0	16.7	0.6%	530
12/14	2,246.5	27.8	1.2%	444
12/13	2,061.6	24.4	1.2%	432
Annual Growth	21.2%	(1.5%)	—	12.0%

2017 Year-End Financials

Return on assets: 0.5%	Dividends
Return on equity: 5.0%	Yield: 0.0%
Long-term debt ($ mil.): —	Payout: 65.1%
No. of shares (mil.): 20.1	Market value ($ mil.): 891.0
Sales ($ mil): 188.6	

	STOCK PRICE ($) FY Close	P/E High/Low	PER SHARE ($) Earnings	Dividends	Book Value
12/17	44.20	34 28	1.32	0.86	26.23
12/16	42.15	20 11	2.12	0.82	22.50
12/15	28.72	33 29	0.94	0.78	21.42
12/14	31.30	15 13	2.01	0.74	17.83
12/13	30.18	17 12	1.80	0.69	16.84
Annual Growth	10.0%	— —	(7.5%)	5.7%	11.7%

BSB Bancorp Inc. (MD)

BSB Bancorp is the holding company for Belmont Savings Bank a community back with about half a dozen branches in southeastern Middlesex County in the suburbs of Boston. Serving local businesses and individuals the $2 billion-asset bank offers checking savings money market retirement accounts and a variety of lending products. Almost 50% of its loan portfolio is made up of one-to-four family residential mortgages while commercial real estate loans make up another 30%. While Belmont Savings Bank traces its roots back to 1885 BSB Bancorp was formed in 2011 to take the company public.

Operations

BSB Bancorp mostly originates one-to-four family residential mortgages and commercial real estate loans for office buildings owner-occupied commercial buildings industrial buildings and strip mall centers. About 46% of its loan portfolio was made up of one-to-four family residential mortgages at the end of 2015 while another 29% was made up of commercial real estate loans. The rest of the portfolio was made up of home equity loans (10% of loan assets) construction (4%) business loans

(3.5%) auto loans (6%) and other consumer loans (less than 1%).

The bank also makes more than 90% of its revenue from interest income. About 87% of its total revenue came from loan interest (including fees) during 2015 while another 7% came from interest on investment securities. The remainder of its revenue came from non-interest income sources including customer service fees.

Geographic Reach

While its primary market area is in the greater Boston area the company serves southeastern Massachusetts in the Essex Middlesex Norfolk and Suffolk Counties from branches in Belmont Watertown Waltham Newton and Cambridge.

Sales and Marketing

BSB Bancorp has been cutting back on its marketing in recent years. It spent $926000 on marketing in 2015 down from $975000 and $999000 in 2014 and 2013 respectively.

Financial Performance

BSB Bancorp's annual revenues have doubled since 2011 as its loan assets have more than tripled to $1.53 billion as a result new branch openings and organic growth with the strengthening economy around Boston. The bank's net income has skyrocketed more than five-fold over the time period as it's kept a lid on rising operating costs and benefited from the low-interest environment.

The bank's revenue jumped 23% to $51.57 million during 2015 mostly as a 30% increase in loan assets spurred higher interest income.

Strong revenue growth in 2015 drove BSB Bancorp's net income higher by 61% to $6.91 million. The bank's operating cash levels fell 14% to $18.1 million for the year mostly after adjusting its earnings for non-cash items related to its net proceeds from loan sales.

Strategy

BSB Bancorp reiterated in 2016 that it planned to continue focusing on growing its one-to-four family residential mortgage commercial real estate and home equity lending business which made up more than 85% of its loan assets in 2015. With its eye on being the "Bank of Choice" for small businesses and municipalities in its core Boston market area it plans to organically grow its deposit and lending business in the parts of Eastern Massachusetts that weren't as affected by the most recent recession.

In 2013 BSB Bancorp expanded its reach by 50% after opening two branches inside Shaw's Supermarkets in Cambridge and Newton (its first supermarket branch was opened in Waltham in 2012).

EXECUTIVES

President CEO and Director BSB Bancorp Inc.; President and CEO Belmont Savings Bank, Robert M. (Bob) Mahoney, age 69
EVP and COO, Hal R. Tovin, age 62
EVP Consumer Lending and Auto Finance Belmont Savings Bank, Christopher Y. (Chris) Downs, age 67
SVP CFO and Secretary BSB Bancorp Inc. and Belmont Savings Bank, John A. Citrano, age 54
President Bob Mahoney, Belmont Bank
Senior Vice President, Morgan Cambern
Board Member, Warren Farrell
Board Member, John Whittemore
Board Member, Richard Fougere

Board Member, Paul Petry
Auditors: Baker Newman & Noyes LLC

LOCATIONS

HQ: BSB Bancorp Inc. (MD)
2 Leonard Street, Belmont, MA 02478
Phone: 617 484-6700
Web: www.belmontsavings.com

COMPETITORS

Bank of America	Hingham Institution
Boston Private	for Savings
Brookline Bancorp	Independent Bank (MA)
Century Bancorp (MA)	Meridian Bancorp
Citizens Financial	Middlesex Savings
Group	Peoples Federal
DCU	Bancshares Inc.
Eastern Bank	Sovereign Bank
Enterprise Bancorp	TD Bank USA

HISTORICAL FINANCIALS

Company Type: Public

Income Statement   FYE: December 31

	ASSETS ($ mil.)	NET INCOME ($ mil.)	INCOME AS % OF ASSETS	EMPLOYEES
12/17	2,676.5	14.3	0.5%	126
12/16	2,158.7	11.9	0.6%	125
12/15	1,812.9	6.9	0.4%	132
12/14	1,425.5	4.2	0.3%	128
12/13	1,054.6	1.9	0.2%	127
Annual Growth	26.2%	64.6%	—	(0.2%)

2017 Year-End Financials

Return on assets: 0.6%	Dividends
Return on equity: 8.4%	Yield: —
Long-term debt ($ mil.): —	Payout: —
No. of shares (mil.): 9.7	Market value ($ mil.): 284.0
Sales ($ mil): 80.7	

	STOCK PRICE ($) FY Close	P/E High/Low	PER SHARE ($) Earnings	Dividends	Book Value
12/17	29.25	20 16	1.55	0.00	18.34
12/16	28.95	21 15	1.33	0.00	17.66
12/15	23.39	30 23	0.78	0.00	16.09
12/14	18.63	38 30	0.49	0.00	15.11
12/13	15.09	69 56	0.22	0.00	14.40
Annual Growth	18.0%	— —	62.9%	—	6.2%

Cabot Microelectronics Corp

Cabot Microelectronics sits atop a mountain of slurry. The company is a top maker of slurries (consumables) used in chemical mechanical planarization (CMP). CMP is a wafer polishing process that enables semiconductor manufacturers to produce smaller faster and more complex devices. Cabot Micro's CMP slurries consist of liquids containing abrasives and chemicals that aid in the CMP process. The company is also a leading provider of polishing pads for CMP and it makes slurries used to polish the substrates and magnetic heads of hard-disk drives. TSMC United Microelectronics Samsung and Intel are among its largest customers.

Operations

Sales of various slurries (tungsten dielectric copper and data storage slurries) and polishing pads account for more than 85% of Cabot Micro's revenues.

In addition the company's Engineered Surface Finishes (ESF) business (5% of sales) develops new polishing techniques and processes that are focused on production efficiency improvements and applications in industries outside of semiconductors. Within the ESF division Cabot Micro's QED Technologies subsidiary makes precision polishing and metrology systems used to shape and surface optical components including lenses mirrors and prisms. Its automated polishing systems use magnetic fluids to polish an array of shapes and finishes. Its metrology systems are based on Subaperture Stitching Interferometer (SSI) which measures non-spherical surfaces.

Geographic Reach

Cabot Micro has five manufacturing plants in Japan Singapore South Korea Taiwan and the US (in Illinois). It has regional sales customer service and technical support offices in Europe Asia and the US. About 80% of sales come from the Asia/Pacific region.

Sales and Marketing

Cabot Micro serves customers that make or provide logic IC (integrated circuit) devices memory IC devices or IC foundry services. Its five largest customers make up more than half of sales. Its top two customers are TSMC and Samsung which respectively account for 18% and 15% of annual sales.

The company primarily uses a direct sales force and depends on independent distributors in some regional markets.

Financial Performance

Sales slid 2.4% in 2015 to $414 million from $424.6 million in 2014. The company had lower sales volumes and was hit by currency exchange rates particularly in Japan and South Korea.

Net income on the other hand rose 10% to $56.5 million in 2015 from $50.7 million in 2014. The company cut some costs including in sales and marketing to achieve the profit gain.

Cash flow from operations was $98 million in 2015 compared to $67 million in 2014.

Strategy

To improve product performance quality and consistency Cabot also works to streamline processes and reduce product variation levels. Some product improvement efforts are conducted in collaboration with customers and strategic partners. In addition to R&D efforts on core lines of slurries and pads for CMP processes the ESF business develops new polishing techniques and processes for applications in industries outside of semiconductors such as precision optics and electronic substrates. These efforts aim to reduce Cabot Micro's dependence on one product for most of its sales which increases its vulnerability to competition.

Mergers and Acquisitions

In 2018 Cabot agreed to buy KMG Chemicals Inc. for $1.2 billion in cash and stock. The deal would strengthen Cabot's position as a supplier to the semiconductor industry by adding KMG's high-purity chemicals to its product portfolio. The transaction was expected to close by the end of 2018.

EXECUTIVES

EVP and CFO, William S. (Bill) Johnson, age 61, $370,000 total compensation

Managing Director China and Korea, David H. Li, age 45, $496,500 total compensation

VP Japan and Asia Operations, Yumiko Damashek, age 62

VP and CTO, Ananth Naman, $338,400 total compensation

VP Secretary and General Counsel, H. Carol Bernstein, $337,800 total compensation

Vice President Global Sales, Richard Hui

Vice President Corporate Development, Brian O'leary

Auditors: PricewaterhouseCoopers LLP

LOCATIONS

HQ: Cabot Microelectronics Corp
870 North Commons Drive, Aurora, IL 60504
Phone: 630 375-6631
Web: www.cabotcmp.com

PRODUCTS/OPERATIONS

2015 Sales

	$ mil.	% of total
Tungsten slurries	178.8	44
Dielectric slurries	96.4	23
Other Metals slurries	71.6	17
Polishing pads	32.0	8
Engineered surface finishes	21.5	5
Data storage slurries	13.7	3
Total	**414.0**	**100**

Selected Products

CMP Polishing Pads
Polished Surface Finishes
Slurries
  Barrier
  Copper
  Data Storage
  Dielectric
  Emerging Applications
  Silicon Carbide Wafer
  Silicon Wafer
  TSV
  Tungsten

COMPETITORS

3M	Fujimi Corp.
ATMI	Hitachi Chemical
Air Products	Praxair
DuPont	Saint-Gobain Abrasives

HISTORICAL FINANCIALS

Company Type: Public

Income Statement   FYE: September 30

	REVENUE ($ mil.)	NET INCOME ($ mil.)	NET PROFIT MARGIN	EMPLOYEES
09/18	590.1	110.0	18.6%	1,219
09/17	507.1	86.9	17.1%	1,179
09/16	430.4	59.8	13.9%	1,145
09/15	414.1	56.1	13.6%	1,111
09/14	424.6	50.7	12.0%	1,054
Annual Growth	**8.6%**	**21.3%**	**—**	**3.7%**

2018 Year-End Financials

Debt ratio: —	No. of shares (mil.): 25.5
Return on equity: 17.4%	Dividends
Cash ($ mil.): 352.9	Yield: 0.0%
Current ratio: 5.17	Payout: 23.8%
Long-term debt ($ mil.): —	Market value ($ mil.): 2,631.0

	STOCK PRICE ($) FY Close	P/E High/Low		PER SHARE ($) Earnings	Dividends	Book Value
09/18	103.17	29	19	4.19	1.00	26.14
09/17	79.93	23	15	3.40	0.78	23.54
09/16	52.91	22	14	2.43	0.54	20.30
09/15	38.74	23	16	2.26	0.00	17.55
09/14	41.45	23	18	2.04	0.00	15.64
Annual Growth	**25.6%**	**—**	**—**	**19.7%**	**—**	**13.7%**

Cadence Bancorporation

Auditors: Ernst & Young LLP

LOCATIONS

HQ: Cadence Bancorporation
2800 Post Oak Boulevard, Suite 3800, Houston, TX 77056
Phone: 713 871-4000
Web: www.cadencebank.com

HISTORICAL FINANCIALS

Company Type: Public

Income Statement   FYE: December 31

	ASSETS ($ mil.)	NET INCOME ($ mil.)	INCOME AS % OF ASSETS	EMPLOYEES
12/17	10,948.9	102.3	0.9%	1,206
12/16	9,530.8	65.7	0.7%	1,193
12/15	8,811.5	39.2	0.4%	0
12/14	0.0	44.8	***************%	0
Annual Growth	**—**	**31.7%**		

2017 Year-End Financials

Return on assets: 1.0%	Dividends
Return on equity: 8.3%	Yield: —
Long-term debt ($ mil.): —	Payout: —
No. of shares (mil.): 83.6	Market value ($ mil.): 2,268.0
Sales ($ mil): 496.7	

	STOCK PRICE ($) FY Close	P/E High/Low		PER SHARE ($) Earnings	Dividends	Book Value
12/17	27.12	22	16	1.25	0.00	16.25
12/16	0.00	—	—	0.87	0.00	14.41
Annual Growth	**—**	**—**	**—**	**43.7%**	**—**	**12.8%**

CAI International Inc

Is it bigger than a breadbox? CAI International can pack it. The company leases large steel boxes to ship freight by plane train or truck around the world. More than 65% of its container fleet is owned by CAI and the balance owned by container investors is managed by CAI. The leasing segment offers 280-plus shipping companies short-term and long-term leases with some leases giving the lessees the option to purchase the container. The container management segment provides container investors with the ability to lease re-lease and dispose of their container portfolio; services also include container repair relocation and storage.

Geographic Reach

CAI caters to 280 customers from 16 offices spanning 13 countries. CAI purchases the majority of its containers in China and operates from offices in Belgium Hong Kong Japan Korea Singapore Taiwan the UK and the US among others.

Sales and Marketing

The top ten largest lessees account for about 60% of its total leasing segment sales (approximately 55% of total sales). Its largest customer CMA CGM generates 11% of sales.

Financial Performance

CAI has enjoyed four straight years of unprecedented growth. Revenues climbed 7% from $212 million in 2013 to reach a historic high of $228 million in 2014. Profits however fell 6% from $64 million in 2013 to $60 million in 2014 due to increased storage handling and other expenses.

The growth for 2014 was driven by a 8% spike in rental revenue due to an increase in the average number of owned containers on lease. The company was also helped by a 11% bump in finance lease sales. This growth was offset by a 17% decrease in management fee revenue.

Company Background

Founded by Hiromitsu Ogawa in 1989 CAI has evolved from solely an intermodal leasing concern to a more ambitious manager of containers owned by investors.

EXECUTIVES

President and CEO, Victor M. Garcia, age 50, $323,833 total compensation
VP Operations, Camille G. Cutino, age 59, $164,800 total compensation
CFO, Timothy Page
Vice President Technical Services, Mike Hohndorf
Vice President, John Pacey
Vice President Marketing, Tina Simner
Vice President Marketing, Geoff Hopkins
Vice President Marketing CAI Rail, Mike MacMahon
Vice President Operations, Freddy Fernandez
Board Member, Gary Sawka
Assistant Treasurer, Sean Nakahara
Auditors: KPMG LLP

LOCATIONS

HQ: CAI International Inc
Steuart Tower, 1 Market Plaza, Suite 900, San Francisco, CA 94105
Phone: 415 788-0100
Web: www.capps.com

PRODUCTS/OPERATIONS

2014 Sales

	% of total
Rental revenue	93
Management fee revenue	3
Finance lease income	4
Gain on sale of container portfolios	0
Total	**100**

Selected Operations

Container leasing
 Container owned by CAI
 Full benefits of ownership
Placed on long- and short-term leases to shipping lines
Container management
 Container sold to investors
 Generate cash flow through management fee revenue and trading income
 Managed by CAI over expected life of asset

COMPETITORS

COSCO Group	Seaco
SeaCube Container	Touax
Seacastle	XTRA Corp.

HISTORICAL FINANCIALS

Company Type: Public

Income Statement				FYE: December 31
	REVENUE ($ mil.)	NET INCOME ($ mil.)	NET PROFIT MARGIN	EMPLOYEES
12/17	348.3	72.0	20.7%	215
12/16	294.3	6.0	2.0%	212
12/15	249.6	26.8	10.7%	128
12/14	227.5	60.2	26.5%	101
12/13	212.4	63.9	30.1%	85
Annual Growth	**13.2%**	**3.0%**	**—**	**26.1%**

2017 Year-End Financials

Debt ratio: 70.0%
Return on equity: 14.1%
Cash ($ mil.): 35.4
Current ratio: 0.54
Long-term debt ($ mil.): 1,570.7
No. of shares (mil.): 20.3
Dividends
 Yield: —
 Payout: —
Market value ($ mil.): 577.0

	STOCK PRICE ($) FY Close	P/E High/Low		PER SHARE ($)		
				Earnings	Dividends	Book Value
12/17	28.32	10	3	3.68	0.00	27.65
12/16	8.67	33	16	0.31	0.00	24.01
12/15	10.08	20	7	1.28	0.00	22.87
12/14	23.20	9	6	2.85	0.00	21.27
12/13	23.57	10	7	2.82	0.00	18.64
Annual Growth	**4.7%**	**—**	**—**	**6.9%**	**—**	**10.4%**

CalAmp Corp

When machines talk CalAmp helps you listen. The former military supplier makes hardware and software to track trucks planes and industrial equipment and to keep them communicating. It provides asset tracking devices mobile telemetry units fixed and mobile wireless gateways and wireless router transmission for machine resource management (MRM) and machine-to-machine (M2M) communication. CalAmp keeps track of it all through cloud-based telematics and applications offered through as-a-service models. The company's customers are in the energy government heavy equipment transportation and automotive markets. CalAmp discontinued its satellite business when EchoStar its only customer consolidated suppliers.

Operations

CalAmp's operations have been segmented into Wireless Datacom and Satellite units.

Some 86% of CalAmp's 2016 (ended February) revenue came from the Wireless Datacom line with the rest generated by Satellite services.

Most of the company's manufacturing and assembly is handled by contractors.

Geographic Reach

Based in Oxnard California the company also operates wireless datacom locations in Virginia and Minnesota in the US and in Quebec Canada and Auckland New Zealand.

About 83% of sales are to customers in the US with international customers supplying the other 17%.

Sales and Marketing

CalAmp offers its wireless datacom through direct and indirect sales force in US and through sales personnel in Latin America Israel and the UK.

Its Satellite segment has sold its products primarily to EchoStar an affiliate of DISH Network which has accounted for a diminishing portion of revenue. It was 14% in 2016 (ended January) 15% in 2015 and 21% in 2014.

Financial Performance

In 2016 (ended January) CalAmp reported revenue growth of 12% to about $281 million driven by higher wireless datacom revenues (up 13%) due to increased sales of MRM products into the fleet management and non-vehicle asset tracking markets. The company also had a boost from an order from a heavy equipment manufacturer.

Net income increased 2.6% in 2016 to about $17 million from 2015. Higher sales combined with a tax benefit to produce a profit.

Cash provided by operations strengthened to $47 million in 2016 from $28.6 million in 2015.

Strategy

CalAmp is not looking back wistfully at its satellite business. With the loss of EchoStar as a customer CalAmp discontinued that part of its operations in its 2017 fiscal year ended February. It is moving deeper into wireless data communications and expects no negative impact from cutting its Satellite business.

A major way CalAmp is expanding its wireless operations is through acquisitions that add technology for MRM and M2M products and services to its lineup.

Mergers and Acquisitions

In 2016 CalAmp spent about $131 million to buy LoJack Corp. a provider of vehicle theft recovery systems and advanced fleet management technologies. The acquisition should accelerate CalAmp's progress into the automotive telematics business.

In 2015 CalAmp Corp. made a similar acquisition with privately held Crashboxx an early stage company focused on insurance telematics applications. The price was $1.5 million.

CalAmp invested in another telematics startup SmartDriverClub Ltd. which develops connected car services and applications aimed at consumers and auto dealers in the UK.

EXECUTIVES

SVP and General Manager Satellite Products, Robert Hannah, $215,000 total compensation
EVP CFO and Secretary, Richard K. (Rick) Vitelle, age 64, $330,000 total compensation
President and CEO, Michael J. Burdiek, age 58, $440,000 total compensation
SVP Operations, John J. Warwick
SVP and General Manager Wireless Networks, Michael P. (Mike) Zachan, age 69
SVP Marketing and Business Development, Justin Schmid

SVP and General Manager MRM/M2M, Greg Gower
Vice President of Engineering, Dave Ghilarducci
Senior Vice President, Richard Rose
Vice President, Peter Byrne
Chairman, A.J. (Bert) Moyer
Auditors: DELOITTE & TOUCHE LLP

LOCATIONS

HQ: CalAmp Corp
15635 Alton Parkway, Suite 250, Irvine, CA 92618
Phone: 949 600-5600
Web: www.calamp.com

PRODUCTS/OPERATIONS

2016 Sales

	$ mil.	% of total
Wireless DataCom	241.4	86
Satellite	39.3	14
Total	**280.7**	**100**

2016 Sales

	$ mil
% of total	
Products	85
Application subscriptions and other services	15
Total	**100**

Selected Products

Satellite components
  Amplifiers
  Downconverters
  Feedhorns
Wireless access equipment
  Antennas
  Broadband analog scrambling/decoding systems
  (MultiCipher)
  Transceivers (passive planar stand-alone)

COMPETITORS

AML Communications	Motorola Solutions
Broadcast Microwave	Novatel Wireless
Services	STC Microwave Systems
COM DEV	Sharp Corp.
Cohu	Sierra Wireless
Enfora	Trimble
Filtronic	WebTech
Kratos Defense &	Wistron NeWeb
Security Solutions	

HISTORICAL FINANCIALS

Company Type: Public

Income Statement   FYE: February 28

	REVENUE ($ mil.)	NET INCOME ($ mil.)	NET PROFIT MARGIN	EMPLOYEES
02/18	365.9	16.6	4.5%	900
02/17	351.1	(7.9)	—	970
02/16	280.7	16.9	6.0%	490
02/15	250.6	16.5	6.6%	530
02/14	235.9	11.8	5.0%	490
Annual Growth	**11.6%**	**8.9%**	**—**	**16.4%**

2018 Year-End Financials

Debt ratio: 32.6%	No. of shares (mil.): 35.7
Return on equity: 9.1%	Dividends
Cash ($ mil.): 132.6	Yield: —
Current ratio: 2.89	Payout: —
Long-term debt ($ mil.): 154.3	Market value ($ mil.): 836.0

	STOCK PRICE ($) FY Close	P/E High/Low	PER SHARE ($) Earnings	Dividends	Book Value
02/18	23.40	53 33	0.46	0.00	5.57
02/17	16.21	— —	(0.22)	0.00	4.62
02/16	17.71	47 33	0.46	0.00	5.17
02/15	19.15	75 33	0.45	0.00	4.18
02/14	32.04	98 27	0.33	0.00	3.71
Annual Growth	**(7.6%)**	**— —**	**8.7%**	**—**	**10.7%**

Calavo Growers, Inc.

Calavo (a combination of "California" and "avocado") began as a growers' marketing cooperative founded in 1924 in order to transform the exotic hobby crop avocados into a culinary staple. Mission accomplished. Since the avocado has become if not a staple a regular in US supermarket shopping carts. Calavo procures and processes avocados papaya pineapple tomatoes and other fresh fruits grown mainly in California but the company also uses fruit from Chile Peru and Mexico. The products are then distributed to retail food outlets food service operators and produce wholesalers throughout the world.

Operations

Calavo operates its business through three segments: Fresh Products (59% of sales in 2015) Calavo Foods (7%) and Renaissance Food Group (RFG 34%).

Some 1900 growers deliver their crops to Calavo for processing. In addition to whole avocados the company manufactures avocado pulp and frozen peeled avocado halves through its Fresh business unit. Meanwhile its Calavo Foods business unit sells guacamole and the Salsa Lisa line of fresh salsas hummus and tortilla chips. RFG produces markets and distributes healthy high-quality products (fresh-cut fruit and vegetables grab-and-go salads snacks and sandwiches) for consumers nationwide through retailers.

FreshRealm is the company's technology firm that's focused on building a platform for those who are in the fresh food business.

Geographic Reach

Calavo operates a number of facilities throughout the US including packaging houses in California and operating and distribution centers in California Arizona Florida Hawaii Minnesota New Jersey and Texas. It also has facilities in Michoacón and Jalisco Mexico.

Sales and Marketing

The company distributes its goods to food service industry and retail customers. It develops various store packaging and displays to entice buyers particularly impulse buyers in the produce section.

The Fresh Products segment's five largest customers accounted for a combined 18% of its consolidated revenues; RFG's top five customers accounted for 23% of its consolidated revenues.

Calavo logged $200000 in advertising expenses in fiscal 2015 and 2014 up from $100000 in 2013.

Financial Performance

Revenues have been on a steady rise for the past five years. In fiscal 2015 revenue increased 9% to $856.8 million largely due to growth in the RFG segment (although the Fresh Products and

Calavo Foods segments also saw sales increases). RFG's growth was attributed to a rise in sales of cut fruits and vegetables and deli products.

After taking a net loss of $97000 in 2014 the company returned to the black in 2015 when net income jumped to $27.2 million. That turnaround was partly due to higher sales but also due to the absence of contingent considerations related to the 2011 acquisition of RFG. Cash flow from operations rose 52% to $37.2 million that year.

Strategy

The Calavo Foods and RFG segments represent the company's move beyond fresh avocados and commodity produce into the market for fresh refrigerated packaged foods. It has expanded such holdings through acquisitions.

In the Fresh Products segment Calavo still seeks to expand its presence in the avocado market but also considers the distribution of other promising crops. In order to grow its business the company pursues partnerships with major food services companies.

In 2015 Calavo added a second packinghouse in Mexico in the prime growing region of Jalisco.

EXECUTIVES

Vice President of Fresh Operations, Mike Browne
Chairman President and CEO, Lecil E. (Lee) Cole, age 79, $635,133 total compensation
VP Sales and Fresh Marketing, Robert J. (Rob) Wedin, age 69, $309,356 total compensation
Director Operations Calavo de México, Dionisio Ortiz
VP Fresh Operations, Michael A. (Mike) Browne, age 60, $309,356 total compensation
CFO and Secretary, B. John Lindeman, $325,000 total compensation
VP Foods Division Sales and Operations, Ron Araiza
Board Member, John Hunt
Board Member, Marc L Brown
Board Member, Dorcas Thille
Auditors: DELOITTE & TOUCHE LLP

LOCATIONS

HQ: Calavo Growers, Inc.
1141-A Cummings Road, Santa Paula, CA 93060
Phone: 805 525-1245   **Fax:** 805 921-3223
Web: www.calavo.com

PRODUCTS/OPERATIONS

2015 Sales

	$ mil.	% of total
Fresh Products	500.7	59
RFG (Renaissance Food Group)	293.9	34
Calavo Foods	62.2	7
Total	**856.8**	**100**

Selected Products

Fresh
  Whole avocado
  Avocado halves
  Avocado pulp
  Papaya
  Pineapple
  Tomato
Calavo Foods
  Guacamole
  Salsa Lisa
  Tortilla chips

Selected Services

Growing
Ripening
Packing

Sales
Warehousing
Shipping & distribution

COMPETITORS

Azteca Foods	Gentile Bros.
BC Hot House Foods	Giumarra Companies
Brooks Tropicals	Goya
Caribe Food	Gruma Corporation
Chiquita Brands	Grupo Bimbo
Coast Citrus	H. J. Heinz Limited
Distributors	Hain Celestial
ConAgra	Index Fresh
Dole Food	Interfresh
Don Miguel Mexican	JR Simplot
Foods	La Tortilla Factory
Eastern Fresh Growers	Oceanside Produce
Inc.	Pacific Tomato Growers
Fresh Del Monte	Pinos Produce
Produce	Rancho Mission Viejo
FreshPoint	Shamrock Foods

HISTORICAL FINANCIALS

Company Type: Public

Income Statement   FYE: October 31

	REVENUE ($ mil.)	NET INCOME ($ mil.)	NET PROFIT MARGIN	EMPLOYEES
10/18	1,088.7	32.2	3.0%	2,979
10/17	1,075.5	37.2	3.5%	2,516
10/16	935.6	38.0	4.1%	2,096
10/15	856.8	27.2	3.2%	2,064
10/14	782.5	0.1	0.0%	1,987
Annual Growth	8.6%	327.1%	—	10.7%

2018 Year-End Financials

Debt ratio: 4.2%
Return on equity: 12.7%
Cash ($ mil.): 1.5
Current ratio: 1.30
Long-term debt ($ mil.): 0.3

No. of shares (mil.): 17.5
Dividends
Yield: 0.0%
Payout: 51.6%
Market value ($ mil.): 1,704.0

	STOCK PRICE ($) FY Close	P/E High/Low	PER SHARE ($) Earnings	Dividends	Book Value
10/18	97.00	58 37	1.84	0.95	14.98
10/17	73.70	36 24	2.13	0.90	13.87
10/16	59.15	32 22	2.18	0.80	12.28
10/15	51.41	39 25	1.57	0.75	10.64
10/14	48.54	48632830	0.01	0.70	10.37
Annual Growth	18.9%	—	−268.3%	7.9%	9.6%

Callon Petroleum Co. (DE)

Callon Petroleum can call on new technologies to find old petroleum resources employing computer-aided techniques such as enhanced 3-D surveys and horizontal drilling to explore and develop oil and gas properties. It also focuses on acquiring properties. Once a major offshore player the firm's holdings are now primarily onshore in Texas. In 2012 Callon's estimated proved reserves stood at 14.1 million barrels of oil equivalent. About 68% of Callon's oil and gas reserves are located onshore in the Permian Basin; 77% of its proved reserve volumes are in the form of crude oil which also accounts for the bulk of its the company's revenues.

Operations

Callon produced nearly 1.6 million barrels of oil equivalent of natural gas and NGLs and crude oil in 2012.

That year the company derived about 87% of its revenues from crude oil sales; the remaining came from natural gas and NGL sales.

Sales and Marketing

Callon's production is sold generally on month-to-month contracts at prevailing prices. Shell Trading Company and Enterprise Crude Oil accounted for 39% and 32% of its 2012 net sales respectively.

Financial Performance

The company's revenues declined by 13% in 2012 due to lower sales of crude oil natural gas and NGLs.

In 2012 Callon's crude oil sales decreased due to lower commodity prices and a drop in production volumes as the result of down-time at the Habanero and Medusa fields and the normal declines from its other offshore properties. These production declines were offset by new production from its Permian wells (22 vertical and two horizontal) which began production that year.

Natural gas revenues also declined in 2012 due to lower production driven by down time at its Haynesville well (which was shut-in for 70 days) and at its East Cameron 257 well (which was suspended due to a natural gas leak in an upstream section of the Stingray Pipeline that transports production volumes from the field). The average realized price for natural gas also decreased by 25% in 2012 although the value of the NGLs in its natural gas stream (from its Permian basin and deepwater production) kept Callon's natural gas sales prices above NYMEX prices.

The company's net income decreased by 97% in 2012 due to lower revenues and higher income tax expenses.

Strategy

To secure better long term returns Callon is shifting its asset base from primarily offshore to primarily onshore. It is focused on bringing its existing Permian acreage position to production and on making opportunistic producing property and leasehold acquisitions. The company is developing an established production base from vertical Wolfberry wells. It is also drilling an inventory of horizontal locations identified in the southern Midland basin and is conducting exploration activities on its acreage in the northern Midland basin.

To pay down debt in 2013 Callon sold its interests in the Medusa field Medusa Spar LLC and all of its Gulf of Mexico shelf assets for $88 million.

The company's estimated proved reserves decreased by 12% in fiscal 2012 due to the sale of its stake in the Habanero field and the downward revision of its Haynesville Shale undeveloped reserves (reduced due to low natural gas pricing assumptions). These decreases were partially offset by the company's development of a portion of its Permian Basin on which it added seven proved developed producing and 19 proved undeveloped reserve wells during 2012.

To increase its financial flexibility in 2012 it sold its 11.25% working interest in the Habanero field (Garden Banks Block 341) to a Royal Dutch Shell unit for $39 million.

Mergers and Acquisitions

In 2016 Callon agreed to buy certain undeveloped acreage and producing oil and gas assets in the Southern Delaware Basin for $615 million.

Company Background

In 2012 Callon spent about $32 million to acquire 16233 gross (14653 net) acres in Borden county Texas (in the northern Midland basin) an additional 8095 gross acres (6964 net) in this area and 2319 gross (1762 net) acres in southern Reagan county Texas

In light of a weak economy the company's strategy (reported in 2009) was to reduce its oil and gas exploration in the Gulf of Mexico focus on longer-lived lower risk onshore US properties (such as its Haynesville Shale development) and to seek partnerships in order to finance its future property acquisitions.

Boosting its onshore assets in 2009 Callon acquired stakes in 22 producing wells in Crockett Ector Midland and Upton counties (in West Texas) for $16.3 million. In 2010 the company received a cash injection of $44.7 million when the federal Bureau of Ocean Energy Management Regulation and Enforcement reimbursed it for overpayment of royalties at its Medusa asset in the Gulf of Mexico.

To raise cash to pay down debt in 2008 it sold a 50% stake in the Entrada Field in the Gulf of Mexico (it acquired an 80% stake a year earlier) to CIECO for $175 million. In 2007 the company sold non-operated onshore royalty and mineral interests for $61.5 million to Indigo Minerals LLC.

Callon was formed in 1994 through the consolidation of a publicly traded limited partnership an independent energy company owned by some members of current Callon management and a joint venture with a consortium of European entities.

EXECUTIVES

Controller Callon Petroleum Company and Callon Petroleum Operating Company, Mitzi P. Conn, age 48, $198,370 total compensation
SVP and COO, Gary A. Newberry, age 63, $367,308 total compensation
President CEO and CFO, Joseph C. Gatto, age 47, $367,308 total compensation
VP Land, Jerry A. Weant, age 59, $250,000 total compensation
VP Permian Operations, Michael O'Connor
Chairman, L. Richard Flury, age 71
Board of Directors, Tony Nocchiero
Auditors: Grant Thornton LLP

LOCATIONS

HQ: Callon Petroleum Co. (DE)
200 North Canal Street, Natchez, MS 39120
Phone: 601 442-1601
Web: www.callon.com

PRODUCTS/OPERATIONS

2015 Sales

	$ mil.	% of total
Oil sales	125.2	91
Natural gas sales	12.3	9
Total	137.5	100

COMPETITORS

Abraxas Petroleum	Parallel Petroleum
Apache	Pioneer Natural
BP	Resources

Carrizo Oil & Gas
Devon Energy
Exxon Mobil
Occidental Oil and Gas

Range Resources
SM Energy
TOTAL

HISTORICAL FINANCIALS
Company Type: Public

Income Statement   FYE: December 31

	REVENUE ($ mil.)	NET INCOME ($ mil.)	NET PROFIT MARGIN	EMPLOYEES
12/17	366.4	120.4	32.9%	169
12/16	200.8	(91.8)	—	121
12/15	137.5	(240.1)	—	93
12/14	151.8	37.7	24.9%	109
12/13	102.5	4.3	4.2%	94
Annual Growth	37.5%	130.0%	—	15.8%

2017 Year-End Financials
Debt ratio: 23.0%
Return on equity: 6.7%
Cash ($ mil.): 28.0
Current ratio: 0.70
Long-term debt ($ mil.): 620.2

No. of shares (mil.): 201.8
Dividends
  Yield: —
  Payout: —
Market value ($ mil.): 2,452.0

	STOCK PRICE ($) FY Close	P/E High/Low	Earnings	PER SHARE ($) Dividends	Book Value
12/17	12.15	29 17	0.56	0.00	9.20
12/16	15.37	— —	(0.78)	0.00	8.62
12/15	8.34	— —	(3.77)	0.00	4.53
12/14	5.45	18 6	0.65	0.00	7.85
12/13	6.53	— —	(0.01)	0.00	6.92
Annual Growth	16.8%	— —	—	—	7.4%

Cambrex Corp

Cambrex focuses on health. Providing products services and technologies which help to accelerate the development and commercialization of small molecule therapeutics the company develops products for the human health care market that include active pharmaceutical ingredients (APIs) and intermediates for over-the-counter and prescription branded and generic pharmaceuticals. Cambrex focuses on developing drug delivery technologies and the manufacture of high-potency compounds and controlled substances.

Geographic Reach
Cambrex has facilities in Italy Sweden and the US. R&D and specialty manufacturing facilities are located in Europe and the US. Europe accounts for more than 60% of sales and North America just over 32%.

Sales and Marketing
The company sells its products through a combination of direct sales and independent agents. Gilead Sciences Inc acconts for 35% of company sales. One active pharmaceutical ingredient (API) sold to multiple customers account for some 30% of Cambrex's revenue.

Financial Performance
Net revenue at Cambrex increased 9% to $534000 from $491000 in 2016 due to higher volumes sold of branded APIs and clinical phase products (8.5%) offset slightly by lower pricing.

Net income went up 25% to $102 million primarily due to higher gross profit (higher royalties and higher production) as well as lower losses from discontinued operations followed by the absence of restructuring expenses.

Cambrex had $183 million in cash holdings at the end of 2017. Operations provided $149 million offset by investments of $49 million while financial activities provided $5 million in cash inflow.

Strategy
Cambrex's stated strategy is to grow its portfolio of customer development projects — primarily those in the latter stages of the clinical trial process — and secure long-term supply agreements to make APIs and intermediates for recently approved drug products. It also seeks to expand sales based on its technologies and to partner with generic drug manufacturers to expand the company's portfolio of APIs. It also drives growth in strategic business segments through the selective acquisition of businesses products product lines technologies and capabilities.

The company holds influential patents (more than 120 worldwide and 100 awaiting) proprietary technology and possesses cutting-edge know-how and trade secrets in manufacturing that enables it to maintain its market position. With a steadily increasing CAPEX (2017: $17 million) the company wants to grow its generic APIs and finished dosage products.

Mergers and Acquisitions
In 2016 the company acquired PharmaCore a privately-owned company located in High Point North Carolina specializing in developing manufacturing and scaling up small molecule APIs for clinical phase projects.

EXECUTIVES
Vice President Operations, Joe Nettleton
EVP Administration, Steven M. (Steve) Klosk, age 61, $533,333 total compensation
Managing Director Cambrex Profarmaco, Aldo Magnini, $338,666 total compensation
EVP Corporate Development and Strategy, Gregory P. (Greg) Sargen, age 52, $400,000 total compensation
EVP and COO, Shawn P. Cavanagh, $412,500 total compensation
Vice President, James Farrell
EVP and CFO, Tom Vadaketh
Tax Director Vice President, Andrew Spada
Vice President Finance, Greg Sargen
Vice President, Robert Congiusti
Vice President Operations, Brian Swierenga
Auditors: BDO USA, LLP

LOCATIONS
HQ: Cambrex Corp
  One Meadowlands Plaza, East Rutherford, NJ 07073
Phone: 201 804-3000   Fax: 201 804-9852
Web: www.cambrex.com

PRODUCTS/OPERATIONS

Selected Mergers and Acquisitions2010Zenara Pharma (51%; India; nicotine replacement therapy)

COMPETITORS
Aceto
Albany Molecular Research
Bausch Health

Boehringer Ingelheim
Sigma-Aldrich
West Pharmaceutical Services

HISTORICAL FINANCIALS
Company Type: Public

Income Statement   FYE: December 31

	REVENUE ($ mil.)	NET INCOME ($ mil.)	NET PROFIT MARGIN	EMPLOYEES
12/17	534.4	102.4	19.2%	1,228
12/16	490.6	81.6	16.6%	1,295
12/15	433.3	57.2	13.2%	1,228
12/14	374.6	57.3	15.3%	1,117
12/13	318.1	25.9	8.1%	936
Annual Growth	13.8%	41.0%	—	7.0%

2017 Year-End Financials
Debt ratio: —
Return on equity: 21.5%
Cash ($ mil.): 183.2
Current ratio: 5.11
Long-term debt ($ mil.): —

No. of shares (mil.): 32.8
Dividends
  Yield: —
  Payout: —
Market value ($ mil.): 1,577.0

	STOCK PRICE ($) FY Close	P/E High/Low	Earnings	PER SHARE ($) Dividends	Book Value
12/17	48.00	20 14	3.06	0.00	16.59
12/16	53.95	23 12	2.48	0.00	12.53
12/15	47.09	30 12	1.76	0.00	9.77
12/14	21.62	13 9	1.81	0.00	8.08
12/13	17.83	23 13	0.84	0.00	6.90
Annual Growth	28.1%	— —	38.2%	—	24.5%

Camden National Corp. (ME)

Camden National Corporation is the holding company for Camden National Bank which boasts nearly 45 branches in about a dozen Maine counties and provides standard deposit products such as checking and savings accounts CDs and IRAs. Commercial mortgages and loans make up 50% of its loan portfolio while residential mortgages make up another 40% and consumer loans constitute the remainder. Subsidiary Acadia Trust provides trust fiduciary investment management and retirement plan administration services while Camden Financial Consultants offers brokerage and insurance services. The largest bank headquartered in Maine Camden National Bank was founded in 1875 and once issued its own US currency.

Operations
About 63% of Camden National's total revenue came from loan interest (including fees) in 2014 while another 15% came from interest on its US government and sponsored enterprise obligations (investment securities). The rest of its revenue came from deposit account service charges (5%) other service charges and fees (5%) income from fiduciary services (4%) brokerage and insurance commissions (2%) and other miscellaneous income sources. The bank had a staff of 471 employees at the end of 2014.

Geographic Reach
Camden National has around 45 branches in 12 counties throughout Maine with one commercial loan office in Manchester New Hampshire. Its

primary markets are in the counties of Androscoggin Cumberland Hancock Kennebec Knox Lincoln Penobscot Piscataquis Somerset Waldo Washington and York.

Sales and Marketing

The company offers deposit and loan services to consumers institutions municipalities non-profits and commercial customers.

Financial Performance

The company has struggled to consistently grow its revenues and profits in recent years mostly due to shrinking interest margins on loans amidst the low-interest environment.

Camden National's revenue dipped by 3% to $112.8 million in 2014 mostly because the bank in 2013 had collected a non-recurring $2.7 million gain from the sale of its five Franklin County branches and because its mortgage banking income fell by $1.1 million as it decided to retain most of its 30-year fixed rate residential mortgage production in 2014.

Despite revenue declines in 2014 the bank's net income jumped by 8% to $24.6 million mostly because in 2013 it had recorded a non-recurring $2.8 million goodwill impairment charge related to its financial services reporting unit. Camden's operating cash levels rose by 1% to $29.9 million for the year on higher cash earnings.

Strategy

The bank competes with larger financial institutions by emphasizing customer service to build customer loyalty and long-term relationships. It also sometimes pursues acquisitions of banks and branches in its target markets in Maine to grow its loan and deposit business.

Camden may also be expanding its franchise beyond Maine in future years. In 2014 it opened a commercial loan office in Manchester New Hampshire enabling it to serve more customers across northern New England.

Mergers and Acquisitions

In March 2015 Camden National Corporation agreed to purchase SBM Financial along with its subsidiary The Bank of Maine subsidiary. The deal expected to be completed in late 2015 would add $813 million in assets and make Camden National Bank Maine's largest community bank.

In late 2012 the bank acquired 15 full-service branches from Bank of America for $12 million.

EXECUTIVES

Vice President risk Management, Steve Matteo
EVP COO and CFO, Deborah A. Jordan, age 52, $223,327 total compensation
EVP Retail Banking, June B. Parent, age 54, $189,248 total compensation
EVP Risk Management, Joanne T. Campbell, age 55, $124,585 total compensation
President and CEO, Gregory A. (Greg) Dufour, age 57, $398,077 total compensation
SVP Information Technology, Scott Buckheit
EVP Commercial Lending, Timothy P. Nightingale, age 60, $213,846 total compensation
Vice President Commercial Portfolio Manager Commercial Loan Administrator Team Leader, Libby Arrico
Vice President, Richard Nickerson
Vice President retail Regional Manager Southern, Nancy Tracy
Vice President, Craig Day
Assistant Vice President, Jody Landrith
Vice President, Cynthia Bergin
Vice President Market Manager, Traci Tenney

Senior Vice President, Vera Rand Roberts
Vice President Commercial Loan Officer, Brent Folster
Vice President Information Security Manager, Anthony Mazzeo
Vice President Credit Risk Officer, Susan Weber
Vice President Commercial Portfolio Manager, Brooke Woodbury
Vice President Loan Servicing, Mark Richards
Senior Vice President, AL Butler
Vice President of Mortgage Operations, Betsy Hauser
Vice President of Mortgage Operations, Paul Palmer
Vice President Collections, Tim Crowe
Senior Vice President Director of Corporate Services, Susan Giffard
Assistant Vice President Senior Client Services Specialist, Amanda Neuts
Vice President Commercial Portfolio Manager, Matthew Gilbert
Vice President Senior Retail Loan Officer, Donna Maynard
AVP IT Systems Management, John Bentley
Senior Vice President Client Advisor, Zach Rubin
Chairman Camden National Corporation and Camden National Bank, Karen W. Stanley, age 72
Auditors: RSM US LLP

LOCATIONS

HQ: Camden National Corp. (ME)
2 Elm Street, Camden, ME 04843
Phone: 207 236-8821   **Fax:** 207 236-6256
Web: www.camdennational.com

PRODUCTS/OPERATIONS

2014 Sales

	$ mil.	% of total
Interest		
Loans including fees	70.7	63
US government & agency securities	17.4	14
Other investments	0.4	1
Noninterest		
Service charges on deposit accounts & others	12.4	11
Income from fiduciary services	5.0	4
Brokerage and insurance commission	1.7	2
Other	5.2	5
Total	**112.8**	**100**

COMPETITORS

Bangor Savings Bank	People's United
Bar Harbor Bankshares	Financial
KeyCorp	TD Bank USA
Northeast Bancorp	The First Bancorp
Norway Bancorp	

HISTORICAL FINANCIALS

Company Type: Public

Income Statement   FYE: December 31

	ASSETS ($ mil.)	NET INCOME ($ mil.)	INCOME AS % OF ASSETS	EMPLOYEES
12/17	4,065.4	28.4	0.7%	636
12/16	3,864.2	40.0	1.0%	631
12/15	3,709.8	20.9	0.6%	652
12/14	2,789.8	24.5	0.9%	471
12/13	2,603.8	22.7	0.9%	481
Annual Growth	**11.8%**	**5.7%**	**—**	**7.2%**

2017 Year-End Financials

Return on assets: 0.7%   Dividends
Return on equity: 7.1%   Yield: 0.0%
Long-term debt ($ mil.): —   Payout: 50.5%
No. of shares (mil.): 15.5   Market value ($ mil.): 654.0
Sales ($ mil): 174.7

	STOCK PRICE ($) FY Close	P/E High/Low	PER SHARE ($) Earnings	Dividends	Book Value
12/17	42.13	26 20	1.82	0.92	25.99
12/16	44.45	19 11	2.57	0.80	25.30
12/15	44.09	26 21	1.73	0.80	23.69
12/14	39.84	19 16	2.19	0.72	22.00
12/13	41.84	22 16	1.98	0.71	20.33
Annual Growth	**0.2%**	**— —**	**(2.1%)**	**6.8%**	**6.3%**

Cantel Medical Corp

Just ask Cantel Medical — cleanliness is second to nothing when it comes to medical and scientific equipment. Through its subsidiaries the firm sells infection prevention and control products to hospitals dentists drug makers researchers and others in the US and abroad in the field of health care. Its diverse offerings include medical device reprocessing systems and disinfectants for dialyzers and endoscopes water purification equipment masks and bibs used in dental offices and therapeutic filtration systems. Fast-growing Cantel Medical employs an active acquisition strategy.

Operations

Cantel Medical's major subsidiaries include: Mar Con Purification (water filtration and purification); Medivators (disposables disinfection sterilization); Crosstex (infection control and prevention); and Saf-T-Pak (packaging medical shipping systems). International units include Cantel Medical (UK) Cantel Medical Asia/Pacific Cantel Medical Devices (China) Biolab Equipment Medivators and Cantel Medical (Italy).

The company operates through four segments: Endoscopy Water Purification and Filtration Healthcare Disposables and Dialysis.

Endoscopy products include medical device reprocessing systems disinfectants detergents and other supplies for disinfection. The segment also provides technical maintenance services. Endoscopy is Cantel Medical's largest segment accounting for more than half of its total revenue.

Water Purification and Filtration offerings include filtration and separation products disinfectants and sterilization and decontamination products for the medical biotech pharmaceutical beverage and commercial industrial industries. That segment accounts for about a quarter of total sales.

Meanwhile Healthcare Disposable offers single-use products such as face masks sterilization pouches towels and bibs tray covers saliva ejectors wipes and disinfectants as well as products for maintaining safe dental unit waterlines. Healthcare Disposables contributes about 15% of Cantel's total sales.

The smallest segment Dialysis (about 5% of sales) provides medical device reprocessing systems sterilants and disinfectants dialysate concentrates and other supplies used in renal dialysis.

Geographic Reach

Cantel Medical rings up about 80% of its sales in the US. Foreign markets include Canada Europe Africa the Middle East South America and the Asia/Pacific region.

Sales and Marketing

Cantel's customers include diagnostic clinical and university laboratories; pharma and biotech companies; US and Canadian government agencies; hospitals; and medical research facilities.

In the US the company uses its own sales force to market its products; in international markets it employs independent distribution companies

In fiscal 2016 (ended July) Cantel Medical spent $3.3 million on advertising in line with what it spent in 2015 and up from the $2.7 million it spent in 2014.

Financial Performance

Cantel Medical's revenues and net income have been steadily rising for the past five years. In fiscal 2016 (ended July) revenue rose 18% to $664.8 million as organic product sales and service income increased. Growing demand in the endoscopy market was a primary driver of the higher sales; additionally in the health care disposables business the company's profits increased as Cantel sold more higher margin product and demand for its products grew in response to the Ebola virus. Overall net income rose 25% to $60 million thanks to the higher revenue but partially offset by higher cost of sales and operating expenses (including growth initiatives).

Strategy

Cantel Medical intends to double its sales and profits within the next five years. It has seen strong growth in its endoscopy and health care disposables businesses thanks partly to acquisitions of other firms that have added to its product portfolio.

The company has grown and diversified by employing an active acquisition strategy. It targets companies in the infection prevention and control market health care disposable products and water purification and filtration markets among others. More recently Cantel has focused on endoscopy its largest segment. It supplements acquisitions with occasional product launches such as the recently introduced SECURE FIT earloop face mask.

In 2015 the company sold its specialty packaging business a non-core operation.

Mergers and Acquisitions

In early 2019 Cantel Medical acquired Vista Research Group which makes water treatment purification and management products for the dental industry. The $10.5 million purchase expanded Cantel's dental water purification portfolio.

The company acquired Belgium-based Aexis Medical for $24.8 million in 2018. Aexis specializes in data analytics particularly around the area of infection prevention.

In mid-2017 Cantel acquired Germany's BHT Group for $60.8 million. BHT holds a portfolio of automatic endoscope reprocessors and endoscope drying and storage cabinets. With the purchase Cantel expanded its international endoscopy business.

EXECUTIVES

President Asia Pacific and Emerging Markets, David Rosen

EVP General Counsel and Secretary, Eric W. Nodiff, age 61, $361,875 total compensation

CEO, Jorgen B. Hansen, age 52, $453,529 total compensation

EVP and CFO, Peter G. Clifford, age 49, $128,077 total compensation

President Medivators Division, David C. Hemink

President Americas Sales and Global Service, Michael G. Spicer

Vice President Market Development, Matt Conlon

Vice Chairman, George L. Fotiades, age 65

Chairman, Charles M. Diker, age 83

Auditors: DELOITTE & TOUCHE LLP

LOCATIONS

HQ: Cantel Medical Corp
150 Clove Road, Little Falls, NJ 07424
Phone: 973 890-7220   **Fax:** 973 890-7270
Web: www.cantelmedical.com

PRODUCTS/OPERATIONS

2016 Sales

	$ mil.	% of total
Endoscopy	341.7	51
Water purification & filtration	177.6	27
Healthcare Disposables	112.6	17
Dialysis	32.8	5
Total	**664.7**	**100**

Selected Acquisitions

FY2014
  PuriCore International Limited ($27 million; Somerset UK; endoscope products)
FY2013
  Jet Prep Ltd ($5 million; Herzliya Israel; developer of JET PREP Flushing device)
FY2012
  Byrne Medical Inc. ($100 million; Houston TX; infection control products)
FY2011
  ConFirm Monitoring Systems Inc. ($7.5 million; Denver Colorado; sterilization monitoring products)
  Gambro Medical Water Systems ($23.7 million; Colorado; production of medical grade water)

Selected Subsidiaries

Biolab Equipment Ltd.
Carsen Group Inc. (Canada)
Crosstex International Inc.
Medivators Inc.
Medivators Japan K.K.
Saf-T-Pak Inc. (Canada)
Strong Dental Products Inc.

COMPETITORS

3M Health Care	Getinge
CONMED Corporation	Johnson & Johnson
Danaher	Kimberly-Clark Health
Dentsply Sirona	Olympus
Ecolab	STERIS
Fresenius	Siemens AG
GE Water and Process Technologies	TIDI Products

HISTORICAL FINANCIALS

Company Type: Public

Income Statement   FYE: July 31

	REVENUE ($ mil.)	NET INCOME ($ mil.)	NET PROFIT MARGIN	EMPLOYEES
07/18	871.9	91.0	10.4%	2,693
07/17	770.1	71.3	9.3%	2,337
07/16	664.7	59.9	9.0%	2,000
07/15	565.0	47.9	8.5%	1,680
07/14	488.7	43.2	8.9%	1,534
Annual Growth	**15.6%**	**20.4%**	**—**	**15.1%**

2018 Year-End Financials

Debt ratio: 20.4%	No. of shares (mil.): 41.7
Return on equity: 16.0%	Dividends
Cash ($ mil.): 94.1	Yield: 0.1%
Current ratio: 2.51	Payout: 7.8%
Long-term debt ($ mil.): 187.3	Market value ($ mil.): 3,867.0

	STOCK PRICE ($) FY Close	P/E High/Low	PER SHARE ($) Earnings	Dividends	Book Value
07/18	92.71	60 34	2.18	0.17	14.60
07/17	74.20	50 40	1.71	0.14	12.56
07/16	66.95	51 34	1.44	0.12	10.89
07/15	54.88	48 29	1.15	0.10	9.77
07/14	33.53	36 25	1.04	0.09	8.81
Annual Growth	**29.0%**	**— —**	**20.3%**	**17.2%**	**13.4%**

Capital Southwest Corp.

A private equity firm Capital Southwest owns significant minority stakes in around 30 companies many of them in Texas. The business development company (BDC) offers growth capital recapitalization and acquisition financing and funding for management buyouts to companies in a variety of industries. It typically invests between $5 million to $15 million per transaction in target firms which do not include troubled companies startups real estate developments or other less-than-stable ventures. The company is also focused on investments in the US especially firms located in the Southwest Southeast Midwest and Mountain regions.

Operations

Its 12 largest holdings including Alamo Group The RectorSeal corporation Trax Holdings and The Whitmore Manufacturing Company account for more than 95% of the value of its investment portfolio. An active investor Capital Southwest is usually represented on its portfolio companies' boards and provides strategic and financial advice in addition to capital. The company claims to have the flexibility to hold onto its investments indefinitely; indeed its average holding period is around 20 years.

Sales and Marketing

Capital Southwest focuses on investing in the energy services industrial technologies and specialty chemicals sectors.

Financial Performance

Capital Southwest has enjoyed a steady rise in revenues over the last three years. Revenues climbed 16% from $9.3 million in 2012 to $10.8 million in 2013 due to increased dividend and interest income. Profits surged 16% from $92 million to $107 million as the company made about $88 million on selling several investments during 2013.

Strategy

Like all private equity firms the company generates additional cash by net realized gain on investments. In 2013 it sold 2774250 shares of common stock in Encore Wire Corporation generating a capital gain of $66 million. It also sold all its ownership in Extreme International generating net cash proceeds of nearly $11 million. In addition it sold all its investment ownership in Heelys and earned cash proceeds of roughly $21 million.

EXECUTIVES

Chairman, Gary L. Martin, age 69, $362,500 total compensation
President and CEO, Joseph B. (Joe) Armes, age 54
Senior Vice President, William M. (Bill) Ashbaugh, age 61, $256,250 total compensation
VP, Jeffrey G. (Jeff) Peterson, age 42, $135,000 total compensation
VP, William R. (Will) Thomas III, age 44, $140,781 total compensation
COO CFO Secretary Treasurer and Chief Compliance Officer, Tracy L. Morris, age 50, $146,250 total compensation
VP, Raymond D. Schwertner, age 68
SVP and Chief Investment Officer, Glenn M. Neblett, age 45
Controller, Jessie Porter
Vice President, Scott Shedd
Vice President, Ray Schwertner
Vice President Learn more, Henry J. Gohlke
Director, John H. Wilson, age 73
Director, Donald W. Burton, age 72
Director, Graeme W. Henderson, age 81
Director, Samuel B. Ligon, age 78
Independent Director, Richard Strup
Independent Director, Duane Morgan
Auditors: RSM LLP

LOCATIONS

HQ: Capital Southwest Corp.
5400 Lyndon B. Johnson Freeway, Suite 1300, Dallas, TX 75240
Phone: 214 238-5700
Web: www.capitalsouthwest.com

PRODUCTS/OPERATIONS

Selected Holdings

Alamo Group Inc. (22% tractor-mounted mowing and agricultural equipment)
Atlantic Capital Bancshares Inc. (2%)
Balco Inc. (91% specialty building products)
Boxx Technologies Inc. (15% graphics workstations)
Cinatra Clean Technologies Inc. (69% environmentally safe storage tank cleaning)
Encore Wire Corporation (17% electrical wire and cable)
iMemories Inc. (27% video and photo storage)
KBI Biopharma Inc. (17% drug development)
Palletone Inc. (8% pallets and pressure-treated wood products)
Palm Harbor Homes Inc. (30% manufactured homes)
The RectorSeal Corporation (specialty chemicals)
Texas Capital Bancshares Inc. (2%)
TitanLiner (30% spill containment system)
Trax Holdings Inc. (31% freight audit and logistics services)
Wellogix Inc. (19% supply chain management software for the oil and gas industry)
The Whitmore Manufacturing Company (80% specialty lubricants)

COMPETITORS

American Capital	Fifth Street Finance
Apollo Investment	Gladstone Capital
Ares Capital	MCG Capital
BlackRock	MVC Capital
CapEx	

HISTORICAL FINANCIALS

Company Type: Public

Income Statement — FYE: March 31

	ASSETS ($ mil.)	NET INCOME ($ mil.)	INCOME AS % OF ASSETS	EMPLOYEES
03/18	417.4	16.2	3.9%	19
03/17	325.7	7.8	2.4%	17
03/16	284.4	(10.6)	—	15
03/15	776.8	(2.4)	—	17
03/14	778.6	4.8	0.6%	14
Annual Growth	(14.4%)	35.0%	—	7.9%

	STOCK PRICE ($) FY Close	P/E High/Low		PER SHARE ($) Earnings	Dividends	Book Value
03/18	17.02	18	15	1.01	0.99	19.08
03/17	16.91	33	27	0.50	0.79	17.80
03/16	13.87	—	—	(0.68)	0.14	17.34
03/15	46.42	—	—	(0.16)	0.20	49.30
03/14	34.72	464	97	0.32	0.89	49.98
Annual Growth (21.4%)	(16.3%)			— —	33.3%	2.8%

Care.com Inc

Care.com lets families shop for child care senior care special needs care pet care tutoring and housekeeping services via web and mobile platforms. The site has more than 14 million members including more than 7.5 million families and more than 6 million caregivers who use Care.com to market their services and find employment. The service which is actively used in more than 15 countries (primarily the US but also Canada the UK and other parts of Western Europe) averages about 6.5 million unique visitors each month including about 4 million visitors per month from mobile devices. Care.com also offers household payroll management (HomePay) and other services. In early 2014 Care.com went public.

IPO

Care.com raised $90 million through its IPO. The company will use the proceeds for working capital and other general corporate purposes including potential acquisitions.

Operations

The majority of the site's listings are for part-time assistance. About 60% of all job postings are for part-time care services with the remaining 40% of postings seeking full-time care.

Care.com's HomePay consumer payments solution which is similar to PayPal lets families electronically pay a caregiver and subscribe to tax preparation services.

Geographic Reach

A little more than 90% of the company's revenue comes from the US though the percentage as been falling slowly as the company expands overseas. It operates in more than 15 countries.

Sales and Marketing

Care.com allows caregivers to create personal profiles listing their skills experience and any other information they would like to include to stand out.

In 2014 Care.com spent about $30.5 million on advertising up from $22.3 million in 2013. The company primarily targets women since they make up the largest percentage of both care-seekers and care-givers.

Financial Performance

The company has enjoyed tremendous growth in its revenue and members. Its revenue grew from $12.9 million in fiscal 2010 to $116.7 million in 2014 which was a 43% increase over the previous year. The bump was due to an increase in paying members and higher revenue per member as well as contributions from an acquisition. However despite the years of revenue growth Care.com has seen increasing net losses culminating in a loss of $80.3 million in 2014 largely due to high operating expenses and acquisition-related goodwill impairment. The losses have lead to a nearly continuous increase is cash used in operations from $12.66 in 2013 to $24.28 million in 2014.

Strategy

Though Care.com has seen years of increasing revenue without being profitable its strategy focuses purely on increasing memberships and revenues expanding internationally and pursuing acquisitions.

Mergers and Acquisitions

In 2013 Care.com acquired certain assets of Big-Tent an online forum for parenting groups for $700000.

The following year it effectively bought all the employees of Consmr Inc. the developer of a mobile review app for $600000. Its biggest purchase to date is the 2014 $31 million acquisition of Citrus Lane a consumer-product subscription service aimed at moms.

EXECUTIVES

Founder Chairwoman and CEO, Sheila Lirio Marcelo, age 48, $269,167 total compensation
General Counsel and Corporate Secretary, Diane Musi
Co-Founder & Chief Technology Officer, Dave Krupinski, age 52, $209,167 total compensation
Co-Founder & VP Policy and CSR, Donna Levin
VP & GM Operations Sales & B2B, Michael Marty
Co-Founder VP & GM US Consumer Subscriptions, Zenobia Moochhala
Interim CFO, Steve Boulanger
Vice President, Nancy Bushkin
Auditors: Ernst & Young LLP

LOCATIONS

HQ: Care.com Inc
77 Fourth Avenue, Fifth Floor, Waltham, MA 02451
Phone: 781 642-5900
Web: www.care.com

COMPETITORS

Bright Horizons Family Solutions	Monster Worldwide
Facebook	PayPal
Google	Yahoo!
	craigslist

HISTORICAL FINANCIALS
Company Type: Public

Income Statement — FYE: December 30

	REVENUE ($ mil.)	NET INCOME ($ mil.)	NET PROFIT MARGIN	EMPLOYEES
12/17	174.0	10.6	6.1%	891
12/16	161.7	7.0	4.4%	787
12/15	138.6	(35.0)	—	799
12/14	116.7	(80.2)	—	853
12/13	81.4	(28.3)	—	835
Annual Growth	20.9%	—	—	1.6%

2017 Year-End Financials
Debt ratio: —
Return on equity: 8.4%
Cash ($ mil.): 86.7
Current ratio: 3.12
Long-term debt ($ mil.): —
No. of shares (mil.): 30.3
Dividends
Yield: —
Payout: —
Market value ($ mil.): 548.0

	STOCK PRICE ($) FY Close	P/E High/Low		PER SHARE ($) Earnings	Dividends	Book Value
12/17	18.04	90	36	0.22	0.00	4.60
12/16	8.57	117	50	0.10	0.00	3.95
12/15	7.27	—	—	(1.09)	0.00	2.73
12/14	8.33	—	—	(2.77)	0.00	3.73
Annual Growth	29.4%	—	—	—	—	7.2%

	STOCK PRICE ($) FY Close	P/E High/Low		PER SHARE ($) Earnings	Dividends	Book Value
12/17	16.76	56	42	0.35	0.74	7.88
12/16	15.32	30	19	0.52	0.68	6.98
12/15	10.95	57	40	0.26	0.64	5.50
12/14	12.33	—	—	(0.36)	6.01	3.63
Annual Growth	10.8%	—	—	—	(50.2%)	29.5%

Carolina Financial Corp (New)

Auditors: Elliott Davis, LLC

LOCATIONS
HQ: Carolina Financial Corp (New)
288 Meeting Street, Charleston, SC 29401
Phone: 843 723-7700

HISTORICAL FINANCIALS
Company Type: Public

Income Statement — FYE: December 31

	ASSETS ($ mil.)	NET INCOME ($ mil.)	INCOME AS % OF ASSETS	EMPLOYEES
12/17	3,519.0	28.5	0.8%	770
12/16	1,683.7	17.5	1.0%	441
12/15	1,409.6	14.4	1.0%	421
12/14	1,199.0	8.3	0.7%	394
12/13	881.5	16.8	1.9%	0
Annual Growth	41.3%	14.2%	—	—

2017 Year-End Financials
Return on assets: 1.1%
Return on equity: 8.9%
Long-term debt ($ mil.): —
No. of shares (mil.): 21.0
Sales ($ mil): 129.0
Dividends
Yield: 0.0%
Payout: 9.8%
Market value ($ mil.): 781.0

	STOCK PRICE ($) FY Close	P/E High/Low		PER SHARE ($) Earnings	Dividends	Book Value
12/17	37.15	22	16	1.73	0.17	22.61
12/16	30.79	21	11	1.42	0.13	13.00
12/15	18.00	12	9	1.48	0.11	11.63
12/14	13.99	48	15	0.88	0.09	9.64
12/13	31.51	22	17	1.77	0.02	8.53
Annual Growth	4.2%	—	—	(0.5%)	69.0%	27.6%

CareTrust REIT Inc

Auditors: Ernst & Young LLP

LOCATIONS
HQ: CareTrust REIT Inc
905 Calle Amanecer, Suite 300, San Clemente, CA 92673
Phone: 949 542-3130
Web: www.caretrustreit.com

HISTORICAL FINANCIALS
Company Type: Public

Income Statement — FYE: December 31

	REVENUE ($ mil.)	NET INCOME ($ mil.)	NET PROFIT MARGIN	EMPLOYEES
12/17	132.9	25.8	19.5%	50
12/16	104.6	29.3	28.0%	50
12/15	74.9	10.0	13.4%	46
12/14	58.9	(8.1)	—	43
12/13	48.8	(0.4)	—	0
Annual Growth	28.5%	—	—	—

2017 Year-End Financials
Debt ratio: 47.1%
Return on equity: 4.9%
Cash ($ mil.): 6.9
Current ratio: 0.39
Long-term debt ($ mil.): 558.9
No. of shares (mil.): 75.4
Dividends
Yield: 0.0%
Payout: 211.4%
Market value ($ mil.): 1,265.0

Carrizo Oil & Gas, Inc.

Carrizo Oil & Gas focuses on exploration development and production of crude oil NGLs and gas in the Eagle Ford Shale in South Texas and the Delaware Basin in West Texas. It specializes in horizontal development drilling and completion in unconventional resource plays. Currently the company holds leases covering approximately 145200 net acres containing more than 560 net oil and gas wells. It boasts proved reserves of 262 MMBoe consisting of 64% crude oil 16% natural gas liquids and 20% natural gas. Its production output is around 54000 Boe/d.

Operations
Carrizo focuses on its oil and gas plays in the Eagle Ford Shale and Delaware Basin producing from some 560 net productive wells.

Its Eagle Ford Shale operations include about 103000 net acres of developed and undeveloped drilling locations where it produces some 38000 barrels of oil equivalent per day with proved reserves of 167 million barrels of oil equivalent.

Delaware Basin operations include about 42000 net acres of developed and undeveloped drilling locations where it produces over 6500 barrels of oil equivalent per day with proved reserves of about 91 million barrels of oil equivalent.

During the course of 2018 Carrizo divested its Niobrara assets in the Eagle Ford Shale. These operations included over 30500 net acres of developed and undeveloped drilling locations where the company produced some 2500 barrels of oil equivalent per day with proved reserves of nearly 4 million barrels of oil equivalent.

Geographic Reach
Carrizo's core Eagle Ford properties are in the LaSalle county and to a lesser extent McMullen Frio and Atascosa counties in Texas. Its Delaware Basin properties are in the Culberson and Reeves counties in Texas with operations in the Wolfcamp Formation.

Sales and Marketing
Shell Trading Company Carrizo's largest customer makes up about 70% of the company's annual sales.

Financial Performance
Revenue at Carrizo went up steadily from $217 million in 2008 to a peak of $710 million in 2014 only to fall below $450 million mark in 2015-16. Though mostly profitable the company lost a combined $1.8 billion the 2015-16 years due to the commodity price downturn.

Revenue jumped 68% in 2017 to $746 million primarily due to higher commodity prices and increased production. Production volumes in 2017 were 53805 Boe/d an increase of 27%.

Net income improved remarkably from a loss of $675 million recorded in 2016 to $87 million posted in 2017 mostly from the absence of $577 million in impairment charges followed by a $300 million increase in YOY sales.

Cash holdings at the end of 2017 stood at $10 million. Operations generated $423 million offset by $1.2 billion going towards investments (CAPEX and new acquisitions taking up the lion's share). The shortfall was made up by $2 billion borrowed under credit agreements resulting in a positive net balance in cash from financial activities at $742 million.

Strategy
In 2017 Carrizo began prioritizing development of crude oil properties in two of the lowest risk resource plays—its traditional Eagle Ford base and more recently the Delaware Basin. The company compliments this with leasehold acquisitions.

Productivity spiked some 35% in 2017 thanks to a solid performance from the new Eagle Ford and Delaware Basin wells. Total production in 2017 increased to 53805 Boe/d from 42276

Boe/d in 2016 primarily due to additional volumes coming from the Sanchez (2016) and ExL (2017) acquisitions.

Carrizo also overhauled its holdings in the fourth quarter of 2017 by selling off assets in the Utica and Marcellus Shales for $137 million followed by the sale of Niobrara Formation assets and parts of Eagle Ford holdings for $383 million. In late 2017 Carrizo also acquired 16508 net acres in the Delaware Basin from ExL in a further sign of its faith in the Basin.

In 2018 the company earmarked a CAPEX in the $750-$800 million range assuming a double-digit increase in oilfield service costs and two drilling rigs in the Eagle Ford Shale plus four in the Delaware Basin.

Mergers and Acquisitions

In mid-2018 Carrizo acquired some Delaware Basin acreage from Devon Enegy Corp. for $215 million. The 9600 net-acre-deal increases Carrizo's Delaware Basin acreage position to 46000 net acres including 26300 net acres in its Phantom area.

Carrizo also acquired 16508 net acres in the Delaware Basin in Reeves and Ward Counties from ExL for some $680 million in the third quarter of 2017 in a further sign of Carrizo's faith in the Delaware Basin. Current net production from the assets is approximately 8000 Boe/d (48% oil) from 11 gross producing horizontal wells. Additionally seven wells are currently in the process of drilling completion or flowback.

Company Background

Getting its start by targeting unconventional properties (for example Coalbed methane gas hydrates shale gas and fractured reservoirs) in the first decade of the 21st century in the Barnett Shale Carrizo established itself as an experienced resource play company in the industry having drilled approximately 1000 horizontal wells across multiple resource plays. Its playing field includes the oil and liquids-rich plays in the Eagle Ford Shale in South Texas and the Delaware Basin in West Texas.

EXECUTIVES

President CEO and Director, S. P. (Chip) Johnson, age 63, $448,000 total compensation
VP and COO, J. Bradley (Brad) Fisher, age 58, $312,000 total compensation
Vice President of Exploration and Development, Gregory E. Evans, age 69, $303,000 total compensation
Vice President of Land, Richard H. Smith, age 61, $221,000 total compensation
CFO Chief Accounting Officer and Treasurer, David L. Pitts, age 52, $303,000 total compensation
VP Business Development (Marcellus), Jim Pritts
General Counsel and VP Business Development, Gerry Morton
Vice President of Investor Relations, Jeff Hayden
Vice President Business Development, Jack Bayless
Vice President Investor Relations, Jeffrey Hayden
Vice President and Chief Accounting Officer, Greg Conaway
Chairman, Steven A. Webster, age 66
Assistant Treasurer, Carrie Semrad
Auditors: Ernst & Young LLP

LOCATIONS

HQ: Carrizo Oil & Gas, Inc.
  500 Dallas Street, Suite 2300, Houston, TX 77002
Phone: 713 328-1000
Web: www.carrizo.com

PRODUCTS/OPERATIONS

2017 Sales

	$ mil.	% of total
Crude Oil	633.2	85
Natural Gas	65.3	9
NGLs	47.4	6
Total	**745.9**	**100**

COMPETITORS

BHP Billiton Plc	Encana Oil & Gas (USA)
Chesapeake Energy	Inc.
Devon Energy	Pioneer Natural
EOG	Resources
EXCO Resources	XTO Energy

HISTORICAL FINANCIALS

Company Type: Public

Income Statement   FYE: December 31

	REVENUE ($ mil.)	NET INCOME ($ mil.)	NET PROFIT MARGIN	EMPLOYEES
12/17	745.8	87.1	11.7%	249
12/16	443.5	(675.4)	—	227
12/15	429.2	(1,155.1)	—	215
12/14	710.1	226.3	31.9%	247
12/13	520.1	43.6	8.4%	229
Annual Growth	**9.4%**	**18.8%**		**2.1%**

2017 Year-End Financials

Debt ratio: 58.6%	No. of shares (mil.): 81.4
Return on equity: 28.6%	Dividends
Cash ($ mil.): 9.5	Yield: —
Current ratio: 0.33	Payout: —
Long-term debt ($ mil.): 1,629.2	Market value ($ mil.): 1,733.0

	STOCK PRICE ($) FY Close	P/E High/Low	PER SHARE ($) Earnings	Dividends	Book Value
12/17	21.28	36 11	1.06	0.00	7.18
12/16	37.35	— —	(11.27)	0.00	0.36
12/15	29.58	— —	(22.45)	0.00	7.61
12/14	41.60	14 7	4.90	0.00	23.92
12/13	44.77	44 18	1.06	0.00	18.51
Annual Growth	**(17.0%)**	**— —**	**(0.0%)**	**—**	**(21.1%)**

Carrols Restaurant Group Inc

This company has some fast food royalty in its blood. Carrols Restaurant Group is a leading quick-service restaurant operator and the world's #1 Burger King franchisee with about 660 locations in the US. Like other franchise operators Carrols pays Burger King Worldwide royalties in order to use the BK banner and other intellectual property for its restaurants. Prior to the July 2012 spin-off of wholly-owned subsidiary Fiesta Restaurant

Group Carrols also operated quick-service chains Taco Cabana and Pollo Tropical. The company has Burger King locations in 15 states.

Geographic Reach

The company's Burger King locations are concentrated in the Midwest the Northeast and the Southeast.

Sales and Marketing

Burger King restaurants rely heavily on national television radio newspaper and magazine marketing campaigns (supplemented by local advertising) and new menu additions to drive guest traffic. Carrols' annual advertising expense is normally about 5% of restaurant sales.

Financial Performance

Carrols reported revenue of $692.7 million in fiscal 2014. That was an increase of more than $29 million compared to the company's fiscal 2013 revenue. Despite the spike in revenue Carrols slumped to a new loss of $38.1 million in fiscal 2014. That was an increase of more than $25 million compared to the loss the company suffered in fiscal 2013.

Carrols ended fiscal 2014 with $14.7 million in cash on hand. That was a decrease of $6.8 million compared to the company's prior fiscal period's cash levels.

Strategy

The company's strategy is focused on remodeling its current restaurants according to the Burger King's 20/20 restaurant image which has improved the customer experience increased traffic and led to a higher average check size.

Carrols remodeled more than 300 of its restaurants in fiscal 2014 and the company plans to remodel another 150 locations by 2017.

The company also plans to acquire select Burger King Restaurants across its service area.

HISTORY

Company Background

Carrols Restaurant Group traces its heritage to the Carrols fast food chain started in 1960. It was acquired by Herbert Slotnick in 1968 who combined the restaurant operation with his movie theater chain to form Carrols Development Corporation and took the combined business public the next year. The company began converting its Carrols locations into Burger King restaurants in 1976 and within two years the Carrols chain had disappeared. The company retained the name however.

Carrols was forced by anti-trust regulators to shed the theaters in 1981. Chairman Alan Vituli led an $88 million management buyout that took the company private in 1986. He was appointed CEO in 1992.

Looking to diversify its revenue streams Carrols acquired Pollo Tropical a chain of Caribbean-themed restaurants for $95 million in 1998. Two years later it bought quick-service Tex-Mex chain Taco Cabana for $155 million. In 2003 Carrols hired John Haywood formerly with Jerrico (which once owned the Long John Silver's chain) to lead the development of the two Tex-Mex concepts. (He later left the company in 2005.)

Carrols announced plans to go public in 2004 but quickly withdrew its planned $475 million IPO later that year. The following year the company shuttered about a dozen underperforming Burger King locations. The company successfully completed a $130 million public offering in 2006.

In May 2012 the company completed the acquisition of 278 corporate-owned Burger King locations from Burger King Worldwide. Not long after that transaction Carrols spun-off wholly-owned subsidiary Fiesta Restaurant Group.

EXECUTIVES

VP; CFO and Treasurer, Paul R. Flanders, age 61, $263,268 total compensation
Chairman; CEO; President and Director, Daniel T. Accordino, age 67, $533,032 total compensation
Auditors: DELOITTE & TOUCHE LLP

LOCATIONS

HQ: Carrols Restaurant Group Inc
  968 James Street, Syracuse, NY 13203
Phone: 315 424-0513
Web: www.carrols.com

COMPETITORS

Akwen	Jack in the Box
American Dairy Queen	McDonald's
Austaco	Morgan's Foods
Biglari Holdings	Panera Bread
Boddie-Noell	Popeyes
Bojangles'	Quiznos
Boston Market	R&L Foods
Carolina Restaurant	Sonic Corp.
Group	Subway
Chick-fil-A	Taco Bueno
Chipotle	V & J Holding
Church's Chicken	Wendy's
Einstein Noah	Whataburger
Restaurant Group	White Castle
Hardee's	YUM!

HISTORICAL FINANCIALS
Company Type: Public

Income Statement   FYE: December 31

	REVENUE ($ mil.)	NET INCOME ($ mil.)	NET PROFIT MARGIN	EMPLOYEES
12/17*	1,088.5	7.1	0.7%	23,500
01/17	943.5	45.4	4.8%	21,500
01/16	859.0	0.0	0.0%	20,350
12/14	692.7	(38.1)	—	20,400
12/13	663.4	(13.5)	—	17,500
Annual Growth	13.2%	—	—	7.6%

*Fiscal year change

2017 Year-End Financials

Debt ratio: 48.4%
Return on equity: 4.4%
Cash ($ mil.): 29.4
Current ratio: 0.75
Long-term debt ($ mil.): 279.7
No. of shares (mil.): 35.4
Dividends
  Yield: —
  Payout: —
Market value ($ mil.): 431.0

	STOCK PRICE ($) FY Close	P/E High/Low		Earnings	PER SHARE ($) Dividends	Book Value
12/17*	12.15	105	63	0.16	0.00	4.77
01/17	15.25	15	11	1.01	0.00	4.39
01/16	11.74	—	—	(0.00)	0.00	3.08
12/14	7.71	—	—	(1.23)	0.00	3.06
12/13	6.66	—	—	(0.59)	0.00	3.35
Annual Growth	16.2%	—	—	—	—	9.2%

*Fiscal year change

Cars.com Inc

Auditors: Ernst & Young LLP

LOCATIONS

HQ: Cars.com Inc
  300 S. Riverside Plaza, Suite 1000, Chicago, IL 60606
Phone: 312 601-5000
Web: www.cars.com

HISTORICAL FINANCIALS
Company Type: Public

Income Statement   FYE: December 31

	REVENUE ($ mil.)	NET INCOME ($ mil.)	NET PROFIT MARGIN	EMPLOYEES
12/17	626.2	224.4	35.8%	1,100
12/16	633.1	176.3	27.9%	1,275
12/15	596.5	157.8	26.5%	0
12/14	145.9	16.2	11.1%	0
Annual Growth	62.5%	140.1%	—	—

2017 Year-End Financials

Debt ratio: 23.0%
Return on equity: 10.9%
Cash ($ mil.): 20.5
Current ratio: 1.58
Long-term debt ($ mil.): 557.1
No. of shares (mil.): 71.6
Dividends
  Yield: —
  Payout: —
Market value ($ mil.): 2,066.0

	STOCK PRICE ($) FY Close	P/E High/Low		Earnings	PER SHARE ($) Dividends	Book Value
12/17	28.84	10	7	3.13	0.00	23.44
12/16	0.00	—	—	1.37	0.00	(0.00)
Annual Growth	—	—	—	128.5%	—	—

Carter Validus Mission Critical REIT Inc

Auditors: KPMG LLP

LOCATIONS

HQ: Carter Validus Mission Critical REIT Inc
  4890 West Kennedy Blvd., Suite 650, Tampa, FL 33609
Phone: 813 287-0101
Web: www.cvmissioncriticalreit.com

HISTORICAL FINANCIALS
Company Type: Public

Income Statement   FYE: December 31

	REVENUE ($ mil.)	NET INCOME ($ mil.)	NET PROFIT MARGIN	EMPLOYEES
12/17	94.4	177.3	187.8%	0
12/16	207.2	31.2	15.1%	0
12/15	214.8	63.4	29.5%	0
12/14	154.2	33.5	21.7%	0
12/13	68.3	12.6	18.5%	0
Annual Growth	8.4%	93.5%	—	—

2017 Year-End Financials

Debt ratio: 8.6%
Return on equity: 12.6%
Cash ($ mil.): 336.5
Current ratio: 12.26
Long-term debt ($ mil.): 140.6
No. of shares (mil.): 186.1
Dividends
  Yield: —
  Payout: 73.6%
Market value ($ mil.): —

Casa Systems Inc

Auditors: PricewaterhouseCoopers LLP

LOCATIONS

HQ: Casa Systems Inc
  100 Old River Road, Andover, MA 01810
Phone: 978 688-6706
Web: www.casa-systems.com

HISTORICAL FINANCIALS
Company Type: Public

Income Statement   FYE: December 31

	REVENUE ($ mil.)	NET INCOME ($ mil.)	NET PROFIT MARGIN	EMPLOYEES
12/17	351.5	88.5	25.2%	680
12/16	316.1	88.6	28.0%	604
12/15	272.4	67.9	24.9%	0
12/14	211.2	59.7	28.3%	352
Annual Growth	18.5%	14.0%	—	24.5%

2017 Year-End Financials

Debt ratio: 63.3%
Return on equity: 233.1%
Cash ($ mil.): 260.8
Current ratio: 4.23
Long-term debt ($ mil.): 295.4
No. of shares (mil.): 81.0
Dividends
  Yield: 0.1%
  Payout: 676.0%
Market value ($ mil.): 1,439.0

	STOCK PRICE ($) FY Close	P/E High/Low		Earnings	PER SHARE ($) Dividends	Book Value
12/17	17.76	52	42	0.26	1.76	0.62
12/16	0.00	—	—	(1.07)	2.92	0.78
Annual Growth (20.3%)	—	—	—	(39.8%)	—	—

Cavco Industries Inc (DE)

Cavco's constructions keep customers covered whether they're at home work or vacation. Cavco Industries designs makes and sells manufactured homes (retail prices range from $26000 to more than $190000) under brands including Cavco Palm Harbor and Fleetwood. Its products include full-sized homes (about 500 sq. ft. to 3300 sq. ft.); park model homes (less than 400 sq. ft.) for use as recreational and retirement units; camping cabins; and commercial structures for use as portable classrooms showrooms and offices. Cavco operates about 15 factories in the West and Midwest; its homes are sold by more than 1000 independent retailers and company-owned outlets in the US Canada Mexico and Japan.

Operations

Cavco operates two business segments: factory-built housing accounting for more than 90% of sales; and a finance and insurance arm which represents the rest. Cavco's mortgage subsidiary CountryPlace Mortgage is an approved Fannie Mae and Ginnie Mae seller and servicer offering mortgages to buyers of the company's homes. Its insurances subsidiary Standard Casualty provides property and casualty insurance to owners of manufactured homes. Cavco owns 51% of Fleetwood Homes (acquired in 2009).

Financial Performance

Cavco's fiscal 2012 (ends March) sales increased 158% vs. the prior year while net income rose 438% over the same period. The triple-digit increase in sales was driven by an 137% increase in sales of its factory-built homes and revenue growth from its financial services segment. The acquisition of the assets of bankrupt Palm Harbor Homes in 2011 increased sales and profits in fiscal 2012. Indeed Cavco sold 7860 homes in fiscal 2012 vs. 4786 in the previous year. Sales by company-owned stores increased dramatically although independent retailers sell more than three times as many Cavco homes.

Strategy

Cavco is the second-largest manufacturer of manufactured homes in the US. It markets a variety of brands styles floor plans and price ranges to appeal to a wide customer base. Cavco primarily targets the manufactured housing industry's mainstream market — high-value homes for entry-level and move-up buyers. It also targets specialty markets such as vacation homebuyers and developers of residential subdivisions and senior living communities. Cavco is one of the nation's largest producers of HUD-code manufactured homes which account for some 80% of the manufacturer's homes.

The company has been successful at capitalizing on the woes of its competitors especially during the recent deep recession which led to consolidation of the industry. By acquiring assets of its former rivals Cavco has added production capacity especially for niche market opportunities. In 2009 acquired nine plants from failed competitor Fleetwood for $22 billion. The deal included mothballed facilities in California and Texas as well as operations in new states for Cavco: Idaho Georgia Oregon Tennessee and Virginia. Two years later Cavco went shopping for another ailing competitor. It formed a new subsidiary Fleetwood Homes which bought the assets of bankrupt Palm Harbor for more than $83 million. The deal included Palm Harbor's construction retail and finance units.

HISTORY

Alfred Ghelfi and partner Bob Curtis began a part-time business in 1965 making pickup truck camper shells. The business Roadrunner Manufacturing became Cavalier Manufacturing in 1966 incorporated in 1968 and went public in 1969. The Cavalier name was already in use so in 1974 the company's name was changed to Cavco. After the 1970s oil crisis nearly wiped out the firm Ghelfi bought out Curtis' share and began making mobile homes. In time Cavco began leasing movable storage buildings but the only successful part of that

business was the security container segment (the rest was sold in 1994). A mid-1980s housing market crash in Arizona spurred Cavco to enter a totally new field — health care utilization management — in 1987.

In 1995 Cavco partnered with Japan's Auto Berg Enterprises to begin selling modular housing in Japan. The next year Cavco teamed up with Arizona Public Service to develop solar-powered manufactured housing and it also sold its health care business. Centex acquired nearly 80% of Cavco for $75 million in 1997. The next year Cavco moved into Texas (one of the biggest markets for factory-built homes) acquiring Texas retailer Boerne Homes.

With demand shrinking and surplus inventory building up the company closed its Belen New Mexico factory in 2000 and moved its production to plants in Phoenix and Seguin Texas. That fall Centex tapped manufactured housing veteran Joseph Stegmayer as chairman of its manufactured housing segment.

In 2001 the company launched Factory Liquidators a new retail concept focusing on repossessed homes.

Centex's board of directors approved the tax-free distribution to its shareholders of all of Cavco's outstanding common stock in 2003. The spin-off was completed in June of that year. Continued weakness within the industry forced Cavco to close eight of its company-owned retail outlets in fiscal 2004 and seven more in 2005.

EXECUTIVES

Chairman President Chief Executive Officer, Steven G. Bunger, age 55
Chairman of the Board; President; Chief Executive Officer, Joseph H. (Joe) Stegmayer, age 65, $236,250 total compensation
Senior Vice President Global Ferroalloys, William C. (Bill) Boor, age 50
VP CFO and Treasurer, Daniel L. Urness, age 47, $175,000 total compensation
VP and General Manager Cavco Park Homes and Cabins, Timothy M. Gage
General Counsel and Secretary, James P. Glew
President of Fleetwood Homes; Inc, Charles Lott
President of Palm Harbor Homes; Inc., Larry Keener
Director, Steven G. Bunger, age 55
Director, William C. (Bill) Boor, age 50
Director, David A. Greenblatt, age 54
Director, Jack Hanna, age 69
Auditors: RSM US LLP

LOCATIONS

HQ: Cavco Industries Inc (DE)
3636 North Central Avenue, Suite 1200, Phoenix, AZ 85012
Phone: 602 256-6263
Web: www.cavco.com

COMPETITORS

All American Group	Fairmont Homes
American Homestar	Liberty Homes
Cavalier Homes	PulteGroup
Champion Home Builders	Skyline
Clayton Homes	Sunshine Homes

HISTORICAL FINANCIALS

Company Type: Public

Income Statement   FYE: March 31

	REVENUE ($ mil.)	NET INCOME ($ mil.)	NET PROFIT MARGIN	EMPLOYEES
03/18*	871.2	61.5	7.1%	4,500
04/17	773.8	37.9	4.9%	4,300
04/16	712.3	28.5	4.0%	3,750
03/15	566.6	23.8	4.2%	3,700
03/14	533.3	16.2	3.0%	3,000
Annual Growth	**13.1%**	**39.5%**	—	**10.7%**

*Fiscal year change

2018 Year-End Financials

Debt ratio: 8.8%	No. of shares (mil.): 9.0
Return on equity: 14.4%	Dividends
Cash ($ mil.): 198.6	Yield: —
Current ratio: 2.37	Payout: —
Long-term debt ($ mil.): 33.7	Market value ($ mil.): 1,572.0

	STOCK PRICE ($) FY Close	P/E High/Low	Earnings	PER SHARE ($) Dividends	Book Value
03/18*	173.75	26 16	6.68	0.00	50.54
04/17	116.40	28 20	4.17	0.00	43.85
04/16	93.20	31 20	3.15	0.00	39.56
03/15	75.03	32 24	2.64	0.00	36.14
03/14	78.64	42 21	1.94	0.00	32.84
Annual Growth	**21.9%**	— —	**36.2%**	—	**11.4%**

*Fiscal year change

CB Financial Services Inc

Business services nec nsk
Auditors: Baker Tilly Virchow Krause, LLP

LOCATIONS

HQ: CB Financial Services Inc
100 N. Market Street, Carmichaels, PA 15320
Phone: 724 966-5041
Web: www.communitybank.tv

HISTORICAL FINANCIALS

Company Type: Public

Income Statement   FYE: December 31

	ASSETS ($ mil.)	NET INCOME ($ mil.)	INCOME AS % OF ASSETS	EMPLOYEES
12/17	934.4	6.9	0.7%	201
12/16	846.0	7.5	0.9%	200
12/15	830.6	8.4	1.0%	198
12/14	846.3	4.2	0.5%	193
12/13	546.4	4.2	0.8%	0
Annual Growth	**14.4%**	**13.0%**	—	—

2017 Year-End Financials

Return on assets: 0.7%	Dividends
Return on equity: 7.6%	Yield: 0.0%
Long-term debt ($ mil.): —	Payout: 52.0%
No. of shares (mil.): 4.1	Market value ($ mil.): 123.0
Sales ($ mil): 40.2	

STOCK PRICE ($)		P/E	PER SHARE ($)		
	FY Close	High/Low	Earnings	Dividends	Book Value
12/17	30.00	18 15	1.69	0.88	22.77
12/16	25.85	14 10	1.86	0.88	21.89
12/15	22.92	11 9	2.07	0.85	21.29
12/14	19.90	13 12	1.63	0.84	20.12
12/13	19.75	13 11	1.72	0.84	18.24
Annual Growth	11.0%	— —	(0.4%)	1.2%	5.7%

Cboe Global Markets Inc

CBOE (or Chicago Board Options Exchange) may no longer be the only options exchange but it's still the US leader in overall volume with 1.2 billion contracts processed per year. CBOE lists options on more than 3300 stocks as well as on interest rates broad-based stock indexes (such as Standard & Poor's S&P 500 Index) exchange-traded products and industry indexes. CBOE operates the fully electronic CBOE Futures Exchange and the CBOE Stock Exchange which goes head-to-head with the NYSE and NASDAQ. CBOE also runs the CBOE Volatility Index (VIX) the C2 all-electronic options market the National Stock Exchange and the Options Institute which has provided training for brokers and investors since 1985.

Operations

CBOE operates markets for the trading of listed options contracts in three broad product categories: the stocks of individual corporations (equity options) various market indexes (index options) and exchange-traded funds and exchange-traded notes. It also offer futures and options on futures products through a futures exchange. In 2015 the company's market for listed options CBOE processed 1.2 billion contracts.

The firm makes the bulk of its money from transaction fees. About 72% of its revenue came from transaction fees during 2015 while the rest came from access fees (8% of revenue) exchange services and other fees (7%) market data fees (5%) regulatory fees (5%) and other income sources.

Sales and Marketing

The firm advertises through print advertising product promotion campaigns and seminars conference convention costs at trade shows and industry events and sponsorships with local professional sports organizations. It spent $4.7 million on advertising during 2915 compared to $4.3 million and $5.4 million in 2014 and 2013 respectively.

Financial Performance

CBOE Holdings' annual revenues have risen 25% since 2011 as the appreciating financial markets have attracted more investors and more trading activity leading to higher transaction revenues and demand for other supplementary services. The company's profits have grown more than 45% over the same period as it's kept a lid on operating expense growth.

The firm's revenue climbed 3% to $634.5 million during 2015 as transaction fees continued to grow with a 17.6% increase in average revenue per contract partially offset by an 11.4% decline in trading volumes perhaps as investors were less driven to trade in the uncertain market. Exchange services and other fees were up 11% thanks to higher fees for technology services and added revenue from its summer 2015 acquisition of Livevol.

Revenue growth in 2015 drove CBOE's net income up 8% to $205 million. The company's operating cash levels dipped 7% to $245.28 million despite earnings growth due to unfavorable changes in working capital including lower deferred income taxes income tax liability and stock-based compensation and higher accounts receivable and income taxes receivable.

Strategy

CBOE outlined its five-part growth strategy in early 2016 which included: expanding its customer base globally by attracting new retail and institutional investors and educating them on how to trade its products developing innovative products that leverage and complement its core products offering a compelling economic model with a more trader-friendly fee schedule continuing to enhance its trading systems and evaluating strategic acquisitions that can leverage and complement its core business.

CBOE regularly creates and acquires new products to drive innovation in the market and attract new trading investors. Some of its most well-known products include the C2 fully electronic trading platform and the CBOE Volatility Index or VIX often called the "fear index" which is a popular measure of the mood on Wall Street and the expected volatility of market trading. During 2015 the company developed its new VIX Weeklys options and futures based on the core VIX product acquired the market data services and analytics platforms of Livevol and began its in-house custom development of its next-generation trading technology the CBOE Vector which lets end-users enjoy enhanced agility speed connectivity and risk controls (expected to be implemented on CBOE Futures Exchange in Q3 2016 and on the CBOE and C2 platforms afterward).

The firm also likes to enter licensing agreements to protect its market position. In 2015 for example it signed a licensing agreement with the London Stock Exchange Group (LSEG) to be the exclusive home for LSEG-owned FTSE and Russell Index options. That year it also extended its trading hours for SPX and VIX options after SPX and VIX options and VIX futures volumes set new records in 2014. In 2014 the firm entered a license agreement to become the exclusive US home for MSCI Index Options and extended its VIX futures trading to 24 hours a day.

Mergers and Acquisitions

In 2017 CBOE bought BATS Global Markets in a $3.2 billion transaction. BATS operates the BZX and BYX exchanges; the purchase expands CBOE's market position (especially in Europe) while providing operating and cost efficiencies. BATS owns its trading technologies making the firm an attractive buy for CBOE.

In 2016 the firm made a major equity investment in investment advisor Vest Financial Group which provides options-centric products.

In 2015 CBOE Holdings expanded more into the market data services business after buying the market data services and trading analytics platforms of Livevol which provides equity and index options technology and market data services to professional and retail traders. The deal included acquiring the Livevol Core Livevol Pro and Livevol X trading analytics platforms as well as other market data solutions products including Livevol Enterprise.

Company Background

In early 2012 the company bought the fully electronic National Stock Exchange which it continues to run as a separate entity. The move boosted the exchange's stock market presence by about half. In 2010 CBOE launched C2 an all-electronic options market capable of trading all of CBOE's products electronically.

CBOE went public in 2010 to better compete in the highly competitive options industry. As a corporation CBOE has better access to capital markets and is able to more easily enter joint ventures or other business combinations. The long-delayed IPO was also part of CBOE's restructuring efforts and a shift from being member-owned to a for-profit corporation.

The company was founded in 1973 by the Chicago Board of Trade (now part of CME Group).

HISTORY

The company was founded in 1973 by the Chicago Board of Trade (now part of CME Group).

CBOE went public in 2010 to better compete in the highly competitive options industry. As a corporation CBOE has better access to capital markets and is able to more easily enter joint ventures or other business combinations. CBOE raised $339 million in a 2010 initial public offering (IPO). The long-delayed IPO was part of CBOE's restructuring efforts and a shift from being member-owned to a for-profit corporation. CBOE allotted funds raised in its IPO for general corporate purposes and for the issuance of common stock shares to existing members.

CBOE launched an all-electronic options market in 2010. Named C2 the new platform was capable of trading all of CBOE's products electronically.

In 2011 the CBOE Stock Exchange moved its trading operations from Chicago to the East Coast to better compete with other stock exchanges and better serve its primarily East Coast-based clientele.

In early 2012 the company bought the fully electronic National Stock Exchange which it continues to run as a separate entity. The move boosted the exchange's stock market presence by about half.

EXECUTIVES

EVP and President Europe of Chicago Board Options Exchange Incorporated, Mark Hemsley, age 55

EVP CFO and Treasurer, Alan J. Dean, age 63, $518,333 total compensation

EVP General Counsel and Corporate Secretary, Joanne Moffic-Silver, age 65, $420,000 total compensation

Chairman and CEO, Edward T. Tilly, age 54, $966,667 total compensation

EVP and CIO, Chris Isaacson, age 39

President and COO, Chris Concannon

Vice President of Facilities, Luann Oshea

Auditors: DELOITTE & TOUCHE LLP

LOCATIONS

HQ: Cboe Global Markets Inc
400 South LaSalle Street, Chicago, IL 60605
Phone: 312 786-5600
Web: www.cboe.com

PRODUCTS/OPERATIONS

Sales 2015

	$ mil.	% of total
Transaction fees	456.0	72
Access fees	53.3	8
Exchange services and other fees	42.2	7
Market data fees	30.0	5
Regulatory fees	33.5	5
Other revenue	19.5	3
Total	**634.5**	**100**

COMPETITORS

Deutsche B ¶rse	Nasdaq
ISE	PHLX
NYSE Holdings	TMX Group
NYSE Liffe	

HISTORICAL FINANCIALS

Company Type: Public

Income Statement   FYE: December 31

	REVENUE ($ mil.)	NET INCOME ($ mil.)	NET PROFIT MARGIN	EMPLOYEES
12/17	2,229.1	401.7	18.0%	889
12/16	656.9	186.8	28.4%	553
12/15	634.5	205.0	32.3%	564
12/14	617.2	189.7	30.7%	520
12/13	572.0	176.0	30.8%	650
Annual Growth	**40.5%**	**22.9%**	**—**	**8.1%**

2017 Year-End Financials

Debt ratio: 23.5%	No. of shares (mil.): 112.7
Return on equity: 23.4%	Dividends
Cash ($ mil.): 143.5	Yield: 0.0%
Current ratio: 1.30	Payout: 28.1%
Long-term debt ($ mil): 1,237.9	Market value ($ mil): 14,046.0

	STOCK PRICE ($) FY Close	P/E High/Low		PER SHARE ($) Earnings	Dividends	Book Value
12/17	124.59	34	20	3.69	1.04	27.59
12/16	73.89	34	26	2.27	0.96	3.91
12/15	64.90	29	23	2.46	0.88	3.16
12/14	63.42	29	21	2.21	0.78	2.97
12/13	51.96	27	15	1.99	1.16	3.28
Annual Growth	**24.4%**	**—**	**—**	**16.7%**	**(2.7%)**	**70.3%**

CenterState Bank Corp

CenterState Banks is the holding company for CenterState Bank of Florida which serves the Sunshine State through about 60 branches. The bank offers standard deposit products such as checking and savings accounts money market accounts and CDs. Real estate loans primarily residential and commercial mortgages make up 85% of the company's loan portfolio while the rest is made up of business loans and consumer loans. The bank's correspondent division provides bond securities accounting and loans to small and mid-sized banks across the Southeast and Texas. It also sells mutual funds annuities and other investment products.

Operations

About 65% of CenterState Banks' total revenue came from loan interest in 2014 while another 10% came from interest on its investment securities. The rest of the bank's revenue came form correspondent banking capital markets revenue and related revenue (11%) deposit account service charges (5%) debit/ATM and merchant card fees (3%) wealth management fees (2%) and other miscellaneous income sources. The company had a staff of 785 employees by the end of 2014.

Geographic Reach

CenterState has nearly 60 branches across 20 counties in central southeast and northeast Florida. Its loan production offices are in Tampa Gainesville Crystal River and Ft. Meyers.

Sales and Marketing

CenterState offers consumer and commercial banking services to individuals businesses and industries across Florida.

Financial Performance

The company has struggled to consistently grow its revenues in recent years due to shrinking interest margins on loans amidst the low-interest environment. Its profits however have been rising thanks to declining loan loss provisions as its loan portfolio's credit quality has improved with higher property valuations in the strengthened economy.

CenterState had a breakout year in 2014 however with its revenue jumping 22% to $164.5 million thanks to higher interest income stemming from new loan business from its acquisitions of First Southern Bancorp and Gulfstream Bancshares during the year.

Higher revenue and stable costs in 2014 also drove the bank's net income higher by 6% to a record $12.96 million. CenterState's operating cash levels plummeted by 90% to $1.4 million after adjusting its earnings for non-cash items mostly related to the net proceeds from its trading securities sales.

Strategy

CenterState Banks continues to seek out additional acquisition opportunities to boost its loan and deposit business and expand into more markets across Florida. To this end the bank's 2014 acquisitions extended its reach into Broward Palm Beach and Martin counties for the first time while adding more than $1.3 billion in new deposits and over $600 million in new loan business to its books.

Struggling to grow its revenues the bank has also worked to become more efficient and profitable through selective branch closures. During 2014 the company closed seven smaller branches and a standalone drive-thru facility to free up resources for more profitable bank acquisitions.

Mergers and Acquisitions

CenterState is buying Platinum Bank Holding Company parent company of Platinum Bank for approximately $83.9 million. The acquisition will add seven banking branches in the Tampa-St. Petersburg-Clearwater and Lakeland-Winter Haven areas. It will also add some $584 million in assets.

In June 2014 CenterState purchased First Southern Bancorp which expanded its market reach into Broward County after adding a net of seven new branches. The deal also added some $600 million in new loan assets and $853 million in deposits.

In January 2014 the company expanded into Palm Beach and Martin counties after buying Gulfstream Bancshares and its four branches with $479 million in deposits.

EXECUTIVES

SVP and CFO, James J. Antal, age 67, $312,750 total compensation
Senior Vice President, Rick Alspaugh
President CEO and Director CenterState Banks Inc. and Centerstate Bank of Florida, John Corbett, age 49, $420,250 total compensation
Corporate Chief Risk Officer, Daniel E. Bockhorst, $217,500 total compensation
Treasurer, Stephen Young, $278,333 total compensation
First Vice President Business Development, Chris Wright
Assistant Vice President Residential Loan Operations Manager, Becky Chiasson
Vice President Retail Service Leader, Annette Fortunato-diaz
Senior Vice President And Commercial Lending Officer, Bill Daniels
Assistant Vice President Merchant Services Divison, Deborah Joyce
Assistant Vice President Business Analyst Ii, Chante Carlson
First Vice President, Stacey A Dunn
Senior Vice President and Chief Operations Officer, Stacy Byrd
Assistant Vice President, Mary Young
Vice President Retail Market Manager, Bretta Christakos
Assistant Vice President Human Resources Employee Relations Officer, Raquel Morales
Senior Vice President, Mark Tucker
Assistant Vice President Project Manager, Lexie Williams
Vice President, Gail Copa
First Vice President, Richard Skopick
Vice President Commercial Lender, Winn Keeton
Senior Vice President Commercial Banking, Garry Lubi
Senior Vice President Community President, Mark Stevens
Vice President, Elfa Mora
First Vice President Prepaid Cards Division, Bruce Davidson
Vice President Commercial Lender, Mike Clanton
Assistant Vice President And Fed Funds Trader, Rebecca Henderson
Assistant Vice President Branch Manager, Denise Tarafa
Chairman, Ernest S. (Ernie) Pinner, age 70
Auditors: Crowe Horwath LLP

LOCATIONS

HQ: CenterState Bank Corp
1101 First Street South, Suite 202, Winter Haven, FL 33880
Phone: 863 293-4710
Web: www.centerstatebanks.com

PRODUCTS/OPERATIONS

2011 Sales

	$ mil.	% of total
Interest		
Loans	65.9	36
Investment securities available for sale	15.7	9
Other	0.6	-
Noninterest		
Bargain purchase gain	57.0	31
Correspondent banking & bond sales	24.9	13
Service charges on deposit accounts	6.3	3

Net gain on sale of securities		3.5	2
Other		10.3	6
Total		**184.2**	**100**

COMPETITORS

BB&T	Regions Financial
BBX Capital	Seacoast Banking
Bank of America	SunTrust
Fifth Third	Wells Fargo
JPMorgan Chase	

HISTORICAL FINANCIALS
Company Type: Public

Income Statement
FYE: December 31

	ASSETS ($ mil.)	NET INCOME ($ mil.)	INCOME AS % OF ASSETS	EMPLOYEES
12/17	7,123.9	55.8	0.8%	1,200
12/16	5,078.5	42.3	0.8%	952
12/15	4,022.7	39.3	1.0%	784
12/14	3,776.8	12.9	0.3%	785
12/13	2,415.5	12.2	0.5%	693
Annual Growth	31.0%	46.1%	—	14.7%

2017 Year-End Financials

Return on assets: 0.9%	Dividends
Return on equity: 7.6%	Yield: 0.0%
Long-term debt ($ mil.): —	Payout: 25.2%
No. of shares (mil.): 60.1	Market value ($ mil.): 1,548.0
Sales ($ mil): 316.5	

	STOCK PRICE ($) FY Close	P/E High/Low	PER SHARE ($) Earnings	Dividends	Book Value
12/17	25.73	29 23	0.95	0.24	15.04
12/16	25.17	29 15	0.88	0.16	11.47
12/15	15.65	19 13	0.85	0.07	10.79
12/14	11.91	37 31	0.31	0.04	9.98
12/13	10.15	26 18	0.41	0.04	9.08
Annual Growth	26.2%	— —	23.4%	56.5%	13.4%

Central Garden & Pet Co

Central Garden & Pet tends to all things pets and pests. It is among the largest US producers and distributors of lawn garden and pet supplies providing its products to retailers home improvement centers nurseries and mass merchandisers among them Wal-Mart. The company operates some 35 manufacturing plants and about 20 distribution centers throughout the US. Central Garden & Pet's sells private label and also branded lines such as AMDRO fire ant bait Four Paws animal products Kaytee bird seed Nylabone dog chews and TFH pet books.

Operations
The company operates two businesses Pet and Garden. The Pet segment generates a little more than 60% of revenue by producing distributing marketing and selling a wide variety of pet-related products for the US. The company mainly targets the pet supplies market which includes edible bones chew toys rawhide pet beds and carriers grooming supplies animal health products aquar-

iums water conditioners and other items. Recognizable brands include Four Paws Coralife Kaytee Breeder?s Choice and Life Sciences. The US pet market is highly fragmented with about 1400 manufacturers. Central Garden & Pet has a competitive advantage in that it operates its own sales and logistics network.

The Garden segment accounts for a little less than 40% of total revenue. It markets and produces grass seed wild bird feed insect control products lawn and garden care items fertilizers and outdoor patio products. Notable brands include Pennington Seed AMDRO Lilly Miller the Pottery Group and Gulfstream.

About 10% of the products sold by Central Garden & Pet are made in China making it susceptible to tariffs placed on Chinese-made goods in the ongoing tensions between the US and China over trade.

Geographic Reach
Walnut Creek California-headquartered Central Garden & Pet operates 35 manufacturing facilities totaling approximately 5.5 million square feet and 60 sales and logistics facilities totaling approximately 4.4 million square feet. Most sales and logistics centers are comprised of office and warehouse space and several large bays for loading and unloading. Each sales and logistics center provides warehouse distribution sales and support functions for its geographic area.

Although most operations and facilities are in the US the company has a presence in Canada China Mexico and the UK.

Sales and Marketing
Central Garden & Pet relies heavily on just a few national retail chains for much of its sales. The company's largest customer Wal-Mart accounts for about 15% of total sales and about 30% of sales for the company's Garden segment. The Home Depot Lowe's Costco PetSmart along with Wal-Mart generate about half of overall revenue. PETCO is also a big customer.

The company relies on a domestic sales network to promote its proprietary brands to thousands of independent specialty stores.

Financial Performance
Central Garden & Pet runs a steady financial organization. For over a decade its revenue remained in a tight range between $1.6 billion and $1.8 billion before breaking the $2 billion mark in 2017 and 2018 (ended September). Net income followed with large gains in the past two years.

In 2018 Central Garden & Pet's built on the previous year's 12% sales increase. Revenue rose 8% to $2.2 billion on 8% increases in sales of pet and garden products. Acquisitions helped the pet segment to the tune of $56 million as well as the garden segment with $84 million.

Net income for the year leaped 58% higher to $123.6 million in 2018 beating the company high established the year before. Costs associated with acquisitions were higher in 2018 but the US Tax Cuts and Jobs Act lowered Central Garden & Pet's income taxes some $43 million.

Cash at the end of 2018 was $482 million up $450 million from the prior year. Cash from operations was stable at $114 million year-to-year while investing activities used $139 million primarily to acquire businesses. Financing activities however provided about $475 million due to about $300 million in debt issued in 2018. In 2017 financing activities used about $10 million mainly for stock buybacks.

Strategy
Central Garden & Pet focuses on building leading brand names by introducing innovative products and packaging extending existing product lines and entering new product categories. It also continues to make selected strategic acquisitions of companies that complement existing brands and product offerings.

Central Garden & Pet is no stranger to acquisitions having purchased more than 40 companies over its lifespan. In 2018 it bought General Pet Supply based in Milwaukee Wisconsin and Bell Nursery which operates in the mid-Atlantic region.

Because a significant portion of its revenue comes from a handful of retailers the company views customer relationships as a key performance indicator. In 2018 it received awards from Lowe?s Petco and Pet Valu for products and service.

The company is streamlining and improving its technologies to enhance efficiency. It has reduced the number of enterprise resource systems from 37 (accumulated through acquisitions) to fewer than 10.

Mergers and Acquisitions
In 2018 Central Garden & Pet purchased General Pet Supply a Midwestern pet food and supplies purveyor for $24 million. The acquisition was expected to expand the company?s pet food and supply distribution footprint and provide access to the veterinary channel.

Also in 2018 the company acquired Bell Nursery a distributor in the mid-Atlantic region for $61 million.

In 2017 Central Garden & Pet purchased K&H Manufacturing a producer of premium pet supplies and the largest marketer of heated pet products in the US for $48 million.

Company Background
Central Garden & Pet Company's roots go back to 1955 when it was founded as a small California distributor of lawn and garden supplies. After nearly three decades of unremarkable growth it was purchased in 1980 by William Brown a former VP of finance at camera maker Vivitar. The company acquired small distributors but let them operate autonomously. By 1987 Central had sales of $25 million with distribution in California.

The company's first major acquisition was the result of a restructuring of forestry giant Weyerhaeuser which had diversified into insurance home building and diapers among other products but was selling noncore divisions to focus solely on timber. It sold Weyerhaeuser Garden Supply to Central in 1990 for $32 million.

Overnight Central became a national powerhouse with 25 distribution centers serving 38 states. In 1991 sales reached $280 million of which acquired operations accounted for nearly 70%. The purchase also gave Central 10 high-volume retail customers — including Costco Kmart and Wal-Mart — which accounted for half of its business. That year the company also acquired a pet distributor its first move into pet supplies.

To pay down debt associated with the Weyerhaeuser acquisition the company (then officially known as Central Garden & Pet Company) went public in 1993 (a 1992 IPO was withdrawn when a warehouse fire damaged inventory). With the capital for growth Central continued to acquire other distributors (from early 1993 to early 1994 it acquired six distributors with about $70 million in sales).

In 1994 the company's largest supplier Solaris (then a unit of Monsanto and maker of Ortho and Roundup products) decided to bypass Central as its distributor and sell products directly. Solaris products accounted for nearly 40% of the company's sales and revenues dipped in 1995. However that year Solaris decided that self-distribution was too difficult and made Central its exclusive distributor. Total sales increased about 65% in 1996.

Broadening its pet supply distribution network in 1996 Central paid $33 million for Kenlin Pet Supply the East Coast's largest pet distributor and Longhorn Pet Supply in Texas. The following year the company bought Four Paws Products and Sandoz Agro.

In 1997 Central paid $132 million for TFH Publications one of the nation's largest producers of pet books and maker of Nylabone dog snacks and Kaytee Products a maker of bird seed. It added Pennington Seed a maker of grass and bird seed in 1998.

The company broadened its scope in 1999 with the purchase of Norcal Pottery Products. It also tried to buy Solaris but that year Monsanto sold its Solaris unit to grass firm The Scotts Co. (now Scotts Miracle-Gro). In a familiar refrain for Central Scotts then decided to shift partially toward self-distribution costing Central between $200 million and $250 million in annual sales; Scotts would completely sever distribution ties with Central the following year leading to countering lawsuits.

Central said in early 2000 it would spin off its lawn and garden distribution business to shareholders but the company abandoned the plan less than a year later. In March 2000 the company acquired AMDRO fire ant killer and IMAGE a weed herbicide from American Home Products (now Wyeth) for $28 million. Later that year Central purchased All-Glass Aquarium Company a manufacturer and marketer of aquariums and related products.

HISTORY

Central Garden & Pet Company's roots go back to 1955 when it was founded as a small California distributor of lawn and garden supplies. After nearly three decades of unremarkable growth it was purchased in 1980 by William Brown a former VP of finance at camera maker Vivitar. The company acquired small distributors but let them operate autonomously. By 1987 Central had sales of $25 million with distribution in California.

The company's first major acquisition was the result of a restructuring of forestry giant Weyerhaeuser which had diversified into insurance home building and diapers among other products but was selling noncore divisions to focus solely on timber. It sold Weyerhaeuser Garden Supply to Central in 1990 for $32 million.

Overnight Central became a national powerhouse with 25 distribution centers serving 38 states. In 1991 sales reached $280 million of which acquired operations accounted for nearly 70%. The purchase also gave Central 10 high-volume retail customers — including Costco Kmart and Wal-Mart — which accounted for half of its business. That year the company also acquired a pet distributor its first move into pet supplies.

To pay down debt associated with the Weyerhaeuser acquisition the company (then officially known as Central Garden & Pet Company) went public in 1993 (a 1992 IPO was withdrawn when

a warehouse fire damaged inventory). With the capital for growth Central continued to acquire other distributors (from early 1993 to early 1994 it acquired six distributors with about $70 million in sales).

In 1994 the company's largest supplier Solaris (then a unit of Monsanto and maker of Ortho and Roundup products) decided to bypass Central as its distributor and sell products directly. Solaris products accounted for nearly 40% of the company's sales and revenues dipped in 1995. However that year Solaris decided that self-distribution was too difficult and made Central its exclusive distributor. Total sales increased about 65% in 1996.

Broadening its pet supply distribution network in 1996 Central paid $33 million for Kenlin Pet Supply the East Coast's largest pet distributor and Longhorn Pet Supply in Texas. The following year the company bought Four Paws Products and Sandoz Agro.

In 1997 Central paid $132 million for TFH Publications one of the nation's largest producers of pet books and maker of Nylabone dog snacks and Kaytee Products a maker of bird seed. It added Pennington Seed a maker of grass and bird seed in 1998.

The company broadened its scope in 1999 with the purchase of Norcal Pottery Products. It also tried to buy Solaris but that year Monsanto sold its Solaris unit to grass firm The Scotts Co. (now Scotts Miracle-Gro). In a familiar refrain for Central Scotts then decided to shift partially toward self-distribution costing Central between $200 million and $250 million in annual sales; Scotts would completely sever distribution ties with Central the following year leading to countering lawsuits.

Central said in early 2000 it would spin off its lawn and garden distribution business to shareholders but the company abandoned the plan less than a year later. In March 2000 the company acquired AMDRO fire ant killer and IMAGE a weed herbicide from American Home Products (now Wyeth) for $28 million. Later that year Central purchased All-Glass Aquarium Company a manufacturer and marketer of aquariums and related products.

EXECUTIVES

President and CEO, George C. Roeth, age 57, $232,500 total compensation
EVP, Michael A. Reed, age 70, $480,808 total compensation
General Counsel and Corporate Secretary, George A. Yuhas, age 65, $459,438 total compensation
CFO, Nicholas (Niko) Lahanas
VICE PRESIDENT, Carl Peterson
Senior Vice President National Account Sales, Roger Mosshart
Senior Vice President Supply Chain, Paul Hibbert
Vice President of Marketing, Kameshia Watkins
Vice President Training And Development, Lisa Lines
Vice President Of Sales Garden Distribution Accounts, Wes Martin
Senior Vice President, Cristina Weekes
Vice President, John Emmons
Vice President of sales, Henry Lam
Vice President Of Consumer Insights, Scott Peterson
Vice President, Joanne Hiras
Vice President of Distribution, Jordan Downs
Senior Vice President Human Resources, Janet M Brady

Vice President Marketing, Stacie Pacheco
Vice President of Sales, Patricia Owens
Executive Vice President, Neill Hines
National Account Manager, Bobby Lechler
Executive Vice President, Ronnie Stapp
National Account Manager, Eric Spiegler
Vice President, Dennis Rowe
Senior Vice President of Sales and Business Unit Leader, Andy Ponte
National Account Manager, Mike Flynn
Vice President Operations, Hank Beattie
Vice President, James Mathews
Vice President of Real Estate, Debbie Framarin
Executive Vice President, Mike Reed
Vice President of Manufacturing and Strategic Procurement, Mike Baker
Senior Vice President Operations, Bill Lynch
Vice President Planning And Procurement, David Norman
Chairman, William E. (Bill) Brown, age 77
Auditors: Deloitte & Touche LLP

LOCATIONS

HQ: Central Garden & Pet Co
1340 Treat Blvd., Suite 600, Walnut Creek, CA 94597
Phone: 925 948-4000
Web: www.central.com

PRODUCTS/OPERATIONS

2018 Sales

	$ mil.	% of total
Pet Products		
Dog and cat products	444.4	20
Other pet products	896.5	40
Garden Products		
Garden controls and fertilizer products	345.7	16
Other garden supplies	528.8	24
Total	**2,215.4**	**100**

Selected Products and Brands

Pet products
  Aquatics
  All-Glass Aquarium
  Kent Marine
  Bird and small animal
  Kaytee
  Dog and cat
  Four Paws
  Interpet
  Nylabone
  Pet Select
  TFH
  Insect control and animal health
  Strike
  Zodiac
Garden products
  Garden decor and pottery
  New England Pottery
  Grass seed
  Lofts Seed
  Pennington
  Rebel
  Weed insect and pest control
  AMDRO
  IMAGE
  Lilly Miller
  Over'n Out
  Sevin
  Wild bird
  Kaytee
  Pennington

COMPETITORS

A.C. Graham
Boss Holdings
Doskocil Manufacturing Company
Dow AgroSciences
Hartz Mountain

Meda Pharmaceuticals
Rollins Inc.
Scotts Miracle-Gro
Spectrum Brands
Virbac Corporation

HISTORICAL FINANCIALS
Company Type: Public

Income Statement
FYE: September 29

	REVENUE ($ mil.)	NET INCOME ($ mil.)	NET PROFIT MARGIN	EMPLOYEES
09/18	2,215.3	123.5	5.6%	5,400
09/17	2,054.4	78.8	3.8%	4,100
09/16	1,829.0	44.5	2.4%	3,600
09/15	1,650.7	31.9	1.9%	3,300
09/14	1,604.3	8.8	0.5%	3,300
Annual Growth	8.4%	93.6%	—	13.1%

2018 Year-End Financials
Debt ratio: 36.2%
Return on equity: 15.6%
Cash ($ mil.): 493.0
Current ratio: 5.72
Long-term debt ($ mil.): 692.0
No. of shares (mil.): 57.7
Dividends
Yield: —
Payout: —
Market value ($ mil.): 1,914.0

	STOCK PRICE ($) FY Close	P/E High/Low	PER SHARE ($) Earnings	Dividends	Book Value
09/18	33.14	17 14	2.32	0.00	16.49
09/17	37.19	24 14	1.52	0.00	12.26
09/16	24.39	28 13	0.87	0.00	10.83
09/15	16.78	26 11	0.64	0.00	10.10
09/14	8.04	53 34	0.18	0.00	9.51
Annual Growth	42.5%	— —	89.5%	—	14.8%

Central Valley Community Bancorp

Central Valley Community Bancorp is the holding company for Central Valley Community Bank which offers individuals and businesses traditional banking services through about 25 offices in California's San Joaquin Valley. Deposit products include checking savings and money market accounts; IRAs; and CDs. The bank founded in 1979 offers credit card services and originates a variety of loans including residential and commercial mortgage Small Business Administration and agricultural loans. Through Central Valley Community Insurance Services it markets health property and casualty insurance products primarily to business customers.

EXECUTIVES

Vice President Operations, Teresa Gilio
Vice President Cash Management Officer, Evey Amado
Vice President and Human Resources Director, Marci Madsen
Vice President and Compliance Officer, Denise Jereb
Vice President, Debra Walker
Vice President Sales, Shannon Reinard
Vice President Commercial Loan, Robert Walker
Vice President Branch Manager, Vicki Nino
Vice President Commercial Loan Officer, Chad Bringe
Vice President Commercial Banking, Brad Wible
Auditors: Crowe Horwath LLP

LOCATIONS

HQ: Central Valley Community Bancorp
7100 N. Financial Drive., Suite 101, Fresno, CA 93720
Phone: 559 298-1775
Web: www.cvcb.com

COMPETITORS

American River Bankshares
Bank of America
Comerica
MUFG Americas Holdings
RCB Corp.
Sierra Bancorp
TriCo Bancshares
United Security Bancshares
Westamerica

HISTORICAL FINANCIALS
Company Type: Public

Income Statement
FYE: December 31

	ASSETS ($ mil.)	NET INCOME ($ mil.)	INCOME AS % OF ASSETS	EMPLOYEES
12/17	1,661.6	14.0	0.8%	316
12/16	1,443.3	15.1	1.1%	287
12/15	1,276.7	10.9	0.9%	282
12/14	1,192.1	5.2	0.4%	290
12/13	1,145.6	8.2	0.7%	290
Annual Growth	9.7%	14.2%	—	2.2%

2017 Year-End Financials
Return on assets: 0.9%
Return on equity: 7.5%
Long-term debt ($ mil.): —
No. of shares (mil.): 13.7
Sales ($ mil): 68.2
Dividends
Yield: 0.0%
Payout: 21.8%
Market value ($ mil.): 276.0

	STOCK PRICE ($) FY Close	P/E High/Low	PER SHARE ($) Earnings	Dividends	Book Value
12/17	20.18	21 16	1.10	0.24	15.30
12/16	19.96	15 8	1.33	0.24	13.51
12/15	12.03	13 10	1.00	0.23	12.67
12/14	11.08	28 22	0.48	0.20	11.93
12/13	11.25	16 10	0.77	0.20	11.00
Annual Growth	15.7%	— —	9.3%	4.7%	8.6%

Century Casinos Inc.

In the 19th century people rushed to Cripple Creek Colorado seeking their fortune in gold. Today thanks to Century Casinos they can do basically the same thing (but via midsized regional casinos rather than through prospecting). The company's Womacks Casino & Hotel in Cripple Creek offers some 440 slot machines and video devices as well as a handful of gaming tables. It also owns the Century Casino & Hotel in Central City Colorado and another Century Casino & Hotel in Edmonton Canada. In addition it operate four cruise ship casinos and is the casino concessionaire for cruise lines run by TUI Cruises a joint venture between German travel operator TUI and #2 cruise ship operator Royal Caribbean.

Strategy
After a period of major expansion Century Casinos has been focused on upgrading its properties and making targeted acquisitions. In early 2010 the company acquired the Silver Dollar casino in Alberta Canada from struggling Evergreen Gam-

ing for some $9.5 million. It spent nearly $2 million to renovate the gaming floor and dining area at Womacks during 2008.

Geographic Reach
Outside of North America Century Casinos continues to own a controlling stake in Casinos Poland Ltd. (CPL) owner and operator of eight casinos in Poland. Century Casinos owns 33% of CPL and in 2012 the company agreed to up its stake to 66.6%.

After a experiencing decreased gaming revenue at all of its properties during the global recession the company disposed of its properties in the Czech Republic and South Africa. It sold the Caledon Hotel Spa & Casino near Cape Town South Africa to Tsogo Sun Gaming in 2009. The deal included a 60% stake in Century Casino Newcastle. Also that year it sold its Century Casino Millennium in the Marriott hotel in Prague to Viva Casino Group.

EXECUTIVES

Vice Chairman President Co Chief Executive Officer, Peter Hoetzinger
Auditors: DELOITTE & TOUCHE LLP

LOCATIONS

HQ: Century Casinos Inc.
455 E. Pikes Peak Ave., Suite 210, Colorado Springs, CO 80903
Phone: 719 527-8300
Web: www.cnty.com

PRODUCTS/OPERATIONS

Selected Properties
North America
  Century Casino & Hotel (Century City Colorado)
  Century Casino & Hotel (Edmonton Alberta Canada)
  Womacks Casino & Hotel (Cripple Creek Colorado)
Poland
  Casinos Poland Ltd. (33% 7 full casinos and one slot casino)

COMPETITORS

Global Casinos
Herbst Gaming
Isle of Capri Casinos
Majestic Star
Nevada Gold & Casinos
Riviera Holdings
Trans World Corporation

HISTORICAL FINANCIALS
Company Type: Public

Income Statement
FYE: December 31

	REVENUE ($ mil.)	NET INCOME ($ mil.)	NET PROFIT MARGIN	EMPLOYEES
12/17	154.0	6.2	4.1%	1,910
12/16	139.2	9.2	6.6%	1,791
12/15	134.4	11.9	8.9%	1,638
12/14	120.0	1.2	1.0%	1,620
12/13	104.5	6.1	5.9%	1,600
Annual Growth	10.2%	0.3%	—	4.5%

2017 Year-End Financials
Debt ratio: 20.6%
Return on equity: 4.0%
Cash ($ mil.): 74.6
Current ratio: 2.45
Long-term debt ($ mil.): 51.0
No. of shares (mil.): 29.3
Dividends
Yield: —
Payout: —
Market value ($ mil.): 268.0

STOCK PRICE ($) FY Close	P/E High/Low	PER SHARE ($) Earnings	Dividends	Book Value
12/17 9.13	39 26	0.24	0.00	6.13
12/16 8.23	22 14	0.37	0.00	5.41
12/15 7.78	16 10	0.49	0.00	5.01
12/14 5.05	161 98	0.05	0.00	4.86
12/13 5.21	24 11	0.26	0.00	5.00
Annual Growth 15.1%	— —	(2.0%)	—	5.2%

Century Communities Inc

Auditors: Ernst & Young LLP

LOCATIONS

HQ: Century Communities Inc
8390 East Crescent Parkway, Suite 650, Greenwood Village, CO 80111
Phone: 303 770-8300

HISTORICAL FINANCIALS

Company Type: Public

Income Statement   FYE: December 31

	REVENUE ($ mil.)	NET INCOME ($ mil.)	NET PROFIT MARGIN	EMPLOYEES
12/17	1,423.8	50.3	3.5%	1,011
12/16	994.4	49.5	5.0%	565
12/15	734.4	39.8	5.4%	510
12/14	362.3	20.0	5.5%	397
12/13	171.1	12.3	7.2%	0
Annual Growth	69.8%	42.0%	—	—

2017 Year-End Financials

Debt ratio: 47.5%	No. of shares (mil.): 29.5
Return on equity: 8.3%	Dividends
Cash ($ mil.): 126.5	Yield: —
Current ratio: 9.08	Payout: —
Long-term debt ($ mil.): 824.6	Market value ($ mil.): 918.0

STOCK PRICE ($) FY Close	P/E High/Low	PER SHARE ($) Earnings	Dividends	Book Value
12/17 31.10	15 10	2.03	0.00	24.92
12/16 21.00	9 6	2.33	0.00	21.91
12/15 17.71	12 8	1.88	0.00	19.22
12/14 17.28	22 15	1.03	0.00	17.49
Annual Growth 21.6%	— —	25.4%	—	12.5%

Ceva Inc

CEVA has a fever for semiconductor design. CEVA specializes in technology — both integrated circuit and software designs — used in cell phones handheld computers MP3 players and other wireless devices as well as smart TVs and set-top boxes. It licenses its silicon intellectual property (SIP) de-

signs to such industry heavyweights as LG Samsung and Sony. CEVA's SIP has been shipped in more than 7 billion devices to date; about 30% of handsets shipped worldwide each year contain its SIP. Most of CEVA's revenue comes from outside the US.

Operations

CEVA generates revenue from licensing and royalties. Licensing accounts for 54% of revenue and royalties bring in the other 45%. Customers find it more efficient to license technology from CEVA and similar companies than develop it on their own.

Geographic Reach

Headquartered in California the company has research and development operations in Israel and Ireland. Other offices are located in China Japan Hong Kong South Korea Sweden and Taiwan.

CEVA generates nearly three-quarters of its revenue from the Asia-Pacific region including sales to customers in China (50% of total revenue). US customers account for 16% of revenue.

Sales and Marketing

CEVA primarily uses a direct sales force. In 2015 it signed 47 licensing deals which included 21 with new customers.

Spreadtrum a chip maker in China is CEVA's biggest customer with 31% of sales. Other customers are Atmel Broadcom Yamaha and ZTE.

Financial Performance

CEVA's revenue and profit increased in 2015. Demand for the company's LTE technology helped drive revenue to $59.5 million a 17% increase from 2014. Intellectual property related to Bluetooth technology and contributions from RiveraWaves (acquired in 2014) also propelled revenue growth.

Net income rose to $6.27 million in 2014 compared to a loss of $819000 in 2014.

Cash flow from operations increased to about $19.3 million in 2015 compared to $9 million in 2014.

Strategy

CEVA operates in a highly competitive sector of the semiconductor industry and aims to expand its business reach beyond cellular baseband markets. It sees a growing demand for high-performance and low-power digital signal processor (DSP) and application-specific platforms incorporating DSP cores for other applications such as wireless infrastructure computational photography computer vision Bluetooth the Internet of Things machine-to-machine applications and storage. As such the company continues to invest in new technologies to enter new markets and capitalize on its relationships with semiconductor and OEM licensees that develop CEVA-based products.

In 2016 CEVA expanded its partnership with Spreadtrum for technology for mid-market and high-end smartphones. Spreadtrum's latest 64-bit Octa-Core LTE SoC platform the SC9860 integrates several CEVA DSPs. It enables signal processing workloads including LTE Cat-7 baseband audio and voice sensor fusion and always-on.

HISTORY

Brian Long and Peter McManamon founded Silicon Systems in 1993. Long's background included a stint at AT&T and 17 years with Digital Equipment; McManamon co-founded a large-screen projector company. Silicon Systems was aided early on by seed capital from Enterprise Ireland a government-run development agency plus

its first customer STMicroelectronics. Long took advantage of his previous contact with the Switzerland-based semiconductor giant to secure early contracts.

Over the next five years Silicon Systems honed its design skills in a number of technologies performing contract work for STMicroelectronics and other chip manufacturers. During this period the company retained ownership and licensing rights to its intellectual property which incorporated expertise in digital analog and mixed-signal chips as well as in software design.

Silicon Systems narrowed its focus in 1998 deciding to concentrate on technology for mobile devices. That year Goldman Sachs invested in the company trading $16 million for a 23% stake (reduced to 19% after the company's public offering and subsequently divested).

In 2000 Silicon Systems changed its name to Parthus Technologies and acquired the Global Positioning System (GPS) division of electronics maker Symmetricom. Later that year the company went public listing on both the Nasdaq and the London Stock Exchange in what was at that time the largest technology float by an Irish company. The offering made the reticent Long (he was often accused of being too modest about the company's achievements) one of the richest men in Ireland.

Parthus secured a number of major contracts in 2000 including licensing deals for its NavStream GPS with ARM Holdings and for its processor design for wireless devices (InfoStream) with Motorola Inc. and Psion. The next year the company bought privately held Chicory Systems (technology for speeding up mobile Internet applications) in a cash and stock deal valued at about $41 million.

In 2002 the company combined its operations with Ceva the IP licensing arm of DSP Group to form a new company called ParthusCeva. Parthus president Kevin Fielding became CEO of the combined company. Fielding stepped down in 2003; Long became interim CEO for a few months until industry veteran Chet Silvestri succeeded him as president and CEO. That same year the company changed its name from ParthusCeva to CEVA. Silvestri added the post of chairman in 2004.

Silvestri resigned as chairman and CEO the following year leaving CEVA's board altogether. Co-founder Peter McManamon replaced him as chairman and EVP/GM Gideon Wertheizer was promoted to CEO.

In 2006 the company sold its Global Positioning System (GPS) technology and associated products to GloNav a fabless semiconductor startup in return for an equity stake of about 20% in the firm. GloNav also licensed the CEVA-TeakLite digital signal processor core for the development of its GPS chipsets. At the end of 2007 however NXP acquired GloNav and CEVA divested its 20% stake.

EXECUTIVES

CEO, Gideon Wertheizer, age 61, $380,627 total compensation
CFO, Yaniv Arieli, age 49, $253,430 total compensation
EVP Worldwide Sales, Issachar Ohana, age 52, $281,400 total compensation
CTO, Erez Bar-Niv
VP and General Manager Connectivity Business Unit, Aviv Malinovitch
VP Research and Development, Ran Snir
VP and General Manager Wireless Business Unit, Michael Boukaya

VP and General Manager Vision Business Unit,
 Ilan Yona
Vice President Sales marketing, James Reinstein
VICE PRESIDENT, Brian Huseman
Vice President Corporate Devel, Eitan Dekel
Vice President Operations, Daryl Pint
Board Member, Sven-Christer Nilsson
Director, Peter McManamon, age 69
Auditors: Kost Forer Gabbay & Kasierer (member of
 Ernst & Young Global)

LOCATIONS

HQ: Ceva Inc
 1174 Castro Street, Suite 210, Mountain View, CA 94040
Phone: 650 417-7900
Web: www.ceva-dsp.com

PRODUCTS/OPERATIONS

2015 Sales

	$ mil.	% of total
Licensing	32.1	54
Royalties	27.4	46
Total	**59.5**	**100**

Selected Products CEVA DSP Cores and Platform-sCEVA Connectivity IPs

COMPETITORS

ARM Holdings	Infineon Technologies
Analog Devices	NXP Semiconductors
Axeon	Patriot Scientific
Fairchild	Silicon Image
Semiconductor	Sonics
Fujitsu Semiconductor	Synopsys
Gennum	Tensilica
Imagination	Texas Instruments
Technologies	VeriSilicon

HISTORICAL FINANCIALS

Company Type: Public

Income Statement

FYE: December 31

	REVENUE ($ mil.)	NET INCOME ($ mil.)	NET PROFIT MARGIN	EMPLOYEES
12/17	87.5	17.0	19.5%	313
12/16	72.6	13.1	18.0%	278
12/15	59.5	6.2	10.5%	259
12/14	50.8	(0.8)	—	242
12/13	48.9	6.6	13.7%	207
Annual Growth	15.7%	26.3%	—	10.9%

2017 Year-End Financials

Debt ratio: —
Return on equity: 7.4%
Cash ($ mil.): 56.1
Current ratio: 6.98
Long-term debt ($ mil.): —

No. of shares (mil.): 22.0
Dividends
 Yield: —
 Payout: —
Market value ($ mil.): 1,018.0

	STOCK PRICE ($) FY Close	P/E High/Low	PER SHARE ($) Earnings	Dividends	Book Value
12/17	46.15	66 41	0.75	0.00	11.09
12/16	33.55	58 28	0.61	0.00	9.94
12/15	23.36	88 55	0.30	0.00	9.06
12/14	18.14	— —	(0.04)	0.00	8.84
12/13	15.22	70 46	0.30	0.00	9.01
Annual Growth	32.0%	— —	25.7%	—	5.3%

Charles River Laboratories International Inc.

Chickens and rats have an important part to play in Charles River Laboratories International's specialty portfolio of medical products. The company produces lab rats and mice bred specifically for use in medical testing through its Research Models and Services (RMS) segment. It also provides contract drug discovery and development services including toxicology and pathology through its RMS Discovery and Safety Assessment and Manufacturing Support segments. To a smaller degree the company also supplies pathogen-free fertilized chicken eggs used in vaccine production. Charles River Laboratories which traces its roots back to 1947 has operations in 17 countries around the world.

Operations

In 2014 Charles River Laboratories realigned its reportable segments after acquiring Argenta and BioFocus. Its three operating segments are now Research Models and Services Discovery and Safety Assessment (DSA) and Manufacturing Support.

The RMS segment accounts for 40% of total revenue and includes the research models and research model services businesses. They offer commercial production and sale of small research models and supply large research models. The Genetically Engineered Model Services unit performs contract breeding and related services while the Research Animal Diagnostic Services unit provides health monitoring and diagnostics services related to research models. IS provides colony management of clients' research operations including recruitment training staffing and management services.

The DSA segment which accounted for 41% of revenue in 2014 includes services required to take a drug through early development including discovery services.

Meanwhile Manufacturing Support (19% of revenue in 2014) includes Endotoxin and Microbial Detection (EMD) including non-animal lot-release testing products and microbial detection and species identification services. It also includes Biologics Testing Services which provides testing of biologics and devices; and Avian Vaccine Services which supplies specific-pathogen-free fertile chicken eggs and chickens. The Accugenix subsidiary provides cGMP-compliant contract microbial identification and genetic sequence testing.

Geographic Reach

Charles River Laboratories has approximately 60 locations in 17 countries. While sales in the US account for about half of its annual revenues the company is also growing its operations in other key markets including Canada Europe and Japan.

Charles River Laboratories has laboratories in the US Germany Scotland and Ireland. It owns large (over 50000 sq. ft. of space) facilities for the DSA segment in Canada Ireland Scotland and the US; it leases large facilities in the US and the UK. For the RMS segment it owns large facilities in Canada China France Germany Japan the UK and the US. The company also owns large Manufacturing Support facilities in the US and China.

Sales and Marketing

Charles River Laboratories provides its products and services directly to customers around the globe. Customers include small and midsized pharmaceutical companies biotechnology firms contract research organizations (CROs) agricultural and chemical companies life science companies and veterinary medicine firms as well as educational health care and government institutions.

The company primarily sells its products and services through a direct sales force and account management teams in North America Europe and the Asia/Pacific region. Its promotional activities include organizing scientific symposia publishing scientific papers and newsletters webinars and presentations at conferences and trade shows in North America Europe and Asia. It also participates in online marketing and direct mail. In some markets the group's direct sales force is assisted by international distributors and agents.

Financial Performance

Charles River Laboratories' revenues were flat between 2010 and 2013 but in 2014 revenue rose 11% to $1.3 billion primarily due to growth in the DSA segment. That segment benefited from the 2014 acquisitions of Argenta and BioFocus which contributed a combined $71.4 million in revenue growth. The Safety Assessment business also saw higher earnings.

Net income which more than doubled in 2011 due to a decline in expenses rose 23% to $127 million in 2014 on higher revenue and lower interest expenses. Cash flow from operations also increased rising 21% to $252 million.

Strategy

Charles River Laboratories' strategy is based on leveraging its deep scientific knowledge and strong client support to deliver a comprehensive and integrated portfolio of quality early-stage products and services. This allows its clients to maintain the flexible infrastructure they need in order to bring new therapies to market faster and more cost effectively.

In 2018 the company expanded into the early discovery market. It began offering high-speed pharmacokinetics screening to help firms identify small-molecule candidates. These capabilities were introduced in Europe and the US.

The firm's acquisition strategy takes into account geographic factors as well as expansion of existing core services. The company is partnering with a number of venture capital firms that invest in life sciences health care and technology companies.

Charles River Laboratories has aligned its sales force to improve its ability to support clients to focus on three particular customer segments: global biopharmaceutical companies mid-tier biopharmaceuticals and academic and government institutions.

Mergers and Acquisitions

Charles River Laboratories has been on a buying spree as of late spending more than $1 billion on acquisitions since 2014. It started off 2016 with a major acquisition buying WIL Research for some $585 million. WIL Research provides safety assessment and contract development and manufacturing services to biopharmaceuticals and chemical companies worldwide; the purchase expands Charles Rivers' presence in Europe as well as its portfolio of service offerings.

Later in 2016 the company acquired Massachusetts-based Agilux a specialist in molecule bioanalytical drug metabolism pharmacology and pharmacokinetic services for $64 million.

In mid-2017 Charles River Laboratories acquired Brains On-Line a CRO with a focus on delivering data on treatments for central nervous system diseases. The deal was valued at some $21 million as well as up to $8 million in performance payments.

In early 2018 the company acquired CRO KWS BioTest which provides in vitro and in vivo discovery testing services for areas including immuno-oncology and inflammatory and infectious diseases for approximately $20 million. The transaction also includes a potential $4 million in performance payments.

The company then bought early-stage drug development CRO MPI Research for some $800 million. MPI has a roster of small and midsized biotech customers which Charles River Laboratories sees as a fast-growing market. That purchase also expanded the company's toxicology testing abilities.

EXECUTIVES

Corporate EVP Human Resources Chief Administrative Officer General Counsel and Secretary, David P. Johst, age 56, $567,496 total compensation
Senior Financial Advisor, Thomas F. Ackerman, age 64, $512,245 total compensation
Chairman President and CEO, James C. Foster, age 67, $1,069,089 total compensation
Corporate SVP; President European Preclinical Services, Brian Bathgate, age 58
Corporate EVP and Chief Scientific Officer, Nancy A. Gillett, age 62, $500,523 total compensation
VP Charles River Europe, J ¶rg M. Geller, age 63, $400,520 total compensation
Corporate EVP and President Global Research Models & Services and Preclinical Services Operations, Davide Molho, $450,853 total compensation
Corporate SVP Global Sales and Marketing, William D. Barbo
SVP Information Technology and CIO, Arthur C. Hubbs
Corporate SVP and General Manager Research Models & Services Europe and Asia, Colin Dunn
EVP and CFO, David R. Smith
Auditors: PricewaterhouseCoopers LLP

LOCATIONS

HQ: Charles River Laboratories International Inc.
251 Ballardvale Street, Wilmington, MA 01887
Phone: 781 222-6000
Web: www.criver.com

PRODUCTS/OPERATIONS

2016 Sales

	$ mil.	% of total
Discovery and safety assessment	836.6	50
Research Models & Services	494.0	29
Manufacturing support	350.8	21
Total	**1,681.4**	**100**

Selected Services

Agrochemical & veterinary services
Antibody production services
Avian products & services
Biopharmaceutical services
Clinical trial services
Consulting & staffing services
Discovery & imaging services
Endotoxin & microbial detection
Equipment & instrumentation
Facilities design & management services
Genetic testing services
Genetically engineered models & services
In Vitro services
Pathology associates
Preclinical services
Program management
Regulatory navigator services
Research animal diagnostic services
Research animal models
Surgical model services

COMPETITORS

Albany Molecular Research	Jackson Laboratory
	MPI Research
BioReliance	Nordion
Bioanalytical Systems	PAREXEL
Covance	PRA Health Sciences
Deltagen	PharmaNet Development
Harlan Laboratories	Group
ICON	Taconic
IQVIA	WuXi PharmaTech

HISTORICAL FINANCIALS

Company Type: Public

Income Statement

FYE: December 30

	REVENUE ($ mil.)	NET INCOME ($ mil.)	NET PROFIT MARGIN	EMPLOYEES
12/17	1,857.6	123.3	6.6%	11,800
12/16	1,681.4	154.7	9.2%	11,000
12/15	1,363.3	149.3	11.0%	8,600
12/14	1,297.6	126.7	9.8%	7,900
12/13	1,165.5	102.8	8.8%	7,700
Annual Growth	**12.4%**	**4.7%**	**—**	**11.3%**

2017 Year-End Financials

Debt ratio: 39.0%	No. of shares (mil.): 47.4
Return on equity: 13.1%	Dividends
Cash ($ mil.): 163.7	Yield: —
Current ratio: 1.78	Payout: —
Long-term debt ($ mil.): 1,114.1	Market value ($ mil.): 5,188.0

	STOCK PRICE ($) FY Close	P/E High/Low	PER SHARE ($) Earnings	Dividends	Book Value
12/17	109.45	45 29	2.54	0.00	22.05
12/16	76.19	27 20	3.23	0.00	17.67
12/15	80.08	26 19	3.13	0.00	15.70
12/14	64.29	24 19	2.66	0.00	14.20
12/13	53.33	25 17	2.12	0.00	13.48
Annual Growth	**19.7%**	**— —**	**4.6%**	**—**	**13.1%**

Chatham Lodging Trust

Self-advised real estate investment trust (REIT) Chatham Lodging acquires upscale extended-stay hotels including Residence Inn by Marriott Homewood Suites by Hilton and Hyatt House locations To a lesser extent the firm will also buy select-service and full-service hotels such as Courtyard by Marriott Hampton Inn and Hilton Garden Inn. Chatham Lodging owns nearly 40 hotels with almost 5700 rooms across 15 US states. Through two joint ventures it also has minority interests in 95 other hotels with 12500 rooms/suites. When assembling its portfolio the REIT seeks properties being sold at a discount particularly in large US metropolitan markets including Dallas Denver and Pittsburgh.

Operations

Chatham Lodging operates mainly select service or limited service hotels and as such does not book significant revenue from food and beverages or group conference facilities. Indeed room revenue accounted for 94% of the REIT's total revenue during 2014.

Geographic Reach

Palm Beach-based Chatham Lodging has properties in 16 states: California Colorado Connecticut Florida Georgia Kentucky Maine Massachusetts Minnesota New Hampshire New York Pennsylvania Tennessee Texas Virginia Washington and Washington DC.

Sales and Marketing

The REIT has been boosting its advertising spend in recent years to support sales growth. It spent $3.7 million on advertising during 2014 up from $2.8 million and $2.3 million in 2013 and 2012 respectively.

Financial Performance

Chatham Lodging's revenue has grown more than eight-fold since 2010 as it has expanded its property portfolio through acquisitions and has charged higher rental rates as the real estate market has strengthened. It's also been climbing back from years of losses as it's kept a lid on operating costs and interest expenses on its long-term debt.

The REIT's revenue spiked 56% to $197.22 million during 2014 mostly thanks to added room revenue stemming from six hotel acquisitions in 2013 and nine hotel acquisitions in 2014.

Strong revenue growth in 2014 drove Chatham Lodging's net income sharply up to $67.1 million (compared to $3 million in 2013). The REIT's operating cash levels jumped 56% to $49.3 million for the year as cash earnings rose.

Strategy

Chatham reiterated in 2016 that it looked to acquire upscale extended-stay hotels and premium branded select-service hotel properties in the 25 largest metro areas in the US that are priced below replacement costs in their markets. Indeed through acquisitions made between 2010 and 2014 the REIT has more than quintupled its hotel property investments from $208 million to nearly $1.1 billion.

While Chatham also takes minority interests in other hotels through joint ventures it also sells off properties that could yield big profits. In 2014 for example the REIT reached an agreement to sell the hotels owned by its joint venture with Cerberus Capital Management (acquired in 2011) to Northstar Realty Finance with Chatham netting a gain of $80 million on the $1.3 billion sale.

EXECUTIVES

Chairman President and CEO, Jeffrey H. Fisher, age 63, $209,589 total compensation
EVP and COO, Dennis M. Craven, age 46, $88,233 total compensation
EVP and Chief Investment Officer, Peter M. Willis, age 51, $199,110 total compensation
CFO, Jeremy Wegner
Auditors: PricewaterhouseCoopers LLP

LOCATIONS

HQ: Chatham Lodging Trust
222 Lakeview Avenue, Suite 200, West Palm Beach, FL 33401
Phone: 561 802-4477
Web: www.chathamlodgingtrust.com

PRODUCTS/OPERATIONS

2014 sales

	% of total
Room	94
Food and Beverage	1
Cost reimbursements	1
Others	4
Total	**100**

COMPETITORS

Ashford Hospitality Trust	Hersha Hospitality
	Host Hotels & Resorts
Chesapeake Lodging	Innkeepers USA
DiamondRock Hospitality	Sunstone Hotel Investors
FelCor	

HISTORICAL FINANCIALS

Company Type: Public

Income Statement — FYE: December 31

	REVENUE ($ mil.)	NET INCOME ($ mil.)	NET PROFIT MARGIN	EMPLOYEES
12/17	298.8	29.4	9.9%	45
12/16	293.8	31.4	10.7%	45
12/15	276.9	32.9	11.9%	47
12/14	197.2	66.8	33.9%	45
12/13	126.2	2.9	2.4%	27
Annual Growth	24.0%	77.3%	—	13.6%

2017 Year-End Financials

Debt ratio: 38.6%	No. of shares (mil.): 45.3
Return on equity: 3.9%	Dividends
Cash ($ mil.): 9.3	Yield: 0.0%
Current ratio: 0.92	Payout: 180.8%
Long-term debt ($ mil.): 538.3	Market value ($ mil.): 1,033.0

	STOCK PRICE ($) FY Close	P/E High/Low	PER SHARE ($) Earnings	Dividends	Book Value
12/17	22.76	33 26	0.73	1.32	17.70
12/16	20.55	30 20	0.81	1.38	17.64
12/15	20.48	36 23	0.86	1.20	18.09
12/14	28.97	13 9	2.30	0.93	17.22
12/13	20.45	163 112	0.13	0.84	14.58
Annual Growth	2.7%	— —	53.9%	12.0%	5.0%

Chefs' Warehouse Inc (The)

Before a gourmet chef can say "bon appétit" he must first procure his ingredients. A distributor of specialty food products Chefs' Warehouse sells such gourmet food items as artisan charcuterie specialty cheeses hormone-free protein truffles caviar and chocolates as well as basic food ingredients like cooking oils flour butter milk and eggs.

The company's core customers include chefs from independent restaurants fine dining establishments culinary schools hotels and country clubs. It is a leading gourmet ingredient distributor in culinary centers like New York City San Francisco Los Angeles and Washington DC. Tracing its roots back to 1985 Chefs' Warehouse went public in 2011.

IPO

Shares climbed following the company's market debut. The supplier for restaurants caterers and other foodservice businesses raised $135 million; the proceeds from the IPO were about $63.1 million after expenses which went to repay debt and fund general corporate activity. Company CEO Christopher Pappas Christopher's brother John Pappas and brother-in-law Dean Facatselis collectively retain control of Chefs' Warehouse.

Geographic Reach

Based in Connecticut Chefs' Warehouse operates in one segment — food product distribution — along the East and West coasts. It serves some of the nation's culinary hot spots including New York California Nevada and Washington as well as in Ohio Maryland Florida and Oregon.

Sales and Marketing

Chefs' Warehouse works to cover a number of popular markets including Philadelphia Boston Napa Valley and Seattle. As part of its business the company serves chefs working in country clubs independent restaurants fine dining establishments culinary schools and hotels.

The company distributes its specialty food products to more than 12500 distinct customer locations from distribution centers located in New York San Francisco Los Angeles Las Vegas Miami Portland Columbus Cincinnati and Washington DC. Its products are sourced from more than 2700 different suppliers.

Financial Performance

Except for revenue slump in 2009 due to the global economic recession Chefs' Warehouse has seen an upward trend in revenue from 2008 to 2012. The company has logged rising net income in all fiscal years from 2008-2012 due to increased net sales and decreased operating expenses. Chefs' Warehouse revenue jumped 20% in fiscal 2012 as compared to 2011 thanks to net sales increases resulting from organic sales growth and the acquisitions of Michael's and Praml in 2012 and Provvista in late 2011. The company's net sales growth was negatively impacted by Hurricane Sandy however during the fourth quarter of 2012 and the prior year impact of an extra week in 2011. Chefs' Warehouse reports $14.51 million in 2012 net income — an 88% increase — due to increased net sales in 2012 and reduced interest expenses.

Strategy

Besides acquiring other companies Chefs' Warehouse is expanding its customer base in existing markets and bolstering its product offerings to its existing customers. It is also taking steps to control costs by improving its logistics and inventory management systems. In recent years Chefs' Warehouse has experienced significant financial growth due in large part to a rise in revenue generated by sales to both new and existing customers.

Mergers and Acquisitions

Going forward Chefs' Warehouse's growth strategy continues to include acquisitions of small food distributors that beef up its entree offerings. In 2013 the company purchased Qzina Specialty Foods North America a Florida-based supplier of gourmet chocolate dessert and pastry products that serves pastry chefs in a deal worth some $32.7 million. In 2012 it bought out Michael's Finer Meats a Midwest distributor of meat and seafood for approximately $54.3 million. The deal was one of several; earlier in the year Chefs' Warehouse purchased Praml International a specialty foods importer and foodservice distributor founded in 1987. The acquisition extended the company's reach to some 500 locations in Las Vegas and Reno. Chefs' Warehouse expanded its operations into south Florida after acquiring Monique & Me Inc. (dba Culinaire Specialty Foods) for $3.7 million in 2010. The previous year it bought the San Francisco division of European Imports for $3.8 million. The transaction bolstered its California operations.

Company Background

The Pappas family originally founded the company in 1985 as Dairyland USA a specialty dairy product distributor that served chefs in the New York metropolitan area. The company later expanded into other large US markets through acquisitions of small specialty food products distributors.

EXECUTIVES

Chief Information Officer, Frank ODowd
CFO, John D. Austin
Regional Vice President, Bruce Luong
Vice President Of Operations West At The Chefs Warehouse, Rodney Aguirre
Vice President Sales, Tina Roberts
Vice President Finance, Brad Lavaty
Vice President of Sales, John Groendyke
VICE PRESIDENT OF BUSINESS DEVELOPMENT WEST, Tara Brennan
Vice President Of Purchasing, Matthew Harris
Vice Chairman, John Pappas, age 54
Board Member, Alan Guarino
Auditors: BDO USA, LLP

LOCATIONS

HQ: Chefs' Warehouse Inc (The)
100 East Ridge Road, Ridgefield, CT 06877
Phone: 203 894-1345
Web: www.chefswarehouse.com

PRODUCTS/OPERATIONS

2015 Products sales

	% of total
Center of plate	46
Dry Goods	18
Pastries and other bakery products	14
Cheeses	8
Dairy Products	6
Oils and Vinegars	6
Kitchen supplies	2
Total	**100**

Selected Products

Baking
Beverages
Caviar
Cheese & dairy
Chocolate
Coffee & tea
Condiments
Dry goods
Foie gras & pate
Fruits & nuts
Gluten-free
Molecular gastronomy
Oil & vinegar
Organic
Pasta

Specialty meats
Specialty seafood
Spices
Regional

COMPETITORS

American Milk Products	European Imports
DPI Specialty Foods	World Finer Foods
Dole & Bailey Inc.	atalanta
Economy Foods	

HISTORICAL FINANCIALS

Company Type: Public

Income Statement   FYE: December 29

	REVENUE ($ mil.)	NET INCOME ($ mil.)	NET PROFIT MARGIN	EMPLOYEES
12/17	1,301.5	14.3	1.1%	1,994
12/16	1,192.8	3.0	0.3%	1,948
12/15	1,059.0	16.2	1.5%	1,693
12/14	836.6	14.2	1.7%	1,281
12/13	673.5	16.9	2.5%	1,160
Annual Growth	17.9%	(4.1%)	—	14.5%

2017 Year-End Financials

Debt ratio: 46.2%	No. of shares (mil.): 28.4
Return on equity: 6.5%	Dividends
Cash ($ mil.) 41.5	Yield: —
Current ratio: 2.74	Payout: —
Long-term debt ($ mil.): 314.0	Market value ($ mil.): 583.0

	STOCK PRICE ($) FY Close	P/E High/Low	PER SHARE ($) Earnings	Dividends	Book Value
12/17	20.50	39 22	0.54	0.00	8.74
12/16	15.80	170 87	0.12	0.00	7.37
12/15	17.37	37 21	0.63	0.00	7.15
12/14	22.03	51 27	0.57	0.00	5.86
12/13	29.14	37 19	0.77	0.00	5.28
Annual Growth	(8.4%)	— —	(8.5%)	—	13.5%

Chemical Financial Corp

Chemical Financial has banking down to a science. It's the holding company for Chemical Bank which provides standard services such as checking and savings accounts CDs and IRAs credit and debit cards and loans and mortgages to individuals and businesses through nearly 190 branches in the lower peninsula of Michigan. The majority of the bank's loan portfolio is made up of commercial loans while consumer loans make up the remainder. Boasting assets of $9 billion Chemical is the second largest bank in Michigan. The company also offers trust investment management brokerage and title insurance services through subsidiaries.

Operations

Its Wealth Management division which has some $4 billion in assets under custody offers trust services estate planning investment management and employee benefit programs. Chemical Financial Advisors offers mutual funds and marketable securities while CFC Title Services issues title insur-

ance for mortgage properties. CFC Capital manages the company's municipal investment securities portfolio.

About 72% of Chemical Financial's total revenue came from loan interest (including fees) in 2014 while another 6% came from interest on its investment securities. The rest of its revenue came from deposit account service charges and fees (8%) wealth management revenue (6%) mortgage banking income (2%) and other miscellaneous sources of income.

Sales and Marketing

Chemical Financial spent $3.45 million on advertising in 2014 up from $2.97 million and $3.11 million in 2013 and 2012 respectively.

Financial Performance

Chemical Financial's revenues and profits have been rising over the past few years thanks growing loan and deposit business from acquisitions lower interest expenses on deposits and declining loan loss provisions as its loan portfolio's credit quality has improved with higher property valuations in the strengthened economy.

The bank's revenue rose by 6% to $290.4 million in 2014 as the bank as its acquisition of Northwestern Bancorp boosted its loan business during the year. Higher revenue lower interest expenses and a continued decline in loan loss provisions drove the bank's net income up by 9% to a record $62.1 million. The bank's operating cash levels inched higher to $89.9 million on higher cash earnings.

Strategy

The bank follows an aggressive acquisition strategy to boost its loan and deposit business while expanding its branch network into key parts of Michigan. Indeed its acquisitions in 2015 and 2014 boosted the bank's presence in northwestern Michigan and along the Michigan-Indiana border. By the end of 2014 the bank had acquired some 21 community banks and 36 branch bank offices.

Mergers and Acquisitions

Chemical Financial agreed in January 2019 to merge with Minnesota-based TCF Financial to form a Midwest bank with about $45 billion in assets $34 billion in total deposits and more than 500 branches in nine states. TCF's large deposit base and national wholesale lending business will complement Chemical's commercial lending and wealth management activities. The combined company which is to retain the TCF brand will have a more diversified deposit mix between retail and commercial lines and a more balanced loan portfolio across geographies asset classes and industries. Following the merger TCF shareholders will have a controlling interest in the combined company.

Company Background

In late 2012 the company acquired 21 branches in northeastern Michigan and Battle Creek from Independent Bank. That more than $8-million transaction further expands Chemical Bank's presence geographically. Additional acquisitions including FDIC-assisted takeovers of failed banks are possible.

EXECUTIVES

SVP CFO and Treasurer, Lori A. Gwizdala, age 60, $344,720 total compensation
Vice Chairman and President Chemical Bank, Thomas C. (Tom) Shafer, age 59

EVP and Senior Credit Officer Chemical Bank, James E. Tomczyk, age 66, $225,504 total compensation
Vice Chairman Chemical Bank and CEO InSite Capital LLC, Thomas W. Kohn, age 64, $329,174 total compensation
EVP Commercial Lending Chemical Bank, Daniel W. Terpsma, age 64
EVP and CFO Chemical Financial and Chemical Bank, Dennis L. Klaeser, age 60, $183,483 total compensation
President and CEO, David T. Provost
Director Chemical Financial and Chairman Chemical Bank, Franklin C. Wheatlake, age 70
EVP and COO Business Operations Chemical Bank, Leonardo Amat, age 49, $309,477 total compensation
EVP and Chief Risk Officer Chemical Bank, Lynn M. Kerber, age 49
EVP General Counsel and Secretary, William C. Collins, age 65
EVP and COO Customer Experience Chemical Bank, Robert S. Rathbun, age 54, $309,477 total compensation
SVP and CIO, Greg Meidt
Vice President of Customer Service, Sue Lynde
Vice President, Robert O Burgess
Assistant Vice President Product Development, Jim Hubinger
Senior Vice President Head of Personal Trust, James Blanchard
Vice President Commercial Loan Officer, Jeff Hyde
Executive Vice President Chief Operating Officer, James Milroy
Senior Vice President Senior Lender, Mike Williams
Vice President Information Systems, Laurie Soren
Senior Vice President and Trust Officer, Jude Patnaude
Vice President Commercial Lending, Kip Miller
Vice President Data Services, Brian Beall
First Vice President, David Vermilye
Vice President, Robin Grove
Vice President and Trust Investment Officer, Glen Matz
Vice President and Community Reinvestment Act Officer, Robert BurgessJr
Assistant Vice President, Jane Pontious
Vice President Secondary Market Manager, Robert Clark
Vice President, Kelly Hutchings
Assistant Vice President, Lorie Moriarty
Vice President Commercial Banking, Melissa Spranger
Vice President Commercial Loan Officer, Catherine Yates
Vice President, Joseph Dick
Vice President, John Laman
Vice President Human Resources, David Ramaker
Vice President Retail Sales Manager, Jeff Sharpe
Vice President Mortgage Originator, Krista Martiny
Vice President Commercial Banking Relationship Manager Commerce Park Interim Vice, Ron Cordaro
Vice President First, Michael Debo
Chairman, Gary H. Torgow, age 60
Board Member, Larry Stauffer
Board Member, James Fitterling
Auditors: KPMG LLP

LOCATIONS

HQ: Chemical Financial Corp
   333 W. Fort Street, Suite 1800, Detroit, MI 48226
Phone: 800 867-9757
Web: www.chemicalbank.com

PRODUCTS/OPERATIONS

2014 Sales

	$ mil.	% of total
Interest		
Loans including fees	209.4	72
Investment securities	17.4	6
Other	0.4	-
Non-interest		
Service charges on deposit accounts	22.3	8
Wealth management revenue	16.0	6
Other customer service charges & fees	18.6	6
Other	6.1	2
Total	**290.4**	**100**

COMPETITORS

1st Source Corporation	Flagstar Bancorp
Bank of America	Huntington Bancshares
Comerica	Independent Bank (MI)
Fifth Third	Mercantile Bank
Firstbank	

HISTORICAL FINANCIALS

Company Type: Public

Income Statement   FYE: December 31

	ASSETS ($ mil.)	NET INCOME ($ mil.)	INCOME AS % OF ASSETS	EMPLOYEES
12/17	19,280.8	149.5	0.8%	3,000
12/16	17,355.1	108.0	0.6%	3,300
12/15	9,188.8	86.8	0.9%	2,100
12/14	7,322.1	62.1	0.8%	2,000
12/13	6,184.7	56.8	0.9%	1,700
Annual Growth	32.9%	27.4%	—	15.3%

2017 Year-End Financials

Return on assets: 0.8%
Return on equity: 5.7%
Long-term debt ($ mil.): —
No. of shares (mil.): 71.2
Sales ($ mil): 776.1
Dividends
Yield: 0.0%
Payout: 52.8%
Market value ($ mil.): 3,807.0

	STOCK PRICE ($) FY Close	P/E High/Low	Earnings	Dividends	Book Value
12/17	53.47	27 21	2.08	1.10	37.48
12/16	54.17	25 13	2.17	1.06	36.57
12/15	34.27	15 12	2.39	1.00	26.62
12/14	30.64	17 13	1.97	0.94	24.32
12/13	31.67	16 12	2.00	0.87	23.38
Annual Growth	14.0%	— —	1.0%	6.0%	12.5%

ChemoCentryx, Inc.

Biopharmaceutical ChemoCentryx is developing drugs that target inflammatory disorders autoimmune diseases and cancer. It focuses on orally administered drugs that block specific chemoattractant receptors. Its lead candidates have an initial focus on kidney disease. Avacopan is being studied for its effectiveness in treating a number of orphan diseases while CCX140 is in development for the treatment of chronic and orphan kidney diseases. ChemoCentryx also has candidates in early stage development.

Operations

In addition to its kidney disease medications ChemoCentryx has early stage candidates aimed at treating inflammatory disease and cancer. CX872 for example is being tested for the treatment of pancreatic cancer.

The company relies on contract manufacturing organizations to produce its drug candidates.

Sales and Marketing

ChemoCentryx plans to build a US sales team to commercialize avacopan and other treatments as they become approved. The company expects to initially target nephrologists but it will also market its products to other specialists including rheumatologists.

Financial Performance

With no approved products ChemoCentryx has yet to generate any product revenue. In 2017 the company received milestone and collaboration payments of $82.5 million related to its partnership with Vifor. This translated to an increase of $591% in revenue versus 2016. Because of this the company entered the black for the first time with a net income of $17.9 million. Operating cash flow fell 88% to $4.9 million primarily due to a decrease in deferred revenue.

As of December 2017 ChemoCentryx had an accumulated deficit of $289.2 million; it expects to continue incurring losses as it works to get products to the market.

Strategy

In 2016 ChemoCentryx established a partnership with European kidney disease specialist Vifor which plans to commercialize Avacopan in Europe and certain other markets. ChemoCentryx retained commercialization rights in the US and China. It formed a similar alliance with Vifor for its CCX140 candidate.

As its drugs advance through their clinical trials the company has increased its research and development spending. It spent $49.5 million on R&D in 2017 versus $37.9 million in 2016 and $33.2 million in 2015.

EXECUTIVES

SVP Finance CFO and Secretary, Susan M. Kanaya, $415,600 total compensation
Chairman President and CEO, Thomas J. Schall, $571,450 total compensation
Chief Business Officer and Treasurer, Markus J. Cappel, $354,543 total compensation
Chief Medical Officer, Petrus J. (Pirow) Bekker, $410,405 total compensation
SVP Research, Rajinder Singh
VP Research and Development, Israel Charo
Senior Vice President, Jan Hillson
Auditors: Ernst & Young LLP

LOCATIONS

HQ: ChemoCentryx, Inc.
850 Maude Avenue, Mountain View, CA 94043
Phone: 650 210-2900   **Fax:** 650 210-2910
Web: www.chemocentryx.com

COMPETITORS

AbbVie	Incyte
Alexion	Johnson & Johnson
Pharmaceuticals	Mallinckrodt
Amgen	Merck
AstraZeneca	Novartis
Bayer HealthCare	Pfizer
Pharmaceuticals	Sanofi
Biogen	Takeda Pharmaceutical
Bristol-Myers Squibb	Teva
Genentech	UCB
GlaxoSmithKline	

HISTORICAL FINANCIALS

Company Type: Public

Income Statement   FYE: December 31

	REVENUE ($ mil.)	NET INCOME ($ mil.)	NET PROFIT MARGIN	EMPLOYEES
12/17	82.5	17.8	21.6%	66
12/16	11.9	(39.9)	—	62
12/15	0.0	(47.3)	—	58
12/14	0.0	(46.9)	—	58
12/13	6.0	(38.6)	—	60
Annual Growth	92.1%	—	—	2.4%

2017 Year-End Financials

Debt ratio: 2.4%
Return on equity: 27.6%
Cash ($ mil.): 40.0
Current ratio: 5.46
Long-term debt ($ mil.): 4.6
No. of shares (mil.): 48.8
Dividends
Yield: —
Payout: —
Market value ($ mil.): 291.0

	STOCK PRICE ($) FY Close	P/E High/Low	Earnings	Dividends	Book Value
12/17	5.95	29 15	0.36	0.00	1.62
12/16	7.40	— —	(0.86)	0.00	1.04
12/15	8.10	— —	(1.08)	0.00	1.64
12/14	6.83	— —	(1.08)	0.00	2.50
12/13	5.79	— —	(0.95)	0.00	3.39
Annual Growth (16.8%)	0.7%	— —	—	—	—

Cherry Hill Mortgage Investment Corp

Cherry Hill Mortgage Investment is interested in real estate assets that lie far beyond Cherry Hill New Jersey. Formed in 2012 Cherry Hill is a real estate investment trust or REIT that looks to acquire invest in and manage real estate assets across the US. It plans to build a portfolio that comprises excess mortgage servicing rights (excess MSRs are servicing fees that exceed basic MSR servicing fees) agency residential mortgage-backed securities (secured by the government agencies like Fannie Mae and Freddie Mac) and other residential mortgage assets. The REIT is externally managed by Cherry Hill Mortgage Management an affiliate of Freedom Mortgage. It went public in 2013.

IPO

Cherry Hill Mortgage intends to use a portion of its $130 million in proceeds to invest in its initial portfolio of excess MSRs and agency RMBS.

Operations

Cherry Hill Mortgage capitalized a taxable REIT subsidiary Cherry Hill TRS LLC at the end of 2013 to obtain mortgage servicing licenses.

Financial Performance

Cherry Hill Mortgage attributes its $6 million in fiscal 2013 operating cash outflow to becoming a public company and executing its initial investment strategy.

Strategy

Cherry Hill Mortgage plans to leverage funds raised through its IPO and other investors to establish its portfolio of excess MSRs and agency RMBS. The REIT also intends to grow the portfolio through subsequent investments in other types of real estate-backed assets including prime jumbo mortgage loans.

The firm looks to leverage its relationship with Freedom Mortgage to continue to acquire Excess MSRs on a flow and bulk basis. It also co-invests in Excess MSRs with Freedom Mortgage.

Auditors: Ernst & Young LLP

LOCATIONS

HQ: Cherry Hill Mortgage Investment Corp
1451 Route 34, Suite 303, Farmingdale, NJ 07727
Phone: 877 870-7005
Web: www.chmireit.com

PRODUCTS/OPERATIONS

Selected Investment Types
Agency Residential Mortgage Backed Securities
Excess Mortgage Servicing Rights

COMPETITORS

ARMOUR Residential REIT	Capstead Mortgage
American Capital Agency Corp.	Invesco Mortgage Capital
Annaly Capital Management	MFA Financial Redwood Trust

HISTORICAL FINANCIALS

Company Type: Public

Income Statement   FYE: December 31

	REVENUE ($ mil.)	NET INCOME ($ mil.)	NET PROFIT MARGIN	EMPLOYEES
12/17	82.4	47.3	57.4%	4
12/16	42.3	24.8	58.7%	4
12/15	25.6	13.2	51.6%	3
12/14	7.8	2.3	30.1%	0
12/13	22.5	21.1	93.6%	0
Annual Growth	38.3%	22.4%	—	—

2017 Year-End Financials

Debt ratio: 2.0%
Return on equity: 19.9%
Cash ($ mil.): 27.3
Current ratio: 0.04
Long-term debt ($ mil.): 42.0

No. of shares (mil.): 12.7
Dividends
  Yield: 0.1%
  Payout: 49.2%
Market value ($ mil.): 229.0

	STOCK PRICE ($) FY Close	P/E High/Low		PER SHARE ($) Earnings	Dividends	Book Value
12/17	17.99	5	4	3.98	1.96	25.15
12/16	18.19	6	4	3.30	2.11	20.50
12/15	13.00	11	7	1.76	1.98	20.13
12/14	18.49	66	57	0.31	2.03	21.28
12/13	17.80	1	1	12.50	0.45	21.44
Annual Growth	0.3%	—	—	(24.9%)	44.5%	4.1%

Chesapeake Lodging Trust

As a real estate investment trust (REIT) focused on the hospitality industry Chesapeake Lodging Trust targets upper-upscale hotels located in major US business centers and popular convention markets. The company owns 22 hotels with a total of nearly 6700 rooms in nine US states and Washington DC. Southern California is a major market for the company. Chesapeake Lodging's properties operate under several major brands including Hyatt Marriott and W Hotels. In evaluating properties for purchase the company considers re-branding and renovation options. Formed in mid-2009 Chesapeake Lodging Trust went public in 2010.

Operations

Chesapeake Lodging Trust generated about 76% of its total revenue from Room revenue in 2014 while another 20% came from its Food and Beverage services.

Geographic Reach

Nearly 50% of the REIT's hotel properties are in California (in Los Angeles San Francisco San Diego and Santa Barbara). Its other hotels are in Massachussetes (Boston and Newton); Seattle; Chicago; Washington DC; Denver; Minneapolis; New York City; and New Orleans.

Financial Performance

The REIT's revenues and profits have been growing at a healthy clip over the past several years as it has quadrupled the amount of rent-generating hotel properties and expanded its room number to nearly 6700 from 1638 in 2010.

Chesapeake's revenue jumped 14% to a record $478 million in 2014 mostly thanks to new hotel acquisitions. About one-quarter of the growth came from comparable hotel growth resulting from increased demand from corporate and leisure for rooms located in San Francisco Boston Seattle and San Diego as well as from higher demand from group customers at its hotels in Boston San Francisco and Denver driven by favorable convention calendars for their respective markets during the year.

Higher revenue and a $7 million gain from the sale of its Courtyard Anaheim hotel property in 2014 drove the REIT's net income higher by 35% to a record $60.95 million while Chesapeake's operating cash levels grew by 20% to $120 million on higher cash earnings.

Strategy

Chesapeake Lodging Trust targets investments in upper-upscale hotels in major business and convention markets and selectively acquires select-services hotels in urban areas or unique locations in the US.

Some of its major acquisitions in 2015 included its $103 million purchase of the historic Ace Hotel Downtown and The Theater at Ace Hotel in Los Angeles which would continue to be managed by Ace Hotel Group; and the $278 million acquisition of The Royal Palm hotel in Miami Beach Florida to be managed by HEI Hotels & Resorts and franchised to Starwood Hotels & Resorts. In 2014 Chesapeake bought the JW Marriott San Francisco Union Square for $147.2 million under the continued management of Marriott International.

The REIT also selectively sells off under-performing properties for a profit and uses the proceeds for investments in new properties in its target markets. In 2014 it sold its 153-room Courtyard Anaheim at Disneyland Resort in California for $32.5 million netting a gain on the sale of $7 million.

EXECUTIVES

EVP and CFO, Douglas W. Vicari, age 59, $475,000 total compensation
President and CEO, James L. Francis, age 56, $700,000 total compensation
SVP Chief Accounting Officer and Secretary, Graham J. Wootten, age 44, $252,000 total compensation
EVP and COO, D. Rick Adams, $400,000 total compensation
Chairman, Thomas A. Natelli
Auditors: Ernst & Young LLP

LOCATIONS

HQ: Chesapeake Lodging Trust
4300 Wilson Boulevard, Suite 625, Arlington, VA 22203
Phone: 571 349-9450
Web: www.chesapeakelodgingtrust.com

COMPETITORS

Ashford Hospitality Trust	LaSalle Hotel Properties
DiamondRock Hospitality	Pebblebrook
FelCor	RLJ Lodging
Hospitality Properties Trust	Ryman
Host Hotels & Resorts	Strategic Hotels Sunstone Hotel Investors

HISTORICAL FINANCIALS

Company Type: Public

Income Statement   FYE: December 31

	REVENUE ($ mil.)	NET INCOME ($ mil.)	NET PROFIT MARGIN	EMPLOYEES
12/17	598.2	76.2	12.7%	14
12/16	619.7	76.7	12.4%	15
12/15	582.6	67.5	11.6%	12
12/14	477.9	60.9	12.8%	13
12/13	420.1	45.3	10.8%	13
Annual Growth	9.2%	13.9%	—	1.9%

2017 Year-End Financials

Debt ratio: 42.0%
Return on equity: 6.8%
Cash ($ mil.): 44.3
Current ratio: 1.45
Long-term debt ($ mil.): 829.5

No. of shares (mil.): 59.9
Dividends
  Yield: 0.0%
  Payout: 144.1%
Market value ($ mil.): 1,624.0

	STOCK PRICE ($) FY Close	P/E High/Low		PER SHARE ($) Earnings	Dividends	Book Value
12/17	27.09	26	20	1.11	1.60	17.49
12/16	25.86	24	18	1.13	1.60	19.92
12/15	25.16	39	25	0.99	1.50	20.27
12/14	37.21	38	23	1.00	1.20	19.74
12/13	25.29	34	27	0.75	1.00	19.09
Annual Growth	1.7%	—	—	10.3%	12.5%	(2.2%)

Chesapeake Utilities Corp.

Chesapeake Utilities gasses up the Chesapeake Bay and then some. Chesapeake's regulated natural gas distribution divisions serve customers in the Northeast and Florida. Another unit distributes electricity to more than 30000 customers in Florida. On the unregulated side the company also serves retail propane customers in Delaware Florida Maryland and Virginia. In addition Chesapeake has interstate gas pipeline and gas marketing operations.

Operations
The utility operates through three divisions: regulated energy unregulated energy and other. Regulated the largest consists of electricity and natural gas distribution and transmission. Unregulated includes propane distribution wholesaling and storage (some 4 million gallons of it) as well as natural gas marketing gathering and processing electricity and steam generation and energy-related services. The segment "Other" covers payment processor SkipJack and Eastern Shore Real Estate.

Geographic Reach
Chesapeake Utilities provides its goods and services in Delaware Virginia Maryland Pennsylvania Ohio and Florida.

Sales and Marketing
Chesapeake Utilities serves more than 235000 customers. The company primarily distributes gas to some 150000 customers in Delaware Maryland and Florida as well as electricity to about 32000 customers in Florida. Additionally through subsidiary Eastern Shore Natural Gas the company engages in gas transmission in the Delmarva Peninsula and Florida.

On the unregulated side Chesapeake manages propane distribution in Delaware Maryland Pennsylvania and Florida serving an additional 55000 customers.

Lastly the company also provides marketing of propane crude oil and natural gas in Delmarva Peninsula Florida and Ohio as well as natural gas supply gathering and processing in Ohio and electricity & steam generation through the Eight Flags co-generation gas plant in Florida.

Financial Performance
Revenue jumped up some 24% in 2017 to some $618 million up from $499 million in 2016. Most of the growth came from a 60% hike in revenue from the unregulated energy businesses of Chesapeake accounting for $325 million. Regulated energy also saw a modest 6% annual sales gain. The revenue boost came from new customers being served and natural gas service expansion in Florida.

Net income soared about 30% to $58 million year-over-year mostly due to a $115 million gain in operating income compared to 2016.

Cash holdings at the end of 2017 stood at $5.6 million. Operations generated $111 million offset by $187 million used by operations. Financing activities contributed $78 million in cash inflows.

Strategy
Chesapeake is actively expanding energy distribution and transmission businesses for the last several years. Its success at both regulated and unregulated energy markets have been striking.

The company's midstream and downstream investment focus especially in Florida is proving successful. Chesapeake made three strategic acquisitions in 2017 all in Florida.

The regulated segment is pursuing two major expansion projects at Eastern Shore Natural Gas (ESNG)/Florida natural gas and at Peninsula Pipeline. The Peninsula project consists of two pipeline constructions one each in Escambia and Palm Beach that will interconnect with the FGT. Chesapeake's unregulated segment grew an impressive 60% thanks to a flourishing propane businesses at Sharp Energy and Flo-gas.

Customer base climbed impressively in Delmarva and Florida and with continued acquisitions the company is slated to grow impressively in the near term.

Mergers and Acquisitions
In December 2018 Chesapeake's subsidiary Sharp Energy purchased the propane assets of R.F. Ohl Fuel Oil for an undisclosed sum with an aim to further expand its Pennsylvania footprint. The acquired company already serves 2500 customers in the Carbon Monroe Northampton Lehigh and Schuylkill counties bringing up Sharp's customers served to 6000.

Chesapeake acquired three companies in year prior. Through Flo-gas it acquired some assets of Central Gas a propane distributor with some 325 residential and commercial customers in Florida. Flo-gas also acquired specific Chipola Propane Gas assets broadening Chesapeake's reach in the Marianna region of the sunshine state. The last acquisition was through its PESCO subsidiary which acquired natural gas marketing assets of ARM for $6.8 million complementing its regional footprint and retail demand.

Company Background
The company was founded in 1859 as the Dover Gas Light Company. It became Chesapeake Utilities Corporation in 1947. In 2003 Chesapeake began to exit the water services business selling six of its seven dealerships. The company sold the remaining water dealership in 2004. Chesapeake Utilities expanded into Florida through the acquisition of Florida Public Utilities Company in 2009 where it is expanding more recently.

EXECUTIVES

SVP CFO and Corporate Secretary, Beth W. Cooper, age 51, $300,625 total compensation
SVP; President and COO Eastern Shore Natural Gas Company and Sandpiper Energy, Stephen C. (Steve) Thompson, age 57, $333,750 total compensation
President CEO and Director, Michael P. (Mike) McMasters, age 60, $531,250 total compensation
President Sharp Energy, S. Robert (Bob) Zola, age 67, $143,750 total compensation
SVP Strategic Development, Elaine B. Bittner, age 49, $271,250 total compensation
President Florida Public Utilities and Peninsula Pipeline Company, Jeffry M. Householder, $291,500 total compensation
President Xeron, Richard G. Garcia
Vice President, Nicole Carter
Vice President, James Moore
Vice President Business Development, Jack Lewnard
VP Regulatory Affairs, Sheri Richard
Vice President, Aleida Socarras
Senior Vice President, Steve Thompson
Chairman, John R. Schimkaitis, age 71
Auditors: Baker Tilly Virchow Krause, LLP

LOCATIONS

HQ: Chesapeake Utilities Corp.
909 Silver Lake Boulevard, Dover, DE 19904
Phone: 302 734-6799
Web: www.chpk.com

PRODUCTS/OPERATIONS

2016 Sales

	$ mil.	% of total
Regulated energy	305.7	60
Unregulated energy	203.8	40
Other	(10.6)	-
Total	**498.9**	**100**

Selected Subsidiaries
Chesapeake Service Company
  BravePoint Inc. (formerly United Systems Inc. information technology)
  Chesapeake Investment Company (real estate investments)
  Eastern Shore Real Estate Inc. (office building leases)
  Skipjack Inc. (office building leases)
Eastern Shore Natural Gas Company (transmission)
Florida Public Utilities Company (gas power and propane distribution)
Flo-Gas Corporation
Peninsula Energy Services Company Inc
Peninsula Pipeline Company Inc.
Sharp Energy Inc. (propane distribution)
  Sharpgas Inc.
Xeron Inc. (propane marketing)

COMPETITORS

Constellation Energy Group	JEA
Delmarva Power	New Jersey Resources
Energy Transfer	NextEra Energy
Ferrellgas Partners	Suburban Propane
	UGI

HISTORICAL FINANCIALS
Company Type: Public

Income Statement
FYE: December 31

	REVENUE ($ mil.)	NET INCOME ($ mil.)	NET PROFIT MARGIN	EMPLOYEES
12/17	617.5	58.1	9.4%	945
12/16	498.8	44.6	9.0%	903
12/15	459.2	41.1	9.0%	832
12/14	498.8	36.0	7.2%	753
12/13	444.3	32.7	7.4%	842
Annual Growth	8.6%	15.4%	—	2.9%

2017 Year-End Financials

Debt ratio: 32.3%	No. of shares (mil.): 16.3
Return on equity: 12.4%	Dividends
Cash ($ mil.): 5.6	Yield: 0.0%
Current ratio: 0.43	Payout: 36.0%
Long-term debt ($ mil.): 197.4	Market value ($ mil.): 1,284.0

	STOCK PRICE ($) FY Close	P/E High/Low		PER SHARE ($) Earnings	Dividends	Book Value
12/17	78.55	24 18		3.55	1.28	29.75
12/16	66.95	24 19		2.86	1.20	27.36
12/15	56.75	22 17		2.72	1.13	23.45
12/14	49.66	29 16		2.47	1.07	20.59
12/13	60.02	27 20		2.26	1.01	19.28
Annual Growth	7.0%	— —		12.0%	6.0%	11.5%

Chimera Investment Corp

This Chimera has the body of a mortgage real estate investment trust (REIT) but its head is that of its external manager FIDAC (Fixed Income Discount Advisory Company) a fixed-income investment management firm wholly-owned by Annaly Capital Management. Formed in 2007 Chimera invests in residential mortgage loans; residential mortgage-backed securities (RMBS) such as those guaranteed by government agencies Fannie Mae and Freddie Mac; real estate-related securities; and other assets including collateralized debt obligations or CDOs. The REIT went public in 2007 shortly after it was formed.

Institutional investors hold approximately 40% of Chimera Investment's stock led by Wellington Management's 11% stake. Annaly owns about 9% of the company.

EXECUTIVES

CFO and Secretary, A. Alexandra Denahan, age 45
Managing Director; Head - Business Development, Matthew Lambiase, age 49
Head of Investments, Christian J. Woschenko, age 55
Head of Underwriting, William B. Dyer, age 69
Chairman, Paul Donlin, age 54
Director, Jeremy Diamond, age 52
Director, Mark Abrams, age 67
Director, Gerard (Gerry) Creagh, age 57
Managing Director; Head - Business Development, Matthew Lambiase, age 49
Director, Paul A. Keenan, age 49
Director, Dennis Mahoney
Independent Director, John Reilly
Auditors: Ernst & Young LLP

LOCATIONS

HQ: Chimera Investment Corp
520 Madison Avenue, 32nd Floor, New York, NY 10022
Phone: 212 626-2300
Web: www.chimerareit.com

COMPETITORS

Annaly Capital Management	MFA Financial
Capstead Mortgage	Walter Investment Management
Impac Mortgage Holdings	

HISTORICAL FINANCIALS

Company Type: Public

Income Statement   FYE: December 31

	REVENUE ($ mil.)	NET INCOME ($ mil.)	NET PROFIT MARGIN	EMPLOYEES
12/17	1,168.3	524.6	44.9%	38
12/16	992.9	551.9	55.6%	38
12/15	603.1	250.3	41.5%	32
12/14	768.3	589.2	76.7%	0
12/13	498.7	362.6	72.7%	0
Annual Growth	23.7%	9.7%	—	—

2017 Year-End Financials

Debt ratio: 45.2%	No. of shares (mil.): 187.8
Return on equity: 15.5%	Dividends
Cash ($ mil.): 63.5	Yield: 0.1%
Current ratio: 0.02	Payout: 76.6%
Long-term debt ($ mil.): 9,594.4	Market value ($ mil.): 3,471.0

	STOCK PRICE ($) FY Close	P/E High/Low		Earnings	PER SHARE ($) Dividends	Book Value
12/17	18.48	8	7	2.61	2.00	19.35
12/16	17.02	6	4	2.92	2.44	16.64
12/15	13.64	13	2	1.25	1.44	15.70
12/14	3.18	1	1	2.85	1.80	17.55
12/13	3.10	2	1	1.75	2.80	16.21
Annual Growth	56.3%	—	—	10.5%	(8.1%)	4.5%

Choice Hotels International, Inc.

This company offers a lot of hospitality choices. Choice Hotels is a leading hotel franchisor with more than 6800 locations and 525000 rooms throughout the US and more than 40 other countries. Its flagship brands include Comfort Inn one of the largest limited-service brands with about 1600 properties (including Comfort Suites) along with Quality Inn which serves the midscale hotel segment. Its Econo Lodge chain offers lodging primarily for budget-minded travelers. Other Choice Hotels brands include the full-service Clarion chain Rodeway Inn budget hotels and Sleep Inn.

Geographic Reach
Rockville Maryland-based Choice Hotels does most of its business in the US although it generates around 10% of sales form its 1130 international hotels. It has properties in Australia Brazil Canada Czech Republic France Germany Honduras Italy New Zealand and Norway.

Sales and Marketing
Choice Hotels advertises on national television radio the internet (including social media) print advertising in consumer and trade media and promotional events such as joint marketing promotions with qualified vendors and corporate partners.

It deploys field-based sales agents to target specific groups such as business travelers senior citizens automobile club members families government and military employees educational organizations and meeting planners.

Financial Performance
Choice Hotels has recorded strong consistent growth over the last five years as it expands its hotel- and room-count. In 2017 the company's revenue crested $1 billion for the first time growing 9% on 2016. Growth was due to higher revenue from the marketing and reservation system which recorded $72.1 million organic growth on new reservation delivery programs and higher revenue from its Choice Privileges loyalty program. It also recognized an additional $30.7 million of previously deferred revenue relating to changes in the Choice Privileges expiration policy. Royalty fees grew $23.2 million thanks to higher revenue per

room a 2% increase in room numbers and an increase in the royalty rate.

Choice Hotel's net income fell 18% to $114.9 million mostly due to higher income taxes due to a one time impact of changes to the US tax code.

The company's tax position improved during the year its coffers expanding $31.5 million to $235.3 million due to a strong increase in cash from operations. Operating cash benefited from adjustments for deferred income taxes and changes in forgivable notes receivable.

Strategy
Choice Hotels is riding high and is making the most of strong revenue profits and cash by investing for the future. It is diversifying and growing its hotel portfolio particularly in the upscale price bracket where it has a smaller market presence. The Cambria brand which charges the highest prices among Choice's brand portfolio has a 70-strong pipeline as of end-2017. The brand targets primary market locations and where markets have a high barrier to new construction entry its approach is to reuse and convert existing buildings. Choice also maintains a healthy pipeline in its core market segments; it had some 850 and 65765 rooms in the pipeline at the end of 2017 an increase of 132 on 2016.

The launch of a new cloud-based global reservation system choiceEDGE in 2018 will position the company to extend its range further into upper upscale and beyond. ChoiceEDGE offers scalability and stability; connectivity with online travel agents global distribution systems and property management systems; and the capability to add disparate inventory types including hotel rooms meeting rooms vacation rentals and package offerings.

Mergers and Acquisitions
In 2018 Choice Hotels acquired WoodSpring Suites a hotel franchisor serving the economy extended-stay market with 240 hotels in 35 states for $231 million.

EXECUTIVES

Chief Development Officer, David A. Pepper, age 51, $488,154 total compensation
SVP General Counsel and Corporate Secretary and External Affairs, Simone Wu, age 53, $422,308 total compensation
SVP Upscale Brands, Janis Cannon
President and CEO, Patrick S. Pacious, age 52, $662,531 total compensation
CIO, Todd Davis, age 55
Chief Commercial Officer, Robert McDowell
CFO, Dominic E. Dragisich
Vice President Advertising and Marketing Communications, Christine Lynn
Regional Vice President Franchise Sales, Thomas Bernardo
Vice President Of Engineering, Tony Pallas
REGIONAL VICE PRESIDENT, Byron Bean
Vice President International Operations, Carl Oldsberg
Vice President Head Of Vacation Rentals, Steve Caron
Vice President External Communications and Public Relations, Lorri Christou
Vice President Internal Audit, David Scott
Vice President Real Estate Investment and Asset Management, Justin Roberts
Vice President Treasurer, Maria Uy
Chairman, Stewart Bainum, age 72
Board Member, Monte Koch
Auditors: Ernst & Young LLP

LOCATIONS

HQ: Choice Hotels International, Inc.
  1 Choice Hotels Circle, Suite 400, Rockville, MD 20850
Phone: 301 592-5000
Web: www.choicehotels.com

PRODUCTS/OPERATIONS

2017 Sales

	$ mil.	% of total
Marketing and reservation	567.1	56
Royalty fees	345.3	34
Procurement services	34.7	4
Initial franchise and re-licensing fees	26.3	2
Other	34.0	4
Total	**1,007.4**	**100**

2017 Sales

	$ mil.	% of total
Franchising	996.5	99
SkyTouch Technology	3.1	-
Corporate & Other	7.8	1
Total	**1,007.4**	**100**

Selected Brands

Ascend Collection
Cambria Suites
Clarion
Comfort Inn
Comfort Suites
Econo Lodge
MainStay Suites
Quality
Rodeway Inn
Sleep Inn
Suburban Extended Stay Hotel
WoodSpring Suites

COMPETITORS

Accor North America
Best Western
Carlson Hotels
Drury Inns
Extended Stay America
  Inc.
Hilton Worldwide
InterContinental
  Hotels
La Quinta
Marriott
Wyndham Destinations

HISTORICAL FINANCIALS

Company Type: Public

Income Statement

FYE: December 31

	REVENUE ($ mil.)	NET INCOME ($ mil.)	NET PROFIT MARGIN	EMPLOYEES
12/17	1,007.3	114.8	11.4%	1,987
12/16	924.6	139.3	15.1%	1,789
12/15	859.8	128.0	14.9%	1,462
12/14	757.9	123.1	16.2%	1,331
12/13	724.3	112.6	15.5%	1,088
Annual Growth	**8.6%**	**0.5%**	**—**	**16.2%**

2017 Year-End Financials

Debt ratio: 78.3%
Return on equity: ***,***.*%
Cash ($ mil.): 235.3
Current ratio: 1.37
Long-term debt ($ mil.): 725.2
No. of shares (mil.): 56.6
Dividends
  Yield: 0.0%
  Payout: 42.5%
Market value ($ mil.): 4,398.0

	STOCK PRICE ($) FY Close	P/E High/Low	Earnings	Dividends	Book Value
12/17	77.60	39 26	2.02	0.86	(3.74)
12/16	56.05	23 17	2.46	0.83	(5.53)
12/15	50.41	29 21	2.22	0.79	(7.03)
12/14	56.02	27 21	2.10	0.75	(7.48)
12/13	49.11	26 18	1.91	0.74	(7.92)
Annual Growth	**12.1%**	**— —**	**1.4%**	**3.8%**	**—**

Chuy's Holdings Inc

Where can Tex-Mex connoisseurs and Elvis fans dine under one roof? Chuy's Holdings operates the Chuy's Tex-Mex casual dining restaurant chain which serves up a menu of enchiladas fajitas tacos and "big as yo' face" burritos as well as signature drinks like fresh-squeezed lime margaritas and Texas Martinis. Each of its nearly 70 restaurants offer patrons a funky vibrant and eclectic atmosphere decked out with Mexican folk art vintage hubcap-coated ceilings and a shrine to the "King of Rock and Roll" himself. Originally founded in Austin Texas in 1982 the company went public in mid-2012.

Operations

Unlike some chains Chuy's owns and operates all of its restaurants and does not offer franchises.

Geographic Reach

Outside of its home state of Texas Chuy's now has locations in Alabama Arkansas Florida Georgia Indiana Kentucky Missouri Ohio Oklahoma North Carolina South Carolina Tennessee and Virginia.

Sales and Marketing

Chuy's markets its restaurants through local advertising e-marketing and social media channels. Its marketing costs include local restaurant marketing programs community service and sponsorship activities.

Financial Performance

Chuy's has enjoyed revenue growth and net income growth during the past several fiscal years. The company's revenue increased to about $287 million in fiscal 2015 up 17% from the $245 million it reported in fiscal 2014. The growth in revenue has come largely from opening new restaurants.

Chuy's net income was $12.89 million in fiscal 2015. That was a 12% increase compared to the prior fiscal period. The company ended fiscal 2015 with more than $45 million in cash on hand which was a 56% increase compared to its cash levels at the conclusion of fiscal 2014.

Strategy

Chuy's has focused on opening restaurants in major cities in Texas and in states in the southeastern US; going forward it plans to open additional locations in new and existing markets. During 2016 Chuy's expects to open at least eleven new restaurants. The company plans to expand at around that same rate of 10-15 new locations per year for the next several years.

EXECUTIVES

CFO, Jon W. Howie, age 50, $250,480 total compensation
President CEO and Director, Steve Hislop, age 58, $392,316 total compensation
VP Operations Southeast Region, Frank Biller, $169,343 total compensation
VP Real Estate and Development, Michael Hatcher, $159,006 total compensation
VP Operations, Ted Zapp, age 66, $178,805 total compensation
Vice President Of Operations South, Tommy Larue
Chairman and Treasurer, Jose (Joe) Ferreira, age 62
Auditors: RSM US LLP

LOCATIONS

HQ: Chuy's Holdings Inc
  1623 Toomey Road, Austin, TX 78704
Phone: 512 473-2783
Web: www.chuys.com

PRODUCTS/OPERATIONS

SELECTED MENU
TORTILLAS
NEVER FROZEN
GREEN CHILES
SAUCES
CHICKEN
LIME JUICE

COMPETITORS

Acapulco/El Torito
  Restaurants
Applebee's
  International
Brinker
Carlson Restaurants
Chipotle
Darden
OSI Restaurant
  Partners
Texas Roadhouse

HISTORICAL FINANCIALS

Company Type: Public

Income Statement

FYE: December 31

	REVENUE ($ mil.)	NET INCOME ($ mil.)	NET PROFIT MARGIN	EMPLOYEES
12/17	369.5	28.9	7.8%	9,000
12/16	330.6	17.2	5.2%	8,200
12/15	287.0	12.9	4.5%	7,295
12/14	245.1	11.4	4.7%	6,567
12/13	204.3	11.0	5.4%	5,712
Annual Growth	**16.0%**	**27.2%**	**—**	**12.0%**

2017 Year-End Financials

Debt ratio: —
Return on equity: 16.4%
Cash ($ mil.): 8.7
Current ratio: 1.04
Long-term debt ($ mil.): —
No. of shares (mil.): 16.9
Dividends
  Yield: —
  Payout: —
Market value ($ mil.): 475.0

	STOCK PRICE ($) FY Close	P/E High/Low	Earnings	Dividends	Book Value
12/17	28.05	19 11	1.70	0.00	11.17
12/16	32.95	37 25	1.02	0.00	9.33
12/15	31.14	44 25	0.77	0.00	8.07
12/14	19.49	62 27	0.69	0.00	7.19
12/13	36.63	64 33	0.66	0.00	6.38
Annual Growth	**(6.5%)**	**— —**	**26.7%**	**—**	**15.0%**

CIB Marine Bancshares Inc

EXECUTIVES

President CEO, Stanley J. Calderon, age 70
President and COO, Charles J. Ponicki, age 65, $206,462 total compensation
Chairman and CEO Citrus Bank, G. Richard Nisbeth
Executive Vice President; General Counsel; Secretary, Daniel J. Rasmussen, age 50

Chairman and CEO, John P. Hickey Jr., age 68, $268,400 total compensation
President CEO, Joe Henderson
Paralegal & Investor Relations Manager, Elizabeth Neighbors
Chief Credit Officer, Paul Melnick
Director, Gary L. Longman, age 67
Director, Charles J. Baker, age 71
Director, Charles D. Mires
Director, Ronald E. Rhoades
Director, Willard Bunn III, age 72
Independent Director, Mark Elste
Auditors: Crowe Horwath LLP

LOCATIONS

HQ: CIB Marine Bancshares Inc
1930 West Bluemound Road, Suite D, Waukesha, WI 53186
Phone: 262 695-6010　　**Fax:** 262 695-6014
Web: www.cibmarine.com

COMPETITORS

Associated Banc-Corp	Northern Trust
BBX Capital	PNC Financial
Bank Mutual	TCF Financial
First Busey	U.S. Bancorp
Harris	

HISTORICAL FINANCIALS

Company Type: Public

Income Statement　　　　　　　　　　　FYE: December 31

	ASSETS ($ mil.)	NET INCOME ($ mil.)	INCOME AS % OF ASSETS	EMPLOYEES
12/17	662.3	26.9	4.1%	183
12/16	653.5	4.0	0.6%	171
12/15	571.2	(0.6)	—	0
12/14	501.9	0.3	0.1%	154
12/13	460.1	(1.3)	—	154
Annual Growth	9.5%	—	—	4.4%

2017 Year-End Financials

Return on assets: 4.1%	Dividends
Return on equity: 32.3%	Yield: —
Long-term debt ($ mil.): —	Payout: —
No. of shares (mil.): 18.1	Market value ($ mil.): 26.0
Sales ($ mil): 32.2	

	STOCK PRICE ($) FY Close	P/E High/Low		PER SHARE ($) Earnings	Dividends	Book Value
12/17	1.42	1	1	0.74	0.00	5.34
12/16	1.08	6	1	0.11	0.00	3.83
12/15	0.43	—	—	(0.03)	0.00	3.62
12/14	0.47	42	22	0.01	0.00	3.72
12/13	0.49	—	—	(0.07)	0.00	3.65
Annual Growth	30.5%	—	—	—	—	10.0%

CIM Commercial Trust Corp

PMC Commercial Trust likes lending to little businesses. The real estate investment trust (REIT) makes small business loans primarily to limited-service hotel franchisees. The loans ranging from $100000 to $4 million are secured by first liens on real estate and written for hotel owner/operators of national franchises such as Comfort Inn and Holiday Inn Express. PMC Commercial Trust also lends to owners of convenience stores restaurants and other small businesses. About 20% of its loan portfolio is concentrated in Texas. Subsidiaries are active in Small Business Administration (SBA) lending and in investing (as small business investment companies or SBICs). The company was founded in 1993.PMC Commercial Trust has ramped up its SBA lending activities.In 2006 the company sold its portfolio of about a dozen hotel properties to concentrate on its lending business. The hotels had previously been leased to Arlington Hospitality which filed for Chapter 11 bankruptcy protection in 2005. After regaining possession of the properties PMC Commercial Trust put them on the market.

Siblings Andrew Rosemore (chairman) Lance Rosemore (CEO) and Martha Greenberg (director) together own more than 10% of PMC Commercial Trust.

EXECUTIVES

EVP COO Chief Investment Officer and Treasurer, Jan F. Salit, age 62, $282,329 total compensation
EVP and CFO, Barry N. Berlin, age 52, $282,329 total compensation
President CEO and Secretary, Lance B. Rosemore, age 64, $418,903 total compensation
Independent Trustee, Nathan G. Cohen, age 70
Independent Trustee, Irving Munn, age 67
Independent Trustee, Barry A. Imber, age 69
Trustee, Martha Morrow
Auditors: BDO USA, LLP

LOCATIONS

HQ: CIM Commercial Trust Corp
17950 Preston Road, Suite 600, Dallas, TX 75252
Phone: 972 349-3200
Web: www.cimcommercial.com

COMPETITORS

Amerisource Funding	JER Investors Trust
Archon Group	Jameson Inns
Ashford Hospitality Trust	Janus Hotels
Capital Trust	Texas Capital Bancshares
Cullen/Frost Bankers	Vestin
FirstCity Financial	

HISTORICAL FINANCIALS

Company Type: Public

Income Statement　　　　　　　　　　　FYE: December 31

	ASSETS ($ mil.)	NET INCOME ($ mil.)	INCOME AS % OF ASSETS	EMPLOYEES
12/17	1,336.3	379.7	28.4%	2
12/16	2,022.8	34.5	1.7%	10
12/15	2,098.1	24.3	1.2%	10
12/14	2,094.6	24.3	1.2%	33
12/13	253.4	2.0	0.8%	32
Annual Growth	51.5%	268.2%	—	(50.0%)

2017 Year-End Financials

Return on assets: 22.6%	Dividends
Return on equity: 46.8%	Yield: 0.2%
Long-term debt ($ mil.): —	Payout: 65.5%
No. of shares (mil.): 43.7	Market value ($ mil.): 836.0
Sales ($ mil): 236.3	

	STOCK PRICE ($) FY Close	P/E High/Low		PER SHARE ($) Earnings	Dividends	Book Value
12/17	19.10	4	3	5.47	3.58	14.93
12/16	15.45	59	44	0.34	0.88	11.51
12/15	15.54	84	58	0.25	0.88	13.28
12/14	15.01	93	18	0.25	0.66	13.93
12/13	8.60	10	7	1.00	2.50	63.77
Annual Growth (30.4%)	22.1%	—	—	52.9%	9.4%	

Cirrus Logic Inc

Cirrus Logic takes a sound approach to computing. The fabless semiconductor company long a leader in audio chips of all kinds develops integrated circuits (ICs) for specialized applications in consumer electronics energy and industrial equipment. Its more than 700 products include audio encoder/decoders (codecs) digital amplifiers digital audio converters and energy management devices. Cirrus Logic's audio chips are used in smartphones tablet and laptop computers Blu-ray Disc players gaming devices and digital TVs. Energy management products include LED driver ICs ADCs and DACs used to make LEDs digital utility meters and power supplies. The company gets most of its sales from customers in China.

HISTORY

Suhas Patil a professor who had developed a chip-level software system for controlling disk drives while at MIT founded Patil Systems in 1981. When his firm failed to find buyers for its advanced products Patil sought advice from semiconductor executive Michael Hackworth. Impressed with the products' possibilities Hackworth joined Patil Systems as CEO. In 1984 the company was renamed Cirrus Logic after the high-flying clouds.

The company initially focused on chips for computer peripherals but during the 1980s it also began making chips for PCs. It debuted the first controller chips small enough to be built directly into a disk drive unit an advance that prompted the PC industry's shift to smaller-profile disk drives. When IBM introduced its Video Graphics Array (VGA) graphics display standard in 1987 Cirrus Logic quickly followed with the market's first VGA controller chip.

Cirrus Logic went public in 1989. Its 1991 acquisitions of Crystal Semiconductor and Pixel Semiconductor provided it with access to audio and video technology for the multimedia and fax/modem markets. It bought PC graphics chip maker Acumos in 1992 and Pacific Communication Sciences (products for cellular communications) in 1993. The next year it bought PicoPower Technology a maker of system controller chips.

In 1996 Cirrus Logic sold its wireless infrastructure equipment unit to ADC Telecommunications. That year the company formed wafer fabrication joint venture Cirent with Lucent's microelectronics unit (which became Agere Systems later acquired by LSI Corp.).

An industry downturn led Cirrus Logic to cut its workforce by 13% in 1996 and by another 15%

PIERCE COLLEGE LIBRARY

in 1997. That year Patil stepped away from the company's day-to-day operations (he continued to serve as chairman emeritus and a director) and Hackworth became chairman.

In 1998 continuing to expand its offerings Cirrus Logic debuted products for DVDs. In response to a prolonged slump in the semiconductor industry it eliminated its PC graphics and video accelerator product lines and sold voice compression technology subsidiary Nuera Communications to management. Also that year Cirrus Logic spun off its PC modem business as Ambient Technologies. Analog Devices VP/GM David French was named president and COO in 1998.

In 1999 about 500 more employees were laid off. In an effort to phase out more of its wafer fabrication operations the company that year handed over control of its MiCRUS joint venture (founded in 1994) to partner IBM and transferred its ownership of Cirent to Lucent (now Alcatel-Lucent). Also that year French became CEO; Hackworth remained chairman.

In 2000 Cirrus Logic moved its headquarters from Fremont California to Austin Texas. The next year the company announced that it would focus growth efforts on semiconductors used in consumer entertainment devices. Despite historically dismal conditions in the chip industry Cirrus Logic took steps to pursue this strategy in 2001 when it acquired private chip makers Peak Audio (digital audio hardware and software) LuxSonor ($65 million DVD video processors) ShareWave ($92 million wireless home networking chips and software) and Stream Machine ($110 million digital video encoding chips).

Later in 2001 the company announced that it would lay off about 300 workers — 30% of its staff — in the face of continued poor conditions in the global chip market. The next year Cirrus exited the magnetic storage chip business in order to focus on products for the consumer entertainment market. In 2003 the company announced more job cuts and discontinued the wireless product line acquired as part of the ShareWave acquisition. It also sold its chip testing facilities to ChipPAC (now part of STATS ChipPAC) which in turn supplied Cirrus Logic with assembly test and packaging services.

As conditions in the worldwide semiconductor market turned choppy again in 2004 Cirrus Logic had a 7% reduction in force more than 50 workers mostly affecting employees in California and Texas.

In 2005 the company received $25 million from a legal settlement with Amkor Technology Fujitsu and Sumitomo Bakelite. The litigation was over faulty semiconductors sold by Cirrus to Fujitsu. Cirrus and Fujitsu first sued each other in 2001; Amkor and Sumitomo were added as parties to the litigation (which shifted from federal court to state court) in 2003. The insurance carriers for the four vendors reached a settlement through arbitration in 2005.

That same year Cirrus Logic sold its digital video IC product line to Magnum Semiconductor an entity formed by investors led by Investcorp and August Capital Management. The company received a minority equity stake in Magnum Semi for the assets of the digital video line.

In 2006 Cirrus acquired Shanghai-based Caretta Integrated Circuits for about $10 million in cash. Caretta designed power management ICs for the large single-cell lithium-ion battery market.

David French resigned as president and CEO in 2007 after a special committee of the board investigated the company's past practices in granting stock options and found that French was significantly involved in backdating certain option grants. Chairman Michael Hackworth stepped in as acting president and CEO. VP/GM Jason Rhode a Cirrus Logic employee since 1995 was named to succeed French as president and CEO.

In 2007 the SEC's Division of Enforcement informed Cirrus Logic that its informal investigation of the company's historical stock option practices initiated a year earlier was elevated to a formal inquiry. The SEC later notified the company that the inquiry was concluded and the commission's staff was not recommending any enforcement action against the company.

Cirrus acquired Apex Microtechnology for $42 million in cash in 2007. Apex Micro developed precision high-power analog amplifiers for aerospace and industrial applications used in motors piezoelectrics programmable power supplies and other devices. Founded in 1980 the company (also known as Apex Precision Products) had some 1200 customers with about $20 million in annual sales and employed around 90 people.

In 2008 the company decided that things weren't working out with Caretta Integrated Circuits in terms of its long-term strategic plan. It shut down the subsidiary and laid off about 30 employees in China as a result.

The global financial crisis of 2008 which restricted the worldwide availability of credit destabilized the general economy and triggered a significant slowdown in orders for Cirrus Logic.

EXECUTIVES

Vice President General Counsel and Corporate Secretary, Gregory S Thomas
VP and Chief Culture Officer, Jo-Dee M. Benson, age 58
President CEO and Director, Jason P. Rhode, age 48, $658,500 total compensation
SVP; General Manager Mixed-Signal Audio Division, Scott A. Anderson, age 64, $322,319 total compensation
VP and CFO, Thurman K. Case, $323,171 total compensation
VP Supply Chain Management, Randy Carlson
VP and General Manager MEMS Division, Brad Fluke
Vice President of Product Marketing, Carl Alberty
Vice President Billing, Isa V Card
Vice President Engineering, Thomas Schoen
Vice President of Marketing Communications, Stan Victor
Vice President and Chief Culture Officer, Jodee Benson
Vice President of Worldwide Sales, Andrew Brannan
Vice President. Corporate Communications and Human Resources, Jo Dee Benson
Vice President Software, Stephen Evans
Vice President of APAC Sales, Peter Zou
Chairman, Alan R. Schuele
Board Member, William Sherman
Board Member, Alexander Davern
Board Member, Christine King
Board Member, David Tupman
Auditors: Ernst & Young LLP

LOCATIONS

HQ: Cirrus Logic Inc
800 W. 6th Street, Austin, TX 78701
Phone: 512 851-4000
Web: www.cirrus.com

PRODUCTS/OPERATIONS

2016 Sales

	$ mil.	% of total
Portable Audio Products	989.1	85
Non-Portable Audio and Other Products	180.2	15
Total	**1,169.3**	**100**

Selected Products

Amplifier integrated circuits
Analog-to-digital converters
Digital amplifiers
Digital interface integrated circuits
Digital-to-analog converters
Linear amplifiers
Volume controls

COMPETITORS

AMD	Macronix International
Actions Semiconductor	Marvell Technology
Analog Devices	Maxim Integrated
Analogic	Products
Asahi Kasei	NXP Semiconductors
Atmel	O2Micro
Conexant Systems	ON Semiconductor
Creative Technology	Power Integrations
Dialog Semiconductor	STMicroelectronics
Fairchild	Samsung Electronics
Semiconductor	Sigma Designs
Infineon Technologies	Sunplus
Integrated Device	Texas Instruments
Technology	VIA Technologies
Intel	Yamaha
Linear Technology	ams AG

HISTORICAL FINANCIALS

Company Type: Public

Income Statement

FYE: March 31

	REVENUE ($ mil.)	NET INCOME ($ mil.)	NET PROFIT MARGIN	EMPLOYEES
03/18	1,532.1	162.0	10.6%	1,596
03/17	1,538.9	261.2	17.0%	1,444
03/16	1,169.2	123.6	10.6%	1,291
03/15	916.5	55.1	6.0%	1,104
03/14	714.3	108.1	15.1%	751
Annual Growth	**21.0%**	**10.6%**	**—**	**20.7%**

2018 Year-End Financials

Debt ratio: —
Return on equity: 13.7%
Cash ($ mil.): 235.6
Current ratio: 4.38
Long-term debt ($ mil.): —

No. of shares (mil.): 61.9
Dividends
  Yield: —
  Payout: —
Market value ($ mil.): 2,517.0

	STOCK PRICE ($) FY Close	P/E High/Low		PER SHARE ($) Earnings	Dividends	Book Value
03/18	40.63	28	15	2.46	0.00	18.75
03/17	60.06	16	8	3.92	0.00	17.91
03/16	34.47	19	13	1.87	0.00	13.72
03/15	33.29	39	19	0.85	0.00	12.00
03/14	19.52	15	10	1.65	0.00	10.29
Annual Growth	**20.1%**	**—**	**—**	**10.5%**	**—**	**16.2%**

CNB Community Bancorp Inc

Auditors: Rehmann Robson LLC

LOCATIONS

HQ: CNB Community Bancorp Inc
One South Howell Street, Hillsdale, MI 49242
Phone: 517 439-0401 **Fax:** 517 439-0403
Web: www.countynationalbank.com

HISTORICAL FINANCIALS

Company Type: Public

Income Statement				FYE: December 31
	REVENUE ($ mil.)	NET INCOME ($ mil.)	NET PROFIT MARGIN	EMPLOYEES
12/17	31.1	6.0	19.4%	3
12/16	28.7	4.7	16.5%	0
12/15	25.3	4.2	16.5%	0
12/14	23.7	3.9	16.7%	0
Annual Growth	9.4%	15.1%	—	—

2017 Year-End Financials

Debt ratio: 4.0%	No. of shares (mil.): 2.1
Return on equity: 12.6%	Dividends
Cash ($ mil.): 64.4	Yield: 0.0%
Current ratio: 0.12	Payout: 13.6%
Long-term debt ($ mil.): 24.9	Market value ($ mil.): 50.0

	STOCK PRICE ($) FY Close	P/E High/Low		PER SHARE ($) Earnings	Dividends	Book Value
12/17	23.60	8	8	2.93	0.40	23.81
12/16	19.50	—	—	2.32	0.90	21.88
12/15	19.50	—	—	2.06	0.88	20.51
12/14	19.50	—	—	1.95	0.86	19.37
/0.00	—			(0.00)	0.00	(0.00)
Annual Growth	—	—	—	—	—	—

CNB Financial Corp. (Clearfield, PA)

CNB Financial is the holding company for CNB Bank ERIEBANK and FCBank. The banks and subsidiaries provide traditional deposit and loan services as well as wealth management merchant credit card processing and life insurance through nearly 30 CNB Bank- and ERIEBANK-branded branches in Pennsylvania and nine FCBank branches in central Ohio. Commercial industrial and agricultural loans make up more than one-third of the bank's loan portfolio while commercial mortgages make up another one-third. It also makes residential mortgages consumer and credit card loans. The company's non-bank subsidiaries include CNB Securities Corporation Holiday Financial Services Corporation and CNB Insurance Agency.

Operations

Commercial industrial and agricultural loans made up 36% of the bank's $16.74 billion loan portfolio at the end of 2015 while commercial mortgages made up another 33%. The rest of the portfolio was made up of residential mortgages (15% of loan assets) consumer (14%) overdrafts (less than 1%) and credit card loans (less than 1%).

The group makes more than 80% of its revenue from interest income. About 70% of its revenue came from loan interest during 2015 while another 15% came from interest income from taxable and tax-exempt securities. The remainder of its revenue came from deposit account service charges (4% of revenue) wealth and asset management fees (3%) and other miscellaneous income sources.

Geographic Reach

Clearfield Pennsylvania-based CNB Financial serves clients in its home state as well as in Ohio. CNB Financial serves a specific market area such as the Pennsylvania counties of Cambria Cameron Centre Clearfield Crawford Elk Erie Indiana Jefferson McKean and Warren.

Sales and Marketing

The group serves individuals businesses government and institutional customers.

CNB Financial has been increasing its advertising spend in recent years. It spent $1.6 million during 2015 up from $1.5 million and $1 million in 2014 and 2013 respectively.

Financial Performance

CNB Financial's revenues have risen more than 30% since 2011 as its loan assets have nearly doubled to $1.58 billion. The firm's profits have grown nearly 50% over the same period as low-interest rates and declining loan loss provisions have lowered operating costs.

The group's revenue climbed 1% to $102 million during 2015 thanks to a modest rise in interest income stemming mostly from 16% loan asset growth.

Despite revenue growth in 2015 CNB Financial's net income dipped 4% to $22.2 million mostly due to nearly 10% rise in salary and employee benefit costs from new hires and more expensive benefits. The group's operating cash levels jumped 16% to $34 million for the year thanks to favorable working capital changes related to accrued interest payables and other liabilities.

Strategy

CNB Financial has been acquiring other banks and opening branches in new geographic markets in recent years to boost its loan and deposit business. As a sign of success the bank noted that its assets have nearly doubled in size since 2009 from $1.16 billion to $2.29 billion at the end of 2015.

Toward its branch expansion plans the group's ERIEBANK brand entered Ohio by opening a loan production office there in 2014 with plans to open another by the end of 2016. After opening an FCBank branch in Dublin Ohio in 2014 the group in 2016 also continued to push its FCBank brand which has been enjoying double-digit loan and deposit business growth in the Columbus and Lancaster regions in Ohio. It plans to open a new FCBank branch in Worthington Ohio by the end of 2016.

Mergers and Acquisitions

In 2016 CNB looked expanded into Northeast Ohio after buying Mentor Ohio-based Lake National Bank — and its $152 million in assets — for nearly $25 million. Lake National Bank's operations were folded into ERIEBANK's operations when the transaction closed.

In 2013 extending its reach in Ohio CNB Financial acquired FC Banc Corp. for $41.6 million. The deal gave CNB Financial Farmers Citizens Bank which serves the northern Ohio communities of Bucyrus Cardington Fredericktown Mount Hope and Shiloh as well as the greater Columbus Ohio area.

Company Background

In 2012 CNB Financial acquired an Ebensburg Pennsylvania-based consumer discount company which brought with it a loan portfolio valued at about $1 million.

EXECUTIVES

EVP Human Resources, Mary Ann Conaway
SEVP and Chief Credit Officer CNB Bank, Mark D. Breakey, age 59, $211,000 total compensation
President and CEO, Joseph B. Bower, age 54, $458,000 total compensation
SEVP and COO CNB Bank, Richard L Greslick, age 42, $221,000 total compensation
EVP CFO and Treasurer CNB Bank and Treasurer Principal Financial Officer and Principal Accounting Officer CNB Financial Corporation, Brian W. Wingard, age 44, $210,000 total compensation
EVP and Chief Commercial Banking Officer CNB Bank, Joseph E. Dell, age 62, $211,000 total compensation
EVP Customer Experience, Leanne D. Kassab
Assistant Vice President of Credit Administration, Gregory Dixon
Assistant Vice President of Mortgage Lending, Eileen Ryan
Assistant Vice President of Regional Branch Administration, Vickie Baker
Vice Presidents Commercial Banking, Joseph Yaros
Assistant Vice President Compliance, Kylie Ogden
Vice President Commercial Lending, Brett Stewart
Chairman, Peter F. Smith, age 63
Senior Vice President Operations and Assistant Secretary, Vincent C Turiano
Auditors: Crowe Horwath LLP

LOCATIONS

HQ: CNB Financial Corp. (Clearfield, PA)
1 South Second Street, P.O. Box 42, Clearfield, PA 16830
Phone: 814 765-9621
Web: www.cnbbank.bank

PRODUCTS/OPERATIONS

2015 Sales

	% of total
Interest and Dividend Income	
Loans including fees	70
Securities	
Taxable	10
Tax-exempt	4
Dividends	1
Non-Interest Income	
Wealth and asset management fees	3
Service charges on deposit accounts	4
Other service charges and fees	3
Other revenues	5
Total	**100**

Selected Services

Checking
Credit cards
Loans
Savings

COMPETITORS

AmeriServ Financial	M&T Bank
CBT Financial	Northwest Bancshares
Citizens Financial	PNC Financial
Group	S&T Bancorp
First Commonwealth	
Financial	

HISTORICAL FINANCIALS

Company Type: Public

Income Statement
FYE: December 31

	ASSETS ($ mil.)	NET INCOME ($ mil.)	INCOME AS % OF ASSETS	EMPLOYEES
12/17	2,768.7	23.8	0.9%	528
12/16	2,573.8	20.5	0.8%	507
12/15	2,285.1	22.2	1.0%	454
12/14	2,189.2	23.0	1.1%	426
12/13	2,131.2	16.6	0.8%	395
Annual Growth	6.8%	9.4%	—	7.5%

2017 Year-End Financials

Return on assets: 0.8%	Dividends
Return on equity: 10.4%	Yield: 0.0%
Long-term debt ($ mil.): —	Payout: 42.0%
No. of shares (mil.): 15.2	Market value ($ mil.): 401.0
Sales ($ mil.): 130.3	

	STOCK PRICE ($) FY Close	P/E High/Low	PER SHARE ($) Earnings	Dividends	Book Value
12/17	26.24	19 13	1.57	0.66	15.98
12/16	26.74	20 12	1.42	0.66	14.64
12/15	18.03	12 11	1.54	0.66	14.01
12/14	18.50	12 10	1.60	0.66	13.09
12/13	19.00	16 12	1.29	0.66	11.43
Annual Growth	8.4%	— —	5.0%	(0.0%)	8.7%

CNX Midstream Partners LP

Auditors: Ernst & Young LLP

LOCATIONS

HQ: CNX Midstream Partners LP
CNX Center, 1000 CONSOL Energy Drive, Canonsburg, PA 15317-6506
Phone: 724 485-4000
Web: www.cnxmidstream.com

HISTORICAL FINANCIALS

Company Type: Public

Income Statement
FYE: December 31

	REVENUE ($ mil.)	NET INCOME ($ mil.)	NET PROFIT MARGIN	EMPLOYEES
12/18	256.6	134.0	52.2%	110
12/17	233.8	114.9	49.2%	100
12/16	239.2	96.4	40.3%	100
12/15	203.4	71.2	35.0%	95
12/14	130.1	56.9	43.8%	90
Annual Growth	18.5%	23.9%	—	5.1%

2018 Year-End Financials

Debt ratio: 51.5%	No. of shares (mil.): 63.6
Return on equity: —	Dividends
Cash ($ mil.): 3.9	Yield: 8.1%
Current ratio: 0.62	Payout: 77.7%
Long-term debt ($ mil.): 477.2	Market value ($ mil.): 1,036.0

	STOCK PRICE ($) FY Close	P/E High/Low	PER SHARE ($) Earnings	Dividends	Book Value
12/18	16.28	11 8	1.89	1.32	5.21
12/17	16.77	14 9	1.72	1.15	6.19
12/16	23.55	15 5	1.58	1.00	5.51
12/15	9.85	21 7	1.20	0.88	5.37
12/14	24.12	— —	(0.00)	0.00	5.03
Annual Growth	(9.4%)	— —	—	—	0.9%

Codorus Valley Bancorp, Inc.

Codorus Valley Bancorp is a people-oriented business. The firm is the holding company for PeoplesBank which operates about 20 branches in southeastern Pennsylvania's York County and Hunt Valley and Bel Air Maryland. The bank offers the standard fare including checking and savings accounts and CDs. It uses funds from deposits to write a variety of loans primarily commercial loans and commercial real estate loans but also residential mortgages and consumer installment loans. Bank subsidiary Codorus Valley Financial Advisors offers investment products while SYC Settlement Services provides real estate settlement services.

EXECUTIVES

VICE PRESIDENT COMMERCIAL TEAM LEADER, Adam Bryner
SENIOR VICE PRESIDENT, Neil Brownawell
Auditors: BDO USA, LLP

LOCATIONS

HQ: Codorus Valley Bancorp, Inc.
105 Leader Heights Road, P.O. Box 2887, York, PA 17405
Phone: 717 747-1519
Web: www.peoplesbanknet.com

COMPETITORS

Citizens Financial	M&T Bank
Group	Northwest Bancshares
Fulton Financial	

HISTORICAL FINANCIALS

Company Type: Public

Income Statement
FYE: December 31

	ASSETS ($ mil.)	NET INCOME ($ mil.)	INCOME AS % OF ASSETS	EMPLOYEES
12/17	1,709.2	12.0	0.7%	339
12/16	1,611.5	13.1	0.8%	304
12/15	1,456.3	11.1	0.8%	292
12/14	1,213.8	11.7	1.0%	258
12/13	1,150.6	10.5	0.9%	248
Annual Growth	10.4%	3.2%	—	8.1%

2017 Year-End Financials

Return on assets: 0.7%	Dividends
Return on equity: 7.5%	Yield: 0.0%
Long-term debt ($ mil.): —	Payout: 38.3%
No. of shares (mil.): 9.3	Market value ($ mil.): 257.0
Sales ($ mil.): 81.9	

	STOCK PRICE ($) FY Close	P/E High/Low	PER SHARE ($) Earnings	Dividends	Book Value
12/17	27.53	27 19	1.28	0.49	17.56
12/16	28.60	21 14	1.41	0.45	16.68
12/15	20.34	14 13	1.51	0.42	17.28
12/14	19.68	14 11	1.67	0.38	16.71
12/13	19.53	13 9	1.67	0.34	17.57
Annual Growth	9.0%	— —	(6.5%)	9.3%	(0.0%)

Cogent Communications Holdings, Inc.

Cogent Communications offers a compelling sales pitch: data at the speed of light. The company operates a fiber-optic data network that serves customers in North America Europe and Asia. It offers dedicated Internet access and data transport services to businesses through Ethernet connections that link its 51 data center facilities directly to customer office buildings. Clients include financial services companies law firms ad agencies and other professional services businesses. Cogent also sells access to its network and provides colocation management services to ISPs hosting companies and other high-volume bandwidth users.

Operations

Cogent does business in 191 metropolitan markets in 41 countries serving almost 2250 connected office buildings most of which are multi-tenant. Its network is made up of in-building riser facilities metropolitan optical fiber networks metropolitan traffic aggregation points and inter-city transport facilities.

The company has more than 56000 route miles of intercity fiber and more than 28100 metro fiber miles.

Geographic Reach

Cogent has offices data centers colocation facilities and points-of-presence across North America and Europe. North America (mostly the US) represents more than 80% of sales with the rest in Europe.

Sales and Marketing

Cogent employs a direct sales approach that includes telemarketing.

Financial Performance

The company generates most of its revenues from customers connected directly to its network (on-net customers) while clients served through other carriers' facilities (off-net customers) account for a quarter of revenues.

Cogent has enjoyed steady revenue growth over the past decade; overall sales increased 6% in 2015 to $404 million as its customer base grew from almost 46000 to 53000. Profits have been less consistent as its business is capital-intensive. Profits jumped 514% higher to $4.9 million in 2015 on higher revenue and in comparison to 2014 when tax provisions were incurred.

Cash flow from operations rose to about $84 million in 2015 compared to $73 million in 2014.

Strategy

The company has said that it is focusing on expanding its on-net customers; with multi-tenant office buildings the customer base is built in. It has also expanded its sales force to address a broader range of clients. Cogent is also investing in its network infrastructure to reach more clients in areas that represent significant concentrations of Internet traffic.

In 2015 Cogent entered into an interconnection agreements with CenturyLink AT&T and Verizon to expand its public IP networks.

EXECUTIVES

Chairman and CEO, David (Dave) Schaeffer, age 61, $332,623 total compensation
VP and Controller, Thaddeus G. (Tad) Weed, age 57, $257,262 total compensation
Senior Vice President;Portfolio Director, Brian Shearrow
National Account Manager, Christopher Castro
Auditors: Ernst & Young LLP

LOCATIONS

HQ: Cogent Communications Holdings, Inc.
2450 N Street N.W., Washington, DC 20037
Phone: 202 295-4200
Web: www.cogentco.com

PRODUCTS/OPERATIONS

2015 Sales

	% of total
On-net	73
Off-net	27
Total	**100**

COMPETITORS

AT&T	Level 3
Covad Communications Group	Verio Inc
	Verizon
EarthLink	XO Holdings
Everest Interlink Broadband	

HISTORICAL FINANCIALS

Company Type: Public

Income Statement

FYE: December 31

	REVENUE ($ mil.)	NET INCOME ($ mil.)	NET PROFIT MARGIN	EMPLOYEES
12/17	485.1	5.8	1.2%	928
12/16	446.9	14.9	3.3%	897
12/15	404.2	4.9	1.2%	836
12/14	380.0	0.8	0.2%	772
12/13	347.9	56.6	16.3%	707
Annual Growth	**8.7%**	**(43.3%)**	**—**	**7.0%**

2017 Year-End Financials

Debt ratio: 101.0%	No. of shares (mil.): 45.9
Return on equity: ***,***.*%	Dividends
Cash ($ mil.): 247.0	Yield: 0.0%
Current ratio: 4.11	Payout: 1,384.6%
Long-term debt ($ mil.): 711.0	Market value ($ mil.): 2,082.0

	STOCK PRICE ($) FY Close	P/E High/Low		PER SHARE ($) Earnings	Dividends	Book Value
12/17	45.30	415293		0.13	1.80	(2.23)
12/16	41.35	132 92		0.33	1.51	(1.17)
12/15	34.69	363238		0.11	1.46	(0.27)
12/14	35.39	21541488		0.02	0.61	1.81
12/13	40.41	34 19		1.21	0.76	4.09
Annual Growth	**2.9%**			**—(42.7%)**	**24.1%**	**—**

Cognex Corp

Machines might not possess big picture vision but Cognex machines have excellent vision when it comes to detail. The company is one of the world's largest producers of systems that linked to a video camera serve as eyes where human vision is insufficient. Manufacturers of consumer electronics and vehicles as well as logistics companies use the company's machine vision and industrial identification systems to position and identify products gauge sizes and locate defects. Cognex's big market is factory automation and it also offers consulting and educational services and tech support for its products. Sales to customers based outside the US account for about three-quarters of sales.

Operations

Cognex offers several types of machine vision products. Its Vision software provides users the general-purpose library of Cognex vision tools with cameras frame grabbers and peripheral equipment. Vision Systems combine camera processor and vision software into a rugged package with a flexible user interface for configuring applications. Vision Sensors are designed to deliver simple and reliable tools for a limited number of common vision applications such as checking the presence and size of parts. The company's ID Products business which includes the DataMan line offers bar code readers for use in automotive pharmaceutical aircraft component and medical device manufacturing.

Geographic Reach

Customers in Europe account for 45% of Cognex's sales while US customers supply about 25% and customers in China generate about 15%

of sales. The company's products are assembled by a contract manufacturer in Indonesia. Testing and shipping is done from its Natick Massachusetts facility for US customers and from its Ireland facility for customers outside the US.

Sales and Marketing

Cognex sells through a worldwide direct sales force and via a global network of integration and distribution partners.

The company's customers are in the consumer electronics automotive consumer products food and beverage medical devices and pharmaceutical industries. About 40% of revenue is from consumer electronics 25% each from automotive and logistics and the rest from other customers.

Cognex has a lot of eggs in the Apple basket with the iPhone and MacBook maker directly and indirectly accounting for about a fifth of Cognex's revenue.

Financial Performance

It doesn't take a Cognex product to recognize the company's sales growth. The company's top line number has increased an annual average of nearly 30% over five years. Sales grew even faster in 2017 from 2016 rising 44% to $748 million. Sales rose more than 60% in Asia 40% in Europe and 33% in the US. Strong sales to logistics customers drove sales in the US and demand from consumer electronics customers boosted results in Europe and Asia.

Net income rose 18% to about $177 million in 2017 from 2016 lifted by higher revenue.

Cash on hand rose to about $106 million in 2017 from about $80 million the year before.

Strategy

Cognex focuses on factory automation as its best bet for continued growth. Its business has grown significantly in China and other parts of Asia where consumer electronics manufacturing is concentrated. Asia and China in particular have been targets of US trade sanctions which include higher tariffs on products made outside the US.

Cognex spends about an eighth of its revenue on research and development (nearly $100 million in 2017). The company continued to expand its 2D vision systems which include the DataMan 70 series of barcode readers that offer better read rates for factories and distribution centers. In 3D systems the company has increased its offerings with the help of six acquisitions since 2016 adding capabilities that allow distribution center robots to process objects of different shapes and sizes. The systems generate about 5% of Cognex's revenue but sales have grown at a fast pace (50% in 2017).

Mergers and Acquisitions

Cognex has built out its 3D vision capabilities with the help of acquisitions. In 2017 the company Cognex acquired ViDi Systems which develops deep learning artificial intelligence software for industrial applications for about $23 million. In another 2017 deal it bought GVi Ventures a maker of preconfigured vision tools for common automotive applications for more than $5 million.

HISTORY

Robert Shillman and two MIT colleagues Marilyn Matz and William Silver started Cognex (short for "cognition experts") in 1981 to create vision replacement machines for factories. Competition and inadequate technology forced the firm to reevaluate its distribution strategy in 1986. Cognex began supplying machine vision technology to original equipment manufacturers. The company introduced the first custom vision chip in 1988 and went public the next year.

Cognex found success where human vision fails — in the high-speed detailed repetitive processes required in making semiconductors. The company expanded by purchasing Acumen a developer of machine vision systems for semiconductor wafer identification (1995); Isys Controls a maker of quality control systems (1996); and Mayan Automation a maker of surface inspection systems (1997).

Low demand for semiconductor and printed circuit board manufacturing equipment in Asia hurt sales in 1998. Nonetheless the company boosted R&D by 10% and acquired some of Rockwell Automation's machine vision operations also becoming the preferred global supplier to Rockwell's plants. Orders picked up in early 1999 and Cognex invested $1 million in upstart Avalon Imaging (machine vision for the plastics industry) its first investment in such a company.

A series of acquisitions and in-house innovations enabled Cognex to expand into factory automation inspection which accounts for more than 90% of its business.

EXECUTIVES

President CEO and Director, Robert Willett, age 50, $377,942 total compensation
SVP and CFO, John J. Curran, age 53
Vice President and Corporate Controller, Laura Macdonald
Vice President MVSD Sales and Service Europe, Dirk Rathsack
Manufacturing Vice President, Jim Quinlivan
Vice President Global Operations, Rocco Volpe
Senior Vice President ww Sales and Marketing, Didier Lacroix
Vice President Operations, Herb Lade
Chairman and Chief Culture Officer, Robert J. (Bob) Shillman, age 71
Auditors: Grant Thornton LLP

LOCATIONS

HQ: Cognex Corp
One Vision Drive, Natick, MA 01760-2059
Phone: 508 650-3000
Web: www.cognex.com

PRODUCTS/OPERATIONS

Selected Products
In-Sight 8000 Series
In-Sight 7000 Series
In-Sight Laser Profiler
3D Vision Systems
VisionPro
Cognex Designer

COMPETITORS

Adept Technology	KLA-Tencor
Camtek	Keyence
Clemex	National Instruments
CyberOptics	OMRON
Data Translation	Orbotech
Elbit Vision	PPT VISION
Electro Scientific	Perceptron
Industries	RoboGroup T.E.K.
Image Sensing Systems	SICK
Integral Vision	Scanner Technologies

HISTORICAL FINANCIALS

Company Type: Public

Income Statement

FYE: December 31

	REVENUE ($ mil.)	NET INCOME ($ mil.)	NET PROFIT MARGIN	EMPLOYEES
12/17	747.9	177.1	23.7%	1,771
12/16	520.7	149.5	28.7%	1,421
12/15	450.5	187.0	41.5%	1,305
12/14	486.2	121.4	25.0%	1,322
12/13	353.8	73.5	20.8%	1,077
Annual Growth	**20.6%**	**24.6%**	**—**	**13.2%**

2017 Year-End Financials

Debt ratio: —
Return on equity: 17.2%
Cash ($ mil.): 106.5
Current ratio: 5.57
Long-term debt ($ mil.): —

No. of shares (mil.): 173.5
Dividends
Yield: 0.0%
Payout: 16.9%
Market value ($ mil.): 10,612.0

	STOCK PRICE ($) FY Close	P/E High/Low	PER SHARE ($) Earnings	Dividends	Book Value
12/17	61.16	142 60	0.99	0.17	6.31
12/16	63.62	74 33	0.86	0.15	5.60
12/15	33.77	48 31	1.07	0.11	4.87
12/14	41.33	63 46	0.68	0.00	4.25
12/13	38.18	152 69	0.42	0.00	3.71
Annual Growth	**12.5%**	**—**	**— 24.3%**	**—**	**14.2%**

Coherent Inc

Coherent's lasers make a lot of sense. The company uses light wave manipulation called photonics to manufacture and market a diverse array of lasers. Its products are used in a host of areas: microelectronics (semiconductor fabrication packaging flat-panel display and solar cell manufacturing) scientific and government research in physical and chemical processes OEM components and instrumentation and materials processing. Its specialty lasers and systems segment (70% of sales) makes configurable laser products while its commercial lasers and components unit (30% of sales) specializes in high-volume products sold in set configurations.

Geographic Reach

The company has more than a dozen manufacturing plants in Germany Malaysia Singapore the UK and the US (in Bloomfield Connecticut; East Hanover New Jersey; Salem New Hampshire; Santa Clara and Sunnyvale California; and Wilsonville Oregon) in addition to customer support and sales offices worldwide.

Coherent's largest market is the US which contributed 27% in 2015 followed by South Korea 24% and Japan 17%.

Sales and Marketing

Coherent uses a direct sales staff located in Canada China France Germany Italy Japan the Netherlands South Korea Taiwan the UK and the US. The company reduced advertising spending to $2.1 million in 2015 down from $2.9 million in 2014 and $3.4 million in 2013.

About half of its sales come from customers in Asia where most of the world's electronics are made. Its largest customer is South Korea-based

semiconductor maker Advanced Process Systems Corporation accounting for 10% of revenue.

Financial Performance

Coherent's revenue has fluctuated in the last five years. In 2015 revenue ticked up 1% to $802 million from $794 million in 2014. The commercial lasers and components segment revenue increased 6% on higher medical bio-instrumentation and flat panel display application sales.

The company's net income jumped 29% higher to $76 million in 2015 from $59 million in 2014. Coherent had lower selling general and administrative expenses because of reduced charges in deferred compensation plan liabilities.

Cash flow from operations increased to about $125 million in 2015 from $91 million in 2014.

Strategy

Coherent's strategy includes expanding its portfolio through acquisitions and internal development in order to enter new markets while extending its leadership in existing markets including microelectronics. The company also collaborates with customers to design and development new products as new technologies emerge and looks to increase its market share using both new product development — it spends upwards of 10% of sales on research and development — and acquisitions to spur growth.

Mergers and Acquisitions

In late 2016 Coherent acquired ROFIN-SINAR Technologies Inc. a developer and manufacturer of high-performance industrial laser sources and laser-based components for $942 million.

In 2015 Coherent bought Raydiance Inc. for $5 million and the Tinsley Optics business from L-3 Communications Corp. for approximately $4.3 million.

HISTORY

Early History

In 1966 the six founders of Coherent Radiation Laboratories created their first product a carbon dioxide laser in a laundry room (the only room in the house with a 220-volt outlet to power the laser). In true Silicon Valley fashion the founders were all disgruntled ex-employees of another established company — in this case Spectra-Physics. With a research contract from DuPont and sales to Boeing Coherent's revenues topped $1 million by 1968. In 1970 the company pioneered lasers for ophthalmologic use and completed an IPO. It introduced a carbon dioxide surgical laser in 1976 and the first true excimer laser (which produces a deep ultraviolet light) in 1977 (the same year it became Coherent Inc.). In 1981 the company acquired a stake in Lambda Physik (founded in 1971 as the commercial arm of Germany's renowned Max Planck Institute).

After limping through the recession of the early 1990s Coherent sold its industrial division in 1993. In 1995 the company expanded its semiconductor diode laser business with several acquisitions including the manufacturing operation of laser maker Uniphase (now part of Viavi Solutions). In 1996 Coherent bought telecommunications microchip laser maker Micracor and a controlling stake in Finnish semiconductor wafer maker Tutcore. That year VP Bernard Couillaud was named CEO.

The 1997 acquisition of UK-based Ealing Electro-Optics added assembly capabilities for medical and other systems. Also that year the company formed a telecommunications market-based joint venture with Fiber Optics Network (closed in 1999). In 1999 Coherent bought Star Medical Technologies a maker of laser hair removal equipment in an effort to expand its medical business.

EXECUTIVES

President CEO and Director, John R. Ambroseo, age 57, $625,019 total compensation
EVP and General Manager Specialty Laser Systems Business Group, Mark Sobey, age 57, $375,992 total compensation
EVP and CTO, Luis Spinelli, age 71, $256,006 total compensation
EVP Worldwide Sales Service and Marketing, Paul W. Sechrist, age 58, $355,663 total compensation
EVP and CFO, Kevin S. Palatnik, age 61
EVP General Counsel and Corporate Secretary, Bret M. DiMarco, age 50, $341,876 total compensation
Vice President Corporate Controller, Dan Hunter
Vice President, Richard Waldermann
Chairman, Garry W. Rogerson, age 66
Board Member, Nicki May
Auditors: DELOITTE & TOUCHE LLP

LOCATIONS

HQ: Coherent Inc
   5100 Patrick Henry Drive, Santa Clara, CA 95054
Phone: 408 764-4000
Web: www.coherent.com

PRODUCTS/OPERATIONS

2015 Sales

	$ mil.	% of total
Specialty laser systems	559.6	70
Commercial lasers & components	242.9	30
Total	**802.5**	**100**

2015 Sales by Market

	$ mil.	% of total
Microelectronics	406.2	51
OEM components & instrumentation	168.7	20
Scientific & government programs	116.5	15
Materials processing	111.1	14
Total	**802.5**	**100**

COMPETITORS

Avensys Inc.	Novanta
Cymer	Princeton Lightwave
Gemfire	Roper Technologies
II-VI	Spectris
IPG Photonics	TRUMPF
Jenoptik	USHIO
Komatsu	Viavi Solutions
Newport Corp.	

HISTORICAL FINANCIALS

Company Type: Public

Income Statement

FYE: September 29

	REVENUE ($ mil.)	NET INCOME ($ mil.)	NET PROFIT MARGIN	EMPLOYEES
09/18	1,902.5	247.3	13.0%	5,418
09/17*	1,723.3	207.1	12.0%	5,218
10/16	857.3	87.5	10.2%	2,787
10/15	802.4	76.4	9.5%	2,586
09/14	794.6	59.1	7.4%	2,519
Annual Growth	**24.4%**	**43.0%**	**—**	**21.1%**

*Fiscal year change

2018 Year-End Financials

Debt ratio: 18.8%	No. of shares (mil.): 24.3
Return on equity: 20.0%	Dividends
Cash ($ mil.): 310.5	Yield: —
Current ratio: 3.32	Payout: —
Long-term debt ($ mil.): 420.7	Market value ($ mil.): 4,184.0

	STOCK PRICE ($) FY Close	P/E High/Low		Earnings	PER SHARE ($) Dividends	Book Value
09/18	172.19	32	15	9.95	0.00	54.10
09/17*	235.17	33	12	8.36	0.00	47.23
10/16	110.54	31	14	3.58	0.00	37.45
10/15	54.68	22	17	3.06	0.00	33.23
09/14	62.94	32	24	2.36	0.00	32.85
Annual Growth	**28.6%**	**—**	**—**	**43.3%**	**—**	**13.3%**

*Fiscal year change

Cohu Inc

Cohu makes equipment that puts semiconductors and light-emitting diodes (LEDs)through their paces when they are tested. It makes pick-and-place equipment and instruments called test handlers that usher semiconductors through the trials of testing to make sure they're in working order. Top customers are Intel (18% of sales) and NXP Semiconductors (11% of sales). The company operates through subsidiaries Delta Design Rasco and Ismeca. Cohu has jettisoned two businesses — video cameras for surveillance and microwave communications systems — to concentrate on chip testing.

Operations
Cohu's Delta Design unit offers pick-and-place test handlers thermal subsystems and environmental chambers to semicondcutor makers. The Rasco unit sells gravity feed test-in-strip handlers and micro-electro mechanical system(MEMS) test units. Ismeca offers turret-based test handling and back-end finishing equipment for integrated circuits and LEDs.

Geographic Reach
Semiconductor testing is often done is low-cost markets which helps explain why Malaysia accounts for Cohu's biggest chunk of revenue 23%. The company generates another 20% in China and claims 19% of sales from chip maker facilities in the US. Another 6% is from the Philippines with the rest of the world accounting for 32% of sales.
Cohu makes its equipment at facilities in California the Philippines Germany Malaysia and China.

Sales and Marketing
Cohu commits its salespeople to geographic markets where it believes the sales potential is the greatest. Otherwise it works through independent sales reps.

Financial Performance
Cohu's revenue slid about 15% in 2015 to some $270 million from 2014 with demand for testing equipment experiencing a down year in the cyclical market.
The company posted a profit of $250000 for 2015 a 97% drop from 2014's $8.7 million profit on the lower revenue. It continued to show losses from discontinued operations.

Cohu managed to generate a $21 million stream of cash in 2015 $1.8 million more than 2014.

Strategy
Cohu has become more lean and focused in the past two years. It sold the Broadcast Microwave Services business in 2015 for $5 million in cash and its video camera business Cohu Electronics in 2014 for $10.3 million. The sales of the extraneous businesses put Cohu whole hog in the test-equipment business which is dependent on the notoriously up-and-down market of the semiconductor industry.

EXECUTIVES

President Delta Design Kit Operations, James G. McFarlane, age 68, $237,016 total compensation
VP Finance and CFO, Jeffrey D. Jones, age 57, $255,008 total compensation
President CEO and Director, Luis A. M ller, age 48, $360,006 total compensation
President Delta Design Systems, Samer Kabbani, age 44, $260,000 total compensation
Chairman, James A. Donahue, age 69
Auditors: Ernst & Young LLP

LOCATIONS

HQ: Cohu Inc
   12367 Crosthwaite Circle, Poway, CA 92064-6817
Phone: 858 848-8100
Web: www.cohu.com

PRODUCTS/OPERATIONS

Operations and Selected Products
Semiconductor Equipment
   Delta Design (semiconductor test handling equipment and thermal technology)
   Automated test handlers
   Burn-in board loaders and unloaders
   Device kits
   Docking interfaces
   Environmental chambers
   Rasco (semiconductor test handling)
   Gravity-feed and test-on-strip systems
Cohu Electronics (closed-circuit television systems)
   Cameras and control equipment
   Control systems
   Design services
   Lenses
   Software
Broadcast Microwave Services (microwave communications equipment)
   Antenna systems
   Microwave radio equipment

COMPETITORS

Advantest	Data I/O
Aetrium	EG Systems
Anaren	Honeywell
Bosch	International
Brooks Automation	Mirae
CalAmp	Vicon Industries
Checkpoint Systems	inTEST
Comtech	
Telecommunications	

HISTORICAL FINANCIALS

Company Type: Public

Income Statement

FYE: December 31

	REVENUE ($ mil.)	NET INCOME ($ mil.)	NET PROFIT MARGIN	EMPLOYEES
12/17	352.7	32.8	9.3%	1,800
12/16	282.0	3.0	1.1%	1,800
12/15	269.6	0.2	0.1%	1,600
12/14	333.3	8.7	2.6%	1,600
12/13	247.3	(33.4)	—	1,400
Annual Growth	9.3%	—	—	6.5%

2017 Year-End Financials

Debt ratio: 2.1%
Return on equity: 12.5%
Cash ($ mil.): 134.2
Current ratio: 3.49
Long-term debt ($ mil.): 4.5
No. of shares (mil.): 28.4
Dividends
Yield: 0.0%
Payout: 21.0%
Market value ($ mil.): 625.0

	STOCK PRICE ($) FY Close	P/E High/Low		PER SHARE ($) Earnings	Dividends	Book Value
12/17	21.95	22	11	1.14	0.24	10.15
12/16	13.90	128	94	0.11	0.24	8.77
12/15	12.93	1377	925	0.01	0.24	9.08
12/14	11.98	38	27	0.33	0.24	9.62
12/13	10.08	—	—	(1.34)	0.24	10.09
Annual Growth	21.5%	—	—	—	(0.0%)	0.1%

Cole Credit Property Trust IV Inc

Auditors: DELOITTE & TOUCHE LLP

LOCATIONS

HQ: Cole Credit Property Trust IV Inc
2325 East Camelback Road, 10th Floor, Phoenix, AZ 85016
Phone: 602 778-8700
Web: www.colecapital.com

HISTORICAL FINANCIALS

Company Type: Public

Income Statement

FYE: December 31

	REVENUE ($ mil.)	NET INCOME ($ mil.)	NET PROFIT MARGIN	EMPLOYEES
12/17	424.1	79.4	18.7%	0
12/16	407.4	71.8	17.6%	0
12/15	367.7	64.7	17.6%	0
12/14	256.2	11.1	4.4%	0
12/13	102.5	(32.8)	—	0
Annual Growth	42.6%	—	—	—

2017 Year-End Financials

Debt ratio: 52.2%
Return on equity: 3.5%
Cash ($ mil.): 4.7
Current ratio: 0.97
Long-term debt ($ mil.): 2,471.7
No. of shares (mil.): 311.5
Dividends
Yield: 0.0%
Payout: 250.0%
Market value ($ mil.): —

	STOCK PRICE ($) FY Close	P/E High/Low		PER SHARE ($) Earnings	Dividends	Book Value
12/17	0.00	28	28	0.25	0.63	6.92
12/16	8.62	37	0	0.23	0.63	7.27
12/15	8.95	43	43	0.21	0.00	7.65
Annual Growth	—	—	—	9.1%	—	(4.9%)

Columbia Banking System Inc

Columbia Banking System (CBS) is the $8.5 billion-asset holding company for Columbia State Bank (also known as Columbia Bank). The regional community bank has about 150 branches in Washington from Puget Sound to the timber country in the southwestern part of the state as well as in northern Oregon and Idaho. Targeting retail and small and medium-sized business customers the bank offers standard retail services such as checking and savings accounts CDs IRAs credit cards loans and mortgages. Commercial and multifamily real estate loans make up more than 40% of the company's loan portfolio while business loans make up another 40%. CBS is expanding in the Pacific Northwest through acquisitions of other community banks.

Operations

The bank's Columbia Private Banking division offers customized financial services for businesses and affluent families. Subsidiary CB Financial Services provides investment products through a pact with third-party provider PrimeVest.

Like other retail banks Columbia makes most of its money from interest income. About 68% of its total revenue came from loan interest during 2015 while another 10% came from interest on taxable and tax-exempt securities. The rest of its revenue came from service charges and other fees (15% of revenue) merchant service fees (2%) and other non-interest income sources.

Geographic Reach

Tacoma-based Columbia Banking System has 149 bank branches (as of mid-2016) with about half in the state of Washington 60 across Oregon and 16 in Idaho.

Sales and Marketing

The bank spent $4.7 million on advertising and promotion in 2015 up from $3.9 million and $4.1 million in 2014 and 2013 respectively.

Financial Performance

Columbia Bank's annual revenues have nearly doubled since 2011 as its loan assets have more than doubled to $5.8 billion (at the end of 2015). Its profits have also doubled over the time period as it's kept a handle on costs.

The bank's revenue jumped 14% to $420.36 million during 2015 on higher interest income as it increased its loan business and interest-earning security assets. The company also earned more in service charges and other non-interest income thanks to its organically growing customer base and its Intermountain acquisition.

Revenue growth in 2015 drove the bank's net income up 21% to $98.83 million. Columbia

Bank's operating cash levels dipped 2% to $134.76 million for the year mostly due to unfavorable working capital changes related to other liabilities.

Strategy

Columbia reiterated in 2016 that it would focus on expanding its branches into new markets (either on its own or through acquisitions) while focusing on high-quality loan growth. One of its most recent acquisitions — the purchase of Intermountain Community Bancorp — expanded its presence in Idaho for the first time.

Mergers and Acquisitions

In November 2014 the bank expanded its presence into Idaho after purchasing $960 million-asset Intermountain Community Bancorp and its Panhandle State Bank branches in the state.

In April 2013 Columbia acquired West Coast Bancorp — the parent company of West Coast Bank which operated nearly 60 bank branches in Oregon and Washington. The purchase boosted Columbia's total assets to more than $7 billion and furthered Columbia's goal of becoming the leading regional community bank in the Pacific Northwest.

Company Background

Columbia Banking System took advantage of the rash of bank failures in past years to increase its presence in the Pacific Northwest region. It added more than 30 branches in 2010 when it acquired most of the deposits and assets of failed banks Columbia River Bank and American Marine Bank a week apart. In similar transactions in 2011 it acquired most of the operations of the failed institutions Summit Bank First Heritage Bank and Bank of Whitman. Those deals added more than a dozen branches in Washington.

EXECUTIVES

EVP and Chief Credit Officer, Andrew L. (Andy) McDonald, age 59, $298,000 total compensation
EVP and CFO, Clint E. Stein, age 47, $345,000 total compensation
CEO, Hadley S. Robbins, age 61, $369,827 total compensation
EVP and General Counsel, Kumi Yamamoto Baruffi, age 48
EVP and Chief Human Resources Officer, David C. (Dave) Lawson, age 60, $247,500 total compensation
Vice President Senior Financial Advisor with CB Financial, John Brunk
Vice President, Thomas Poole
Senior Vice President and Banking Solutions Manager, Bruce Morehead
Vice President Commercial Banking Officer, Antoine White
Senior Vice President, Gus Martin
Vice President, Jennifer Kinkade
Vice President, Harold Boucher
Vice President, Saira Russell
Vice President, Rhonda Seagraves
Chairman, William T. Weyerhaeuser, age 75
Auditors: DELOITTE & TOUCHE LLP

LOCATIONS

HQ: Columbia Banking System Inc
1301 "A" Street, Tacoma, WA 98402-2156
Phone: 253 305-1900
Web: www.columbiabank.com

PRODUCTS/OPERATIONS

2015 Sales

	$ mil.	% of total
Interest Income:		
Loans	286.2	68
Taxable securities	30.8	7
Tax-exempt securities	11.8	3
Deposits in banks	0.1	-
Non-interest Income:		
Service charges and other fees	61.9	15
Merchant services fees	9.0	2
Other	24.6	5
FDIC loss-sharing asset	(4.0)	-
Total	**420.4**	**100**

COMPETITORS

BECU	JPMorgan Chase
Bank of America	KeyCorp
Banner Corp	U.S. Bancorp
Heritage Financial	Washington Federal
HomeStreet	Wells Fargo

HISTORICAL FINANCIALS

Company Type: Public

Income Statement — FYE: December 31

	ASSETS ($ mil.)	NET INCOME ($ mil.)	INCOME AS % OF ASSETS	EMPLOYEES
12/17	12,716.8	112.8	0.9%	2,120
12/16	9,509.6	104.8	1.1%	1,819
12/15	8,951.7	98.8	1.1%	1,868
12/14	8,578.8	81.5	1.0%	1,844
12/13	7,161.5	60.0	0.8%	1,695
Annual Growth	**15.4%**	**17.1%**	**—**	**5.8%**

2017 Year-End Financials

Return on assets: 1.0%	Dividends
Return on equity: 7.0%	Yield: 0.0%
Long-term debt ($ mil.): —	Payout: 47.3%
No. of shares (mil.): 73.0	Market value ($ mil.): 3,172.0
Sales ($ mil): 484.3	

	STOCK PRICE ($) FY Close	P/E High/Low		PER SHARE ($) Earnings	Dividends	Book Value
12/17	43.44	25	19	1.86	0.88	26.70
12/16	44.68	25	15	1.81	1.53	21.55
12/15	32.51	21	15	1.71	1.34	21.52
12/14	27.61	19	16	1.52	0.94	21.38
12/13	27.49	23	14	1.21	0.41	20.55
Annual Growth	**12.1%**	**—**	**—**	**11.3%**	**21.0%**	**6.8%**

Columbia Sportswear Co.

Gertrude Boyle is one tough mother. The nonagenarian is the face of leading active outerwear company Columbia Sportswear's "tough mother" ads. Columbia develops markets and distributes upscale outdoor wear such as its trademark Bugaboo parka with weatherproof shell that put the company on the map. As well as the Bugaboo Columbia offers performance apparel sportswear accessories and rugged footwear for various outdoor activities. Its key brands are Columbia Mountain Hardwear Sorel prAna and Montrail. Founded as a hat company in 1938 Columbia Sportswear is controlled by the Boyle family and run by president and CEO Tim Boyle son of Gert.

Operations

Columbia Sportswear's operations are divided between two product categories: The largest category apparel accessories and equipment generates some 80% of total revenue. Footwear including Sorel brand boots accounted for the rest.

In the US the sportswear maker operates more than 90 outlet stores 24 branded retail stores two employee stores and five brand-specific e-commerce sites. The company has nearly 120 concession-based branded outlet and shop-in-shop locations in Japan and over 200 additional such stores in Korea. It had a handful of retail stores in Canada and around 20 outlet and shop-in-shop retail stores and one branded retail store in the EMEA region.

Geographic Reach

Columbia Sportswear's products are sold in North America and over 90 more countries worldwide. The company generates some 65% of its sales in the US and 20% from its second-largest market LAAP (Latin America and the Asia-Pacific region). Europe the Middle East and Africa account for some 10% while the remaining +5% comes from Canada.

Sales and Marketing

Columbia's products are primarily sold through 8500-plus wholesale distributors to specialty outdoor and sporting goods stores and major retail chains. The company also sells directly to consumers through domestic and international banner retail outlets and stores (Columbia-operated and dealer-operated) as well as online. In countries where it does not trade the Columbia sells to about twenty independent distributors. Almost all of Columbia's items are made in Asia by independent manufacturers.

The company uses a variety of media to market its products including online advertising and social media sites TV and print. It also sponsors events and operates branded and outlet retail stores in high-profile locations.

Financial Performance

Columbia Sportswear's sales and profits have been creeping up in recent years thanks to the success of its direct-to-consumer channel which sells through company-operated retail stores and e-commerce sites.

In fiscal 2016 sales increased 2% to $2.4 billion with the majority coming from the US direct-to-consumer business. The US wholesale business declined due to customer bankruptcies. Sales in the EMEA region (Europe Middle East and Africa) climbed 9% or $20 million on the back of strength in the direct business. In the Latin America and Asia-Pacific region a fall in demand in Korea for outdoor clothing created a product surplus driving down prices and causing sales to fall $15.5 million.

By brand sales growth was concentrated in the Columbia brand up 2% or around $45 million.

Net income was up 10% to $17.6 million due to a higher proportion of higher-margin direct-to-consumer sales.

Cash from operating activities increased from $95.1 million to $275.2 million due to a lower increase in inventory levels.

Strategy

Columbia Sportswear has strategically expanded its geographic presence and product offerings through acquisitions alliances and licensing deals.

The company typically acquires or partners with brands that move it into new and complementary consumer categories especially ones that reduce its dependence on cold-weather products. In 2016 Columbia became the official outdoor apparel supplier for Manchester United Football Club and the following year became the official outfitter of the UK National Parks' rangers and staff.

In 2015 Columbia expanded into new clothing territory after forming an exclusive licensing agreement with Delta Galil Industries which would begin developing producing and distributing performance-based underwear under the Columbia Sportswear brand.

HISTORY

Paul Lanfrom acquired a small hat distributor in 1938 which he renamed Columbia Hat Co. His daughter Gertrude married Neal Boyle in the late 1940s and Neal took control of the firm when Lanfrom died in 1963. Building on a fishing vest designed by Gertrude Columbia Sportswear moved into hunting and fishing apparel. When Neal died suddenly in 1970 Gertrude assumed control of the floundering company.

Columbia struggled as Gertrude and her son Tim learned to run the business; but in the 1980s the company introduced its breakthrough product: the Bugaboo jacket with a shell and lining that can be worn separately or zipped together for added warmth.

Columbia launched its rugged footwear and Tough Mother denim lines in 1993. It opened its flagship Portland Oregon retail outlet in 1996 then launched its Asian retail operations with a Seoul Korea store in 1997. Columbia Sportswear went public in March of the following year.

To consolidate the company shuttered its only owned manufacturing facility in 1999 cutting nearly 15% of its workforce. Columbia Sportswear also launched a program that year licensing its name for socks and other items. In early 2000 it cut licensing deals with leather goods manufacturer Humphreys for belts and other leather accessories and with Cerf Brothers for travel bags. Also in 2000 Columbia acquired Sorel a well-known but bankrupt boot maker.

To further advance its outdoor brand the company signed a licensing agreement with L'Amy Group for the design manufacture and marketing of a line of men's and women's sunglasses and ski goggles (which hit stores in 2003). Also in 2003 Columbia increased distribution of its apparel and footwear in Europe by beginning operations at its distribution center in France. It also acquired climbing gear and apparel company Mountain Hardware.

In 2004 Columbia signed a licensing agreement with Granger's International for shoe and apparel care products including repellents cleaners and conditioners.

Columbia purchased outdoor footwear maker Montrail for $15 million in 2006. The Montrail brand is known for its IntegraFit technology for running walking and hiking. And at auction the company was the winning bidder for outerwear and sportswear brand Pacific Trail which was sold by the bankrupt London Fog Industries in 2006 for $20 million.

Trying something new Columbia in 2007 began to license its name for pet products made by RC Pet Products. Items include dog coats and pet accessories.

EXECUTIVES

President CEO and Director, Timothy P. (Tim) Boyle, age 68, $922,846 total compensation
EVP Chief Administrative Officer General Counsel and Secretary, Peter J. Bragdon, age 56, $470,193 total compensation
President SOREL Brand, Mark Nenow, age 61
President Mountain Hardware, Joe Vernachio
VP and Corporate Controller, Thomas B. Cusick, age 51, $572,970 total compensation
EVP and General Manager Americas, Franco Fogliato, age 48, $451,214 total compensation
VP Design and Innovation Columbia Brand, Michael W. (Woody) Blackford, age 49
EVP and Columbia Brand President, Joseph P. (Joe) Boyle, age 37
VP E-Commerce, Patricia E. Higgins, age 50
President Prana, Russell B. (Russ) Hopcus, age 58
VP and CIO, Michael Hirt
SVP Global Sourcing and Manufacturing, Stephen P. (Steve) Woodside, age 53
SVP and CFO, Jim Swanson, age 44
SVP Emerging Brands and APAC, Douglas H. (Doug) Morse
Vice President Ecommerce, Tricia Higgins
Senior Vice President Chro, Richelle Luther
Global Vice President Marketing Mountain Hardware, Dennis Randall
Vice President Strategic and Financial Planning, Allison Ogilvy
NATIONAL SALES MANAGER, Paul Mayrs
Vice President Global Distribution, Alonzo Plater
Vice President and Chief Accounting Officer, Melissa Dugan
Chairman, Gertrude (Gert) Boyle, age 93
Board Member, Stephen Babson
Board Member, Malia Wasson
Auditors: DELOITTE & TOUCHE LLP

LOCATIONS

HQ: Columbia Sportswear Co.
14375 Northwest Science Park Drive, Portland, OR 97229
Phone: 503 985-4000
Web: www.columbia.com

PRODUCTS/OPERATIONS

2017 Sales

	$ mil.	% of total
Apparel accessories & equipment	1,928.0	78
Footwear	538.1	22
Total	**2,466.1**	**100**

2017 Sales by Brand

	$ mil.	% of total
Columbia	1,990.3	81
Sorel	228.8	9
prAna	140.9	6
Mountain Hardwear	101.6	4
Other	4.5	-
Total	**2,466.1**	**100**

Selected Brands

Bugaboo
Columbia
Convert
Mountain Hardwear
Montrail
OutDry
Pacific Trail
prAna
Sorel

COMPETITORS

Amerex	NIKE
American Eagle Outfitters	Nautica Apparel
	North Face
American Recreation Products	PVH
Benetton	Patagonia Inc.
Berghaus	Quiksilver
Burton	REI
Carhartt	Ralph Lauren
Crocs	Skechers U.S.A.
Deckers Outdoor	Spyder
Fila USA	The Gap
Hanesbrands	VF Corporation
Kellwood	Williamson-Dickie Manufacturing
L.L. Bean	Wolverine World Wide
Lafuma	Woolrich Inc.
Lands' End	adidas
Levi Strauss	

HISTORICAL FINANCIALS

Company Type: Public

Income Statement

FYE: December 31

	REVENUE ($ mil.)	NET INCOME ($ mil.)	NET PROFIT MARGIN	EMPLOYEES
12/17	2,466.1	105.1	4.3%	6,188
12/16	2,377.0	191.9	8.1%	6,023
12/15	2,326.1	174.3	7.5%	5,978
12/14	2,100.5	137.1	6.5%	5,326
12/13	1,685.0	94.3	5.6%	4,320
Annual Growth	**10.0%**	**2.7%**	**—**	**9.4%**

2017 Year-End Financials

Debt ratio: —	No. of shares (mil.): 70.0
Return on equity: 6.6%	Dividends
Cash ($ mil.): 673.1	Yield: 0.0%
Current ratio: 3.64	Payout: 48.9%
Long-term debt ($ mil.): —	Market value ($ mil.): 5,031.0

	STOCK PRICE ($) FY Close	P/E High/Low	PER SHARE ($) Earnings	Dividends	Book Value
12/17	71.88	48 34	1.49	0.73	23.17
12/16	58.30	23 17	2.72	0.69	22.34
12/15	48.76	29 17	2.45	0.62	20.21
12/14	44.54	44 18	1.94	0.57	19.24
12/13	78.75	58 36	1.36	0.46	18.00
Annual Growth	**(2.3%)**	**— —**	**2.3%**	**12.5%**	**6.5%**

Columbus McKinnon Corp. (NY)

Columbus McKinnon's machinery products can be extremely uplifting — literally. Founded in 1875 the company is one of North America's largest producers of equipment for lifting positioning or securing all kinds of large materials. Columbus McKinnon's hoists cranes actuators and steel lifting and rigging tools are used in construction general manufacturing and industrial machinery forestry mining and even wind energy. Well known in the marketplace its brand names include Coffing Duff-Norton Shaw-Box and Yale (made by NACCO). Hoists are the company's biggest seller generating almost 60% sales. In addition to OEMs the company sells to hardware distributors and rental outlets.

Operations

Hoists account for 59% of the company's total revenue while chain and rigging tools account for 13%. Other products include industrial cranes (5%) actuators and rotary unions (11%) digital power control and delivery systems (8%) elevator application drive systems (2%) and other products (2%).

Geographic Reach

New York-based Columbus McKinnon operates 19 principal manufacturing facilities in China France Germany Hungary Mexico the UK and the US. It has a network of roughly 38 sales and service offices in 23 countries and nine warehouse facilities spanning five countries. The US accounts for about 64% of sales followed by Europe with 25%.

Sales and Marketing

The company sells its products via a sales force of more than 165 sales people and independent sales representatives worldwide. The products are sold to over 15500 general and specialty distributors end users and OEMs globally.

Financial Performance

The company's sales increased 3% in fiscal 2015 (ended March) versus the prior year to $597 million. The growth was fueled by a 15% bump in industrial cranes sales particularly within the US. Columbus McKinnon's net income however fell 28% from 2014 to 2015 to $20 million. This was attributed to additional costs associated with acquisitions and losses affiliated with unfavorable foreign currency translations.

Strategy

Columbus McKinnon's sights are set on South America and China where industrial opportunities are expected to be strong. Its direction is supported by a number of product introductions relevant to developing economies including lightweight high-speed industrial air hoists forged lifting attachments and hand hoists and lever tools made at lower-cost facilities in China.

Mergers and Acquisitions

In 2016 Columbus McKinnon agreed to acquire Konecranes' Germany business Stahl for around $240 million.

In 2015 the company paid almost $183 million to acquire Magnetek a designer and manufacturer of digital power and motion control systems for material handling elevators and mining applications. The transaction enhanced Columbus McKinnon's development of "smart" and integrated technology into its own portfolio of hoisting systems.

In February 2014 Columbus McKinnon acquired Michigan-based Unified Industries a privately-owned company with annual sales of about $13 million. Unified Industries designs makes and sells overhead aluminum light rail workstations that are primarily used in automotive and other industrial applications.

EXECUTIVES

President Magnetek, Peter M. (Pete) McCormick, age 59
President CEO and Director, Mark D. Morelli, age 55
VP North America, Gene P. Buer, age 66, $300,998 total compensation
VP Europe Middle East Africa (EMEA), Ivo Celi, age 56, $289,176 total compensation
VP and CFO, Gregory P. Rustowicz, age 58, $337,653 total compensation

VP Americas, Kurt F. Wozniak, age 54, $288,200 total compensation
VP Information Services, Mark Paradowski, age 48
VP Asia Pacific (APAC), Benjamin AuYeung, age 54
Executive Director and Chief Procurement Officer, Lawrence Gavin
Vice President and Chief Information Officer, Richard Knoffloch
Vice President Human Resources, Randy Biggs
Chairman, Ernest R. (Ernie) Verebelyi, age 70
Auditors: Ernst & Young LLP

LOCATIONS

HQ: Columbus McKinnon Corp. (NY)
205 Crosspoint Parkway, Getzville, NY 14068
Phone: 716 689-5400
Web: www.cmworks.com

PRODUCTS/OPERATIONS

2016 sales

	$ mil.	% of total
Hoists	352.0	59
Actuators and rotary unions	63.9	11
Chain & forged attachments	75.4	13
Digital power control and delivery system	50.4	8
Industrial cranes	30.5	5
Other	24.9	4
Total	**597.1**	**100**

Selected Products

Hoists
  Electrification (cable/cable reels conductor bar festoon)
  Load chain (disc grade/manual star grade/electric)
  Manual (hand chain lever)
  Powered (air chain air wire rope electric chain electric wire rope)
  Trolleys (manual powered)
Rigging
  Below the hook (pallet lifters coil lifters lifting beams sheet lifters bartender rack)
  Carbon chain and attachments (cold shuts rings chain links)
  CM rigging (hoist rings clamps wire rope clips/thimbles shackles hooks rigging accessories/turnbuckles)
  Dixie forestry (hookaroons handled product tongs)
  Farm hardware and fence tools (pins clevis)
  Heavy duty truck (binders tire chain tire chain hooks binder chain assemblies towing/trucking heavy duty components)
  Overhead lifting (attachments hooks chain slings)
  Towing (bridle assemblies tow chain assemblies)
Cranes
  Components (rotating axle fixed axle top/under running channel type high-cap single girder)
  Enclosed track (freestanding ceiling mounted jib cranes components)
  Jib cranes (base mounted pillar wall mounted)

Selected Brands

Abell Howe
Alltec
Budgit Hoists
Cady Lifters
CES (Crane Equipment & Service Inc.)
Chester Hoist
Coffing Hoists
CM (Columbus McKinnon)
Duff Norton
Little Mule
LodeRail
Pfaff Silberblau
Shaw-Box
WECO (Washington Equipment Co.)
Yale

COMPETITORS

Aluminum Ladder	Linamar Corp.
Bridon Group	Nook Industries
CLARK Material Handling	Parker-Hannifin
Cascade Corp.	Taylor Group
Deublin	Terex
JLG Industries	Terex MHPS
Kito	Toyota Material Handling
Konecranes	Werner Co.

HISTORICAL FINANCIALS

Company Type: Public

Income Statement   FYE: March 31

	REVENUE ($ mil.)	NET INCOME ($ mil.)	NET PROFIT MARGIN	EMPLOYEES
03/18	839.4	22.0	2.6%	3,328
03/17	637.1	8.9	1.4%	3,107
03/16	597.1	19.5	3.3%	2,896
03/15	579.6	27.1	4.7%	2,747
03/14	583.2	30.4	5.2%	2,626
Annual Growth	**9.5%**	**(7.7%)**	**—**	**6.1%**

2018 Year-End Financials

Debt ratio: 31.8%
Return on equity: 5.8%
Cash ($ mil.): 63.0
Current ratio: 1.74
Long-term debt ($ mil.): 303.2

No. of shares (mil.): 23.0
Dividends
  Yield: 0.0%
  Payout: 16.8%
Market value ($ mil.): 826.0

	STOCK PRICE ($) FY Close	P/E High/Low	PER SHARE ($) Earnings	Dividends	Book Value
03/18	35.84	46 24	0.95	0.16	17.71
03/17	24.82	65 32	0.43	0.16	15.13
03/16	15.76	28 14	0.96	0.16	14.24
03/15	26.94	22 15	1.34	0.16	13.44
03/14	26.79	18 11	1.52	0.00	14.71
Annual Growth	**7.5%**	**— —**	**(11.1%)**	**—**	**4.8%**

Community Bank System Inc

Community Bank System is right up front about what it is. The holding company owns Community Bank which operates about 195 branches across upstate New York and northeastern Pennsylvania where it operates as First Liberty Bank and Trust. Focusing on small underserved towns and non-urban markets the bank offers standard products and services such as checking and savings accounts certificates of deposit and loans and mortgages to consumer business and government clients. Boasting over $11.0 billion in assets the bank's loan portfolio consists of mostly business loans residential mortgages and consumer loans. Community Bank System's subsidiaries offer employee benefit services wealth management and insurance products and services.

Operations

Community Bank System operates three business segments. The Banking segment which made up 83% of the company's total revenue during 2015 provides lending and deposit services to individuals businesses and municipalities. Employee Benefit Services (12% of revenue) offers trust investment fund retirement plan actuarial healthcare consulting and other administrative services through Benefit Plan Administrative Services (BPAS). The All Other segment (5% of revenue) includes its Wealth Management (operating through Community Investment Services) and Insurance businesses (operating through CBNA Insurance Agency).

Nearly 70% of the company's revenue comes from interest income. About 49% of its revenue came from loan interest during 2015 while another 19% came from interest on taxable and nontaxable investments. The rest of its revenue came from deposit service fees (14% of revenue) employee benefit services (12%) wealth management and insurance services (5%) and other banking revenues (1%).

Geographic Reach

Community Bank System operated 194 branches and six back-office operating facilities in 36 counties in upstate New York and six counties in northeastern Pennsylvania at the end of 2015.

Sales and Marketing

The bank has been ramping up its advertising spend in recent years. It spent $3.6 million on advertising during 2015 up from $3.2 million and $3.0 million in 2014 and 2013 respectively.

Financial Performance

Community Bank System's annual revenues have been slowly trending higher since 2013 despite a decline in loan interest mostly as it's been building its non-interest related business lines. Meanwhile its net income has risen more than 15% as it's had to pay less in interest expenses on deposits amidst the low interest environment.

The bank's revenue grew 2% to $382.92 million during 2015 thanks to a combination of employee benefit services business growth from new customers and expanding business relationships with existing customers as well as from new service offerings; higher interest income from loans and taxable investments as such interest-earning asset balances grew modestly; and a 13% jump in wealth management and insurance services revenue stemming from the acquisition of OneGroup from the Oneida Financial Group acquisition.

Despite revenue growth in 2015 Community's net income dipped less than 1% to $91.23 million for the year due to costs related to the Oneida acquisition. The company's operating cash levels shrank 5% to $116.46 million mostly due to unfavorable working capital changes related to deferred income tax provisions and changes in other assets and liabilities.

Strategy

Community Bank System looks to continue building its loan and deposit business as well as its non-interest service lines organically and through strategic acquisitions of other banks and financial companies. The financial company in 2015 began exploring expansion opportunities into neighboring markets in eastern Ohio upper New England and New Jersey and in 2017 acquired Northeast Retirement Services (NRS) for around $146 million. NRS provides institutional transfer agency master recordkeeping services custom target date fund administration trust product administration and customized reporting services to institutional clients.

Mergers and Acquisitions

Community Bank System agreed to acquire Kinderhook Bank for $93.4 million. Kinderhook has 11 offices in five New York counties (including in the Capital District of upstate New York) and holds nearly $640 million in assets and about $560 million in deposits. The deal extends Community Bank's reach into the Capital District markets.

In spring 2017 Community Bank acquired Vermont-based Merchants Bancshares. Merchants operates nearly 35 branches and has assets in excess of $1.8 billion; the acquisition will expand Community Bank's operations into Vermont and western Massachusetts.

Company Background

In mid-2012 the bank purchased about 20 branches in upstate New York from HSBC. The deal which was made to satisfy antitrust concerns regarding First Niagara's purchase of 195 branches in New York from HSBC strengthened Community Bank Systems' geographic footprint.

In 2011 the company bought bank holding company The Wilber Corporation adding about 20 locations in the Catskills Mountains region of central New York.

In 2011 expanding its trust and benefits administration business it bought retirement plan administrator CAI Benefits which has offices in New York and Northern New Jersey.

EXECUTIVES

EVP and CFO, Scott A. Kingsley, age 53, $422,500 total compensation

President CEO and Director, Mark E. Tryniski, age 57, $725,000 total compensation

EVP and Chief Banking Officer, Brian D. Donahue, age 62, $350,000 total compensation

SVP and CTO, J. Michael Wilson, age 47

SVP Retail Banking Sales and Marketing, Harold M. (Harry) Wentworth, age 53

SVP and Chief Investment Officer, Joseph J. Lemchak, age 56

President Pennsylvania Banking, Robert P. Matley, age 66

SVP Municipal Banking Director, Joseph E. Sutaris, age 50

SVP and Senior Commercial Lending Officer Northern New York, Nicholas S. (Nick) Russell, age 50

SVP and Chief Credit Administrator, Stephen G. Hardy, age 63

EVP and General Counsel, George J. Getman, age 61, $375,000 total compensation

SVP and Chief Risk Officer, Paul J. Ward

SVP and Chief Credit Officer, Joseph Serbun, $248,107 total compensation

Vice President and Security Officer, Stuart Smith

Assistant Vice President Marketing an, Mary K Barnette

Executive Vice President Marketing, Aaron Kurtz

Vice President, Patrick Gorman

Executive Vice President Marketing, Deborah Fitch

Vice President Marketing, Art Gentry

Executive Vice President, Barbara Call

Vice President and Manager Financial Analysis, Robert Frost

Vice President Director Mortgage Lending, George J Burke

Vice President and Information Technology Manager, James Wilson

Vice President Administration, Eric Wollman

Senior Vice President and Chief Credit Officer, Joe Serbun

Finance Senior Vice President, Richard Heidrick

Vice President Commercial Banker, Allison Mosher

Vice President Commercial Banking, Craig Stevens

Assistant Vice President And General Accounting MA, Laura Mattice

Chair, Sally A. Steele, age 62

Auditors: PricewaterhouseCoopers LLP

LOCATIONS

HQ: Community Bank System Inc
5790 Widewaters Parkway, DeWitt, NY 13214-1883
Phone: 315 445-2282
Web: www.communitybankna.com

PRODUCTS/OPERATIONS

2015 Sales

	$ mil.	% of total
Interest Income:		
Interest and fees on loans	187.7	49
Taxable investments	52.9	14
Nontaxable investments	19.0	5
Noninterest		
Deposit service fees	52.7	14
Employee benefit services	45.4	12
Wealth management	20.2	5
Other	5.0	1
Total	**382.9**	**100**

Selected Subsidiaries & Affiliates

Benefit Plans Administrative Services Inc.
Benefit Plans Administrative Services LLC
Brilie Corporation
CBNA Insurance Agency Inc.
CBNA Preferred Funding Corp.
CBNA Treasury Management Corporation
Community Bank N.A. (also dba First Liberty Bank & Trust)
Community Investment Services Inc.
First of Jermyn Realty Company
First Liberty Service Corporation
Flex Corporation
Hand Benefit & Trust Company
Hand Securities Inc.
Harbridge Consulting Group LLP
Nottingham Advisors Inc.
Town & Country Agency LLC
Western Catskill Realty Inc.

COMPETITORS

Arrow Financial	Financial Institutions
Bank of America	HSBC USA
Canandaigua National	JPMorgan Chase
Chemung Financial	KeyCorp
Citizens Financial Group	M&T Bank
Elmira Savings Bank	NBT Bancorp

HISTORICAL FINANCIALS

Company Type: Public

Income Statement | | | | FYE: December 31

	ASSETS ($ mil.)	NET INCOME ($ mil.)	INCOME AS % OF ASSETS	EMPLOYEES
12/17	10,746.2	150.7	1.4%	2,874
12/16	8,666.4	103.8	1.2%	2,499
12/15	8,552.6	91.2	1.1%	2,490
12/14	7,489.4	91.3	1.2%	2,182
12/13	7,095.8	78.8	1.1%	2,215
Annual Growth	**10.9%**	**17.6%**	**—**	**6.7%**

2017 Year-End Financials

Return on assets: 1.5%
Return on equity: 10.6%
Long-term debt ($ mil.): —
No. of shares (mil.): 50.7
Sales ($ mil): 531.8

Dividends
Yield: 0.0%
Payout: 43.5%
Market value ($ mil.): 2,725.0

	STOCK PRICE ($) FY Close	P/E High/Low	PER SHARE ($) Earnings	Dividends	Book Value
12/17	53.75	20 16	3.03	1.32	32.26
12/16	61.79	27 15	2.32	1.26	26.96
12/15	39.94	20 15	2.19	1.22	26.06
12/14	38.13	18 15	2.22	1.16	24.24
12/13	39.68	21 14	1.94	1.10	21.66
Annual Growth	**7.9%**	**— —**	**11.8%**	**4.7%**	**10.5%**

Comtech Telecommunications Corp.

Comtech means contact. Through its subsidiaries Comtech Telecommunications operates in three divisions: mobile data communications telecommunications transmission and radio-frequency (RF) microwave amplifiers. Comtech makes equipment used largely by the US government and related defense contractors. Other customers include satellite systems integrators communications service providers and oil companies. Its transmission equipment includes modems frequency converters very-small-aperture terminal (VSAT) satellite transceivers and antennas and microwave radios. Comtech's RF amplifiers enable wireless instrumentation and medical systems and provide satellite-based messaging services and location tracking.

Operations

Comtech's biggest segment with 67% of revenue is Telecommunications Transmission which provides equipment and systems that enhance satellite transmission efficiency and that enable wireless communications in environments where terrestrial communications are unavailable or impractical. The RF Microwave Amplifiers segment contributes 25% of sales from satellite earth station traveling wave tube amplifiers and solid-state high-power narrow and broadband amplifiers. About 8% of revenue is from Mobile Data Communications which provides customers with integrated systems for global satellite-based communications when mobile real-time secure transmission is required.

Geographic Reach

Headquartered in Melville New York Comtech makes its products in Santa Clara California and Germantown Maryland. Its telecommunications transmission segment also has offices in Brazil Canada China India North Africa Singapore and the UK. Its sales to international customers jumped to 59% of revenue in 2014 (ended July) from 50% in 2013.

Sales and Marketing

Comtech sells through its sales staff and through independent sales companies and value-added resellers. Customers include AT&T Inc. China Mobile Limited Raytheon Company and Varian Medical Systems. The company sales to US government entities were 28% of total revenue in 2014 off from about 35% in 2013.

Financial Performance

While revenue in 2014 (ended July) rose 8% from 2013 it was still less than the $747 million in revenue its posted in 2010. Sales declined in the following years with fewer orders from the US Army which has been Comtech's biggest customer. In 2014 revenue was $347 million compared to about $320 million the year before. Sales were boosted from a contract with a North African government to design and supply in a communication network. A decrease in mobile data communications revenue was attributed to lower funding and the timing of work performed related to BFT-1 sustainment services for the US Army.

Comtech's net income jumped 41% to $25 million in 2014 from 2013's $17.8 million with the higher revenue and a drop in interest expense as the result of the settlement of $200 million principal of 3% convertible senior notes.

The company's cash flow from operations dropped by about $3 million in 2014 to $34.6 million because of high capital requirements and the timing of billings and commission payments on contracts for over-the-horizon microwave system contracts.

Strategy

Comtech plans to stretch its international sales beyond the 59% it now has by expanding international marketing efforts with more independent sales reps distributors and value-added resellers. It also intends to set up more foreign sales offices.

For it RF Microwave Amplifiers segment Comtech plans to set itself up as one-stop shop approach for RF microwave amplifiers; to =handle more amplifier production outsourced by other companies; and exploit its traveling wave tube amplifier in the direct-to-home market. The company's mobile data communications unit seeks opportunities with the US Army including blue force tracking (BFT) 2.5 and seek expansion into foreign military markets.

The BFT efforts paid off in 2014 when Comtech won two new contracts for BFT-1 sustainment totaling more than $68 million.

EXECUTIVES

SVP and President Comtech Systems Inc., Richard L. Burt, age 77, $380,000 total compensation
Chairman President and CEO, Fred V. Kornberg, age 82, $760,000 total compensation
SVP and CFO, Michael D. Porcelain, age 49, $395,000 total compensation
President Enterprise Technologies, Jay F. Whitehurst, age 58
SVP and President Comtech EF Data Corp. and Xicom Technology Inc., John Branscum
President Comtech PST Corp., Michael Hrybenko
COO, Michael Galletti
President Safety and Security Technologies, Lynne Houserman
President Command and Control Technologies, Michael Atcheson
Auditors: DELOITTE & TOUCHE LLP

LOCATIONS

HQ: Comtech Telecommunications Corp.
68 South Service Road, Suite 230, Melville, NY 11747
Phone: 631 962-7000   **Fax:** 631 962-7001
Web: www.comtechtel.com

PRODUCTS/OPERATIONS

2016 Sales

	$ mil.	% of total
Commercial Solutions	249.0	61
Government Solutions	162.0	39
Total	**411.0**	**100**

Selected Products

Mobile data communications services
   Location tracking
   Two-way messaging
Telecommunications transmission equipment
   Error-correction and compression chips
   Over-the-horizon microwave communications products
   Satellite earth station equipment (modems frequency converters amplifiers transceivers)
Radio-frequency microwave amplifiers

COMPETITORS

Advantech	Northrop Grumman
CPI International	QUALCOMM
Ericsson	Raytheon
General Dynamics	Surrey Satellite
Gilat Satellite	Technology
Harmonic	Teledyne Technologies
Harris Corp.	VT iDirect
Lockheed Martin	ViaSat

HISTORICAL FINANCIALS

Company Type: Public

Income Statement   FYE: July 31

	REVENUE ($ mil.)	NET INCOME ($ mil.)	NET PROFIT MARGIN	EMPLOYEES
07/18	570.5	29.7	5.2%	1,852
07/17	550.3	15.8	2.9%	1,813
07/16	411.0	(7.7)	—	2,031
07/15	307.2	23.2	7.6%	978
07/14	347.1	25.1	7.2%	1,069
Annual Growth	13.2%	4.3%		14.7%

2018 Year-End Financials

Debt ratio: 19.8%	No. of shares (mil.): 23.8
Return on equity: 6.0%	Dividends
Cash ($ mil.): 43.4	Yield: 1.1%
Current ratio: 1.69	Payout: 32.2%
Long-term debt ($ mil.): 148.8	Market value ($ mil.): 801.0

	STOCK PRICE ($) FY Close	P/E High/Low	PER SHARE ($) Earnings	Dividends	Book Value
07/18	33.60	28 14	1.24	0.40	21.22
07/17	18.00	29 14	0.68	0.60	20.36
07/16	13.07	— —	(0.46)	1.20	20.16
07/15	28.81	28 19	1.42	1.20	24.88
07/14	33.80	25 15	1.37	1.18	24.56
Annual Growth	(0.1%)	— —	(2.5%)	(23.6%)	(3.6%)

Concert Pharmaceuticals Inc

Concert Pharmaceuticals wants to use deuterium chemistry to conduct a symphony of drugs. The company's process lets it substitute deuterium (also called heavy hydrogen) for hydrogen in a chemical compound thereby making the compound more stable without changing its other properties. It believes this process will lead to shorter time from discovery to trial for certain drugs. Concert has a handful of clinical-stage candidates in various stages of the approval process including treatments for spasticity kidney disease and neurologic disorders. It collaborates with Avanir Celgene and Jazz Pharmaceuticals on development.

Operations

Concert Pharmaceuticals gets revenue from development and commercialization collaborations and from not-for-profit organizations. Collaboration income includes licensing revenue R&D services option agreements and milestone payments.

Geographic Reach

Concert Pharmaceutical operates office research and lab space in Lexington Massachusetts.

Sales and Marketing

Concert plans to pursue strategic development and marketing partnerships while retaining full rights to and control over certain drugs. It intends to build out its production and marketing capability in the US.

Financial Performance

Since Concert doesn't have a product on the market yet its revenue (from stock offerings licensing and R&D payments and patent arrangements) was minimal until 2017. The company has lost money most years it has been in operation with the exception of 2015 and 2017 when significant transactions provided an influx of cash. It expects the trend to continue for several years as it works to get its drugs commercialized. At the end of 2017 it had an accumulated deficit of $76.2 million.

Revenue increased from $174000 in 2016 to $143.9 million in 2017. Most of that increase came from the sale of CTP-656 (now VX-561) and other cystic fibrosis assets to Vertex Pharmaceuticals. It was partially offset by a decline in license and R&D revenue which dropped because the company had already completed work performed for Celgene and Jazz Pharmaceuticals.

Thanks to the higher revenue Concert netted $95.6 million in 2017. It had posted a $50.7 million loss in 2016.

The company ended 2017 with $27.7 million in net cash $12.9 million less than it had at the end of 2016. Operating activities provided $102.9 million in cash and financing activities provided $5.5 million while investing activities used $121.3 million.

Strategy

Concert Pharmaceuticals plans to continue pushing its pipeline candidates through FDA approval acquiring rights to additional candidates and seeking collaborative partners to help it develop and commercialize its products. It is betting on its deuterium substitution candidates which it believes could be safer more easily tolerated and more effective than other drugs.

EXECUTIVES

SVP and Chief Development Officer, James V. (Jim) Cassella, age 63, $392,700 total compensation
COO, Nancy Stuart, age 60, $384,780 total compensation
President and CEO, Roger D. Tung, age 58, $499,905 total compensation
VP Regulatory Affairs, Christine Boisclair
Chairman, Richard H. Aldrich, age 64
Board Member, Thomas Auchincloss
Auditors: Ernst & Young LLP

LOCATIONS

HQ: Concert Pharmaceuticals Inc
99 Hayden Avenue, Suite 3000N, Lexington, MA 02421
Phone: 781 860-0045
Web: www.concertpharma.com

PRODUCTS/OPERATIONS

2017 Sales

	$ mil.	% of total
License & R&D	0.1	-
Other	143.8	100
Total	**143.9**	**100**

COMPETITORS

ACADIA Pharmaceuticals	LEO Pharma
AbbVie	Lundbeck Inc.
AstraZeneca	Merck
Auspex	Novartis
Bayer AG	Pfizer
GW Pharmaceuticals	Roche Holding
GlaxoSmithKline	Sanofi

HISTORICAL FINANCIALS

Company Type: Public

Income Statement
FYE: December 31

	REVENUE ($ mil.)	NET INCOME ($ mil.)	NET PROFIT MARGIN	EMPLOYEES
12/17	143.8	95.6	66.5%	64
12/16	0.1	(50.7)	—	69
12/15	66.7	24.1	36.2%	59
12/14	8.5	(31.7)	—	55
12/13	25.4	(6.0)	—	45
Annual Growth	**54.3%**	**—**	**—**	**9.2%**

2017 Year-End Financials

Debt ratio: —
Return on equity: 67.8%
Cash ($ mil.): 27.6
Current ratio: 31.92
Long-term debt ($ mil.): —
No. of shares (mil.): 23.1
Dividends
 Yield: —
 Payout: —
Market value ($ mil.): 599.0

	STOCK PRICE ($) FY Close	P/E High/Low		PER SHARE ($) Earnings	Dividends	Book Value
12/17	25.87	7	2	4.06	0.00	8.49
12/16	10.29	—	—	(2.28)	0.00	3.84
12/15	18.97	22	11	1.09	0.00	5.89
12/14	13.32	—	—	(2.00)	0.00	3.01
Annual Growth	**24.8%**	**—**	**—**	**—**	**—**	**41.3%**

ConnectOne Bancorp Inc (New)

ConnectOne Bancorp (formerly Center Bancorp) is the holding company for ConnectOne Bank which operates some two dozen branches across New Jersey. Serving individuals and local businesses the bank offers such deposit products as checking savings and money market accounts; CDs; and IRAs. It also performs trust services. Commercial loans account for about 60% of the bank's loan portfolio; residential mortgages ac-

count for most of the remainder. It also has a subsidiary that sells annuities and property/casualty life and health coverage. The former Center Bancorp acquired rival community bank ConnectOne Bancorp in 2014 and took that name.

Geographic Reach

ConnectOne has 24 branches in Bergen Essex Hudson Manhattan Mercer Monmouth Morris and Union Counties in New Jersey.

Mergers and Acquisitions

In 2014 Center Bancorp acquired ConnectOne Bancorp in an all-stock deal valued at approximately $243 million. The merged bank with nearly $4 billion in assets now does business under the ConnectOne brand name.

EXECUTIVES

President; Chief Executive Officer; Director, Anthony C. (Tony) Weagley, age 55, $225,000 total compensation
VP; SVP Union Center National Bank, Lori A. Wunder, age 51, $128,750 total compensation
Chairman Center Bancorp and Union Center National Bank, Alexander A. Bol, age 68
VP; SVP and Branch Administrator Union Center National Bank, Mark S. Cardone, age 53, $119,525 total compensation
VP and Credit Administrator Union Center National Bank, John J. Lukens
VP; SVP Union Center National Bank, William J. Boylan, age 51, $125,000 total compensation
VP and Senior Lending Officer; SVP and Senior Lending Officer Union Center National Bank, Ronald M. Shapiro, age 64, $132,500 total compensation
Executive Assistant Investor Relations Officer and Secretary Center Bancorp and Union Center National Bank, Joseph D. Gangemi
VP and Senior Auditor Union Center National Bank, George J. Theiller
Chief Operating Officer; Vice President, Arthur Wein
Vice President and Director - Communications & Public Relations, France Donne
Vice President; Compliance Officer, James Sorge
Senior Vice President; Loan Officer, Nicholas Anthony
Vice President; Chief Loan Officer, Vincent Bagarozza
Chief Financial Officer; Vice President; Treasurer, Vincent Tozzi
President CEO and Director Center Bancorp and Union Center National Bank, Anthony C. (Tony) Weagley, age 55
Director, Lawrence B. Seidman, age 68
Director, William A. Thompson, age 58
Director, James J. Kennedy, age 60
Director, Harold A. Schechter, age 70
Director, Raymond Vanaria, age 57
Director, Howard Kent, age 68
Director, Nicholas Minoia, age 61
Director, Phyllis S. Klein, age 53
Director, Allan H. Strauss
Independent Director, Frederick Fish
Auditors: Crowe Horwath LLP

LOCATIONS

HQ: ConnectOne Bancorp Inc (New)
301 Sylvan Avenue, Englewood Cliffs, NJ 07632
Phone: 201 816-8900
Web: www.centerbancorp.com

COMPETITORS

BCB Bancorp	New York Community
Bank of America	Bancorp
Citizens Financial	Oritani Financial
Corp.	PNC Financial
Fulton Financial	Provident Financial
Hudson City Bancorp	Services
Investors Bancorp	Sovereign Bank
JPMorgan Chase	Valley National
Kearny Financial	Bancorp
Lakeland Bancorp	Westamerica

HISTORICAL FINANCIALS

Company Type: Public

Income Statement
FYE: December 31

	ASSETS ($ mil.)	NET INCOME ($ mil.)	INCOME AS % OF ASSETS	EMPLOYEES
12/17	5,108.4	43.2	0.8%	0
12/16	4,426.3	31.0	0.7%	0
12/15	4,016.7	41.3	1.0%	0
12/14	3,448.5	18.5	0.5%	0
12/13	1,673.0	19.9	1.2%	166
Annual Growth	**32.2%**	**21.4%**	**—**	**—**

2017 Year-End Financials

Return on assets: 0.9%
Return on equity: 7.8%
Long-term debt ($ mil.): —
No. of shares (mil.): 32.0
Sales ($ mil): 189.5
Dividends
 Yield: 0.0%
 Payout: 22.3%
Market value ($ mil.): 826.0

	STOCK PRICE ($) FY Close	P/E High/Low		PER SHARE ($) Earnings	Dividends	Book Value
12/17	25.75	21	16	1.34	0.30	17.63
12/16	25.95	26	15	1.01	0.30	16.62
12/15	18.69	16	13	1.36	0.30	15.87
12/14	19.00	25	21	0.79	0.30	15.03
12/13	18.76	16	10	1.21	0.26	10.30
Annual Growth	**8.2%**	**—**	**—**	**2.6%**	**3.6%**	**14.4%**

Consolidated Communications Holdings Inc

Consolidated Communications is just what its name implies. The rural local exchange carrier operates systems in Illinois Kansas Missouri Pennsylvania Texas and California providing voice and data telecommunications to business and residential customers. It operates RLECs that offer local access and long-distance internet and TV business phone systems and related services through about 270000 local access lines 167000 voice connections and 290000 data and Internet connections. It also offers directory publishing and carrier services. Subsidiaries include Illinois Consolidated Telephone Company Consolidated Communications of Fort Bend Company and Consolidated Communications of Texas Company.

Operations

Video data and Internet services generate 45% of Consolidated's revenue with local calling services and network access services providing 17% each.

Geographic Reach

In its home base of Illinois (the headquarters is in Mattoon) Consolidated operates 35 incumbent local exchanges serving primarily small towns and rural areas mostly in the central part of the state. It also has operations in East Texas western Pennsylvania around Sacramento Calif. and around Kansas City in Missouri and Kansas.

Sales and Marketing

Consolidated markets services individually and in bundles such as the 'triple-play' of voice data and video services. The company boosted its advertising spending to $8.2 million in 2014 from $7.6 million in 2013.

Financial Performance

Consolidated reported revenue of $635.7 million for 2014 up about 7% from $601.5 million in 2013. The acquisition of Enventis a Mlinnesota telecom lifted revenue. However only video data and Internet services posted a year-to-year revenue gain while revenue from other segments fell.

Net income dropped 51% to $15 million in 2014 from $31 million in 2013. Acquisitions were accompanied by higher operating costs which cut into net income as did depreciation and amortization expenses.

Cash from operations rose to $189 million in 2014 from $164 million in 2013 because of a change in working capital items.

Strategy

One way to view Consolidated's strategy is to look at a map. Starting in Illinois the company has expanded to Pennsylvania Texas Missouri and Kansas and California gobbling up similar telecoms that serve small towns and rural areas. It's tweaking that approach with its move to the Kansas City area and into the Dallas-Fort Worth suburbs.

As the company's wireline business decreases (as it has with most telecom companies) Consolidated is moving to add more Internet data and video services to its lineup. The company is expanding its services in a big way in the Dallas-Fort Worth area where it has 30000 miles of fiber ready to light up with Internet access wide area networks and hosted iPBX for commercial customer. The network had been used for wholesale and carrier customers.

Consolidated offers high-speed Internet service through fiber optic lines in Kansas City and Conroe and Katy Texas. The company gained about 4200 miles of fiber lines with its acquisition of Eventis. Consolidate's capital expenditure budgets include money for continued expansion of fiber in its service areas.

Consolidated also is expanding its services to provide carrier hotel space and data center space in its markets and to support fiber backhaul services to cell sites. It is to have nearly 700 cell tower sites completed by the end of 2014.

Mergers and Acquisitions

Acquisitions play a key role in Consolidated Communications growth strategy and the company continued in 2016 with a deal to buy Fair-Point Communications for $1.5 billion (including debt). FairPoint Communications operates in the Eastern US and has a strong network in New England. The deal would extend Consolidated's reach to some 24 states from California to North Carolina and other points on the eastern seaboard. FairPoint's assets bring Consolidated route miles

of fiber optic cable to 35100. The transaction is expected to close in mid-2017.

In 2014 Consolidated bought Enventis which has service in Iowa Minnesota North Dakota South Dakota and Wisconsin for about $350 million. Enventis brings about 39000 access lines 21000 high-speed Internet customers 12000 digital TV customers and 90 fiber-to-the tower sites as well as $123 million in revenue.

In 2012 Consolidated bought SureWest Communications a provider of residential and commercial communications and broadband services in the Sacramento California and Kansas City markets in a deal valued at $324 million excluding debt.

EXECUTIVES

CFO, Steven L. (Steve) Childers, age 63, $276,542 total compensation
SVP CIO and Corporate Secretary, Steven J. (Steve) Shirar, age 60, $238,346 total compensation
President and CEO, C. Robert (Bob) Udell, age 52, $415,385 total compensation
VP Operations, Gabe Waggoner
CTO, Tom White
Vice President Customer Service, Dawn Frost
Chairman, Robert J. (Bob) Currey, age 73
Auditors: Ernst & Young LLP

LOCATIONS

HQ: Consolidated Communications Holdings Inc
121 South 17th Street, Mattoon, IL 61938-3987
Phone: 217 235-3311
Web: www.consolidated.com

PRODUCTS/OPERATIONS

2014 Sales

	$ mil.	% of total
Telephone		
Data Internet & video	287.5	45
Local calling 108.3	17	
Network access	106.3	17
Subsidies	53.2	8
Long distance	19.6	3
Other services	60.8	10
Total	**635.7**	**100**

COMPETITORS

AT&T	Sprint Communications
Comcast	Suddenlink
Google	Communications
Mediacom	Time Warner Cable
Communications	Verizon

HISTORICAL FINANCIALS

Company Type: Public

Income Statement — FYE: December 31

	REVENUE ($ mil.)	NET INCOME ($ mil.)	NET PROFIT MARGIN	EMPLOYEES
12/17	1,059.5	64.9	6.1%	3,930
12/16	743.1	14.9	2.0%	1,676
12/15	775.7	(0.8)	—	1,783
12/14	635.7	15.0	2.4%	1,960
12/13	601.5	30.8	5.1%	1,521
Annual Growth	15.2%	20.5%	—	26.8%

2017 Year-End Financials

Debt ratio: 62.9%	No. of shares (mil.): 70.7
Return on equity: 17.5%	Dividends
Cash ($ mil.): 15.6	Yield: 0.0%
Current ratio: 0.83	Payout: 144.8%
Long-term debt ($ mil.): 2,311.5	Market value ($ mil.): 863.0

	STOCK PRICE ($) FY Close	P/E High/Low	PER SHARE ($) Earnings	Dividends	Book Value
12/17	12.19	26 11	1.07	1.55	8.03
12/16	26.85	102 64	0.29	1.55	3.38
12/15	20.95	— —	(0.02)	1.55	4.87
12/14	27.83	82 53	0.35	1.55	6.40
12/13	19.63	26 21	0.76	1.55	3.69
Annual Growth (11.2%)	— —	8.9%	(0.0%)	21.5%	

Consolidated-Tomoka Land Co.

From golf courses and retail centers to timber and hay farms land developer Consolidated-Tomoka owns a chunk of the Southeast. The company focuses on Florida but also has holdings in other neighboring states. Its portfolio includes retail properties (tenants include Bank of America CVS Walgreens a couple of golf courses (including the national headquarters of the LPGA) and some 10000 acres of agricultural land that the company is converting into other income properties. Through its subsidiaries it also holds subsurface oil gas and mineral interests on land throughout Florida and properties in North Carolina and Georgia. Consolidated-Tomoka was founded in 1902.

Operations

The company divides its operations across four segments: real estate operations income property golf and investment in a commercial mortgage loan collateralized by a hotel property in Atlanta.

Its income properties are the biggest money-maker accounting for about half of overall sales. It owns 35 single-tenant income properties in seven states that are triple or double net leases and ground leases where the tenant pays for all real estate taxes insurance utilities maintenance and capital expenditures.

Geographic Reach

Consolidated-Tomoka is headquartered in Florida. The majority of its real estate is located there but other properties are in Arizona California Colorado Georgia Illinois and North Carolina.

Financial Performance

Overall sales grew almost 50% in 2013 to $25 million after the company recognized rents from nine properties bought in 2013 and a full year of results for six properties bought in late 2012. In addition Consolidated-Tomoka bought a mortgage loan in 2013 and began adding the accrued interest to its revenue mix. Profits grew 514% from $600000 in 2013 to $3 million in 2013.

Mergers and Acquisitions

As part of its strategy of investing in income-producing properties in 2013 Consolidated-Tomoka bought nine income properties for a combined $39 million including four buildings leased to Bank of America in Southern California and two office complexes leased to Hilton in Florida. At the same time it sold five properties for $18.6 million.

EXECUTIVES

SVP General Counsel and Corporate Secretary, Daniel E. Smith, $185,000 total compensation
President and CEO, John P. Albright, $500,000 total compensation
SVP and CFO, Mark E. Patten, $220,500 total compensation
SVP Investments, Steven R. Greathouse
Vice Chairman, A. Chester Skinner
Chairman, Thomas P. Warlow
Auditors: GRANT THORNTON LLP

LOCATIONS

HQ: Consolidated-Tomoka Land Co.
1140 N. Williamson Blvd., Suite 140, Daytona Beach, FL 32114
Phone: 386 274-2202   **Fax:** 386 274-1223
Web: www.ctlc.com

PRODUCTS/OPERATIONS

2015 Sales

	% of total
Income Properties	44
Real Estate Operations	37
Golf Operations	12
Interest Income from Commercial Loan Investments	7
Agriculture and Other income	-
Total	**100**

COMPETITORS

AV Homes	Rayonier
Alico Inc.	St. Joe
Anthony Forest Products	Stiles
	Stratus Properties
Echelon Development	Tejon Ranch
Forestar	Turnberry Associates

HISTORICAL FINANCIALS

Company Type: Public

Income Statement				FYE: December 31
	REVENUE ($ mil.)	NET INCOME ($ mil.)	NET PROFIT MARGIN	EMPLOYEES
12/17	91.4	41.7	45.6%	14
12/16	71.0	16.2	22.9%	14
12/15	43.0	8.3	19.4%	14
12/14	35.5	6.3	18.0%	14
12/13	25.8	3.6	14.3%	13
Annual Growth	37.1%	83.5%	—	1.9%

2017 Year-End Financials

Debt ratio: 42.0%
Return on equity: 25.1%
Cash ($ mil.): 6.5
Current ratio: 0.34
Long-term debt ($ mil.): 195.8
No. of shares (mil.): 5.5
Dividends
  Yield: 0.0%
  Payout: 2.4%
Market value ($ mil.): 355.0

	STOCK PRICE ($) FY Close	P/E High/Low		PER SHARE ($) Earnings	Dividends	Book Value
12/17	63.50	8	7	7.48	0.18	32.98
12/16	53.42	19	15	2.85	0.12	25.97
12/15	52.71	44	34	1.43	0.08	22.81
12/14	55.80	54	30	1.10	0.07	21.83
12/13	36.29	66	48	0.64	0.06	20.53
Annual Growth	15.0%	—	—	84.9%	31.6%	12.6%

Continental Building Products Inc

Continental Building Products (CBP) has got homeowners surrounded. The company is a leading manufacturer of gypsum wallboard (aka drywall) and complementary finishing products used in new residential and commercial construction and for repairs and remodels. CBP manufactures its products at plants in Florida Kentucky and New York for sale east of the Mississippi River and in eastern Canada. The company claims to be the only US producer of gypsum wallboard to use only 100% synthetic gypsum. Product lines include LiftLite a lightweight product Mold Defense which protects against mildew and Weather Defense exterior sheeting. The wallboard producer went public in 2014 in an offering valued at $185 million.

IPO
The company's February 2014 IPO was timed to capitalize on the rebound in housing starts. The offering raised $185.3 million or $14 per share significantly below its expected range of $16 to $18. CBP used the proceeds to retire debt.

Geographic Reach
Virginia-based CBP rings up nearly 90% of its sales in the US. Canada accounts for the rest. The company has manufacturing facilities and sales efforts concentrated in the eastern US and eastern Canada. It operates automated manufacturing facilities in Silver Grove Kentucky; Palatka Florida; and Buchanan New York.

Sales and Marketing
CBP serves the residential commercial and repair and remodel construction markets. The company sells its products through several different channels and to a broad group of customers including gypsum wallboard distributors buying groups wholesalers and mass merchants. Lowes its largest customer represented 16% 15% and 14% of its net sales in 2015 2014 and 2013 respectively

Financial Performance
After posting milestone revenues of for $425 million in 2014 CBP saw its revenues dip marginally by 1% to $422 million in 2015. The decline was attributed to the unfavorable impact of foreign currency and lower sales of its non-wallboard products during 2015.

The company's profits jumped 5% from $15.9 million in 2014 to $16.7 million in 2015. The was fueled by decreased expenses mainly non-recurring costs incurred in the first quarter of 2014 including the prepayment premium for the repayment of loans.

Company Background
CBP was created after the $700 million sale of Lafarge SA's North America Inc.'s gypsum business to private equity firm Lone Star Funds in August 2013.

EXECUTIVES

SVP Sales Marketing and Supply Chain, Muhammad Shahbaz (Boz) Malik, age 50
President and CEO, James (Jay) Bachmann, age 49
SVP and CFO, Dennis Schemm, age 51
SVP Manufacturing, David Obergefell, age 64
Vice President Strategy and Strategic Sourcing, Bruce Major

Chairman, Edward M. (Ed) Bosowski, age 63
Auditors: Ernst & Young LLP

LOCATIONS

HQ: Continental Building Products Inc
12950 Worldgate Drive, Suite 700, Herndon, VA 20170
Phone: 703 480-3800
Web: www.continental-bp.com

PRODUCTS/OPERATIONS

2015 Sales

	$ mil.	% of total
Wallboard	408.0	97
Other	13.7	3
Total	**421.7**	**100**

Selected Products/trademarks
Firecheck
LiftLite
Mold Defense
Rapid Coat
Weather Defense

COMPETITORS

American Gypsum	New NGC
CertainTeed	USG
Georgia-Pacific	

HISTORICAL FINANCIALS

Company Type: Public

Income Statement				FYE: December 31
	REVENUE ($ mil.)	NET INCOME ($ mil.)	NET PROFIT MARGIN	EMPLOYEES
12/17	489.1	59.8	12.2%	621
12/16	461.3	44.0	9.5%	617
12/15	421.6	16.7	4.0%	546
12/14	424.5	15.8	3.7%	538
12/13	150.0	2.1	1.4%	480
Annual Growth	34.4%	130.9%	—	6.7%

2017 Year-End Financials

Debt ratio: 41.3%
Return on equity: 19.0%
Cash ($ mil.): 72.5
Current ratio: 3.32
Long-term debt ($ mil.): 263.6
No. of shares (mil.): 37.5
Dividends
  Yield: —
  Payout: —
Market value ($ mil.): 1,057.0

	STOCK PRICE ($) FY Close	P/E High/Low		PER SHARE ($) Earnings	Dividends	Book Value
12/17	28.15	18	14	1.54	0.00	8.47
12/16	23.10	23	13	1.08	0.00	7.79
12/15	17.46	61	42	0.39	0.00	7.20
12/14	17.73	54	34	0.37	0.00	6.88
Annual Growth	16.7%	—	—	60.9%	—	7.2%

Control4 Corp

Control4 gives homes a personal touch far beyond throw pillows and new paint. The company makes and sells home automation systems that allow users to control music video lighting temperature and security systems with the touch of a button on a wall panel or mobile device. For example homeowners may program their system to lock the doors close the blinds and turn on the alarm when they leave for work and open the garage door and adjust the thermostat to a particular temperature upon arrival. Control4 systems are only sold through authorized dealers and distributors who design a custom solution for each home (and to a smaller extent businesses).

Operations
Control4's software is designed to work with other software and networks such as a cable TV or security system and its software platform operates with more than 8700 third-party devices. The company's systems range in price from $1200 for a single-room automation installation to more than $25000 for a complete integrated system.

The company relies on two contract manufacturers Sanmina and Lite-On to make the majority of its products. Another six contract manufacturers also located in Asia make the remaining 20% of its products.

Geographic Reach
Control4 sells its products directly through a network of 3400 dealers in the US Canada the UK and 40 other countries. In addition it has partnership agreements with about 30 distributors in 41 other countries. The US and Canada are its largest markets accounting for 75% of sales.

Sales and Marketing
The company's dealer network ranges from small businesses to large organizations. Using a dealer network for its sales model allows the company to create custom projects programmed specifically for each residence; its systems need to be installed and maintained by a technician.

Financial Performance
Control4 has seen its revenues grow consistently every year. Revenues jumped 16% from $129 million in 2013 to peak at a record-setting $149 million in 2014. Profits also more than doubled $3.5 million to $8.2 million during that same time period mostly due to a major decline in legal settlement costs.

The historic growth for 2014 was fueled by surges in sales across all its geographical segments: the US (16%) Canada (2%) and other countries (21%). This was mainly due to an overall increase in the number of dealers and distributors selling its products and services.

Strategy
Control4 recorded milestone revenues in 2014 primarily by expanding its global dealer and distributor network. It will continue to adhere to this strategy going forward and will focus on increasing penetration of its North America core market expanding its focus on adjacent markets and enhancing its products and services through streaming technology and mobile apps.

Mergers and Acquisitions
Control4 also plans to grow through the use of acquisitions. In 2015 it obtained Nexus Technologies Pty an Australia-based provider of audio and video distribution products. Through the acquisition Control4 gained access to Nexus' broad array of Leaf-branded audio and video distribution products.

EXECUTIVES

Chairman President and CEO, Martin H. Plaehn, age 60, $280,000 total compensation
SVP Marketing, Susan K. Cashen, age 57
General Counsel and Chief Compliance Officer, Greg Bishop, age 59, $240,000 total compensation
SVP Products, Eric Anderson, age 59

SVP Supply Chain Operations and Business Development, Jefferson (Jeff) Dungan, age 48
CFO, Mark Novakovich, age 50, $229,000 total compensation
Auditors: Ernst & Young LLP

LOCATIONS

HQ: Control4 Corp
11734 S. Election Road, Salt Lake City, UT 84020
Phone: 801 523-3100
Web: www.control4.com

COMPETITORS

ADT	Logitech
AMX Corp.	Russound
Comcast	Simtrol
Crestron Electronics	SmartLabs
Leviton	Verizon

HISTORICAL FINANCIALS
Company Type: Public

Income Statement
FYE: December 31

	REVENUE ($ mil.)	NET INCOME ($ mil.)	NET PROFIT MARGIN	EMPLOYEES
12/17	244.7	15.9	6.5%	635
12/16	208.8	12.9	6.2%	546
12/15	163.1	(1.6)		449
12/14	148.8	8.1	5.5%	417
12/13	128.5	3.5	2.7%	386
Annual Growth	17.5%	46.1%	—	13.3%

2017 Year-End Financials

Debt ratio: —	No. of shares (mil.): 25.8
Return on equity: 10.2%	Dividends
Cash ($ mil.): 29.7	Yield: —
Current ratio: 3.75	Payout: —
Long-term debt ($ mil.): —	Market value ($ mil.): 769.0

	STOCK PRICE ($) FY Close	P/E High/Low	PER SHARE ($) Earnings	Dividends	Book Value
12/17	29.76	56 17	0.60	0.00	6.77
12/16	10.20	22 10	0.53	0.00	5.77
12/15	7.27	— —	(0.07)	0.00	4.93
12/14	15.37	93 35	0.32	0.00	4.87
12/13	17.70	72 43	0.16	0.00	4.32
Annual Growth	13.9%	— —	39.2%	—	11.9%

Copart Inc

What happens after cars are totaled in wrecks or natural disasters? How about stolen cars recovered after the insurance settlement? Perhaps Copart happens; it takes junked cars and auctions them for insurers auto dealers and car rental agencies. The buyers are mostly rebuilders licensed dismantlers and used-car dealers and exporters. It's replaced live auctions with Internet auctions using a platform known as Virtual Bidding Third Generation (VB3 for short). Copart also provides services such as towing and storage to buyers and other salvage companies as well as an online database and search engine for used parts. Copart serves customers throughout North America Europe the Middle East and Brazil.

Operations
The majority of the vehicles Copart processes are auctioned under an incentive program in which Copart gets a percentage of the proceeds; the rest are auctioned under a fixed-fee consignment basis (generally $50 to $175). Copart's other services include Copart Dealer Services which sells trade-ins for franchises and independent dealerships using VB3 and CoPartfinder which enables customers to bid on a vehicle search for parts from Keystone Automotive Industries and receive e-mail notifications when cars matching their criteria come up for sale.

About 86% of Copart's revenue came from its service offerings in fiscal 2015 (ended July 2015) while the remainder came from vehicle sales.

Geographic Reach
North America is by far Copart's largest market accounting for 80% of sales in fiscal 2015 (ended July 2015). The UK generated another 18% of the company's sales that year. Copart also serves customers in the United Arab Emirates (UAE) Oman Bahrain India and Brazil and provides vehicle remarketing services in Germany and Spain.

Sales and Marketing
Copart's customer base of vehicle sellers mostly consists of insurance companies (which make up more than 80% of the vehicles Copart processes each year) though it also includes banks and financial institutions charities car dealerships fleet operators and vehicle rental companies. Copart sells its vehicles mostly to licensed vehicle dismantlers rebuilders repair licensees used vehicle dealers and exporters and to the general public in select locations.

Overall the company spent $4.9 million on advertising in fiscal 2015 (ended July 2015) compared to $5 million per year in both FY2014 and FY2013.

Financial Performance
Copart's annual revenues and profits have been trending higher over the past several years.

The company's sales dipped by less than 2% to $1.15 billion in fiscal 2015 (ended July 31 2015) mostly because vehicle sales fell 22% as volumes from insurance sellers declined and as auction selling prices dipped as well. Service revenue (the company's main revenue driver) grew thanks to higher volume as the company boosted its market share and enjoyed a marginal increase in revenue per car serviced. By geography revenue grew by 1% in North America (its largest market) and declined by 10% or more in the UK and other countries.

Despite modest revenue declines in FY2015 Copart's net income spiked 23% to a record $219.8 million for the year mostly because in FY2014 it incurred asset impairment charges after terminating its contract with KPIT (formerly known as Sparta Consulting); KPIT would have designed and implemented an SAP-based replacement for Copart's business operating software that would have addressed Coparts international expansion needs among other things. Copart's operating cash levels inched up 1% to $265 million for the year on higher cash earnings.

Strategy
With its market in the US maturing Copart continues to expand into more foreign markets and online through acquisitions and new facility openings. During 2015 the company opened new facilities in Manama Bahrain; Muscat Oman; and Moncton Canada. In 2014 it opened new facilities

in Seaford Delaware; Itaquaquecetuba Brazil; and India while also acquiring online rights to hundreds of potentially valuable web domains to boost its online presence.

Copart also planned in 2015 to pursue more national and regional vehicle supply agreements expand its online auctions and vehicle remarketing service offerings to more sellers and members and extend the application of its latest Virtual Bidding platform (VB3) into new markets and to new sellers across the vehicle market.

Mergers and Acquisitions

During fiscal 2014 (ended July 31 2014) Copart purchased a facility in Montreal Canada; a salvage vehicle auction business in Brazil; and the assets of an online marketing company and rights to hundreds of web domains including www.cashforcars.com and www.cash4cars.com. The total purchase price of these assets amounted to $14.5 million.

HISTORY

Copart was co-founded in 1982 by Willis Johnson who had owned and operated an auto dismantling business for more than 10 years. After buying out his partner in 1986 he became CEO and used his own money to expand the company into a network of four California salvage yards by 1991. In the next two years Copart nearly tripled the number of salvage operations it owned by acquiring companies throughout the US. HPB Associates a private investor group came on board in 1993 buying 26% of the firm for $10 million and the company went public the next year.

Copart doubled its total facilities in 1995 with the acquisition of NER Auction Systems the largest privately held salvage auction company in the US. The firm acquired or opened more than 30 facilities between 1995 and 1997. In 1998 the company started an online auction site; expanded through acquisitions into Alabama Iowa Michigan and South Carolina; and opened new locations in California and Minnesota. The next year rival Insurance Auto Auctions spurned its merger overtures.

In 2000 Copart opened three new salvage vehicle auction facilities and acquired eight more. That year the company also signed an agreement to sell Keystone Automotive Industries' parts through its Web site. In 2001 and 2002 the company acquired or opened 13 new locations. Continuing its acquisition strategy the company opened or acquired five more facilities in 2004.

In 2005 the company made two acquisitions for about $4.5 million: Kentucky Auto Salvage Pool a 25-acre salvage facility in Lexington Kentucky; and Insurance Auctions of Missouri. In November Copart acquired the salvage pool assets of Central Penn Sales a vehicle salvage disposal company with four sites in Pennsylvania and Maryland totaling 255 acres. In December the company opened a second salvage facility in Michigan.

In June 2007 Copart acquired Universal Salvage the operator of about 10 salvage yards in the UK and a vehicle remarketer to the insurance and automotive industries for about $120 million. Adding to its UK holdings in August Copart purchased Century Salvage Sales Limited which has three salvage yards and AG Watson which has four salvage yards in England and Scotland.

During 2008 the company launched CopartDirect. The service allows Copart to sell cars to the general public using its VB 2 application so that

individuals can avoid the inconvenience of selling a vehicle themselves.

In February 2010 Willis Johnson relinquished the CEO's title to A. Jayson Adair who formerly served as president of Copart. Johnson continued as chairman of the company.

In 2011 Copart acquired the Indiana-based auto auction firm Barodge Auto Pool expanding its presence in Indiana and surrounding states. The company also broadened its existing range of farming equipment in the UK when it acquired Hewitt International an auctioneer of agricultural vehicles and equipment based in central England in 2011.

In 2012 the company made several acquisitions in international markets including Brazil Canada Germany and Dubai UAE. That year Copart expanded into Germany (the world's fourth largest auto market) with the purchase of WOM Wreck Online Marketing a leading European salvage vehicle auction platform there. Earlier in the year it bought Canada's Diamond Auto Bids and Disposals a privately-held automotive auction that gives Copart a foothold in Western Canada specifically Calgary and Edmonton. It also extended the reach of its business into South America through its purchase of Central de Leiloes LTDA based in Sao Paulo Brazil.

EXECUTIVES

CEO, A. Jayson Adair, age 48
EVP, William E. Franklin, age 62, $363,423 total compensation
President, Vincent W. Mitz, age 55, $265,000 total compensation
SVP and CFO, Jeffrey Liaw, age 42
Senior Vice President of Strategic Growth, John Lindle
National Sales Manager, Jim Miller
National Account Manager, Chris Hanks
National Account Manager, Daniel Smith
Copart Direct VPA, Marlon Ford
Vice President, Richard Kruse
Vice President of Sales and Account Management, Scott Christy
Auditors: Ernst & Young LLP

LOCATIONS

HQ: Copart Inc
14185 Dallas Parkway, Suite 300, Dallas, TX 75254
Phone: 972 391-5000
Web: www.copart.com

PRODUCTS/OPERATIONS

2015 Sales

	$ mil.	% of total
Services	985.4	86
Vehicles	160.7	14
Total	**1,146.1**	**100**

Selected Services

Copart Access (online vehicle information retrieval)
Copart Dealer Services (online trade-in vehicle sales)
Copart Direct (online used car sales)
CoPartfinder (online used-parts search engine)
DMV processing (title document processing)
Monthly reporting (summary of all vehicles processed by company for suppliers)
Online bidding (online auctions)
Salvage brokerage network (coordination of vehicle disposal outside areas of current operation)
Salvage Lynk (software providing online information on vehicles being processed)
Transportation services (fleet of transport trucks)

Vehicle inspection stations (central locations for insurance companies to inspect vehicles)
Vehicle preparation and merchandising (cleaning and weather protection direct mailings to buyers)

COMPETITORS

Advance Auto Parts	KAR Auction Services
Columbus Fair Auto	LKQ
Auction	Pittsburgh Independent
Cox Automotive	Auto Auction
Cox Enterprises	

HISTORICAL FINANCIALS

Company Type: Public

Income Statement

FYE: July 31

	REVENUE ($ mil.)	NET INCOME ($ mil.)	NET PROFIT MARGIN	EMPLOYEES
07/18	1,805.7	417.8	23.1%	6,026
07/17	1,447.9	394.2	27.2%	5,323
07/16	1,268.4	270.3	21.3%	4,844
07/15	1,146.0	219.7	19.2%	4,267
07/14	1,163.4	178.6	15.4%	4,179
Annual Growth	**11.6%**	**23.7%**	—	**9.6%**

2018 Year-End Financials

Debt ratio: 17.3%	No. of shares (mil.): 233.9
Return on equity: 31.1%	Dividends
Cash ($ mil.): 274.5	Yield: —
Current ratio: 2.56	Payout: —
Long-term debt ($ mil.): 398.7	Market value ($ mil.): 13,423.0

	STOCK PRICE ($) FY Close	P/E High/Low		PER SHARE ($) Earnings	Dividends	Book Value
07/18	57.39	33	17	1.73	0.00	6.76
07/17	31.49	36	17	1.66	0.00	4.76
07/16	50.44	43	28	1.11	0.00	3.52
07/15	36.03	44	35	0.84	0.00	4.01
07/14	33.38	52	44	0.68	0.00	3.98
Annual Growth	**14.5%**	—	—	**26.3%**	—	**14.2%**

Corcept Therapeutics Inc

Corcept Therapeutics wants to help people who are beyond blue. The biotechnology firm is exploring treatments that regulate the presence of cortisol a steroid hormone associated with some psychiatric and metabolic disorders. Its sole commercial product Korlym is a version of the compound mifepristone (commonly known as RU-486 or the "abortion pill") used to regulate release patterns of cortisol. The drug is approved in the US for use in patients with Cushing's Syndrome a metabolic disorder caused by high levels of cortisol in the blood. The company is also developing mifepristone for treatment of patients with psychotic depression.

Operations

Corcept is investigating three additional proprietary selective cortisol modulators for the treatment of Cushing syndrome and of solid-tumor cancers. In certain cancers cortisol activity promotes the growth of tumors; Corcept is studying the idea that adding a cortisol modulator to a patient's treatment will activate the body's immune system.

The company does not manufacture Korlym or its drug candidates but rather relies on contract manufacturers Produits Chimiques Auxiliaires et de Synthese and Alcami Corporation.

Geographic Reach

Corcept sells Korlym in the US. It does not have immediate plans to market the drug in other markets.

Sales and Marketing

Corcept markets Korlym in the US through direct sales representatives health care providers and via medical science liaisons.The company has significantly increased the size of its sales force in recent years.

Financial Performance

Corcept's revenues have been rising rapidly over the past five years thanks to higher sales volumes and price increases. In 2016 revenue increased 62% to $81.3 million. With the higher revenue the company became profitable that year netting $8.1 million (versus losses of $6.4 million in 2015 and $31.4 million in 2014).

Cash flow from operations has also been steadily increasing. In 2016 it totaled $18.4 million more than quadruple the $3.1 million it totaled in 2015.

Strategy

Corcept typically allots about 30% of its operating expenses to research and development. In fiscal 2016 the company spent $23.8 million on R&D up from $15.4 million in 2015 and $18.4 million in 2014. It expects these expenses to rise as its clinical studies activities ramp up and it hires additional clinical staff.

Right now the company is reliant on Korlym for its growth as its other candidates won't be commercialized for years. Although sales of Korlym have been on the rise the drug faces competition from Novartis' Signifor which is also approved to treat adults with Cushing's disease (which the majority of patients with Cushing's syndrome have).

EXECUTIVES

President and CEO, Joseph K. Belanoff, age 60, $597,670 total compensation
CFO, G. Charles Robb, age 55, $363,472 total compensation
SVP Commercial, Sean Maduck
Chief Medical Officer, Robert S. Fishman, age 56, $104,956 total compensation
VP Regulatory Affairs, Susan Rinne
Vice President Marketing and Training, Rob Adamoski
Chairman, James N. Wilson
Treasurer, David Penake
Auditors: Ernst & Young LLP

LOCATIONS

HQ: Corcept Therapeutics Inc
149 Commonwealth Drive, Menlo Park, CA 94025
Phone: 650 327-3270
Web: www.corcept.com

COMPETITORS

AstraZeneca	Janssen
Bayer HealthCare	Pharmaceuticals
Pharmaceuticals	Merck
Bristol-Myers Squibb	Mylan
Eli Lilly	Novartis
GlaxoSmithKline	Pfizer

HISTORICAL FINANCIALS

Company Type: Public

Income Statement

FYE: December 31

	REVENUE ($ mil.)	NET INCOME ($ mil.)	NET PROFIT MARGIN	EMPLOYEES
12/17	159.2	129.1	81.1%	136
12/16	81.3	8.1	10.0%	103
12/15	50.2	(6.4)	—	96
12/14	26.5	(31.3)	—	92
12/13	10.3	(46.0)	—	77
Annual Growth	**98.0%**	**—**	**—**	**15.3%**

2017 Year-End Financials

Debt ratio: —
Return on equity: —
Cash ($ mil.): 31.0
Current ratio: 4.20
Long-term debt ($ mil.): —
No. of shares (mil.): 114.7
Dividends
Yield: —
Payout: —
Market value ($ mil.): 2,072.0

	STOCK PRICE ($) FY Close	P/E High/Low		PER SHARE ($) Earnings	Dividends	Book Value
12/17	18.06	18	6	1.04	0.00	1.66
12/16	7.26	139	47	0.07	0.00	0.37
12/15	4.98	—	—	(0.06)	0.00	0.17
12/14	3.00	—	—	(0.31)	0.00	(0.03)
12/13	3.21	—	—	(0.46)	0.00	0.21
Annual Growth	**54.0%**			**—**	**—**	**67.7%**

CoreLogic Inc.

Auditors: PricewaterhouseCoopers LLP

LOCATIONS

HQ: CoreLogic Inc.
40 Pacifica, Irvine, CA 92618-7471
Phone: 949 214-1000
Web: www.corelogic.com

HISTORICAL FINANCIALS

Company Type: Public

Income Statement

FYE: December 31

	REVENUE ($ mil.)	NET INCOME ($ mil.)	NET PROFIT MARGIN	EMPLOYEES
12/17	1,851.1	152.1	8.2%	5,900
12/16	1,952.5	106.5	5.5%	6,300
12/15	1,528.1	127.8	8.4%	6,500
12/14	1,405.0	73.2	5.2%	4,820
12/13	1,330.6	107.7	8.1%	5,242
Annual Growth	**8.6%**	**9.0%**	**—**	**3.0%**

2017 Year-End Financials

Debt ratio: 43.0%
Return on equity: 15.1%
Cash ($ mil.): 118.8
Current ratio: 0.70
Long-term debt ($ mil.): 1,683.5
No. of shares (mil.): 80.8
Dividends
Yield: —
Payout: —
Market value ($ mil.): 3,738.0

	STOCK PRICE ($) FY Close	P/E High/Low		PER SHARE ($) Earnings	Dividends	Book Value
12/17	46.21	27	19	1.78	0.00	12.46
12/16	36.83	35	26	1.19	0.00	11.89
12/15	33.86	29	22	1.41	0.00	11.90
12/14	31.59	44	32	0.79	0.00	11.35
12/13	35.53	32	19	1.11	0.00	11.44
Annual Growth	**6.8%**	**—**	**—**	**12.5%**	**—**	**2.1%**

CorEnergy Infrastructure Trust Inc

A closed-end investment management firm CorEnergy Infrastructure Trust (formerly Tortoise Capital Resources) invests in privately held and public micro-cap energy companies including midstream and downstream oil and gas companies and coal companies. The firm typically makes equity or debt investments in low-risk established energy companies that will generate steadily increasing returns on its investments over the long term. CorEnergy which has more than $90 million in assets under management is managed by Tortoise Capital Advisors a fund manager with five other publicly traded funds under management.

EXECUTIVES

President CEO and Director, David J. Schulte, age 57
Chief Accounting Officer Treasurer and Secretary, Rebecca Sandring
Vice President Finance, Jeff Teeven
Auditors: Ernst & Young LLP

LOCATIONS

HQ: CorEnergy Infrastructure Trust Inc
1100 Walnut, Suite 3350, Kansas City, MO 64106
Phone: 816 875-3705
Web: www.corenergy.corridortrust.com

PRODUCTS/OPERATIONS

2015 Sales

	% of total
Lease	68
Transportation	20
Sales	10
Financing	2
Total	**100**

COMPETITORS

Adams Express	Petroleum & Resources
FMR	Corporation
First Reserve	Prospect Capital
OHA Investment	The Vanguard Group

HISTORICAL FINANCIALS
Company Type: Public

Income Statement
FYE: December 31

	REVENUE ($ mil.)	NET INCOME ($ mil.)	NET PROFIT MARGIN	EMPLOYEES
12/17	88.7	32.6	36.7%	20
12/16	89.2	29.6	33.2%	22
12/15	71.2	12.3	17.3%	22
12/14	40.3	7.0	17.4%	21
12/13	31.2	4.5	14.4%	0
Annual Growth	29.8%	64.0%	—	—

2017 Year-End Financials
Debt ratio: 24.1%
Return on equity: 7.5%
Cash ($ mil.): 15.7
Current ratio: 6.98
Long-term debt ($ mil.): 152.7

No. of shares (mil.): 11.9
Dividends
Yield: 0.0%
Payout: 144.9%
Market value ($ mil.): 455.0

	STOCK PRICE ($) FY Close	P/E High/Low		PER SHARE ($) Earnings	Dividends	Book Value
12/17	38.20	19	15	2.07	3.00	38.75
12/16	34.88	17	5	2.14	3.00	34.20
12/15	14.84	30	5	0.79	2.75	35.01
12/14	6.48	8	6	1.05	2.57	33.31
12/13	7.12	8	6	0.95	1.88	36.68
Annual Growth	52.2%	—	—	21.5%	12.5%	1.4%

CoreSite Realty Corp

CoreSite Realty leases data center space to those with data center needs. The real estate investment trust (REIT) owns develops and operates these specialized facilities which require enough power security and network interconnection to handle often complex IT operations. Its property portfolio includes more than 15 operating data center facilities with additional space under development. These properties comprise around 3 million rentable sq. ft. and are located in major US tech hubs including Silicon Valley. Tenants include enterprise organizations communications service providers media and content companies government agencies and schools. The REIT has grown along with demand for data center space.

Operations
Unlike most REITs which earn virtually all of their revenue from lease income CoreSite also makes money from the power and cross connections it supplies to its tenants. About 56% of its total revenue came from rental income during 2015 while about 27% came from power revenue and 13% came from interconnection revenue.

Geographic Reach
Denver-based CoreSite Realty operates 17 data center campuses in nine North American markets. Almost 75% of the REIT's rental income came from its properties in Los Angeles San Francisco Bay and Northern Virginia during 2015 while another nearly 25% came from its properties in Chicago Boston and New York. The rest came from its Miami- and Denver-based properties.

Sales and Marketing
The REIT boasts a global customer base of more than 900 tenants (as of early 2016) including ISPs (Internet Service Providers) and telecommunications carriers (including AT&T Verizon Comcast Time Warner China Mobile and Tata Communications) content and media entertainment providers (such as Facebook Google Microsoft and DreamWorks Animation) cloud providers (Amazon Computer Science Corp. Hewlett-Packard) as well as enterprise financial educational institutions and government agencies.

CoreSite's 10 largest tenants made up 35.6% of its annualized rent during 2015 reflecting a diversified tenant base.

Financial Performance
CoreSite Realty's annual revenues have nearly doubled since 2011 as new property acquisitions and demand for data center space has driven higher rental income. The REIT's profits have skyrocketed as it has managed to keep a lid on the growth of operating costs.

The REIT's revenue jumped 22% to a record $333.29 million during 2015 as new and expansion leases increased its occupied space by 20% to 1.49 million net rental square feet (NRSF) boosting rental and power income sources. Interconnection revenue also rose 25% as new and existing customers added 2226 new cross connections.

Strong revenue growth in 2015 drove CoreSite's net income up 52% to a record $34.71 million. The company's operating cash levels spiked 43% to $142.6 million for the year as its cash-based rental power and interconnection revenues increased.

Strategy
The properties in CoreSite's portfolio are strategically located in major metropolitan cities known for being high-tech hotbeds such as Boston Chicago Los Angeles New York City and the San Francisco Bay and Northern Virginia areas. Data centers especially outsourced ones (which are cheaper than in-house ones) are growing in these cities and others because they meet specific technology needs with specialized infrastructures that supply multiple network connectivity uninterruptible power backup generators cooling equipment fire suppression systems and physical security.

The company hopes to capitalize on demand that is outpacing supply for outsourced data centers in these markets. Supply of new data center facilities has been hampered in part by industry consolidation and lack of capital to develop additional space. CoreSite intends to market its existing portfolio — coupled with its development capabilities and the network interconnection services it offers — to attract more quality tenants.

Company Background
The company's first data center was purchased in 2000. Acquisitions of these properties throughout its history have been funded and held through real estate funds affiliated with global private equity firm The Carlyle Group.

CoreSite Realty Corp. started in 2001 as CRG West a portfolio company of The Carlyle Group. CoreSite Realty went public in September 2010 with an offering worth $270.4 million. CoreSite used the proceeds of its IPO to develop and redevelop additional data centers and to retire debt.

EXECUTIVES

President and CEO, Paul E. Szurek, age 58
CFO, Jeffrey S. (Jeff) Finnin, age 54, $382,308 total compensation

SVP Field Operations and Network Engineering, Dominic M. Tobin, age 64, $203,750 total compensation
SVP General Counsel and Secretary, Derek S. McCandless, age 47, $291,635 total compensation
SVP Engineering and Product, Brian P. Warren, age 48, $225,961 total compensation
SVP Sales and Marketing, Steven J. Smith, age 53, $310,961 total compensation
Vice President Controller, Mark Jones
Senior Management (Senior Vice President General Manager Director), Matt Gleason
Vice President Investor Relations and Corporate Communications, Greer Aviv
Vice President Sales Va, Juan Font
Vice President, Yvonne Deir
Senior Vice President Sales, Maile Kaiser
Vice President, Gerry Fassig
Vice President Of Sales Network And Mobility, Ben Green
Auditors: KPMG LLP

LOCATIONS

HQ: CoreSite Realty Corp
1001 17th Street, Suite 500, Denver, CO 80202
Phone: 866 777-2673
Web: www.coresite.com

PRODUCTS/OPERATIONS

2015 Sales

	$ mil.	% of total
Data Center:		
Rental	183.3	56
Power	89.4	27
Interconnection	44.2	13
Tenant reimbursement & other	8.3	2
Office light-industrial & other	8.0	2
Total	333.2	100

COMPETITORS

AT&T	Internap
CenturyLink	QTS Realty Trust Inc.
CyrusOne	SAVVIS
Digital Realty	Telx Group
DuPont Fabros	Terremark Worldwide
Equinix	Zayo Group

HISTORICAL FINANCIALS
Company Type: Public

Income Statement
FYE: December 31

	REVENUE ($ mil.)	NET INCOME ($ mil.)	NET PROFIT MARGIN	EMPLOYEES
12/17	481.8	74.8	15.5%	465
12/16	400.3	58.7	14.7%	422
12/15	333.2	34.7	10.4%	391
12/14	272.4	22.7	8.4%	354
12/13	234.8	18.8	8.0%	363
Annual Growth	19.7%	41.2%	—	6.4%

2017 Year-End Financials
Debt ratio: 61.3%
Return on equity: 20.8%
Cash ($ mil.): 5.2
Current ratio: 0.25
Long-term debt ($ mil.): 939.5

No. of shares (mil.): 34.2
Dividends
Yield: 0.0%
Payout: 194.5%
Market value ($ mil.): 3,900.0

Corporate Property Associates 18 Global Inc

	STOCK PRICE ($) FY Close	P/E High/Low	PER SHARE ($) Earnings	Dividends	Book Value
12/17	113.90	65 44	1.84	3.58	8.21
12/16	79.37	59 35	1.54	2.39	12.85
12/15	56.72	57 37	1.03	1.79	13.58
12/14	39.05	58 44	0.66	1.47	14.83
12/13	32.19	77 55	0.49	1.16	15.54
Annual Growth (14.8%)	37.2%	— —		39.2%	32.5%

Auditors: PricewaterhouseCoopers LLP

LOCATIONS

HQ: Corporate Property Associates 18 Global Inc
50 Rockefeller Plaza, New York, NY 10020
Phone: 212 492-1100
Web: www.cpa18global.com

HISTORICAL FINANCIALS
Company Type: Public

Income Statement — FYE: December 31

	REVENUE ($ mil.)	NET INCOME ($ mil.)	NET PROFIT MARGIN	EMPLOYEES
12/17	205.6	26.5	12.9%	0
12/16	184.3	(30.0)	—	0
12/15	135.9	(57.7)	—	0
12/14	54.3	(55.8)	—	0
12/13	3.2	(0.6)	—	0
Annual Growth	181.1%	—	—	—

2017 Year-End Financials

Debt ratio: 48.7%	No. of shares (mil.): 142.3
Return on equity: 3.3%	Dividends
Cash ($ mil.): 71.0	Yield: —
Current ratio: 0.27	Payout: 619.7%
Long-term debt ($ mil.): 1,136.1	Market value ($ mil.): —

CoStar Group, Inc.

CoStar has all the dirt on the commercial real estate industry. A provider of commercial real estate information CoStar has a proprietary database of some 4 million properties in the US the UK and France. The database contains information on more than 10 billion square feet of sale and lease listings. It also has more than 12 million digital images of buildings floor plans and maps. Its hundreds of data fields include location ownership and tenant names. CoStar additionally offers marketing and analytic services. Clients include government agencies real estate brokerages real estate invest-ment trusts (REITs) and property owners and managers. Most of CoStar's sales come from subscription fees.

Operations
The company employs a team of more than 1000 research professionals and contractors who collect and analyze commercial real estate information. Its subscription-based services consist primarily of CoStar Property Professional (comprehensive inventory) CoStar Tenant (tenant information) CoStar COMPS Professional (comparable sales information) FOCUS (data on UK market) and Propex (UK market info for professional investors). It does business in England through CoStar UK.

Geographic Reach
The company's sales teams are located in 30 field sales offices throughout the US and in offices located in London England; Manchester England; Glasgow Scotland and Paris France. Sales in the US accounted for about 95% of total revenues in fiscal 2012.

Sales and Marketing
The company draws its customers from commercial real estate and related business community. Commercial real estate brokers have traditionally formed the largest portion of CoStar clients. The company also provides services to owners landlords financial institutions retailers vendors appraisers investment banks governmental agencies and other parties involved in commercial real estate.

CoStar sells its products and services through a direct sales force located in field sales offices. Its E-commerce advertising expenses were approximately $3 million in fiscal 2012.

Financial Performance
CoStar's revenue has spiked nearly 40% in fiscal 2012 compared to the previous year. The company brought in almost $350 million in revenue during fiscal 2012 after reporting about $251.7 million in fiscal 2011 and $226.3 million back in fiscal 2010.

The increase in revenues during fiscal 2012 was primarily attributable to additional revenue from the acquisition of LoopNet the penetration of the subscription-based information services and successful cross-selling of the company's services to its customers in existing markets combined with continued high renewal rates.

Net income decreased in fiscal 2012 mainly due to the increase in income tax expense and the impact of costs related to the LoopNet acquisition that are not deductible for tax purposes.

Mergers and Acquisitions
In 2012 the company significantly expanded its holdings with the $860 million purchase of Loop-Net a complementary provider of online commercial real estate information. The deal doubled the size of CoStar's paid subscriber base to some 160000. The previous year CoStar enhanced its real estate brokerage offerings when it obtained Virtual Premise a provider of real estate management software and lease abstraction services. Each month Virtual Premise manages over $1 billion in rent payments for its customers.

EXECUTIVES

Vice President Research, Craig Farrington
President CEO and Director, Andrew C. Florance, age 54, $561,267 total compensation
CTO and SVP Information Technology Loopnet, Wayne B. Warthen, age 55
CIO, Frank Simuro, age 51
EVP, Brian J. Radecki, age 47, $357,031 total compensation
EVP Sales, Max Linnington
President LoopNet, Curtis M. Kroeker, age 47
EVP Operations, Francis (Frank) Carchedi, $287,273 total compensation
President Apartments.com, Brad Long
CEO Resolve Technology, Eric C. Forman, age 58
Managing Director CoStar UK Limited, Giles R. Newman
Managing Director PPR, Hans G. Nordby, age 51
President Virtual Premise, M. Andrew Thomas, age 55
CFO, Scott Wheeler
Vice President Major Accounts, Gerry Perrine
Vice President Finance, Scott Yinger
Vice President Investor Relations, Richard Simonelli
Senior Vice President Operations, Simon Law
Vice President Research, Dean Dean L Violagis Violagis
Vice President Software Development, Jason Butler
Regional Vice President Sales, Jeffrey Reesing
Regional Vice President West, Jamie Jump
Vice President, David Sambrook
Vice President Software Development, Jerry Rodgers
General Counsel and Secretary, Jonathan Coleman
Chairman, Michael R. Klein, age 76
Auditors: Ernst & Young LLP

LOCATIONS

HQ: CoStar Group, Inc.
1331 L Street, N.W., Washington, DC 20005
Phone: 202 346-6500   **Fax:** 877 739-0486
Web: www.costargroup.com

PRODUCTS/OPERATIONS

Selected Subscription Products
CoStar COMPS Professional (comparable sales information)
CoStar Property Professional (flagship real estate database)
CoStar Tenant (tenant information)
FOCUS (UK real estate information)

Selected Data
Building characteristics
Contact information
Demographic information
For-sale information
Historical trends
Income and expense histories
Lease expirations
Mortgage and deed information
Number of retail stores
Ownership
Retail sales per square foot
Sales and lease comparables
Site and zoning information
Space availability
Tax assessments
Tenant names

COMPETITORS

First American	Reed Business
Market Leader	Information
Move Inc.	Reis
PropertyInfo	Zillow

HISTORICAL FINANCIALS

Company Type: Public

Income Statement

FYE: December 31

	REVENUE ($ mil.)	NET INCOME ($ mil.)	NET PROFIT MARGIN	EMPLOYEES
12/17	965.2	122.7	12.7%	3,711
12/16	837.6	85.0	10.2%	3,064
12/15	711.7	(3.4)	—	2,631
12/14	575.9	44.8	7.8%	2,444
12/13	440.9	29.7	6.7%	2,046
Annual Growth	21.6%	42.5%	—	16.1%

2017 Year-End Financials

Debt ratio: —	No. of shares (mil.): 36.1
Return on equity: 5.7%	Dividends
Cash ($ mil.): 1,211.4	Yield: —
Current ratio: 8.78	Payout: —
Long-term debt ($ mil.): —	Market value ($ mil.): 10,722.0

	STOCK PRICE ($) FY Close	P/E High/Low	PER SHARE ($) Earnings	Dividends	Book Value
12/17	296.95	84 50	3.66	0.00	73.43
12/16	188.49	85 56	2.62	0.00	50.73
12/15	206.69	— —	(0.11)	0.00	47.49
12/14	183.63	145 93	1.46	0.00	46.83
12/13	184.58	174 83	1.05	0.00	32.16
Annual Growth	12.6%	— —	36.6%	—	22.9%

County Bancorp, Inc.

Auditors: Plante & Moran, PLLC

LOCATIONS

HQ: County Bancorp, Inc.
 2400 South 44th Street, Manitowoc, WI 54221
Phone: 920 686-9998
Web: www.investorscommunitybank.com

HISTORICAL FINANCIALS

Company Type: Public

Income Statement

FYE: December 31

	ASSETS ($ mil.)	NET INCOME ($ mil.)	INCOME AS % OF ASSETS	EMPLOYEES
12/17	1,397.0	10.4	0.7%	156
12/16	1,242.6	10.6	0.9%	150
12/15	884.8	10.9	1.2%	111
12/14	771.7	8.2	1.1%	103
12/13	757.8	7.0	0.9%	100
Annual Growth	16.5%	10.4%	—	11.8%

2017 Year-End Financials

Return on assets: 0.7%	Dividends
Return on equity: 7.6%	Yield: 0.0%
Long-term debt ($ mil.): —	Payout: 16.1%
No. of shares (mil.): 6.6	Market value ($ mil.): 199.0
Sales ($ mil): 60.7	

	STOCK PRICE ($) FY Close	P/E High/Low	PER SHARE ($) Earnings	Dividends	Book Value
12/17	29.76	23 15	1.49	0.24	21.13
12/16	26.97	16 11	1.61	0.20	19.93
12/15	19.50	13 9	1.82	0.16	21.14
Annual Growth	23.5%	— —	(9.5%)	22.5%	(0.0%)

Cousins Properties Inc

Cousins Properties only wants the best office properties in the Deep South. The real estate investment trust (REIT) buys develops and manages Class-A office properties mainly in high-growth markets in the Sunbelt region of the US. Its portfolio includes around 41 office properties with almost 20 million sq. ft. of space in Atlanta Austin Houston and Charlotte. While the REIT also owns a handful of retail centers and apartment complexes in Atlanta it's been winding those down to focus on prime office properties. Cousins Properties also provides property and construction management services and develops properties for third parties.

Operations

Cousins Properties' highest-grossing office rental properties include the Greenway Plaza (which made up 33% of its net operating income in 2015) and the Post Oak Central (12%) properties in Houston; and the Northpark Town Center property in Atlanta (10%).

Geographic Reach

The Atlanta-based REIT owns properties in its Atlanta; Austin Texas; Houston and Charlotte. About 40% of the company's net operating income came from its office properties in Houston during 2015 while another 39% came from its office properties in Atlanta. The rest came from its properties in Austin (8% of net operating income) and Charlotte (6%).

Sales and Marketing

Reflecting a broad tenant base the REIT's top 20 tenants made up 41% of its annualized base rental income during 2015 with no single tenant accounting for more than 8% of its rental income. More than 20% of its rental base comes from tenants in the energy sector.

Some of the REIT's tenants include the American Cancer Society and Fifth Third Bank. Past tenants have included Bank of America and Dimensional Fund Advisors.

Financial Performance

The REIT's annual revenues have more than tripled since 2011 as property acquisitions in new markets have spurred additional rental income. Its profits have also skyrocketed over the same period thanks to property sale gains and tight operating cost controls.

Cousins Properties' revenue climbed 6% to $381.6 million during 2015 mostly thanks to added rental income stemming from its newly-operational Colorado Tower property and its 2014 property acquisitions. Its same-property rental revenue increased by 0.2%.

Revenue growth in 2015 combined with higher property sale gains from its North Point Center East The Points at Waterview and 2100 Ross dispositions more than doubled the REIT's net income to $125.5 million. Cousins Properties' operating cash levels rose 7% to $151.6 million for the year thanks to a rise in cash-based earnings.

Strategy

Cousins Properties acquires develops and manages Class-A office properties in high-growth Sunbelt markets though it also may buy mixed-use commercial buildings if the right opportunity arises. To diversify its revenue streams it continues to to acquire properties outside of Atlanta moving into the Houston and Austin markets in Texas and also into Charlotte North Carolina in recent years.

Some of its more recent acquisitions include the proposed $1.95 billion acquisition of Parkway Properties and its 41 properties in the Southeast in 2016; the $27 million-purchase of 4.2 acres of land in Atlanta to build NCR's corporate headquarters in 2015 and the the $348 million-acquisition of the 1.5 million sq. ft. Northpark Town Center in Atlanta in 2014; and the 2014 purchase of the almost 700000 sq. ft. Fifth Third Center in Charlotte for $215 million.

Mergers and Acquisitions

In October 2016 Cousins Properties acquired Orlando-based Parkway Properties for $1.95 billion in stock. The deal expanded Cousins' presence to 41 properties in the Southeast.

The combined group immediately spun off its Houston-based assets creating a new public REIT named Parkway.

Company Background

Cousins Properties experienced challenges from the depressed economy and the downturn in the real estate markets following the financial crisis. The REIT responded by restructuring reducing headcount selling non-core assets and curtailing new development projects. It sold all of its industrial properties to focus on Class-A office properties. It also continues to wind down its multifamily residential portfolio.

Institutional investors own about a third of Cousins Properties' stock. Morgan Stanley holds the largest stake at more than 11% followed by BlackRock Inc. and The Vanguard Group. Chairman Emeritus Thomas G. Cousins owns about 11% of the firm's shares.

EXECUTIVES

Senior Vice President and Director of Leasing, Darryl Bonner
EVP and CFO, Gregg D. Adzema, age 53, $390,000 total compensation
Chairman and CEO The Cousins Foundation Inc., Lillian C. Giornelli, age 57
EVP, John S. McColl, age 56, $341,453 total compensation
Chairman and CEO, Lawrence L. Gellerstedt, age 62, $600,000 total compensation
SVP, J. Thad Ellis, $294,175 total compensation
President and COO, M. Colin Connolly, age 42, $250,000 total compensation
Vice President Human Resources, Marva Lewis
Senior Vice President, Thad Ellis
Vice President, Chip Andrews
Vice President Internal Audit, Timothy A O'Connell
Vice President Treasurer, Mary Caneer
Executive Vice President And Director Of Development Retail Division, William Bassett
Senior Vice President Leasing, Bill Hollett
Vice President SEC Reporting, Patricia Grimes
Vice President Financial Reporting, Matt Ams
Auditors: DELOITTE & TOUCHE LLP

LOCATIONS

HQ: Cousins Properties Inc
 3344 Peachtree Road NE, Suite 1800, Atlanta, GA 30326-4802
Phone: 404 407-1000
Web: www.cousinsproperties.com

PRODUCTS/OPERATIONS

2011 Sales

	$ mil.	% of total
Rental property	135.6	76
Third-party management & leasing	19.4	11
Fee income	13.8	8
Multifamily residential unit sales	4.7	3
Residential & outparcel	3.0	2
Other	2.0	-
Total	**178.5**	**100**

COMPETITORS

American Realty Investors	Highwoods Properties
Chelsea Property	Macerich
DDR	Poag & McEwen
Duke Realty	Lifestyle Centers
Equity Office	Simon Property Group
GGP	Trammell Crow Residential

HISTORICAL FINANCIALS

Company Type: Public

Income Statement   FYE: December 31

	REVENUE ($ mil.)	NET INCOME ($ mil.)	NET PROFIT MARGIN	EMPLOYEES
12/17	466.1	216.2	46.4%	261
12/16	259.2	79.1	30.5%	279
12/15	381.6	125.5	32.9%	257
12/14	361.3	52.0	14.4%	257
12/13	210.7	121.7	57.8%	237
Annual Growth	**22.0%**	**15.4%**	**—**	**2.4%**

2017 Year-End Financials

Debt ratio: 26.0%	No. of shares (mil.): 420.0
Return on equity: 8.2%	Dividends
Cash ($ mil.): 148.9	Yield: 0.0%
Current ratio: 1.59	Payout: 57.6%
Long-term debt ($ mil.): 1,093.2	Market value ($ mil.): 3,885.0

	STOCK PRICE ($) FY Close	P/E High/Low		PER SHARE ($) Earnings	Dividends	Book Value
12/17	9.25	18	15	0.52	0.30	6.60
12/16	8.51	37	23	0.31	0.24	6.24
12/15	9.43	20	15	0.58	0.32	7.96
12/14	11.42	60	46	0.22	0.30	7.73
12/13	10.30	15	11	0.76	0.18	7.68
Annual Growth	**(2.7%)**	**—**	**—**	**(9.1%)**	**13.6%**	**(3.7%)**

Credit Acceptance Corp (MI)

In the world of Credit Acceptance Corporation (CAC) to purchase a car is not an impossible dream for problem borrowers. CAC makes the effort a reality. Working with more than 55000 independent and franchised automobile dealers in the US CAC provides capital for auto loans to people with substandard credit. The company also provides other services to dealers including payment servicing receivables management marketing and service contracts. CAC which concentrates its operations in a handful of US states typically funds about 1.5 million auto loans per year.

Operations

CAC steps in to help finance auto purchases for those whose credit histories aren't ideal. Auto dealers in turn benefit from the vehicle sales and from repeat and referral sales generated by these customers.

Geographic Reach

Michigan-based CAC serves consumers nationwide. Its largest markets include New York Texas Ohio and Pennsylvania.

Sales and Marketing

CAC caters to and partners with some 56000 independent and franchised automobile dealers throughout the US.

Financial Performance

The company's revenue has been growing for several years. In fiscal 2013 CAC posted 12% increases in revenue to $682.1 million as compared to 2012's $609.2 million. CAC points to a 10% boost in finance charges due to an increase in the average net loans receivable balance for the 2013 gains. These were offset however by a drop in the average yield on loan portfolio. Thanks to a new profit-sharing arrangement CAC entered in 2012 with third party providers (TPPs) other income jumped some 68% during the reporting period. Helping other income was an increase in GPS-SID fee income due to rising fee earned per unit purchased primarily resulting from new the new profit-sharing agreement. CAC's net income has been on the same trajectory. In 2013 net income rose some 15% to $253.1 million vs. 2012's $219.7 million bolstered by the company's higher revenue offset in part by an increased provision for income tax. Cash flow from operations also rose in 2013 — from $308.6 million in 2012 to $325.7 million in 2013 — attributable to higher net income a decrease in the provision for credit losses and a change in working capital.

Strategy

The company funds loans in two ways. It advances money to its dealer-partners in exchange for the servicing rights to the underlying loan or it purchases loans directly from dealers. CAC earns most of its revenues from finance charges servicing fees and monthly program fees it charges its dealer partners. Indeed finance charges in 2013 accounted for 87% of revenue.

HISTORY

Donald Foss was a used-car dealer in Detroit where to make sales he sometimes financed cars out of his own pocket. As Foss' chain of dealerships grew so did his financing business. In 1972 he established it as a separate company and 20 years later took it public.

For most of its history CAC stood alone in the field of subprime auto lending but stagnating salaries made it a competitive growth business in the early 1990s. At mid-decade the company entered Canada and the UK to tap similar markets there. In 1996 CAC acquired Montana Investment Group a credit reporting service.

Even as rising consumer debt and bad credit continued to pump buyers into CAC's loan pipeline the economic boom of the mid-1990s paradoxically made used cars less desirable. The soft used-car market squeezed several of CAC's competitors out of business; a staggering default rate — nearing 40% — also pressured CAC whose auditors insisted it increase reserves to cover losses. The subsequent earnings dive spurred a shareholder lawsuit accusing CAC of hiding its poor fiscal health. Although bad loans had damaged its bottom line the company adopted more stringent lending policies to reduce risk. Consumers filed class-action suits alleging unethical practices in 1998 but many claims were dismissed.

To pay off debt acquired through bad loans CAC sold Montana Investment Group in 1999. In 2000 it launched CAC Leasing to further offset losses from a decrease in subprime lending but in 2002 the company exited that line deciding the lending field was more profitable. CAC stopped originating new loans in the UK and Canada in 2003.

In 2005 the SEC investigated CAC's accounting methods specifically related to its loan portfolio and the company restated portions of its past financial results.

The company found itself in hot water again in 2008 when it agreed to pay some 15000 Missouri customers to settle a class action lawsuit. The lawsuit filed more than a decade prior alleged that CAC overcharged customers for fees and interest on their loans. As part of the settlement CAC said it would write off $39 million in outstanding accounts and distribute another $13 million to customers.

EXECUTIVES

Senior Vice President, Douglas Busk

CEO, Brett A. Roberts, age 51, $1,025,000 total compensation

President, Steven M. Jones, age 54, $625,000 total compensation

CFO, Kenneth S. Booth, age 50, $414,792 total compensation

CIO, John S. Soave, age 53

Vice President Of Sales, Jeffrey Brock

Senior Vice President Accounting And Financial Reporting, Jay Martin

Vice President Business Information Services, Noah Kotch

Vice President, Wayne Mancini

Chairman, Donald A. Foss, age 73

Auditors: GRANT THORNTON LLP

LOCATIONS

HQ: Credit Acceptance Corp (MI)
25505 West Twelve Mile Road, Southfield, MI 48034-8339
Phone: 248 353-2700

PRODUCTS/OPERATIONS

2016 Sales

	$ mil.	% of total
Finance charges	874.3	90
Premiums earned	43.0	5
Other	51.9	5
Total	**969.2**	**100**

Selected Subsidiaries

Buyers Vehicle Protection Plan Inc.
CAC Leasing Inc.
CAC Reinsurance Ltd.
CAC Warehouse Funding Corp. II III IV
Credit Acceptance Wholesale Buyers Club Inc.
Vehicle Remarketing Services Inc.
VSC Re Company

COMPETITORS

Ally Financial
American Honda Finance
Bank of America
Capital One Auto Finance

First Investors Financial Services
Ford Motor Credit
GM Financial
Mercedes-Benz Credit
Mercedes-Benz Financial Services USA
Toyota Motor Credit
Volkswagen Financial Services
Volvo Car Finance

HISTORICAL FINANCIALS
Company Type: Public

Income Statement   FYE: December 31

	REVENUE ($ mil.)	NET INCOME ($ mil.)	NET PROFIT MARGIN	EMPLOYEES
12/17	1,110.0	470.2	42.4%	1,817
12/16	969.2	332.8	34.3%	1,609
12/15	825.3	299.7	36.3%	1,425
12/14	723.5	266.2	36.8%	1,303
12/13	682.1	253.1	37.1%	1,317
Annual Growth	12.9%	16.7%	—	8.4%

2017 Year-End Financials

Debt ratio: 61.5%
Return on equity: 34.7%
Cash ($ mil.): 8.2
Current ratio: 1.63
Long-term debt ($ mil.): 3,070.8

No. of shares (mil.): 19.3
Dividends
  Yield: —
  Payout: —
Market value ($ mil.): 6,246.0

	STOCK PRICE ($) FY Close	P/E High/Low		PER SHARE ($) Earnings	Dividends	Book Value
12/17	323.48	14	8	24.04	0.00	79.53
12/16	217.51	13	10	16.31	0.00	59.05
12/15	214.02	19	9	14.28	0.00	46.10
12/14	136.41	14	9	11.92	0.00	34.09
12/13	129.99	12	9	10.54	0.00	32.69
Annual Growth	25.6%	—	—	22.9%	—	24.9%

Croghan Bancshares, Inc.

Croghan Bancshares is helping to share the wealth in the Buckeye state. The firm is the holding company for Croghan Colonial Bank which has about 10 branches in northern Ohio. Founded in 1888 the bank provides standard products and services including checking and savings accounts money market accounts certificates of deposit and credit cards Its lending activities primarily consist of residential and commercial mortgages and to a lesser extent agricultural business construction and consumer loans. In addition the bank offers wealth management investments estate planning private banking and trust services.

EXECUTIVES

Secretary; VP and Trust Officer Croghan Colonial Bank, Barry F. Luse, age 63, $99,600 total compensation
VP and Chief Lending Officer Croghan Colonial Bank, Thomas J. Elder, age 68, $110,000 total compensation

Treasurer; VP CFO and COO Croghan Colonial Bank, Kendall W. Rieman, age 45, $119,000 total compensation
President and CEO, Rick M. Robertson, age 63
Investor Relations, Amy LeJeune
Senior Vice President; Chief Operations Officer of the Bank, Stacy Cox
Auditors: Plante & Moran, PLLC

LOCATIONS

HQ: Croghan Bancshares, Inc.
  323 Croghan Street, Fremont, OH 43420
Phone: 419 332-7301
Web: www.croghan.com

COMPETITORS

Commercial Bancshares	KeyCorp
Fifth Third	United Community
First Citizens Banc	Financial
Corp	

HISTORICAL FINANCIALS
Company Type: Public

Income Statement   FYE: December 31

	ASSETS ($ mil.)	NET INCOME ($ mil.)	INCOME AS % OF ASSETS	EMPLOYEES
12/17	843.0	10.2	1.2%	205
12/16	819.5	9.0	1.1%	208
12/15	797.4	8.4	1.1%	205
12/14	779.4	8.6	1.1%	203
12/13	817.8	4.4	0.5%	209
Annual Growth	0.8%	23.2%	—	(0.5%)

2017 Year-End Financials

Return on assets: 1.2%
Return on equity: 9.7%
Long-term debt ($ mil.): —
No. of shares (mil.): 2.2
Sales ($ mil): 39.3

Dividends
  Yield: 0.0%
  Payout: 32.5%
Market value ($ mil.): 115.0

	STOCK PRICE ($) FY Close	P/E High/Low		PER SHARE ($) Earnings	Dividends	Book Value
12/17	50.30	12	10	4.48	1.46	47.64
12/16	45.95	12	9	3.98	1.41	44.61
12/15	35.50	10	9	3.67	1.36	43.22
12/14	35.18	9	9	3.78	1.29	41.01
12/13	34.25	14	12	2.57	1.28	37.45
Annual Growth	10.1%	—	—	14.9%	3.3%	6.2%

Cross Country Healthcare Inc

Cross Country Healthcare is one of the largest health care staffing firms in the US. Under several brands the company places traveling nurses and other health care professionals through about 9500 contracts with acute care hospitals pharmaceutical companies nursing homes schools and other related facilities across the nation. The firm coordinates travel and housing arrangements for its nurses whose assignments usually last about three months at a time. Cross Country also pro-

vides health care education training and recruiting services for doctors and health care executives. Subsidiaries and brands include Assignment America Allied Health Group NovaPro Med-Staff TravCorps and Cejka Search.
Operations
The company operates through three reportable segments: nurse and allied staffing (81% of net sales) physician staffing (15%) and other human capital management services (4%).
Geographic Reach
The company's nurse staffing services business segment is headquartered in Boca Raton Florida. Its travel staffing business has operation centers in Florida Georgia Massachusetts and Pennsylvania. Its Cross Country Education (CCE) subsidiary is headquartered in Brentwood Tennessee while its Cejka Search subsidiary is headquartered in Creve Coeur Missouri.
Sales and Marketing
Cross Country markets is services through direct mail marketing online advertising print media and promotional material. It spends about $5 million each year on advertising.
Financial Performance
Cross Country has achieved unprecedented growth the last few years with revenues jumping 24% to peak at a record-setting $767 million in 2015. After posting three straight years of net losses the company also posted $4 million in positive net income in 2015.

The historic growth for 2015 was driven by a 35% bump in nurse and allied staffing segment sales. This was attributed to both organic growth and additional revenue from acquisitions.
Strategy
Cross Country is counting on its diverse portfolio of services and its strong relationships with hospitals all over the country to sustain itself until the conditions of the broader labor market improve.

To focus on its core markets and to streamline its operations in 2013 Cross Country sold its former clinical trial services division to contract research firm ICON for some $52 million.
Mergers and Acquisitions
Cross Country plans to grow by focusing on making strategic acquisitions in high growth high margin businesses and by seeking additional MSP contracts and EMR engagements with hospitals and health systems.

The company in 2015 purchased Mediscan for a purchase price of almost $30 million in cash. Mediscan provides temporary healthcare staffing and workforce services to both the health care and education markets especially public and charter schools. While largely concentrated in California Mediscan provides services across 11 states to more than 300 clients through more than 70 specialties. The deal gave Cross Country a new customer base in the health care staffing market for public and charter schools.

In 2014 the company acquired Medical Staffing Network a comprehensive healthcare staffing company with 55 locations throughout the US that provides per diem local contract travel and permanent hire staffing services. Cross Country paid $48 million on the deal which increased its branch network and market share and diversified its customer base and brings them new service lines.

EXECUTIVES

CIO, William G. (Bill) Halnon, age 60
President and CEO, William J. Grubbs, age 61, $625,000 total compensation
CFO, William J. Burns, age 49, $400,000 total compensation
SVP Sales and Marketing, Deborah Dean, age 58, $125,000 total compensation
President Cross Country Staffing, Vickie L. Anenberg, age 54, $357,500 total compensation
President Cejka Search, John Gramer
President MDA Holdings Inc., Timothy Fischer, age 52
President Mediscan Staffing Services, Dennis Ducham, age 59
REGIONAL VICE PRESIDENT, Erik Dokken
Vice President Nursing, Wendi Dusseault
Vice President of Finance Corporate Controller and Treasurer, Christopher Pizzi
Vice President Allied, Lydia Fort
Vice President Procurement, Jerry Chico
Regional Vice President Strategic Partnerships, Deena Harpham
Vice President Sales, Darren Montgomery
Vice President Consulting, Kerry Torres
SENIOR VICE PRESIDENT, Rishabh Parmar
Senior Vice President Recruiting Strategy Operations, BUFFY WHITE
Regional Vice President Strategic Accounts Cross Country Healthcare, Jeannine Kelley
Chairman, Thomas C. Dircks, age 61
Board Member, Gale Fitzgerald
Auditors: DELOITTE & TOUCHE LLP

LOCATIONS

HQ: Cross Country Healthcare Inc
5201 Congress Avenue, Suite 100B, Boca Raton, FL 33487
Phone: 561 998-2232
Web: www.crosscountryhealthcare.com

PRODUCTS/OPERATIONS

Brands
Cross Country Staffing
Medical Staffing Network
Allied Health Group
Mediscan
DirectEd
Business Model
Marketing and Recruiting Healthcare Professionals
Sales and Marketing to Hospitals and Healthcare Facilities
Credentialing and Quality Management
Client Billing

OPERATIONS

2015 Sales

	$ mil.	% of total
Nurse & allied staffing	621.3	81
Physician staffing	115.3	15
Other human capital management services	30.8	4
Total	**767.4**	**100**

Selected Subsidiaries

Education and training
  Cross Country Education
Search and recruitment
  Cejka
Nurse Staffing
  Cross Country Staffing
  MedStaff
Nurse Recruiting
  Assignment America
  Cross Country Local
  Cross Country TravCorps
  MedStaff

NovaPro
Physician staffing
  MDA Holdings (MDA)

COMPETITORS

AMN Healthcare
ATC Healthcare
Adecco
CHG Healthcare
Gentiva
Jackson Healthcare
Kelly Services
Kforce
ManpowerGroup
On Assignment
RehabCare
TeamStaff
inVentiv Health

HISTORICAL FINANCIALS

Company Type: Public

Income Statement — FYE: December 31

	REVENUE ($ mil.)	NET INCOME ($ mil.)	NET PROFIT MARGIN	EMPLOYEES
12/17	865.0	37.5	4.3%	1,800
12/16	833.5	7.9	1.0%	1,737
12/15	767.4	4.4	0.6%	1,585
12/14	617.8	(31.7)	—	1,630
12/13	438.3	(51.9)	—	1,100
Annual Growth	**18.5%**	**—**	**—**	**13.1%**

2017 Year-End Financials

Debt ratio: 21.2%	No. of shares (mil.): 35.8
Return on equity: 19.3%	Dividends
Cash ($ mil.): 25.5	Yield: —
Current ratio: 2.21	Payout: —
Long-term debt ($ mil.): 92.2	Market value ($ mil.): 457.0

	STOCK PRICE ($) FY Close	P/E High/Low	PER SHARE ($) Earnings	Dividends	Book Value
12/17	12.76	15 11	1.01	0.00	6.62
12/16	15.61	66 43	0.15	0.00	4.68
12/15	16.39	130 72	0.14	0.00	4.41
12/14	12.48	— —	(1.02)	0.00	4.15
12/13	9.98	— —	(1.68)	0.00	5.17
Annual Growth	**6.3%**	**— —**	**—**	**—**	**6.4%**

CubeSmart

CubeSmart (formerly U-Store-It Trust) is a real estate investment trust (REIT) that owns more than 420 self-storage facilities with nearly 30 million sq. ft. of rentable space in about 25 states and Washington DC. The company also manages manages more than 100 self-storage facilities for third parties. Amenities at its properties include security systems and wider aisles for larger vehicles as well as climate-controlled units and outdoor storage for vehicles and boats at selected sites. The REIT also sells storage-related items such as packing supplies and locks to tenants who typically rent units on a month-to-month basis.

Operations

Operating through partnership CubeSmart L.P the company generates just under 90% of its revenue from rental income from leasing out its storage units. About 10% of revenue comes from other property-related income including administrative charges late fees tenant insurance commissions and sales of storage supplies. The rest of CubeSmart's revenue comes from property man-

agement fee income (primarily from its third-party management business).

Geographic Reach

CubeSmart owns or manages facilities in more than 20 states across the US with facilities in New York Florida Texas and California producing over 50% of total revenues. Another 15% of the company's revenue comes from New Jersey Illinois and Connecticut. Cubesmart also owns or manages facilities in Puerto Rico.

Sales and Marketing

The company spent $7.7 million on advertising and marketing in 2014 compared to $7.6 million and $8.1 million in 2013 and 2012 respectively.

Financial Performance

CubeSmart's revenues and profits have trended sharply higher over the past several years as the REIT has enjoyed more rental income from acquisitions and rental rate increases buoyed by the strengthened US economy.

The REIT's revenue jumped by 18% to $377 million in 2014 mostly thanks to higher rental income from 2014 and 2013 property acquisitions but also thanks to higher net rental rates and higher average occupancy rates on existing properties. CubeSmart's property management fee income also rose by 26% for the year as its third-party management business grew which further helped the REIT's top line.

Despite higher revenue in 2014 CubeSmart's net income dove 36% to $26.4 million mostly as the REIT made $27.4 million in property sale gains in 2013 compared to no comparable gains during 2014. CubeSmart's operating cash levels grew by 16% to $166 million however mostly as it generated more cash income from new property acquisitions.

Strategy

CubeSmart's strategy is to grow through acquisitions mainly in high-growth areas such as the Northeastern and Middle Atlantic regions in the US along with Georgia Florida Texas Illinois and California. The company hopes to gradually increase rental income by selectively acquiring properties in markets with high barriers to entry strong demographic fundamentals and high demand. In addition more locations offer higher economies of scale and greater operating efficiencies for higher operating margins.

Indeed from 2011 through late 2014 management had announced more than 100 facility acquisitions totaling roughly $1.3 billion. During 2014 alone CubeSmart acquired 53 self-storage facilities for a total price of $568.2 million including a $223 million purchase of 26 facilities across six states from Harrison Street Real Estate Capital in late 2014.

The company also plans to continue selling facilities in slower growing low barrier-to-entry locations and using proceeds to purchase new facilities in target markets. In 2013 for example it sold 35 locations mostly in California Indiana Tennessee and Texas for approximately $126.4 million. In 2012 it sold 26 locations (including 14 from New Mexico and Ohio) for $60 million.

Besides expansion CubeSmart plans to maximize rental revenues from existing facilities by raising rent increasing occupancy levels (which are around 90% up from 80% in 2011) controlling operating expenses and expanding and enhancing the facilities themselves. As a final step for growth CubeSmart will utilize relationships with third-party owners to help source future acquisitions and expand through these existing relationships.

Company Background

As part of a rebranding initiative CubeSmart changed its name from U-Store-It in 2011.

EXECUTIVES

CEO, Christopher P. (Chris) Marr, age 53, $600,000 total compensation

CFO, Timothy M. (Tim) Martin, age 47, $390,000 total compensation

SVP and CIO, Ajai Nair

SVP and Chief Investment Officer, Jonathan Perry

Chairman, William M. Diefenderfer, age 73

Auditors: KPMG LLP

LOCATIONS

HQ: CubeSmart
5 Old Lancaster Road, Malvern, PA 19355
Phone: 610 535-5000
Web: www.cubesmart.com

PRODUCTS/OPERATIONS

2015 Sales

	$ mil.	% of total
Rental income	392.4	88
Property management fees	7.0	10
Other property-related income	45.1	2
Total	**444.5**	**100**

COMPETITORS

AMERCO	Mobile Mini
Extra Space	PODS Enterprises
Life Storage	Public Storage

HISTORICAL FINANCIALS

Company Type: Public

Income Statement

FYE: December 31

	REVENUE ($ mil.)	NET INCOME ($ mil.)	NET PROFIT MARGIN	EMPLOYEES
12/17	558.9	134.2	24.0%	2,508
12/16	510.0	87.9	17.2%	2,136
12/15	444.5	77.7	17.5%	1,837
12/14	376.9	26.3	7.0%	1,640
12/13	318.4	41.4	13.0%	1,442
Annual Growth	15.1%	34.2%	—	14.8%

2017 Year-End Financials

Debt ratio: 46.1%	No. of shares (mil.): 182.2
Return on equity: 8.1%	Dividends
Cash ($ mil.): 5.2	Yield: 0.0%
Current ratio: 0.19	Payout: 150.0%
Long-term debt ($ mil.): 1,634.9	Market value ($ mil.): 5,270.0

	STOCK PRICE ($) FY Close	P/E High/Low		PER SHARE ($) Earnings	Dividends	Book Value
12/17	28.92	40	31	0.74	1.11	8.94
12/16	26.77	74	53	0.45	0.90	9.19
12/15	30.62	73	51	0.42	0.69	9.41
12/14	22.07	164	112	0.14	0.55	8.83
12/13	15.94	75	55	0.26	0.46	7.84
Annual Growth	16.1%	—	—	29.9%	24.6%	3.3%

Customers Bancorp Inc

Customers Bancorp makes it pretty clear who they want to serve. Boasting some $8.5 billion in assets the bank holding company operates about 15 branches mostly in southeastern Pennsylvania but also in New York and New Jersey. It offers personal and business checking savings and money market accounts as well as loans certificates of deposit credit cards and concierge or appointment banking (they come to you seven days a week). Around 95% of the bank's loan portfolio is made up of commercial loans while the rest consists of consumer loans. It was formed in 2010 as a holding company for Customers Bank which was created in 1994 as New Century Bank.

Operations

Customers Bancorp operates two main business lines: Commercial Lending and Consumer Lending. Its Commercial Lending business provides commercial and industrial loans small and middle-market business banking and small business administration (SBA) loans multi-family and commercial real estate loans and commercial loans to mortgage originators. Its Consumer Lending division mostly makes local market mortgage loans and home equity loans. More than 95% of the bank's loan portfolio was made up of commercial loans at the end of 2015 while the rest consisted of consumer loans.

Broadly speaking the bank makes roughly 90% of its revenue from interest income. About 66% of its revenue came from loan interest during 2015 while another 19% came from interest loans held for sale and 4% came from interest on investment securities. The remainder of its revenue came from mortgage warehouse transactional fees (4%) and other miscellaneous and non-recurring sources.

Geographic Reach

The bank had 14 branches at the end of 2015 including nine in Philadelphia and Southeastern Pennsylvania; four in Berks County Pennsylvania; one in Westchester County New York; and one in Mercer County New Jersey. It also had a handful of additional offices in Boston; New York City; Portsmouth New Hampshire; Providence Rhode Island; and Suffolk County New York.

Sales and Marketing

Customers Bancorp's customers include private businesses business customers non-profits and consumers. Its commercial lending division typically makes loans to companies with revenues between $1 million to $50 million needing between $0.5 million to $10 million in credit.

The bank has been ramping up its advertising spend in recent years. It spent $1.48 million on advertising in 2015 up from $1.33 million and $1.27 million in 2014 and 2013 respectively.

Financial Performance

The bank's annual revenues have nearly quadrupled since 2011 as its loan assets have more than tripled (its loan assets reached $5.45 billion by of the end of 2015). Meanwhile growing revenues strong cost controls and low interest rates have pushed the bank's annual profits up almost 15-fold over the same period.

Customers Bancorp's revenue jumped 29% to $277.5 million during 2015 mostly as its average balance of interest-earning loan and securities assets rose by 31% to $6.7 billion for the year.

Revenue growth in 2015 drove the bank's net income up 36% to $58.5 million. Customer Bancorp's operating cash levels declined sharply to $356.6 million for the year as the bank originated more loans held for sale than it actually sold.

Strategy

With its eye on becoming the leading regional bank holding company Customers Bancorp continued in 2016 to focus on expanding its market share with its high-touch personalized Concierge Banking services and its "high-tech" BankMobile offerings which include remote account opening remote deposit capture and mobile banking. The BankMobile and online banking channels allow Customers Bancorp to slow expensive branch-expansion plans and cut operating costs significantly while giving customers faster access to banking services.

But even with digital banking the bank occasionally opens new branches (and selectively acquire others) to grow its loan and deposit business. In January 2016 it opened and replaced an existing branch in Hamilton New Jersey onto Route 33 in the same city. In June 2015 Customers opened a new Long Island location in Mellville New York to expand its private and commercial banking services to local clients there.

Mergers and Acquisitions

In December 2015 Customers Bank expanded its deposit business and added 2 million new student customers after buying the One Account Student Checking and Refund Management Disbursement Services business from higher education refund disbursement provider Higher One Inc for $42 million.

Company Background

In late 2011 Customers purchased Berkshire Bancorp and picked up five branches in Berks County Pennsylvania for about $11.3 million.

EXECUTIVES

Chairman and CEO, Jay S. Sidhu, age 66, $300,000 total compensation

President and COO, Richard A. Ehst, age 72, $225,000 total compensation

Executive Vice President President of Community Banking, Warren Taylor, age 60, $190,000 total compensation

EVP and Chief Credit Officer, Thomas Jastrem

EVP and Chief Administrative Officer, Jim Collins

EVP and Chief Lending Officer, Timothy D. Romig

EVP and President Special Assets Group, Robert A. White

EVP and and Director Enterprise Risk Management, James D. Hogan

EVP and Director Multi-Family and Investment CRE Lending, Kenneth A. Keiser

Executive Vice President And Chief Financial Officer, Robert Wahlman

Vice President Assistant Loan Administration Manager and Loan Operations Manager, Michael McCarrie

VICE PRESIDENT, John Gerhart

ASSISTANT VICE PRESIDENT AND APPRAISAL REVIEW OFFICER, Richard Nagy

Senior Vice President Berks County Commercial Banking Group, Mary Moffitt

Vp Assistant Bsa Officer, Melissa Krueger

Senior Vice President. Credit Officer, Barbara Bergman

SENIOR VICE PRESIDENT, William Hirst

Vice President Collections Manager, Robert Deyoung

Executive Vice President Market Chief Lending
  Officer, George Maroulis
Vice President of Operations, Richard Kirk
Vice President Government Guaranteed Lending,
  Lisa Kennedy
Vice President Government Guaranteed Lending,
  Michele Vervlied
Assistant Vice President Capital Markets, Dana
  Galvin
Assistant Vice President And Assistant Branch
  Manager, Lisa Gearheart
Assistant Vice President Sox Internal Control
  Manager, Frank Bommentre
Senior Vice President, Kevin Cornwall
Assistant Vice President, Terry Meehan
ASSISTANT VICE PRESIDENT AND CREDIT
  ANALYST, Angela Edwards
Assistant Vice President Client Relations,
  Benjamin Harris
Senior Vice President NE Director of Pla, Paula
  Pais
Senior Vice President, Michael Solomon
Senior Vice President Philadelphia Market Leader,
  Varsovia Fernandez
Vice President And Government Guaranteed
  Lender, Stephanie Schwandt
Senior Vice President Commercial Finance
  Group, Sam Smith
Vice President SBA Loan Specialist, Stacey
  Kuzniasz
Vice President, Laura Simon
Vice President, Elizabeth Le
Senior Vice President Regional Chief Lending
  Officer, Robert Fischer
SENIOR VICE PRESIDENT AND LOAN REVIEW
  DIRECTOR, David Dowd
Vice President Commercial Lending Philadelphia
  Market, Edwin Roman
ASSISTANT VICE PRESIDENT MEMBER
  SERVICES AND TALENT ACQUISITION, Amy
  Shaughnessy
Business Development Officer Vice President,
  Sunita Raina
Senior Vice President, Veder Reddick
Senior Vice President And Director Of Corporate
  Planning, Tammy Sibalic
VICE PRESIDENT COMMERCIAL LENDING,
  Brett V Long
VICE PRESIDENT AND CREDIT OFFICER, Gary
  Arnold
SENIOR VICE PRESIDENT DIRECTOR OF
  OPERATIONS DEPOSIT ADMINISTRATION,
  Robert J Diegel
Vice President Special Assets Financial
  Reporting, Doan Dang
Assistant Vice President And Lead Information
  Technology Auditor, Patrick Direnzo
Vice President, S Gates
ASSISTANT VICE PRESIDENT, John Chung
Vice President, Diane Billman
Vice President, Keith Munley
VICE PRESIDENT CONSUMER LENDING
  COMPLIANCE, Matt Kachurka
VICE PRESIDENT MANAGER OF NETWORK
  ADMINISTRATION, Joseph Thren
VICE PRESIDENT AND SENIOR ANALYST,
  Joann Zerbo
SENIOR VICE PRESIDENT OF WAREHOUSE
  LENDING, Kenneth Blume
Auditors: BDO USA, LLP

LOCATIONS

HQ: Customers Bancorp Inc
  1015 Penn Avenue, Suite 103, Wyomissing, PA 19610
Phone: 610 933-2000
Web: www.customersbank.com

PRODUCTS/OPERATIONS

2015

	% of total
Interest income	
Loans receivable including fees	66
Loans held for sale	19
Investment securities	4
Other	2
Non interest income	
Mortgage warehouse transnational fees	4
Bank-owned life insurance	3
Gains on sales of loans	1
Deposit fees	0
Mortgage loan and banking income	0
Gain (loss) on sale of investment securities)	0
Other	1
Total	**100**

Products include
Equipment Loans
Mortgage Warehouse Loans
Multi-Family And Commercial Real Estate Loans
Residential Mortgage Loans
Small Business Loans

COMPETITORS

Bank of America	Huntington Bancshares
Capital One	JPMorgan Chase
Citigroup	KeyCorp
Comerica	PNC Financial
Fifth Third	U.S. Bancorp
HSBC	Wells Fargo

HISTORICAL FINANCIALS

Company Type: Public

Income Statement   FYE: December 31

	ASSETS ($ mil.)	NET INCOME ($ mil.)	INCOME AS % OF ASSETS	EMPLOYEES
12/17	9,839.5	78.8	0.8%	765
12/16	9,382.7	78.7	0.8%	739
12/15	8,401.3	58.5	0.7%	517
12/14	6,825.3	43.2	0.6%	426
12/13	4,153.1	32.6	0.8%	388
Annual Growth	24.1%	24.6%	—	18.5%

2017 Year-End Financials

Return on assets: 0.8%	Dividends
Return on equity: 8.8%	Yield: —
Long-term debt ($ mil.): —	Payout: —
No. of shares (mil.): 31.3	Market value ($ mil.): 816.0
Sales ($ mil): 451.7	

	STOCK PRICE ($) FY Close	P/E High/Low	PER SHARE ($) Earnings	Dividends	Book Value
12/17	25.99	17 12	1.97	0.00	29.35
12/16	35.82	15 9	2.31	0.00	28.26
12/15	27.22	15 9	1.96	0.00	20.59
12/14	19.46	14 11	1.55	0.00	16.57
12/13	20.46	15 11	1.30	0.00	14.51
Annual Growth	6.2%	— —	11.0%	—	19.3%

Cutera Inc

Cutera has a handle on hairy situations and a firm plan for flabby faces. The company makes lasers for medical and aesthetic use in doctors' offices and spas. Cutera markets its FDA-approved devices for hair removal and treatments to reduce pigmented lesions (age and sun spots) wrinkles and veins. Products are sold under the names CoolGlide Solera and Xeo. Its Titan line of products use deep tissue heating to firm up saggy skin. Other products provide body contouring for fat reduction and tattoo removal. In the US the company markets its products through a direct sales force and through distributors; in more than 40 other countries it relies on a small sales group and distributors. Cutera also sells a limited number of products online.

Operations

Cutera boasts more than 30 issued US patents and a handful of pending US patent applications. Beyond dermatologists and plastic surgeons Cutera sells its products to gynecologists primary care physicians and medically supervised spas. Its products portfolio has grown by its adding upgrade options and expanding its international reach. To support equipment sales the company offers upgrade hand-piece refill dermal filler and cosmetic pharmaceutical products as well as equipment support services.

In addition to its CoolGlide Solera Xeo and Titan lines the company sells products under the brand names Cutera Enlighten Excel GenesisPlus and TruSculpt.

Product sales account for some three-fourths of Cutera's total revenues.

Geographic Reach

The US is Cutera's largest market accounting for more than half of total revenue.

The company also has service support offices in Australia Belgium Canada France Hong Kong Japan Spain and Switzerland. In 40-plus other countries it works with a network of distributors and third-party service providers.

Sales and Marketing

Cutera markets and sells its products in the US through its own sales organization of about 35 representatives; abroad it also has a direct sales force with some 30 representatives as well as a network of distributors. The company sells a limited number of its products such as its Titan hand piece refills online.

The firm markets its products by making office visits attending trade shows presenting workshops and webinars and by publishing in trade journals.

Financial Performance

In fiscal 2015 Cutera's revenue rose 21% to $94.8 million. That gain was due to higher product sales which rose 34% (largely due to the launches of new products under the Enlighten and Excel HR brands but partially offset by declining sales of legacy products); service revenue remained relatively flat that year.

However the company has been operating at a loss for the past few years. Net loss which had fallen to $10.6 million in 2014 due to a one-time impairment charge related to an acquisition recovered somewhat to $4.4 million in 2015.

Strategy

The multi-billion dollar aesthetic market is expected to grow at some $2 billion annually with tattoo removal hair removal and skin rejuvenation as some of the leading drivers of that growth. Cutera is positioned to take advantage of this market growth; it aims to boost its product sales through the introduction of new technologies and by gaining approvals for additional uses for its existing best-sellers.

By obtaining more approvals for additional treatments from the FDA Cutera continues to make money on an existing device without having to start the R&D process from scratch. Some of Cutera's more recent product introductions include the GenesisPlus which builds on the company's existing Genesis platform to treat toenail fungus and to provide skin rejuvenation as well as the Excel V a vascular device to treat a wide variety of cosmetic vascular conditions (such as visible blood vessels). The Excel V complements the company's previous Excel Laser treatment which is also used to treat vascular conditions.

In late 2016 Cutera launched PICO Genesis a non-thermal procedure to treat pigmentary skin conditions.

EXECUTIVES

Consultant CFO, Sandra A. Gardiner, age 53
VP Global Marketing, Marina Kamenakis, age 59
President and CEO, James A. Reinstein, age 54
EVP International, Miguel A. Pardos, age 50, $251,394 total compensation
EVP Sales North America, Larry E. Laber, age 47, $437,500 total compensation
VP Operations, Bernie Schneider
Vice President Legal Compliance And Equity, Eduardo Martins
VP Marketing, Jonathan Pearson
VP Regulatory Affairs, Brad Renton
Vice President, Brian Hall
National Sales Manager, Keith Adams
Vice President Business Process Management, Michael Ammen
Board of Director, Timothy O'Shea
Chairman, J. Daniel Plants
Auditors: BDO USA, LLP

LOCATIONS

HQ: Cutera Inc
   3240 Bayshore Blvd., Brisbane, CA 94005
Phone: 415 657-5500
Web: www.cutera.com

PRODUCTS/OPERATIONS

2015 Sales

	% of total
Products	75
Hand Piece Refills	3
Skincare	3
Service	19
Total	**100**

Selected products

Acutip
CoolGlide
CoolGlide Platform
Excel
Excel V
GenesisPlus
LimeLight
Pearl
Pearl Fractional
Pearl Fusion
ProWave
Solera Platform
Titan
Xeo Platform

COMPETITORS

Allergan Limited	Palomar Medical
Alma Lasers	PhotoMedex
Cynosure	SkinMedica
IRIDEX	Solta Medical
Lumenis	Syneron
Osyris Medical	TRIA Beauty

HISTORICAL FINANCIALS

Company Type: Public

Income Statement

FYE: December 31

	REVENUE ($ mil.)	NET INCOME ($ mil.)	NET PROFIT MARGIN	EMPLOYEES
12/17	151.4	29.9	19.8%	367
12/16	118.0	2.5	2.2%	297
12/15	94.7	(4.4)	—	262
12/14	78.1	(10.6)	—	266
12/13	74.5	(4.7)	—	238
Annual Growth	**19.4%**	**—**	**—**	**11.4%**

2017 Year-End Financials

Debt ratio: —	No. of shares (mil.): 13.4
Return on equity: 47.6%	Dividends
Cash ($ mil.): 14.1	Yield: —
Current ratio: 2.04	Payout: —
Long-term debt ($ mil.): —	Market value ($ mil.): 611.0

	STOCK PRICE ($) FY Close	P/E High/Low		PER SHARE ($) Earnings	Dividends	Book Value
12/17	45.35	22	8	2.04	0.00	4.81
12/16	17.35	92	53	0.19	0.00	4.43
12/15	12.79	—	—	(0.32)	0.00	3.85
12/14	10.68	—	—	(0.74)	0.00	5.57
12/13	10.18	—	—	(0.33)	0.00	6.05
Annual Growth	**45.3%**	**—**	**—**	**—**	**—**	**(5.5%)**

Dave & Busters Entertainment Inc

Fun and games collide with food and drink at these nightspots. Dave & Buster's Entertainment owns and operates more than 85 entertainment complexes that offer casual dining full bar service and a cavernous game room. The adult fun centers feature the latest in video games and motion simulators as well as games of skill played for prizes. For dining Dave & Buster's offers a menu that features traditional American fare such as burgers seafood and steak. Partners David Corriveau and James "Buster" Corley opened the first Dave & Buster's in 1982. It went public in late 2014.

Operations

Slightly less than 50% of sales come from food and beverages while the remaining sales come from amusements such as air hockey skee-ball and video games.

Geographic Reach

Dave & Buster's owns and operates locations in 33 states and Canada. About 27 of the company's 87 entertainment complexes are concentrated within the three states of California New York and Texas.

Sales and Marketing

Dave & Buster's is concentrating on increased sales and marketing efforts to reinvigorate its brand and grow the special events portion of its business. The chain helped pioneer a new segment in casual dining but few adult fun arcade chains have followed and flourished. One notable exception is Champps a chain of suburban nightspots popular for live music games and karaoke. Dave

& Buster's also faces stiff competition in the general food and drink category from such franchises as Applebee's Buffalo Wild Wings and Hooters.

Financial Performance

The company reported revenue of $866.98 million for fiscal 2016 which was an increase of $120.23 million (or 16%) compared to its fiscal 2015 revenue. The primary reason for the spike was increased revenues from comparable store sales driven by a continued focus on sports viewing new game launches and new menu offerings.

Dave & Buster's net income was $59.61 million in fiscal 2016 which was an increase of $51.98 million compared to its fiscal 2015 net income.

The company ended fiscal 2016 with $186.98 million in cash flow from operations. That was an increase of a little more than $100 million compared to Dave & Buster's cash on hand at the end of fiscal 2015.

Strategy

The chain's recent expansion efforts have slanted towards opening new units that are a smaller format store the company developed out of the need to reduce construction and operating costs. The company is focused on its growth through geographic expansion.

HISTORY

Late in the 1970s David Corriveau and James "Buster" Corley were running two businesses located next to each other in Little Rock Arkansas. Corriveau operated a billiards and game parlor called Slick Willie's and Corley ran Buster's a restaurant that Corriveau helped finance. The two noticed a large amount of traffic between the two locales and the idea of Dave & Buster's was formed. The first site opened in a converted Dallas warehouse in 1982; the second opened six years later. Eager for expansion Corriveau and Corley sold an 80% stake in the business to Dallas retailer Edison Brothers in 1990. Edison grew weary of the cash drain however and divested its stake in 1995. The company went public that year.

The company picked up its expansion pace in 1996 opening three more locations. The next year the first West Coast Dave & Buster's opened in Ontario California and brewer Bass (later Six Continents) opened the first international site in the UK. (A second UK location opened the following year.) In 1998 Dave & Buster's signed a franchise agreement with TaiMall Development to open seven locations across the Pacific Rim (the first of which opened that year in Taiwan) and an agreement with SVAG Development to open several stores in Germany Switzerland and Austria.

New stores opened in Texas and Florida the following year. Dave & Buster's also inked an agreement with Funtime Hospitality to open 10 locations in Canada. (The company opened a single location in Toronto in 2000; it acquired Funtime's assets and terminated its development rights in 2003.) Results during 1999 were disappointing however causing the company to slow its expansion plans in 2000. That year Bass terminated its license agreement and closed the UK locations. SVAG cancelled its development deal the next year. Also in 2001 the company signed an agreement to develop five locations in South Korea.

A group led by management and backed by Investcorp agreed to buy the company and take it private for $255 million in 2002. Unable to get financing however the deal was called off late that year prompting public complaints from investors.

With the founders at the helm for years Dave & Buster's separated the offices of chairman and CEO in 2003. Former co-chairs and co-CEOs Corriveau and Corley gained new titles (president and CEO respectively) and director Peter Edison was named non-executive chairman.

The company opened no new stores in 2003 and only one in 2004. However in 2004 the company purchased nine Jillian's locations and the Jillian's trade name for $47 million $20 million more than the original proposal. Most of the entertainment night spots were converted to Dave & Buster's locations.

Wellspring Capital Management took Dave & Buster's private in 2006 for $375 million. Corley stepped down as CEO following the deal and turned the reins over to Stephen King formerly head of international operations for Carlson Restaurants (T.G.I. Friday's). Corriveau was replaced the following year by Starlette Johnson.

In 2008 Dave & Buster's announced plans to go public again through an IPO but that deal was later shelved due to the deteriorating economy. Wellspring sold the restaurant business to private-equity firm Oak Hill Capital for $570 million in 2010. Dave & Buster's eventually filed its IPO in 2011 only to cancel those plans in 2012.

EXECUTIVES

SVP and CFO, Brian A. Jenkins, age 56, $316,731 total compensation
SVP Purchasing and International Operations, J. Michael (Mike) Plunkett, age 67, $194,615 total compensation
CEO, Stephen M. King, age 60, $600,000 total compensation
President and COO, Dolf Berle, age 55
SVP Entertainment and Games Strategy, Kevin Bachus
SVP Human Resources And Training, Margo Manning
Chairman, Alan J. Lacy
Auditors: KPMG LLP

LOCATIONS

HQ: Dave & Busters Entertainment Inc
2481 Manana Drive, Dallas, TX 75220
Phone: 214 357-9588
Web: www.daveandbusters.com

PRODUCTS/OPERATIONS

2017 Sales

	$ mil.	% of total
Amusement and other revenues	553.0	55
Food and beverage revenues	452.2	45
Total	**1,005.2**	**100**

COMPETITORS

AMF Bowling	Champps Entertainment
Applebee's	Damon's
International	Hooters
Brinker	Houlihan's
Brunswick Corp.	Rock Bottom
Buffalo Wild Wings	Restaurants
Carlson Restaurants	

HISTORICAL FINANCIALS

Company Type: Public

Income Statement

	REVENUE ($ mil.)	NET INCOME ($ mil.)	NET PROFIT MARGIN	FYE: February 4 EMPLOYEES
02/18*	1,139.7	120.9	10.6%	14,840
01/17	1,005.1	90.8	9.0%	13,983
01/16	866.9	59.6	6.9%	12,495
02/15	746.7	7.6	1.0%	10,930
02/14	635.5	2.1	0.3%	10,961
Annual Growth	**15.7%**	**173.3%**	**—**	**7.9%**

*Fiscal year change

2018 Year-End Financials

Debt ratio: 30.6%	No. of shares (mil.): 40.1
Return on equity: 27.5%	Dividends
Cash ($ mil.): 18.8	Yield: —
Current ratio: 0.46	Payout: —
Long-term debt ($ mil.): 351.2	Market value ($ mil.): 1,913.0

	STOCK PRICE ($) FY Close	P/E High/Low	PER SHARE ($) Earnings	Dividends	Book Value
02/18*	47.70	25 15	2.84	0.00	10.51
01/17	54.80	27 14	2.10	0.00	10.41
01/16	36.27	29 19	1.39	0.00	8.32
02/15	28.74	140 78	0.21	0.00	6.47
Annual Growth	**18.4%**		**—138.3%**	**—**	**17.6%**

*Fiscal year change

Deckers Outdoor Corp.

There's no business like the specialty shoe business for Deckers Outdoor. It designs and markets the iconic UGG brand of luxury sheepskin footwear in addition to Teva sports sandals — a cross between a hiking boot and a flip-flop used for walking hiking and rafting among other pursuits. Other product lines include Sanuk Hoka One One and Koolaburra. While imitations flood the market the company distinguishes UGG and Teva from its competitors by avoiding distribution in off-price outlets. Deckers Outdoor's products are made by independent contractors primarily in Asia. The company sells its footwear through about 150 retail stores worldwide independent distributors catalogs and online.

Operations

Deckers operates across five segments: UGG Wholesale (45% of net sales) Direct-to-Consumer (35%) Teva Wholesale (5%) Sanuk Wholesale (5%) and Other Brands (5%).Its wholesale units ring up sales through higher-end department stores lifestyle retailers and specialty retailers as well as the likes of Amazon and Zappo's. The direct-to-consumer business consists of Deckers' retail stores and its owned e-commerce websites. It operates 160 retail stores worldwide consisting of 96 concept stores and 64 outlet stores primarily under the UGG banner.

Geographic Reach

Deckers Outdoors boasts a global presence with a foothold in the US Canada Australia Europe Japan and China. The US generates 65% of its net sales.

Sales and Marketing

The footwear firm markets its products under three primary brand names: UGG Teva and Sanuk.

The UGG brand is one of the industry's most recognized shoe brands. Deckers Outdoors sells its products through both domestic and international retailers international distributors and directly to end-user customers worldwide. It also uses websites call centers retail concept stores and retail outlets stores to get its products in consumers' hands.

Customers have included such big names as Nordstrom Neiman Marcus Bloomingdale's Dillard's Zappos.com REI Dick's Sporting Goods and The Sports Authority among others. The company's five largest customers accounted for some 20% of its net sales in 2016 (ended in March).

Financial Performance

In fiscal 2017 (ended March) Deckers saw sales fall for the first time in over five years. Revenue decreased 5% to $1.8 billion. Lower pricing per pair and lower pairs sold dragged down sales in UGG and Teva wholesale partially offset by an increase in the direct-to-consumer (DTC) channel. DTC grew on the back of higher online sales.

The company posted razor-thin profit of $5.7 million in 2017 a sharp decrease on the $122.3 million profit recorded the year before. The increase was down to an increase in selling and general expenses as the company undertook restructuring as well as impairment charges on the Sanuk brand's goodwill.

Cash from operations increased 58% to $198.7 million was a result of the net impact of impairment charges and positive changes in working capital partially offset by lower net income.

Strategy

As the explosive growth in UGG sales slows to increase profits in 2016 the company undertook restructuring. The process included retail store and office consolidations as the company repositioned its brands across the product groups Fashion Lifestyle and Performance Lifestyle. The restructuring is hoped to reduce overheads and create operating efficiencies as well as improve cross-team collaboration. It closed 25 stores and relocated Sanuk headquarters to corporate HQ in Goleta California. It also closed its Ahnu brand operations in Richmond CA and consolidated its European offices. It will further reduce its physical store presence by 30-40 stores; it targets 125 stores operations in 2020. The plan in total is hoped to drive $100 million in operating profit each year by 2020. It is also weighing up the sale of brands or even the entire company.

Company Background

Douglas Otto and his former partner Karl Lopker founded Styled Steers in 1973. But the small obscure maker of leather sandals gained prominence with a line of multicolored rubber sandals. Surfers in Hawaii called them "deckers" and the company soon adopted the name. In 1985 Deckers Outdoor licensed Teva from river guide Mark Thatcher who invented the Teva strapping system for rafters to ensure sandals remained attached in turbulent waters. Teva sport sandals became a popular form of casual footwear largely through word of mouth.

A continuing rise in UGG sales has extended debates over whether the name is generic or a trademark that could possibly be defended over international boundaries. Australian makers of the sheepskin boots traditionally called uggs contend that the name is generic akin to trying to protect the name "sneaker" as a trademark.

EXECUTIVES

CFO, Thomas A. George, age 63, $510,000 total compensation
President Performance Lifestyle Brands, Wendy Yang
President Omnichannel, Stefano Caroti
President Global Direct to Consumer, Dave Powers, $600,000 total compensation
COO, David E. Lafitte, $100,000 total compensation
President Fashion Lifestyle, Andrea O'Donnell
Auditors: KPMG LLP

LOCATIONS

HQ: Deckers Outdoor Corp.
250 Coromar Drive, Goleta, CA 93117
Phone: 805 967-7611
Web: www.deckers.com

PRODUCTS/OPERATIONS

2016 Sales

	$ mil.	% of total
Wholesale	1,230.8	66
Direct-to-Consumer	644.3	34
Total	**1,875.1**	**100**

2016 Sales

	$ mil.	% of total
UGG wholesale	918.1	49
Direct-to-Consumer	644.3	34
Teva wholesale	121.2	6
Sanuk wholesale	90.7	5
Other brands wholesale	100.8	6
Total	**1,875.1**	**100**

Selected Brands

Ahnu
HOKA One One
Sanuk
Teva
UGG Australia

COMPETITORS

Birkenstock USA	NIKE
C&J Clark	North Face
Cole Haan	PUMA SE
Columbia Sportswear	Patagonia Inc.
Converse	Phoenix Footwear
Crocs	Quiksilver
Diesel SpA	R. Griggs
Fila USA	Rocky Brands
Guess?	Skechers U.S.A.
Jimlar	Steven Madden
K-Swiss	Timberland
Keds	Vans
Kenneth Cole	Wolverine World Wide
L.L. Bean	adidas
LaCrosse Footwear	

HISTORICAL FINANCIALS

Company Type: Public

Income Statement				FYE: March 31
	REVENUE ($ mil.)	NET INCOME ($ mil.)	NET PROFIT MARGIN	EMPLOYEES
03/18	1,903.3	114.3	6.0%	3,500
03/17	1,790.1	5.7	0.3%	3,300
03/16	1,875.2	122.2	6.5%	3,500
03/15	1,817.0	161.7	8.9%	3,400
03/14	294.7	(2.6)	—	0
Annual Growth	**59.4%**	**—**	**—**	**—**

2018 Year-End Financials

Debt ratio: 2.5%
Return on equity: 12.0%
Cash ($ mil.): 429.9
Current ratio: 4.81
Long-term debt ($ mil.): 31.5
No. of shares (mil.): 30.4
Dividends
  Yield: —
  Payout: —
Market value ($ mil.): 2,741.0

	STOCK PRICE ($) FY Close	P/E High/Low		PER SHARE ($) Earnings	Dividends	Book Value
03/18	90.03	27	15	3.58	0.00	30.90
03/17	59.73	381	250	0.18	0.00	29.83
03/16	59.91	20	11	3.70	0.00	30.21
03/15	72.87	21	14	4.66	0.00	28.15
03/14	79.73	—	—	(0.08)	0.00	25.67
Annual Growth	**3.1%**	—	—	—	—	**4.7%**

Diamond Hill Investment Group Inc.

Diamond Hill Investment Group takes a shine to investment management. Operating through flagship subsidiary Diamond Hill Capital Management the firm oversees some $11.5 billion in assets most of it invested in mutual funds. Serving institutional and individual clients the company administers several mutual funds and sells them mainly through independent investment advisers brokerdealers financial planners investment consultants and third-party marketing firms. The firm hews to a value-based investment philosophy and takes a long-term perspective to investing. Formed in 1990 Diamond Hill Investment Group also manages separate accounts and hedge funds.

Operations

Diamond Hill Investment Group operates through its subsidiaries: Diamond Hill Capital Management; and Beacon Hill Fund Services and BHIL Distributors collectively known as Beacon Hill. Beacon Hill provides fund administration and statutory underwriting services to various clients including Diamond Hill Funds.

Financial Performance

Diamond Hill Investment Group's revenue rose 4% in 2012 versus 2011 to $66.6 million. The increase was due to a 13% rise in fees from mutual fund administration while investment advisory fees rose a more modest 3%. Net income rose 18% over the same period to $16.9 million. Assets under management at the end of 2012 exceeded $9.4 billion an increase of nearly 9% over the prior year. The firm's revenue and profits have increased steadily since 2008 after taking a hit during the financial crisis as investors retreated from the market.

EXECUTIVES

Co-Chief Investment Officer, Christopher A. (Chris) Welch
COO, Lisa M. Wesolek, age 55
Managing Director Investments and Portfolio Manager, Chuck Bath
President CEO and Portfolio Manager, Christopher (Chris) Bingaman, age 53
CFO, Thomas E. (Tom) Line, age 52

Co-Chief Investment Officer and Portfolio Manager, Austin Hawley
Vice President, Karen Colvin
Chairman, Roderick H. (Ric) Dillon, age 61
Auditors: KPMG LLP

LOCATIONS

HQ: Diamond Hill Investment Group Inc.
325 John H. McConnell Blvd., Suite 200, Columbus, OH 43215
Phone: 614 255-3333
Web: www.diamond-hill.com

PRODUCTS/OPERATIONS

2015 Sales

	$ mil.	% of total
Investment advisory	107.9	87
Mutual fund administration	16.5	13
Total	**124.4**	**100**

Selected Products

Diamond Hill Small Cap Fund
Diamond Hill Small-Mid Cap Fund
Diamond Hill Large Cap Fund
Diamond Hill Select Fund Fund
Diamond Hill Long-Short Fund
Diamond Hill Strategic Income Fund

COMPETITORS

AllianceBernstein	GAMCO Investors
American Century	Legg Mason
Calamos Asset Management	MFS
	Putnam
Cohen & Steers	Pzena Investment
Columbia Management	Management
Davis Advisers	Raymond James
Duncan-Hurst	Financial
Eaton Vance	SEI Investments
Edelman Financial	T. Rowe Price
Edward Jones	The Vanguard Group
Epoch	Waddell & Reed
FMR	Westwood Holdings
Franklin Templeton	

HISTORICAL FINANCIALS

Company Type: Public

Income Statement				FYE: December 31
	REVENUE ($ mil.)	NET INCOME ($ mil.)	NET PROFIT MARGIN	EMPLOYEES
12/17	145.2	49.9	34.4%	118
12/16	136.1	46.0	33.8%	112
12/15	124.4	37.0	29.8%	126
12/14	104.5	31.5	30.2%	107
12/13	81.4	22.1	27.2%	98
Annual Growth	**15.6%**	**22.6%**	**—**	**4.8%**

2017 Year-End Financials

Debt ratio: —
Return on equity: 32.0%
Cash ($ mil.): 76.6
Current ratio: 2.67
Long-term debt ($ mil.): —
No. of shares (mil.): 3.4
Dividends
  Yield: 0.0%
  Payout: 48.3%
Market value ($ mil.): 717.0

	STOCK PRICE ($) FY Close	P/E High/Low		PER SHARE ($) Earnings	Dividends	Book Value
12/17	206.66	15	13	14.48	7.00	49.69
12/16	210.38	16	11	13.49	6.00	40.81
12/15	189.00	20	11	11.03	5.00	30.84
12/14	138.04	14	11	9.67	4.00	22.40
12/13	118.34	18	10	6.94	3.00	13.80
Annual Growth	**15.0%**	—	—	**20.2%**	**23.6%**	**37.8%**

Diamondback Energy, Inc.

Auditors: Grant Thornton LLP

LOCATIONS

HQ: Diamondback Energy, Inc.
500 West Texas, Suite 1200, Midland, TX 79701
Phone: 432 221-7400
Web: www.diamondbackenergy.com

HISTORICAL FINANCIALS

Company Type: Public

Income Statement   FYE: December 31

	REVENUE ($ mil.)	NET INCOME ($ mil.)	NET PROFIT MARGIN	EMPLOYEES
12/17	1,205.1	482.2	40.0%	251
12/16	527.1	(165.0)	—	158
12/15	446.7	(550.6)	—	141
12/14	495.7	193.7	39.1%	114
12/13	208.0	54.5	26.2%	68
Annual Growth	55.1%	72.4%	—	38.6%

2017 Year-End Financials

Debt ratio: 19.0%	No. of shares (mil.): 98.1
Return on equity: 10.7%	Dividends
Cash ($ mil.): 112.4	Yield: —
Current ratio: 0.62	Payout: —
Long-term debt ($ mil.): 1,477.3	Market value ($ mil.): 12,394.0

	STOCK PRICE ($) FY Close	P/E High/Low	PER SHARE ($) Earnings	Dividends	Book Value
12/17	126.25	26 17	4.94	0.00	53.53
12/16	101.06	— —	(2.20)	0.00	41.02
12/15	66.90	— —	(8.74)	0.00	28.08
12/14	59.78	25 12	3.64	0.00	30.78
12/13	52.88	42 15	1.29	0.00	17.95
Annual Growth	24.3%	— —	39.9%	—	31.4%

Digital Realty Trust Inc

We can't yet build buildings in the clouds but Digital Realty Trust builds clouds in its buildings. The real estate investment trust (REIT) owns and leases data centers in some 145 technology properties with more than 26 million sq. ft. of rentable space. Active in around 35 metropolitan technology hubs in the US Europe and Asia the company provides data center colocation and interconnection services for tenants in fields such as financial services cloud and IT tech manufacturing energy healthcare and consumer products. It also holds 14 properties with 1.9 million rentable square feet as investments. The company operates through Digital Realty Trust LP.

Operations

Digital Realty Trust (DRT) operates some 26.1 million rentable sq. ft. It also has some 2.0 million sq. ft. under development and 1.1 million sq. ft. held for future development. The company has 2200 tenants across its properties.

The company offers products and services across three categories: Interconnection Cloud Connectivity and Data Center services. Its interconnection services include cross connects metro connect internet exchange dedicated internet access and service exchange. It cloud services consist of public private and hybrid clouds managed services Amazon web services and Google cloud interconnection. Data Center activities include remote IT support disaster recovery Data Center Infrastructure Management implementation and MarketplacePORTAL.

Geographic Reach

Digital Realty Trust focuses on major metropolitan areas with high concentrations of data center and technology tenants.

In the US Digital Realty Trust (DRT) has properties in the Atlanta Boston Chicago Dallas Los Angeles New York Northern Virginia Phoenix San Francisco Seattle and Silicon Valley metropolitan areas. In Europe is operates in Amsterdam Dublin Frankfurt London and Paris; and in the Asia-Pacific region in Singapore Sydney Melbourne Hong Kong and Osaka.

New York Northern Virginia London and Dallas are the company's four largest metropolitan markets and each accounts for more than 10% of total sales.

The US accounts for around 80% of total sales and the UK 10%. Other territories account for the remainder.

Sales and Marketing

Digital Realty Trust's occupancy rate is around 90%. The company's top 20 tenants account for around 45% of sales.

The REIT's tenants come from a wide variety of sectors around the world including financial services cloud and IT services manufacturing gaming energy life sciences and consumer products. It's largest tenants by rental revenue include IBM CenturyLink Equinix AT&T Facebook LinkedIn and Oracle.

Financial Performance

Digital Realty Trust's (DRT) revenue has been trending upwards for several years as it adds new data center properties to capitalize on growth in cloud computing demand.

In fiscal 2016 revenue increased 23% to $2.1 billion as eight acquisitions in Europe added to rental and interconnection sales. Net income increased a strong 43% to $431.9 million thanks to higher revenue and gains on property sales. Cash from operations increased 14% to $912.3 million thanks primarily to the Telx and European acquisitions.

Strategy

Digital Realty Trust's growth strategy is based on real estate acquisitions and the redevelopment of its existing properties. It pursues growth in high-barrier markets around clusters of telecommunication service providers. The company believes that upgrades to its properties lead to low tenant turnover and longer lease terms. From 2011 through the end of 2016 Digital Realty has expanded its portfolio from just over 100 properties to more than 145.

Expanding into Japan Digital Realty entered into a joint venture — MC Digital Realty — with Mitsubishi to set up data center in the country. Japanese companies operate in-house data centers at far higher rates than US and European companies offering a solid market opportunity. The joint venture is aiming to hold around $1.76 billion in assets by 2022.

Mergers and Acquisitions

In 2018 Digital Realty agreed to acquire Ascenty a Brazil-based data center provider for $1.8 billion. The company is also investing an additional $425 million in capital expenditures to facilitate the construction of a data center that will be part of the transaction. In all the deal which will expand Digital Realty's footprint into Latin America is valued at $2.25 billion. Ascenty's eight data centers are located in major Brazilian metropolitan areas; Digital Realty intends to bolster Ascenty's data center presence in Brazil and eventually expand into other regions in Latin America.

In 2017 Digital Realty Trust acquired DuPont Fabros Technology in a $7.6 billion deal. The acquisition brings data centers in California Virginia and Chicago to Digital Realty expanding its footprint in key markets. The companies said they could save about $18 million a year in costs.

In 2016 the company acquired 8 data centers in Amsterdam Frankfurt and London from Equinix for $818.9 million.

Company Background

Digital Realty Trust acquired 15 properties in 2010 (the busiest that the company had been since 2007) including some in new markets. The REIT added its first property in Asia when it bought a data center in Singapore. It entered Massachusetts and Connecticut with the acquisition of three data centers there.

Digital Realty Trust purchased more than a dozen properties in 2011 and 2012 including some in new markets such as London and Sydney. The latter deals added to the company's international presence in Dublin Melbourne Paris and Singapore.

EXECUTIVES

CEO, A. William (Bill) Stein, age 64, $750,000 total compensation

Managing Director Asia Pacific, Edward T. (Ted) Higase, age 51

Chief Investment Officer, Scott E. Peterson, age 56, $514,671 total compensation

COO, Jarrett B. Appleby, age 56, $297,822 total compensation

SVP and CIO, Michael Henry

CFO, Andrew P. Power, age 38, $283,333 total compensation

CTO, Chris Sharp

SVP Global Sales And Marketing, Daniel Papes

Senior Vice President Sales and Marketing, Matthew Miszewski

Senior Vice President of Construction, Anthony Caracino

Vice President Global Customer Operations, Mike Davis

Senior Vice President Human Resources, Ellen Jacobs

Vice President Tax, Brian Keyser

Senior Vice President, Sean Mccarthy

Vice President Platforms and Integration, Steve Chaput

Senior Vice President Global Sales Operations Partnerships and Alliances, Colin McLean

Vice President Network Solutions, John Bonczek

Vice President Cloud Strategic Business Development, Suzie Gleeson

Vice President, Doug Steinberg

Vice President Network Sector West, Lisa Grasse

Vice Chairman, Laurence A. Chapman, age 68

Chairman, Dennis E. Singleton, age 73

Auditors: KPMG LLP

LOCATIONS

HQ: Digital Realty Trust Inc
Four Embarcadero Center, Suite 3200, San Francisco, CA 94111
Phone: 415 738-6500   **Fax:** 415 738-6501
Web: www.digitalrealty.com

PRODUCTS/OPERATIONS

2015 Sales

	$ mil.	% of total
Rental	1,355.0	77
Tenant reimbursements	359.9	21
Interconnection and other	40.7	2
Fee income and other	7.7	-
Total	**1,763.3**	**100**

COMPETITORS

CenterPoint Properties	Kilroy Realty
CoreSite	Mack-Cali
CyrusOne	Prologis
Duke Realty	QTS Realty Trust Inc.
EastGroup Properties	Vornado Realty
Equinix	
First Industrial Realty	

HISTORICAL FINANCIALS

Company Type: Public

Income Statement

FYE: December 31

	REVENUE ($ mil.)	NET INCOME ($ mil.)	NET PROFIT MARGIN	EMPLOYEES
12/17	2,457.9	248.2	10.1%	1,436
12/16	2,142.2	426.1	19.9%	1,345
12/15	1,763.3	296.6	16.8%	1,295
12/14	1,616.4	200.1	12.4%	860
12/13	1,482.2	314.4	21.2%	784
Annual Growth	**13.5%**	**(5.7%)**	**—**	**16.3%**

2017 Year-End Financials

Debt ratio: 40.4%
Return on equity: 3.2%
Cash ($ mil.): 0.0
Current ratio: 0.25
Long-term debt ($ mil.): 8,648.6
No. of shares (mil.): 205.4
Dividends
  Yield: 0.0%
  Payout: 375.7%
Market value ($ mil.): 23,403.0

	STOCK PRICE ($) FY Close	P/E High/Low	PER SHARE ($) Earnings	Dividends	Book Value
12/17	113.90	127 100	0.99	3.72	50.63
12/16	98.26	51 33	2.20	3.52	32.05
12/15	75.62	49 39	1.56	3.40	30.74
12/14	66.30	70 49	0.99	3.32	28.60
12/13	49.12	35 21	2.12	3.12	28.11
Annual Growth	**23.4%**	**— —**	**(17.3%)**	**4.5%**	**15.9%**

Diversified Gas & Oil PLC

Auditors: Crowe Clark Whitehill LLP

LOCATIONS

HQ: Diversified Gas & Oil PLC
1100 Corporate Drive, Birmingham, AL 35242
Phone:
Web: www.dgoc.com

HISTORICAL FINANCIALS

Company Type: Public

Income Statement

FYE: December 31

	REVENUE ($ mil.)	NET INCOME ($ mil.)	NET PROFIT MARGIN	EMPLOYEES
12/17	41.7	8.8	21.2%	162
12/16	18.2	17.6	96.7%	74
12/15	6.3	(0.4)	—	39
12/14	7.3	(0.2)	—	32
Annual Growth	**78.4%**	**—**		**71.7%**

2017 Year-End Financials

Debt ratio: 31.5%
Return on equity: 17.9%
Cash ($ mil.): 15.1
Current ratio: 1.93
Long-term debt ($ mil.): 71.4
No. of shares (mil.): 145.0
Dividends
  Yield: —
  Payout: 77.7%
Market value ($ mil.): —

	STOCK PRICE ($) FY Close	P/E High/Low	PER SHARE ($) Earnings	Dividends	Book Value
12/17	0.00	— —	0.07	0.05	0.62
Annual Growth	**—**	**— —**	**—**	**—**	**—**

DNB Financial Corp.

DNB Financial Corporation is the holding company for DNB First a bank with about 15 branches in Chester and Delaware counties in southeastern Pennsylvania. Founded in 1861 the bank serves area consumers but mainly lends to small and mid-sized businesses with mortgages secured by commercial property (approximately 35% of its loan portfolio) commercial operating loans (more than 25%) and equipment leases representing most of its financing activity. The bank also writes residential mortgages and consumer loans. Deposit products include checking savings and money market accounts.

The bank's DNB Advisors division provides wealth management and trust services while subsidiary DNB Financial Services sells insurance and investment products.

EXECUTIVES

EVP and Chief Accounting Officer DNB Financial and DNB First, Bruce E. Moroney, age 59, $125,131 total compensation
President Chief Risk and Credit Officer DNB Financial and DNB First and Director DNB Financial, William J. Hieb, age 59, $210,100 total compensation
Director Retail Services DNB First, Christopher M. Breslin
EVP CFO and Secretary DNB Financial and DNB First, Gerald F. Sopp, age 60
Chairman and CEO DNB Financial and DNB First, William S. Latoff, age 67, $295,100 total compensation
EVP and Chief Lending Officer DNB Financial and DNB First, Albert J. (Al) Melfi Jr., age 64, $203,408 total compensation
SVP and Marketing Director DNB First, Catherine H. Hall
SVP Operations DNB First, Frank S. Monterosso

Managing Director Wealth Management, Richard Weber
President Chief Risk and Credit Officer DNB Financial and DNB First and Director DNB Financial, William J. Hieb, age 59
Director, James J. Koegel, age 69
Director, James H. Thornton, age 70
Director, Mildred C. Joyner, age 66
Director, Gerard F. Griesser, age 65
Director, Thomas A. Fillippo, age 68
Auditors: BDO USA, LLP

LOCATIONS

HQ: DNB Financial Corp.
4 Brandywine Avenue, Downingtown, PA 19335
Phone: 610 269-1040
Web: www.dnbfirst.com

COMPETITORS

Bank of America	Fulton Financial
Citizens Financial Group	PNC Financial
Fox Chase Bancorp	Sovereign Bank

HISTORICAL FINANCIALS

Company Type: Public

Income Statement

FYE: December 31

	ASSETS ($ mil.)	NET INCOME ($ mil.)	INCOME AS % OF ASSETS	EMPLOYEES
12/17	1,081.9	7.9	0.7%	183
12/16	1,070.6	4.9	0.5%	166
12/15	748.8	5.1	0.7%	129
12/14	723.3	4.8	0.7%	133
12/13	661.4	3.9	0.6%	139
Annual Growth	**13.1%**	**19.3%**	**—**	**7.1%**

2017 Year-End Financials

Return on assets: 0.7%
Return on equity: 8.0%
Long-term debt ($ mil.): —
No. of shares (mil.): 4.2
Sales ($ mil): 48.8
Dividends
  Yield: 0.0%
  Payout: 15.1%
Market value ($ mil.): 144.0

	STOCK PRICE ($) FY Close	P/E High/Low	PER SHARE ($) Earnings	Dividends	Book Value
12/17	33.70	19 15	1.85	0.28	23.78
12/16	28.40	19 15	1.55	0.28	22.36
12/15	29.50	16 12	1.79	0.28	19.65
12/14	21.60	14 11	1.66	0.28	23.00
12/13	20.75	16 11	1.36	0.28	21.27
Annual Growth	**12.9%**	**— —**	**8.0%**	**(0.0%)**	**2.8%**

Dolphin Entertainment Inc

EXECUTIVES

Chb-ceo-cfo; Pres, William O'Dowd
Auditors: BDO USA, LLP

LOCATIONS

HQ: Dolphin Entertainment Inc
2151 LeJeune Road, Suite 150 - Mezzanine, Coral Gables, FL 33134
Phone: 305 774-0407
Web: www.dolphinentertainment.com

HISTORICAL FINANCIALS

Company Type: Public

Income Statement				FYE: December 31
	REVENUE ($ mil.)	NET INCOME ($ mil.)	NET PROFIT MARGIN	EMPLOYEES
12/17	22.4	6.9	30.8%	87
12/16	9.4	(37.1)	—	97
12/15	3.0	(4.0)	—	20
12/14	2.0	(1.8)	—	20
12/13	2.2	(2.4)	—	0
Annual Growth 76.8%		—	—	—

2017 Year-End Financials

Debt ratio: 24.4%
Return on equity: ***,***.*%
Cash ($ mil.): 5.3
Current ratio: 0.47
Long-term debt ($ mil.): 0.6

No. of shares (mil.): 10.5
Dividends
Yield: —
Payout: —
Market value ($ mil.): 38.0

	STOCK PRICE ($) FY Close	P/E High/Low		Earnings	PER SHARE ($) Dividends	Book Value
12/17	3.60	14	4	(0.20)	0.00	0.58
12/16	6.00	—	—	(9.66)	0.00	(4.43)
12/15	0.20	—	—	(2.00)	0.00	(7.74)
12/14	0.04	—	—	(0.80)	0.00	(5.76)
12/13	0.06	—	—	(1.20)	0.00	(4.84)
Annual Growth 178.3%		—	—	—	—	—

Douglas Dynamics, Inc.

Let it snow Let it snow Let it snow! It's a song made to order for Douglas Dynamics. The company makes snowplows and sand-and-salt spreading equipment for light trucks. One of the biggest manufacturers in its industry the company sells its lineup under brand names Western Fisher Snowex Turfex Sweepex and Blizzard via equipment distributors. It also supplies related parts and accessories. End customers are mainly snowplowers in the business of removing snow and ice for municipalities and commercial and private owners in the Midwest East and Northeast US as well as throughout Canada. Douglas traces its roots back to the 1970s.

Geographic Reach

Douglas has manufacturing facilities in Milwaukee; Rockland Maine; and Madison Heights Michigan. Most of its distributors are located throughout the snow belt regions in North America (primarily the Midwest East and Northeast regions of the US as well as all provinces of Canada) and also cater to many parts of Europe and China.

Sales and Marketing

The company sells its products through a distributor network primarily to professional snowplowers who are contracted to remove snow and ice from commercial municipal and residential areas. Douglas spent $4.5 million $4.3 million and $3 million for 2015 2014 and 2013 respectively on advertising expenses.

Financial Performance

Douglas experienced unprecedented growth for 2015 with revenues peaking at a record-setting $400 million and profits reaching $44 million another company milestone. In addition its cash flow

from operations jumped 5% in 2015. The historic growth for 2015 was fueled by a 37% surge in equipment sales and an additional $96 million in sales from a previous acquisition.

Strategy

Douglas has cultivated sales by gradually expanding its distribution relationships and by purchasing related businesses. In 2014 it acquired Henderson Products a North American manufacturer of customized turnkey snow and ice control equipment for heavy-duty trucks focused on government departments for $95 million. The purchase strengthened its market position in snow and ice control across all truck segments and created new opportunities for growth in attractive adjacent markets. It also contributed to Douglas' milestone revenue totals for 2015.

EXECUTIVES

Chairman President and CEO, James L. Janik, $490,348 total compensation
EVP and CFO, Robert McCormick, $310,724 total compensation
SVP Sales and Marketing, Mark Adamson, age 61, $237,461 total compensation
SVP Operations, Keith Hagelin, age 58, $227,660 total compensation
Auditors: Ernst & Young LLP

LOCATIONS

HQ: Douglas Dynamics, Inc.
7777 North 73rd Street, Milwaukee, WI 53223
Phone: 414 354-2310
Web: www.douglasdynamics.com

PRODUCTS/OPERATIONS

2015 Sales

	$ mil.	% of total
Equipment	349.4	87
Parts & accessories	51.0	13
Total	**400.4**	**100**

Selected Brands

Blizzard
Fisher
Snowex
Sweepex
Turfex
Western

COMPETITORS

Dana	Visteon
Tenneco	ZF Friedrichshafen

HISTORICAL FINANCIALS

Company Type: Public

Income Statement				FYE: December 31
	REVENUE ($ mil.)	NET INCOME ($ mil.)	NET PROFIT MARGIN	EMPLOYEES
12/17	474.9	55.3	11.6%	1,664
12/16	416.2	39.0	9.4%	1,633
12/15	400.4	44.1	11.0%	1,104
12/14	303.5	39.9	13.2%	993
12/13	194.3	11.6	6.0%	520
Annual Growth 25.0%		47.7%	—	33.7%

2017 Year-End Financials

Debt ratio: 44.9%
Return on equity: 23.1%
Cash ($ mil.): 36.8
Current ratio: 2.45
Long-term debt ($ mil.): 274.8

No. of shares (mil.): 22.5
Dividends
Yield: 0.0%
Payout: 40.0%
Market value ($ mil.): 854.0

	STOCK PRICE ($) FY Close	P/E High/Low		Earnings	PER SHARE ($) Dividends	Book Value
12/17	37.80	18	12	2.40	0.96	11.36
12/16	33.65	20	10	1.70	0.94	9.80
12/15	21.07	12	10	1.94	0.89	8.96
12/14	21.43	14	8	1.77	0.87	7.78
12/13	16.82	33	25	0.51	0.84	6.99
Annual Growth 22.4%		—	—	47.3%	3.5%	12.9%

Douglas Emmett Inc

Office Space is more than the name of a cult movie to Douglas Emmett. The self-administered and self-managed real estate investment trust (REIT) invests in commercial real estate in Southern California and Hawaii. It owns about 50 Class A office properties (totaling 13.3 million sq. ft.) mostly in the heart of Hollywood and surrounding areas. Its office holdings account for about 85% of its total revenues. The REIT also owns nearly 2900 apartment units in tony neighborhoods of West Los Angeles and Honolulu. Douglas Emmett's portfolio includes some of the most notable addresses on the West Coast including the famed Sherman Oaks Galleria Burbank's Studio Plaza and office tower 100 Wilshire.

Geographic Reach

The Santa Monica-based firm's portfolio includes properties in California and Hawaii. Submarkets include Los Angeles County (Brentwood Olympic Corridor Century City Santa Monica Beverly Hills Westwood Sherman Oaks/Encino Warner Center/Woodland Hills and Burbank) and Honolulu. Douglas Emmett has a growing presence in Honolulu where it controls about 35% of the office market.

Financial Performance

The REIT reported $591.5 million in revenue in 2013 a 2% gain versus 2012. Net income rose 98% to $45.3 million over the same period. Indeed 2013 marked the third consecutive year of rising revenue and profit — as well as rising average office rental rates — for the firm after the economic recession caused some tenants to downsize or default on rents in 2009 and 2010. Revenue from the REIT's multifamily properties increased by about 4% year over year while office rental revenue was up less than by nearly 1%.

Strategy

Douglas Emmett which targets tenants in the health care legal entertainment and technology industries operates in markets where high barriers to entry such as environmental restrictions or steep property values limit new competition. Its properties are often located in communities with high-end lifestyle amenities and a diverse economic base. The company is a relatively conservative investor maintaining its portfolio while slowly making new acquisitions and considering new markets.

Focusing on its core submarkets the REIT is working on two multifamily projects one in Brentwood in Los Angeles and the other in Honolulu. It expects to break ground on another 452 apartments at its Moanalua Hillside Apartments in Honolulu by mid-2014. It's also seeking to build a high-rise apartment project in Los Angeles although construction isn't expected to begin before at least mid-2015.

Mergers and Acquisitions

In August 2013 the REIT purchased a 191000-square-foot Class A office building on Ventura Blvd. for $61 million. In MayDouglas Emmett bought a 225000-square-foot Class A office building at 8484 Wilshire Blvd. in Beverly Hills for $89 million.

In 2010 the REIT acquired Bishop Square the largest office project in Hawaii.

EXECUTIVES

Chief Investment Officer, Kevin A. Crummy, $600,000 total compensation
President and CEO, Jordan L. Kaplan, age 57, $1,000,000 total compensation
COO, Kenneth M. (Ken) Panzer, age 58, $1,000,000 total compensation
CFO, Mona Gisler, age 46
Senior Vice President, Kevin Kuritani
Senior Vice President Leasing, Andrew Goodman
Senior Vice President, Michele Aronson
Chairman, Dan A. Emmett, age 78
Auditors: Ernst & Young LLP

LOCATIONS

HQ: Douglas Emmett Inc
808 Wilshire Boulevard, Suite 200, Santa Monica, CA 90401
Phone: 310 255-7700
Web: www.douglasemmett.com

PRODUCTS/OPERATIONS

2015 Sales

	$ mil.	% of total
Office rental		
Rental revenues	412.5	65
Parking and other income	85.4	13
Tenant recoveries	43.1	7
Multifamily rental		
Rental revenues	87.9	14
Parking and other income	6.9	1
Total	**635.8**	**100**

COMPETITORS

Apartment Investment and Management	Hudson Pacific
	Intergroup
C.J. Segerstrom & Sons	Irvine Company
Castle & Cooke	Kilroy Realty
Equity Residential	Majestic Realty
Essex Property Trust	UDR
Gables Residential Services	Vestar Development

HISTORICAL FINANCIALS

Company Type: Public

Income Statement   FYE: December 31

	REVENUE ($ mil.)	NET INCOME ($ mil.)	NET PROFIT MARGIN	EMPLOYEES
12/17	812.0	94.4	11.6%	600
12/16	742.5	85.4	11.5%	600
12/15	635.7	58.3	9.2%	600
12/14	599.5	44.6	7.4%	560
12/13	591.5	45.3	7.7%	500
Annual Growth	**8.2%**	**20.2%**	**—**	**4.7%**

2017 Year-End Financials

Debt ratio: 49.6%
Return on equity: 4.3%
Cash ($ mil.): 176.6
Current ratio: 1.08
Long-term debt ($ mil.): 4,117.3

No. of shares (mil.): 169.5
Dividends
Yield: 0.0%
Payout: 162.0%
Market value ($ mil.): 6,962.0

	STOCK PRICE ($) FY Close	P/E High/Low	Earnings	PER SHARE ($) Dividends	Book Value
12/17	41.06	71 63	0.58	0.94	14.38
12/16	36.56	68 44	0.55	0.89	12.68
12/15	31.18	80 67	0.39	0.85	13.11
12/14	28.40	95 75	0.30	0.81	13.42
12/13	23.29	88 70	0.31	0.74	13.82
Annual Growth	**15.2%**	**— —**	**17.0%**	**6.2%**	**1.0%**

Duluth Holdings Inc

Auditors: GRANT THORNTON LLP

LOCATIONS

HQ: Duluth Holdings Inc
201 East Front Street, Mount Horeb, WI 53572
Phone: 608 424-1544
Web: www.duluthtrading.com

HISTORICAL FINANCIALS

Company Type: Public

Income Statement   FYE: January 28

	REVENUE ($ mil.)	NET INCOME ($ mil.)	NET PROFIT MARGIN	EMPLOYEES
01/18	471.4	23.3	5.0%	2,172
01/17	376.1	21.3	5.7%	1,627
01/16*	304.1	27.4	9.0%	1,187
02/15	231.8	23.6	10.2%	1,316
02/14	163.0	15.5	9.5%	0
Annual Growth	**30.4%**	**10.8%**	**—**	**—**

*Fiscal year change

2018 Year-End Financials

Debt ratio: 12.5%
Return on equity: 18.9%
Cash ($ mil.): 2.8
Current ratio: 2.02
Long-term debt ($ mil.): 28.0

No. of shares (mil.): 32.4
Dividends
Yield: —
Payout: —
Market value ($ mil.): 606.0

	STOCK PRICE ($) FY Close	P/E High/Low	Earnings	PER SHARE ($) Dividends	Book Value
01/18	18.68	32 21	0.72	0.00	4.19
01/17	22.97	55 21	0.66	0.00	3.43
01/16*	16.51	16 13	1.06	0.00	2.75
Annual Growth	**6.4%**	**— —**	**(17.6%)**	**—**	**23.5%**

*Fiscal year change

e.l.f. Beauty Inc

Auditors: DELOITTE & TOUCHE LLP

LOCATIONS

HQ: e.l.f. Beauty Inc
570 10th Street, Oakland, CA 94607
Phone: 510 778-7787
Web: www.elfcosmetics.com

HISTORICAL FINANCIALS

Company Type: Public

Income Statement   FYE: December 31

	REVENUE ($ mil.)	NET INCOME ($ mil.)	NET PROFIT MARGIN	EMPLOYEES
12/17	269.8	33.4	12.4%	413
12/16	229.5	5.3	2.3%	351
12/15	191.4	4.3	2.3%	231
12/14	135.1	(9.2)	—	0
Annual Growth	**25.9%**	**—**	**—**	**—**

2017 Year-End Financials

Debt ratio: 37.4%
Return on equity: 20.0%
Cash ($ mil.): 10.0
Current ratio: 2.41
Long-term debt ($ mil.): 147.7

No. of shares (mil.): 46.6
Dividends
Yield: —
Payout: —
Market value ($ mil.): 1,040.0

	STOCK PRICE ($) FY Close	P/E High/Low	Earnings	PER SHARE ($) Dividends	Book Value
12/17	22.31	40 26	0.68	0.00	4.16
12/16	28.94	— —	(39.47)	0.00	3.11
12/15	0.00	— —	(1,560.00)	0.00	
3,968.83					
Annual Growth (96.8%)		**— —**	**—**	**—**	**—**

EACO Corp

EACO Corporation lost its appetite for the buffet business. For a half-dozen years after selling its restaurant operations to pursue a new line of business the company generated revenues from a handful of rental properties including restaurant and industrial properties. (Tenant NES Rentals accounts for about half of its rental revenues.) In 2010 the company acquired Bisco Industries which distributes electronics components in the US and Canada. EACO was once the sole franchisee of Ryan's Restaurant Group restaurants in Florida; it also owned a chain of 16 Whistle Junction and Florida Buffet locations. CEO Glen Ceiley owns 98.9% of EACO.

EACO (formerly Family Steak Houses of Florida) struggled for years to make a profit before it sold off its restaurant business to the privately-owned Banner Buffets but Banner didn't fare much better and ceased operations in 2007 resulting in the leases of two restaurant properties reverting back to EACO.

EXECUTIVES

Chairman and CEO; CEO Bisco, Glen F. Ceiley, age 67
Director; VP Technology Bisco, William L. Means, age 69
President and COO Bisco, Donald S. (Don) Wagner, age 51
Controller, Michael Bains
Auditors: SQUAR MILNER LLP

LOCATIONS

HQ: EACO Corp
1500 North Lakeview Loop, Anaheim, CA 92807
Phone: 714 876-2490
Web: www.eacocorp.com

COMPETITORS

Allied Electronics	Newark Corporation
Digi-Key	Realty Income
GE Franchise Finance	

HISTORICAL FINANCIALS

Company Type: Public

Income Statement   FYE: August 31

	REVENUE ($ mil.)	NET INCOME ($ mil.)	NET PROFIT MARGIN	EMPLOYEES
08/18	193.2	6.9	3.6%	464
08/17	156.9	4.0	2.6%	407
08/16	148.5	4.1	2.8%	414
08/15	140.2	3.7	2.7%	424
08/14	134.7	5.6	4.2%	426
Annual Growth	9.4%	5.5%	—	2.2%

2018 Year-End Financials

Debt ratio: 10.9%	No. of shares (mil.): 4.8
Return on equity: 18.1%	Dividends
Cash ($ mil.): 2.7	Yield: —
Current ratio: 2.48	Payout: —
Long-term debt ($ mil.): 8.2	Market value ($ mil.): 68.0

	STOCK PRICE ($) FY Close	P/E High/Low		PER SHARE ($) Earnings	Dividends	Book Value
08/18	14.00	10	4	1.41	0.00	8.62
08/17	6.32	11	7	0.82	0.00	7.16
08/16	5.96	7	6	0.83	0.00	6.34
08/15	5.20	25	6	0.75	0.00	5.54
08/14	7.25	7	3	1.14	0.00	4.83
Annual Growth	17.9%	—	—	5.5%	—	15.6%

Eagle Bancorp Inc (MD)

For those nest eggs that need a little help hatching holding company Eagle Bancorp would recommend its community-oriented EagleBank subsidiary. The bank serves businesses and individuals through more than 20 branches in Maryland Virginia and Washington DC and its suburbs. Deposit products include checking savings and money market accounts; certificates of deposit; and IRAs. Commercial real estate loans represent more than 70% of its loan portfolio while construction loans make up another more than 20%. The bank which has significant expertise as a Small Business Administration lender also writes business consumer and home equity loans. EagleBank offers insurance products through an agreement with The Meltzer Group.

Operations
Like other retail banks Eagle Bancorp makes the bulk of its money from loan interest. About 86% of its total revenue came from loan interest (including fees) during 2015 while another 4% came from interest on investment securities. The rest of its revenue came from deposit account service charges (2% of revenue) and non-recurring income sources.

The bank has two direct subsidiaries: Bethesda Leasing LLC which holds the bank's foreclosed real estate (owned and acquired); and Eagle Insurance Services LLC which provides commercial and retail insurance products through a referral arrangement with insurance broker The Meltzer Group.

Geographic Reach
The Bethesda Maryland-based bank operates 21 branches in Maryland Virginia and Washington DC (as of mid-2016) including nine in Northern Virginia seven in Montgomery County and five in the District of Columbia.

Sales and Marketing
Eagle Bancorp serves local businesses professional clients individuals sole proprietors small and medium-sized businesses non-profits and investors. Other clients are from the healthcare accountant and attorney markets.

The bank spent $2.7 million on marketing and advertising during 2015 up 38% from the $2 million it spent in 2014 mostly due to higher digital and print advertising and sponsorship costs.

Financial Performance
Eagle Bancorp's annual revenue has more than doubled since 2011 mostly thanks to strong loan growth with the addition of new branches. Meanwhile its net income has more than tripled as the bank has kept a lid on credit loss provisions and overhead costs.

The bank's revenue jumped 33% to $279.8 million during 2015 largely thanks to a rise in interest income as its loan assets grew 16%.

Strong revenue growth in 2015 coupled with an absence of merger expenses drove Eagle Bancorp's net income up 55% to $84.1 million. The bank's operating cash levels spiked 66% to $98.5 million for the year thanks to a strong rise in cash-based earnings.

Strategy
The company has been focused on growing within its existing markets. Its strategy for further growth includes continuing to seek opportunities to open or acquire new banking locations while waiting out record low interest rates. Eagle's strict loan underwriting standards — it didn't write subprime residential mortgages and didn't buy securities backed by subprime mortgages — has helped it have fewer problem loans the downfall for many banks.

Beyond its core lending and deposit businesses Eagle Bancorp continues to expand its other product offerings as well. In 2015 it introduced a Full Service Equipment Leasing program which provided alternative and convenient financing for all types of business equipment for customers.

Mergers and Acquisitions
In November 2014 Eagle Bancorp significantly expanded its presence in Northern Virginia after it purchased Fairfax County-based Virginia Heritage. The deal added six Virginia Heritage Bank branches (renamed as EagleBank) in northern Virginia along with $917.4 million in assets — including $715 million in loans and $737 million in deposits.

EXECUTIVES

EVP; SEVP and COO EagleBank, Susan G. Riel, age 69, $478,806 total compensation
Chairman President and CEO; Chairman and CEO EagleBank; President Ronald D. Paul Cos., Ronald D. Paul, age 63, $863,565 total compensation
EVP; EVP and Chief Credit Officer EagleBank, Janice L. Williams, age 61, $391,758 total compensation
EVP and General Counsel Eagle Bancorp and EagleBank, Laurence E. Bensignor, age 62
EVP; EVP and Chief Lending Officer Commercial Real Estate EagleBank, Antonio F. Marquez, age 60, $368,256 total compensation
EVP; EVP and Chief Lending Officer Commercial and Industrial EagleBank, Lindsey S. Rheaume, age 58
EVP and CFO, Charles D. Levingston, age 38
Vice President, Joan Grant
Senior Vice President Commercial Banking Team Leader, Derek Whitwer
Vice President Facilities Operations Manager, Shawn Cox
Executive Vice President Chief Real Estate, Tony Marquez
Vice President Treasurer, Scott Clark
Auditors: Dixon Hughes Goodman LLP

LOCATIONS

HQ: Eagle Bancorp Inc (MD)
7830 Old Georgetown Road, Third Floor, Bethesda, MD 20814
Phone: 301 986-1800
Web: www.eaglebankcorp.com

PRODUCTS/OPERATIONS

Selected Subsidiaries
EagleBank
    Bethesda Leasing LLC
    Eagle Insurance Services LLC
    Fidelity Mortgage Inc.
Eagle Commercial Ventures LLC

COMPETITORS

BB&T	OBA Financial Services
Bank of America	PNC Financial
Capital One	Sandy Spring Bancorp
M&T Bank	SunTrust

Income Statement   FYE: December 31

	ASSETS ($ mil.)	NET INCOME ($ mil.)	INCOME AS % OF ASSETS	EMPLOYEES
12/17	7,479.0	100.2	1.3%	466
12/16	6,890.1	97.7	1.4%	469
12/15	6,076.6	84.1	1.4%	434
12/14	5,247.8	54.2	1.0%	427
12/13	3,771.5	47.0	1.2%	386
Annual Growth	18.7%	20.8%	—	4.8%

2017 Year-End Financials

Return on assets: 1.4%
Return on equity: 11.1%
Long-term debt ($ mil.): —
No. of shares (mil.): 34.1
Sales ($ mil): 353.4

Dividends
Yield: —
Payout: —
Market value ($ mil.): 1,979.0

	STOCK PRICE ($) FY Close	P/E High/Low	PER SHARE ($) Earnings	Dividends	Book Value
12/17	57.90	23 17	2.92	0.00	27.80
12/16	60.95	22 15	2.86	0.00	24.77
12/15	50.47	22 13	2.50	0.00	22.07
12/14	35.52	18 15	1.95	0.00	20.60
12/13	30.63	18 11	1.76	0.00	15.22
Annual Growth	17.3%	— —	13.5%	—	16.3%

Eagle Materials Inc

Eagle Materials is perched near the top of the building materials business. The company manufactures and distributes cement and gypsum wallboard which together account for nearly 75% of its total sales. Eagle Materials also produces readymix concrete aggregates and recycled paperboard. Its products are sold to residential commercial and industrial construction customers throughout the US. The company operates about 25 plants and manufacturing facilities. It also has about 100 railcars for shipping its wallboard products to customers across the country. Founded in 1963 Eagle Materials was spun off by homebuilder Centex Corporation in 2004.

Operations

Eagle Materials operates five main business segments: Cement Concrete and Aggregates Gypsum Wallboard Recycled Paperboard and Oil and Gas Proppants.

Cement sales accounts for nearly 40% of Eagle's total sales while Gypsum Wallboard accounts for another 35%. Its Paperboard and Concrete and Aggregates segments each make up another roughly 10% of total sales while Oil and Gas Proppants generate around 5%.

In addition to wholly-owned plants in Illinois Wyoming and Nevada Eagle owns a 50% stake in Texas Lehigh Cement Co. in Buda Texas. Eagle manufactures gypsum wallboard at five plants representing about 35% of sales. Republic Paperboard Co. the company's paperboard business is located in Oklahoma and accounts for about 20% Eagle's sales. Concrete and aggregates make up the rest.

Geographic Reach

Dallas-based Eagle Materials sells its gypsum wallboard throughout the US focusing on markets nearest its production facilities. The company sells cement in six regional markets including northern Nevada and California the greater Chicago area the Rocky Mountain region the Central Plains region and Texas.

Sales and Marketing

Most of the demand for Eagle's cement products come from the infrastructure commercial construction and residential construction. About 50% of the total demand comes from public works infrastructure projects.

Financial Performance

Eagle's sales and profits have been rising at a healthy clip over the past few years thanks to increased demand for cement concrete and other aggregate materials amidst the strengthening US economy. The company's more recent Oil and Gas Proppants business has also been boosting annual sales.

Eagle Materials' revenue jumped by 19% to a record $1.07 billion in fiscal 2015 (ended March) thanks to a combination of its CRS acquisition in the Oil and Proppants business higher average net selling prices across all of its materials segments and higher sales volumes across all segments except aggregates.

Higher revenue in FY2015 drove the company's profits higher by 50% to $186.85 million (the highest level since 2007) while operating cash spiked by 37% to $234.12 million thanks to higher cash earnings.

Strategy

Strengthened demand for construction products as the US economy has gained steam has buoyed Eagle's prospects for 2015 and beyond. With its cement sales network spanning the entire nation and with infrastructure spending industrial construction and residential building activity expected to heat up the company anticipated that calender year 2015 would be good for cement demand across all of its regional cement markets.

Besides growing on its own the company likes to acquire aggregate cement or other raw building material-producers that complement or bolster its material product offerings. In recent years the company has been looking to acquire frac-sand producers to expand its service offerings in lucrative shale regions.

Mergers and Acquisitions

In 2014 Eagle Materials agreed to purchase CRS Proppants as well as its subsidiaries including Great Northern Sand LLC which has long supplied high-quality northern-white frac-sand to the energy industry. The company expressed that CRS Proppants' services were highly complementary to its own frac-sand operations.

Eagle's Audubon Materials subsidiary agreed in late 2012 to purchase a pair of cement plants in Missouri and Oklahoma from rival Lafarge North America for about $446 million in cash. The purchase which included six distribution terminals two aggregates quarries eight ready-mix concrete plants and a fly ash business marked Eagle's return to acquisition mode.

Company Background

Prior to the recession the firm had designs on expansion especially in its core wallboard and cement business. The company opened a fifth gypsum wallboard plant in 2007 to increase production capacity but the addition proved untimely.

EXECUTIVES

EVP Strategy Corporate Development and Communications, Robert S. (Bob) Stewart, age 64, $420,500 total compensation
EVP General Counsel and Secretary, James H. (Jim) Graass, age 60, $399,000 total compensation
EVP Cement Aggregates and Concrete, Gerald J. (Gerry) Essl, age 68, $386,000 total compensation
President and CEO, David B. (Dave) Powers, age 68, $800,000 total compensation
EVP Finance and Administration and CFO, D. Craig Kesler, age 42, $420,000 total compensation
COO, Michael Haack, $530,500 total compensation
Senior Vice President Finance And Treasurer, Arthur R Zunker, age 77
Vice Chairman, Michael R. Nicolais, age 60
Chairman, Richard R. Stewart, age 68
Auditors: Ernst & Young LLP

LOCATIONS

HQ: Eagle Materials Inc
5960 Berkshire Lane, Suite 900, Dallas, TX 75225
Phone: 214 432-2000   **Fax:** 214 432-2100
Web: www.eaglematerials.com

PRODUCTS/OPERATIONS

2015 Sales

	$ mil.	% of total
Cement	488.6	39
Gypsum wallboard	437.5	35
Recycled paperboard	142.8	11
Concrete & aggregates	107.9	9
Oil and Gas Proppants	81.4	6
Adjustments	(191.8)	-
Total	**1,066.4**	**100**

Selected Subsidiaries

American Gypsum Company
Centex Materials
Illinois Cement Company
Mathews Readymix
Mountain Cement Company
Nevada Cement Company
Republic Paperboard Company
Texas Leigh Cement Company (50%)
Western Aggregates

COMPETITORS

Boral	Martin Marietta
CEMEX Inc.	Aggregates
Caraustar	Martin Marietta
Georgia-Pacific	Materials
Holcim (US)	New NGC
Lafarge North America	TXI
Lehigh Cement	U.S. Concrete
Lehigh Hanson	USG

HISTORICAL FINANCIALS
Company Type: Public

Income Statement   FYE: March 31

	REVENUE ($ mil.)	NET INCOME ($ mil.)	NET PROFIT MARGIN	EMPLOYEES
03/18	1,386.5	256.6	18.5%	2,200
03/17	1,211.2	198.2	16.4%	2,200
03/16	1,143.4	152.5	13.3%	2,000
03/15	1,066.3	186.8	17.5%	2,000
03/14	898.4	124.2	13.8%	1,800
Annual Growth	11.5%	19.9%	—	5.1%

Debt ratio: 26.2%
Return on equity: 19.5%
Cash ($ mil.): 9.3
Current ratio: 2.56
Long-term debt ($ mil.): 620.9

No. of shares (mil.): 48.2
Dividends
  Yield: 0.0%
  Payout: 7.5%
Market value ($ mil.): 4,976.0

	STOCK PRICE ($) FY Close	P/E High/Low	PER SHARE ($) Earnings	Dividends	Book Value
03/18	103.05	23 16	5.28	0.40	29.36
03/17	97.14	26 17	4.10	0.40	24.84
03/16	70.11	28 15	3.05	0.40	21.44
03/15	83.56	28 19	3.71	0.40	20.11
03/14	88.66	36 24	2.49	0.40	16.61
Annual Growth	3.8%	— —	20.7%	(0.0%)	15.3%

Eagle Pharmaceuticals, Inc.

Like the talons of its namesake Eagle Pharmaceuticals specializes in sharps. The firm develops and commercializes injectable treatments primarily to address unmet needs in oncology and critical care. The company has five FDA-approved products — blood thinner Argatroban malignant hyperthermia treatment Ryanodex anti-inflammatory drug diclofenac-misoprostol cancer drug Non-Alcohol Docetaxel Injection and leukemia and non-Hodgkin lymphoma treatment Bendeka. Eagle Pharmaceuticals also has a handful of candidates under development. Commercial and development partners include Cephalon Albany Molecular Research Sandoz and The Medicines Company.

Operations

Eagle Pharmaceuticals has four candidates either in late-stage development or under FDA review.

Sales and Marketing

Going forward Eagle plans to keep its US sales and marketing efforts in-house while using partners and third-parties for European distribution.

Financial Performance

In 2014 Eagle changed its fiscal year end from September to December. When combining the revenue for the entire year the company made $24.7 million in 2014. The following year revenue rose 168% to $66.2 million. This was primarily due to $45 million in licensing and other revenue but also largely due to an increase in product sales and a doubling of royalty earnings. The company recognizes licensing revenue from Teva subsidiary Cephalon related to sales of Bendeka.

After years of losing money and thanks to the increased revenue Eagle entered the black in 2015 with $2.6 million in net income (compared to a loss of $23.5 million in 2014).

Strategy

A big part of Eagle's strategy for success is to be ready when the patent expires on a popular drug and release its "new and improved" version no later than the first generic. It feels it can offer a price point and efficacy improvement over the name brand while offering something closer to a brand than the generics. The company intends to leverage its knowledge of the approval process to line up improved drugs for launch. It will partner for European sales and handle domestic sales and marketing itself while continuing to expand its intellectual property portfolio.

Mergers and Acquisitions

In late 2016 Eagle agreed to buy Arsia Therapeutics for some $30 million plus up to an additional $48 million in milestone payments. That deal will mark the company's entry into the biosimilar market.

EXECUTIVES

President CEO and Director, Scott L. Tarriff, age 58, $645,590 total compensation
EVP Research and Development, Peter E. Grebow, age 71
CFO, David E. Riggs, age 66, $390,913 total compensation
EVP and Chief Scientific Officer, Steven L. Krill, age 58, $390,913 total compensation
EVP Clinical Research Medical and Regulatory Affairs, Adrian Hepner, age 56, $311,766 total compensation
EVP and General Counsel, John LaRocca
SVP Sales and Marketing, Sherry Korczynski
Chairman, Michael (Mike) Graves, age 55
Auditors: BDO USA, LLP

LOCATIONS

HQ: Eagle Pharmaceuticals, Inc.
  50 Tice Boulevard, Suite 315, Woodcliff Lake, NJ 07677
Phone: 201 326-5300
Web: www.eagleus.com

PRODUCTS/OPERATIONS

2016 Sales

	$ mil.	% of total
Product sales	13.0	20
Royalty income	8.2	12
License and other income	45.0	68
Total	66.2	100

COMPETITORS

Abbott Labs	Merck
Allergan plc	Mylan
AstraZeneca	Novartis
Bayer HealthCare	Pfizer
Pharmaceuticals Inc.	Sandoz International
Biogen	GmbH
Bristol-Myers Squibb	Sanofi
GlaxoSmithKline	Teva
Johnson & Johnson	

HISTORICAL FINANCIALS

Company Type: Public

Income Statement				FYE: December 31
	REVENUE ($ mil.)	NET INCOME ($ mil.)	NET PROFIT MARGIN	EMPLOYEES
12/17	236.7	51.9	21.9%	108
12/16	189.4	81.4	43.0%	77
12/15	66.2	2.5	3.9%	41
12/14*	5.6	(5.5)	—	0
09/14	19.1	(17.9)	—	31
Annual Growth	87.6%	—		36.6%

*Fiscal year change

Debt ratio: 17.6%
Return on equity: 31.4%
Cash ($ mil.): 114.6
Current ratio: 3.99
Long-term debt ($ mil.): 42.9

No. of shares (mil.): 14.8
Dividends
  Yield: —
  Payout: —
Market value ($ mil.): 793.0

	STOCK PRICE ($) FY Close	P/E High/Low	PER SHARE ($) Earnings	Dividends	Book Value
12/17	53.42	28 14	3.27	0.00	12.07
12/16	79.34	17 6	4.96	0.00	9.87
12/15	88.67	592 90	0.16	0.00	5.78
12/14*	15.50	— —	(0.39)	0.00	1.99
09/14	12.65	— —	(1.97)	0.00	2.36
Annual Growth	43.4%	— —	—		50.4%

*Fiscal year change

East West Bancorp, Inc

East West Bancorp banks in both hemispheres of the world. It's the holding company for East West Bank which provides standard banking services and loans through more than 130 branches in major US metropolitan areas and about 10 offices across in China Hong Kong and Taiwan. Boasting $29 billion in assets East West Bank focuses on making commercial and industrial real estate loans which account for the majority of the company's loan portfolio. Catering to the Asian-American community it also provides international banking and trade financing to importers/exporters doing business in the Asia/Pacific region. East West Bank offers multilingual service in English Cantonese Mandarin Vietnamese and Spanish.

Operations

East West Bancorp operates two business segments. The commercial banking segment (which generated 62% of its total revenue in 2014) includes commercial industrial and commercial real estate primarily generates commercial and industrial real estate loans and offers a wide variety of international finance and trade services and products. The retail banking segment (33% of total revenue) focuses primarily on retail operations through the East West Bank's branch network. The bank also offers insurance products through East West Insurance.

Broadly speaking the bank made 93% of its revenue from loan interest (including fees) in 2014 and another 7% from interest on investment securities investment in Federal Home Loan Bank and Federal Reserve Bank Stock and short-term investments. It had a staff of roughly 2700 employees at the end of 2014.

Geographic Reach

East West's bank network in the US is mainly in California (in and around Los Angeles the San Francisco Bay area Orange County and Silicon Valley) and in the Atlanta Boston Houston New York and Seattle metropolitan areas. Internationally the bank has five branches in Hong Kong and Greater China (Shanghai Shantou and Shenzhen) and five representative offices in Beijing Chongqing Guangzhou Xiamen and Taiwan.

Sales and Marketing

East West Bancorp caters its banking and loan business to companies in the manufacturing wholesale trade and service sectors.

Financial Performance

The bank has struggled to consistently grow its revenues in recent years due to shrinking interest margins on loans amidst the low-interest environment. Its profits however have been rising thanks to declining loan loss provisions as its loan portfolio's credit quality has improved with higher property valuations in the strengthened economy.

East West had a breakout year in 2014 as its revenue climbed by 17% to $1.14 billion mostly thanks to an increase in non-covered loan volumes. Higher revenue in 2014 drove East West Bancorp's net income higher by 16% to $342.5 million. Lower income tax provisions resulting from additional purchases of affordable housing partnerships and tax-credited investments also help pad the bank's bottom line.

The bank's operating cash levels dipped by 8% to $392.9 million mostly due to unfavorable working capital changes related to accrued interest receivables and other asset balances.

Strategy

East West Bancorp's long-term vision reiterated in 2015 is to "serve as the financial bridge between the United States and Greater China" by reaching more customers with its cross-border products and capabilities. Its full-service branches in Greater China offer traditional letters of credit and trade finance between businesses while also providing the bank a way to serve existing clients and establish new business relationships.

Toward its international expansion plans the company opened two new branches in Greater China's Shenzhen and Shanghai Pilot Free Trade Zone during 2014 which would better position it to help its customers and facilitate their financial needs between Greater China and the US.

The bank may also occasionally pursue acquisitions of other banks to broaden its market reach and grow its loan and deposit business.

Mergers and Acquisitions

In 2014 East West Bancorp expanded its presence in Texas and California after it purchased Metrocorp along with its 19 MetroBank and Metro United Bank branches in the Houston Dallas and San Diego markets. The deal also added $1.7 billion in assets and $1.4 billion in new loan assets.

Company Background

East West Bancorp was founded in 1998.

In 2009 the company acquired more than 60 branches and most of the banking operations of larger rival United Commercial Bank which had been seized by regulators. The deal gave East West Bank about 40 more California branches plus some 20 additional US locations beyond the state.

EXECUTIVES

EVP Chief Risk Officer General Counsel and Secretary East West Bancorp and East West Bank, Douglas P. Krause, age 62, $403,090 total compensation

Chairman and CEO East West Bancorp and East West Bank, Dominic Ng, age 59, $1,000,000 total compensation

Vice Chairman East West Bancorp and East West Bank, John M. Lee, age 86

EVP and Head of International and Commercial Banking, Andy Yen, age 60, $370,977 total compensation

EVP and CFO East West Bancorp and East West Bank, Irene H. Oh, age 40, $403,090 total compensation

EVP and Chief Credit Officer East West Bank, Albert Sun, age 63

President and COO East West Bancorp and East West Bank, Gregory L. Guyett, age 54

EVP Head of U.S. Eastern and Texas Regions and Head of Consumer and Business Banking, Wendy Cai-Lee

Vice President, Sue Chao

First Vice President Consumer Banking Regional Manager, Renee Chang

First Vice President Relationship Manager, Dorothy Zhao

Vice President Business Development Officer, Ellen Chiang

Avp Loan Portfolio Manager, Sheng-ta Tsai

Avp Loan Documentation And Funding, Jacquelynn Forte

Vice President, Ann Huynh

Assistant Vice President Credit Analyst, Joseph Au

Auditors: KPMG LLP

LOCATIONS

HQ: East West Bancorp, Inc
135 North Los Robles Ave., 7th Floor, Pasadena, CA 91101
Phone: 626 768-6000
Web: www.eastwestbank.com

PRODUCTS/OPERATIONS

2011 Sales

	$ mil.	% of total
Commercial lending	619.8	57
Retail banking	358.8	33
Other & adjustments	112.8	10
Total	**1,091.4**	**100**

COMPETITORS

Bank of America	Hanmi Financial
Bank of East Asia	Hope Bancorp
Cathay General Bancorp	JPMorgan Chase
Citibank	U.S. Bancorp
City National	Wells Fargo
Comerica	

HISTORICAL FINANCIALS

Company Type: Public

Income Statement

FYE: December 31

	ASSETS ($ mil.)	NET INCOME ($ mil.)	INCOME AS % OF ASSETS	EMPLOYEES
12/17	37,150.2	505.6	1.4%	3,000
12/16	34,788.8	431.6	1.2%	2,873
12/15	32,350.9	384.6	1.2%	2,833
12/14	28,738.0	342.4	1.2%	2,709
12/13	24,730.0	295.0	1.2%	2,542
Annual Growth	**10.7%**	**14.4%**	**—**	**4.2%**

2017 Year-End Financials

Return on assets: 1.4%
Return on equity: 13.9%
Long-term debt ($ mil.): —
No. of shares (mil.): 144.5
Sales ($ mil): 1,583.5

Dividends
Yield: 0.0%
Payout: 23.0%
Market value ($ mil.): 8,793.0

	STOCK PRICE ($) FY Close	P/E High/Low		PER SHARE ($) Earnings	Dividends	Book Value
12/17	60.83	18	14	3.47	0.80	26.58
12/16	50.83	17	9	2.97	0.80	23.78
12/15	41.56	17	13	2.66	0.80	21.70
12/14	38.71	16	13	2.38	0.72	19.85
12/13	34.97	17	10	2.10	0.60	17.18
Annual Growth	**14.8%**	**—**	**—**	**13.4%**	**7.5%**	**11.5%**

Eastman Kodak Co.

Eastman Kodak the inventor of the Brownie camera has put consumer photography in albums on a shelf to focus on imaging for businesses. The company generates nearly two-thirds of sales from print systems and services for the book publishing newspaper and magazine publishing commercial printing and packaging industries among others. It makes presses and imprinting systems as well as technology to print documents publications and product packaging. Kodak's other operations include hardware software consumables and services related to printing and imaging for consumers and customers in a host of industries. The company which generates most of its sales outside the US was founded in 1880 by George Eastman.

Operations

Kodak operates through seven segments. Its largest Print Systems includes prepress and electrophotographic printing systems and services and accounts for more than 60% of total revenue. The Consumer and Film segment which generates nearly 15% of revenue includes licensing of the Kodak name for consumer products (batteries cameras accessories) as well as industrial film and chemicals and motion picture film and film processing services. Enterprise Inkjet Systems (ink and inkjet components and services) and Flexographic Packaging (imaging equipment printing plates and consumables for customized packaging materials) each contribute about 10% of revenue. Kodak is selling its Flexographic Packaging segment.

The company's other segments include Software and Solutions (workflow and document management managed print services) Advanced Materials and 3D Printing (emerging operations IP licensing) and Eastman Business Park (activities of Kodak's 1200-acre industrial complex in Rochester New York).

Geographic Reach

Kodak generates about a third of its revenue from the US with another third coming from the Europe Middle East and Africa (EMEA) region. The Asia-Pacific region and Canada and Latin America account for about 25% and 10% respectively.

The Rochester New York-based company has manufacturing and R&D facilities in the US (Georgia Ohio Minnesota New York Oklahoma) as well as Canada China Germany Israel and Japan.

Sales and Marketing

Kodak serves a broad range of customers in the graphic arts commercial print publishing packaging electronic displays entertainment and commercial films and consumer products markets.

The company markets its products and services through a direct sales team as well as through dealers.

Financial Performance

Kodak has seen a significant decline in revenue over the past five years with total sales falling about 35% since 2013. After a few years of net losses however net income is slowing growing.

In 2017 the company reported revenue of $1.5 billion down 7% from the prior year. Growth in the Flexographic Packaging segment (which Kodak is selling) was not enough to offset declines in the other segments particularly volume and pricing declines in Print Systems.

Net income that year jumped to $94 million compared to $15 million in 2016. The gain is mostly the result of a benefit for income taxes related to the 2017 Tax Act.

Cash at the end of 2017 was $369 million a decrease of $109 million from the prior year. Cash from operations used $67 million while investing activities used $24 million mainly for additions to properties. Financing activities used another $29 million for dividends to stockholders and other items.

Strategy

As Kodak's mature businesses including much of the Print Systems segment continue to decline the company plans to focus on those products and services its sees as possible growth engines. Those include Sonora (process free digital plates for more efficient and environmentally friendly printing) Prosper and Ultrastream (next-generation inkjet technology) and advanced materials and 3D printing (which includes intellectual property licensing.

In order to free up investment resources and pay down some its debt Kodak is looking to cash in on one of the bright spots of its recent performance — the growing Flexographic Packaging segment. The company put the division up for sale in mid-2018.

HISTORY

After developing a method for dry-plate photography George Eastman established The Eastman Dry Plate and Film Company in 1884. In 1888 it introduced its first camera a small easy-to-use device that was loaded with enough film for 100 pictures. Owners mailed the camera back to the company which returned it with the pictures and more film. The firm settled on the name Eastman Kodak in 1892 after Eastman tried many combinations of letters starting and ending with "k" which he thought was a "strong incisive sort of letter." The user-friendly Brownie camera followed in 1900. Three years later Kodak introduced a home movie camera projector and film.

Ailing and convinced that his work was done Eastman committed suicide in 1932. Kodak continued to dominate the photography industry with the introduction of color film (Kodachrome 1935) and a handheld movie camera (1951). The company established US plants to produce the chemicals plastics and fibers used in its film production.

The Instamatic introduced in 1963 became Kodak's biggest success. The camera's foolproof film cartridge eliminated the need for loading in the dark. By 1976 Kodak had sold an estimated 60 million Instamatics 50 million more cameras than all its competitors combined.

EXECUTIVES

CEO, Jeffrey J. (Jeff) Clarke, age 56, $1,034,843 total compensation
SVP and President Print Systems Division, Brad W. Kruchten, age 58, $481,203 total compensation
SVP and CIO, Kim E. VanGelder
SVP CTO and President Intellectual Property Solutions, Terry R. Taber, age 64
VP and General Manager Worldwide Sales Print Systems Division, John O'Grady, age 54
SVP Chief Marketing Officer and President Consumer and Film Division, Steven Overman, age 50
SVP and Director Sales Strategy and Operations, Eric-Yves Mahe, age 55, $436,830 total compensation
VP and Managing Director ALMA Region, Lo s Lebegue
SVP and President Enterprise Inkjet Systems Division and Micro 3D Printing and Packaging Division, Philip Cullimore, age 52, $561,696 total compensation
President Motion Picture and Entertainment, Steve Bellamy
SVP and CFO, David E. Bullwinkle, age 44
Chairman, James V. (Jim) Continenza, age 55
Auditors: PricewaterhouseCoopers LLP

LOCATIONS

HQ: Eastman Kodak Co.
343 State Street, Rochester, NY 14650
Phone: 585 724-4000
Web: www.kodak.com

PRODUCTS/OPERATIONS

2017 Sales

	% of total
Sales	80
Services	20
Total	**100**

2017 Sales

	% of total
Print Systems	62
Consumer and Film	13
Flexographic Packaging	9
Enterprise Inkjet Systems	9
Software and Solutions	6
Eastman Business Park	1
Advanced Materials and 3D Printing Technology	-
Total	**100**

Selected Products and Services

Commercial inkjet printing systems
Commercial printing workflow software
Consumer and professional photographic film
Digital picture frames
Document scanners
Electrophotographic equipment
Inkjet printers
Origination and print films
Photographic paper
Prepress equipment
Processing chemicals
Retail printing kiosks APEX drylab systems and related media
Wholesale photofinishing services

COMPETITORS

3M	Konica Minolta
Agfa	Lexmark
Canon	Olympus
Dell	Panasonic Corp
EskoArtwork	Philips Electronics
FUJIFILM	Ricoh Company
HP	SCREEN Holdings
Heidelberger Druckmaschinen	Sharp Corp.
	Xerox

HISTORICAL FINANCIALS

Company Type: Public

Income Statement

FYE: December 31

	REVENUE ($ mil.)	NET INCOME ($ mil.)	NET PROFIT MARGIN	EMPLOYEES
12/17	1,531.0	94.0	6.1%	5,800
12/16	1,543.0	15.0	1.0%	6,100
12/15	1,798.0	(80.0)	—	6,400
12/14	2,102.0	(123.0)	—	7,300
12/13	805.0	(81.0)	—	8,800
Annual Growth	**17.4%**	—		**(9.9%)**

2017 Year-End Financials

Debt ratio: 23.6%	No. of shares (mil.): 42.6
Return on equity: 61.8%	Dividends
Cash ($ mil.): 344.0	Yield: —
Current ratio: 2.29	Payout: —
Long-term debt ($ mil.): 399.0	Market value ($ mil.): 132.0

	STOCK PRICE ($) FY Close	P/E High/Low		PER SHARE ($) Earnings	Dividends	Book Value
12/17	3.10	9	2	1.76	0.00	5.18
12/16	15.50	62	29	0.28	0.00	1.96
12/15	12.54	—	—	(1.91)	0.00	1.86
12/14	21.71	—	—	(2.95)	0.00	6.61
12/13	34.71	—	—	(1.94)	0.00	15.10
Annual Growth	**(45.3%)** (23.5%)	—	—	—	—	—

Ebix Inc

Ebix Inc. helps the worlds of several information-dependent industries go ?round. The company supplies on-demand software and ecommerce services for insurance financial and healthcare. Its Ebix-Exchange service acts as an online auction house where buyers and carriers can exchange bids for auto home health life and other types of insurance while paying Ebix a fee on each transaction. Ebix also provides agency management software that includes workflow and customer relationship management (CRM) capabilities as well as other back-office functions for insurance brokers and insurance carriers. Ebix also offers money transfer services in India and Asia.

Operations

Ebix operates through four channels: Exchanges Broker P&C (property and casualty) Systems Risk Compliance Solutions (RCS) and Carrier P&C Systems.

Exchanges which generate about 70% of the company?s revenue are data exchanges for finance travel life insurance annuities employee health benefits risk management workers compensation insurance underwriting and property and casualty. The exchanges connect multiple entities in financial and insurance markets enabling the participant to carry and process data from one end to another.

The focus of Broker P&C Systems 4% revenue is outside the US. Ebix operates three back-end systems: eGlobal which targets multinational P&C insurance brokers; WinBeat which targets P&C brokers in Australia and New Zealand; and Ebix-

ASP which is a system for the P&C insurance brokers in the US.

Through RCS about a quarter of revenue Ebix provides business process outsourcing services that include domain intensive project management time and material-based consulting the creation and tracking of certificates of insurance issued in the US and Australia the provision of claims adjudication and settlement call center and back office support.

Ebix has reduced emphasis on Carrier P&C Systems about 1% of revenue in favor of its other businesses. The unit designs and deploys on-demand back-end systems for P&C insurance companies.

Geographic Reach

Atlanta-based Ebix's #1 market is the US accounting for nearly 60% of its sales with India and Australia accounting for about 20% and 9% respectively. The firm's international operations are managed from Dubai. The company has more than 50 offices across the Australia Brazil New Zealand Singapore the UK Canada and India.

Financial Performance

Ebix Inc.?s revenue and profit have grown fortified by the several acquisitions the company makes each year. Revenue has risen for the past decade while profit has been on a steady rise higher for the past four years.

In 2017 the company?s revenue increased 22% to about $364 million from 2016 pushed by the latest round of acquisitions. The Exchange division?s revenues jumped 26% with help from the acquisitions of ItzCash YouFirst Wall Street Paul Merchants and Via. The Risk Compliance Solutions division?s revenue rose 17% on new e-governance sales from operations in India and consulting service sales from the Wdev acquisition. A 4% increase in Broker P&C Systems revenue was aided by the effects of currency exchange rates. Carrier P&C Systems division revenues fell 16% with the end of some large projects.

Higher revenue drove net income to more than $100 million in 2017 a 7% increase from 2016.

Ebix had about $64 million in cash and cash equivalents at the end of 2017 down from about $114 million in 2016. The company spent about $200 million on acquisitions in 2017 about $190 million than it spent on acquisitions in 2016.

Strategy

Ebix finds companies that add to or fill in its portfolio of products and services buys them and integrates them into its framework. The plan has built revenue from about $75 million in 2008 to about $364 million in 2017.

With this strategy Ebix has expanded beyond insurance and into financials and healthcare markets as well as geographic markets. Geographically India has become an important market for Ebix. The company?s revenue from India grew to more than $61 million in 2017 from less than $4 million in 2015 making the country its second-biggest market. In India and other southeast Asia countries Ebix through its EbixCash Financial Exchange offerings provides domestic and international money remittance travel pre-paid and gift cards utility payments and more.

Mergers and Acquisitions

The Ebix mergers and acquisitions team had to be one of the busiest such units in 2017 when the company made six acquisitions some of which boosted its business in India.

The biggest deal came in a joint venture with the India-based Essel Group. Ebix and Essel acquired an 80% stake in ItzCash Indiós leading payment exchange for about $120 million.

The other acquisitions were of:
— Via an online travel and assisted ecommerce exchange in India. Ebix paid about $80 million.
— The Money Transfer Service Scheme (MTSS) Business of Paul Merchants the largest international remittance service provider in India. Ebix paid about $37 million.
— The MTSS Business of YouFirst another international remittance service provider in India. The cost was about $10 million.
— The MTSS Business of Wall Street an international remittance service provider in India and its subsidiary Goldman Securities Limited. The price was about $7 million.
— The assets of beBetter a technology-enabled corporate wellness provider of tools and programs such as health screening coaching tobacco cessation weight and stress management health information and others. Ebix paid about $1 million.

EXECUTIVES

Chairman President and CEO, Robin Raina, age 49, $1,300,000 total compensation
EVP and Corporate Officer of Mergers & Acquisitions and Special Projects, Robert F. (Bob) Kerris, age 64, $225,000 total compensation
SVP Agency Systems, Graham Prior, age 61, $154,126 total compensation
SVP Ebix Health, James (Jim) Senge, age 57, $225,000 total compensation
Managing Director Ebix Australia Group, Leon d'Apice, age 61, $164,250 total compensation
Managing Director Ebix New Zealand, Tony Wisniewski
Head of Enterprise Solutions EbixExchange, Ash Sawhney
CFO, Sean T. Donaghy, age 53
Vice President Of Operations, Ashley Franco
Assistant Vice President Professional Services, Albert Golbasarians
Vice President Sales, David Greiff
Vice President, Alex Mattelaer
Vice President Software Development Rcs, Bhoga Pappu
Vice President Operations, Tom Lebleu
Vice President Solution Architecture and Implementation, Andy Labrot
Board Member, George Hebard
Auditors: T. R. Chadha & Co., LLP

LOCATIONS

HQ: Ebix Inc
1 Ebix Way, Johns Creek, GA 30097
Phone: 678 281-2020
Web: www.ebix.com

PRODUCTS/OPERATIONS

2017 Sales

	$ mil.	% of total
Exchanges	259,470.0	71
Risk Compliance Solutions	86,832.0	24
Broker systems	14,672.0	4
Carrier systems	2,995.0	1
Total	**363,971.0**	**100**

COMPETITORS

Answer Financial	InsWeb
Applied Systems	Intuit
BenefitMall	Life Quotes
CCC Information	SunGard
Computer Sciences Corp.	The Hartford
Cover-All	TriZetto
Crawford & Company	Ultimate Software
Datamonitor	Vertafore
Guidewire Software	salesforce.com

HISTORICAL FINANCIALS

Company Type: Public

Income Statement				FYE: December 31
	REVENUE ($ mil.)	NET INCOME ($ mil.)	NET PROFIT MARGIN	EMPLOYEES
12/17	363.9	100.6	27.6%	4,515
12/16	298.2	93.8	31.5%	2,988
12/15	265.4	79.5	30.0%	2,707
12/14	214.3	63.5	29.7%	2,343
12/13	204.7	59.2	29.0%	1,927
Annual Growth	**15.5%**	**14.1%**	**—**	**23.7%**

2017 Year-End Financials

Debt ratio: 35.9%	No. of shares (mil.): 157.3
Return on equity: 21.9%	Dividends
Cash ($ mil.): 63.9	Yield: 0.0%
Current ratio: 1.72	Payout: 47.3%
Long-term debt ($ mil.): 385.5	Market value ($ mil.): 12,473.0

	STOCK PRICE ($) FY Close	P/E High/Low		PER SHARE ($)		
			Earnings	Dividends	Book Value
12/17	79.25	128 84	0.63	0.30	3.12
12/16	57.05	109 51	0.57	0.30	2.66
12/15	32.79	83 36	0.46	0.30	2.45
12/14	16.99	53 36	0.06	0.30	2.39
12/13	14.71	65 29	0.31	0.08	2.20
Annual Growth	**52.4%**	**— —**	**20.0%**	**41.4%**	**9.2%**

Echo Global Logistics Inc

By land air or sea Echo Global Logistics delivers the goods. The company provides a wide range of transportation and supply chain management services using a proprietary technology platform for truckload quoting and transit times. Its main business is arranging transportation by truckload (TL) and less than truckload (LTL) carriers. It also offers intermodal services—a combination of truck and rail delivery—and some air and ocean delivery services. Its logistics solutions encompass services such as rate negotiation shipment tracking and freight management and reporting.

Operations

About 40000 transportation providers make up Echo Global's carrier network which consists of small and midsized fleets trucking companies and single-truck owners.

Echo Global offers mode-specific transportation services as well as logistics services on a shipment-to-shipment basis (transactional) or via long-term contracts (managed transportation). Its truckload (TL) shipping service generates close to 70% of net sales and includes dry van temperature-controlled and flatbed trucks. TL services utilizes its Truckload Quoting Tool technology which uses predictive pricing algorithms and capacity data to provide the best rates for its customers. Echo's less than truckload business (LTL) accounts for more than 25% of net sales. LTL services uses its RateIQ 2.0 technology to get real-time price and transit times for all LTL shipments.

The company also provides intermodal transportation services (a combination of truck and rail) small parcel shipping domestic air shipments and international ocean freight services. These account for about 5% of revenue.

As part of its shipping business the company offers logistics services including customized freight management solutions such as rate negotiation procurement shipment tracking and reporting freight bill payment and audit and integration of shipping applications into customers' e-commerce sites.

Geographic Reach

Echo is stationed in Chicago and has about 30 sales offices located across the US as well as two data centers.

Sales and Marketing

The company caters to a wide range of industries including manufacturing construction food and beverage consumer products and retail. Its customers are divided into two types: transactional (services provided on a shipment-by-shipment basis) and managed transportation (under multiyear contracts). Transactional clients represent about 80% of total revenue with 20% generated by managed transportation clients.

Financial Performance

Echo Global Logistics has experienced doubledigit growth over the last five years. Net sales increased to $1.9 billion in 2017 a $227 million increase (or 13%) from 2016. The increase is attributed to higher shipment volume and revenue per shipment driven by an increase in truckload rates.

The company reported net income of $12.6 million in 2017 compared with $1.6 million the previous year primarily due to an $8.3 million tax benefit and an increase in net revenue. Negatively affecting Echo Global's bottom line were an increase in transportation costs driven by higher carrier rates. Transportation costs as a percentage of revenue increased by more than 1%.

Cash at the end of fiscal 2017 was $23.5 million an increase of $6.9 million from the prior year. Cash from operations contributed $48.7 million to the coffers while investing activities used $20.7 million mainly for purchases of property and equipment. Financing activities used another $21.1 million for the company's stock repurchase program.

Strategy

Echo Global Logistics plans to continue to grow through investments in technology and through acquisitions.

Echo Global's proprietary technology platforms are driving revenue growth. With logistics being one of the fastest growing industries Echo continues to leverage its expertise in technology-based logistics solutions and plans to hire more than 70 technology professionals in 2018. With a focus on its client portal EchoShip and its carrier portal and mobile platform EchoDrive the company aims to continue to develop tools to further automate and digitize data such as capacity rates shipment status and settlement documents. It has also invested in productivity tools for its sales force.

Echo Global is also focused on acquisitions to further growth. Its 2018 acquisition of Freight Management Plus (FMP) adds approximately $15 million in annual revenue experienced LTL sales talent and expands its reach to small and middle-market shippers.

Mergers and Acquisitions

In 2018 Echo acquired Freight Management Plus Inc. (FMP) a third-party logistics company headquartered in Allison Park PA. FMP specializes in LTL managed transportation solutions. With the purchase of FMP Echo hopes to expand its portfolio of small to middle-market shippers.

EXECUTIVES

President and COO, David B. (Dave) Menzel, age 56, $546,000 total compensation
Chairman and CEO, Douglas R. (Doug) Waggoner, age 59, $760,000 total compensation
CIO, Tim Kutz
CFO, Kyle L. Sauers, age 47, $425,000 total compensation
SVP Marketing, Christopher N. Clemmensen
Senior Vice President of Talent, Cheryl Johnson
National Account Manager, Brian Godla
Vice President Of Sales, Jamie Petrzelka
National Account Manager, Jared Rames
National Account Manager, Alex Rossi
National Account Manager, Jordan Alterbaum
Executive Vice President, Andy Arquette
National Account Manager, Kevin Holtrup
National Account Manager, Ben Boelter
National Account Manager, Jason Agostino
National Account Manager, Dustin Williams
National Account Manager, Natalie Benedettini
National Account Manager, Alex Fitzpatrick
National Account Manager, Dean DeWilder
Senior Vice President of Marketing, Chris Clemmensen
National Accounts Manager, Pete Haitaian
NATIONAL ACCOUNT MANAGER, Lyndsey Whelan
NATIONAL ACCOUNT MANAGER, Jon Lisek
National Account Manager, Brandon Scott
National Account Manager, Jason Dutcher
Regional Vice President, Paul Warren
Regional Vice President, Steve Rotondi
National Accounts Manager, Erika Klatte
National Account Manager, Minos Glykofridis
Vice President Sales, Michael Zamost
Regional Vice President Rochester, Dave Buschner
National Account Manager, John Mercer
Vice President of Solutions and Implementation, Bill Homoky
NATIONAL ACCOUNT MANAGER, Adam Wall
REGIONAL VICE PRESIDENT, Daniel Despain
Board Member, Paul Loeb
Auditors: Ernst & Young LLP

LOCATIONS

HQ: Echo Global Logistics Inc
  600 West Chicago Avenue, Suite 725, Chicago, IL 60654
Phone: 800 354-7993
Web: www.echo.com

PRODUCTS/OPERATIONS

2017 Sales

	% of total
Truckload (TL)	68
Less Than Truckload (LTL)	27
Intermodal	3
Transportation	2
Total	**100**

Selected Services

Truckload services (TL)
Less than Truckload services (LTL)
Intermodal services
Domestic air and expedited services
International air and ocean transportation services
Small Parcel services
EchoTrak
EchoIQ
RateIQ 2.0
FastLane
Truckload Quoting Tool
EchoDrive carrier portal
EchoShip client portal

COMPETITORS

ABF Freight System
C.H. Robinson Worldwide
Expeditors
FedEx
Hub Group
J.B. Hunt
MIQ Logistics
Ozburn-Hessey Logistics
Roadrunner Transportation Systems
Ryder System
Schneider Logistics
Total Quality Logistics
Transplace
UPS
XPO logistics

HISTORICAL FINANCIALS

Company Type: Public

Income Statement   FYE: December 31

	REVENUE ($ mil.)	NET INCOME ($ mil.)	NET PROFIT MARGIN	EMPLOYEES
12/17	1,943.0	12.6	0.6%	2,453
12/16	1,716.1	1.5	0.1%	2,350
12/15	1,512.3	7.8	0.5%	2,335
12/14	1,173.3	16.7	1.4%	1,734
12/13	884.1	14.2	1.6%	1,297
Annual Growth	21.8%	(2.9%)	—	17.3%

2017 Year-End Financials

Debt ratio: 25.3%
Return on equity: 3.5%
Cash ($ mil.): 23.5
Current ratio: 1.49
Long-term debt ($ mil.): 212.0
No. of shares (mil.): 27.2
Dividends
  Yield: —
  Payout: —
Market value ($ mil.): 763.0

	STOCK PRICE ($) FY Close	P/E High/Low	PER SHARE ($) Earnings	Dividends	Book Value
12/17	28.00	62 29	0.45	0.00	13.17
12/16	25.05	475 317	0.05	0.00	12.73
12/15	20.39	118 59	0.28	0.00	13.30
12/14	29.20	41 22	0.71	0.00	7.84
12/13	21.48	36 28	0.61	0.00	6.95
Annual Growth	6.9%	— —	(7.3%)	—	17.3%

Eclipse Resources Corp

Looking to eclipse its oil and gas rivals Eclipse Resources is an independent exploration and production company active in the Appalachian Basin. It has 227230 net acres in Eastern Ohio including 96240 net acres in the most prolific and economic area of the Utica Shale fairway (Utica Core Area) with 25740 net acres targeted as a highly liquids-rich area in the Marcellus Shale in Eastern Ohio (Marcellus Project Area). Eclipse operates 81% of its net acreage within the Utica Core and Marcellus Project areas. In 2014 the company reported estimated proved reserves of 109.6 billion cu. ft. equivalent and 18.3 million barrels of oil equivalent. It went public in June of that year.

IPO
The company plans to use its IPO proceeds of $818.1 million to pay down debt and fund its capital expenditure plan. Following the public offering Eclipse Resource Holdings L.P. held 81% of the company.

Operations
In 2014 Eclipse had identified 668 net horizontal drilling locations in the Utica Core and 195 locations in the Marcellus Project. That year the company and/or its operating partners had commenced drilling 72 gross wells within the Utica Core and 3 gross wells within the Marcellus Project.

Strategy
Eclipse intends to focus on developing its substantial inventory of horizontal drilling locations and will continue to add to this acreage position by acquiring acreage at attractive prices.

EXECUTIVES

EVP and COO, Thomas S. Liberatore, age 62, $261,038 total compensation

Chairman President and CEO, Benjamin W. Hulburt, age 44, $585,225 total compensation

EVP Secretary General Counsel and Director, Christopher K. Hulburt, age 47, $327,116 total compensation

EVP and CFO, Matthew R. DeNezza, age 47, $329,244 total compensation

Auditors: GRANT THORNTON LLP

LOCATIONS

HQ: Eclipse Resources Corp
2121 Old Gatesburg Rd, Suite 110, State College, PA 16803
Phone: 814 308-9754
Web: www.eclipseresources.com

PRODUCTS/OPERATIONS

2015 Sales

	$ mil.	% of total
Natural gas sales	69.5	51
Oil sales	47.3	34
NGLs sales	21.0	15
Total	**137.8**	**100**

COMPETITORS

Avenue Group	Penn Virginia
Carrizo Oil & Gas	Stone Energy
Chesapeake Energy	XTO Energy

HISTORICAL FINANCIALS
Company Type: Public

Income Statement
FYE: December 31

	REVENUE ($ mil.)	NET INCOME ($ mil.)	NET PROFIT MARGIN	EMPLOYEES
12/17	383.6	8.5	2.2%	171
12/16	235.0	(203.8)	—	138
12/15	255.3	(971.4)	—	210
12/14	137.8	(183.1)	—	227
12/13	12.9	(43.5)	—	159
Annual Growth	**133.4%**	—	—	**1.8%**

2017 Year-End Financials
Debt ratio: 40.4%
Return on equity: 1.5%
Cash ($ mil.): 17.2
Current ratio: 0.72
Long-term debt ($ mil.): 495.0
No. of shares (mil.): 262.7
Dividends
 Yield: —
 Payout: —
Market value ($ mil.): 631.0

	STOCK PRICE ($) FY Close	P/E High/Low	Earnings	Dividends	Book Value
12/17	2.40	103 59	0.03	0.00	2.18
12/16	2.67	— —	(0.84)	0.00	2.10
12/15	1.82	— —	(4.46)	0.00	2.79
12/14	7.03	— —	(1.27)	0.00	7.20
Annual Growth	**(30.1%)**	— —	**(32.9%)**	—	—

Eldorado Resorts Inc

Auditors: Ernst & Young LLP

LOCATIONS

HQ: Eldorado Resorts Inc
100 West Liberty Street, Suite 1150, Reno, NV 89501
Phone: 775 328-0100
Web: www.eldoradoresorts.com

HISTORICAL FINANCIALS
Company Type: Public

Income Statement
FYE: December 31

	REVENUE ($ mil.)	NET INCOME ($ mil.)	NET PROFIT MARGIN	EMPLOYEES
12/17	1,473.5	73.9	5.0%	12,500
12/16	892.9	24.8	2.8%	7,400
12/15	719.7	114.1	15.9%	7,800
12/14	361.8	(14.4)	—	7,100
12/13	247.1	18.9	7.6%	0
Annual Growth	**56.3%**	**40.6%**	—	—

2017 Year-End Financials
Debt ratio: 61.7%
Return on equity: 11.8%
Cash ($ mil.): 152.2
Current ratio: 1.15
Long-term debt ($ mil.): 2,189.5
No. of shares (mil.): 76.8
Dividends
 Yield: —
 Payout: —
Market value ($ mil.): 2,547.0

	STOCK PRICE ($) FY Close	P/E High/Low	Earnings	Dividends	Book Value
12/17	33.15	31 14	1.09	0.00	12.30
12/16	16.95	32 17	0.52	0.00	6.34
12/15	11.00	5 2	2.43	0.00	5.78
12/14	4.05	— —	(0.48)	0.00	3.26
Annual Growth	**101.5%**	— —	—	—	**55.6%**

Ellie Mae Inc

Ellie Mae might sound like Fannie Mae's cousin but they're just in related industries not bloodlines. The company provides automation software and operates the Ellie Mae Network that facilitates the residential mortgage origination and funding process. Its Encompass software suite combines loan origination with CRM (customer relationship management) to gather review and verify data from a single database. Other programs handle regulatory compliance appraisal and title services underwriting tax transcripts and document preparation and management. More than 136000 mortgage professionals use its software and network to process more than 3 million new mortgages an estimated 20% of its addressable market.

Geographic Reach
Ellie Mae operates in the US from offices in California Missouri Nebraska (technical support) and New Jersey.

Sales and Marketing
The company's sales force is divided into four teams that handle account management new account acquisition sales development and solution engineering. Customers include American Home Bank HighTechLending Skyline Financial and Supreme Lending.

Mortgage originators that use Encompass software pay for it either as a service with monthly fees based on the number of users and mortgages funded or through licensing and recurring subscription fees. Lenders and service providers that use the Ellie Mae Network pay fees per transaction for business received from Encompass users.

Financial Performance
Sales grew some 57% in 2015 jumping from $161 million to $254 million year-over-year. The substantial increase was primarily due to Encompass users working with the on-demand Software-as-a-Service model. The company has grown its base of active Encompass SaaS users from about 109000 in 2014 to 136000 in 2014. Profits jumped from $15 million in 2014 to $22 million in 2015.

Strategy
A major part of Ellie Mae's SaaS focus is its "success-based" pricing model that allows customers to pay at the time loans are closed. Besides its objectives to add new Encompass users and cross-sell to existing ones the company plans to enhance its Ellie Mae Network with increased functionality and services and expand the use of settlement services on the system. Industry trends are also influencing strategy. The software industry has gone cloud crazy over the past few years and Ellie Mae has not been immune. A key part of its

strategy is to emphasize the software-as-a-service (SaaS) incarnations of its Encompass offerings.

Mergers and Acquisitions

In October 2015 Ellie Mae acquired Mortgage Returns a provider of on-demand customer relationship management and marketing automation tools for mortgage lenders.

Company Background

Ellie Mae was founded in 1997 and launched the first version of its transaction network in 2000. The Encompass software suite came out in 2003.

EXECUTIVES

EVP Sales and Marketing, Cathleen Schreiner Gates, $272,083 total compensation
President and CEO, Jonathan H. Corr, age 51, $375,000 total compensation
SVP Insurance Services, Joseph Tyrrell, $272,500 total compensation
CFO, Matthew LaVay, age 49
EVP Technology and Operations, Peter Hirsch
EVP Human Resources, Melanie Simpson
SVP and CIO, John Abel
SVP Engineering, Dinesh Shahane
Vice President Product Strategy, Jonas Moe
Senior Vice President Marketing, Susan Scarth
Senior Vice President Marketing, Susan Chenoweth
Vice President Professional Services, Kathleen Haley
Vice President Legal Services, Wendy Nemeroff
Vice President General Manager, Terri Davis
Vice President CRM Solutions, Jim Blatt
Vice President Cloud Infrastructure and Operations, Satheesh Ravala
Vice President Human Resources, Sunita Liggin
Vice President Of Operations, Ketan Joshi
Chairman, Sig Anderman
Auditors: Grant Thornton LLP

LOCATIONS

HQ: Ellie Mae Inc
4420 Rosewood Drive, Suite 500, Pleasanton, CA 94588
Phone: 925 227-7000   **Fax:** 925 227-9030
Web: www.elliemae.com

PRODUCTS/OPERATIONS

2015 Sales

	% of total
On-demand	98
On-premise	2
Total	**100**

Selected Products and Services
Encompass Compliance Service
Encompass Product & Pricing Service
Encompass Fraud Service
Encompass Flood Service
Encompass 4506-T Service
Encompass Appraisal Service
Encompass Title & Closing Center
Implementation Packages
Implementation Education Packages
Additional Implementation Services
Customer Acquisition and Relationship Management
Processing
Risk Management and Business Reporting
Connectivity Personalization and Integration
Underwriting
Secondary Marketing and Trade Management
Closing and Funding
Credit Report
Product Eligibility and Pricing Engine
Automated Underwriting

COMPETITORS

D+H USA	Prymak
DH Corporation	Verisk
Dexma	Wolters Kluwer
FirstPoint Inc	WowTools
Fiserv	Xerox
ISGN	eLynx
MGIC Investment	
McCracken Financial Solutions	

HISTORICAL FINANCIALS
Company Type: Public

Income Statement   FYE: December 31

	REVENUE ($ mil.)	NET INCOME ($ mil.)	NET PROFIT MARGIN	EMPLOYEES
12/17	417.0	52.8	12.7%	1,480
12/16	360.2	37.7	10.5%	1,069
12/15	253.9	22.2	8.8%	857
12/14	161.5	14.8	9.2%	640
12/13	128.4	12.5	9.8%	407
Annual Growth	**34.2%**	**43.2%**	**—**	**38.1%**

2017 Year-End Financials

Debt ratio: —
Return on equity: 7.6%
Cash ($ mil.): 137.7
Current ratio: 3.91
Long-term debt ($ mil.): —
No. of shares (mil.): 34.2
Dividends
Yield: —
Payout: —
Market value ($ mil.): 3,060.0

	STOCK PRICE ($) FY Close	P/E High/Low	PER SHARE ($) Earnings	Dividends	Book Value
12/17	89.40	74 52	1.48	0.00	21.48
12/16	83.68	89 49	1.15	0.00	19.44
12/15	60.23	109 53	0.72	0.00	9.84
12/14	40.32	80 45	0.50	0.00	8.75
12/13	26.87	70 40	0.44	0.00	7.49
Annual Growth	**35.1%**	**— —**	**35.4%**	**—**	**30.1%**

Ellington Residential Mortgaging Real Estate Investment Trust

Ellington Financial LLC is ready to double its money. The investment firm formed Ellington Residential Mortgage REIT a real estate residential trust (REIT) to invest in agency residential mortgage-backed securities (Agency RMBS) or those guaranteed by federally sponsored entities Fannie Mae Freddie Mac and Ginnie Mae. (Agency RMBS carry less risk than privately issued mortgage securities.) The trust's portfolio is balanced out with about 10% non-Agency RMBS such as residential whole mortgage loans mortgage servicing rights (MSRs) and residential real properties. (Non-Agency RMBS carry more risk but might offer better returns.) The trust went public in 2013.

IPO

The trust plans to spend at least 80% of the proceeds from its $129 million IPO to invest in Agency RMBS backed by 15-year and 30-year fixed rate mortgages. The remaining 20% will be used to invest in Agency RMBS backed by hybrid and adjustable rate mortgages and non-Agency RMBS backed by Alt-A prime and subprime mortgages.

Operations

Ellington Residential Mortgage REIT formed in August 2012 by affiliates of Ellington Financial and investment firm The Blackstone Group. As a REIT it is exempt from paying federal income tax as long as it makes a quarterly distribution to shareholders. And as a trust Ellington Residential Mortgage does not have any employees. It is externally managed and advised by Ellington Residential Mortgage Management LLC.

Strategy

The company's investment philosophy revolves around pursuing various types of mortgage-backed securities and related assets without any restriction as to ratings structure or position in the capital structure. Of course there are risks associated with mortgage investments but Ellington believes balancing its portfolio with agency-backed securities somewhat levels its risk.

Auditors: PricewaterhouseCoopers LLP

LOCATIONS

HQ: Ellington Residential Mortgaging Real Estate Investment Trust
53 Forest Avenue, Old Greenwich, CT 06870
Phone: 203 698-1200
Web: www.earnreit.com

COMPETITORS

AG Mortgage Investment Trust	JAVELIN Mortgage MFA Financial
American Capital Agency Corp.	New York Mortgage Trust
Bimini Capital Management	Putnam Mortgage Two Harbors
Hatteras Financial	Western Asset Mortgage
Invesco Mortgage Capital	ZAIS Financial

HISTORICAL FINANCIALS
Company Type: Public

Income Statement   FYE: December 31

	REVENUE ($ mil.)	NET INCOME ($ mil.)	NET PROFIT MARGIN	EMPLOYEES
12/17	35.5	10.7	30.4%	160
12/16	26.1	11.9	45.5%	160
12/15	11.4	0.0	0.3%	160
12/14	26.4	16.1	61.2%	150
12/13	5.4	(1.9)	—	130
Annual Growth	**59.7%**	**—**	**—**	**5.3%**

2017 Year-End Financials

Debt ratio: —
Return on equity: 6.4%
Cash ($ mil.): 56.1
Current ratio: 0.11
Long-term debt ($ mil.): —
No. of shares (mil.): 13.3
Dividends
Yield: 0.1%
Payout: 168.8%
Market value ($ mil.): 161.0

	STOCK PRICE ($) FY Close	P/E High/Low	PER SHARE ($) Earnings	Dividends	Book Value
12/17	12.04	17 13	0.93	1.57	14.45
12/16	13.01	11 8	1.31	1.65	15.52
12/15	12.35	— —	(0.00)	2.00	15.86
12/14	16.27	10 9	1.77	2.20	17.86
12/13	15.38	— —	(0.29)	1.14	18.29
Annual Growth	**(5.9%)**	**— —**	**—**	**8.3%**	**(5.7%)**

Embassy Bancorp Inc

EXECUTIVES

Prin, David M Lobach
Auditors: Baker Tilly Virchow Krause, LLP

LOCATIONS

HQ: Embassy Bancorp Inc
One Hundred Gateway Drive, Suite 100, Bethlehem, PA
18017
Phone: 610 882-8800
Web: www.embassybank.com

HISTORICAL FINANCIALS
Company Type: Public

Income Statement   FYE: December 31

	ASSETS ($ mil.)	NET INCOME ($ mil.)	INCOME AS % OF ASSETS	EMPLOYEES
12/17	996.9	7.3	0.7%	84
12/16	924.2	7.1	0.8%	83
12/15	804.0	7.4	0.9%	76
12/14	719.0	6.4	0.9%	69
12/13	670.8	5.5	0.8%	71
Annual Growth 10.4%		7.2%	—	4.3%

2017 Year-End Financials

Return on assets: 0.7%
Return on equity: 9.5%
Long-term debt ($ mil.): —
No. of shares (mil.): 7.4
Sales ($ mil): 37.0

Dividends
Yield: 0.0%
Payout: 14.4%
Market value ($ mil.): 119.0

	STOCK PRICE ($) FY Close	P/E High/Low	PER SHARE ($) Earnings	Dividends	Book Value
12/17	16.00	16 13	0.97	0.14	10.71
12/16	13.00	14 11	0.96	0.13	9.84
12/15	10.91	11 10	1.00	0.10	9.19
12/14	10.30	12 9	0.87	0.06	8.34
12/13	7.65	12 7	0.76	0.05	7.38
Annual Growth 20.3%		— —	6.3%	29.4%	9.7%

Emerald Expositions Events Inc

Auditors: PricewaterhouseCoopers LLP

LOCATIONS

HQ: Emerald Expositions Events Inc
31910 Del Obispo Street, Suite 200, San Juan Capistrano,
CA 92675
Phone: 949 226-5700
Web: www.emeraldexpositions.com

HISTORICAL FINANCIALS
Company Type: Public

Income Statement   FYE: December 31

	REVENUE ($ mil.)	NET INCOME ($ mil.)	NET PROFIT MARGIN	EMPLOYEES
12/17	348.2	81.8	23.5%	427
12/16	323.7	22.1	6.8%	430
12/15	306.4	19.6	6.4%	0
12/14	273.5	(7.6)	—	0
Annual Growth 8.4%		—	—	—

2017 Year-End Financials

Debt ratio: 33.8%
Return on equity: 12.6%
Cash ($ mil.): 10.9
Current ratio: 0.42
Long-term debt ($ mil.): 548.5

No. of shares (mil.): 72.6
Dividends
Yield: 0.0%
Payout: 18.5%
Market value ($ mil.): 1,477.0

	STOCK PRICE ($) FY Close	P/E High/Low	PER SHARE ($) Earnings	Dividends	Book Value
12/17	20.34	20 16	1.13	0.21	10.48
12/16	0.00	— —	0.35	0.00	8.53
Annual Growth —		— —222.9%	—	22.9%	

Emergent BioSolutions Inc

Emergent BioSolutions is preparing for a bioterrorism or pandemic worst-case scenario. The company develops and produces vaccines that treat or protect against infectious diseases and bio-agents. The company supplies BioThrax (the US's only FDA-approved anthrax vaccine) primarily to the US Department of Defense (DOD) Centers for Disease Control (CDC) and the US Department of Health and Human Services (HHS). It is also developing a post-exposure treatment for anthrax. In 2016 the firm spun off its biosciences division which works on therapies for leukemia and lymphona and vaccines for such infectious diseases as influenza as the new public company Aptevo Therapeutics.

Operations

Prior to the split Emergent BioSolutions operated in two segments: Biodefense (more than 80% of revenue) and Biosciences. The Biodefense segment focuses on chemical biological radiological nuclear and explosives threats while Biosciences focused on therapeutics and vaccines in hematology cancer transplantation infectious disease and autoimmunity.

Products marketed by Biodefense include Bio-Thrax BAT (the only FDA-approved heptavalent for the treatment of botulinum disease) Anthrasil (pending approval for the treatment of anthrax) VIGIV (the only FDA-licensed therapeutic addressing adverse effects of smallpox vaccination) and Reactive Skin Decontamination Lotion or RSDL (for the removal or neutralization of chemical agents from the skin). Its investigational candidates are anthrax vaccines NuThrax and PreviThrax and GC-072 the lead compound in the EV-035 series of broad spectrum antibiotics (acquired from Evolva in late 2014).

Meanshile the Biosciences' portfolio comprised four products acquired with Cangene Corporation in 2014 (WinRho SDF for the treatment of autoimmune platelet disorder HepaGam for the treatment of hepatitis B VARIZIG for the treatment of chicken pox and shingles and episil for pain relief) as well as investigational state candidates (IXINITY for bleeding episodes in people with hemophilia B ES414 for the treatment of prostate cancer and otlertuzumab for chronic lymphocytic leukemia). Biosciences also provided contract manufacturing services.

Emergent BioSolutions contracts with a third-party filling laboratory to measure BioThrax into dosage vials.

Geographic Reach

Emergent BioSolutions manufactures BioThrax at its production facility in Lansing Michigan. It also operates offices and laboratories in Maryland and Washington as well as in Germany. With its acquisition of Cangene Corporation in 2014 the company gained facilities in Winnipeg Manitoba in Canada.

International markets include Europe the Middle East and the Asia/Pacific region.

Sales and Marketing

Emergent BioSolutions markets its products primarily to US state and local governments and domestic non-governmental organizations. The US is the primary buyer of its Biodefense products providing funding for the development of drug candidates.

Its commercial operations team focuses on selling to hospitals hematology clinics medical oncology clinics and transplant centers. Products are distributed in the US through wholesalers including Cardinal Health McKesson and Amerisource-Bergen. In Canada commercial products are distributed exclusively by Canadian Blood Services and Héma-Québec.

Financial Performance

Emergent BioSolutions' revenues had been growing slowly until 2014 when they rose 44% to $450.1 million on higher product sales contract manufacturing business and contracts grants and collaborations. The firm's RSDL product had increased sales that year; additionally products and contract manufacturing business gained from the Cangene acquisition provided new revenue sources. Finally contracts grants and collaborations revenues increased due to funding for the development of Anthrasil and BAT both acquired during 2014.

Net income has followed revenue trends. In 2014 it rose 18% to $37 million driven by the higher revenue but partially offset by a decrease in other income. Cash flow from operations rose 16% to $112 million due to an increase in cash provided by inventories and other factors.

Strategy

While Emergent BioSolutions dominates the anthrax vaccine niche its focus on a single niche product can leave it vulnerable to fluctuations in demand from a relatively narrow customer base. To reduce its vulnerability the company has broadened its customer base in recent years to include state and local governments (who might want their own stockpiles for first responders) as well as foreign governments. It has also built up its non-anthrax pipeline through acquisitions.

The company's overall product development strategy includes acquiring new candidates through company acquisitions and in-licensing transactions. In 2013 it bought the Healthcare Protective Products Division of Bracco Diagnostics Inc. and added the division's RSDL to its product offerings. Two years later it acquired biopharmaceutical Cangene Corporation adding BAT Anthrasil VIGIV WinRho Hepagam VARIZIG to its portfolio. In addition to its acquisitions the company has also divested its stake in a tuberculosis vaccine candidate and saw Pfizer terminate a collaboration agreement related to the development of a rheumatoid arthritis treatment and Abbott Laboratories terminate a collaboration for development of a leukemia treatment.

In 2015 the FDA approved IXINITY and AIGIV for the treatment of bleeding episodes in patients with hemophilia B and inhalational anthrax respectively.

Emergent BioSolutions entered into an agreement with MorphSys in 2014; they will co-develop and commercialize the novel oncology immunotherapeutic MOR 209/ES414 which targets prostate cancer.

In 2016 the company spun off its Biosciences division into Aptevo Therapeutics a separate standalone public company. The move allows each division to operate as pure-play companies with separate areas of focus.

Mergers and Acquisitions

In 2018 Emergent BioSolutions acquired private firm Adapt Pharma which makes Narcan the only needle-free drug that treats opioid overdose. The deal was valued at up to $735 million including an upfront payment of $635 million.

Later that year the company acquired specialty vaccines firm PaxVax for $270 million. That deal brought Emergent Solutions two marketed vaccines — Vivotif (for typhoid fever) and Vaxchora (for cholera).

EXECUTIVES

SVP and Chief Scientific Officer, W. James Jackson, age 58
President and CEO, Daniel J. Abdun-Nabi, age 63, $589,695 total compensation
EVP Corporate Services Division CFO and Treasurer, Robert G. (Bob) Kramer, age 61, $428,560 total compensation
EVP and President Corporate Affairs Division, Allen Shofe
EVP and President BioDefense Division, Adam R. Havey, age 47, $332,648 total compensation
EVP and General Counsel, A.B. Cruz
VP Regulatory Affairs, David Wonnacott
Senior Vice President Corporate Development, Yasmine Gibellini
Vice President And Chief Security Officer, Jeff Hauk
Vice President Commercial Markets, Jeff Hackman
Vice President Manufacturing Operations, Shawn Kirk
Senior Vice President Antibody Therapeutics Business Unit Head, Laura Saward
Chairman, Fuad El-Hibri, age 60
Auditors: Ernst & Young LLP

LOCATIONS

HQ: Emergent BioSolutions Inc
400 Professional Drive, Suite 400, Gaithersburg, MD 20879
Phone: 240 631-3200
Web: www.emergentbiosolutions.com

PRODUCTS/OPERATIONS

2014 Sales

	$ mil.	% of total
Products	308.3	68
Contracts & grants	110.9	25
Contract manufacturing	30.9	7
Total	**450.1**	**100**

2014 Sales

	% of total
Biodefense	82
Biosciences	18
Total	**100**

Selected Acquisitions and Ventures

COMPETITORS

Altimmune	Human Genome Sciences
Amgen	Pfenex
Biogen	Pfizer
Elusys Therapeutics	Roche Holding
Genentech	Soligenix

HISTORICAL FINANCIALS
Company Type: Public

Income Statement
FYE: December 31

	REVENUE ($ mil.)	NET INCOME ($ mil.)	NET PROFIT MARGIN	EMPLOYEES
12/17	560.8	82.5	14.7%	1,256
12/16	488.7	51.7	10.6%	1,098
12/15	522.7	62.8	12.0%	1,292
12/14	450.1	36.7	8.2%	1,280
12/13	312.7	31.1	10.0%	1,353
Annual Growth	**15.7%**	**27.6%**	**—**	**(1.8%)**

2017 Year-End Financials

Debt ratio: 1.2%	No. of shares (mil.): 49.4
Return on equity: 10.9%	Dividends
Cash ($ mil.): 178.2	Yield: —
Current ratio: 4.85	Payout: —
Long-term debt ($ mil.): 13.4	Market value ($ mil.): 2,296.0

	STOCK PRICE ($) FY Close	P/E High/Low	PER SHARE ($) Earnings	Dividends	Book Value
12/17	46.47	24 14	1.71	0.00	18.47
12/16	32.84	34 19	1.13	0.00	14.69
12/15	40.01	25 16	1.41	0.00	16.75
12/14	27.23	29 20	0.88	0.00	14.67
12/13	22.99	28 15	0.85	0.00	13.37
Annual Growth	**19.2%**	**— —**	**19.1%**	**—**	**8.4%**

Empire State Realty OP LP

Auditors: Ernst & Young LLP

LOCATIONS

HQ: Empire State Realty OP LP
111 West 33rd Street, 12th Floor, New York, NY 10120
Phone: 212 687-8700
Web: www.empirestaterealtytrust.com

HISTORICAL FINANCIALS
Company Type: Public

Income Statement
FYE: December 31

	REVENUE ($ mil.)	NET INCOME ($ mil.)	NET PROFIT MARGIN	EMPLOYEES
12/17	712.4	118.2	16.6%	831
12/16	678.0	107.2	15.8%	819
12/15	657.6	79.9	12.2%	850
12/14	635.3	70.2	11.1%	862
12/13	127.5	193.4	151.6%	607
Annual Growth	**53.7%**	**(11.6%)**	**—**	**8.2%**

2017 Year-End Financials

Debt ratio: 42.9%	No. of shares (mil.): 300.4
Return on equity: —	Dividends
Cash ($ mil.): 530.2	Yield: 0.0%
Current ratio: 0.89	Payout: 107.6%
Long-term debt ($ mil.): 971.5	Market value ($ mil.): 6,212.0

	STOCK PRICE ($) FY Close	P/E High/Low	PER SHARE ($) Earnings	Dividends	Book Value
12/17	20.68	56 50	0.39	0.42	6.58
12/16	19.98	58 38	0.38	0.40	6.63
12/15	18.04	65 54	0.29	0.34	5.13
12/14	17.49	66 48	0.27	0.34	5.17
12/13	14.07	104 16	0.79	0.08	4.09
Annual Growth	**10.1%**	**— —**	**(16.2%)**	**51.6%**	**12.7%**

Empire State Realty Trust Inc

If King Kong were around he'd be an executive at Empire State Realty Trust. The self-administered and self-managed real estate investment trust (REIT) formed in mid-2011 to take over a portfolio of high-profile Manhattan properties from its previous owners the Malkin family. Its flagship property is of course the 102-story Empire State Building but the trust also owns more than a dozen other buildings in the greater New York area totaling almost 7.7 million sq. ft. of office and retail space. In addition it plans to build a 340000-sq.-ft. building at the train station in Stamford Connecticut. Empire State Realty Trust went public in 2013 raising $929 million.

Operations

As a REIT Empire State Realty Trust doesn't pay federal income tax as long as it distributes 90% of its income back to stockholders in the form of dividends. Empire State Realty Trust was formed to consolidate a number of companies owned by the Malkin family including Malkin Properties a property manager and leasing agent and Malkin Construction a general contractor for its renovation projects. Since REITs can't have a shareholder owning more than 10% Empire State Realty Trust plans to use the proceeds from its IPO to pay off existing shareholders namely the Malkin family and loans the Malkin family made to the company.

The 2.8 million-sq.-ft. Empire State Building is the tallest building in Manhattan. Its top five tenants are Coty the FDIC Host Services Li & Fung and Walgreen's. Besides tenant revenue it makes money from two observatories and broadcasting facilities. Tourists pay anywhere from $20 to $50 to ride the elevators to the building's observation decks on either the 86th or 102nd floors and the company sold more than 4 million tickets in 2010. In addition to being a tourist attraction the Empire State Building also serves as an antenna site for broadcasting operations with more than a dozen licensed TV stations and about 20 licensed radio stations using the building to transmit signals. Empire State Realty Trust has spent $123 million renovating the building and estimates another $230 million is needed to finish the job by 2016.

Company Background

Chairman Emeritus Peter Malkin joined his father-in-law Lawrence Wien in the real estate business back in 1958. Wien had been the real estate partner of Harry Helmsley (who founded Helmsley Enterprises) since the 1940s. (Peter's son Anthony Malkin is now Chairman CEO and President of Empire State Realty Trust.) The Manhattan office properties that make up Empire State Realty Trust's portfolio were acquired between 1950 and 1979 (Wien first bought the Empire State Building in 1961 for $65 million). The Empire State Building has changed hands over the years and been involved in lawsuits with affiliates of the Helmsley family (including the notorious Leona Helmsley) and Donald Trump whose Trump Organization sold its stake in 2002. Malkin Properties gained day-to-day management of the Empire State Building in 2006.

EXECUTIVES

Senior Vice President Leasing Marketing, Fred Posniak
Senior Vice president, Mark Labell
Executive Vice President General Counsel and Secretary, Thomas N Keltner
Senior Vice President Director of Leasing and Marketing, Ryan Kass
Vice President Controller, Pierre Nelson
VICE PRESIDENT SENIOR CREDIT OFFICER, John Hogg
Vice President Senior Property Controller, Tammy Fisher
Auditors: Ernst & Young LLP

LOCATIONS

HQ: Empire State Realty Trust Inc
111 West 33rd Street, 12th Floor, New York, NY 10120
Phone: 212 687-8700
Web: www.empirestaterealtytrust.com

COMPETITORS

Boston Properties	Silverstein Properties
Brookfield Office Properties	The Trump Organization
Equity Office	Tishman Construction
LeFrak Organization	Tishman Hotel
Related	Tishman Speyer
SL Green Realty	Vornado Realty

HISTORICAL FINANCIALS

Company Type: Public

Income Statement   FYE: December 31

	REVENUE ($ mil.)	NET INCOME ($ mil.)	NET PROFIT MARGIN	EMPLOYEES
12/17	712.4	63.5	8.9%	831
12/16	678.0	52.3	7.7%	819
12/15	657.6	34.6	5.3%	850
12/14	635.3	27.1	4.3%	862
12/13	127.5	75.2	59.0%	607
Annual Growth	53.7%	(4.1%)	—	8.2%

2017 Year-End Financials

Debt ratio: 42.9%
Return on equity: 5.4%
Cash ($ mil.): 464.3
Current ratio: 3.36
Long-term debt ($ mil.): 1,688.7

No. of shares (mil.): 161.4
Dividends
  Yield: 0.0%
  Payout: 107.6%
Market value ($ mil.): 3,315.0

	STOCK PRICE ($) FY Close	P/E High/Low		PER SHARE ($) Earnings	Dividends	Book Value
12/17	20.53	55	49	0.39	0.42	7.28
12/16	20.19	58	39	0.38	0.40	7.46
12/15	18.07	63	53	0.29	0.34	4.44
12/14	17.58	66	53	0.27	0.34	4.45
12/13	15.30	20	17	0.79	0.08	4.03
Annual Growth	7.6%	—	—	(16.2%)	51.6%	16.0%

Enanta Pharmaceuticals Inc

Enanta Pharmaceuticals is getting hip to Hep C. The biotech firm is developing treatments for viral infections including hepatitis C (HCV) a virus that can lead to chronic liver diseases such as cirrhosis organ failure and cancer. The company's first licensed product which is licensed to AbbVie is paritaprevir is a protease inhibitor for use against HCV. Enanta also has four small molecule drugs under development: glecaprevir another protease inhibitor for the treatment for HCV; the similar EDP-239 and EDP-494; and EDP-305 which is being studied for the treatment of non-alcoholic steatohepatitis (NASH) and primary biliary cholangitis (PBC). In late 2014 Enanta discontinued its biodefense antibiotic program.

Operations

Enanta Pharmaceuticals makes most of its money from royalties for its protease inhibitors. It also earns milestone payments related to those same compounds.

Financial Performance

The biotech has yet to make any revenue from product sales but rather has earned money on collaborations with other pharmaceuticals (primarily AbbVie) and from a now-closed government contract to develop antibiotics for biodefense purposes.

In fiscal 2016 (ended September) Enanta had revenue of $88.3 million a 45% decline from the previous year. This was primarily due to a significant drop in milestone payments from AbbVie as well as a drop in funding from the government (its antibiotics contract ended during 2015). Net in-

come that year totaled $21.7 million a 73% decline from fiscal 2015. Lower revenue and higher R&D expenses led to the drop in net income.

Strategy

Enanta Pharmaceuticals is currently focused on three disease areas: the liver disease NASH respiratory syncytial virus (RSV) and hepatitis B. It also continues to develop treatments for HCV. The company sees plenty of opportunity and hopes to introduce new treatments for unmet medical needs in these areas (NASH has no approved treatments for instance.). It uses funding from its AbbVie collaboration to advance its development pipeline; it is also open to other partnerships to finance its R&D activities.

EXECUTIVES

SVP Finance and Administration and CFO, Paul J. Mellett, age 63, $344,862 total compensation
President CEO and Director, Jay R. Luly, age 62, $520,748 total compensation
SVP and General Counsel, Nathaniel S. Gardiner, age 65
SVP New Product Strategy and Development, Timothy D. Ocain, age 61
SVP and Chief Medical Officer, Nathalie Adda
Chairman, Bruce L.A. Carter
Auditors: PricewaterhouseCoopers LLP

LOCATIONS

HQ: Enanta Pharmaceuticals Inc
500 Arsenal Street, Watertown, MA 02472
Phone: 617 607-0800
Web: www.enanta.com

PRODUCTS/OPERATIONS

2016 Sales

	$ mil.	% of total
AbbVie Agreement		
Royalties	57.7	65
Milestones	30.0	34
NIAID contract	0.6	1
Total	**88.3**	**100**

COMPETITORS

Achillion	Johnson & Johnson
Boehringer Ingelheim	Merck
Bristol-Myers Squibb	PTC Therapeutics
Gilead Sciences	Vertex Pharmaceuticals

HISTORICAL FINANCIALS

Company Type: Public

Income Statement   FYE: September 30

	REVENUE ($ mil.)	NET INCOME ($ mil.)	NET PROFIT MARGIN	EMPLOYEES
09/18	206.6	71.9	34.8%	113
09/17	102.8	17.7	17.2%	89
09/16	88.2	21.6	24.5%	76
09/15	160.8	78.9	49.1%	69
09/14	47.7	34.4	72.1%	52
Annual Growth	44.2%	20.2%	—	21.4%

2018 Year-End Financials

Debt ratio: 0.0%
Return on equity: 20.7%
Cash ($ mil.): 63.9
Current ratio: 23.74
Long-term debt ($ mil.): 0.2

No. of shares (mil.): 19.4
Dividends
  Yield: —
  Payout: —
Market value ($ mil.): 1,657.0

STOCK PRICE ($) FY Close	P/E High/Low	PER SHARE ($) Earnings	Dividends	Book Value
09/18	85.46	34 12	3.48	0.00	20.30
09/17	46.80	50 24	0.91	0.00	15.78
09/16	26.61	36 18	1.13	0.00	14.18
09/15	36.14	12 7	4.09	0.00	12.62
09/14	39.57	25 10	1.80	0.00	7.99
Annual Growth	21.2%	— —	17.9%	—	26.2%

Encore Capital Group Inc

Encore Capital Group hopes to collect from stubborn borrowers again and again. The firm and its Midland Credit Management subsidiary purchase discounted non-performing consumer receivables that banks credit unions consumer and auto finance companies credit card issuers telecommunications firms retailers and other lenders have given up on. The group then does its best to collect the money via phone direct mail third-party collection agencies and legal action; it employs skip-tracing to track down stubborn debtors. Subsidiary Ascension Capital Group provides bankruptcy support services to the financial services industry. Encore collects debts in the US the UK Ireland Colombia Peru New Zealand and the Philippines.

Operations
Encore Capital operated two business segments during 2015: Portfolio Purchasing and Recovery (which made up 97% of the company's total revenue) and Tax Liens (3%) through Propel Financial Services (which it sold in early 2016).

The company boasts one of the debt collection industry's largest financially distressed consumer databases. Volume is important for Encore Capital as the company pursues collections on only a fraction of accounts and generates payments from less than 1% of them. Practicing a "friendly but firm approach" its account managers evaluate customers' ability to pay then develop tailored payment programs. The company utilizes proprietary statistical and behavioral models account-level valuation methods customized software applications and purchased credit bureau information to determine its collection strategies.

Some of the Encore Capital's major subsidiaries include Cabot Credit Management in the UK US-based Asset Acceptance Capital Corp Baycorp in the Australasia region Europe's Grove Capital Management and Latin America's Refinancia S.A. among others.

Geographic Reach
The San Diego-headquartered collection company operates in 14 countries worldwide in the Americas Europe and the Australasia region. Its largest market is the US where it generated 64% of its revenue during 2015 while Europe (including the UK Spain and Australia) accounted for another 32%. Encore US operating centers are in San Diego; Phoenix; Houston; Dallas; San Antonio; McAllen Texas; St. Cloud Minnesota; Warren Michigan; New Freedom Pennsylvania; and Roanoke Virginia.

Sales and Marketing
Encore Capital markets its services through direct mail call centers and third-party collection agencies.

Financial Performance
The debt collector's annual revenues have more than doubled since 2011 as portfolio acquisitions and higher gross collections have been rising over the years. Encore Capital's profits have also been trending higher as the firm has kept a lid on rising costs.

Encore Capital's revenue climbed 8% to $1.2 billion during 2015 as its portfolio recoveries rose by 8% for the year with higher portfolio balances and better recovery rates.

Despite revenue growth in 2015 the company's net income fell 56% to $45.14 million for the year mostly as it took a $49 million loss on the sale of its tax lien business subsidiary Propel Financial Services. Encore Capital's operating cash levels rose 3% to $114 million thanks to favorable working capital changes related to its accounts payable accrued liabilities and other liabilities.

Strategy
Encore Capital continues to acquire new portfolios of card telecom and consumer bankruptcy charge-offs. The firm is also expanding its international reach through portfolio acquisitions and recovery operations in Latin America Australasia and India (as of early 2016).

Mergers and Acquisitions
In September 2015 expanding its reach into the Australia and New Zealand markets Encore Capital bought a 50.25% stake in debt resolution specialist Baycorp.

In June 2015 UK-subsidiary Cabot Credit Management Limited bought UK-based consumer debt acquirer and collector Hillesden Securities Ltd for ó180.6 million.

In August 2014 the company purchased Atlantic Credit & Finance (ACF) a collector of fresh higher-balance accounts in the US for approximately $70 million in cash.

In April 2014 Encore acquired a controlling stake in Grove Capital Management a purchaser of credit portfolios specializing on UK insolvencies and Spanish assets.

In February 2014 under Encore's ownership Cabot bought Marlin Financial Group an acquirer of non-performing consumer debt in the UK for ó295 million ($481 million).

In December 2013 it purchased Refinancia S.A. a manager of non-performing loans in Colombia and Peru. Refinancia also offered portfolio management services to banks for non-performing loans.

In July 2013 Encore Capital expanded its business in the UK with the purchase of Cabot Credit Management a debt management firm that operates in England and Ireland for ó115 million ($177 million).

In June 2013 Encore acquired Asset Acceptance Capital Corp. a debt recovery firm in the US.

Company Background
In early 2016 the company sold its San Antonio Texas-based Propel Acquisition LLC subsidiary which acquired and serviced residential and commercial tax liens on property. The firm was the largest tax lien company in Texas.

EXECUTIVES

Senior Vice President Operations, Jim Syran
President International, Paul J. Grinberg, age 57, $563,750 total compensation
SVP Information Technology and CIO, Carl Eberling
President and CEO, Ashish Masih, age 52, $375,417 total compensation
SVP; Managing Director India Operations, Anupam Arun
EVP and CFO, Jonathan C. Clark, age 59, $508,333 total compensation
Vice President Business Development, Amy Anuk
Vice President Operations, Iliana Gonzalez
Senior Vice President Chief Scientific Officer, Christopher Trepel
Vice President Consumer Marketing, Brian Enneking
Senior Vice President Indian Operations, Manu Rikhye
Vice President Investor Relations, Bruce Thomas
Vice President India Operations, Manu Sharma
Vice President Finance, Greg Moy
Vice President Human Resources, Marie Burris
Vice President Legal and Corporate Affairs, Melissa Resslar
Assistant Vice President Call Center Technology, Deepak Cherukuri
Vice President And Controller, Glen Freter
Vice President of Information Technology, David Yoo
Vice President Information Technology, Vikas Sehgal
Vice President Human Resources, Michael Haubenstock
VICE PRESIDENT DEPUTY GENERAL COUNSEL, Steve Dietz
VICE PRESIDENT OPERATIONS, Darin B Herring
Vice President Operations Strategy and Analytics, Deepak Maheshwari
Chairman, T. Willem (Will) Mesdag, age 65
Board Member, Francis Quinlan
Board Member, Norman Sorensen
Auditors: BDO USA, LLP

LOCATIONS

HQ: Encore Capital Group Inc
3111 Camino Del Rio North, Suite 103, San Diego, CA 92108
Phone: 877 445-4581
Web: www.encorecapital.com

PRODUCTS/OPERATIONS

2015 Sales

	$ mil.	% of total
Portfolio purchasing and recovery	1,130.0	97
Tax lien business	31.6	3
Total	1,161.6	100

Selected Subsidiaries
Ascension Capital Group Inc.
Cabot Financial (UK Ireland)
Grove Financial (UK)
Marlin Financial Group (UK)
MCM Midland Management Costa Rica S.r.l.
Midland Credit Management Inc.
Midland Credit Management India Private Limited
Midland Funding LLC
Midland Funding NCC-2 Corporation
Midland India LLC
Midland International LLC
Midland Portfolio Services Inc.
MRC Receivables Corporation
Propel Financial Services (US)
Refinancia S.A. (Colombia Peru)

COMPETITORS

Asta Funding
Expert Global
  Solutions
FirstCity Financial
GC Services
Genesis Financial
  Solutions
Leland Scott &
  Associates
Nationwide Recovery
  Systems
PRA Group

HISTORICAL FINANCIALS

Company Type: Public

Income Statement   FYE: December 31

	REVENUE ($ mil.)	NET INCOME ($ mil.)	NET PROFIT MARGIN	EMPLOYEES
12/17	1,187.0	83.2	7.0%	8,200
12/16	1,029.2	76.5	7.4%	6,700
12/15	1,161.5	45.1	3.9%	6,700
12/14	1,072.7	103.7	9.7%	5,400
12/13	773.3	75.3	9.7%	5,300
Annual Growth	11.3%	2.5%	—	11.5%

2017 Year-End Financials

Debt ratio: 76.7%
Return on equity: 14.5%
Cash ($ mil.): 212.1
Current ratio: 1.10
Long-term debt ($ mil.): 3,446.8

No. of shares (mil.): 25.8
Dividends
  Yield: —
  Payout: —
Market value ($ mil.): 1,086.0

	STOCK PRICE ($) FY Close	P/E High/Low		PER SHARE ($) Earnings	Dividends	Book Value
12/17	42.10	15	9	3.15	0.00	22.55
12/16	28.65	10	6	2.96	0.00	21.85
12/15	29.08	25	16	1.69	0.00	23.59
12/14	44.40	13	10	3.77	0.00	24.15
12/13	50.26	17	9	2.87	0.00	22.47
Annual Growth	(4.3%)	—	—	2.4%	—	0.1%

Energy Recovery Inc

Desalination makes seawater potable; Energy Recovery (ERI) makes desalination practical. The company designs develops and manufactures energy recovery devices used in sea water reverse osmosis (SWRO) desalination plants. The SWRO process is energy intensive using high pressure to drive salt water through membranes to produce fresh water. The company's main product the PX Pressure Exchanger helps recapture and recycle up to 98% of the energy available in the high-pressure reject stream a by-product of the SWRO process. The PX can reduce the energy consumption of a desalination plant by up to 60% compared with a plant lacking an energy recovery device. Subsidiary Pump Engineering also makes high pressure pumps.

Geographic Reach

ERI has its headquarters and main manufacturing center located in California. Other offices reside in Shanghai and Dubai.

Sales and Marketing

Primary customers for ERI consist of international engineering procurement and construction firms that build large desalination plants. Energy Recovery also sells its products and services to OEMs of pumps and other water-related equip-

ment for small to mid-size plants used in hotels cruise ships farm operations and power plants. Major customers have included IDE Technologies Ltd Thiess Degremont J.V. Hydrochem Acciona Agua and UTE Mostaganem.

Financial Performance

ERI's revenues decreased 29% from 2013 to 2014. The decrease was primarily due to significantly lower mega-project (MPD) shipments as well as lower OEM shipments. The decreases in MPD and OEM sales were offset by higher aftermarket shipments and revenue attributable to an oil and gas operating lease and lease buy-out.

ERI has suffered five straight years of net losses. Its $19 million net loss in 2014 was fueled by higher sales and marketing expenses coupled with the lower net revenue. Research and development expenses also spiked during 2014.

Strategy

Going forward ERI intends to benefit from a significant presence in Spain and other countries. Energy Recovery's lineup for example supports most of Spain's desalination plants. ERI also plans to enter into the material science and manufacturing of ceramics — a key component of its PX devices. The strategy aims to boost device production cut costs and improve product quality.

EXECUTIVES

Vp Of Corporate Strategy, Eric Siebert
VP Human Resources, Andrew Stroud
Auditors: DELOITTE & TOUCHE LLP

LOCATIONS

HQ: Energy Recovery Inc
  1717 Doolittle Drive, San Leandro, CA 94577
Phone: 510 483-7370
Web: www.energyrecovery.com

PRODUCTS/OPERATIONS

2014 Sales

	$ mil.	% of total
PX devices & related products & services	20.9	69
Turbochargers & pumps	8.7	29
Oil and gas product operating lease	0.8	2
Total	**30.4**	**100**

PRODUCTS

VorTeq
IsoBoost
IsoGen
IsoBoost for Syngas & Ammonia
PX Pressure Exchanger
Turbochargers
Pumping Systems

Selected Products

Energy recovery devices
  PX pressure exchanger devices (PX-300 the 65 series the 4S series and brackish PX devices)
  Turbochargers (HTCAT series the HALO line and the LPT series for brackish water desalination)
  High pressure and circulation pumps (AquaBold series the AquaSpire series and a line of small circulation pumps)
  Technical support and replacement parts

COMPETITORS

Flowserve
GE Water and Process
  Technologies
KSB AG
Seprotech
Siemens Water
  Technologies
Sulzer

HISTORICAL FINANCIALS

Company Type: Public

Income Statement   FYE: December 31

	REVENUE ($ mil.)	NET INCOME ($ mil.)	NET PROFIT MARGIN	EMPLOYEES
12/17	63.1	12.3	19.6%	133
12/16	54.7	1.0	1.9%	120
12/15	44.7	(11.6)	—	114
12/14	30.4	(18.7)	—	124
12/13	43.0	(3.1)	—	112
Annual Growth	10.1%	—	—	4.4%

2017 Year-End Financials

Debt ratio: 0.0%
Return on equity: 16.7%
Cash ($ mil.): 27.7
Current ratio: 6.36
Long-term debt ($ mil.): 0.0

No. of shares (mil.): 53.9
Dividends
  Yield: —
  Payout: —
Market value ($ mil.): 472.0

	STOCK PRICE ($) FY Close	P/E High/Low		PER SHARE ($) Earnings	Dividends	Book Value
12/17	8.75	49	27	0.22	0.00	1.53
12/16	10.35	818	268	0.02	0.00	1.23
12/15	7.07	—	—	(0.22)	0.00	1.21
12/14	5.27	—	—	(0.36)	0.00	1.35
12/13	5.55	—	—	(0.06)	0.00	1.69
Annual Growth	12.1%	—	—	—	—	(2.5%)

Ensign Group Inc

The Ensign Group hangs its insignia at more than 200 senior living facilities. Most of its facilities are skilled nursing homes but it also operates a number of assisted-living and independent-living facilities as well as combination nursing assisted and independent-living centers. Some locations also offer rehabilitation hospice and physical therapy services. Ensign's facilities are either owned by the company or operated under lease agreements. The health care provider operates some 120 long-term care centers with a capacity of some 13200 beds in about a dozen states in the southwestern and western US. Ensign also operates home health and hospice agencies.

Operations

Ensign is a holding company that counts among its operations more than 140 facilities 15 hospice companies and about 20 home health businesses. The company has a decentralized operating structure with its portfolio of homes organized into five regional operating companies. Each home operates under local — and largely independent — management. As part of its business the company relies on reimbursement from government and commercial health insurance plans as well as sales to private pay customers. It generates about three-fourths of its revenues from Medicaid and Medicare programs.

Geographic Reach

California-based Ensign has facilities in California Arizona Texas Washington Utah Idaho Colorado Nevada Iowa Nebraska Oregon South Carolina and Wisconsin. California and Texas are the company's largest markets home to more than 50% of its beds.

Financial Performance

Ensign reported revenue of $904.6 million in 2013 an increase of 10% versus 2012 on rising Medicare Medicaid managed care and private revenue. (The Medicare and Medicaid programs are Ensign's biggest payors contributing 72% of revenue in 2013.) Despite the double-digit rise in revenue net income declined 41% over the same period to $24 million due to US government settlement expenses incurred and an increase in the loss from discontinued operations. Some of Ensign's subsidiaries were the subject of an investigation (launched in 2006 and eventually settled in 2013) by the Department of Justice regarding claims submitted to the Medicare program.

Strategy

The company split its health care and real estate business into two separate publicly traded companies in June 2014. Ensign continued to provide health care services through its existing operations while the underlying real estate became owned by CareTrust REIT.

The company's growth strategy — and a growing population of increasingly infirm patients — has resulted in a decade of steady and significant revenue growth. Ensign primarily expands its operations by snapping up underperforming nursing homes in existing or new territories and turning them around both in terms of operating performance and clinical quality. In addition to acquiring new facilities and establishing local leadership teams the company works to boost patient occupancy at its existing facilities especially those facing financial troubles and extremely low occupancy rates. It does this by developing quality staff and clinical processes and through facility upgrades as well as by adding services such as outpatient therapy services. It is also focused on attracting more high-acuity patients who require higher levels of medical and rehabilitative care and for whom the company is generally reimbursed at higher rates.

Ensign branched out into a new area of operations in 2012 when it formed a joint venture with a group of physicians to establish or acquire urgent care centers in select communities. The Immediate Clinic venture intended to provide walk-in medical care to fill the gap between primary care doctor's offices and hospital emergency rooms a growing area of need as health reform measures take effect in the US. Its first acquisition in 2012 was Doctors Express which boasts about 50 franchised urgent care centers nationwide. However Immediate Clinic turned around and sold the Doctors Express business to American Family Care in 2013 while retaining a number of urgent care clinics in the greater Seattle area; in late 2016 Ensign sold its remaining Immediate Clinic operations to Multi-Care Health System. Ensign plans to focus more directly on its post-acute care operations.

Mergers and Acquisitions

In late 2014 Ensign purchased nine skilled nursing and assisted living facilities in the San Diego area from Shea Family Care. The closing of the Shea Family deal brought Ensign's growing portfolio to 136 healthcare facilities (nine of which will be owned) nine hospice companies 12 home health agencies two home care businesses and 14 urgent care clinics in 12 states. Also that year the company bought Sherwood Village Assisted Living and Memory Care a 135-unit assisted living facility in Tucson Arizona for $4.8 million.

In 2015 the company acquired Managed Care at Home and Apismellis Homecare adding to its home health operations; and skilled nursing facility Olympia Transitional Care and Rehabilitation in Washington. It also bought facilities in Arizona California and Wisconsin and expanded eastward with the purchase of a facility in skilled nursing facility in South Carolina. Ensign started off 2016 with the purchases of three more South Carolina skilled nursing facilities and separately 18 skilled nursing facilities in Texas.

Ensign capped off 2016 with the purchase of 15 assisted living facilities in Wisconsin.

EXECUTIVES

Executive Vice President and Secretary, Gregory K Stapley

President CEO and Director, Christopher R. Christensen, age 50, $462,327 total compensation

COO Ensign Services Inc., Barry R. Port, age 44, $326,227 total compensation

President Bandera Healthcare, John P. Albrechtsen, age 41, $164,687 total compensation

CFO, Suzanne D. Snapper, age 44, $307,500 total compensation

VP and General Counsel, Beverly B. Wittekind, age 53, $410,612 total compensation

President Cornerstone Healthcare, Daniel H. (Danny) Walker

President Bridgestone Living, John Guerreri

President Milestone Healthcare, Jorge Rojas

EVP and Secretary, Chad A. Keetch, age 40, $280,833 total compensation

President Pennant Healthcare, Spencer Burton

President Keystone Healthcare, Kevin Reese

Director Of Nursing Services, Traishon Lockett

Director Of Nursing Services, Kay Gudgell

Vice President Organizational Development, David Sedgwick

Director of Clinical Services, Mira Jensen

Director of Nursing, Linda Kolpin

Chairman, Roy E. Christensen, age 85

Auditors: Deloitte & Touche LLP

LOCATIONS

HQ: Ensign Group Inc
  27101 Puerta Real, Suite 450, Mission Viejo, CA 92691
Phone: 949 487-9500
Web: www.ensigngroup.net

PRODUCTS/OPERATIONS

2016 Sales

	$ mil.	% of total
Medicaid	558.0	34
Medicare	477.0	29
Private & other	266.9	16
Managed care	265.5	16
Medicaid - skilled	87.5	5
Total	**1,654.9**	**100**

2016 Sales

	$ mil.	% of total
Transitional and Skilled Services	1,377.7	83
Assisted and Independent Living Services	123.7	7
Home Health and Hospice Services	115.8	7
All Other	42.8	3
Elimination -5.1 -		
Total	**1,341.8**	**100**

COMPETITORS

Amedisys	Enlivant
American Baptist Homes of the West	Five Star Senior Living
Apria Healthcare	Genesis Healthcare
Brookdale Senior Living	Golden Horizons
	Kindred Healthcare
Covenant Care	Life Care Centers
Dignity Health	RehabCare
Diversicare Healthcare Services	SavaSeniorCare
Encompass Health	Sunrise Senior Living

HISTORICAL FINANCIALS

Company Type: Public

Income Statement

FYE: December 31

	REVENUE ($ mil.)	NET INCOME ($ mil.)	NET PROFIT MARGIN	EMPLOYEES
12/18	2,040.6	92.3	4.5%	23,463
12/17	1,849.3	40.4	2.2%	21,301
12/16	1,654.8	49.9	3.0%	19,482
12/15	1,341.8	55.4	4.1%	16,494
12/14	1,027.4	35.9	3.5%	13,229
Annual Growth	**18.7%**	**26.6%**	**—**	**15.4%**

2018 Year-End Financials

Debt ratio: 20.5%
Return on equity: 17.0%
Cash ($ mil.): 31.0
Current ratio: 1.29
Long-term debt ($ mil.): 233.1

No. of shares (mil.): 52.5
Dividends
  Yield: 0.4%
  Payout: 12.7%
Market value ($ mil.): 2,040.0

	STOCK PRICE ($) FY Close	P/E High/Low	PER SHARE ($) Earnings	Dividends	Book Value
12/18	38.79	27 13	1.70	0.18	11.24
12/17	22.20	31 22	0.77	0.17	9.59
12/16	22.21	24 18	0.96	0.16	8.98
12/15	22.63	49 20	1.06	0.15	8.32
12/14	44.39	59 35	0.78	0.14	5.73
Annual Growth	**(3.3%)**	**— —**	**21.5%**	**6.4%**	**18.3%**

Entegris Inc

Entegris makes products integral to the manufacture of semiconductors and computer disk drives. The company makes some 20000 standard and custom products used to transport and protect semiconductor and disk drive materials during processing. Its semiconductor products include wafer carriers storage boxes and chip trays as well as chemical delivery products such as pipes fittings and valves. Its disk drive offerings include shippers stamper cases and transport trays. Top customers include Applied Materials ASML MEMC Siltronic Tokyo Electron and Taiwan Semiconductor Manufacturing. In 2019 Entegris and Versum Materials agreed to merge in an all-stock deal valued at about $4 billion.

Operations

Entegris identifies its products as capital-driven (dependent on capital spending to expand manufacturing capacity) and unit-driven and consumable (products that are used or consumed in the manufacturing process). Unit-driven products which make up nearly four-fifths of sales include liquid filters specialized graphite components and wafers shippers. They provide some protection against industry cycles by providing a recurring source of revenue. Capital-driven products 20% of revenue include wafer process carriers and gas microcontamination control systems. Those products give the company access to more capital when chip makers retrofit or expand production facilities.

Geographic Reach

Entegris has manufacturing and research and development facilities in France German Israel Singapore China Japan Malaysia South Korea Taiwan and the US. It also has sales and service offices throughout Asia and Europe.

The US and Taiwan each account for 23% of the company's revenue followed by South Korea with 14% and Japan with 12%. Combined customers in Asia account for more than 60% of its revenue.

Sales and Marketing

The company sells its products through a direct sales force and strategic distributors serving a range of markets including Semiconductor Flat Panel Display Manufacturing Compound Semiconductor Disk Data Storage Aerospace Solar/Clean Energy Life Sciences Emerging Technologies and Water Treatment industries.

In 2015 sales to the company's 10 biggest customers accounted for 44% of revenue. It sold products to 2400 companies.

Financial Performance

Entegris posted a 12% gain in revenue to reach $1.08 billion in 2015. The company realized $105.3 million in revenue from the ATMI acquisition. The company said the strong US dollar cost it almost $7 million in 2015.

The company's profit jumped sharply — more than 900% -to $80 million in 2015 from just about $8 million in 2014. A gain related to the sale of an equity investment and lack of ATMI merger costs as well as reduced integration expenditures boosted net income.

Entegris had about $121 million in cash flow in 2015 compared to $126.42 million in 2014. The company carried higher inventories in 2015.

Strategy

In order to counter the cycles of the semiconductor industry Entegris has expanded into adjacent and ancillary markets including applications in solar flat-panel displays and high-purity chemicals. Non-semiconductor industries include the aerospace biomedical glass container and electrical discharge machining markets. Its focus includes strategic acquisitions and partnerships and related transactions that enable it to complement its product markets and broaden its technological capabilities and product offerings.

It expanded its operations in Taiwan to provide manufacturing capabilities to support important customers in the region and also established sales and service offices in China in anticipation of a growing semiconductor manufacturing base in that region and expanded its presence in Singapore to enhance its global and regional management of supply chain and manufacturing processes.

The company expanded engineering research and development operations in South Korea and Taiwan in late 2015 and early 2016. Entegris said the operations are to enhance collaboration between its engineers and its customers in designing and manufacturing products.

Mergers and Acquisitions

In 2019 Entegris and Versum Materials based in Tempe Arizona agreed to merge in a $4 billion all-stock deal that would give Entegris shareholders 52.5% ownership while Versum shareholders would own the rest. The combined company would have annual revenue of about $3 billion based on

each firm's 2018 revenue. The companies said that combined operations would lead to $75 million in cost reductions. The companies said that their complementary products and operations would broaden the new entity's reach as the semiconductor industry adopts new manufacturing materials and methods in the coming years. The deal is expected to close in the second half of 2019.

EXECUTIVES

President and CEO, Bertrand Loy, age 52, $625,000 total compensation
EVP and CFO, Gregory B. (Greg) Graves, age 57, $321,826 total compensation
SVP and COO, Todd Edlund, age 55, $291,577 total compensation
Chairman, Paul L. H. Olson, age 67
Auditors: KPMG LLP

LOCATIONS

HQ: Entegris Inc
 129 Concord Road, Billerica, MA 01821
Phone: 978 436-6500   **Fax:** 952 556-1880
Web: www.entegris.com

PRODUCTS/OPERATIONS

2015 Sales

	$ mil.	% of total
Critical Materials Handling	671.3	62
Electronic Materials	409.8	38
Total	**1,081.1**	**100**

COMPETITORS

3M	Pall Corporation
Air Products	Parker-Hannifin
Brooks Automation	Peak International
Donaldson Company	SAES Getters
Illinois Tool Works	Saint-Gobain
L'Air Liquide	Schweiter Technologies
MKS Instruments	Shin-Etsu Chemical
Mersen Group	Tokai Carbon
Mirae	

HISTORICAL FINANCIALS

Company Type: Public

Income Statement

FYE: December 31

	REVENUE ($ mil.)	NET INCOME ($ mil.)	NET PROFIT MARGIN	EMPLOYEES
12/17	1,342.5	85.0	6.3%	3,900
12/16	1,175.2	97.1	8.3%	3,727
12/15	1,081.1	80.3	7.4%	3,557
12/14	962.0	7.8	0.8%	3,528
12/13	693.4	74.5	10.7%	3,200
Annual Growth	**18.0%**	**3.4%**	**—**	**5.1%**

2017 Year-End Financials

Debt ratio: 34.1%	No. of shares (mil.): 141.2
Return on equity: 8.9%	Dividends
Cash ($ mil.): 625.4	Yield: 0.0%
Current ratio: 3.63	Payout: 11.8%
Long-term debt ($ mil.): 574.3	Market value ($ mil.): 4,302.0

	STOCK PRICE ($) FY Close	P/E High/Low	PER SHARE ($) Earnings	Dividends	Book Value
12/17	30.45	55 30	0.59	0.07	7.03
12/16	17.90	27 15	0.68	0.00	6.36
12/15	13.27	26 21	0.57	0.00	5.71
12/14	13.21	234171	0.06	0.00	5.35
12/13	11.59	21 17	0.53	0.00	5.46
Annual Growth	**27.3%**	**—**	**2.7%**	**—**	**6.5%**

Entercom Communications Corp

The signals from Entercom Communications come through loud and clear. The company is among the largest radio broadcasters in the US with about 125 stations clustered in more than 25 markets including Austin Boston Denver Kansas City New Orleans San Francisco and Seattle. Operating a number of stations in one market allows the company to combine such back office functions as finance and accounting as well as advertising sales and marketing. Its stations program a variety of formats including oldies country and adult contemporary as well as talk sports and news. The Field family including founder and chairman Joseph Field controls more than 65% of Entercom.

Sales and Marketing

Entercom has broadcast partnerships with the Boston Red Sox Boston Celtics Kansas City Royals New Orleans Saints and the Buffalo Sabres. The company has also been investing in high-definition digital radio (HD Radio) a developing business that could allow its stations to increase the number of signals they program.

Financial Performance

The company reported $379.8 million in revenue for fiscal 2014. That was an increase of 1% compared to the prior fiscal period. The company's net income was $26.9 million in fiscal 2014 which was an increase of slightly less than $1 million compared to its fiscal 2013 net income.

Entercom's cash flow increased by $1.9 million during fiscal 2014 and the company ended the year with about $65.3 in cash on hand.

Strategy

In the past Entercom has grown through acquisitions.

Mergers and Acquisitions

In fiscal 2014 the company acquired Lincoln Financial Media from Lincoln Financial Group for $105 million. The deal included 15 radio stations in the Atlanta Denver Miami and San Diego markets.

EXECUTIVES

Vice President Sales, Lisa Powell
Executive Vice President Human Resources, John C Donlevie
Vice President General Manager, Dick O'Neil
President and CEO, David J. Field, age 55, $974,853 total compensation

COO, Louise C. (Weezie) Kramer, age 62, $561,000 total compensation
President Sales, Deborah Kane
President Programming, Pat Paxton
VP Controller Treasurer and Principal Accounting Officer, Eugene D. Levin, age 67, $216,750 total compensation
EVP and CFO, Richard J. Schmaeling, age 53
Regional President, Michael Doyle
Vice President General Manager, Greg Ried
Senior Vice President Digital, Sandy Smallens
Vice President Of Programming, Jim Fox
Vice President of Digital Audience Engagement, Kim Reis
Vice President Market Manager, Jennifer Skjodt
Vice President General Manager, Amy Griesheimer
Vice President Market Manager, Matt Hanlon
National Sales Manager, Brooke Maratos
Vice President and General Manager, Steve Sinicropi
National Sales Manager, Jennifer Hart
Vice President Revenue Management, Geoff Spencer
Vice President Programming Operations, Mike Peterson
Vice President General Manager of Kswd, Peter Burton
VICE PRESIDENT SALES, Tim Holly
VICE PRESIDENT, James E Verzella
Vice President of Programming Innovation, Liana Huth
Vice President Market Manager, Mike Fowler
National Account Manager, Michelle Kazian
Chairman, Joseph M. Field, age 86
Auditors: PricewaterhouseCoopers LLP

LOCATIONS

HQ: Entercom Communications Corp
401 E. City Avenue, Suite 809, Bala Cynwyd, PA 19004
Phone: 610 660-5610
Web: www.entercom.com

COMPETITORS

Beasley Broadcast Group	Radio One Inc.
Bonneville International	SIRIUS XM
CBS Radio	Saga Communications
Cumulus Media	Salem Media
Emmis Communications	Simmons Media
Entravision	Wilks Broadcast Group
Journal Broadcast Group	iHeartCommunications

HISTORICAL FINANCIALS

Company Type: Public

Income Statement   FYE: December 31

	REVENUE ($ mil.)	NET INCOME ($ mil.)	NET PROFIT MARGIN	EMPLOYEES
12/17	592.8	233.0	39.3%	7,614
12/16	460.2	38.0	8.3%	2,828
12/15	411.3	29.1	7.1%	2,529
12/14	379.7	26.8	7.1%	2,315
12/13	377.6	26.0	6.9%	2,252
Annual Growth	11.9%	73.0%	—	35.6%

2017 Year-End Financials

Debt ratio: 41.2%	No. of shares (mil.): 143.7
Return on equity: 21.3%	Dividends
Cash ($ mil.): 34.1	Yield: 0.0%
Current ratio: 2.02	Payout: 11.7%
Long-term debt ($ mil.): 1,859.4	Market value ($ mil.): 1,552.0

	STOCK PRICE ($) FY Close	P/E High/Low		PER SHARE ($) Earnings	Dividends	Book Value
12/17	10.80	4	2	4.38	0.52	12.28
12/16	15.30	17	10	0.91	0.23	10.34
12/15	11.23	18	13	0.73	0.00	9.81
12/14	12.16	18	11	0.69	0.00	8.42
12/13	10.51	16	10	0.68	0.00	7.75
Annual Growth	0.7%	—	—	59.3%	—	12.2%

Enterprise Bancorp, Inc. (MA)

Enterprise Bancorp caters to more customers than just entrepreneurs. The holding company owns Enterprise Bank and Trust which operates more than 20 branches in north-central Massachusetts and southern New Hampshire. The $2 billion-asset bank offers traditional deposit and loan products specializing in lending to businesses professionals high-net-worth individuals and not-for-profits. About half of its loan portfolio is tied to commercial real estate while another one-third is tied to commercial and industrial and commercial construction loans. Subsidiaries Enterprise Investment Services and Enterprise Insurance Services provide investments and insurance geared to the bank's target business customers.

Operations

More than 50% of Enterprise Bancorp's $1.86 billion loan portfolio was tied to commercial real estate loans at the end of 2015 while commercial and industrial and commercial construction loans made up another 25% and 11% of the bank's loan assets. The rest of the bank's portfolio was tied to residential mortgages (9% of loan assets) home equity loans and lines of credit (4%) and consumer loans (less than 1%).

Nearly 80% of the bank's total revenue comes from loan interest while investment advisory fees and deposit and interchange fees each make up another 5%.

Geographic Reach

The Lowell Massachusetts-based bank operated 23 branches mostly located in the greater Merrimack Valley and North Central regions of Massachusetts and Southern New Hampshire at the end of 2015.

Sales and Marketing

Enterprise spent $2.7 million on advertising and public relations during 2015 down from $2.9 million in 2014.

Financial Performance

The bank's annual revenues have risen more than 40% since 2011 as its loan assets have swelled by 50% to $1.86 billion. Meanwhile its net income has grown more than 50% as it's kept a lid on loan loss provisions and operating costs.

Enterprise Bancorp's revenue climbed 8% to $98.4 million during 2015 thanks to 11% loan asset growth driven by a "seasoned" lending team a sales and service culture and geographic market expansion. Commercial construction loans grew the fastest rate during the year though all loans grew albeit at a slightly slower rate.

Revenue growth in 2015 drove the bank's net income up 10% to $16.1 million despite higher salary and employee benefit expenses. Enterprise Bancorp's operating cash levels nearly doubled to $25.7 million for the year largely thanks to positive changes in working capital mainly related to prepaid expenses and other assets.

Strategy

Enterprise Bancorp has traditionally expanded its loan and deposit business by opening new branches rather than by acquiring other banks. Enterprise hopes to take advantage of the trend to switch from larger banks to smaller community-oriented institutions. The company has also invested in upgrading its branches and operations systems.

EXECUTIVES

EVP and CFO Enterprise Bancorp and Enterprise Bank and Trust, James A. (Jim) Marcotte, age 60, $194,806 total compensation
CEO Enterprise Bancorp and Enterprise Bank and Trust, John P. (Jack) Clancy, age 60, $400,000 total compensation
President Enterprise Bancorp and Enterprise Bank and Trust, Richard W. (Dick) Main, age 70, $258,918 total compensation
EVP and COO Enterprise Bank and Trust, Stephen J. Irish, age 63, $194,804 total compensation
SVP and Chief Commercial Lender, Brian H. Bullock, age 60
EVP and Chief Banking Officer Enterprise Bank and Trust, Steven R. Larochelle, age 54
EVP and Chief Sales and Marketing Officer Enterprise Bank and Trust, Chester J. (Chet) Szablak, age 60
Vice President, Paul Rousseau
Vice Chairman Enterprise Bancorp and Enterprise Bank and Trust, Arnold S. Lerner, age 88
Chairman Enterprise Bancorp and Enterprise Bank and Trust, George L. Duncan, age 77
Auditors: RSM US LLP

LOCATIONS

HQ: Enterprise Bancorp, Inc. (MA)
222 Merrimack Street, Lowell, MA 01852
Phone: 978 459-9000

PRODUCTS/OPERATIONS

2015 Sales

	$ mil.	% of total
Interest and dividend income:		
Loans and loans held for sale	77.9	79
Investment securities	5.3	5
Other interest-earning assets	0.2	-
Non-interest income:		
Investment advisory fees	4.8	5
Deposit and interchange fees	4.9	5
Net gains on sales of investment securities	1.8	2
Income on bank-owned life insurance net	0.5	1
Gains on sales of loans	0.5	1
Other income	2.5	3
Total	**98.4**	**100**

PRODUCTS AND SERVICES

Lending Products:
Residential Loans
Home Equity Loans and Lines of Credit
Consumer Loans
Credit Risk and Allowance for Loan Losses
Deposit Products:
Cash Management Services
Product Delivery Channels
Investment Services
Insurance Services

COMPETITORS

Bank of America
Citizens Financial
 Group
Eastern Bank

Peoples Federal
 Bancshares Inc.
Sovereign Bank
TD Bank USA

HISTORICAL FINANCIALS

Company Type: Public

Income Statement

FYE: December 31

	ASSETS ($ mil.)	NET INCOME ($ mil.)	INCOME AS % OF ASSETS	EMPLOYEES
12/17	2,817.5	19.3	0.7%	482
12/16	2,526.2	18.7	0.7%	468
12/15	2,285.5	16.1	0.7%	426
12/14	2,022.2	14.6	0.7%	412
12/13	1,849.9	13.5	0.7%	398
Annual Growth	11.1%	9.4%	—	4.9%

2017 Year-End Financials

Return on assets: 0.7%	Dividends
Return on equity: 8.6%	Yield: 0.0%
Long-term debt ($ mil.): —	Payout: 32.5%
No. of shares (mil.): 11.6	Market value ($ mil.): 395.0
Sales ($ mil): 120.7	

	STOCK PRICE ($) FY Close	P/E High/Low		PER SHARE ($) Earnings	Dividends	Book Value
12/17	34.05	23	18	1.66	0.54	19.97
12/16	37.56	22	12	1.70	0.52	18.72
12/15	22.85	16	13	1.55	0.50	17.38
12/14	25.25	18	12	1.44	0.48	16.35
12/13	21.17	16	11	1.36	0.46	15.14
Annual Growth	12.6%	—	—	5.1%	4.1%	7.2%

Enterprise Financial Services Corp

Enterprise Financial Services wants you to boldly bank where many have banked before. It's the holding company for Enterprise Bank & Trust which mostly targets closely-held businesses and their owners but also serves individuals in the St. Louis Kansas City and Phoenix metropolitan areas. Boasting $3.8 billion in assets and 16 branches Enterprise offers standard products such as checking savings and money market accounts and CDs. Commercial and industrial loans make up over half of the company's lending activities while real estate loans make up another 45%. The bank also writes consumer and residential mortgage loans. Bank subsidiary Enterprise Trust offers wealth management services.

Operations

Enterprise Trust the company's wealth management unit targets business owners wealthy individuals and institutional investors providing financial planning business succession planning and related services. The unit also invests in Missouri state tax credits from funds for affordable housing development which it then sells to clients and others.

About 82% of Enterprise Financial's total revenue came from loan interest (including fees) in 2014 while another 7% came from interest on its taxable and tax-exempt investment securities. The rest of its revenue came from wealth management income (4%) service fees (3%) gains on state tax credits (1%) and other miscellaneous income sources. The bank had a staff of 452 full-time employees at the end of 2014.

Geographic Reach

Enterprise Bank & Trust operates eight banking locations in or around Kansas City six banking locations and a support center in the St. Louis area and two banking locations in the Phoenix metro area.

Financial Performance

The company has struggled to consistently grow its revenues in recent years mostly due to shrinking interest margins on its loans amidst the low-interest environment. Its profits however have mostly trended higher thanks to declining loan loss provisions as its loan portfolio's credit quality has improved with higher property valuations in the strengthened economy.

Enterprise Financials' revenue fell by 9% to $148.4 million in 2014 mostly due to double-digit declines in interest income as its purchased credit-impaired (PCI) loan balances and accelerated payments declined and as interest margins on its loans continued to shrink. The bank's portfolio loan balances increased however helping to offset some of its interest income decline.

Lower revenue and higher loan loss provisions (it received a loan loss benefit of $642 thousand in 2013) in 2014 caused the bank's net income to dive 18% to $27.2 million. Enterprise Financial's operating cash levels rose by 7% to $31.5 million despite lower earnings for the year mostly thanks to favorable changes in its working capital related to a $12-million change in other asset balances.

Strategy

Enterprise Financial Services planned in 2015 to continue its long-term strategy of keeping a "relationship-oriented distribution and sales approach"; growing its fee income and niche businesses; practicing "prudent" credit and interest rate risk management; and using advanced technology and controlled-expense growth. The company added that it planned on "operating branches with larger average deposits and employing experienced staff who are compensated on the basis of performance and customer service."

Though it just had two branches in Phoenix in 2015 the bank believes the fast-growing Phoenix market offers long-term growth opportunities for the company with its underlying demographic and geographic factors. Indeed at the end of 2014 the market had over 90000 privately-held businesses and 80000-plus households each with investable assets of more than $1 million.

Mergers and Acquisitions

In 2017 Enterprise Financial Services completed the acquisition of Jefferson County Bancshares the holding company of Eagle Bank and Trust Company in Missouri. The deal added 13 branches in metropolitan St. Louis and Perry County Missouri. The acquisition expanded EFS's assets to nearly $5 billion.

Company Background

In a restructuring move Enterprise Financial Services sold life insurance arm Millennium Brokerage in 2010 five years after investing in the company.

EXECUTIVES

President Enterprise Bank and Trust, Scott R. Goodman, age 54, $318,150 total compensation
EVP and CFO, Keene S. Turner, age 38, $333,125 total compensation
CEO, James B. Lally, age 50, $331,342 total compensation
Chief Credit Officer Enterprise Bank & Trust, Douglas N. Bauche, age 49, $253,270 total compensation
Senior Vice President Loan Review, Jeremy Jameson
Vice President Relationship Manager, Brian Glarner
Vice President Branch Manager, Hidy Ortiz
Assistant Vice President Relationship Manager, Tom Noel
Assistant Vice President Business Banking Specialist, Arnold Otero
AVP Relationship Manager, Bob Sivewright
Vice President Relationship Manager, Michael Hasenkamp
Assistant Vice President Business Banking, Molly McKay
Assistant Vice President Business Banking Specialist, Jessica Nollett
Assistant Vice President Business Banking Specialist, Brandy Kimble
Assistant Vice President Relationship Manager, John Garrett
Chairman, John S. Eulich, age 67
Auditors: DELOITTE & TOUCHE LLP

LOCATIONS

HQ: Enterprise Financial Services Corp
 150 North Meramec, Clayton, MO 63105
Phone: 314 725-5500
Web: www.enterprisebank.com

PRODUCTS/OPERATIONS

2011 Sales

	$ mil.	% of total
Interest		
Loans including fees	130.1	79
Securities	11.8	7
Other	0.9	1
Noninterest		
Wealth management	6.8	4
Service charges on deposit accounts	5.1	3
Gain on state tax credits net	3.7	2
Other service charges and fee income	1.7	1
Other	4.7	3
Adjustments	(3.5)	-
Total	161.3	100

Selected Acquisitions

COMPETITORS

BOK Financial
Bank of America
Commerce Bancshares
First Clover Leaf
 Financial

Midwest BankCentre
Pulaski Financial
U.S. Bancorp
Wells Fargo

HISTORICAL FINANCIALS
Company Type: Public

Income Statement — FYE: December 31

	ASSETS ($ mil.)	NET INCOME ($ mil.)	INCOME AS % OF ASSETS	EMPLOYEES
12/17	5,289.2	48.1	0.9%	635
12/16	4,081.3	48.8	1.2%	479
12/15	3,608.4	38.4	1.1%	459
12/14	3,277.0	27.1	0.8%	452
12/13	3,170.2	33.1	1.0%	455
Annual Growth	13.7%	9.8%	—	8.7%

2017 Year-End Financials
Return on assets: 1.0%
Return on equity: 10.3%
Long-term debt ($ mil.): —
No. of shares (mil.): 23.0
Sales ($ mil): 236.9
Dividends
Yield: 0.0%
Payout: 21.2%
Market value ($ mil.): 1,042.0

	STOCK PRICE ($) FY Close	P/E High/Low	PER SHARE ($) Earnings	Dividends	Book Value
12/17	45.15	22 18	2.07	0.44	23.76
12/16	43.00	18 10	2.41	0.41	19.31
12/15	28.35	16 10	1.89	0.26	17.53
12/14	19.73	15 12	1.35	0.21	15.94
12/13	20.42	12 7	1.73	0.21	14.47
Annual Growth	21.9%	— —	4.6%	20.3%	13.2%

Entravision Communications Corp.

This company helps advertisers trying to reach the US Hispanic market. Entravision Communications is the #2 Spanish-language media company in the country (behind Univision Communications) with about 55 television stations and 50 radio stations located mostly in the Southwest. It is the largest affiliate of Univision's two Spanish-language television networks Univision and TeleFutura; Entravision's TV portfolio also includes a small number of stations affiliated with The CW Network FOX and MyNetworkTV. On the radio the company offers a variety of programming formats including music news sports and talk radio.

Operations
The Company operates in two reportable segments: television broadcasting and radio broadcasting. Its radio operations combine network and local programming with local time slots available for advertising news traffic weather promotions and community events.

Geographic Reach
The company has a presence in 20 of the top 50 US Hispanic markets in California Colorado Connecticut Florida Massachusetts Nevada New Mexico Texas and Washington DC. Entravision's radio operations consist of 49 radio stations (38 FM and 11 AM) in 19 markets located primarily in Arizona California Colorado Florida Nevada New Mexico and Texas.

Strategy
Entravision is focused on attracting advertising revenue from companies trying to reach the fast-growing Spanish-speaking demographic. Part of its strategy involves cross-selling ad spots between radio and television in markets where it has both operations. The company is also working to expand its digital and mobile reach.

EXECUTIVES
Executive Vice President, Karl Meyer
Chairman and CEO, Walter F. Ulloa, age 69, $1,030,000 total compensation
EVP CFO and Treasurer, Christopher T. Young, age 49, $424,360 total compensation
President and COO, Jeffrey A. Liberman, age 59, $424,360 total compensation
Chief Strategy Officer, Esteban Lopez Blanco
President Entravision National Sales, Jose M. Villafane
National Sales Manager, Karla Barreto
Vice President Sales And Marketing, Greg Heitzman
Auditors: BDO USA, LLP

LOCATIONS
HQ: Entravision Communications Corp.
2425 Olympic Boulevard, Suite 6000 West, Santa Monica, CA 90404
Phone: 310 447-3870

PRODUCTS/OPERATIONS

Selected Television Stations
KAJB (TeleFutura; Yuma AZ)
KCEC Univision Denver)
KINC (Univision Las Vegas)
KINT (Univision; El Paso TX)
KLDO (Univision; Laredo TX)
KLUZ (Univision; Albuquerque NM)
KNVO (Univision; McAllen TX)
KORO (Univision; Corpus Christi TX)
KPMR (Univision; Santa Barbara CA)
KREN (Univision; Reno NV)
KSMS (Univision; Monterey-Santa Cruz CA)
KTFD (TeleFutura Denver)
KTFN (TeleFutura; El Paso TX)
KUPB (Univision; Odessa-Midland TX)
KVSN (Univision; Colorado Springs CO)
KVYE (Univision; Yuma AZ)
WFDC (Univision; Washington DC)
WJAL (Ind.; Washington DC)
WOTF (TeleFutura; Orlando FL)
WUNI (Univision Boston)
WUTF (TeleFutura Boston)
WUVN (Univision Hartford CT)
WVEA (Univision Tampa)
WVEN (Univision; Orlando FL)

COMPETITORS
Barrington Broadcasting
CBS Corp
Cox Enterprises
Entercom
Evening Post
Gray Television
Hearst Television
LIN Media
Lotus Communications
S&P Global
SIRIUS XM
Salem Media
Spanish Broadcasting
TEGNA
TV Azteca
Telemundo Communications
Televisa
Tribune Media
Univision
iHeartCommunications

HISTORICAL FINANCIALS
Company Type: Public

Income Statement — FYE: December 31

	REVENUE ($ mil.)	NET INCOME ($ mil.)	NET PROFIT MARGIN	EMPLOYEES
12/17	536.0	176.2	32.9%	1,259
12/16	258.5	20.4	7.9%	1,111
12/15	254.1	25.6	10.1%	1,165
12/14	242.0	27.1	11.2%	1,010
12/13	223.9	133.8	59.8%	962
Annual Growth	24.4%	7.1%	—	7.0%

2017 Year-End Financials
Debt ratio: 38.5%
Return on equity: 66.2%
Cash ($ mil.): 39.5
Current ratio: 5.64
Long-term debt ($ mil.): 292.4
No. of shares (mil.): 90.3
Dividends
Yield: 0.0%
Payout: 8.4%
Market value ($ mil.): 646.0

	STOCK PRICE ($) FY Close	P/E High/Low	PER SHARE ($) Earnings	Dividends	Book Value
12/17	7.15	4 3	1.92	0.16	3.86
12/16	7.00	36 26	0.22	0.13	2.03
12/15	7.71	32 20	0.28	0.11	1.88
12/14	6.48	24 13	0.30	0.10	1.67
12/13	6.09	5 1	1.50	0.13	1.54
Annual Growth	4.1%	— —	6.4%	6.8%	25.8%

Enviva Partners LP

Auditors: KPMG LLP

LOCATIONS
HQ: Enviva Partners LP
7200 Wisconsin Ave., Suite 1000, Bethesda, MD 20814
Phone: 301 657-5560
Web: www.envivabiomass.com

HISTORICAL FINANCIALS
Company Type: Public

Income Statement — FYE: December 31

	REVENUE ($ mil.)	NET INCOME ($ mil.)	NET PROFIT MARGIN	EMPLOYEES
12/17	543.2	17.5	3.2%	0
12/16	464.2	21.3	4.6%	0
12/15	457.3	23.1	5.1%	0
12/14	290.1	0.2	0.1%	338
12/13	179.8	(5.4)	—	0
Annual Growth	31.8%	—	—	—

2017 Year-End Financials
Debt ratio: 62.4%
Return on equity: —
Cash ($ mil.): 0.5
Current ratio: 1.47
Long-term debt ($ mil.): 468.8
No. of shares (mil.): 26.3
Dividends
Yield: 0.0%
Payout: 372.9%
Market value ($ mil.): 728.0

	STOCK PRICE ($) FY Close	P/E High/Low	PER SHARE ($) Earnings	Dividends	Book Value
12/17	27.65	48 38	0.61	2.28	7.99
12/16	26.80	30 15	0.91	2.03	11.90
12/15	18.15	14 7	1.58	0.70	13.05
Annual Growth	23.4%	—	— (37.9%)	79.9%	(21.8%)

Epam Systems, Inc.

EPAM provides software development and other IT services to US and European customers primarily from development centers in Russia Belarus Hungary Ukraine Kazakhstan and Poland. In addition to software product development the company offers services in such areas as e-commerce support data warehousing customer relationship management and application integration. EPAM also offers its own hosted and stand-alone enterprise software for sales force automation content management order management and other business processes. Half of sales come from North America.

Operations
EPAM generates 69% of its revenue from software development. Another 19% comes from testing applications with application maintenance accounting for 8%.

Geographic Reach
North America is EPAM's biggest market accounting for 50% of revenue. European customers provide 39%. Russia and former members of the Soviet Union account for 15% of revenue.

The company has expanded geographically by adding client management offices in locations that are close to customers — including the US UK Germany Sweden Switzerland Russia and Kazakhstan — and by adding new development centers. In certain cases (such as Russia and Kazakhstan) EPAM has both development centers and client management offices in the same country.

Financial Performance
EPAM has posted steady growth in revenue and net income over the past several years. Revenue increased 31% in 2014 to $730 million. The company broadened its sales to existing customers and found new ones to drive up revenue. Sales jumped 30% in North America in 2014.

Net income rose 12% in 2014 to $69.6 million. Cash flow from operations also rose in 2014 reaching $104 million compared to $58 million in 2013.

Strategy
The company is looking to extend its expertise in targeted industry verticals which include independent software vendors banking and financial services business information and media hospitality and travel and retail and consumer. To do this EPAM continues to recruit IT professionals with specific industry knowledge and to pursue acquisitions that add to its service portfolio and customer base. Another part of EPAM's growth strategy is to make acquisitions of companies that have a significant presence in China Latin America and other emerging markets.

Mergers and Acquisitions
EPAM widened the services it offers with the 2014 acquisitions of Netsoft Holdings Joint Technology Development Limited GGA Software Services and Great Fridays Ltd. The expanded capabilities are in health care financial services and digital design areas.

EXECUTIVES

President and CEO, Arkadiy Dobkin, age 58, $437,500 total compensation
SVP and CFO, Jason Peterson
SVP and Co-Head of Global Business, Balazs Fejes, age 43, $292,326 total compensation
Head of Global Operations, Yuriy Goliyad
Co-Head of Global Business, Boris Shnayder, age 52, $257,500 total compensation
Co-Head Global Delivery, Sergey Yezhkov
Co-Head Global Delivery, Victor Dvorkin
Senior Vice President Head of Global Business Development, Robert Corace
Auditors: DELOITTE & TOUCHE LLP

LOCATIONS

HQ: Epam Systems, Inc.
41 University Drive, Suite 202, Newtown, PA 18940
Phone: 267 759-9000
Web: www.epam.com

PRODUCTS/OPERATIONS

2014 Sales

	$ mil.	% of total
Software development	504.6	69
Application testing services	140.4	19
Application maintenance & support	58.8	8
Infrastructure services	14.2	2
Licensing	3.6	1
Reimbursable expenses & other revenues	8.4	1
Total	**730.0**	**100**

2014 Sales by Industry

	$ mil.	% of total
Banking & financial services	215.4	29
Independent software vendors & technology	157.9	22
Travel & hospitality	157.8	22
Business information & media	91.7	13
Other verticals	98.8	13
Reimbursable expenses & other revenues	8.4	1
Total	**730.0**	**100**

Selected Services
Application development
Application maintenance and support
Application testing
Business intelligence
Business process management
Content management
Customer Relationship Management (CRM)
Data warehousing and business intelligence
E-commerce
Enterprise application integration
Enterprise resource planning
Infrastructure and hosting
Knowledge management
Localization
Offshore software development
Quality assurance consulting and testing strategy transformation
Server and network management

COMPETITORS

Accenture	Infosys
Atos	MindTree
Camelot Information	Pactera
Capgemini	Sapient
Cognizant Tech Solutions	Symphony Technology Group LLC
Computer Sciences Corp.	Tata Consultancy VanceInfo
GlobalLogic	Wipro
HCL Technologies	iSoftStone
IBM Global Services	

HISTORICAL FINANCIALS
Company Type: Public

Income Statement
FYE: December 31

	REVENUE ($ mil.)	NET INCOME ($ mil.)	NET PROFIT MARGIN	EMPLOYEES
12/17	1,450.4	72.7	5.0%	25,962
12/16	1,160.1	99.2	8.6%	22,383
12/15	914.1	84.4	9.2%	18,354
12/14	730.0	69.6	9.5%	14,109
12/13	555.1	61.9	11.2%	11,056
Annual Growth	**27.1%**	**4.1%**	**—**	**23.8%**

2017 Year-End Financials

Debt ratio: 2.0%	No. of shares (mil.): 52.9
Return on equity: 8.2%	Dividends
Cash ($ mil.): 582.5	Yield: —
Current ratio: 5.31	Payout: —
Long-term debt ($ mil.): 25.0	Market value ($ mil.): 5,692.0

	STOCK PRICE ($) FY Close	P/E High/Low	PER SHARE ($) Earnings	Dividends	Book Value
12/17	107.43	78 45	1.32	0.00	18.40
12/16	64.31	40 29	1.87	0.00	15.29
12/15	78.62	48 26	1.62	0.00	12.22
12/14	47.75	35 20	1.40	0.00	9.61
12/13	34.94	29 13	1.28	0.00	8.07
Annual Growth	**32.4%**	**— —**	**0.8%**	**—**	**22.9%**

EPR Properties

EPR Properties (formerly Entertainment Properties Trust) invests in places to play and learn. The self-administered real estate investment trust (REIT) owns around 140 movie megaplex theaters and theater-anchored entertainment retail centers around the US and Canada. The REIT buys properties from theater operators and leases them back to the original owners. Many of its theaters are leased to AMC Entertainment. EPR also owns ski resorts (for clients including Camelback Mountain Resorts) golf resorts (for operator TopGolf) waterparks (including Schlitterbahn parks) public charter schools early education centers and private schools.

Operations
The REIT owns three main types of properties: Entertainment Education and Recreation. Its Entertainment properties which generated 63% of its total revenue during 2015 in the form of rental income include multiplex theaters entertainment retail centers and family entertainment centers. Its Education properties (19% of revenue) consists of 70 public charter school properties 18 early childhood centers and three private schools.

Its Recreation properties (17% of revenue) consist of ski areas waterparks and golf courses. Its Metro Daily Ski business consists of 14 ski properties located close to metropolitan areas including: Camelback Mountain Resort in Pennsylvania; Vermont's Mt. Snow; and a dozen other properties in Ohio and nine other mostly eastern states. EPR's waterpark properties are leased to Schlitterbahn. Its four Texas golf properties are operated by TopGolf.

Geographic Reach

The Kansas City Missouri-based REITs five largest markets are in Texas (13% of 2015 revenues) Ontario (10%) California (9%) Arizona (7%) and Illinois (6%).

Sales and Marketing

The REIT has more than 250 tenants and about 99% of its properties are currently leased. Its largest tenant is theater operator AMC which accounted for about 20% of its annual revenue during 2015. Other tenants include Schlitterbahn Regal Studio Movie Grill Altitude Trampoline Park TopGolf and Carolina Cinemas.

Financial Performance

EPR Properties' annual revenues have risen 40% since 2011 as new property acquisitions have spurred additional rental income. Its annual profits have grown nearly 70% over the same period as the REIT has kept a lid on rising operating and overhead costs.

The REIT's revenue climbed 9% to $421 million during 2015 as property acquisitions (mostly movie theaters) and build-to-suite projects added to its rental revenue.

Strong revenue growth and gains from property sales in 2015 boosted EPR's net income by 8% to $194.5 million for the year. The REIT's operating cash levels rose 11% to $278.5 million thanks to the rise in cash-denominated earnings.

Strategy

EPR Properties remains focused on its core movie theater business as Americans continue to flock to the movies even in uncertain markets. In April 2014 the company invested $118 million on 11 theater properties in seven states continuing to build its massive collection.

Although megaplexes account for the majority of its holdings the company continues to look for opportunities to diversify its real estate holdings.

EXECUTIVES

President and CEO, Gregory K. (Greg) Silvers, age 54, $484,500 total compensation
SVP and Chief Investment Officer, Morgan G. (Jerry) Earnest, age 62, $392,700 total compensation
SVP CFO and Treasurer, Mark A. Peterson, age 54, $346,500 total compensation
SVP Secretary and General Counsel, Neil E. Sprague, age 62, $300,000 total compensation
Chairman, Robert J. Druten, age 71
Auditors: KPMC LLP

LOCATIONS

HQ: EPR Properties
909 Walnut Street, Suite 200, Kansas City, MO 64106
Phone: 816 472-1700   **Fax:** 816 472-5794
Web: www.eprkc.com

PRODUCTS/OPERATIONS

2015 Sales

	$ mil.	% of total
Rental Revenue	330.9	78
Mortgage and other financing income	70.2	17
Tenant reimbursements	16.3	4
Other income	3.6	1
Total	**421.0**	**100**

2015 Sales

	$ mil.	% of total
Entertainment	262.9	63
Education	82.1	19
Recreation	72.6	17
Corporate	3.0	1
Other	0.4	-

Total	**421.0**	**100**

COMPETITORS

Acadia Realty Trust	Realty Income
Cousins Properties	Regal Entertainment
Lexington Realty Trust	Simon Property Group
National Retail	Tanger Factory Outlet
Properties	Taubman Centers
One Liberty Properties	Vornado Realty
Reading International	

HISTORICAL FINANCIALS

Company Type: Public

Income Statement   FYE: December 31

	REVENUE ($ mil.)	NET INCOME ($ mil.)	NET PROFIT MARGIN	EMPLOYEES
12/17	575.9	262.9	45.7%	63
12/16	493.2	224.9	45.6%	57
12/15	421.0	194.5	46.2%	49
12/14	385.0	179.6	46.7%	40
12/13	343.0	180.2	52.5%	38
Annual Growth	**13.8%**	**9.9%**	**—**	**13.5%**

2017 Year-End Financials

Debt ratio: 48.9%
Return on equity: 10.2%
Cash ($ mil.): 41.9
Current ratio: 0.65
Long-term debt ($ mil.): 3,028.8
No. of shares (mil.): 74.1
Dividends
  Yield: 0.0%
  Payout: 124.0%
Market value ($ mil.): 4,852.0

	STOCK PRICE ($) FY Close	P/E High/Low		Earnings	Dividends	Book Value
12/17	65.46	24	19	3.29	4.08	39.49
12/16	71.77	27	17	3.17	3.84	34.34
12/15	58.45	22	17	2.93	3.63	34.10
12/14	57.63	21	17	2.86	3.42	33.72
12/13	49.16	19	14	3.24	3.16	32.67
Annual Growth	**7.4%**		**—**	**—**	**0.4%**	**6.6%** 4.9%

EQM Midstream Partners LP

Auditors: Ernst & Young, LLP

LOCATIONS

HQ: EQM Midstream Partners LP
625 Liberty Avenue, Suite 2000, Pittsburgh, PA 15222
Phone: 412 553-5700
Web: www.eqtmidstreampartners.com

HISTORICAL FINANCIALS

Company Type: Public

Income Statement   FYE: December 31

	REVENUE ($ mil.)	NET INCOME ($ mil.)	NET PROFIT MARGIN	EMPLOYEES
12/17	834.1	571.9	68.6%	0
12/16	735.6	537.9	73.1%	0
12/15	614.1	393.4	64.1%	0
12/14	392.9	232.7	59.2%	0
12/13	185.8	109.7	59.0%	0
Annual Growth	**45.5%**	**51.1%**	**—**	**—**

2017 Year-End Financials

Debt ratio: 32.8%
Return on equity: —
Cash ($ mil.): 2.5
Current ratio: 0.69
Long-term debt ($ mil.): 1,167.3
No. of shares (mil.): 82.0
Dividends
  Yield: 0.0%
  Payout: 70.4%
Market value ($ mil.): 5,996.0

	STOCK PRICE ($) FY Close	P/E High/Low		Earnings	Dividends	Book Value
12/17	73.10	16	13	5.19	3.66	26.20
12/16	76.68	15	11	5.21	3.05	24.30
12/15	75.46	19	13	4.70	2.51	19.85
12/14	88.00	28	17	3.52	2.02	11.16
12/13	58.79	24	13	2.46	1.55	13.20
Annual Growth	**5.6%**		**—**	**—**	**20.5%**	**23.9%** 18.7%

Equity Bancshares Inc

Auditors: Crowe Chizek LLP

LOCATIONS

HQ: Equity Bancshares Inc
7701 East Kellogg Drive, Suite 300, Wichita, KS 67207
Phone: 316 612 6000
Web: www.equitybank.com

HISTORICAL FINANCIALS

Company Type: Public

Income Statement   FYE: December 31

	ASSETS ($ mil.)	NET INCOME ($ mil.)	INCOME AS % OF ASSETS	EMPLOYEES
12/17	3,170.5	20.6	0.7%	526
12/16	2,192.1	9.3	0.4%	415
12/15	1,585.7	10.3	0.6%	297
12/14	1,175.3	8.9	0.8%	262
12/13	1,140.0	7.8	0.7%	0
Annual Growth	**29.1%**	**27.3%**	**—**	**—**

2017 Year-End Financials

Return on assets: 0.7%
Return on equity: 6.5%
Long-term debt ($ mil.): —
No. of shares (mil.): 14.6
Sales ($ mil.): 118.1
Dividends
  Yield: —
  Payout: —
Market value ($ mil.): 517.0

	STOCK PRICE ($) FY Close	P/E High/Low		Earnings	Dividends	Book Value
12/17	35.41	22	18	1.62	0.00	25.62
12/16	33.64	34	19	1.07	0.00	22.09
12/15	23.39	16	15	1.54	0.00	20.37
Annual Growth	**23.0%**		**—**	**—**	**2.6%**	**—** 12.2%

ESCO Technologies, Inc.

Diversified manufacturing company ESCO Technologies focuses on three business segments: Utility Solutions (automation and communication devices for utilities) Filtration/Fluid Flow and RF Shielding and Test. ESCO's communications equipment includes meter-reading technology and video surveillance systems used to monitor industrial applications. The company's filters are used in industrial applications fuel systems medical applications and appliances. Test products include electromagnetic compatibility equipment such as antennas probes turntables and calibration equipment as well as radio-frequency shielding products.

Operations

In ESCO's Utility Solutions segment Aclara is the industry leader in advanced metering infrastructure solutions and analytics for gas water and electric utilities. Doble partners with electric utilities providing more than 5500 companies with diagnostic test instruments consulting and testing services and the world's largest database of infrastructure asset test results.

Building on a heritage of innovation ESCO's Filtration/Fluid Flow segment companies — Crissair PTI Technologies and VACCO Industries deliver highly engineered fluid control services an technologies for mission critical systems. The segment's markets include commercial aerospace space and defense satellite communications medical industrial and automotive.

In ESCO's RF Shielding and Test segment the ETS Lindgren subsidiary is the world's leading supplier of electromagnetic compatibility (EMC) and radio frequency (RP) test facilities as well as shielded enclosures for medical and security applications.

Financial Performance

ESCO's revenues decreased by 0.8% in fiscal year 2012 due to a 9.1% decrease in utility segment revenues thanks to a $34.6 million decrease in net sales from Aclara caused by lower deliveries of Advanced Metering Infrastructure products for the New York City water project ($17.4 million) the Pacific Gas & Electric Company gas project ($18.4 million) and the Federal Commission of Electricity electric project in Mexico ($29.6 million).

Other factors included a 0.3% decrease in Test sales revenues due to a $6 million decrease in net sales from the segment's US operations primarily driven by lower shipments of shielding for a NASA project in Florida and a $1.3 million decrease in net sales from the segment's European operations.

However weaker sales elsewhere were offset by a 16.2% increase in Filtration net sales due to higher shipments of its Space products; a $6.6 million increase in net sales from its Thermoform Engineered Quality unit mainly due to higher shipments to commercial customers; a $6.5 million increase in net sales from PTI Technologies driven by higher shipments of aerospace assemblies elements and couplings; and a $5.5 million increase at Crissair mainly due to higher product shipments and price increases on its products.

ESCO's net income decreased by 11% in fiscal year 2012 driven by lower revenues an increase in SG&A expenses due to new product development costs for additional Space product applications additional content on Airbus platforms and an increase in head count.

Strategy

ESCO has been expanding its Utility Solutions business via acquisitions and investing in new products; the business accounted for 46% of the company's total revenues in fiscal year 2012. The company boosted its utility offerings in early 2013 with the acquisition of smart grid services provider Metrum Technologies.

In 2010 ESCO acquired Crissair a Palmdale California maker of hydraulic fuel and pneumatic system products for commercial and military aircraft. Crissair became part of ESCO's filtration and fluid flow business segment and its $27 million in annual revenue is projected to double the segment's revenues. ESCO also acquired Xtensible Solutions a leading provider of semantic-based information management and integration services. The deal boosted the company's capacity to support utilities in implementing Smart Grid technology.

Mergers and Acquisitions

ESCO through its subsidiary NRG systems acquired a portfolio of advanced Lidar technology developed by Pentalum in 2018.

Founded in 2009 Pentalum an Israeli company pioneered low-cost solutions for wind-resource assessment and forecasting with its patented Direct Detect Lidar technology delivering high precision and reliability at a significantly lower cost compared to conventional Doppler Lidar technologies.

The acquisition will help NRG expand its role in the global wind energy market.

HISTORY

`ESCO Electronics was formed in 1990 as a subsidiary of Emerson Electric. It was created to be a holding company for several Emerson subsidiaries but Emerson spun it off within two months. ESCO operated in defense systems defense electronics filtration/fluid flow communications/test and other industrial and government products.

Most of ESCO's growth in the early 1990s came from the defense sector. Its Southwest Mobile Systems won a US Army contract to provide battle tank transporters in 1992. That year ESCO bought the filtration systems unit of Textron.

In the face of a shrinking defense industry ESCO began to build up its commercial products in 1993 focusing on its areas of expertise: valves and filters communications test instrumentation and motion control. In 1994 it won a US Postal Service contract for a mail-handling system and an Air Force contract for aircraft cargo loaders. The company restructured in 1995 and recorded a loss that fiscal year. It sold its Hazeltine subsidiary in 1996 to GEC-Marconi. The divestiture reduced ESCO's defense operations to two-thirds of its total sales and caused a fiscal 1997 sales dip.

Furthering its pursuit of the commercial market ESCO bought plastic-filter maker Filtertek from Schawk (later renamed SGK LLC) in 1997. The next year ESCO acquired Euroshield a Finland-based maker of high-quality shielding products and Advanced Membrane Technology a manufacturer of filter membranes. ESCO also won a $7.5 million settlement from the US Army in a dispute over an M1000 Tank Transporter contract. In 1999 the company sold its defense-related Systems & Electronics subsidiary to Engineered Support Systems for $85 million.

Continuing the sale of its defense interests in 2000 ESCO sold its Rantec microwave antenna products business. The company changed its name to ESCO Technologies the same year. Also in 2000 ESCO picked up Eaton's fluid flow components business and Minnesota-based Holaday Industries a maker of specialty measurement probes.

In 2001 the company increased its presence in Europe with the acquisition of Italy-based Bea Filtri a supplier of filtration products for pharmaceutical food and beverage healthcare and petrochemical

applications. In 2002 ESCO acquired the rights to the intellectual assets held by North Carolina Separations Research Technology a provider of cross-flow filtration devices. Later that year the company promoted Vic Richey to CEO.

In January 2003 ESCO acquired the assets of Austin Acoustics Systems a provider of noise control test chambers. In April 2003 the company completed the sale of its Rantec Power Systems subsidiary.

ESCO continued divesting its noncore operations in 2004 when it sold its PTI Advanced Filtration and PTI Technologies subsidiaries to dominick hunter. It also sold its PTI S.p.A. subsidiary that year.

In 2005 the company bought Nexus Energy Software which makes software used by utilities for functions such as billing customer service and forecasting.

In 2006 ESCO acquired Hexagram a provider of radio frequency fixed-network automatic meter reading services. Hexagram which had contracts with some 75 utilities had posted annual revenue has ranged between $20 million and $35 million since 2003.

In 2008 ESCO acquired LDIC GmbH (now Doble Lemke GmbH) a diagnostic test business serving the international electric utility industry with operations in Dresden Germany and Rheinfelden Switzerland.

EXECUTIVES

EVP and CFO, Gary E. Muenster, age 56, $526,000 total compensation
SVP Secretary and General Counsel, Alyson S. Barclay, age 57, $312,000 total compensation
Chairman President and CEO, Victor L. (Vic) Richey, age 61, $790,000 total compensation
Vice President Human Resources, Deborah Hanlon
Auditors: KPMG LLP

LOCATIONS

HQ: ESCO Technologies, Inc.
9900A Clayton Road, St. Louis, MO 63124-1186
Phone: 314 213-7200
Web: www.escotechnologies.com

PRODUCTS/OPERATIONS

2015 Sales

	$ mil.	% of total
Utility Solutions Group	123.6	23
Filtration/Fluid Flow	236.1	44
RF Shielding & Test	177.6	33
Total	**537.3**	**100**

Selected Operating Units

Utility Solutions
  Comtrak Technologies L.L.C.
  Distribution Control Systems Caribe Inc.
  Distribution Control Systems Inc. (DCSI)
  Doble Engineering Company
  Hexagram Inc.
  Nexus Energy Software Inc.
Filtration/Fluid Flow
  Crissair Inc.
  PTI Technologies Inc.
  Thermoform Engineered Quality LLC
  VACCO Industries
RF Shielding and Test
  Beijing Lindgren ElectronMagnetic Technology Co. Ltd.
  EMV Elektronische Messgeräte Vertriebs-GmbH
  ETS-Lindgren Japan Inc.
  ETS-Lindgren L.P.
  Lindgren RF Enclosures Inc.

COMPETITORS

3M Purification
Atos
CLARCOR
Comverge
Elster Group SE

Itron
Moog
Oracle
Pall Corporation

HISTORICAL FINANCIALS

Company Type: Public

Income Statement   FYE: September 30

	REVENUE ($ mil.)	NET INCOME ($ mil.)	NET PROFIT MARGIN	EMPLOYEES
09/18	771.5	92.1	11.9%	3,117
09/17	685.7	53.7	7.8%	3,254
09/16	571.4	45.8	8.0%	2,643
09/15	537.2	42.5	7.9%	2,323
09/14	531.1	0.4	0.1%	2,103
Annual Growth	9.8%	287.2%	—	10.3%

2018 Year-End Financials

Debt ratio: 17.3%
Return on equity: 12.8%
Cash ($ mil.): 30.4
Current ratio: 1.97
Long-term debt ($ mil.): 200.0

No. of shares (mil.): 25.9
Dividends
  Yield: 0.0%
  Payout: 9.0%
Market value ($ mil.): 1,763.0

	STOCK PRICE ($) FY Close	P/E High/Low		PER SHARE ($) Earnings	Dividends	Book Value
09/18	68.05	20	16	3.54	0.32	29.31
09/17	59.95	30	21	2.07	0.24	26.01
09/16	46.42	26	18	1.77	0.32	23.92
09/15	35.90	24	20	1.62	0.32	22.63
09/14	34.78	3679	3238	0.02	0.32	22.14
Annual Growth	18.3%	—		—264.7%	(0.0%)	7.3%

Essex Property Trust Inc

Essex Property Trust acquires develops redevelops and manages apartment communities focusing on the metropolitan areas of Los Angeles San Diego San Francisco and Seattle. The self-managed and self-administered real estate investment trust (REIT) owns more than 240 apartment communities — mostly in Southern California — and eight community properties under development. Essex also owns a handful of office buildings in its home state and has partial stakes in several apartment communities through joint ventures. The REIT adds to its portfolio through acquisitions and through the development and renovation of properties. Essex significantly expanded its property base after its 2014 acquisition of BRE Properties in a $4.3 billion deal.

Operations

Essex Property had interests in 246 communities (mostly garden-style but some mid-rise and high-rise) spanning 59160 apartment homes on the West Coast at the end of 2015. It also had stakes in four commercial buildings spanning over 319000 sq. ft. and eight active development projects with nearly 2450 apartment homes in various stages of development. Its property occupancy rates exceeded 96%.

Rent from the apartment communities generated more than 99% of the company's total revenue in 2015.

Geographic Reach

Palo Alto-based Essex Property's generated 44% of its revenue from properties in Southern California (in Los Angeles Orange San Diego and Ventura counties) during 2015; about 35% of its revenue from properties in Northern California (in the San Francisco Bay area); and 17% of its revenue from properties in the Seattle metro area. The REIT has offices in Woodland Hills Irvine San Jose and San Diego California; and in Bellevue Washington.

Financial Performance

Essex Property's annual revenues have more than doubled while its profits have grown nearly five-fold since 2011 thanks to rent-boosting property acquisitions and rising rental rates stemming from the strengthened economy.

The REIT's revenue jumped 23% to $1.19 billion during 2015 mostly as newly acquired properties from the BRE merger and 10 other communities boosted rental revenues. Same-property revenues also increased thanks to an 8.1% rise in average rental rates (which reached $1741 per apartment home) as housing demand continued to strengthen.

Strong revenue growth in 2015 allowed Essex Property's net income to nearly double to $232.12 million for the year. Its operating cash levels climbed 25% to $617.4 million on rising cash earnings.

Strategy

When making acquisitions Essex usually targets multifamily properties with more than 100 units and spends from $300 million to $500 million per transaction. It likes to be active in supply-constrained markets with populations of at least one million and drives rent growth through high occupancy rates (approximately 96% at year-end 2015).

The REIT continually monitors its existing markets and isn't afraid to exit if the housing supply increases too much. The company sells off assets if they no longer fit into its strategy and often uses the money raised to buy newer communities and parcels of land.

Mergers and Acquisitions

During 2015 Essex bought interests in seven communities spanning 1722 apartment homes for $638 million which included the 8th & New Hope The Huxley The Dylan Reveal Avant Avant II and Enso community properties.

In April 2014 Essex Property Trust acquired California-based BRE Properties forming a combined company in which former Essex shareholders hold about 63% of the combined company's stock and former BRE shareholders hold 37%. (The combined company retained the name Essex Property Trust.) The deal valued at about $4.3 billion greatly bolstered the REIT's presence in the multifamily market on the West Coast.

In 2013 Essex acquired ownership interests in eight communities comprising 1472 units for $462.5 million. The acquired apartment complexes are in San Francisco (2) Los Angeles Mountain View and San Diego California and in Kirkland and Seattle (2) Washington.

EXECUTIVES

Senior Vice President, Mark Mikl
EVP Acquisitions, Craig K. Zimmerman, age 67, $325,000 total compensation
EVP Development, John D. Eudy, age 63, $325,000 total compensation
President and CEO, Michael J. (Mike) Schall, age 60, $450,000 total compensation
VP Fund Manager, John F. Burkart, $275,000 total compensation
Vice Chairman, Keith R. Guericke, age 69
Chairman, George M. Marcus, age 77
Auditors: KPMG LLP

LOCATIONS

HQ: Essex Property Trust Inc
  1100 Park Place Suite 200, San Mateo, CA 94403
Phone: 650 655-7800
Web: www.essex.com

PRODUCTS/OPERATIONS

2015 Sales

	$ mil.	% of total
Rental & other property revenues		
Southern California	529.4	44
Northern California	416.3	35
Seattle Metro	201.4	17
Other real estate assets	38.3	3
Management & other fees from affiliates	9.0	1
Total	1,194.4	100

COMPETITORS

Apartment Investment
  and Management
AvalonBay
Camden Property
Equity Residential

Fairfield Residential
Irvine Apartment
  Communities
UDR

HISTORICAL FINANCIALS

Company Type: Public

Income Statement   FYE: December 31

	REVENUE ($ mil.)	NET INCOME ($ mil.)	NET PROFIT MARGIN	EMPLOYEES
12/17	1,363.9	433.0	31.8%	1,835
12/16	1,294.0	414.9	32.1%	1,799
12/15	1,194.4	232.1	19.4%	1,806
12/14	969.3	122.1	12.6%	1,725
12/13	613.7	156.2	25.5%	1,173
Annual Growth	22.1%	29.0%	—	11.8%

2017 Year-End Financials

Debt ratio: 45.5%
Return on equity: 6.9%
Cash ($ mil.): 61.1
Current ratio: 1.17
Long-term debt ($ mil.): 5,689.1

No. of shares (mil.): 66.0
Dividends
  Yield: 0.0%
  Payout: 106.5%
Market value ($ mil.): 15,944.0

	STOCK PRICE ($) FY Close	P/E High/Low		PER SHARE ($) Earnings	Dividends	Book Value
12/17	241.37	41	34	6.57	7.00	95.03
12/16	232.50	38	31	6.27	6.40	94.50
12/15	239.41	70	59	3.49	5.76	95.41
12/14	206.60	103	69	2.06	5.11	94.57
12/13	143.51	42	35	4.04	4.84	50.48
Annual Growth	13.9%	—		—12.9%	9.7%	17.1%

Etsy Inc

Auditors: PricewaterhouseCoopers LLP

LOCATIONS

HQ: Etsy Inc
   117 Adams Street, Brooklyn, NY 11201
Phone: 718 880-3660
Web: www.etsy.com

HISTORICAL FINANCIALS

Company Type: Public

Income Statement   FYE: December 31

	REVENUE ($ mil.)	NET INCOME ($ mil.)	NET PROFIT MARGIN	EMPLOYEES
12/17	441.2	81.8	18.5%	744
12/16	364.9	(29.9)	—	1,043
12/15	273.5	(54.0)	—	819
12/14	195.5	(15.2)	—	685
12/13	125.0	(0.8)	—	0
Annual Growth	37.1%	—	—	—

2017 Year-End Financials

Debt ratio: 11.5%
Return on equity: 22.0%
Cash ($ mil.): 315.4
Current ratio: 4.29
Long-term debt ($ mil.): 64.1

No. of shares (mil.): 121.7
Dividends
   Yield: —
   Payout: —
Market value ($ mil.): 2,490.0

	STOCK PRICE ($) FY Close	P/E High/Low	Earnings	PER SHARE ($) Dividends	Book Value
12/17	20.45	32 14	0.68	0.00	3.26
12/16	11.78	— —	(0.26)	0.00	2.97
12/15	8.26	— —	(0.59)	0.00	2.94
Annual Growth	57.3%	— —	—	—	5.4%

Euronet Worldwide Inc.

Euronet Worldwide might soon have the whole world in its net — thanks to the growing electronic payments industry. The company offers money transfer and processing services and manages ATM networks and point-of-sale (POS) terminals for itself and others. It operates three primary businesses: epay (which sells prepaid mobile airtime and related products and services) EFT (electronic financial transaction processing software and ATM/POS management services); and consumer-to-consumer money transfer. Traditionally Euronet is highly acquisitive and has snatched up money transfer processing and similar companies around the world. Founded in 1994 Euronet operates in 160 countries and its top markets are the US Germany and the UK.

Operations

Euronet Worldwide operates through three business segments: epay ETF Processing and Money Transfer.

Money Transfer generates around 40% of sales and provides cross-globe consumer-to-consumer money transfer services under the brands Ria AFEX Money Express and IME. It also runs global account-to-account money transfer services under the brands HiFX and xe. It operates through a network of sending agents company-owned stores and websites.

The epay segment accounts for around 35% of sales and provides electronic distribution and processing of prepaid mobile airtime. Its network covers 661000 point-of-sale terminals that process pre-paid "top-up" services. It also sells vouchers and physical gift fulfillment in Europe and gift card distribution across the world.

The ETF Processing segment generates about 25% of sales and processes transactions across a network of nearly 34000 ATMs and 163000 point-of-sale (POS) terminals across Europe the Middle East and the Asia-Pacific region. It also carries out POS currency conversion advertising card issuing and merchant acquiring.

Geographic Reach

Kansas-based Euronet does business in 160 countries across 61 offices and 13 transaction processing centers. The US is Euronet's largest market at roughly 30% of sales followed by Germany at more than 20% and the UK and Poland at more than 5% each. Other large markets include Spain Australia and India.

Sales and Marketing

Euronet Worldwide's clients include financial institutions retailers service providers and consumers.

Financial Performance

Euronet's revenues and profits have been rising over the past few years fueled by company acquisitions global network expansion and an overall strong consumer demand for digital payment mediums.

In fiscal 2016 sales climbed a further 11% to $2.0 billion thanks to the IME acquisition in mid-2015 and the continued growth of the Wal-mart-2-Wal-mart money transfer service since 2014. The company also witnesses growth in the number of money transfers processing by the Ria business and growth in ATM numbers under management (relating to the YourCash acquisition). On the downside prepaid mobile transactions fell.

Net income increased 77% to $174.4 million due to higher operating income a decrease in foreign exchange losses and an increase in investment gains. On the downside income tax increased by $16.2 million and interest expense by $3.5 million.

Cash from operations increased 71% to $368.2 million due to fluctuations in working capital relating to payment timings.

Strategy

Euronet Worldwide has historically bolstered its three main business lines and entered new geographic markets by acquiring money transfer processing and similar companies in mature and emerging markets. Its 2016 acquisition of Your-Cash added independent ATM networks in 21 European countries.

The epay segment is facing declining revenue as the number of consumers on contract plans increases more and more. Its strategy is to defend margins which it aims to do by providing value added services to mobile operators and reduce reliance on mobile top up by increasing distribution of other digital content. Product initiatives include prepaid debit cards music software and games backed by relationships with global consumer product brands such as iTunes Google Play and Microsoft.

In the Money Transfer segment Euronet works to increase the volume of money transferred across its network by deepening its correspondent networks in existing corridors. US-Mexico is its primary transfer corridor (thanks to family ties between the two countries) but the company is developing new transfer corridors from the US to other territories. It is also looking at greater cross-sell opportunities between the Money Transfer and ETF Processing segments.

Mergers and Acquisitions

In October 2016 the company acquired UK-based ATM operator YourCash adding some 5000 ATMs in the UK Ireland Belgium and the Netherlands. With that deal Euronet has independent ATM networks in 21 European countries.

Company Background

In late 2012 epay New Zealand acquired ezi-pay Ltd. making epay New Zealand the largest distributor of prepaid mobile and non-mobile content in the country. In late 2011 Euronet acquired German company cadooz AG from Palamon Capital Partners. cadooz provides vouchers and rewards for sales incentives customer acquisition and loyalty and employee satisfaction campaigns for the German Austrian and Polish markets across a broad range of industries. The unit joined Euronet's epay division.

Also in 2011 Euronet expanded its network in Poland with the acquisition of ATMs from Diebold. The deal added 535 ATMs to Euronet's Polish network (the largest in that country). In another 2011 deal Euronet acquired Smart PayNetwork which provides ATM outsourcing services card issuing and acquiring and merchant servicing in Romania. Previously in 2010 epay expanded into the growing South American markets with its acquisition of Brazil-based Telecom Net (which was known as Ativi but has since been renamed epay Brazil).

EXECUTIVES

Chairman President and CEO, Michael J. (Mike) Brown, age 61, $600,000 total compensation
EVP and General Counsel, Jeffrey B. (Jeff) Newman, age 64, $300,000 total compensation
EVP and CFO, Rick L. Weller, age 61, $365,000 total compensation
EVP and CEO Money Transfer Division, Juan C. Bianchi, age 47, $320,769 total compensation
EVP and CEO epay and EFT Asia Pacific Division, Kevin J. Caponecchi, age 52, $365,000 total compensation
EVP and CEO EFT Europe Middle East and Africa, Nikos Fountas, $353,701 total compensation
SVP and CTO, Martin L. Br ckner
Auditors: KPMG LLP

LOCATIONS

HQ: Euronet Worldwide Inc.
   3500 College Boulevard, Leawood, KS 66211
Phone: 913 327-4200   **Fax:** 913 327-1921
Web: www.euronetservices.com

PRODUCTS/OPERATIONS

2014 Sales

	% of total
Epay	47
Money Transfer	31
EFT Processing	22
Adjustments	0
Total	**100**

Selected Subsidiaries

Bankomat 24/Euronet Sp. z o.o. (Poland)
Delta Euronet GmbH (Germany)
EFT Services Holding B.V. (Netherlands)
   Cashlink Bangladesh Ltd. (10%)
e-pay Holdings Limited (UK)
Euronet Adminisztracios Szolgaltato Kft (Hungary)
Euronet Business Holdings S.L. (Spain)
Euronet Card Services S.A. (Greece)
Euronet Services SRL (Romania)
Euronet TeleRecarga S.L. (Spain)
   Euronet MovilCarga S.L. (Spain 80%)
EWI Foreign Holdings Limited (Cyprus)
Gescoro Inc. (Canada)
RIA de Centroamérica S.A. de C.V. (El Salvador)
RIA Telecommunications of Canada Inc.
transact Elektronische Zahlungssysteme GmbH
   (Germany)

COMPETITORS

ACE Cash Express	MoneyGram
First Data	International
Fiserv	PULSE Network
Global Payments	Western Union

HISTORICAL FINANCIALS

Company Type: Public

Income Statement

FYE: December 31

	REVENUE ($ mil.)	NET INCOME ($ mil.)	NET PROFIT MARGIN	EMPLOYEES
12/17	2,252.4	156.8	7.0%	6,600
12/16	1,958.6	174.4	8.9%	6,200
12/15	1,772.2	98.8	5.6%	5,600
12/14	1,664.1	101.6	6.1%	4,600
12/13	1,413.1	87.9	6.2%	4,100
Annual Growth	12.4%	15.5%	—	12.6%

2017 Year-End Financials

Debt ratio: 14.6%
Return on equity: 14.9%
Cash ($ mil.): 819.1
Current ratio: 1.34
Long-term debt ($ mil.): 413.7

No. of shares (mil.): 52.8
Dividends
  Yield: —
  Payout: —
Market value ($ mil.): 4,450.0

	STOCK PRICE ($) FY Close	P/E High/Low	PER SHARE ($) Earnings	Dividends	Book Value
12/17	84.27	33 24	2.85	0.00	22.70
12/16	72.43	25 17	3.23	0.00	17.20
12/15	72.43	43 24	1.83	0.00	15.55
12/14	54.90	30 18	1.89	0.00	14.16
12/13	47.85	28 13	1.69	0.00	12.57
Annual Growth	15.2%	— —	14.0%	—	15.9%

Evans Bancorp, Inc.

Evans National Bank wants to take care of Buffalo's bills. The subsidiary of Evans Bancorp operates about a dozen branches in western New York (including Buffalo). The bank primarily uses funds gathered from deposits to originate commercial and residential real estate loans (more than 70% of its loan portfolio) and to invest in securities. Subsidiaries include ENB Insurance Agency which sells property/casualty insurance; ENB Associates offering mutual funds and annuities to bank customers; and Evans National Leasing which provides financing for business equipment throughout the US. In 2009 Evans Bancorp acquired the assets

and single branch of the failed Waterford Village Bank in Clarence New York.

In addition to Buffalo Evans National Bank operates branches in Amherst Angola Derby Evans Forestville Hamburg Lancaster and North Boston New York.

The company wants to more than double in size over the next five years. It plans to open new de novo branches and acquire existing ones within its market area with a particular focus on Buffalo and the Northtowns. It is also interested in acquiring companies that will help it build its in-house capabilities. Its late 2008 purchase of Suchak Data Systems which provides data processing services to financial institutions expands Evans Bancorp's IT platform.

A group of 14 officers and directors controls about 9% of Evans Bancorp.

EXECUTIVES

President and CEO Evans Bancorp and Evans National Bank and Director, David J. Nasca, age 58, $227,692 total compensation
Chairman, Phillip Brothman, age 77
Secretary; SVP Evans National Bank; CEO Evans National Leasing, William R. Glass, age 69, $186,740 total compensation
Director; President TEA and ENB Associates, Robert G. Miller Jr., age 59, $213,584 total compensation
Vice Chairman, John R. O'Brien, age 66
Treasurer; SVP and CFO Evans National Bank, Gary A. Kajtoch, age 49, $156,231 total compensation
Independent Chairman of the Board, John OBrien
IR Contact Officer, Michelle Baumgarden
Director, Lee C. Wortham
President and CEO Evans Bancorp and Evans National Bank and Director, David J. Nasca, age 58
Director, James Tilley, age 73
Director; President TEA and ENB Associates, Robert G. Miller Jr., age 59
Director, James E. Biddle Jr., age 54
Director, Thomas H. Waring Jr., age 58
Director, Nancy W. Ware, age 59
Vice Chairman, John R. O'Brien, age 66
Director, Mary Catherine Militello, age 57
Director, Kenneth C. Kirst, age 63
Director, Marsha S. Henderson
Auditors: KPMG LLP

LOCATIONS

HQ: Evans Bancorp, Inc.
  One Grimsby Drive, Hamburg, NY 14075
Phone: 716 926-2000
Web: www.evansbancorp.com

COMPETITORS

HSBC USA	M&T Bank
KeyCorp	Northwest Bancshares

HISTORICAL FINANCIALS

Company Type: Public

Income Statement

FYE: December 31

	ASSETS ($ mil.)	NET INCOME ($ mil.)	INCOME AS % OF ASSETS	EMPLOYEES
12/17	1,295.6	10.4	0.8%	271
12/16	1,100.7	8.2	0.8%	254
12/15	939.1	7.8	0.8%	258
12/14	846.8	8.1	1.0%	251
12/13	833.5	7.8	0.9%	241
Annual Growth	11.7%	7.5%	—	3.0%

2017 Year-End Financials

Return on assets: 0.8%
Return on equity: 9.7%
Long-term debt ($ mil.): —
No. of shares (mil.): 4.7
Sales ($ mil): 60.7

Dividends
  Yield: 0.0%
  Payout: 37.0%
Market value ($ mil.): 200.0

	STOCK PRICE ($) FY Close	P/E High/Low	PER SHARE ($) Earnings	Dividends	Book Value
12/17	41.90	20 15	2.16	0.80	24.74
12/16	31.55	19 12	1.90	0.76	22.50
12/15	25.72	14 12	1.82	0.72	21.44
12/14	24.31	13 11	1.95	0.65	20.41
12/13	21.10	11 8	1.85	0.50	19.21
Annual Growth	18.7%	— —	3.9%	12.5%	6.5%

Evercore Inc

Evercore Partners makes Investment Banking advisory its core business. It provides advisory services on mergers and acquisitions restructurings divestitures and financing to corporate clients. Boasting some $14 billion in assets under management the firm's investment management business principally manages and invests capital for clients including institutional investors such as corporate and public pension funds endowments insurance companies and high net-worth individuals. Evercore also makes private equity investments. Beyond the US the company operates globally through subsidiaries such as Evercore Europe in London. Evercore also has offices in Brazil Hong Kong and Singapore.

Operations

The firm's Investment Banking advisory segment is its core business accounting for 88% of its revenue in 2014. Evercore's Institutional Equities services offering equity research and securities trading for institutional clients resides under the Investment banking umbrella.

Its Investment Management segment (12% of revenue) focuses on asset management for institutions wealthy individuals and private equity clients. The segment had $14 million in assets under management at the end of 2014 with $8.1 million of that attributable to Institutional Asset Management $5.7 billion attributable to Wealth Management and $0.3 billion attributable to Private Equity Clients. As part of this segment Evercore Trust provides investment management and trustee services to employee benefits plans.

Geographic Reach

While Evercore Partners operates globally the US accounted for about 65% of the firm's revenue in 2014. Latin America accounted for 7% while Europe and other countries made up 27%. Evercore's offices are in the US the UK Brazil Hong Kong and Singapore. It also has strategic alliances with leading firms in China Japan India Korea and Argentina.

Sales and Marketing

Evercore Partners had a staff of 1300 employees worldwide at the end of 2014.

Financial Performance

Evercore Partner's rising revenues and profits over the last several years have been fueled by higher demand for its advisory services amidst a surge of merger and acquisition activity as the financial markets in the US and UK have become increasingly more attractive to investors.

The firm's annual revenue jumped 20% to $915.8 million in 2014 mostly as its Investment Banking revenue rose from increased advisory fees from US- and UK-based businesses partially stemming from its late-2014 acquisition of ISI. The Investment Banking segment served some 418 clients during the year with 173 fees valued in excess of $1 million. The firm's investment advisory and management fees grew by 4% year-over-year as its assets under management in its Wealth Management unit continued to grow.

Higher revenue and an absence of loss from discontinued operations in 2014 pushed Evercore's net income higher by 63% to $86.9 million while the firm's operating cash levels rose by 9% to $216 million on higher cash earnings.

Strategy

Evercore continues to grow by acquiring financial advisory firms that enhance its capabilities and by bolstering its Investment Banking business through expanding the number of sectors it serves. In 2014 Evercore continued to expand the scope of its core Advisory business by hiring experienced talent to bolster its proficiency in the fast-growing Technology Media and Telecommunications sector as well as the technology healthcare telecom and oil & gas sectors in the US and Europe. Its

The firm also continues to move into new geographic markets that are receptive to its Investment Banking business model. In recent years Evercore has expanded into Canada and Singapore while forming advisory affiliates and alliances in Brazil Argentina Japan China South Korea and India as well as in Australia in early 2015.

As an independent investment banking firm that isn't involved in commercial banking or proprietary trading Evercore has avoided the controversy swirling around competitors such as Goldman Sachs that results from the conflicts of interest that may occur at larger firms that both underwrite and invest in their clients.

Mergers and Acquisitions

In May 2015 Evercore expanded its reach into Germany and enhanced its sector expertise after buying the Frankfurt-based investment banking advisory boutique Kuna & Co. KG which specialized in real estate in Germany.

In November 2014 the firm purchased ISI International Strategy & Investment bolstering its Investment Banking business' position as a scaled provider of non-proprietary capital markets advice and execution. The acquired company which was renamed Evercore ISI would start by providing macro research and fundamental coverage of more than 600 companies across 12 industries (60% of the S&P 500's market capitalization value).

Company Background

Some of Evercore's past high-profile transactions include the 2012 breakup of Kraft Foods (now Mondelez International) the recapitalizations of GM and CIT Group and the acquisition of Lubrizol by Berkshire Hathaway.

Evercore was launched in 1996 (it went public 10 years later) by Roger Altman who formerly led investment banking and merger advisory practices at Lehman Brothers and The Blackstone Group. Altman resigned as CEO in 2009 and was succeeded by Ralph Schlosstein co-founder of asset management giant BlackRock; Altman remained executive chairman.

EXECUTIVES

President and CEO, Ralph L. Schlosstein, age 67, $500,000 total compensation
Senior Managing Director and General Counsel, Adam B. Frankel, age 50
Senior Managing Director and CEO Evercore Partners Mexico and Evercore Partners Mexico S. de R.L., Augusto Arellano, age 43
Senior Managing Director and CFO, Robert B. Walsh, age 62, $500,000 total compensation
Senior Managing Director and CEO Europe Investment Banking, Andrew Sibbald, age 51, $400,000 total compensation
Chairman Evercore ISI and Head Economic Research Team, Edward S. (Ed) Hyman, age 73
CEO Evercore Asia (Singapore), Keith Magnus
Founder and Senior Chairman, Roger C. Altman, age 73
Chairman, John S. Weinberg, age 61
Auditors: Deloitte & Touche LLP

LOCATIONS

HQ: Evercore Inc
55 East 52nd Street, 38th floor, New York, NY 10055
Phone: 212 857-3100   **Fax:** 212 857-3101
Web: www.evercore.com

PRODUCTS/OPERATIONS

2011 Sales

	$ mil.	% of total
Investment banking	430.6	80
Investment management	99.2	18
Other	13.9	2
Total	**543.7**	**100**

COMPETITORS

Allen & Company	Greenhill
Atalanta Sosnoff	JPMorgan Chase
Bank of America	Lazard
Barclays Capital	Merrill Lynch
Blackstone Group	Moelis & Company
Citigroup Global	Morgan Stanley
Markets	Rothschild North
Credit Suisse	America
Deutsche Bank	UBS Investment Bank
Goldman Sachs	

HISTORICAL FINANCIALS

Company Type: Public

Income Statement   FYE: December 31

	REVENUE ($ mil.)	NET INCOME ($ mil.)	NET PROFIT MARGIN	EMPLOYEES
12/17	1,704.3	125.4	7.4%	1,600
12/16	1,440.0	107.5	7.5%	1,475
12/15	1,223.2	42.8	3.5%	1,400
12/14	915.8	86.8	9.5%	1,300
12/13	765.4	53.2	7.0%	1,000
Annual Growth	**22.2%**	**23.9%**	**—**	**12.5%**

2017 Year-End Financials

Debt ratio: 11.0%	No. of shares (mil.): 39.1
Return on equity: 23.4%	Dividends
Cash ($ mil.): 620.2	Yield: 0.0%
Current ratio: 2.16	Payout: 50.7%
Long-term debt ($ mil.): 175.1	Market value ($ mil.): 3,519.0

	STOCK PRICE ($) FY Close	P/E High/Low	PER SHARE ($)		
			Earnings	Dividends	Book Value
12/17	90.00	29 21	2.80	1.42	13.91
12/16	68.70	26 15	2.43	1.27	13.45
12/15	54.07	51 41	0.98	1.15	12.73
12/14	52.37	26 19	2.08	1.03	15.21
12/13	59.78	37 18	1.38	0.91	15.20
Annual Growth	**10.8%**	**— —**	**19.3%**	**11.8%**	**(2.2%)**

Evolution Petroleum Corp

Just as petroleum and natural gas evolves from old living forms Evolution Petroleum has evolved by producing these ancient hydrocarbons. The company operates oil and gas producing fields in Louisiana Oklahoma and Texas. Its strategy is to acquire already-established properties and redevelop them making the fields more profitable. One method it uses is gas flooding which uses carbon dioxide to free up trapped oil deposits. Assets include a CO2-project in Louisiana's Delhi Field and patented artificial lift technology to extend the life and ultimate recoveries of wells with oil or associated water production. It reported 10.8 million barrels of oil equivalent proved reserves in fiscal 2016.

Operations

Evolution Petroleum is engaged in the acquisition exploitation and development of properties for the production of crude oil and natural gas. It five major projects are Delhi Field Enhanced Oil Recovery(EOR)-Northeast Louisiana (which has produced 192 million barrels of crude oil and substantial amounts of natural gas to date); Mississippi Lime-North Central Oklahoma Kay County (a limestone formation that horizontal drilling combined with multistage hydraulic fracturing has opened up to redevelopment); GARP (Gas Assisted Rod Pump artificial lift technology being commercialized through subsidiary NGS Technologies; and Giddings Field-Central Texas (2180 net developed acres); and Lopez Field-South Texas (782 net acres).

Geographic Reach

The company has operations in Northeast Louisiana Southeast Oklahoma South Texas Central Texas and North Central Oklahoma.

Sales and Marketing

The company markets its production to third parties. It sells its crude oil under the Delhi Field operator's agreement with Plains Marketing LP for the delivery and pricing.

Financial Performance

Evolution Petroleum's revenues decreased by 5.4% to $26.35 million in fiscal 2016 (June year end) due to a 55% slump in realized prices which more than offset a 45% increase in production volumes.

The company's net income increased by 394% in fiscal 2016 to $24.7 million due to litigation settlement proceeds insurance proceeds and realized hedging gains offset in part by increased DD&A expenses litigation expenses and higher income tax expense. The company settled outstanding litigation with the operator of Delhi field during the year. In the settlement Evolution Petroleum received $27.5 million in cash.

In fiscal 2016 cash flows provided by operating activities of $30.7 million reflected $28.9 million provided by operations and $1.8 million provided by other working capital changes. Of the $28.9 million provided before working capital changes some $24.7 million came from net income and $4.2 million from non-cash expenses and gains.

Strategy

Evolution Petroleum acquires known underdeveloped oil and natural gas resources and exploit them through the application of capital sound engineering and modern technology to increase production ultimate recoveries or both.

It strategy is intended to generate scalable low unit cost development and re-development opportunities that minimize or eliminate exploration risks. These opportunities involve the application of modern technology its own proprietary technology and its specific expertise in overlooked areas of the United States where it may or may not choose to be the operator. The assets it exploits currently fit into three types of project opportunities: EOR Bypassed Primary Resources and Unconventional Development using its staff expertise in horizontal drilling.

Company Background

In 2013 to raise cash the company sold all of its non-GARP producing wells and drilling locations in its Giddings assets.

In 2008 in order to raise cash Evolution Petroleum sold its working interests in some oil fields in LaSalle and Winn Parishes Louisiana to a private buyer for $4.6 million.

The company was formed in 2003.

EXECUTIVES

President and CEO, Randall D. Keys, age 58, $295,500 total compensation
SVP and CFO, David Joe, age 53, $205,000 total compensation
Chairman, Robert S. Herlin, age 63
Auditors: Moss Adams LLP

LOCATIONS

HQ: Evolution Petroleum Corp
 1155 Dairy Ashford Road, Suite 425, Houston, TX 77079
Phone: 713 935-0122   **Fax:** 713 935-0199
Web: www.evolutionpetroleum.com

PRODUCTS/OPERATIONS

2016 Sales

	% of total
Crude oil	99
Artificial lift technology services	1
Total	**100**

Selected Operations

CO2-based enhanced oil recovery
Low-permeablitiy reservoir development
Technology-based redevelopment of old oil and gas fields

COMPETITORS

Abraxas Petroleum	EOG
Anadarko Petroleum	Midstates Petroleum
Callon Petroleum	Saratoga Resources
Carrizo Oil & Gas	Triangle Petroleum
Chesapeake Energy	

HISTORICAL FINANCIALS
Company Type: Public

Income Statement
FYE: June 30

	REVENUE ($ mil.)	NET INCOME ($ mil.)	NET PROFIT MARGIN	EMPLOYEES
06/18	41.2	19.6	47.5%	4
06/17	34.4	8.0	23.3%	5
06/16	26.3	24.6	93.6%	6
06/15	27.8	4.9	17.9%	10
06/14	17.6	3.6	20.4%	8
Annual Growth	**23.6%**	**52.8%**	**—**	**(15.9%)**

2018 Year-End Financials

Debt ratio: —	No. of shares (mil.): 33.0
Return on equity: 26.9%	Dividends
Cash ($ mil.): 24.9	Yield: 0.0%
Current ratio: 7.26	Payout: 59.3%
Long-term debt ($ mil.): —	Market value ($ mil.): 326.0

	STOCK PRICE ($) FY Close	P/E High/Low		PER SHARE ($) Earnings	Dividends	Book Value
06/18	9.85	17	11	0.59	0.35	2.34
06/17	8.10	48	25	0.21	0.26	2.07
06/16	5.47	10	5	0.73	0.20	2.32
06/15	6.59	85	44	0.13	0.30	1.48
06/14	10.95	151	118	0.09	0.30	1.59
Annual Growth	**(2.6%)**			**60.0%**	**3.9%**	**10.1%**

Evoqua Water Technologies Corp

Auditors: Ernst & Young LLP

LOCATIONS

HQ: Evoqua Water Technologies Corp
 210 Sixth Avenue, Pittsburgh, PA 15222
Phone: 724 772-0044
Web: www.evoqua.com

HISTORICAL FINANCIALS
Company Type: Public

Income Statement
FYE: September 30

	REVENUE ($ mil.)	NET INCOME ($ mil.)	NET PROFIT MARGIN	EMPLOYEES
09/18	1,339.5	6.1	0.5%	4,000
09/17	1,247.4	2.1	0.2%	3,958
09/16	1,137.2	11.6	1.0%	200
09/15	1,060.9	(86.0)	—	0
09/14	791.1	(97.7)	—	0
Annual Growth	**14.1%**	**—**	**—**	**—**

2018 Year-End Financials

Debt ratio: 57.2%	No. of shares (mil.): 113.9
Return on equity: 2.1%	Dividends
Cash ($ mil.): 82.3	Yield: —
Current ratio: 1.99	Payout: —
Long-term debt ($ mil.): 928.0	Market value ($ mil.): 2,026.0

	STOCK PRICE ($) FY Close	P/E High/Low		PER SHARE ($) Earnings	Dividends	Book Value
09/18	17.78	504	352	0.05	0.00	3.15
Annual Growth	**—**			**—**	**—**	**—**

Exelixis Inc

We've come a long way baby but we still have a lot in common with the fruit fly. Exelixis a pharmaceutical research and development firm got its start analyzing genetic data from fruit flies and other organisms as a means to speed the development of drugs and other products. Its early genomic work has yielded a pipeline of drug candidates primarily in the area of cancer therapies as well as some potential treatments for metabolic and cardiovascular diseases. Lead candidate Cometriq gained FDA approval for treatment of thyroid cancer in late 2012 and was launched in the US in early 2013. Exelixis takes its name from the Greek word for evolution.

Operations

Exelixis has built upon its past in genomics research to become a full-fledged drug development company focusing increasingly on its pharmaceuticals pipeline. Exelixis has historically relied on licensing and co-development partnerships to fund its operations. In fact most of its development-stage candidates are licensed out to third parties though the company retains some marketing rights on select candidates (including Cometriq). Development and licensing partners include Bristol-Myers Squibb Merck Daiichi Sankyo Genentech and Sanofi. The company expects sales of Cometriq to further support its R&D efforts.

The Exelixis-discovered cobimetinib compound a selective inhibitor of mitogen-activated protein kinase (MEK) is being studied by Roche and Genentech in collaboration with Exelixis. Roche has completed a Market Authorization Application (MAA) for the compound to be used in combination with vemurafenib in Europe; in the US the FDA has granted the compound's New Drug Application. Another compound XL888 is an HSP90 inhibitor under investigation.

Other pipeline products include METEOR (a phase III pivotal trial in second-line metastatic renal carcinoma) and CELESTIAL (a phase III pivotal trial in second-line hepatocellular cancer).

Geographic Reach

The company leases 367773 sq. ft. of office and lab space in San Francisco.

Sales and Marketing

In 2014 Diplomat Specialty Pharmacy accounted for 99% of the company's revenues. Commerical product Cometriq is distributed by Diplomat Specialty Pharmacy in the US market and is warehoused and shipped by a third-party logistics firm.

Exelixis contracts with third parties to manufacture the active pharmaceutical ingredients (APIs) and finished drug products for use in clinical studies.

Financial Performance

As a development-stage company Exelixis has struggled to turn a profit. It did manage to grow its revenues each year for several years by entering new partnerships and licensing agreements and by achieving milestone payouts on existing contracts including a 55% increase to $289.6 million in 2011. However the rise in revenue and was due primarily to accelerated payouts from discontinued licensing agreements and therefore revenues dropped 84% the following year. Revenues have declined since then; in 2014 it decreased 20% to $25 million on lower license and contract revenues.

Net loss increased by 10% in 2014 to $268 million on higher R&D costs related to an increase in clinical trial activity as well as on charges related to a corporate restructuring initiated that year. Exelixis has lost money every year since its founding with the exception of fiscal 2011. At the end of 2014 it has accumulated debt of $1.8 billion.

Operating cash outflow increased 18% to $235 million in 2014 due to factors such as a decline in cash provided by clinical trial liability and changes in accounts payable.

Strategy

Exelixis is focused on development of proprietary partnered and licensed candidates for cancer cardiovascular and metabolic candidates. In addition it is focused on promoting Cometriq as well as other candidates once they gain approval. Exelixis also seeks out new development and licensing partners to fuel its research programs.

Cometriq (cabozantinib) was the company's main research focus prior to approval; in addition to the approved application for thyroid cancer the company is developing Cometriq for treatment of prostate breast renal and other cancers. In 2014 the drug was approved in Europe for the treatment of adults with progressive unresectable medullary thyroid cancer. In 2015 the firm extended its agreement with Swedish Orphan Biovitrum to support the distribution and commercialization of Cometriq in certain European markets.

After cabozantinib failed in one of its phase III pivotal trials in 2014 Exelixis initiated a corporate restructuring reducing its workforce. It recorded some $6 million in aggregate restructuring charges of which approximately 95% was recorded that year. (The rest is expected to be recorded in 2015.) The company is changing its focus to other phase III pivotal trials of cabozantinib.

Also in 2014 GlaxoSmithKline (GSK) terminated the development of foretinib returning it to Exelixis for development and commercialization; GSK remains entitled to a 3% royalty on net sales of any product with cabozantinib (including Cometriq) and a 4% royalty on net sales of any product containing foretinib.

EXECUTIVES

President Product Development and Medical Affairs; Chief Medical Officer, Gisela M. Schwab, age 61, $513,906 total compensation
President and CEO, Michael M. Morrissey, age 57, $755,192 total compensation
EVP Scientific Strategy and Chief Scientific Officer, Peter Lamb, age 57, $407,042 total compensation
EVP and CFO, Christopher J. (Chris) Senner
EVP and General Counsel, Jeffrey J. Hessekiel, age 48, $380,769 total compensation
SVP Medical Affairs, William Berg
VP Marketing, Gregg Bernier
Executive Vice President, Pamela A Simonton
Chairman, Stelios Papadopoulos, age 70
Auditors: Ernst & Young LLP

LOCATIONS

HQ: Exelixis Inc
1851 Harbor Bay Parkway, Alameda, CA 94502
Phone: 650 837-7000
Web: www.exelixis.com

COMPETITORS

Amgen	Keryx
ArQule	Biopharmaceuticals
Array BioPharma	Madrigal
AstraZeneca	Pharmaceuticals
Bayer HealthCare	Millennium: The Takeda
Pharmaceuticals Inc.	Oncology Company
Biogen	Novartis
Bristol-Myers Squibb	OSI Pharmaceuticals
Eli Lilly	Onyx Pharmaceuticals
Genentech	Pfizer
Genmab	Sanofi
Genzyme	Semafore
GlaxoSmithKline	Pharmaceuticals

HISTORICAL FINANCIALS

Company Type: Public

Income Statement

FYE: December 29

	REVENUE ($ mil.)	NET INCOME ($ mil.)	NET PROFIT MARGIN	EMPLOYEES
12/17	452.4	154.2	34.1%	372
12/16	191.4	(70.2)	—	287
12/15	37.1	(169.7)	—	115
12/14	25.1	(268.5)	—	98
12/13	31.3	(244.7)	—	227
Annual Growth	**94.9%**	**—**		**13.1%**

2017 Year-End Financials

Debt ratio: —
Return on equity: 82.6%
Cash ($ mil.): 183.1
Current ratio: 4.21
Long-term debt ($ mil.): —

No. of shares (mil.): 296.2
Dividends
Yield: —
Payout: —
Market value ($ mil.): 9,005.0

	STOCK PRICE ($) FY Close	P/E High/Low	PER SHARE ($) Earnings	Dividends	Book Value
12/17	30.40	59 28	0.49	0.00	0.96
12/16	14.91	— —	(0.28)	0.00	0.31
12/15	5.64	— —	(0.81)	0.00	(0.46)
12/14	1.44	— —	(1.38)	0.00	(0.59)
12/13	6.13	— —	(1.33)	0.00	0.36
Annual Growth	**49.2%**	— —	—	**—**	**27.9%**

ExlService Holdings Inc

Have an extra-large task you'd rather not take on? Outsource it to ExlService Holdings. The company known as EXL offers business process outsourcing (BPO) research and analytics and consulting services. EXL's BPO offerings which generate most of its sales include claims processing collections customer support and finance and accounting. Customers come mainly from the banking financial services and insurance industries as well as from the utilities and telecommunications sectors. EXL operates offices around the world including the US and countries in Eastern Europe and Asia. The company was established in 1999.

Geographic Reach

EXL operates through six offices in the US 19 offices in India as well as through a half-a-dozen locations in the Czech Republic Bulgaria Romania Malaysia and the Philippines. The company also has a sales office in the UK and networking and telecommunications centers in California New Jersey and New York.

Sales and Marketing

EXL earned revenue from more than 600 clients in 2014 with its top three clients generating 22% of its revenue.

Financial Performance

The company's revenue was $499 million in fiscal 2014. That was an increase of more than $20 million compared to the prior fiscal period. EXL's net income was $32.4 million in fiscal 2014 which was a decrease of $15.7 million compared to its fiscal 2013 net income. The company's cash flow from operations decreased by more than $16 million during fiscal 2014 compared to the prior fiscal period but the company still ended the year with $66.7 million in cash on hand.

EXECUTIVES

Vice Chairman and CEO, Rohit Kapoor, age 53, $600,000 total compensation
President and COO, Pavan Bagai, age 56, $242,590 total compensation
VP and Business Leader, Vikas Bhalla, age 46
EVP and Business Head Health Care, Rembert de Villa, age 61, $382,534 total compensation
EVP and CFO, Vishal Chhibbar, age 50, $251,341 total compensation
EVP General Counsel and Corporate Secretary, Nancy Saltzman, age 52
CTO, Mike Toma
EVP and Chief Human Resource Officer, Nalin Miglani, age 57, $400,000 total compensation
Chairman, Garen K. Staglin, age 73
Auditors: DELOITTE & TOUCHE LLP

LOCATIONS

HQ: ExlService Holdings Inc
280 Park Avenue, 38th Floor, New York, NY 10017
Phone: 212 277-7100
Web: www.exlservice.com

PRODUCTS/OPERATIONS

2014 Sales

	$ mil.	% of total
Operations Management	388.7	78
Analytics and Business Transformation	110.6	22
Total	**499.3**	**100**

COMPETITORS

Accenture	Infosys
Genpact	Tata Consultancy
HP Enterprise Services	WNS (Holdings)
IBM Global Services	Wipro

HISTORICAL FINANCIALS

Company Type: Public

Income Statement

FYE: December 31

	REVENUE ($ mil.)	NET INCOME ($ mil.)	NET PROFIT MARGIN	EMPLOYEES
12/17	762.3	48.8	6.4%	27,800
12/16	685.9	61.7	9.0%	26,000
12/15	628.4	51.5	8.2%	24,100
12/14	499.2	32.4	6.5%	22,800
12/13	478.4	48.1	10.1%	22,200
Annual Growth	**12.4%**	**0.4%**	**—**	**5.8%**

2017 Year-End Financials

Debt ratio: 7.4%
Return on equity: 8.6%
Cash ($ mil.): 265.2
Current ratio: 3.14
Long-term debt ($ mil.): 50.7

No. of shares (mil.): 33.8
Dividends
Yield: —
Payout: —
Market value ($ mil.): 2,045.0

	STOCK PRICE ($) FY Close	P/E High/Low	PER SHARE ($) Earnings	Dividends	Book Value
12/17	60.35	43 31	1.39	0.00	17.70
12/16	50.44	29 23	1.79	0.00	15.82
12/15	44.93	31 18	1.51	0.00	14.07
12/14	28.71	31 25	0.96	0.00	12.74
12/13	27.62	22 16	1.42	0.00	11.38
Annual Growth	21.6%	—	(0.5%)	—	11.7%

Extra Space Storage Inc

When closets are bursting at the seams and garages are overflowing Extra Space Storage gives its customers room to breathe. One of the largest operators and managers of self-storage properties in the US the self-administered self-managed real estate investment trust (REIT) wholly-owns owns in joint-venture partnerships or operates for third parties about 1030 facilities with some 680000 units totaling nearly 76 million sq. ft. of rentable space. Active in metropolitan areas in nearly 35 states and Washington DC the company also offers business boat and RV storage and leases to nearly 600000 tenants nationwide.

Operations
Extra Space Storage operates through three segments: rental operations; tenant reinsurance; and property management acquisition and development.

The rental operations segment focuses on rentals of the self-storage facilities it owns. Tenant reinsurance covers the reinsurance of risks relating to the loss of goods stored by tenants in the company's self-storage facilities. Its last segment — property management acquisition and development — manages acquires develops and sells self-storage facilities.

Geographic Reach
Utah-based Extra Space Storage operates its business throughout the US in 35 states Puerto Rico and Washington DC.

Financial Performance
The storage company's revenue rose some $111.22 million in fiscal 2013 or 27% to $520.6 million continuing several years of incremental growth. It attributes the increases to a boost in property rental and tenant reinsurance revenue. Property rental revenue rose thanks to its purchase of 78 properties during 2013 and 91 properties during 2012.

Extra Space Storage logged $172.1 million in net income in fiscal 2013 representing a $54.78 million increase or a 47% jump overall. Higher revenues a gain on the sale of real estate assets and the purchase of a joint venture partners' interest all contributed to the spike.

Cash flow from operations also increased — by $55.38 million in 2013 — to $271.26 million from higher net income and the net change in working capital.

Strategy
The REIT has relied on acquisitions in growing markets to expand its business. In 2014 Extra Space Storage acquired a self-storage portfolio of 17 assets located in Virginia for about $200 million. The deal gave the company 1.5 million sq. ft. of net rentable space across 14000 units. The company also has another five properties under contract for an approximate purchase price of $58 million. In 2012 Extra Space Storage added to its holdings with the acquisition of 21 properties in about a dozen states from a joint venture partner. It acquired a noteworthy 55 properties in 2011.

Extra Space Storage is also looking to expand Extra Space Management its third-party property management subsidiary.

EXECUTIVES

CEO and Director, Joseph D. (Joe) Margolis, age 57, $290,000 total compensation
SVP Accounting, P. Scott Stubbs, $437,750 total compensation
EVP and Chief Marketing Officer, James Overturf
EVP Operations, Samrat Sondhi
EVP and Chief Legal Officer, Gwyn McNeal
Senior Vice President, Timothy Arthurs
Vice President And Corporate Controller, Grace Kunde
Vice President, Bron McCall
Executive Vice President And Chief Financial Officer, Kent Christensen
Vice President Of Learning And Development, Karen Pierce
Vice President Asset Management, Matthias Kellmer
Chairman, Kenneth M. Woolley, age 71
Board Member, Spencer Kirk
Auditors: Ernst & Young LLP

LOCATIONS

HQ: Extra Space Storage Inc
2795 East Cottonwood Parkway, Suite 300, Salt Lake City, UT 84121
Phone: 801 365-4600
Web: www.extraspace.com

PRODUCTS/OPERATIONS

2015 Sales

	$ mil.	% of total
Property rental	676.1	87
Tenant reinsurance	72.0	9
Management & franchise fees	34.2	4
Total	**782.3**	**100**

COMPETITORS

AMERCO	Mobile Mini
CubeSmart	PODS Enterprises
Life Storage	Public Storage

HISTORICAL FINANCIALS
Company Type: Public

Income Statement — FYE: December 31

	REVENUE ($ mil.)	NET INCOME ($ mil.)	NET PROFIT MARGIN	EMPLOYEES
12/17	1,105.0	479.0	43.3%	3,380
12/16	991.8	366.1	36.9%	3,287
12/15	782.2	189.4	24.2%	3,209
12/14	647.1	178.3	27.6%	2,643
12/13	520.6	172.0	33.1%	2,584
Annual Growth	20.7%	29.2%		6.9%

2017 Year-End Financials

Debt ratio: 61.0%
Return on equity: 20.8%
Cash ($ mil.): 55.6
Current ratio: 0.47
Long-term debt ($ mil.): 4,460.2

No. of shares (mil.): 126.0
Dividends
Yield: 0.0%
Payout: 82.9%
Market value ($ mil.): 11,019.0

	STOCK PRICE ($) FY Close	P/E High/Low	PER SHARE ($) Earnings	Dividends	Book Value
12/17	87.45	23 19	3.76	3.12	18.66
12/16	77.24	32 24	2.91	2.93	17.83
12/15	88.21	57 37	1.56	2.24	16.83
12/14	58.64	39 27	1.53	1.81	14.93
12/13	42.13	32 24	1.53	1.45	15.19
Annual Growth	20.0%	—	25.2%	21.1%	5.3%

F & M Bank Corp.

F & M Bank has deep roots in Virginia's Shenandoah Valley. Founded in 1908 the holding company operates about 10 Farmers & Merchants Bank branches in the northern Virginia counties of Rockingham and Shenandoah. Farmers & Merchants caters to individuals and businesses. It provides typical deposit products including checking and savings accounts CDs and IRAs. Some 40% of its loans are mortgages; it also writes agricultural business construction and consumer loans. The company offers insurance brokerage and financial services through TEB Life Insurance and Farmers & Merchants Financial Services.

EVP Larry Caplinger is the only beneficial owner of F & M with just over a 5% stake.

EXECUTIVES

Vice President, Teresa Helmick
Senior Vice President, Ed Strunk
Auditors: Yount, Hyde & Barbour, P.C.

LOCATIONS

HQ: F & M Bank Corp.
P.O. Box 1111, Timberville, VA 22853
Phone: 540 896-8941
Web: www.FMBankVA.com

COMPETITORS

Ames National	First United
BB&T	Highlands Bankshares
Bank of America	Inc.
Community Financial (VA)	Pioneer Bankshares
	Summit Financial (WV)
Fauquier Bankshares	SunTrust
First National	Village Bank & Trust

HISTORICAL FINANCIALS

Company Type: Public

Income Statement
FYE: December 31

	ASSETS ($ mil.)	NET INCOME ($ mil.)	INCOME AS % OF ASSETS	EMPLOYEES
12/17	753.2	9.0	1.2%	178
12/16	744.8	9.5	1.3%	173
12/15	665.3	8.4	1.3%	168
12/14	605.3	5.8	1.0%	156
12/13	552.7	4.7	0.9%	153
Annual Growth	8.0%	17.6%	—	3.9%

2017 Year-End Financials

Return on assets: 1.2%	Dividends
Return on equity: 10.2%	Yield: 0.0%
Long-term debt ($ mil.): —	Payout: 36.6%
No. of shares (mil.): 3.2	Market value ($ mil.): 108.0
Sales ($ mil): 41.9	

	STOCK PRICE ($) FY Close	P/E High/Low	PER SHARE ($) Earnings	Dividends	Book Value
12/17	33.10	13 10	2.48	0.91	27.86
12/16	26.05	10 8	2.57	0.80	26.29
12/15	22.70	10 8	2.25	0.73	25.07
12/14	19.50	11 9	1.80	0.68	23.50
12/13	18.50	10 8	1.88	0.68	21.39
Annual Growth	15.7%	— —	7.2%	7.6%	6.8%

FactSet Research Systems Inc.

Analysts portfolio managers and investment bankers know FactSet Research Systems has the facts down pat. The company offers global financial and economic information for investment analysis. FactSet also offers software for use in downloading and manipulating the data. (Its products can be fully integrated with Microsoft applications such as Excel and PowerPoint.) Among the company's applications are tools for presentations data warehousing portfolio analysis and report writing. Revenues are derived from month-to-month subscriptions to services databases and financial applications. More than 80% of revenue comes from investment managers; investment banking clients account for the rest.

Geographic Reach

About 30% of the company's revenues come from outside the US. Recent geographic growth efforts include the build out of new space in Paris and New York as well as the continued expansion of offices in India and the Philippines. It opened its 24th office located in Dubai in 2011. In addition to those locations FactSet has international offices in Australia Germany Italy Japan Hong Kong and the Netherlands.

Strategy

The company's success is in part due to its focus on growing its proprietary content collection efforts as well as investing in products and applications. Concurrent with the growth of its products and services the company has gained new clients and users both in the US and internationally.

HISTORY

Howard Wille and Charles Snyder founded FactSet in 1978. Both had previously worked for Wall Street investment firm Faulkner Dawkins & Sullivan (acquired by Shearson Hayden Stone in 1977). The company spent the 1980s building its client base and developing software that allowed clients to manipulate data on their own PCs.

FactSet opened an office in London in 1993 and one in Tokyo the next year. In 1994 the company added Morgan Stanley Capital International and EDGAR SEC filings to its database offerings. It added World Bank subsidiary International Finance Corp. in 1995 and the Russell U.S. Equity Profile report and Toyo Keizai a Japanese company database the next year. FactSet went public in 1996. Market Guide's information on US firms and ADRs (American depositary receipts) as well as the economic and financial databases of DRI/McGraw-Hill were added in 1997.

Snyder retired in 1999 but remained vice chairman. The following year Wille retired and Philip Hadley became chairman and CEO. The company made its first acquisition in 2000 when it bought Innovative Systems Techniques (Insyte) a maker of database management and decision support systems.

The company then began acquiring several content businesses. Its 2003 purchase of Mergerstat gave the company a database of global merger and acquisition and related information. In 2004 the company purchased JCF Group a provider of broker estimates and other financial data to institutional investors and CallStreet a provider of quarterly earnings call transcripts to the investment community. The following year the company purchased TrueCourse a provider of corporate competitive intelligence.

FactSet continued its acquisition spree with the 2005 purchase of Derivative Solutions (DSI) which offers fixed income analytics portfolio management and risk management services to financial institutions and the 2006 purchase of AlphaMetrics which provides institutional clients with software for capturing measuring and ranking financial information.

FactSet in 2007 released its ExcelConnect offering which enables data and analytics to be compatible with Microsoft Excel. Also that year the company enhanced its wireless capabilities giving users access to market company and portfolio information via PDAs and other wireless devices.

In 2008 FactSet expanded with the acquisition of the Thomson Fundamentals business which includes a global financial database with coverage of more than 43000 companies. The company also purchased investment banking workflow tool DealMaven reflecting its strategy of developing tools to make client workflows more efficient.

The company expanded in 2010 with the purchase of Market Metrics a US-based market research firm focused on advisor-sold investments and insurance products. FactSet used the acquisition to increase its global sales leveraging its own international network to sell Market Metrics products outside the US.

In 2011 FactSet expanded its presence in the Middle East when it opened an office in Dubai.

EXECUTIVES

Senior Vice President Director of Learning and Development, Laura Ruhe

Comptroller, Maurizio Nicolelli, age 50, $225,000 total compensation

SVP Strategic Resources and General Counsel, Rachel R. Stern

President CEO and Director, F. Philip Snow, age 53, $290,000 total compensation

EVP Chief Technology and Product Officer, Gene Fernandez

EVP and Global Head of Sales and Client Solutions, John W. Wiseman

SVP and CHRO, Edward Baker-Greene

Senior Vice President Director of Software Engineering, Daniel Weinstein

Vice President Director Information Systems, Lucy Tancredi

Vice President, James Porter

Vice President, Jia-Lin Fu

Vice President, Thomas Aratari

Vice President Business Analyst, Amanda Harchuck

Vice President Institutional Sales, Kathy Maridou

Senior Vice President Director Content Integration Engineering, Mark Thomford

Vice President Human Resources, Dan Viens

Vice President, Lisa Knoll

Assistant Vice President Key Accounts, W M Taylor

Vice President Global Account Manager, Terence Yarde

Senior Vice President Product Sales Specialist, Robert Robie

Vice President Associate Director, Ken Ambrosio

Vice President Information Systems, Jonathan Shea

Vice President Associate Director, Michael Cheng

Vice President, Rick Barrett

SENIOR VICE PRESIDENT DIRECTOR CORE TECHNOLOGIES, Jason Dennis

Vice President Institutional Sales, Jill Fisher

Assistant Vice President, Ryan Birrell

Vice President Brand Management, John Sanders

SENIOR VICE PRESIDENT, Anthony Jetnil

VICE PRESIDENT ASSOCIATE DIRECTOR, Kristin Bedoukian

Vice President Senior Human Resources Manager, Leonard F Johnson

VICE PRESIDENT PRODUCT MANAGER, Julie Kinney

Vice President Associate Director Content Integration Engineering, Jon Loach

VICE PRESIDENT INSTITUTIONAL SALES, Meredith Schiffer

VICE PRESIDENT INVESTOR RELATIONS, Rima Hyder

VICE PRESIDENT MULTI ASSET CLASS RISK SOLUTIONS, Shamin Parikh

VICE PRESIDENT HUMAN RESOURCES GLOBAL PRODUCT CONTENT AND TECHNOLOGY, Katherine Parente

EXECUTIVE VICE PRESIDENT GLOBAL DIRECTOR OF SALES, Scott G Miller

Senior Vice President RMS Solutions, Tim Gavin

Vice President and General Manager Wealth Management Solutions North America, Bill Chambers

VICE PRESIDENT INSTITUTIONAL SALES REPRESENTATIVE, Akw Vizag

VICE PRESIDENT SALES MANAGER, Andrea Williams

VICE PRESIDENT DIRECTOR, Jeffrey Schuller

VICE PRESIDENT SALES MANAGER, Michael Schiffer

Chairman, Philip A. Hadley, age 56

Board Member, James McGonigle

Board Member, Laurie Siegel

Board Member, Sheila Jordan

Board Member, Malcolm Frank

Auditors: Ernst & Young LLP

LOCATIONS

HQ: FactSet Research Systems Inc.
601 Merritt 7, Norwalk, CT 06851
Phone: 203 810-1000 **Fax:** 203 810-1001
Web: www.factset.com

PRODUCTS/OPERATIONS

2015 Sales

	% of total
US	67
Europe	25
Asia/Pacific	8
Total	**100**

Selected Applications

Company Analysis
Data Warehousing
Economic Analysis
Fixed Income Analysis
Pitchbook Building
Portfolio Analysis
Quantitative Analysis
Real-time Market Data

Selected Content Providers

Dow Jones & Company
Global Insight
Interactive Data Corporation
Merrill Lynch
Morningstar
Standard and Poor's
Thomson Reuters

Selected Product and Service Offerings:

Investment Managers
Equity Analysis
Quant and Risk Analysis
Portfolio Analysis
Markets and Economics
Fixed Income Analysis
Data Integration
Charting
Wireless Connectivity
Global Banking & Brokerage Professionals
Models and Presentations
Company and Industry Analytics
Deal Analytics
Idea Screening
People Intelligence
Accountability
Corporate Governance
Wireless Connectivity
Other Global Professionals
Hedge Funds
Private Equity and Venture Capital
Sell-Side Research
Equity Sales
Trading and Managing Market Data
Consultants and Advisors
Investor Relations and Corporate Strategy
Legal Accounting Management Consulting and Other
   Professionals
Academia - Professors and Students

COMPETITORS

Avention	MSCI
Bloomberg L.P.	Pearson plc
CME	Telvent DTN
Capital IQ	Thomson Reuters
Dealogic	Track Data
Hoover's Inc.	thinkorswim
LexisNexis	

HISTORICAL FINANCIALS

Company Type: Public

Income Statement — FYE: August 31

	REVENUE ($ mil.)	NET INCOME ($ mil.)	NET PROFIT MARGIN	EMPLOYEES
08/18	1,350.1	267.0	19.8%	9,571
08/17	1,221.1	258.2	21.1%	9,074
08/16	1,127.0	338.8	30.1%	8,375
08/15	1,006.7	241.0	23.9%	7,360
08/14	920.3	211.5	23.0%	6,639
Annual Growth	**10.1%**	**6.0%**	**—**	**9.6%**

2018 Year-End Financials

Debt ratio: 40.4%
Return on equity: 49.2%
Cash ($ mil.): 208.6
Current ratio: 1.95
Long-term debt ($ mil.): 574.7

No. of shares (mil.): 38.1
Dividends
   Yield: 1.0%
   Payout: 35.4%
Market value ($ mil.): 8,761.0

	STOCK PRICE ($) FY Close	P/E High/Low	PER SHARE ($) Earnings	Dividends	Book Value
08/18	229.39	33 23	6.78	2.40	13.77
08/17	157.18	28 23	6.51	2.12	14.34
08/16	178.03	22 16	8.19	1.88	12.92
08/15	157.92	30 20	5.71	1.66	12.87
08/14	127.40	26 20	4.92	1.48	12.23
Annual Growth	**15.8%**	**—**	**8.3%**	**12.8%**	**3.0%**

HISTORICAL FINANCIALS

Company Type: Public

Income Statement — FYE: December 31

	ASSETS ($ mil.)	NET INCOME ($ mil.)	INCOME AS % OF ASSETS	EMPLOYEES
12/17	3,075.4	28.3	0.9%	330
12/16	2,922.1	29.7	1.0%	339
12/15	2,615.3	27.3	1.0%	316
12/14	2,360.5	25.4	1.1%	310
12/13	2,076.0	24.0	1.2%	299
Annual Growth	**10.3%**	**4.2%**	**—**	**2.5%**

2017 Year-End Financials

Return on assets: 0.9%
Return on equity: 9.7%
Long-term debt ($ mil.): —
No. of shares (mil.): 0.8
Sales ($ mil): 131.3

Dividends
   Yield: 0.0%
   Payout: 38.6%
Market value ($ mil.): 549.0

	STOCK PRICE ($) FY Close	P/E High/Low	PER SHARE ($) Earnings	Dividends	Book Value
12/17	676.00	20 17	35.03	13.55	368.90
12/16	640.00	17 13	37.44	13.10	346.80
12/15	540.00	17 13	34.82	12.90	318.46
12/14	463.00	14 13	32.64	12.70	297.39
12/13	417.00	16 12	30.93	12.50	269.84
Annual Growth	**12.8%**	**—**	**3.2%**	**2.0%**	**8.1%**

Farmers & Merchants Bancorp (Lodi, CA)

EXECUTIVES

Chb-pres-ceo, Kent A Steinwert
Vice President, Denise Goodell
Assistant Vice President, Benea Schmidt
Vice President, Chris Winek
Executive Vice President Senior Credit Officer, Ken Smith
Executive Vice President, Deborah Hodkin
Vice President And Chief Appraiser, Jon Schrader
VICE PRESIDENT COMMERCIAL LOAN OFFICER, Claire Forsythe
VICE PRESIDENT TREASURY RELATIONSHIP MANAGER, Mike Caselli
SENIOR VICE PRESIDENT, Carol Murray
Senior Vice President Human Resources, Charles Broom
Assistant Vice President Operations Supervisor, Carrie Henshaw
Auditors: Moss Adams LLP

LOCATIONS

HQ: Farmers & Merchants Bancorp (Lodi, CA)
   111 W. Pine Street, Lodi, CA 95240
Phone: 209 367-2300
Web: www.fmbonline.com

Farmers National Banc Corp. (Canfield,OH)

Farmers National Banc is willing to help even nonfarmers grow their seed income into thriving bounties of wealth. The bank provides commercial and personal banking from nearly 20 branches in Ohio. Founded in 1887 Farmers National Banc offers checking and savings accounts credit cards and loans and mortgages. Farmers' lending portfolio is composed of real estate mortgages consumer loans and commercial loans. The company also includes Farmers National Insurance and Farmers Trust Company a non-depository trust bank that offers wealth management and trust services.

Geographic Reach

Farmers National Banc operates 19 branches located throughout Mahoning Trumbull Columbiana Stark and Cuyahoga Counties. Farmers Trust Company operates two offices located in Boardman and Howland Ohio.

Financial Performance

The company's revenues have ranged from $40 million to $60 million in the past decade. In 2013 overall sales fell 1% to $54 million; the slight dip was due to lessened interest income on loans and taxable securities. (Financial institutions make their money on interest income from loans and non-interest income from fees.) Its non-interest income experienced growth from service charges insurance agency commissions and consulting fees for retirement planning.

Profits decreased by 22% to $8 million in 2013 due to increase in a provision for loan losses and non-interest expenses such as salary and employee benefits.

Mergers and Acquisitions

In 2013 the bank added retirement planning services to their portfolio with the acquisition of Cleveland-based National Associates Inc. for $4.4 million. The acquisition was part of its plan to boost noninterest income and complement its existing retirement services.

EXECUTIVES

Assistant Vice President, Francis Gallagher
Vice President And Treasury Manager, Bobbi Harding
Vice President Commercial Lending Relationship Manager, James Rhodes
Vice President Commercial Lending Relationship Manager, Andrew Estock
Vice President Commercial Lending Relationship Manager, Darrell Smucker
Vice President Commercial Lending Relationship Manager, Suzanne Rinehart
Assistant Vice President Small Business Lender, Dean Karhan
Senior Vice President Commercial Lending Team Leader, Thomas Stocksdale
Assistant Vice President Relationship Manager Treasury Management, Jessica Kane
Auditors: CliftonLarsonAllen, LLP

LOCATIONS

HQ: Farmers National Banc Corp. (Canfield,OH)
20 South Broad Street, Canfield, OH 44406
Phone: 330 533-3341
Web: www.farmersbankgroup.com

PRODUCTS/OPERATIONS

Selected Products
Personal
Certificate of DepositChecking AccountsChildren's AccountsConsumer LoansHome Equity Loans & LinesMortgage LoansOnline BankingPersonal Credit CardPersonal Debit CardPhone BankingRetirementSavings Accounts
Business
Business Credit CardBusiness Debit CardBusiness DepositsBusiness LoansCash ManagementRemote Deposit Capture
Wealth Management and Insurance
Farmers Trust CompanyFarmers National InvestmentsFarmers National Insurance
On-line banking

COMPETITORS

CSB Bancorp	JPMorgan Chase
Central Federal	Killbuck Bancshares
Consumers Bancorp	National Bancshares
Cortland Bancorp	Ohio Legacy
FFD Financial	Tri-State 1st Banc
Fifth Third	United Community
First Financial	Financial
Bancorp	Wayne Savings
First Niles Financial	Bancshares
Home Loan Financial	

HISTORICAL FINANCIALS
Company Type: Public

Income Statement
FYE: December 31

	ASSETS ($ mil.)	NET INCOME ($ mil.)	INCOME AS % OF ASSETS	EMPLOYEES
12/17	2,159.0	22.7	1.1%	445
12/16	1,966.1	20.5	1.0%	441
12/15	1,869.9	8.0	0.4%	432
12/14	1,136.9	8.9	0.8%	327
12/13	1,137.3	7.7	0.7%	328
Annual Growth	**17.4%**	**30.7%**	**—**	**7.9%**

2017 Year-End Financials

Return on assets: 1.1%
Return on equity: 9.9%
Long-term debt ($ mil.): —
No. of shares (mil.): 27.5
Sales ($ mil): 104.5

Dividends
Yield: 0.0%
Payout: 26.8%
Market value ($ mil.): 406.0

	STOCK PRICE ($) FY Close	P/E High/Low		Earnings	PER SHARE ($) Dividends	Book Value
12/17	14.75	19	15	0.82	0.22	8.79
12/16	14.20	20	11	0.76	0.16	7.88
12/15	8.60	24	20	0.36	0.12	7.35
12/14	8.35	18	14	0.48	0.12	6.71
12/13	6.55	17	14	0.41	0.12	6.02
Annual Growth	**22.5%**	**—**	**—**	**18.9%**	**16.4%**	**9.9%**

Farmland Partners Inc

Auditors: Plante & Moran, PLLC

LOCATIONS

HQ: Farmland Partners Inc
4600 South Syracuse Street, Suite 1450, Denver, CO 80237-2766
Phone: 720 452-3100
Web: www.farmlandpartners.com

HISTORICAL FINANCIALS
Company Type: Public

Income Statement
FYE: December 31

	REVENUE ($ mil.)	NET INCOME ($ mil.)	NET PROFIT MARGIN	EMPLOYEES
12/17	46.2	7.9	17.1%	16
12/16	31.0	4.3	13.9%	18
12/15	13.7	1.2	8.9%	13
12/14	4.2	(0.5)	—	7
12/13	2.3	0.0	1.5%	2
Annual Growth	**110.6%**	**290.1%**	**—**	**68.2%**

2017 Year-End Financials

Debt ratio: 44.0%
Return on equity: 2.5%
Cash ($ mil.): 53.5
Current ratio: 3.71
Long-term debt ($ mil.): 514.0

No. of shares (mil.): 33.3
Dividends
Yield: 0.0%
Payout: 1,700.0%
Market value ($ mil.): 289.0

	STOCK PRICE ($) FY Close	P/E High/Low		Earnings	PER SHARE ($) Dividends	Book Value
12/17	8.68	381274		0.03	0.51	14.06
12/16	11.16	133111		0.09	0.51	9.33
12/15	10.97	155123		0.08	0.50	9.05
12/14	10.41	—	—	(0.15)	0.33	8.58
Annual Growth	**(5.9%)**	**—**	**—**	**—**	**16.1%**	**17.9%**

FB Financial Corp

Auditors: Crowe Horwath LLP

LOCATIONS

HQ: FB Financial Corp
211 Commerce Street, Suite 300, Nashville, TN 37201
Phone: 615 564-1212
Web: www.firstbankonline.com

HISTORICAL FINANCIALS
Company Type: Public

Income Statement
FYE: December 31

	ASSETS ($ mil.)	NET INCOME ($ mil.)	INCOME AS % OF ASSETS	EMPLOYEES
12/17	4,727.7	52.4	1.1%	1,386
12/16	3,276.8	40.5	1.2%	1,108
12/15	2,899.4	47.8	1.7%	1,038
12/14	2,428.1	32.4	1.3%	0
12/13	2,258.3	26.9	1.2%	0
Annual Growth	**20.3%**	**18.1%**	**—**	**—**

2017 Year-End Financials

Return on assets: 1.3%
Return on equity: 11.3%
Long-term debt ($ mil.): —
No. of shares (mil.): 30.5
Sales ($ mil): 311.1

Dividends
Yield: 0.0%
Payout: —
Market value ($ mil.): 1,282.0

	STOCK PRICE ($) FY Close	P/E High/Low		Earnings	PER SHARE ($) Dividends	Book Value
12/17	41.99	23	13	1.86	0.00	19.54
12/16	25.95	12	9	2.10	4.03	13.71
Annual Growth	**61.8%**	**—**	**—**	**(11.4%)**	**—**	**42.5%**

Federal Agricultural Mortgage Corp

Farmer Mac (Federal Agricultural Mortgage Corporation) is Fannie Mae and Freddie Mac's country cousin. Like its city-slicker kin it provides liquidity in its markets (agricultural real estate and rural housing mortgages) by buying loans from lenders and then securitizing the loans into Farmer Mac Guaranteed Securities. Farmer Mac buys both conventional loans and those guaranteed by the US Department of Agriculture. Farmer Mac was created by Congress in 1987 to establish a secondary market for agricultural mortgage and rural utilities loans. It is a stockholder-owned publicly-traded corporation based in Washington DC with an underwriting office in Iowa.

Operations

Farmer Mac operates four segments: Farm & Ranch which accounted for 39% of revenue during 2015 purchases mortgage loans secured by first liens on agricultural real estate including part-time farms and rural housing; Institutional Credit (28% of revenue) which buys or guarantees general lender obligations secured by eligible pools of loans; the USDA Guarantees segment (18%) which buys USDA-backed agricultural rural development business and industry and community facilities loans; and Rural Utilities (10%) which buys mortgages tied to eligible rural utilities loans.The organization generates more than 90% of its revenue from interest income stemming from a roughly even mix of loans and backed loan securities. About 47% of its revenue came from interest on Farmer Mac Guaranteed or USDA securities during 2015 while another 41% came from interest on loans. The rest came from interest on other investments (5% of revenue) guarantee and commitment fees (5%) and gains on financial derivatives and hedging activities (1%).

Geographic Reach

The Washington DC-based group serves the US from satellite operations in Ames Iowa; Boise Idaho; Canton Michigan; Fresno California; Johnston Iowa; and Scottsdale Arizona.

Sales and Marketing

Farmer Mac markets its services personally and directly to agricultural lenders by participating regularly in events such as state and national banking conferences. It also has alliances with the American Bankers Association and the Independent Community Bankers of Alliances and has a business relationship with the members of the Farm Credit System.

Financial Performance

Farmer Mac's annual revenues have risen more than 25% since 2011 thanks to a stronger agricultural economy as well as product developments which have driven customer and overall loan asset growth over the years. Its annual profits have also trended higher but have fluctuated more due to the volatility of the gains it's made from financial derivatives hedging activities and other trading securities.

The group's revenue climbed 4% to $284 million during 2015 mostly thanks to double-digit interest income growth as its loan assets grew 12% to $3.96 billion and as its Farm & Ranch loans USDA Securities and AgVantage securities balances grew as well. Farmer Mac's non-interest income shrank 39% as it collected $37.4 million less in trading securities gains as it did in 2014.

Revenue growth and a decline in interest expenses in 2015 drove Farmer Mac's net income up 43% to $68.7 million. The lender's operating cash levels jumped 19% to $184 million as its cash-based earnings rose and as working capital increased with changes in other assets.

Strategy

Farmer Mac seeks to improve the availability of long-term credit at stable interest rates to rural communities. To this end its primary strategy for managing interest rate risk is to fund asset purchases with liabilities that have similar duration and cash flow characteristics so that they will perform similarly as interest rates change.

EXECUTIVES

President and CEO, Timothy L. (Tim) Buzby, age 49, $643,750 total compensation
EVP CFO and Treasurer, R. Dale Lynch, age 51, $375,950 total compensation
SVP Agricultural Finance, J. Curtis Covington, age 62
SVP General Counsel and Secretary, Stephen P. Mullery, age 51, $340,930 total compensation
Vice President Corporate Affairs, Chris Bohanon
Senior Vice President Agricultural Finance, Curt Covington
Chairman, Lowell L. Junkins, age 74
Vice Chairman, Myles J. Watts, age 67
Auditors: PricewaterhouseCoopers LLP

LOCATIONS

HQ: Federal Agricultural Mortgage Corp
  1999 K Street, N.W., 4th Floor, Washington, DC 20006
Phone: 202 872-7700   **Fax:** 202 872-7713
Web: www.farmermac.com

PRODUCTS/OPERATIONS

2015 Sales

	% of total
Interest income	
Farmer Mac Guaranteed Securities and USDA Securities	47
Loans	41
Investments and cash equivalents	5
Noninterest income	
Guarantee and commitment fees	5
Gains on financial derivatives and hedging activities	1
Other	1
Total	**100**

2015 Sales

	% of total
Farm & Ranch	39
USDA Guarantees	28
Rural Utilities	18
Institutional Credit	10
Corporate	4
Reconciling Adjustments	1
Total	**100**

Selected Operations

Farm & Ranch (Farmer Mac I)
USDA Guarantees (Farmer Mac II)
Rural Utilities

COMPETITORS

AgFirst	Fannie Mae
AgStar	Farm Credit Services
AgriBank	of Mid-America
Bank of America	Freddie Mac
Citigroup	

HISTORICAL FINANCIALS

Company Type: Public

Income Statement

FYE: December 31

	ASSETS ($ mil.)	NET INCOME ($ mil.)	INCOME AS % OF ASSETS	EMPLOYEES
12/17	17,792.2	84.4	0.5%	88
12/16	15,606.0	77.3	0.5%	81
12/15	15,540.3	68.7	0.4%	71
12/14	14,287.8	48.0	0.3%	71
12/13	13,361.7	75.3	0.6%	67
Annual Growth	**7.4%**	**2.9%**	**—**	**7.1%**

2017 Year-End Financials

Return on assets: 0.5%	Dividends
Return on equity: 12.5%	Yield: 0.0%
Long-term debt ($ mil.): —	Payout: 21.8%
No. of shares (mil.): 10.6	Market value ($ mil.): 831.0
Sales ($ mil): 418.0	

	STOCK PRICE ($) FY Close	P/E High/Low		PER SHARE ($) Earnings	Dividends	Book Value
12/17	78.24	12	8	6.60	1.44	66.69
12/16	57.27	10	4	5.97	1.04	61.05
12/15	31.57	8	5	4.19	0.64	51.79
12/14	30.34	10	8	3.37	0.56	49.90
12/13	34.25	6	4	6.41	0.48	30.55
Annual Growth	**22.9%**	**—**	**—**	**0.7%**	**31.6%**	**21.5%**

Federal Home Loan Bank Boston

Federal Home Loan Bank of Boston (FHLB Boston) is banking on the continued support of other banks. The government-supported enterprise provides funds for residential mortgages and community development loans to its members which consist of more than 440 financial institutions across New England including banks thrifts credit unions and insurance companies. The bank also lends to nonmember institutions the likes of state housing finance agencies primarily to promote the funding of low to moderate income housing in the region. FHLB Boston is one of 12 regional wholesale banks in the Federal Home Loan Bank System. Its region includes Connecticut Maine Massachusetts New Hampshire Rhode Island and Vermont.

Operations

FHLB Boston provides its members with loans or advances and other services to promote community development. As a government-sponsored enterprise the bank enjoys favorable interest rates on its own borrowings. It is overseen by the Federal Housing Finance Agency.

Financial Performance

FHLB Boston logged its highest annual net income in its history in fiscal 2013 posting $212.3 million — a $5.2 million increase from 2012's $207.1 million. It attributes this to $53.3 million in litigation settlements related to certain investments in private-label mortgage-backed securities.

Strategy

The bank's performance is closely tied with the economy including the current low-interest rate environment and the value of its investments in private-label mortgage-backed securities. Ongoing factors contributing to the health (or non-health) of those securities are high unemployment widespread foreclosures and the number of borrowers who are underwater on their homes. While the stormy financial climate has had and will continue to have a negative impact on the bank net income has been rising.

EXECUTIVES

Vice President Deputy Director Housing A, Mary Jutras

Vice President Corporate and Finance Counsel, Keith Walsh

Assistant Vice President Residential Field Review Manager, Matthew Mcdermod

Assistant Vice President Human Resources Manager and Senior Business Partner, Brenda Kirouac

Vice President, George Maroun

Assistant Vice President Technical Research and De, William Evans

Senior Vice President Executive Director Human Resources, Barry Gale

Vice President Director, Joanne Sullivan

Assistant Vice President Compliance Officer, Melissa Benson

Vice President Operations, Rachele McDonough

Senior Vice President and General Counsel, Carol Pratt

Vice President Director of Internal Audit, Brian Chase

Vice President Assistant General Counsel, Jane Harper

Assistant Vice President Collateral Manager, David Trant

Vice President Relationship Management, Matt Stewart

Auditors: PricewaterhouseCoopers LLP

LOCATIONS

HQ: Federal Home Loan Bank Boston
800 Boylston Street, Boston, MA 02199
Phone: 617 292-9600
Web: www.fhlbboston.com

HISTORICAL FINANCIALS

Company Type: Public

Income Statement

	REVENUE ($ mil.)	NET INCOME ($ mil.)	NET PROFIT MARGIN	EMPLOYEES
12/17	959.8	190.2	19.8%	203
12/16	737.4	173.2	23.5%	202
12/15	756.9	289.3	38.2%	206
12/14	578.4	149.7	25.9%	200
12/13	630.2	212.3	33.7%	199
Annual Growth	11.1%	(2.7%)	—	0.5%

2017 Year-End Financials

Debt ratio: 92.8%
Return on equity: 5.8%
Cash ($ mil.): 9,060.9
Current ratio: 0.32
Long-term debt ($ mil.): 28,344.6
No. of shares (mil.): 22.8
Dividends
  Yield: —
  Payout: 51.9%
Market value ($ mil.): —

Federal Home Loan Bank Indianapolis

Auditors: PricewaterhouseCoopers LLP

LOCATIONS

HQ: Federal Home Loan Bank Indianapolis
8250 Woodfield Crossing Boulevard, Indianapolis, IN 46240
Phone: 317 465-0200
Web: www.fhlbi.com

HISTORICAL FINANCIALS

Company Type: Public

Income Statement   FYE: December 31

	REVENUE ($ mil.)	NET INCOME ($ mil.)	NET PROFIT MARGIN	EMPLOYEES
12/17	1,016.6	156.4	15.4%	241
12/16	694.8	113.0	16.3%	218
12/15	543.7	120.9	22.2%	216
12/14	495.2	116.6	23.5%	215
12/13	552.4	203.3	36.8%	0
Annual Growth	16.5%	(6.3%)	—	—

2017 Year-End Financials

Debt ratio: 93.4%
Return on equity: 5.8%
Cash ($ mil.): 4,601.0
Current ratio: 0.22
Long-term debt ($ mil.): 37,895.6
No. of shares (mil.): 18.5
Dividends
  Yield: —
  Payout: 43.0%
Market value ($ mil.): —

Federal Home Loan Bank New York

Federal Home Loan Bank of New York (FHLBNY) provides funds for residential mortgages and community development to more than 330 member banks savings and loans credit unions and life insurance companies in New York New Jersey Puerto Rico and the US Virgin Islands. One of a dozen Federal Home Loan Banks in the US it is cooperatively owned by its member institutions and supervised by the Federal Housing Finance Agency. FHLBNY like others in the system is privately capitalized; it receives no taxpayer funding. The bank instead raises funds mainly by issuing debt instruments in the capital markets.

Operations

FHLBNY is a secured lender that requires collateral for its advances which are typically used by members to underwrite residential mortgages or to invest in US Treasury and agency securities mortgage-backed securities and other real estate-related assets.

A large part of FHLBNY's business is in making collateralized loans or advances to members. It serves the public through its mortgage programs. Three members — Citibank (25%) Met Life (14%) and New York Community Bank (11%) — accounted for half of total advances.

Geographic Reach

Based in New York FHLBNY serves not only New York but New Jersey Puerto Rico and the US Virgin Islands.

Sales and Marketing

FHLBNY caters to more than 330 member banks credit unions life insurance companies and savings and loans.

Financial Performance

Revenue dropped by 14% to $801 million in fiscal 2013 from 2012's $934.9 million. FHLBNY attributes the decline to a decrease in interest income and other income. Net income also dropped some 16% in 2013 to $304.6 million vs. $360.7 million in 2012. It attributes net income decreases to declining revenue and rising other expenses. Operating cash flow decreased in fiscal 2013 to $525.6 million compared to 2012's $678.9 million.

Strategy

Credit unions are a possible area of growth for FHLBNY. The bank has identified more than 50 credit unions and banks that are not members but are eligible. To be under consideration an institution must have more than $50 million in assets ($100 million for banks) be an established wholesale lender maintain a high deposit-to-loan ratio and have management that has done business with an FHLB in the past.

Beginning in 2014 it's also funding — with the help of $35.5 million in subsidies — 48 affordable housing initiatives throughout New Jersey New York Puerto Rico the US Virgin Islands Florida Maryland and Pennsylvania. The effort involves the creation or rehabilitation of more than 3000 affordable housing units.

EXECUTIVES

Vice President Director of Human Resources, Mildred Tse-Gonzalez

Assistant Vice President, Diahann Rothstein

Senior Vice President Director of Bank Relations, Eric Amig

Vice President Sales And Marketing And C, Alfred O'Connell

Vice President Manager Business Research and Devolpment, John Brandon

Senior Vice President Chief Capital Markets Officer, Phil Scott

Vice President, Eugene Khesin

Assistant Vice President, Kristen Lalama

Assistant Vice President Fina, Kimberly Whitenack

Auditors: PricewaterhouseCoopers LLP

LOCATIONS

HQ: Federal Home Loan Bank New York
101 Park Avenue, New York, NY 10178
Phone: 212 681-6000
Web: www.fhlbny.com

PRODUCTS/OPERATIONS

2013 Sales

	$ mil.	% of total
Interest		
Advances	444.5	55
Long-term securities	244.0	30
Mortgage loans held for portfolio	68.3	9
Available-for-sale securities	16.6	2
Other	14.3	2
Non-interest	13.3	2
Total	801.0	100

HISTORICAL FINANCIALS

Company Type: Public

Income Statement   FYE: December 31

	ASSETS ($ mil.)	NET INCOME ($ mil.)	INCOME AS % OF ASSETS	EMPLOYEES
12/17	158,918.3	479.4	0.3%	308
12/16	143,606.2	401.1	0.3%	280
12/15	123,248.3	414.8	0.3%	273
12/14	132,825.3	314.9	0.2%	258
12/13	128,332.9	304.6	0.2%	258
Annual Growth	5.5%	12.0%	—	4.5%

2017 Year-End Financials

Return on assets: 0.3%
Return on equity: 6.0%
Long-term debt ($ mil.): —
No. of shares (mil.): 67.5
Sales ($ mil): 2,184.3

Dividends
Yield: —
Payout: 72.3%
Market value ($ mil.): —

Federal Home Loan Bank Of Cincinnati

Auditors: PricewaterhouseCoopers LLP

LOCATIONS

HQ: Federal Home Loan Bank Of Cincinnati
600 Atrium Two, P.O Box 598, Cincinnati, OH 45201-0598
Phone: 513 852-7500
Web: www.fhlbcin.com

HISTORICAL FINANCIALS
Company Type: Public

Income Statement				FYE: December 31
	ASSETS ($ mil.)	NET INCOME ($ mil.)	INCOME AS % OF ASSETS	EMPLOYEES
12/17	106,895.2	313.5	0.3%	226
12/16	104,635.2	268.1	0.3%	211
12/15	118,796.7	248.7	0.2%	203
12/14	106,640.4	244.2	0.2%	204
12/13	103,180.7	261.0	0.3%	0
Annual Growth	0.9%	4.7%	—	—

2017 Year-End Financials

Return on assets: 0.3%
Return on equity: 6.1%
Long-term debt ($ mil.): —
No. of shares (mil.): 42.4
Sales ($ mil): 1,621.1

Dividends
Yield: —
Payout: 66.3%
Market value ($ mil.): —

Federal Home Loan Bank Of Dallas

Auditors: PricewaterhouseCoopers LLP

LOCATIONS

HQ: Federal Home Loan Bank Of Dallas
8500 Freeport Parkway South, Suite 600, Irving, TX 75063-2547
Phone: 214 441-8500

HISTORICAL FINANCIALS
Company Type: Public

Income Statement				FYE: December 31
	ASSETS ($ mil.)	NET INCOME ($ mil.)	INCOME AS % OF ASSETS	EMPLOYEES
12/17	68,524.3	150.2	0.2%	205
12/16	58,212.0	79.4	0.1%	218
12/15	42,083.2	67.1	0.2%	207
12/14	38,045.8	48.5	0.1%	192
12/13	30,221.8	87.8	0.3%	0
Annual Growth	22.7%	14.4%	—	—

2017 Year-End Financials

Return on assets: 0.2%
Return on equity: 4.7%
Long-term debt ($ mil.): —
No. of shares (mil.): 23.1
Sales ($ mil): 831.1

Dividends
Yield: —
Payout: 21.6%
Market value ($ mil.): —

Federal Home Loan Bank Of Des Moines

Auditors: PricewaterhouseCoopers LLP

LOCATIONS

HQ: Federal Home Loan Bank Of Des Moines
909 Locust Street, Des Moines, IA 50309
Phone: 515 412-2100
Web: www.fhlbdm.com

HISTORICAL FINANCIALS
Company Type: Public

Income Statement				FYE: December 31
	ASSETS ($ mil.)	NET INCOME ($ mil.)	INCOME AS % OF ASSETS	EMPLOYEES
12/17	145,099.0	518.0	0.4%	351
12/16	180,605.0	649.0	0.4%	307
12/15	137,381.0	131.0	0.1%	279
12/14	95,523.9	121.0	0.1%	228
12/13	73,004.0	109.8	0.2%	0
Annual Growth	18.7%	47.4%	—	—

2017 Year-End Financials

Return on assets: 0.3%
Return on equity: 7.1%
Long-term debt ($ mil.): —
No. of shares (mil.): 51.0
Sales ($ mil): 2,485.0

Dividends
Yield: —
Payout: 24.9%
Market value ($ mil.): —

Federal Home Loan Bank of Pittsburgh

The Federal Home Loan Bank of Pittsburgh helps revitalize neighborhoods and fund low-income housing in the City of Champions and beyond. One of a dozen banks in the Federal Home Loan Bank System the government-sponsored entity (FHLB Pittsburgh for short) uses private capital and public sponsorships to provide low-cost funding for residential mortgages and community and economic development loans in Delaware Pennsylvania and West Virginia. It is cooperatively owned by about 300 member banks thrifts credit unions and insurance companies in its three-state district. The bank also offers member banks correspondent banking services such as depository funds transfer settlement and safekeeping services.

Financial Performance

FHLB Pittsburgh which boasts $71 billion in assets logged net income of $147.8 million in fiscal 2013 up $18.1 million from 2012's $129.7 million. The institution attributes the boost to higher net gains on derivatives and hedging activities lower net other-than-temporary-impairment (OTTI) credit losses and net gains on the early extinguishment of debt. These gains however were partially offset by lower net interest income and higher other expenses.

Strategy

The wholesale bank has been shying away from higher-yielding assets including private label mortgage-backed securities and replacing those with less risky agency securities. While demand for advances remains low the bank plans to prudently manage its capital position and continue enhancing its risk management practices.

While FHLB Pittsburgh earns the largest portion of its revenue from investments in securities such as US Treasurys and mortgage-backed securities about a third comes from accrued interest on loan advances to other financial institutions. Its five largest customers — Ally Bank PNC Bank Sovereign Bank Susquehanna Bank and TD Bank— account for more than 70% of its credit products and own around 45% of its stock.

The Federal Housing Finance Agency oversees the twelve Federal Home Loan Banks. FHLB Pittsburgh members include any eligible institution in Delaware Pennsylvania or West Virginia.

Company Background

As a mortgage lender for other banks the Federal Home Loan Bank of Pittsburgh suffered during the mortgage crisis. The Pittsburgh bank experienced its first-ever net loss in 2009 and was unable to set aside the usual 10% for the FDIC's Affordable Housing Program. In 2010 bank executives began reducing its use of derivatives improving processes and systems and employing outside experts on risk management. The moves helped FHLB Pittsburgh to return to profitability. Also that year as part of the Housing and Economic Recovery Act Community Development Financial Institutions including community development loan funds venture capital firms and state-chartered credit unions without federal deposit insurance became eligible to become members of a Federal Home Loan Bank.

EXECUTIVES

Managing Director, Dana Yealy
Auditors: PricewaterhouseCoopers LLP

LOCATIONS

HQ: Federal Home Loan Bank of Pittsburgh
601 Grant Street, Pittsburgh, PA 15219
Phone: 412 288-3400
Web: www.fhlb-pgh.com

HISTORICAL FINANCIALS
Company Type: Public

Income Statement				FYE: December 31
	REVENUE ($ mil.)	NET INCOME ($ mil.)	NET PROFIT MARGIN	EMPLOYEES
12/17	1,485.9	339.6	22.9%	215
12/16	1,010.5	260.0	25.7%	214
12/15	740.0	256.5	34.7%	215
12/14	701.7	255.7	36.4%	219
12/13	644.0	147.8	23.0%	210
Annual Growth	23.2%	23.1%	—	0.6%

Debt ratio: 94.0%
Return on equity: 6.9%
Cash ($ mil.): 9,845.3
Current ratio: 15.85
Long-term debt ($ mil.): 93,727.0
No. of shares (mil.): 36.5
Dividends
  Yield: —
  Payout: 49.4%
Market value ($ mil.): —

Federal Home Loan Bank Of San Francisco

The city by the bay is the home to the Federal Home Loan Bank of San Francisco one ofA a dozenA regional banks in the Federal Home Loan Bank System chartered by Congress inA 1932 to provide credit to residential mortgage lenders. TheA government-sponsored enterpriseA is privately owned by its members which include some 400 commercial banks credit unions industrial loan companies savings and loans insurance companies and housing associatesA headquartered in Arizona California and Nevada. The bank links members to worldwide capital markets which provide them with low-cost funding. Members then pass these advances along to their customers in the form of affordable home mortgage and economic development loans.

EXECUTIVES

Assistant Vice President Compliance, Jamie Leong
Auditors: PricewaterhouseCoopers LLP

LOCATIONS

HQ: Federal Home Loan Bank Of San Francisco
  600 California Street, San Francisco, CA 94108
Phone: 415 616-1000
Web: www.fhlbsf.com

PRODUCTS/OPERATIONS

2013

	$ mil.	% of total
Interest income	1,086.0	97
Other income	5.0	3
Total	**1,091.0**	**100**

HISTORICAL FINANCIALS

Company Type: Public

Income Statement | | | FYE: December 31

	ASSETS ($ mil.)	NET INCOME ($ mil.)	NET INCOME AS % OF ASSETS	EMPLOYEES
12/17	123,385.0	376.0	0.3%	287
12/16	91,941.0	712.0	0.8%	274
12/15	85,707.0	638.0	0.7%	263
12/14	75,807.0	205.0	0.3%	255
12/13	85,774.0	308.0	0.4%	262
Annual Growth	**9.5%**	**5.1%**	**—**	**2.3%**

2017 Year-End Financials

Return on assets: 0.3%
Return on equity: 6.0%
Long-term debt ($ mil.): —
No. of shares (mil.): 32.0
Sales ($ mil): 1,678.0
Dividends
  Yield: —
  Payout: 49.7%
Market value ($ mil.): —

Federal Home Loan Bank Topeka

Don't worry Toto Federal Home Loan Bank of Topeka is in Kansas. The institution created by Congress provides funds for residential mortgages and community-development loans to almost 900 member banks thrifts credit unions and insurance companies in Arizona Colorado Kansas Nebraska New Mexico Oklahoma and Wyoming. FHLBank Topeka also provides members with other financial services such as safekeeping shelf funding and wire transfer services. One of a dozen Federal Home Loan Banks in the US FHLBank Topeka is cooperatively owned by its member institutions.

EXECUTIVES

Vice President and Marketing Director, Julie Devader
Vice President of Network Services, Kathleen Grote
Vice President Director Of Member Services, Julia Burghart
Vice President and Portfolio Manager, Gregory Mclaren
First Vice President, Tom Thull
Vice President, Brad Gentry
Assistant Vice President And Product; Product Administration, Gant Welborn
Vice President Risk Management, Michael Surface
Vice President Director, Tom Bliss
First Vice President Funding And Treasurer, Matt Boatwright
Vice President and Controller, Denise Cauthon
Vice President, Greg Mclaren
First Vice President Internal Audit, Tom Millburn
Vice President Public Relations, Julie Devadar
Assistant Vice President And Regional Account Manager, Donald Cushing
Auditors: PricewaterhouseCoopers LLP

LOCATIONS

HQ: Federal Home Loan Bank Topeka
  500 SW Wanamaker Road, Topeka, KS 66606
Phone: 785 233-0507
Web: www.fhlbtopeka.com

HISTORICAL FINANCIALS

Company Type: Public

Income Statement | | | | FYE: December 31

	REVENUE ($ mil.)	NET INCOME ($ mil.)	NET PROFIT MARGIN	EMPLOYEES
12/17	831.9	197.2	23.7%	233
12/16	580.4	161.7	27.9%	238
12/15	465.4	93.3	20.1%	218
12/14	428.3	106.0	24.7%	217
12/13	443.0	119.0	26.9%	210
Annual Growth	**17.1%**	**13.5%**	**—**	**2.6%**

2017 Year-End Financials

Debt ratio: 93.4%
Return on equity: 8.8%
Cash ($ mil.): 14,266.6
Current ratio: 27.71
Long-term debt ($ mil.): 44,935.1
No. of shares (mil.): 16.4
Dividends
  Yield: —
  Payout: —
Market value ($ mil.): —

FedNat Holding Co

Trashed trailer crashed car damaged dwelling? Federated National Holding Company has a policy to cover that. Through Federated National Insurance Company and other subsidiaries it underwrites a variety of personal property/casualty insurance lines in Florida. Products include homeowners flood liability and nonstandard automobile coverage. Recently formed property insurance unit Monarch National (established in 2015) offers a complete homeowners policy special form (HO-3) multi-peril insurance product for Florida homeowners (and plans to introduce a similar product for condominiums). The firm distributes its products through independent agents and its Insure-Link agency.

Operations

Federated National underwrites homeowners commercial general liability federal flood personal auto and other lines of insurance. It is licensed as an admitted carrier for more than 300 classes of commercial general liability coverage in Alabama Georgia Louisiana and Texas. The company's affiliates are also able to market and underwrite other carriers' lines of business and process and adjust claims for third-party carriers.

The firm's independent agency Insure-Link distributes all of the company's products. Such vertical integration is unusual for small regional insurers but is part of Federated National's strategy to control all aspects of the insurance underwriting distribution and claims process.

Homeowners accounted for more than 90% of the firm's net premiums earned in fiscal 2014.

Geographic Reach

Federated National operates in the US Europe and Asia. In the US it primarily operates in the Southeast: Alabama Florida Georgia Louisiana Mississippi Missouri Nevada South Carolina and Texas.

Sales and Marketing

The company markets and distributes its and other carriers' products and services through its Insure-Link network of independent agents and through general agents.

Financial Performance

Federated National's revenues have spiked over the past couple of years on increases in homeowners' net premiums earned (thanks to more policies being sold) and higher commissions. In 2014 revenue increased 65% to $201 million; also contributing to the rise was higher investment earnings. Net income has followed revenue and in 2014 it rose 192% to $37 million.

However cash flow from operations fell 21% to $63 million as more cash was used in prepaid reinsurance premiums and for other expenses.

Strategy

Federated National is working on expanding its product offerings and underwriting additional profitable types of coverage. It also plans on introducing its wares in more states building on its Florida base. In 2015 its formed Monarch Insurance a new property/casualty insurance provider in Florida offering homeowners' policies.

EXECUTIVES

Vice President Accounting And Financial Reporting, Donald G Braun

President and CEO, Michael H. Braun, age 50,
$229,824 total compensation
CFO, Ronald Jordan, age 50
Vice President Marketing, Marty Kramer
Assistant Vice President Claims, Gordon Baker
Vice President Operations, Steve Young
Chairman, Bruce F. Simberg, age 69
Assistant Treasurer, Faye Henry
Secretary, Becky Sanchez
Auditors: Ernst & Young LLP

LOCATIONS

HQ: FedNat Holding Co
14050 N.W. 14th Street, Suite 180, Sunrise, FL 33323
Phone: 800 293-2532
Web: www.FedNat.com

PRODUCTS/OPERATIONS

2014 Premiums

	% of total
Homeowners	92
Commercial general liability	6
Automobile	2
Total	**100**

2014 Revenue

	$ mil.	% of total
Net premiums earned	170.9	86
Direct written policy fees	8.7	4
Net investment income	5.4	3
Commission income	4.5	2
Net realized investment gains	4.4	2
Finance revenue	1.5	1
Quota share profit sharing	2.8	1
Other income	2.5	1
Total	**200.7**	**100**

COMPETITORS

Allstate	Safeco
AssuranceAmerica	Safeway Insurance
Bankers Financial	State Farm
GEICO	Universal Insurance
Main Street America	Holdings
Progressive	
Corporation	

HISTORICAL FINANCIALS

Company Type: Public

Income Statement   FYE: December 31

	ASSETS ($ mil.)	NET INCOME ($ mil.)	INCOME AS % OF ASSETS	EMPLOYEES
12/17	904.8	7.9	0.9%	419
12/16	813.1	(0.2)	—	381
12/15	638.3	40.8	6.4%	297
12/14	503.6	37.2	7.4%	219
12/13	316.7	12.7	4.0%	153
Annual Growth	**30.0%**	**(11.0%)**	**—**	**28.6%**

2017 Year-End Financials

Return on assets: 0.9%
Return on equity: 3.7%
Long-term debt ($ mil.): —
No. of shares (mil.): 12.9
Sales ($ mil): 391.6
Dividends
Yield: 0.0%
Payout: 52.4%
Market value ($ mil.): 215.0

	STOCK PRICE ($) FY Close	P/E High/Low	Earnings	PER SHARE ($) Dividends	Book Value
12/17	16.57	34 17	0.61	0.32	16.29
12/16	18.69	— —	(0.01)	0.25	16.26
12/15	29.56	11 7	2.92	0.17	16.86
12/14	24.16	11 4	2.99	0.12	14.13
12/13	14.67	10 4	1.45	0.13	9.95
Annual Growth	**3.1%**	**— —**	**(19.5%)**	**25.3%**	**13.1%**

Fentura Financial Inc

It just makes cents to say that Fentura Financial has its hands full. Fentura Financial is the holding company for Michigan community banks The State Bank Davison State Bank West Michigan Community Bank and Community Bancorp. From about 20 branch locations the banks provide commercial and consumer banking services and products including checking and savings accounts and loans. Commercial loans account for some two-thirds of the bank's combined loan portfolio. The State Bank Fentura's first subsidiary traces its origins to 1898. Fentura acquired St. Charles-based Community Bancorp in late 2016.

EXECUTIVES

President CEO and Director Fentura Financial
and The State Bank, Donald L. Grill, age 68,
$235,434 total compensation
SVP and Secretary; President and CEO West
Michigan Community Bank, Ronald L. Justice, age
51, $139,646 total compensation
Independent Vice Chairman of the Board, Brian P.
Petty, age 58
Vice Chairman, Thomas P. McKenney, age 64
SVP The State Bank, Dennis E. Leyder, age 62,
$145,000 total compensation
SVP; President Davison State Bank, Holly J.
Pingatore, age 58, $104,181 total compensation
Chief Financial Officer, James W. Distelrath
President CEO and Director Fentura Financial
and The State Bank, Donald L. Grill, age 68
Vice Chairman, Thomas P. McKenney, age 63
Independent Director, William Dery
Independent Director, Frederick Dillingham
Independent Director, Joanne Shaw
Independent Director, Ronald Rybar
Independent Director, Randy Hicks
Auditors: Rehmann Robson LLC

LOCATIONS

HQ: Fentura Financial Inc
175 North Leroy, P.O. Box 725, Fenton, MI 48430-3805
Phone: 810 629-2263
Web: www.fentura.com

COMPETITORS

Clarkston Financial
FNBH Bancorp
Fifth Third
First Federal of Northern Michigan Bancorp
Flagstar Bancorp
Oxford Bank

HISTORICAL FINANCIALS

Company Type: Public

Income Statement   FYE: December 31

	ASSETS ($ mil.)	NET INCOME ($ mil.)	INCOME AS % OF ASSETS	EMPLOYEES
12/17	781.4	8.6	1.1%	0
12/16	703.3	4.4	0.6%	0
12/15	446.4	4.6	1.1%	0
12/14	393.5	3.3	0.9%	0
12/13	335.2	8.4	2.5%	0
Annual Growth	**23.6%**	**0.6%**	**—**	**—**

2017 Year-End Financials

Return on assets: 1.1%
Return on equity: 15.7%
Long-term debt ($ mil.): —
No. of shares (mil.): 3.6
Sales ($ mil): 39.1
Dividends
Yield: 0.0%
Payout: 8.3%
Market value ($ mil.): 69.0

	STOCK PRICE ($) FY Close	P/E High/Low	Earnings	PER SHARE ($) Dividends	Book Value
12/17	18.88	8 6	2.39	0.20	16.37
12/16	16.00	9 8	1.70	0.40	14.00
12/15	13.86	8 5	1.87	0.12	12.90
12/14	9.90	10 5	1.35	0.09	11.24
12/13	6.97	2 1	3.44	0.00	9.97
Annual Growth	**28.3%**	**— —**	**(8.7%)**	**—**	**13.2%**

Fidelity Southern Corp

Fidelity Southern Corp. is the holding company for Fidelity Bank which boasts over $3 billion in assets and some 45 branches in the Atlanta metro and in northern Florida markets. The bank offers traditional deposit services such as checking and savings accounts CDs and IRAs. Consumer loans primarily indirect auto loans which the company purchases from auto franchises and independent dealers throughout the Southeast make up more than 50% of its loan portfolio. Real estate construction commercial real estate business residential mortgage and other consumer loans round out Fidelity Southern's lending activities. Subsidiary LionMark Insurance Company offers consumer credit-related insurance products.

Operations

About 50% of Fidelity Southern's total revenue came from loan interest (including fees) in 2014 while another 2% came from interest on its investment securities. The rest of its revenue came from mortgage banking income (28%) indirect lending activities (9%) SBA Lending (3%) service charges on deposit accounts (2%) and other miscellaneous income sources. The bank had a staff of roughly 1040 employees at the end of 2014.

Geographic Reach

While the company mostly has a branch presence in Georgia and Florida it also offers mortgage loans indirect auto loans and Small Business Administration (SBA) loans in a dozen Southern states.

Sales and Marketing

Fidelity Southern mostly serves individuals and small to medium-sized businesses. The company spent $2.34 million on advertising and promotions in 2014 up from $1.69 million and $1.13 million in 2013 and 2012 respectively.

Financial Performance

Fidelity Southern's revenues and profits have risen over the past several years thanks to growing loan and deposit business from branch openings and acquisitions lower interest expenses and declining loan loss provisions as its loan portfolio's credit quality has improved with higher property valuations in the strengthened economy.

The company's revenue inched higher by 1% to $197 million in 2014 mostly as its loan balances grew organically by 8% during the year with higher loan originations and market expansion.

Higher revenue and lower interest expenses in 2014 boosted Fidelity Southern's net income by 9% to a record $30 million. Its cash levels plummeted during the year with operations using a net $141 million for the year after adjusting its earnings for non-cash items related to its net proceeds from its loans held for sale.

Strategy

Fidelity Southern has focused on building and diversifying its loan portfolio including originating more residential mortgages commercial loans and consumer installment loans. The bank has been opening new branches as part of this organic growth strategy. During 2014 it opened 12 new branches including five in Georgia and seven in Florida.

It's also pursued small bank and branch acquisitions to grow its loan and deposit business while expanding its geographic reach in Florida and Georgia.

Mergers and Acquisitions

In October 2015 the Fidelity Bank agreed to purchase The Bank of Georgia including its $295 million in total assets $280 million in deposits and seven branches in Peachtree City Fayetteville Tyrone Sharpsburg Newnan and Fairburn.

September 2015 Fidelity Southern purchased eight branches in Florida from First Bank including $154 million in deposits and $31.6 million in loans. The deal expanded Fidelity's presence in counties surrounding Bradenton Palmetto and Longboat Key.

In September 2014 the company purchased six branches of CenterState Bank of Florida including $174.2 million in deposits. The deal expanded Fidelity's presence in counties surrounding Orlando and Jacksonville.

HISTORY

WWII veteran Clark Harrison and five others founded Fidelity National Bank in 1973. The first office opened in downtown Decatur Georgia the next year. Fidelity National Bank opened its second branch and formed Fidelity Southern Corporation as a holding company in 1979; it formed Fidelity National Mortgage a year later. In 1984 the company received trust powers opened two new branches and began a major credit card marketing program.

The acquisition of two branches from the Resolution Trust Corporation in 1992 brought the number of branches to 10 and increased assets to $257 million. Fidelity National Capital Investors a retail brokerage was incorporated that year. In 1993 Fidelity National Bank began a consumer sales finance department to buy auto loans from car dealers.

The company opened an office in Jacksonville in 1995 to offer mortgage car and construction lending. Also that year the firm changed the name of its holding company to Fidelity National Corporation.

Fidelity National acquired Friendship Community Bank in Florida and bought six branches from First Union and NationsBank in 1996; rapid expansion and unexpectedly high credit card chargeoffs that year slashed earnings and prevented Fidelity National from opening three of its newly acquired branches. Under the scrutiny of federal regulators the bank discontinued its high-default card program the next year and shored up its finances raising capital through a stock offering.

In 1998 Fidelity National focused on maintaining capital levels and recovering from its losses while other banks expanded. Fidelity National Bank finally gained regulatory approval to open the three remaining branches acquired from NationsBank and First Union later that year. Regulators released the bank from capital and dividend restrictions in 1999 but Fidelity National had to restate its earnings for 1997 citing overestimation of an asset's value.

Fidelity National experienced moderate growth in 2001. Inspections by the Federal Reserve Board in 2000 and 2001 led to Fidelity National's adoption of a resolution that prohibits Fidelity National from redeeming its capital stock paying dividends on its common stock or incurring debt without prior approval of the Federal Reserve Board. In light of a softening economy in 2001 Fidelity National placed greater significance on credit risk management and building the secured portion of its consumer loan portfolio. The company sold its credit card business to Bank One in December.

In 2003 the company changed its name back to Fidelity Southern Corporation and its branches converted to the shortened Fidelity Bank; the bank also switched from a national to a state charter.

EXECUTIVES

President Fidelity Southern; CEO Fidelity Bank, H. Palmer Proctor, age 50, $500,000 total compensation

Chairman and CEO, James B. Miller, age 78, $800,000 total compensation

VP; EVP Fidelity Bank; President LionMark Insurance, David Buchanan, age 60, $400,000 total compensation

CFO, Charles D. Christy

Senior Vice President, Sam Mathis

Vice President Business Bankin, Scott Wright

Vice President Commercial Banking, Kevin Lubitz

Executive Vice President, Michael Pierson

Vice President, Ron Hendrix

Vice President, Josh Savage

Senior Vice President Regional Manager, John Andrews

Vice President Assistant Compliance Officer, Neda Tabaridunn

Vice President Loan Operations Manager, Maria Becerra

Senior Vice President Wealth Management, Dave Johnston

Vice President, Christine Hobert

Vice President Corporate Insurance and Accounting Operations Manager Fidelity Bank, Laura Eastman

Vice President, Nina Efird

Senior Vice President, Michelle McCorvey

Senior Vice President, Gerald Kemp

VICE PRESIDENT MORTGAGE ACCOUNTING, Joshua Savage

Auditors: Ernst & Young LLP

LOCATIONS

HQ: Fidelity Southern Corp
3490 Piedmont Road, Suite 1550, Atlanta, GA 30305
Phone: 404 639-6500
Web: www.FidelitySouthern.com

PRODUCTS/OPERATIONS

2014 Sales

	$ mil.	% of total
Interest		
Loans including fees	96.7	50
Investment securities	4.9	2
Federal funds sold & bank deposits	0.1	-
Noninterest		
Mortgage banking activities	55.8	28
Indirect lending activities	18.5	9
SBA lending activities	5.0	3
Service charges on deposit accounts	4.4	2
Bank owned life insurance	1.7	1
Other fees & charges	4.3	2
Other	5.6	3
Total	**197.0**	**100**

COMPETITORS

BB&T	SunTrust
Bank of America	Synovus
Citizens Bancshares	Wells Fargo
Regions Financial	

HISTORICAL FINANCIALS

Company Type: Public

Income Statement   FYE: December 31

	ASSETS ($ mil.)	NET INCOME ($ mil.)	INCOME AS % OF ASSETS	EMPLOYEES
12/17	4,576.8	39.8	0.9%	1,394
12/16	4,389.6	38.7	0.9%	1,284
12/15	3,849.0	39.1	1.0%	1,242
12/14	3,085.2	30.0	1.0%	1,038
12/13	2,564.1	27.6	1.1%	890
Annual Growth	**15.6%**	**9.5%**	**—**	**11.9%**

2017 Year-End Financials

Return on assets: 0.8%	Dividends
Return on equity: 10.4%	Yield: 0.0%
Long-term debt ($ mil.): —	Payout: 32.2%
No. of shares (mil.): 27.0	Market value ($ mil.): 589.0
Sales ($ mil): 292.9	

	STOCK PRICE ($) FY Close	P/E High/Low		PER SHARE ($) Earnings	Dividends	Book Value
12/17	21.80	17	13	1.49	0.48	14.86
12/16	23.67	16	9	1.50	0.48	13.78
12/15	22.31	13	9	1.64	0.39	13.03
12/14	16.11	12	9	1.28	0.30	12.40
12/13	16.61	13	7	1.21	0.05	11.07
Annual Growth	**7.0%**	**—**	**—**	**5.3%**	**76.0%**	**7.7%**

Finjan Holdings Inc

Converted Organics is not a group of new and fervent farmers but a company that is religiously developing a process to turn food into fertilizer. The company uses organic food waste as raw material to make all-natural fertilizers that combine both disease suppression and nutritional characteristics. Its manufacturing process uses heat and bacteria to transform food waste into a high-value natural fertilizer. It sells its environmentally friendly products in the agribusiness turf management and retail markets. The company which acquired vertical farming operation TerraSphere Systems in 2010 also has an industrial wastewater treatment unit. Converted Organics is restructuring to streamline operations.

The company acquired two smaller companies operating in the same business areas during 2008. The acquisition of United Organic Products and Waste Recovery Limited made Converted Organics the sole owner of the High Temperature Liquid Composting system the manufacturing process the company uses to make its fertilizers. The deal for United Organic Products brought the company its California manufacturing facility which began operations in early 2008 and gave Converted Organics its first sales revenue. It also bought a poultry-based fertilizer line in early 2010 that the company expects to boost fertilzer sales by almost half.

Converted Organics was formed in 2006 and merged with its predecessor organizations Mining Organics Management LLC and Mining Organics Harlem River Rail Yard LLC. The company used a significant part of the proceeds from its 2007 IPO to develop and build the organic waste conversion plant in New Jersey. That facility began operation in mid-2008.

EXECUTIVES

Chairman President and CEO, Edward J. (Ed) Gildea, age 62, $222,879 total compensation
EVP Administration and CFO, David R. (Dave) Allen, age 59, $152,376 total compensation
VP Waste Management, John A. (Jack) Walsdorf, age 66, $104,230 total compensation
Director Product Research and Development, William A. (Bill) Torello, age 63
Director Finance and Accounting, Ellen P. O'Neil
VP Marketing, David A. Flannery
Director Sales, Gerard H. (Gerry) Gould
General Manager President of Industrial Waste Water Division, Kristen Brandt
Auditors: Marcum LLP

LOCATIONS

HQ: Finjan Holdings Inc
2000 University Avenue, Suite 600, East Palo Alto, CA 94303
Phone: 650 282-3228
Web: www.finjan.com

COMPETITORS

CF Industries	The Mosaic Company
Koch Industries Inc.	Yara North America

HISTORICAL FINANCIALS
Company Type: Public

Income Statement   FYE: December 31

	REVENUE ($ mil.)	NET INCOME ($ mil.)	NET PROFIT MARGIN	EMPLOYEES
12/17	50.4	22.8	45.2%	10
12/16	18.3	0.3	1.9%	12
12/15	4.6	(12.6)	—	14
12/14	5.0	(10.4)	—	14
12/13	0.7	(6.0)	—	20
Annual Growth	187.0%	—	—	(15.9%)

2017 Year-End Financials

Debt ratio: —	No. of shares (mil.): 27.7
Return on equity: 73.7%	Dividends
Cash ($ mil.): 41.1	Yield: —
Current ratio: 5.39	Payout: —
Long-term debt ($ mil.): —	Market value ($ mil.): 60.0

	STOCK PRICE ($) FY Close	P/E High/Low		PER SHARE ($) Earnings	Dividends	Book Value
12/17	2.16	5	2	0.68	0.00	1.71
12/16	1.13	—	—	(0.28)	0.00	0.62
12/15	1.15	—	—	(0.56)	0.00	0.28
12/14	2.70	—	—	(0.47)	0.00	0.81
12/13	6.43	—	—	(0.28)	0.00	1.21
Annual Growth	(23.9%)	—	—	—	—	9.1%

First Bancshares Inc (MS)

Hoping to be first in the hearts of its customers The First Bancshares is the holding company for The First a community bank with some two dozen branch locations in southern Mississippi's Hattiesburg Alabama and Louisiana. The company provides such standard deposit products as checking and savings accounts NOW and money market accounts and IRAs. Real estate loans account for about 80% of the bank's lending portfolio including about equal portions of residential mortgages commercial mortgages and construction loans. The bank also writes business loans and consumer loans. The bank which has expanded beyond Mississippi through several acquisitions has approximately $970 million in assets.Mergers and AcquisitionsIn April 2013 The First Bancshares acquired First National Bank (FNB) of Baldwin Country a community bank in Alabama with five branches along the Gulf Coast. The purchase of FNB marked The First's entry into the Alabama market. In 2011 The First expanded into Louisiana and strengthened its hold on southern Mississippi with the acquisition of seven branch banks from Whitney National Bank and one branch from Hancock Bank of Louisiana for an undisclosed amount.

EXECUTIVES

Vice President, Kevin Miller
Vice President, Ken Kennedy
Auditors: Crowe Horwath LLP

LOCATIONS

HQ: First Bancshares Inc (MS)
6480 U.S. Highway 98 West, Suite A, Hattiesburg, MS 39402
Phone: 601 268-8998
Web: www.thefirstbank.com

COMPETITORS

BancorpSouth	Peoples Financial
Community Bancshares of Mississippi	Renasant
Hancock Holding	Trustmark

HISTORICAL FINANCIALS
Company Type: Public

Income Statement   FYE: December 31

	ASSETS ($ mil.)	NET INCOME ($ mil.)	INCOME AS % OF ASSETS	EMPLOYEES
12/17	1,813.2	10.6	0.6%	487
12/16	1,277.3	10.1	0.8%	315
12/15	1,145.1	8.8	0.8%	305
12/14	1,093.7	6.6	0.6%	278
12/13	940.8	4.6	0.5%	266
Annual Growth	17.8%	23.0%	—	16.3%

2017 Year-End Financials

Return on assets: 0.6%	Dividends
Return on equity: 5.6%	Yield: 0.0%
Long-term debt ($ mil.): —	Payout: 13.5%
No. of shares (mil.): 11.1	Market value ($ mil.): 382.0
Sales ($ mil): 80.4	

	STOCK PRICE ($) FY Close	P/E High/Low		PER SHARE ($) Earnings	Dividends	Book Value
12/17	34.20	31	24	1.11	0.15	19.92
12/16	27.50	15	8	1.64	0.15	17.19
12/15	18.34	11	8	1.62	0.15	19.24
12/14	14.51	12	11	1.25	0.15	18.10
12/13	14.02	16	9	1.06	0.15	16.70
Annual Growth	25.0%	—	—	1.2%	(0.0%)	4.5%

First Bank (Williamstown, NJ)

EXECUTIVES

Coo, Ryan K Manville
Vice President Compliance and CRA Officer, Luisa Franco
Auditors: RSM US LLP

LOCATIONS

HQ: First Bank (Williamstown, NJ)
2465 Kuser Road, Hamilton, NJ 08690
Phone: 609 643-4211
Web: www.FirstBankNJ.com

HISTORICAL FINANCIALS
Company Type: Public

Income Statement   FYE: December 31

	ASSETS ($ mil.)	NET INCOME ($ mil.)	INCOME AS % OF ASSETS	EMPLOYEES
12/17	1,452.3	6.9	0.5%	153
12/16	1,073.2	6.4	0.6%	110
12/15	855.5	3.8	0.5%	101
12/14	677.4	5.8	0.9%	96
12/13	466.7	1.7	0.4%	60
Annual Growth	32.8%	42.2%	—	26.4%

2017 Year-End Financials

Return on assets: 0.5%	Dividends
Return on equity: 5.5%	Yield: 0.0%
Long-term debt ($ mil.): —	Payout: 16.6%
No. of shares (mil.): 17.4	Market value ($ mil.): 242.0
Sales ($ mil): 53.3	

STOCK PRICE ($)		P/E	PER SHARE ($)		
	FY Close	High/Low	Earnings	Dividends	Book Value
12/17	13.85	30 23	0.48	0.08	9.36
12/16	11.60	20 10	0.61	0.00	7.78
12/15	6.61	17 14	0.41	0.00	7.26
12/14	6.24	11 9	0.63	0.00	6.88
12/13	6.34	20 15	0.33	0.00	6.16
Annual Growth	21.6%	— —	9.8%	—	11.0%

First Busey Corp

First Busey Corporation keeps itself busy taking care of deposits and making loans. It's the holding company for Busey Bank which boasts $4 billion in assets and 40 branches across Illinois Florida and Indiana. The bank offers standard deposit products and services using funds from deposits to originate primarily real estate loans and mortgages. Subsidiary Busey Wealth Management which manages $5 billion in assets provides asset management trust brokerage and related services to individuals businesses and foundations while FirsTech provides retail payment processing services. Most of Busey Bank's branches are located in downstate Illinois.

Operations

First Busey Corporation operates three business segments Busey Bank which generated more than 99% of its total revenue in 2014 and serves retail and corporate customers; FirsTech which provides remittance processing for online bill payments lock box and walk-in payments; and Busey Wealth Management which provides asset management tax preparation philanthropic advisory services and investment and fiduciary services to individuals businesses and foundations.

Real estate loans including commercial and residential mortgages accounted for 70% of the bank's loan portfolio in 2014 while commercial loans (25%) construction loans (4%) and consumer installments and other loans (0.5%) comprised the rest.

About 55% of First Busey's total revenue came from loan interest (including fees) while another 10% came from interest income on taxable and non-taxable investment securities. The rest of its revenue came from trust fees (11%) deposit account service charges (7%) remittance processing fees (6%) commissions and brokers' fees (2%) and various types of gains on securities and loan sales.

Geographic Reach

Busey Bank has nearly 30 branches in Illinois seven locations in southwest Florida and another office in Indianapolis. Its FirsTech subsidiary accepts payments from its 3000 agent locations across 36 US states.

Sales and Marketing

The bank which staffed 801 employees at the end of 2014 serves individuals businesses and foundations.

Financial Performance

First Busey's revenues have declined in recent years due to shrinking interest margins on loans amidst the low-interest environment. Its profits however have been rising thanks to lower interest expenses on deposits and declining loan loss pro-

visions as its loan portfolio's credit quality has improved with higher property valuations in the strengthened economy.

The bank's revenue dipped by 2% to $167 million mostly as it collected smaller gains from loan sales due to lower refinancing volumes as interest rates began to rise. The bank's loan interest income also continued to decline with lower yields on loan and security assets in the low-interest environment.

Despite generating less revenue in 2014 First Busey's net income jumped by 14% to $32.8 million thanks to continued declines in interest expenses on deposits and lower loan loss provisions. The company's operating cash levels fell by 31% to $68.1 million after adjusting its earnings for non-cash items related to its net proceeds from its loans held-for-sale.

Strategy

First Busey sometimes strategically acquires smaller banks in its target markets to boost its market share broaden its service offerings and boost its loan and deposit business.

Mergers and Acquisitions

In December 2015 First Busey Corporation expanded into Missouri for the first time after it agreed to buy Pulaski Financial Corporation— along with its $1.5 billion in assets (including $1.3 billion in loans $1.1 billion in deposits) and 13 Pulaski Bank branches in the St. Louis metro area — for around $210.7 million.

In January 2015 First Busey boosted its market share in Illinois after purchasing Pekin-based Herget Financial and its three Herget Bank branches in the area. The $34.1 million-deal extended Busey Bank's presence in Pekin and the greater Peoria market added Herget Financials "dominant" deposit market position in its community and bolstered its service offerings with trust estate and asset management services as well as competitive commercial loan and mortgage offerings.

EXECUTIVES

EVP and Chief Risk Officer, Barbara J. Harrington, age 58
President CEO and Director, Van A. Dukeman, age 59, $537,308 total compensation
Chief Credit Officer, Robert F. (Bob) Plecki, age 57, $268,654 total compensation
President and CEO FirsTech, Howard F. Mooney, age 53, $240,216 total compensation
EVP and Regional President Busey Bank, Christopher M. (Chris) Shroyer, age 52, $268,654 total compensation
EVP and General Counsel, John J. Powers
COO and CFO, Robin N. Elliott, $256,731 total compensation
Assistant Vice President Advisor Wealth Busey Wealth Management, Melissa Hendricks
Vice President Senior Retirement Plan Services Advisor, Charlee Seaton
Assistant Vice President Special Assets, Shana Reed-harper
Executive Vice President Managing Director Busey Wealth Management, Mark Wisniewski
Senior Vice President, Cheryl Chisholm
Vice President Retail Market Manager, Tami Crouch
Assistant Vice President Risk Management Analyst, Annie Feleccia
Senior Vice President Relationship Manager, David Bealke
Vice President Senior Mortgage Originator, Kent Hackstadt

Vice President, Briggett Carter
Assistant Vice President Wealth Advisor Assistant, Monya Russell
Vice President Mortgage Operations Manager, Kevin Hoogeveen
Assistant Vice President Wire Services Manager, Karen Aulph
Senior Vice President Cash Management Executive, Brian Hintz
Assistant Vice President, Valerie Garrett
Senior Vice President, Harry Mcsteen
Vice President Commercial Lending, Ross Rotherham
Chairman, Gregory B. (Greg) Lykins, age 70
Auditors: RSM US LLP

LOCATIONS

HQ: First Busey Corp
100 W. University Ave., Champaign, IL 61820
Phone: 217 365-4544
Web: www.busey.com

PRODUCTS/OPERATIONS

2014 Sales

	$ mil.	% of total
Interest		
Loans including fees	92.4	55
Interest & dividends on securities	15.7	10
Noninterest		
Trust fees	19.6	11
Service charges on deposit accounts	12.0	7
Remittance processing	9.4	6
Gain on sales of loans	4.7	3
Commissions and broker's fees net	2.7	2
Other	10.5	6
Total	**167.0**	**100**

COMPETITORS

Bank of America	First Midwest Bancorp
CIB Marine Bancshares	JPMorgan Chase
Fifth Third	Mercantile Bancorp
First Mid-Illinois Bancshares	PNC Financial
	Wintrust Financial

HISTORICAL FINANCIALS

Company Type: Public

Income Statement

FYE: December 31

	ASSETS ($ mil.)	NET INCOME ($ mil.)	INCOME AS % OF ASSETS	EMPLOYEES
12/17	7,860.6	62.7	0.8%	1,347
12/16	5,425.1	49.6	0.9%	1,295
12/15	3,998.9	39.0	1.0%	795
12/14	3,665.6	32.7	0.9%	801
12/13	3,539.5	28.7	0.8%	849
Annual Growth	**22.1%**	**21.6%**	**—**	**12.2%**

2017 Year-End Financials

Return on assets: 0.9%	Dividends
Return on equity: 8.2%	Yield: 0.0%
Long-term debt ($ mil.): —	Payout: 49.6%
No. of shares (mil.): 48.6	Market value ($ mil.): 1,458.0
Sales ($ mil): 308.7	

	STOCK PRICE ($)	P/E	PER SHARE ($)		
	FY Close	High/Low	Earnings	Dividends	Book Value
12/17	29.94	22 19	1.45	0.72	19.21
12/16	30.78	22 13	1.40	0.68	15.54
12/15	20.63	17 5	1.32	0.17	13.01
12/14	6.51	6 5	1.11	0.57	14.98
12/13	5.80	7 5	0.87	0.36	14.36
Annual Growth	50.7%	— —	13.6%	18.9%	7.5%

First Business Financial Services, Inc.

Business comes first at First Business Financial Services which serves small and midsized companies entrepreneurs professionals and high-networth individuals through First Business Bank and First Business Bank - Milwaukee. The banks offer deposits loans cash management and trust services from a handful of offices in Wisconsin and Kansas. Over 60% of the company's loan portfolio is made up of commercial real estate loans. Subsidiary First Business Capital specializes in asset-based lending while First Business Equipment Finance provides commercial equipment financing. First Business Trust & Investments offers investment management and retirement services.

Operations

First Business Financial Services backs its subsidiaries with low-cost corporate services such as human resources finance IT and marketing. First Business Credit Cards provides revolving lines of credit and term loans for financial and strategic acquisitions capital expenditures working capital used to support rapid growth bank debt refinancing debt restructuring and other corporate financing needs.

The company generated 80% of its total revenue from interest on loans and leases in 2014 and another 5% from interest on its securities. About 7% of revenue came from trust and investment services fee income while service charges on deposits and loan fees made up 4% and 2% of revenue respectively.

Geographic Reach

The company's primary market areas are in Wisconsin Kansas and Missouri. First Business's loan production offices are in Wisconsin in Oshkosh Green Bay Appleton and Kenosha while its two Kansas offices are in Leawood and Overland Park. In Wisconsin it targets Madison Milwaukee Appleton Green Bay Oshkosh and their surrounding communities.

Sales and Marketing

Beyond individual customers the bank generally targets businesses with annual sales between $2 million and $75 million.

Financial Performance

The company has struggled to consistently grow its revenues in recent years due to shrinking interest margins on loans amidst the low-interest environment. Its profits however have been rising thanks to declining loan loss provisions as its loan portfolio's credit quality has improved with higher property valuations in a strengthened economy.

First Business had a breakout year in 2014 however as its revenue rose 9% to $67.8 million on higher loan interest as its commercial and industrial loans comercial real estate and other mortgage loans and direct financing leases businesses all enjoyed "favorable volume variances." The bank's non-interest income also jumped by 20% which was mostly driven by growth in trust and investment services fee income on higher assets under management.

Higher revenue and lower interest expenses on deposits in 2014 pushed the company's net income up by 3% to $14.1 million. First Business' operating cash levels fell by 25% to $11.9 million due to unfavorable changes in working capital related to an increase in accrued interest payable and other liabilities.

Strategy

First Business Financial Services continued in 2015 to focus on maintaining its loan asset quality while organically growing its loan and lease portfolio in addition to growing its customer account based to increase its fee-based revenues on its variety of treasury management trust and investment services and SBA loans. It also planned to boost its investment in utilizing technology to support these initiatives while staying efficient as the business grows.

The company occasionally opens new offices or strategically acquires other banks and financial companies to extend its reach into its target markets and to grow its loan and deposit business. In 2014 its FBB-Milwaukee bank subsidiary expanded more into the southeastern area of Wisconsin after opening a loan production office in Kenosha; while its acquisition of Aslin Group and Alterra Bank furthered its exposure to new markets and loan and deposit business in Kansas.

Mergers and Acquisitions

In November 2014 First Business Financial Services expanded its Midwest market and extended its reach into Kansas after its acquisition of Leawood-based Aslin Group including its Alterra Bank subsidiary. The deal added $223 million in total assets including $182 million in new loan assets and $192 million in new deposits.

EXECUTIVES

President and CEO, Corey A. Chambas, age 55, $416,000 total compensation
SVP and Chief Credit Officer, Michael J. Losenegger, age 60, $221,950 total compensation
President and CEO First Business Capital, Charles H. (Chuck) Batson, age 64, $242,927 total compensation
President and CEO First Business Bank - Madison, Mark J. Meloy, age 56, $201,800 total compensation
President First Business Trust & Investments, Joan A. Burke, age 66
President and CEO First Business Bank - Milwaukee, David J. (Dave) Vetta, age 63
CFO, Edward G. (Ed) Sloane, age 57
President Kenosha Region, Wesley Ricchio
SVP and COO First Business Capital Corp., Peter Lowney
COO and Interim President and CEO Alterra Bank, David R. Seiler
CIO, Daniel S. Ovokaitys, age 44
Vice President Business Development, Tom Rude
Vice President Operations Manager First Business Factors, Jorge Varela
Vice President, Cymbre Van Fossen
Vice President, Josh Hoesch
Assistant Vice President Treasury Management, Wade Hanna
Vice President, Mark Buchert
Vice President Private Wealth Management, Monica Schlicht
Senior Vice President, Bill Blenderman
VICE PRESIDENT BUSINESS DEVELOPMENT OFFICER, Chris Mckernan
Vice President Business Development Officer, Jay Peterson
Vice President Internal Loan Review, Gretchen Griffin
Vice President, Nancy Johnshoy

ASSISTANT VICE PRESIDENT TREASURY MANAGEMENT, Laura Shoemaker
Vice President Commercial Banking, Jessica Meier
Chairman, Jerome R. (Jerry) Smith, age 67
Board Member, Jim Hartlieb
Auditors: KPMG LLP

LOCATIONS

HQ: First Business Financial Services, Inc.
401 Charmany Drive, Madison, WI 53719
Phone: 608 238-8008
Web: www.firstbusiness.com

COMPETITORS

Associated Banc-Corp	TCF Financial
Bank Mutual	U.S. Bancorp
Harris	

HISTORICAL FINANCIALS

Company Type: Public

Income Statement   FYE: December 31

	ASSETS ($ mil.)	NET INCOME ($ mil.)	INCOME AS % OF ASSETS	EMPLOYEES
12/17	1,794.0	11.9	0.7%	264
12/16	1,780.7	14.9	0.8%	272
12/15	1,782.8	16.5	0.9%	258
12/14	1,629.3	14.1	0.9%	231
12/13	1,268.6	13.7	1.1%	164
Annual Growth	9.0%	(3.5%)	—	12.6%

2017 Year-End Financials

Return on assets: 0.6%	Dividends
Return on equity: 7.1%	Yield: 0.0%
Long-term debt ($ mil.): —	Payout: 38.2%
No. of shares (mil.): 8.7	Market value ($ mil.): 194.0
Sales ($ mil): 92.4	

	STOCK PRICE ($) FY Close	P/E High/Low	Earnings	Dividends	Book Value
12/17	22.12	21 15	1.36	0.52	19.32
12/16	23.72	15 11	1.71	0.48	18.55
12/15	25.01	25 12	1.90	0.44	17.34
12/14	47.91	28 21	1.76	0.42	15.88
12/13	37.63	22 13	1.75	0.32	13.85
Annual Growth	(12.4%)	— —	(6.0%)	13.4%	8.7%

First Capital Inc.

First Capital is the holding company for First Harrison Bank which operates about a dozen branches in Clark Floyd Harrison and Washington counties in southern Indiana. Targeting area consumers and small to midsized businesses the bank offers standard deposit products such as checking and savings accounts certificates of deposit and individual retirement accounts. Residential mortgages make up nearly half of the company's loan portfolio; consumer loans and commercial mortgages are around 20% apiece. First Harrison Bank also offers access to investments such as stocks bonds and mutual funds.

EXECUTIVES

Board Member, William Orwick
Board Member, Mark D Shireman
Auditors: Monroe Shine & Co., Inc.

LOCATIONS

HQ: First Capital Inc.
220 Federal Drive N.W., Corydon, IN 47112
Phone: 812 738-2198
Web: www.firstharrison.com

COMPETITORS

First Savings	Regions Financial
Financial	Stock Yards Bancorp
JPMorgan Chase	U.S. Bancorp
PNC Financial	

HISTORICAL FINANCIALS

Company Type: Public

Income Statement				FYE: December 31
	ASSETS ($ mil.)	NET INCOME ($ mil.)	INCOME AS % OF ASSETS	EMPLOYEES
12/17	758.9	7.4	1.0%	206
12/16	743.6	6.8	0.9%	204
12/15	715.8	5.2	0.7%	191
12/14	472.7	5.5	1.2%	150
12/13	444.3	5.0	1.1%	145
Annual Growth	14.3%	10.0%	—	9.2%

2017 Year-End Financials

Return on assets: 0.9%	Dividends
Return on equity: 9.5%	Yield: 0.0%
Long-term debt ($ mil.): —	Payout: 38.5%
No. of shares (mil.): 3.3	Market value ($ mil.): 123.0
Sales ($ mil): 33.1	

	STOCK PRICE ($) FY Close	P/E High/Low	PER SHARE ($) Earnings	Dividends	Book Value
12/17	36.74	17 13	2.23	0.86	24.25
12/16	32.42	17 12	2.05	0.84	22.69
12/15	26.10	15 12	1.87	0.84	22.28
12/14	24.34	12 10	2.03	0.84	20.84
12/13	21.26	12 11	1.82	0.80	19.12
Annual Growth	14.7%	— —	5.2%	1.8%	6.1%

First Choice Bancorp

Auditors: Vavrinek Trine Day & Co., LLP

LOCATIONS

HQ: First Choice Bancorp
17785 Center Court Drive N, Suite 750, Cerritos, CA 90703
Phone: 562 345-9092
Web: www.firstchoicebankca.com

HISTORICAL FINANCIALS

Company Type: Public

Income Statement				FYE: December 31
	ASSETS ($ mil.)	NET INCOME ($ mil.)	INCOME AS % OF ASSETS	EMPLOYEES
12/17	903.8	7.3	0.8%	0
12/16	863.4	8.2	1.0%	0
12/15	811.9	5.3	0.7%	0
12/14	626.4	4.0	0.6%	0
12/13	440.0	2.6	0.6%	0
Annual Growth	19.7%	28.7%	—	—

2017 Year-End Financials

Return on assets: 0.8%	Dividends
Return on equity: 7.1%	Yield: —
Long-term debt ($ mil.): —	Payout: 78.4%
No. of shares (mil.): 7.2	Market value ($ mil.): —
Sales ($ mil): 45.8	

First Citizens BancShares Inc (NC)

First Citizens BancShares owns First-Citizens Bank which operates more than 550 branches in 20 states mainly in the southeastern and western US and urban areas scattered nationwide. The $32 billion-asset bank provides standard services such as deposits loans mortgages and trust services in addition to processing and operational support to other banks. Real estate loans including commercial residential and revolving mortgages and construction and land development loans comprise most of its loan portfolio. Subsidiaries First Citizens Investor Services First Citizens Securities Corporation and First Citizens Asset Management offers investment and discount brokerage services to bank clients.

Operations

The company provides consumer business and commercial banking wealth investments and insurance through a network of branch offices internet banking mobile banking telephone banking and ATMs.

More than 60% of the bank's total revenue came from loan and lease interest during 2015 while another 6% came from interest income on investment securities. The rest of its revenue came from merchant services (6% of revenue) service charges on deposit accounts (6%) wealth management services (6%) cardholder services (4%) mortgage income (1%) insurance commissions (1%) and other miscellaneous income sources.

Geographic Reach

First Citizens BancShares has nearly 560 branches in almost 20 states (Arizona California Colorado Florida Georgia Kansas Maryland Missouri New Mexico North Carolina Oklahoma Oregon South Carolina Tennessee Texas Virginia Washington and West Virginia) and Washington DC.

Sales and Marketing

First Citizens BancShares serves both individuals and commercial entities operating in the healthcare dental practices legal services property management agribusiness nonprofit and trade association markets.

The bank has been ramping up its advertising spend in recent years. It spent $12.4 million in 2015 up from $11.4 million and $8.2 million in 2014 and 2013 respectively.

Financial Performance

First Citizens BancShares' annual revenues have risen more than 35% since 2013 thanks to growth in its variety of non-banking business. Its profits have also been trending higher thanks to declining loan loss provisions as its loan portfolio's credit quality has improved with higher property valuations in the strengthened economy.

The bank's revenue jumped 30% to $1.44 billion during 2015 mostly thanks to higher loan and lease interest income stemming from added loan business from the acquisition of First Citizens Bancorporation. Its non-interest income sources grew 36% during the year as well.

Strong revenue growth in 2015 drove First Citizen's net income up 52% to $210.3 million. The bank's operating cash levels rose 28% to $233 million with the rise in cash-based earnings.

Strategy

FCB has expanded its branch network into new markets while bolstering its loan and deposit business by acquiring small community banks in new territory.

Mergers and Acquisitions

In May 2016 the bank made an agreement with the FDIC to buy select assets and liabilities of First Cornerstone Bank of King of Prussia in Pennsylvania. It made a similar FDIC transaction to buy North Milwaukee State Bank in March 2016. Later that year the company acquired Cordia Bancorp and its six-branch subsidiary Bank of Virginia.

In February 2015 also through the FDIC First Citizens bought select assets and deposits of Capitol City Bank & Trust (CCBT) expanding into Georgia with eight branches in Atlanta Albany Augusta Stone Mountain and Savannah.

In January 2015 First Citizens BancShares expanded its loan business and expanded into South Carolina after buying First Citizens Bancorporation and its subsidiary First Citizens Bank and Trust Company.

Company Background

First Citizens BancShares has been fortifying its presence along the West Coast by snapping up failed financial institutions. Since 2009 it has acquired most of the banking operations of Temecula Valley Bank Washington-based Venture Bank and First Regional Bank in Southern California. It also acquired the failed Florida-based bank Sun American and entered Colorado through the acquisitions of United Western Bank and Colorado Capital Bank. All were FDIC-assisted transactions and each acquired institution became branches of First-Citizens Bank. The deals added about 50 branches to the bank's network. First Citizens BancShares continues to seek out acquisitions of other seized institutions.

Though the company has been able to grow geographically thanks to the economic downturn its IronStone Bank division which focused on business customers suffered from weakened markets in Florida and Georgia. (First Citizens Bancshares merged IronStone into First-Citizens Bank in 2011 to increase efficiency and unify the company's brand.) It has remained profitable thanks in part to its acquisitions which include loss-sharing agreements with the FDIC but has had to increase its provisions for loan losses each of the last five years.

The Holding family which occupies several positions in the company's board room and executive suite controls First Citizens BancShares.

EXECUTIVES

COO BancShares and First-Citizens Bank & Trust Company, Edward L. (Ed) Willingham, age 63, $585,125 total compensation
President and Corporate Sales Executive of BancShares and First-Citizens Bank & Trust Company, Peter M. Bristow, age 52

Chairman and CEO First Citizens BancShares First-Citizens Bank & Trust and IronStone Bank, Frank B. Holding, age 57, $902,875 total compensation

EVP Finance and CFO, Craig L. Nix, age 46

EVP Business Banking Segment Manager and Director First-Citizens Bank & Trust; President IronStone Bank, Hope Holding Connell, age 55, $563,750 total compensation

Chief Human Resources Officer; Executive Vice President of FCB, Lou J. Davis, age 65

EVP and Chief Credit Officer First-Citizens Bank & Trust; Group VP and Chief Credit Officer IronStone, Ricky T. Holland, age 64

Executive Vice President and General Auditor of FCB, Donald Preskenis

Vice President, Rhonda Chapman

Vice President Marketing, Christine Thompson

Vice President, Scott German

Assistant Vice President of Information Technology, Kim Whalen

Vice President Commercial Banking, Drew Schiavone

Auditors: Dixon Hughes Goodman LLP

LOCATIONS

HQ: First Citizens BancShares Inc (NC)
4300 Six Forks Road, Raleigh, NC 27609
Phone: 919 716-7000
Web: www.firstcitizens.com

PRODUCTS/OPERATIONS

2013 Sales

	$ mil.	% of total
Interest		
Loans & leases	757.2	72
Investment securities including dividends	36.9	3
Overnight investments	2.7	-
Noninterest		
Service charges on deposit accounts	60.7	5
Wealth management services	59.6	5
Merchant services	56.0	4
Cardholder services	48.4	4
Fees from processing services	22.1	1
Other service charges and fees	15.7	1
Adjustments	(72.3)	-
Other	72.8	5
Total	**1,060.4**	**100**

COMPETITORS

BB&T	JPMorgan Chase
BBVA Compass Bancshares	PNC Financial
Bank of America	Regions Financial
Capital One	SunTrust
Citibank	Synovus
First Horizon	Wachovia Corp
	Wells Fargo

HISTORICAL FINANCIALS

Company Type: Public

Income Statement				FYE: December 31
	ASSETS ($ mil.)	NET INCOME ($ mil.)	INCOME AS % OF ASSETS	EMPLOYEES
12/17	34,527.5	323.7	0.9%	6,799
12/16	32,990.8	225.4	0.7%	6,296
12/15	31,475.9	210.3	0.7%	6,232
12/14	30,075.1	138.5	0.5%	6,440
12/13	21,199.0	167.7	0.8%	4,875
Annual Growth	**13.0%**	**17.9%**	**—**	**8.7%**

First Community Corp (SC)

Putting first things first First Community is the holding company for First Community Bank which serves individuals and smaller businesses in central South Carolina. Through about a dozen offices the bank which was founded in 1995 offers such products and services as checking and savings accounts money market accounts CDs IRAs credit cards insurance and investment services. Commercial mortgages make up about 60% of First Community Bank's loan portfolio which also includes residential mortgages and business consumer and construction loans. The company's First Community Financial Consultants division offers asset management and estate planning.

EXECUTIVES

Vice Chairman; Vice Chairman and EVP First Community Bank, J. Thomas (Tommy) Johnson, age 69, $142,786 total compensation

President CEO and Director First Community Corporation and First Community Bank, Michael C. (Mike) Crapps, age 56, $247,636 total compensation

Chairman, Mitchell M. Willoughby, age 68

SVP and Chief Credit Officer, David K. Proctor, age 59, $126,500 total compensation

SVP and CFO, Joseph G. Sawyer, age 65, $138,833 total compensation

SVP and Director Commercial and Retail Banking, J. Ted Nissen, age 54, $116,600 total compensation

SVP and Director Human Resources and Marketing, Robin D. Brown

VP Commercial Lender First Community Bank, Harry Deith

Vice Chairman; Vice Chairman and EVP First Community Bank, J. Thomas (Tommy) Johnson, age 69

Independent Director, Richard K. (Rick) Bogan, age 70

President CEO and Director First Community Corporation and First Community Bank, Michael C. (Mike) Crapps, age 56

Independent Director, Anita B. Easter, age 71

Independent Director, George H. Fann Jr., age 71

Independent Director, Chimin J. Chao, age 59

Independent Director, Loretta R. Whitehead, age 73

Independent Director, Roderick M. Todd, age 51

Independent Director, Alexander Snipe

Independent Director, James Kitchens

Independent Director, O. Ethridge

Auditors: Elliott Davis, LLC

LOCATIONS

HQ: First Community Corp (SC)
5455 Sunset Boulevard, Lexington, SC 29072
Phone: 803 951-2265
Web: www.firstcommunitysc.com

COMPETITORS

BB&T	Regions Financial
Bank of America	Security Federal
First Citizens Bancorporation	Synovus

HISTORICAL FINANCIALS

Company Type: Public

Income Statement				FYE: December 31
	ASSETS ($ mil.)	NET INCOME ($ mil.)	INCOME AS % OF ASSETS	EMPLOYEES
12/17	1,050.7	5.8	0.6%	224
12/16	914.7	6.6	0.7%	202
12/15	862.7	6.1	0.7%	186
12/14	812.3	5.1	0.6%	185
12/13	633.3	4.1	0.7%	171
Annual Growth	**13.5%**	**8.9%**	**—**	**7.0%**

2017 Year-End Financials

Return on assets: 0.5%
Return on equity: 6.2%
Long-term debt ($ mil.): —
No. of shares (mil.): 7.5
Sales ($ mil): 41.8

Dividends
Yield: 0.0%
Payout: 43.3%
Market value ($ mil.): 171.0

	STOCK PRICE ($) FY Close	P/E High/Low	Earnings	PER SHARE ($) Dividends	Book Value
12/17	22.60	29 21	0.83	0.36	13.93
12/16	18.05	19 13	0.98	0.32	12.20
12/15	14.92	16 12	0.91	0.28	11.81
12/14	11.31	15 13	0.78	0.24	11.18
12/13	10.40	14 11	0.78	0.22	9.93
Annual Growth	**21.4%**	**— —**	**1.6%**	**13.1%**	**8.8%**

First Defiance Financial Corp

Named for its hometown not its attitude First Defiance Financial is the holding company for First Federal Bank of the Midwest which operates more than 30 branches serving northwestern Ohio western Indiana and southern Michigan. The thrift offers standard deposit products including checking savings and money market accounts and CDs. Commercial real estate loans account for more than half of the bank's loan portfolio; commercial loans make up another quarter of all loans. The company's insurance agency subsidiary First Insurance Group of the Midwest which accounts for

---

2017 Year-End Financials (First Citizens BancShares)

Return on assets: 0.9%
Return on equity: 10.2%
Long-term debt ($ mil.): —
No. of shares (mil.): 12.0
Sales ($ mil): 1,744.7

Dividends
Yield: 0.0%
Payout: 4.6%
Market value ($ mil.): 4,840.0

	STOCK PRICE ($) FY Close	P/E High/Low	Earnings	PER SHARE ($) Dividends	Book Value
12/17	403.00	16 12	26.96	1.25	277.60
12/16	355.00	19 12	18.77	1.20	250.82
12/15	258.17	15 12	17.52	1.20	239.14
12/14	252.79	20 16	13.56	1.20	223.77
12/13	222.63	13 9	17.43	1.20	215.89
Annual Growth	**16.0%**	**— —**	**11.5%**	**1.0%**	**6.5%**

some 7% of the company's revenues provides life insurance property/casualty coverage and investments.

Strategy

First Defiance Financial has boosted its non-banking product lines via acquisitions. It bought the employee benefits insurance business of another local agency Andres O'Neil & Lowe in 2010; and property/casualty agency Payak-Dubbs Insurance Agency in 2011. Both additions became part of First Insurance Group of the Midwest (formerly named First Insurance & Investments).

In 2016 the company agreed to buy another bank serving northwest Ohio Commercial Bancshares. The deal is valued at some $63 million and adds seven branches and $342 million in assets.

EXECUTIVES

EVP Business Banking First Federal Bank, Dennis E. Rose, age 49, $144,077 total compensation
President and CEO First Defiance Financial and First Federal Bank, Donald P. Hileman, age 65, $400,000 total compensation
EVP General Counsel and Chief Risk Officer First Defiance Financial Corp and First Federal Bank, John R. Reisner, age 62, $180,147 total compensation
EVP and Community Banking President – First Federal Bank, Gregory R. Allen, age 54, $200,000 total compensation
EVP and President Western Market Area First Federal Bank, James R. Williams, age 50
EVP and President Eastern Market Area First Federal Bank, Timothy K. (Tim) Harris, age 59
SVP Credit Administration First Federal Bank of the Midwest, Michael D. Mulford, age 53, $149,387 total compensation
EVP and President Northern Market Area First Federal Bank, Marybeth Shunck, age 48
EVP and CFO First Defiance Financial Corp. and First Federal Bank, Kent T. Thompson, age 64, $218,360 total compensation
EVP and Director Human Resources First Defiance Financial Corp. and First Federal Bank, Sharon L. Davis, age 36
EVP and President Southern Market Area First Federal Bank, Amy L. Hackenberg, age 47
Vice President, Gary Verhoff
Assistant Vice President Human Resources, Diane Beam
Assistant Vice President, Julie Harris
Senior Vice President, Lisa R Christy
Vice President Senior Accountant, Steve Giesige
Executive Vice President Eastern Market Area President, Tim Harris
Chairman, William J. (Bill) Small, age 67
Vice Chairman, Stephen L. Boomer, age 67
Auditors: Crowe Horwath LLP

LOCATIONS

HQ: First Defiance Financial Corp
601 Clinton Street, Defiance, OH 43512
Phone: 419 782-5015
Web: www.fdef.com

PRODUCTS/OPERATIONS

2016 Sales

	$ mil.	% of total
Interest		
Loans	80.2	66
Investment securities		
Taxable	3.2	3
Tax-exempt	3.0	2
Interest-bearing deposits	0.4	
FHLB stock dividends	0.6	1

Non-interest		
Service fees & other charges	10.9	9
Insurance commissions	10.4	9
Mortgage banking income	7.3	6
Trust income	1.7	1
Gain on sale of non-mortgage loans	0.8	1
Income from bank owned life insurance	0.9	1
Gain on sale or call of securities	0.5	-
Other	1.5	1
Total	**121.4**	**100**

COMPETITORS

Farmers National	Huntington Bancshares
Fifth Third	KeyCorp
First Citizens Banc Corp	PNC Financial
First Financial Bancorp	SB Financial Group

HISTORICAL FINANCIALS

Company Type: Public

Income Statement
FYE: December 31

	ASSETS ($ mil.)	NET INCOME ($ mil.)	INCOME AS % OF ASSETS	EMPLOYEES
12/17	2,993.4	32.2	1.1%	674
12/16	2,477.6	28.8	1.2%	581
12/15	2,297.6	26.4	1.2%	586
12/14	2,178.9	24.2	1.1%	555
12/13	2,137.1	22.2	1.0%	549
Annual Growth	**8.8%**	**9.8%**	**—**	**5.3%**

2017 Year-End Financials

Return on assets: 1.1%	Dividends
Return on equity: 9.6%	Yield: 0.0%
Long-term debt ($ mil.): —	Payout: 31.0%
No. of shares (mil.): 20.3	Market value ($ mil.): 1,056.0
Sales ($ mil): 148.1	

	STOCK PRICE ($) FY Close	P/E High/Low	Earnings	PER SHARE ($) Dividends	Book Value
12/17	51.97	35 29	1.61	0.50	18.38
12/16	50.74	32 22	1.60	0.44	16.31
12/15	37.78	29 21	1.41	0.39	15.39
12/14	34.06	27 19	1.22	0.31	15.13
12/13	25.97	25 17	1.10	0.23	14.00
Annual Growth	**18.9%**	**— —**	**10.1%**	**22.1%**	**7.0%**

First Financial Bankshares, Inc.

Texas hold 'em? Well sort of. First Financial Bankshares is the holding company for eleven banks consolidated under the First Financial brand all of which are located in small and midsized markets in Texas. Together they have about 50 locations. The company maintains a decentralized management structure with each of the subsidiary banks having their own local leadership and decision-making authority. Its First Financial Trust & Asset Management subsidiary administers retirement and employee benefit plans in addition to providing trust services. First Financial Bankshares also owns an insurance agency.

EXECUTIVES

Chairman President and CEO; Chairman First Financial Bank N.A., F. Scott Dueser, age 65, $754,167 total compensation
EVP and CFO, J. Bruce Hildebrand, age 63, $445,000 total compensation
EVP and Chief Administrative Officer, Ronald D. (Ron) Butler, age 57, $405,000 total compensation
EVP Lending, Marna Yerigan
EVP Lending, T. Luke Longhofer
EVP and CIO, Thomas S. (Stan) Limerick
EVP and Lending Officer, Gary S.Gragg, age 58, $325,000 total compensation
EVP Retail and Training, Monica Houston
EVP Chief Risk Officer, Randy Roewe
Vice President of Commercial Loans, Chris Evatt
Senior Vice President, Kay Berry
Assistant Vice President Human Resources, Racheal Carter
Senior Vice President Consumer Lending, Chris Schjetnan
Senior Vice President and Credit Administration, Clay Trumble
Vice President, Wade Spain
Vice President, Isabel Montoya
Board Member, Tim Lancaster
Auditors: Ernst & Young LLP

LOCATIONS

HQ: First Financial Bankshares, Inc.
400 Pine Street, Abilene, TX 79601
Phone: 325 627-7155
Web: www.ffin.com

PRODUCTS/OPERATIONS

2015 sales

	$ mil.	% of total
Interest Income		
Interest and fees on loans	151.7	51
Interest on investment securities	69.7	24
Interest on federal funds sold and interest-bearing deposits in banks		0.2
Non-Interest Income		
ATM interchange and credit card fees	21.9	7
Trust fees	19.2	6
Service charges on deposit accounts	17.2	6
Real estate mortgage operations	10.4	4
Net gain on sale of available-for-sale securities	0.5	-
Net gain on sale of foreclosed assets	0.5	-
Net loss on sale of assets	(0.8)	-
Other	4.6	2
Total	**295.1**	**100**

PRODUCTS/SERVICESPERSONAL

Learn
Online Banking
Mobile Banking
Consumer Education
FAQS
Privacy & Security Information
Resources
Testimonials
Tools
Bank
Checking
Savings
Invest
CDS & IRAS
Broker Services
Borrow
Mortgage Loans
Mortgage Lenders
Auto Loans
Recreational Loans
Home Equity Loans
Personal Line of Credit
CD Secured Loans
Banking with First Financial

Mobile Banking
Online Banking
Pay Bills
Get Cash
Make Deposit
Move Money
Keep Track
Business
Learn
Online Banking
Mobile Banking
Business Education
Starting your Business
Growing your Business
Tools
Business Banking Services
Manage Cash
Send Payments
Receive Payments
Manage Fraud and Risk
Other Services
Trust & Wealth Management
Investment Management
Trust Management
Estate Management
Oil & Gas Management
Real Estate and Property Management
Company Retirement Plans

Selected Subsidiaries

First Financial Bank National Association Abilene Texas.
First Technology Services Inc. Abilene Texas (wholly owned subsidiary of First Financial Bank National Association Abilene Texas).
First Financial Trust & Asset Management Company National Association Abilene Texas.
First Financial Insurance Agency Inc. Abilene Texas.
First Financial Investments Inc. Abilene Texas.

COMPETITORS

BBVA Compass Bancshares	JPMorgan Chase
Bank of America	Wells Fargo
Cullen/Frost Bankers	Woodforest Financial

HISTORICAL FINANCIALS

Company Type: Public

Income Statement

FYE: December 31

	ASSETS ($ mil.)	NET INCOME ($ mil.)	INCOME AS % OF ASSETS	EMPLOYEES
12/17	7,254.7	120.3	1.7%	1,300
12/16	6,809.9	104.7	1.5%	1,300
12/15	6,665.0	100.3	1.5%	1,270
12/14	5,848.2	89.5	1.5%	1,140
12/13	5,222.2	78.8	1.5%	1,100
Annual Growth	8.6%	11.1%	—	4.3%

2017 Year-End Financials

Return on assets: 1.7%
Return on equity: 13.6%
Long-term debt ($ mil.): —
No. of shares (mil.): 65.7
Sales ($ mil): 336.9

Dividends
Yield: 0.0%
Payout: 41.4%
Market value ($ mil.): 2,963.0

	STOCK PRICE ($) FY Close	P/E High/Low		PER SHARE ($) Earnings	Dividends	Book Value
12/17	45.05	27	20	1.81	0.75	14.03
12/16	45.20	29	15	1.59	0.70	12.78
12/15	30.17	23	16	1.54	0.62	12.30
12/14	29.88	47	20	1.39	0.55	10.72
12/13	66.11	54	31	1.24	0.52	9.26
Annual Growth	(9.1%)	—	—	10.0%	9.9%	10.9%

First Foundation Inc

Auditors: Vavrinek, Trine, Day & Co., LLP

LOCATIONS

HQ: First Foundation Inc
18101 Von Karman Avenue, Suite 700, Irvine, CA 92612
Phone: 949 202-4160
Web: www.ff-inc.com

HISTORICAL FINANCIALS

Company Type: Public

Income Statement

FYE: December 31

	ASSETS ($ mil.)	NET INCOME ($ mil.)	INCOME AS % OF ASSETS	EMPLOYEES
12/17	4,541.1	27.5	0.6%	394
12/16	3,975.4	23.3	0.6%	335
12/15	2,592.5	13.3	0.5%	295
12/14	1,355.4	8.3	0.6%	207
12/13	1,037.3	7.8	0.8%	187
Annual Growth	44.6%	36.9%	—	20.4%

2017 Year-End Financials

Return on assets: 0.6%
Return on equity: 8.1%
Long-term debt ($ mil.): —
No. of shares (mil.): 38.2
Sales ($ mil): 175.5

Dividends
Yield: —
Payout: —
Market value ($ mil.): 708.0

	STOCK PRICE ($) FY Close	P/E High/Low		PER SHARE ($) Earnings	Dividends	Book Value
12/17	18.54	36	17	0.78	0.00	10.34
12/16	28.50	41	28	0.70	0.00	8.69
12/15	23.59	41	29	0.58	0.00	8.13
12/14	18.14	37	33	0.52	0.00	6.34
Annual Growth	0.7%	—	—	14.8%	—	17.7%

First Internet Bancorp

First Internet Bancorp was formed in 2006 to be the holding company for First Internet Bank of Indiana (First IB). Launched in 1999 the bank was the first state-chartered FDIC-insured institution to operate solely via the Internet. It now operates two locations in Indianapolis after adding one via its 2007 purchase of Landmark Financial (the parent of Landmark Savings Bank) a deal that also brought aboard residential mortgage brokerage Landmark Mortgage. First IB offers traditional checking and savings accounts in addition to CDs IRAs credit and check cards consumer installment and residential mortgage loans and lines of credit. It serves customers in all 50 states.

EXECUTIVES

Vice President Treasury Management, Maria Bryce
Vice President Commercial Lender, Carl Osberg
Vice President Commercial Lending, Jim Laine
Vice President Commercial Lending, Kevin Lynch
Vice President Commercial Banking, Christy Smith
Vice President Commercial Banking, Suzy Sottong
VP Human Resources, Angie Redmon

VP of Information Technology, Craig Fortner
VICE PRESIDENT OF APPRAISAL REVIEW, John Reed
Auditors: BKD, LLP

LOCATIONS

HQ: First Internet Bancorp
11201 USA Parkway, Fishers, IN 46037
Phone: 317 532-7900
Web: www.firstinternetbancorp.com

COMPETITORS

Bank of America	Citibank
BofI	E*TRADE Bank

HISTORICAL FINANCIALS

Company Type: Public

Income Statement

FYE: December 31

	ASSETS ($ mil)	NET INCOME ($ mil)	INCOME AS % OF ASSETS	EMPLOYEES
12/17	2,767.6	15.2	0.6%	206
12/16	1,854.3	12.0	0.7%	192
12/15	1,269.8	8.9	0.7%	152
12/14	970.5	4.3	0.4%	143
12/13	802.3	4.5	0.6%	130
Annual Growth	36.3%	34.9%	—	12.2%

2017 Year-End Financials

Return on assets: 0.6%
Return on equity: 8.0%
Long-term debt ($ mil.): —
No. of shares (mil.): 8.4
Sales ($ mil): 95.2

Dividends
Yield: 0.0%
Payout: 11.2%
Market value ($ mil.): 321.0

	STOCK PRICE ($) FY Close	P/E High/Low		PER SHARE ($) Earnings	Dividends	Book Value
12/17	38.15	19	12	2.13	0.24	26.65
12/16	32.00	14	10	2.30	0.24	23.76
12/15	28.69	18	7	1.96	0.24	23.28
12/14	16.74	26	16	0.96	0.24	21.80
12/13	22.50	22	13	1.51	0.22	20.44
Annual Growth	14.1%	—	—	9.0%	2.2%	6.9%

First Interstate BancSystem Inc

This Treasure State bank wants to be your treasury. First Interstate BancSystem is the holding company for First Interstate Bank which has about 80 branches in Montana western South Dakota and Wyoming. Serving area consumers businesses and municipalities the bank provides traditional services including deposit accounts wealth management and loans. Commercial loans including mortgages make up more than half of the bank's loan portfolio; residential real estate agricultural and construction loans round out its lending activities. On the wealth management side the bank has more than $8 billion in trust assets held in a fiduciary or agent capacity.

Financial Performance

The company's revenue decreased in fiscal 2013 compared to the previous period. It reported $369.3 million in revenue for fiscal 2013 down from $388.8 million in fiscal 2012. However despite the decreased annual revenue the company's net income increased in fiscal 2013 to $86 million up from a net income of $58 million the prior fiscal year. Cash flow increased by about $15 million in fiscal 2013 compared to 2012 levels.

Strategy

The company is always looking for opportunities for expansion including organic growth as well as growth through acquisitions. It expanded into the northwest growth market with the acquisition of Cascade Bancorp for around $589 million.

EXECUTIVES

SVP and CIO, Kevin J. Guenthner, age 54, $205,385 total compensation

President and CEO, Kevin P. Riley, age 58, $307,270 total compensation

EVP and Chief Banking Officer, Bill Gottwals

EVP and CFO, Marcy D. Mutch, age 58

Executive Vice President and Chief Banking Officer, Michael Huston

Chairman, James R. Scott, age 68

Auditors: RSM US LLP

LOCATIONS

HQ: First Interstate BancSystem Inc
401 North 31st Street, Billings, MT 59116-0918
Phone: 406 255-5390
Web: www.fibk.com

PRODUCTS/OPERATIONS

Selected ServicesBanking
Checking Accounts
Credit Cards
Debit Cards
Escrow Services
Foreign Currency
Overdraft Protection
Personal Resources
Prepaid Cards
Savings Accounts
Borrowing
AdvanceLine
Auto & Recreation
Debt Consolidation
Home Equity
Home Mortgage
Personal Loans
Create & Build Wealth
Long-Term Planning
Planning for the Unexpected
Saving for College
Saving for Retirement
Wealth Resources
Protect & Preserve Wealth
Asset Management
Employee Exit Strategies
Health Concerns
Investment Services
Retirement Plan Services

Sales 2015

	$ mil.	% of total
Interest income	282.4	70
Non-interest income	121.0	30
Total	**403.4**	**100**

COMPETITORS

Bank of the West	Great Western Bancorp
Crazy Woman Creek	U.S. Bancorp
Eagle Bancorp	Wells Fargo
Glacier Bancorp	

HISTORICAL FINANCIALS

Company Type: Public

Income Statement   FYE: December 31

	ASSETS ($ mil.)	NET INCOME ($ mil.)	INCOME AS % OF ASSETS	EMPLOYEES
12/17	12,213.2	106.5	0.9%	2,207
12/16	9,063.9	95.6	1.1%	1,721
12/15	8,728.2	86.8	1.0%	1,742
12/14	8,609.9	84.4	1.0%	1,705
12/13	7,564.6	86.1	1.1%	1,635
Annual Growth	**12.7%**	**5.5%**	**—**	**7.8%**

2017 Year-End Financials

Return on assets: 1.0%
Return on equity: 8.8%
Long-term debt ($ mil.): —
No. of shares (mil.): 56.4
Sales ($ mil): 519.5

Dividends
Yield: 0.0%
Payout: 46.8%
Market value ($ mil.): 2,261.0

	STOCK PRICE ($) FY Close	P/E High/Low	Earnings	PER SHARE ($) Dividends	Book Value
12/17	40.05	22 16	2.05	0.96	25.28
12/16	42.55	20 12	2.13	0.88	21.87
12/15	29.07	16 12	1.90	0.80	20.92
12/14	27.82	16 13	1.87	0.64	19.85
12/13	28.37	15 8	1.96	0.54	18.15
Annual Growth	**9.0%**	**— —**	**1.1%**	**15.5%**	**8.6%**

First Merchants Corp

First Merchants is the holding company that owns First Merchants Bank which operates some 120 branches in Indiana Illinois and western Ohio. Through its Lafayette Bank & Trust and First Merchants Private Wealth Advisors divisions the bank provides standard consumer and commercial banking services including checking and savings accounts CDs check cards and consumer commercial agricultural and real estate mortgage loans. First Merchants also provides trust and asset management services. Founded in 1982 First Merchants has nearly $9.4 billion worth of consolidated assets.

Operations

Real estate loans made up about 70% of First Merchants's loan portfolio while commercial and industrial agricultural and consumer loans account for the remainder of the bank's lending activity.

Geographic Reach

Muncie Indiana-based First Merchants's 120-plus bank branches are located across Indiana and in two counties each in Illinois and Ohio.

Sales and Marketing

First Merchants's marketing expense was $3.73 million in 2017 $3 million (2016) and $3.5 million (2015).

Financial Performance

Revenue jumped by 19% to $348.2 million in 2017 driven by higher interest income from more organic and inorganic loan business and more investment security income following the bank's recent acquisitions. The bank also collected significantly more non-interest income from deposit account service charges electronic card fees and insurance-related gains as it grew its customer base through acquisitions. Higher revenue drove the bank's net income up 18% to $96 million.

Total cash on hand at the end of fiscal 2017 stood at $154.9 million which was $27 million higher than cash at the start of the year. Cash from operations contributed $126 million and cash generated through financing activities added $535.8 while investments in securities and other uses used $635.3 million.

Strategy

A key part of the First Merchants's growth strategy is to expand geographically through acquisitions of small community banks operating in its key Indiana Illinois and western Ohio markets.

In 2017 and 2018 First Merchants added more nearly 3 dozen branches to its banking network after acquiring Michigan-based Monroe Bank & Trust Ohio-based Arlington Bank and Independent Alliance Banks located in Indiana. The bank has in recent years acquired 1-2 community banks operating in these states each year often adding a handful of branches as well as loans and other assets through each transaction.

Mergers and Acquisitions

In 2018 First Merchants acquired MBT Financial Corporation the holding company for Monroe Bank & Trust and its 20 branches serving Monroe Michigan and the southeastern Michigan area.

In 2017 First Merchants bought Columbus Ohio-based Arlington Bank. for $82.6 million. The same year it spent $238.8 million to acquire a majority stake in Independent Alliance Banks and IAB's 16 banking centers located in and around Fort Wayne Indiana.

EXECUTIVES

EVP and CFO, Mark K. Hardwick, age 47, $317,347 total compensation

CTO, Stephan H. Fluhler, $205,268 total compensation

President and CEO, Michael C. (Mike) Rechin, age 59, $502,181 total compensation

EVP and Chief Banking Officer, Michael J. (Mike) Stewart, age 52, $310,077 total compensation

EVP and Chief Credit Officer, John J. Martin, age 51, $249,193 total compensation

SVP and Chief Risk Officer, Jeffery B. Lorentson

Vice President, Brad Wise

First Vice President and Director Investor Relations, David Ortega

Vice President oF marketing, Deanne Beard

Vice President, Tom Dunson

Vice President of Loans, Christopher Allen

Vice President Marketing Manager, Dana Talaga

Vice President, Lentz Gregory

Executive Vice President Mortgage Operations, Debra Rynearson

Vice President and Purchasing Director, Lisa Brothers

Senior Vice President Chief Accounting Officer, Jami Bradshaw

Vice President, Joseph Keyler

Vice President, Alex Jones

Assistant Vice President Relationship Manager, Michael Kahne

Vice President, Margaret Hoke

Avp Review Appraiser, Joanilla Barker

Vice President Manager Small Business Credit, Robert Spencer

Vice President Business Banking, Chris Chatfield

Senior Vice President Chief Sales Officer Lakeshore Region, Dale Clapp

Senior Vice President and Director of Human Resources, Kim A Ellington

Vice President Retail Market Leader, Roberta Salway
Vice President Structured Finance, Dave Decraene
Vice President Retail Lending Leader, Jill Engerer
Assistant Vice President, Tammy Hall
First Vice President, Mark Stevenson
Vice President, Jeffrey Lorentson
Vice President, Josh McKenney
ASSISTANT VICE PRESIDENT, Jacob Crouch
Vice President, Adam Treibic
VICE PRESIDENT MANAGER MORTGAGE SALES, Elizabeth Chenore
Assistant Vice President Business Banking Officer, Duane Kamminga
Assistant Vice President, Jeffrey Chadwell
VICE PRESIDENT HUMAN RESOURCES MANAGER, Agnes Lasics
ASSISTANT VICE PRESIDENT, Rob Garrett
VICE PRESIDENT, William Robertson
VICE PRESIDENT AND CLIENT ADVISOR, Rita K Smith
VICE PRESIDENT, Benjamin J Hartings
ASSISTANT VICE PRESIDENT MANAGER FACILITIES PROJECTS AND PLANNING, Lindsay S Sweet
VICE PRESIDENT RELATIONSHIP MANAGER III, Kevin M Orourke
Vice President Regional Sales Manager Muncie East and Ohio Region, Scott Vermillion
Vice President, Bill Robertson
Vice President Manager Commercial Lending, Scott Casbon
VICE PRESIDENT, Benjamin Hartings
Senior Vice President, Joseph Peterson
ASSISTANT VICE PRESIDENT MANAGER FACILITIES PROJECTS AND PLANNING, Lindsay Sweet
First Vice President Director Talent Development, Sharissa Ulrey
Vice President, Hohl Matt
Board Member, Terry Walker
Chairman, Charles E. Schalliol, age 71
Board Member, Patrick Sherman
Auditors: BKD, LLP

LOCATIONS

HQ: First Merchants Corp
200 East Jackson Street, Muncie, IN 47305-2814
Phone: 765 747-1500
Web: www.firstmerchants.com

PRODUCTS/OPERATIONS

2017 Sales

	$ mil.	% of total
Interest		
Loans	274.4	71
Investment Securities	38.9	10
Federal Reserve and Federal Home Loan Bank stock	.9	-
Interest Expense/Other	(36.9)	-
Non-interest		
Service charges on deposits	18.7	5
Fiduciary activities	11.6	3
Other customer fees	20.9	5
Earnings on cash surrender value of life insurance	3.9	1
Net gains and fees on sales of loans	7.6	2
Net realized gains on sales of available for sale securities	2.6	1
Others	5.7	2
Total	348.3	100

COMPETITORS

Ameriana Bancorp
Bank of America
Citigroup
Harris
JPMorgan Chase
MutualFirst Financial
NorthWest Indiana Bancorp
Old National Bancorp
STAR Financial Group
U.S. Bancorp

HISTORICAL FINANCIALS

Company Type: Public

Income Statement
FYE: December 31

	ASSETS ($ mil.)	NET INCOME ($ mil.)	INCOME AS % OF ASSETS	EMPLOYEES
12/17	9,367.4	96.0	1.0%	1,684
12/16	7,211.6	81.0	1.1%	1,449
12/15	6,761.0	65.3	1.0%	1,529
12/14	5,824.1	60.1	1.0%	1,415
12/13	5,437.2	44.5	0.8%	1,449
Annual Growth	14.6%	21.2%	—	3.8%

2017 Year-End Financials

Return on assets: 1.1%
Return on equity: 8.7%
Long-term debt ($ mil.): —
No. of shares (mil.): 49.1
Sales ($ mil): 385.9

Dividends
Yield: 0.0%
Payout: 32.5%
Market value ($ mil.): 2,068.0

	STOCK PRICE ($) FY Close	P/E High/Low	PER SHARE ($) Earnings	Dividends	Book Value
12/17	42.06	21 17	2.12	0.69	26.52
12/16	37.65	19 11	1.98	0.54	22.04
12/15	25.42	16 13	1.72	0.41	20.92
12/14	22.75	14 12	1.65	0.29	19.29
12/13	22.72	16 10	1.41	0.18	17.68
Annual Growth	16.6%	— —	10.7%	39.9%	10.7%

First Mid-Illinois Bancshares Inc

Money doesn't grow on trees so when farmers in Illinois need a little cash they turn to First Mid-Illinois Bank & Trust. The primary subsidiary of First Mid-Illinois Bancshares is a major supplier of farm credit (including real estate machinery and production loans; inventory financing; and lines of credit) in its market area. In addition to agricultural loans the bank offers commercial consumer and real estate lending. It also provides deposit products such as savings and checking accounts plus trust and investment services through a partnership with Raymond James. First Mid-Illinois Bank & Trust has about 40 branches.Other subsidiaries provide data processing services and insurance products and services.

First Mid-Illinois experienced a 12% increase in revenue in 2011 and net income grew by nearly 30% that year. Growth was attributed to an increase in the size of the company's balance sheet and lower interest rates on deposit balances which resulted in less interest expense. The company also has been growing geographically. In 2010 it acquired 10 branches in northern Illinois that belonged to First Banks. The deal helped First Mid-Illinois expand its footprint but it also added to its deposit base by gaining new customers.

The company is focused on growing business operating and real estate loans. Another area of focus is growing its commercial and retail deposit base. The company's wealth management business has directed its attention to estate planning investment and farm management services. The com-

pany's insurance arm has a strategy to increase property and casualty insurance for businesses and individuals.

EXECUTIVES

Vice President Branch Operations and Cashier, Rhonda Rawlings
Senior Vice President Of Business Development, Clay Dean
Senior Management (Senior Vice President General Manager Director), Jason Tucker
Vice President And Chief Audit Executive, Melissa Wilhelm
Assistant Vice President Mortgage Lending, Mary White
SENIOR VICE PRESIDENT, Andrew Zavarella
Assistant Vice President And Dep Statement Services, Joan Kirk
Assistant Vice President Mortgage Loan Administration, Sue Radloff
Vice President, Nancy Zike
Vice President Director of Marketing, Laura Zuhone
Vice President, Gant Harper
Assistant Vice President Human Resource Generalist II, Tyla Larson
Auditors: BKD, LLP

LOCATIONS

HQ: First Mid-Illinois Bancshares Inc
1421 Charleston Avenue, Mattoon, IL 61938
Phone: 217 234-7454   Fax: 217 258-0485
Web: www.firstmid.com

PRODUCTS/OPERATIONS

Selected Subsidiaries
The Checkley Agency Inc. (dba First Mid Insurance Group)
First Mid-Illinois Bank & Trust N.A.
First Mid-Illinois Statutory Trust I II
Mid-Illinois Data Services Inc.

COMPETITORS

Bank of America
Fifth Third
First BancTrust
First Busey
Northern Trust
PNC Financial
U.S. Bancorp

HISTORICAL FINANCIALS

Company Type: Public

Income Statement
FYE: December 31

	ASSETS ($ mil.)	NET INCOME ($ mil.)	INCOME AS % OF ASSETS	EMPLOYEES
12/17	2,841.5	26.6	0.9%	592
12/16	2,884.5	21.8	0.8%	598
12/15	2,114.5	16.5	0.8%	513
12/14	1,607.1	15.4	1.0%	400
12/13	1,605.5	14.7	0.9%	406
Annual Growth	15.3%	16.0%	—	9.9%

2017 Year-End Financials

Return on assets: 0.9%
Return on equity: 9.0%
Long-term debt ($ mil.): —
No. of shares (mil.): 12.6
Sales ($ mil): 129.8

Dividends
Yield: 0.0%
Payout: 30.9%
Market value ($ mil.): 488.0

	STOCK PRICE ($)	P/E	PER SHARE ($)		
	FY Close	High/Low	Earnings	Dividends	Book Value
12/17	38.54	20 14	2.13	0.66	24.32
12/16	34.00	17 11	2.05	0.62	22.51
12/15	26.00	14 10	1.81	0.59	24.25
12/14	18.55	13 9	1.85	0.55	23.45
12/13	22.00	14 12	1.73	0.46	25.39
Annual Growth	15.0%	— —	5.3%	9.4%	(1.1%)

First Midwest Bancorp, Inc. (Naperville, IL)

There's a lot of cabbage in corn country. Just ask First Midwest Bancorp the holding company for First Midwest Bank. Through nearly 110 branches the bank mainly serves suburban Chicago though its market extends into central and western Illinois and neighboring portions of Iowa and Indiana. Focusing on area small to mid-sized businesses it offers deposit products loans trust services wealth management insurance and retirement plan services; it has $7.2 billion of client trust and investment assets under management. Commercial real estate loans account for more than half of the company's portfolio.

Operations

More than 85% of the company's loan portfolio consists of corporate loans (the majority of which are secured by commercial real estate) while the remainder of the portfolio consists of consumer loans (which include home equity loans lines of credit and 1-4 family mortgages). Illustrative of its commitment to business lending First Midwest does not originate sub-prime lending or investment banking activities.

The bank's subsidiaries include: equipment leasing and commercial financier First Midwest Equipment Finance Co.; investment security managers First Midwest Securities Management LLC and First Midwest Holdings Inc.; Section 8 housing venture investor LIH Holdings; and Synergy Property Holdings LLC which manages the bank's OREO properties.

Geographic Reach

The company operates 109 banking offices largely located in various communities throughout the suburban metropolitan Chicago market as well as central and western Illinois and eastern Iowa. It owns 145 automated teller machines most of which are housed at banking locations. First Midwest and Allpoint together provide access to more than 50000 free ATMs worldwide.

Sales and Marketing

The company serves different industry segments including manufacturing health care pharmaceutical higher education wholesale and retail trade service and agricultural. First Midwest spent about $8.2 million on advertising and promotions in 2014 up from $7.8 million in 2013 and $5.1 million in 2012.

Financial Performance

Following a modest rebound in 2013 First Midwest's revenue in 2014 dipped by less than 1% to $426.48 million mostly because of a 76% drop in net securities gains as the bank in 2013 was able to collect a non-recurring equity investment sale gain of $34 million. Lower mortgage banking income resulting from lower market pricing also contributed to the modest dip in revenue. The bank did however report higher interest income as its loan business grew higher wealth management fees with growth in assets under management and higher service charge fees as deposit accounts grew.

After healthy profit growth in 2013 net income fell by nearly 13% to $69.31 million in 2014 mostly as the bank incurred higher costs associated with the acquisition and integration of Popular and Great Lakes and because the bank had higher loan loss provision expenses. In 2013 First Midwest had posted a large jump in net income thanks to higher revenue a decrease in the provision for loan and covered loan losses and lower interest and non-interest expenses.

Continuing its annual cash declines the bank's operations provided $122.93 million (or 10% less cash than in 2013) mostly due to lower earnings.

Mergers and Acquisitions

In 2014 First Midwest acquired south suburban Chicago-based Great Lakes Financial Resources Inc. the holding company for Great Lakes Bank National Association. As part of the $58 million deal the company gained eight locations $490 million in deposits and $234 million in loans.

That year it also bought the Chicago banking operations of Popular Community Bank a subsidiary of Popular Inc. (12 full-service retail branches and its small business and middle market commercial lending activities in the Chicago metropolitan area which included $726 million in deposits and $562 million in loans).

In early 2017 the company completed the acquisition of another Chicago-area bank Standard Bancshares. The deal will add 35 branches $2.3 billion in assets $2.1 billion in deposits and $1.9 million in loans.

Company Background

First Midwest capitalized on the rash of bank failures that have occurred in the Chicago area amid the recessionary economy. Its relative financial soundness put it in a position to acquire three failed Illinois banks through separate FDIC-facilitated transactions in 2009 and 2010: First DuPage Bank Peotone Bank and Trust and Palos Bank and Trust. The deals which included loss-sharing agreements with the regulator added a total of nearly 10 branches. In 2012 the company acquired the deposits and loans of Waukegan Savings Bank in another FDIC-assisted deal that added two more branches to its network. First Midwest will continue to consider acquisitions of failed banks in the Chicago area.

EXECUTIVES

President CEO and Director; Chairman and CEO First Midwest Bank, Michael L. Scudder, age 57, $750,000 total compensation

EVP CIO and COO First Midwest Bank, Kent S. Belasco, age 67, $224,000 total compensation

EVP and CFO First Midwest Bancorp Inc. & First Midwest Bank, Paul F. Clemens, age 66, $376,000 total compensation

SEVP and COO; Vice Chairman and President First Midwest Bank, Mark G. Sander, age 59, $545,000 total compensation

EVP and Treasurer First Midwest Bancorp Inc. & First Midwest Bank, James P. Hotchkiss, age 61

EVP and Chief Risk Officer First Midwest Bancorp Inc. & First Midwest Bank, Kevin L. Moffitt

EVP Corporate Secretary and General Counsel, Nicholas J. Chulos

Vice President, Juan Cortez

Executive Vice President Bank Operations Director, David Kullander

Executive Vice President and Director Commercial Banking First Midwest Bank, Victor Carapella

Vice President, Ed Garner

Senior Vice President, Rob Schultz

Executive Vice President Director of Employee Resources First Midwest Bank, Caryn Guinta

Vice President, Cheri Rubocki

Vice President Administration, Connie Steinke

Senior Vice President, Carlos Touza

Vice President, Jodie Speers

Senior Vice President Director Applic, John Hudak

Senior Vice President Financial Planning, Rich Padula

Vice President Area Sales Manager, Evan Klee

Assistant Vice President Branch Manager, Josie Pacheco

Vice President Public Funds, Susan Wade

Vice President, Tami Johnson

Vice President, Chris Sawyer

Senior Vice President BusinessBanking Group Manager, Chris Esposito

Vice President, Brian Ruos

Assistant Vice President Branch Manager II, Michael Barbari

Vice President Treasury Management, Ala Swais

Vice President, Phillip Greiner

Assistant Vice President, Megan Miller

Vice President Business Banking, Dave Kurow

Vice President, Chad Lyons

Vice President Commercial Banking, Abdullah Tadros

Vice President Community Banking Officer Community Real Estate Group, Richard Rischall

Senior Vice President and Commercial Banking Manager, John Twohy

Executive Vice President CHRO, Michelle Hoskins

Vice President, Angela Hart

Executive Vice President Chief Credit Officer, Mike Kozak

Senior Vice President Commercial Banking, James Schramm

Assistant Vice President, Andrew Trasatt

Vice President Business Banking, Tony Martino

Vice President Sales Regional Sales Manager, Joe Creamons

Vice President, Tim Woodcock

Vice President, Michael Chin

Vice President ABL Relationship Manager Business Credit, Thomas Brennan

Senior Vice President, Tom Neylon

Assistant Vice President Bank Manager, Giuseppe Veneziano

Senior Vice President, Aaron Markos

Vice President CRA Manager, Mary Morstadt

Vice President, Robert Rodie

Senior Vice President Manager Business Banking, Brian Burke

Vice President Group Sales Manager, Joseph Palazzolo

Vice President Senior Human Resources Consultant, Anita Dwyer

Senior Vice President, Phil Ostroski

Senior Vice President, Neil Prendergast

AVP HR Consultant (Business Partner), Amy Crabbe

Senior Vice President Healthcare Banking Coverage Group, James Goody

Executive Vice President And Senior Counsel, James Carroll
Chairman, Robert P. (Bob) O'Meara, age 80
Board Member, Phupinder Gill
Board Member, Frank Modruson
Board Member, Kathryn Hayley
Auditors: Ernst & Young LLP

LOCATIONS

HQ: First Midwest Bancorp, Inc. (Naperville, IL)
8750 West Bryn Mawr Avenue, Suite 1300, Chicago, IL 60631-3655
Phone: 703 831-7483
Web: www.firstmidwest.com

PRODUCTS/OPERATIONS

2016

	$ mil.	% of total
Interest Income		
Loans	338.0	63
Investment securities - taxable	28.7	5
Investment securities - tax-exempt	8.7	2
Other short-term investments	2.9	0
Noninterest Income		
Service charges on deposit accounts	40.7	8
Wealth management fees	33.1	6
Card-based fees	29.1	5
Merchant servicing fees	12.5	2
Mortgage banking income	10.1	2
Capital market products income	10.0	2
Other service charges commissions and fees	9.6	2
Net gain on sale-leaseback transaction	5.5	1
BOLI income	3.7	1
Net securities gains	1.4	0
Other income	3.6	1
Total	**537.6**	**100**

COMPETITORS

Bank of America	Meta Financial Group
BankFinancial	Northern Trust
Cummins-Allison	PrivateBank
Fifth Third	QCR Holdings
First Busey	West Suburban Bancorp
Harris	Wintrust Financial
JPMorgan Chase	

HISTORICAL FINANCIALS

Company Type: Public

Income Statement — FYE: December 31

	ASSETS ($ mil.)	NET INCOME ($ mil.)	INCOME AS % OF ASSETS	EMPLOYEES
12/17	14,077.0	98.3	0.7%	2,152
12/16	11,422.5	92.3	0.8%	1,882
12/15	9,732.6	82.0	0.8%	1,790
12/14	9,445.1	69.3	0.7%	1,788
12/13	8,253.4	79.3	1.0%	1,647
Annual Growth	**14.3%**	**5.5%**	**—**	**6.9%**

2017 Year-End Financials

Return on assets: 0.7%	Dividends
Return on equity: 6.3%	Yield: 0.0%
Long-term debt ($ mil.): —	Payout: 40.6%
No. of shares (mil.): 102.7	Market value ($ mil.): 2,466.0
Sales ($ mil): 672.8	

	STOCK PRICE ($) FY Close	P/E High/Low		PER SHARE ($) Earnings	Dividends	Book Value
12/17	24.01	27	22	0.96	0.39	18.16
12/16	25.23	22	14	1.14	0.36	15.46
12/15	18.43	19	15	1.05	0.36	14.70
12/14	17.11	19	17	0.92	0.31	14.17
12/13	17.53	17	11	1.06	0.16	13.34
Annual Growth	**8.2%**	**—**	**—**	**(2.4%)**	**25.0%**	**8.0%**

First of Long Island Corp

When it comes to banking The First of Long Island wants to be the first thing on Long Islanders' minds. The company owns The First National Bank of Long Island which offers a variety of lending investment and deposit services through around 45 commercial and retail branches on New York's Long Island and the boroughs of Manhattan and Queens. Residential and Commercial Mortgages (particularly tied to multifamily properties) make up more than 90% of the bank's loan portfolio though the bank also writes revolving home equity business and consumer loans. Its two bank subsidiaries include insurance agency The First of Long Island Agency and investment firm FNY Service.

Operations

The First National Bank of Long Island also operates an investment management division that offers trust and investment management estate and custody services.

The bank makes more than 90% of its revenue from interest income. About 70% of its total revenue came from loan interest during 2015 while another 21% came from interest income on taxable and non-taxable investment securities. The rest of its revenue came from deposit account service charges (3% of revenue) investment management division income (2%) gains on securities sales (1%) and other income sources.

Geographic Reach

The New York City-based bank operated 45 branches at the end of 2015 including 41 in Long Island and two each in Manhattan and Queens.

Sales and Marketing

First serves individuals professionals corporations institutions and governmental clients through its branches.

The bank markets its services through customer service personnel tele-sales lending relationships referral sources and advertisements. It spent $877000 on marketing during 2015 compared to $927000 and $670000 in 2014 and 2013 respectively.

Financial Performance

The First of Long Island's annual revenues have risen more than 20% since 2011 as its loan assets have more than doubled to $2.25 billion. Meanwhile the bank's profits have swelled more than 30% thanks to revenue growth and low interest expenses.

First's revenue jumped 13% to $101 million during 2015 mostly thanks to higher interest income as its average loan balances grew 26% and as its non-taxable security assets rose by 6%. The bulk of the loan asset growth was tied to residential mortgages while most of the rest came from multifamily commercial mortgage growth.

Double-digit revenue growth drove the bank's net income up 12% to $25.9 million. First's operating cash levels dipped 1% to $35 million despite the rise in earnings due to unfavorable working capital changes mostly related to a decrease in accrued expenses and other liabilities.

Strategy

The bank has been opening new branches utilizing "effective relationship management" using targeted solicitation efforts and expanding its product and service offerings to boost its loan and deposit business in recent years.

In early 2016 the company planned to open between eight and 12 more The First National Bank of Long Island branches in Queens after opening two branches there in Howard Beach and Whitestone in 2015. It also planned to open branches in Brooklyn. Expanding its branch network on Long Island the bank in 2015 launched new branches in Patchogue and Melville.

EXECUTIVES

SVP and EVP and Senior Lending Officer Commercial Lending The First National Bank Long Island, Donald L. Manfredonia, age 66, $222,500 total compensation
SVP, Richard Kick, age 60, $230,100 total compensation
SVP and Treasurer; EVP CFO and Cashier The First National Bank of Long Island, Mark D. Curtis, age 63, $242,700 total compensation
President and CEO The First of Long Island Corporation and The First National Bank of Long Island, Michael N. Vittorio, age 65, $468,000 total compensation
SVP and Secretary; SEVP The First National Bank of Long Island, Sallyanne K. Ballweg, age 62, $264,000 total compensation
EVP and Chief Risk Officer First National Bank of Long Island, Christopher Becker
Vice President, Jane Reed
Assistant Vice President, Giuseppe Sparacino
Vice President, Robert Eisen
Vice President Sales Manager, Rick Hughes
Vice President Director Of Human Resources, Sue Hempton
Vice President, Susan Donovan
Vice President Financial Reporting Manager, Dina Cascione
Vice President Of Marketing, Laura Ierulli
Vice President and Controller, Maria Doyle
Chairman The First of Long Island Corporation and The First National Bank of Long Island, Walter C. Teagle, age 68
Auditors: Crowe Horwath LLP

LOCATIONS

HQ: First of Long Island Corp
10 Glen Head Road, Glen Head, NY 11545
Phone: 516 671-4900
Web: www.fnbli.com

PRODUCTS/OPERATIONS

2015 Sales

	$ mil.	% of total
Interest and dividend income:		
Loans	70.6	70
Investment securities		
Taxable	8.0	8
Nontaxable	13.6	13
Noninterest income		
Investment Management Division income	2.0	2
Service charges on deposit accounts	2.6	3
Net gains on sales of securities	1.3	1
Other	2.8	3
Total	**100.9**	**100**

Selected Services:

Checking
Savings
Saving for Retirement & Education
Online Banking & Bill Pay
FirstLink Online Banking
Quicken/Quickbooks
FirstPay Bill Pay
PopMoney
Account to Account Transfers

COMPETITORS

Astoria Financial	JPMorgan Chase
Bank of America	New York Community
Citibank	Bancorp
Dime Community	Ridgewood Savings Bank
Bancshares	Suffolk Bancorp
Flushing Financial	

HISTORICAL FINANCIALS

Company Type: Public

Income Statement

FYE: December 31

	ASSETS ($ mil.)	NET INCOME ($ mil.)	INCOME AS % OF ASSETS	EMPLOYEES
12/17	3,894.7	35.1	0.9%	333
12/16	3,510.3	30.8	0.9%	314
12/15	3,130.3	25.8	0.8%	302
12/14	2,721.4	23.0	0.8%	284
12/13	2,399.8	21.3	0.9%	260
Annual Growth	12.9%	13.3%	—	6.4%

2017 Year-End Financials

Return on assets: 0.9%	Dividends
Return on equity: 10.6%	Yield: 0.0%
Long-term debt ($ mil.): —	Payout: 40.5%
No. of shares (mil.): 24.6	Market value ($ mil.): 703.0
Sales ($ mil): 125.0	

	STOCK PRICE ($) FY Close	P/E High/Low		PER SHARE ($) Earnings	Dividends	Book Value
12/17	28.50	22	18	1.43	0.58	14.37
12/16	28.55	30	19	1.34	0.55	12.90
12/15	30.00	26	19	1.22	0.52	11.85
12/14	28.37	39	21	1.10	0.47	11.20
12/13	42.87	41	27	1.03	0.45	10.04
Annual Growth	(9.7%)	—	—	8.5%	6.4%	9.4%

First Savings Financial Group Inc

First Savings Financial Group was formed in 2008 to be the holding company for First Savings Bank a community bank serving consumers and small businesses in southern Indiana. Through more than a dozen branches the bank offers standard deposit services like savings checking and retirement accounts as well as a variety of lending services. One- to four- family residential loans make up about 60% of First Savings Bank's loan portfolio; other loans in the bank's portfolio include commercial real estate construction consumer and commercial business. In 2012 First Savings Financial expanded its footprint by acquiring the four Indiana branches of First Financial Service Corporation.

Founded in 1937 as First Federal Savings and Loan First Savings Bank changed its name in 1996 and went public in 2008 as part of a conversion from a mutual savings bank to a stock form of ownership.

EXECUTIVES

President CEO and Director, Larry W. Myers, age 57, $174,100 total compensation
COO and Director, John P. Lawson Jr., age 58, $121,800 total compensation
Chairman, Michael F. Ludden, age 66
CFO, Anthony A. (Tony) Schoen
Assistant VP and Branch Manager Jeffersonville, Nancy Boman
Executive Vice President; Director; Area President of First Savings Bank, Samuel Eckart
President CEO and Director, Larry W. Myers, age 57
COO and Director, John P. Lawson Jr., age 58
Director, Charles E. Becht Jr., age 67
Director, Cecile A. Blau, age 70
Director, Gerald Wayne Clapp Jr., age 66
Director, Douglas A. York, age 53
Independent Director, Frank Czeschin
Auditors: Monroe Shine & Co., Inc.

LOCATIONS

HQ: First Savings Financial Group Inc
501 East Lewis & Clark Parkway, Clarksville, IN 47129
Phone: 812 283-0724
Web: www.fsbbank.net

COMPETITORS

First Capital	Regions Financial
JPMorgan Chase	River Valley Bancorp
PNC Financial	

HISTORICAL FINANCIALS

Company Type: Public

Income Statement

FYE: September 30

	ASSETS ($ mil.)	NET INCOME ($ mil.)	INCOME AS % OF ASSETS	EMPLOYEES
09/18	1,034.4	10.9	1.1%	364
09/17	891.1	9.3	1.0%	201
09/16	796.5	7.9	1.0%	178
09/15	749.9	6.7	0.9%	170
09/14	713.1	5.3	0.8%	168
Annual Growth	9.7%	19.3%	—	21.3%

2018 Year-End Financials

Return on assets: 1.1%	Dividends
Return on equity: 11.3%	Yield: 0.0%
Long-term debt ($ mil.): —	Payout: 12.8%
No. of shares (mil.): 2.2	Market value ($ mil.): 156.0
Sales ($ mil): 55.4	

	STOCK PRICE ($) FY Close	P/E High/Low		PER SHARE ($) Earnings	Dividends	Book Value
09/18	68.28	15	11	4.60	0.59	43.11
09/17	53.40	13	8	3.97	0.55	41.52
09/16	36.16	10	9	3.41	0.51	39.27
09/15	34.00	11	8	2.93	0.47	43.21
09/14	24.96	10	9	2.34	0.43	40.10
Annual Growth	28.6%	—	—	18.4%	8.2%	1.8%

FirstCash Inc

FirstCash operates more than 2000 pawnshops and cash advance stores in the US Mexico El Salvador and Guatemala. The company lends money secured by such personal property as jewelry electronics tools sporting goods musical equipment and firearms (in select markets). Its First Cash Pawn and Famous Pawn shops sell merchandise forfeited by borrowers. The company's Fast Cash Advance locations offer short-term and payday loans. The company exited the check cashing business in late 2014 when it discontinued its Cash & Go joint venture. The company then named First Cash Financial Services merged with US pawn rival Cash America International in September 2016.

Change in Company Type

In 2016 First Cash Financial Services and Cash America International completed a $2.4 billion "merger of equals" deal to form a new company FirstCash. The merger combined First Cash Financial's large store count in Mexico and presence in Guatemala and El Salvador with Cash America's large store count in the US creating one of the largest pawn store networks in the US and Latin America with more than 2000 stores across four countries.

Operations

Prior to the merger First Cash Financial Services made most of its money from merchandise sales. About 63% of its total revenue came from retail merchandise sales of collateral forfeitures and over-the-counter store purchases during 2015 while another 28% of revenue came from pawn loan fees. The rest of its income came from wholesale scrap jewelry revenue (5% of revenue) and consumer loan and credit services fees (4%).

Geographic Reach

In 2015 Texas-based First Cash Financial Services operated 705 stores in 29 states in Mexico another 338 shops in 14 US states (with its largest markets being in Texas Colorado Maryland and the Carolinas) and 32 stores in Guatemala. The company generated 52% of its revenue from its shops in the Latin American countries during 2015 with most of that coming from Mexico.

Sales and Marketing

The company has been cutting back on its advertising spend in recent years. It spent $679000 on advertising during 2015 down from $1.33 million and $2.24 million in 2014 and 2013 respectively.

Financial Performance

Fueled by rapid store expansion and growing merchandise sales annual revenues and profits have been trending higher over the past few years.

The company's revenue dipped 1% to $704.6 million during 2015 however mostly due to a decline in wholesale scrap jewelry sales as it sold less gold and as gold prices fell from $1268 per ounce to just $1145 per ounce for the year. Its consumer loan income shrank 24% as it continued to wind down its Cash & Go business and due to increased competition and regulation.

Revenue declines in 2015 combined with an uptick in interest expenses and store operating expenses from newly acquired or opened stores made net income plunge 29% to $60.7 million for the year. Operating cash levels tumbled 5% to $92.7 million in 2015 as cash-based earnings declined.

Strategy

FirstCash continues to expand its store network (either organically or by acquiring existing store fronts) especially in Mexico and broader Latin America to boost its business. Mexico has been a ripe market for years as the country's 6000 to

8000 competing pawn stores are mostly jewelry-focused businesses. The company also continues grow in the US by opening new shops or buying individual pawn shops.

As part of its store expansion strategy the company made its largest move into Latin America to date in early 2016 after buying 211 full-service pawn stores mostly in Mexico but also in the new markets of Guatemala and El Salvador. It also bought 33 US pawn stores in six US states during 2015.

To reduce its risk to new regulations associated with payday lending First Cash began winding down its short term loan and credit business in the US in 2014 through the discontinuation of Cash & Go which operated 37 check cashing and financial services kiosks located inside convenience stores in Texas.

Mergers and Acquisitions

In September 2016 First Cash Financial Services merged with US rival Cash America International to form FirstCash.

In January 2016 the company expanded into Mexico and entered two new Latin American markets after buying 211 full-service pawn stores in the region including 166 pawn shops in Mexico 32 pawn locations in Guatemala (via its $10.45 million-acquisition of Maxi Prenda Guatemala S.A.) and 13 pawn locations in El Salvador.

In June 2015 First Cash bought 24 large-format pawn shops in North Carolina along with less than a handful of additional locations in Virginia and Kentucky.

In October 2014 First Cash acquired a chain of 15 large-format pawn stores located in Kentucky Missouri Tennessee and South Carolina. The purchase came on the heels of its purchase of 47 pawn shops in Mexico Colorado and Texas in August.

In 2012 First Cash announced a larger US deal with the acquisition of a 24-store chain of pawn stores operating under the Mister Money brand. The $25.5 million transaction expanded First Cash's geographic footprint in Colorado Kentucky Wyoming and Nebraska. The company later arranged to purchase 16 pawn stores operating as Fast Cash Pawn in the Denver area. That deal carried an approximately $46 million price tag.

Company Background

The company first expanded its presence into Mexico in 2008 with the acquisition of Presta Max a chain of 16 pawn shops in southern Mexico.

HISTORY

First Cash grew from a single pawnshop in Dallas. John Payne traded some land in Colorado for the store after selling his Dallas bank in 1979. He and his wife ran the shop until 1985 when they sold it and built a new shop in the suburbs aiming to achieve the ambience of a video store.

It was an opportune moment: The Texas economy particularly the banking industry was just beginning its slide. Payne (who later left the company) incorporated First Cash in 1988 and brought in professional management under former banker Rick Powell in 1990.

Eight-store First Cash went public in 1991. Acquisitions and expansions included the 1994 purchase of a Baltimore/Washington DC area chain. The next year First Cash upgraded its computers to improve inventory control and loan valuations and became the first major pawn chain to stop selling or making loans on handguns.

In 1996 and 1997 First Cash added stores in Maryland and Texas. The next year it bought 10-store chain JB Pawn (from a brother of First Cash director Richard Burke) and about 20 individual shops. First Cash also moved into check-cashing buying 11-store Miraglia.

To reflect the diversification the company changed its name to First Cash Financial Services in early 1999. That year First Cash joined other pawnbrokers and short-term lenders in moving into Mexico. In 2000 First Cash partnered with Pawnbroker.com to provide online financial and support services to pawn shops.

First Cash discontinued its auto loan operations in 2008 two years after purchasing dealer and lender Auto Master. In the midst of a worldwide credit crunch First Cash sold Auto Master to Minneapolis-based Interstate Auto Group (dba CarHop).

The company first expanded its presence into Mexico in 2008 with the acquisition of Presta Max a chain of 16 pawn shops in southern Mexico.

EXECUTIVES

Vice President Human Resources and Administration, Jan Hartz

Chairman President and CEO, Rick L. Wessel, age 59, $963,040 total compensation

EVP CFO Secretary and Treasurer, R. Douglas (Doug) Orr, age 57, $454,480 total compensation

General Counsel, Peter H. Watson, age 68, $386,250 total compensation

SVP Latin American Operations, Raul R. Ramos, age 51, $322,537 total compensation

SVP Store Development and Facilities, Sean D. Moore, age 40, $286,038 total compensation

Vice President Facility maintenance, Rick Work

Auditors: RSM US LLP

LOCATIONS

HQ: FirstCash Inc
1600 West 7th Street, Fort Worth, TX 76102
Phone: 817 335-1100
Web: www.firstcash.com

PRODUCTS/OPERATIONS

2015 Sales

	$ mil.	% of total
Retail merchandise	449.3	63
Pawn loan fees	195.4	28
Wholesale Scrap jewelry	32.0	5
Consumer loan and credit services fees	27.9	4
Total	**704.6**	**100**

Selected Subsidiaries

All Access Special Events LLC
American Loan Employee Services S.A. de C.V. (Mexico)
Cardplus Inc.
College Park Jewelers Inc.
Famous Pawn Inc.
FCFS MO Inc.
FCFS OK Inc.
FCFS SC Inc.
First Cash Corp.
First Cash Credit Ltd.
First Cash Inc.
First Cash Credit Management LLC
First Cash Ltd.
First Cash Management LLC
First Cash S.A. de C.V. (Mexico)
King Pawn Inc.
King Pawn II Inc.
Maryland Precious Metals Inc.
SHAC LLC
T.J. Unlimited LLC

COMPETITORS

ACE Cash Express	World Acceptance
EZCORP	Xponential

HISTORICAL FINANCIALS

Company Type: Public

Income Statement				FYE: December 31
	REVENUE ($ mil.)	NET INCOME ($ mil.)	NET PROFIT MARGIN	EMPLOYEES
12/18	1,780.8	153.2	8.6%	19,000
12/17	1,779.8	143.8	8.1%	17,000
12/16	1,088.3	60.1	5.5%	16,200
12/15	704.6	60.7	8.6%	8,600
12/14	712.8	85.1	11.9%	7,900
Annual Growth	25.7%	15.8%	—	24.5%

2018 Year-End Financials

Debt ratio: 28.0%
Return on equity: 10.9%
Cash ($ mil.): 71.7
Current ratio: 5.94
Long-term debt ($ mil.): 590.8

No. of shares (mil.): 43.6
Dividends
  Yield: 1.2%
  Payout: 24.2%
Market value ($ mil.): 3,155.0

	STOCK PRICE ($) FY Close	P/E High/Low	PER SHARE ($) Earnings	Dividends	Book Value
12/18	72.35	28 20	3.41	0.91	30.23
12/17	67.45	23 14	3.00	0.77	31.46
12/16	47.00	31 18	1.72	0.57	29.89
12/15	37.43	26 17	2.14	0.00	15.28
12/14	55.67	21 16	2.93	0.00	15.73
Annual Growth	6.8%		3.9%	—	17.7%

Five Below Inc

Five Below may be growing as quickly as its youthful clientele. Operating a fast-growing chain of specialty retail stores it sells a broad range of trend-right products all priced under $5. The company which targets teen and pre-teen girls and boys operates some 750 stores in shopping centers in 30-plus US states; it also operates an e-commerce site. Core merchandise includes fun but inexpensive items meant to entice teens such as jewelry and accessories novelty T-shirts casual footwear sports gear decor and crafts and mobile phone accessories. Five Below was founded in 2002.

Operations

Five Below has three categories of youth-oriented merchandise: leisure fashion and home and party and snack. Leisure is the largest segment accounting for about 50% of revenue and includes games electronics accessories and sporting goods among other products. Fashion and home (more than 30%) includes T-shirts personal accessories and beauty offerings while party and snack (nearly 20%) includes candy and beverages greeting cards and party goods.

Working with a large number of vendors allows the chain to switch products quickly as it tries to capitalize on the popular items of the moment. Its stores measure about 8000 square feet.

Geographic Reach

From its base in the Northeast (the company is headquartered in Philadelphia) Five Below has aggressively expanded into the Southeast and Midwest. With additional moves into Texas and California the company has stores in about 35 states across all regions of the country. Texas Pennsylvania and New York are its largest markets.

The company has distribution centers in Pedricktown New Jersey and Olive Branch Mississippi. It is building a new distribution center in Monroe County Georgia (just south of Atlanta).

Sales and Marketing

Five Below's marketing strategy includes traditional advertising in newspapers and on television as well as digital advertising and a growing social media presence. New store openings which are grouped by market to leverage the company's efforts generally include contests giveaways and signature events such as "Five Cent" hot dogs.

As its geography and store count has increased so has Five Below's spending on advertising. It spent $31 million $27 million and $22 million in fiscal years 2017 2016 and 2015 respectively.

Financial Performance

Amid a rapidly expanding network of stores Five Below has seen strong growth over the past five years. Revenue has more than doubled since fiscal 2014 (ended January 2015) and net income has more than tripled.

In fiscal 2017 (ended January 2018) the company reported revenue of $1.3 billion up more than 25% from the prior year. The results were driven primarily by new store openings (some 100 that year) but same-store sales were also up 6.5%.

Primarily as a result of the strong revenue growth net income was also up in fiscal 2017. It jumped more than 40% to $103 million.

Cash at the end of fiscal 2017 was $113 million an increase of $37 million from the prior year. Cash from operations contributed $167 million to the coffers while investing activities used $139 million mainly for purchases of investment securities. Financing activities added another $8 million from proceeds of exercise of stock options and vesting of restricted stock units.

Strategy

Like many deep-discount retailers Five Below is expanding its store base at a rapid clip. Indeed it added more than 100 new locations in fiscal 2017 (ended January 2018) with plans for 125 more in 2018. The company expects it can eventually build a store network across the US of some 2500 locations.

In addition to new store growth merchandising is also key to Five Below's strategy. It is very focused on its teen and pre-teen customer base stocking what it considers to be fun exciting and dynamic products at prices those customers can afford. The company works with hundreds of different vendors so it can monitor trends and quickly respond when products move into the mainstream. This pricing and selection strategy has helped Five Below withstand the Amazon effect by undercutting the online behemoth in price while creating a "treasure hunt" vibe (you never know what you might find) that attracts young shoppers to its stores.

E-commerce is not as important for Five Below as it is for some other retailers but the company is working to establish an online presence. It got a bit of late start as it didn't begin selling through its fivebelow.com site until August 2016 and is still developing its online capabilities and determining how to maintain the $5 and below price point.

Company Background

Five Below was founded in 2002 as Cheap Holdings by former CEO Thomas Vellios and David Schlessinger. The company changed its name to Five Below later in 2002 and went public in 2012.

EXECUTIVES

Chief Administrative Officer, Eric M. Specter, age 60, $500,000 total compensation
CFO Secretary and Treasurer, Kenneth R. Bull, age 55, $400,000 total compensation
President CEO and Director, Joel D. Anderson, age 53, $700,000 total compensation
EVP Merchandising, Michael F. Romanko, age 52, $450,000 total compensation
EVP Retail Operations, George Hill
Vice President Information Technology, Chris DeMeester
Operations Senior Vice President, Eugene Rosadino
Executive Vice President Real Estate, Linda Moser
Vice President of Information Technology, Robert Millman
Senior Vice President Marketing, David Makuen
Senior Vice President Human Resources, Bill Clark
Chairman, Thomas G. (Tom) Vellios, age 63
Auditors: KPMG LLP

LOCATIONS

HQ: Five Below Inc
701 Market Street, Suite 300, Philadelphia, PA 19106
Phone: 215 546-7909
Web: www.fivebelow.com

PRODUCTS/OPERATIONS

2017 Sales

	% of total
Leisure	51
Fashion & home	32
Party & snack	18
Total	**100**

COMPETITORS

Big Lots	Hot Topic
CVS	Kmart
Claire's Stores	Rite Aid
Dollar General	TJX Companies
Dollar Tree	Target Corporation
Family Dollar Stores	Wal-Mart
Forever 21	Walgreen

HISTORICAL FINANCIALS

Company Type: Public

Income Statement				FYE: February 3
	REVENUE ($ mil.)	NET INCOME ($ mil.)	NET PROFIT MARGIN	EMPLOYEES
02/18*	1,278.2	102.4	8.0%	12,100
01/17	1,000.4	71.8	7.2%	9,500
01/16	831.9	57.6	6.9%	7,600
01/15	680.2	48.0	7.1%	6,700
02/14	535.4	32.1	6.0%	5,500
Annual Growth	**24.3%**	**33.6%**	**—**	**21.8%**

*Fiscal year change

2018 Year-End Financials

Debt ratio: —	No. of shares (mil.): 55.4
Return on equity: 25.5%	Dividends
Cash ($ mil.): 112.6	Yield: —
Current ratio: 2.91	Payout: —
Long-term debt ($ mil.): —	Market value ($ mil.): 3,489.0

	STOCK PRICE ($) FY Close	P/E High/Low	PER SHARE ($)		
			Earnings	Dividends	Book Value
02/18*	62.94	39 20	1.84	0.00	8.27
01/17	37.60	40 25	1.30	0.00	6.04
01/16	35.23	38 26	1.05	0.00	4.48
01/15	33.32	52 37	0.88	0.00	3.20
02/14	36.65	92 60	0.59	0.00	2.16
Annual Growth	**14.5%**	**— —**	**32.9%**	**—**	**39.9%**

*Fiscal year change

FleetCor Technologies Inc

Helping companies manage motor fleets is at the core of FLEETCOR's mission. The company is a leading provider of fleet cards and payment processing services aimed at commercial and government fleets. Its cards carry the names Fuelman CFN Keyfuels CCS and Fuelcard. The fleet cards function like typical charge cards and can be used to purchase fuel and lodging. FLEETCOR tracks purchases to help manage employee spending. The company serves more than 500000 accounts and has millions of cards active in the US the UK and Brazil as well as 50 other countries around the world. Major customers include oil giants BP Shell and Speedway. The company fuels growth through acquisitions.

Operations

FLEETCOR makes the majority of its sales from fuel card payments corporate payments and toll products as well as gift and lodging cards. It also offers fleet-related and workforce payment services such as fleet maintenance management and employee benefit payments.

The company processes around 3 billion transactions each year. It makes its money from transaction fees card fees and network fees and charges which can be fixed fees cost-plus-mark-up or percentage based. It also charges late payment fees based on customer credit risk.

By product category fuel cards account for some 50% of revenue; tolls generate about 15% corporate payments and gift cards supply about 10% each and lodging accounts for about 5%.

It operates its own "closed-loop" networks — under the brands Fuelman Comdata Commercial fueling Network and Pacific Pride — where possible but also makes use of third-party networks to broaden its card acceptance and use. These include MasterCard and Carnet in Mexico.

Geographic Reach

North America accounts for around 65% of Norcross Georgia-based FLEETCOR's sales. Brazil generates about 20% and the UK supplies more than 10%. Beyond those three the company does business in more than 55 other countries across Africa Europe (including Russia) Latin America and Australasia.

Sales and Marketing

FLEETCOR offers its commercial payment services to retailers commercial fleets major oil companies petroleum marketers and government entities in a variety of industries such as retail healthcare construction and hospitality. The company has relationships with 800 such partners.

Financial Performance
Fueled by smaller fleet service and portfolio acquisitions FLEETCOR's annual revenues have tripled and its profits doubled since 2011 (the company went public in 2010).

In 2017 sales grew 22% to $2.2 billion as total transactions increased 33% to 2.9 billion boosted by a 122% increase in international transactions due to acquisitions.

Net income jumped more than 60% in 2017 to $740 million from $452 million in 2016 driven by the strong revenue growth. The company recorded a $44 million impairment loss from its Masternaut investment.

Cash in FLEETCOR's coffers totaled $913 million in 2017 compared to $475 million in 2016.

Strategy
FLEETCOR's primary means of growth is through acquisitions: it has made more than 70 since 2002. It targets smaller and regional fleet service providers in markets it currently serves and in new markets overseas. It also looks to buy commercial account portfolios technologies services and products.

Its acquisition activity has taken FLEETCOR international. The company has snapped up companies in growing markets in Europe Asia and Latin America. It expanded in Brazil when it bought San Paulo-based electronic toll payment company STP in mid-2016.

FLEETCOR sold its NexTraq telematics business to Michelin in 2017. FLEETCOR divested the business because it did not fit with the company's core payments business. Terms were not disclosed. The company bought NexTraq in 2013.

Mergers and Acquisitions
In 2017 FLEETCOR acquired Creative Lodging Solutions a provider of long-term stay lodging for businesses.

In another 2017 acquisition FLEETCOR bought Cambridge Global Payments an international payments provider for about $690 million. The deal puts FLEETCOR in the business-to-business cross-border payments market.In August 2016 FLEETCOR paid $1.2 billion to acquire San Paulo-based electronic toll payment company Servicos e Tecnologia de Pagamentos S.A (STP). The firm collects some $2.5 billion in toll parking and fuel payments from 4.5 million active users annually and provided cardless fuel payments at Shell sites throughout Brazil.

Company Background
Founded in 2000 FleetCor went public in December 2010 via an initial public offering that raised about $290 million. The proceeds went to FleetCor's private equity shareholders Advent International Bain Capital and Summit Partners.

EXECUTIVES

President Global Fuel Cards, Steve Greene
Chairman and CEO, Ronald F. (Ron) Clarke, age 62, $1,000,000 total compensation
CFO, Eric R. Dey, age 58, $373,077 total compensation
President North American Partners, David D. Maxsimic, age 58
President International Corporate Development, Andrew R. Blazye, age 59, $340,137 total compensation
President North America Fuel Cards, Todd W. House, age 46, $398,077 total compensation

EVP Global Sales, Charles R. Freund, age 45, $343,077 total compensation
EVP Global Corporate Development, John S. Coughlin, age 50, $398,077 total compensation
CIO, John A. Reed, age 63
President Brazil, Armando L. Netto, age 49, $280,048 total compensation
President Comdata Corporate Payments, Kurt P. Adams, age 48
President Continental Europe, Alexey Gavrilenya, age 41
President UK Australia and New Zealand, Alan King, age 41
President North American Trucking, Greg L. Secord, age 55
Vice President of Sales, Chet Panhans
Vice President Process Excellence and Program Management, Ed Thomas
Vice President Corporate Devel, James Howle
Vice President Product Management, Wes Williams
Vice President Global Sales Planning and Analysis, Jason Cole
Vice President Information Security, Bruce R Evans, age 61
Executive Vice President Business Development, John Couglin
Vice President US Sales Operations, Steve Casper
Senior Vice President of Financial Planning and Analysis, Chad Richardson
Senior Vice President Inside Sales, Christopher Alff
Vice President and GM North American Partners, Kelly Fifarek
Senior Vice President and Chief Information Security Officer CISO, James Edgar
Board Member, Richard Macchia
Board Member, Steven Stull
Board Member, Jeffrey Sloan
Board Member, Joseph Farrelly
Board Member, Thomas Hagerty
Auditors: Ernst & Young LLP

LOCATIONS

HQ: FleetCor Technologies Inc
5445 Triangle Parkway, Peachtree Corners, GA 30092
Phone: 770 449-0479
Web: www.fleetcor.com

PRODUCTS/OPERATIONS

2017 Sales

	% of total
Fuel	49
Tolls	14
Corporate Payments	12
Gift	9
Lodging	5
Other	11
Total	**100**

Selected Brands and Subsidiaries
CCS
CFN Holding Co.
CLC Group
Corporate Lodging Consultants Inc.
FleetCards
FleetNet
Fuelman
The Fuelcard Company
Fuel Vend Limited
Keyfuels
Mannatec Inc.
Transit Card

COMPETITORS

American Express	Sodexo USA
Arval	U.S. Bancorp
Edenred	WEX
Multi Service	World Fuel Services
Retail Decisions	

HISTORICAL FINANCIALS
Company Type: Public

Income Statement
FYE: December 31

	REVENUE ($ mil.)	NET INCOME ($ mil.)	NET PROFIT MARGIN	EMPLOYEES
12/17	2,249.5	740.2	32.9%	7,890
12/16	1,831.5	452.3	24.7%	7,100
12/15	1,702.8	362.4	21.3%	5,330
12/14	1,199.3	368.7	30.7%	4,780
12/13	895.1	284.5	31.8%	3,500
Annual Growth	**25.9%**	**27.0%**	**—**	**22.5%**

2017 Year-End Financials

Debt ratio: 32.7%	No. of shares (mil.): 89.8
Return on equity: 21.9%	Dividends
Cash ($ mil.): 913.6	Yield: —
Current ratio: 0.87	Payout: —
Long-term debt ($ mil.): 2,902.1	Market value ($ mil.): 17,281.0

	STOCK PRICE ($) FY Close	P/E High/Low	PER SHARE ($) Earnings	Dividends	Book Value
12/17	192.43	24 16	7.91	0.00	40.94
12/16	141.52	36 23	4.75	0.00	33.58
12/15	142.93	42 35	3.85	0.00	30.64
12/14	148.71	36 23	4.24	0.00	30.04
12/13	117.17	35 15	3.36	0.00	15.08
Annual Growth	**13.2%**	**— —**	**23.9%**	**—**	**28.4%**

Floor & Decor Holdings Inc

Auditors: Ernst & Young LLP

LOCATIONS

HQ: Floor & Decor Holdings Inc
2233 Lake Park Drive, Smyrna, GA 30080
Phone: 404 471-1634
Web: www.FloorandDecor.com

HISTORICAL FINANCIALS
Company Type: Public

Income Statement
FYE: December 28

	REVENUE ($ mil.)	NET INCOME ($ mil.)	NET PROFIT MARGIN	EMPLOYEES
12/17	1,384.7	102.7	7.4%	5,534
12/16	1,050.7	43.0	4.1%	4,391
12/15	784.0	26.8	3.4%	0
12/14	584.5	15.1	2.6%	0
Annual Growth	**33.3%**	**89.5%**	**—**	**—**

2017 Year-End Financials

Debt ratio: 17.7%	No. of shares (mil.): 95.5
Return on equity: 35.8%	Dividends
Cash ($ mil.): 0.5	Yield: —
Current ratio: 1.40	Payout: —
Long-term debt ($ mil.): 185.5	Market value ($ mil.): 4,736.0

	STOCK PRICE ($) FY Close	P/E High/Low	PER SHARE ($) Earnings	Dividends	Book Value
12/17	49.59	43 28	1.03	0.00	4.64
12/16	0.00	— —	0.49	0.00	1.61
Annual Growth	**—**	**— —**	**110.2%**	**—**	**188.4%**

FNB Corp

F.N.B. Corporation is the holding company for First National Bank of Pennsylvania which serves consumers and small to midsized businesses though almost 290 bank branches in Pennsylvania northeastern Ohio and Maryland. The company also has more than 70 consumer finance offices operating as Regency Finance in those states as well as Tennessee and Kentucky. In addition to community banking and consumer finance F.N.B. also has segments devoted to insurance and wealth management. It also offers leasing and merchant banking services. F.N.B. has extended its reach in its target states through acquisitions of banks including Metro Bancorp Annapolis Bancorp and PVF Capital Corp.

Operations

F.N.B operates four segments. The Community Banking segment which made up almost 90% of the company's total revenue during 2015 provides commercial and consumer banking services including corporate banking small business banking investment real estate financing asset-based lending capital markets services and lease financing as well as traditional consumer banking products.

The company's Wealth Management segment (5% of revenue) offers trust and other fiduciary services while the Insurance segment (2% of revenue) offers commercial and personal insurance through major carriers. F.N.B.'s Consumer Finance segment (6% of revenue) which operates through subsidiary Regency Finance Company provides installment loans to individuals and buys installment loans from retail merchants.

Like other retail banks F.N.B. makes the bulk of its money from interest income. Nearly 70% of the bank's total revenue came from loan and lease interest (including fees) during 2015 while 9% came from interest on taxable and non-taxable securities. The rest of money came from service charges (10% of revenue) trust income (3%) insurance commissions and fees (2%) securities commissions and fees (2%) mortgage banking (1%) and other non-interest income sources.

Geographic Reach

Most of the Pittsburgh-based company's branches are concentrated in Pennsylvania with the next largest markets being in Ohio Maryland and West Virginia. Its consumer finance offices are mostly in Pennsylvania and Tennessee with others in Kentucky and Ohio.

Sales and Marketing

F.N.B. boosted its advertising and promotional spend by 7% to $8.4 million during 2015 mostly because of higher expenses associated with the bank's recent acquisitions as it worked to get the name out in new territories such as in Cleveland Ohio and Baltimore.

Financial Performance

F.N.B. Corporation's annual revenues have risen nearly 40% since 2011 as its loan assets have nearly doubled with new branch openings and acquisitions. Its profits have doubled as well over the period as the company has kept a lid on growing costs.

The bank's revenue climbed 6% to $709.21 million during 2015 thanks to continued loan business growth stemming from recent bank acquisitions.

Revenue growth in 2015 drove F.N.B.'s net income up 11% to $159.65 million. The company's operating cash levels plunged 50% to $223.48 million for the year due to unfavorable changes in working capital related to securities classified as trading in business combination and sold.

Strategy

F.N.B. Corporation grows its loan and deposit business while expanding into new markets by acquiring smaller banks and select bank branches. In 2016 it agreed to buy North Carolina-based Yadkin Financial for $1.4 billion. That deal will add around 100 banking locations in the Carolinas and some $7.5 billion in assets. The combined bank will have some 400 branches across the Mid-Atlantic and Southeast US.

Mergers and Acquisitions

In April 2016 the company bought 17 branch locations in the Pittsburgh area from Fifth Third Bank as well as $100000 in loans and over $300000 in deposits.

In February 2016 F.N.B. Corporation purchased Metro Bancorp along with its $3 billion in assets and more than 30 Metro Bank branches in south-central Pennsylvania. The deal effectively merged Metro Bank into F.N.B.'s First National Bank of Pennsylvania subsidiary.

In September 2015 the bank purchased five branches in southeastern Pennsylvania from Bank of America along with almost $155000 in associated deposits.

In October 2013 F.N.B. moved to expand its presence in the greater Cleveland area by purchasing PVF Capital Corp. which owned Park View Federal Savings Bank with some 20 offices in Cleveland and northeastern Ohio.

In April 2013 F.N.B. purchased Annapolis Bancorp the parent company of BankAnnapolis in an all-stock transaction valued at about $51 million. The deal expanded F.N.B.'s reach into Maryland.

Company Background

F.N.B. which moved its headquarters from Pennsylvania to Florida in 2001 spun off First National Bankshares of Florida at the start of 2004 and returned to the Pittsburgh area. F.N.B. still operates two loan offices in Florida but these primarily manage the company's legacy loan portfolio there.

The bank is again rooted firmly in the Keystone State and bordering markets. After returning it expanded via several acquisitions prior to the Parkvale deal including bank holding companies NSD Bancorp Slippery Rock Financial North East Bancshares Omega Financial and Iron and Glass Bancorp. In 2011 F.N.B. expanded in northeastern Pennsylvania through the acquisition of Comm Bancorp. The deal valued at some $70 million brought in 15 branches.

EXECUTIVES

SVP and Corporate Controller, Timothy G. Rubritz, age 65, $215,016 total compensation
Chief Legal Officer, James G. Orie, age 59, $165,000 total compensation
CFO, Vincent J. Calabrese, age 55, $385,008 total compensation
Chief Credit Officer, Gary Guerrieri, age 57, $350,016 total compensation
President and CEO; CEO First National Bank, Vincent J. (Vince) Delie, age 53, $770,016 total compensation
President First National Bank, John C. Williams, $385,008 total compensation
President Charlotte Region, Gregory L. (Greg) Heaton
Vice President Business Development Officer, Leslie Harrison
Vice President, Gregory Robb
Senior Vice President, Craig Muthler
Vice President, Michael Griffo
Vice President Private Banking, Donna Logan
Vice President, Mike DeRosa
Vice President Wealth Advisor Maryland Region, Nick Ey
SENIOR VICE PRESIDENT MANAGING DIRECTOR, Nick Bellino
Chairman, Stephen J. (Steve) Gurgovits, age 74
Board Member, Stephen Martz
Board Member, Heidi Nicholas
Auditors: Ernst & Young LLP

LOCATIONS

HQ: FNB Corp
 One North Shore Center, 12 Federal Street, Pittsburgh, PA 15212
Phone: 800 555-5455
Web: www.fnb-online.com

PRODUCTS/OPERATIONS

2015 Sales by Segment

	$ mil.	% of total
Community banking	616.2	87
Consumer finance	42.8	6
Wealth management	35.2	5
Insurance	13.1	2
parent & other	1.8	-
Total	**709.1**	**100**

2015 Sales

	$ mil.	% of total
Interest		
Loans including fees	482.1	68
Securities including dividends	64.6	9
Other	0.1	-
Non-interest		
Service charges	70.7	10
Trust Services	20.8	3
Insurance commissions & fees	16.3	2
Securities commissions & fees	13.6	2
Other	40.9	6
Total	**709.1**	**100**

Selected Subsidiaries

F.N.B. Capital Corporation (merchant banking)
First National Bank of Pennsylvania
 Bank Capital Services LLC (also dba F.N.B. Commercial Leasing)
 First National Trust Company
 F.N.B. Investment Advisors
 First National Investment Services Company
First National Insurance Agency LLC
Regency Finance Company
 Citizens Financial Services Inc.
 F.N.B. Consumer Discount Company
 Finance and Mortgage Acceptance Corporation

COMPETITORS

Bank of America	Huntington Bancshares
Citizens Financial Group	M&T Bank
	Northwest Bancshares
Dollar Bank	PNC Financial
Fifth Third	S&T Bancorp
First Commonwealth Financial	Sandy Spring Bancorp
	Sovereign Bank
Fulton Financial	United Community Financial
Glen Burnie Bancorp	

HISTORICAL FINANCIALS
Company Type: Public

Income Statement
FYE: December 31

	ASSETS ($ mil.)	NET INCOME ($ mil.)	INCOME AS % OF ASSETS	EMPLOYEES
12/17	31,417.6	199.2	0.6%	4,748
12/16	21,844.8	170.8	0.8%	3,821
12/15	17,557.6	159.6	0.9%	3,205
12/14	16,127.0	144.0	0.9%	3,145
12/13	13,563.4	117.8	0.9%	3,103
Annual Growth	23.4%	14.0%	—	11.2%

2017 Year-End Financials

Return on assets: 0.7%	Dividends
Return on equity: 5.7%	Yield: 0.0%
Long-term debt ($ mil.): —	Payout: 76.1%
No. of shares (mil.): 323.4	Market value ($ mil.): 4,470.0
Sales ($ mil): 1,232.7	

	STOCK PRICE ($) FY Close	P/E High/Low	PER SHARE ($) Earnings	Dividends	Book Value
12/17	13.82	26 19	0.63	0.48	13.63
12/16	16.03	21 14	0.78	0.48	12.18
12/15	13.34	17 14	0.86	0.48	11.95
12/14	13.32	17 14	0.80	0.48	11.62
12/13	12.62	16 13	0.80	0.48	11.16
Annual Growth	2.3%	— —	(5.8%)	(0.0%)	5.1%

FormFactor Inc

Why test each microchip one by one when you can test them all in one place? That's the question FormFactor answers with its interconnect technology called MicroSpring. The companyy makes wafer probe cards that test semiconductor circuits (especially memory chips) while they are still part of semiconductor wafers — before the wafers are cut into individual chips. FormFactor touts the process for its cost-effectiveness since it allows testing of many chips at once across a range of scales and temperatures. While the most of the company's products are made in the US the majority of sales are to customers in the Asia/Pacific region.

Geographic Reach
FormFactor primarily manufactures its products in California but it also has smaller manufacturing facilities in China and Japan. It also has sales and services offices in China Germany Japan Singapore South Korea and Taiwan. South Korea is the biggest market for FormFactor products accounting for 20% of revenue followed by Taiwan with 18%. About 28% of sales come from customers in North America.

Sales and Marketing
Sales to its largest customer Intel accounted for about 20% of 2014 sales up from about 18% in 2013. Another top customer SK Hynix accounted for about 15% of sales in 2014. Micron's business was about 15% of revenue in 2014 up from 11% in 2013.

Financial Performance
Sales jumped 16% higher in 2014 to $268.5 million boosted by increases in the System-on-a-Chip (SOC) and DRAM markets. Flash memory revenue

were down 34%. SOC sales were driven by demand from the mobile PC and automotive microcontroller markets. FormFactor cut its loss to $19 million in 2014 from $57.6 million in 2013. Stronger revenue and lower operating costs combined to reduce the loss. Cash flow improved $17 million in 2014 from a negative $5.8 million in 2013.

Strategy
The company responds to changes in the global semiconductor market by restructuring including several rounds of minor workforce reductions. Following workforce reductions in 2011 2012 and 2013 the company cut about 50 jobs in 2014.

Looking to improve its business in the flash memory market FormFactor introduced a new product for testing NAND flash devices in 2014. Gaining a foothold in the growing flash storage sector is important for the company's growth.

Like all semiconductor equipment manufacturers FormFactor makes substantial investments in R&D in order to develop next-generation process architecture and testing products. The company is focused on new product development for the SoC market which is less volatile than the memory market. It also invests in technology through acquisitions.

EXECUTIVES

Chief Financial Officer, Michael M. Ludwig, age 56, $282,692 total compensation
SVP General Counsel and Secretary, Stuart L. Merkadeau, age 56, $273,269 total compensation
CEO and Director, Michael (Mikie) Slessor, age 50, $300,000 total compensation
CTO and SVP Engineering & Product Development, Jarek (January) Kister
VP Marketing, Amy Leong
Vice President Of Administrative Services, Prahlad Moharir
Vice President Strategic And Product Management, Tim Eichenseer
Senior Vice President, Richard Freeman
Vice President and General Counsel, Jason Cohen
Chairman, Thomas (Tom) St. Dennis, age 65
Auditors: KPMG LLP

LOCATIONS

HQ: FormFactor Inc
7005 Southfront Road, Livermore, CA 94551
Phone: 925 290-4000
Web: www.formfactor.com

PRODUCTS/OPERATIONS

2014 Sales by Market

	$ mil.	% of total
System-on-a-Chip (SoC)	142.3	53
DRAM	110.8	41
Flash memory devices	15.4	6
Total	**268.5**	**100**

Selected Products
DRAM
  Harmony eXP
  PH150XP and PH Series
Flash
  Harmony OneTouch
Known good die (KGD)
  HFTAP (K1 K3 K5)
Logic/SoC
  BladeRunner 175
  TrueScale PP40
MicroSpring interconnect technology
Probe cards

Probe heads (PH50 PH75 PH100 PH150 models)
Special Products
  Parametric
  Takumi Pico
  Takumi Femto
TRE test technology

COMPETITORS

ASE Test
Advantest
Aehr Test Systems
Cascade Microtech
EG Systems
Everett Charles Technologies
Interconnect Devices
JAPAN ELECTRONIC MATERIALS CORPORATION
MICRONICS JAPAN CO. LTD.
Mirae
QualiTau
Synopsys
Teradyne
Tokyo Electron
Xcerra

HISTORICAL FINANCIALS
Company Type: Public

Income Statement
FYE: December 30

	REVENUE ($ mil.)	NET INCOME ($ mil.)	NET PROFIT MARGIN	EMPLOYEES
12/17	548.4	40.9	7.5%	1,685
12/16	383.8	(6.5)	—	1,571
12/15	282.3	(1.5)	—	958
12/14	268.5	(19.1)	—	907
12/13	231.5	(57.6)	—	961
Annual Growth	24.1%	—		15.1%

2017 Year-End Financials

Debt ratio: 16.3%	No. of shares (mil.): 72.5
Return on equity: 9.5%	Dividends
Cash ($ mil.): 91.1	Yield: —
Current ratio: 3.32	Payout: —
Long-term debt ($ mil.): 87.2	Market value ($ mil.): 1,135.0

	STOCK PRICE ($) FY Close	P/E High/Low	PER SHARE ($) Earnings	Dividends	Book Value
12/17	15.65	32 19	0.55	0.00	6.32
12/16	11.20	— —	(0.10)	0.00	5.66
12/15	9.11	— —	(0.03)	0.00	5.07
12/14	8.65	— —	(0.34)	0.00	5.12
12/13	6.14	— —	(1.06)	0.00	5.38
Annual Growth	26.4%	— —	—	—	4.1%

Fortinet Inc

Fortinet secures the fortress against Internet marauders. The company makes network security appliances (sold under its FortiGate line) and software that integrate antivirus firewall content filtering intrusion prevention systems (IPS) and antispam functions to protect against computer viruses worms and inappropriate Web content. Its FortiGuard subscription services offer continuous updates on all new threats to provide real-time network protection. The company also offers complementary products that include its FortiManager security management and FortiAnalyzer event analysis systems.

Operations

While service revenues — an important source of recurring income — account for 53% of sales product revenues — 47% of sales — have taken an increasingly important place in Fortinet's earnings as well. Fortinet outsources the manufacturing of its appliance products to contract manufacturers and original design manufacturers (ODMs). The company's manufacturers include Flextronics International Ltd. Micro-Star International Co. Ltd. Adlink Technology Inc. Senao Networks Inc. and several Taiwan-based manufacturers.

Geographic Reach

Fortinet's largest geographic segment is the Americas which accounts for 42% of revenues. The Europe Middle East and Africa (EMEA) segment accounts for about 35% of sales while the Asia/Pacific region accounts for the remainder. The company operates sales and service offices in about 30 countries worldwide.

Sales and Marketing

Fortinet sells through channel partners to end-customers that range from from small businesses to large enterprises and industries that include government telecommunications technology government financial services education retail manufacturing and health care. In 2014 distributor Exclusive Networks Group accounted for 15% of revenue.

Financial Performance

Fortinet has posted steady revenue growth over the years and that continued in 2014 when revenue increased 25% to $770 million. Product revenue rose 30% driven by sales of its FortiGate product to enterprise and service provider customers. Services and other revenue increased 22% on the strength of FortiGuard security subscriptions and FortiCare technical support contracts.

The company recorded its second straight year of declining revenue in 2014 with a 43% decrease to $25.3 million. It had higher costs and paid more taxes in 2014.

Cash flow from operations was $196 million at the end of 2014 up from $147 million at the end of 2013. The increased cash flow was due to changes in working capital because of deferred revenue.

Strategy

Fortinet sells its products to distributors and resellers who have significant purchasing power and deployment capabilities while at the same time strengthening its customer support network in high-growth regions. It also works to build a solid base of subscription and service customers.

In addition to expand its product offerings Fortinet conducts research and development efforts to create new software and hardware offerings for customers. The company employs about 600 R&D employees in Canada China and the US and spends some $112 million annually on research projects about 14% of revenue.

Fortinet's products are being incorporated into networking products from NTT Com Security according to an agreement the companies reached in 2015. In another 2015 agreement Fortinet has access to information about security threats from the federal Department of Homeland Security. With the agreement Fortinet participates in the Cyber Information and Sharing and Collaboration Program (CISCP) which entails sharing cyber threat incident and vulnerability information in near real-time drawing on data of observed threat activity submitted by CISCP participants.

Mergers and Acquisitions

Fortinet acquired Meru Networks an intelligent Wi-Fi networking developer in 2015. The acquisition expands Fortinet's capabilities in $5 billion market for enterprise Wi-Fi security.

EXECUTIVES

Chairman and CEO, Ken Xie, age 55, $406,372 total compensation
President and CTO, Michael Xie, age 49, $360,490 total compensation
SVP International Sales and Support, Patrice Perche
CFO, Andrew (Drew) Del Matto, $381,401 total compensation
VP Corporate Development and Strategic Alliances and General Counsel, John Whittle, $332,695 total compensation
Director Of Surgery, JANE ZHU
Vice President Carrier and Service Provider Group, Matthew Pley
Vice President Product Marketing, Patrick Bedwell
Senior Vice President Products and Solutions, John Maddison
Vice President Marketing At Fortinet Inc, Tamir Hardof
Vice President Us Enterprise Sales, Scott Lewis
National Account Manager, Hooman Minai
Vice President Cloud Services, Chad Whalen
Vice President Finance And Operations, Linda Liang
Vice President Support And Services, Dave Monery
National Account Manager, Jeffrey Laniewski
Vice President Quality, Dayong Zhou
Vice President Engineering, Venkat Adusumilli
Vice President Global Corporate Communications, Sandra Wheatley
Vice President Mexico, Manuel Acosta
National Account Manager, Cassie Rupp
Vice President Strategic Accounts, John DiFerdinando
Senior Vice President People, Lisa McGill
VP Finance, Christiane Ohlgart
Vice President of Strategic Programs, Jonathan Nguyen-Duy
Vice President Europe, Yann Pradelle
Vice President of Sales Atandt, Chris Sousa
Vice President, XJ Zhong
Vice President Sales Central US, Jim Overbeck
National Account Manager, Carrie Sinnott
Board Member, Pehong Chen
Auditors: Deloitte & Touche LLP

LOCATIONS

HQ: Fortinet Inc
899 Kifer Road, Sunnyvale, CA 94086
Phone: 408 235-7700   **Fax:** 408 235-7737
Web: www.fortinet.com

PRODUCTS/OPERATIONS

2014 Sales

	$ mil.	% of total
Products	360.6	53
Services and others	409.8	47
Total	**770.7**	**100**

Selected Products

Database security appliance (FortiDB)
E-mail antispam (FortiMail)
Endpoint security software (FortiClient)
Endpoint vulnerability management appliance (FortiScan)

Network event correlation and content archiving (FortiAnalyzer)
Network security appliances (FortiGate)
Secure wireless access product (FortiAP)
Security management (FortiManager)
Spam and virus control subscription (FortiGuard)
Support (FortiCare)
Web application firewall appliance (FortiWeb)

COMPETITORS

Bivio Networks	NetWolves
Blue Coat	Palo Alto Networks
CA Inc.	Proofpoint
Check Point Software	SteelCloud
Cisco Systems	Symantec
F5 Networks	Trend Micro
Fortrex	VeriSign
Infoblox	WatchGuard
Juniper Networks	Technologies
McAfee	e-DMZ Security
Microsoft	zvelo

HISTORICAL FINANCIALS

Company Type: Public

Income Statement

FYE: December 31

	REVENUE ($ mil.)	NET INCOME ($ mil.)	NET PROFIT MARGIN	EMPLOYEES
12/17	1,494.9	31.4	2.1%	5,066
12/16	1,275.4	32.1	2.5%	4,665
12/15	1,009.2	7.9	0.8%	4,018
12/14	770.3	25.3	3.3%	2,854
12/13	615.3	44.2	7.2%	2,308
Annual Growth	**24.8%**	**(8.2%)**	**—**	**21.7%**

2017 Year-End Financials

Debt ratio: —	No. of shares (mil.): 167.8
Return on equity: 4.4%	Dividends
Cash ($ mil.): 811.0	Yield: —
Current ratio: 1.67	Payout: —
Long-term debt ($ mil.): —	Market value ($ mil.): 7,335.0

	STOCK PRICE ($) FY Close	P/E High/Low	PER SHARE ($) Earnings	Dividends	Book Value
12/17	43.69	251 167	0.18	0.00	3.51
12/16	30.12	196 125	0.18	0.00	4.84
12/15	31.17	977 584	0.05	0.00	4.41
12/14	30.66	209 127	0.15	0.00	4.06
12/13	19.13	93 61	0.26	0.00	3.63
Annual Growth	**22.9%**	**— —**	**(8.8%)**	**—**	**(0.8%)**

Forward Air Corp

When it's time to haul freight Forward Air never looks back. The company transports deferred airfreight by truck — cargo that requires specific-time delivery but is less time-sensitive than airfreight. Forward Air typically receives freight that has been transported by plane sends it to a sorting facility then dispatches it by truck to a terminal near its destination. The company has nearly 3777 trailers and more than 570 owned and 100 leased tractors and straight trucks in its fleet. It operates from about 85 terminals at or near airports in the US and Canada including about a dozen regional hubs. It also provides services such as warehousing and local pick-up and delivery.

Operations

The company markets its services to airfreight forwarders air cargo carriers and airlines rather than directly to shippers. Although Forward Air does facilitate overnight delivery of freight the company doesn't compete in the parcel delivery market because it handles larger shipments.

Besides its expedited transportation business the company offers pool distribution services through a second business segment Forward Air Solutions. (Pool distribution involves combining goods from multiple shippers into loads headed to the same location.) Forward Air Solutions maintains about 30 terminals near airport in major cities. Because the segment's customers tend to be retailers located in malls and outlet-based chains revenues are dependent upon the health of the retail industry.

As with its competitors Forward Air uses a fuel surcharge as a way to compensate for fluctuating fuel prices. The rates are based upon the national average price of diesel per gallon and tonnage delivered.

Geographic Reach

Forward Air operates regional hubs in Atlanta; Charlotte North Carolina; Chicago Dallas/Ft. Worth; Denver Kansas City; Los Angeles; New Orleans; Newark New Jersey; Newburgh New York; Orlando Florida; and Sacramento California. Its airport-to-airport network consists of terminals located in 87 cities.

In addition the company leases and maintains 76 additional terminals including its pool distribution terminals located in major cities throughout the US and Canada.

Financial Performance

Forward Air has enjoyed several straight years of unprecedented growth. Revenues spiked 20% from $652 million in 2013 to peak at a record-shattering $781 million in 2014. Profits also jumped 12% from $54 million in 2013 to $61 million in 2014 another milestone.

The historic growth for 2014 was driven by surges across all its segments: Forward Air (22%) Forward Air Solutions (16%) and Total Quality (6%). The growth was mostly due to additional revenue from previous acquisitions.

In addition to rises in revenue and net income Forward Air's operating cash flow surged during 2013 and 2014.

Strategy

The company intents to grow by adding new services to its lineup and by acquiring other transportation services companies. In 2013 Forward Air acquired Total Quality a provider of temperature-controlled logistics services serving the life science and pharmaceutical sector for $66 million. The deal added a new service to Forward Air's logistics portfolio and widened its client base.

In 2014 Forward Air acquired Central States Trucking Co. and Central States Logistics (CST). CST provides container and intermodal drayage services primarily within the Midwest region of the US. CST also provides dedicated contract and container freight station warehouse and handling services. Forward Air made the transaction for $83 million in net cash and $11 million in assumed debt.

EXECUTIVES

Senior Vice President Sales, Craig Drum

Chairman President and CEO, Bruce A. Campbell, age 67, $620,999 total compensation
EVP Operations, Chris C. Ruble, age 56, $414,072 total compensation
EVP Intermodal Services and Chief Strategy Officer, Matthew J. Jewell, age 52, $413,240 total compensation
SVP Chief Legal Officer and Secretary, Michael L. Hance, age 46, $334,200 total compensation
SVP CFO and Treasurer, Michael J. Morris, age 50
VICE PRESIDENT OF SYSTEMS AND PROCESS ENGINEERING, Kelly Brown
Vice President Operations, Mike Serth
Board Member, Ana Amicarella
Auditors: Ernst & Young LLP

LOCATIONS

HQ: Forward Air Corp
1915 Snapps Ferry Road, Building N, Greeneville, TN 37745
Phone: 423 636-7000
Web: www.forwardair.com

PRODUCTS/OPERATIONS

2014 Sales

	$ mil.	% of total
Forward Air	608.1	78
Forward Air Solutions	124.4	16
TQI	48.5	6
Total	**7,801.0**	**100**

Services
Expedited Linehaul Service
Forward Air Complete
Canadian Transborder Service
Airline Logistics Services
Freight Management Services
Container Freight Stations
Truckload Services

COMPETITORS

Alliance Air	Old Dominion Freight
CRST Expedited	Panther Expedited
CRST International	Services
Daylight Transport	Schneider National
FedEx Freight	Towne Air Freight
New Penn Motor Express	XPO logistics

HISTORICAL FINANCIALS

Company Type: Public

Income Statement

FYE: December 31

	REVENUE ($ mil.)	NET INCOME ($ mil.)	NET PROFIT MARGIN	EMPLOYEES
12/17	1,100.8	87.3	7.9%	4,898
12/16	982.5	27.6	2.8%	4,868
12/15	959.1	55.5	5.8%	4,536
12/14	780.9	61.1	7.8%	3,902
12/13	652.4	54.4	8.3%	3,537
Annual Growth	**14.0%**	**12.5%**	**—**	**8.5%**

2017 Year-End Financials

Debt ratio: 5.9%
Return on equity: 16.9%
Cash ($ mil.): 3.8
Current ratio: 2.71
Long-term debt ($ mil.): 40.5
No. of shares (mil.): 29.4
Dividends
  Yield: 0.0%
  Payout: 20.7%
Market value ($ mil.): 1,692.0

	STOCK PRICE ($) FY Close	P/E High/Low		PER SHARE ($) Earnings	Dividends	Book Value
12/17	57.44	20	16	2.89	0.60	18.11
12/16	47.38	55	40	0.90	0.51	16.59
12/15	43.01	32	23	1.78	0.48	16.70
12/14	50.37	25	21	1.96	0.48	15.32
12/13	43.91	24	19	1.77	0.40	14.28
Annual Growth	**6.9%**	**—**		**13.0%**	**10.7%**	**6.1%**

Foundation Building Materials Inc

Auditors: DELOITTE & TOUCHE LLP

LOCATIONS

HQ: Foundation Building Materials Inc
2741 Walnut Avenue, Suite 200, Tustin, CA 92780
Phone: 714 380-3127
Web: www.fbmsales.com

HISTORICAL FINANCIALS

Company Type: Public

Income Statement

FYE: December 31

	REVENUE ($ mil.)	NET INCOME ($ mil.)	NET PROFIT MARGIN	EMPLOYEES
12/17	2,060.9	82.4	4.0%	3,782
12/16	1,392.5	(28.3)	—	3,500
12/15*	192.5	(7.9)	—	0
10/15	628.0	(29.4)	—	0
12/14	508.8	(1.8)	—	0
Annual Growth	**41.9%**	**—**	**—**	**—**

*Fiscal year change

2017 Year-End Financials

Debt ratio: 42.9%
Return on equity: 23.3%
Cash ($ mil.): 12.1
Current ratio: 2.26
Long-term debt ($ mil.): 581.8
No. of shares (mil.): 42.8
Dividends
  Yield: —
  Payout: —
Market value ($ mil.): 634.0

	STOCK PRICE ($) FY Close	P/E High/Low		PER SHARE ($) Earnings	Dividends	Book Value
12/17	14.79	9	6	1.99	0.00	8.83
Annual Growth	**—**	**—**		**—**	**—**	**—**

Four Corners Property Trust Inc

Auditors: KPMG LLP

LOCATIONS

HQ: Four Corners Property Trust Inc
591 Redwood Highway, Suite 1150, Mill Valley, CA 94941
Phone: 415 965-8030
Web: www.fcpt.com

HISTORICAL FINANCIALS

Company Type: Public

Income Statement
FYE: December 31

	REVENUE ($ mil.)	NET INCOME ($ mil.)	NET PROFIT MARGIN	EMPLOYEES
12/17	133.2	71.3	53.6%	342
12/16	124.0	156.8	126.4%	324
12/15	33.4	5.7	17.0%	334
12/14	17.7	0.0	0.2%	350
12/13	16.9	0.0	0.2%	0
Annual Growth	67.5%	604.4%	—	—

2017 Year-End Financials

Debt ratio: 48.2%
Return on equity: 14.5%
Cash ($ mil.): 64.4
Current ratio: 14.73
Long-term debt ($ mil.): 515.5

No. of shares (mil.): 61.3
Dividends
  Yield: 0.0%
  Payout: 84.9%
Market value ($ mil.): 1,576.0

	STOCK PRICE ($) FY Close	P/E High/Low		PER SHARE ($) Earnings	Dividends	Book Value
12/17	25.70	23	17	1.18	1.00	8.39
12/16	20.52	9	5	2.63	9.29	7.76
12/15	24.16	26	19	0.91	0.00	10.33
Annual Growth	3.1%	—	—	13.9%	—	(9.9%)

Fox Factory Holding Corp

Talk about shock value. Fox Factory makes suspension products — i.e. shocks — for high-performance mountain bikes and other powered vehicles that give riders a smooth ride over rough terrain. Some two-thirds of sales are for shocks for bicycles but the other third of revenue comes from shocks for ATVs motorcycles snowmobiles and off-road vehicles and trucks. Fox Factory sells its shocks to original equipment manufacturers (OEMs) such as Specialized and Trek (bikes) and Ford and Polaris (powered vehicles). It also sells branded apparel such as T-shirts sweatshirts and hats. Fox Factory went public in 2013.

Geographic Reach
Sales outside the US account for about two-thirds of revenue because Fox Factory sells directly to OEMs that have primary manufacturing operations in Asia. The majority of its own manufacturing operations are in California but Fox Factory does have a plant in Taiwan. The company is shifting all of its manufacturing to Taiwan by 2016.

Sales and Marketing
Fox Factory sells its suspension products to more than 150 OEMs and distributes its products to more than 2300 retail dealers and distributors worldwide. In 2012 80% of sales were to OEM customers and 20% were to dealers and distributors for resale in the aftermarket channel.

Financial Performance
The company has experienced steady growth over the years. Sales increased about 20% in 2012 due to increased demand from both OEMs and aftermarket customers. Fox Factory has also been consistently profitable.

Company Background
Fox Factory was founded in 1974 by Robert Fox who built a racing suspension shock in his friend's garage. The company was bought by Compass Diversified Holdings in 2008. In 2013 Fox Factory went public and Compass held onto a majority share; Compass subsequently divested shares in Fox Factory but still maintains a minority ownership stake.

EXECUTIVES

CEO, Larry L. Enterline, age 65, $702,821 total compensation
CFO, Zvi Glasman, age 54, $270,100 total compensation
President, Mario Galasso, age 52, $295,654 total compensation
SVP Global Operations, William H. (Bill) Katherman
Chairman, Elias J. Sabo, age 47
Auditors: GRANT THORNTON LLP

LOCATIONS

HQ: Fox Factory Holding Corp
  915 Disc Drive, Scotts Valley, CA 95066
Phone: 831 274-6500
Web: www.ridefox.com

PRODUCTS/OPERATIONS

2015 Sales

	$ mil.	% of total
Bikes	211.7	58
Power vehicles	155.1	42
Total	**366.8**	**100**

COMPETITORS

Cannondale	SRAM
Giant Manufacturing	Tenneco
KAYABA INDUSTRY CO. LTD.	Truck-Lite
	ZF Group NAO

HISTORICAL FINANCIALS

Company Type: Public

Income Statement
FYE: December 29

	REVENUE ($ mil.)	NET INCOME ($ mil.)	NET PROFIT MARGIN	EMPLOYEES
12/17	475.6	43.1	9.1%	1,800
12/16	403.0	35.6	8.9%	1,700
12/15	366.8	24.9	6.8%	1,500
12/14	306.7	27.6	9.0%	1,000
12/13	272.7	24.1	8.8%	670
Annual Growth	14.9%	15.7%	—	28.0%

2017 Year-End Financials

Debt ratio: 23.0%
Return on equity: 20.6%
Cash ($ mil.): 35.9
Current ratio: 2.35
Long-term debt ($ mil.): 93.6

No. of shares (mil.): 37.6
Dividends
  Yield: —
  Payout: —
Market value ($ mil.): 1,461.0

	STOCK PRICE ($) FY Close	P/E High/Low		PER SHARE ($) Earnings	Dividends	Book Value
12/17	38.85	38	22	1.11	0.00	6.24
12/16	27.75	29	15	0.94	0.00	5.01
12/15	16.53	29	22	0.66	0.00	4.11
12/14	16.23	25	18	0.73	0.00	3.47
12/13	17.62	28	23	0.68	0.00	2.54
Annual Growth	21.9%	—	—	13.0%	—	25.2%

Francesca's Holdings Corp

Auditors: Ernst & Young LLP

LOCATIONS

HQ: Francesca's Holdings Corp
  8760 Clay Road, Houston, TX 77080
Phone: 713 864-1358   **Fax:** 713 426-2751
Web: www.francescas.com

HISTORICAL FINANCIALS

Company Type: Public

Income Statement
FYE: February 3

	REVENUE ($ mil.)	NET INCOME ($ mil.)	NET PROFIT MARGIN	EMPLOYEES
02/18*	471.6	15.5	3.3%	6,447
01/17	487.1	42.0	8.6%	6,701
01/16	439.3	38.1	8.7%	5,211
01/15	377.5	32.1	8.5%	4,056
02/14	340.3	44.8	13.2%	3,217
Annual Growth	8.5%	(23.2%)	—	19.0%

*Fiscal year change

2018 Year-End Financials

Debt ratio: —
Return on equity: 13.2%
Cash ($ mil.): 31.3
Current ratio: 2.60
Long-term debt ($ mil.): —

No. of shares (mil.): 36.0
Dividends
  Yield: —
  Payout: —
Market value ($ mil.): 199.0

	STOCK PRICE ($) FY Close	P/E High/Low		PER SHARE ($) Earnings	Dividends	Book Value
02/18*	5.52	44	13	0.43	0.00	3.18
01/17	16.98	20	9	1.09	0.00	3.10
01/16	18.23	20	11	0.91	0.00	3.08
01/15	15.86	27	15	0.76	0.00	2.58
02/14	19.00	31	16	1.02	0.00	1.85
Annual Growth	(26.6%)	—	—	(19.4%)	—	14.6%

*Fiscal year change

Franklin Financial Network Inc

Auditors: Crowe Horwath LLP

LOCATIONS

HQ: Franklin Financial Network Inc
  722 Columbia Avenue, Franklin, TN 37064
Phone: 615 236-2265
Web: www.franklinsynergybank.com

HISTORICAL FINANCIALS
Company Type: Public

Income Statement
FYE: December 31

	ASSETS ($ mil.)	NET INCOME ($ mil.)	INCOME AS % OF ASSETS	EMPLOYEES
12/17	3,843.5	28.0	0.7%	281
12/16	2,943.1	28.0	1.0%	268
12/15	2,167.7	16.0	0.7%	226
12/14	1,355.8	8.4	0.6%	220
12/13	796.3	4.5	0.6%	0
Annual Growth	48.2%	57.5%	—	—

2017 Year-End Financials

Return on assets: 0.8%	Dividends
Return on equity: 9.7%	Yield: —
Long-term debt ($ mil.): —	Payout: —
No. of shares (mil.): 13.2	Market value ($ mil.): 451.0
Sales ($ mil): 147.1	

	STOCK PRICE ($) FY Close	P/E High/Low		PER SHARE ($) Earnings	Dividends	Book Value
12/17	34.10	20	14	2.04	0.00	23.01
12/16	41.85	17	10	2.42	0.00	20.73
12/15	31.38	20	11	1.54	0.00	17.86
12/14	17.30	17	13	1.27	0.00	15.70
12/13	12.90	11	11	1.10	0.00	13.40
Annual Growth	27.5%	—		16.7%	—	14.5%

	STOCK PRICE ($) FY Close	P/E High/Low		PER SHARE ($) Earnings	Dividends	Book Value
05/18	8.25	41	13	0.32	0.00	2.72
05/17	4.40	71	49	0.08	0.00	2.35
05/16	5.30	102	50	0.09	0.00	2.19
05/15	9.05	84	65	0.11	0.00	2.34
05/14	9.05	103	42	0.09	0.00	2.16
Annual Growth	(2.3%)	—	—	37.3%	—	5.9%

FS Bancorp Inc (Washington)

FS Bancorp is the holding company for 1st Security Bank of Washington which operates six branches in the Puget Sound region. The bank provides standard deposit products such as checking and savings accounts CDs and IRAs to area businesses and consumers. Its lending activities are focused on consumer loans (more than half of its portfolio) including home improvement boat and automobile loans. The bank also writes business and construction loans and commercial and residential mortgages. FS Bancorp went public via in initial public offering in 2012.

The company plans proceeds from its IPO to fund new loans purchase securities and scale up the bank's operations. Also as part of the offering the bank converted from a mutual to a stock form of ownership.

EXECUTIVES
Vice President Indirect Sales Manager, Craig Brown
Vice President Of Finance and Treasurer, David Tun
Vice President Consumer Lending Manager, Sue Coldwell
Auditors: Moss Adams LLP

LOCATIONS
HQ: FS Bancorp Inc (Washington)
6920 220th Street SW, Mountlake Terrace, WA 98043
Phone: 425 771-5299
Web: www.fsbwa.com

COMPETITORS

Bank of America	KeyCorp
Banner Corp	Washington Banking
Columbia Banking	Washington Federal
Heritage Financial	Wells Fargo

FRMO Corp.

EXECUTIVES
Chb-ceo, Murray Stahl
Auditors: Baker Tilly Virchow Krause, LLP

LOCATIONS
HQ: FRMO Corp.
1 North Lexington Avenue, Suite 12C, White Plains, NY 10601
Phone: 914 632-6730   **Fax:** 914 636-0388
Web: www.frmocorp.com

HISTORICAL FINANCIALS
Company Type: Public

Income Statement
FYE: May 31

	REVENUE ($ mil.)	NET INCOME ($ mil.)	NET PROFIT MARGIN	EMPLOYEES
05/18	16.4	14.0	85.6%	0
05/17	7.6	3.4	45.9%	0
05/16	8.4	3.8	44.8%	0
05/15	7.9	4.9	61.8%	0
05/14	7.6	3.8	51.0%	0
Annual Growth	21.2%	38.0%	—	—

2018 Year-End Financials

Debt ratio: —	No. of shares (mil.): 43.9
Return on equity: 12.6%	Dividends
Cash ($ mil.): 53.6	Yield: —
Current ratio: 16.39	Payout: —
Long-term debt ($ mil.): —	Market value ($ mil.): 363.0

HISTORICAL FINANCIALS
Company Type: Public

Income Statement
FYE: December 31

	ASSETS ($ mil.)	NET INCOME ($ mil.)	INCOME AS % OF ASSETS	EMPLOYEES
12/17	981.7	14.0	1.4%	326
12/16	827.9	10.5	1.3%	306
12/15	677.5	8.8	1.3%	241
12/14	509.7	4.5	0.9%	210
12/13	419.1	3.9	0.9%	160
Annual Growth	23.7%	37.7%	—	19.5%

2017 Year-End Financials

Return on assets: 1.5%	Dividends
Return on equity: 13.8%	Yield: 0.0%
Long-term debt ($ mil.): —	Payout: 10.0%
No. of shares (mil.): 3.6	Market value ($ mil.): 201.0
Sales ($ mil): 70.2	

	STOCK PRICE ($) FY Close	P/E High/Low		PER SHARE ($) Earnings	Dividends	Book Value
12/17	54.57	13	8	4.28	0.43	33.15
12/16	35.95	10	6	3.51	0.37	26.49
12/15	26.00	9	6	2.93	0.27	23.24
12/14	18.25	12	11	1.52	0.23	20.35
12/13	17.15	14	10	1.29	0.15	19.23
Annual Growth	33.6%	—		35.0%	30.1%	14.6%

FS Energy & Power Fund

Auditors: RSM LLP

LOCATIONS
HQ: FS Energy & Power Fund
201 Rouse Boulevard, Philadelphia, PA 19112
Phone: 215 495-1150
Web: www.fsinvestments.com

HISTORICAL FINANCIALS
Company Type: Public

Income Statement
FYE: December 31

	REVENUE ($ mil.)	NET INCOME ($ mil.)	NET PROFIT MARGIN	EMPLOYEES
12/17	418.7	286.5	68.4%	0
12/16	369.7	231.6	62.7%	0
12/15	379.6	227.6	59.9%	0
12/14	289.9	174.8	60.3%	0
12/13	132.0	66.8	50.6%	0
Annual Growth	33.5%	43.9%	—	—

2017 Year-End Financials

Debt ratio: 28.2%	No. of shares (mil.): 446.0
Return on equity: 9.0%	Dividends
Cash ($ mil.): 195.3	Yield: —
Current ratio: 2.37	Payout: 109.0%
Long-term debt ($ mil.): 1,218.1	Market value ($ mil.): —

	STOCK PRICE ($) FY Close	P/E High/Low		PER SHARE ($) Earnings	Dividends	Book Value
12/17	0.00	—	—	0.65	0.71	6.65
Annual Growth		—	—	—		

FVCBankcorp Inc

Auditors: Yount Hyde & Barbour, P.C.

LOCATIONS

HQ: FVCBankcorp Inc
  11325 Random Hills Road,, Suite 240, Fairfax, VA 22030
Phone: 703 436-3800
Web: www.fvcbank.com

HISTORICAL FINANCIALS

Company Type: Public

Income Statement   FYE: December 31

	ASSETS ($ mil.)	NET INCOME ($ mil.)	INCOME AS % OF ASSETS	EMPLOYEES
12/17	1,053.2	7.6	0.7%	0
12/16	909.3	6.9	0.8%	0
12/15	736.8	5.4	0.7%	0
12/14	604.7	4.1	0.7%	0
12/13	506.7	2.2	0.4%	0
Annual Growth	20.1%	36.3%	—	—

2017 Year-End Financials

Return on assets: 0.7%
Return on equity: 8.6%
Long-term debt ($ mil.): —
No. of shares (mil.): 10.8
Sales ($ mil): 43.2

Dividends
  Yield: —
  Payout: —
Market value ($ mil.): 190.0

	STOCK PRICE ($) FY Close	P/E High/Low	Earnings	PER SHARE ($) Dividends	Book Value
12/17	17.52	28 23	0.67	0.00	9.04
12/16	16.80	29 23	0.63	0.00	7.84
12/15	17.25	45 25	0.51	0.00	7.17
12/14	15.50	44 37	0.40	0.00	6.59
12/13	17.00	68 60	0.25	0.00	6.02
Annual Growth	0.8%	— —	28.5%	—	10.7%

Gaming & Leisure Properties, Inc

Auditors: Deloitte & Touche LLP

LOCATIONS

HQ: Gaming & Leisure Properties, Inc
  845 Berkshire Blvd., Suite 200, Wyomissing, PA 19610
Phone: 610 401-2900
Web: www.glpropinc.com

HISTORICAL FINANCIALS

Company Type: Public

Income Statement   FYE: December 31

	REVENUE ($ mil.)	NET INCOME ($ mil.)	NET PROFIT MARGIN	EMPLOYEES
12/17	971.3	380.6	39.2%	714
12/16	828.2	289.3	34.9%	751
12/15	575.0	128.1	22.3%	792
12/14	635.9	185.3	29.2%	807
12/13	242.1	19.8	8.2%	866
Annual Growth	41.5%	109.3%	—	(4.7%)

2017 Year-End Financials

Debt ratio: 61.3%
Return on equity: 15.5%
Cash ($ mil.): 29.0
Current ratio: 0.43
Long-term debt ($ mil.): 4,442.8

No. of shares (mil.): 212.7
Dividends
  Yield: 0.0%
  Payout: 139.6%
Market value ($ mil.): 7,871.0

	STOCK PRICE ($) FY Close	P/E High/Low	Earnings	PER SHARE ($) Dividends	Book Value
12/17	37.00	22 17	1.79	2.50	11.56
12/16	30.62	22 15	1.60	2.32	11.72
12/15	27.80	34 23	1.08	2.18	(2.19)
12/14	29.34	31 17	1.58	14.32	(1.10)
12/13	50.81	282229	0.17	0.00	1.61
Annual Growth	(7.6%)	— —	80.1%	—	63.8%

Gencor Industries Inc

Gencor Industries is a US manufacturer of heavy machinery used in the production of highway construction materials synthetic fuels and environmental control equipment. Subsidiary Bituma designs and manufactures hot-mix asphalt batch plants used in the production of asphalt paving materials. Subsidiary General Combustion engineers combustion systems namely large burners that can transform almost any fuel into energy or burn multiple fuels simultaneously and fluid heat transfer systems under the Hy-Way and Beverley brands. With two manufacturing facilities in the US it sells products through its own sales force and independent dealers and agents located throughout the world.

Operations

Gencor's operations are comprised of Hetherington and Berner (H&B) Hy-Way Heat Bituma Corporation Thermotech Systems and General Combustion.

H&B is a manufacturer of asphalt batch mixing plants while Hy-Way produces thermal fluid process equipment and targets the industrial and asphalt markets. Bituma builds hot mix storage silo systems and Thermotech Systems offers a portable patented thermal absorption process used for processing contaminated soil. General Combustion specializes in advanced combustion technology.

Geographic Reach

Gencor is stationed in Orlando Florida and has two manufacturing facilities in Iowa and Florida. It serves North America Europe the Middle East and Asia. All of its revenue comes from the US.

Sales and Marketing

Gencor's products are sold through sales representatives and independent dealers and agents located throughout the world. It primarily targets the highway construction industry.

Financial Performance

After experiencing two straight years of growth Gencor saw its revenues decrease 23% from $63 million in 2012 to $49 million in 2013. Its profits however surged by 50% from $4.5 million to $6.7 million.

The revenue decline for 2013 was the result of the completion of a large asphalt plant delivered in 2012 and continued weak domestic road construction activity. In addition its Canadian sales declined as various Canadian government's infrastructure spend programs neared completion.

The surge in profits was fueled by continued improvements in production lower purchasing costs reduced product engineering and development expenses and tight controls on selling general and administrative expenses.

Strategy

In response to lower demand for its products and services Gencor is focused on conserving cash and streamlining its operations and cost structure. These actions included adjustments to its workforce reduced purchases of raw materials and reductions in selling general and administrative expenses. In addition it reviews its internal processes to identify inefficiencies and cost reduction opportunities.

HISTORY

The company started out making combustion systems for paving contractors in the 1940s. It incorporated in Florida in 1960 as Mechtron Corporation. In 1969 it merged with Ohio-based General Combustion and Genco Manufacturing. E. J. "Mike" Elliott chairman of General Combustion was named president of the combined company rechristened Mechtron International in 1970. In 1987 it adopted its present name.

In the 1980s Gencor began beefing up its process machinery business moving into thermal fluid heaters industrial incinerators and asphalt-making systems. Asphalt machinery accounted for 70% of sales but the business suffered from cyclical swings. To smooth the ups and downs in 1996 Gencor bought Ingersoll-Rand's food equipment division a maker of pelleting grinding flaking and filtration machines. The buy catapulted Gencor into a leading position in the food processing machinery field. In 1997 it made a series of acquisitions in South America including Brazilian citrus processing equipment maker Gumaco.

In 1998 the company bought ACP Holdings PLC (an asphalt production business with operations in the UK and Australia). It also acquired a 45% interest in Carbontronics and made machinery that company is using to produce synthetic fuel from coal waste. The firm suffered some serious setbacks that year: Bad weather damaged much of Brazil's orange crop hurting results of Gencor's Gumaco subsidiary. The Asian financial crisis also slugged its Gencor ACP unit. Gencor ACP's chairman and CFO were both terminated after irregularities in accounting practices were discovered.

Gencor filed for Chapter 11 bankruptcy protection in 2000 and emerged from Chapter 11 at the end of 2001. The company sold its food processing machinery business for $52 million in 2001.

EXECUTIVES

Secretary, Jeanne M. Lyons
President and Director, Marc G. Elliott, $384,000
  total compensation
Chairman of the Board; Chief Executive Officer,
  E. J. (Mike) Elliott, $600,000 total compensation
VP and Controller, Lawrence C. Maingot, age 55
SVP Sales and Marketing, Dennis B. Hunt, $250,000
  total compensation
CFO, Eric E. Mellen
VP Product Support, Larry K. Miles
Controller, Allen Bradley
President and Director, Marc G. Elliott

Director, Randolph H. Fields
Director, David A. Air
Director, Cort J. Dondero
Director, James P. Sharp
Auditors: Moore Stephens Lovelace, P.A.

LOCATIONS

HQ: Gencor Industries Inc
5201 North Orange Blossom Trail, Orlando, FL 32810
Phone: 407 290-6000
Web: www.gencor.com

PRODUCTS/OPERATIONS

Selected Products and Services

Asphalt Storage Tanks
Baghouse Filtration
Batch Plants
Burners and Combustion Systems
Cold Feed Systems
Gencor Control Automation
Drag Slat Conveyors
Drum Mix Plants
Heat Thermal Fluid Systems
Hot Mix Silos
Mineral Additive Systems
(RAP) Recycle Systems
Soil Remediation Plants
Used Equipment

COMPETITORS

Astec Industries	Coen Company
CMI Terex	Forney Corporation
Caterpillar	Paul Mueller
Cleaver-Brooks	

HISTORICAL FINANCIALS

Company Type: Public

Income Statement   FYE: September 30

	REVENUE ($ mil.)	NET INCOME ($ mil.)	NET PROFIT MARGIN	EMPLOYEES
09/18	98.6	12.5	12.7%	372
09/17	80.6	8.4	10.4%	335
09/16	69.9	7.0	10.1%	273
09/15	39.2	(1.8)	—	216
09/14	40.0	3.4	8.7%	222
Annual Growth	25.3%	37.9%	—	13.8%

2018 Year-End Financials

Debt ratio: —	No. of shares (mil.): 14.5
Return on equity: 9.2%	Dividends
Cash ($ mil.): 8.0	Yield: —
Current ratio: 17.10	Payout: —
Long-term debt ($ mil.): —	Market value ($ mil.): 175.0

	STOCK PRICE ($) FY Close	P/E High/Low	PER SHARE ($) Earnings	Dividends	Book Value
09/18	12.05	21 14	0.85	0.00	9.78
09/17	17.65	31 19	0.57	0.00	8.94
09/16	11.98	37 18	0.49	0.00	8.36
09/15	9.04	— —	(0.13)	0.00	7.88
09/14	9.82	48 35	0.24	0.00	8.00
Annual Growth	5.2%	— —	37.2%	—	5.2%

Genesee & Wyoming Inc.

Genesee & Wyoming (GWI) owns stakes in more than 120 freight railroads. Its network includes 115 short-line and regional freight railroads that operate over a total of more than 22000 miles of track. Among this total about 15900 miles of track are owned and leased by the company and another 3300 miles additional miles are under contractual track access arrangements to more than 40 ports in North America Europe and Australia. Freight transported by GWI railroads includes coal forest products agricultural products automobiles and auto parts chemicals and plastics metallic ores petroleum products and pulp and paper.

Operations

GWI's rolling stock consists of some 1350 locomotives of which 1000 are owned and around 310 are leased. It also maintains 29430 railcars of which 8690 are owned and nearly 20740 are leased.

The company generates non-freight revenues from its railcar switching car hire and rental services demurrage and storage car repair services railroad construction and fuel sales to third-parties. Freight revenues represent around 70% of total sales while non-freight revenues generate about 25%.

Geographic Reach

GWI owns short line and regional freight railroads in the US Australia and Europe. Within North America the company operates through eight regions: Coastal (which includes industrial switching and port operations) Pacific Mountain West Central Southern Midwest Ohio Valley and Canada and the Northeast.

Sales and Marketing

GWI serves some 3000 customers. Its 10 largest customers account for more than 20% of revenue of which two customers (within the iron ore mining agricultural and coal sectors) are located in Australia and two in the UK (maritime shipping firm and infrastructure manager).

Financial Performance

GWI has seen revenue growth over the last five years; however revenues remained static for 2015 and 2016 hovering around the $2 billion mark for both years.

Total traffic from its North American operations in 2016 decreased by 4% mainly due to less traffic from carloads of coal and coke minerals chemicals and plastics metallic ores and pulp and paper. In addition the company's UK/European operations traffic jumped by 24% in 2016 mostly due to new operations partially offset from a 2% decrease form its existing operations which included carloads of coal and minerals.

GWI's net income decreased 37% from $225 million in 2015 to $141 million in 2016 mainly due to a 6% spike in operating expenses. This included additional impairment and related charges mainly related to its European intermodal business and more than $20 million in charges associated with an iron ore customer in Australia that entered voluntary bankruptcy protection.

The company's operating cash flows have decreased the last few years dipping from $475 million in 2015 to $407 million in 2016. This was

due to additional cash it paid for property and equipment and acquisition-related purchases during 2016.

Strategy

The company which has primarily expanded over the years via acquisitions continues to grow by buying railroads not only in North America and Australia but also in European markets. It is focused on growing its rail traffic through regional marketing along with efficiently operating costs as it invests in track and rolling stock to ensure safe operations. It is also focused on equipment investments in Australia and additional investments in its UK intermodal operations.

Mergers and Acquisitions

GWI often uses acquisitions to extend its railroad network in strategic areas. In mid-2017 it purchased Atlantic Western Transportation the parent company of Heart of Georgia Railroad (HOG). The deal extended GWI's network in Georgia as HOG operates on 219 miles of track leased from the Georgia Department of Transportation and connects with two of GWI's railroads. HOG transports 10000 annual carloads of agricultural products feed fertilizer and lumber and forest products.

Enhancing its market position in Australia GWI purchased Glencore Rail (GRail) one of Australió's largest coal haulage businesses in late 2016. The $845 million deal added a significant presence in the Hunter Valley coal supply chain and complemented GWós existing intermodal agricultural and mining operations in South Australia and the Northern Territory.

Company Background

GWI's $1.4 billion milestone deal to purchase RailAmerica in 2012 created the largest short-line railroad operator in the US with about 110 railroads and 15000 miles of track. The transaction helped to skyrocket GWI's revenues by nearly 80% from $875 million in 2012 to $1.57 billion in 2013.

In addition to that significant deal GWI expects freight business in Australia to pick up as the grain harvest in that country increased over the previous year's totals. To that end GWI purchased Australia's FreightLink rail network for about $332 million Australian dollars ($319 million). FreightLink which serves general freight and mining customers in South Australia will operate as part of Genesee & Wyoming Australia (GWA). GWA has managed FreightLink's rail services and operations and provided it with locomotives and crews since its inception.

The original 14-mile Genesee & Wyoming railroad was purchased out of bankruptcy in 1899 by Edward Fuller and his financial partners to transport salt from their mine in Western New York State.

EXECUTIVES

Vice President, Paul Victor
Chairman President and CEO, John C. (Jack) Hellmann, age 47, $849,750 total compensation
SVP Coastal Region Companies Genesee & Wyoming Railroad Services Inc., Andrew T. Chunko, age 49
VP Corporate Development and Treasurer, Matthew O. Walsh, age 43, $500,000 total compensation
SVP Information Technology Genesee & Wyoming Railroad Services Inc., Mike Meyers
CFO, Timothy J. Gallagher, age 55, $466,796 total compensation

SVP Southern Region Railroads Genesee &
Wyoming Railroad Services Inc., Bill Jasper
Managing Director Rotterdam Rail Feeding,
Arnoud de Rade
SVP Pacific Region Railroads Genesee &
Wyoming Railroad Services Inc., James E. Irvin
SVP Central Region Railroads Genesee &
Wyoming Railroad Services Inc., Dewayne
Swindall
COO, David A. Brown, age 59, $414,812 total
compensation
SVP Northeast Region Railroads Genesee &
Wyoming Railroad Services Inc., Dave Ebbrecht
SVP Canada Region Railroads and President
Genesee & Wyoming Canada Inc., Louis Gravel
SVP Midwest Region Railroads Genesee &
Wyoming Railroad Services Inc., Gary R. Long
SVP Mountain West Region Railroads Genesee &
Wyoming Railroad Services Inc., J. Bradley Ovitt
Executive Director and Chief Commercial Officer
Genesee & Wyoming Australia Pty Ltd., John
McArthur
CEO Freightliner Group Ltd., Russell Mears
Managing Director Freightliner Ltd. UK, Adam
Cunliffe
Managing Director Freightliner Maintenance Ltd.,
Dave Curtis
Managing Director Freightliner Poland, Konstantin
Skorik
Senior Vice President Information Technology,
Jean Wilson
Vice President Environmental Compliance, Rick
Norris
Senior Vice President Safety and Compliance,
Tyrone James
Executive Vice President International Business
Development, Mark Hastings
Vice President Finance And Administration,
Gerald Sattora
Vice President ?? Commercial Counsel, Kenneth
Charron
Senior Vice President Corporate Development and
Treasurer, Thomas Savage
Senior Vice President Operations, Bill Riehl
Vice President Sales and Marketing, Micah Powell
Vice President Marketing and Sales, Russ Smitley
Vice President, Kirk Bedford
Assistant Vice President, Kevin Phillips
Vice President of Safety Pacific Region, Craig
Ashenfelter
Board Member, Richard Bott
Board Member, Hunter Smith
Board Member, Hans Norkus
Board Member, Albert Neupaver
Board Member, Joseph Pyne
Auditors: PricewaterhouseCoopers LLP

LOCATIONS

HQ: Genesee & Wyoming Inc.
20 West Avenue, Darien, CT 06820
Phone: 203 202-8900
Web: www.gwrr.com

PRODUCTS/OPERATIONS

2016 Sales

	$ mil.	% of total
Freight	1,371.6	68
Freight-related	536.3	27
All Other	93.6	5
Total	**2,001.5**	**100**

COMPETITORS

Anacostia Rail Holdings	Iowa Interstate Railroad

Arkansas & Missouri Railroad	Kansas City Southern
Burlington Northern Santa Fe	Montana Rail Link
	Norfolk Southern
CSX	OmniTRAX
Canadian National Railway	Pan Am Railways
	Pinsly Railroad
Canadian Pacific Railway	Pioneer Railcorp
	Providence and Worcester Railroad
Dakota Minnesota & Eastern Railroad	Union Pacific
	Watco Companies

HISTORICAL FINANCIALS

Company Type: Public

Income Statement   FYE: December 31

	REVENUE ($ mil.)	NET INCOME ($ mil.)	NET PROFIT MARGIN	EMPLOYEES
12/17	2,208.0	549.0	24.9%	8,000
12/16	2,001.5	141.1	7.1%	7,300
12/15	2,000.4	225.0	11.2%	7,500
12/14	1,639.0	260.7	15.9%	5,200
12/13	1,569.0	271.3	17.3%	4,800
Annual Growth	**8.9%**	**19.3%**	**—**	**13.6%**

2017 Year-End Financials

Debt ratio: 29.0%
Return on equity: 16.9%
Cash ($ mil.): 80.4
Current ratio: 1.26
Long-term debt ($ mil.): 2,303.4

No. of shares (mil.): 62.6
Dividends
Yield: —
Payout: —
Market value ($ mil.): 4,932.0

	STOCK PRICE ($) FY Close	P/E High/Low		PER SHARE ($) Earnings	Dividends	Book Value
12/17	78.73	9	7	8.79	0.00	57.12
12/16	69.41	33	18	2.42	0.00	46.60
12/15	53.69	26	13	3.89	0.00	43.64
12/14	89.92	22	18	4.58	0.00	43.68
12/13	96.05	20	15	4.79	0.00	40.11
Annual Growth	**(4.8%)**	**—**	**—**	**16.4%**		**9.2%**

Gentex Corp.

Gentex would agree that competitors never look better than when they are in the rearview. The company focuses on designing making and marketing interior and exterior auto-dimming rearview mirrors and camera-based driver-assist systems for the automotive market. It serves customers worldwide but its largest base includes big carmakers such as Toyota General Motors and Volkswagen. Its products are found as standard or optional features on hundreds of vehicle models. To a lesser degree Gentex also makes dimmable aircraft windows found on commercial aircraft and fire protection products — including smoke detectors fire alarms and signaling devices — primarily for commercial buildings.

Operations

The company's fire protection products are primarily sold to domestic distributors and OEMs of fire and security systems. Within the aerospace industry Gentex has delivered dimmable aircraft windows to the production line of Boeing's new 787 Dreamliner series and to Hawker Beechcraft for its business-class Beechcraft King Air 350i airplane. Gentex's dimmable window systems are

marketed by PPG Aerospace under the brand name Alteos Interactive Window Systems.

Geographic Reach

Operating through five manufacturing facilities in Michigan Gentex has additional offices in the US Korea Canada France Mexico China Japan Sweden Hungary and the UK. Unsurprisingly the company's largest markets are the leading car production countries of the US (32% of net sales) Germany (19%) and Japan (10%).

Sales and Marketing

The company's top customer is Volkswagen (14% of sales). Other major clients have included BMW Ford Chrysler and Nissan. Gentex markets its products directly to OEMs as well as through Tier 1 suppliers.

Financial Performance

The company has achieved unprecedented growth over the years with revenues jumping 17% from $223 million in 2013 to $289 million in 2014. Profits also surged 29% from $223 million to $289 million over that same time period. (Both 2014 totals counted as historical milestones for the company.)

The historic growth for 2014 was fueled by increased sales from automotive products and other products. Automotive net sales spiked due to its acquisition of HomeLink and an 11% increase in auto-dimming mirror shipments. Dimmable aircraft window sales also increased 54% year over year and fire protection sales surged by 4%.

Strategy

To boost production capacity and support growth in its core geographic territories Gentex is busy making investments in its facilities. It constructed a new technology center adjacent to its headquarters in Zeeland Michigan and it is making a number of facility upgrades and renovations. The investments support the company's optimistic sales forecast and anticipated growing demand for high-tech camera-based automotive products such as Gentex's rear camera displays which consist of a liquid crystal display (LCD) that works with a rear-mounted video camera to provide a rear view while backing up and its SmartBeam high-beam assist system which uses a camera-on-a-chip to maximize forward lighting while eliminating the task of turning the high beams on and off manually. Both are integrated into Gentex auto-dimming mirrors.

Mergers and Acquisitions

Gentex has also achieved milestone revenues due to acquisitions. In 2013 it obtained HomeLink a wireless vehicle/home communications product that enables drivers to remotely activate garage door openers entry door locks home lighting security systems entry gates and other radio frequency convenience products. Gentex integrated HomeLink into its interior auto-dimming rearview mirrors product portfolio.

In 2014 Gentex acquired Helmet Integrated Systems Ltd (HISL). Headquartered in the UK HISL provides helmets communications equipment and respiratory protection for civil defense security and industrial personnel. The addition of HISL accelerated Gentex's international growth by providing it immediate access to new markets particularly within the UK.

HISTORY

At 23 Fred Bauer had already started and sold one company before founding Gentex in 1974. A maker of dual-cell photoelectric smoke detectors Gentex found its niche with products that had fewer false alarms and could detect slow smoldering fires. The company went public in 1981.

The next year Gentex entered the automotive market with the first electromechanical dimming mirror to beat the glare of nighttime driving. (Electrochromic technology uses electricity to darken a material.) The product was soon snapped up by Ford and General Motors to the tune of 200000 units a year. Five years later Gentex debuted the interior Night Vision Safety (NVS) electrochromic automatic-dimming mirror. Exterior NVS mirrors were introduced in 1991.

Gentex entered an agreement in 1992 with Japan's Ichikoh Industries to market mirrors in Asia. The following year it established a European office. Returning to its roots Gentex in 1993 introduced an AC/DC smoke detector. That year rival Donnelly paid $3.6 million in damages for infringing on Gentex's electrochromic mirror patent. Gentex formed a German subsidiary Gentex GmbH in 1994 and two years later opened an $8 million plant near its Michigan headquarters.

In 1997 Gentex developed a compass mirror a headlamp control mirror and a mirror that displays outside temperature. The next year it bought a stake in Photobit a developer of pixel sensor technology and sold more than 3.3 million NVS mirrors. In 1999 DaimlerChrysler agreed to equip all its models with Gentex mirrors.

Adding to its manufacturing capacity Gentex in 2000 completed the construction of a $12 million mirror manufacturing plant in Zeeland Michigan and made plans to build a factory in Europe. Adding more equipment to rearview mirrors paid off when GM announced that it would place the OnStar communications system in Gentex's interior mirrors in 1 million automobiles.

In 2002 Gentex announced that it would bring its new SmartBeam product to market by mid-2004. SmartBeam allowed drivers to use their bright lights more easily because the high beam self-dimmed when it detected an oncoming car. SureBeam came to market in 2004 the same year Gentex finished constructing a sales and engineering facility in Erlenbach Germany. The facility was intended to help Gentex better serve its European customers by offering greater logistics sales and engineering support.

EXECUTIVES

Chairman and CEO, Fred T. Bauer, age 76, $464,031 total compensation
VP Purchasing and Advanced Technology, Mark Newton, age 59, $257,040 total compensation
VP Operations, Paul Flynn, $153,273 total compensation
VP Europe, Brad Bosma
President COO Interim CFO and Treasurer, Steve Downing
Vice President Operations, John Arnold
Treasurer, Randy Beute
Auditors: Ernst & Young LLP

LOCATIONS

HQ: Gentex Corp.
600 N. Centennial, Zeeland, MI 49464
Phone: 616 772-1800   **Fax:** 616 772-7348
Web: www.gentex.com

PRODUCTS/OPERATIONS

Selected Products
Automotive
  Auto-dimming mirrors
  Curved glass mirrors
  Custom sensors (for detecting velocity rain and humidity)
  Interior lighting
  Microphones
  Mirror-based displays
  Side blind zone indicators
  SmartBeam (automatic high beam system integrated into auto-dimming mirror)
  Telematics systems
  Razor (turn signal lights)
  Rear camera display (LCD display integrated into auto-dimming mirror that works with a video camera mounted at rear of vehicle)
Fire protection
  Audio and visual signaling appliances
  Bells and speakers
  Carbon monoxide alarms
  Photoelectric smoke alarms and detectors
Other
  Dimmable aircraft windows

COMPETITORS

Ficosa
Guardian Industries
Ichikoh
Ingersoll-Rand Security Technologies
Magna Mirrors
Murakami Corp.
Safety Vision
SimplexGrinnell
UTC Climate Controls & Security
Universal Security Instruments
Visteon

HISTORICAL FINANCIALS

Company Type: Public

Income Statement   FYE: December 31

	REVENUE ($ mil.)	NET INCOME ($ mil.)	NET PROFIT MARGIN	EMPLOYEES
12/17	1,794.8	406.7	22.7%	5,481
12/16	1,678.9	347.5	20.7%	5,315
12/15	1,543.6	318.4	20.6%	4,757
12/14	1,375.5	288.6	21.0%	4,196
12/13	1,171.8	222.9	19.0%	3,801
Annual Growth	11.2%	16.2%	—	9.6%

2017 Year-End Financials

Debt ratio: 3.3%	No. of shares (mil.): 280.2
Return on equity: 20.5%	Dividends
Cash ($ mil.): 569.7	Yield: 0.0%
Current ratio: 4.86	Payout: 26.9%
Long-term debt ($ mil.): —	Market value ($ mil.): 5,872.0

	STOCK PRICE ($) FY Close	P/E High/Low		PER SHARE ($) Earnings	Dividends	Book Value
12/17	20.95	16	12	1.41	0.38	7.31
12/16	19.69	17	11	1.19	0.35	6.64
12/15	16.01	33	14	1.08	0.33	5.91
12/14	36.13	38	27	0.98	0.30	5.32
12/13	32.98	43	24	0.78	0.28	4.56
Annual Growth	(10.7%)	—	—	16.1%	8.4%	12.5%

Gentherm Inc

Don't worry TED can keep your car seat warm ... or cool. Gentherm develops thermoelectric device (TED) technology for its climate-control seats (CCS) for vehicles. CCS products can be found on the vehicles of nearly every automotive manufacturer in North America Europe and Asia. Other Gentherm products include heated and cooled cup holders steering wheel heaters and heated door and armrests. The company's industrial segment also makes battery thermal management products waste heat recovery products and hospital patient temperature management systems. The company sells its products worldwide but the US represents its largest market.

Operations

Gentherm has two reportable segments: Automotive and Industrial. The Automotive segment accounts for about 90% of total revenue and is comprised of the company's global automotive business and individual convenience products. This business makes seat comfort systems including seat heaters variable temperature Climate Control Seats (CCS) and integrated electronic components such as blowers and electronic control units. It also produces specialized automotive cable system products such as ready-made wire harnesses and related wiring products. Other automotive products in this segment are steering wheel heaters heated door and armrests heated and cooled cup holders and thermal storage bins.

The Industrial segment (10% of revenue) consists of patient temperature management systems that manage patient body and blood temperatures in hospitals and its advanced research and product development division that develops products that improve the efficiency of thermal management technologies.

Geographic Reach

Gentherm is based in Northville MI and has facilities in the US Canada Mexico China Vietnam Germany Hungary Macedonia and the Ukraine. The US accounts for 45% of its total sales while China generates about 10%. Other major markets include Germany South Korea Japan and Canada.

Sales and Marketing

Gentherm depends on its three largest customers to generate about 45% of its total sales. These include Lear Corporation (20% of total sales) Adient (more than 15%) and Bosch Automotive (about 10%). The company actually markets its products however to OEMs such as General Motors Ford Volkswagen and Fiat Chrysler to name a few. These auto manufacturers then direct their suppliers to work with Gentherm.

Financial Performance

Gentherm has seen steady growth over the last five years. Its 2017 revenues reached $985.7 million a 7% increase compared with 2016. Gentherm cited increased sales from its recent acquisitions of CSZ in 2016 and Etratech in late 2017 for the increase as well as the favorable impact of foreign currency rates.

Net income however dropped to $35.2 million down more than $41 million from 2016 the second consecutive year of decline in net profits. The decrease in 2017 was primarily due to higher research and development expenses and higher interest expenses.

Cash at the end of fiscal 2017 was $103.2 million a decrease of $74.0 million from the prior year. Cash from operations contributed $49.9 million to the coffers while investing activities used $117.7 million mainly for its acquisition of Etratech and purchases of property and equipment. Financing activities used another $31.6 million mainly for repayments of debt.

Strategy

Going forward Gentherm plans to expand its core technologies and portfolio of products in the automotive industry and penetrate new markets. The company introduced a "Fit-for-Growth" plan in 2018 aimed at divesting non-core businesses such as its Global Power Technologies (GPT) subsidiary (serves the oil and gas market) and products related to furniture and aviation. Instead it is focusing on increasing efficiency and expanding its engineering operations.

In its automotive segment the company is adding application engineers to develop the next generation of seat comfort products automotive cooled storage devices and interior thermal management devices. The company also plans to leverage the rapid development of fully electric and autonomous vehicles by focusing on new products related to battery-related applications.

In the industrial sector the company is targeting medical applications to increase sales of its patient thermal management products including its Hemotherm blood heater and cooler and Blanketrol hyper-hypothermia system that manages body temperature.

The company is also investing in other key technologies including thermophysiology software and electronics simulation and thermal engines.

Mergers and Acquisitions

The company has achieved historic revenue growth over the years primarily through the use of acquisitions. In 2017 Gentherm acquired Etratech an electronics market leader specializing in design development and manufacturing of advanced electronic controls.

In 2016 it acquired Cincinnati Sub-Zero Products (CSZ) a leading provider of temperature management equipment serving the medical industrial and testing industries.

EXECUTIVES

VP CFO and Treasurer, Barry G. Steele, age 47, $350,000 total compensation
VP and General Counsel, Kenneth J. (Ken) Phillips, $370,000 total compensation
President Automotive Business Unit, Frithjof Oldorff, $404,575 total compensation
President and CEO, Daniel R. Coker, age 66, $700,000 total compensation
VP Product Development, Darren A. Schumacher, $319,300 total compensation
Vice President Product Strategy and Business Planning, John Marx
Vice President, Jim Mertes
Chairman, Oscar B. (Bud) Marx, age 79
Board Member, Lewis Booth
Board Member, Byron Shaw
Auditors: Grant Thornton LLP

LOCATIONS

HQ: Gentherm Inc
21680 Haggerty Road, Northville, MI 48167
Phone: 248 504-0500
Web: www.gentherm.com

PRODUCTS/OPERATIONS

2017 Sales

	% of total
Automotive	89
Industrial	11
Total	**100**

Selected Products

Climate Control Seat (CCS)
ComfortBalance Seat
Steering wheel heating
Vehicle surface heating
Battery thermal management
Automotive Cable Technology (ACT)
CSZ patient temperature management subsidiary
Hemotherm blood heater and cooler
Blanketrol hyper-hypothermia systems
Etratech electronics subsidiary

COMPETITORS

Commercial Vehicle	Magna International
Delphi Automotive Systems	Toyota Boshoku
Leggett & Platt	Visteon

HISTORICAL FINANCIALS

Company Type: Public

Income Statement

FYE: December 31

	REVENUE ($ mil.)	NET INCOME ($ mil.)	NET PROFIT MARGIN	EMPLOYEES
12/17	985.6	35.2	3.6%	13,069
12/16	917.6	76.6	8.3%	11,685
12/15	856.4	95.3	11.1%	10,098
12/14	811.3	70.1	8.6%	8,607
12/13	662.0	33.8	5.1%	7,403
Annual Growth	**10.5%**	**1.0%**	**—**	**15.3%**

2017 Year-End Financials

Debt ratio: 16.3%
Return on equity: 6.9%
Cash ($ mil.): 103.1
Current ratio: 2.69
Long-term debt ($ mil.): 141.2
No. of shares (mil.): 36.7
Dividends
Yield: —
Payout: —
Market value ($ mil.): 1,167.0

	STOCK PRICE ($) FY Close	P/E High/Low	PER SHARE ($) Earnings	Dividends	Book Value
12/17	31.75	42 31	0.96	0.00	15.07
12/16	33.85	23 13	2.09	0.00	12.60
12/15	47.40	22 14	2.62	0.00	10.58
12/14	36.62	26 12	1.95	0.00	8.24
12/13	26.81	27 14	0.94	0.00	6.64
Annual Growth	**4.3%**	**— —**	**0.5%**	**—**	**22.7%**

GEO Group Inc (The) (New)

The GEO Group sticks to its convictions and it relies on them to generate business. It is one of the largest correctional systems in the US with operations in more than 30 states and electronic monitoring services in every state. It operates more than 140 correctional detention and mental health facilities with some 96000 beds. Besides incarceration GEO offers educational rehabilitative and vocational training programs at its facilities. The firm offers mental health and residential treatment services through its GEO Care subsidiary.

HISTORY

The company that became The Geo Group began as part of the Wackenhut Corporation (now known as G4S Secure Solutions (USA)) which was founded in 1954 as an investigation firm and moved into the security guard business the next year. When the prison population began to grow in the late 1970s and early 1980s (because of tougher sentences and new federal drug laws) Wackenhut established its Wackenhut Corrections division in 1984 to focus on prison management.

In 1986 the division won its first contract to construct a Colorado facility for the Immigration and Naturalization Service. Two years later Wackenhut Corrections became a full-fledged subsidiary of its parent. Wackenhut Corrections ventured overseas in 1992 when it began operating a prison in Australia and formed a joint venture Premier Prison Services with Serco Group to provide prison management services in the UK.

The company's next step was to go public which it did in 1994 when Wackenhut Corporation sold a minority stake. Also that year Premier Prison Services won its first contract to operate a prison in the town of Doncaster in the UK. The joint venture won another deal in 1997 to manage a 500-bed prison in Kilmarnock Scotland. However Wackenhut Corrections was forced to change policies after violence at some of its foreign prisons. To solve the problem the company replaced American guards with native hires and began paying more attention to troublesome inmates.

Wackenhut Corrections moved beyond prisons in 1997 buying an 86-bed psychiatric hospital in Fort Lauderdale Florida. The next year Wackenhut Corrections spun off a real estate investment trust (REIT) Correctional Properties Trust to buy and build prison facilities and lease them back to the company. (The REIT was later renamed Centra-Core Properties Trust.)

Wackenhut Corrections stumbled in 1999 when the state of Texas took over control of a Wackenhut-operated prison in Austin after allegations that guards had had sex with female inmates. In addition a riot at a New Mexico prison sparked bad publicity. But business continued to roll in and the company gained contracts to run a prison in New Zealand and a hospital in Florida.

After its closure in 2000 Wackenhut's juvenile facility in Jena Louisiana was named in a lawsuit brought by the US Justice Department against Louisiana prisons. The company shifted focus to its international operations in 2001 — it expanded existing prisons in Australia and opened prisons in South Africa and the UK.

Danish security firm Group 4 Falck gained control of Wackenhut Corrections in 2002 when it acquired Wackenhut Corporation. Late in the year Wackenhut Corrections acquired four additional facilities in Michigan New Mexico North Carolina and Texas.

In an effort to raise capital needed to expand its prison systems Wackenhut Corrections sold its 50% stake in Premier Custodial Group to Serco in 2003. Also that year Wackenhut Corrections bought back the 57% stake that Group 4 Falck held in the company. As a condition of the purchase the company changed its name to The GEO

Group and abandoned its connection to the Wackenhut trademark and name.

GEO expanded in 2005 by buying smaller US rival Correctional Services Corporation. GEO paid about $62 million in cash for Correctional Services and assumed about $124 million of the company's debt. Upon the deal's closing GEO sold Correctional Services' juvenile operations to Correctional Services CEO James Slattery. Correctional Services' adult operations — 16 facilities with an overall capacity of about 8000 beds — were absorbed into those of GEO.

In 2006 the company sold its mental health subsidiary Atlantic Shores Healthcare (ASH) which included a 72-bed mental health hospital for approximately $11.5 million. Also that year GEO renewed its contract (for an additional five years) with the US Department of State and the US Department of Homeland Security to operate the Migrant Operations Center (MOC) at Guantanamo Bay. The MOC a separate facility from the controversial GITMO detention center is intended for immigrants caught at sea without US entry documents.

In 2009 GEO opened a new $62 million Florida Civil Commitment Center (FCCC) in Arcadia Florida. The facility has a capacity of 720 residents and provides treatment services to sexually violent predators. FCCC is operated by GEO Care under a management contract with the Florida Department of Children and Families. Also that year GEO purchased Just Care a provider of medical and mental health services to detainees primarily in Georgia and South Carolina for about $40 million.

Events in 2010 included the company's $730 million acquisition of rival Cornell Companies a private provider of educational treatment and correctional services. Cornell's business which comprises outsourced-contracts with federal state and local governmental agencies is included in GEO's US Detention & Corrections and GEO Care segments which due to the Cornell acquisition generated sales of about $85 and $66 million respectively. The Cornell investment came subsequent to GEO's

GEO also wrapped up a number of projects in 2010 including the completion of the Aurora ICE Processing Center (Colorado) Blackwater River Correctional Facility (Florida) and Harmondsworth Immigration Removal Centre (London). Additionally it landed a new management contract with the D. Ray James Correctional Facility (Georgia).

EXECUTIVES

Vice President Programs, Gary Templeton
Vice President Corporate Relations, Pablo Paez
Chairman and CEO, George C. Zoley, age 68, $1,179,350 total compensation
SVP North American Operations, John M. Hurley, age 70, $515,000 total compensation
SVP and CFO, Brian R. Evans, age 50, $515,000 total compensation
SVP; President GEO Community Services, Ann M. Schlarb
Vp Finance And Treasurer, Shayn P March, age 54
Divisional Vice President Finance, Larry Sherman
Vice President Finance, Blake Barras
Senior Vice President General Counsel and Secretary, John Bulfin
Senior Vice President Development, Thomas Wierdsma
Vice President Construction Services, Rick Zahner

Executive Vice President Contract Compliance, Patricia Persante
Senior Vice President, David Venturella
Vice President Office Of Professional Responsibility, Joseph Woodring
Vice President of Risk Management, Philip Dugger
Divisional Vice President Community, Loren Grayer
Divisional Vice President Continuum of Care, John Thurston
Vice President Operations, Blake Davis
Executive Vice President, Ernesto Alvarez
Executive Vice President Business Development, Adam Hasner
Board Member, Anne Foreman
Auditors: GRANT THORNTON LLP

LOCATIONS

HQ: GEO Group Inc (The) (New)
One Park Place, 621 NW 53rd Street, Suite 700, Boca Raton, FL 33487
Phone: 561 893-0101
Web: www.geogroup.com

PRODUCTS/OPERATIONS

2017 Revenue by Segment

	$ mil.	% of total
US Corrections & Detention	1,438.0	63
GEO Care	514.2	23
International Services	195.8	9
Facility Construction & Design	115.4	5
Total	**2,263.4**	**100**

Selected Products and Services

Adult inmate management
Behavioral health and residential treatment services for youthful offenders
Community-based residential re-entry services
Construction management
Correctional health care services
Electronic monitoring devices
Facility design
Facility maintenance
Facility management
Facility operation
Infrastructure financing
Pre-trial and immigration custody services
Residential mental health / special needs services
Secure prisoner escort

Selected Facilities

Arizona State Prison - Phoenix West (Phoenix Arizona)
Aurora ICE Processing Center (Aurora Colorado)
Blackwater River Correctional Facility (Milton Florida)
Bronx Community Re-Entry Center (Bronx New York)
Broward Transition Center (Deerfield Beach Florida)
D. Ray James Correctional Facility (Folkston Georgia)
Harmondsworth Immigration Removal Centre (London England)
Lawrenceville Correctional Center (Lawrenceville Virginia)
South Bay Correctional Facility (South Bay Florida)

COMPETITORS

3M
Avalon Correctional Services
Corizon
Corrections Corporation of America
G4S
MHM Services
Management & Training
Res-Care
Sodexo

HISTORICAL FINANCIALS

Company Type: Public

Income Statement
FYE: December 31

	REVENUE ($ mil.)	NET INCOME ($ mil.)	NET PROFIT MARGIN	EMPLOYEES
12/17	2,263.4	146.2	6.5%	18,512
12/16	2,179.4	148.7	6.8%	19,370
12/15	1,843.3	139.4	7.6%	15,806
12/14	1,691.6	143.9	8.5%	17,479
12/13	1,522.0	115.1	7.6%	16,292
Annual Growth	10.4%	6.2%	—	3.2%

2017 Year-End Financials

Debt ratio: 61.0%
Return on equity: 13.4%
Cash ($ mil.): 81.3
Current ratio: 1.57
Long-term debt ($ mil.): 2,552.9

No. of shares (mil.): 124.0
Dividends
  Yield: 0.0%
  Payout: 155.1%
Market value ($ mil.): 2,927.0

	STOCK PRICE ($) FY Close	P/E High/Low	PER SHARE ($) Earnings	Dividends	Book Value
12/17	23.60	40 19	1.21	1.88	9.67
12/16	35.93	27 15	1.33	1.73	8.66
12/15	28.91	36 21	1.25	1.67	8.99
12/14	40.36	31 23	1.32	0.41	9.40
12/13	32.22	36 26	1.07	0.00	9.47
Annual Growth	(7.5%)		3.0%	—	0.5%

German American Bancorp Inc

German American Bancorp is the holding company for German American Bank which operates some 65 branches in southern Indiana and Kentucky. Founded in 1910 the bank offers such standard retail products as checking and savings accounts certificates of deposit and IRAs. It also provides trust services while sister company German American Investment Services provides trust investment advisory and brokerage services. German American Bancorp also owns German American Insurance which offers corporate and personal insurance products. The group's core banking operations provide more than 90% of its total sales.

Geographic Reach

German American is headquartered in Jasper Indiana. Its subsidiaries operate from more than 60 locations in southern Indiana and Kentucky.

Sales and Marketing

German American Bancorp spent $3.5 million on advertising in 2017. Advertising expenses totaled $2.7 million in 2016 and $3.7 million in 2015.

Financial Performance

German American's revenue has been climbing steadily for the past five years thanks to the company's acquisitions of other area banks. Similarly net income has also been on the rise. In 2017 the company marked its eighth consecutive year of record earnings.

In 2017 revenue increased 4% to $131.8 million. That increase was partially due to the addition of River Valley Financial Bank which German American acquired in 2016. Growth in the company's loan portfolio also boosted net interest income. This was slightly offset by a 1% decline in non-interest income. Although trust and insurance operations rose other operating income declined $1.1 million (29%).

Net income rose 16% to $35.2 million in 2017; in addition to having higher revenue the company recognized a benefit related to the reduced corporate tax rate that year.

German American ended 2017 with $70.4 million in net cash $5.5 million more than it had at the end of 2016. Operating activities provided $54.9 million in cash and financing activities provided $139.9 million. Investing activities used $189.3 million.

Strategy

German American Bancorp has grown recently through a number of acquisitions including bank branches an insurance office and other bank holding companies. These acquisitions have also helped the company grow into new geographic markets including locations in Kentucky.

Growth by acquisition can be somewhat risky though. The company could unknowingly acquire problem assets or have difficulties integrating other banks it purchases. These issues could bring down its financial performance.

German American operates in a relatively small region which leaves it vulnerable to economic downturns in that area. If economic conditions in its market decline German American faces the risk of increased delinquencies and charge-offs. The company's larger more widespread competitors would be less impacted in such a case.

Mergers and Acquisitions

In October 2018 German American Bancorp acquired Kentucky's First Security Bank for $101 million. With that deal the company expanded into Kentucky's Owensboro Bowling Green and Lexington markets.

Earlier that year the company purchased five Indiana branches from First Financial Bank. That acquisition helped quell regulatory concerns about the merger between First Financial and MainSource Bank.

In 2016 German American acquired River Valley Bancorp and its River Valley Financial Bank subsidiary. It entered the Kentucky market through that purchase.

EXECUTIVES

Vice President, Lisa Matheis

General technical; Senior Vice President, Floyd Alsman

Chairman and CEO, Mark A. Schroeder, age 65, $342,500 total compensation

President, Clay W. Ewing, age 63, $250,000 total compensation

EVP CFO and Senior Administrative Officer, Bradley M. Rust, age 52, $210,000 total compensation

SVP and Chief Credit Officer, Keith A. Leinenbach, age 59, $180,000 total compensation

SVP and Head of Retail Banking, Randall L. Braun, age 58, $180,000 total compensation

Senior Vice President Trust Officer, Dave Mitchell

Vice President Deposit Services Secruity, Dale Altstadt

Senior Vice President of Technology and Operations, Clay Barrett

Senior Vice President Commercial Banking, Joe Hauersperger

Senior Vice President Commercial Banking, Julie Donham

Regional Senior Vice President, Jim Thomas

Vice President, Christina Lebeau

Senior Vice President Commercial Lender, Jane Thoma

Regional Vice President, Jean Emery

Vice President Private Banking, Sherri Alley

Vice President Senior Wealth Advisor, Jim Godsey

Executive Vice President Head of Trust, Brent Sternberg

Vice President, John Schroeder

Regional Vice President Commercial Lending, Doug Bell

Vice President Commercial Banking, Rob Bingham

Vice President Commercial Banking, John Newcomer

Senior Vice President Commercial Banking, Greg Cardinal

Vice President Commercial Banking, Randy Goodman

Senior Vice President Senior Wealth Advisor, Alan VanCleef

Vice President Agriculture and Commercial Banking, Gaven Oexmann

Regional Senior Vice President, Steve Walker

Board Member, Chris Ramsey

Auditors: Crowe Horwath LLP

LOCATIONS

HQ: German American Bancorp Inc
711 Main Street, Jasper, IN 47546
Phone: 812 482-1314
Web: www.germanamerican.com

PRODUCTS/OPERATIONS

2017 Sales

	$ mil.	% of total
Interest		
Loans including fees	91.7	64
Securities including dividends	19.2	13
Short-term investments	0.1	-
Non-interest		
Insurance	8.0	6
Service charges on deposit accounts	6.2	4
Trust & investment product fees	5.3	4
Other	12.4	9
Adjustments	(11.1)	-
Total	**131.8**	**100**

COMPETITORS

Fidelity Federal	Home Financial Bancorp
Fifth Third	Old National Bancorp
First Bancorp of Indiana	Porter Bancorp
First Capital	SVB&T

HISTORICAL FINANCIALS

Company Type: Public

Income Statement

FYE: December 31

	ASSETS ($ mil.)	NET INCOME ($ mil.)	INCOME AS % OF ASSETS	EMPLOYEES
12/17	3,144.3	40.6	1.3%	614
12/16	2,955.9	35.1	1.2%	597
12/15	2,373.7	30.0	1.3%	596
12/14	2,237.1	28.3	1.3%	484
12/13	2,163.8	25.4	1.2%	480
Annual Growth	**9.8%**	**12.5%**	**—**	**6.3%**

2017 Year-End Financials

Return on assets: 1.3%
Return on equity: 11.7%
Long-term debt ($ mil.): —
No. of shares (mil.): 22.9
Sales ($ mil): 142.8

Dividends
Yield: 0.0%
Payout: 29.1%
Market value ($ mil.): 810.0

	STOCK PRICE ($) FY Close	P/E High/Low	PER SHARE ($) Earnings	Dividends	Book Value
12/17	35.33	30 17	1.77	0.52	15.90
12/16	52.61	34 19	1.57	0.48	14.43
12/15	33.32	23 18	1.51	0.45	12.67
12/14	30.52	22 17	1.43	0.43	11.54
12/13	28.42	23 15	1.32	0.40	10.13
Annual Growth	**5.6%**	**— —**	**7.6%**	**6.6%**	**11.9%**

Glacier Bancorp, Inc.

Glacier Bancorp is on a Rocky Mountain high. The holding company owns about a dozen community bank divisions with about 100 locations in Montana Idaho Utah Washington Arizona Colorado and Wyoming. Serving individuals small to midsized businesses not-for-profits and public entities the banks offer traditional deposit products and credit cards in addition to retail brokerage and investment services through agreements with third-party providers. Its lending activities consist of commercial real estate loans (about half of the company's loan portfolio) as well as residential mortgages business loans and consumer loans.

Financial Performance

Glacier's financial results are on a steady upward swing since 2012 with yearly increases in interest income and near-annual improvement in non-interest income and net income.

In 2017 the company generated $375 million in interest income and $112 million in non-interest income for total revenue of $487 million. Its loan portfolio grew by $601 million or 11% in the year bringing the size of its loan portfolio to just less than $6.5 billion.

Net income for the year was $116 million 4% more than 2016 due to the higher revenue partially offset by an increase in loan loss provisions employee compensation and income tax expense.

Glacier Bancorp ended 2017 with $200 million in cash an increase of nearly $50 million over the previous year. Financing activities used $230 million for loan repayments stock dividends and a decrease in deposits. Investing activities added $24 million to the coffers and operating activities contributed $255 million mostly from net income a deferred tax expense and proceeds from selling some of its loan portfolio.

Strategy

Glacier Bancorp hopes to capitalize on additional acquisition opportunities that it expects to arise as small banks deal with new industry regulations. To this end it has been on a buying spree in recent years. In early 2018 it acquired Inter-Mountain Bancorp (Montana) Columbine Capital Corporation (Colorado); in 2017 it purchased TFB Bancorp (Arizona); in 2016 it bought Treasure State Bank (Montana) and in 2015 Glacier acquired Canon Bank Corporation (Colorado) and Montana Community Banks (Montana). In total these purchases cost $377 million.

The company is also banking on organic growth with the populations of the states in its market area growing faster than the national average thanks to an influx of retiring Baby Boomers and an increase in energy- and natural resource-related jobs.

EXECUTIVES

EVP and CFO, Ron J. Copher, $352,651 total compensation
EVP and Chief Administrative Officer, Don J. Cherry, $299,950 total compensation
President and CEO, Randall M. (Randy) Chesler, age 60, $153,846 total compensation
Vice President And Cra And Compliance Officer, Lanette Marcum
Senior Vice President, Robert Taylor
Vice President Internal Auditor, Judy Overcast
Vice President Marketing North America, Martha Tannehill
Vice President, Ryan T Screnar
Assistant Vice President, Judy Gohsman
Vice President, Donald Mccarthy
Executive Vice President Chief Admin Officer, Don Chery
Senior Vice President of Human Resources, Robin S Roush
Vice President of Human Resources, Christopher Murphy
Vice President Internal Auditor, Leslie Thompson
Vice President, Melody Pieri
VP Corporate BSA Officer, Mary Strozzi
Vice President and Risk Manager, Emily Lamb
Senior Vice President Enterprise wide Risk Manager, T Frickle
Assistant Vice President Benefits Administrator, Jill Klocke
Vice President Risk Management, T J Frickle
Real Estate Lender Vice President, Toby Gilchrist
Board Member, Craig A Langel
Chairman, Dallas I. Herron, age 73
Board Member, Sherry Cladouhos
Board Member, Annie Goodwin
Board Member, Douglas Mcbride
Board Member, James English
Board Member, Mark Semmens
Auditors: BKD, LLP

LOCATIONS

HQ: Glacier Bancorp, Inc.
49 Commons Loop, Kalispell, MT 59901
Phone: 406 756-4200
Web: www.glacierbank.com

PRODUCTS/OPERATIONS

2016 Sales

	% of total
Interest income	
Commercial loans	47
Investment securities	17
Residential real estate loans	7
Consumer and other loans	7
Non-interest income	
Service charges and other fees	14
Gain on sale of loans	6
Miscellaneous loan fees and charges	1
(Loss) gain on sale of investments	-
Other income	2
Total	**100**

Selected Services

Commercial loan
Consumer loan
Deposits
Mortgage origination services
Real estate loan
Retail brokerage services
Transaction and savings

Selected Bank Divisions

1st Bank (Wyoming)
Bank of the San Juans (Colorado)
Big Sky Western Bank (Montana)
Citizens Community Bank (Idaho)
Collegiate Peaks Bank
First Bank of Montana
First Bank of Wyoming
First Security Bank (Montana)
First State Bank (Wyoming)
Foothills Bank
Glacier Bank (Montana)
Mountain West Bank (Idaho)
North Cascades Bank (Washington)
Valley Bank of Helena (Montana)
Western Security Bank (Montana)

COMPETITORS

Eagle Bancorp
First Citizens Banc Corp
First Interstate
U.S. Bancorp
Wells Fargo
Zions Bancorporation

HISTORICAL FINANCIALS

Company Type: Public

Income Statement

FYE: December 31

	ASSETS ($ mil.)	NET INCOME ($ mil.)	INCOME AS % OF ASSETS	EMPLOYEES
12/17	9,706.3	116.3	1.2%	2,354
12/16	9,450.6	121.1	1.3%	2,291
12/15	9,089.2	116.1	1.3%	2,245
12/14	8,306.5	112.7	1.4%	2,030
12/13	7,884.3	95.6	1.2%	1,919
Annual Growth	**5.3%**	**5.0%**	—	**5.2%**

2017 Year-End Financials

Return on assets: 1.2%	Dividends
Return on equity: 10.0%	Yield: 0.0%
Long-term debt ($ mil.): —	Payout: 96.0%
No. of shares (mil.): 78.0	Market value ($ mil.): 3,073.0
Sales ($ mil): 487.2	

	STOCK PRICE ($) FY Close	P/E High/Low	PER SHARE ($) Earnings	Dividends	Book Value
12/17	39.39	27 21	1.50	1.44	15.37
12/16	36.23	24 14	1.59	1.10	14.59
12/15	26.53	20 14	1.54	1.05	14.15
12/14	27.77	20 16	1.51	0.68	13.70
12/13	29.79	24 11	1.31	0.60	12.95
Annual Growth	**7.2%**	— —	**3.4%**	**24.5%**	**4.4%**

Gladstone Commercial Corp

Gladstone Commercial a real estate investment trust (REIT) invests in and owns office and industrial real estate properties. The company owns about 100 properties in around 25 states with assets that include office buildings medical office buildings warehouses retail stores and manufacturing facilities. Gladstone generally provides net leases with terms between seven and 15 years for small to very large private and public companies. Tenants include General Motors Morgan Stanley and T-Mobile. The business is managed by its external adviser Gladstone Management which is also headed by chairman and CEO David Gladstone.

Operations

Gladstone Commercial owns about 100 properties totaling nearly 12 million sq. ft. — including office buildings medical office buildings warehouses retail stores and manufacturing facilities — in around 25 states. Virtually all of the REIT's revenue comes from rental income from tenants most of whom sign net leases which require them to pay most or all of a property's operating maintenance repair and insurance costs and real estate taxes.

Geographic Reach

Headquartered in McLean Virginia Gladstone Commercial owns properties in about 25 states. Texas accounts for the most rental revenue with more than 15% followed by Pennsylvania (more than 10%) and Ohio (about 10%). Other large markets include Florida North Carolina Georgia and South Carolina.

Sales and Marketing

Gladstone derives at least 10% of its rental revenue from tenants in each of the telecommunications healthcare automobile and diversified/conglomerate services industries. Its five largest tenants account for nearly 20% of rental revenue.

Financial Performance

Since 2013 Gladstone Commercial's net income has skyrocketed nearly 300% alongside substantial revenue expansion of over 50%. The REIT's growth has accelerated as office and industrial properties in the US see vacancy rates fall and rental rates rise both of which have contributed to an increase in construction in many markets.

In 2017 the company reported revenue of $94.8 million which is up 10% from the prior year. The top line was boosted by increased rent revenue following Gladstone's acquisition of seven properties that year.

The REIT's net income increased 50% to $5.9 million in 2017 owing to increased rental revenue and a gain from the sale of four properties.

Cash at the end of fiscal 2017 was $6.7 million an increase of 43% from the prior year. Cash from operations contributed $46.8 while investing activities used $99.2 million mainly for property acquisitions. Financing activities added another $54.4 million.

Strategy

Gladstone Commercial seeks to assemble a diversified property portfolio both geographically and by tenant and industry type. The REIT's tenants span about 20 different industries including telecommunications healthcare and automobiles from small businesses to very large public and private companies. Geographically its target markets include Washington Oregon Nevada Arizona Tennessee and Kentucky.

The company is working to increase acquisitions of industrial properties. As of late 2018 the company had a potential acquisition pipeline of nearly 20 properties about half of them industrial. Gladstone is seeking fully developed industrial parks with areas of 50000 to 300000 square feet in size and warehouse clear heights of 24 to 28 feet and trailer parking that are occupied by middle-market non-rated tenants.

The company is conducting a capital recycling program wherein it sells properties outside of its core markets to fund acquisitions in target secondary growth markets or repay debt. In 2017 the company sold four non-core properties totaling about 590000 square feet and used the proceeds to pay down some debt and fund the acquisition of seven new properties. The strategy continued in 2018 when Gladstone divested a property in Texas.

Mergers and Acquisitions

In 2017 Gladstone Commercial a REIT purchased seven new properties including buildings leased to Jacobs Engineering Group the National Archives and Records Administration federal records center Automatic Data Processing and Morgan Stanley. It continued adding properties to its portfolio in 2018 including industrial properties in Alabama Michigan and Ohio.

Company Background

The REIT Gladstone Commercial is part of the Gladstone Companies which include the three affiliated public entities Gladstone Capital Gladstone Investment and Gladstone Land. Gladstone Capital and Gladstone Investment invest in small and medium sized private businesses while Gladstone Land invests in farmland.

EXECUTIVES

Chairman and CEO, David J. Gladstone, age 76, $68,833 total compensation
Managing Director, Matt Tucker
Vice Chairman and COO, Terry Lee Brubaker
President, Robert G. Cutlip
Senior Managing Director, Buzz Cooper
Managing Director, Andrew White
CFO, Michael Sodo
Board Member, Caren Merrick
Auditors: PricewaterhouseCoopers LLP

LOCATIONS

HQ: Gladstone Commercial Corp
 1521 Westbranch Drive, Suite 100, McLean, VA 22102
Phone: 703 287-5800   **Fax:** 703 287-5801
Web: www.GladstoneCommercial.com

PRODUCTS/OPERATIONS

2017 Sales

	$ mil.	% of total
Rental	92.8	98
Tenant recovery	2.0	2
Total	**94.8**	**100**

COMPETITORS

Colony Northstar	Monmouth Real Estate
Equity Commonwealth	One Liberty Properties
Mack-Cali	PS Business Parks
Meredith Enterprises	iStar Financial Inc

HISTORICAL FINANCIALS

Company Type: Public

Income Statement

FYE: December 31

	REVENUE ($ mil.)	NET INCOME ($ mil.)	NET PROFIT MARGIN	EMPLOYEES
12/17	94.8	5.9	6.3%	0
12/16	86.3	3.9	4.6%	0
12/15	83.7	3.6	4.3%	66
12/14	73.7	(5.9)	—	0
12/13	61.3	1.5	2.5%	0
Annual Growth	**11.5%**	**40.4%**	**—**	**—**

2017 Year-End Financials

Debt ratio: 58.4%
Return on equity: 1.8%
Cash ($ mil.): 6.6
Current ratio: 1.89
Long-term debt ($ mil.): 542.6

No. of shares (mil.): 29.2
Dividends
 Yield: 0.0%
 Payout: —
Market value ($ mil.): 617.0

STOCK PRICE ($) FY Close	P/E High/Low	PER SHARE ($) Earnings	PER SHARE ($) Dividends	PER SHARE ($) Book Value
12/17	21.06	— —	(0.19)	1.50	11.96
12/16	20.10	— —	(0.16)	1.50	12.02
12/15	14.59	— —	(0.07)	1.50	9.97
12/14	17.17	— —	(0.61)	1.50	10.67
12/13	17.97	— —	(0.22)	1.50	11.42
Annual Growth	**4.0%**	**— —**	**—**	**(0.0%)**	**1.2%**

Global Net Lease Inc

Auditors: PricewaterhouseCoopers LLP

LOCATIONS

HQ: Global Net Lease Inc
 405 Park Ave., 3rd Floor, New York, NY 10022
Phone: 212 415-6500

HISTORICAL FINANCIALS

Company Type: Public

Income Statement

FYE: December 31

	REVENUE ($ mil.)	NET INCOME ($ mil.)	NET PROFIT MARGIN	EMPLOYEES
12/17	259.3	23.5	9.1%	1
12/16	214.1	47.1	22.0%	1
12/15	205.3	(2.0)	—	0
12/14	93.3	(53.5)	—	0
12/13	3.9	(6.9)	—	0
Annual Growth	**184.6%**	**—**	**—**	**—**

2017 Year-End Financials

Debt ratio: 49.8%
Return on equity: 1.7%
Cash ($ mil.): 102.4
Current ratio: 5.25
Long-term debt ($ mil.): 1,513.6

No. of shares (mil.): 67.2
Dividends
 Yield: 0.0%
 Payout: 591.6%
Market value ($ mil.): 1,385.0

STOCK PRICE ($) FY Close	P/E High/Low	PER SHARE ($) Earnings	PER SHARE ($) Dividends	PER SHARE ($) Book Value
12/17	20.58	83 25	0.30	1.78	21.00
12/16	7.83	11 8	0.81	0.00	20.34
12/15	7.95	— —	(0.03)	2.13	21.41
Annual Growth	**60.9%**	**— —**	**—**	**(8.7%)**	**(0.9%)**

Globus Medical Inc

If Globus Medical helps you stand up straight then the company's products are working. Globus Medical makes medical devices used during spinal surgery to treat a variety of spinal disorders and assist surgeons with different types of spinal procedures from screws and plates to disc replacement systems and biomaterials for bone grafts. Top sellers include the REVERE screw-and-rod system and the COALITION cervical fusion device. Altogether Globus Medical has more than 100 spinal devices on the market in the US; its products are also sold in about 25 international markets.

Operations

Globus Medical divides its products into two categories — innovative fusion or disruptive technologies. Innovative fusion products are used in spinal fusion surgery a common and traditional procedure where two individual vertebrae are fused together. This division accounts for about 60% of sales.

The other 40% is made up of products in the disruptive technologies segment a growing category of newer generation products used in novel surgical procedures or as improvements to existing procedures as well as for minimally invasive procedures used as an alternative to surgery.

Geographic Reach

Even though international sales accounts for less than 10% of Globus Medical's overall revenues sales outside the US are growing rapidly.

Sales and Marketing

Globus Medical uses direct sales to promote its products in the US primarily to spine surgeons and hospitals. The company is rapidly adding direct sales personnel in international countries; it also uses distributor representatives to sell in some global markets. Global sales are conducted in Europe Australia India South Africa South America and the Middle East.

Strategy

Putting new products on the market is crucial in the medical device industry and Globus Medical has launched more than 110 new products since its inception. The firm introduced 14 new products in 2012 including the MARS anterior retractor and the SECURE-C cervical artificial disc. The company has also entered a new market by introducing the Algea Therapies line of pain management products. Globus Medical is pursuing R&D projects in both the innovative fusion and disruptive technology segments; in addition to new product development the firm works to improve existing products.

Other means of growth include pursuit of acquisitions or strategic alliances increasing market penetration growing the sales force and hiring and retaining personnel with market experience.

Mergers and Acquisitions

Globus Medical acquired privately held firm Nemaris in 2018. Nemaris developed the Surgimap surgical planning software platform for the spinal surgery market.

In 2017 Globus Medical acquired KB Medical a Swiss robotics developer. That transaction underscored the firm's commitment to producing robotic technology for surgeries.

In 2016 Globus Medical acquired the international business of medical device firm Alphatec for $80 million. The deal includes the international distribution business including units in Japan Brazil the UK and Italy.

Company Background

Globus Medical was founded in 2003 by CEO David Paul a former product development director at bone-related medical device maker Synthes. Globus Medical relied on venture capital funding prior to its 2012 IPO.

EXECUTIVES

CEO, David M. (Dave) Demski, age 60, $337,765 total compensation
Group President Commercial Operations, A. Brett Murphy, age 54, $309,309 total compensation

SVP Operations, David D. Davidar, age 52, $234,738 total compensation
SVP and CFO, Daniel T. Scavilla, age 53
Vice President of Business Development, Brian Kearns
Vice President Of Sales, Jay Martin
Vice President Business Development, Rick Kreppel
Vice President US Sales West Zone, David Hole
Chairman, David C. Paul, age 51
Auditors: Deloitte & Touche LLP

LOCATIONS

HQ: Globus Medical Inc
2560 General Armistead Avenue, Audubon, PA 19403
Phone: 610 930-1800   **Fax:** 302 636-5454
Web: www.globusmedical.com

PRODUCTS/OPERATIONS

2015 Sales

	$ mil.	% of total
Innovative fusion	288.1	53
Disruptive technologies	256.7	47
Total	**544.8**	**100**

Selected Products

Innovative Fusion Products:
Cervical
ASSURE (anterior cervical plate system)
ELLIPSE (posterior occipital cervical thoracic stabilization system)
PROVIDENCE (anterior cervical plate system)
VIP (anterior cervical plate system)
XTEND (anterior cervical plate system)
Thoracolumbar:
BEACON Posted Screw (posted pedicle screw system)
REVERE Degen (comprehensive pedicle screw and rod system)
SI-LOK (sacroiliac joint fixation system)
Interbody/Corpectomy
COALITION (anterior cervical stand-alone fusion device)
COLONIAL (anterior cervical interbody fusion device)
FORTIFY (self-locking expandable corpectomy device)
INDEPENDENCE (anterior lumbar stand-alone fusion device)
SUSTAIN (spacers for partial or complete vertebrectomy)
XPAND (expandable corpectomy spacer)
Deformity Tumor and Trauma
REVERE Anterior (pedicle screw and rod deformity system)
REVERE Deformity (comprehensive pedicle screw hook and rod deformity system)
TRUSS (lateral compressible thoracolumbar plate system)
Minimally Invasive Surgery Products:
CALIBER (expandable posterior lumbar interbody fusion device)
CALIBER-L (expandable lateral lumbar interbody fusion device)
INTERCONTINENTAL (lateral lumbar interbody fusion device)
MARS 3V (three-blade retractor system)
REVOLVE (minimally invasive pedicle screw and rod system)
SIGNATURE (articulating transforaminal interbody fusion device)
TRANSCONTINENTAL (lateral lumbar interbody fusion device)
Motion Preservation:
FLEXUS (minimally invasive unilateral PEEK interspinous process spacer)
ORBIT-R (anterior lumbar disc replacement)
SECURE-CR (articulating cervical disc replacement device)
SP-FIX (interspinous process fusion device)
TRANSITION (stabilization system)
TRIUMPH (transforaminal lumbar disc replacement device)
ZYFLEX (stabilization system)

COMPETITORS

Alphatec Spine	NuVasive
DePuy Spine	Orthofix
Integra LifeSciences	Stryker
Medtronic	Synthes
Medtronic Sofamor Danek	Zimmer Biomet

HISTORICAL FINANCIALS

Company Type: Public

Income Statement   FYE: December 31

	REVENUE ($ mil.)	NET INCOME ($ mil.)	NET PROFIT MARGIN	EMPLOYEES
12/17	635.9	107.3	16.9%	1,500
12/16	563.9	104.3	18.5%	1,400
12/15	544.7	112.7	20.7%	1,200
12/14	474.3	92.4	19.5%	900
12/13	434.4	68.6	15.8%	850
Annual Growth	**10.0%**	**11.8%**	**—**	**15.3%**

2017 Year-End Financials

Debt ratio: —
Return on equity: 11.9%
Cash ($ mil.): 118.8
Current ratio: 6.67
Long-term debt ($ mil.): —
No. of shares (mil.): 96.6
Dividends
Yield: —
Payout: —
Market value ($ mil.): 3,973.0

	STOCK PRICE ($) FY Close	P/E High/Low	Earnings	Dividends	Book Value
12/17	41.10	37 22	1.10	0.00	10.01
12/16	24.81	26 19	1.08	0.00	8.67
12/15	27.82	24 17	1.17	0.00	7.50
12/14	23.77	28 19	0.97	0.00	6.18
12/13	20.18	27 14	0.73	0.00	5.06
Annual Growth	**19.5%**	**— —**	**10.8%**	**—**	**18.6%**

GoDaddy Inc

Auditors: Ernst & Young LLP

LOCATIONS

HQ: GoDaddy Inc
14455 N. Hayden Road, Scottsdale, AZ 85260
Phone: 480 505-8800
Web: www.godaddy.com

HISTORICAL FINANCIALS

Company Type: Public

Income Statement   FYE: December 31

	REVENUE ($ mil.)	NET INCOME ($ mil.)	NET PROFIT MARGIN	EMPLOYEES
12/17	2,231.9	136.4	6.1%	5,990
12/16	1,847.9	(16.5)	—	4,749
12/15	1,607.3	(47.4)	—	4,761
12/14	1,387.2	(143.3)	—	4,908
12/13	1,130.8	(199.8)	—	0
Annual Growth	**18.5%**	**—**	**—**	**—**

2017 Year-End Financials

Debt ratio: 42.3%
Return on equity: 26.0%
Cash ($ mil.): 582.7
Current ratio: 0.59
Long-term debt ($ mil.): 2,410.8
No. of shares (mil.): 168.0
Dividends
Yield: —
Payout: —
Market value ($ mil.): 8,447.0

	STOCK PRICE ($) FY Close	P/E High/Low	Earnings	Dividends	Book Value
12/17	50.28	41 28	0.79	0.00	2.90
12/16	34.95	— —	(0.21)	0.00	3.37
12/15	32.06	— —	(0.81)	0.00	2.70
Annual Growth	**25.2%**	**— —**	**—**	**—**	**3.5%**

Goldman Sachs BDC Inc

Auditors: PricewaterhouseCoopers LLP

LOCATIONS

HQ: Goldman Sachs BDC Inc
200 West Street, New York, NY 10282
Phone: 212 902-0300
Web: www.goldmansachsbdc.com

HISTORICAL FINANCIALS

Company Type: Public

Income Statement   FYE: December 31

	REVENUE ($ mil.)	NET INCOME ($ mil.)	NET PROFIT MARGIN	EMPLOYEES
12/17	136.7	79.9	58.5%	0
12/16	125.1	76.2	60.9%	0
12/15	118.4	74.5	63.0%	0
12/14	73.2	52.7	72.0%	0
12/13	22.8	15.9	69.8%	0
Annual Growth	**56.4%**	**49.7%**	**—**	**—**

2017 Year-End Financials

Debt ratio: 41.7%
Return on equity: 11.5%
Cash ($ mil.): 11.6
Current ratio: 0.85
Long-term debt ($ mil.): 542.5
No. of shares (mil.): 40.1
Dividends
Yield: 0.0%
Payout: 140.6%
Market value ($ mil.): 890.0

	STOCK PRICE ($) FY Close	P/E High/Low	Earnings	Dividends	Book Value
12/17	22.18	20 17	1.28	1.80	18.09
12/16	23.52	21 16	1.12	1.80	18.31
12/15	19.00	12 8	2.14	1.80	18.97
Annual Growth	**8.0%**	**— —**	**(22.7%)**	**(0.0%)**	**(2.3%)**

Grand Canyon Education Inc

Grand Canyon Education (dba Grand Canyon University) spans a broad educational horizon. The regionally accredited Christian educator offers graduate and undergraduate degrees online at its campus in Phoenix and onsite at corporate facilities. Grand Canyon University offers career-oriented degree programs focused on the core disciplines of business education health care and liberal arts. Working adults make up most of the school's student body. Grand Canyon University enrolls almost 82000 students annually; about 79% are in online programs and about 50% of those pursue advanced degrees. Most classes have a student-teacher ratio of about 25:1. The company was formed in 1949 as a not-for-profit college.

Operations

Grand Canyon University keeps its enrollment numbers up by marketing itself to working adults (whom the company defines as 25 years and older) seeking to complete their education switch careers or earn a higher degree in the field in which they already work. Grand Canyon University attracts adult students with the flexibility and convenience of online classes and conversely adult students are attractive to Grand Canyon University because they are generally more stable able to finance their education and have higher completion rates than younger students. The school offers more than 100 degrees and concentrations.

Grand Canyon University derives more than 70% of its income from tuition that is financed under Title IV programs (federal grants and loans to students awarded on the basis of their financial need). Other sources of income come from self-funding private loans other financial aid programs and employer tuition reimbursements.

Geographic Reach

Grand Canyon University has a traditional campus in Phoenix and it enrolls students from all 50 states and the District of Columbia in its online and corporate classes.

Sales and Marketing

Grand Canyon University markets the flexibility and convenience of online classes to working adults and traditional students.

Financial Performance

Grand Canyon has reported several years of rising revenue. In 2016 revenue rose by 12% to $873 million thanks to a jump in enrollment from 74506 in 2015 to 81908 that year.

Net income increased by 13% to $149 million and higher enrollment more than offset the increase in operating expenses.

Cash from operations grew to $218.3 million in 2016 (from $173.9 million in 2015) due to higher provisions for bad debt and depreciation and amortization and an increase in deferred income taxes.

Strategy

To enhance its brand and continue to attract students Grand Canyon University invests in technology to update its infrastructure and expanding its physical campus. Improvements have included constructing its first parking garage a basketball and entertainment arena a new dorm an activity center an Arts and Sciences classroom and a new general office building. The university also keeps tabs on industry trends and adjusts its course offerings accordingly. For example increased demand for nursing programs led the school to establish satellite locations at multiple hospitals where nursing students can complete their clinical education while also completing other course work online. It has similar onsite arrangements with certain employers such as schools and school districts through which students can pursue a profession in teaching.

Mergers and Acquisitions

In late 2018 Grand Canyon agreed to buy Orbis Education Services for some $362 million. Orbis provides health care education programs to around 20 universities around the nation. The addition complements the education services partnerships Grand Canyon already offers and helps the university better address the shortage of health care professionals.

Company Background

Founded as Grand Canyon College a private not-for-profit college in 1949 the university moved to its existing campus in Phoenix in 1951. In 2004 several of its stockholders acquired Grand Canyon University and converted it to a for-profit institution. The company then raised about $126 million through a public offering which was completed in 2008 after a four-month-long IPO drought in the US.

EXECUTIVES

CFO, Daniel E. (Dan) Bachus, age 47, $362,250 total compensation
President and CEO, Brian E. Mueller, age 64, $621,000 total compensation
COO, W. Stan Meyer, age 57, $362,250 total compensation
Provost, Hank Radda
Senior Vice President, Bart Burkert
Chairman, Brent D. Richardson, age 56
Auditors: KPMG LLP

LOCATIONS

HQ: Grand Canyon Education Inc
2600 W. Camelback Road, Phoenix, AZ 85017
Phone: 602 247-4400
Web: www.gcu.edu

PRODUCTS/OPERATIONS

2016 Student Enrollment by Degree Type

	No. of students
Undergraduate degree	48,693
Graduate degree	33,215
Total	**81,908**

2016 Enrollment by Instructional Delivery Method

	No of students
Online	64,646
Ground	17,262
Total	**81,908**

Selected Colleges

College of Humanities and Social Sciences
College of Theology
College of Education
College of Doctoral Studies
College of Fine Arts and Production
College of Nursing and Health Care Professions
College of Business
College of Science Engineering and Technology
Honors College

Selected Degree Programs

Athletic Training & Exercise Science
Business & Leadership
Computer Science & Information Technology
Health Care
Health Sciences & Pre-Med
Liberal Arts
MBA & EMBA
Nursing
Performing Arts & Digital Design
Psychology & Counseling
Teaching & Education Administration
Theology & Youth Ministry

COMPETITORS

Adtalem	Bridgepoint Education
American Public	Career Education
Education	Education Management
Apollo Education	ITT Educational
Arizona State	Northern Arizona
University	University
Azusa Pacific	Strayer Education
University	UTI
Baylor University	University of Arizona

HISTORICAL FINANCIALS

Company Type: Public

Income Statement

FYE: December 31

	REVENUE ($ mil.)	NET INCOME ($ mil.)	NET PROFIT MARGIN	EMPLOYEES
12/17	974.1	203.3	20.9%	10,000
12/16	873.3	148.5	17.0%	3,850
12/15	778.2	131.4	16.9%	3,650
12/14	691.0	111.4	16.1%	3,600
12/13	598.3	88.7	14.8%	3,100
Annual Growth	**13.0%**	**23.0%**	—	**34.0%**

2017 Year-End Financials

Debt ratio: 5.1%
Return on equity: 23.1%
Cash ($ mil.): 153.4
Current ratio: 1.57
Long-term debt ($ mil.): 59.9
No. of shares (mil.): 48.1
Dividends
Yield: —
Payout: —
Market value ($ mil.): 4,309.0

	STOCK PRICE ($) FY Close	P/E High/Low		PER SHARE ($) Earnings	Dividends	Book Value
12/17	89.53	22	13	4.22	0.00	20.49
12/16	58.45	19	10	3.15	0.00	16.27
12/15	40.12	16	13	2.78	0.00	13.02
12/14	46.66	21	15	2.37	0.00	10.19
12/13	43.60	24	11	1.92	0.00	7.49
Annual Growth	**19.7%**	—	—	**21.8%**	—	**28.6%**

Gray Television Inc

Gray Television has The Eye for local television markets. The company is the largest independent operator of TV stations affiliated with the CBS network with 17 stations in more than a dozen states. In total the company operates more than 35 stations in 30 midsized and smaller markets mostly in the Midwest and South. Its other stations are affiliated with ABC NBC and FOX. In addition to traditional analog signals Gray Television broadcasts an additional 40 digital channels mostly carrying programming from The CW and MyNetworkTV. Former CEO J. Mack Robinson and his family control nearly 40% of the company.

Operations

Approximately 70% of the company's revenues are generated from local advertising including political ads. The company also earns revenue from national ads retransmission consent (charging a fee to cable operators to carry its stations) and consulting as well as from a management contract with New Young Broadcasting Holding Company (formerly Young Broadcasting) to manage several of Young's stations.

Financial Performance

The company's revenue declined from $404 million in fiscal 2012 down to $346 million in fiscal 2013. Its net income and cash flow also decreased in fiscal 2013 compared to the previous period.

Strategy

Gray Television has benefited from its large portfolio of CBS affiliated stations as the Eye network has typically dominated the primetime ratings.

EXECUTIVES

EVP and CFO, James C. (Jim) Ryan, age 57, $500,000 total compensation
Vice Chairman, Hilton H. Howell, age 55, $850,000 total compensation
EVP and Co-COO, Bob Smith, age 55
EVP and Co-COO, Nick Waller, age 64
EVP and Chief Digital and Technology Officer, Jason Effinger
EVP and Chief Legal and Development Officer, Kevin P. Latek, age 47, $550,000 total compensation
Auditors: RSM US LLP

LOCATIONS

HQ: Gray Television Inc
4370 Peachtree Road N.E., Atlanta, GA 30319
Phone: 404 504-9828
Web: www.gray.tv

PRODUCTS/OPERATIONS

2016 sales

	% of total
Local	50
National	12
Political	11
Retransmission consent	25
Other	2
Total	**100**

Selected Television Stations
KAKE (ABC; Wichita-Hutchinson KS)
KBTX (CBS; Bryan TX)
KCRG (ABC MY ANT; Cedar Rapids IA)
KCWY (NBC; Casper WY)
KGIN (CBS; Grand Island NE)
KGWN (CBS NBC CW; Cheyenne WY)
KKCO (NBC; Grand Junction CO)
KKTV (CBS; Colorado Springs CO)
KLBY (ABC; Colby KS)
KMVT (CBS CWTwin Falls ID)
KNOE (CBS CW ABC; Monroe-El Dorado LA)
KOLN (CBS; Lincoln-Hastings-Kearney NE)
KOLO (ABC; Reno NV)
KOSA(CBS MY; Odessa - Midland TX)
KSNB (NBC MY; Lincoln - Hastings - Kearney NE)
KSTB (CBS CW; Scottsbluff NE)
KSVT (FOX MY; Twin Falls ID)
KUPK (ABC; Garden City KS)
KWTX (CBS; Waco-Temple-Bryan TX)
KXII (CBS; ShermanTX)
WAGM (FOX CBS; Presque Isle ME)
WAHU (FOX; Charlottesville VA)
WBKO (ABC; Bowling Green KY)
WCAV (CBS; Charlottesville VA)
WCTV (CBS; Tallahassee FL)
WEAU (NBC La Crosse-Eau Claire WI)
WHSV (ABC; Harrisonburg VA)
WIBW (CBS; Topeka KS)
WIFR (CBS; Rockford IL)
WILX (NBC; Lansing MI)
WITN (NBC; Greenville NC)
WJHG (NBC; Panama City FL)
WKYT (CBS; Lexington KY)
WMTV (NBC; Madison WI)
WNDU (NBC; South Bend IN)
WOWT (NBC; Omaha NE)
WRDW (CBS; Augusta GA)
WSAW (CBS; Wausau-Rhinelander WI)
WSAZ (NBC; Charleston WV)
WSWG (CBS; Albany GA)
WTAP (NBC; Parkersburg WV)
WTOK (ABC; Meridian MS)
WTVY (CBS; Dothan AL)
WVAW (ABC; Charlottesville VA)
WVLT (CBS; Knoxville TN)
WYMT (CBS; Hazard KY)

COMPETITORS

ACME Communications
Barrington Broadcasting
Evening Post
Hoak Media
Journal Broadcast Group
Media General
Morris Multimedia
New Young Broadcasting
Nexstar Broadcasting
Quincy Newspapers
Raycom Media
Schurz Communications
Sinclair Broadcast Group

HISTORICAL FINANCIALS

Company Type: Public

Income Statement　　　　　　　FYE: December 31

	REVENUE ($ mil.)	NET INCOME ($ mil.)	NET PROFIT MARGIN	EMPLOYEES
12/17	882.7	261.9	29.7%	3,938
12/16	812.4	62.2	7.7%	3,996
12/15	597.3	39.3	6.6%	3,819
12/14	508.1	48.0	9.5%	2,937
12/13	346.3	18.2	5.3%	2,248
Annual Growth	**26.4%**	**94.5%**	**—**	**15.0%**

2017 Year-End Financials

Debt ratio: 56.3%
Return on equity: 35.2%
Cash ($ mil.): 462.4
Current ratio: 5.08
Long-term debt ($ mil.): 1,831.0
No. of shares (mil.): 89.8
Dividends
　Yield: —
　Payout: —
Market value ($ mil.): 1,505.0

	STOCK PRICE ($) FY Close	P/E High/Low	Earnings	Dividends	Book Value
12/17	16.75	5　3	3.55	0.00	11.05
12/16	10.85	19　8	0.86	0.00	6.80
12/15	16.30	31 16	0.57	0.00	5.93
12/14	11.20	18　9	0.82	0.00	3.70
12/13	14.88	46　7	0.32	0.00	3.00
Annual Growth	**3.0%**	**—**	**82.5%**	**—**	**38.5%**

Great Ajax Corp

Auditors: Moss Adams LLP

LOCATIONS

HQ: Great Ajax Corp
9400 SW Beaverton-Hillsdale Hwy, Suite 131, Beaverton, OR 97005
Phone: 503 505-5670
Web: www.great-ajax.com

HISTORICAL FINANCIALS

Company Type: Public

Income Statement　　　　　　　FYE: December 31

	REVENUE ($ mil.)	NET INCOME ($ mil.)	NET PROFIT MARGIN	EMPLOYEES
12/17	93.9	28.9	30.8%	0
12/16	70.2	27.8	39.6%	0
12/15	48.9	24.7	50.6%	0
12/14*	7.0	3.4	48.8%	0
09/14	2.2	1.0	43.5%	0
Annual Growth	**153.0%**	**132.1%**	**—**	**—**

*Fiscal year change

2017 Year-End Financials

Debt ratio: 57.0%
Return on equity: 10.2%
Cash ($ mil.): 54.0
Current ratio: 0.19
Long-term debt ($ mil.): 796.6
No. of shares (mil.): 18.5
Dividends
　Yield: 0.0%
　Payout: 74.8%
Market value ($ mil.): 257.0

	STOCK PRICE ($) FY Close	P/E High/Low	Earnings	Dividends	Book Value
12/17	13.82	9　8	1.51	1.13	15.62
12/16	13.27	9　6	1.65	0.99	15.03
12/15	12.12	9　7	1.68	0.64	14.89
Annual Growth	**6.8%**	**—**	**(5.2%)**	**32.9%**	**2.4%**

Great Western Bancorp Inc

Auditors: Ernst & Young LLP

LOCATIONS

HQ: Great Western Bancorp Inc
225 South Main Avenue, Sioux Falls, SD 57104
Phone: 605 334-2548
Web: www.greatwesternbank.com

HISTORICAL FINANCIALS

Company Type: Public

Income Statement　　　　　　　FYE: September 30

	ASSETS ($ mil.)	NET INCOME ($ mil.)	INCOME AS % OF ASSETS	EMPLOYEES
09/18	12,116.8	157.9	1.3%	1,664
09/17	11,690.0	144.7	1.2%	1,689
09/16	11,531.1	121.2	1.1%	1,649
09/15	9,798.6	109.0	1.1%	1,475
09/14	9,371.4	104.9	1.1%	1,492
Annual Growth	**6.6%**	**10.8%**	**—**	**2.8%**

2018 Year-End Financials

Return on assets: 1.3%
Return on equity: 8.7%
Long-term debt ($ mil.): —
No. of shares (mil.): 58.9
Sales ($ mil): 555.4
Dividends
　Yield: 0.0%
　Payout: 33.7%
Market value ($ mil.): 2,486.0

	STOCK PRICE ($) FY Close	P/E High/Low	Earnings	Dividends	Book Value
09/18	42.19	17 14	2.67	0.90	31.24
09/17	41.28	18 13	2.45	0.74	29.83
09/16	33.32	16 11	2.14	0.56	28.34
09/15	25.37	14　9	1.90	0.36	26.43
Annual Growth	**18.5%**	**—**	**12.0%**	**35.7%**	**5.7%**

Green Dot Corp

If you've got the green but not the plastic Green Dot would like to help. The company offers prepaid debit cards through more than 100000 retail locations in the US. The MasterCard- and Visa-branded reloadable cards function like credit cards for purchases and cash withdrawals. Green Dot which has about 4.5 million cards in circulation partners with Wal-Mart Kmart Walgreens Home Depot and other retailers to enable its customers to add funds to their accounts. The company's products are designed for people who aren't able to or choose not to utilize traditional credit card and banking services. Green Dot makes most of its money from new card monthly maintenance and ATM fees.

Operations

As the pioneer of the prepaid debit card industry Green Dot is the largest provider of reloadable prepaid debit cards and cash reload processing services in the US. Roughly 40% of its revenue comes from card revenues and other fees while cash transfer revenue and interchange revenue each make up around 30% of the company's total revenue.

Green Dot also offers mobile banking services through its GoBank mobile checking account. Green Dot subsidiary TPG is largest processor of tax refund disbursements in the nation.The company also boasts the Green Dot Network which provides reload services to more than 120 third-party prepaid card programs including programs offered by UniRush and H&R Block. The Green Dot Network even facilitates cash reload services for members programs that are part of MasterCard's RePower Reload Network.

Geographic Reach

California-based Green Dot has sales and support offices in Tampa Florida; Bentonville Arkansas; and in Pasadena Palo Alto and Westlake Village California.

Sales and Marketing

Green Dot provides its products and services to consumers through a "branchless bank" distribution network. The network spans more than 100000 U.S. retail locations thousands of local financial service center locations an online website major mobile app stores as well as through 25000 tax preparation offices and major online tax preparation providers.

Green Dot has been the exclusive distributor of Walmart-branded general purpose reloadable (GPR) cards sold at Walmart stores since 2007. Indeed Wal-Mart Stores is the company's largest retail distributor representing 54% of its total operating revenue in 2014. Green Dot's cards are sold by mass merchants including Walmart and Kmart discount retailers (including dollar stores) drugstores convenience stores supermarkets and by financial service centers.

The company has been increasing its sales and marketing spend in recent years which has mostly been tied to sales commission expenses. Green Dot spent $235.23 million on sales and marketing expenses in 2014 up from $218.37 million in 2013 and $209.87 million in 2012.

Financial Performance

Green Dot has enjoyed rising revenue over the past several years as consumers warm up to prepaid cards. The company's revenue in 2014 rose nearly 5% to a record $601.55 million mostly thanks to higher monthly maintenance fees as the number of active cards in its network grew and because more of these cards were Green Dot-branded products which carry higher average maintenance fees. Interchange revenue also grew by $6.2 million thanks to a 6% increase in purchase volume while cash transfer revenue declined

slightly as the company offered more fee-free cash transfers during the year.

Following two years of losses net income in 2014 rebounded by 25% to $42.69 million thanks to a combination of higher revenue and non-recurring net cash proceeds of $7.1 million which the company collected from the settlement of a lawsuit.

Despite higher cash earnings in 2014 cash from operations dropped by 44% to 68.97 million primarily because it paid $48.7 million in amounts due to card issuing banks for overdrawn accounts. These payments were mostly related to Green Dot's liability settlement with GE Capital Retail Bank which involved overdrawn cardholder account balances.

Strategy

Green Dot has been adding new lines of financial products to diversify its revenue streams either through acquisitions or on its own. In 2014 for example it purchased Santa Barbara Tax Products Group to create a new income stream enhance margins and add a new distribution network to sell more of its products and services. In February 2014 Green Dot finished transitioning its card issuing program with GE Capital Retail Bank to Green Dot Bank. As a result all Walmart Money-Cards are now issued by Green Dot Bank. In 2013 the firm launched its GoBank mobile checking account developed for smartphones and other mobile devices.

In 2012 in a move to become more vertically integrated the company acquired certain processing and hardware assets of eCommLink for some $2.5 million. The move allowed Green Dot to bring its transaction processing in house rather than rely on outsourced parties such as TSYS. Also in 2012 to help attract and retain customers and expand its tech capabilities Greent Dot acquired mobile app start-up Loopt which provides mobile location-based services for consumers to learn about local business deals for some $43 million.

Like other electronic payments companies serving the underbanked community Green Dot has also attracted fully banked consumers seeking to safely shop online using separate accounts. Using prepaid cards as a companion to their primary accounts also allows users to control spending and prevent overdrafts. As the electronics payments industry evolves and competitors continue to introduce new products such as contactless cards Green Dot is exploring its various technological options. In addition to technological innovations card companies like Green Dot are also focusing on maintaining a stable and secure technology infrastructure.

Company Background

The company's July 2010 initial public offering exceeded its own expectations raising nearly $165 million. Although the IPO of secondary shares raised a significant amount Green Dot did not keep any of the money for itself. Instead the money was distributed to existing shareholders the most prominent being Wal-Mart. Prior to the IPO the retail giant took a minority stake in Green Dot — a move that cemented the pair's partnership.

EXECUTIVES

CEO and Director, Steven W. Streit, age 57, $666,000 total compensation

SVP Corporate Strategy and Mergers and Acquisitions and Acting CFO, Mark Shifke, age 59, $450,000 total compensation

COO, Kuan Archer, age 46, $440,000 total compensation

CEO Green Dot Bank, Mary J. Dent

Senior Vice President Customer Operations, Madeline Fernandez

Vice President Product Development GM Gobank, Alok Deshpande

Vice President, Dave Banta

Senior Vice President Information Technology Governance and Shared Services, Christopher Strader

Vice President Banking Operations, Kathy Clark

Vice President Product, Michael Panzarella

Vice President User Experience and Design, Jason Conness

Vice President Communications, Michelle Blaya

Senior Vice President, Mark Lauderdale

VICE PRESIDENT PRODUCT MANAGEMENT, William Coats

Chairman, William I. Jacobs, age 77

Treasurer, Matt Kohler

Auditors: Ernst & Young LLP

LOCATIONS

HQ: Green Dot Corp
3465 E. Foothill Blvd., Pasadena, CA 91107
Phone: 626 765-2000
Web: www.greendot.com

PRODUCTS/OPERATIONS

2014 Sales

	$ mil.	% of total
Card revenues & other fees	253.2	40
Cash transfer revenues	179.3	30
Interchange revenues	178.0	30
Adjustments	(8.9)	-
Total	**601.6**	**100**

COMPETITORS

American Express	MoneyGram
Blackhawk Network	International
DFC Global	NetSpend
FSV Payment Systems	PreCash
First Data	U.S. Bancorp
H&R Block	Visa Inc
JPMorgan Chase	Western Union
Jackson Hewitt	nFinanSe

HISTORICAL FINANCIALS

Company Type: Public

Income Statement

FYE: December 31

	REVENUE ($ mil.)	NET INCOME ($ mil.)	NET PROFIT MARGIN	EMPLOYEES
12/17	890.1	85.8	9.6%	1,152
12/16	718.7	41.6	5.8%	974
12/15	694.7	38.4	5.5%	1,012
12/14	601.5	42.6	7.1%	857
12/13	573.6	34.0	5.9%	562
Annual Growth	11.6%	26.0%	—	19.7%

2017 Year-End Financials

Debt ratio: 2.6%	No. of shares (mil.): 51.1
Return on equity: 11.8%	Dividends
Cash ($ mil.): 919.2	Yield: —
Current ratio: 0.99	Payout: —
Long-term debt ($ mil.): 58.7	Market value ($ mil.): 3,081.0

	STOCK PRICE ($)	P/E	PER SHARE ($)		
	FY Close	High/Low	Earnings	Dividends	Book Value
12/17	60.26	38 14	1.61	0.00	14.95
12/16	23.55	31 19	0.80	0.00	13.54
12/15	16.42	29 19	0.72	0.00	13.13
12/14	20.49	29 18	0.90	0.00	12.30
12/13	25.15	34 16	0.76	0.00	10.66
Annual Growth	24.4%	—	20.6%	—	8.8%

Green Plains Partners LP

Auditors: KPMG LLP

LOCATIONS

HQ: Green Plains Partners LP
1811 Aksarben Drive, Omaha, NE 68106
Phone: 402 884-8700
Web: www.greenplainspartners.com

HISTORICAL FINANCIALS

Company Type: Public

Income Statement				FYE: December 31
	REVENUE ($ mil.)	NET INCOME ($ mil.)	NET PROFIT MARGIN	EMPLOYEES
12/17	106.9	58.8	55.0%	45
12/16	103.7	56.8	54.7%	0
12/15	50.9	16.3	32.2%	0
12/14	12.8	2.1	16.6%	0
12/13	11.0	0.9	8.3%	0
Annual Growth	76.5%	183.3%		

2017 Year-End Financials

Debt ratio: 146.1%
Return on equity: —
Cash ($ mil.): 0.5
Current ratio: 1.35
Long-term debt ($ mil.): 134.8
No. of shares (mil.): 31.8
Dividends
  Yield: 0.0%
  Payout: 98.3%
Market value ($ mil.): 595.0

	STOCK PRICE ($)	P/E	PER SHARE ($)		
	FY Close	High/Low	Earnings	Dividends	Book Value
12/17	18.70	12 10	1.81	1.78	(1.98)
12/16	19.80	12 7	1.75	1.64	(2.02)
12/15	16.25	23 18	0.71	0.40	2.06
Annual Growth	7.3%	—	59.7%	111.0%	—

Greene County Bancorp Inc

This company helps put the "green" in upstate New York. Greene County Bancorp is the holding company for The Bank of Greene County serving New York's Catskill Mountains region from about a dozen branches. Founded in 1889 as a building and loan association the bank offers traditional retail products such as savings NOW checking and money market accounts; IRAs; and CDs. Real estate loans make up about 85% of the bank's lending activities; it also writes business and consumer loans. Through affiliations with Fenimore Asset Management and Essex Corp. Greene County Bancorp offers investment products. Subsidiary Greene County Commercial Bank is a state-chartered limited purpose commercial bank.

The Bank of Greene County established Greene County Commercial Bank in 2004. Operating as a subsidiary of The Bank of Greene County it provides banking services to area municipalities.

EXECUTIVES

VP Secretary and Human Resources Director The Bank of Greene County, Rebecca R. Main
EVP COO and CFO Greene County Bancorp and The Bank of Greene County, Michelle M. Plummer, age 50, $144,700 total compensation
Executive Vice President; Chief Lending Officer, Stephen E. Nelson, age 49, $112,800 total compensation
Chairman, Martin C. Smith, age 71
President and CEO Greene County Bancorp and The Bank of Greene County and Director, Donald E. Gibson, age 51, $164,100 total compensation
CIO The Bank of Greene County, Gregory W. Spampinato
VP Operations The Bank of Greene County, John Olivett
VP and Mortgage Officer The Bank of Greene County, Charles McEntee
VP Municipal Banking and Commercial Services The Bank of Greene County, Kresten M. Bjornsson
VP Investment Services The Bank of Greene County, Timothy J. Bartholomew
Manager Core Systems The Bank of Greene County, Marge Tobiassen
Assistant VP and Director Marketing The Bank of Greene County, Martha Keeler
Controller The Bank of Greene County, Betsy Darrow
VP Branch Administration and BSA Officer The Bank of Greene County, Cynthia DuPilka
VP and Mortgage Officer The Bank of Greene County, Trisha Lamb
VP Commercial Lending The Bank of Greene County, Perry M. Lasher
Auditors: Bonadio & Co., LLP

LOCATIONS

HQ: Greene County Bancorp Inc
302 Main Street, Catskill, NY 12414
Phone: 518 943-2600
Web: www.tbogc.com

COMPETITORS

HSBC USA	M&T Bank
KeyCorp	TrustCo Bank Corp NY

HISTORICAL FINANCIALS

Company Type: Public

Income Statement				FYE: June 30
	ASSETS ($ mil.)	NET INCOME ($ mil.)	INCOME AS % OF ASSETS	EMPLOYEES
06/18	1,151.4	14.4	1.3%	164
06/17	982.2	11.1	1.1%	146
06/16	868.7	8.9	1.0%	140
06/15	738.6	7.1	1.0%	136
06/14	674.1	6.5	1.0%	133
Annual Growth	14.3%	21.9%	—	5.4%

2018 Year-End Financials

Return on assets: 1.3%
Return on equity: 16.0%
Long-term debt ($ mil.): —
No. of shares (mil.): 8.5
Sales ($ mil): 46.4
Dividends
  Yield: 0.0%
  Payout: 23.0%
Market value ($ mil.): 289.0

	STOCK PRICE ($)	P/E	PER SHARE ($)		
	FY Close	High/Low	Earnings	Dividends	Book Value
06/18	33.90	22 13	1.69	0.39	11.27
06/17	27.20	21 12	1.31	0.38	9.82
06/16	16.27	40 15	1.06	0.37	8.77
06/15	28.49	36 30	0.85	0.36	7.92
06/14	26.55	39 27	0.77	0.35	7.26
Annual Growth	6.3%	—	21.7%	2.7%	11.6%

GrubHub Inc

Auditors: Crowe Horwath LLP

LOCATIONS

HQ: GrubHub Inc
111 W. Washington Street, Suite 2100, Chicago, IL 60602
Phone: 877 585-7878
Web: www.grubhub.com

HISTORICAL FINANCIALS

Company Type: Public

Income Statement				FYE: December 31
	REVENUE ($ mil.)	NET INCOME ($ mil.)	NET PROFIT MARGIN	EMPLOYEES
12/17	683.0	98.9	14.5%	2,125
12/16	493.3	49.5	10.0%	1,518
12/15	361.8	38.0	10.5%	1,105
12/14	253.8	24.2	9.6%	1,090
12/13	137.1	6.7	4.9%	680
Annual Growth	49.4%	95.7%	—	33.0%

2017 Year-End Financials

Debt ratio: 11.2%
Return on equity: 9.4%
Cash ($ mil.): 234.0
Current ratio: 2.07
Long-term debt ($ mil.): 169.6
No. of shares (mil.): 86.7
Dividends
  Yield: —
  Payout: —
Market value ($ mil.): 6,232.0

	STOCK PRICE ($)	P/E	PER SHARE ($)		
	FY Close	High/Low	Earnings	Dividends	Book Value
12/17	71.80	64 29	1.12	0.00	12.88
12/16	37.62	76 32	0.58	0.00	11.34
12/15	24.20	105 51	0.44	0.00	10.33
12/14	36.32	137 91	0.30	0.00	9.41
Annual Growth	25.5%	—	55.1%	—	11.0%

Guaranty Bancshares Inc

Auditors: Whitley Penn LLP

LOCATIONS

HQ: Guaranty Bancshares Inc
201 South Jefferson Avenue, Mount Pleasant, TX 75455
Phone: 903 572-9881
Web: www.gnty.com

PRODUCTS/OPERATIONS

2008 Sales

	$ mil.	% of total
Interest		
Loans including fees	31.2	70
Securities	6.3	13
Other	1.1	2
Noninterest		
Service charges	4.2	8
Other	3.3	7
Total	**46.1**	**100**

COMPETITORS

BancorpSouth	Southside Bancshares
Bank of America	Wells Fargo
Capital One	Woodforest Financial
Cullen/Frost Bankers	

HISTORICAL FINANCIALS

Company Type: Public

Income Statement

FYE: December 31

	ASSETS ($ mil.)	NET INCOME ($ mil.)	INCOME AS % OF ASSETS	EMPLOYEES
12/17	1,962.6	14.4	0.7%	407
12/16	1,828.3	12.1	0.7%	397
12/15	1,682.6	10.1	0.6%	0
12/14	1,334.0	9.7	0.7%	0
12/13	1,247.0	14.7	1.2%	0
Annual Growth	**12.0%**	**(0.6%)**	**—**	**—**

2017 Year-End Financials

Return on assets: 0.7%	Dividends
Return on equity: 8.2%	Yield: 0.0%
Long-term debt ($ mil.): —	Payout: 28.5%
No. of shares (mil.): 11.0	Market value ($ mil.): 339.0
Sales ($ mil): 83.9	

	STOCK PRICE ($) FY Close	P/E High/Low	PER SHARE ($) Earnings	Dividends	Book Value
12/17	30.65	25 20	1.40	0.40	18.75
12/16	26.50	— —	1.35	0.52	16.22
12/15	26.50	— —	1.15	0.50	15.47
12/14	26.50	— —	1.25	1.50	14.01
12/13	26.50	— —	2.40	1.90	13.25
Annual Growth	**3.7%**	**— —**	**(12.6%)**	**(32.3%)**	**9.1%**

Gulfport Energy Corp.

Gulfport Energy put its energy into exploring for hydrocarbons near the Gulf of Mexico and elsewhere. The oil and gas exploration and production company' main producing properties are located along the Louisiana Gulf Coast in the Permian basin in West Texas in the Niobrara Shale Formation in western Colorado and in the Utica Shale in eastern Ohio. Additionally Gulfport Energy holds a sizeable acreage position in the Alberta oil sands in Canada through its interest in Grizzly Oil Sands ULC and it has interests in entities that operate in the Phu Horm gas field in northern Thailand. In 2015 the company reported proved reserves of 6.4 million barrels of oil and 1.5 trillion cu. ft. of natural gas.

Operations

Gulfport Energy's average daily net production from its Utica Shale in 205 was 586.9 barrels of oil equivalent 59% of which was from natural gas.

In 2015 it drilled 49 gross (38.4 net) wells participated in an additional 25 gross (7.3 net) wells that were drilled by other operators on Utica Shale acreage and recompleted 72 gross and net wells. Of 49 new wells drilled ten were completed as producing wells and at year end 36 were in various stages of completion and three were drilling. That year it recompleted 35 existing wells. In the Hackberry Field Gulfport Energy recompleted 37 existing wells.

During the year gas accounted for 72% of revenues; oil and condensate 20%; and natural gas liquids 8%.

Geographic Reach

The company's principal operating area inc ludes Louisiana's West Cote Blanche Bay field East Hackberry field (in the Permian Basin) Utica shale in Ohio the Niobrara Shale in Colorado Canadian oil sands in Alberta and the Phu Horm gas field in Thailand.

Sales and Marketing

In 2015 Gulfport Energy sold 90% and 10% of its oil production to Shell and Marathon Oil respectively; 76% and 24% of its natural gas liquids production to MarkWest and Antero Resources respectively; and 79% 14% and 5% of its natural gas production to BP DTE Energy and Hess respectively.

In Ohio the company entered into firm transportation contracts to deliver 725000 MMBtu to 775000 MMBtu per day for 2016.

For 2017 it entered into firm transportation contracts to deliver 775000 MMBtu to 1125000 MMBtu per day. For 2018 through 2020 the company had firm transportation contracts to deliver 1125000 MMBtu per day.

Financial Performance

In 2015 Gulfport Energy's net revenues increased by 6% due to a 128% increase in net production partially offset by a 54% decrease in realized Mcfe prices as the result of a decline in commodity prices and a shift in the company's production mix toward natural gas and NGLs in 2015.

The company incurred a huge net loss of $1.22 billion (and overall decrease of 595% compared to net income in 2014). This loss was mainly due to impairment of oil and gas properties of $1.4 billion.

In 2015 cash from operating activities declined by 21% due to impairment charges.

Strategy

The company sells some assets to pay down debt. It is also focused on building up its lucrative Utica shale assets. Gulfport Energy's strategy includes well development reserve acquisitions midstream infrastructure and other activities.

A key part of our strategy involves using some of the latest available horizontal drilling and completion techniques.

It spud 49 gross (38.4 net) wells on Utica Shale acreage and in 2016 (through February 10 2016) they had spud four gross (2.2 net) wells. As of February 2016 one well was waiting on completion and three were still being drilled.

In 2016 the company planned to drill 29 to 32 gross (19 to 21 net) horizontal wells and commence sales from 44 to 48 gross (28 to 30 net) horizontal wells on Utica Shale acreage for an estimated aggregate cost of $219 million to $247. It anticipated 17 to 19 gross (two to three net) horizontal wells will be drilled and sales commenced from 30 to 34 gross (eight to nine net) horizontal wells by other operators on our Utica Shale acreage during 2016 for an estimated net cost to us of $90 million to $100 million.

In 2014 Gulfport Energy sold Blackhawk Midstream's (50% owned by Gulfport) equity interest in two entities Ohio Gathering Company LLC and Ohio Condensate Company LLC to Summit Midstream Partners for $190 million.

Mergers and Acquisitions

In 2016 Gulfport Energy agreed to buy 12600 net undeveloped acres in northern Monroe County Ohio in the core of the dry gas window of the Utica Shale for $87 million.

In 2015 the company acquired Paloma for $301.9 million. Paloma holds approximately 24000 net nonproducing acres in the Utica Shale of Ohio. It also bought 6198 gross and net acres located in Belmont and Jefferson Counties Ohio from AEU for $68.2 million.

Gulfport Energy also bought 38965 gross (27228 net) acres located in Monroe County Ohio 14.6 MMcf per day of average net production 18 gross (11.3 net) drilled but uncompleted wells an 11 mile gas gathering system and a four well pad location from AEU for a total purchase price of approximately $319.0 million

Company Background

In 2013 Gulfport Energy acquired 22000 net acres in the Utica Shale from Windsor Ohio LLC an affiliate of Wexford Capital for $220 million; with an expectation of net production to be about 22200 barrels of oil equivalent per day.

In 2012 the company purchased 37000 net acres in the Utica Shale for about $372 million boosting its leasehold interests in the shale play to 137000 gross (106000 net) acres.

In 2012 the company completed its contribution of its oil and gas interests in the Permian Basin to Diamondback prior to the closing of the Diamondback IPO. In 2013 the company received an additional payment from Diamondback of $19 million.

EXECUTIVES

CEO; Director, Michael G. (Mike) Moore, age 61, $460,000 total compensation
VP Geological and Geophysical, Stuart A. Maier, age 65, $400,000 total compensation
VP Reservoir Engineering, Steve R. Baldwin, age 65

CFO, Keri Crowell, age 44, $250,000 total compensation
VP Land, Lester Zitkus
VP Operations, Mark Malone
VP Drilling, Rob Jones
Managing Director Midstream Operations, Ty Peck
Vice President, Jonathon Hines
Chairman, David L. Houston, age 65
Auditors: Grant Thornton LLP

LOCATIONS

HQ: Gulfport Energy Corp.
3001 Quail Springs Parkway, Oklahoma City, OK 73134
Phone: 405 252-4600
Web: www.gulfportenergy.com

PRODUCTS/OPERATIONS

2015 Sales

	$ mil.	% of total
Gas	507.7	72
Oil & condensate	142.0	20
Natural gas liquids	59.4	8
Other	0.4	-
Total	**709.5**	**100**

COMPETITORS

Abraxas Petroleum	EOG
Apache	Exxon Mobil
Bill Barrett	FieldPoint Petroleum
BreitBurn	MarkWest Energy
Cabot Oil & Gas	Partners
Chesapeake Energy	XTO Energy
Devon Energy	

HISTORICAL FINANCIALS

Company Type: Public

Income Statement				FYE: December 31
	REVENUE ($ mil.)	NET INCOME ($ mil.)	NET PROFIT MARGIN	EMPLOYEES
12/17	1,320.3	435.1	33.0%	331
12/16	385.9	(979.7)	—	241
12/15	709.4	(1,224.8)	—	230
12/14	671.2	247.4	36.9%	203
12/13	262.7	153.1	58.3%	118
Annual Growth	49.7%	29.8%	—	29.4%

2017 Year-End Financials

Debt ratio: 35.1%
Return on equity: 16.4%
Cash ($ mil.): 99.5
Current ratio: 0.62
Long-term debt ($ mil.): 2,038.3

No. of shares (mil.): 183.1
Dividends
Yield: —
Payout: —
Market value ($ mil.): 2,336.0

	STOCK PRICE ($) FY Close	P/E High/Low		PER SHARE ($) Earnings	Dividends	Book Value
12/17	12.76	9	5	2.41	0.00	16.94
12/16	21.64	—	—	(7.97)	0.00	13.75
12/15	24.57	—	—	(12.27)	0.00	18.82
12/14	41.74	26	13	2.88	0.00	26.81
12/13	63.13	35	18	1.97	0.00	24.07
Annual Growth	(32.9%)	—	—	5.2%	—	(8.4%)

Hallador Energy Co

Hallador Energy puts most of its energy into selling coal from its Carlisle Mine in Indiana to three utilities in the Midwest and one in Florida. Hallador has recoverable coal reserves of 43.5 million tons (34.2 million tons proven and 9.3 million tons probable). In addition to the Carlisle Mine it get coals from a mine in Clay County Indiana and has two inactive mines in Illinois. The company is exploring the possibility of other contracts with a number of coal purchasers. Additionally Hallador has a 45% stake in Savoy Energy L.P. an oil and gas company with operations in Michigan and a 50% interest in Sunrise Energy LLC a private oil and gas exploration and production company with assets in Indiana.

Sales and Marketing
Hallador sells coal in the Midwest to Duke Energy Hoosier Energy and Indianapolis Power & Light. It also sells coal to JEA in Florida.

Financial Performance
In 2012 the company's revenues declined by 10% due to a price decrease and unfavorable weather conditions crimping demand. Hallador's net income decreased by 34% due to lower net sales and higher operating costs.

Strategy
Expanding its geographic coverage in 2011 the company sold 300000 tons of coal to JEA its first such sale to a Florida-based customer. It sold 18500 tons to JEA in 2012.

Company Background
Hallador was founded in 1949. In 1997 investment company Yorktown Energy Partners II and affiliates invested $5 million in Hallador.

Despite its Harry Potter-like name Hallador Petroleum could find no magic in oil and natural gas exploration and production — just a lot of hard and dirty work. It therefore decided to focus on its coal operations. The company acquired control of Sunrise Coal co-developer of the Carlisle Mine in 2008.

Hallador in Spanish means "finder" or "discoverer" or "one who leads the way."

EXECUTIVES

Chairman, David Hardie, age 66
Chief Executive Officer, Victor P. Stabio, age 69, $180,000 total compensation
CFO Sunrise Coal, Larry Martin, age 51, $102,000 total compensation
Chief Financial Officer; Chief Accounting Officer, William A. (Andy) Bishop, age 63
President and appointed to our board, Brent Bilsland
Director, Sheldon B. Lubar, age 87
Director, Bryan H. Lawrence, age 74
CEO and Director, Victor P. Stabio, age 68
Independent Director, John Heuvelen
Auditors: Plante & Moran PLLC

LOCATIONS

HQ: Hallador Energy Co
1660 Lincoln Street, Suite 2700, Denver, CO 80264-2701
Phone: 303 839-5504
Web: www.halladorenergy.com

PRODUCTS/OPERATIONS

2015 Sales

	$ mil.	% of total
Coal sales	339.5	99
Other	2.2	1
Equity loss - Savoy	(1.5)	-
Equity loss - Sunrise Energy	(0.1)	-
Total	**340.1**	**100**

COMPETITORS

Alpha Natural Resources	Noble Energy
	Peabody Energy
Anadarko Petroleum	Pioneer Natural
Arch Coal	Resources
CONSOL Energy	SandRidge Energy
Chesapeake Energy	

HISTORICAL FINANCIALS

Company Type: Public

Income Statement				FYE: December 31
	REVENUE ($ mil.)	NET INCOME ($ mil.)	NET PROFIT MARGIN	EMPLOYEES
12/17	271.6	33.0	12.2%	742
12/16	281.4	12.5	4.4%	748
12/15	340.1	20.1	5.9%	740
12/14	241.1	10.2	4.2%	1,027
12/13	153.8	23.1	15.0%	376
Annual Growth	15.3%	9.3%	—	18.5%

2017 Year-End Financials

Debt ratio: 38.3%
Return on equity: 14.1%
Cash ($ mil.): 12.4
Current ratio: 1.32
Long-term debt ($ mil.): 165.7

No. of shares (mil.): 29.9
Dividends
Yield: 0.0%
Payout: 14.8%
Market value ($ mil.): 182.0

	STOCK PRICE ($) FY Close	P/E High/Low		PER SHARE ($) Earnings	Dividends	Book Value
12/17	6.09	9	5	1.08	0.16	8.32
12/16	9.09	24	10	0.42	0.16	7.37
12/15	4.56	19	7	0.68	0.16	7.07
12/14	11.01	41	22	0.34	0.16	6.56
12/13	8.06	11	8	0.80	0.28	6.38
Annual Growth	(6.8%)	—	—	7.8%	(13.1%)	6.9%

Halozyme Therapeutics Inc

Halozyme Therapeutics is searching for cures through a number of "ologys" by developing treatments for use in endocrinology oncology and dermatology fields. It is also creating products for the drug delivery market. Its Hylenex recombinant is used as an adjuvant for drug and fluid infusions. Most of Halozyme's products and candidates (including Hylenex) are based on rHuPH20 its patented recombinant human hyaluronidase enzyme while its lead cancer program is PEGPH20 which targets solid tumors. Halozyme partners with such pharmaceuticals as Roche Pfizer Janssen Baxalta and AbbVie for its ENHANZE drug delivery platform which enables biologics and small molecule compounds to be delivered subcutaneously.

Operations

The firm's commercial products are marketed through distribution agreements primarily in the US and Europe. It also receives revenue from its development partnerships. Halozyme has a development and marketing agreement with Baxter International to develop an under-the-skin delivery technology for Baxter's Gammagard Liquid immunodeficiency treatment using Halozyme's Enhanze platform. The two companies did partner on sales of Hylenex as well however in 2011 Baxter returned its marketing rights back to Halozyme. Halozyme intends to take advantage of the inroads already made by Baxter to commercialize the product further.

Geographic Reach

Halozyme is headquartered in and has research facilities in San Diego California.

Switzerland accounts for about 60% of the firm's revenue and the US accounts for about 40%.

Sales and Marketing

Roche accounts for more than half of Halozyme's total revenue while Janssen accounts for about 20%.

Integrated Commercial Solutions a division of AmerisourceBergen is the exclusive distributor for Hylenex recombinant in the US.

The company employs outside vendors such as advertising agencies market research firms and marketing firms to help support its commercial activities.

Financial Performance

With the exception of 2012 revenue has been on the rise for the past five years. It rose 37% to $75 million in 2014 as product sales and royalty earnings increased. Bulk sales of rHuPH20 for the firm's collaboration with Roche grew by nearly $10 million that year while Hylenex sales grew by more than $4 million. Royalties primarily increased due to sales of Roche's Herceptin SC (subcutaneous) which was launched in 2013.

Halozyme has operated at a loss every year since its inception but thanks to the higher revenue in 2014 that loss declined to $68 million (versus $83 million in 2013). At the end of 2014 its accumulated deficit totaled some $450.4 million.

Operating cash outflow dropped 2% to $48 million in 2014.

Strategy

Halozyme's two primary goals are to continue developing its PEGPH20 oncology program and entering more collaborations for its Enhanze technology. For instance Halozyme has a collaboration with Roche to apply its ENHANZE technology to Roche's therapeutic biological compounds in areas including oncology and immunology. And in 2015 the company signed a collaboration agreement with Eisai to investigate Eisai's eribulin and PEGPH20 in metastatic breast cancer.

The company has made a number of related moves in the past couple of years. Also in 2015 it signed a global collaboration and license agreement with AbbVie to develop and commercialize products that combine Halozyme's ENHANZE platform with AbbVie compounds. In 2014 it entered into a similar agreement with Janssen which will focus on the rHuPH20 enzyme and Janssen's proprietary biologics.

In 2014 Baxter launched HyQvia a subcutaneous immunoglobulin treatment for patients with primary immunodeficiency in the US. Also that year Roche launched the subcutaneous formulation of MabThera in Europe for the treatment of non-Hodgkin lymphoma. Both of those treatments utilize Halozyme's rHuPH20 enzyme.

Halozyme's proprietary Ultrafast Insulin program combines the company's enzyme with mealtime insulins to increase absorption speed of action and glycemic control. Additional candidates target bladder cancer solid tumors and aesthetic dermatology conditions.

During 2014 the company terminated a collaboration agreement with ViroPharma and a license agreement with Intrexon.

EXECUTIVES

SVP and COO, Mark J. Gergen, age 55
President CEO and Director, Helen I. Torley, age 55, $624,000 total compensation
VP and Chief Scientific Officer, Michael J. LaBarre
SVP and CFO, Laurie D. Stelzer, age 50, $229,115 total compensation
SVP and Chief Medical Officer, Athena Countouriotis, age 46, $426,967 total compensation
Chair, Connie L. Matsui, age 64
Auditors: Ernst & Young LLP

LOCATIONS

HQ: Halozyme Therapeutics Inc
11388 Sorrento Valley Road, San Diego, CA 92121
Phone: 858 794-8889
Web: www.halozyme.com

PRODUCTS/OPERATIONS

2014 Revenues

	$ mil.	% of total
Product sales	37.8	50
Collaborative agreements	28.1	37
Royalties	9.4	13
Total	**75.3**	**100**

COMPETITORS

Abeona	Dyadic
Amphastar	ISTA Pharmaceuticals
Biodel	Irvine Scientific
Cook Group	Novo Nordisk
CooperSurgical	PhaseBio

HISTORICAL FINANCIALS

Company Type: Public

Income Statement				FYE: December 31
	REVENUE ($ mil.)	NET INCOME ($ mil.)	NET PROFIT MARGIN	EMPLOYEES
12/17	316.6	62.9	19.9%	255
12/16	146.6	(103.0)	—	259
12/15	135.0	(32.2)	—	216
12/14	75.3	(68.3)	—	153
12/13	54.8	(83.4)	—	170
Annual Growth	**55.0%**	**—**	**—**	**10.7%**

2017 Year-End Financials

Debt ratio: 38.9%	No. of shares (mil.): 142.7
Return on equity: 71.6%	Dividends
Cash ($ mil.): 168.7	Yield: —
Current ratio: 3.89	Payout: —
Long-term debt ($ mil.): 125.1	Market value ($ mil.): 2,893.0

	STOCK PRICE ($) FY Close	P/E High/Low	PER SHARE ($) Earnings	Dividends	Book Value
12/17	20.26	45 22	0.45	0.00	1.46
12/16	9.88	— —	(0.81)	0.00	(0.25)
12/15	17.33	— —	(0.25)	0.00	0.34
12/14	9.65	— —	(0.56)	0.00	0.33
12/13	14.99	— —	(0.74)	0.00	(0.17)
Annual Growth	**7.8%**	**—**	**—**	**—**	**—**

Hamilton Lane Inc

Auditors: Ernst & Young LLP

LOCATIONS

HQ: Hamilton Lane Inc
One Presidential Blvd., 4th Floor, Bala Cynwyd, PA 19004
Phone: 610 934-2222
Web: www.hamiltonlane.com

HISTORICAL FINANCIALS

Company Type: Public

Income Statement				FYE: March 31
	REVENUE ($ mil.)	NET INCOME ($ mil.)	NET PROFIT MARGIN	EMPLOYEES
03/18	244.0	17.3	7.1%	340
03/17	179.8	0.6	0.3%	290
03/16	180.8	57.1	31.6%	290
03/15	155.3	69.2	44.6%	0
03/14	139.7	62.4	44.7%	0
Annual Growth	**15.0%**	**(27.4%)**	**—**	**—**

2018 Year-End Financials

Debt ratio: 28.6%	No. of shares (mil.): 48.8
Return on equity: 25.0%	Dividends
Cash ($ mil.): 47.6	Yield: 0.0%
Current ratio: 1.06	Payout: 75.2%
Long-term debt ($ mil.): 84.1	Market value ($ mil.): 1,818.0

	STOCK PRICE ($) FY Close	P/E High/Low	PER SHARE ($) Earnings	Dividends	Book Value
03/18	37.23	42 19	0.93	0.70	1.61
03/17	18.67	642601	0.03	0.00	1.28
Annual Growth	**99.4%**	**—**	**—3000.0%**	**—**	**25.6%**

Hanmi Financial Corp.

Hanmi Financial owns Hanmi Bank which serves Korean-American and other ethnic communities in California Colorado Georgia Illinois New Jersey New York Texas Virginia and Washington. The company which holds $5.5 billion in assets offers traditional banking services to small and midsized businesses from about 40 branches and eight loan offices. Real estate loans — including for retail hospitality mixed-use apartment office industrial gas station faith-based facility and warehouse properties — account for about 80% of its loan portfolio; commercial and industrial loans and leases receivable make up most of the rest.

Operations

Hanmi Financial originates real estate loans (including commercial construction and residential property) commercial and industrial loans (including commercial term commercial lines of credit and international) equipment lease financing consumer loans and Small Business Administration (SBA) loans. The bank also offers traditional deposit products including checking savings negotiable order of withdrawal (NOW) and money market accounts and CDs.

Hanmi's $4.6 billion loan portfolio is made up mostly of real estate loans – particularly commercial property loans including retail (about 20% of total portfolio) hospitality (20%) and other loans (30%). Other loans include loans for mixed-use apartment office industrial gas station faith-based facility and warehouse properties. Residential property loans comprise around 10%.

Commercial and industrial loans and leases receivable together make up about 15% of the bank's portfolio.

Geographic Reach

Headquartered in a penthouse suite on Los Angeles' Wilshire Boulevard Hanmi Financial has one bank branch in each of New Jersey New York and Virginia; some five branches in Illinois; about 10 branches in Texas; and around 25 branches in California. The majority of its loan and deposit concentration is in Southern California.

Sales and Marketing

Hanmi Financial's lending is concentrated in real estate loans commercial loans and leases and Small Business Administration (SBA) loans for small and middle market businesses in California Texas Illinois and New York — primarily among Korean-American and other multi-ethnic communities.

Financial Performance

Since 2013 Hanmi Financial has grown its revenue and net income by about 60% and 40% respectively thanks to increasing net interest income. But the company also depleted its cash stores by about 15% and more than doubled its long-term debt in that time mostly due to Federal Home Loan Bank advances in 2016.

The bank's revenue increased 9% in 2017 compared with 2016 reaching $210.2 million. Higher interest and fees on loans and leases drove the improvement which was partially offset by higher expense for interest on deposits. Average loans and leases and the percentage of loans and leases in Hanmi's mix of interest-earning assets both increased in 2017.

Net income slipped 3% to $54.7 million owing mostly to an increase in the bank's income tax provision which included a $3.9 million charge for a one-time revaluation adjustment connected with the Tax Cuts and Jobs Act (TCJA).

Hanmi added $6.6 million to its cash stores in 2017 for a total of $153.8 million. Operations and financings provided $79.9 million and $445.1 million respectively. Investment activity used $518.4 million.

Strategy

Hanmi Financial is working to diversify its loan portfolio to reduce its reliance on commercial real estate and increase its composition of leases and commercial industrial and residential real estate loans. Since 2014 the company has increased the proportion of its portfolio made up of leases and residential real estate while maintaining the proportion of commercial and industrial loans.

After a review of its cost structure and operating efficiency in 2018 the company is moderating its growth expectations lowering its non-interest expenses and consolidating about 10% of its branches.

Hanmi also hired a Chief Technology officer in 2018 to implement a strategy to improve the company's use of technology including using it to increase efficiency of regulatory compliance activities (for which the company heavily relies on human capital).

Mergers and Acquisitions

In its first foray outside of California in late 2013 Hanmi agreed to acquire Central Bancorp Inc. the parent of Texas-based United Central Bank. United Central Bank serves multi-ethnic communities in Texas Illinois Virginia California New York and New Jersey through some two dozen branches. Once the acquisition is complete Hanmi will have about 50 branches and two loan production offices serving a broad range of ethnic communities in California Texas Illinois New York New Jersey Virginia and Georgia.

Company Background

Hanmi Financial was founded in 1982.

EXECUTIVES

SEVP and COO, Bonita I. (Bonnie) Lee, age 55
Chief Compliance and BSA Officer, Jean Lim
EVP and CFO, Michael W. McCall
President CEO and Director, Chong Guk (C. G.) Kum
EVP and Chief Credit Officer, Randall G. Ewig
EVP and Chief Administrative Officer, Greg D. Kim
EVP and Chief Banking Officer, Peter Yang
EVP and Chief Lending Officer, Anthony Kim
Vice President and Loan Officer, Yong Park
Assistant Vice President Compliance Officer, Michael Santiago
Assistant Vice President Treasury Management, Debby Sassoon
Senior Vice President Senior Credit Administrator, Oliver Kim
Vice President, Maheboob Kurani
Vice President Loss Share Accounting Manager, Brian Rogers
Assistant Vice President andamp; SBA Loan Officer, Sharon Min
Vice President Human Resources Officer, Ashley Sowa
Vice President and Accounting Officer Accounting Department, Jin Shin
Chairman, Joseph K. Rho, age 77
Auditors: KPMG LLP

LOCATIONS

HQ: Hanmi Financial Corp.
3660 Wilshire Boulevard, Penthouse Suite A, Los Angeles, CA 90010
Phone: 213 382-2200
Web: www.hanmi.com

PRODUCTS/OPERATIONS

2017 Sales

	$ mil.	% of total
Net interest income	176.8	84
Non-interest income	33.4	16
Total	**210.2**	**100**

COMPETITORS

Bank of America	Far East National Bank
Broadway Financial	Hope Bancorp
Cathay General Bancorp	JPMorgan Chase
East West Bancorp	Woori

HISTORICAL FINANCIALS

Company Type: Public

Income Statement
FYE: December 31

	ASSETS ($ mil.)	NET INCOME ($ mil.)	INCOME AS % OF ASSETS	EMPLOYEES
12/17	5,210.4	54.6	1.0%	642
12/16	4,701.3	56.4	1.2%	638
12/15	4,234.5	53.8	1.3%	622
12/14	4,232.4	49.7	1.2%	699
12/13	3,055.5	39.9	1.3%	499
Annual Growth	**14.3%**	**8.2%**	**—**	**6.5%**

2017 Year-End Financials

Return on assets: 1.1%
Return on equity: 10.0%
Long-term debt ($ mil.): —
No. of shares (mil.): 32.4
Sales ($ mil): 242.7
Dividends
Yield: 0.0%
Payout: 47.3%
Market value ($ mil.): 984.0

	STOCK PRICE ($) FY Close	P/E High/Low	PER SHARE ($) Earnings	Dividends	Book Value
12/17	30.35	21 15	1.69	0.80	17.34
12/16	34.90	20 11	1.75	0.66	16.42
12/15	23.72	16 12	1.68	0.47	15.45
12/14	21.81	16 12	1.56	0.28	14.21
12/13	21.89	18 11	1.26	0.14	12.63
Annual Growth	**8.5%**	**— —**	**7.6%**	**54.6%**	**8.2%**

Hannon Armstrong Sustainable Infrastructure Capital Inc

Hannon Armstrong Sustainable Infrastructure Capital has its hands in both kinds of green. The REIT provides securitized funding for environmentally friendly infrastructure projects. It is a key provider of financing for the US government's energy efficiency projects. Hannon Armstrong focuses on energy efficiency clean energy (solar and wind) and other sustainable projects including water and communications that improve energy consumption and the use of natural resources. The company manages some $5 billion in assets and operates mostly in the US.

Operations

Hannon Armstrong manages about $5 billion in assets across more than 175 investments in projects to improve energy efficiency and develop renewable energy sources and sustainable infrastructure. About 45% of the REIT's projects are focused on solar energy; wind nearly 30%; energy efficiency more than 20%; and sustainable infrastructure (which includes water and seismic retrofit projects) about 5%.

Nearly 55% of the company's revenue is derived from interest income on receivables. Almost 20% each comes from rental income and gain on sale of receivables and investments.

When making investment decisions Hannon Armstrong calculates the estimated metric tons of carbon emissions or equivalent avoided a calculation it calls CarbonCount. The company's 2017 CarbonCount calculation estimates its investments will reduce carbon emissions by about 530000 metric tons.

Geographic Reach

Based in Annapolis Maryland Hannon Armstrong operates primarily in the US.

Sales and Marketing

Hannon Armstrong provides securitized funding for environmentally friendly infrastructure projects by US federal state and local governments and high credit quality institutions.

Financial Performance

Thanks to growing popularity and falling costs of efficient and renewable energy Hannon Armstrong has seen more than a 325% expansion of revenue in the last five years accompanying a jump in net income to more than $30 million in 2017 compared with a loss of more than $10 million in 2013. Meanwhile the company bolstered its cash stores by about 270% while long-term debt climbed around 325%.

In 2017 the REIT reported revenue of $105.6 million up 30% from the prior year. Interest income on receivables and rental income each account for more than 30% of that growth; around 15% each came from gain on sale of receivables and investments and interest income on investments.

Hannon Armstrong's net income in 2017 ballooned 111% to $30.9 million thanks to improvements in revenue and income from investments.

Cash at the end of fiscal 2017 was $118.1 million double that of the prior year. Cash from operations provided $11.7 million while investing activities used $297.9 million due mostly to equity method investments and purchases of real estate. Financing activities added another $345.2 million primarily from proceeds from non-recourse debt.

Strategy

Hannon Armstrong intends to continue investing in clean energy technologies that it believes benefit society and that generally are tied to long-term utility contracts.

In November 2018 SunStong Capital Holdings a joint venture between the REIT and solar energy company SunPower completed a $400 million asset-backed securitization to refinance the JV's residential lease portfolio debt.

In October 2018 Hannon Armstrong Sustainable Real Estate (HASRE) a collaboration between Hannon Armstrong and Counterpoint Sustainable Real Estate completed a 25-year $10.5 million Commercial Property Assessed Clean Energy (C-PACE) financing for energy efficiency standards and seismic retrofitting of a Hyatt hotel in Sacramento California. Through C-PACE property owners can access inexpensive long-term financing for conservation renewable energy and hazard reduction projects.

In March 2017 Hannon Armstrong closed an $84 million offering of sustainable yield bonds to fund energy efficiency and solar energy projects for more than 90 public schools and 20 local governments.

In February 2017 the company paid $144 million for more than 4000 acres of land leased to 20 solar energy projects under long-term contracts.

Company Background

Formed in 2012 to be a REIT the company went public in 2013 though it traces its roots to the 1980s and Hannon Armstrong Capital LLC.

EXECUTIVES

EVP and CFO, J. Brendan Herron, age 57, $295,000 total compensation

Chairman President and CEO, Jeffrey W. Eckel, age 59, $495,000 total compensation

EVP and General Counsel, Steven L. (Steve) Chuslo, age 60, $300,000 total compensation

EVP Origination, M. Rhem Wooten, age 58, $285,000 total compensation

SVP and Chief Investment Officer, Nathaniel J. Rose, age 40, $275,000 total compensation

EVP, Daniel K. McMahon, age 46

Auditors: Ernst & Young LLP

LOCATIONS

HQ: Hannon Armstrong Sustainable Infrastructure Capital Inc
1906 Towne Centre Blvd., Suite 370, Annapolis, MD 21401
Phone: 410 571-9860
Web: www.hannonarmstrong.com

PRODUCTS/OPERATIONS

2017 Sales

	$ mil.	% of total
Interest income financing receivables	56.7	53
Rental income	19.8	19
Gain on sale of receivables and investments	21.0	20
Interest income investments	5.1	5
Fee income	3.0	3
Total	**105.6**	**100**

Selected Project Types

Clean Energy
Energy Efficiency
Other Sustainable Infrastructure

COMPETITORS

Bank of America	JPMorgan Chase
Goldman Sachs	Wells Fargo

HISTORICAL FINANCIALS

Company Type: Public

Income Statement
FYE: December 31

	REVENUE ($ mil.)	NET INCOME ($ mil.)	NET PROFIT MARGIN	EMPLOYEES
12/17	105.5	30.8	29.2%	47
12/16	81.2	14.6	18.0%	40
12/15	32.2	7.9	24.6%	32
12/14	28.6	9.6	33.6%	28
12/13	3.6	(10.4)	—	22
Annual Growth	132.2%	—	—	20.9%

2017 Year-End Financials

Debt ratio: 63.4%
Return on equity: 5.1%
Cash ($ mil.): 57.2
Current ratio: 11.19
Long-term debt ($ mil.): 1,358.5

No. of shares (mil.): 51.6
Dividends
  Yield: 0.0%
  Payout: 231.5%
Market value ($ mil.): 1,243.0

	STOCK PRICE ($) FY Close	P/E High/Low		Earnings	PER SHARE ($) Dividends	Book Value
12/17	24.06	44	32	0.57	1.32	12.37
12/16	18.99	78	52	0.32	1.23	12.27
12/15	18.92	102	65	0.21	1.08	11.57
12/14	14.23	35	30	0.43	0.92	10.21
12/13	13.96	—	—	(0.68)	0.42	9.22
Annual Growth	14.6%	—	—	—	33.1%	7.6%

HarborOne Bancorp Inc

Auditors: Wolf & Company, P.C.

LOCATIONS

HQ: HarborOne Bancorp Inc
770 Oak Street, Brockton, MA 02301
Phone: 508 895-1000
Web: www.harborone.com

HISTORICAL FINANCIALS

Company Type: Public

Income Statement
FYE: December 31

	ASSETS ($ mil.)	NET INCOME ($ mil.)	INCOME AS % OF ASSETS	EMPLOYEES
12/17	2,684.9	10.3	0.4%	581
12/16	2,448.3	5.9	0.2%	614
12/15	2,163.1	5.7	0.3%	387
12/14	2,041.8	2.5	0.1%	0
Annual Growth	9.6%	59.2%	—	—

2017 Year-End Financials

Return on assets: 0.4%
Return on equity: 3.0%
Long-term debt ($ mil.): —
No. of shares (mil.): 32.6
Sales ($ mil): 144.8

Dividends
  Yield: —
  Payout: —
Market value ($ mil.): 626.0

	STOCK PRICE ($) FY Close	P/E High/Low		Earnings	PER SHARE ($) Dividends	Book Value
12/17	19.16	67	49	0.33	0.00	10.52
12/16	19.34	—	—	(0.00)	0.00	10.25
12/15	0.00	—	—	(0.00)	0.00	(0.00)
Annual Growth	—	—	—	—	—	—

Health Insurance Innovations Inc

Auditors: Grant Thornton LLP

LOCATIONS

HQ: Health Insurance Innovations Inc
15438 North Florida Avenue, Suite 201, Tampa, FL 33613
Phone: 813 397-1187
Web: www.hiiquote.com

HISTORICAL FINANCIALS
Company Type: Public

Income Statement   FYE: December 31

	REVENUE ($ mil.)	NET INCOME ($ mil.)	NET PROFIT MARGIN	EMPLOYEES
12/17	250.4	17.8	7.1%	199
12/16	184.5	4.5	2.4%	174
12/15	104.7	0.6	0.6%	192
12/14	88.7	(0.3)	—	285
12/13	56.6	(3.3)	—	168
Annual Growth	45.0%	—	—	4.3%

2017 Year-End Financials

Debt ratio: —
Return on equity: 27.0%
Cash ($ mil.): 39.3
Current ratio: 2.27
Long-term debt ($ mil.): —

No. of shares (mil.): 16.1
Dividends
  Yield: —
  Payout: —
Market value ($ mil.): 404.0

	STOCK PRICE ($) FY Close	P/E High/Low		Earnings	PER SHARE ($) Dividends	Book Value
12/17	24.95	22	9	1.50	0.00	5.20
12/16	17.85	32	7	0.57	0.00	3.24
12/15	6.70	117	52	0.08	0.00	2.74
12/14	7.16	—	—	(0.06)	0.00	2.63
12/13	10.11	—	—	(0.70)	0.00	1.74
Annual Growth	25.3%			—	—	31.5%

Healthcare Services Group, Inc.

Healthcare Services Group gets swept up in the work it does for health care facilities. The company provides housekeeping laundry and linen food and maintenance services to hospitals nursing homes rehabilitation centers and retirement facilities. It tidies up around 3500 long-term care facilities across the US. Housekeeping and laundry and linen services are the company's top revenue generators. The company's dietary division prepares food for residents and monitors nutritional needs in more than 1500 facilities. Healthcare Services Group was established in 1976.

Operations
Healthcare Services Group's operations are divided in two business units: Housekeeping and Dietary.

The company's Housekeeping unit manages clients' housekeeping departments which are responsible for the cleaning disinfecting and sanitizing patient rooms and common areas of clients' facilities. The business unit also offers laundering and processing of patient clothing.

Its Dietary unit manages food purchasing meal preparation and dietary consulting. Consulting services including creating meal plans based on individual patient's dietary needs.

Revenue is split between the two segments with Housekeeping and Dietary services each contributing about 50%.

Geographic Reach
Healthcare Services Group based in Bensalem Pennsylvania operates in 48 states. The company manages operations regionally through offices in Pennsylvania Colorado South Carolina Connecticut Georgia California and New Jersey.

Sales and Marketing
Sales and marketing activities at Healthcare Services Group include referrals and in-person solicitation of target facilities. The company regularly industry trade shows health care trade associations and healthcare support service seminars.

Significant customers include Genesis Healthcare. While it does business with numerous companies Healthcare Services Group's largest customer accounts for more than 17% of its total revenue.

Financial Performance
Revenue and net income at Healthcare Services Group have trended upwards over the past decade.

In 2017 revenue jumped 19% rising to $1.8 billion from $1.5 billion in 2016. The biggest increase came from its Dietary business which extended Dietary contracts to clients using the company's Housekeeping services. Its Housekeeping business also saw a small increase in revenue with contracts landed with new clients driving the increase.

Higher revenue lead to a 14% rise in net income in 2017 with net income increasing to $88.2 million from $77.3 million in 2016.

Total cash flow at the end of fiscal 2017 sat at $9.5 million a decrease from the $23.8 million at the start of the year. The company used $14.9 million in investing activities and $6.9 million in financing activities while cash from operations contributed $7.6 million. Its operating cash flow was significantly lower than in previous years due in large part to an increase in accounts receivables which consists largely outstanding or delayed payments by clients.

Strategy
Healthcare Services Group's growth strategy centers on renewing and extending contracts with existing clients. Much of the company's recent financial success is driven by aggressive cross-selling of its Dietary service to its existing Housekeeping services clients. This strategic approach drove a 46% jump in revenue in its Dietary business unit in 2017.

The company's growth strategy also includes pursuing new clients operating in the health care and senior care industries and Healthcare Services Group reports consistent revenue growth year over year that's driven by landing contracts with new clients.

EXECUTIVES

Executive Vice President, Joseph McCartney
VP Mid-Atlantic Division, Michael E. McBryan, $102,492 total compensation
EVP, Bryan D. McCartney, $102,492 total compensation
President and CEO, Theodore Wahl, age 44, $996,255 total compensation
CFO, John Shea, $389,039 total compensation
Vice President of Human Resources, Jeannie Fissinger
Regional Vice President, Josh Dubler
Vice President, Jim Keeley
Divisional Vice President, Stephen Foresman
Regional Vice President, Jim Bleming
Divisional Vice President, Jason Lecroy
Divisional Vice President, Donnie Warren
Regional Vice President, Tim Hubka
Vice President, John Bullock
Chairman, Daniel P. McCartney, age 66
Board Member, Robbie Moss
Auditors: Grant Thornton LLP

LOCATIONS
HQ: Healthcare Services Group, Inc.
3220 Tillman Drive, Suite 300, Bensalem, PA 19020
Phone: 215 639-4274   **Fax:** 215 639-2152
Web: www.hcsgcorp.com

PRODUCTS/OPERATIONS

2017 Sales

	$ mil.	% of total
Housekeeping services	979.6	52
Dietary services	886.5	48
Total	1,866.1	100

Selected Services
Senior living housekeeping & laundry services
Senior living dining & nutrition services
Hospital environmental services
Hospital dining & nutrition services

COMPETITORS

ABM Industries
ARAMARK
Alsco
Angelica Corporation
Crothall Healthcare

Ecolab
G&K Services
Sodexo USA
SureQuest Systems

HISTORICAL FINANCIALS
Company Type: Public

Income Statement   FYE: December 31

	REVENUE ($ mil.)	NET INCOME ($ mil.)	NET PROFIT MARGIN	EMPLOYEES
12/17	1,866.1	88.2	4.7%	55,000
12/16	1,562.6	77.4	5.0%	48,900
12/15	1,436.8	58.0	4.0%	8,600
12/14	1,293.1	21.8	1.7%	8,600
12/13	1,149.8	47.1	4.1%	7,600
Annual Growth	12.9%	17.0%	—	64.0%

2017 Year-End Financials

Debt ratio: 5.2%
Return on equity: 23.8%
Cash ($ mil.): 9.5
Current ratio: 2.86
Long-term debt ($ mil.): —

No. of shares (mil.): 73.4
Dividends
  Yield: 0.0%
  Payout: 63.2%
Market value ($ mil.): 3,872.0

	STOCK PRICE ($) FY Close	P/E High/Low		Earnings	PER SHARE ($) Dividends	Book Value
12/17	52.72	46	32	1.19	0.75	5.45
12/16	39.17	40	31	1.05	0.73	4.67
12/15	34.87	47	37	0.80	0.71	4.12
12/14	30.93	103	83	0.31	0.69	3.88
12/13	28.37	43	32	0.67	0.67	4.07
Annual Growth	16.8%	—	—	15.4%	2.8%	7.5%

Healthcare Trust Of America Inc

EXECUTIVES

Chb-pres-ceo, Scott D Peters
Executive Vice President Acquisitions, Mark Engstrom
Senior Vice President Leasing, Jaime Northam
Board Of Directors, Gary Wescombe
Auditors: Deloitte & Touche LLP

LOCATIONS

HQ: Healthcare Trust Of America Inc
16435 N. Scottsdale Road, Suite 320, Scottsdale, AZ
85254

Phone: 480 998-3478   **Fax:** 480 991-0755
Web: www.htareit.com

HISTORICAL FINANCIALS
Company Type: Public

Income Statement
FYE: December 31

	REVENUE ($ mil.)	NET INCOME ($ mil.)	NET PROFIT MARGIN	EMPLOYEES
12/17	613.9	63.9	10.4%	270
12/16	460.9	45.9	10.0%	214
12/15	403.8	32.9	8.2%	181
12/14	371.5	45.3	12.2%	170
12/13	319.9	24.2	7.6%	160
Annual Growth	17.7%	27.4%	—	14.0%

2017 Year-End Financials

Debt ratio: 43.1%
Return on equity: 2.5%
Cash ($ mil.): 118.5
Current ratio: 0.71
Long-term debt ($ mil.): 2,781.0

No. of shares (mil.): 204.8
Dividends
Yield: 0.0%
Payout: 355.8%
Market value ($ mil.): 6,155.0

	STOCK PRICE ($) FY Close	P/E High/Low		Earnings	PER SHARE ($) Dividends	Book Value
12/17	30.04	94	82	0.34	1.21	16.00
12/16	29.11	102	77	0.33	1.19	11.91
12/15	26.97	115	87	0.26	1.17	10.86
12/14	26.94	72	26	0.37	0.29	11.57
12/13	9.84	66	49	0.20	0.00	11.71
Annual Growth	32.2%	—	—	14.2%	—	8.1%

HealthEquity Inc

Auditors: PricewaterhouseCoopers LLP

LOCATIONS

HQ: HealthEquity Inc
15 West Scenic Pointe Drive, Suite 100, Draper, UT
84020
Phone: 801 727-1000
Web: www.healthequity.com

HISTORICAL FINANCIALS
Company Type: Public

Income Statement
FYE: January 31

	REVENUE ($ mil.)	NET INCOME ($ mil.)	NET PROFIT MARGIN	EMPLOYEES
01/18	229.5	47.3	20.6%	1,027
01/17	178.3	26.3	14.8%	875
01/16	126.7	16.6	13.1%	636
01/15	87.8	10.1	11.6%	455
01/14	62.0	1.2	2.0%	381
Annual Growth	38.7%	149.0%	—	28.1%

2018 Year-End Financials

Debt ratio: —
Return on equity: 15.5%
Cash ($ mil.): 240.2
Current ratio: 12.95
Long-term debt ($ mil.): —

No. of shares (mil.): 60.8
Dividends
Yield: —
Payout: —
Market value ($ mil.): 3,079.0

	STOCK PRICE ($) FY Close	P/E High/Low		Earnings	PER SHARE ($) Dividends	Book Value
01/18	50.62	69	50	0.77	0.00	5.69
01/17	46.25	108	35	0.44	0.00	4.40
01/16	21.55	121	65	0.28	0.00	3.52
01/15	20.77	66	43	0.21	0.00	2.63
Annual Growth	34.6%	—	—	54.2%	—	29.4%

Healthstream Inc

HealthStream supplies internet-based learning and research content to help US health care organizations meet their training certification and development needs. HealthStream's core learning product is HealthStream Learning Center (HLC) which offers educational and training courseware to about 4.8 million subscribers (representing some 45000 hospitals) via a software-as-a-service (SaaS) model. In early 2018 the company sold its research offerings which included quality and satisfaction surveys data analysis and other research-based management tools to Press Ganey.

Operations

HealthStream's offerings are organized into two segments: Workforce Solutions and Provider Solutions.

Workforce Solutions products are focused on employee training and development; they account for some 70% of HealthStream's total sales.

Provider Solutions include credentialing privileging call center services and enrollment. These offerings contribute about 15% of total sales.

In 2018 HealthStream sold its former Patient Experience Solutions segment which provided surveys and other research for $65.5 million. Before the divestiture the unit brought in some 10% of total revenue.

Geographic Reach

HealthStream serves customers in the US from its corporate headquarters in Nashville and its satellite offices in San Diego California; Chicago; Columbia Maryland; Brentwood Tennessee; Jericho New York; and Boulder Colorado.

Sales and Marketing

HealthStream generates sales from subscription fees based on the number of users and type of content provided. Clients include US health care organizations — primarily acute care hospitals such as HCA Community Health Systems and Tenet Healthcare — and pharmaceutical and medical device companies. Other clients include private not-for-profit and government organizations.

HealthStream markets its products primarily through direct sales teams consultants and account relationship managers. Its marketing programs include catalogs trade shows online promotions telemarketing campaigns public relations direct mail and advertising.

Advertising expenses in 2017 totaled some $1 million the same as in 2016 and down from $1.1 million in 2015.

Financial Performance

HealthStream's revenues have climbed steadily over the last decade but net income has been somewhat more volatile.

In 2017 revenue increased 10% to $247.7 million. The Workforce Solutions segment had 6% growth as subscriptions increased and enterprise applications sales rose. Those gains were partially offset by an expected decline in ICD-10 readiness products. The Provider Solutions segment grew 53% that year — largely due to the 2016 acquisition of Morrisey Associates. The now-divested Patient Experience Solutions segment decreased 3% in 2017.

The increase in revenue led to a boost in profits. Net income which had fallen in 2015 and 2016 rebounded the following year when it rose 163% to $10 million.

The company ended 2017 with $84.8 million in cash and cash equivalents almost double what it began the year with. This was largely due to operating activities which provided $46.7 million.

Strategy

While many of its competitors are offering course material in a range of formats (print online instructor-led) HealthStream focuses on its internet-based offerings. In order to remain competitive HealthStream tailors its HLC course delivery methods to provide clients with access to the specific educational resources they need. While HealthStream is focused on adding subscribers to the HLC platform it also aims to have existing subscribers order additional courses and new software applications.

To take advantage of the increasing use of simulation technology to educate students and medical professionals HealthStream partnered with Laerdal Medical in a joint venture called SimVentures. The venture sold patient simulation scenarios through a simulation management platform called SimCenter but SimVentures was terminated in early 2018.

Mergers and Acquisitions

HealthStream has made a string of acquisitions to expand its services and product offerings. In early 2019 it purchased Providigm which provides quality assurance to skilled nursing facilities and other health care facilities. The Denver-based firm's system abaqis should help HealthStream's customers meet new federal regulations to better manage health care services at nursing homes.

EXECUTIVES

Chairman President and CEO, Robert A. Frist, age 50, $305,600 total compensation
SVP and CFO, Gerard M. (Gerry) Hayden, age 63, $264,898 total compensation
SVP and COO, J. Edward Pearson, age 55, $288,815 total compensation
SVP and CIO, Jeffrey S. Doster, age 53, $128,077 total compensation
VP and Head of Sales, Scott Fenstermacher
SVP and President Provider Solutions, Michael J. Sousa, age 49, $278,800 total compensation
SVP and CTO, Jeff Cunningham
Senior Vice President of Sales, Thomas Schultz
Vice President Strategic Accounts, Jim Reeves
Vice President Developer, Joe Christopher
Vice President of Information Technology, Tom Dugger
Vice President Compliance Solutions, Ben Diamond
Auditors: Ernst & Young LLP

LOCATIONS

HQ: Healthstream Inc
   209 10th Avenue South, Suite 450, Nashville, TN 37203
Phone: 615 301-3100
Web: www.healthstream.com

PRODUCTS/OPERATIONS

2017 Sales by Segment

	$ mil.	% of total
Workforce Solutions	178.1	72
Provider Solutions	36.8	15
Patient Experience	32.8	13
Total	**247.7**	**100**

COMPETITORS

Bertelsmann	Saba Software
Cornerstone OnDemand	SumTotal
Kenexa	Wolters Kluwer
Medscape llc	Workday Inc.
Oracle	

HISTORICAL FINANCIALS

Company Type: Public

Income Statement
FYE: December 31

	REVENUE ($ mil.)	NET INCOME ($ mil.)	NET PROFIT MARGIN	EMPLOYEES
12/17	247.6	10.0	4.0%	1,027
12/16	225.9	3.7	1.7%	1,120
12/15	209.0	8.6	4.1%	972
12/14	170.6	10.3	6.1%	787
12/13	132.2	8.4	6.4%	686
Annual Growth	**17.0%**	**4.4%**	—	**10.6%**

2017 Year-End Financials

Debt ratio: —
Return on equity: 3.4%
Cash ($ mil.): 84.7
Current ratio: 1.98
Long-term debt ($ mil.): —
No. of shares (mil.): 31.9
Dividends
Yield: —
Payout: —
Market value ($ mil.): 739.0

	STOCK PRICE ($) FY Close	P/E High/Low		Earnings	PER SHARE ($) Dividends	Book Value
12/17	23.16	100	69	0.31	0.00	9.41
12/16	25.05	237	152	0.12	0.00	9.01
12/15	22.00	111	73	0.28	0.00	8.86
12/14	29.48	91	55	0.37	0.00	6.06
12/13	32.63	127	65	0.30	0.00	5.47
Annual Growth	**(8.2%)**	—	—	**0.8%**	—	**14.5%**

Heartland BancCorp

EXECUTIVES

Chb-ceo, Scott G McComb
Assistant Vice President, Bennett Musselman
Assistant Vice President Agribusiness Banker,
   Seth Middleton

LOCATIONS

HQ: Heartland BancCorp
   850 North Hamilton Road, Gahanna, OH 43230
Phone: 614 337-4600
Web: www.heartlandbank.com

HISTORICAL FINANCIALS

Company Type: Public

Income Statement
FYE: December 31

	ASSETS ($ mil.)	NET INCOME ($ mil.)	INCOME AS % OF ASSETS	EMPLOYEES
12/17	900.9	8.8	1.0%	0
12/16	781.3	7.9	1.0%	0
12/15	729.5	8.1	1.1%	0
12/14	649.6	6.0	0.9%	0
12/13	580.3	5.2	0.9%	0
Annual Growth	**11.6%**	**14.2%**	—	—

2017 Year-End Financials

Return on assets: 1.0%
Return on equity: 11.8%
Long-term debt ($ mil.): —
No. of shares (mil.): 1.6
Sales ($ mil) 40.6
Dividends
Yield: 0.0%
Payout: 31.8%
Market value ($ mil.): 133.0

	STOCK PRICE ($) FY Close	P/E High/Low		Earnings	PER SHARE ($) Dividends	Book Value
12/17	82.60	15	12	5.40	1.72	48.77
12/16	64.01	14	9	4.97	1.55	45.10
12/15	45.00	10	8	5.13	1.47	42.61
12/14	40.00	11	8	3.87	1.42	39.05
12/13	35.00	11	9	3.34	1.30	35.00
Annual Growth	**23.9%**	—	—	**12.8%**	**7.2%**	**8.7%**

Heartland Financial USA, Inc. (Dubuque, IA)

Heartland Financial USA is an $11.3 billion multi-bank holding company that owns flagship subsidiary Dubuque Bank and Trust (Iowa) and ten other banks that together operate more than 120 branches in about a dozen states primarily in the West and Midwest. In addition to standard deposit loan and mortgage services the banks also offer retirement wealth management trust insurance and investment services. Heartland also owns consumer lender Citizens Finance which has about a dozen offices in Illinois Iowa and Wisconsin.

Operations

Heartland Financial USA operates two main segments: community and other banking and retail mortgage banking services which account for about 90% and 10% of revenue respectively. The community banking business generates revenue from interest earned on loans and investment securities and fees from deposit services. Its retail mortgage banking services division collects revenue from interest from mortgage loans held for sale gains on sales of loans on the secondary market the servicing of mortgage loans for investors and loan origination fee income.

About three-quarters of Heartland's loan portfolio comes from commercial and commercial real estate loans but — in keeping with the bank's Midwestern identity — it also makes agricultural residential mortgage and consumer loans.

Heartland's subsidiaries include: Citywide Banks (approximately $1.9 billion total deposits) New Mexico Bank & Trust ($1.2 billion) Dubuque Bank and Trust Company ($1.1 billion) Wisconsin Bank & Trust ($890 million) First Bank & Trust ($820 million) Premier Valley Bank ($710 million) Illinois Bank & Trust ($690 million) Morrill & Janes Bank and Trust ($560 million) Arizona Bank & Trust ($520 million) Rocky Mountain Bank ($420 million) and Minnesota Bank & Trust ($180 million).

Geographic Reach

Dubuque Iowa-based Heartland Financial USA operates through about 145 locations (including branches and loan production offices in local communities in Iowa Illinois Wisconsin New Mexico Arizona Montana Colorado Minnesota Kansas Missouri Texas and California. The company's three largest bank subsidiaries by number of locations are Colorado's Citywide Banks with about 25 and Wisconsin Bank & Trust and New Mexico Bank & Trust with about 20 each.

Sales and Marketing

Heartland Financial USA offers its banking services to businesses public sector and non-profit entities and individuals.

The company's Commercial Card team works with its commercial clients to help cut manual processes and costs from employee travel entertainment spending and vendor payments.

Financial Performance

As it grows its assets and loan portfolio via acquisitions Heartland Financial USA had positive overall performance in the last five years increasing revenue by some 70% and net income by more than 100% — all while expanding its cash by about 55% and reducing long-term debt by nearly 20%.

Revenue ticked up 6% to $432.3 million in 2017 on increased interest income mostly from interest and fees on a larger loan portfolio following the company's acquisitions of Citywide Banks and Founders Bancorp.

Net income trended down 6% to $75.3 million owing to higher income taxes salaries employee benefits and professional fees.

Heartland added $37.3 million to its cash stores in 2017 to end the year with $196 million. Operations and investments brought in $155.9 million and $27.3 million respectively. Financing activities used up $145.9 million due to a net decrease from savings accounts and repayments of short term Federal Home Loan Bank advances.

Strategy

Heartland Financial USA's strategy for the past two decades is centered on expanding through acquisitions in its existing and adjacent markets while balancing growth in newer western markets with the stability of its established midwestern markets. The company's goal is to have at least $1 billion in assets in each state where it operates.

Mergers and Acquisitions

Heartland added its eleventh subsidiary in May 2018 through its acquisition of Lubbock Texas-based First Bank Lubbock Bancshares for $189.9 million. Operating under the name First Bank & Trust (which Heartland retained) the bank held $681.1 million in gross loans held to maturity and deposits of $893.8 million. First Bank & Trust has eight branches in West Texas and eight mortgage lending services offices throughout Texas.

In February 2018 the company acquired Minnetonka Minnesota-based Signature Bancshares for $61.4 million and incorporated it into its Minnesota Bank & Trust subsidiary. Signature had two branches in the Twin Cities metropolitan area with $324.5 million in gross loans held to maturity and deposits of $357.3 million.

Heartland acquired Citywide Banks (headquartered in Aurora Colorado) in July 2017 for $211.2 million. At the time of purchase Citywide had $985.4 million in net loans outstanding and $1.2 billion in deposits. Following incorporation of Citywide into its Centennial Bank and Trust subsidiary (which then adopted Citywide's name) Heartland had more than 25 branches in Colorado.

In February 2017 Heartland Financial USA acquired San Luis Obispo California-based Founders Bancorp which it incorporated into its Premier Valley Bank subsidiary for $31 million. The company's Founders Community Bank held loans totaling $96.4 million and the purchase increased Heartland's total number of branches in California from five to nine.

Company Background

Heartland Financial USA was founded in 1981 although it traces its roots back to the 1935 establishment of Dubuque Bank and Trust. It made its first bank acquisition in in 1989 - Key City Bank - and has continued acquiring community banks since.

EXECUTIVES

President and CEO Minnesota Bank & Trust, Catherine T. (Kate) Kelly

Chairman President and CEO Heartland Financial USA Inc.; Vice Chairman Dubuque Bank & Trust Wisconsin Bank & Trust New Mexico Bank & Trust Arizona Bank & Trust Rocky Mountain Bank Centennial Bank and Trust(1) Minnesota Bank & Trust and Premier Valley Bank, Lynn B. Fuller, age 68, $486,388 total compensation

EVP Lending, Douglas J. Horstmann, age 64, $275,156 total compensation

President and CEO New Mexico Bank & Trust, R. Greg Leyendecker

President and CEO Wisconsin Bank & Trust, Kevin S. Tenpas

President of Heartland Director Rocky Mountain Bank and President Heartland Financial USA Inc. Insurance Services, Bruce K. Lee, age 57, $383,519 total compensation

EVP Human Resources and Organizational Development, Mark G. Murtha, age 56

SVP Chief Accounting Officer, Janet M. Quick

President and CEO Riverside Community Bank, Steven E. Ward

EVP Wealth Management, Bruce C. Rehmke

EVP Commercial Sales, Frank E. Walter, age 71

EVP Senior General Counsel and Corporate Secretary, Michael J. Coyle, age 72

EVP Operations, Brian J. Fox, age 69, $190,000 total compensation

EVP and Chief Risk Officer, Rodney L. Sloan, age 58

EVP and CFO Heartland Financial USA Treasurer Citizens Finance Parent Co.. and Director Heartland Financial USA Inc. Insurance Services, Bryan R. McKeag, age 57, $305,625 total compensation

EVP Finance and Corporate Strategy, David L. Horstmann, age 68

President and CEO Arizona Bank & Trust, Jerry L. Schwallier

President and CEO Rocky Mountain Bank, Curtis Chrystal

President and CEO Morrill & Janes Bank and Trust Co., Kurt M. Saylor

EVP Private Client Services, Kelly J. Johnson, age 56

President and CEO Illinois Bank and Trust, Jeff Hultman

Chief Investment Officer, Nancy Tengler

EVP and Chief Credit Officer, Drew Townsend

EVP and Private Wealth Management Director, Rick O. Terry

President and CEO Heartland Mortgage, Paul Johnstun

CEO Centennial Bank and Trust, Jim Basey

President Heartland Mortgage, Jack Lloyd

Vice President Finance, Sandra Wild

Vice President Administrative Services, Joseph V Berretta

Vice President, Jean Harkey

Assistant Vice President Commercial Services, Lynn Stoffregen

Vice President, Shelley Phillips

Vice President, Craig Sciara

Senior Vice President Credit Administration, Brian McCarthy

Assistant Vice President, Michelle Schoen

Assistant Vice President Information Services, Brent Wilke

VICE PRESIDENT DIRECTOR FINANCIAL PLANNING AND PERFORMANCE MANAGEMENT, Michael G Flood

CREDIT ADMIN OFFICER IV SENIOR VICE PRESIDENT, Ralph Atkinson

PCS DIRECTOR OF FINANCIAL PLANNING VICE PRESIDENT, Chrisanna Elser

VICE PRESIDENT DIRECTOR FINANCIAL PLANNING AND PERFORMANCE MANAGEMENT, Michael Flood

Vice Chairman of the Board of Heartland Financial USA Inc.; Chairman and Director of Dubuque Bank and Trust, Mark C. Falb, age 70

Vice Chairman of the Board of Heartland Financial USA Inc.; Director and Vice Chairman of the Board of Dubuque Bank and Trust, Thomas L. Flynn, age 62

Board Member, Duane White

Auditors: KPMG LLP

LOCATIONS

HQ: Heartland Financial USA, Inc. (Dubuque, IA)
1398 Central Avenue, Dubuque, IA 52001
Phone: 563 589-2100   **Fax:** 563 589-2011
Web: www.htlf.com

PRODUCTS/OPERATIONS

2017 Sales

	$ mil.	% of total
Interest		
Loans & leases including fees	304.0	65
Securities	58.1	13
Other	1.6	-
Interest expense	(33.3)	
Noninterest		
Gains on sales of loans	22.2	5
Service charges and fees	39.2	8
Trust fees	15.8	3
Loan serving income	5.6	1
Brokerage & insurance commissions	4.0	1
Security gains	7.0	2
Other	8.1	2
Total	**432.3**	**100**

Selected Subsidiaries

Arizona Bank & Trust
Citywide Banks (Colorado)
Dubuque Bank and Trust Company (Iowa)
  DB&T Community Development Corp.
  DB&T Insurance
Illinois Bank & Trust
Minnesota Bank & Trust
Morrill & Janes Bank and Trust Company (Kansas)
New Mexico Bank & Trust
Premier Valley Bank (California)
Rocky Mountain Bank (Montana)
Wisconsin Bank & Trust

COMPETITORS

Associated Banc-Corp	First Banks
BBVA Compass	U.S. Bancorp
Bancshares	Wells Fargo
Bank of America	Zions Bancorporation
Bank of the West	

HISTORICAL FINANCIALS

Company Type: Public

Income Statement
FYE: December 31

	ASSETS ($ mil.)	NET INCOME ($ mil.)	INCOME AS % OF ASSETS	EMPLOYEES
12/17	9,810.7	75.2	0.8%	2,008
12/16	8,247.0	80.3	1.0%	1,864
12/15	7,694.7	60.0	0.8%	1,799
12/14	6,052.3	41.9	0.7%	1,631
12/13	5,923.7	36.7	0.6%	1,676
Annual Growth	**13.4%**	**19.6%**	**—**	**4.6%**

2017 Year-End Financials

Return on assets: 0.8%	Dividends
Return on equity: 8.6%	Yield: 0.0%
Long-term debt ($ mil.): —	Payout: 19.2%
No. of shares (mil.): 29.9	Market value ($ mil): 1,607.0
Sales ($ mil): 465.6	

	STOCK PRICE ($) FY Close	P/E High/Low		PER SHARE ($) Earnings	Dividends	Book Value
12/17	53.65	20	16	2.65	0.51	33.10
12/16	48.00	15	8	3.22	0.50	28.37
12/15	31.36	14	9	2.83	0.45	29.56
12/14	27.10	13	10	2.19	0.40	26.81
12/13	28.79	14	11	2.04	0.50	23.88
Annual Growth	**16.8%**	**—**	**—**	**6.8%**	**0.5%**	**8.5%**

HEICO Corp

HEICO Corporation helps jets get airborne. Its Flight Support Group consisting of HEICO Aerospace and its subsidiaries makes FAA-approved replacement parts for jet engines that can be substituted for original parts including airfoils bearings and fuel pump gears. Flight Support also repairs overhauls and distributes jet engine parts as well as avionics and instruments for commercial air carriers. HEICO's second segment Electronic Technologies Group makes a variety of electronic equipment for the aerospace/defense electronic medical and telecommunications industries.

Operations

HEICO's business is comprised of two operating segments the Flight Support Group (FSG; about 65% of net sales) and the Electronic Technologies Group (ETG; 35%).

FSG competes with industry leading OEMs and to a lesser extent with smaller independent parts distributors. Historically the three main jet engine OEMs General Electric Pratt & Whitney and Rolls Royce have been the source of substantially all jet engine replacement parts for their own jet engines. HEICO is seeking to capture some of that market by adding new products at a rate of 300 to 500 manufacturer-approved parts (also called PMAs) per year.

Geographic Reach

HEICO has its operations and facilities in China India Singapore Canada France Korea Laos the

Netherlands the UK and the US. The company markets its products and services in approximately 100 countries with the US counting for more than 65% of its net sales.

Sales and Marketing

HEICO sells its products through in-house personnel and independent manufacturers' representatives. It targets a broad customer base consisting of domestic and foreign commercial and cargo airlines repair and overhaul facilities other aftermarket suppliers of aircraft engine and airframe materials OEMs domestic and foreign military units electronic manufacturing services companies US and foreign governments manufacturers for the defense industry as well as medical telecommunications scientific and industrial companies. Net sales to its five largest customers account for around 20% of net sales each year.

Financial Performance

HEICO has achieved unprecedented growth over the years with revenues jumping 16% from $1.19 billion in 2015 to peak at a record-setting $1.38 billion in 2016. Profits also surged 17% from $134 million in 2015 to $156 million in 2016 another company milestone. In 2016 cash flow from operating activities increased due to a $37 million decrease in working capital a $23 million increase in net income from consolidated operations and a $12 million increase in depreciation and amortization expense (a non-cash item).

The historic growth for 2016 was fueled by increases in both of its segments. FSG jumped by 8% due to organic growth as well as additional net sales from a previous acquisition. The organic growth reflected new product offerings and favorable market conditions resulting in net sales within the aftermarket replacement parts and repair and overhaul services product lines.

ETG revenue soared by 31% due to additional net sales from a previous acquisition as well as organic growth of approximately 4%. The organic growth reflected an increase in demand for certain space and aerospace products.

Mergers and Acquisitions

HEICO uses acquisitions to build out a diverse product and service portfolio in order to reduce exposure to cyclical swings in any single market. Its current set of offerings have broad-range applications in aircraft missiles ships surveillance systems computer and networking devices telecom equipment surgical equipment CT scanners and X-ray systems.

In 2016 the company's ETG division acquired Arizona-based Robertson Fuel Systems for $255 million. Robertson has expertise in the design and production of mission-extending crashworthy and ballistically self-sealing auxiliary fuel systems for military rotorcraft. The acquisition will enhance the company's fuel systems product portfolio.

In 2015 the company's FSG division purchased Astroseal Products Manufacturing Corp. Astroseal makes expanded foil mesh that is integrated into composite aerospace structures for lightning strike protection in fixed and rotary wing aircraft. The deal expanded the group's offerings of aerospace composite products.

HISTORY

Founded in 1957 as Heinicke Instruments to make laboratory products the company moved into jet engine parts in 1974 with the acquisition of Jet Avion. The company changed its name to HEICO (a shortened version of its previous name) in 1985.

After a faulty combustion chamber erupted in flames that year the FAA ordered all combustion chambers on US jets to be inspected and if necessary replaced. HEICO's sales skyrocketed but descended back to earth after airlines found they had overstocked.

EXECUTIVES

Co-President and Director; President and CEO HEICO Electronic Technologies, Victor H. Mendelson, age 50, $519,178 total compensation
Co-President and Director; President and CEO HEICO Aerospace Holdings, Eric A. Mendelson, age 53, $519,178 total compensation
Senior Executive Vice President, Thomas S. Irwin, age 72, $238,299 total compensation
Chairman and CEO, Laurans A. Mendelson, age 80, $973,425 total compensation
EVP CFO and Treasurer, Carlos L. Macau, $553,014 total compensation
Vice President Acquisitions, Adam Bentkover
Vice President Sales (HPG) Latin America, Mike Garcia
Vice President, Pat Markham
Executive Vice President Operations, John Hunter
Auditors: DELOITTE & TOUCHE LLP

LOCATIONS

HQ: HEICO Corp
3000 Taft Street, Hollywood, FL 33021
Phone: 954 987-4000
Web: www.heico.com

PRODUCTS/OPERATIONS

2016 Sales

	$ mil.	% of total
Flight Support Group	875.9	63
Electronic Technologies Group	511.3	37
Intersegment sales	(10.9)	-
Total	**1,376.3**	**100**

Selected Products

Flight Support Group
  Cockpit/avionics parts
  Electro-mechanical components
  Engine parts
  Fuselage/interior parts
  Wing parts
Electronic Technologies Group
  Aircraft power supplies and batteries
  Circuit board shielding
  Electro-optical infrared simulation and test equipment
  Electro-optical laser products
  High-voltage interconnect and cable assembly devices
  Medical power supplies and power generators

COMPETITORS

AAR Corp.	Kellstrom Industries
ATI Ladish	LMI Aerospace
BBA Aviation	Pratt & Whitney
Barnes Group	Rolls-Royce
CIC International	SAFRAN
Doncasters	SIFCO
GE Aviation	TIMCO Aviation
Honeywell Aerospace	Triumph Group

HISTORICAL FINANCIALS

Company Type: Public

Income Statement

FYE: October 31

	REVENUE ($ mil.)	NET INCOME ($ mil.)	NET PROFIT MARGIN	EMPLOYEES
10/18	1,777.7	259.2	14.6%	5,400
10/17	1,524.8	185.9	12.2%	5,100
10/16	1,376.2	156.1	11.3%	4,700
10/15	1,188.6	133.3	11.2%	4,600
10/14	1,132.3	121.2	10.7%	3,500
Annual Growth	**11.9%**	**20.9%**	**—**	**11.5%**

2018 Year-End Financials

Debt ratio: 20.0%	No. of shares (mil.): 132.9
Return on equity: 20.2%	Dividends
Cash ($ mil.): 59.6	Yield: 0.1%
Current ratio: 2.60	Payout: 6.1%
Long-term debt ($ mil.): 531.6	Market value ($ mil.): 11,144.0

	STOCK PRICE ($) FY Close	P/E High/Low	PER SHARE ($) Earnings	Dividends	Book Value
10/18	83.83	50 37	1.90	0.12	10.52
10/17	90.68	65 47	1.37	0.10	8.80
10/16	67.56	62 41	1.17	0.08	7.33
10/15	50.44	61 46	1.01	0.07	6.20
10/14	54.24	69 50	0.92	0.24	5.38
Annual Growth	**11.5%**	**— —**	**19.8%**	**(16.7%)**	**18.2%**

Hennessy Advisors Inc

EXECUTIVES

Chb-pres-ceo; Chief Information Officer, Neil J Hennessy
Vice President Of Operations, Ana Miner
Senior Vice President Business Development, Dan Steadman
Vice President, Michael Perrella
VICE PRESIDENT NATIONAL ACCOUNTS, Darcy Limanni
BOARD MEMBER, Henry Hansel
Board Member, Thomas Seavey
Board Member, Susan Pomilia
Board Member, Daniel Libarle
Auditors: Marcum LLP

LOCATIONS

HQ: Hennessy Advisors Inc
7250 Redwood Blvd., Suite 200, Novato, CA 94945
Phone: 415 899-1555   **Fax:** 415 899-1559
Web: www.hennessyadvisors.com

HISTORICAL FINANCIALS

Company Type: Public

Income Statement

FYE: September 30

	REVENUE ($ mil.)	NET INCOME ($ mil.)	NET PROFIT MARGIN	EMPLOYEES
09/18	54.5	20.6	37.8%	23
09/17	52.9	14.9	28.2%	23
09/16	51.4	14.3	27.9%	22
09/15	44.7	11.3	25.5%	21
09/14	34.5	7.6	22.2%	19
Annual Growth	**12.1%**	**28.1%**	**—**	**4.9%**

2018 Year-End Financials

Debt ratio: 19.8%
Return on equity: 33.6%
Cash ($ mil.): 25.4
Current ratio: 2.55
Long-term debt ($ mil.): 17.5

No. of shares (mil.): 7.9
Dividends
  Yield: 0.0%
  Payout: 14.3%
Market value ($ mil.): 109.0

	STOCK PRICE ($) FY Close	P/E High/Low		PER SHARE ($) Earnings	Dividends	Book Value
09/18	13.85	8	5	2.61	0.38	8.99
09/17	15.44	18	7	1.92	0.29	6.63
09/16	35.47	21	13	1.86	0.20	4.87
09/15	23.76	19	14	1.27	0.15	3.05
09/14	19.88	22	14	0.87	0.10	4.14
Annual Growth	(8.6%)	—	—	31.7%	38.9%	21.4%

Heritage Commerce Corp

If you know the way to San Jose you may also know the way to Heritage Commerce. It is the holding company for Heritage Bank of Commerce which operates 10 branches in the South Bay region of the San Francisco area. Serving consumers and small to midsized businesses and their owners and managers the bank offers savings and checking accounts money market and retirement accounts and CDs as well as cash management services and loans. Commercial construction land and mortgage loans make up most of the company's loan portfolio which is rounded out by home equity and consumer loans. The bank was founded in 1994.

EXECUTIVES

EVP and CFO, Lawrence D. McGovern, age 63, $260,753 total compensation
President and CEO, Walter T. (Walt) Kaczmarek, age 66, $368,509 total compensation
EVP and Director Business Development, Robert P. (Bob) Gionfriddo, age 72
EVP Banking Division, Michael E. Benito, $244,826 total compensation
COO, Keith A. Wilton, $243,025 total compensation
EVP and Chief Credit Officer, David E. Porter, $260,738 total compensation
EVP and Corporate Secretary, Deborah K. (Debbie) Reuter
EVP HOA and Deposit Services, Teresa Powell
Vice President Business Development Officer, David Beronio
Vice President Cash Management Officer, Kelly Swanson
Chairman, Jack W. Conner, age 78
Auditors: Crowe Horwath LLP

LOCATIONS

HQ: Heritage Commerce Corp
  150 Almaden Boulevard, San Jose, CA 95113
Phone: 408 947-6900
Web: www.heritagecommercecorp.com

PRODUCTS/OPERATIONS

2017 Sales

	$ mil.	% of total
Interest		
Loans including fees	86.4	74
Taxable securities	13.7	12
Other	6.8	6
Interest expense	(5.4)	-
Noninterest		
Service charges & fees on deposit accounts	3.2	3
Increase in cash surrender value of life insurance	1.7	1
Gain on sales of SBA loans	1.1	1
Servicing income	1.0	1
Other	2.6	2
Total	**111.1**	**100**

COMPETITORS

Bank of America	JPMorgan Chase
Bank of the West	MUFG Americas Holdings
Citibank	SVB Financial
Comerica	U.S. Bancorp
First Republic (CA)	Wells Fargo

HISTORICAL FINANCIALS

Company Type: Public

Income Statement   FYE: December 31

	ASSETS ($ mil.)	NET INCOME ($ mil.)	INCOME AS % OF ASSETS	EMPLOYEES
12/17	2,843.4	23.8	0.8%	278
12/16	2,570.8	27.3	1.1%	263
12/15	2,361.5	16.5	0.7%	260
12/14	1,617.1	13.4	0.8%	242
12/13	1,491.6	11.5	0.8%	193
Annual Growth	17.5%	19.9%	—	9.6%

2017 Year-End Financials

Return on assets: 0.8%
Return on equity: 8.9%
Long-term debt ($ mil.): —
No. of shares (mil.): 38.2
Sales ($ mil): 116.5

Dividends
  Yield: 0.0%
  Payout: 64.5%
Market value ($ mil.): 585.0

	STOCK PRICE ($) FY Close	P/E High/Low		PER SHARE ($) Earnings	Dividends	Book Value
12/17	15.32	26	21	0.62	0.40	7.10
12/16	14.43	20	13	0.72	0.36	6.85
12/15	11.96	26	17	0.48	0.32	7.64
12/14	8.83	21	19	0.42	0.18	6.96
12/13	8.24	23	18	0.36	0.06	6.58
Annual Growth	16.8%	—	—	14.6%	60.7%	1.9%

Heritage Financial Corp (WA)

Heritage Financial is ready to answer the call of Pacific Northwesterners seeking to preserve their heritage. Heritage Financial is the holding company for Heritage Bank which operates more than 65 branches throughout Washington and Oregon. Boasting nearly $4 billion in assets the bank offers a range of deposit products to consumers and businesses such as CDs IRAs and checking savings NOW and money market accounts. Commercial and industrial loans account for over 50% of Heritage Financial's loan portfolio while mortgages secured by multi-family real estate comprise about 5%. The bank also originates single-family mortgages land development construction loans and consumer loans.

Operations

The bank also does business under the Central Valley Bank name in the Yakima and Kittitas counties of Washington and under the Whidbey Island Bank name on Whidbey Island.

About 79% of Heritage Financial's total revenue came from loan interest (including fees) in 2014 while another 7% came from interest on its investment securities. The rest of its revenue came from service charges and other fees (8%) Merchant Visa income (1%) and other miscellaneous fees. The company had a staff of 748 employees at the end of that year.

Geographic Reach

The Olympia-based bank operates more than 65 branches across Washington and the greater Portland area. It has additional offices in eastern Washington mostly in Yakima county.

Sales and Marketing

Heritage targets small and medium-sized businesses along with their owners as well as individuals.

Financial Performance

Fueled by loan and deposit growth from a series of bank acquisitions Heritage Financial's revenues and profits have been on the rise in recent years.

The company's revenue jumped 70% to a record $137.6 million in 2014 mostly thanks to new loan business stemming from its acquisition of Washington Banking Company. Deposit service charge income also increased thanks to new deposit business from the acquisition.

Higher revenue in 2014 allowed Heritage Financial's net income to more than double to a record $21 million while its operating cash levels rose 66% to $51.3 million on higher cash earnings and net proceeds from the sale of its loans.

Strategy

The bank reiterated in 2015 that it would continue to pursue strategic acquisitions of community banks to grow market share across the Pacific Northwest (its region of expertise) expand its business lines and grow its loan and deposit business.

With its focus on business and commercial lending the bank also in 2015 emphasized the importance of seeking high asset quality loans lending to familiar markets that have a historical record of success. Recruiting and retaining "highly competent personnel" to execute its strategies was also key to its long-term agenda.

Mergers and Acquisitions

In May 2014 Heritage acquired Washington Banking Company and its Whidbey Island Bank subsidiary for $265 million which "significantly expanded and enhanced" its product offerings across its core geographic market.

In July 2013 the bank acquired Puyallup Washington-based Valley Community Bancshares and its eight Valley Bank branches for $44 million.

In January 2013 the company purchased Lakewood Washington-based Northwest Commercial Bank along with its two branch locations in Washington state for $5 million.

EXECUTIVES

President CEO and Director Heritage Financial and CEO Heritage Bank, Brian L. Vance, age 63, $494,316 total compensation

EVP and CFO Heritage Financial and Heritage Bank, Donald J. Hinson, age 57, $255,084 total compensation

EVP and Chief Credit Officer Heritage Bank, David A. Spurling, age 65, $237,342 total compensation

EVP Heritage Financial and President and COO Heritage Bank, Jeffrey J. (Jeff) Deuel, $291,516 total compensation

EVP and Chief Lending Officer Heritage Bank, Bryan D. McDonald, age 46, $261,374 total compensation

Vice President And Financial Reporting Manager, Patrice Hernandez

Chairman, Brian S. Charneski, age 56

Auditors: Crowe Horwath LLP

LOCATIONS

HQ: Heritage Financial Corp (WA)
201 Fifth Avenue S.W., Olympia, WA 98501
Phone: 360 943-1500
Web: www.HF-WA.com

PRODUCTS/OPERATIONS

2014 Sales

	$ mil.	% of total
Interest income		
Interest and fees on loans	110.4	79
Investment securities	10.2	7
Others	0.5	-
Non-interest income		
Service charges and others	11.1	8
Merchant Visa income	1.1	1
Others	4.3	5
Total	**137.6**	**100**

COMPETITORS

Bank of America	U.S. Bancorp
Columbia Banking	Washington Federal
FS Bancorp	Wells Fargo
KeyCorp	

HISTORICAL FINANCIALS

Company Type: Public

Income Statement

FYE: December 31

	ASSETS ($ mil.)	NET INCOME ($ mil.)	INCOME AS % OF ASSETS	EMPLOYEES
12/17	4,113.2	41.7	1.0%	735
12/16	3,878.9	38.9	1.0%	760
12/15	3,650.7	37.4	1.0%	717
12/14	3,457.7	21.0	0.6%	748
12/13	1,659.0	9.5	0.6%	373
Annual Growth	**25.5%**	**44.5%**	**—**	**18.5%**

2017 Year-End Financials

Return on assets: 1.0%	Dividends
Return on equity: 8.4%	Yield: 0.0%
Long-term debt ($ mil.): —	Payout: 43.8%
No. of shares (mil.): 29.9	Market value ($ mil.): 922.0
Sales ($ mil): 183.2	

	STOCK PRICE ($) FY Close	P/E High/Low	PER SHARE ($) Earnings	Dividends	Book Value
12/17	30.80	23 16	1.39	0.61	16.98
12/16	25.75	20 13	1.30	0.72	16.08
12/15	18.84	16 12	1.25	0.69	15.68
12/14	17.55	23 19	0.82	0.50	15.02
12/13	17.10	29 22	0.61	0.42	13.31
Annual Growth	**15.8%**	**— —**	**22.9%**	**9.8%**	**6.3%**

Hersha Hospitality Trust

Hersha Hospitality Trust's fortune is in hotels not chocolate. The self-advised real estate investment trust (REIT) invests in hotel properties primarily midscale upscale and extended stay properties in metropolitan markets across the US. It owns or co-owns more than 50 hotels containing nearly 8000 rooms most of them in Boston New York and Washington DC as well as in Miami and Los Angeles. The properties are operated under such brand names as Marriott International Hilton Hotels Starwood Hotels and Hyatt. Hersha Hospitality Trust owns a minority stake in Hersha Hospitality Management which manages the REIT's properties. Starwood Capital Group owns the remainder of Hersha Hospitality Management.

Operations

Hersha Hospitality Trust's property portfolio consisted of 46 wholly-owned limited and full-service hotel properties with nearly 6600 rooms in 2014. Through joint ventures it held five limited and full-service properties with nearly 1370 rooms. The hotels mostly operated under brands owned by Marriott International Hilton Worldwide Intercontinental Hotels Group Hyatt Corporation and Starwood Hotels and Resorts Worldwide.

Geographic Reach

More than 45% of Hersha's rental income came from its properties in New York City in 2014. Its other hotel properties were in mostly major urban areas in nearly a dozen states including Arizona California Connecticut Delaware Washington DC Florida Maryland Massachusetts New York Pennsylvania and Virginia.

Financial Performance

Hersha Hospitality's revenues and profits have been growing over the past few years as it has expanded its property portfolio through acquisitions and has charged higher rental rates as its property valuations have improved.

The company's revenue rose 23% to $417.2 million in 2014 mostly thanks to property acquisitions from 2014 and 2013. Hersha's same-store revenues also improved during the year.

Higher revenue and larger gains on its hotel property sales in 2014 drove the REIT's net income up 37% to $68.3 million for the year. Its operating cash levels jumped 25% to $112.9 million on higher cash earnings.

Strategy

Hersha Hospitality focuses on investing in high-quality upscale mid-scale and extended-stay hotels in urban high-barrier gateway markets. In recent years the company has targeted such properties in New York Washington DC Boston Philadelphia South Florida and select markets on the West Coast.

During 2014 Hersha purchased 107 hotels including its $42-million purchase of Hotel Milo in Santa Barbara and four strategic hotels in California South Florida and Manhattan. The company that year expressed particular interest in the Santa Barbara hotel market which it said carried some of the highest revPAR rates in the country with minimal new supply.

In addition to acquisitions in urban areas the REIT is focused on property renovations designed to boost occupancy rates and enhance hotel value — which allow the company to raise room rates. In 2014 Hersha completed renovations on properties in Philadelphia (at its luxury-urban resort The Rittenhouse Spa Club Salon and Pool) as well as in Boston Los Angeles Washington DC and South Florida.

EXECUTIVES

President and COO, Neil H. Shah, age 44, $400,000 total compensation

Chief Executive Officer; Trustee, Jay H. Shah, age 49, $425,000 total compensation

VP Finance, Bennett Thomas

Vice President Of Purchasing, Bhavesh Vekaria

Vice President Of Human Resources, Keith Black

Vice President Of Financial Services, Jay Linsey

Executive Vice President, David McCaslin

Executive Vice President Of Operations, Greg Adee

VICE PRESIDENT ASSET MANAGEMENT, Pamela Mathiowetz

VICE PRESIDENT ACQUISITIONS AND DEVELOPMENT, Chas Hyatt

Chairman, Hasu P. Shah, age 73

Auditors: KPMG LLP

LOCATIONS

HQ: Hersha Hospitality Trust
44 Hersha Drive, Harrisburg, PA 17102
Phone: 717 236-4400 **Fax:** 717 774-7383
Web: www.hersha.com

PRODUCTS/OPERATIONS

2014 Sales

	$ mil.	% of total
Hotel operating revenues	417.2	100
Interest from development loans - -		
Other	0.2	-
Total	**417.4**	**100**

2014 Property Management

Hotels	Rooms	
Hersha Hospitality Management	45.0	6,439
Waterford HOtel Group Inc	3.0	1,087
South Bay Boston Management Inc	2.0	282
Northwood Management LLC	1.0	148
Total	**51.0**	**7,956**

COMPETITORS

Ashford Hospitality Trust	Host Hotels & Resorts
Condor Hospitality	Innkeepers USA
DiamondRock Hospitality	LaSalle Hotel Properties
FelCor	Shaner Hotel Group
Hospitality Properties Trust	Strategic Hotels
	Sunstone Hotel Investors

Company Type: Public

Income Statement — FYE: December 31

	REVENUE ($ mil.)	NET INCOME ($ mil.)	NET PROFIT MARGIN	EMPLOYEES
12/17	498.2	99.8	20.0%	51
12/16	466.6	116.9	25.1%	49
12/15	470.3	41.8	8.9%	51
12/14	417.4	67.2	16.1%	48
12/13	338.4	49.6	14.7%	49
Annual Growth	10.2%	19.1%	—	1.0%

2017 Year-End Financials

Debt ratio: 51.1%
Return on equity: 11.9%
Cash ($ mil.): 17.9
Current ratio: 0.53
Long-term debt ($ mil.): 1,093.0

No. of shares (mil.): 39.9
Dividends
Yield: 0.0%
Payout: 73.7%
Market value ($ mil.): 695.0

	STOCK PRICE ($) FY Close	P/E High/Low		PER SHARE ($) Earnings	Dividends	Book Value
12/17	17.40	12	9	1.79	1.32	20.89
12/16	21.50	10	7	2.18	0.84	20.00
12/15	21.76	51	11	0.56	0.84	15.25
12/14	7.03	7	5	1.04	1.04	16.68
12/13	5.57	10	8	0.64	0.96	16.53
Annual Growth	32.9%	—	—	29.3%	8.3%	6.0%

Heska Corp.

If you lie down with dogs Heska makes sure you don't get up with fleas. The company makes diagnostic products vaccines and pharmaceuticals for domestic animals primarily cats and dogs. Its products — both on the market and in development — include diagnostics and treatments for allergies arthritis cancer fleas heartworms skin problems thyroid problems and viral infections. As part of its business Heska also operates a diagnostic lab and manufactures veterinary diagnostic and monitoring devices. The company develops vaccines for cattle small mammals and fish as well. Products are sold worldwide through direct sales representatives and independent distributors.

Sales and Marketing

The company markets its animal health products in the US to veterinarians through an outside sales force of 40 individuals an inside sales force of 20 and a few independent distributors. Internationally Heska markets its products to veterinarians primarily through third-party veterinary diagnostic laboratories independent distributors and through a collaboration with Novartis Japan. Novartis Japan exclusively markets and distributes SOLO STEP CH and Heska's line of ERD HEALTHSCREEN urine test products in Japan.

Financial Performance

Net revenue for Heska rose some 7% in 2011 vs. 2010 boosted across its core business segments: core companion animal health and other vaccines pharmaceuticals and products. Sales of cattle vaccine helped this latter OVP segment's revenue rise thanks in part to its fruitful contract with AgriLabs and sales of other cattle vaccines.

Revenue increases were offset however by slower sales of its bulk bovine biological product.

Heska has been vulnerable to the economic problems that have plagued the US in recent years as families put off vet visits and subsequently vets themselves delay making major purchases. Additionally the loss of a key supplier of Heska's handheld blood analyzer equipment had an adverse effect during both 2009 and 2010 on its core companion animal health business which brings in roughly 82% of Heska's income. This macroeconomic drag on Heska's business in recent years puts into perspective the positive push the AgriLabs agreement has made to level out its revenue.

Strategy

Some of Heska's top products include the SOLO STEP line of heartworm diagnostic tests for cats and dogs HEMATRUE Hematology Analyzer to measure a variety of blood parameters including white and red blood cell counts and hemoglobin levels and the DRI-CHEM 7000 which has the capacity to run more than 20 tests with a single blood sample.

The DRI-CHEM 7000 is a next-generation version of the DRI-CHEM 4000 and an example of how Heska grows its product lines by revamping best-sellers with additional features and capabilities. In 2012 Heska's wholly owned subsidiary Diamond Animal Health began to manufacture Pet-Trust Plus a heartworm preventative product that's based on an existing FDA-approved product. Once its products are sold Heska continues to garner income on many of them through the sale of adjunct supplies and services.

Heska is focused on developing external licensing deals and creating new collaborations to expand its product lines in both the CCA and its Other Vaccines Pharmaceuticals and Products (OVP) divisions. As part of this effort Heska in 2011 expanded its products portfolio of in-clinic blood analyzers by launching a lactate meter analyzer.

In the OVP segment Heska is keenly focused on marketing and growing its line of bovine vaccines licensed by the USDA. Heska also has a long-term non-exclusive agreement with Agri Laboratories to market and sell some of Heska's bovine vaccines — sold primarily under the Titanium and Master-Guard brands. The partnership generates a significant portion of OVP's revenue. OVP also produces vaccines and pharmaceuticals for other third parties.

EXECUTIVES

COO and Chief Strategist, Jason A. Napolitano, age 49, $316,775 total compensation
EVP Diagnostic Operations and Product Development, Nancy Wisnewski, age 55, $260,104 total compensation
EVP Companion Animal Health Sales, Rodney A. Lippincott, age 44, $175,000 total compensation
President and CEO, Kevin S. Wilson, age 46, $275,000 total compensation
EVP Companion Animal Health Sales, Steven M. Asakowicz, age 52, $175,000 total compensation
EVP Global Sales and Marketing, Steven M. (Steve) Eyl, age 52, $261,458 total compensation
CFO, John McMahon, age 53
Executive Vice President, Steve Eyl
Chair, Sharon L. Riley, age 57
Auditors: Plante & Moran PLLC

LOCATIONS

HQ: Heska Corp.
3760 Rocky Mountain Avenue, Loveland, CO 80538
Phone: 970 493-7272
Web: www.heska.com

COMPETITORS

Abaxis	Merck
American Animal Health	Merck Animal Health
Bayer AG	Merial
Bayer Animal Health	Neogen
Drs. Foster & Smith	Novartis
ECO Animal Health	Pfizer
Eli Lilly	Sanofi-Aventis U.S
Farnam Companies	Skystar
IDEXX Labs	Virbac

HISTORICAL FINANCIALS

Company Type: Public

Income Statement — FYE: December 31

	REVENUE ($ mil.)	NET INCOME ($ mil.)	NET PROFIT MARGIN	EMPLOYEES
12/17	129.3	9.9	7.7%	345
12/16	130.0	10.5	8.1%	327
12/15	104.6	5.2	5.0%	310
12/14	89.8	2.6	2.9%	301
12/13	78.3	(1.2)	—	290
Annual Growth	13.4%	—	—	4.4%

2017 Year-End Financials

Debt ratio: 4.4%
Return on equity: 10.6%
Cash ($ mil.): 9.6
Current ratio: 2.45
Long-term debt ($ mil.): —

No. of shares (mil.): 7.3
Dividends
Yield: —
Payout: —
Market value ($ mil.): 586.0

	STOCK PRICE ($) FY Close	P/E High/Low		PER SHARE ($) Earnings	Dividends	Book Value
12/17	80.21	78	50	1.30	0.00	13.75
12/16	71.60	47	17	1.43	0.00	12.38
12/15	38.68	50	20	0.74	0.00	9.59
12/14	18.13	41	20	0.41	0.00	8.38
12/13	8.72	—	—	(0.21)	0.00	8.64
Annual Growth	74.2%	—	—	—		12.3%

HFF Inc

Don't huff and puff — HFF will help you finance that high-rise. The company's Holliday Fenoglio Fowler subsidiary is a large commercial real estate capital intermediary. The firm provides capital markets services including structured financing commercial loan servicing investment sales loan sales and debt placement. Real estate investment banking subsidiary HFF Securities provides advisory services seeks private and joint venture equity capital places private listings and provides institutional marketing for property investments. Unlike most commercial property brokerage firms HFF does not provide leasing or property management services. The company operates about 20 offices throughout the US.

Geographic Reach

The company operates more than 20 offices throughout the US. HFF offers capital markets services throughout Canada Mexico Puerto Rico and the US.

Financial Performance

The company has seen its revenues rebound after they plummeted during the global financial downturn when frozen credit markets reduced liquidity and severely impacted commercial real estate activity. From 2011 to 2012 the firm's revenues jumped 12% from $255 million to $285 million. This was driven by an 11% surge in capital markets services revenue as a result of production volumes and related revenues in a majority of its capital markets services platforms. The company also enjoyed an 85% increase in interest on mortgage notes due to a higher average loan value and a higher number of loans originated.

Strategy

The company continues to seek to improve its market share by penetrating national and regional markets. The company's biggest capital services market is Texas accounting for about 20% of total revenues. Other key markets include Florida Massachusetts and the DC area. HFF hopes to grow by opening additional offices in key US markets and it is also looking at expanding in foreign markets.

EXECUTIVES

CEO and Executive Managing Director, Mark D. Gibson, age 59, $500,000 total compensation
CFO, Gregory R. Conley, age 57, $375,000 total compensation
Executive Managing Director, Gerard Sansosti
Executive Managing Director, Manny De Zarraga, $250,000 total compensation
Executive Managing Director, Scott Galloway
Executive Managing Director, Matthew D. Lawton, $250,000 total compensation
Vice Chairman President and Executive Managing Director, Joe B. (Jody) Thornton, $500,000 total compensation
Auditors: Ernst & Young LLP

LOCATIONS

HQ: HFF Inc
One Victory Park, 2323 Victory Avenue, Suite 1200, Dallas, TX 75219
Phone: 214 265-0880
Web: www.hfflp.com

PRODUCTS/OPERATIONS

2015 Sales

	$ mil.	% of total
Capital markets services	487.9	97
Interest on mortgage notes receivable	11.2	2
Other	2.9	1
Total	**502.0**	**100**

Selected Services

Advisory Services
Case Studies
Debt Placement
Equity Placement
Foreign Capital
Investment Sales
Loan Sales
Loan Servicing
Special Assets

COMPETITORS

Arbor Commercial	Cushman & Wakefield
BGC Partners	Eastdil Secured
Boston Capital	Jones Lang LaSalle
CBRE Group	NorthMarq Capital
Capmark	Trammell Crow Company

HISTORICAL FINANCIALS

Company Type: Public

Income Statement

FYE: December 31

	REVENUE ($ mil.)	NET INCOME ($ mil.)	NET PROFIT MARGIN	EMPLOYEES
12/17	609.4	94.9	15.6%	982
12/16	517.4	77.2	14.9%	891
12/15	501.9	83.9	16.7%	810
12/14	425.9	61.2	14.4%	721
12/13	355.6	51.4	14.5%	637
Annual Growth	**14.4%**	**16.6%**	**—**	**11.4%**

2017 Year-End Financials

Debt ratio: 50.5%
Return on equity: 36.3%
Cash ($ mil.): 272.8
Current ratio: 1.37
Long-term debt ($ mil.): 0.1

No. of shares (mil.): 38.5
Dividends
Yield: 0.0%
Payout: 65.6%
Market value ($ mil.): 1,877.0

	STOCK PRICE ($) FY Close	P/E High/Low	Earnings	PER SHARE ($) Dividends	Book Value
12/17	48.64	20 11	2.39	1.57	7.43
12/16	30.25	16 11	1.99	1.80	6.21
12/15	31.07	21 14	2.18	1.80	5.67
12/14	35.92	24 16	1.61	1.83	4.95
12/13	26.85	20 11	1.36	0.00	4.71
Annual Growth	**16.0%**	**— —**	**15.1%**	**—**	**12.0%**

Hi-Crush Partners LP

Auditors: Deloitte & Touche LLP

LOCATIONS

HQ: Hi-Crush Partners LP
1330 Post Oak Blvd, Suite 600, Houston, TX 77056
Phone: 713 980-6200   **Fax:** 713 963-0088
Web: www.hicrushpartners.com

HISTORICAL FINANCIALS

Company Type: Public

Income Statement

FYE: December 31

	REVENUE ($ mil.)	NET INCOME ($ mil.)	NET PROFIT MARGIN	EMPLOYEES
12/17	602.6	82.5	13.7%	0
12/16	204.4	(81.0)	—	0
12/15	339.6	28.2	8.3%	0
12/14	386.5	123.0	31.8%	0
12/13	141.7	58.5	41.3%	0
Annual Growth	**43.6%**	**9.0%**	**—**	**—**

2017 Year-End Financials

Debt ratio: 17.5%
Return on equity: —
Cash ($ mil.): 5.6
Current ratio: 1.99
Long-term debt ($ mil.): 194.4

No. of shares (mil.): 89.0
Dividends
Yield: 0.0%
Payout: 15.6%
Market value ($ mil.): 952.0

	STOCK PRICE ($) FY Close	P/E High/Low	Earnings	PER SHARE ($) Dividends	Book Value
12/17	10.70	23 8	0.96	0.15	8.94
12/16	19.80	— —	(1.64)	0.00	4.56
12/15	5.92	54 7	0.73	1.83	3.70
12/14	31.03	22 10	3.00	2.24	4.76
12/13	37.98	17 7	2.08	1.92	4.51
Annual Growth	**(27.1%)**	**— —**	**(17.6%)**	**(47.1%)**	**18.7%**

Hilltop Holdings, Inc.

Hilltop Holdings sits on top of a mound of money-related businesses. The company's PlainsCapital subsidiary operates more than 80 branches in Texas and an offshore branch in the Caymans offers residential mortgages through 200 PrimeLending offices in 40-plus and provides securities brokerage and investment banking through HilltopSecurities. Subsidiary National Lloyds Corporation (NLC) offers fire and home-owners' coverage for low-value and manufactured homes and insurance through independent agents in Texas and more than 25 other (mostly) southern states. NLC operates as National Lloyds Insurance and American Summit Insurance. Hilltop has more than $13 billion in assets under management.

Operations

The purchase of PlainsCapital in a transaction valued at about $700 million moved Hilltop from insurance as its primary revenue generator to banking. It now operates in banking mortgage origination insurance and financial advisory services.

The PlainsCapital entities serve niche markets such as midsized businesses investors and high-net worth individuals. NLC's operating subsidiaries primarily write the kind of lower-cost homeowners' policies that only pay out cash value instead of replacement costs and most of its policies exclude coverage for water or mold damage. Texas accounts for over 70% of the company's premiums. While personal lines account for more than 90% of its premiums the company does write a small amount of commercial insurance covering builders' risk sports liability and transportation insurance which is known as "inland marine" policies.

Geographic Reach

PlainsCapital's banking operations are in Texas and its mortgages are secured by property in Texas mostly in or around major cities. NLC is licensed in 42 states and sells in 27 but primarily does business in Texas Oklahoma Arizona Tennessee Georgia and Louisiana with Texas accounting for more than 60% of sales. PrimeLending concentrates on nine states and does most of its business in Texas California and North Carolina.

Financial Performance

The PlainsCapital acquisition did what it was meant to do - gave the company a shot in the arm. For 2013 revenue rose nearly 350% to $1.3 billion. Net loss in 2012 became a net income of $125 million and cash from operations grew 71%.

Strategy

After the 2012 purchase of PlainsCapital Hilltop began to focus on being a Texas-based bank and financial services company. It plans to continue expanding its empire through organic growth and acquisitions. To that end in 2013 PlainsCapital purchased First National Bank a Texas-based company and its 51 branches. The same year Hilltop subsidiary NLASCO changed its name to National Lloyds Corporation or NLC as part of an overall re-branding effort.

Mergers and Acquisitions

Through its PlainsCapital subsidiary Hilltop in 2018 agreed to acquire The River Oaks Bank located in a posh region of Houston TX for $85 million.

In 2015 Hilltop purchased Dallas-based SWS Group Inc. which was comprised of Southwest Securities FSB (a $1.2 billion bank) Southwest Securities Inc. (broker-dealer subsidiaries) and SWS Financial Services Inc.

In 2013 the company purchased Texas-based First National Bank with about 50 branches mostly in South Texas. It followed that up in early 2015 with the acquisition of Dallas-based securities brokerage SWS Group. In 2016 Hilltop merged its broker-dealer subsidiaries First Southwest Company and Hilltop Securities (formerly Southwest Securities) to create HilltopSecurities. (HilltopSecurities division FirstSouthwest will continue to offer municipal advisory services.)

Company Background

The company began life as Affordable Residential Communities (ARC) and spent its early days as a real estate investment trust (REIT). It went public in 2004 dropped its REIT status in 2006 and built up its collection of manufactured housing communities through acquisitions.

After several years of losses in the housing business the company chose to transition into another industry. It acquired NLASCO a niche provider of fire and homeowners insurance for manufactured homes and other low-value properties at the start of 2007. The company then renamed itself Hilltop Holdings.

EXECUTIVES

President and Co-CEO, Jeremy B. Ford, age 43, $700,000 total compensation
Vice Chairman and Co-CEO; Chairman PlainsCapital Bank, Alan B. White, age 69, $1,350,000 total compensation
COO Subsidiaries, James R. Huffines, age 67, $690,000 total compensation
Chief Administrative Officer, Darren E. Parmenter, age 55, $335,000 total compensation
Chairman and CEO Hilltop Securities, Hill A. Feinberg, age 71, $500,000 total compensation
President and CEO PlainsCapital Bank, Jerry L. Schaffner, age 60
CFO, William B. Furr, age 40, $143,438 total compensation
CEO PrimeLending, Todd L. Salmans, age 69, $750,000 total compensation
CIO, Toby Pennycuff
Executive Vice President Chief Financial Officer of PlainsCapital, John A Martin
Senior Vice President Corporate Development, Erik Yohe
SENIOR VICE PRESIDENT, David Commons
SENIOR VICE PRESIDENT, Ashlee Miller
Vice President, Taylor Pool
VICE PRESIDENT, Matthew Weaver
EXECUTIVE VICE PRESIDENT, Thomas Dallam
Chairman, Gerald J. Ford, age 74
Board Member, Charles R Cummings
Board Of Directors, Markham Green

Board Member, Andrew Littlefair
Board Member, Lee Lewis
Board Member, Robert Taylor
Auditors: PricewaterhouseCoopers LLP

LOCATIONS

HQ: Hilltop Holdings, Inc.
2323 Victory Avenue, Suite 1400, Dallas, TX 75219
Phone: 214 855-2177
Web: www.hilltop-holdings.com

PRODUCTS/OPERATIONS

2016 Sales

	% of total
Interest income	
Loans including fees	22
Securities borrowed	2
Taxable Securities	2
Tax-exempt securities	-
Other	-
Non-interest income	
Net gains from sale of loans and other mortgage production income	35
Net insurance premiums earned	9
Securities commissions and fees	9
Investment and securities advisory fees and commissions	7
Mortgage loan origination fees	5
Other	9
Total	**100**

Selected Services

Financial Advisory
Clearing
Retail Brokerage
Investment Banking Services
Internet Banking
Business Check Cards

Selected Subsidiaries

PlainsCapital Bank
PrimeLending
HilltopSecurities
National Lloyds Corporation

COMPETITORS

American Modern Insurance	International Bancshares
BBVA Compass Bancshares	JPMorgan Chase
	Morgan Keegan
Bank of America	Raymond James Financial
Comerica	
Costco Wholesale	Republic Group
Cullen/Frost Bankers	Texas Capital Bancshares
Fannie Mae	
Foremost Insurance	Travelers Companies
Freddie Mac	Wells Fargo
ING	

HISTORICAL FINANCIALS

Company Type: Public

Income Statement

FYE: December 31

	ASSETS ($ mil.)	NET INCOME ($ mil.)	INCOME AS % OF ASSETS	EMPLOYEES
12/17	13,365.7	132.5	1.0%	5,500
12/16	12,738.0	145.8	1.1%	5,400
12/15	11,867.0	210.9	1.8%	5,300
12/14	9,242.4	111.6	1.2%	4,400
12/13	8,903.2	125.3	1.4%	4,550
Annual Growth	**10.7%**	**1.4%**	**—**	**4.9%**

2017 Year-End Financials

Return on assets: 1.0%	Dividends
Return on equity: 7.0%	Yield: 0.0%
Long-term debt ($ mil.): —	Payout: 17.6%
No. of shares (mil.): 95.9	Market value ($ mil.): 2,431.0
Sales ($ mil): 1,712.2	

	STOCK PRICE ($) FY Close	P/E High/Low		PER SHARE ($) Earnings	Dividends	Book Value
12/17	25.33	22	16	1.36	0.24	19.92
12/16	29.80	20	10	1.48	0.06	18.98
12/15	19.22	12	8	2.09	0.00	17.56
12/14	19.95	22	16	1.17	0.00	16.19
12/13	23.13	17	9	1.40	0.00	14.54
Annual Growth	**2.3%**	**—**	**—**	**(0.7%)**	**—**	**8.2%**

Hilton Grand Vacations Inc

Auditors: Ernst & Young LLP

LOCATIONS

HQ: Hilton Grand Vacations Inc
6355 MetroWest Boulevard, Suite 180, Orlando, FL 32835
Phone: 407 613-3100
Web: www.hiltongrandvacations.com

HISTORICAL FINANCIALS

Company Type: Public

Income Statement

FYE: December 31

	REVENUE ($ mil.)	NET INCOME ($ mil.)	NET PROFIT MARGIN	EMPLOYEES
12/17	1,711.0	327.0	19.1%	8,000
12/16	1,583.0	168.0	10.6%	7,750
12/15	1,475.0	174.0	11.8%	6,650
12/14	1,317.0	167.0	12.7%	0
12/13	1,224.0	128.0	10.5%	0
Annual Growth	**8.7%**	**26.4%**	**—**	**—**

2017 Year-End Financials

Debt ratio: 44.6%	No. of shares (mil.): 99.1
Return on equity: 95.4%	Dividends
Cash ($ mil.): 246.0	Yield: —
Current ratio: 4.49	Payout: —
Long-term debt ($ mil.): 1,065.0	Market value ($ mil.): 4,159.0

	STOCK PRICE ($) FY Close	P/E High/Low		PER SHARE ($) Earnings	Dividends	Book Value
12/17	41.95	13	8	3.28	0.00	5.23
Annual Growth	**—**	**—**	**—**	**—**	**—**	**—**

Hingham Institution for Savings

The Hingham Institution for Savings serves businesses and retail customers in Boston's south shore communities operating more than 10 branches in Massachusetts in Boston Cohasset Hingham Hull Norwell Scituate South Hingham and South Weymouth. Founded in 1834 the bank offers traditional deposit products such as checking and savings accounts IRAs and certificates of deposit. More than 90% of its loan portfolio is split between commercial mortgages and residential mortgages (including home equity loans) though the bank also originates construction business and consumer loans. More than 95% of the company's revenue comes from loan interest.

Operations

The Hingham Institution for Savings made 96% of its total revenue from loan interest during 2015 while about 2% came from interest in equities CODs and other investments. The rest of its revenue mostly came from service fees on deposit accounts.

Of its $1.4 billion loan portfolio (at the end of 2015) about 48% was made up of commercial real estate mortgages (including multi-family housing) while 45% was tied to residential mortgages (including home equity). The remainder of the portfolio was made up of residential and commercial construction loans (7% of loan assets) and commercial business loans and consumer loans (1%).

Subsidiary Hingham Unpledged Securities Corporation holds title to certain securities available for sale.

Geographic Reach

The company mostly serves clients in Boston the South Shore and the island of Nantucket. Its branches are in Boston Cohasset Hingham Hull Nantucket Norwell Scituate South Hingham and South Weymouth Massachusetts.

Sales and Marketing

The Hingham Institution for Savings serves both individuals and small businesses in its three target markets in Massachusetts. Some of its clients (as of mid-2016) include Lyons Associates The Hub TCR Development SYA+FH Steven Young Architect + Fine Home Builder and Park Drive Inc.

The bank spent $489000 on marketing expenses during 2015 down from $557000 in each of 2014 and 2013.

Financial Performance

The bank's annual revenues have slowly trended higher over the past several years as the promising Boston real estate market has fueled its commercial real estate and residential loan business growth.

Hingham's revenue dipped 1% to $64.34 million during 2015 despite 13% mortgage loan growth mostly because in 2014 it earned a gains on life insurance distributions. The bank also continued to lose fee income as it has eliminated many fees on its deposit products to simplify offerings and attract customer deposits.

Revenue declines and higher income tax provisions in 2015 (in 2014 it earned non-taxed death benefit proceeds) caused the bank's net income to fall 13% to $19.34 million. Hingham's operating cash levels rose 11% to $20.2 million for the year thanks to a jump in cash-based earnings.

Strategy

The Hingham Institution for Savings continued in 2016 to focus on originating commercial multi-family and single-family mortgage loans in its target markets of Boston the South Shore and the island of Nantucket in Massachusetts especially as the healthy real estate market in and around Boston has provided a tailwind for its lending business.

EXECUTIVES

Chief Executive Officer; President; Director, Robert H. Gaughen, $319,615 total compensation
Assistant Vice President Retail Lending, Pat Talbot
Auditors: Wolf & Company, P.C.

LOCATIONS

HQ: Hingham Institution for Savings
55 Main Street, Hingham, MA 02043
Phone: 781 749-2200 **Fax:** 781 740-4889
Web: www.hinghamsavings.com

COMPETITORS

Bank of America	Independent Bank (MA)
Citizens Financial Group	Peoples Federal Bancshares Inc.
Eastern Bank	Sovereign Bank

HISTORICAL FINANCIALS

Company Type: Public

Income Statement

FYE: December 31

	ASSETS ($ mil.)	NET INCOME ($ mil.)	INCOME AS % OF ASSETS	EMPLOYEES
12/17	2,284.6	25.7	1.1%	101
12/16	2,014.6	23.4	1.2%	103
12/15	1,768.5	19.3	1.1%	111
12/14	1,552.2	22.2	1.4%	121
12/13	1,356.4	13.3	1.0%	131
Annual Growth	13.9%	17.8%	—	(6.3%)

2017 Year-End Financials

Return on assets: 1.2%	Dividends
Return on equity: 14.8%	Yield: 0.0%
Long-term debt ($ mil.): —	Payout: 13.7%
No. of shares (mil.): 2.1	Market value ($ mil.): 441.0
Sales ($ mil): 82.4	

	STOCK PRICE ($) FY Close	P/E High/Low	Earnings	Dividends	Book Value
12/17	207.00	19 14	11.81	1.62	87.29
12/16	196.78	18 11	10.89	1.52	75.50
12/15	119.80	15 9	9.02	2.14	64.83
12/14	87.01	9 7	10.44	1.37	57.08
12/13	78.49	13 10	6.28	1.32	48.49
Annual Growth	27.4%	— —	17.1%	5.3%	15.8%

Holly Energy Partners LP

Holly Energy Partners pipes petroleum products and crude oil from refineries. It operates petroleum product and crude gathering pipelines (in New Mexico Oklahoma Texas and Utah) distribution terminals (in Arizona Idaho New Mexico Oklahoma Texas Utah and Washington) and refinery tankage in New Mexico and Utah. It operates 1330 miles of refined petroleum pipelines (340 miles leased) 960 miles of crude oil trunk lines 10 refined product terminals one jet fuel terminal and two truck-loading facilities. It also has three 65-mile pipelines that ship feedstocks and crude oil. HollyFrontier holds a 41% stake in Holly Energy Partners.

EXECUTIVES

Vice President of Human Resources, Nancy Hartmann
Vice President Finance, Scott Surplus
Vice President and Treasurer, Stephen Wise
Auditors: Ernst & Young LLP

LOCATIONS

HQ: Holly Energy Partners LP
2828 N. Harwood, Suite 1300, Dallas, TX 75201
Phone: 214 871-3555
Web: www.hollyenergy.com

COMPETITORS

ExxonMobil Pipeline	Shell Pipeline
Magellan Midstream	Wolverine Pipe Line Company
NuStar Energy	

HISTORICAL FINANCIALS

Company Type: Public

Income Statement

FYE: December 31

	REVENUE ($ mil.)	NET INCOME ($ mil.)	NET PROFIT MARGIN	EMPLOYEES
12/17	454.3	195.0	42.9%	269
12/16	402.0	147.5	36.7%	249
12/15	358.8	137.2	38.2%	245
12/14	332.5	105.5	31.7%	273
12/13	305.1	79.4	26.0%	257
Annual Growth	10.5%	25.2%	—	1.1%

2017 Year-End Financials

Debt ratio: 69.9%	No. of shares (mil.): 101.5
Return on equity: —	Dividends
Cash ($ mil.): 7.7	Yield: 0.0%
Current ratio: 1.34	Payout: 109.8%
Long-term debt ($ mil.): 1,507.3	Market value ($ mil.): 3,300.0

	STOCK PRICE ($) FY Close	P/E High/Low	Earnings	Dividends	Book Value
12/17	32.49	17 13	2.28	2.51	3.88
12/16	32.06	22 13	1.69	2.32	6.02
12/15	31.14	23 17	1.60	2.17	4.92
12/14	29.91	31 24	1.20	2.05	5.46
12/13	32.33	82 34	0.88	1.93	6.30
Annual Growth (11.4%)	0.1%	— —	26.9%	6.8%	

Home Bancorp Inc

Making its home in Cajun Country Home Bancorp is the holding company for Home Bank a community bank which offers deposit and loan services to consumers and small to midsized businesses in southern Louisiana. Through about two dozen branches the bank offers standard savings and checking accounts as well as lending services such as mortgages consumer loans and credit cards. Its loan portfolio includes commercial real estate commercial and industrial loans as well as construction and land loans. Home Bancorp also operates about half a dozen bank branches in west Mississippi which were formerly part of Britton & Koontz Bank.

Geographic Reach

Home Bancorp serves the Louisiana areas of Greater Lafayette Baton Rouge Greater New Orleans and Northshore (of Lake Pontchartrain). Its markets in Mississippi include Vicksburg and Natchez.

Financial Performance

Although the company saw assets and loans grow in 2013 net income fell 20% that year to $7.3 million on lower operating income.

Mergers and Acquisitions

In early 2014 Home Bancorp spent about $35 million on Britton & Koontz Capital Corporation the holding company of Britton & Koontz Bank; the deal added five branches in west Mississippi to Home Bancorp's operations.

EXECUTIVES

Executive Vice President, Darren Guidry
Auditors: Porter Keadle Moore, LLC

LOCATIONS

HQ: Home Bancorp Inc
503 Kaliste Saloom Road, Lafayette, LA 70508
Phone: 337 237-1960   **Fax:** 337 264-9280
Web: www.home24bank.com

COMPETITORS

Capital One	MidSouth Bancorp
IBERIABANK	Regions Financial
JPMorgan Chase	Teche Holding
Louisiana Bancorp	

HISTORICAL FINANCIALS

Company Type: Public

Income Statement

FYE: December 31

	ASSETS ($ mil.)	NET INCOME ($ mil.)	INCOME AS % OF ASSETS	EMPLOYEES
12/17	2,228.1	16.8	0.8%	0
12/16	1,556.7	16.0	1.0%	0
12/15	1,551.9	12.5	0.8%	0
12/14	1,221.4	9.8	0.8%	0
12/13	984.2	7.2	0.7%	0
Annual Growth	22.7%	23.2%	—	—

2017 Year-End Financials

Return on assets: 0.8%	Dividends
Return on equity: 7.3%	Yield: 0.0%
Long-term debt ($ mil.): —	Payout: 24.1%
No. of shares (mil.): 9.4	Market value ($ mil.): 406.0
Sales ($ mil): 84.3	

	STOCK PRICE ($) FY Close	P/E High/Low	PER SHARE ($) Earnings	Dividends	Book Value
12/17	43.22	19 14	2.28	0.55	29.57
12/16	38.61	17 10	2.25	0.41	24.47
12/15	25.98	14 11	1.79	0.37	22.80
12/14	22.94	15 12	1.42	0.07	21.64
12/13	18.85	17 15	1.06	0.00	19.99
Annual Growth	23.1%	— —	21.1%	—	10.3%

Home BancShares Inc

Home BancShares is the holding company for Centennial Bank which operates some 160 branches in Arkansas Florida and Alabama with an additional branch in each of New York City and Los Angeles (through which the company is building out a national lending platform). With $14.9 billion in assets the bank offers traditional services such as checking savings and money market accounts and CDs. About 60% of its lending portfolio is focused on commercial real estate loans — including non-farm and non-residential and construction and land development. The bank also writes residential mortgages and business and consumer loans. Through a subsidiary Home BancShares offers insurance services.

Operations

About 80% of Home Bancshares' $10.8 billion loan portfolio comprises real estate loans including non-farm and non-residential commercial loans which make up more than 40% of the total. Residential one-to-four-family loans and commercial construction and land development loans contribute about 20% and 15% respectively. Commercial and industrial loans make up around 10%.

The holding company has built a $6.3 billion portfolio of non-farm and non-residential commercial real estate loans primarily secured by commercial real estate. Around 50% 30% and 15% of the company's commercial real estate loan portfolio is in Florida Arkansas and with its Centennial Finance Group (CFG). Home Bancshares established the group in 2015 to manage loans acquired in the company's acquisition of the Florida Panhandle business of Banco Popular and to originate new loans (with a focus on commercial real estate and commercial and industrial loans) via a national lending platform.

About 30% and 60% of the company's $2.6 billion residential real estate loan portfolio are for one-to-four-family properties and non-owner occupied one-to-four family properties respectively.

The company's commercial and industrial loans account for about $1.3 billion of the portfolio; Arkansas Florida and Centennial CFG house about 40% 35% and 25% of that segment respectively.

Geographic Reach

Conway Arkansas-based Home Bancshares' holding company's Centennial Bank operates about 90 branches in Florida more than 75 in Arkansas around five in Southern Alabama and one in each of New York City and Los Angeles.

Sales and Marketing

Home Bancshares' non-farm and non-residential lending (comprising about 40% of the total) is made up of loans for shopping and retail centers hotels and motels offices industrial warehouses churches marinas and nursing homes.

Residential one-to-four-family residential mortgages for individuals make up some 20% of the company's portfolio. About 30% and 60% of its residential mortgage loans are for one-to-four-family owner-occupied and non-owner-occupied properties respectively.

The holding company also lends heavily to residential and commercial developers to construct commercial properties and develop land. Construction and land development loans make up about 15% of its portfolio.

Around 10% of the value of Home Bancshares' loans go to commercial and industrial clients.

Financial Performance

Home Bancshares reported revenue of $555.5 million in 2017 up 174% from 2013 and net income of $135.1 million up 103% over the same period. The company's cash stores and long-term debt both about tripled during that time to $635.9 million and $1.7 billion respectively.

The holding company's revenue increased 13% in 2017 compared with 2016 owing to increased interest income from loans.

Home Bancshares' net income fell 24% due mostly to an increase in income tax expense related to the passage of the Tax Cuts and Jobs Act.

The company's $419.3 million to its cash in 2017. Operating activities provided $176.9 million down from the previous year based on decreased net income and increased charges from indemnification and other assets and accrued interest payable on other liabilities. Investments used $355.5 million while financings added $597.8 million driven mostly by proceeds from issuance of subordinated debentures.

Strategy

Home Bancshares' strategy is focused on expanding in its core Florida market through the purchase of local managed community banks including four in 2017 and 2018.

In addition to growing its geographic footprint Home Bancshares is also diversifying its product offerings through acquisitions. In 2018 the company bought the Shore Premier Finance division of Union Bankshares. Shore originated direct consumer loans for high-end sail and power boats in southeast Florida.

Mergers and Acquisitions

Home Bancshares acquired Giant Holdings The Bank of Commerce and Stonegate Bank in 2017 as well as former Union Bankshares subsidiary Shore Premier Finance in 2018.

The holding company purchased Giant Holdings for $96 million. Giant operated six branches in the Ft. Lauderdale Florida area and had $398.1 million in total assets $327.8 million in loans and $304 million in deposits.

Home Bancshares acquired The Bank of Commerce from Bank of Commerce Holdings as part of that company's bankruptcy for $4.2 million. Bank of Commerce - which had $182.5 million in assets $127.5 million in loans and $141.7 million in deposits - operated three branches in the Sarasota Florida area.

Home Bancshares bought Stonegate Bank for $820 million adding the company's $3.1 billion in total assets $2.4 billion in loans and $2.6 billion in deposits to its books. Stonegate had 24 offices in Florida markets including Broward and Sarasota counties.

In 2018 the company acquired the Shore Premier Finance division of Union Bankshares for $374.5 million in cash and 1.3 million shares. Shore originates direct consumer loans for high-end sail and power boats at 16 locations in southeast Florida. At the deal's close Shore had $384.2 million in assets including $383.4 million in total loans.

Company Background

Home Bancshares formed in 1998 as First State Bank.

EXECUTIVES

CFO and Treasurer and Director, Randy E. Mayor, age 53, $300,000 total compensation
President and CEO, C. Randall (Randy) Sims, age 63, $390,000 total compensation
Regional President Centennial Bank, Robert F. Birch, age 68, $290,000 total compensation
President and CEO Centennial Bank, Tracy M. French, age 56, $290,000 total compensation
Chief Lending Officer, Kevin D. Hester, age 54
COO Home BancShares Inc. and Centennial Bank, John (Stephen) Tipton
Vice President Security, Jenni Holbrook
Vice President, Brian Jackson
Chairman, John W. Allison, age 71
Vice Chairman, Robert H. Adcock, age 69
Board Member, Alex Lieblong
Board Member, James G Hinkle
Board Member, Thomas Longe
Board Member, Mike Beebe
Auditors: BKD, LLP

LOCATIONS

HQ: Home BancShares Inc
719 Harkrider, Suite 100, Conway, AR 72032
Phone: 501 339-2929
Web: www.homebancshares.com

COMPETITORS

Arvest Bank	Bear State Financial
BB&T	Regions Financial
BBX Capital	Simmons First
Bank of America	Woodforest Financial
Bank of the Ozarks	

HISTORICAL FINANCIALS

Company Type: Public

Income Statement				FYE: December 31
	ASSETS ($ mil.)	NET INCOME ($ mil.)	INCOME AS % OF ASSETS	EMPLOYEES
12/17	14,449.7	135.0	0.9%	1,744
12/16	9,808.4	177.1	1.8%	1,503
12/15	9,289.1	138.2	1.5%	1,424
12/14	7,403.2	113.0	1.5%	1,376
12/13	6,811.8	66.5	1.0%	1,497
Annual Growth	20.7%	19.4%	—	3.9%

2017 Year-End Financials

Return on assets: 1.1%
Return on equity: 7.6%
Long-term debt ($ mil.): —
No. of shares (mil.): 173.6
Sales ($ mil): 619.8

Dividends
Yield: 0.0%
Payout: 44.9%
Market value ($ mil.): 4,037.0

	STOCK PRICE ($) FY Close	P/E High/Low	PER SHARE ($) Earnings	Dividends	Book Value
12/17	23.25	33 24	0.89	0.40	12.70
12/16	27.77	35 15	1.26	0.34	9.45
12/15	40.52	46 28	1.01	0.28	8.55
12/14	32.16	44 33	0.85	0.18	7.51
12/13	37.35	75 36	0.57	0.18	6.46
Annual Growth	(11.2%)	—	11.8%	22.5%	18.4%

Homefed Corp.

HomeFed won't provide you with room and board but it can help you get a home. The company earns its keep by investing in and developing residential real estate. Through subsidiaries Home-Fed is developing a master-planned community in San Diego County called San Elijo Hills which contains approximately 3500 residences as well as commercial space and a town center. In 2014 Leucadia Financial increased its ownership in Home-Fed from 31% to 65%. It also enhanced Home-Fed's geographic presence by adding land and commercial real estate assets in New York Florida Maine and South Carolina.

Like many real estate developers in California HomeFed has been affected by the battered housing market. San Elijo Hills is more than 80% sold but the company completed only one residential lot sale between 2006 and 2009. HomeFed also owns a portion of another community under development Otay Ranch in addition to some 1500 acres of a grape vineyard in California that is not zoned for residential or commercial use. It did not any real estate at Otay Ranch from 2007 to 2009.

Leucadia from which the company acquired the San Elijo Hills and Otay Ranch projects controls more than 30% of HomeFed's stock. Jospeh Steinberg president of Leucadia and chairman of Home-Fed owns almost 10%. Ian Cumming who is chairman of Leucadia and a director of HomeFed holds more than 7%.

EXECUTIVES

President and Director, Paul J. Borden, age 63, $255,742 total compensation
Chairman, Joseph S. Steinberg, age 68
Secretary, Corinne A. Maki
VP, Curt R. Noland, age 55, $165,500 total compensation
VP Treasurer and Controller, Erin N. Ruhe, age 46, $133,900 total compensation
President and Director, Paul J. Borden, age 63
Director, Ian M. Cumming, age 72
Director, Patrick D. Bienvenue, age 57
Director, Timothy M. Considine, age 71
Director, Michael A. Lobatz, age 63
Auditors: PricewaterhouseCoopers LLP

LOCATIONS

HQ: Homefed Corp.
1903 Wright Place, Suite 220, Carlsbad, CA 92008
Phone: 760 918-8200
Web: www.homefedcorporation.com

COMPETITORS

Brookfield Homes	Newhall Land
Corky McMillin	Tejon Ranch
Irvine Company	

HISTORICAL FINANCIALS

Company Type: Public

Income Statement				FYE: December 31
	REVENUE ($ mil.)	NET INCOME ($ mil.)	NET PROFIT MARGIN	EMPLOYEES
12/17	78.6	11.8	15.1%	35
12/16	81.0	36.6	45.3%	33
12/15	69.5	5.8	8.4%	31
12/14	59.5	3.8	6.5%	27
12/13	56.6	11.2	19.9%	16
Annual Growth	8.6%	1.3%	—	21.6%

2017 Year-End Financials

Debt ratio: 19.2%
Return on equity: 2.6%
Cash ($ mil.): 40.4
Current ratio: 2.59
Long-term debt ($ mil.): 118.2

No. of shares (mil.): 15.4
Dividends
Yield: —
Payout: —
Market value ($ mil.): 809.0

	STOCK PRICE ($) FY Close	P/E High/Low	PER SHARE ($) Earnings	Dividends	Book Value
12/17	52.25	68 55	0.77	0.00	29.55
12/16	45.00	21 13	2.38	0.00	28.75
12/15	34.05	132 89	0.38	0.00	26.38
12/14	45.00	207124	0.29	0.00	25.99
12/13	36.60	27 19	1.43	0.00	22.82
Annual Growth	9.3%	—	(14.3%)	—	6.7%

HomeStreet Inc

HomeStreet aims to offer home and business mortgages to all in the Pacific Northwest and Hawaii. Its subsidiary HomeStreet Bank offers traditional consumer banking accounts as well as commercial and private banking investment and insurance products and services through 45 branches and 65 loan offices in the Pacific Northwest California and Hawaii. Specializing in residential and commercial mortgages the bank and fellow subsidiary Homestreet Capital Corp originate home loans both directly and through a joint venture Windermere Real Estate which operates about 40 offices in Washington and Oregon. HomeStreet also provides specialty financing for income-producing properties.

Operations

HomeStreet operates two lines of business: Commercial and Consumer Banking and Mortgage Banking which originates residential mortgage loans for wale in the secondary markets to be securitized by GSAs. Its primary subsidiaries are HomeStreet Bank and HomeStreet Capital Corp. (HCC). HCC sells and services multifamily mortgage loans in conjunction with HomeStreet Bank.

HomeStreet gets most of its business from mortgage originations and sales. About 53% of the company's revenue came from its mortgage banking business (origination and sales) during 2015 while another 6% came from mortgage servicing income. Another 34% of its revenue came from loan interest.

Geographic Reach

Seattle-based HomeStreet operates bank branches in Arizona California Colorado Hawaii Idaho Oregon Utah and Washington.

Sales and Marketing
HomeStreet provides financial services for small- and middle-market businesses as well as consumers.

Financial Performance
HomeStreet's annual revenues and profits have more than doubled since 2011 thanks to strong mortgage banking and loan business growth driven by a strengthening housing market.

The company's revenue spiked 50% to $446.35 million during 2015 mostly thanks to a 64% increase in gains on mortgage loan origination sales resulting from a rise in single family mortgage interest rate lock commitments.

Strong revenue growth in 2015 caused HomeStreet's net income to nearly double to $41.32 million. The company's operating cash levels spiked to $8.31 million for the year (operations had used $348.6 million in 2014) mostly because it collected more in cash-denominated proceeds from its mortgage loan sales than it did in 2014.

Strategy
HomeStreet has been moving more toward commercial mortgage and SBA originations in recent years launching its HomeStreet commercial capital business in Orange County California in 2015. It also continues to acquire other small community banks in its region to grow its loan and deposit business and expand into new geographic markets.

Additionally it's been expanding its retail operations its own opening two new branches in San Diego's Mission Gorge and Kearny Mesa markets in March 2016. To boost profitability HomeStreet looked in 2016 to enhance productivity and cut costs by streamlining operations.

Mergers and Acquisitions
The company plans to buy two Southern California banks from Boston Private Bank & Trust. Through that acquisition HomeStreet will gain some $110 million in deposit accounts. It will then have a dozen retail branches in Southern California.

In February 2016 the company purchased Orange County Business Bank for $55 million extending its reach into "one of the premier commercial and consumer banking markets in the country" according to HomeStreet CEO and chairman Mark Mason.

In March 2015 HomeStreet expanded into Southern California's retail banking market after acquiring Simplicity Bancorp and its seven Simply Bank retail deposit branches in the greater Los Angeles area. Beyond geographic expansion the deal added valuable retail deposit and loan assets.

In November 2013 HomeStreet acquired Fortune Bank a community bank with two branches in Seattle and Bellevue for about $27 million. Concurrently it purchased YNB Financial Services Corp. the parent company of Yakima National Bank which operates four branches in Yakima Selah Sunnyside and Kennewick for about $10.3 million. The twin purchases along with the acquisition of two branches from AmericanWest Bank increased the number of retail deposit branches operates by HomeStreet to 29.

Company Background
HomeStreet went public in February 2012 with an offering worth $55 million. The company sold 1.6 million shares priced at $44 each. HomeStreet had postponed two previous attempts to go public in 2011 that had planned to sell many more shares. Proceeds from the 2012 IPO were used to meet capital-ratio requirements required by regulators in the wake of allegations that the bank engaged in unsafe practices.

HomeStreet was hit hard by the economic downturn and slowdown in the housing market. Trouble in its core mortgage lending business led to losses in 2009 and 2010 and the bank entered into agreements with regulators to improve its capital position earnings and management. It brought in a new management team and launched a turnaround plan to stabilize the business which included tightening its lending standards restructuring troubled loans when necessary and the sale of real estate backed by nonperforming loans. The measures helped HomeStreet return to profitability in 2011 and remain in the black for several years thereafter.

EXECUTIVES

Chairman President and CEO HomeStreet Inc. and HomeStreet Bank, Mark K. Mason, age 58, $537,500 total compensation

EVP Chief Administrative Officer General Counsel and Corporate Secretary Homestreet Inc. and Homestreet Bank, Godfrey B. Evans, age 64, $247,200 total compensation

SEVP Commercial Banking HomeStreet Bank, David H. Straus, age 71

EVP HomeStreet Inc. and EVP Residential Construction and Affiliated Businesses HomeStreet Bank, Richard W. H. (Rich) Bennion, age 68, $203,000 total compensation

EVP and Retail Banking Director HomeStreet Bank, Paulette Lemon, age 61

EVP and Human Resources Director Homestreet Bank, Pamela J. (Pam) Taylor, age 66

EVP Chief Risk Officer and Chief Credit Officer HomeStreet Inc. and Homestreet Bank, Jay C. Iseman, age 58, $200,000 total compensation

SEVP Mortgage Lending Director, Rose Marie David, age 54, $200,000 total compensation

EVP Commercial Real Estate and Commercial Capital President HomeStreet Bank, William D. Endresen, age 63

EVP and Residential Construction Lending Director HomeStreet Bank, Jeff Todhunter

EVP Chief Investment Officer and Treasurer HomeStreet Inc. and HomeStreet Bank, Darrell S. van Amen, age 52

Vice President Commercial Lending Manager, George Brace

Vice President Loan Officer, Carmen Esteban

Auditors: DELOITTE & TOUCHE LLP

LOCATIONS
HQ: HomeStreet Inc
601 Union Street, Suite 2000, Seattle, WA 98101
Phone: 206 623-3050
Web: www.homestreet.com

PRODUCTS/OPERATIONS

2015 Sales

	$ mil.	% of total
Interest		
Loans	152.6	34
Investment securities available for sale	11.6	3
Other	0.9	-
Non-interest		
Net gains on mortgage origination & sales activities	236.4	53
Mortgage servicing	24.4	6
Depositor & other retail banking fees	5.9	1
Gain on sale of investment securities available for sale	2.4	1
Bargain purchase gain	7.7	2
Insurance agency commission Income from WMS Series LLC and other	4.4	-
Total	**446.3**	**100**

Selected Services
Personal Banking
Home LoansInvestmentInsurancePrivate Bank
Commercial Banking
Builder Financing/Residential ConstructionCommercial LendingCommercial Real EstatePartnership Programs

COMPETITORS

American Savings Bank	KeyCorp
Bank of America	Sound Financial
Bank of Hawaii	U.S. Bancorp
Banner Corp	Umpqua Holdings
First Hawaiian	Washington Federal
JPMorgan Chase	Wells Fargo

HISTORICAL FINANCIALS
Company Type: Public

Income Statement
FYE: December 31

	ASSETS ($ mil.)	NET INCOME ($ mil.)	INCOME AS % OF ASSETS	EMPLOYEES
12/17	6,742.0	68.9	1.0%	2,419
12/16	6,243.7	58.1	0.9%	2,552
12/15	4,894.5	41.3	0.8%	2,139
12/14	3,535.0	22.2	0.6%	1,611
12/13	3,066.0	23.8	0.8%	1,502
Annual Growth	**21.8%**	**30.4%**	**—**	**12.7%**

2017 Year-End Financials
Return on assets: 1.0%
Return on equity: 10.3%
Long-term debt ($ mil.): —
No. of shares (mil.): 26.8
Sales ($ mil): 549.8

Dividends
Yield: —
Payout: —
Market value ($ mil.): 778.0

	STOCK PRICE ($) FY Close	P/E High/Low		Earnings	PER SHARE ($) Dividends	Book Value
12/17	28.95	13	9	2.54	0.00	26.20
12/16	31.60	14	8	2.34	0.00	23.48
12/15	21.71	12	9	1.96	0.00	21.08
12/14	17.41	14	11	1.49	0.44	20.34
12/13	20.00	17	11	1.61	0.33	17.97
Annual Growth	**9.7%**	**—**	**—**	**12.1%**	**—**	**9.9%**

HomeTrust Bancshares Inc.

Auditors: Dixon Hughes Goodman LLP

LOCATIONS
HQ: HomeTrust Bancshares Inc.
10 Woodfin Street, Asheville, NC 28801
Phone: 828 259-3939
Web: www.hometrustbancshares.com

HISTORICAL FINANCIALS

Company Type: Public

Income Statement

FYE: June 30

	ASSETS ($ mil.)	NET INCOME ($ mil.)	INCOME AS % OF ASSETS	EMPLOYEES
06/18	3,304.1	8.2	0.2%	520
06/17	3,206.5	11.8	0.4%	486
06/16	2,717.6	11.4	0.4%	465
06/15	2,783.1	8.0	0.3%	505
06/14	2,074.4	10.3	0.5%	471
Annual Growth	12.3%	(5.5%)	—	2.5%

2018 Year-End Financials

Return on assets: 0.2%	Dividends
Return on equity: 2.0%	Yield: —
Long-term debt ($ mil.): —	Payout: —
No. of shares (mil.): 19.0	Market value ($ mil.): 536.0
Sales ($ mil): 136.3	

	STOCK PRICE ($) FY Close	P/E High/Low	PER SHARE ($) Earnings	Dividends	Book Value
06/18	28.15	65 50	0.44	0.00	21.49
06/17	24.40	41 27	0.65	0.00	20.96
06/16	18.50	32 26	0.65	0.00	20.00
06/15	16.76	40 35	0.42	0.00	19.04
06/14	15.77	31 28	0.54	0.00	18.28
Annual Growth	15.6%	— —	(5.0%)	—	4.1%

Hooker Furniture Corp

Hooker Furniture wants to sell you the pieces that will turn your house into a home. The company offers hardwood and metal furniture including wall units home office items home theater cabinets living and dining room tables bedroom furniture and accent pieces. Its youth furniture is sold under the Opus Designs by Hooker label. Hooker Furniture's popular Bradington-Young line of residential upholstered furniture features leather reclining chairs and sofas. The furniture manufacturer's Sam Moore unit makes high-end chairs. Hooker Furniture's products are sold through specialty shops (Star Furniture Nebraska Furniture Mart) and department stores (Dillard's). Hooker Furniture was founded in 1924.

Operations

Hooker's operating segments casegoods (wood and metal furniture) and upholstery account for roughly two-thirds and a third of sales respectively. The upholstery segment includes the company's leather seating business Bradington-Young and chair settee and sectionals maker Sam Moore furniture. It also houses Opus Designs Hooker's youth bedroom lines division.

The company imports all of its wood furniture primarily purchased from China Guatemala Honduras Indonesia the Philippines Mexico and Vietnam. The furniture is sent to market through the company's half-dozen distribution centers located in the US and China. Hooker also operates one furniture showroom in High Point North Carolina.

Geographic Reach

Virginia-based Hooker Furniture generates more than 95% of its sales domestically. The company employs about 800 people in Virginia and North Carolina. In addition to factories in Bedford Virginia and Hickory North Carolina the company imports wood and some leather furniture from factories in Asia (China Indonesia Vietnam) Mexico and Central America.

Financial Performance

After a rough patch during the Great Recession and housing crisis Hooker Furniture is showing signs of life. The company reported sales of $228.3 million in fiscal 2014 (ended January) an increase of nearly $10 million or 4.5% versus the prior year. The increase in sales was primarily due to higher average selling prices on both casegoods and upholstered furniture partially offset by higher discounting and returns and allowances in the casegoods business. Net income declined 8% year over year to $7.9 million due primarily to start-up costs for Hooker's two new businesses: H Contract which furnishes upscale senior living facilities; and Homeware a direct-to-consumer e-commerce operation. Despite the positive news that Hooker's sales have risen in three of the past four years the $228.3 million the company rang up in fiscal 2014 is well below Hooker's record high of $350 million achieved in 2006.

Cash flow from operations has been erratic — posting large swings — over the past four years. In fiscal 2014 (ended January) cash generated from operations totaled $5.7 million compared with negative cash flow of $3.3 million in fiscal 2013.

Strategy

Optimistic about the health of the broader economy (housing job growth and the stock market) growing consumer confidence and improving retail conditions Hooker is planning for growth by expanding its domestic upholstery capacity warehousing and distribution in both the US and Asia and capital spending on information systems. The company sees potential for its two new businesses — H Contract and Homeware — targeting Millennials and Baby Boomers seeking senior living options.

The new H Contract product line supplies upholstered seating and casegoods to upscale senior living facilities while the Homeware product line offers direct-to-consumer customer-assembled modular upholstered and casegoods products designed for younger and more mobile furniture customers (think IKEA).

Hooker Furniture continues to focus on expanding the number of brand names and product categories it offers furniture retailers. To cater to a younger more frugal customer the company makes Envision furniture. Its youth design category was expanded through its purchase of kids furniture manufacturer Opus Designs in a deal valued at more than $5 million and builds on its acquisition of upholstered seating firm Bradington-Young. From its purchase of La-Z-Boy's Sam Moore Furniture business Hooker Furniture offers customized chairs.

Mergers and Acquisitions

In February 2016 Hooker Furniture made its largest ever acquisition in buying Home Meridian International (HMI). The $100 million-acquisition more than doubled Hooker's sales volume making it one of the top five furniture suppliers in the US furniture market. The combined companies annual revenues would be in excess of $550 million.

EXECUTIVES

Chairman and CEO, Paul B. Toms, age 64, $370,000 total compensation
President Sam Moore, Frank Richardson
COO, George Revington, age 71
President Bradington-Young, Craig Young
SVP Finance and Accounting and CFO, Paul A. Huckfeldt, age 61, $214,500 total compensation
President, Michael W. Delgatti, age 64, $300,000 total compensation
CIO, Charlene Bowling
President Hooker Casegoods, Steve Lush
President Hooker Upholstery, Jeremy Hoff
Auditors: KPMG LLP

LOCATIONS

HQ: Hooker Furniture Corp
440 East Commonwealth Boulevard, Martinsville, VA 24112
Phone: 276 632-2133
Web: www.hookerfurniture.com

PRODUCTS/OPERATIONS

FY017 Sales by Segment

	% of total
Home Meridian	60
Hooker Casegoods	25
Upholstery	14
All other	1
Total	**100**

Selected Brands and Collections

Bradington-Young
H Contract
Homeware
Prime Resources
Pulaski Furniture
Right 2 Home
Sanctuary
Sam Moore
Samuel Lawrence Hospitality
Waverly Place

COMPETITORS

Ashley Furniture	Herman Miller
Bassett Furniture	Klaussner Furniture
Broyhill	La-Z-Boy
Bush Industries	Sauder Woodworking
DMI Furniture	Stanley Furniture
Drexel Heritage	Vaughan-Bassett
Ethan Allen	Furniture
Heritage Home Group	Williams-Sonoma

HISTORICAL FINANCIALS

Company Type: Public

Income Statement

FYE: January 28

	REVENUE ($ mil.)	NET INCOME ($ mil.)	NET PROFIT MARGIN	EMPLOYEES
01/18	620.6	28.2	4.6%	1,216
01/17	577.2	25.2	4.4%	952
01/16*	247.0	16.1	6.6%	645
02/15	244.3	12.5	5.1%	674
02/14	228.2	7.9	3.5%	670
Annual Growth	28.4%	37.4%	—	16.1%

*Fiscal year change

2018 Year-End Financials

Debt ratio: 15.2%	No. of shares (mil.): 11.7
Return on equity: 13.2%	Dividends
Cash ($ mil.): 30.9	Yield: 0.0%
Current ratio: 3.55	Payout: 20.6%
Long-term debt ($ mil.): 45.7	Market value ($ mil.): 465.0

STOCK PRICE ($)		P/E		PER SHARE ($)		
	FY Close	High/Low		Earnings	Dividends	Book Value
01/18	39.55	21	12	2.42	0.50	19.51
01/17	33.95	18	10	2.18	0.42	17.12
01/16*	28.71	20	12	1.49	0.40	14.43
02/15	18.04	16	12	1.16	0.40	13.26
02/14	15.15	24	18	0.74	0.40	12.54
Annual Growth 27.1%		— —		34.5%	5.7%	11.7%

*Fiscal year change

Hope Bancorp Inc

Hope Bancorp (formerly BBCN Bancorp) is the holding company for Bank of Hope (formerly BBCN Bank) the largest Korean-American bank in the US. Bank of Hope caters to individuals and small business owners from 85 branches in California Alabama Georgia Illinois New Jersey New York Texas Virginia and Washington. Some 80% of its loan portfolio consists of commercial real estate loans though it also offers auto loans credit cards commercial and construction loans SBA loans and international banking services. The bank has expanded its footprint through bank acquisitions in recent years; it acquired top rival Wilshire Bancorp for $1 billion in mid-2016.

OperationsHope Bancorp makes nearly 90% of its revenue from interest income. About 82% of its total revenue came from loan interest (including fees) during 2015 while another 6% came from interest on securities and other investments. The rest of its revenue came from gains on SBA loan sales (4% of revenue) deposit account service fees (3%) international service fees (1%) loan servicing fees (1%) and wire transfer fees (1%).About 78% of its loan portfolio consisted of commercial real estate loans at the end of 2015 while 16% of loan assets were tied to commercial business loans. The rest of the portfolio consisted of construction mortgages (2% of loan assets) trade finance loans (2%) and consumer and other loans (2%).Geographic ReachBBCN Bank boasted 50 branches in six states at the end of 2015 including 28 in California (Los Angeles Orange County Oakland and Silicon Valley areas); eight branches in New York City metro area and New Jersey; eight branches in the Chicago metro area; four branches in the Seattle metro area; and two branches in Virginia. The merger with Wilshire Bancorp added some 35 branches including locations in Alabama Georgia Illinois and Washington.It also had eight loan production offices in Seattle Denver Dallas Atlanta Northern California Portland and Annandale Virginia. Wilshire brought an SBA loan office in Fremont California.

Internationally Hope has a representative office in Seoul Korea that serves international businesses with US subsidiaries.Sales and MarketingThe bank spent $5.1 million on advertising and marketing during 2015 down slightly from $5.4 million and $5.2 million in 2014 and 2013 respectively.Financial PerformanceThe company's annual revenues have doubled since 2011 as its loan assets have swelled by nearly 70% to $6.25 billion. Meanwhile the bank's net income has more than quadrupled thanks to declining loan loss provisions as its loan portfolio's credit quality has improved with the strengthened economy. The bank's revenue climbed 3% to $357.3 million during 2015 mostly thanks to higher interest income stemming from 12% organic loan asset growth. Non-interest income slid 1% as the bank collected less in deposit account service charges and earned less in gains on SBA loan sales.Revenue growth and a continued decline in loan loss provisions in 2015 drove BBCN's net income up 4% to $92.2 million. The company's operating cash levels fell 9% to $122.89 million for the year mostly due to unfavorable working capital changes mostly related to changes in other assets.StrategyThe nation's largest Korean-American bank differentiates itself by honing in on its target customer base being sure to be present in areas with high concentrations of Korean Americans (such as in California). Bank of Hope has been acquiring smaller banks in recent years to expand its footprint into such markets while growing its deposit and loan business. Its mid-2016 acquisition of top Korean-American rival Wilshire Bancorp solidified its position ahead of its closest rival Hamni Financial.

Mergers and Acquisitions

In December 2015 BBCN Bancorp agreed to buy Wilshire Bancorp (the second-largest US Korean-American bank) for $1 billion in an all-stock offer. Completed in mid-2016 the combined banks control more than $13 billion in assets effectively creating the seventh-largest bank in California and the largest Korean-American bank (and only super-regional Korean-American bank) in the US ahead of rival Hamni Financial. In 2013 it bought Pacific International Bancorp which came with four branches in Seattle and Foster Bankshares which had nine branches — eight in Illinois and one in Virginia.Company BackgroundBBCN Bancorp formed in 2011 from the merger of Center Bank and Nara Bank two rivals headquartered a few blocks away from each other in the Koreatown neighborhood of Los Angeles. (Its name stood for Business Bank of Center and Nara.)

EXECUTIVES

Vice President And Systems Support Manager, Joshua Chu
Senior Vice President and Chief Credit Officer, Peter Koh
Senior Vice President and Manager Loan Center III We Are Now Bank of Hope, Christie Yoo
VICE PRESIDENT INFORMATION TECHNOLOGY PROCUREMENT MANAGER, Karina Moran
FVP and Manager General Services Department, Brandon Lee
Vice President Desktop Analyst II, Eunmoo Choi
Vice President Desktop Manager We Are Now Bank of Hope, Charles Yoo
Senior Vice President Institutional Banking Director Business Aircraft, Scott Schaidle
Senior Vice President Manager Vendor Risk Management, Bradley Martin
AAP Senior Vice President TMS Operations Manager, Rachel Lim
Senior Vice President and Director of Investment Banking Operations, Charuka Sinhabahu
Vice President and Operational Risk Management Assistant, Katelyn Kang
First Vice President and Senior Financial Analyst, Joonhyok Shin
AVP and Loan Officer Bank of Hope, James Chong

Senior Vice President and Marketing Manager Senior Business Analyst Loan Department, Gene Pak
Auditors: Crowe Horwath LLP

LOCATIONS

HQ: Hope Bancorp Inc
3200 Wilshire Boulevard, Suite 1400, Los Angeles, CA 90010
Phone: 213 639-1700   **Fax:** 213 235-3033
Web: www.bankofhope.com

PRODUCTS/OPERATIONS

2015 Sales

	$ mil.	% of total
Interest income	313.7	88
Non-interest income	43.7	12
Total	**357.4**	**100**

COMPETITORS

Bank of America	Grandpoint
Broadway Financial	Hanmi Financial
Cathay General Bancorp	U.S. Bancorp
East West Bancorp	Wells Fargo
Far East National Bank	Woori

HISTORICAL FINANCIALS

Company Type: Public

Income Statement				FYE: December 31
	ASSETS ($ mil.)	NET INCOME ($ mil.)	INCOME AS % OF ASSETS	EMPLOYEES
12/17	14,206.7	139.4	1.0%	1,470
12/16	13,441.4	113.7	0.8%	1,372
12/15	7,912.6	92.2	1.2%	938
12/14	7,140.3	88.6	1.2%	915
12/13	6,475.2	81.7	1.3%	835
Annual Growth 21.7%		14.3%	—	15.2%

2017 Year-End Financials

Return on assets: 1.0%	Dividends
Return on equity: 7.3%	Yield: 0.0%
Long-term debt ($ mil.): —	Payout: 48.5%
No. of shares (mil.): 135.5	Market value ($ mil.): 2,473.0
Sales ($ mil): 638.5	

	STOCK PRICE ($)	P/E		PER SHARE ($)		
	FY Close	High/Low		Earnings	Dividends	Book Value
12/17	18.25	22	15	1.03	0.50	14.23
12/16	21.89	20	13	1.10	0.45	13.72
12/15	17.22	17	11	1.16	0.42	11.79
12/14	14.38	16	12	1.11	0.35	11.10
12/13	16.59	16	11	1.03	0.25	10.19
Annual Growth 2.4%		— —		(0.0%)	18.9%	8.7%

Horizon Bancorp Inc

For those in Indiana and Michigan Horizon Bancorp stretches as far as the eye can see. The company is the holding company for Horizon Bank (and its Heartland Community Bank division) which provides checking and savings accounts IRAs CDs and credit cards to customers through more than 50 branches in north and central Indiana and southwest and central Michigan. Commercial financial and agricultural loans make up the largest segment of its loan portfolio which also includes mortgage warehouse loans (loans earmarked for sale into the secondary market) consumer loans and residential mortgages. Through subsidiaries the bank offers trust and investment management services; life health and property/casualty insurance; and annuities.

Operations

Horizon boasted more than $2.08 billion in total assets and $1.48 billion in deposits in 2014. Commercial loans made up 49% of the bank's total loan portfolio. The bank employed nearly 450 full and part time employees that year.

Horizon's subsidiaries include: Horizon Investments which manages the bank's investment portfolio; Horizon Properties which manages the real estate investment trust; Horizon Insurance Services which sells through the company's Wealth Management; and Horizon Grantor Trust which holds title to certain company-owned life insurance policies.

The bank generated 61% of its revenue from interest income on loans in 2014 while another 13% came from interest on its taxable and tax-exempt investments. About 8% of revenues came from gains on its mortgage sales while the remainder of revenues were mostly generated by a mix of service charges on deposit accounts interchange fees and fiduciary activities fees.

Geographic Reach

The bank's more than 30 branches serve customers in north and central Indiana and southwest and central Michigan. Its mortgage-banking services are offered across the Midwest.

Financial Performance

Horizon Bancorp's revenues and profits have been trending higher over the past few years mostly as it's continued to grow its loan business and deposit customer base through acquisitions.

The bank's revenue rose by 2% to $102.5 million in 2014 mostly as the bank increased its interest-earning assets during the year. Its non-interest income also increased thanks to higher service charges on deposits and interchange fee income resulting from the growth in transactional deposit accounts and volume.

Despite higher revenue in 2014 the company's net income fell by 9% to $18.1 million for the year on higher provisions for loan losses due to loan growth and a write off of a commercial account coupled with an increase in transaction costs related to its Summit acquisition and an increase in salaries and employee benefits due to growth. Horizon's operating cash levels fell by 62% to $17.7 million after adjusting its earnings for non-cash items related to its net proceeds on the sale of its held-for-sale loans.

Strategy

Horizon Bancorp continues to expand its geographic reach and loan business through acquisitions and new branches. It acquired several banks and opened new branches throughout 2016 and 2017.

Mergers and Acquisitions

In 2017 Horizon Bancorp agreed to buy Wolverine Bancorp for $92 million and Lafayette Community Bancorp for $32 million

In 2016 Horizon Bancorp bought LaPorte Bancorp for $98.9 million boosting its total assets by 20% to more than $3.24 billion while expanding its branch reach into the LaPorte area of Indiana.

It also agreed to buy CNB Bancorp which operates Central National Bank & Trust in Attica Indiana.

In 2015 Horizon Bancorp agreed to buy Peoples Bancorp and subsidiary Peoples Federal Savings Bank of DeKalb County.

In April 2014 the company purchased SCP Bancorp including subsidiary Summit Community Bank and its two branches.

EXECUTIVES

President CEO Chief Administrative Officer and Director; Chairman and CEO Horizon Bank, Craig M. Dwight, age 61, $300,000 total compensation
EVP; President and COO Horizon Bank, Thomas H. Edwards, age 65, $187,000 total compensation
CFO, Mark E. Secor, age 52, $131,921 total compensation
President LaPorte County Indiana Horizon Bank, Steven C. Kring
President Southwest Michigan Horizon Bank, Donald E. (Don) Radde, age 65, $166,000 total compensation
President Porter County Indiana Horizon Bank, David G. Rose
Vice President Data Processing, Bradford Smith
Chairman, Robert C. Dabagia, age 79
Auditors: BKD, LLP

LOCATIONS

HQ: Horizon Bancorp Inc
515 Franklin Square, Michigan City, IN 46360
Phone: 219 879-0211
Web: www.horizonbank.com

PRODUCTS/OPERATIONS

Selected Subsidiaries
Horizon Bank National Association
   Horizon Insurance Services Inc.
   Horizon Investments Inc.
   Horizon Trust & Investment Management N.A.

COMPETITORS

1st Source Corporation	Farmers Mutual of NE
American United Mutual	Fifth Third
Bank of America	First Merchants
Brotherhood Mutual	Indiana Farmers Mutual

HISTORICAL FINANCIALS

Company Type: Public

Income Statement				FYE: December 31
	ASSETS ($ mil.)	NET INCOME ($ mil.)	INCOME AS % OF ASSETS	EMPLOYEES
12/17	3,964.3	33.1	0.8%	701
12/16	3,141.1	23.9	0.8%	665
12/15	2,652.4	20.5	0.8%	558
12/14	2,076.9	18.1	0.9%	448
12/13	1,758.2	19.8	1.1%	421
Annual Growth	22.5%	13.6%	—	13.6%

2017 Year-End Financials

Return on assets: 0.9%
Return on equity: 8.3%
Long-term debt ($ mil.): —
No. of shares (mil.): 38.2
Sales ($ mil): 161.6

Dividends
Yield: 0.0%
Payout: 33.5%
Market value ($ mil.): 1,065.0

	STOCK PRICE ($)	P/E	PER SHARE ($)		
	FY Close	High/Low	Earnings	Dividends	Book Value
12/17	27.80	30 26	0.95	0.32	11.94
12/16	28.00	40 26	0.79	0.27	10.25
12/15	27.96	33 26	0.84	0.25	9.93
12/14	26.14	30 22	0.84	0.23	9.38
12/13	25.33	26 19	0.96	0.19	8.47
Annual Growth	2.4%	— —	(0.3%)	14.4%	8.9%

Hospitality Properties Trust

Hospitality Properties Trust (HPT) rolls out the welcome mat for the road-weary. The real estate investment trust (REIT) owns more than 320 hotels throughout the US Canada Puerto Rico as well as around 200 full-service truck stops operating as TravelCenters of America and Petro Stopping Centers. Unlike some hospitality REITs HPT is not affiliated with any one hotel company. Its properties target different markets from upscale (Crowne Plaza Hotels & Resorts) to business and family travelers on long-term trips (Residence Inn by Marriott). HPT maintains a geographically diverse portfolio with hotels or travel centers (usually both) in nearly 45 states.

Operations

Hospitality Properties Trust (HPT) operates two business segments: Hotel Real Estate Investments (HREI) and Travel Center Real Estate Investments (TCREI).

The HREI segment generates around 85% of HPT's total revenue and consists of the operations of its more nearly 50000 rooms across more than 320 hotel properties. Its hotels operate under some 20 different brands including Courtyard by Marriott; Royal Sonesta; Candlewood Suites; Residence Inn by Marriott; Crowne Plaza; Staybridge Suites; Radisson.

The TCREI segment accounts for the remaining 15% and generates lease income from some 200 travel center properties leased to TravelCenters of America LLC (or subsidiaries). About 75% of its travel centers operate under the TravelCenters of America or TA brand while the remainder operate under the Petro Stopping Centers or Petro brand name.

Geographic Reach

Massachusetts-based Hospitality Properties Trust's properties span nearly 45 US states as well as Canada and Puerto Rico. The states in which it has the largest percent of its properties are California Texas Georgia and Illinois.

Financial Performance

HPT's revenues and profits have been trending higher over the past few years mostly from added revenues from new hotel property acquisitions. Net income has been above $100 million and sometimes exceeding $200 million over the same period.

Revenue in 2017 grew 6% to $2.2 billion with increases in both hotel operating revenues and rental income. Although average hotel occupancy slid 0.4% the average daily rate per room increased nearly 1%.

Despite higher revenue net income fell marginally to $215 million. The decrease was due to across-the-board higher expenses as evidenced by the 2017 operating margin of 17.5% compared to 2016?s 18.9%.

Cash at year end was $24 million up $13 million from the previous year. Financing activities contributed $193 million mostly from an increase in borrowings. Investing activities used $734 million for real estate acquisitions and improvements to its existing properties. Operating activities added $554 million from the company?s net income and large adjustments for depreciation & amortization.

Strategy

As a real estate investment trust Hospitality Properties is all about generating dependable cash flows at the lowest risk possible. While economic activity is in growth mode its properties ride the wave higher but when negative economic cycles appear its risk management kicks in. It believes its hotel and travel centers incur growth and risk at different points of economic cycles spreading risk across a time duration. Additionally the company has in place for all but two of its properties agreements that guarantee minimum return or rent. Its hotel properties are operated by brand owners instead of third party management groups which it believes ensures a higher degree of commitment and resolution on the part of the hotel managers.

HPT snapped up additional properties in 2017: 20 hotels a travel center and various parcels of land. It spent more than $600 million on the acquisitions.

Company Background

HPT made a bold move beyond hotels when it acquired truck stop chain TravelCenters of America (TA) in 2007 for almost $2 billion signifying the REIT's first foray into the travel convenience industry. While the hotel industry is cyclical HPT wanted to capitalize on the fact that travel centers which are located along most major US interstate highways perform well even in recession. TA was spun off not long after the acquisition and now operates as a separate company leasing all travel center properties from owner HPT.

HISTORY

Lawyer Barry Portnoy founded Health and Retirement Properties Trust (now HRPT Properties Trust) in 1986 to finance New MediCo a chain of nursing homes and head injury centers owned by one of his law clients and the client's cousin Gerard Martin. When New MediCo ran into financial trouble in 1992 HRPT privately restructured the debt and took over eight of the facilities.

In 1995 HRPT established and spun off Hospitality Properties Trust (HPT) as a separate public company with an initial portfolio of 21 Marriott International mid-market hotels. Over the next several years HPT bought hundreds of hotel properties often in large blocks; an example was its 1997 acquisition of 45 Marriott-branded hotels.

The company continued to add properties as REIT stock prices soared in the 1990s. But in 1999 REITs (particularly hospitality REITs) fell out of favor because of a perceived oversupply of rooms. Nevertheless the company succeeded in raising capital in 1999 to continue enlarging its portfolio. In early 2005 it acquired a portfolio of about a dozen properties from hotel management company InterContinental Hotels Group. The package

included one hotel in San Juan Puerto Rico and two in Toronto that represent HPT's first non-US properties.

EXECUTIVES

Secretary, Jennifer B. Clark, age 57
SVP, Ethan S. Bornstein, age 44, $214,275 total compensation
President and COO, John G. Murray, age 57, $214,275 total compensation
CFO and Treasurer, Mark L. Kleifges, age 57, $214,275 total compensation
Auditors: Ernst & Young LLP

LOCATIONS

HQ: Hospitality Properties Trust
Two Newton Place, 255 Washington Street, Suite 300, Newton, MA 02458
Phone: 617 964-8389
Web: www.hptreit.com

PRODUCTS/OPERATIONS

2017 Sales

	$ mil.	% of total
Hotel operating revenues	1,843.5	85
Rental income	323.7	15
FF&E reserve income	4.7	-
Total	**2,171.9**	**100**

Selected Hotel Tenants

Candlewood Suites
Crowne Plaza Hotels & Resorts
Country Inns & Suites by Carlson
Courtyard by Marriott
Holiday Inn Hotels & Resorts
Hyatt Place
InterContinental Hotels & Resorts
Marriott Hotels and Resorts
Park Plaza Hotels & Resorts
Radisson Hotels & Resorts
Residence Inn by Marriott
SpringHill Suites by Marriott
Staybridge Suites
TownePlace Suites by Marriott

COMPETITORS

Ashford Hospitality Trust
Berkshire Hathaway
FelCor
Hersha Hospitality
Host Hotels & Resorts
LaSalle Hotel Properties
Love's Country Stores
Pebblebrook
Pilot Flying J
Shaner Hotel Group
Starwood Hotels & Resorts
Strategic Hotels
Sunstone Hotel Investors

HISTORICAL FINANCIALS

Company Type: Public

Income Statement — FYE: December 31

	REVENUE ($ mil.)	NET INCOME ($ mil.)	NET PROFIT MARGIN	EMPLOYEES
12/17	2,171.9	215.1	9.9%	0
12/16	2,047.2	223.1	10.9%	0
12/15	1,921.9	166.4	8.7%	0
12/14	1,736.3	197.1	11.4%	0
12/13	1,563.8	133.1	8.5%	0
Annual Growth	**8.6%**	**12.7%**	**—**	**—**

2017 Year-End Financials

Debt ratio: 55.9%	No. of shares (mil.): 164.3
Return on equity: 7.3%	Dividends
Cash ($ mil.): 24.1	Yield: 0.0%
Current ratio: 0.25	Payout: 166.9%
Long-term debt ($ mil.): 4,001.0	Market value ($ mil.): 4,906.0

	STOCK PRICE ($) FY Close	P/E High/Low	Earnings	PER SHARE ($) Dividends	Book Value
12/17	29.85	26 22	1.24	2.07	16.77
12/16	31.74	25 17	1.30	2.03	19.05
12/15	26.15	35 26	0.97	1.99	18.56
12/14	31.00	27 21	1.18	1.95	19.94
12/13	27.03	44 32	0.73	1.89	20.63
Annual Growth	**2.5%**	**— —**	**14.2%**	**2.3%**	**(5.1%)**

Houlihan Lokey Inc

Auditors: KPMG LLP

LOCATIONS

HQ: Houlihan Lokey Inc
10250 Constellation Blvd., 5th Floor, Los Angeles, CA 90067
Phone: 310 788-5200
Web: www.hl.com

HISTORICAL FINANCIALS

Company Type: Public

Income Statement — FYE: March 31

	REVENUE ($ mil.)	NET INCOME ($ mil.)	NET PROFIT MARGIN	EMPLOYEES
03/18	963.3	172.2	17.9%	884
03/17	872.0	108.3	12.4%	832
03/16	693.7	69.7	10.1%	1,171
03/15	680.8	79.8	11.7%	981
03/14	592.4	61.3	10.4%	871
Annual Growth	**12.9%**	**29.5%**	**—**	**0.4%**

2018 Year-End Financials

Debt ratio: 0.8%	No. of shares (mil.): 67.7
Return on equity: 21.8%	Dividends
Cash ($ mil.): 416.0	Yield: 0.0%
Current ratio: 1.17	Payout: 30.7%
Long-term debt ($ mil.): 11.8	Market value ($ mil.): 3,024.0

	STOCK PRICE ($) FY Close	P/E High/Low	Earnings	PER SHARE ($) Dividends	Book Value
03/18	44.60	19 12	2.60	0.80	12.58
03/17	34.45	19 12	1.63	0.71	9.97
03/16	24.90	22 18	1.10	0.30	9.97
Annual Growth	**33.8%**	**— —**	**53.7%**	**63.3%**	**12.3%**

Howard Bancorp Inc

Auditors: Dixon Hughes Goodman LLP

LOCATIONS

HQ: Howard Bancorp Inc
3301 Boston Street, Baltimore, MD 21224
Phone: 410 750-0020
Web: www.howardbank.com

HISTORICAL FINANCIALS

Company Type: Public

Income Statement

FYE: December 31

	ASSETS ($ mil.)	NET INCOME ($ mil.)	INCOME AS % OF ASSETS	EMPLOYEES
12/17	1,149.9	7.2	0.6%	306
12/16	1,026.9	5.3	0.5%	300
12/15	946.7	1.1	0.1%	257
12/14	691.4	10.4	1.5%	218
12/13	499.9	1.9	0.4%	102
Annual Growth	23.2%	38.4%	—	31.6%

2017 Year-End Financials

Return on assets: 0.6%
Return on equity: 6.6%
Long-term debt ($ mil.): —
No. of shares (mil.): 9.8
Sales ($ mil): 62.5

Dividends
Yield: —
Payout: —
Market value ($ mil.): 216.0

	STOCK PRICE ($) FY Close	P/E High/Low	PER SHARE ($) Earnings	Dividends	Book Value
12/17	22.00	31 20	0.75	0.00	13.47
12/16	15.10	20 16	0.73	0.00	12.27
12/15	13.24	94 69	0.16	0.00	13.34
12/14	11.40	5 4	2.48	0.00	14.39
12/13	9.42	22 14	0.44	0.00	11.87
Annual Growth	23.6%	— —	14.3%	—	3.2%

Howard Hughes Corp

The Howard Hughes Corporation (THHC) is involved in neither planes movies or medical research but one of the 20th century entrepreneur's later interests real estate. The company arose from the bankruptcy restructuring of shopping mall developer General Growth Properties (GGP) to oversee much of GGP's non-retail assets. THHC owns GGP's former portfolio of four master planned communities outside Columbia Maryland; Houston Texas; and Summerlin Nevada; as well as about two dozen other as-yet undeveloped sites and commercial properties in 16 states from New York to Hawaii including GGP's own headquarters building in downtown Chicago. Unlike GGP THHC does not operate as a REIT.

Operations

THHC owns manages and develops commercial residential and mixed-use real estate throughout the US. It organizes its business into three segments: master planned communities; operating assets; and strategic developments. THHC's holdings include eight mixed-use and retail properties nine office properties an apartment building a resort and conference center a 36-hole golf course and country club three equity investments and four other revenue-generating assets.

The firm's 22500-acre flagship property outside Las Vegas Summerlin is home to about 100000 people and has another 7000 acres for sale and redevelopment. Its other three communities in Texas and Maryland have a combined 7000 acres for sale and redevelopment. Beyond that other holdings include nine mixed-use development projects four mall developments and seven distressed mall properties slated for redevelopment.

Geographic Reach

Dallas-based THHC has offices at select properties and in New York City and Los Angeles. The firm operates master planned communities in Houston and The Woodlands Texas; Howard and Price George's counties in Maryland; and in Las Vegas.

Financial Performance

THHC has logged substantial revenue growth in recent years. Indeed in 2013 the firm reported $474.6 million in revenue a 26% increase versus 2012. Driving the double-digit gain was growth in master planned communities due to higher demand for its residential superpad sites in Summerlin (Las Vegas) and finished lots in The Woodlands and $33 million in revenue generated from the sale of condominium rights in Hawaii to a 50:50 joint venture. Despite the revenue gain THHC posted a loss of nearly $73.8 million in 2013 versus a deeper loss in 2012. Indeed the firm has posted losses in four of the last five years.

Strategy

After taking a pounding at the hands of Superstorm Sandy in 2013 which resulted in damage and lost revenue THHC is doubling down on its investment in the South Street Seaport District in lower Manhattan with the proposed acquisition of 80 South Street. The firm is rebuilding pier 17 and is working with the community on a proposal for a mixed-use project that increased a hotel and residential units a new marina restoration of the Tin Building an extension of the East River Esplanade a food market and a plan to ensure the long-term future of the financially troubled Seaport Museum. Its plans for a 50-story hotel/condo tower on the site of the former historic Fulton Fish Market is meeting resistance from the community.

Mergers and Acquisitions

In 2011 THHC acquired the remainder of The Woodlands master planned community in Houston that it already didn't own from Morgan Stanley Real Estate Investing. The $117.5 million deal gave the company complete control over the The Woodlands brand. In addition to its residential properties Howard Hughes plans to focus on developing commercial properties within The Woodlands.

Company Background

The Summerlin name is also the company's tie to Howard Hughes. In the 1950s Mr. Hughes bought 25000 acres outside Las Vegas and named it Summerlin his maternal grandmother's maiden name. Three years before he died in 1973 Mr. Hughes created Summa Corporation which became Summerlin's new owner. Hughes' heirs sold Summa to The Rouse Company in 1996 for about $500 million. GGP bought The Rouse Company in 2004. During the bankruptcy GGP paid Hughes' heirs $230 million to settle Summerlin and in return named the new company after him.

EXECUTIVES

Executive Vice President Master Planned Communities, Paul Layne
Senior Vice President Development, Adam Meister
Senior Vice President Development, David Kautz
VICE PRESIDENT FINANCE, Robert Carroll
Executive Vice President Management and Operations, Sarah Vasquez
Managing Director Events and Entertainment, Alan Kashian
Vice President Community Development, Todd Apo
Executive Vice President Leasing, Rick Strauss
Senior Vice President Sales And Marketing, Bill Pisetsky
Vice President Tenant Coordination Design, Boun Somphanh
Assistant Treasurer, Robert McDonald
Auditors: Ernst & Young LLP

LOCATIONS

HQ: Howard Hughes Corp
13355 Noel Road, 22nd Floor, Dallas, TX 75240
Phone: 214 741-7744   **Fax:** 214 741-3021
Web: www.howardhughes.com

PRODUCTS/OPERATIONS

Selected Propeties

American City Building (office building in Columbia MD)
Bridgeland (master-planned community in Houston)
Century Plaza (future development in Birmingham AL)
Columbia (master-planned community in Maryland)
Kendall Town Center (future mixed-use development near Miami FL)
Landmark Mall (mall in Alexandria VA)
Ridgley Building (office building in Columbia MD)
Riverwalk Marketplace (mall in New Orleans LA)
South Street Seaport (retail site in Manhattan NY)
Summerlin (master-planned community near Las Vegas)
The Woodlands (master-planned community in Houston)

COMPETITORS

Bresler & Reiner	Macerich
CBL & Associates Properties	Newhall Land Related
Deltona	Taubman Centers
Hillwood	Washington Real Estate
Hines	Weingarten Realty

HISTORICAL FINANCIALS

Company Type: Public

Income Statement

FYE: December 31

	REVENUE ($ mil.)	NET INCOME ($ mil.)	NET PROFIT MARGIN	EMPLOYEES
12/17	1,100.1	168.4	15.3%	1,100
12/16	1,035.0	202.3	19.5%	1,100
12/15	797.0	126.7	15.9%	1,000
12/14	634.5	(23.5)	—	1,100
12/13	474.6	(73.7)	—	1,000
Annual Growth	23.4%	—	—	2.4%

2017 Year-End Financials

Debt ratio: 42.4%
Return on equity: 5.8%
Cash ($ mil.): 861.0
Current ratio: 1.56
Long-term debt ($ mil.): 2,857.9

No. of shares (mil.): 43.2
Dividends
Yield: —
Payout: —
Market value ($ mil.): 5,680.0

	STOCK PRICE ($) FY Close	P/E High/Low	PER SHARE ($) Earnings	Dividends	Book Value
12/17	131.27	32 26	3.91	0.00	73.56
12/16	114.10	24 16	4.73	0.00	64.53
12/15	113.16	50 34	1.60	0.00	59.43
12/14	130.42	— —	(0.60)	0.00	56.10
12/13	120.10	— —	(1.87)	0.00	56.56
Annual Growth	2.2%	— —	—	—	6.8%

Hudson Pacific Properties Inc

Hudson Pacific Properties wants to be the landlord to the stars. One of Hollywood's biggest landlords the real estate investment trust (REIT) buys and manages primarily office buildings but also and media and entertainment properties in California and the Pacific Northwest in cities such as Los Angeles Orange County San Diego San Francisco and Seattle. It owns more than 55 properties totaling some 15 million sq. ft. including two production studios on Hollywood's Sunset Boulevard. Its largest tenants range from tech giants such as Google Cisco Systems Uber to Hollywood producers including Warner Bros. Entertainment and Warner Music Group.

Operations

Hudson Pacific's portfolio consisted of 54 office properties spanning 14 million square feet and two Hollywood-based media and entertainment properties (the Sunset Gower property and Sunset Bronson property) with 0.9 million sq. ft. of space at the end of 2015.

Rental income from its office properties made up 93% of its total revenue that year while the media and entertainment properties accounted for the remainder.

Geographic Reach

The Los Angeles-based REIT's properties are mostly in Northern and Southern California and the Pacific Northwest (mainly in Seattle). Its target markets include Los Angeles Orange County San Diego San Francisco Seattle Silicon Valley the East Bay and the Pacific Northwest.

Sales and Marketing

The REIT's largest tenants during 2015 were Google Inc. and Weil Gotshal & Manges LLP which together made up 8% of its annualized base rent. Other major tenants included Riot Games Cisco Systems Uber Technologies Square Salesforce Warner Bros. Entertainment Warner Music Group. and EMC Corp.

Financial Performance

Hudson Pacific's annual revenues have more than quadrupled since 2011 thanks to rent-boosting property acquisitions and as rental rates have risen with increased demand for office properties in its target markets.

The REIT's revenue more than doubled to $520.8 million during 2015 on added rental income mostly stemming from its April 2015 acquisition of office properties from Blackstone which doubled the size of its portfolio. Same-store office property revenues rose 4.5% as the REIT signed new leases for Uber and Square at its 1455 Market property and a new lease for Sales Force at its Rincon Center property. Same-store media and entertainment property revenue dipped 1% as the REIT had to take certain buildings and stages offline to allow developers to work on its Sunset Bronson property.

Despite exceptional revenue growth and stable operating income in 2015 Hudson Pacific suffered a $16.08 million loss for the year due to a combination of interest expenses on long-term debt and acquisition-related expenses. The REIT's operating cash nearly tripled to $174.86 million during 2015 as it generated more in cash-based rental income.

Strategy

Hudson Pacific continued in 2016 to focus on acquiring office and media and entertainment properties situated in high barrier-to-entry submarkets in North and South California and in the Pacific Northwest. It also searches out distressed commercial properties in densely populated urban areas in these top markets where property is always in high demand.

In one of its most significant property acquisitions to date Hudson in April 2015 doubled its property holdings and reached further into the hot Silicon Valley real estate market through its $3.5 billion cash and stock purchase of 26 Bay Area office properties spanning 8.2 million sq. ft. from Blackstone Group. In mid-2015 the REIT also purchased the three-story 121000 sq.ft. "4th and Traction" manufacturing facility in Los Angeles's for $49 million; and a three-building 83200-sq. ft. redevelopment project in downtown Los Angeles' Arts District for $40 million.

Hudson also continues to expand in the fast-growing Seattle market. In February 2014 the REIT acquired an office building in Santa Monica California for $18.5 million and an office and retail property in downtown Seattle for $57.7 million. In July 2013 the company bought an 848001 square-foot office portfolio in Seattle from Spear Street Capital for approximately $368.4 million. The purchase included a two-building waterfront property in downtown Seattle occupied by tenants including Capital One and EMC Corp. and an office building occupied by Internet giant Amazon.com under a 10-year lease that commenced in late 2013.

Company Background

Hudson Pacific went public in June 2010 with an initial public offering worth $217.6 million. The firm used the proceeds from its IPO to pay off mortgage-related debt and acquire new properties.

Hudson Pacific Properties was founded by CEO Victor J. Coleman and President Howard S. Stern two former executives at another Los Angeles-based REIT Arden Realty. Arden Realty was sold to GE Real Estate in 2006.

EXECUTIVES

Chairman President and CEO, Victor J. Coleman, age 57, $600,000 total compensation
COO CFO and Treasurer, Mark T. Lammas, age 52, $450,000 total compensation
EVP Operations and Development, Christopher J. Barton, age 53, $375,000 total compensation
EVP Finance, Dale Shimoda, age 50, $300,000 total compensation
Chief Investment Officer, Alexander (Alex) Vouvalides, age 39, $310,000 total compensation
EVP General Counsel and Secretary, Kay L. Tidwell
SVP Northern California, Drew B. Gordon
SVP Southern California, Gary Hansel
SVP Pacific Northwest, David Tye
VICE PRESIDENT CONTROLLER, Elva Hernandez
Vice President of Engineering, Jim Soutter
Executive Vice President Operations, Josh Hatfield
Vice President Leasing, Jeff Lasky
Vice President Portfolio Management, Anne Mehrtens
Vice President of IT, Jeff Ballard
VICE PRESIDENT LEASING, Jeffrey Lasky
Auditors: Ernst & Young LLP

LOCATIONS

HQ: Hudson Pacific Properties Inc
11601 Wilshire Blvd., Ninth Floor, Los Angeles, CA 90025
Phone: 310 445-5700 **Fax:** 310 445-5710
Web: www.hudsonpacificproperties.com

PRODUCTS/OPERATIONS

2015 sales

	% of total
Non-Same-Store	57
Same-Store	43
Total	**100**

HUDSON PACIFIC MEDIA SERVICES
Catering
Control Room Rentals
Entertainment & Sports VIP Client Service
HD Camera Rentals
Lighting & Grip Rentals
Office / Facility Management
Production Office Space Rentals
Real Estate Professional Services
Recording Studio Rentals
Sound Stage Rentals

2015 Sales

	% of total
Office	
Rental	76
Tenant recoveries	13
Parking and other	4
Media & entertainment	
Rental	4
Tenant recoveries	0
Other property-related revenue	3
Others	0
Total	**100**

COMPETITORS

Douglas Emmett	Meredith Enterprises
EVOQ Properties	Newhall Land
Irvine Company	Pacific Office
J. H. Snyder	Properties Trust
Kilroy Realty	Watson Land Co.
Majestic Realty	

HISTORICAL FINANCIALS

Company Type: Public

Income Statement
FYE: December 31

	REVENUE ($ mil.)	NET INCOME ($ mil.)	NET PROFIT MARGIN	EMPLOYEES
12/17	728.1	68.5	9.4%	293
12/16	639.6	27.9	4.4%	257
12/15	520.8	(16.4)	—	234
12/14	253.4	9.9	3.9%	151
12/13	205.5	(14.8)	—	130
Annual Growth	**37.2%**	**—**		**22.5%**

2017 Year-End Financials

Debt ratio: 36.5%	No. of shares (mil.): 155.6
Return on equity: 2.0%	Dividends
Cash ($ mil.): 101.2	Yield: 0.0%
Current ratio: 0.77	Payout: 227.2%
Long-term debt ($ mil.): 2,421.3	Market value ($ mil.): 5,329.0

	STOCK PRICE ($) FY Close	P/E High/Low	PER SHARE ($) Earnings	Dividends	Book Value
12/17	34.25	83 72	0.44	1.00	23.44
12/16	34.78	136 88	0.25	0.80	22.81
12/15	28.14	— —	(0.19)	0.58	18.80
12/14	30.06	202143	0.15	0.50	17.81
12/13	21.87	— —	(0.27)	0.50	17.72
Annual Growth	**11.9%**		**—**	**18.9%**	**7.3%**

Hudson Technologies Inc

Hudson Technologies defends the ozone. Using proprietary reclamation technology to remove moisture and impurities from refrigeration systems it recovers and reclaims chlorofluorocarbons (CFCs) used in commercial air-conditioning and refrigeration systems. The company sells both reclaimed and new refrigerants and also buys used refrigerants for reclamation and sale. In addition Hudson Technologies offers on-site decontamination services as well as services designed to improve the efficiency of customers' refrigeration systems. Customers include commercial and industrial enterprises and government entities along with refrigerant contractors distributors and wholesalers and makers of refrigeration equipment.

To expand its presence both in the US and overseas Hudson Technologies formed an alliance with BOC Group a UK-based producer of industrial and specialty gases that has since been acquired by and integrated into Linde.

EXECUTIVES

VP Sales and Marketing, Charles F. Harkins Jr., age 54, $164,019 total compensation
Director Engineering, Joseph Longo
VP Legal and Regulatory and Secretary, Stephen P. Mandracchia, age 56, $129,879 total compensation
President COO and Director, Brian F. Coleman, age 54, $175,377 total compensation
Chairman and CEO, Kevin J. Zugibe, age 52, $198,021 total compensation
CFO, James R. Buscemi, age 63, $113,091 total compensation
Director Energy Assets and Optimization, Riyaz Papar
Account Manager All, Marla Waggoner
Vice President - Marketing, Greg Heilbrunn
President COO and Director, Brian F. Coleman, age 54
Director, Vincent P. Abbatecola, age 70
Director, Dominic J. Monetta, age 75
Director, Otto C. Morch, age 83
Auditors: BDO USA, LLP

LOCATIONS

HQ: Hudson Technologies Inc
1 Blue Hill Plaza, P.O. Box 1541, Pearl River, NY 10965
Phone: 845 735-6000
Web: www.hudsontech.com

PRODUCTS/OPERATIONS

2014 Sales

	% of total
Refrigerant and reclamation sales	90
RefrigerantSide	10
Total	**100**

COMPETITORS

Airgas	Hatco
C. C. Dickson	Kyzen

HISTORICAL FINANCIALS

Company Type: Public

Income Statement
FYE: December 31

	REVENUE ($ mil.)	NET INCOME ($ mil.)	NET PROFIT MARGIN	EMPLOYEES
12/17	140.3	11.1	7.9%	262
12/16	105.4	10.6	10.1%	137
12/15	79.7	4.7	6.0%	136
12/14	55.8	(0.7)	—	131
12/13	58.6	(5.8)	—	93
Annual Growth	**24.4%**	—	—	**29.6%**

2017 Year-End Financials

Debt ratio: 52.0%
Return on equity: 9.4%
Cash ($ mil.): 5.0
Current ratio: 2.19
Long-term debt ($ mil.): 101.1
No. of shares (mil.): 42.4
Dividends
Yield: —
Payout: —
Market value ($ mil.): 257.0

	STOCK PRICE ($) FY Close	P/E High/Low	PER SHARE ($) Earnings	Dividends	Book Value
12/17	6.07	35 20	0.26	0.00	2.91
12/16	8.01	27 9	0.30	0.00	2.70
12/15	2.97	30 18	0.14	0.00	1.51
12/14	3.77	— —	(0.02)	0.00	1.36
12/13	3.70	— —	(0.24)	0.00	1.12
Annual Growth	**13.2%**		—	—	**27.0%**

IBERIABANK Corp

Holding company IBERIABANK Corporation through its flagship bank subsidiary IBERIABANK operates some 230 branches in Louisiana and about 10 other states. It also has about 30 title insurance offices in Louisiana Arkansas and Tennessee in addition to some 90 mortgage loan offices in a dozen states and about 20 wealth management offices in four states. Offering deposit products such as checking and savings accounts CDs and IRAs the bank uses funds gathered mainly to make loans. Commercial loans and leases make up around two-thirds of the company's $22.3 billion loan portfolio which also includes consumer loans and residential mortgages. IBERIABANK Corp. has $30.1 billion in assets.

Operations

IBERIABANK operates through its IBERIABANK mortgage and LTC segments.

The IBERIABANK segment — which includes commercial and retail banking wealth management capital markets and other corporate functions — accounts for about 90% of revenue. Net interest income comprises about 85% of the segment's revenue. Commercial loans provide about 70% of the holding company's loan interest income; consumer and other loans generate about 20% of its loan interest income.

The mortgage segment accounts for nearly 10% of revenue. Through that business IBERIABANK originates funds and sells one-to-four family residential mortgages. Such loans accounts for about 10% of the company's loan interest income.

IBERIABANK offers title insurance and loan closing services through its LTC segment.

Geographic Reach

IBERIABANK operates about 330 combined offices including around 230 bank branch offices and two loan production offices in Louisiana Arkansas Tennessee Alabama Texas Florida Georgia South Carolina New York and North Carolina; about 30 title insurance offices in Arkansas Tennessee and Louisiana; and mortgage representatives at some 90 locations in 12 US states.

Some 40% 20% and 10% of the company's loans are in Florida Louisiana and Texas respectively.

Financial Performance

IBERIABANK has seen strong revenue and net income growth from 2013 to 2017 adding 82% and 119% respectively. Cash stores increased 60% to $625.7 million while long-term debt ballooned by 433% to $1.5 billion.

The holding company's revenue trended up 15% to $1 billion in 2017 compared with 2016 thanks to increased interest and fees from loans caused by improvements in loan yields and average earning assets. The growth was offset slightly by a decline in non-interest income primarily from the residential mortgage business.

Net income however fell 24% to $142.4 million in that time owing to non-interest expenses related to IBERIABANK's acquisition of southeastern Florida bank chain Sabadell United Bank and a $51 million increase in income tax expense caused by the 2017 Tax Cuts and Jobs Act.

The bank's cash stores were depleted by $736.4 million in 2017. Operations added $263.6 million and investments used $1.9 billion including $490.4 million for acquisitions. Financings added another $908.5 million from proceeds from long-term debt and common stock issuances.

Strategy

IBERIABANK announced its 2020 strategic goals in April 2018 which include improving operating efficiency using a “branch-lite” approach that involves digitalization of client services and back-office processes. Since 2012 the company has increased the proportion of its alternative transactions — including via online digital and smart device delivery systems — by 10 percentage points. The bank opened 28 offices and closed 11 branches in 2017 and scheduled more than 20 branch closures or consolidations for 2018.

In 2018 IBERIABANK also launched a mobile banking app introduced robotic process automation back offices created a mortgage self-fulfillment application and announced plans to update its internet banking website.

IBERIABANK is working to increase its presence in Miami Florida which holds $226 billion in total market deposits. IBERIABANK acquired Southeast Florida-based Sabadell United Bank in July 2017. The deal gave IBERIABANK 25 offices serving the Miami metropolitan area and three offices in Naples Sarasota and Tampa. In March 2018 the bank acquired Gibraltar Private Bank & Trust another Florida bank with seven offices in the Miami Key West and Naples metropolitan areas and one in New York City.

The bank owns around 90 branches in Florida with about $9 billion total deposits. The company has significantly increased its presence in Florida; since 2014 it has grown the share of its portfolio comprising loans and deposits in that state by 13 and 22 percentage points respectively. Other growth markets for the company include Dallas and Houston as well as Atlanta Orlando and Tampa.

Mergers and Acquisitions

Since 2008 IBERIABANK has made more than 20 acquisitions of live and failing banks branches and wealth management and title insurance companies.

IBERIABANK acquired Gibraltar Private Bank & Trust another Florida bank in March 2018 for about $214.7 million. Gibraltar had seven offices in the Miami Key West and Naples metropolitan areas and one in New York City prior to the acquisition. The agreement conferred $1.5 billion in loans and $1.1 billion in deposits to IBERIABANK's portfolio.

The bank acquired SolomonParks Title & Escrow in January 2018 for $3.3 million thereby gaining eight title offices in the Nashville Tennessee area.

In July 2017 IBERIABANK acquired Southeast Florida-based Sabadell United Bank for $809.2 million in cash and 2.6 million IBERIABANK shares. The deal gave IBERIABANK $4 billion in loans and $4.4 billion in deposits as well as 25 offices serving the Miami metropolitan area and three offices in Naples Sarasota and Tampa.

Company Background

IBERIABANK was founded in 1887 in New Iberia Louisiana. It operated in just two states - Louisiana and Arkansas - until 2008 when it began spreading across the Southeast.

EXECUTIVES

President and CEO, Daryl G. Byrd, age 63, $1,015,000 total compensation

SEVP Mergers and Acquisitions Finance and Investor Relations; Director Financial Strategy and Mortgage, John R. Davis, age 57, $456,154 total compensation

Vice Chairman and Managing Director of Brokerage Trust and Wealth Management, Jefferson G. (Jeff) Parker, age 65, $480,192 total compensation

SEVP and Director Communications Facilities and Human Resources, Elizabeth A. (Beth) Ardoin, age 49

SEVP and CFO, Anthony J. Restel, age 48, $480,385 total compensation

Vice Chairman; SEVP and COO, Michael J. (Mike) Brown, age 54, $598,269 total compensation

President and CEO IberiaBank Mortgage, Bill Edwards

EVP and Director Retail Small Business and Mortgage, Robert M. (Bob) Kottler, age 59

EVP and Executive Credit Officer, H. Spurgeon Mackie, age 67

EVP and Chief Risk Officer, J. Randolph Bryan, age 50

EVP Corporate Secretary and General Counsel, Robert B. Worley, age 58

President and CEO Lender's Title Company, David B. Erb

Assistant Vice President Retail Support Specialist, Sheila Montgomery

Senior Vice President, Steve Krueger

Assistant Vice President, Dolores Hernandez

Vice President, Tom Chelewski

Vice President Bcs Ore Officer, Neel Stacy

Vice President, Bruce Reid

Vice President Support Services, Jerry Prejean

Vice President And Senior Business Relationship Manager, Ty Powell

Executive Vice President, Ken Brown

Vice President Commercial Lending, Jeremy Young

Assistant Vice President, Misty Labat

Vice President, Mary Rice

Senior Vice President Network Support Manager, Chris Berthaut

Vice President, Nancy Dost

Vice President Business Banking, Shannon Pemberton

Senior Vice President, Missy S Krantz

Vice President, Craig Peak

Senior Vice President, Greg Mendez

Vice President Of Product Management, Paula Allred

Senior Vice President, Eric Movassaghi

Vice President Retail Administration, Linda Swinkey

Vice President ORE Property Manager, Brian Buczko

Senior Vice President Corporate Banking, C Mizelle

Vice President, Michael Hallmark

Vice President Branch Manager Business Development Officer, Pedro Diaz

Vice President Business Credit Services Officer, Michael Schaefer

Vice President Business Credit Services, Timothy Wilson

Vice President Human Resources, Jayne Socotch

Vice President, Howard Mary

Senior Vice President Commercial Banking, Holly Popham

Vice President Finance, Joel Jewell

Vice President Human Resources And Employee Development And Training, Mike Pelletier

Vice President Controllera, Angela Robert

Senior Vice President, Pat Yates

Vice President Business Credit Services, David Krage

Bank Manager Vice President, Melanie Savell

Executive Vice President And Director Enterprise Risk Ma, Elise Latimer

Senior Vice President And Commercial Rel, Jamey Vaught

Vice President Corporate Security, Warren Bujol

Executive Vice President, Beth Ardoin

Vice President Benefits and Recruiting Director, Greg Rizzuto

Senior Vice President, Richard Perdue

Executive Vice President, Norman Vascocu

Vice President Business Banking, William Biossat

Vice President Compliance Officer, Winifred Stamps

Treasury Management Consultant And Vice President, Steven Perez

Mortgage Executive Vice President, Susie Boudreaux

Senior Vice President And Business And Retail Market Manger, Maurice Butler

Senior Vice President Consumer Credit Risk Director, Wayne Stone

VICE PRESIDENT, William Morrow

Senior Vice President Business Credit Se, Fred Malzahn

Senior Vice President and Manager of Financial Analytics, Shawn Jordan

Vice President Branch Manager, Samantha McDermott

Vice President Commercial Relationship Manager, Layne Dodd

Vice President Mortgage Executive, Mark Young

Senior Vice President Special Assets Manager, Karen Repas

Vice President Mortgage Executive, Connie Fernandez

Senior Vice President Treasury Management, Kathaleen Parks

Assistant Vice President, Felesha Finch

Vice President Central Retail Administration, Donna Pye

Vice President Corporate Counsel, Lynn Dodd

Assistant Vice President Relationship Manager, Millard Morrison

Senior Vice President, Mary Morgan

Vice President, Linda Rodriguez

Vice President Private Banking Relationship Manager, Carrie Standlee

Vice President Business Banking, Tim Finn

Vice President, Cody Walker

Vice President, Leigh Seago

Vice President, Matthew Rink

Vice President Deposit Operations, Felicia Weeks

Senior Vice President, Doug Woodman

Vice President Quality Control, Cheryl Terry

Vice President, Marc Massad

Senior Vice President Commercial Relationship Manager Assistant Rebecca Oberg, Kelly Gegerson

Vice President, Karen Hardy

Vice President Manager Commercial Cash Vault, Anna Taylor

Business Intelligence Analyst Assistant Vice President, Kevin Cagle

Assistant Vice President Business Banking Relationship Manager, Deborah Sefcik

Senior Vice President Private Lending Relationship Manager, Maria Ferrer

Assistant Vice President Retail Support Specialist, Heather Wade

Assistant Vice President, Christie Bell

Asst. Vice President Branch Manager, Tamela Leger

Vice President Treasury Management Operations Manager, Kevin Northcutt

Assistant Vice President, Erica Murphy

Vice President Private Banking, Casey Lawhead

Vice President Treasury Management Product Management, Cindy Wolbach

Assistant Vice President Branch Manager, Colleen Lemoine

Vp Business Banking Relationship Manager, Kristen Strickland

Vice President Retail Support Lead, Terri Bridges

Executive Vice President and Commercial Group Manager, John Reingardt

Senior Vice President Compliance Manager Central Florida CRA Liaison, Susan DeFreese

Vice President, Glenn O'Leary

Vice President Human Resources Manager, Karla Newan

Vice President Treasury Management Implementations Manager, Megan Alesci

VICE PRESIDENT AND COMMERCIAL RELATIONSHIP MANAGER, Kevin Tarleton

Vice President Senior Business Analyst Development Officer, Martin Chapman

Assistant Vice President Branch Manager, Heather Ross

Senior Vice President, Michael Alcantar

Vice President Relationship Manager, Amy Moore

Senior Vice President Commercial Manager Collin County, Shannon Bettis

Chairman, William H. Fenstermaker, age 69

Vice Chairman, E. Stewart Shea, age 66

Board Member, Angus Cooper

Board Member, Rick Maples

Auditors: Ernst & Young LLP

LOCATIONS

HQ: IBERIABANK Corp
200 West Congress Street, Lafayette, LA 70501
Phone: 337 521-4003
Web: www.iberiabank.com

COMPETITORS

BancorpSouth	Investar
Bank of America	JPMorgan Chase
Bank of the Ozarks	Louisiana Bancorp
Capital One	MidSouth Bancorp
Hancock Holding	Regions Financial
Home Banc	Teche Holding

HISTORICAL FINANCIALS

Company Type: Public

Income Statement

FYE: December 31

	ASSETS ($ mil.)	NET INCOME ($ mil.)	INCOME AS % OF ASSETS	EMPLOYEES
12/17	27,904.1	142.4	0.5%	3,604
12/16	21,659.1	186.7	0.9%	3,155
12/15	19,504.0	142.8	0.7%	3,216
12/14	15,758.6	105.4	0.7%	2,825
12/13	13,365.5	65.1	0.5%	2,638
Annual Growth	20.2%	21.6%	—	8.1%

2017 Year-End Financials

Return on assets: 0.5%
Return on equity: 4.2%
Long-term debt ($ mil.): —
No. of shares (mil.): 53.8
Sales ($ mil): 1,124.8

Dividends
Yield: 0.0%
Payout: 56.3%
Market value ($ mil.): 4,175.0

	STOCK PRICE ($) FY Close	P/E High/Low	PER SHARE ($) Earnings	Dividends	Book Value
12/17	77.50	33 27	2.59	1.46	68.62
12/16	83.75	21 10	4.30	1.40	65.62
12/15	55.07	19 15	3.68	1.36	60.74
12/14	64.85	22 18	3.30	1.36	55.39
12/13	62.85	29 20	2.20	1.36	51.40
Annual Growth	5.4%	— —	4.2%	1.8%	7.5%

Ichor Holdings Ltd

Auditors: KPMG LLP

LOCATIONS

HQ: Ichor Holdings Ltd
3185 Laurelview Court, Fremont, CA 94538
Phone: 510 897-5200
Web: www.ichorsystems.com

HISTORICAL FINANCIALS

Company Type: Public

Income Statement

FYE: December 29

	REVENUE ($ mil.)	NET INCOME ($ mil.)	NET PROFIT MARGIN	EMPLOYEES
12/17	655.8	56.4	8.6%	1,760
12/16	405.7	16.6	4.1%	787
12/15	290.6	5.6	1.9%	671
12/14	249.0	6.1	2.5%	0
Annual Growth	38.1%	109.2%	—	—

2017 Year-End Financials

Debt ratio: 33.4%
Return on equity: 31.6%
Cash ($ mil.): 69.3
Current ratio: 1.89
Long-term debt ($ mil.): 180.2

No. of shares (mil.): 25.8
Dividends
Yield: —
Payout: —
Market value ($ mil.): —

	STOCK PRICE ($) FY Close	P/E High/Low	PER SHARE ($) Earnings	Dividends	Book Value
12/17	0.00	— —	2.15	0.00	8.37
Annual Growth	—	— —	—	—	—

ICU Medical Inc

ICU Medical sees the future of infection prevention. The company's devices protect health care workers and patients from the spread of diseases such as HIV and hepatitis. Its primary products are intravenous (IV) connection devices called Clave needleless connectors that reduce the risk of needle sticks and disconnections. The firm also makes custom IV sets many of which use Clave connectors and other ICU products for third parties. Additionally ICU Medical makes critical care equipment such as angiography kits and heart monitors. ICU Medical sells its products to other equipment makers and distributors throughout the US and internationally.

Operations

ICU Medical develops makes and sells innovative medical devices used in vascular therapy oncology and critical care applications. Its products improve patient outcomes by helping prevent bloodstream infections and protecting health care workers from exposure to infectious diseases or hazardous drugs. The company's products include custom IV systems closed delivery systems for hazardous drugs needlefree IV connectors catheters and cardiac monitoring systems. About 70% of total revenue comes from infusion therapy services while critical care accounts about 20%: the remainder comes from oncology and other services.

Geographic Reach

The company sells its products to more than 60 countries in Europe the Middle East Africa the Asia/Pacific region Latin America and North America. Its administrative office are in San Clemente California; Vrable Slovakia; Roncanova Italy; Utrecht Netherlands; Bella Vista Australia; and Ludenscheid Germany. Customers in Europe are served by facilities in Slovakia and Germany. Customers elsewhere are served from facilities in the US and Mexico. ICU Medical operates a plant in Mexico with about 1350 workers in Ensenada; it has another plant in Vrable Slovakia (with about 240 employees). The company also maintains a plant in Salt Lake City Utah.

The US accounted for about 70% of total revenue in 2014.

Sales and Marketing

On the sales side the company is increasingly directing its marketing efforts toward securing long-term contracts with large buying organizations. ICU Medical is reacting to an increasingly consolidated health care provider marketplace because the providers have more buying power as they get larger. Long-term contracts help the company lock in prices even as the market changes around them.

Medical device maker Hospira is ICU Medical's biggest customer - it accounts for around 35% of revenue annually.

The company also sells to independent distributors and to end users through a direct sales force.

In 2014 advertising expenses totaled $0.1 million down from $0.3 million in 2013 and $0.2 million in 2012.

Financial Performance

After several years of increasing revenue in 2013 ICU Medical reported a 10% decrease from $316.9 million to $313.7 million due to lower infusion therapy sales to key American customer Hospira. Revenue fell a marginal 1% to $309 million in 2014 for the same reason. Higher international and critical care revenue helped offset the decline.

Net income has been falling the last few years and 2014 delivered a 35% drop to $26 million on lower sales and higher operating expenses (including R&D and restructuring costs). Cash flow from operations has also been on a slow decline: In 2014 it fell 8% to $61 million due to the decrease in net income and a change in inventories.

Strategy

ICU Medical has a long-standing relationship with Hospira. Way back in 2005 ICU Medical purchased Hospira's Salt Lake City manufacturing plant which produces catheters angiography kits and cardiac monitors among other devices. At that time the two entered a 20-year agreement under which ICU Medical will manufacture the products and Hospira will purchase them. Then in 2009 ICU Medical purchased the commercial rights and physical assets from Hospira's critical care product line giving ICU Medical complete control of manufacturing and marketing rights of the critical care line.

Through yet another agreement with Hospira ICU Medical makes and co-promotes custom IV systems under the name SetSource. That agreement is set to last through 2018. All told sales to Hospira account for about 35% of ICU Medical's yearly income.

Aside from bringing home the bacon ICU Medical's dealings with Hospira provide ICU Medical access to the IV set market in the US in which Hospira has a significant share. The company expects Hospira will be important to growing its CLAVE line custom infusion sets and its other products worldwide.

Outside of its dealings with Hospira ICU Medical's growth strategy hinges upon its ability to continue to develop and introduce new products to its customers particularly in the face of upcoming patent expirations on some of its products. Much like pharmaceutical companies medical device manufacturers enjoy a certain amount of market exclusivity on their patented products but once those patents expire competitors are free to introduce their own versions of the devices.

ICU Medical is preparing for patent expirations by diversifying its product line internally developing products and systems and by acquiring product lines. These products include the TEGO for use in dialysis the Orbit 90 diabetes set and a line of oncology products including the Spiros male luer connector device the Genie vial access device custom IV sets and ancillary products specifically designed for chemotherapy. The company is busy working on a new hemodynamic monitor part of its Critical Care business.

Mergers and Acquisitions

In 2015 ICU Medical acquired the New Jersey-based Excelsior Medical Corporation a medical device maker also focused on infection prevention for $59.5 million.

In early 2017 the company acquired Pfizer's global infusion therapy business Hospira Infusion Systems for $1 billion. The deal creates a company with a complete IV therapy product portfolio.

EXECUTIVES

Vice President Marketing, Evelyn Foss
Chairman President and CEO, George A. Lopez, age 71, $690,100 total compensation
VP Operations, Steven C. (Steve) Riggs, age 60, $339,900 total compensation
CEO, Vivek Jain, age 57
CFO Secretary and Treasurer, Scott E. Lamb, age 56, $378,448 total compensation
President Europe, Gabriele Giovanelli
Vice President of Quality Assurance and Regulatory Affairs, Dan Wait
Vice President International Sales and Marketing, Gregory P Pratt
Vice President Quality and Regulatory Affairs, Krishna Uppugonduri
Vice President General Counsel, Virginia Sanzone
Medical Director, JW Beard
Auditors: DELOITTE & TOUCHE LLP

LOCATIONS

HQ: ICU Medical Inc
951 Calle Amanecer, San Clemente, CA 92673
Phone: 949 366-2183
Web: www.icumed.com

PRODUCTS/OPERATIONS

2014 Sales

	% of total
Infusion Therapy	70
Critical Care	18
Oncology	12
Other	-
Total	**100**

COMPETITORS

B. Braun Melsungen	Edwards Lifesciences
Baxter International	Fresenius
Becton Dickinson	Merit Medical Systems
Cardinal Health	Navilyst Medical
CareFusion	

HISTORICAL FINANCIALS

Company Type: Public

Income Statement

FYE: December 31

	REVENUE ($ mil.)	NET INCOME ($ mil.)	NET PROFIT MARGIN	EMPLOYEES
12/17	1,292.6	68.6	5.3%	6,802
12/16	379.3	63.0	16.6%	2,803
12/15	341.6	44.9	13.2%	2,446
12/14	309.2	26.3	8.5%	2,280
12/13	313.7	40.4	12.9%	2,269
Annual Growth	**42.5%**	**14.2%**	**—**	**31.6%**

2017 Year-End Financials

Debt ratio: —
Return on equity: 7.3%
Cash ($ mil.): 300.1
Current ratio: 4.11
Long-term debt ($ mil.): —
No. of shares (mil.): 20.2
Dividends
  Yield: —
  Payout: —
Market value ($ mil.): 4,365.0

	STOCK PRICE ($) FY Close	P/E High/Low		PER SHARE ($) Earnings	Dividends	Book Value
12/17	216.00	63	38	3.29	0.00	59.29
12/16	147.35	39	22	3.66	0.00	40.41
12/15	112.78	43	28	2.73	0.00	36.05
12/14	81.90	50	32	1.68	0.00	32.59
12/13	63.71	28	20	2.65	0.00	30.77
Annual Growth	**35.7%**	**—**	**—**	**5.6%**	**—**	**17.8%**

Idexx Laboratories, Inc.

IDEXX can identify what's wrong with Fluffy Fido Flossie or Flicka. A leading animal health care company IDEXX develops manufactures and distributes products for pets livestock dairy and poultry markets. Veterinarians use the company's VetTest analyzers for blood and urine chemistry and its SNAP in-office test kits to detect heartworms feline leukemia and other diseases. The company also provides lab testing services and practice management software. In addition IDEXX makes products to test for contaminants in water. The company sells its products worldwide but the Americas account for more than half of its total revenue.

Operations

IDEXX operates through three primary segments: Companion Animal Group (CAG) Water Quality Products (Water) and Livestock Poultry and Dairy (LPD).

Products and services for companion animals (aka: pets) account for more than 80% of IDEXX's sales. Most of that revenue comes from diagnostic products and services including chemistry analyzers rapid test kits and laboratory services. The company operates a network of laboratories to which vets can send patient samples for analysis.

The LPD segment (horses cows pigs and chickens) is the second-largest business bringing in about 10% of total revenue. The segment sells diagnostic tests services and related instrumentation. Its products can test for Bovine Spongiform Encephalopathy (BSE or "mad cow" disease) as well as porcine illnesses and poultry diseases. Equine products make up a smaller portion of the company's sales.

The Water segment (about 5% of sales) makes tests which detect coliforms and E. coli in water. Water utilities and government laboratories are the primary customers for these products.

The company also makes and distributes diagnostics for the human market but those are not a substantial part of its business

Geographic Reach

More than half of IDEXX's sales are made in the US but it also maintains sales offices outside the US in Africa the Asia/Pacific region Europe the Middle East North America and Latin America. Many of its products and materials are manufactured by third parties but the company also maintains manufacturing and assembly facilities in Georgia and Maine and in Bern Switzerland and Montpellier France.

Sales and Marketing

IDEXX distributes its products through its own marketing and sales force and through independent distributors and resellers. In the US it solely relies on internal sales representatives to sell its companion animal diagnostics products.

Financial Performance

IDEXX's revenue has been growing for the past five years and in 2017 it rose 11% to $2 billion. This was due to increases in both product and sales revenues. In the CAG segment growth was driven by higher demand for lab diagnostics services and VetLab consumables as well as higher prices for certain products. Higher prices also boosted returns for the Water segment as did higher sales of the Colilert line of E. coli tests in the Asia/Pacific region and North America. The LPD segment had higher sales of swine tests in China as well as pregnancy tests in Europe and North America.

Thanks to the increasing revenues net income has also been on the rise. It increased 19% to $263.1 million in 2017. Similarly operating cash flow rose 10% to $373.3 million.

Strategy

IDEXX continues to grow by focusing on launching new products and consumables for its instruments and test kits. For example in 2017 it installed some 4000 new chemistry analyzers more than half of which were sold to new customers. These installations are a good sign of recurring revenue for the company as customers will then typically buy related consumables. New products include the SediVue DX urine sediment analyzer designed for use in veterinary clinics and the Catalyst SDMA Test to test for kidney disease.

The company enhances its offerings with companion software for veterinarians.

HISTORY

David Shaw founded IDEXX in 1984 as AgriTech Systems. An MBA who had specialized in agribusiness consulting Shaw wanted to cut the costs and time involved in lab testing for diseases by producing kits that could be used on-site; an initial line of poultry disease tests proved successful. The company changed its name to IDEXX in 1988 and went public in 1991.

In 1994 IDEXX acquired AMIS International a leading Japanese test lab for veterinarians. The next year the company opened offices in Spain and the Netherlands and introduced the SNAP test which detects allergies in dogs.

In 1997 IDEXX acquired two software companies Advanced Veterinary Systems and Professionals Software and merged them to create IDEXX Informatics. That year the firm also bought Acumedia Manufacturers a producer of more than 300 varieties of dehydrated culture media. Looking to expand into animal drug development the company bought animal health firm Blue Ridge Pharmaceuticals in 1998. In 2000 IDEXX sold Acumedia as well as its food microbiology operations. It also launched VetConnect.com which provides veterinary information and support and product sales.

In 2008 the company sold its veterinary pharmaceutical operations which were miniscule to focus on its core test kit and consumable business.

EXECUTIVES

Vice President of Purchasing, Rick Cotta
Chairman President and CEO, Jonathan W. (Jon) Ayers, age 61, $800,000 total compensation

EVP CFO and Treasurer, Brian P. McKeon, age 56, $496,153 total compensation

EVP, Johnny D. Powers, age 56, $416,923 total compensation

EVP, Michael J. Williams, age 50, $416,923 total compensation

EVP, Jay Mazelsky, $416,923 total compensation

Vice President Human Resource, Sue Rochon

Vice President General Manager, Scott Hamilton

Facilities Maintenance Senior Vice President Senior, Michael Flaherty

Vice President, George Fennell

Vice President and General Manager, Mike Erickson

Vice President Finance, Bob Burns

Vice President of Information Technology, Alexander Peterson

Vice President, Daniel Meyaard

Vice President, Kathy Turner

Corporate Vice President Research and Development, Jeffrey Thomas

Vice President of Strategy and Business Development, Kerry Bennett

Corporate Vice President Sales Marketing and Business Development, Tj Dupree

Vice President of Information Technology, Arin Brost

Corporate Vice President General Counsel and Secretary, Jackie Studer

Board Member, Rebecca Henderson

Board Member, Christine Lane

Board Member, Daniel M Junius

Auditors: PricewaterhouseCoopers LLP

LOCATIONS

HQ: Idexx Laboratories, Inc.
One IDEXX Drive, Westbrook, ME 04092
Phone: 207 556-0300   **Fax:** 207 856-0346
Web: www.idexx.com

PRODUCTS/OPERATIONS

2016 Sales

	$ mil.	% of total
CAG	1,522.7	86
Water	103.6	6
LPD	126.5	7
Other	22.6	1
Total	**1,775.4**	**100**

2016 Sales

	$ mil.	% of total
Product	1,071.0	60
Service	704.4	40
Total	**1,775.4**	**100**

COMPETITORS

Abaxis	Neogen
Abbott Labs	Sdix
Henry Schein	VCA
Heska	Zoetis
Instrumentation	
Laboratory Company	

HISTORICAL FINANCIALS

Company Type: Public

Income Statement
FYE: December 31

	REVENUE ($ mil.)	NET INCOME ($ mil.)	NET PROFIT MARGIN	EMPLOYEES
12/17	1,969.0	263.1	13.4%	7,600
12/16	1,775.4	222.0	12.5%	7,365
12/15	1,601.8	192.0	12.0%	6,800
12/14	1,485.8	181.9	12.2%	6,400
12/13	1,377.0	187.8	13.6%	5,700
Annual Growth	**9.4%**	**8.8%**	**—**	**7.5%**

2017 Year-End Financials

Debt ratio: 73.6%	No. of shares (mil.): 87.1
Return on equity: ***,***.*%	Dividends
Cash ($ mil.): 187.6	Yield: —
Current ratio: 0.97	Payout: —
Long-term debt ($ mil.): 606.0	Market value ($ mil.): 13,621.0

	STOCK PRICE ($) FY Close	P/E High/Low	PER SHARE ($) Earnings	Dividends	Book Value
12/17	156.38	57 39	2.94	0.00	(0.62)
12/16	117.27	49 26	2.44	0.00	(1.23)
12/15	72.92	81 30	2.05	0.00	(0.93)
12/14	148.27	84 58	1.79	0.00	1.24
12/13	106.37	62 47	1.74	0.00	5.03
Annual Growth	**10.1%**	**—**	**14.0%**	**—**	**—**

II-VI Inc

II-VI could play a mean game of laser tag but it's more interested in making things. The company (its name is pronounced "two-six") makes lenses mirrors prisms and other optical components and materials. II-VI's clients — drawn from the aerospace health care industrial military and telecom equipment sectors — use these components in lasers and other systems used in precision manufacturing communications networks military targeting and navigation systems and other applications. The company has manufacturing operations throughout the US as well as in Asia and Germany. Customers have included Caterpillar Volkswagen Raytheon and the US government.

Operations

II-VI's biggest source of revenue is its Laser Solutions unit which accounts for 39% of sales. It is followed by Photonics 35% of revenue and Performance Products 26%.

Geographic Reach

The US is II-VI's largest market accounting for 32% of its sales. China is next representing more than 19% of annual sales while Hong Kong represents about 15% and Germany 10%. The company has production facilities in 10 US states including its home state of Pennsylvania and half a dozen foreign countries such as China and Vietnam.

Financial Performance

II-VI's sales have increased each of past six years. The company set another revenue record for itself in 2015 (ended June) posting $742 million in sale — a 9% increase from 2014. Its photonics segment paced sales for the year with a 20% increase based on customer demand for optical fil-

ters optical components and assemblies pump lasers and fiber amplifier modules. Sales in the Performance Products unit however fell 9%.

Net income shot up 71% in 2015 as II-VI began to realize contributions from acquisitions that resulted in bigger market share higher revenue and operationing efficiencies. Net income was $66 million in 2015 compared to $38 million the year before. Net earnings also benefited from a one-time settlement related to obligations from previous acquisitions of $7.1 million (after-tax).

II-VI had $1299 million cash flow from operations in 2015 compared to $95 million in 2014.

Strategy

II-VI continued a restructuring program in its Photonics and Performance Products segments to adjust costs. It recorded after-tax restructuring charges of $4.1 million in 2015 compared to $3.4 million in f2014.

Research and development is vital to the company's success. Indeed II-VI aims to invest between 5% and 7% of its revenues each year in R&D (the figure was 6.9% in 2015). Its recent focus has been in silicon carbide substrates chemical vapor deposition (CVD) synthetic diamond materials photonics and thermoelectric materials and devices. II-VI uses a mix of internal and external funding for most areas but devotes only internal funds to CVD diamond and photonics.

II-VI's Pacific Rare Specialty Metals & Chemicals (PRM) subsidiary in 2013 discontinued its tellurium line and downsized its selenium production line to focus on providing selenium metal to the company's Infrared Optics business while distancing the business from volatile metal index price fluctuations. !—[if gte mso 9]

The company uses acquisitions to build its business around core strengths in engineered materials and components.

Mergers and Acquisitions

In early 2016 II-VI agreed to buy two businesses to expand its technology platforms and production capacity for semiconductor lasers for $110 million. The acquisitions of EpiWorks and ANADIGICS position II-VI for the fast-growing markets for Vertical Cavity Surface Emitting Lasers (VCSELs). The lasers are used in consumer electronics data centers sensing medical and industrial markets.

In September 2013 the company acquired the Switzerland-based semiconductor laser business of Oclaro Inc. for $115 million. II-VI will operate the newly acquired business as II-VI Laser Enterprise GmbH.

In 2012 it bought Connecticut-based M Cubed Technologies for about $71 million and California-based LightWorks Optics for about half that amount. M Cubed manufactures advanced ceramic materials and precision motion control products and LightWorks supplies advanced optical systems used in defense aerospace and commercial operations. The prior year brought the acquisition of Massachusetts-based Aegis Lightwave for $52 million. Aegis' tunable optical devices are used to expand bandwidth in high speed optical networks and will contribute to II-VI's near-infrared optics business.

HISTORY

Electrical engineer Carl Johnson who had worked at Bell Labs (now part of Alcatel-Lucent) among other companies founded II-VI in 1971 to produce infrared optical materials for the emerging laser market. These materials — including cadmium zinc telluride zinc selenide and zinc sulfide — gave the company its name; they are from the "two-six" family of materials. (Cadmium and zinc are from column two on the periodic table; tellurium and selenium are from column six.)

By the 1980s II-VI was the leading maker of optical components for carbon dioxide lasers. The company went public in 1987 and the next year added a factory in Singapore.

EXECUTIVES

VP Military and Materials Businesses, James Martinelli, age 58, $194,000 total compensation
President and CEO, Francis J. Kramer, age 67, $433,000 total compensation
Chairman, Carl J. Johnson, age 74, $212,000 total compensation
CFO and Treasurer, Craig A. Creaturo, age 46, $227,125 total compensation
EVP, Vincent D. (Chuck) Mattera Jr., age 60, $208,500 total compensation
Secretary, Robert D. German
Director, Marc Y. E. Pelaez, age 70
Director, Joseph J. (Joe) Corasanti, age 52
President CEO and Director, Francis J. Kramer, age 66
Director, Wendy F. DiCicco, age 49
Director, Peter W. Sognefest, age 75
Director, Thomas E. Mistler, age 74
Independent Director, Howard Xia
Auditors: Ernst & Young LLP

LOCATIONS

HQ: II-VI Inc
375 Saxonburg Boulevard, Saxonburg, PA 16056
Phone: 724 352-4455
Web: www.ii-vi.com

COMPETITORS

AXSUN Technologies
CVI Laser
Coherent Inc.
CoorsTek
Cree
Cymer
DRS Technologies
Dow Corning
Ferrotec
Goodrich Corp.
Jenoptik
Komatsu
Laird Technologies
LightPath
Newport Corp.
Nippon Steel & Sumitomo Metal Corporation
Northrop Grumman
Oplink Communications
Orbotech
ROFIN-SINAR
Raytheon
Saint-Gobain
Spectra-Physics
Sumitomo Electric
Umicore
Zygo

HISTORICAL FINANCIALS

Company Type: Public

Income Statement
FYE: June 30

	REVENUE ($ mil.)	NET INCOME ($ mil.)	NET PROFIT MARGIN	EMPLOYEES
06/18	1,158.7	88.0	7.6%	11,443
06/17	972.0	95.2	9.8%	10,349
06/16	827.2	65.4	7.9%	8,927
06/15	741.9	65.9	8.9%	8,490
06/14	683.2	38.4	5.6%	6,796
Annual Growth	14.1%	23.0%	—	13.9%

2018 Year-End Financials

Debt ratio: 24.9%
Return on equity: 9.1%
Cash ($ mil.): 247.0
Current ratio: 3.22
Long-term debt ($ mil.): 419.0

No. of shares (mil.): 63.3
Dividends
  Yield: —
  Payout: —
Market value ($ mil.): 2,750.0

	STOCK PRICE ($) FY Close	P/E High/Low	Earnings	Dividends	Book Value
06/18	43.45	38 24	1.35	0.00	16.18
06/17	34.30	26 12	1.48	0.00	14.26
06/16	18.76	22 14	1.04	0.00	12.64
06/15	18.98	18 10	1.05	0.00	11.91
06/14	14.46	33 21	0.60	0.00	10.98
Annual Growth	31.7%	— —	22.5%	—	10.2%

Independence Realty Trust Inc

Auditors: KPMG LLP

LOCATIONS

HQ: Independence Realty Trust Inc
Two Liberty Place, 50 S. 16th Street, Suite 3575, Philadelphia, PA 19102
Phone: 267 270-4800
Web: www.irtliving.com

HISTORICAL FINANCIALS

Company Type: Public

Income Statement
FYE: December 31

	REVENUE ($ mil.)	NET INCOME ($ mil.)	NET PROFIT MARGIN	EMPLOYEES
12/17	161.2	30.2	18.7%	421
12/16	153.3	(9.8)		395
12/15	109.5	28.2	25.8%	0
12/14	49.2	2.9	6.0%	0
12/13	19.9	0.6	3.1%	0
Annual Growth	68.6%	163.7%	—	—

2017 Year-End Financials

Debt ratio: 53.6%
Return on equity: 5.3%
Cash ($ mil.): 9.9
Current ratio: 1.30
Long-term debt ($ mil.): 778.4

No. of shares (mil.): 84.7
Dividends
  Yield: 0.0%
  Payout: 175.6%
Market value ($ mil.): 855.0

	STOCK PRICE ($) FY Close	P/E High/Low	Earnings	Dividends	Book Value
12/17	10.09	26 21	0.41	0.72	7.37
12/16	8.92	— —	(0.19)	0.72	7.35
12/15	7.51	13 9	0.78	0.72	7.74
12/14	9.31	76 59	0.14	0.72	7.90
12/13	8.34	73 66	0.12	0.27	7.76
Annual Growth	4.9%	— —	36.0%	28.2%	(1.3%)

Independent Bank Group Inc.

It makes sense that a company that calls itself Independent Bank Group (IBG) would do business in a state that was once its own country. The bank holding company does business through subsidiary Independent Bank which operates about 40 banking offices and 70 branches in North and Central Texas Houston and Colorado. The banks offer standard personal and business accounts and services including some focused on small business owners. IBG has total assets of nearly $8.9 billion and loans of about $6.4 billion. The company traces its roots back 100 years but took its current shape in 2002.

Operations

In addition to its banking activities Independent Bank Group (IBG)also owns IBG Adriatica a mixed use development in the Dallas-Fort Worth area. The company does not intend to move into real estate but purchased the development where one of its branches is located to help maintain business in the area. It had also made commercial loans to several tenants of the development and saw the purchase as a way to protect its investments rather than have the entire property go into foreclosure.

Financial Performance

Independent Bank Group has shown increasing net income for several years and in fiscal 2016 grew revenue a further 20% to $210.0 million. Net income has likewise been consistently growing reaching $53.5 million up 39%. Cash from operations increased 85% to $80.3 million.

Strategy

Independent Bank Group's strategy is all about growth. It seeks organic growth in loans and deposits in existing locations by developing customer relationships while maintaining the quality of its loan portfolio. It also makes acquisitions: since 2010 it has made nine acquisitions most recently of Carlile Bancshares and its subsidiary Northstar Bank and Grand Bank in Dallas.

Mergers and Acquisitions

Independent Bank Group acquired Carlile Bancshares and its subsidiary Northstar Bank for around $434 million in 2017.

EXECUTIVES

Chairman President and CEO, David R. Brooks, age 60, $650,000 total compensation
EVP and COO, James C. (Jim) White, age 53

Vice Chairman and Chief Lending Officer and
President Independent Bank Central Texas, Brian
E. Hobart, age 53, $350,000 total compensation
Executive Vice President and Chief Financial
Officer, Michelle S. Hickox, age 51, $265,000 total
compensation
EVP and Secretary and EVP and Senior
Operations Officer Independent Bank, Jan C.
Webb, age 60
Vice President Commercial Banking, Ethan Everett
Vice President Market Manager, Tisha Reyes
Senior Vice President, Kaitlin Mahard
Senior Vice President Director Of Financial
Reporting, Leslie Beseda
Assistant Vice President, Scott Daniels
Senior Vice President, Jenny Steelman
Vice President Commercial Lending, Ozzie
Martinez
AVP Area Banking Manager, Marcey Bench
SVP Director HR, Lisa Murray
SVP HR Director Texas, Pam Murray
Executive Vice President, Duane Reaves
Senior Vice President, Julie Crump
Vice Chairman and Chief Risk Officer, Daniel W.
Brooks, age 58
Auditors: RSM US LLP

LOCATIONS

HQ: Independent Bank Group Inc.
1600 Redbud Boulevard, Suite 400, McKinney, TX 75069-
3257
Phone: 972 562-9004
Web: www.ibtx.com

PRODUCTS/OPERATIONS

2012 Loan Portfolio

	% of total
Real estate	
Commercial	47
Residential	23
Construction land & land development	7
Single-family interim construction	5
Commercial	12
Agricultural	3
Consumer	3
Total	**100**

Selected Acquisition

Town Center Bank (2010 North Texas)
Farmersville Bancshares Inc. (2010 North Texas)
I Bank Holding Company Inc. (2012 Austin/Central
Texas)
The Community Group Inc. (2012 Dallas/North Texas)

COMPETITORS

BBVA Compass Bancshares	HSBC International Bancshares
Bank of America	JPMorgan Chase
Broadway Bancshares	Lone Star Bank
Capital One	PlainsCapital
Citigroup	Prosperity Bancshares
Comerica	Texas Capital Bancshares
Cullen/Frost Bankers	Wells Fargo
Extraco	Woodforest Financial
First Financial Bankshares	

HISTORICAL FINANCIALS

Company Type: Public

Income Statement   FYE: December 31

	ASSETS ($ mil.)	NET INCOME ($ mil.)	INCOME AS % OF ASSETS	EMPLOYEES
12/17	8,684.4	76.5	0.9%	924
12/16	5,852.8	53.5	0.9%	577
12/15	5,055.0	38.7	0.8%	587
12/14	4,132.6	28.9	0.7%	511
12/13	2,163.9	19.8	0.9%	340
Annual Growth	**41.5%**	**40.2%**	**—**	**28.4%**

2017 Year-End Financials

Return on assets: 1.0%
Return on equity: 7.6%
Long-term debt ($ mil.): —
No. of shares (mil.): 28.2
Sales ($ mil): 349.2

Dividends
Yield: 0.0%
Payout: 13.4%
Market value ($ mil.): 1,910.0

	STOCK PRICE ($) FY Close	P/E High/Low	Earnings	Dividends	Book Value
12/17	67.60	24 18	2.97	0.40	47.28
12/16	62.40	22 9	2.88	0.34	35.63
12/15	32.00	21 13	2.21	0.32	34.09
12/14	39.06	33 21	1.85	0.24	31.75
12/13	49.66	28 16	1.77	0.12	18.96
Annual Growth	**8.0%**	**— —**	**13.8%**	**35.1%**	**25.7%**

InfraREIT Inc

Auditors: Ernst & Young LLP

LOCATIONS

HQ: InfraREIT Inc
1900 North Akard Street, Dallas, TX 75201
Phone: 214 855-6700
Web: www.infrareitinc.com

HISTORICAL FINANCIALS

Company Type: Public

Income Statement   FYE: December 31

	REVENUE ($ mil.)	NET INCOME ($ mil.)	NET PROFIT MARGIN	EMPLOYEES
12/17	134.5	12.3	9.1%	0
12/16	172.1	49.9	29.0%	0
12/15	151.2	13.2	8.8%	0
12/14	1.6	(86.3)	—	0
12/13	73.1	32.1	43.9%	0
Annual Growth	**16.4%**	**(21.3%)**	**—**	**—**

2017 Year-End Financials

Debt ratio: 47.6%
Return on equity: 1.8%
Cash ($ mil.): 4.5
Current ratio: 0.32
Long-term debt ($ mil.): 841.2

No. of shares (mil.): 43.8
Dividends
Yield: 0.0%
Payout: 357.1%
Market value ($ mil.): 814.0

	STOCK PRICE ($) FY Close	P/E High/Low	Earnings	Dividends	Book Value
12/17	18.58	83 58	0.28	1.00	15.00
12/16	17.91	19 13	1.14	1.00	15.72
12/15	18.50	109 58	0.31	0.82	15.57
Annual Growth	**0.2%**	**— —**	**(5.0%)**	**10.8%**	**(1.8%)**

Innospec Inc

Innospec has concluded that the company's future lies in applying innovative ideas to its specialty chemicals businesses by developing fuel additives and niche performance chemicals. Innospec's Fuel Specialties segment makes chemical additives that enhance fuel efficiency and engine performance and its Performance Chemicals unit makes several products used in the personal care home care agrochemical and mining. Meanwhile the oilfield services provide drilling and production chemical. It is also the sole producer of TEL (tetra ethyl lead) product an anti-knock gas additive sold to oil refineries worldwide.

Operations

Innospec operated through Fuel Specialties Performance Chemicals Oilfield Services and Octane Additives.

The company's Fuel Specialties segment accounts for 40% its total sales. It produces a range of specialty chemical products used as additives to help improve fuel efficiency boost engine performance and reduce harmful emissions. They are used to support the efficient operation of automotive marine and aviation engines power plant generators and heating oil.

Its Performance Chemicals segment (about 30%) provides technology-based solutions for customers' processes in the personal care home care agrochemical and mining markets.

Its Octane Additives segment (5%) sells TEL for use in automotive gasoline and trading provides services as part of the company's environmental remediation business.

Its Oilfield Services accounts for roughly 25% of revenue and develops and sells products to drilling operations chemical solutions stimulations and completion operations and products for oil and gas production.

Geographic Reach

Innospec operates in Belgium Brazil China France Germany Italy Singapore Switzerland the UK and the US. The US accounts for 40% of its sales.

Sales and Marketing

The company's products are sold primarily to oil and gas exploration and production companies oil refineries personal care and home care companies formulators of agrochemical and mining preparations and other chemical and industrial companies throughout the world.

Financial Performance

IIn 2017 revenue soared almost 50% to $1.3 billion up from $883 million the year before thanks to a sales increases from performance chemicals (due to Huntsman acquisition) and oilfield services due to higher demand triggered by oil price increases.

Net income for the year decreased to $62 million from $81 million in 2016 mostly due to a $40 million YOY increase in income tax expense.

Cash from operating activities was $83 million in 2017 compared to $106 million in 2016 mostly due to the $28 million used for the Huntsman acquisition.

Strategy

Innospec performed well in 2017 thanks to recovering oil prices and successful acquisition leading to better results in performance chemicals. The company had strong cash flows despite acquisition costs While the company is banking on fuel specialties and performance chemicals to deliver growth oilfield services to remain stable due to recovered oil prices a major concern is the future of its octane additives business which is struggling with its recent contract failure. However recent investments in specialty surfactants for its Iselux business as well as a new subsidiary in China to cater to growing demand for specialty chemicals should secure positive momentum.

Mergers and Acquisitions

In 2017 Innospec completed the acquisition of Huntsman's European Differentiated Surfactants business valued at about $200 million. The acquisition provides a small presence in new markets to Innospec including Agriculture Mining and Construction.

EXECUTIVES

COO, Philip J. (Phil) Boon, age 59, $322,590 total compensation
SVP and CTO, Ian M. McRobbie, age 69, $279,453 total compensation
President and CEO, Patrick S. Williams, age 53, $910,340 total compensation
EVP and CFO, Ian P. Cleminson, age 52, $352,064 total compensation
VP Strategic Planning and Regulatory Affairs, Brian R. Watt, age 59, $277,415 total compensation
Vice President of Sales, Jim Vrzak
Senior Vice President Applied Technology, Jeff Dawson
Vice President Human Resources, Rya Stone
Senior Vice President Business Development, Butch Gothard
Vice President Permian Region, Larry Hodnett
Senior Vice President Production Chemical, Jake Hammond
Chairman, Milton C. (Bud) Blackmore, age 70
Board Member, Hugh Aldous
Board Member, Larry Padfield
Board Member, David Landless
Auditors: KPMG LLP

LOCATIONS

HQ: Innospec Inc
8310 South Valley Highway, Suite 350, Englewood, CO 80112
Phone: 303 792-5554
Web: www.innospecinc.com

PRODUCTS/OPERATIONS

2015 sales

	$ mil.	% of total
Fuel Specialties	758.3	75
Performance chemical	194.5	19
Octane Additives	59.5	6
Total	**1,012.3**	**100**

COMPETITORS

BASF SE	Infineum
Clean Diesel	KMG Chemicals
Detrex	Lubrizol
Dow Chemical	NewMarket
Ethyl Corporation	TPC Group

HISTORICAL FINANCIALS

Company Type: Public

Income Statement

FYE: December 31

	REVENUE ($ mil.)	NET INCOME ($ mil.)	NET PROFIT MARGIN	EMPLOYEES
12/17	1,306.8	61.8	4.7%	1,900
12/16	883.4	81.3	9.2%	1,800
12/15	1,012.3	119.5	11.8%	1,300
12/14	960.9	84.1	8.8%	1,300
12/13	818.8	77.8	9.5%	1,100
Annual Growth	**12.4%**	**(5.6%)**	**—**	**14.6%**

2017 Year-End Financials

Debt ratio: 15.9%
Return on equity: 8.5%
Cash ($ mil.): 90.2
Current ratio: 2.15
Long-term debt ($ mil.): 205.8

No. of shares (mil.): 24.3
Dividends
Yield: 0.0%
Payout: 30.5%
Market value ($ mil.): 1,719.0

	STOCK PRICE ($) FY Close	P/E High/Low		PER SHARE ($) Earnings	Dividends	Book Value
12/17	70.60	29	21	2.52	0.77	32.60
12/16	68.50	21	13	3.33	0.67	27.15
12/15	54.31	12	8	4.86	0.61	25.10
12/14	42.70	13	10	3.38	0.55	21.24
12/13	46.22	15	10	3.22	2.50	16.82
Annual Growth	**11.2%**	**—**	**—**	**(5.9%)**	**(25.5%)**	**18.0%**

Innoviva Inc

Innoviva (formerly Theravance) figures there's no sense in re-inventing the wheel. The biotech takes aim at already proven biological targets taking advantage of existing research to create next-generation treatments. The firm is focused on the discovery development and commercialization of small molecule medicines across a number of therapeutic areas including respiratory disease bacterial infections and central nervous system pain. Its VIBATIV product (an injectable antibiotic approved to treat skin infections and hospital-acquired pneumonia) was successfully developed and commercialized with partner Astellas. It also develops chronic obstructive pulmonary disease (COPD) products with GlaxoSmithKline (GSK).

Operations

VIBATIV is approved in the US and Europe for the treatment of certain difficult-to-treat infections. Other products include TD-4208 which is being investigated for the treatment of COPD; and Axelopran (TD-1211) a potential treatment for opioid-induced constipation. Earlier-stage assets are being tested for the treatment of diseases of the lung and gastrointestinal tract and infectious diseases.

Collaboration partner GSK has launched RELVAR/BREO ELLIPTA in a number of markets including the US Canada Japan the UK and Germany. GSK is also responsible for the commercialization of ANORO ELLIPTA.

Theravance Biopharma a subsidiary established in 2014 handles the company's R&D development operations. The unit was created when then-named Theravance split its R&D operations from its late-stage partnered respiratory assets.

Geographic Reach

Innoviva sells its products in the US Japan and Canada and in Western Europe.

Financial Performance

The company's revenues grew by a whopping 454% to $135.8 million in 2012 thanks to the recognition of deferred income from its collaboration with Astellas for VIBATIV which achieved commercialization in early 2012 (the agreement has since been dissolved). Revenues dropped back down in 2013 but rose 86% to $8.4 million in 2014 on royalties from the sale of RELVAR/BREO ELLIPTA and ANORO ELLIPTA (launched that year).

Innoviva has reported net losses every year since its inception. In 2014 its net loss decreased 1% to $168 million due to a decline in losses from discontinued operations. At the end of 2015 its accumulated deficit totaled approximately $1.7 billion.

Operating cash outflow increased 1% to $130 million in 2014.

Strategy

Innoviva actively seeks partnerships with global pharmaceutical companies to allow for faster development and marketing of its pipeline candidates.

Through an exclusive alliance with minority shareholder GSK Innoviva is developing a next-generation version of GSK's asthma medication Advair and other products. The company's collaboration with GSK is focused on its Advair-replacement candidate RELVAR/BREO ELLIPTA to treat asthma and COPD that was launched in the US Japan and Europe. The companies have additional collaborative respiratory treatments (MABA and LAMA) under development. GSK also has the option to exclusively license other Innoviva pipeline products in areas including gastrointestinal ailments and pain. In mid-2014 the partners submitted a supplemental New Drug Application to the FDA for an asthma treatment in patients aged 12 years and older.

Other projects in the pipeline include treatments for gastrointestinal motility disorders such as chronic constipation. It also has candidates in the works to treat infection chronic pain and Alzheimer's disease. The company plans to continue to add new therapeutic candidates and enhance its R&D capabilities. It also hopes to find development partners for all of its programs especially as they get closer to commercialization stages where teaming up with a larger company with an established sales and marketing organization would be beneficial.

Company Background

Innoviva began operating in 1997 under the name Advanced Medicine.

EXECUTIVES

President and CEO, Michael W. Aguiar, age 51, $441,726 total compensation
Head - Business Development, David L. Brinkley, age 60, $301,102 total compensation
VP and Research and Development Program Leader, Edmund J. Moran, age 56
SVP Research and Early Clinical Development, Mathai Mammen, age 51, $411,925 total compensation
VP Clinical and Medical Affairs, Steve Barriere
VP Pharmacology, Sharath S. Hegde
VP Medicinal Chemistry, Dan Marquess

VP Drug Metabolism and Pharmacokinetics, Philip Worboys

Vice President Molecular and Cellular Biology, Jeffrey T. Finer

Vice President Clinical Development, Daniel M. Canafax

SVP Operations, Frank Pasqualone

SVP and CFO, Eric d'Esparbes

Chairman, Rick E. Winningham, age 58

Auditors: Ernst & Young LLP

LOCATIONS

HQ: Innoviva Inc
2000 Sierra Point Parkway, Suite 500, Brisbane, CA 94005
Phone: 650 238-9600
Web: www.inva.com

PRODUCTS/OPERATIONS

2014 Sales

	% of total
Royalty revenue	87
MABA program license	13
Total	**100**

Selected Development Products

Bacterial Infections
TD-1792 (antibiotic for staph infections)
VIBATIV (telavancin for complicated skin and skin structure infections or cSSSI including staph infections)
Central Nervous System/Pain
TD-1211 (opioid-induced constipation)
TD-9855 (chronic pain)
Cognitive Disorders
TD-5108 (Alzheimer's disease)
Gastrointestinal
TD-5108 (for severe constipation and irritable bowel syndrome)
TD-8954 (motility)
Respiratory
LAMA/LABA (or GSK573719/Vilanterol for chronic obstructive pulmonary disease or COPD with GlaxoSmithKline)
MABA (or GSK961081 for COPD with GlaxoSmithKline)
RELOVAIR (for asthma with GlaxoSmithKline)

COMPETITORS

Abbott Labs	NovaBay
Achillion	Novartis
AstraZeneca	Pfizer
Boehringer Ingelheim	Progenics
Cubist Pharmaceuticals	Pharmaceuticals
Eli Lilly	SkyePharma
Johnson & Johnson	Sucampo
Merck	Sunovion

HISTORICAL FINANCIALS

Company Type: Public

Income Statement				FYE: December 31
	REVENUE ($ mil.)	NET INCOME ($ mil.)	NET PROFIT MARGIN	EMPLOYEES
12/17	217.2	134.1	61.8%	12
12/16	133.5	59.5	44.6%	14
12/15	53.9	(18.7)	—	13
12/14	8.4	(168.4)	—	10
12/13	4.7	(170.7)	—	241
Annual Growth	**159.9%**	—	—	**(52.8%)**

2017 Year-End Financials

Debt ratio: 163.1%	No. of shares (mil.): 101.9
Return on equity: ***,***.*%	Dividends
Cash ($ mil.): 73.3	Yield: —
Current ratio: 5.77	Payout: —
Long-term debt ($ mil.): 574.3	Market value ($ mil.): 1,446.0

	STOCK PRICE ($) FY Close	P/E High/Low		PER SHARE ($) Earnings	Dividends	Book Value
12/17	14.19	12	8	1.17	0.00	(2.38)
12/16	10.70	26	15	0.53	0.00	(3.26)
12/15	10.54	—	—	(0.16)	1.00	(2.99)
12/14	14.15	—	—	(1.50)	0.50	(1.92)
12/13	35.65	—	—	(1.67)	0.00	2.68
Annual Growth	**(20.6%)**	—	—	—	—	—

Inogen, Inc

Combine innovation with oxygen and you've got Inogen. The company makes portable oxygen-concentrators that provide supplemental oxygen by people with chronic respiratory conditions. Oxygen concentrators pull nitrogen from ambient air to supply an oxygen-rich mix through a breathing tube. Its 4.8- and 7-pound models are meant to replace both large in-home concentrators as well as portable tank systems which also eliminates the need for home delivery of oxygen tanks. Unlike most suppliers in the market Inogen sells and rents directly to patients. International customers account for about a third of revenue. Inogen was formed in 2001 and went public in early 2014.

IPO

The company plans to use its $70.6 million in IPO proceeds to increase its rental-unit capacity to improve and expand its manufacturing facilities to expand its sales and marketing force and for R&D.

Operations

The majority of Inogen's revenue comes from consumer-direct supplies but it does operate though oxygen supply companies as well mostly in international markets. A growing portion of its revenues come from equipment rental which it prefers doing to the predictable and recurring nature of rental income. The company develops and manufacturers its products.

Geographic Reach

Inogen sells to more than 40 countries mostly in Europe and believes its product is poised to do well internationally for several reasons. Some countries including the UK and France have insurance or other payors that reimburse better for portable oxygen concentrators than the US while other countries have infrastructure (or a lack thereof) that makes a self-sustaining portable option best. And in some countries including Australia insurance doesn't pay for portable oxygen at all making light-weight mobility and low-cost key factors for customers who have to foot the bill themselves.

Sales and Marketing

In the US about 70% of sales Inogen primarily markets directly to consumers while it uses mostly large oxygen supply distributors and gas companies overseas.

The company believes its system gives it an advantage in the marketplace since traditional sys-

tems require a delivery network for regular replacement of oxygen tanks making supply in rural areas difficult and costly. It markets directly to consumers to avoid the traditional model which is geared toward delivering oxygen tanks or supplying large home concentrators.

Financial Performance

Inogen recognizes revenue from sales rentals Medicare reimbursements sales of used equipment and from warranties service contracts and shipping markups (categorized as 'other'). In 2012 the company reported a 59% increase in total revenue as it sold and rented more units for higher prices. Accordingly it went from a net loss of about 2 million to a modest gain of .6 million and cash flow improved about 5% as operating and financing activities both improved.

Strategy

Going forward Inogen plans to leverage its direct relationship with costumers to improve existing products and develop new ones. It also intends to expand its sales and marketing efforts and sign contracts with private insurance and Medicaid.

EXECUTIVES

President and CEO, Scott Wilkinson, age 52, $278,000 total compensation

EVP Finance and CFO, Alison Bauerlein, age 36, $293,461 total compensation

EVP Operations, Matt Scribner, age 50

EVP Engineering, Brenton Taylor, age 36

EVP Sales and Marketing, Byron Myers, age 38

Chairman, Heath Lukatch, age 50

Auditors: Deloitte & Touche LLP

LOCATIONS

HQ: Inogen, Inc
326 Bollay Drive, Goleta, CA 93117
Phone: 805 562-0500
Web: www.inogen.com

PRODUCTS/OPERATIONS

2014 Sales

	$ mil.	% of total
Sales	73.1	65
Rentals	39.4	35
Total	**112.5**	**100**

Selected Products

G2 Systems & Accessories
G3 Systems & Accessories
Inogen At Home Oxygen Concentrator
Inogen Freedom Bundle
Inogen Oxygen Accessories
Inogen Oxygen Concentrators for Sale

COMPETITORS

American HomePatient	Lincare Holdings
Apria Healthcare	Philips Electronics
Chart Industries	Praxair
DeVilbiss	Rotech Healthcare
Invacare	

HISTORICAL FINANCIALS

Company Type: Public

Income Statement				FYE: December 31
	REVENUE ($ mil.)	NET INCOME ($ mil.)	NET PROFIT MARGIN	EMPLOYEES
12/17	249.4	21.0	8.4%	770
12/16	202.8	20.5	10.1%	602
12/15	159.0	11.5	7.3%	547
12/14	112.5	6.8	6.1%	411
12/13	75.4	25.4	33.7%	354
Annual Growth	34.8%	(4.7%)	—	21.4%

2017 Year-End Financials

Debt ratio: —
Return on equity: 10.2%
Cash ($ mil.): 173.9
Current ratio: 6.74
Long-term debt ($ mil.): —

No. of shares (mil.): 20.9
Dividends
Yield: —
Payout: —
Market value ($ mil.): 2,498.0

	STOCK PRICE ($) FY Close	P/E High/Low		PER SHARE ($)		
				Earnings	Dividends	Book Value
12/17	119.08	126	62	0.96	0.00	10.82
12/16	67.17	67	29	0.97	0.00	8.93
12/15	40.09	91	50	0.56	0.00	6.77
12/14	31.37	95	42	0.30	0.00	6.20
Annual Growth	56.0%	—	—	47.4%	—	20.4%

Inovalon Holdings Inc

Auditors: DELOITTE & TOUCHE LLP

LOCATIONS

HQ: Inovalon Holdings Inc
4321 Collington Road, Bowie, MD 20716
Phone: 301 809-4000
Web: www.inovalon.com

HISTORICAL FINANCIALS

Company Type: Public

Income Statement				FYE: December 31
	REVENUE ($ mil.)	NET INCOME ($ mil.)	NET PROFIT MARGIN	EMPLOYEES
12/17	449.3	34.8	7.7%	2,480
12/16	427.5	27.1	6.3%	2,453
12/15	437.2	66.0	15.1%	3,323
12/14	361.5	65.3	18.1%	2,474
12/13	295.8	32.7	11.1%	2,474
Annual Growth	11.0%	1.6%	—	0.1%

2017 Year-End Financials

Debt ratio: 24.9%
Return on equity: 5.2%
Cash ($ mil.): 208.9
Current ratio: 4.82
Long-term debt ($ mil.): 203.3

No. of shares (mil.): 143.9
Dividends
Yield: —
Payout: —
Market value ($ mil.): 2,159.0

	STOCK PRICE ($) FY Close	P/E High/Low		PER SHARE ($)		
				Earnings	Dividends	Book Value
12/17	15.00	73	43	0.24	0.00	4.47
12/16	10.30	111	49	0.18	0.00	4.62
12/15	17.00	71	37	0.45	0.00	4.87
Annual Growth	(6.1%)	—	—	(27.0%)	—	(4.3%)

Installed Building Products Inc

Installed Building Products (IBP) wants to insulate its customers from the elements. The company is a leading new residential insulation installer with more than 100 branches in about 45 states. IBP manages all aspects of the installation process for its customers including direct purchases of materials from national manufacturers to delivery and installation. In addition to insulation IBP installs garage doors rain gutters shower doors shelving fireplaces locksets and hardware and mirrors. The company's primary market is residential new home construction (about three-quarters of sales). Seeking to capitalize on the recovery in new home building IBP went public in 2014.

IPO

Installed Building Products (IBP) went public in February 2014 with an offering valued at $82 million (or $11 per share) well below the company's forecast of $14 to $16 per share. It also sold fewer shares than anticipated. The company plans to use the proceeds to repay debt and for general corporate purposes.

Geographic Reach

Ohio-based IBP has branches in 44 states including California Florida Indiana New York Ohio and Texas.

Financial Performance

The residential insulation installer's revenue increased 26% in 2012 versus 2011 to $301.3 million. It narrowed its loss from $9 million in 2011 to $1.9 million in 2012. (For the nine months ended September 2013 the firm turned a profit of nearly $3.7 million.)

Strategy

Founded in 1977 IBP has built its national presence through an aggressive acquisition strategy including more than 90 purchases since 1999. Indeed in 2012 the firm completed seven acquisitions. The firm has grown its share of the US residential new construction insulation installation market from about 5% in 2005 to approximately 16% in 2013.

Mergers and Acquisitions

In October 2016 IBP acquired East Coast Insulators expanding its presence in the mid-Atlantic region. It was the seventh acquisition made that year and the company continues to pursue additional buying opportunities.

EXECUTIVES

Chairman President and CEO, Jeffrey w. Edwards, age 54, $83,077 total compensation
EVP CFO and Director, Michael T. Miller, age 53, $194,900 total compensation
COO, Jay P. Elliott, age 56, $194,900 total compensation
President External Affairs, W. Jeffrey Hire, age 66
Regional President, R. Scott Jenkins, age 62
Regional President, Matthew J. Momper, age 57
Regional President, Warren W. Pearce, age 59
Regional President, Randall S. Williamson, age 55
Auditors: Deloitte & Touche LLP

LOCATIONS

HQ: Installed Building Products Inc
495 South High Street, Suite 50, Columbus, OH 43215
Phone: 614 221-3399
Web: www.installedbuildingproducts.com

PRODUCTS/OPERATIONS

2017 Sales

	% of total
Residential new construction and repair and remodel	83
Commercial construction	17
Total	**100**

2017 Sales

	% of total
Insulation	67
Waterproofing	8
Shower doors shelving & mirrors	7
Garage doors	5
Rain gutters	4
Other	9
Total	**100**

COMPETITORS

ABC Supply　　　　　　HD Supply

HISTORICAL FINANCIALS

Company Type: Public

Income Statement				FYE: December 31
	REVENUE ($ mil.)	NET INCOME ($ mil.)	NET PROFIT MARGIN	EMPLOYEES
12/17	1,132.9	41.1	3.6%	6,900
12/16	862.9	38.4	4.5%	5,292
12/15	662.7	26.5	4.0%	4,510
12/14	518.0	13.9	2.7%	3,600
12/13	431.9	6.0	1.4%	3,200
Annual Growth	27.3%	61.6%	—	21.2%

2017 Year-End Financials

Debt ratio: 48.6%
Return on equity: 22.5%
Cash ($ mil.): 92.5
Current ratio: 2.22
Long-term debt ($ mil.): 337.4

No. of shares (mil.): 31.8
Dividends
Yield: —
Payout: —
Market value ($ mil.): 2,420.0

	STOCK PRICE ($) FY Close	P/E High/Low		PER SHARE ($)		
				Earnings	Dividends	Book Value
12/17	75.95	60	31	1.30	0.00	6.61
12/16	41.30	36	15	1.23	0.00	4.89
12/15	24.83	35	20	0.85	0.00	3.65
12/14	17.82	—	—	(0.20)	0.00	2.91
Annual Growth	62.1%	—	—	—	—	31.4%

Integer Holdings Corp

The beat goes on with Integer Holdings products. The heartbeat that is. The company is a leading maker of batteries used in implantable medical devices such as pacemakers and implantable cardioverter defibrillators (ICDs). Other medical components include electrodes capacitors engineered components enclosures and feedthroughs (used to deliver electrical signals from an implantable medical device to an electrode). Integer Holdings also makes batteries for demanding energy military and environmental applications. The business gets more than half of its sales from US clients.

Operations

Integer Holdings a medical device outsourcer operates through two segments: medical and non-medical.

Three product lines comprise the medical segment. The Cardio & Vascular segment accounting for more than 35% of revenue offers products and services for the development of diagnostic and interventional cardiac and endovascular devices.

The Advanced Surgical Orthopedics & Portable Medical segment about 30% of revenue offers advanced development engineering and program management.

The Cardio & Neuromodulation business about 30% of revenue provides batteries capacitors filtered and unfiltered feedthroughs engineered components implantable stimulation leads and enclosures used in implantable medical devices (IMDs).

The non-medical segment less than 5% of revenue produces Electrochem-branded customized battery power management systems charging and docking stations and power supplies.

Geographic Reach

Integer Holdings is based in Frisco Texas and it has operations including 25 manufacturing facilities in Canada Mexico Switzerland and the US. About 60% of its sales come from the US while Puerto Rico generates 10% with other countries accounting for the other 30%.

Sales and Marketing

Integer's medical customers include large multinational medical device OEMs such as Abbott Laboratories Boston Scientific Johnson & Johnson and Medtronic which collectively account for 55% of sales. Non-medical customers include Halliburton Teledyne Technologies and Weatherford International.

Financial Performance

Revenue generated by Integer Holdings jumped nearly 75% 2016 with the company's merger with LRM in 2015. The growth rate slowed to about 5% in 2017 when the company posted revenue of about $1.5 billion. Gains were driven by market growth and new business. Revenue growth was slowed by price concessions the company made to its larger OEM customers in return for long-term volume commitments.

Integer's profit jumped to about $66 million in 2017 from $6 million in 2016 because of lower costs in 2017 after integrating Integer and LRM operations. The company also received a tax benefit of about $40 million from the US Tax Cuts and Jobs Act.

Cash and cash equivalents fell about $8 million to $44 million in 2017 from 2016 because the company used excess cash flow from operations to pay down debt.

Strategy

Integer started a makeover in 2015 when it merged with rival LRM to form one of the largest medical device outsourcing (MDO) manufacturing companies in the world. In 2016 it spun off the QiG Group subsidiary and its neuromodulation medical device business known as Nuvectra.

LRM and Integer spent time and money in 2016 and 2017 integrating and consolidating their operations to make them more efficient and less costly. In 2017 the company conducted a strategic review of customers competitors and markets. The review prompted Integer to better align its re-sources which means focusing investment to conduct research and development and improve manufacturing operations improving business processes and redirecting investments away from projects without significant market potential.

The company intends to invest in its Cardio & Vascular Neuromodulation and Electrochem where its sees potential for growth. It also plans to protect its Cardiac Rhythm Management product line while shoring up profitability in its orthopedics advanced surgical and power solutions businesses.

Mergers and Acquisitions

Integer Holdings uses acquisitions primarily to expand its product lines and related markets. In 2014 it obtained Centro de Construcción de Cardioestimuladores del Uruguay (CCC) headquartered in Montevideo Uruguay. CCC is an implantable neuromodulation medical device systems developer and manufacturer that produces a range of medical devices including implantable pulse generators programmer systems battery chargers patient wands and leads.

EXECUTIVES

President and COO, Thomas J. Hook, age 55, $719,192 total compensation
EVP and COO, Jeremy A. Friedman
EVP Quality and Regulatory Affairs, Joseph F. (Joe) Flanagan
EVP and Chief Human Resources Officer, Kristin E. Trecker
President Advanced Surgical and Orthopaedics, Declan Smyth
President Cardiac Rhythm Management (CRM) and Neuromodulation, Tony Gonzalez
President Electrochem, Jennifer Bolt
EVP and CFO, Gary Haire
Interim President Cardio and Vascular, John Harris
Executive Vice President Global Sales and Marketing, Thomas Hickman
Vice President and Chief Audit Executive, Dave Bolton
Senior Vice President and Chief Technology Officer, George Cintra
Vice President Of Research and Development, Dominick Frustaci
Chairman, William R. (Bill) Sanford, age 73
Auditors: DELOITTE & TOUCHE LLP

LOCATIONS

HQ: Integer Holdings Corp
5830 Granite Parkway, Suite 1150, Plano, TX 75024
Phone: 214 618-5243
Web: www.integer.net

PRODUCTS/OPERATIONS

2017 Sales

	$ mil.	% of total
Cardio & Vascular	536.8	37
Advanced Surgical Orthopedics & Portable Medical	439.8	30
Cardio & Neuromodulation	428.3	29
Non-medical	69.0	4
Total	**1,461.9**	**100**

Selected Operations

Medical   Cardio & Vascular   Introducers Steerable Sheaths   Guidewires   Catheters and Stimulation Therapy Components   Subassemblies and Finished Device   Cardiac & Neuromodulation Batteries   Capacitors   Fil

COMPETITORS

AVX   Orthofix

Accellent
CONMED Corporation
Cardinal Health
Eagle-Picher
Edwards Lifesciences
Heraeus Holding
Integra LifeSciences
Johnson & Johnson
Laird Technologies
Medtronic
Merit Medical Systems
Morgan Advanced
  Materials

Paragon Medical
SAFT
Smith & Nephew
SonoSite
St. Jude Medical
Stryker
Teleflex
Thoratec Corp
Ultralife
West Pharmaceutical
  Services
ZOLL
Zimmer Biomet

HISTORICAL FINANCIALS

Company Type: Public

Income Statement

FYE: December 29

	REVENUE ($ mil.)	NET INCOME ($ mil.)	NET PROFIT MARGIN	EMPLOYEES
12/17	1,461.9	66.6	4.6%	9,700
12/16*	1,386.7	5.9	0.4%	9,400
01/16	800.4	(7.5)	—	9,559
01/15	687.7	55.4	8.1%	3,690
01/14	663.9	36.2	5.5%	3,385
Annual Growth	**21.8%**	**16.4%**	**—**	**30.1%**

*Fiscal year change

2017 Year-End Financials

Debt ratio: 56.4%
Return on equity: 8.2%
Cash ($ mil.): 44.1
Current ratio: 2.54
Long-term debt ($ mil.): 1,578.7

No. of shares (mil.): 31.8
Dividends
  Yield: —
  Payout: —
Market value ($ mil.): 1,444.0

	STOCK PRICE ($) FY Close	P/E High/Low		PER SHARE ($) Earnings	Dividends	Book Value
12/17	45.30	26	14	2.09	0.00	28.03
12/16*	29.45	284	96	0.19	0.00	23.45
01/16	52.50	—		(0.29)	0.00	27.80
01/15	48.66	23	18	2.14	0.00	24.47
01/14	43.80	29	16	1.43	0.00	22.19
Annual Growth	**0.8%**	**—**	**—**	**10.0%**	**—**	**6.0%**

*Fiscal year change

Integra LifeSciences Holdings Corp

Integra LifeSciences a regenerative medicine specialist develops medical equipment for use in cranial procedures small bone and joint reconstruction and the repair and reconstruction of soft tissue. Integra makes surgical equipment including bone fixation devices spinal fixation systems tissue ablation equipment and drainage catheters used in neurosurgery and orthopedic reconstruction as well as basic surgical instruments. Its products are marketed worldwide through direct sales and distributors. Integra operates in two segments: Specialty Surgical Solutions (the larger segment it brings in some two-thirds of revenues) and Orthopedics and Tissue Technologies.

Operations

The Specialty Surgical Solutions segment makes products in the area of dural repair tissue ablation precision tools and neuro critical care. Meanwhile the Orthopedics and Tissue Technologies segments offers small bone repair and joint replacement hardware products for extremities as well as private-label regenerative medicine technologies.

The company's products are intended mainly for niche markets not targeted by larger medical device firms. Most of Integra's orthopedic products for instance are designed for orthopedic reconstruction of the extremities such as the feet and ankles (rather than the hip and knee replacement products offered by the likes of Zimmer and DePuy). However the company has reached those larger and more diverse markets through a select number of original equipment manufacturer deals with firms such as Medtronic and Zimmer.

Geographic Reach
The company's principal manufacturing and research facilities are located in the US (Massachusetts New Jersey Ohio and Pennsylvania) and in France Germany Ireland Mexico and Puerto Rico. Its distribution centers are in the US (Nevada Ohio and Pennsylvania) Australia Belgium Canada and France.

Integra also has repair centers in the US (California Massachusetts and Ohio) Australia and Germany.

The US accounts for more than three-fourths of total revenue; Europe accounts for 12%.

Sales and Marketing
The group sells its products through an internal sales force and through distributors and wholesalers. It also markets some products domestically through strategic partnerships.

Financial Performance
Integra's revenue had been on the rise until 2015 when revenue fell 5% to $883 million. That drop was due to the spin-off of SeaSpine Holdings; both segments actually had higher sales that year thanks largely to a number of acquisitions.

Net income which has been fluctuating for the past five years dropped in 2015. The company lost a net $4 million that year as selling general and administrative spending increased (again largely due to acquisition activity as well as the spin-off of the spine business). Cash flow from operations has been rising; it increased 19% to $94 million due to decline in inventories and changes in liabilities.

Strategy
Integra has expanded its operations over the years through acquisitions geographic expansion and product R&D efforts. It has expanded both its product lines and geographic reach through some 45 acquisitions since its formation including recent additions of direct distribution assets in Australia and the UK.

As a result of its growth efforts and string of acquisitions the company has implemented a number of cost-cutting measures. It has consolidated manufacturing and distribution facilities. In 2015 Integra separated its orthobiologics and spinal fusion hardware business SeaSpine Holdings which became a public company. The split will help both surviving entities operate in their respective arenas more effectively.

Additionally it has nearly completed the integration of a common enterprise resource planning (ERP) system.

Integra plans to launch its Omnigraft product for the treatment of diabetic foot ulcers.

Mergers and Acquisitions
Integra reached an agreement to acquire Derma Sciences a tissue regeneration company focused on advanced wound and burn care for around $204 million in early 2017. Also that year it bought Johnson & Johnson's Codman neurosurgery business which provides devices for areas including hydrocephaly neurocritical care and operative neurosurgery for $1.05 billion.

In 2015 the company acquired TEI Biosciences and TEI Medical for $312 million. That purchase boosted its offerings in regenerative wound care and tissue repair. Integra also purchased a line of lower extremity implants from Metasurg that year as well as the US rights to Tornier's Talari and Talaris XT ankle replacement products and its Futura toe replacement products. Finally it acquired Italian distribution arm Tekmed Instruments.

Integra gets a majority of its sales from its orthopedic segment and its neurosciences segment each accounting for about 40% of sales; nearly one-third of those segment revenues come from regenerative medicine supplies. Traditional medical instruments such as surgical forceps scopes lights and retractors account for about 20% of revenues.

EXECUTIVES

Senior Vice President Corporate Development, Maria Platsis

VP; President International, Dan Reuvers

CEO President and Director, Peter J. Arduini, age 53, $787,115 total compensation

President Instruments, Debbie Leonetti, age 62

VP; President Advanced Wound Care, Robert D. Paltridge, age 60, $215,000 total compensation

VP and CFO, Glenn Coleman, age 50

VP Global Operations and Supply Chain, John Mooradian

VP; President Neurosurgery, Robert T. Davis, $335,115 total compensation

Vice President Product Development, Jerry Klawitter

Vice President Product Development, Christopher Fedele

Vice President Global Total Rewards, Barbara Vietor

Board Member, Keith Bradley

Chairman, Stuart M. Essig, age 56

Auditors: PricewaterhouseCoopers LLP

LOCATIONS

HQ: Integra LifeSciences Holdings Corp
311 Enterprise Drive, Plainsboro, NJ 08536
Phone: 609 275-0500
Web: www.integralife.com

PRODUCTS/OPERATIONS

2015 Sales

	$ mil.	% of total
Specialty Surgical Solutions	586.9	66
Orthopedics and Tissue Technologies	295.8	34
Total	**882.7**	**100**

COMPETITORS

Accuray	Organogenesis
Alphatec Spine	Orthofix
B. Braun Medical (UK)	RTI Surgical
CareFusion	Smith & Nephew
Genzyme Biosurgery	Stryker
Globus Medical	Synovis Life
Johnson & Johnson	Technologies
Medtronic	Synthes
NuVasive	Zimmer Biomet

HISTORICAL FINANCIALS
Company Type: Public

Income Statement				FYE: December 31
	REVENUE ($ mil.)	NET INCOME ($ mil.)	NET PROFIT MARGIN	EMPLOYEES
12/17	1,188.2	64.7	5.4%	4,400
12/16	992.0	74.5	7.5%	3,700
12/15	882.7	(3.5)	—	3,500
12/14	928.3	34.0	3.7%	3,400
12/13	836.2	(16.9)	—	3,300
Annual Growth	**9.2%**	**—**	**—**	**7.5%**

2017 Year-End Financials

Debt ratio: 57.3%
Return on equity: 7.1%
Cash ($ mil.): 174.9
Current ratio: 2.36
Long-term debt ($ mil.): 1,781.1
No. of shares (mil.): 78.3
Dividends
  Yield: —
  Payout: —
Market value ($ mil.): 3,752.0

	STOCK PRICE ($) FY Close	P/E High/Low		PER SHARE ($)		
				Earnings	Dividends	Book Value
12/17	47.86	101	49	0.82	0.00	12.28
12/16	85.79	87	55	0.94	0.00	11.24
12/15	67.78	—	—	(0.05)	0.00	10.17
12/14	54.23	104	84	0.52	0.00	10.76
12/13	47.71	—	—	(0.30)	0.00	10.43
Annual Growth	**0.1%**	**—**	**—**	**—**	**—**	**4.2%**

Interactive Brokers Group Inc

Interactive Brokers Group serves investors who interact with world markets. The global electronic broker and market maker performs low-cost trade order management execution and portfolio management services through its Interactive Brokers subsidiaries and electronic market-maker Timber Hill. Catering to institutional and experienced individual investors the US' largest electronic broker by revenue offers access to more than 100 electronic exchanges and trading centers worldwide executing one million trades per day in stocks options futures foreign exchange instruments bonds and mutual funds. The company also licenses its trading interface to large banks and brokerages through white-label agreements.

Operations
The firm operates through a pair of business segments: Electronic Brokerage which accounted for 79% of the company's total revenue during 2015; and Market Making (21% of revenue).

Reflecting a diversified revenue base Interactive Brokers Group generated 45% of its total revenue from commissions and execution fees during 2015 while another 35% came from interest income and 20% came from trading gains.

Geographic Reach
Greenwich Connecticut-based Interactive Brokers Group serves customers from nearly 200 countries. It operates US offices in Boston Chicago Jersey City San Francisco Washington DC and West Palm Beach. Abroad it has offices in Canada England Hungary Russia Estonia Liechtenstein

Switzerland Hong Kong Shanghai India Australia and Japan.

Sales and Marketing

Interactive Brokers Group which uses automated systems and word-of-mouth advertising served some 331000 institutional and individual brokerage customers at the end of 2015.

Its customers fall into three groups based on their service needs: cleared customers (small market making groups individual market makers institutional and individual traders financial advisors and introducing brokers); trade execution customers (prime brokers custodian banks); and wholesale customers (large banks and retail electronic brokers) to which it licenses its trading interface through white-label agreements.

Financial Performance

While a continued decline in trading gains have caused headwinds for Interactive Brokers Group's annual revenues and profits over the past several years rising commission fees and interest income have more recently been leading the company to growth.

Interactive Brokers' revenue jumped 13% to $1.2 billion during 2015 thanks to a combination of: higher interest income from higher average customer margin borrowings average customer cash balances (which were invested in interest-bearing vehicles) and net fees earned from securities lending transactions; and an increase in commissions and executions fees driven by customer account growth and trading activity despite lower average commission per customer order.

Strong revenue growth in 2015 drove the firm's net income up 10% to $49 million despite an uptick in customer bad debt expenses driven by customer losses that stemmed from movements in the Swiss franc and market volatility in late August. Interactive Brokers' operating cash levels spiked 74% to $725 million during the year as it collected more in cash-denominated revenues.

Strategy

Interactive Brokers Group develops proprietary technologies to stay competitive and weather market fluctuations. It also acquires electronic trading-focused companies and platforms when the technology they offer can't be quickly replicated such as with its 2015 acquisition of Covestor which launched Interactive Brokers into the robo advisors business.

Some of the new technology and products launched during 2015 included the Investors' Marketplace platform which allowed traders analysts advisors fund managers technology providers and business developers to do business; a new CRM (customer relationship management) platform for advisors to centrally manage their customer relationship life cycles; the RIA Compliance Center to offer resource help for advisors registering and starting their own advisory firms; and the Portfolio Builder trading tool which allowed traders to create investment strategies (with back-testing capability) using Interactive Brokers Groups' research and fundamentals data.

Interactive Brokers Group has invested in or helped to form several stock exchanges and trading platforms including the CBOE Stock Exchange (founded by the CBOE Holdings in 2007) the OneChicago single-stock futures exchange and the Boston Options Exchange (established by Interactive Brokers Bourse de Montréal and the Boston Stock Exchange).

Mergers and Acquisitions

In April 2015 Interactive Brokers effectively entered the fast-growing "robo advisors" market after acquiring Boston-based Covestor an online investment marketplace and the first digital asset management company to offer both active and passive investment options.

Company Background

Founder chairman and CEO Thomas Peterffy controls Interactive Brokers Group.

EXECUTIVES

Chairman and CEO, Thomas Peterffy, age 73, $1,350,000 total compensation
CFO Treasurer Secretary and Director, Paul J. Brody, age 57, $380,000 total compensation
Executive Vice President; Chief Information Officer, Thomas A. J. Frank, $380,000 total compensation
EVP Marketing and Product Development, Steve Sanders
President and Director, Milan Galik, age 51, $380,000 total compensation
Vice Chairman, Earl H. Nemser, age 71
Auditors: DELOITTE & TOUCHE LLP

LOCATIONS

HQ: Interactive Brokers Group Inc
One Pickwick Plaza, Greenwich, CT 06830
Phone: 203 618-5800
Web: www.interactivebrokers.com

PRODUCTS/OPERATIONS

Trading Services
Account Management
Employee Track Management
Funding Reference
Investors' Marketplace
IRA Information
New Features Poll
Securities Financing

2015 Sales

	$ mil.	% of total
Commissions & execution fees	617.0	45
Interest income	492.0	35
Trading gains	269.0	20
Other	(122)	-
Total	**1,256.0**	**100**

COMPETITORS

Charles Schwab
Citigroup Global Markets Limited
E*TRADE Financial
GSEC
KCG Holdings
Merrill Lynch
Morgan Stanley
PEAK6 Investments
Susquehanna International Group LLP
TD Ameritrade
UBS

HISTORICAL FINANCIALS

Company Type: Public

Income Statement — FYE: December 31

	REVENUE ($ mil.)	NET INCOME ($ mil.)	NET PROFIT MARGIN	EMPLOYEES
12/17	1,702.0	76.0	4.5%	1,228
12/16	1,396.0	84.0	6.0%	1,204
12/15	1,189.0	49.0	4.1%	1,087
12/14	1,043.2	44.5	4.3%	960
12/13	1,076.1	37.0	3.4%	880
Annual Growth	12.1%	19.7%	—	8.7%

2017 Year-End Financials

Debt ratio: 7.2%
Return on equity: 7.3%
Cash ($ mil.): 23,999.0
Current ratio: 1.06
Long-term debt ($ mil.): —
No. of shares (mil.): 71.4
Dividends
Yield: 0.0%
Payout: 37.3%
Market value ($ mil.): 4,232.0

	STOCK PRICE ($) FY Close	P/E High/Low		Earnings	Dividends	Book Value
12/17	59.21	57	31	1.07	0.40	15.25
12/16	36.51	34	24	1.25	0.40	14.33
12/15	43.60	57	35	0.78	0.40	13.49
12/14	29.16	37	26	0.77	0.40	13.11
12/13	24.34	34	18	0.73	0.40	12.94
Annual Growth	24.9%	—	—	10.0%	(0.0%)	4.2%

Interdigital Inc (PA)

InterDigital is more than just interested in wireless digital telecommunications. The company develops and licenses circuitry designs software and other technology using CDMA (code-division multiple access) and other wireless communications standards. Altogether it holds a patent portfolio of about 2200 US patents and 10900 foreign patents. InterDigital licenses its technology patents to companies that make smartphones tablets notebook computers and wireless personal digital assistants as well as wireless infrastructure equipment such as base stations and components dongles and modules for wireless devices. Top customers include Sony Samsung HTC and other makers of chips software and telecom equipment.

Geographic Reach

InterDigital operates from six research and development offices in the US one in Canada one in the UK and one in South Korea.

Taiwan is its biggest market generating about half of revenue. South Korea the US and Japan account for 16% 15% and 12% of revenue respectively.

Sales and Marketing

Historically the company generates most of its revenues from Asia where the world's electronics are manufactured. The US accounts for one-third of sales. It also relies on a small number of customers - in 2015 Pegatron Samsung and Sony Corporation of America combined accounted for 60% of sales.

Financial Performance

InterDigital's revenue rose 6% in 2015 to $441 million from $415 million in 2014. The company had higher per-unit royalties in 2015 driven by more shipments to Pegatron. It also saw a rise in fixed-fee revenue.

Net income increased 14% hitting $119 million in 2015 compared to $104 million in 2014. The company had lower administration and licensing expenses in 2015. Litigation expenses decreased to $31 million in 2015 from $52 million and $75 million in 2014 and 2013 respectively.

Cash flow from operations was $114 million in 2015 down from $242 million the previous year.

Strategy

As a patent licensing firm InterDigital must continually expand its pool of licensing customers to continue its growth and the company has a limited number of licensees contributing most of its revenues. InterDigital must also spend money on developing patentable technologies and it has had to litigate to defend the patents it holds for years at a time in some cases. In mid-2014 it settled with Samsung over mobile technology royalties for Samsung's 3G and 4G products. Over the next five years InterDigital will receive millions from Samsung.

InterDigital is developing technologies for 5G wireless networks and the Internet of Things. In 2015 it launched the MPOWER platform which enables interoperability and scalability across verticals networks and devices. It renewed a joint venture with Sony and Convida Wireless for development in 5G and the Internet of Things.

InterDigital's R&D spending was $73 million in 2015 $75 million in 2014 and $65 million in 2013.

EXECUTIVES

President and CEO, William J. Merritt, age 59, $575,000 total compensation

EVP Intellectual Property and Chief Intellectual Property Counsel; President InterDigital Patent Holding Subsidiaries, Lawrence F. Shay, age 59, $410,000 total compensation

SEVP Innovation, Scott A. McQuilkin, age 63, $375,000 total compensation

EVP InterDigital Solutions, James J. (Jim) Nolan, age 58, $325,000 total compensation

CFO, Richard J. Brezski, age 47, $285,000 total compensation

EVP General Counsel and Secretary, Jannie K. Lau
EVP InterDigital Labs and CTO, Byung K. Yi
Chairman, Steven T. (Terry) Clontz, age 67
Auditors: PricewaterhouseCoopers LLP

LOCATIONS

HQ: Interdigital Inc (PA)
200 Bellevue Parkway, Suite 300, Wilmington, DE 19809-3727
Phone: 302 281-3600
Web: www.interdigital.com

PRODUCTS/OPERATIONS

2015 Sales

	$ mil.	% of total
Per-unit royalty	234.8	53
Fixed-fee amortized royalty	131.8	30
Past patent royalties	65.8	15
Current technology solutions	6.1	1
Past technology solutions	2.9	1
Total	**441.4**	**100**

2015 Sales

	$ mil.	% of total
Patent licensing royalties	432.5	98
Technology solutions	8.9	2
Total	**441.4**	**100**

COMPETITORS

Alcatel-Lucent	QUALCOMM
Conexant Systems	Sonics
IBM Microelectronics	Texas Instruments
Infineon Technologies	Unwired Planet
Intel	VirnetX
Marvell Technology	Xora
Nokia	

HISTORICAL FINANCIALS
Company Type: Public

Income Statement
FYE: December 31

	REVENUE ($ mil.)	NET INCOME ($ mil.)	NET PROFIT MARGIN	EMPLOYEES
12/17	532.9	174.2	32.7%	350
12/16	665.8	309.0	46.4%	360
12/15	441.4	119.2	27.0%	330
12/14	415.8	104.3	25.1%	320
12/13	325.3	38.1	11.7%	290
Annual Growth	**13.1%**	**46.2%**	**—**	**4.8%**

2017 Year-End Financials

Debt ratio: 15.3%
Return on equity: 21.8%
Cash ($ mil.): 433.0
Current ratio: 3.71
Long-term debt ($ mil.): 285.1

No. of shares (mil.): 34.6
Dividends
Yield: 0.0%
Payout: 25.6%
Market value ($ mil.): 2,636.0

	STOCK PRICE ($) FY Close	P/E High/Low		PER SHARE ($) Earnings	Dividends	Book Value
12/17	76.15	20	14	4.87	1.25	24.70
12/16	91.35	10	5	8.78	0.90	21.57
12/15	49.04	18	14	3.27	0.80	14.42
12/14	52.90	21	10	2.62	0.60	12.68
12/13	29.49	52	31	0.92	1.90	13.12
Annual Growth	**26.8%**	**—**		**51.7%**	**(9.9%)**	**17.1%**

Investar Holding Corp

Auditors: Ernst & Young LLP

LOCATIONS

HQ: Investar Holding Corp
7244 Perkins Road, Baton Rouge, LA 70808
Phone: 225 227-2222

HISTORICAL FINANCIALS
Company Type: Public

Income Statement
FYE: December 31

	ASSETS ($ mil.)	NET INCOME ($ mil.)	INCOME AS % OF ASSETS	EMPLOYEES
12/17	1,622.7	8.2	0.5%	258
12/16	1,158.9	7.8	0.7%	152
12/15	1,031.5	7.0	0.7%	951
12/14	879.3	5.4	0.6%	179
12/13	634.9	3.1	0.5%	171
Annual Growth	**26.4%**	**26.8%**	**—**	**10.8%**

2017 Year-End Financials

Return on assets: 0.5%
Return on equity: 5.7%
Long-term debt ($ mil.): —
No. of shares (mil.): 9.5
Sales ($ mil): 57.1

Dividends
Yield: 0.0%
Payout: 7.5%
Market value ($ mil.): 229.0

	STOCK PRICE ($) FY Close	P/E High/Low		PER SHARE ($) Earnings	Dividends	Book Value
12/17	24.10	26	20	0.96	0.07	18.15
12/16	18.65	18	12	1.10	0.04	15.88
12/15	17.60	18	14	0.97	0.03	15.05
12/14	13.85	15	13	0.93	0.01	14.24
Annual Growth	**20.3%**	**—**		**1.1%**	**73.4%**	**8.4%**

Investors Bancorp Inc (New)

Investors Bancorp is the holding company for Investors Savings Bank which serves New Jersey and New York from more than 130 branch offices. Founded in 1926 the bank offers such standard deposit products as savings and checking accounts CDs money market accounts and IRAs. Nearly 40% of the bank's loan portfolio is made up of residential mortgages while multi-family loans and commercial real estate loans make up more than 50% combined. The bank also originates business industrial and consumer loans. Founded in 1926 Investors Bancorp's assets now exceed $20 billion.

Operations

About 86% of Investors Bancorp's revenue came from interest income from loans and loans held-for sale in 2014 while another 8% came from interest income on the bank's mortgage-backed securities municipal bonds and other debt. The remainder of its revenue came from fees and service charges (3%) and other miscellaneous income sources. Investors Bancorp boasted a staff of more than 1700 at the end of 2014.

Geographic Reach

Based in Short Hills New Jersey Investors Bancorp has more than 130 branches across New Jersey and New York. It also has lending offices in New York City Short Hills Spring Lake Newark Astoria and Brooklyn. Its operation center is in Iselin New Jersey.

Sales and Marketing

The company offers retail and commercial banking services to individuals professional service firms municipalities small and middle-market companies commercial and industrial firms and other businesses.

Financial Performance

Investors Bancorp's revenues and profits have been rising thanks to strong loan growth from bank acquisitions falling interest expenses on deposits and declining loan loss provisions as its loan portfolio's credit quality has improved with higher property valuations in the strengthened economy.

The bank's revenue jumped by 21% to a record $702.7 million in 2014 mostly thanks to loan asset growth stemming from the bank's 2014 acquisition of Gateway Community Financial.

Higher revenue and a continued decline in loan loss provisions in 2014 drove the bank's net income higher by 18% to a record $131.7 million. Investor Bancorp's operating cash levels spiked by 58% to $277.4 million for the year on higher cash earnings and favorable changes in its working capital.

Strategy

Investors Bancorp continues to expand its geographic reach in its core New Jersey and New York markets and boost its loan and deposit business mainly through select bank and branch acquisitions. Indeed the bank noted in 2015 that it had made eight bank or branch acquisitions since 2008 adding that they have counted for "a significant portion" of the bank's historic growth.

The company's 2014 and 2013 bank acquisitions bolstered its expansion in New Jersey into the suburbs of Philadelphia the boroughs of New York City the Nassau and Suffolk Counties on Long Island and historic markets throughout New Jersey.

Mergers and Acquisitions

In May 2016 Investors Bancorp agreed to purchase the $1 billion-asset The Bank of Princeton along with its 13 branches in the greater Princeton New Jersey and Philadelphia Pennsylvania areas. The added locations would grow Investors Bancorp's branch network by almost 10% to 156 branches in the Philadelphia to New York City corridor.

In January 2014 Investors Bancorp purchased Gateway Community Financial Corp along with its four branches in Gloucester County New Jersey. The deal added nearly $255 million in customer deposits and $195 million in new loan business to its books.

In December 2013 the company bought Roma Financial Corporation and its 26 branches in Burlington Ocean Mercer Camden and Middlesex counties in New Jersey. The deal added $1.34 billion in deposits and $991 million in loan assets while expanding the company's reach into the Philadelphia suburbs of New Jersey.

Company Background

In late 2012 the company acquired Marathon Banking Corporation (a subsidiary of Greece-based Piraeus Bank) for $135 million adding 13 branches in the New York metro area and more than doubling its branches in New York. The deal also would mark Investors Bancorp's entry into Manhattan and Staten Island.

EXECUTIVES

SEVP and COO, Domenick A. Cama, age 62, $621,000 total compensation

President and CEO, Kevin Cummings, age 63, $935,000 total compensation

EVP and Chief Lending Officer, Richard S. Spengler, age 56, $400,000 total compensation

EVP and Chief Retail Banking Officer, Paul Kalamaras, $375,000 total compensation

SVP and CFO, Sean Burke

Senior Vice President, Jawad Chaudhry

Vice President Information Security Officer

Director of Information Security, David Van

Vice President Systems, Charles Little

Chairman, Robert M. Cashill, age 75

Auditors: KPMG LLP

LOCATIONS

HQ: Investors Bancorp Inc (New)
101 JFK Parkway, Short Hills, NJ 07078
Phone: 973 924-5100
Web: www.myinvestorsbank.com

PRODUCTS/OPERATIONS

2014 Sales

	$ mil.	% of total
Interest		
Loans receivable and held-for-sale	603.4	86
Mortgage-backed securities	44.2	6
Federal Home Loan Bank stock	6.9	1
Municipal bonds & other debt	5.7	1
Other	0.7	-
Non-interest		
Fees & service charges	19.3	3
Gain on loan transaction	5.3	2
Others	17.2	1
Total	**702.7**	**100**

COMPETITORS

Bank of America
Bank of New York Mellon
Citigroup
ConnectOne Bancorp
Fulton Financial
M&T Bank
New York Community Bancorp
OceanFirst Financial
PNC Financial

HISTORICAL FINANCIALS

Company Type: Public

Income Statement — FYE: December 31

	ASSETS ($ mil.)	NET INCOME ($ mil.)	INCOME AS % OF ASSETS	EMPLOYEES
12/17	25,129.2	126.7	0.5%	1,959
12/16	23,174.6	192.1	0.8%	1,829
12/15	20,888.6	181.5	0.9%	1,768
12/14	18,773.6	131.7	0.7%	1,708
12/13	15,623.0	112.0	0.7%	1,597
Annual Growth	**12.6%**	**3.1%**	**—**	**5.2%**

2017 Year-End Financials

Return on assets: 0.5%
Return on equity: 4.0%
Long-term debt ($ mil.): —
No. of shares (mil.): 306.1
Sales ($ mil): 917.3

Dividends
Yield: 0.0%
Payout: 76.7%
Market value ($ mil.): 4,249.0

	STOCK PRICE ($) FY Close	P/E High/Low	Earnings	Dividends	Book Value
12/17	13.88	34 29	0.43	0.33	10.21
12/16	13.95	22 16	0.64	0.26	10.09
12/15	12.44	24 19	0.55	0.25	9.89
12/14	11.23	74 26	0.38	0.08	9.99
12/13	25.58	64 44	0.40	0.00	3.78
Annual Growth	**(14.2%)**	**— —**	**2.1%**	**—**	**28.2%**

IPG Photonics Corp

IPG Photonics has a laser focus on spreading the use of lasers. The company makes fiber lasers and amplifiers and diode lasers which are primarily used in materials processing applications (nearly 90% of sales) such as welding cutting marking and engraving. Its fiber lasers are used in 3D printing and telecommunications. IPG Photonics is moving into automotive manufacturing applications and the developing market for medical uses. The company's customers have included BAE SYSTEMS Mitsubishi Heavy Industries and Nippon Steel. Deriving about 85% of its sales outside North America IPG Photonics operates sales offices in more than a dozen countries in Asia and Europe.

Operations

The vertically integrated manufacturer designs and makes most of the components used in its finished products (which can cost hundreds of thousands of dollars) from semiconductor diodes to optical fiber preforms finished fiber lasers and amplifiers. It also manufactures other products used in its lasers including optical delivery cables fiber couplers beam switches optical heads and chillers. By not outsourcing its manufacturing to third-party companies IPG Photonics is able to better control its proprietary processes and technologies as well as the supply of its materials.

The company's biggest market is in materials processing which accounts for 94% of revenue.

Geographic Reach

The company conducts R&D in the same city as its headquarters as well as in New Hampshire and overseas in the German city of Burbach (near Frankfurt) and in Fryazino Russia (outside Moscow).

It has four manufacturing facilities for lasers amplifiers and components one in each of its R&D cities and the fourth one in Cerro Maggiore Italy outside Milan. Manufacturing facilities for optical components are in India and China.

In terms of geographic markets China is the company's biggest accounting for 35% of revenue. The next biggest single country is the US generating 15% followed by Germany with 10% and Japan with 8%.

Sales and Marketing

IPG Photonics primarily uses a direct sales force. It has a diverse customer base - its five-largest customers only account for about 25% of sales. Its biggest customer is in China and accounts for 13% of sales. In 2015 the company shipped nearly 33000 units to moire than 3000 customers worldwide.

It has sales offices at each of its manufacturing facilities as well as in Michigan and California in the US. International sales offices are located in China Czech Republic France India Italy South Korea Spain Singapore Turkey and the UK.

Financial Performance

IPG Photonics is beaming after a 17% revenue increase in 2015. The company's sales reach $901 million for the year from $770 million in 2014. Materials processing of course provided most of the increase rising 16% with higher sales of quasi-continuous wave (QCW) pulsed lasers for welding and cutting. The company's smaller segments also grew in 2015 with the medical segment rising 100% for the year.

The rising sales at IPG Photonics drove profit 21% higher in 2015 to $242 million. Cash from operating activities also rose in 2015 from 2014.

Strategy

IPG remains focused on fiber lasers as an alternative to conventional lasers such as gas or crystal. Its strategy is to exploit the advantages that fiber lasers offer such as superiority in electrical efficiency beam quality and control maintenance costs longevity flexibility and usability. Traditional laser technologies have advantages that make them more suitable for some applications but fiber lasers continue to gain ground. Crystal lasers generate higher peak power pulses fiber lasers don't achieve the deep ultraviolet light needed for some semiconductor applications and carbon dioxide lasers are better for non-metallic applications such has plastics. Fiber lasers however have made improvements in power output that has opened them up to new markets and IPG believes the technology can reach additional nascent applications such as natural resource extraction.

IPG released a threebeam fiber laser system for brazing zinc-coated steel a process used in the automobile industry. The company is positioning fiber laser products for the auto industry and the trend toward the lighter weight metals such as high strength steel and aluminum. We are also encouraged by the potential for increased volumes of our laser seam stepper that welds auto bodies.

In 2015 some makers of consumer electronics adopted the company's QCW lasers for making their products and multi-hundred volume orders.

IPG formed a separate company IPG Medical in 2015 to focus on medical applications. The company is developing its Thulium fiber laser to break up kidney stones faster and and more simply than current technologies.

Mergers and Acquisitions

Increasing demand has led IPG to pursue operational expansion in Russia Germany and the US. In 2012 the company paid $55.4 million to acquire the 22.5% of Russia-based subsidiary NTO IRE-Polus that it did not already own to extend its control over R&D sales and manufacturing infrastructure in the country.

Also in 2012 IPG bought privately held J.P. Sercel Associates (JPSA) a New Hampshire-based supplier of UV excimer and diode-pumped solid-state industrial laser micromachining systems used in high-volume biomedical industrial automation LED microelectromechanical systems (MEMS) microfluidics thin-film solar panel and semiconductor manufacturing applications. The purchase expands IPG's custom laser system offerings to include fine processing precision cutting drilling and micromachining of ceramics glass and semiconductors. The company further enhanced its UV laser development with the purchase the following year of California-based Mobius Photonics.

HISTORY

IPG Photonics raised about $100 million in private equity funding with its investors including Apax Partners Merrill Lynch TA Associates and Winston Partners. The company filed for an IPO in 2000 and withdrew the registration statement six months later. It filed for another IPO in 2006 and completed the offering by the end of the year.

The company used proceeds of its public offering to repurchase warrants pay off debts and for general corporate purposes including working capital expansion of manufacturing facilities purchases of equipment and expansion of applications development and services.

In 2007 IPG Photonics acquired its Chinese distributor HM Laser and established a subsidiary IPG China with an office in Beijing. China is one of IPG's principal markets along with Germany Japan Russia and the US.

The company stepped forward with its purchase of laser material manufacturer Photonics Innovations (PII) in January 2010. The acquisition expanded IPG's products and services portfolio for optical and laser materials fabrication tunable laser design and optical and sensing systems. Transaction details were not divulged.

EXECUTIVES

Vice President Communications Products, George Buabbud

Chairman and CEO, Valentin P. Gapontsev, age 80, $687,981 total compensation

COO, Eugene Scherbakov, age 70, $450,449 total compensation

SVP and CFO, Timothy P. V. Mammen, age 49, $440,067 total compensation

Director of Research and Development IPG Laser, Igor Samartsev, age 56

SVP Components, Alexander (Alex) Ovtchinnikov, age 57, $400,579 total compensation

SVP U.S. Operations, Felix Stukalin, age 56

Upper Management Vice President, Laura Richards

Vice President of Human Resources Worldwide, John Weaver

Vice President Strategic Marketing, Yuri Erokhin

Vice President Advanced Industrial Applications, Leonid Lev

Auditors: Deloitte & Touche LLP

LOCATIONS

HQ: IPG Photonics Corp
50 Old Webster Road, Oxford, MA 01540
Phone: 508 373-1100
Web: www.ipgphotonics.com

PRODUCTS/OPERATIONS

2015 Sales by Market

	$ mil.	% of total
Materials processing	849.3	94
Advanced applications	28.9	3
Communications	14.4	2
Medical	8.6	1
Total	**901.2**	**100**

Selected Products

Broadband light sources
Continuous wave lasers
Diode laser systems
Diode-pumped solid-state laser systems
Erbium lasers
Fiber amplifiers
Fiber lasers
Fiber-coupled direct diode laser systems
Pulsed fiber lasers
Raman pump lasers
Thulium lasers
UV excimer laser systems
Ytterbium lasers

COMPETITORS

Cisco Systems	Newport Corp.
Coherent Inc.	Novanta
EMCORE	Oclaro
FANUC	Presstek
Furukawa Electric	Swatch
Huawei Technologies	TRUMPF
Mitsubishi Materials	Viavi Solutions

HISTORICAL FINANCIALS

Company Type: Public

Income Statement — FYE: December 31

	REVENUE ($ mil.)	NET INCOME ($ mil.)	NET PROFIT MARGIN	EMPLOYEES
12/17	1,408.8	347.6	24.7%	5,390
12/16	1,006.1	260.7	25.9%	4,510
12/15	901.2	242.1	26.9%	4,020
12/14	769.8	200.4	26.0%	3,370
12/13	648.0	155.7	24.0%	2,800
Annual Growth	**21.4%**	**22.2%**	**—**	**17.8%**

2017 Year-End Financials

Debt ratio: 2.0%
Return on equity: 19.4%
Cash ($ mil.): 909.9
Current ratio: 8.82
Long-term debt ($ mil.): 45.3
No. of shares (mil.): 53.6
Dividends
Yield: —
Payout: —
Market value ($ mil.): 11,484.0

	STOCK PRICE ($) FY Close	P/E High/Low	Earnings	Dividends	Book Value
12/17	214.13	38 15	6.36	0.00	37.71
12/16	98.71	21 15	4.85	0.00	29.25
12/15	89.16	22 15	4.53	0.00	23.82
12/14	74.92	20 16	3.79	0.00	19.98
12/13	77.61	26 18	2.97	0.00	17.87
Annual Growth	**28.9%**	**— —**	**21.0%**	**—**	**20.5%**

iRobot Corp

If you want a glimpse of the robot future cast your eyes to the floor. That's where iRobot's Roomba vacuums scurry to and fro sweeping up dirt and dust bunnies. Models range from basic sweepers to higher end devices that can be programmed for specific houses. iRobot has offices in the US UK China and Hong Kong and sells its home products worldwide through retailers and distributors. Just more than half of its annual sales are in the US. Since its founding in 1990 by engineers from the Massachusetts Institute of Technology iRobot has sold more than 20 million robots.

Operations

iRobot sells consumer products that are designed for both indoor and outdoor cleaning applications. It offers Roomba floor vacuuming robots at prices ranging from $299 to $899. The company also offers the Braava family of mopping robots. In association with Aquatron Inc. iRobot sells the Mirra Pool Cleaning Robot for cleaning residential pools.

In 2016 iRobot sold its defense and security business unit and exited the remote presence market to focus on the consumer market.

Geographic Reach

Bedford Massachusetts-based iRobot has offices in the US the UK China Austria Belgium France Germany Netherlands Portugal Spain Japan and Hong Kong. Its research and development facilities are in Bedford and Pasadena California. Sales to customers outside the US account for nearly half of the company's revenue.

The company contracts manufacturing to third parties in China. Strained trade relations between the US and China that involve higher tariffs could have a negative impact on iRobot's sales.

Sales and Marketing

iRobot sells through distributors and retailers as well as online. Its biggest customer is Amazon.com which accounts for about 15% of revenue. About 60% of the company's revenue comes from 15 customers who are distributors or retailers.

The company markets its products through national advertising consumer and industry trade shows and direct marketing. The company increased its ad spending by about a third to about $92 million in 2017.

Financial Performance

iRobot has enjoyed rising sales and profit over the past few years thanks to its home robot line. Revenue rose about 33% to $883 million in 2017 from 2016 on a 25% increase in units shipped and an 11% increase in average selling price. US consumer revenue rose about 42% in 2017 which the company attributed to its investments in advertising and promotions and adoption of its Roomba 900 and Roomba 600 series robots. International consumer revenue rose about 28% in 2017 from 2016. The company shipped about 3.7 million robots in 2017 compared to about 2.9 million the year before.

The company's profit rose 21% to $51 million in 2017 from 2016 as it reduced cost of revenue and general and administrative expenses as a percentage of sales. Those savings were somewhat offset by higher expenses for research and development and sales and marketing.

Cash holdings at iRobot stood at about $128 million at the end of 2017 compared to about $214 million in 2016. The company spent about $150 million in 2017 to acquire distributors SODC and Robopolis. It also invested $23 million in property and equipment including machinery and tooling for new products.

Strategy

iRobot has locked in on the consumer market after selling off its defense-related business and getting out of the remote presence for medical applications business. The company has developed new products with a software that enables iRobot products to better understand the homes in which they operate.

The company's recent models extend mapping visual navigation and cloud connectivity to a wider range of customers. The iRobot HOME App allows users them to choose the appropriate cleaning options for their home. iRobot uses Amazon Web Services cloud to increase the number of connected robots it supports globally and provide more smart home capabilities.

The connectivity capabilities thrust iRobot into the news in 2017 over fears that the vacuums were spying on customers and that the company would sell customer information to third parties. iRobot officials said connectivity was necessary to communicate with customers' smart phones that most data would be kept in the vacuum's memory and that the company would not sell data.

iRobot invested in driving international sales with the acquisitions of key distributors in Europe (Robopolis) and Japan (Sales On Demand Corp. (SODC)) for about $150 million total. The acquisitions provide iRobot with greater control of the sales and marketing of its products in key overseas markets.

Mergers and Acquisitions

In 2017 iRobot acquired Robopolis SAS a French company to expand its enhance distribution network provide consistent branding and improved service for European customers.

Also in 2017 iRobot bought Sales On Demand Corp. (SODC) in Japan for the same reasons it acquired Robopolis.

EXECUTIVES

EVP Human Resources and Corporate Communications, Russell J. (Russ) Campanello, age 62, $51,923 total compensation

Chairman and CEO, Colin M. Angle, age 50, $463,897 total compensation

EVP and Chief Legal Counsel, Glen D. Weinstein, age 47, $290,353 total compensation

EVP and CFO, Alison Dean, age 53, $228,654 total compensation

COO, Christian Cerda

Vice President Investor Relations, Elise Caffrey

SVP SALES, Steven Rogers

Vice President and Assistant General Counsel, Tonya Drake

Vice President Advanced Development, Mark Chiappetta

Board Member, Andrew Miller

Auditors: PricewaterhouseCoopers LLP

LOCATIONS

HQ: iRobot Corp
8 Crosby Drive, Bedford, MA 01730
Phone: 781 430-3000
Web: www.irobot.com

COMPETITORS

AM General	General Dynamics
Allen-Vanguard Corporation	LG Electronics
BAE SYSTEMS	Lockheed Martin
BISSELL	Miele
Electrolux	QinetiQ
GE Appliances & Lighting	Samsung Electronics
	Whirlpool

HISTORICAL FINANCIALS

Company Type: Public

Income Statement				FYE: December 31
	REVENUE ($ mil.)	NET INCOME ($ mil.)	NET PROFIT MARGIN	EMPLOYEES
12/17	883.9	50.9	5.8%	920
12/16*	660.6	41.9	6.3%	607
01/16	616.7	44.1	7.2%	622
12/14	556.8	37.8	6.8%	572
12/13	487.4	27.6	5.7%	528
Annual Growth	16.0%	16.5%	—	14.9%

*Fiscal year change

2017 Year-End Financials

Debt ratio: —
Return on equity: 11.8%
Cash ($ mil.): 128.6
Current ratio: 2.20
Long-term debt ($ mil.): —

No. of shares (mil.): 27.9
Dividends
  Yield: —
  Payout: —
Market value ($ mil.): 2,143.0

	STOCK PRICE ($)	P/E	PER SHARE ($)		
	FY Close	High/Low	Earnings	Dividends	Book Value
12/17	76.70	58 29	1.77	0.00	16.83
12/16*	58.45	40 19	1.48	0.00	14.28
01/16	35.40	25 19	1.47	0.00	14.35
12/14	34.81	36 24	1.25	0.00	13.17
12/13	35.41	42 19	0.94	0.00	11.43
Annual Growth	21.3%	— —	17.1%	—	10.2%

*Fiscal year change

iStar Inc

iStar Financial is a real estate investment trust (REIT) that acts as a private banker for owners of high-end commercial real estate in the US and abroad. Its financing activities include first mortgages senior and mezzanine real estate debt and corporate capital net lease financing and equity investments. The REIT's loans typically range in size from $20 million to $150 million and are mainly secured by apartments or other residential properties office complexes land hotels or industrial retail entertainment or mixed-use properties. Office or industrial properties make up 25% of its secured assets while land makes up another 20%.

Operations

iStar operates four business segments based on portfolio strategy. The Real Estate Finance portfolio is primarily comprised of senior and mezzanine real estate loans that may be either fixed-rate or variable-rate. It also includes senior and subordinated loans to corporations. The Net Lease portfolio is made up of company-owned properties leased to tenants where the properties are subject to long-term leases.

The Operating Properties portfolio represent a diverse pool of assets across a broad range of geographies and property types. The commercial properties within this portfolio include office retail and hotel properties. The residential properties within this portfolio are generally luxury condominium projects. iStar seeks to reposition or redevelop these assets with the objective of maximizing their value through the infusion of capital and/or intensive asset management efforts. Finally the Land portfolio is made up of master planned communities as well as waterfront and urban infill land parcels.

The REIT makes more than 50% of its revenue from operating lease income which the firm gets from its net lease assets and commercial operating properties. About 25% of iStar's revenue comes from interest income from its financing services.

Geographic Reach

The New York-based company has regional offices in Atlanta; Dallas; Hartford Connecticut; San Francisco and Los Angeles. Its properties are located across 33 US states with about 25% of property assets in the Northeast 20% in the West 15% in the Mid-Atlantic 15% in the Southeast and 13% in the Southwest.

Sales and Marketing

Some iStar's customers include AT&T Drake Hotel Landmark Apartment Trust Marina Palms La Kapolei Van Dyke Commons The Ilikai Hotel Paramount Bay Ocean House University Technical Institute (UTI) and Solo Cup.

Financial Performance

iStar's revenue has been on the uptrend in recent years mostly thanks to rising operating lease income as the firm has acquired more property assets charged higher rent and increased occupancy rates over time.

iStar's revenue jumped by 18% to $462 million in 2014 mostly as it made a $19.5 million gain on sales of non-performing loans and $16.5 million on asset-related settlements. Additionally the firm enjoyed 4% growth in operating lease income from higher rental prices and occupancy rates during the year as well as 14% growth in interest income as the firm originated more investments and financed a higher volume of loans during the year.

Following three years of losses stemming from the company's high interest expenses iStar reported a profit of $16.45 million in 2014 mostly as interest expenses declined sharply during the year as it continued to reduce its long-term debt . In addition the firm's equity method investment gains increased by $50 million compared to the prior year further padding its bottom line. iStar's operating cash also improved sharply thanks to higher cash earnings.

Strategy

As its Net Lease property business continues to grow even driving the company to a profit in 2014 for the first time since 2010 iStar has been looking for more ways to make money in the landlord business. In 2014 for example the company partnered with a sovereign wealth fund to form its Net Lease Venture with plans to invest $500 million in equity to acquire and develop up to $1.25 billion worth of net lease assets. iStar would own a majority non-controlling interest in the venture.

Struggling to dig out of liabilities stemming from the real estate slump the company's core strategy is to sell non-core assets and raise capital (including secured and unsecured debt financing debt exchanges asset sales issuances of equity joint ventures and other third party capital arrangements) and invest in its core business. Accordingly the firm often divests in properties to lock in gains for future investments. In 2013 iState sold its 24% stake in LNR Property LLC for $220 million. During 2012 the company sold a portfolio of 12 net lease assets for a gain of $24.9 million. It also sold net lease assets for a gain of $2.4 million and sold commercial properties valued at $29.3 million and land assets ($72.1 million).

On the growth side of the business in 2013 the company sold the entire inventory of homes in phase two of its VIVE luxury townhome community project in Asbury Park New Jersey.

Company Background

The economic recession that began in 2008 impacted iStar in two critical ways. The tightening credit markets made it more difficult for the company to secure both debt and equity financing for its commercial real estate lending and investment activities. And the deterioration of the real estate markets caused the firm's nonperforming loans to balloon. iStar began limiting its new investments while focusing on resolving non-performing loans and improving credit quality.

EXECUTIVES

Chairman and CEO, Jay Sugarman, age 55, $1,000,000 total compensation
EVP Land and Development, Steven P. Magee
EVP Chief Investment Officer and Chief Legal Officer, Nina B. Matis, age 70, $500,000 total compensation
EVP Investments, Barclay G. Jones, age 57
EVP Investments and Head Capital Markets, Michelle M. Mackay, $400,000 total compensation
SVP, Chase S. Curtis
EVP Investments, Vernon B. Schwartz, age 63
COO and CFO, Geoffrey G. Jervis, age 46
EVP Land and Development, Karl Frey
Vice President Information Technology Security, Phil Burke
Auditors: PricewaterhouseCoopers LLP

LOCATIONS

HQ: iStar Inc
1114 Avenue of the Americas, 39th Floor, New York, NY 10036
Phone: 212 930-9400   **Fax:** 212 930-9494
Web: www.istar.com

PRODUCTS/OPERATIONS

2014 Sales

	% of total
Interest	53
Operating lease income	27
Other	20
Total	**100**

2014 Property Distribution

Property/Collateral Type	% of total
Office/Industrial	26
Land	22
Mixed Use/Mixed Colleteral	13
Entertainment/Leisure	11
Hotel	9
Retail	6
Condominim	5
Strategic Investments	2
Others	6
Total	**100**

COMPETITORS

Annaly Capital Management	Dynex Capital
CIFC	MFA Financial
Capital Trust	NovaStar Financial
Capstead Mortgage	Redwood Trust

HISTORICAL FINANCIALS

Company Type: Public

Income Statement				FYE: December 31
	REVENUE ($ mil.)	NET INCOME ($ mil.)	NET PROFIT MARGIN	EMPLOYEES
12/17	679.2	175.6	25.9%	186
12/16	477.0	95.3	20.0%	193
12/15	514.5	(2.4)	—	188
12/14	462.0	16.4	3.6%	182
12/13	390.7	(111.9)	—	175
Annual Growth	**14.8%**	**—**	**—**	**1.5%**

2017 Year-End Financials

Debt ratio: 73.4%
Return on equity: 18.5%
Cash ($ mil.): 657.6
Current ratio: 3.29
Long-term debt ($ mil.): 3,476.4
No. of shares (mil.): 68.2
Dividends
 Yield: —
 Payout: —
Market value ($ mil.): 771.0

	STOCK PRICE ($) FY Close	P/E High/Low		PER SHARE ($) Earnings	Dividends	Book Value
12/17	11.30	8	7	1.56	0.00	12.89
12/16	12.37	21	13	0.55	0.00	14.11
12/15	11.73	—	—	(0.62)	0.00	13.06
12/14	13.65	—	—	(0.40)	0.00	14.05
12/13	14.27	—	—	(1.83)	0.00	14.85
Annual Growth	**(5.7%)**	—	—	—	—	**(3.5%)**

J.Jill Inc

Auditors: PricewaterhouseCoopers LLP

LOCATIONS

HQ: J.Jill Inc
4 Batterymarch Park, Quincy, MA 02169
Phone: 617 376-4300
Web: www.jjill.com

HISTORICAL FINANCIALS

Company Type: Public

Income Statement				FYE: February 3
	REVENUE ($ mil.)	NET INCOME ($ mil.)	NET PROFIT MARGIN	EMPLOYEES
02/18*	698.1	55.3	7.9%	3,755
01/17	639.0	24.0	3.8%	3,801
01/16	420.0	4.3	1.0%	3,801
05/15	141.9	(1.9)	—	0
01/15	483.4	10.3	2.1%	0
Annual Growth	**9.6%**	**52.3%**	**—**	**—**

*Fiscal year change

2018 Year-End Financials

Debt ratio: 40.4%
Return on equity: 36.2%
Cash ($ mil.): 25.9
Current ratio: 1.26
Long-term debt ($ mil.): 238.8
No. of shares (mil.): 43.7
Dividends
 Yield: —
 Payout: —
Market value ($ mil.): 358.0

	STOCK PRICE ($) FY Close	P/E High/Low		PER SHARE ($) Earnings	Dividends	Book Value
02/18*	8.18	11	4	1.27	0.00	4.10
Annual Growth	**—**	—	—	**—**	**—**	**—**

*Fiscal year change

---

j2 Global Inc (New)

EXECUTIVES

VP Engineering, Vincent P. (Vince) Niedzielski
VP Human Resources, Patty Brunton
EVP Corporate Strategy, Zohar Loshitzer, age 58
CEO, Nehemia (Hemi) Zucker, age 59, $459,000 total compensation
Chairman, Richard S. Ressler, age 58, $144,000 total compensation
CFO, Kathleen M. (Kathy) Griggs, age 62, $270,000 total compensation
President, R. Scott Turicchi, age 53, $375,000 total compensation
VP Products, Michael W. Harris, age 53
VP General Counsel and Secretary, Jeffrey D. (Jeff) Adelman, age 49, $270,000 total compensation
Vice President Marketing, Mike Pugh
VP Corporate Development, Ken Truesdale
VP Network Operations, Alan Alters
Vice President International, Tim McLean
VP and General Manager Europe, Paul Kinsella
Manager of Operations, Warner Bros
Vice President General Counsel Secretary, Jeff Adelman
Vice President Engineering, Vince Niedzielski
Chief Accounting Officer, Steve Dunn
Director, William B. (Brian) Kretzmer, age 61
Director, Douglas Y. Bech, age 71
Director, Robert J. Cresci, age 72
Director, John F. Rieley, age 73
Director, Michael P. Schulhof, age 74
Director, Stephen Ross, age 67
Auditors: BDO USA, LLP

LOCATIONS

HQ: j2 Global Inc (New)
6922 Hollywood Boulevard, Suite 500, Los Angeles, CA
90028
Phone: 323 860-9200
Web: www.j2.com

COMPETITORS

CommTouch Software	Notify Technology
Deltathree	Open Text
EasyLink	Satellink
FuzeBox	

HISTORICAL FINANCIALS

Company Type: Public

Income Statement				FYE: December 31
	REVENUE ($ mil.)	NET INCOME ($ mil.)	NET PROFIT MARGIN	EMPLOYEES
12/17	1,117.8	139.4	12.5%	2,487
12/16	874.2	152.4	17.4%	2,426
12/15	720.8	133.6	18.5%	1,608
12/14	599.0	124.3	20.8%	1,410
12/13	520.8	107.5	20.6%	1,130
Annual Growth	21.0%	6.7%		21.8%

2017 Year-End Financials

Debt ratio: 40.8%	No. of shares (mil.): 47.8
Return on equity: 14.4%	Dividends
Cash ($ mil.): 350.9	Yield: 0.0%
Current ratio: 2.34	Payout: 53.7%
Long-term debt ($ mil.): 1,001.9	Market value ($ mil.): 3,591.0

	STOCK PRICE ($) FY Close	P/E High/Low	PER SHARE ($) Earnings	Dividends	Book Value
12/17	75.03	32 25	2.83	1.52	21.32
12/16	81.80	26 18	3.13	1.36	19.28
12/15	82.32	30 21	2.73	1.22	18.57
12/14	62.00	24 17	2.58	0.56	17.30
12/13	50.01	24 13	2.28	0.98	15.32
Annual Growth	10.7%	— —	5.6%	11.6%	8 6%

John Bean Technologies Corp

John Bean Technologies Corporation (JBT) keeps food cold and jets in the air. JBT manufactures industrial equipment for the food processing and air transportation industries. Its JBT FoodTech segment makes commercial-grade refrigeration systems freezers ovens canning equipment and food processing systems for fruit meats seafood and ready-to-eat meals. JBT AeroTech manufactures and services ground support equipment (plane deicers aircraft tow vehicles and cargo loading systems) airport gate equipment (its Jetway brand) and military equipment. More than half of JBT's revenue is generated in the US.

Operations

JBT operates through two segments: FoodTech and AeroTech.

The FoodTech business (contributing more than 70% of total revenue) includes protein technology such as systems for chilling mixing grinding portioning and packaging meats; liquid foods solutions for extracting concentrating and preserving fruit juices; and automated systems including robotic vehicle systems for material handling in manufacturing and warehouse facilities.

Its AeroTech segment (close to 30%) provides airport ground support and services for airport authorities airlines airfreight companies military forces and defense contractors. Products include mobile equipment such as its Commander and Ranger cargo loaders and aircraft towing and deicing equipment; fixed equipment (its Jetway gate equipment for passenger boarding); and airport services such as maintenance for airport equipment systems and facilities.

Geographic Reach

JBT owns production facilities located in seven US states and six European countries as well as in South America South Africa and China. It also has several technical centers and sales and service offices located worldwide.

The company sells its products to more than 100 countries. The US accounts for more than half its sales.

Sales and Marketing

JBT sells and markets its products and services primarily through a direct sales force supplemented with independent distributors and sales representatives. It also educates its customers about products through newsletters websites seminars trade shows user groups and conferences.

Financial Performance

JBT's revenue increased 21% to $1.6 billion in 2017 compared with 2016. The increase in revenue was driven by sales from acquisitions in 2017.

Operating expenses for both products and services as well as research and development costs have increased significantly for JBT. Net income however has risen dramatically over the past three years with an increase of 19% to $80.5 million in 2017 and a 21% jump to $67.6 million in 2016. The increase in 2017 was mainly due to higher revenue as well as a $10.6 million decrease in restructuring expenses and a $15.5 million tax benefit due to the Tax Cuts and Jobs Act.

Cash at the end of fiscal 2017 was $34.0 million an increase of $800000 from the prior year. Cash from operations contributed $104.6 million to the coffers while investing activities used $139.9 million mainly for acquisitions. Financing activities used another $34.7 million for dividends to stockholders and the company's stock repurchase program.

Strategy

JBT is in the midst of its "Elevate" strategy launched in 2017 which encompasses four key priorities: new product development recurring revenue organic growth and efficiency and acquisitions.

New products include JBT's advanced DSI system which uses vision technology and software along with high-velocity water streams to cut poultry and other proteins into specific portions. The company also introduced its iOPS technology which uses data collection and advanced algorithms to monitor its customers' JBT equipment. iOPS provides automatic fault alerts reducing equipment down time. JBT is also tailoring its products to the exploding Asian market and has established a technology center in Kunshan China. In addition it's expanding the functionality of its automated guided vehicles (AGVs) for tasks such as repetitive forklift work and introducing new food equipment technology that automates manual tasks in food production facilities.

Acquisitions continue to be one of the company's key growth drivers. JBT has made more than six acquisitions in the past three years adding to its products and capabilities and expanding its geographic reach.

Mergers and Acquisitions

In 2018 JBT acquired Netherlands-based FTNON a provider of equipment and solutions for the fresh produce ready meals and pet food industries for €32 million. FTNON offers robotic technology for cutting coring and peeling fruits and vegetables allowing JBT to penetrate the fresh cut equipment market and leveraging the increasing demand for ready-to-eat fresh produce.

JBT made three acquisitions in 2017 aimed at bolstering revenue and adding to its portfolio of businesses. The company acquired Europe-based PLF International a provider of powder filling systems (for flour spices baby formula etc.) for the global food and beverage markets for £28 million. PLF adds complementary products and expertise to JBT's operations expands its business geographically and strengthens its aftermarket opportunities. In the same year it purchased Avure Technologies for $57 million. Avure makes high pressure processing (HPP) systems a cold pasteurization technology that ensures food safety and freshness without heat or preservatives. Avure will benefit from JBT's global sales force service support and extensive customer relationships.

Also in 2017 the company bought Aircraft Maintenance Support Services (AMSS) a privately held manufacturer of military aviation equipment based in the UK for £10 million. AMSS enhances JBT's AeroTech segment with military offerings and expanded access to foreign military organizations.

Company Background

John Bean Technologies was spun off from FMC Technologies in 2008. JBT Corporation takes its name from John Bean a California inventor who founded Bean Spray Pump Company in 1884 the company which eventually became Food Machinery Corporation (FMC) through a series of mergers and acquisitions in the 20th century. (The original Bean Spray Pump technology was adapted to make a plane deicer in the 1960s.)

EXECUTIVES

EVP and President JBT AeroTech, David C. Burdakin, age 63, $365,000 total compensation
Chairman President and CEO, Thomas W. Giacomini, age 53, $733,333 total compensation
EVP Human Resources, Mark K. Montague, $342,539 total compensation
EVP CFO and Treasurer, Brian A. Deck, $334,583 total compensation
EVP and President JBT FoodTech, Steven R. (Steve) Smith, $367,449 total compensation
EVP General Counsel and Secretary, James L. Marvin
Auditors: KPMG LLP

LOCATIONS

HQ: John Bean Technologies Corp
70 West Madison Street, Suite 4400, Chicago, IL 60602
Phone: 312 861-5900
Web: www.jbtcorporation.com

PRODUCTS/OPERATIONS

2017 Sales

	$ mil.	% of total
JBT FoodTech	1,171.9	72
JBT AeroTech	463.0	28
Other revenue and eliminations	0.2	-
Total	**1,635.1**	**100**

2017 Sales

	$ mil.	% of total
Product revenue	1,376.8	84
Service revenue	258.3	16
Total	**1,635.1**	**100**

Selected Products & Services

JBT FoodTech
- Blow-Molders
- Brine Preparation
- Choppers Corers Cutters Emulsifiers & Peelers
- High Pressure Processors (HPP)
- Injection Equipment
- Installation Services
- Juicers Finishers & Extractors
- Laboratory Devices
- Liquid Process Engineering/Design & Build
- Lubricants
- Massagers (Polar)
- Ovens & Cookers
- Pasteurizers & Sterilizers
- Portioners & Slicers
- Product Labeling
- Tanks & ASME Pressure Vessels
- Tenderizers Macerators & Presses
- Washers Loaders Sizers & Conveyors

AeroTech
- Cargo Loaders
- Tempest Deicers
- Conventional Tow Bar Tractors
- Expediter Towbarless Tractors
- Jetaire Pre-Conditioned Air
- Jetpower Mobile GPUs
- Passenger Steps
- Belt Loaders
- Ambulift
- Fuel Tank Repair Trolley

COMPETITORS

Air T	Heat and Control
Alarko	Hobart Corp.
Barry-Wehmiller	Illinois Tool Works
Carlisle FoodService	Manitowoc
Duke Manufacturing	Middleby
GEA Group	ThyssenKrupp Elevator

HISTORICAL FINANCIALS

Company Type: Public

Income Statement

FYE: December 31

	REVENUE ($ mil.)	NET INCOME ($ mil.)	NET PROFIT MARGIN	EMPLOYEES
12/17	1,635.1	80.5	4.9%	5,800
12/16	1,350.5	67.6	5.0%	5,000
12/15	1,107.3	55.9	5.0%	4,200
12/14	984.2	30.8	3.1%	3,500
12/13	934.2	33.1	3.5%	3,330
Annual Growth	**15.0%**	**24.9%**	**—**	**14.9%**

2017 Year-End Financials

Debt ratio: 27.5%	No. of shares (mil.): 31.5
Return on equity: 25.8%	Dividends
Cash ($ mil.): 34.0	Yield: 0.0%
Current ratio: 1.33	Payout: 15.8%
Long-term debt ($ mil.): 372.7	Market value ($ mil.): 3,499.0

	STOCK PRICE ($) FY Close	P/E High/Low		PER SHARE ($) Earnings	Dividends	Book Value
12/17	110.80	47	32	2.53	0.40	13.99
12/16	85.95	40	18	2.27	0.40	6.17
12/15	49.83	27	16	1.88	0.37	4.45
12/14	32.86	33	25	1.03	0.36	4.10
12/13	29.33	26	16	1.11	0.34	5.33
Annual Growth	**39.4%**	**—**		**22.9%**	**4.1%**	**27.3%**

Kaanapali Land LLC

EXECUTIVES

Pres-ceo, Gary Nickele
Auditors: GRANT THORNTON LLP

LOCATIONS

HQ: Kaanapali Land LLC
900 N. Michigan Ave., Chicago, IL 60611
Phone: 312 915-1987
Web: www.kaanapalidevelopment.com

HISTORICAL FINANCIALS

Company Type: Public

Income Statement

FYE: December 31

	REVENUE ($ mil.)	NET INCOME ($ mil.)	NET PROFIT MARGIN	EMPLOYEES
12/17	15.9	10.7	67.1%	23
12/16	8.3	(16.6)	—	25
12/15	6.8	(3.5)	—	26
12/14	19.0	(1.5)	—	26
12/13	8.8	(2.9)	—	20
Annual Growth	**15.9%**	**—**	**—**	**3.6%**

2017 Year-End Financials

Debt ratio: —	No. of shares (mil.): 1.8
Return on equity: 13.2%	Dividends
Cash ($ mil.): 30.5	Yield: —
Current ratio: 2.23	Payout: —
Long-term debt ($ mil.): —	Market value ($ mil.): 63.0

	STOCK PRICE ($) FY Close	P/E High/Low		PER SHARE ($) Earnings	Dividends	Book Value
12/17	34.00	7	5	5.81	0.00	46.55
12/16	28.58	—	—	(9.03)	0.00	40.85
12/15	24.65	—	—	(1.91)	0.00	44.91
12/14	25.00	—	—	(0.82)	0.00	47.73
12/13	21.80	—	—	(1.61)	0.00	50.20
Annual Growth	**11.8%**	**—**	**—**	**—**	**—**	**(1.9%)**

Kadant Inc

Kadant wants to hear the ka-ching of profits being made from its papermaking equipment. The company's papermaking machinery and components which Kadant develops and manufactures can be found in most of the world's pulp and paper mills. Its products include stock preparation; doctoring cleaning and filtration (for cleaning of paper rolls); and fluid handling (mainly drying). Its wood processing offerings include stranders debarkers chippers and logging machinery. It also recycles papermaking byproducts into biodegradable fiber-based granules for oil and grease absorption and lawn and garden applications. Kadant has operations in North America South America Europe and Asia. Most of Kadant's revenues are generated outside the US.

Operations

Kadant generates its revenue through its three segments: Papermaking Systems (close to 80% of revenue) Wood Processing Systems (nearly 20%) and Fiber-based Products (less than 5%).

The Papermaking Systems segment develops and manufactures equipment for the global papermaking recycling waste management and other process industries. Its principal products include stock-preparation systems for wastepaper conversion into recycled paper and balers for processing recycled materials; fluid-handling systems and equipment used in industrial piping systems to transfer fluid power and data; doctoring systems and equipment for paper machines; and filtration and cleaning systems for draining purifying and recycling water and for cleaning fabrics belts and rolls.

Through its Wood Processing Systems segment Kadant makes market stranders debarkers chippers and logging machinery used in the harvesting and production of lumber and OSB (oriented strand board). This segment also refurbishes and repairs pulping equipment for the pulp and paper industry.

The Fiber-based Products business sells biodegradable absorbent granules made from papermaking by-products that are used in agricultural for home and professional lawn and garden applications and for oil and grease absorption.

Geographic Reach

Kadant has 21 manufacturing facilities in 11 countries in Europe North and South America and Asia. Approximately 65% of its sales are to customers outside the US principally in Canada Europe and China.

Sales and Marketing

Kadant sells its products services and systems using a combination of direct sales independent sales agents and distributors. Technical service personnel product specialists and independent sales agents and distributors are utilized in certain markets and for certain product lines.

Financial Performance

Kadant has seen a general upward trend in revenue since 2013 with a significant increase of 24% to record sales of $515.0 million in 2017 (sales were also up a 43% in 2016 compared with 2015). The increase in 2017 is attributed to sales generated by acquisitions and favorable foreign currency translation.

Net income however slumped 3% in 2017 to $31.0 million (2016 net income was also down 7% from 2015). An increase in selling general and administrative (SG&A) expenses a higher provision for income taxes and increased R&D costs ate into Kadant's profits for 2017.

Cash at the end of fiscal 2017 was $75.4 million an increase of $3.9 million from the prior year. Cash from operations contributed $65.2 million to the coffers while investing activities used $221.9 million mainly for acquisitions. Financing activities provided $151.4 primarily from borrowings.

Strategy

Kadant's strategic growth initiatives involve increasing its penetration into emerging markets and expand its parts and consumables revenue by leveraging its low-cost manufacturing operations. It also continues to acquire well-positioned companies that offer differentiated products for process industries. The company recently agreed to purchase material handling equipment maker Syntron which has opened up new markets in the mining food processing and packaging industries. The acquisition of expansion joint maker Unaflex has increased sales in Kadant's parts and consumables business.

Mergers and Acquisitions

Kadant has seen its revenues soar with major strategic acquisitions in recent years. In 2018 the company agreed to purchase Syntron Material Handling Group for approximately $179 million. Syntron makes material handling equipment and systems such as conveying and vibratory equipment at its facilities in Tupelo MS and Changshu China under the Link-Belt and Syntron brands. The acquisition extends Kadant's footprint into new process industries such as mining aggregates food processing and packaging.

In 2017 Kadant acquired NII FPG Company's forest products business for approximately $170.8 million. Kadant aims to bolster its aftermarket business with NII FPG's products including equipment for sawmills veneer mills and other manufacturers in the forest products industry. Later that year it also acquired certain assets of Unaflex a maker of expansion joints and related products for process industries for $31.3 million. With Unaflex's business made up of primarliy parts and consumables the acquisition is aligned with Kadant's strategy to grow its aftermarket business.

EXECUTIVES

VP General Counsel and Secretary, Sandra L. Lambert, age 62, $290,000 total compensation
President and CEO, Jonathan W. (Jon) Painter, age 59, $586,000 total compensation
SVP and CFO, Michael J. McKenney, age 56, $253,000 total compensation
EVP and COO, Eric T. Langevin, age 55, $376,000 total compensation
EVP, Jeffrey L. Powell, age 59, $360,000 total compensation
CTO, Bilal Mehmood
National Sales Manager, Chris Skibba
Vice President Sales And Marketing, Frederic Bontempelli
Treasurer, Daniel Walsh
Chairman, William A. (Bill) Rainville, age 76
Auditors: KPMG LLP

LOCATIONS

HQ: Kadant Inc
One Technology Park Drive, Westford, MA 01886
Phone: 978 776-2000
Web: www.kadant.com

PRODUCTS/OPERATIONS

2017 Sales

	$ mil.	% of total
Papermaking Systems		
Stock Preparation	193.8	38
Doctoring Cleaning & Filtration	109.6	21
Fluid Handling	104.1	20
Wood Processing Systems	95.1	19
Fiber-based Products	12.4	2
Total	**515.0**	**100**

Selected Products

Doctoring Cleaning and Filtration
  Doctoring
  Cleaning
  Filtration
  Forming
Fluid Handling
  Rotary joints and unions
  Expansion joints and flexible connectors
  Jet devices
  Condensate pumps
  Steam systems
  Accessories
Fiber Processing
  OCC recycled stock and pulp preparation
  Chemical pulping
Recycling Machinery
  Balers for recyclable materials
  Balers for waste RDF alfalfa
  Conveyors
Wood Processing
  Engineered wood (OSB)
  Chipping/screening
  Debarking
  Granules

COMPETITORS

Andritz AG
AstenJohnson
Barco
Columbus McKinnon
Deublin
Lorentzen & Wettre
Metso
Ovivo
Sandusky International
Voith

HISTORICAL FINANCIALS

Company Type: Public

Income Statement
FYE: December 30

	REVENUE ($ mil.)	NET INCOME ($ mil.)	NET PROFIT MARGIN	EMPLOYEES
12/17	515.0	31.0	6.0%	2,400
12/16*	414.1	32.0	7.7%	2,000
01/16	390.1	34.3	8.8%	1,800
01/15	402.1	28.6	7.1%	1,800
12/13	344.5	23.4	6.8%	1,800
Annual Growth	**10.6%**	**7.3%**	**—**	**7.5%**

*Fiscal year change

2017 Year-End Financials

Debt ratio: 31.8%
Return on equity: 10.1%
Cash ($ mil.): 75.4
Current ratio: 2.01
Long-term debt ($ mil.): 241.3

No. of shares (mil.): 11.0
Dividends
  Yield: 0.0%
  Payout: 29.8%
Market value ($ mil.): 1,105.0

	STOCK PRICE ($) FY Close	P/E High/Low	PER SHARE ($) Earnings	Dividends	Book Value
12/17	100.40	40 20	2.75	0.82	30.06
12/16*	61.20	22 12	2.88	0.74	25.84
01/16	40.61	18 12	3.10	0.66	24.75
01/15	42.38	17 13	2.56	0.58	24.33
12/13	40.79	20 12	2.07	0.38	24.28
Annual Growth	**25.3%**	**— —**	**7.4%**	**21.6%**	**5.5%**

*Fiscal year change

KBS Strategic Opportunity REIT Inc

Auditors: Ernst & Young LLP

LOCATIONS

HQ: KBS Strategic Opportunity REIT Inc
800 Newport Center Drive, Suite 700, Newport Beach, CA 92660
Phone: 949 417-6500
Web: www.kbsstrategicopportunityreit.com

HISTORICAL FINANCIALS

Company Type: Public

Income Statement
FYE: December 31

	REVENUE ($ mil.)	NET INCOME ($ mil.)	NET PROFIT MARGIN	EMPLOYEES
12/17	140.7	210.6	149.7%	0
12/16	134.2	(28.9)	—	0
12/15	112.1	2.4	2.2%	0
12/14	106.1	(23.1)	—	0
12/13	68.5	11.4	16.8%	0
Annual Growth	**19.7%**	**106.9%**		

2017 Year-End Financials

Debt ratio: 54.7%
Return on equity: 75.6%
Cash ($ mil.): 377.1
Current ratio: 23.16
Long-term debt ($ mil.): 603.0

No. of shares (mil.): 52.0
Dividends
  Yield: —
  Payout: 96.7%
Market value ($ mil.): —

Kearny Financial Corp (MD)

Auditors: Crowe LLP

LOCATIONS

HQ: Kearny Financial Corp (MD)
120 Passaic Avenue, Fairfield, NJ 07004
Phone: 973 244-4500
Web: www.kearnybank.com

HISTORICAL FINANCIALS

Company Type: Public

Income Statement
FYE: June 30

	ASSETS ($ mil.)	NET INCOME ($ mil.)	INCOME AS % OF ASSETS	EMPLOYEES
06/18	6,579.8	19.6	0.3%	565
06/17	4,818.1	18.6	0.4%	466
06/16	4,500.0	15.8	0.4%	459
06/15	4,237.1	5.6	0.1%	491
06/14	3,510.0	10.1	0.3%	474
Annual Growth	**17.0%**	**17.8%**	**—**	**4.5%**

2018 Year-End Financials

Return on assets: 0.3%
Return on equity: 1.6%
Long-term debt ($ mil.): —
No. of shares (mil.): 99.6
Sales ($ mil): 184.6

Dividends
  Yield: 0.0%
  Payout: 104.1%
Market value ($ mil.): 1,340.0

	STOCK PRICE ($)		P/E		PER SHARE ($)		
	FY Close		High/Low	Earnings	Dividends	Book Value	
06/18	13.45		65 54	0.24	0.25	12.74	
06/17	14.85		73 57	0.22	0.10	12.53	
06/16	12.58		74 62	0.18	0.08	12.50	
06/15	11.16		191179	0.06	0.00	12.48	
Annual Growth	6.4%		— —	58.7%	—	0.7%	

KEMET Corp.

KEMET is one of the world's largest makers of tantalum and multilayer ceramic capacitors — devices that store filter and regulate electrical energy and that are used in virtually all electronic devices. KEMET makes about 35 billion capacitors a year; its focus is on surface-mount capacitors including specialized units for aerospace automotive communications systems computers and military equipment. The company also makes solid aluminum capacitors for high-frequency applications. More than 70% of its sales come from outside the US.

Operations
KEMET makes about three quarters of its revenue from its solid capacitors group which produces tantalum aluminum polymer and ceramic capacitors with the rest coming from film and electrolytic which produces film paper and wet aluminum electrolytic capacitors.

Geographic Reach
Based in South Carolina KEMET operates 21 production facilities in Mexico China Italy the U.K. Portugal Finland Sweden Indonesia Germany Bulgaria and Macedonia. It has two specialty electronics companies — FELCO in Illinois and Dectron in Sweden.

Sales and Marketing
KEMET sells its vast array of products (it has nearly 250000 distinct part configurations) primarily to manufacturers such as Alcatel-Lucent Cisco Dell Hewlett-Packard IBM and Intel. Electronics accounted for 45% of sales 2015 with 10% of sales going to one distributor.

Financial Performance
Since revenue peaked at more than $1 billion in 2011 KEMET's revenue has declined year-to-year. It ended 2015 (ended March) with $823 million in revenue a 1.24% drop from 2014. Sales in its biggest segment solid capacitors were down 1%. Foreign exchange rates and fewer sales of lower margin products cut tantalum product sales.

KEMET trimmed its loss for the second straight year reporting a $14 million loss in 2015 compared to a loss of $68 million in 2014. In 2015 proceeds from the sale of its machinery division and lower operating costs contributed to reduce the loss.

The company reported positive cash flow of $24.4 million in 2015 compared to outflow of $6.7 million in 2014.

Strategy
KEMET is making changes through a program it calls the One KEMET campaign. The company has implemented standard practices and procedures throughout its businesses by working through programs such as Oracle 11iEBS and Lean and Six Sigma initiatives.

As part of its campaign to sharpen its corporate focus KEMET sold its machinery division in 2014 to Manz AG. KEMET had acquired the business as part of its purchase of Arcotronics Italia in 2007. The deal will help KEMET focus on designing producing and distributing electronic components as well as strategic initiatives such as its joint venture with NEC TOKIN in which KEMET has 34% economic interest and 51% voting interest.

Among KEMET's new products in the past year are tantalum capacitors for the automotive industry which buys an increasing amount of electronic components. The new line of tantalum capacitors help automotive electronics handle the demands placed on systems such as driver assistance energy recovery and infotainment.

Mergers and Acquisitions
KEMET bought IntelliData Inc. a developer of digital technologies for discovery decision support and the sales and marketing of electronic components. The company has been a KEMET vendor since 2000.

EXECUTIVES

Vice President and Chief Information Officer, Brian Burch
EVP and CFO, William M. Lowe, age 65, $492,500 total compensation
Senior Vice President Chief Technology and Marketing Officer, Philip M. (Phil) Lessner, age 59
Executive Vice President Solid Capacitor Business Group, Charles C. (Chuck) Meeks, age 57, $313,314 total compensation
Executive Vice President Tantalum Business Group, Conrado Hinojosa, age 53, $302,500 total compensation
Executive Vice President Ceramic Film and Electrolytics Business Group, Chuck Meeks
Vice President Ceramic Business Group, John Powers
Vice President Film and Electrolytic Business Group, Bob Willoughby
SVP Global Sales and Marketing, Claudio Lollini
CEO, Per-Olof Loof
Vice President Marketing, Johnny Boan
Chairman, Frank G. Brandenberg, age 71
Auditors: Ernst & Young LLP

LOCATIONS

HQ: KEMET Corp.
KEMET Tower, One East Broward Blvd, Fort Lauderdale, FL 33301
Phone: 954 766-2800
Web: www.kemet.com

PRODUCTS/OPERATIONS

2015 Sales

	$ mil.	% of total
Solid Capacitors	621.3	75
Film & electrolytic	201.9	25
Total	823.2	100

Selected Products
Capacitors
  Aluminum (wet electrolytic and solid polymer)
  Multilayer ceramic
  Film
  Paper
  Tantalum

COMPETITORS

AVX	Panasonic Corp
Anhui Tongfeng	ROHM

Electronics	SANYO Semiconductor
Dover Corp.	Samsung Electronics
EPCOS	TDK
Man Yue	Taiyo Yuden
Maxwell Technologies	Vishay Intertechnology
Murata Manufacturing	

HISTORICAL FINANCIALS
Company Type: Public

Income Statement
FYE: March 31

	REVENUE ($ mil.)	NET INCOME ($ mil.)	NET PROFIT MARGIN	EMPLOYEES
03/18	1,199.9	254.5	21.2%	14,850
03/17	757.7	47.9	6.3%	9,100
03/16	734.8	(53.6)	—	8,800
03/15	823.1	(14.1)	—	9,225
03/14	833.6	(68.5)	—	9,625
Annual Growth	9.5%	—		11.5%

2018 Year-End Financials

Debt ratio: 26.6%
Return on equity: 82.4%
Cash ($ mil.): 286.8
Current ratio: 2.37
Long-term debt ($ mil.): 304.0

No. of shares (mil.): 56.6
Dividends
  Yield: —
  Payout: —
Market value ($ mil.): 1,027.0

	STOCK PRICE ($)		P/E		PER SHARE ($)		
	FY Close		High/Low	Earnings	Dividends	Book Value	
03/18	18.13		6 2	4.34	0.00	8.17	
03/17	12.00		12 2	0.87	0.00	3.31	
03/16	1.93		— —	(1.17)	0.00	2.45	
03/15	4.14		— —	(0.31)	0.00	3.62	
03/14	5.81		— —	(1.52)	0.00	4.91	
Annual Growth	32.9%		— —	—		13.6%	

Kennedy-Wilson Holdings Inc

Kennedy-Wilson doesn't run for office it invests in them. The international real estate company invests in and leases mostly commercial properties and some multi-family properties while also offering a slew of real estate services in the US UK Ireland Spain and Japan. In addition to office space the company's KW Investments unit acquires and manages portfolios of multifamily loans retail space hotels condos and land. Its KW Services division provides property and asset management auction and residential sales and brokerage services. Kennedy-Wilson which has nearly $20 billion in assets under management manages more than 40 million sq. ft. of property.

Operations
Kennedy-Wilson operates two segments: KW Investments which made up 89% of its revenue (mostly in the form of rental income) during 2015 and invests in real estate properties (mostly commercial with some multifamily and student housing properties) and real estate-secured loans on its own or through its investment management platform; and KW Services (11% of revenue) which generates commissions by providing investment

management property services research brokerage and auction and conventional sales services.

The firm makes most of its revenue from rental income. About 67% of Kennedy-Wilson's total revenue came from rental income during 2015 while another 18% came from hotel property room and operating revenue. The rest came from its real estate services (11% of revenue) and loan purchase and origination fees (3%).

Geographic Reach

The Beverly Hills-based company has 25 offices in the US (mostly in major real estate markets) and one office each in Dublin London Madrid and Tokyo. Its largest market is in Europe (including the UK Ireland and Spain) where it generated 60% of its revenue during 2015. Its next largest markets are in the Western US (38% of revenue) and Japan (2%).

Financial Performance

Kennedy-Wilson's annual revenues have risen nearly 10-fold since 2011 mostly as new property acquisitions have spurred additional rental income. The firm's profits have come back strong from losses in 2011-2013 caused by financing and acquisition costs used to its support growth.

The firm's revenue jumped 52% to $603.7 million during 2015 mostly as new property acquisitions continued to boost its rental income. Its same-store rental revenue climbed 10% for its 5296 existing multifamily units and 4% for its 2.2 million existing square feet on its commercial properties. Kennedy-Wilson also collected 68% more in hotel revenue thanks to added rooms from three hotels it acquired in mid-2014 in Europe. The company's service revenue slipped 16% as it sold some of its service-oriented properties mostly in Dublin Ireland.

Despite strong revenue and operating income growth in 2015 Kennedy-Wilson's net income tumbled 35% to $59 million as mostly on doubling interest expenses as it used more financing to acquire properties during the year. The company's operating cash levels climbed 82% to $178.2 million for the year thanks to strong cash-denominated revenue growth.

Strategy

Unlike real estate investment trusts which strictly focus on investments Kennedy-Wilson's unique advantage over competitors is that it can offer a full array of real estate services to the properties and tenants that it manages. As is the case with many real estate companies Kennedy-Wilson relies on bargain-priced property acquisitions to boost its rental revenue over time.

During 2015 the firm used a significantly larger portion of its $3.2 billion acquisition budget to buy properties in the more promising Western US region especially in fast-growing real estate markets such as Seattle. In 2014 Kennedy-Wilson purchased an office building in Pasadena California for around $40 million. In the first half of 2014 as the market lagged a bit in Europe the company invested nearly $800 million in the UK and Ireland after spending close to $400 million there the year before. In 2013 it bought eight UK shopping centers out of bankruptcy a Hollywood office complex and an apartment complex in Salt Lake City for a total of close to $600 million.

Company Background

While many real estate companies struggled during the recession Kennedy-Wilson took advantage of the slumping US real estate market by acquiring assets at discounted prices.

Kennedy-Wilson was founded in 1977 as a real estate auction firm.

EXECUTIVES

Chief Administrative Officer, Barry S. Schlesinger, $600,000 total compensation
Chairman and CEO, William J. McMorrow, $950,000 total compensation
President and CEO Kennedy Wilson Europe, Mary L. Ricks, $750,000 total compensation
EVP and President Capital Markets Group, Donald J. Herrema
President Properties Group, James A. (Jim) Rosten
President Auction Group, Richard Rhett Winchell
President Commercial Investment Group, John C. Prabhu
President Residential Investment Group, Stuart Cramer
President Multifamily Management Group, Kurt Zech
EVP, Matt Windisch, $340,000 total compensation
CFO, Justin Enbody, $277,000 total compensation
President of Commercial Investments and Fund Management, Nicholas Colonna
Senior Vice President Finance, Ken Smotrys
Vice President, Omar Macedo
Vice President Brokerage, Charlotte Pruitt
Vice President, Jordan Rubinstein
Auditors: KPMG LLP

LOCATIONS

HQ: Kennedy-Wilson Holdings Inc
151 S. El Camino Drive, Beverly Hills, CA 90212
Phone: 310 887-6400
Web: www.kennedywilson.com

PRODUCTS/OPERATIONS

2015 Sales

	% of total
Investments	89
Services	11
Total	**100**

2015 Sales

	% of total
Rental	67
Hotel	18
Sale of real estate	1
Investment management property service and research fee	11
Loan purchases origination and others	3
Total	**100**

Selected Services

Auction and Conventional Sales
Property Services
Brokerage
Construction Management and Engineering
Investment Management
Research
Trust Services

COMPETITORS

Baird & Warner	Cushman & Wakefield
Brookfield Office Properties	Gale Company
	Jones Lang LaSalle
CBRE Group	Lincoln Property
Colliers International	Newmark Knight Frank

HISTORICAL FINANCIALS

Company Type: Public

Income Statement

FYE: December 31

	REVENUE ($ mil.)	NET INCOME ($ mil.)	NET PROFIT MARGIN	EMPLOYEES
12/17	810.6	100.5	12.4%	498
12/16	703.4	5.6	0.8%	500
12/15	603.7	74.7	12.4%	495
12/14	398.6	21.9	5.5%	450
12/13	121.2	(6.4)	—	400
Annual Growth	**60.8%**	**—**		**5.6%**

2017 Year-End Financials

Debt ratio: 73.3%	No. of shares (mil.): 151.5
Return on equity: 8.3%	Dividends
Cash ($ mil.): 351.3	Yield: 0.0%
Current ratio: 0.85	Payout: 84.3%
Long-term debt ($ mil.): 5,661.9	Market value ($ mil.): 2,630.0

	STOCK PRICE ($) FY Close	P/E High/Low	PER SHARE ($) Earnings	Dividends	Book Value
12/17	17.35	27 21	0.83	0.70	9.01
12/16	20.50	2408 1584	0.01	0.56	9.05
12/15	24.08	43 34	0.66	0.48	9.90
12/14	25.30	199 149	0.14	0.36	9.38
12/13	22.25	— —	(0.21)	0.28	9.30
Annual Growth	**(6.0%)**	**— —**	**—**	**25.7%**	**(0.8%)**

Kentucky Bancshares Inc

State commercial banks

EXECUTIVES

Chb, Buckner Woodford
Auditors: Crowe Horwath LLP

LOCATIONS

HQ: Kentucky Bancshares Inc
P.O. Box 157, Paris, KY 40362-0157
Phone: 859 987-1795
Web: www.kybank.com

HISTORICAL FINANCIALS

Company Type: Public

Income Statement

FYE: December 31

	ASSETS ($ mil.)	NET INCOME ($ mil.)	INCOME AS % OF ASSETS	EMPLOYEES
12/17	1,053.1	10.7	1.0%	233
12/16	1,028.4	8.5	0.8%	241
12/15	974.6	6.8	0.7%	243
12/14	855.2	7.0	0.8%	215
12/13	770.5	5.8	0.8%	208
Annual Growth	**8.1%**	**16.5%**	**—**	**2.9%**

2017 Year-End Financials

Return on assets: 1.0%	Dividends
Return on equity: 11.0%	Yield: 0.0%
Long-term debt ($ mil.): —	Payout: 64.2%
No. of shares (mil.): 5.9	Market value ($ mil.): 274.0
Sales ($ mil): 52.4	

	STOCK PRICE ($) FY Close	P/E High/Low	PER SHARE ($) Earnings	Dividends	Book Value
12/17	46.05	26 18	1.81	1.16	16.88
12/16	32.50	23 18	1.44	1.08	15.63
12/15	29.65	28 23	1.20	0.52	14.96
12/14	27.35	22 18	1.30	0.50	14.33
12/13	24.24	26 17	1.08	0.96	12.45
Annual Growth	17.4%	— —	13.8%	4.8%	7.9%

	STOCK PRICE ($) FY Close	P/E High/Low	PER SHARE ($) Earnings	Dividends	Book Value
12/17	74.65	51 44	1.51	1.65	37.53
12/16	73.22	26 16	2.97	3.38	38.01
12/15	63.28	32 26	2.42	1.40	34.37
12/14	69.07	36 25	1.95	1.40	30.91
12/13	50.18	161128	0.36	1.40	29.96
Annual Growth	10.4%	— —	43.1%	4.2%	5.8%

Kilroy Realty Corp

Kilroy is still here especially if you're referring to the West Coast. A self-administered real estate investment trust (REIT) Kilroy Realty owns manages and develops Class A office space mostly in suburban Southern California's Orange County San Diego and Los Angeles but it has since expanded to the San Francisco Bay and greater Seattle area to woo technology companies as tenants. Its portfolio includes about 115 office properties encompassing more than 13 million square feet of leasable space. A majority of Kilroy Realty's 500-plus tenants are involved in technology media financial services and real estate.

Geographic Reach
Besides 10 office buildings in Washington all of the REIT's property is located in California.

Sales and Marketing
Its 15 largest tenants accounted for 34% of the REIT's base rental revenue in 2012; these include DIRECTV Intuit and Bridgepoint Education. Its properties are 92% occupied.

Financial Performance
Overall sales grew 10% to $405 million in 2012. Profits jumped more than 300% to $270 million after the trust recorded gains on properties it sold.

As a REIT Kilroy Realty is exempt from paying federal income tax as long as it distributes quarterly dividends to shareholders.

Strategy
Kilroy Realty has moved away from owning industrial properties in order to focus on office buildings which generally earn more in rental income. In late 2012 it sold its entire portfolio of 44 industrial properties in California to two unnamed buyers for $355 million. The industrial properties totaled almost 4 million-sq.-ft. of space.

At the same time the trust boosted its portfolio of office buildings in San Francisco and Seattle home to many of the nation's wealthy tech companies. In 2012 it paid $330 million for three properties totaling 837000 square feet in Seattle $162 million for a 374000-sq.-ft. office park in Silicon Valley and it paid $52 million for a building in downtown San Francisco that it will spend another $200 million redeveloping into a 27-story glass office tower for new tenant salesforce.com. In addition the trust is spending $315 million to develop a 587000-sq.-ft. office complex for LinkedIn in Sunnyvale California.

Not missing a beat in 2013 the trust boosted its Bay Area construction pipeline to more than 1.8 million square feet with new developments in Redwood City and downtown San Francisco (most of the space is pre-leased).

In addition Kilroy Realty has approximately 110 acres of undeveloped land in San Diego with the capacity for more than 2 million sq. ft. of rentable office space.

EXECUTIVES

EVP and CFO, Tyler H. Rose, age 58, $500,000 total compensation

EVP and COO, Jeffrey C. Hawken, age 60, $675,000 total compensation

Chairman President and CEO, John B. Kilroy, age 70, $1,225,000 total compensation

EVP Asset Management, John T. Fucci

EVP Development and Construction Services, Justin W. Smart, $500,000 total compensation

EVP Chief Accounting Officer and Controller, Heidi R. Roth

EVP Southern California, David Simon

EVP Leasing and Business Development, A. Robert Paratte

EVP Northern California, Mike L. Sanford

Vice President Coporate Finance And Corporate Counsel, Joseph Magri

Treasurer, Michelle Ngo

Auditors: Deloitte & Touche LLP

LOCATIONS

HQ: Kilroy Realty Corp
12200 W. Olympic Boulevard, Suite 200, Los Angeles, CA 90064
Phone: 310 481-8400
Web: www.kilroyrealty.com

PRODUCTS/OPERATIONS

2015 Sales

	% of total
Rental income	91
Tenant reimbursements	9
Other property income	-
Total	100

COMPETITORS

BioMed Realty	Irvine Company
Brandywine Realty	Majestic Realty
Digital Realty	PS Business Parks
Douglas Emmett	Prologis
Equity Commonwealth	Shorenstein
Equity Office	The Koll Company
Hudson Pacific	Trammell Crow Company

HISTORICAL FINANCIALS
Company Type: Public

Income Statement
FYE: December 31

	REVENUE ($ mil.)	NET INCOME ($ mil.)	NET PROFIT MARGIN	EMPLOYEES
12/17	719.0	164.6	22.9%	251
12/16	642.5	293.7	45.7%	245
12/15	581.2	234.0	40.3%	232
12/14	521.7	180.2	34.5%	226
12/13	465.1	43.8	9.4%	219
Annual Growth	11.5%	39.2%	—	3.5%

2017 Year-End Financials

Debt ratio: 34.5%
Return on equity: 4.5%
Cash ($ mil.): 57.6
Current ratio: 1.20
Long-term debt ($ mil.): 2,347.0

No. of shares (mil.): 98.6
Dividends
  Yield: 0.0%
  Payout: 109.2%
Market value ($ mil.): 7,362.0

Kilroy Realty L.P.

Auditors: Deloitte & Touche LLP

LOCATIONS

HQ: Kilroy Realty L.P.
12200 W. Olympic Boulevard, Suite 200, Los Angeles, CA 90064
Phone: 310 481-8400
Web: www.kilroyrealty.com

HISTORICAL FINANCIALS
Company Type: Public

Income Statement
FYE: December 31

	REVENUE ($ mil.)	NET INCOME ($ mil.)	NET PROFIT MARGIN	EMPLOYEES
12/17	719.0	167.4	23.3%	251
12/16	642.5	300.0	46.7%	245
12/15	581.2	238.1	41.0%	232
12/14	521.7	183.5	35.2%	226
12/13	465.1	44.3	9.5%	219
Annual Growth	11.5%	39.4%	—	3.5%

2017 Year-End Financials

Debt ratio: 34.5%
Return on equity: —
Cash ($ mil.): 57.6
Current ratio: 0.30
Long-term debt ($ mil.): 2,347.0

No. of shares (mil.): 100.7
Dividends
  Yield: —
  Payout: 109.2%
Market value ($ mil.): —

Kimball Electronics Inc

Auditors: DELOITTE & TOUCHE LLP

LOCATIONS

HQ: Kimball Electronics Inc
1205 Kimball Boulevard, Jasper, IN 47546
Phone: 812 634-4000
Web: www.kimballelectronics.com

HISTORICAL FINANCIALS
Company Type: Public

Income Statement — FYE: June 30

	REVENUE ($ mil.)	NET INCOME ($ mil.)	NET PROFIT MARGIN	EMPLOYEES
06/18	1,072.0	16.7	1.6%	5,700
06/17	930.9	34.1	3.7%	5,400
06/16	842.0	22.2	2.6%	4,500
06/15	819.3	26.2	3.2%	4,300
06/14	741.5	24.6	3.3%	3,800
Annual Growth	9.7%	(9.2%)	—	10.7%

2018 Year-End Financials

Debt ratio: 1.3%
Return on equity: 4.8%
Cash ($ mil.): 46.4
Current ratio: 1.91
Long-term debt ($ mil.): —

No. of shares (mil.): 26.5
Dividends
Yield: —
Payout: —
Market value ($ mil.): 486.0

	STOCK PRICE ($) FY Close	P/E High/Low		PER SHARE ($) Earnings	Dividends	Book Value
06/18	18.30	35	25	0.62	0.00	13.40
06/17	18.05	15	10	1.24	0.00	12.75
06/16	12.45	19	12	0.76	0.00	11.49
06/15	14.59	18	8	0.89	0.00	10.71
Annual Growth	7.8%			— (11.4%)	—	7.8%

Kingstone Companies Inc

Kingstone Companies (formerly DCAP Group) keeps things covered. While the company has transformed itself from a broker into an underwriter its main business is still insurance. Its Kingstone Insurance Company (formerly Commercial Mutual Insurance Company) provides property/casualty insurance policies for individuals and businesses in New York State. Its products including auto business and homeowners' policies are sold through independent agents. The company has divested its former insurance brokerage business which offered life and property/casualty policies through owned and franchised retail locations in New York and eastern Pennsylvania.

In mid-2009 the company completed the divestiture of its more than 70 owned or franchised retail locations in New York and eastern Pennsylvania which operated under the brand names DCAP Barry Scott and Atlantic Insurance. The retail locations offered insurance policies underwritten by third parties and some of the group's locations offered income tax preparation services.

Around the same time the company acquired Commercial Mutual Insurance Company a mutual insurance underwriting firm. Commercial Mutual was converted into a stock company and was renamed Kingstone Insurance. Parent company DCAP Group changed its name to Kingstone Companies following the transaction.

CEO Barry Goldstein owns 25% of Kingstone Companies and director Michael Feinsod owns about 16% through Infinity Capital Partners.

EXECUTIVES

Chairman President CEO and Treasurer, Barry B. Goldstein, age 59, $275,000 total compensation
CFO and Secretary, Victor Brodsky, age 54
Executive Vice President of Kingstone Insurance Company, John Reiersen
Auditors: Marcum LLP

LOCATIONS

HQ: Kingstone Companies Inc
15 Joys Lane, Kingston, NY 12401
Phone: 845 802-7900
Web: www.kingstonecompanies.com

COMPETITORS

AIG	New York Life
Allstate	Progressive
GEICO	Corporation
GNY Mutual Insurance	The Hartford
NYCM	

HISTORICAL FINANCIALS
Company Type: Public

Income Statement — FYE: December 31

	REVENUE ($ mil.)	NET INCOME ($ mil.)	NET PROFIT MARGIN	EMPLOYEES
12/17	92.7	9.9	10.8%	97
12/16	77.4	8.9	11.5%	80
12/15	64.1	6.9	10.8%	69
12/14	50.0	5.3	10.6%	66
12/13	36.5	2.0	5.5%	59
Annual Growth	26.2%	49.3%	—	13.2%

2017 Year-End Financials

Debt ratio: 11.4%
Return on equity: 13.2%
Cash ($ mil.): 48.3
Current ratio: 7.99
Long-term debt ($ mil.): 29.1

No. of shares (mil.): 10.6
Dividends
Yield: 0.0%
Payout: 32.1%
Market value ($ mil.): 200.0

	STOCK PRICE ($) FY Close	P/E High/Low		PER SHARE ($) Earnings	Dividends	Book Value
12/17	18.80	20	12	0.94	0.30	8.90
12/16	13.75	12	6	1.14	0.25	7.15
12/15	9.00	11	7	0.94	0.21	6.18
12/14	8.15	12	8	0.72	0.18	5.54
12/13	7.27	14	9	0.50	0.16	4.91
Annual Growth	26.8%			— 17.1%	17.3%	16.0%

Kinsale Capital Group Inc

Auditors: KPMG LLP

LOCATIONS

HQ: Kinsale Capital Group Inc
2221 Edward Holland Drive, Suite 600, Richmond, VA 23230
Phone: 804 289-1300   **Fax:** 804 673-5697
Web: www.kinsalecapitalgroup.com

HISTORICAL FINANCIALS
Company Type: Public

Income Statement — FYE: December 31

	ASSETS ($ mil.)	NET INCOME ($ mil.)	INCOME AS % OF ASSETS	EMPLOYEES
12/17	667.8	24.9	3.7%	164
12/16	614.3	26.1	4.3%	145
12/15	545.2	22.2	4.1%	145
12/14	437.6	12.9	3.0%	0
12/13	0.0	12.2	-	0
Annual Growth	—	19.4%		—

2017 Year-End Financials

Return on assets: 3.8%
Return on equity: 11.1%
Long-term debt ($ mil.): —
No. of shares (mil.): 21.0
Sales ($ mil): 186.7

Dividends
Yield: 0.0%
Payout: 20.6%
Market value ($ mil.): 947.0

	STOCK PRICE ($) FY Close	P/E High/Low		PER SHARE ($) Earnings	Dividends	Book Value
12/17	45.00	38	24	1.16	0.24	11.32
12/16	34.01	61	32	0.56	0.10	10.03
Annual Growth	32.3%			—107.1%	140.0%	12.9%

Kite Realty Group Trust

Kite Realty Group Trust has been flying high as a developer and operator of retail properties. The growing real estate investment trust (REIT) owns interests in more than 110 strip malls and anchored shopping centers totaling some 22.4 million sq. ft. of space in some 20 US states with about half of its rent streaming from Florida Indiana and Texas. Kite Realty also provides third-party management development and construction services. Its largest tenants include Walmart Target and Lowe's.

Operations

Kite Realty Group Trust owns interests in more than 110 properties and generates virtually all its revenue through rental income. About 80% of the REIT's properties are community centers anchored by groceries or convenience-oriented businesses. It has leased out about 95% of its properties.

Geographic Reach

Indianapolis-based Kite Realty Group Trust has properties in about 20 US states with holdings concentrated in Florida (about 25% of annualized base rent) Indiana (nearly 15%) and Texas (more than 10%). Other significant markets include Nevada and North Carolina.

Sales and Marketing

About 80% of Kite Realty Group Trust's properties are community centers anchored by groceries or convenience-oriented businesses and include some of the nation's best-known retailers. The REIT's largest tenants are The TJX Companies Publix Super Markets Petsmart Bed Bath & Beyond and Ross Stores which together represent more than 10% of annualized base rent. Other significant tenants include Lowe's Office Depot/Office Max and Dick's Sporting Goods.

Financial Performance

Kite Realty Group Trust has seen massive growth in the last five years increasing revenue by more than 175% to $358.8 million and pushing 2017 net income to $11.9 million from a loss of $2.9 million in 2013. The REIT's debt has doubled in that time and its cash stores grew by a third.

Despite a huge overall five-year improvement in revenue Kite's growth has slowed consistently since 2014 when its year-over-year revenue doubled following the company's acquisition of Inland Diversified Real Estate Trust. The company's 2017 revenue ticked up only 1% to $358.8 million because of increases in rental rates and occupancy.

The company's net income increased tenfold in 2017 owing to a nearly fourfold increase in gains from the sale of four properties: Florida locations Cove Center and The Shops at Village Walk Alabama's Clay Marketplace and Texan strip mall Wheatland Towne Crossing.

Kite's cash grew $4.2 million to $24.1 million in 2017. Operations provided $153.7 million while investments used $126000 as proceeds from property sales mostly offset capital expenditures. Financing activities reduced cash a further $149.3 million due to loan payments and shareholder distributions.

Strategy

Kite's growth strategy includes the operation development and redevelopment of properties in well-located community and neighborhood shopping centers using cash debt and equity capital as well as pruning its least profitable properties.

Since nearly doubling its portfolio of properties in 2014 with its acquisition of Inland Diversified Real Estate Kite shifted its focus to redeveloping repositioning and repurposing its holdings - what it calls its 3-R initiative. In 2017 the REIT completed construction on seven 3-R projects with total costs of $23.5 million and an estimated combined return on investment of 12.3%. Between January 2017 and November 2018 Kite sold nine properties and had another nine under active redevelopment. During that time one development property became operational.

The company is also seeking to incorporate more office multifamily housing and hotel projects in its portfolio. Through a joint venture the company opened an Embassy Suites at its Eddy Street Commons mixed use development in South Bend Indiana in 2018. Kite holds a 35% interest in the hotel.

EXECUTIVES

Chairman and CEO, John A. Kite, age 52, $700,000 total compensation
President and COO, Thomas K. McGowan, age 53, $450,000 total compensation
EVP and CFO, Daniel R. Sink, age 50, $400,000 total compensation
EVP General Counsel and Corporate Secretary, Scott E. Murray, $320,000 total compensation
Senior Vice President, Gregg Poetz
Executive Vice President Leasing, Bud Moll
Vice President Leasing, Jason Samreny
Senior Vice President Human Capital, Melissa Boggs
VICE PRESIDENT TAX MANAGEMENT, Vickie Norman
Auditors: Ernst & Young LLP

LOCATIONS

HQ: Kite Realty Group Trust
30 S. Meridian Street, Suite 1100, Indianapolis, IN 46204
Phone: 317 577-5600
Web: www.kiterealty.com

PRODUCTS/OPERATIONS

2017 Sales

	$ mil.	% of total
Minimum rent	273.4	76
Tenant reimbursements	73.0	21
Other property-related revenue	12.0	3
Fee income	0.4	-
Total	**358.8**	**100**

COMPETITORS

Acadia Realty Trust	Regency Centers
Cedar Realty Trust	Regency Commercial
DDR	Associates
GGP	Simon Property Group
Kimco Realty	Weingarten Realty
Lauth	

HISTORICAL FINANCIALS

Company Type: Public

Income Statement				FYE: December 31
	REVENUE ($ mil.)	NET INCOME ($ mil.)	NET PROFIT MARGIN	EMPLOYEES
12/17	358.8	11.8	3.3%	147
12/16	354.1	1.1	0.3%	153
12/15	347.0	27.1	7.8%	145
12/14	259.5	(5.7)	—	141
12/13	129.4	(2.8)	—	95
Annual Growth	**29.0%**	—	—	**11.5%**

2017 Year-End Financials

Debt ratio: 48.3%
Return on equity: 0.7%
Cash ($ mil.): 24.0
Current ratio: 1.05
Long-term debt ($ mil.): 1,699.2
No. of shares (mil.): 83.6
Dividends
  Yield: 0.0%
  Payout: 864.2%
Market value ($ mil.): 1,639.0

	STOCK PRICE ($) FY Close	P/E High/Low		PER SHARE ($) Earnings	Dividends	Book Value
12/17	19.60	173	127	0.14	1.21	18.72
12/16	23.48	3041	2268	0.01	1.14	19.67
12/15	25.93	165	121	0.18	1.08	20.71
12/14	28.74	—	—	(0.24)	0.26	22.74
12/13	6.57	—	—	(0.48)	0.96	23.04
Annual Growth	**31.4%**	—	—	—	**6.0%**	**(5.1%)**

Knight-Swift Transportation Holdings Inc

Auditors: GRANT THORNTON LLP

LOCATIONS

HQ: Knight-Swift Transportation Holdings Inc
20002 North 19th Avenue, Phoenix, AZ 85027
Phone: 602 269-2000
Web: www.swifttrans.com

HISTORICAL FINANCIALS

Company Type: Public

Income Statement				FYE: December 31
	REVENUE ($ mil.)	NET INCOME ($ mil.)	NET PROFIT MARGIN	EMPLOYEES
12/17	2,425.4	484.2	20.0%	25,400
12/16	1,118.0	93.8	8.4%	5,971
12/15	1,182.9	116.7	9.9%	6,196
12/14	1,102.3	102.8	9.3%	5,485
12/13	969.2	69.2	7.1%	5,177
Annual Growth	**25.8%**	**62.6%**	—	**48.8%**

2017 Year-End Financials

Debt ratio: 8.6%
Return on equity: 16.0%
Cash ($ mil.): 150.3
Current ratio: 1.51
Long-term debt ($ mil.): 616.9
No. of shares (mil.): 178.0
Dividends
  Yield: 0.0%
  Payout: 1.3%
Market value ($ mil.): 7,782.0

	STOCK PRICE ($) FY Close	P/E High/Low		PER SHARE ($) Earnings	Dividends	Book Value
12/17	43.72	10	4	4.34	0.06	29.43
12/16	24.36	23	11	1.16	0.00	9.80
12/15	13.82	20	9	1.42	0.00	9.12
12/14	28.63	23	15	1.25	0.00	8.28
12/13	22.21	27	10	0.86	0.24	6.88
Annual Growth	**18.4%**	—	—	**49.9%**	**(29.3%)**	**43.8%**

Korn Ferry

High-level executives can jump ship via Korn/Ferry International. The world's largest executive recruitment firm Korn/Ferry has almost 75 offices in more than 35 countries. The company's more than 600 consultants help prominent public and private companies as well as government and not-for-profit organizations find qualified job applicants for openings in a variety of executive level positions (including CEOs CFOs and other senior-level jobs). Through Futurestep job seekers use the Internet and videotaped job interviews to find mid-level management positions. In addition the company provides management assessment as well as coaching and executive development services. Korn/Ferry was founded in 1969.

HISTORY

Korn/Ferry was founded in 1969 by Lester Korn and Richard Ferry. A year later the firm debuted its first specialty division a unit serving the national real estate industry. Its specialization approach was a unique (and successful) slant on the practice of headhunting and the company soon added more specialties. Korn/Ferry went public in 1972; it also expanded overseas with offices in Brussels and London that year and in Tokyo a year later. Volatile stock prices became a distraction to the two founders so in 1974 they took the company private by repurchasing all its stock. Korn/Ferry moved into Latin America in 1977 by acquiring 49% of Hazzard & Associates.

By 1980 steady growth had made Korn/Ferry one of the top headhunting firms in the country. A decade later the firm established a foothold in central Europe by opening an office in Budapest Hungary; it further strengthened its old-country presence by acquiring European search firm Carre/Orban (at the time it was the largest merger in search firm history). Traditionally a search firm for high-level executives Korn/Ferry pushed into the middle management arena in 1998 with its Internet-based Futurestep service. Also that year former COO Windle Priem took over the company from Michael Boxberger who left after 19 months.

Korn/Ferry went public again in 1999. The following year it acquired online college recruitment service JobDirect. In 2001 Priem stepped down as president and CEO and was replaced by Paul Reilly former CEO of KPMG International. Also that year in an effort to strengthen its Web offerings the company cobranded its Futurestep site with online giant Yahoo! Later in 2001 Korn/Ferry cut 500 jobs or 20% of its workforce and reduced salaries. It also reorganized management and closed JobDirect. In 2002 and 2003 the company continued reducing its workforce and streamlining its operations.

Over the next few years Korn/Ferry expanded beyond its traditional executive recruitment services (by beefing up its management assessment business among others). In 2006 Korn/Ferry primarily focusing on its information technology products portfolio launched its K/F One software platform. The product aggregates Microsoft Outlook the Internet and proprietary Korn/Ferry software. Keeping this focus on technology the company acquired Lominger Limited a provider of leadership development software for $24 million later in the year.

Gary Burnison the company's former COO and CFO took over the reins as CEO in mid-2007 while Reilly remained chairman.

To further boost its leadership and talent consulting business Korn/Ferry in late 2008 acquired Lore International a provider of leadership development executive education and coaching services that has offices in the US and Europe.

EXECUTIVES

President Global Productized Services, Andrew Huddart, age 50

President Asia Pacific Executive Search, Charles Tseng

President Global Industrial Market Executive Search, Yannick Binvel

EVP CFO and Chief Corporate Officer, Robert P. Rozek, age 57, $516,667 total compensation

President CEO and Director, Gary D. Burnison, age 57, $910,000 total compensation

President Financial Executive Search, Michael Franzino, age 68

CEO Futurestep, Byrne K. Mulrooney, age 57, $450,000 total compensation

SVP Chief Marketing Officer and President Korn Ferry Institute, Michael Distefano

President Asia Pacific Futurestep, Chong Ng

President Life Sciences Executive Search, Jay Kizer

CEO Korn Ferry Hay Group, Stephen Kaye, $187,500 total compensation

President South America Executive Search, Dominique Virchaux

President Technology Executive Search, Werner Penk

EVP Global Human Resources, Linda Hyman

President Europe Middle East and Africa (EMEA) and Chair Global Industrial and Consumer Markets Executive Search, Bernard S. Zen-Ruffinen

President Americas Executive Search, Doug Charles

SVP and CIO, Bryan Ackermann

Vice President Finance And Assistant Controller, Erika Joseph

Chairman, George T. Shaheen, age 73

Secretary, Peter Dunn

Auditors: Ernst & Young LLP

LOCATIONS

HQ: Korn Ferry
1900 Avenue of the Stars, Suite 2600, Los Angeles, CA 90067
Phone: 310 552-1834
Web: www.kornferry.com

PRODUCTS/OPERATIONS

2016 Sales

	$ mil.	% of total
Executive Search		
North America	371.3	28
EMEA	144.3	11
Asia Pacific	80.5	6
Latin America	26.7	2
Hay Group	471.2	35
Futurestep	198.1	15
Reimbursed out-of-pocket engagement expense	54.6	3
Total	**1,346.7**	**100**

Solutions
Assessment & Succession
Board & CEO Services
Employer Branding
Executive Search
Leadership Development
Professional Search
Recruitment Process Outsourcing
Rewards & Benefits
Strategy Execution & Organization Design
Talent Strategy & Organizational Alignment
Workforce performance Inclusion & Diversity

COMPETITORS

A.T. Kearney	Handler & Associates
CCL	Heidrick & Struggles
CTPartners	J.C. Wilson Associates
Development Dimensions International	PageGroup
	Russell Reynolds
Diversified Search	Solomon Page
Egon Zehnder	Spencer Stuart
Gap International	

HISTORICAL FINANCIALS

Company Type: Public

Income Statement

FYE: April 30

	REVENUE ($ mil.)	NET INCOME ($ mil.)	NET PROFIT MARGIN	EMPLOYEES
04/18	1,819.5	133.7	7.4%	7,643
04/17	1,621.6	84.1	5.2%	7,232
04/16	1,346.7	30.9	2.3%	6,947
04/15	1,066.0	88.3	8.3%	3,687
04/14	995.5	72.6	7.3%	3,396
Annual Growth	**16.3%**	**16.5%**	**—**	**22.5%**

2018 Year-End Financials

Debt ratio: 10.3%	No. of shares (mil.): 56.5
Return on equity: 11.6%	Dividends
Cash ($ mil.): 520.8	Yield: 0.7%
Current ratio: 1.82	Payout: 17.0%
Long-term debt ($ mil.): 211.3	Market value ($ mil.): 3,021.0

	STOCK PRICE ($) FY Close	P/E High/Low		PER SHARE ($) Earnings	Dividends	Book Value
04/18	53.46	23	13	2.35	0.40	21.53
04/17	32.40	22	13	1.47	0.40	19.03
04/16	27.14	66	44	0.58	0.40	18.25
04/15	31.53	19	14	1.76	0.10	16.12
04/14	29.05	20	10	1.48	0.00	15.17
Annual Growth	**16.5%**	**—**		**12.3%**	**—**	**9.1%**

Kraton Corp

If you brushed your teeth or shaved this morning you probably touched a Kraton product. Through Kraton Polymers the company makes unhydrogenated styrenic block copolymers (USBCs) polymersand hydrogenated styrenic block copolymers (HSBC). SBCs are used in adhesives coatings sealants lubricants packaging and other applications across a range of industries such as paving and roofing automotive and personal care products. Under its Cariflex brand it sells isoprene rubber latex products. In 2016 the company sold its compounding business to PolyOne for $72 million.

Operations

The company operates through Polymer Segment and Chemical Segment.

The polymer segment accounts for about 60% of total revenue. It makes styrenic block copolymers used in a wide range of application including adhesives coatings consumer and personal care products sealants lubricants medical packaging automotive paving roofing and footware products.

Chemical segment (40% of sales) sells pine wood pulping co-products and feedstocks like crude tall oil and crude sulfate turpentine. Products are made for adhesive roads and construction and automotive industries.

Geographic Reach

Kraton has operations across North America South America Europe and Asia. The US generates about 35% of revenues and 65% comes from outside of US.

Sales and Marketing

Kraton has a direct sales force (the bulk of its sales) marketing representatives and distributors. It has 800 customers in more than 70 countries.

Financial Performance

Revenue was $1.9 billion for 2017 a 12% increase from the prior year primarily due to sales volume growth in its polymer products (by $175 million) particularly in performance products which saw higher average selling prices. and improved sales volumes from its chemicals segment ($41 million) especially adhesives.

Net income for 2017 was $98 million a decrease of $10 million over the previous year primarily due to a YOY $30 million reduction in income tax benefit with an increase of $20 million in losses from debt extinguishment.

Cash holdings at the end of 2017 was $89 million. Operations generated $256 million offset by $123 million going towards investments and a further $175 million in financial activities.

Mergers and Acquisitions

In 2016 Kraton completed the acquisition of Arizona Chemical Holdings Corporation the largest global provider of pine-based specialty chemicals for $1.3 million. Through the business combination the company expanded its offerings of polymers and specialty chemicals.

EXECUTIVES

EVP and CFO, Stephen E. Tremblay, age 59, $450,000 total compensation
President and CEO, Kevin M. Fogarty, age 53, $875,000 total compensation
SVP and CTO, Lothar P. Freund, age 58, $350,000 total compensation
SVP and Chief Commercial Officer, Holger R. Jung, age 55, $375,000 total compensation
VP and Chief Human Resources Officer, Melinda S. Conley, age 52, $311,875 total compensation
Vice President General Counsel Secretary, James Simmons
BOARD MEMBER, Richard Brown
Chairman, Dan F. Smith, age 71
Board Member, Dominique Fournier
Auditors: KPMG LLP

LOCATIONS

HQ: Kraton Corp
  15710 John F. Kennedy Blvd., Suite 300, Houston, TX 77032
Phone: 281 504-4700
Web: www.kraton.com

PRODUCTS/OPERATIONS

2015 Sales

	% of total
Performance Products	52
Specialty Polymers	34
Cariflex	14
Other	0
Total	**100**

2015 Application sales

	% of total
Paving	27
Personal care	20
Roofing	18
Packaging & industrial adhesives	18
Industrial	7
Other	10
Total	**100**

COMPETITORS

Kumho Petrochemical	Polimeri Europa
Kuraray	Sinopec Corp.
LG Chem	Zeon

HISTORICAL FINANCIALS

Company Type: Public

Income Statement

FYE: December 31

	REVENUE ($ mil.)	NET INCOME ($ mil.)	NET PROFIT MARGIN	EMPLOYEES
12/17	1,960.3	97.5	5.0%	1,931
12/16	1,744.1	107.3	6.2%	1,971
12/15	1,034.6	(10.5)	—	917
12/14	1,230.4	2.4	0.2%	934
12/13	1,292.1	(0.6)	—	936
Annual Growth	**11.0%**	**—**	**—**	**19.8%**

2017 Year-End Financials

Debt ratio: 55.1%	No. of shares (mil.): 31.6
Return on equity: 17.8%	Dividends
Cash ($ mil.): 89.0	Yield: —
Current ratio: 2.08	Payout: —
Long-term debt ($ mil.): 1,574.8	Market value ($ mil.): 1,522.0

STOCK PRICE ($) FY Close	P/E High/Low		PER SHARE ($) Earnings	Dividends	Book Value
12/17	48.17	16	8	3.07	0.00	20.14
12/16	28.48	11	4	3.43	0.00	14.79
12/15	16.61	—	—	(0.34)	0.00	11.74
12/14	20.79	404223		0.07	0.00	13.52
12/13	23.05	—	—	(0.02)	0.00	15.78
Annual Growth	**20.2%**	—	—	—	—	**6.3%**

Ladenburg Thalmann Financial Services Inc

Ladenburg Thalmann Financial Services provides brokerage asset management and investment research banking and wholesale life insurance services to corporate institutional and individual clients throughout the US. The company serves primarily retail clients through independent broker-dealer subsidiaries which together have some 4300 financial advisors and manage about $160 billion in assets. The company's investment bank provides investment research on small- to mid-cap companies and finance and strategic advisory services to middle-market companies. Its asset management unit offers mutual funds alternative investments and investment counseling. Ladenburg's insurance subsidiaries provide support services to life insurance advisors and institutions.

Operations

The clear majority of Ladenburg Thalmann's revenue (about 90%) is generated by its independent advisory and brokerage services business. Through five subsidiaries employing about 4300 representatives Ladenburg provides financial advice primarily to retail investors especially individuals and households with $100000 to $1.5 million in net investible assets.

Ladenburg's investment banking practice which it calls its Ladenburg segment generates about 5% of revenue and includes Ladenburg Thalmann & Co. and Ladenburg Thalmann Asset Management (LTAM). The investment bank mostly finances companies with market caps below $500 million through underwritten public registered direct and at-the-market offerings and private placements. LTAM manages about $2.5 billion in assets for more than 14500 clients.

Ladenburg's insurance brokerage business also contributes about 5% of revenue. The company's Highland Capital Brokerage subsidiary provides life insurance and fixed and equity indexed annuities to investment and insurance providers. Highland and the Ladenburg Thalmann Annuity Insurance division provide services including risk underwriting back office processing advanced planning marketing strategy and point of sale support.

Geographic Reach

Ladenburg Thalmann is stationed in Miami. Its branch offices are in Naples and Boca Raton Florida; Melville Westhampton Beach and New York New York; Boston Massachusetts; Dallas Texas; and Calabasas and Irvine California. Substantially all of the company's revenue comes from

the US where all of its long-lived assets are located.

Sales and Marketing

Ladenburg Thalmann's independent advisory and brokerage services business provides financial advice primarily to retail investors especially what the company calls “mass affluent” customers — individuals and households with $100000 to $1.5 million in net investible assets.

Financial Performance

Ladenburg Thalmann's revenue and cash have grown impressively in the last five years (63% and 242% respectively) while 2017 saw the company's net income regain some ground following huge losses in 2016 and 2015.

The company reported revenue of $1.3 billion in 2017 up 15% from the previous year driven primarily by a $96.8 million jump in fees from its independent advisory and brokerage subsidiaries as a result of improved market conditions. Commissions investment banking revenue and interest and dividends also rose.

The firm's net income increased by $7.7 million in 2017 a stark contrast to 2016 and 2015 when the company lost $22.3 million and $11.2 million respectively. The bounce-back was fueled by accelerating revenues and a $16.5 million cut in income tax expense which followed a $10 million tax expense increase in 2016 caused by the company's tax valuation allowance.

Cash at the end of fiscal 2017 was $172.1 million an increase of $73.2 million from the prior year. Cash from operations contributed $16.2 million while investing activities used $9.8 million — mainly for furniture and equipment purchases and leasehold improvements. Financing activities provided another $66.8 million due to several stock issuances.

Strategy

Key to Ladenburg Thalmann's strategy is expanding its network of independent advisors and equipping them with technologies and tools to grow their businesses. The company added about 300 advisors to its roster in 2017. Ladenburg gives all advisors access to its products and services including its wealth management division capital markets products investment banking services and investment research. The company also provides advisors with business coaching services and applications such as its Succession Continuity & Acquisitions (SCA) program; Retirement Plan Consulting Platform; and Behavioral Financial Advice Training Program.

Company Background

Founded in 1876 Ladenburg Thalmann boasts of having had Albert Einstein as a client. The company is the sixth oldest member on record as a New York Stock Exchange member.

EXECUTIVES

President CEO and Director, Richard J. (Dick) Lampen, age 64, $200,000 total compensation
EVP and Director, Mark Zeitchick, age 52, $375,000 total compensation
SVP and CIO, Doreen Griffith
SVP Wealth Management, Paul Lofties
SVP and CFO, Brett H. Kaufman, age 46, $325,000 total compensation
EVP and COO, Adam Malamed, age 46, $350,000 total compensation
Chief Risk Officer, Craig Timm
Senior Vice President Enterprise Initiatives, Carly Maher

Chairman, Phillip Frost, age 82
Vice Chairman, Howard M. Lorber, age 69
Auditors: EisnerAmper LLP

LOCATIONS

HQ: Ladenburg Thalmann Financial Services Inc
4400 Biscayne Boulevard, 12th Floor, Miami, FL 33137
Phone: 305 572-4100
Web: www.ladenburg.com

PRODUCTS/OPERATIONS

2017 Sales

	$ mil.	% of total
Commissions	536.0	42
Advisory fees	560.9	44
Investment banking	46.5	4
Interest & dividends	25.0	2
Principal transactions	0.9	-
Service fees & other	98.9	8
Total	**1,268.2**	**100**

2017 Sales

	$ mil.	% of total
Independent Advisory & Brokerage	1,140.4	90
Ladenburg	66.7	5
Insurance Brokerage	57.1	5
Corporate	4.0	-
Total	**1,268.2**	**100**

COMPETITORS

Citigroup Global Markets	LPL Financial
Detwiler Fenton	Morgan Stanley
Investors Capital Holdings	National Holdings
JPMorgan Chase	Sage Advisory Services
	UBS Financial Services

HISTORICAL FINANCIALS

Company Type: Public

Income Statement
FYE: December 31

	REVENUE ($ mil.)	NET INCOME ($ mil.)	NET PROFIT MARGIN	EMPLOYEES
12/17	1,268.1	7.7	0.6%	1,379
12/16	1,106.9	(22.2)	—	1,299
12/15	1,152.1	(11.1)	—	1,307
12/14	921.2	33.4	3.6%	1,109
12/13	793.1	(0.4)	—	715
Annual Growth	**12.4%**	—	—	**17.8%**

2017 Year-End Financials

Debt ratio: 15.3%
Return on equity: 2.1%
Cash ($ mil.): 172.1
Current ratio: 1.58
Long-term debt ($ mil.): 96.8

No. of shares (mil.): 198.5
Dividends
  Yield: 0.0%
  Payout: —
Market value ($ mil.): 628.0

	STOCK PRICE ($) FY Close	P/E High/Low	PER SHARE ($) Earnings	Dividends	Book Value
12/17	3.16	— —	(0.13)	0.02	1.87
12/16	2.44	— —	(0.29)	0.00	1.87
12/15	2.76	— —	(0.21)	0.00	2.06
12/14	3.95	49 26	0.08	0.00	1.82
12/13	3.13	— —	(0.04)	0.00	1.07
Annual Growth	**0.2%**	— —	—	—	**15.0%**

Lakeland Bancorp, Inc.

Lakeland Bancorp is the holding company for Lakeland Bank which serves northern and central New Jersey from around 50 branch offices. Targeting individuals and small to midsized businesses the bank offers standard retail products such as checking and savings accounts money market and NOW accounts and CDs. It also offers financial planning and advisory services for consumers. The bank's lending activities primarily consist of commercial loans and mortgages (around three-quarters of the company's loan portfolio) and residential mortgages. Lakeland also offers commercial lease financing for commercial equipment.

Operations

Lakeland Bancorp operates through a single business segment. Around 70% of its $4.3 billion loan portfolio is made up of commercial mortgages. Industrial commercial loans residential mortgages real estate construction loans and home equity and consumer loans each represent between 5%-10% of the company's lending activity. The company holds $5.5 billion in assets and $4.4 billion in deposits.

Geographic Reach

Headquartered in Oak Ridge New Jersey Lakeland Bancorp boasts about 50 banking offices across the New Jersey counties of Bergen Essex Morris Ocean Passaic Somerset Sussex Union and Warren. The company also has a branch in Highland Mills New York; six New Jersey regional commercial lending centers in Bernardsville Jackson Montville Newton Teaneck and Waldwick; and two commercial loan production offices serving Middlesex and Monmouth counties in New Jersey and the Hudson Valley region of New York.

Sales and Marketing

Lakeland Bancorp serves a variety of customers from individuals to businesses to municipalities.

One-fifth of Lakeland's commercial loan segment - the largest in its portfolio - is made up of owner-occupied real estate loans. Multifamily and retail loans make up about 15% each and industrial and office loans each comprise around 10%.

Financial Performance

Lakeland Bancorp has seen major five-year growth expanding revenue by 53% to $190.7 million net income by 111% to $52.6 million and cash by 39% to $142.9 million between 2013 and 2017. However the company's debt has risen 85% to $296.9 million in that time.

The holding company's revenue increased 14% in 2017 owing primarily to increased net interest income from growing average earning assets. Net income added 27% on the strength of those gains.

Lakeland's cash dipped $32.9 million in 2017. Operations and financings contributed $67.5 million and investments used $355.1 million. Financings provided $254.8 million down nearly $200 million from the previous year following an increase in net deposits federal funds purchased and securities sold under repurchase agreements.

Strategy

Lakeland Bancorp is focused on growth through acquisitions. The company has acquired at least eight community banks since its inception including Highlands Bancorp. which operates in northern New Jersey. The company also offers internet banking mobile banking and cash management services.

Mergers and Acquisitions

In January 2019 Lakeland Bancorp acquired Vernon New Jersey-based Highlands Bancorp in a deal valued at $56.7 million. The holding company - which operated branches in the New Jersey municipalities of Sparta Totowa and Denville - had consolidated total assets of $5.53 billion.

Company Background

Lakeland Bancorp was founded in 1969. It organized into a bank holding company in 1989.

EXECUTIVES

President and CEO Lakeland Bancorp and Lakeland Bank, Thomas J. Shara, age 60, $650,000 total compensation
SEVP and COO, Ronald E. (Ron) Schwarz, age 61, $266,769 total compensation
SEVP and Regional President, Robert A. Vandenbergh, age 66, $360,212 total compensation
EVP and Senior Government Banking and Financial Services Officer, Jeffrey J. Buonforte, age 66, $205,075 total compensation
SVP and Chief Credit Officer Lakeland Bank, James R. Noonan, age 66
EVP and Chief Risk Officer, James M. Nigro
CFO, Thomas F. Splaine, age 53
First SVP and Chief Technology and Information Security Officer, Mary Kaye Nardone
EVP and Chief Retail Officer, Ellen Lalwani
EVP and Chief Lending Officer, David S. Yanagisawa, $220,000 total compensation
EVP Chief Administrative Officer General Counsel and Corporate Secretary, Timothy J. Matteson, age 48
EVP and Regional President, Michael A. Schutzer
Senior Vice President and Team Leader of Commercial Lending, Michael Vessa
Vice President Asset Based Lending, Steven Breeman
Vice President, Russell Dunn
Vice President Commercial Lending, Bruce Bready
Vice President, Scott Heiman
Vice President Area Manager, Hafeza Mohammed
Vice President Director of Hurman Resource, Connie Meehan
Vice President, Connie Feeney
Senior Vice President and Director of Marketing, Maureen Martin
Vice President, Rasiel Kleiner
Vice President, Betsy Kalman
Vice President In the Investment Program, Joseph P Dolan
Vice President, Cynthia SanPhillip
Vice President, Jane Quinn
Vice President Business Development, Bill Schachtel
Assistant Vice President Branch Manager, Kim Trimmer
Vice President and Business Development Officer, Mark McCoy
Vice President and Investment Representative, Jeffrey Beebe
Vice President and Associate Counsel, Saily Avelenda
Assistant Vice President, Robert Surovich
Vice President Compliance Officer, Lisa Nienaber
Vice President Facilities Manager, Tina George
Vice President, Debra Zimmerly
Vice President Data Operations and Data Security Officer, Elizabeth Martin
Vice President Commercial Lending, Beth Johns
Vice President Secondary Marketing and Product Development, Jorge Ferrer
Vice President Area Manager, Jerry Slavik
Vice President, John Allen

Vice President Information Security Officer, Marty
 Puzio
Assistant Vice President, Richard Machtinger
Senior Vice President, Samuel Wilson
First Senior Vice President, John Rath
Vice President Relationship Manager, Tony Creanza
Vice President Consumer Loan Officer, James
 Trotta
Vice President Area Manager, Rehab Elmoslemany
Avp Portfolio Manager, Christopher Barbarino
Board Member, Janeth Hendershot
Board Member, Stephen Tilton
Vice Chairman, Bruce G Bohuny
Chairman Lakeland Bancorp and Lakeland Bank,
 Mary Ann Deacon, age 66
Board Member, Mark J Fredericks
Board Member, Robert Nicholson
Board Member, Thomas Marino
Assistant Treasurer Branch Manager, Carianne
 Reeber
ASSISTANT TREASURER, Debra Burke
Auditors: KPMG LLP

LOCATIONS

HQ: Lakeland Bancorp, Inc.
 250 Oak Ridge Road, Oak Ridge, NJ 07438
Phone: 973 697-2000
Web: www.lakelandbank.com

PRODUCTS/OPERATIONS

2017 Sales

	$ mil.	% of total
Interest		
Loans & fees	172.3	80
Investment securities and other	17.9	8
Interest expense	(25.0)	-
Non-interest		
Service charges on deposit accounts	10.7	5
Commissions & fees	4.9	2
Income on bank owned life insurance	2.4	1
Other	7.5	4
Total	190.7	100

Selected Services

401K and IRA Rollovers
Certificates of deposit & individual retirement accounts
Checking accounts
Consumer loans
Home loans
Insurance
Investment management
Online services
Retirement income planning
Savings and money market accounts

COMPETITORS

Bank of America	PNC Financial
Bank of New York	Sovereign Bank
Mellon	Sussex Bancorp
Capital One	TD Bank USA
Clifton Bancorp	Valley National
Hudson City Bancorp	Bancorp
Investors Bancorp	Wells Fargo
JPMorgan Chase	
New York Community	
Bancorp	

HISTORICAL FINANCIALS

Company Type: Public

Income Statement

FYE: December 31

	ASSETS ($ mil.)	NET INCOME ($ mil.)	INCOME AS % OF ASSETS	EMPLOYEES
12/17	5,405.6	52.5	1.0%	621
12/16	5,093.1	41.5	0.8%	592
12/15	3,869.5	32.4	0.8%	551
12/14	3,538.3	31.1	0.9%	566
12/13	3,317.7	24.9	0.8%	550
Annual Growth	13.0%	20.5%	—	3.1%

2017 Year-End Financials

Return on assets: 1.0%	Dividends
Return on equity: 9.2%	Yield: 0.0%
Long-term debt ($ mil.): —	Payout: 36.2%
No. of shares (mil.): 47.3	Market value ($ mil.): 912.0
Sales ($ mil): 215.6	

	STOCK PRICE ($) FY Close	P/E High/Low		PER SHARE ($) Earnings	Dividends	Book Value
12/17	19.25	20	16	1.09	0.40	12.31
12/16	19.50	21	10	0.95	0.37	11.65
12/15	11.79	15	12	0.85	0.33	10.57
12/14	11.70	15	12	0.82	0.29	10.01
12/13	12.37	18	13	0.71	0.27	9.28
Annual Growth	11.7%	—	—	11.1%	9.8%	7.3%

Lakeland Financial Corp

American dollars are preferred over Polish zloty in this Warsaw bank. Lakeland Financial is the holding company for Lake City Bank which serves area business customers and individuals through more than 40 branches scattered across about a dozen northern Indiana counties. Founded in 1872 in Warsaw Indiana the bank offers such standard retail services as checking and savings accounts money market accounts and CDs. Commercial loans including agricultural loans and mortgages make up about 80% of the bank's loan portfolio. Lake City Bank also offers investment products and services such as corporate and personal trust brokerage employee benefit plans and estate planning.

EXECUTIVES

EVP and Retail Banking Manager, Kevin L.
 Deardorff, age 57, $217,963 total compensation
President and CEO Lakeland Financial and Lake
 City Bank, David M. Findlay, age 56, $493,360 total
 compensation
EVP and Chief Credit Officer, Michael E. Gavin
EVP and CFO, Lisa M. O'Neill, age 50, $206,286 total
 compensation
SVP and General Counsel, Kristin L. Pruitt, age 46
EVP and Commercial Banking Manager, Eric H.
 Ottinger, $218,263 total compensation
Vice President And Trust Officer, Patricia Culp
Vice President Controller, Teresa Bartman
Senior Vice President Human Resources Training,
 Jill DeBatty

Senior Vice President and Commercial
 Indianapolis Regional Manager, Bill Redman
Vice President and Trust Officer, Jennifer King
Chairman Lakeland Financial and Lake City Bank,
 Michael L. Kubacki, age 66
Auditors: Crowe Horwath LLP

LOCATIONS

HQ: Lakeland Financial Corp
 202 East Center Street, P.O. Box 1387, Warsaw, IN
 46581-1387
Phone: 574 267-6144
Web: www.lakecitybank.com

PRODUCTS/OPERATIONS

2017 Sales

	$ mil.	% of total
Interest		
Loans	151.0	75
Securities	14.3	7
Other	0.3	-
Interest expense	(29.8)	-
Noninteresst		
Service charges on deposit accounts	13.7	7
Loan and service fees	7.9	4
Wealth advisory fees	5.5	3
Investment brokerage fees	1.3	-
Other	7.7	4
Total	171.9	100

COMPETITORS

1st Source Corporation	PNC Financial
KeyCorp	Peoples Bancorp (IN)
Northeast Indiana	
Bancorp	

HISTORICAL FINANCIALS

Company Type: Public

Income Statement

FYE: December 31

	ASSETS ($ mil.)	NET INCOME ($ mil.)	INCOME AS % OF ASSETS	EMPLOYEES
12/17	4,682.9	57.3	1.2%	539
12/16	4,290.0	52.0	1.2%	524
12/15	3,766.2	46.3	1.2%	518
12/14	3,443.2	43.8	1.3%	496
12/13	3,175.7	38.8	1.2%	497
Annual Growth	10.2%	10.2%	—	2.0%

2017 Year-End Financials

Return on assets: 1.2%	Dividends
Return on equity: 12.8%	Yield: 0.0%
Long-term debt ($ mil.): —	Payout: 28.2%
No. of shares (mil.): 25.0	Market value ($ mil.): 1,214.0
Sales ($ mil): 201.7	

	STOCK PRICE ($) FY Close	P/E High/Low		PER SHARE ($) Earnings	Dividends	Book Value
12/17	48.49	23	18	2.23	0.63	18.72
12/16	47.36	26	16	2.05	0.73	17.12
12/15	46.62	26	20	1.83	0.63	15.83
12/14	43.47	25	20	1.74	0.55	14.63
12/13	39.00	25	15	1.55	0.49	13.10
Annual Growth	5.6%	—	—	9.5%	6.3%	9.3%

Landmark Infrastructure Partners LP

Auditors: Ernst & Young LLP

LOCATIONS

HQ: Landmark Infrastructure Partners LP
400 N. Continental Blvd., Suite 500, P.O. Box 3429, El Segundo, CA 90245
Phone: 310 598-3173
Web: www.landmarkmlp.com

HISTORICAL FINANCIALS

Company Type: Public

Income Statement — FYE: December 31

	REVENUE ($ mil.)	NET INCOME ($ mil.)	NET PROFIT MARGIN	EMPLOYEES
12/17	52.6	19.2	36.6%	30
12/16	42.4	9.9	23.4%	30
12/15	27.7	(0.4)	—	20
12/14	14.2	0.5	3.8%	20
12/13	12.6	5.7	45.6%	20
Annual Growth	42.9%	35.2%	—	10.7%

2017 Year-End Financials

Debt ratio: 63.9%
Return on equity: 7.7%
Cash ($ mil.): 9.1
Current ratio: 7.41
Long-term debt ($ mil.): 491.2

No. of shares (mil.): 23.2
Dividends
Yield: 0.0%
Payout: 266.9%
Market value ($ mil.): 421.0

	STOCK PRICE ($) FY Close	P/E High/Low	Earnings	PER SHARE ($) Dividends	Book Value
12/17	18.10	34 27	0.53	1.42	10.92
12/16	15.25	40 27	0.41	1.33	10.82
12/15	14.64	116 82	0.07	1.06	8.92
12/14	16.92	—	(0.34)	0.00	13.32
Annual Growth	2.3%	— —	—	—	(6.4%)

Lannett Co., Inc.

Lannett banks on the designation of "bioequivalent" for its products. The firm develops manufactures packages markets and distributes generic prescription drugs in the US including thyroid treatment levothyroxine digoxin for congestive heart failure migraine drug butalbital and ursodiol for gallstones. Such medicines are pharmaceutical equivalents or bioequivalents of branded medicines made by other drug companies. While Lannett maintains two plants it also relies on manufacturer Jerome Stevens Pharmaceuticals for a significant portion of its inventories. The company produces medicines in oral solid (tablets liquids and capsules) and topical dosages forms.

Operations

Two of Lannett's product lines levothyroxine sodium and digoxin collectively accounted for 50% of the company's net sales in fiscal year 2015 (ended June). Both of the top products are primarily manufactured by Jerome Stevens Pharmaceuticals.

Pain management products include Cocaine Topical Solution which is primarily used during ear nose or throat surgery; Morphine Sulfate oral Solution for pain in adults; and Oxycodone HCl Oral Solution for moderate to moderately severe pain. Through the 2015 acquisition of Silarx Pharmaceuticals Lannett added several more pain management products.

Sales and Marketing

Lannett's customers include the big wholesale US pharmaceutical distributors as well as group purchasing organizations chain drug stores and other pharmaceutical companies. Top customers include AmerisourceBergen (30% of net sales in fiscal 2015) McKesson (11%) and Cardinal Health (7%).

Lannett employs a direct sales force; it also promotes products through trade shows and publications.

Financial Performance

Revenues rose modestly in fiscal 2012 and 2013 and dramatically in 2014 and 2015. In fiscal 2015 (ended June) revenue increased 49% to $407 million largely due to tremendous growth in gallstone treatments. This in turn was driven by price increases for Ursodiol. Other treatment areas that saw growth that year included migraine glaucoma and thyroid deficiency; a new muscle relaxant product also helped revenue.

Net income which has also been on the rise rose 162% to $150 million in fiscal 2015. Higher revenue led to that growth but was partially offset by higher operating expenses and reduced gains on investments.

Following suit cash flow from operations increased 185% to $128 million in 2015.

Strategy

Like any drug developer Lannett maintains a steady stream of potential drugs in its pipeline. New product introductions are key to keeping ahead of its competitors and as such the firm focuses on developing products with few or no generic competitors. The company maintains its own R&D staff partners with third-party developers and sometimes simply purchases new products from other generic makers or buys other pharmaceutical companies outright.

In 2015 the company's newly acquired subsidiary Silarx Pharmaceuticals received FDA approval for its generic version of antidepressant Abilify. This followed the 2014 approval of Lannett's generic versions of Novartis' Femara Tablets (for treatment of breast cancer) and Lehigh Valley Technology's Oxycodone Hydrochloride Oral Solution.

One of the company's focus areas of development is the market of narcotics and controlled substances as Lannett believes the demand for pain medicine will continue to increase as the Baby Boomer generation ages. Lannett is also looking to grow in new specialty fields of medicine as well as new dosage formulations (such as ophthalmic or nasal products) through strategic relationships or acquisitions.

Lannett signed an agreement with Symplmed in mid-2014 through which Symplmed became the exclusive US distributor of Lannett's generic version of ACEON a treatment for high blood pressure.

In early 2016 Lannett made a number of changes to cut costs including cutting 10% of its total staff (with plans to ultimately cut 20% over the next three years). It also closed the Princeton New Jersey corporate offices of the recently acquired Kremers Urban Pharmaceuticals. The restructuring efforts which aim to streamline and consolidate operations are expected to generate some $40 million in savings within 12 months.

Mergers and Acquisitions

In 2015 Lannett bought Kremers Urban Pharmaceuticals for $1.23 billion. Formerly the US generics business of Belgian firm UCB Kremers makes treatments for such ailments as ADHD and gastroesophageal reflux. The deal is one of several that have been announced or completed in the generics arena which is growing in importance as more drugs lose patent protection.

Also that year the company acquired New York-based Silarx Pharmaceuticals for $42.5 million. Silarx makes and markets liquid pharmaceutical products including generic and over-the-counter products.

Company Background

Formed in 1942 Lannett is one of the oldest generics manufacturers in the US.

EXECUTIVES

CEO, Arthur P. Bedrosian, age 73, $555,170 total compensation
VP Sales and Marketing, Kevin R. Smith, age 59, $286,340 total compensation
VP Logistics and CIO, Robert Ehlinger, age 62, $170,000 total compensation
VP Finance CFO and Treasurer, Martin P. Galvan, age 67, $326,510 total compensation
Vice President Quality, John Abt
Chairman, William Farber, age 87
Secretary, Jeffrey K. Farber, age 59
Auditors: Grant Thornton LLP

LOCATIONS

HQ: Lannett Co., Inc.
9000 State Road, Philadelphia, PA 19136
Phone: 215 333-9000
Web: www.lannett.com

PRODUCTS/OPERATIONS

2015 Sales

	$ mil.	% of total
Wholesalers	297.7	73
Retail chains	65.1	16
Mail-order pharmacy	44.0	11
Total	**406.8**	**100**

2015 Sales

	% of total
Thyroid Deficiency	38
Gallstone	16
Cardiovascular	14
Migraine	6
Pain management	6
Glaucoma	5
Antibiotic	3
Gout	2
Muscle Relaxant	2
Obesity	1
Other	7
Total	**100**

Selected Products

Amantadine (generic Symmetrel Parkinson's Disease)
Butalbital (generic Fiorinal migraine)
Clindamycin (generic Cleocin antibiotic)
C-Topical solution (anesthetic)

Danazol (generic Danocrine endometriosis)
Dicyclomine (generic Bentyl irritable bowel syndrome)
Diethylpropion (generic Tenuate obesity)
Digoxin (generic Lanoxin congestive heart failure)
Doxycycline (generic Adoxa antibiotic)
Fluphenazine (generic Proxlixin antipsychotic)
Hydromorphone (generic Dilaudid pain management)
Levothyroxine (generic Levoxyl thyroid deficiency)
Loxapine (generic Loxitane antipsychotic)
Morphine sulfate (pain)
Oxycodone (generic Roxicodone pain management)
Phentermine (generic Adipex obesity)
Pilocarpine (generic Salagen dry mouth)
Primidone (generic Mysoline epilepsy)
Probenecid (generic Benemid gout)
Rifampin (generic Rifadin antibiotic for meningitis)
Terbutaline (generic Brethine bronchospasms)
Triamterene with hydrochlorothiazide (generic Byazide hypertension)
Unithroid (thyroid deficiency)
Ursodiol (generic Actigall gallstone)

COMPETITORS

Abbott Labs	Mylan
Akorn	Obagi Medical
Allergan plc	Par Pharmaceutical
Chiesi USA	Companies
Cumberland	Pfizer
Pharmaceuticals	Purdue Pharma
Derma Sciences	Roxane Laboratories
GlaxoSmithKline	Salix Pharmaceuticals
Hi-Tech Pharmacal	Sandoz International
Jazz Pharmaceuticals	GmbH
Momenta	SciClone
Pharmaceuticals	Teva

HISTORICAL FINANCIALS

Company Type: Public

Income Statement   FYE: June 30

	REVENUE ($ mil.)	NET INCOME ($ mil.)	NET PROFIT MARGIN	EMPLOYEES
06/18	684.5	28.6	4.2%	1,251
06/17	633.3	(0.5)	—	1,126
06/16	542.4	44.7	8.3%	1,149
06/15	406.8	149.9	36.8%	502
06/14	273.7	57.1	20.9%	399
Annual Growth	25.7%	(15.8%)	—	33.1%

2018 Year-End Financials

Debt ratio: 53.2%
Return on equity: 4.9%
Cash ($ mil.): 98.5
Current ratio: 2.62
Long-term debt ($ mil.): 772.4

No. of shares (mil.): 37.3
Dividends
  Yield: —
  Payout: —
Market value ($ mil.): 508.0

	STOCK PRICE ($) FY Close	P/E High/Low		PER SHARE ($) Earnings	Dividends	Book Value
06/18	13.60	38	17	0.75	0.00	16.02
06/17	20.40	—	—	(0.02)	0.00	15.20
06/16	23.79	51	14	1.20	0.00	15.14
06/15	59.44	17	8	4.04	0.00	12.78
06/14	49.62	29	7	1.62	0.00	8.28
Annual Growth	(27.6%)	—	—	(17.5%)	—	17.9%

LCI Industries

Drew Industries makes wanderlust — in comfort and style — a possibility. The company manufac-tures aluminum and vinyl windows and doors and other products (furniture and slide-out walls) for travel trailers and fifth-wheel recreational vehicles (RVs) (some 85% of sales) and manufactured housing (MH). Drew does business via two sub-sidiaries: Kinro produces windows doors and screens and Lippert Components churns out axles ramps and chassis parts as well as specialty trailers for hauling boats and snowmobiles. Brands include Equa-Flex Happijac RV Lock Solera Ground Con-trol and Level Up.

Operations

Drew operates through two segments: RV prod-ucts and manufactured housing products (MH). About 90% of its RV segment's net sales in 2015 were of products to manufacturers of travel trailer and fifth-wheel RVs. The MH segment makes fab-ricating welding thermoforming painting and as-sembling components into finished products and operates through 13 manufacturing and ware-house facilities throughout the US.

Geographic Reach

Drew operates about 45 facilities throughout the US. About half of its manufacturing plants are concentrated in Indiana.

Sales and Marketing

RV products are sold primarily to major manu-facturers of RVs such as Thor Industries Forest River Jayco and other OEMs. Drew's MH products are sold primarily to major producers of manufac-tured homes such as Clayton Homes Cavco Indus-tries and other OEMs. The company also sells both segments' products to distributors and retail deal-ers of aftermarket products.

Financial Performance

With the painful effects of the recession firmly behind it Drew has enjoyed unprecedented growth over the last five years. Revenues jumped 18% to peak at $1.4 billion in 2015. Profits also surged 19% to reach $74 million in 2015. (Both these to-tals represented historic milestones for the com-pany.)

The historic growth for 2015 was driven by a 20% rise in RV sales thanks to an increase in in-dustry-wide wholesale shipments of travel trailer and fifth-wheel RVs the company's primary RV market. Drew also experienced a bump in MH rev-enue as industry-wide wholesale shipments of manufactured homes increased as well as sales of components for new manufactured homes.

Mergers and Acquisitions

The company has made its mark in the RV and manufactured housing industries primarily by growing through acquisitions. As a result of the economic downturn certain distressed manufac-turers have placed their assets and intellectual property rights on the sales block and Drew's sub-sidiaries have taken advantage of those opportu-nities.

In 2015 the company purchased Signature Seat-ing an Indiana-based manufacturer of furniture products and services for fresh water boat manu-facturers. It also purchased Spectal Industries a Canada-based manufacturer of windows and doors.

Later in 2015 it picked up EA Technologies an Indiana-based manufacturer of custom steel and aluminum parts. EA is also a provider of electro-deposition and powder coating services for RV bus medium-duty truck automotive recreational marine specialty and utility trailer and military applica-tions.

In 2014 Drew for $36 million obtained Innova-tive Design Solutions (IDS) located in Troy Michi-gan. IDS is a designer developer and manufacturer of electronic systems encompassing a wide variety of RV applications. The acquisition provided Drew with further access to cutting-edge electronic prod-ucts for the RV industry as well as adjacent indus-tries.

EXECUTIVES

CEO, Jason D. Lippert, age 46, $856,800 total compensation
President and COO, Scott T. Mereness, age 46, $589,050 total compensation
CFO, Brian M. Hall, age 43, $225,727 total compensation
Chairman, James F. Gero, age 74
Board Member, David Reed
Board Member, John Lowe
Auditors: KPMG LLP

LOCATIONS

HQ: LCI Industries
  3501 County Road 6 East, Elkhart, IN 46514
Phone: 574 535-1125
Web: www.lci1.com

PRODUCTS/OPERATIONS

2013 Sales

	$ mil.	% of total
Recreational vehicles	893.7	88
Manufactured housing	121.9	12
Total	**1,015.6**	**100**

Selected Products

Manufactured housing (MH) products
  Aluminum and vinyl patio doors
  Axles
  Entry doors
  Steel and fiberglass entry doors
  Steel chassis
  Steel chassis parts
  Replacement windows doors thermoformed bath products
  Thermoformed bath and kitchen products
  Vinyl and aluminum windows and screens
Recreational vehicle (RV) products (travel trailers and fifth-wheel RVs)
  Aluminum windows and screens
  Chassis components
  Entry and baggage doors
  Entry steps
  Furniture and mattresses
  Manual electric and hydraulic stabilizer and lifting systems
  Patio doors
  Slide-out mechanisms
  Specialty trailers for hauling boats personal watercraft snowmobiles and equipment
  Thermoformed bath kitchen and other products
  Towable axles and suspensions
  Towable steel chassis
  Toy hauler ramp doors

COMPETITORS

Atwood Mobile	Meritor
Coast Distribution	Patrick Industries
Elixir Industries	Quality Trailer
Euramax	Products
Featherlite	Tuthill
LaSalle Bristol	Wozniak Industries

HISTORICAL FINANCIALS
Company Type: Public

Income Statement
FYE: December 31

	REVENUE ($ mil.)	NET INCOME ($ mil.)	NET PROFIT MARGIN	EMPLOYEES
12/17	2,147.7	132.8	6.2%	9,852
12/16	1,678.9	129.6	7.7%	7,654
12/15	1,403.0	74.3	5.3%	6,576
12/14	1,190.7	62.2	5.2%	5,845
12/13	1,015.5	50.1	4.9%	5,109
Annual Growth	20.6%	27.6%	—	17.8%

2017 Year-End Financials

Debt ratio: 5.2%	No. of shares (mil.): 24.9
Return on equity: 22.0%	Dividends
Cash ($ mil.): 26.0	Yield: 0.0%
Current ratio: 2.29	Payout: 39.1%
Long-term debt ($ mil.): 49.9	Market value ($ mil.): 3,249.0

	STOCK PRICE ($) FY Close	P/E High/Low		PER SHARE ($) Earnings	Dividends	Book Value
12/17	130.00	25	17	5.24	2.05	26.12
12/16	107.75	21	10	5.20	1.40	22.23
12/15	60.89	21	16	3.02	2.00	18.01
12/14	51.07	21	16	2.56	0.00	16.56
12/13	51.20	25	15	2.11	2.00	13.42
Annual Growth	26.2%			25.5%	0.6%	18.1%

LegacyTexas Financial Group Inc

With its eye on the Lone Star State LegacyTexas Financial (formerly ViewPoint Financial) provides retail and commercial banking through its LegacyTexas Bank subsidiary which operates about 50 branches located mostly in the Dallas/Fort Worth area. LegacyTexas offers standard deposit products such as checking and savings accounts and CDs and uses deposit funds to originate primarily real estate loans: Commercial Real Estate loans account for nearly 50% of its lending portfolio while consumer real estate loans make up another nearly 20%. Non-real estate commercial loans make up almost 30% of its loan portfolio.

Operations
Outside of banking services the LegacyTexas offers brokerage services to buy and sell investments and insurance products through a third-party brokerage arrangement.

About 82% of the company's total revenue came from loan interest (including fees) in 2014 and another 6% came from interest on its taxable and non-taxable securities. Most of LegacyTexas' remaining revenue came from service charges and fees on deposit accounts.

Geographic Reach
The Plano-based company boasts 51 Texas branches with 48 of them located in the Dallas-Fort Worth Metroplex. Its two First National Bank of Jacksboro branches are in Jack in Wise counties in Texas.

Sales and Marketing

LegacyTexas' serves a diverse market of management professional and sales personnel office employees manufacturing and transportation workers service industry workers government employees and self-employed individuals. It spent $1.54 million on advertising in 2014 compared to $2.69 million and $1.75 million in 2013 and 2012 respectively.

Financial Performance
The company has struggled to consistently grow its revenues and profits in recent years despite growing loan business mostly stemming from lost revenues from the sale of its mortgage-banking subsidiary in 2012.

LegacyTexas' revenue rebounded by 7% to $31.3 million in 2014 primarily thanks to double-digit growth in its loan interest income driven by higher commercial loan volume.

Despite higher revenue in 2014 the company's net income dipped by 1% to $31.3 million mostly due to higher loan loss provisions as commercial loan production picked up. LegacyTexas' operating cash levels fell by 21% to $52 million mostly from unfavorable changes in working capital related to its assets and liabilities.

Strategy
The company formerly known as ViewPoint Financial significantly boosted its loan and deposit business and the size of its branch network through its early 2015 acquisition LegacyTexas Group. The deal made its branch network swell to 48 offices from just 31 before while adding some $1.63 billion in deposits and $1.4 billion in new loan business. The new LegacyTexas Group planned in 2015 to organically grow its loan portfolio focusing especially on making commercial real estate commercial and industrial and energy loans tied to high-quality assets. To cheaply raise funding for loans the bank plans to promote its non-interest-bearing demand deposit accounts especially in the commercial sector and using its treasury management services to provide a "catalyst for deposit growth."

Mergers and Acquisitions
In January 2015 the former ViewPoint Financial acquired LegacyTexas Group in a $300 million deal to create one of the largest independent banks in Texas with assets of nearly $6 billion. The parent company then changed its name to LegacyTexas Financial and the bank changed its name to LegacyTexas Bank.

Company Background
LegacyTexas Financial converted from a mutual holding company to a stock holding company in 2010. It sold its mortgage subsidiary VPM which operated a dozen loan production offices in Texas and Oklahoma in late 2012.

EXECUTIVES

EVP Chief Lending Officer, Thomas S. Swiley, age 68, $277,300 total compensation
EVP COO Chief Risk Officer and General Counsel, Scott A. Almy, age 51, $277,300 total compensation
President CEO and Director, Kevin J. Hanigan, age 61, $549,450 total compensation
EVP Community Banking, Charles D. Eikenberg, age 63, $277,300 total compensation
EVP and CFO, J. Mays Davenport, age 50
Senior Vice President Credit Officer, Sam Duff
Vice President Banking Center Manager, Monisa Barbosa
Vice President Business Development, Ginger Johnson
Vice President Warehouse Lending, Michelle Marrapodi
Chairman, Anthony J. LeVecchio, age 71
Vice Chairman, George Fisk
Auditors: Ernst & Young LLP

LOCATIONS
HQ: LegacyTexas Financial Group Inc
5851 Legacy Circle, Plano, TX 75024
Phone: 972 578-5000
Web: www.legacytexasfinancialgroup.com

PRODUCTS/OPERATIONS

2014 Sales

	% of total
Interest and dividend income	88
Non interest income	12
Total	**100**

COMPETITORS

Amegy	PlainsCapital
BBVA Compass	SP Bancorp
Bancshares	Texas Capital
Bank of America	Bancshares
Cullen/Frost Bankers	Wells Fargo
North Dallas Bank	

HISTORICAL FINANCIALS
Company Type: Public

Income Statement
FYE: December 31

	ASSETS ($ mil.)	NET INCOME ($ mil.)	INCOME AS % OF ASSETS	EMPLOYEES
12/17	9,086.2	89.4	1.0%	869
12/16	8,362.2	97.8	1.2%	896
12/15	7,691.9	70.9	0.9%	856
12/14	4,164.1	31.2	0.8%	530
12/13	3,525.2	31.6	0.9%	576
Annual Growth	26.7%	29.6%	—	10.8%

2017 Year-End Financials

Return on assets: 1.0%	Dividends
Return on equity: 9.7%	Yield: 0.0%
Long-term debt ($ mil.): —	Payout: 32.2%
No. of shares (mil.): 48.1	Market value ($ mil.): 2,031.0
Sales ($ mil): 410.4	

	STOCK PRICE ($) FY Close	P/E High/Low		PER SHARE ($) Earnings	Dividends	Book Value
12/17	42.21	23	18	1.89	0.61	19.95
12/16	43.06	21	8	2.09	0.58	18.49
12/15	25.02	21	13	1.53	0.54	16.88
12/14	23.85	36	26	0.81	0.48	14.20
12/13	27.45	33	22	0.83	0.42	13.63
Annual Growth	11.4%		—	22.8%	9.8%	10.0%

LeMaitre Vascular Inc

LeMaitre Vascular makes the veins run on time. The company makes both disposable and implanted surgical vascular devices including catheters and stents under such brands as AnastoClip EndoFit and Pruitt-Inahara. Originally founded by a vascular surgeon to develop a valvulotome to prepare veins for arterial bypass surgery the company has since expanded its offerings to include a device to create dialysis access sites and another to treat aortic aneurysms. Le Maitre sells 12 product lines most of which are used in open vascular surgery and some of which are used in endovascular procedures. Its products are sold to hospitals in North America Europe and Japan through a direct sales force.

Geographic Reach

LeMaitre manufactures most of its products in a single facility in Massachusetts.

In an effort to tap into the world's third-largest medical device market LaMaitre opened its first office in China in mid-2014.

Sales and Marketing

LeMaitre sells its products through a direct sales force but also relies on a few distributors in several countries. The company however is expanding its sales force to reach its customers more directly.

Strategy

LeMaitre has grown by competing in niche markets expanding its worldwide direct sales force and acquiring and developing complementary vascular devices. LeMaitre also intends to grow by pursuing regulatory approval of its products in new markets.

Along with acquisitions product enhancements and developments are at the heart of the firm's growth strategy. As new products are acquired or launched the company also cleans out its closet and discontinues or divests products it no longer considers complementary.

Mergers and Acquisitions

LeMaitre acquired the assets of Cardial a Becton Dickinson subsidiary for $2.3 million in 2018. Cardial makes knitted and woven vascular grafts valvulotomes and surgical glue. Earlier that year the company paid $14.2 million for the vascular clot business including a number of catheter products of Applied Medical Resources.

In 2016 LeMaitre acquired Restore Flow Allografts for $14 million plus potential performance payments. Restore Flow processes and cryopreserves vascular veins and arteries which LeMaitre will use as it expands its range of biologic products. Other recent acquisitions for the company include OmniFlow II and ProCol.

Company Background

LeMaitre was founded in 1983 by vascular surgeon George D. LeMaitre to develop a valvulotome to prepare veins for arterial bypass surgery.

In 2006 LeMaitre Vascular raised more than $30 million from its initial public offering. The company spent part of the proceeds to pay off debt; it also used proceeds toward its goals of increasing research and development efforts hiring new sales representatives and acquiring complementary products or businesses.

EXECUTIVES

Vice President General Counsel and Secretary, Aaron Grossman

Chairman and CEO, George W. LeMaitre, age 53, $315,580 total compensation

President, David B. (Dave) Roberts, age 54, $333,174 total compensation

President International Operations, Peter R. Gebauer, age 64, $295,149 total compensation

SVP Operations, Trent G. Kamke, age 47, $162,500 total compensation

CFO, Joseph P. Pellegrino, age 53, $247,236 total compensation

VP Central Europe and Sales, Maik D. Helmers, age 44

VP Information Technology, Jonathan W. Ngau, age 44

Country Manager Japan, Nobuhiro Okabe, age 65

VP Research and Development, Ryan H. Connelly, age 40

SVP Clinical Regulatory & Quality Affairs, Andrew Hodgkinson, age 42

Country Manager Italy, Giovannella Deiure

General Counsel, Laurie A. Churchill

Vice President, Cornelia Lemaitre

Board of Director, Michael Jackson

Auditors: GRANT THORNTON LLP

LOCATIONS

HQ: LeMaitre Vascular Inc
63 Second Avenue, Burlington, MA 01803
Phone: 781 221-2266
Web: www.lemaitre.com

PRODUCTS/OPERATIONS

Selected Products

Vascular
  Balloon catheters (for removing blood clots; occlusion and facilitation of blood flow)
  Carotid shunts (facilitation of blood flow to brain during carotid plaque removal)
  Remote endarterectomy devices (for removing blockages in major arteries in the leg)
  Valvulotomes (destroys vein valves to create vein bypass grafts)
  Vascular grafts (synthetic vessels used in bypass and replacement procedures)
  Vascular patches (synthetic and biological patches used in closing incisions in a blood vessel)
  Vein strippers (single-incision removal of varicose veins)
  Vessel closure systems (attachment of blood vessels mainly for dialysis access)
Endovascular
  Aortic stent grafts (endovascular repair of abdominal and thoracic aortic aneurysms and thoracic dissections; in clinical studies)
  Manual contrast injectors (contrast media injection into blood vessels)
  Modeling catheters (for improved sealing of aortic stent grafts; application submitted)
  Radiopaque tape (for improved precision of vascular and endovascular procedures)
General surgery
  Laparoscopic cholecystectomy devices (for introducing dye into the cystic duct and related uses)

COMPETITORS

Bard	Getinge
Cardiovascular Systems	Medtronic
Cook Group	Terumo
Edwards Lifesciences	W.L. Gore

HISTORICAL FINANCIALS

Company Type: Public

Income Statement — FYE: December 31

	REVENUE ($ mil.)	NET INCOME ($ mil.)	NET PROFIT MARGIN	EMPLOYEES
12/17	100.8	17.1	17.0%	423
12/16	89.1	10.5	11.9%	397
12/15	78.3	7.7	9.9%	356
12/14	71.1	3.9	5.5%	341
12/13	64.5	3.2	5.0%	334
Annual Growth	**11.8%**	**52.2%**	**—**	**6.1%**

2017 Year-End Financials

Debt ratio: —	No. of shares (mil.): 19.2
Return on equity: 17.4%	Dividends
Cash ($ mil.): 19.1	Yield: 0.0%
Current ratio: 6.09	Payout: 25.5%
Long-term debt ($ mil.): —	Market value ($ mil.): 613.0

	STOCK PRICE ($) FY Close	P/E High/Low		PER SHARE ($) Earnings	Dividends	Book Value
12/17	31.84	43	24	0.86	0.22	5.70
12/16	25.34	45	22	0.55	0.18	4.71
12/15	17.25	40	17	0.42	0.16	4.25
12/14	7.65	35	28	0.23	0.14	3.93
12/13	8.01	41	27	0.20	0.12	3.63
Annual Growth	**41.2%**	**—**	**—**	**44.0%**	**16.4%**	**11.9%**

LendingTree Inc (New)

LendingTree (formerly Tree.com) helps consumers cut through a forest of options in financing education insurance home services and more. The company allows users to comparison shop for home loans through its most prominent branch LendingTree which helps match home buyers with lenders. Its lending network includes over 350 banks and other lenders. Other subsidiaries help consumers choose between colleges and home service providers. LendingTree also markets auto loans and credit cards. Services are free to consumers as the firm collects fees from the companies to which it refers business.

Operations

LendingTree operates four main business segments: Lending for consumers seeking home mortgage loans lines of credit reverse mortgages and personal loans; Auto which includes its auto refinance and purchase loan products; Education which includes a student enrollment product and student loan products; and Home Services which helps consumers research and find home improvement professional services through its marketplace of local and national contractors.

Overall 80% of the company's total revenue in 2014 came from mortgage products while nonmortgage lending products (such as personal loans home equity reverse mortgages and credit cards) made up another 12%.

Sales and Marketing

The online company has been ramping up its advertising in recent years. It spent $102.2 million on advertising in 2014 up from $80.7 million and $40.8 million in 2013 and 2012 respectively.

Financial Performance

LendingTree's revenues have more than tripled since 2011 thanks to a strengthened housing market which has driven more demand for its mortgage loan marketplace services. Its profits have also trended higher with business growth. (Note: The company's profit spiked in 2012 thanks to significant gains from the $56 million sale of its LendingTree Loans business to Discover.)

The firm's revenue jumped 20% to $167.4 million in 2014 mostly thanks to strong growth in its nonmortgage lending products stemming from its 2013 introduction of its reverse mortgage credit card and personal loan products. Mortgage lending product revenue also rose by 9% on notable increases in its purchase product supported by growth of its rate table offering launched in early 2013. The number of consumers matched on its lending marketplace spiked by 64% during the year though its average revenue earned from marketplace lenders per matched customer fell by 26% as more users went for lower-margin non-mortgage lending products.

Higher revenue in 2014 allowed the company's net income to more than double to $9.4 million. LendingTree's operating cash levels fell by 11% to $9.1 million due to unfavorable changes in working capital related mostly to its accounts payable accrued expenses and other current liabilities balances.

Strategy

LendingTree regularly introduces new products across new markets to keep consumers interested. In mid-2015 expanding beyond its mortgage-related wheelhouse LendingTree launched its new personal loan rates product which allowed consumers to shop among multiple lenders for personal loans. In 2014 the company introduced its new Small Business Loan marketplace (which included peer-to-peer lenders) and an online marketplace for car shoppers (via autos.lendingtree.com) to shop more than 2.5 million new and used cars and find auto financing through its marketplace services.

The company also releases new tools to keep visitors coming back to its website. In 2014 the company relaunched its My LendingTree platform that offered personalized loan comparison shopping free credit scores credit score analysis and an in-depth review of a consumer's credit profile.

Mergers and Acquisitions

LendingTree agreed in 2018 to acquire Value Holding the parent company of personal finance website ValuePenguin.com for $105 million in cash. The site provides financial analysis to consumers for products including insurance and credit cards. LendingTree believes the purchase will drive acquisition of insurance customers. The deal is expected to close in the first quarter of 2019.

In 2017 LendingTree acquired financial advice website MoneyTree.com for around $30 million.

Company Background

The company's roots formed with LendingTree which was founded by CEO Doug Lebda in 1996 and acquired by IAC/InterActiveCorp (IAC) in 2003. Five years later IAC spun off LendingTree and three other subsidiaries: ILG Ticketmaster and HSN. As part of the spinoff Tree.com was formed to operate LendingTree along with its other lending and real estate businesses as a separate publicly traded company.

EXECUTIVES

Chairman and CEO, Douglas R. (Doug) Lebda, age 48, $600,000 total compensation
President, Neil Salvage, age 45, $391,538 total compensation
Chief Product and Strategy Officer, Nikul Patel, age 45, $318,615 total compensation
SVP Chief Accounting Officer and Treasurer, Carla Shumate, $236,538 total compensation
SVP Sales and General Manager Mortgage, Sam Mischner
CFO, J.D. Moriarty, age 46
Auditors: PricewaterhouseCoopers LLP

LOCATIONS

HQ: LendingTree Inc (New)
11115 Rushmore Drive, Charlotte, NC 28277
Phone: 704 541-5351
Web: www.lendingtree.com

PRODUCTS/OPERATIONS

2014 Sales

	$ mil.	% of total
Lending		
Mortgage Products	134.2	80
Non-mortgage Products	20.4	12
Others	12.8	8
Total	**167.4**	**100**

Selected Brands

DegreeTree.com
DoneRight.com
GetSmart.com
HealthTree.com
InsuranceTree.com
LendingTreeAutos.com
LendingTree.com
ServiceTree.com

COMPETITORS

Bankrate	XO Group
Internet Brands	ditech

HISTORICAL FINANCIALS

Company Type: Public

Income Statement

FYE: December 31

	REVENUE ($ mil.)	NET INCOME ($ mil.)	NET PROFIT MARGIN	EMPLOYEES
12/17	617.7	15.5	2.5%	535
12/16	384.4	27.4	7.2%	399
12/15	254.2	48.0	18.9%	312
12/14	167.3	9.3	5.6%	218
12/13	139.2	3.9	2.8%	192
Annual Growth	45.1%	40.9%	—	29.2%

2017 Year-End Financials

Debt ratio: 34.3%	No. of shares (mil.): 11.9	
Return on equity: 5.9%	Dividends	
Cash ($ mil.): 368.5	Yield: —	
Current ratio: 2.97	Payout: —	
Long-term debt ($ mil.): 238.2	Market value ($ mil.): 4,078.0	

	STOCK PRICE ($) FY Close	P/E High/Low	Earnings	Dividends	Book Value
12/17	340.45	271 76	1.14	0.00	24.57
12/16	101.35	48 24	2.15	0.00	19.63
12/15	89.28	33 10	3.83	0.00	19.46
12/14	48.34	57 28	0.84	0.00	8.46
12/13	32.84	91 45	0.36	0.00	7.73
Annual Growth	79.4%		— 33.4%	—	33.5%

LGI Homes, Inc.

LGI Homes wants everyone to stop wasting money on rent. Targeting first-time homebuyers the residential builder develops homes that appeal to renters looking to buy an affordable home in Texas Florida the Southwest the Southeast or the Northwest. During 2015 its homes were priced between $110000 and $475000 and ranged from 1100 to 4000 sq. ft. with each home selling for an average price of $185100. The builder's higher-quality Terrata Homes started at $350000 for a 2500 sq. ft. home. LGI Homes has sold more than 12000 homes since its founding in 2003. It went public in 2013.

Operations

The builder operates five segments organized by region: Texas Florida the Southwest (Arizona Colorado New Mexico) the Southeast (Florida Georgia North Carolina South Carolina) the Northwest (Washington).

Geographic Reach

The Woodlands Texas-based LGI Homes builds in 20 states with its largest state market being in Texas (particularly around the major cities) where it made 56% of its total sales during 2015. Its next largest market was Florida (especially in Tampa and Orlando) which accounted for 12% of sales. The rest of its sales came from states in the Southwest (17% of sales) Southeast (15%) and the Northwest (less than 1%).

Sales and Marketing

The homebuilder targets mostly home and apartment renters and markets products through print and digital advertising including direct mail newspaper ads social media and interactive online media as well as via directional signage and billboards.

It's been ramping up its advertising and direct mail spend in recent years to support sales growth. The builder spent $9.3 million on advertising and direct mail during 2015 up from $8.6 million and $3.3 million in 2014 and 2013 respectively.

Financial Performance

LGI's annual sales and profits have swelled more than ten-fold since 2011 as it's expanded into more states and as the housing market has heated up with higher home prices and more demand.

The homebuilder's sales spiked 64% to a record $630.24 million during 2015 mostly thanks to a 45% rise in home closings (which totaled 3404 home deliveries for the year) but also because its average home sale prices increased by 13.8% to $185146 per home thanks to product mix changes higher price points in new markets and a more favorable environment for growing home prices. Its Oakmont acquisition which led to 269 more home closing during the year also helped boost total sales.

Strong revenue growth in 2015 drove LGI Homes' net income up 87% to a record $53 million. While the homebuilder's operations used $89 million in cash for the year toward building its land inventory to support future home sales it spent about half as much cash as in 2014 as it eased up on inventory purchases.

Strategy

LGI Homes continued in 2016 to focus on acquiring land lots and building in its core markets which include Houston San Antonio Dallas/Fort Worth Austin Phoenix Tucson Tampa Orlando Atlanta Albuquerque Charlotte and Denver. The homebuilder hopes record-high rental rates especially in these markets will entice more potential first-time homebuyers to look at its homes.

Mergers and Acquisitions

In October 2014 LGI entered the Charlotte North Carolina market after acquiring Oakmont Home Builders as well as its 150 homes under construction and 1000 owned and controlled lots for a total price of $17.3 million.

Company Background

LGI Homes went public in 2013 raising $99 million which it used to buy back stock from investment firm GTIS Partners as well as to buy land develop lots and build more homes.

EXECUTIVES

Chairman and CEO, Eric Lipar, age 48
President and COO, Michael Snider, age 47
CFO, Charles Merdian, age 49
EVP Acquisitions, Jack Lipar, age 50
EVP and Chief Marketing Officer, Rachel Eaton, age 37
Auditors: Ernst & Young

LOCATIONS

HQ: LGI Homes, Inc.
1450 Lake Robbins Drive, Suite 430, The Woodlands, TX 77380
Phone: 281 362-8998
Web: www.lgihomes.com

COMPETITORS

AV Homes	M.D.C.
Beazer Homes	M/I Homes
CalAtlantic	Meritage Homes
D.R. Horton	NVR
Drees Homes	PulteGroup
KB Home	Taylor Morrison
Lennar	Toll Brothers

HISTORICAL FINANCIALS

Company Type: Public

Income Statement

FYE: December 31

	REVENUE ($ mil.)	NET INCOME ($ mil.)	NET PROFIT MARGIN	EMPLOYEES
12/17	1,257.9	113.3	9.0%	726
12/16	838.3	75.0	9.0%	591
12/15	630.2	52.8	8.4%	489
12/14	383.2	28.2	7.4%	390
12/13	162.8	22.3	13.7%	253
Annual Growth	66.7%	50.1%	—	30.2%

2017 Year-End Financials

Debt ratio: 44.0%
Return on equity: 26.8%
Cash ($ mil.): 67.5
Current ratio: 9.14
Long-term debt ($ mil.): 475.2

No. of shares (mil.): 21.8
Dividends
Yield: —
Payout: —
Market value ($ mil.): 1,639.0

	STOCK PRICE ($) FY Close	P/E High/Low		PER SHARE ($) Earnings	Dividends	Book Value
12/17	75.03	15	5	4.73	0.00	22.42
12/16	28.73	11	5	3.41	0.00	16.67
12/15	24.33	13	5	2.44	0.00	12.20
12/14	14.92	15	10	1.33	0.00	9.19
12/13	17.79	54	37	0.34	0.00	7.92
Annual Growth	43.3%	—	—	93.1%	—	29.7%

LHC Group Inc

The injured and ailing in need of a little TLC need look no further than LHC. LHC Group administers post-acute health care services through more than 780 home nursing agencies hospices and long-term acute care hospitals (LTACH). The company operates through two segments: home-based services and facility-based services in rural areas in about 25 US states. LHC's home health nursing agencies provide care to Medicare beneficiaries offering such services as private duty nursing physical therapy and medically-oriented social services. Its hospices provide palliative care for terminal patients while its LTACHs serve patients who no longer need intensive care but still require complex care in a hospital setting. In 2018 LHC Group merged with Almost Family a provider of home health care services.

Operations

LHC also operates a handful of rehabilitation disease management and other specialty health facilities. Its Telehealth Services segment delivers medical care remotely via telephone Web-based applications and e-mail. The use of telehealth expands access to care to more patients and rural locations as well as provides for better monitoring of patients with chronic health problems.

The company gets the majority of its revenue from its home-based health services units located primarily in the Southeast and Midwest regions of the country. Medicare payments account for the bulk of its service income. Given that such a significant portion of the company's revenue is derived from federal payments LHC is vulnerable to changes in reimbursement levels to Medicare.

LHC also partners with not-for-profit hospitals because such joint ventures tend to provide a more attractive return on investment for the company. It has such agreements with Baptist Health System (Alabama) West Tennessee Healthcare Southeast Alabama Medical Center East Alabama Medical Center Three Rivers Community Hospital (Oregon) Woods Memorial Hospital (Tennessee) the continuing care arm of CHRISTUS Health (northeast Texas) Texas Health Resources and Methodist Health System (Texas). In total it has more than 100 joint venture locations in close to 20 states across its home nursing hospice and LTAC agencies although most are in collaboration with hospitals.

In addition to the home nursing agencies and hospices that it owns or operates (its home-based segment) the company's facility-based services include six LTACHs with nine locations a health clinic and a pharmacy.

Geographic Reach

LHC operates in 36 states.

Strategy

Unlike its Medicare-funded activities demand for services is an area that LHC is not expected to have problems with. Home health care long-term care and nursing services are expected to see a surge in demand with the aging US population.

The company pursues a strategy of expanding into new markets through organic development or acquisitions as well as by forming new partnerships.

Mergers and Acquisitions

In 2017 LHC agreed to merge with Almost Family. Post-merger LHC shareholders own 58.5% of the combined entity while Almost Family shareholders own the rest.

The company bought Georgia-based Halcyon Hospice for $58.5 million in 2015. That purchase expanded LHC's hospice operations into new markets and deepens its presence in the Southeast. Later that year it acquired assets in Kentucky (Nurses Registry — now operating as Commonwealth Home Health — and Home Health Corp. as well as the Kentucky operations of The Visiting Nurses Association of Greater Cincinnati and Northern Kentucky) and made plans to buy a Missouri hospice.

EXECUTIVES

Vice President of Operations, Morris Sanford
Chairman and CEO, Keith G. Myers, age 59, $542,303 total compensation
President and COO, Donald D. (Don) Stelly, age 50, $395,816 total compensation
VP and Chief Administrative Officer, Marcus D. Macip
CIO, Rajesh (Raj) Shetye
EVP CFO and Treasurer, Joshua L. Proffitt
Director Of Nursing, Toya Brown
Director of HIM, Suzonne Borque
Medical Director, Robert Ewing
Director Of Nursing, Marsha Smith
Director Of Medical Records, Ann Faile
Director Of Nursing, Barbara Jones
Division Vice President Of Sales, Rob Little
Interim Vice President Revenue Strategy, Gwen Guillotte
Auditors: KPMG LLP

LOCATIONS

HQ: LHC Group Inc
901 Hugh Wallis Road South, Lafayette, LA 70508
Phone: 337 233-1307　　**Fax:** 337 235-8037
Web: www.lhcgroup.com

PRODUCTS/OPERATIONS

2015 Sales

	$ mil.	% of total
Home health services	613.2	75
Hospice services	85.9	11
Facility-based services	76.1	9
Community-based services	41.2	5
Total	**816.4**	**100**

Selected services

Community-Based Services
Home Health Services
Hospice Services

COMPETITORS

Amedisys	Health First
American HomePatient	Home Instead
Apria Healthcare	Kindred Healthcare
Consulate Health Care	NHC
Critical Homecare Solutions	National Home Health
Ensign Group	Personal-Touch Home Care
Gentiva	RehabCare
Girling Health Care	Trinity HomeCare
Guardian Home Care Holdings	VITAS Healthcare

HISTORICAL FINANCIALS

Company Type: Public

Income Statement				FYE: December 31
	REVENUE ($ mil.)	NET INCOME ($ mil.)	NET PROFIT MARGIN	EMPLOYEES
12/17	1,072.0	50.1	4.7%	14,554
12/16	914.8	36.5	4.0%	11,598
12/15	816.3	32.3	4.0%	10,922
12/14	733.6	21.8	3.0%	10,767
12/13	658.2	22.3	3.4%	8,186
Annual Growth	13.0%	22.4%	—	15.5%

2017 Year-End Financials

Debt ratio: 18.1%
Return on equity: 11.8%
Cash ($ mil.): 2.8
Current ratio: 1.97
Long-term debt ($ mil.): 144.0
No. of shares (mil.): 17.7
Dividends
Yield: —
Payout: —
Market value ($ mil.): 1,087.0

	STOCK PRICE ($) FY Close	P/E High/Low		PER SHARE ($)		
			Earnings	Dividends	Book Value
12/17	61.25	25 16	2.79	0.00	25.29
12/16	45.70	22 16	2.07	0.00	22.45
12/15	45.29	27 16	1.84	0.00	20.32
12/14	31.18	25 16	1.26	0.00	18.44
12/13	24.04	20 15	1.30	0.00	17.13
Annual Growth	26.3%	— —	21.0%	—	10.2%

Life Storage Inc

A self-administered real estate investment trust (REIT) Life Storage operates some 700 facilities with more than 50 million sq. ft. of storage space. Its properties usually offer features such as humidity-controlled spaces; outdoor storage for cars boats and RVs; and the use of a free truck to help clients haul their stuff. Serving both individual and business customers the company owns properties in about 30 states. In mid-2016 it effected its corporate name change and began transitioning the name of its facilities from Uncle Bob's Self Storage to Life Storage.

Geographic Reach

Life Storage based in Buffalo New York owns about 700 self-storage properties in some 30 states. Its largest markets are Texas (22% of properties and revenue) and Florida (13% of properties and revenue).

Sales and Marketing

Life Storage uses internet marketing and its fleet of trucks to create brand awareness.

Financial Performance

Life Storage has reported steadily increasing revenue over the past five years. In 2017 sales rose 13% to about $530 million in 2016 on higher rents and more units rented. Same-store sales (430 core properties) were up about 1.6% for the year.

Net income increased about $11 million to $96 million in 2017 from 2016 boosted by higher revenue.

Cash and cash equivalents fell to about $9 million in 2017 from about $24 million in 2016.

Strategy

Life Storage pursues growth by purchasing self-storage facilities in a largely fragmented industry

dominated by independent operators. The REIT concentrates its acquisition efforts in metropolitan areas of the South and Southeast; occasionally it acquires multiple facilities in new markets.

In 2017 the company integrated with LifeStorage an operator of 84 self-storage facilities acquired in 2016 for $1.3 billion. The combined company changed its name to Life Storage and has run branding campaigns centered around the name. The transaction slotted the company into Sacramento California and Las Vegas.

Life Storage introduced a way to book a storage space completely online in 2018. The Rent Now platform allows renters to book space select the specific space and gain access to it. The platform was to roll out to Life Storage's markets in 2018 and 2019.

EXECUTIVES

Vice President Real Estate Asset Management, Michael Rogers
CEO, David L. Rogers, age 62, $484,000 total compensation
President and Director, Kenneth F. Myszka, age 69, $484,000 total compensation
CFO, Andrew J. Gregoire, $250,000 total compensation
COO, Edward F. Killeen, $250,000 total compensation
Regional VP, Jeffrey Myszka
Chief Investment Officer, Paul T. Powell, $250,000 total compensation
Regional VP, Randy Hillman
Regional VP, Christopher Runckel
Regional VP, Jim Kwitchoff
Director Information Technologies, Jeffrey O'Donnell
Regional VP, Philip Wilfong
Vice President Marketing, Chris Laczi
Chairman, Robert J. Attea, age 76
Auditors: Ernst & Young LLP

LOCATIONS

HQ: Life Storage Inc
6467 Main Street, Williamsville, NY 14221
Phone: 716 633-1850 **Fax:** 716 633-1860
Web: www.unclebobs.com

PRODUCTS/OPERATIONS

2017 Sales

	$ mil.	% of total
Rental income	485.3	92
Other	44.4	8
Total	529.7	100

Selected Services

Storage
Truck Rental
Moving Boxes
Vehicle Storage
Commercial Storage

COMPETITORS

AMERCO	PODS Enterprises
CubeSmart	Public Storage
Extra Space	Smart Move
Mobile Mini	

HISTORICAL FINANCIALS

Company Type: Public

Income Statement				FYE: December 31
	REVENUE ($ mil.)	NET INCOME ($ mil.)	NET PROFIT MARGIN	EMPLOYEES
12/17	529.7	96.3	18.2%	1,792
12/16	462.6	85.2	18.4%	1,537
12/15	366.6	112.5	30.7%	1,429
12/14	326.0	88.5	27.2%	1,378
12/13	273.5	74.1	27.1%	1,268
Annual Growth	18.0%	6.8%	—	9.0%

2017 Year-End Financials

Debt ratio: 44.5%
Return on equity: 4.6%
Cash ($ mil.): 9.1
Current ratio: 0.24
Long-term debt ($ mil.): 1,726.7
No. of shares (mil.): 46.5
Dividends
Yield: 0.0%
Payout: 190.8%
Market value ($ mil.): 4,146.0

	STOCK PRICE ($) FY Close	P/E High/Low		PER SHARE ($)		
			Earnings	Dividends	Book Value
12/17	89.07	44 34	2.07	3.95	43.57
12/16	85.26	60 40	1.96	3.70	44.96
12/15	107.31	35 27	3.16	3.20	32.75
12/14	87.22	33 24	2.67	2.72	28.61
12/13	65.17	33 26	2.36	2.02	26.76
Annual Growth	8.1%	— —	(3.2%)	18.3%	13.0%

Ligand Pharmaceuticals Inc

Biopharmaceutical firm Ligand Pharmaceuticals seeks to discover disease-curing molecules. The drug development company works with gene transcription technology to address assorted illnesses. Its research and development projects include treatments for thrombocytopenia (low blood platelet count) osteoporosis cardiovascular disease cancer and diabetes. Ligand conducts many of its programs through partnerships with other drug makers including CyDex Pharmaceuticals Pfizer and Lilly. The company is focused on expanding its development pipeline through additional partnerships and technology licensing agreements as well as via acquisitions.

Operations

Ligand makes its money in three ways: from royalties from commercialized products (around two-thirds of revenue) from license and milestone payments (some 20% of revenue) and the development and commercialization of drugs using Captisol technology by CyDex Pharmaceuticals (around 15% of revenue).

Captisol is a formulation technology that has led to a number of FDA-approved products including Amgen's Spectrum. It is also being developed through clinical-stage partner programs.

The company's pipeline products include a receptor antagonist a selective androgen receptor modulator and Captisol-enabled Clopidogrel.

Strategy

Ligand's growth strategy is focused around increasing licensing milestone and royalty fees from its partners. The company has a vast portfolio of current and development-stage programs most of which are being developed through partnerships with other drug makers.

The company relies heavily on revenues from the sales of Promacta and Kyprolis for which it receives royalties from Novartis and Amgen respectively. Any slowdown in sales of those products — from causes such as the introduction of generics manufacturing issues or lower demand — would significantly impact Ligand's financial performance.

Mergers and Acquisitions

In 2018 Ligand acquired UK-based biotech firm Vernalis for some $42.3 million. The purchase brought the company programs in respiratory oncology and central nervous system therapies.

In 2017 the company purchased Crystal Bioscience along with its OmniChicken antibody discovery platform for $25 million. That deal boosted Ligand's work in developing antibodies for challenging targets.

EXECUTIVES

CEO, John L. Higgins, $500,331 total compensation
Vice President; General Counsel; Secretary, Charles S. Berkman, age 49, $283,351 total compensation
VP Biology, Keith Marschke
VP Chemistry and Pharmaceutical Sciences, Lin Zhi
President and COO, Matthew W. Foehr, $368,101 total compensation
CFO and Vice President Finance and Strategy, Nishan Silva
Chairman, John W. Kozarich
Auditors: Ernst & Young LLP

LOCATIONS

HQ: Ligand Pharmaceuticals Inc
3911 Sorrento Valley Boulevard, Suite 110, San Diego, CA 92121
Phone: 858 550-7500
Web: www.ligand.com

PRODUCTS/OPERATIONS

2017 Sales

	$ mil.	% of total
Royalties	88.7	63
Material sales (Captisol)	22.1	16
License fees milestones & other	30.3	21
Total	**141.1**	**100**

COMPETITORS

Adherex Technologies	Merck
Amgen	NPS Pharmaceuticals
AstraZeneca	Novartis Corporation
Bayer HealthCare Pharmaceuticals	Protalex
Biogen	Roche Holding
Chugai	Sanofi
Cytokinetics	Sunovion
Eli Lilly	Valeant
Evotec	Vertex Pharmaceuticals
GTx	Xencor

HISTORICAL FINANCIALS

Company Type: Public

Income Statement

FYE: December 31

	REVENUE ($ mil.)	NET INCOME ($ mil.)	NET PROFIT MARGIN	EMPLOYEES
12/17	141.1	12.5	8.9%	39
12/16	108.9	(1.6)	—	22
12/15	71.9	257.3	357.8%	21
12/14	64.5	12.0	18.6%	19
12/13	48.9	11.4	23.3%	20
Annual Growth	**30.3%**	**2.4%**	**—**	**18.2%**

2017 Year-End Financials

Debt ratio: 33.4%
Return on equity: 3.1%
Cash ($ mil.): 20.6
Current ratio: 0.99
Long-term debt ($ mil.): —

No. of shares (mil.): 21.1
Dividends
Yield: —
Payout: —
Market value ($ mil.): 2,896.0

	STOCK PRICE ($) FY Close	P/E High/Low	PER SHARE ($) Earnings	Dividends	Book Value
12/17	136.93	245 167	0.53	0.00	19.80
12/16	101.61	— —	(0.08)	0.00	17.74
12/15	108.42	9 4	12.12	0.00	15.26
12/14	53.21	135 72	0.56	0.00	1.34
12/13	52.60	103 34	0.55	0.00	2.42
Annual Growth	**27.0%**	**— —**	**(0.9%)**	**—**	**69.0%**

Littelfuse Inc

Littelfuse is big on circuit protection. The company is one of the world's largest fuse makers. In addition to its fuses Littelfuse's other circuit protection devices include positive temperature coefficient devices that limit current when too much is being supplied and electrostatic discharge suppressors that redirect transient high voltage. The company's thyristors protect telecommunications circuits from transient voltage caused by lightning strikes. It also supplies fuses for HVAC systems elevators and machine tools. Littelfuse's 5800 customers include electronics manufacturers (Hewlett-Packard and Samsung) automakers (Ford and GM) and the automotive aftermarket (O'Reilly Automotive and Pep Boys).

Operations

The company operates through three business unit segments. Electronics includes circuit protection products for wireless telephones consumer electronics computers modems and telecommunications equipment and markets the products under brand names PICO and NANO. Considering the average car contains 30 to 100 fuses the automotive segment stays busy making fuses for gas and electric automobiles trucks and buses and to protect electrical power to operate lights heating air conditioning radios windows and other controls.

Some automotive brand names include ATO MasterFuse JCASE and CablePro. In addition to fuses electrical makes ground-fault and protection relays to safeguard personnel and equipment from electrical shock hazards in industrial environments and underground mining or water treatment applications. Brand names include POWR-GARD.

Geographic Reach

The company operates in three geographic territories — the Americas Europe and Asia/Pacific — and has 30 manufacturing and distribution facilities in about 15 countries. The company gets about 40% of its sales outside the US. China is another large market representing 22% of sales.

Sales and Marketing

Littelfuse markets its products indirectly through a worldwide organization of 60 manufacturers' representatives and distributes through a network of electronics automotive and electrical distributors. Its domestic sales and marketing staff of over 100 people maintains relationships with major OEMs and distributors.

Financial Performance

Littelfuse enjoyed unprecedented growth in 2015 as sales peaked at a record-setting $868 million. Profits however decreased by 17% due to additional pension settlement charges and expenses related with acquisitions. Littelfuse's operating cash flow has trended upward over the last four years and surged by 8% in 2015.

The historic growth for 2015 was fueled by an uptick in automotive sales and strong growth for automotive sensor products as a result of continued strength in the heavy truck market. This growth was offset by a general market slowdown within the construction agriculture and global mining industries.

Strategy

Littelfuse operates in a highly competitive industry matching up against much larger manufacturers by focusing on brand name price quality and service. The automotive industry witnessed a rash of bankruptcies before and during the recession and the electronics industry reeled from the economic downturn as well. The company's dependence on customers in the automotive communications and consumer electronics industries leaves Littelfuse vulnerable to cyclicality in those industries.

One important element of Littelfuse's strategy is product development which has resulted in about 200 patents in North America some 85 in the European Union and more than 60 in other foreign countries. After consulting with customers sales and marketing staff often suggest new products which then undergo a development process that can last from a few months to up to 18 months.

Mergers and Acquisitions

In 2017 Littelfuse acquired IXYS a maker of power semiconductors and integrated circuits for about $750 million in cash and stock. IXYS focuses on medium to high voltage power control chips for industrial communications consumer and medical markets. Littelfuse was to use IXYS technologies to expand in the industrial and automotive markets. The deal was Littelfuse's biggest.

In 2015 the company acquired TE Connectivity's circuit protection business (CPD) which has expertise in polymer-based resettable circuit protection devices. The business was acquired for $350 million and has operations in Menlo Park California and manufacturing facilities in Tsukuba Japan; and Shanghai and Kunshan China. The acquisition expanded the company's capabilities in the battery and automotive market and increased its presence in Japan.

Company Background

Littelfuse was formed in 1927 to make the first small fast-acting fuse able to protect test meters. In 1968 military electronics firm Tracor (later part of the UK's General Electric Company now telent) bought the company. Littelfuse entered the power (industrial) fuse market in 1983. Tracor ran into financial troubles with the end of the Cold War and filed for bankruptcy protection in 1991. As a result of Tracor's reorganization Littelfuse became an independent company in 1992.

EXECUTIVES

VP; General Manager Custom Products, Dal Ferbert, age 64, $232,662 total compensation
President CEO and Director, David W. Heinzmann, age 54, $477,532 total compensation
EVP and Chief Legal and Human Resources Officer, Ryan K. Stafford, age 51, $387,320 total compensation
SVP; General Manager Automotive, Dieter Roeder, age 61
SVP; General Manager Industrial, Matthew J. Cole
SVP; General Manager Electronics, Deepak Nayar
SVP and CTO; General Manager Semiconductor Products, Ian Highley
SVP Global Operations, Michael P. Rutz, $353,273 total compensation
EVP and CFO, Meenal A. Sethna, age 48
Chairman, Gordon B. Hunter, age 67
Auditors: GRANT THORNTON LLP

LOCATIONS

HQ: Littelfuse Inc
8755 West Higgins Road, Suite 500, Chicago, IL 60631
Phone: 773 628-1000
Web: www.littelfuse.com

PRODUCTS/OPERATIONS

2015 Sales

	$ mil.	% of total
Electronics	405.5	47
Automotive	340.0	39
Electrical	122.4	14
Total	**867.9**	**100**

Selected Brands
ATO
JCASE Fuse
MAXI
MEGA
MIDI
MINI
NANO2
OMNI-BLOK
PICO II
POWR-GARD
PulseGuard

Selected Products
Automotive Sensors
Battery Management
Custom-Engineered Electrical Equipment
DC Power Distribution Modules
DC Solenoids and Relays
Fuse Blocks Fuse Holders and Fuse Accessories
Fuses
Fusible Switches and Panels
Gas Discharge Tubes
Magnetic Sensors and Reed Switches
Other Products and Accessories
Power Semiconductors
Protection Relays and Controls
Polymer ESD Suppressors
Resettable PTC Fuses
Semiconductors
Shock-Block GFCI
Surge Protection Module
Switches
Varistors

Selected Services
Custom Circuit Protection Solutions
Custom Power Centers and Electrical Equipment
Electrical Safety Services
MROplus Industrial Fuse Consolidation
Testing Services

COMPETITORS

AVX	ON Semiconductor
Bel Fuse	S&C Electric
Bourns	STMicroelectronics
EPCOS	TE Connectivity
Mersen Group	

HISTORICAL FINANCIALS
Company Type: Public

Income Statement
FYE: December 30

	REVENUE ($ mil.)	NET INCOME ($ mil.)	NET PROFIT MARGIN	EMPLOYEES
12/17	1,221.5	119.5	9.8%	10,700
12/16*	1,056.1	104.4	9.9%	10,300
01/16	867.8	82.4	9.5%	8,800
12/14	852.0	99.4	11.7%	7,900
12/13	757.8	88.7	11.7%	7,400
Annual Growth	12.7%	7.7%	—	9.7%

*Fiscal year change

2017 Year-End Financials
Debt ratio: 28.4%
Return on equity: 13.7%
Cash ($ mil.): 429.6
Current ratio: 3.52
Long-term debt ($ mil.): 489.3
No. of shares (mil.): 22.2
Dividends
  Yield: 0.0%
  Payout: 26.8%
Market value ($ mil.): 4,406.0

	STOCK PRICE ($) FY Close	P/E High/Low	Earnings	Dividends	Book Value
12/17	197.82	40 28	5.21	1.40	41.64
12/16*	151.77	34 20	4.60	1.24	36.67
01/16	107.01	31 23	3.63	1.08	33.73
12/14	98.76	23 18	4.37	0.94	32.21
12/13	92.67	24 15	3.94	0.84	30.57
Annual Growth	20.9%	— —	7.2%	13.6%	8.0%

*Fiscal year change

Live Oak Bancshares Inc

LOCATIONS

HQ: Live Oak Bancshares Inc
1741 Tiburon Drive, Wilmington, NC 28403
Phone: 910 790-5867
Web: www.liveoakbank.com

HISTORICAL FINANCIALS
Company Type: Public

Income Statement
FYE: December 31

	ASSETS ($ mil.)	NET INCOME ($ mil.)	INCOME AS % OF ASSETS	EMPLOYEES
12/17	2,758.4	100.5	3.6%	528
12/16	1,755.2	13.7	0.8%	425
12/15	1,052.6	20.6	2.0%	366
12/14	673.3	10.0	1.5%	263
12/13	430.3	28.0	6.5%	0
Annual Growth	59.1%	37.6%	—	—

2017 Year-End Financials
Return on assets: 4.4%
Return on equity: 30.4%
Long-term debt ($ mil.): —
No. of shares (mil.): 39.9
Sales ($ mil): 276.3
Dividends
  Yield: 0.0%
  Payout: 3.7%
Market value ($ mil.): 952.0

	STOCK PRICE ($) FY Close	P/E High/Low	Earnings	Dividends	Book Value
12/17	23.85	9 7	2.65	0.10	10.95
12/16	18.50	50 30	0.39	0.07	6.51
12/15	14.20	31 20	0.65	0.02	5.84
Annual Growth	29.6%	—	—101.9%	123.6%	37.0%

Live Ventures Inc

LiveDeal (formerly YP Corp.) is an Internet yellow pages and local online classifieds provider. The company offers goods and services listed for sale through its online classified marketplace at classifieds.livedeal.com; LiveDeal also publishes about 17 million business listings via its business directory at yellowpages.livedeal.com. Sources of revenue include advertising sales a pay-per-lead program with major auto dealers and optional listing upgrade and e-commerce/fraud prevention fees. The company changed its name from YP Corp. after its 2007 purchase of online local classifieds marketplace LiveDeal.

The company has been focused on shifting away from its traditional listing business in order to focus on Internet services including customer acquisition. It sold approximately 14000 customers from its directory business for more than $3 million in 2009. With losses mounting however LiveDeal is exploring alternatives including selling the business.

Richard Sommer resigned as CEO in early 2010 after less than a year on the job. The company appointed Kevin Hall to lead the business as interim COO. The executive shake up was the latest in several changes at LiveDeal in recent years. Sommer had replaced Mike Edelhart who was appointed CEO in 2008.

EXECUTIVES

President; Chief Executive Officer; Director, Jon Isaac
Director, Thomas J. (Tom) Clarke Jr., age 60
Director, Greg A. LeClaire, age 47
Director, Richard D. Butler Jr., age 67
Independent Director, Dennis Gao
Auditors: WSRP, LLC

LOCATIONS

HQ: Live Ventures Inc
325 E Warm Springs Road, Suite 102, Las Vegas, NV 89119
Phone: 702 997-5968
Web: www.liveventures.com

COMPETITORS

Amazon.com	The Berry Company
Blucora	YPM
Buy.com	Yahoo!

Dex Media
Google
Infogroup
Overstock.com

Yellowbook
craigslist
eBay

HISTORICAL FINANCIALS
Company Type: Public

Income Statement — FYE: September 30

	REVENUE ($ mil.)	NET INCOME ($ mil.)	NET PROFIT MARGIN	EMPLOYEES
09/18	199.6	5.9	3.0%	1,155
09/17	152.0	6.5	4.3%	1,211
09/16	78.9	17.8	22.6%	277
09/15	33.3	(14.6)	—	302
09/14	7.2	(4.6)	—	112
Annual Growth	129.0%	—	—	79.2%

2018 Year-End Financials
Debt ratio: 55.2%	No. of shares (mil.): 1.9
Return on equity: 16.2%	Dividends
Cash ($ mil.): 1.9	Yield: —
Current ratio: 1.76	Payout: —
Long-term debt ($ mil.): 64.2	Market value ($ mil.): 18.0

	STOCK PRICE ($) FY Close	P/E High/Low		PER SHARE ($) Earnings	Dividends	Book Value
09/18	9.00	7	3	1.58	0.00	20.28
09/17	12.40	9	1	1.61	0.00	16.86
09/16	1.91	0	0	5.40	0.00	8.67
09/15	1.68	—	—	(5.58)	0.00	2.24
09/14	2.98	—	—	(2.10)	0.00	5.50
Annual Growth	31.8%		—	—	—	38.6%

LogMeIn Inc

LogMeIn wants to help you stay productive even on the go. The company provides Web-based remote access software and services to consumers small and midsized businesses and IT service providers. Its user access and remote collaboration offerings serve consumers and business users while businesses and IT service providers use LogMeIn's technology to provide remote management and support. LogMeIn offers both free and subscription-based services. Its paid services add advanced features such as file transfer remote printing and drive mapping. Corporate customers include 3M AMD and IBM. About two-thirds of LogMeIn's sales come from US clients. In 2017 LogMeIn merged with GoToBusiness in a $1.8 billion transaction.

Change in Company Type
In 2017 LogMeIn merged with GoToBusiness which was spun out of Citrix Systems. The merged company is owned by Citrix (50.1%) and LogMeIn (48.9%) shareholders. The transaction was valued at about $1.8 billion. Adding GoTo products to its portfolio increases LogMeIn's presence in the small and medium business markets. The products are GoToAssist GoToMeeting GoToMyPC GoToTraining GoToWebinar Grasshopper and OpenVoice. The combined company expects annual revenue of about $1 billion.

Operations

Other advanced features of LogMeIn's paid services include high-definition remote control and content streaming remote sound and file sharing and syncing.

Services used by internal IT departments and customer care teams include device management disaster recovery and software update automation.

Geographic Reach
The company's services are available in 12 languages and are used in more than 240 countries. It has international sales offices in Australia Europe (Dublin and London) and India as well as two offshore IT offices in Hungary.

Sales and Marketing
LogMeIn uses free trials of its services to woo users and turn them into paying customers. Some of its funded marketing efforts include both online and offline advertising such as trade magazines newspapers and radio as well as tradeshows and events. With its extensive global presence and most sales still coming from the US the company plans to increase its spending on international sales and marketing. It also invests in expanding its range of connectivity services whether through internal development or strategic acquisitions. The company increased its advertising in 2014 spending $36.8 million up from $27.8 million in 2013.

Financial Performance
LogMeIn continued to generate revenue growth in 2014 raising its top line 34% to about $222 million. Much of that came from new customers as the number of subscribers to its premium join.me pro collaboration service grew. The company discontinued LogMeIn Free a free remote access service to focus on faster growing free services including join.me. The company reversed a $7 loss in 2013 (due in part to a legal settlement) to post a $7 million profit in 2014.

Strategy
LogMeIn is aiming to leverage its capabilities of connecting remote devices to become a player in the Internet of Things (the networking of sensors and other devices). Its Xively platform helps customers managed their connected devices and analyze the information collected by the devices. The 2014 acquisition of Ionia Corporation is part of LogMeIn's Internet of Things push.

Mergers and Acquisitions
LogMeIn acquired BBA Inc. known as Meldium for $10.6 million. Meldium provides single sign-on password management software and it expands LogMeIn's popular portfolio.

In an effort to capitalize on opportunities provided by the Internet of Things (allowing common objects to be connected to the network to send and receive data) LogMeIn purchased Ionia Corporation in 2014; Ionia is a systems integrator focused on connected solutions.

EXECUTIVES
SVP and Chief Marketing Officer, W. Sean Ford, age 49, $299,653 total compensation
President and CEO, William R. Wagner, age 51, $410,000 total compensation
CFO, Edward K. (Ed) Herdiech, age 51, $228,000 total compensation
CTO, Sandor Palfy
Vice President Data Management Products, Andras Lang
Vice President Network Operations, Joel Peterson
Senior Vice President Of Products, Andrew Burton
Vice President Customer Experience, Paddy Srinivasan
Vice President Business Development, Richard Redding
Vice President Product Development, Kevin Bardos
Vice President Customer Support, Andrew Thompson
Vice President Sales NA, Larry D'Angelo
Senior Vice President Strategy, Rob Lawrence
Vice President Customer Care, Bryce Cote
Vice President Business Development, Deepak Puri
Senior Vice President Chief Marketing Officer, W Ford
Vice President Corporate Marketing, Alison Durant
Vice President Marketing, Lauren McCollem
Vice President Sales, Michelle Benfer
Vice President Engineering, Jason Luce
Senior Vice President of Sales, Lawrence D'Angelo
Vice President Corporate Development, Jeremy Segal
Vice President Sales Operations, Sharon Gould
Vice President, David Kubick
VICE PRESIDENT REAL ESTATE AND FACILITIES, Steve Nicholson
Senior Vice President Of Engineering, James Lok
Chairman, Michael K. Simon, age 53
Board Member, David Henshall
Auditors: DELOITTE & TOUCHE LLP

LOCATIONS
HQ: LogMeIn Inc
320 Summer Street, Boston, MA 02210
Phone: 781 638-9050   **Fax:** 781 437-1803
Web: www.LogMeIn.com

PRODUCTS/OPERATIONS

Selected Products
AppGuru
BoldChat
Cubby
join.me
LogMeIn Backup
LogMeIn Central
LogMeIn Hamachi
LogMeIn Pro
LogMeIn Rescue
Meldium
RemotelyAnywhere
Xively

COMPETITORS
Adobe Systems	LivePerson
Apple Inc.	Microsoft
Box Inc.	NetSuite
Cisco Systems	Oracle
Citrix Systems	Symantec
Google	

HISTORICAL FINANCIALS
Company Type: Public

Income Statement — FYE: December 31

	REVENUE ($ mil.)	NET INCOME ($ mil.)	NET PROFIT MARGIN	EMPLOYEES
12/17	989.7	99.5	10.1%	2,760
12/16	336.0	2.6	0.8%	1,124
12/15	271.6	14.5	5.4%	1,006
12/14	221.9	7.9	3.6%	804
12/13	166.2	(7.6)	—	613
Annual Growth	56.2%	—	—	45.7%

2017 Year-End Financials
Debt ratio: —	No. of shares (mil.): 52.5
Return on equity: 5.9%	Dividends
Cash ($ mil.): 252.4	Yield: 0.0%
Current ratio: 0.90	Payout: 64.7%
Long-term debt ($ mil.): —	Market value ($ mil.): 6,019.0

	STOCK PRICE ($)	P/E	PER SHARE ($)		
	FY Close	High/Low	Earnings	Dividends	Book Value
12/17	114.50	64 47	1.93	1.25	60.19
12/16	96.55	1089432	0.10	1.00	7.68
12/15	67.10	125 78	0.56	0.00	8.27
12/14	49.34	160 95	0.31	0.00	7.12
12/13	33.55	— —	(0.32)	0.00	6.94
Annual Growth	35.9%	— —	—	—	71.6%

LTC Properties, Inc.

Specializing in TLC LTC Properties sees long-term care real estate as a healthy investment. The self-administered real estate investment trust (REIT) mostly invests in health care and long-term care facilities. Its portfolio includes more than 220 assisted living skilled-nursing and other healthcare properties with nearly 15000 living units across 30 states with its largest markets being in Texas Florida Colorado and Arizona. Its top tenant operators include Brookdale Senior Living Prestige Healthcare Senior Care Centers and Senior Lifestyle Corporation which in aggregate contribute around 45% to its total rental income. The REIT also invests in mortgage loans tied to long-term care properties.

Operations

The REIT's portfolio consisted of 224 properties at the end of 2015 including 104 assisted living centers (homes for elderly residents not requiring constant supervision) 100 skilled nursing facilities (which provide rehabilitative and restorative nursing care) seven other health care properties (such as independent living behavioral or memory care) a school and 11 land parcels. The assisted living and skilled nursing properties made up more than 90% of the REIT's rental income.

As with most leasing REITs LTC Properties makes most of its revenue from rental income from tenants/operators. About 83% of its total revenue came from rental income during 2015 while interest income from mortgage loans made up another 16%.

Geographic Reach

LTC's properties are located in 30 states. Texas Florida Colorado and Arizona are its largest markets.

Sales and Marketing

LTC Property's top tenant operators in 2015 included: Prestige Healthcare (which contributed 15% to the REIT's rental income) Brookdale Senior Living (11%) Senior Care Centers (9%) and Senior Lifestyle Corporation (9%) which in aggregate contributed around 45% to its total rental income.

Financial Performance

The REIT's annual revenues have risen more than 60% since 2011 thanks to regular rental rate increases and some rent-boosting property acquisitions. Its net income has nearly doubled over the same period on property sale gains and as it's managed to keep its operating and overhead costs in check.

LTC Property's revenue jumped 14% to $136.2 million during 2015 mostly thanks to rental rate increases associated with renewals though a two

new skilled-nursing property acquisitions also helped increase its rental income. The REIT's interest income from its mortgage loans grew 34% as the company acquired more interest-earning loan assets.

Despite strong revenue growth in 2015 the REIT's net income dipped less than 1% to $73.08 million mostly as it didn't earn as much from property sale gains. Its operating cash levels climbed 7% to $102.34 million as it collected more in cash-denominated earnings.

Strategy

LTC Properties mostly invests in assisted living and skilled nursing facilities though it also invests in related healthcare facilities and even mortgages tied to such properties. To diversify its portfolio the REIT likes to buy properties in new geographic locations with new tenant operators.

EXECUTIVES

Chairman CEO and President, Wendy L. Simpson, age 68, $610,500 total compensation
EVP CFO and Secretary, Pamela J. (Pam) Shelley-Kessler, age 52, $365,833 total compensation
EVP and Chief Investment Officer, Clint B. Malin, age 46, $365,833 total compensation
SVP Controller and Treasurer, Caroline L. (Cece) Chikhale, age 41, $163,327 total compensation
SVP Investment and Portfolio Management, Brent P. Chappell, age 53, $245,833 total compensation
Auditors: Ernst & Young LLP

LOCATIONS

HQ: LTC Properties, Inc.
2829 Townsgate Road, Suite 350, Westlake Village, CA 91361
Phone: 805 981-8655
Web: www.ltcreit.com

PRODUCTS/OPERATIONS

2015 Sales

	$ mil.	% of total
Rental income	113.1	83
Interest income from mortgage loans	22.1	16
Interest & other income	1.0	1
Total	**136.2**	**100**

COMPETITORS

Chartwell Seniors Housing	Omega Healthcare Investors
HCP	Sabra Health Care
Healthcare Realty Trust	Senior Housing Properties
Legacy Healthcare	Tiptree
NHC	Ventas
National Health Investors	Welltower
NorthStar Healthcare Investors	

HISTORICAL FINANCIALS

Company Type: Public

Income Statement

FYE: December 31

	REVENUE ($ mil.)	NET INCOME ($ mil.)	NET PROFIT MARGIN	EMPLOYEES
12/17	168.0	87.3	52.0%	20
12/16	161.5	85.1	52.7%	24
12/15	136.2	73.0	53.7%	22
12/14	118.9	73.4	61.7%	19
12/13	104.9	57.8	55.1%	18
Annual Growth	12.5%	10.9%	—	2.7%

2017 Year-End Financials

Debt ratio: 45.5%	No. of shares (mil.): 39.5
Return on equity: 11.6%	Dividends
Cash ($ mil.): 5.2	Yield: 0.0%
Current ratio: 0.77	Payout: 103.6%
Long-term debt ($ mil.): 571.0	Market value ($ mil.): 1,723.0

	STOCK PRICE ($)	P/E	PER SHARE ($)		
	FY Close	High/Low	Earnings	Dividends	Book Value
12/17	43.55	24 20	2.20	2.28	19.08
12/16	46.98	25 19	2.21	2.19	18.87
12/15	43.14	25 20	1.94	2.07	17.56
12/14	43.17	22 18	1.99	2.04	18.61
12/13	35.39	29 21	1.63	1.91	18.20
Annual Growth	5.3%	— —	7.8%	4.6%	1.2%

Lumentum Holdings Inc

Auditors: DELOITTE & TOUCHE LLP

LOCATIONS

HQ: Lumentum Holdings Inc
400 North McCarthy Boulevard, Milpitas, CA 95035
Phone: 408 546-5483
Web: www.lumentum.com

HISTORICAL FINANCIALS

Company Type: Public

Income Statement

FYE: June 30

	REVENUE ($ mil.)	NET INCOME ($ mil.)	NET PROFIT MARGIN	EMPLOYEES
06/18*	1,247.7	248.1	19.9%	2,930
07/17	1,001.6	(102.5)	—	2,057
07/16	903.0	9.3	1.0%	1,850
06/15	837.1	(3.4)	—	1,550
06/14	817.9	10.7	1.3%	1,550
Annual Growth	11.1%	119.4%	—	17.3%

*Fiscal year change

2018 Year-End Financials

Debt ratio: 21.6%	No. of shares (mil.): 62.7
Return on equity: 32.2%	Dividends
Cash ($ mil.): 397.3	Yield: —
Current ratio: 5.27	Payout: —
Long-term debt ($ mil.): 334.6	Market value ($ mil.): 3,636.0

	STOCK PRICE ($) FY Close	P/E High/Low	PER SHARE ($) Earnings	Dividends	Book Value
06/18*	57.90	19 11	3.82	0.00	14.75
07/17	57.05	— —	(1.71)	0.00	10.07
07/16	23.65	— —	(0.05)	0.00	8.35
Annual Growth	56.5%	— —	—	—	32.9%

*Fiscal year change

Luminex Corp

William Blake could "see a world in a grain of sand" and Luminex can reveal hundreds of secrets in a drop of fluid. Its xMAP (Multi-Analyte Profiling) technology allows simultaneous analysis of up to 500 bioassays or tests from a single drop of fluid. xMAP consists of instruments software and disposable microspheres (microscopic polystyrene beads on which tests are performed). Luminex also uses MultiCode real-time polymerase chain reaction and xTAG technology. Luminex's systems are used by clinical and research laboratories and are distributed through strategic partnerships with other life sciences firms. Luminex also develops testing assays and disposable testing supplies for the clinical diagnostics market.

Operations

The company's xMAP technology is being used in various segments of the life sciences industry including drug discovery and development clinical diagnostics genetic analysis bio-defense food safety and biomedical research. The MultiCode assay chemistry provides real-time polymerase chain reaction (PCR) and multiplex PCR-based applications.

Geographic Reach

More than 80% of Luminex's sales are made in the US. It also sells to customers in other countries in North America Europe and the Asia/Pacific region. Luminex has facilities in Australia Canada China Japan the Netherlands and the US.

Sales and Marketing

The company's technology is available commercially around the world; it is used by major pharmaceutical diagnostic biotechnology and life science companies. Luminex's largest customers include Laboratory Corporation of America (21% of revenue in 2014) Thermo Fisher Scientific (17% of revenue) and Bio-Rad Laboratories (7%).

Advertising expenses including trade show and convention activities were some $2.3 million in 2014 down from $2.6 million in in 2013 and $2.4 million in 2012.

Financial Performance

Revenue has grown over the past five years. It rose 6% to $227 million in 2014 on an increase in assay revenue and royalty earnings. Net income which had fallen for two years spiked 450% to $39 million that year as operating expenses declined.

Cash flow from operations also rose increasing 83% to $49 million in 2014.

Strategy

The technology-based firm has implemented a strategy to transform itself into a market-driven customer-focused company. To achieve this goal Luminex is focusing on key markets including life

sciences research molecular infectious disease genetic disease pharmacogenetic testing bio-defense testing and immunodiagnostics. In addition it aims to develop next-generation systems to bring efficient portable testing solutions to market as well as market-leading assays in the human molecular diagnostic testing market. It is also working to develop strategic partnerships in its key markets and to pursue acquisitions that could hasten its goals.

Luminex is largely focused on the final development of its ARIES system; it hopes to improve the simplicity and ease of use of its multiplex products through the development of a new version of its multiplex PCR technology. In the area of molecular diagnostics the company is working to grow both its cleared Cytochrome P450 assays and the pharmacognetic lab-developed test portfolios of its clinical customers.

The FDA cleared three new targets to the company's xTAG Gastrointestinal Pathogen Panel (GPP) in 2014; it also cleared xTAG GPP for use with specimens in Cary-Blair medium a common transport medium for the collection and preservation of microbiological specimens. The following year Luminex received Health Canada Class 3 Device License approval for its xTAG CYP2D6 Kit v. 3 comprehensive genotyping assay.

During 2014 Luminex's 46 partners who have commercialized xMAP-based assay products accounted for two-thirds of total revenue while all of its strategic partners represented some 70% of revenue.

Luminex closed its manufacturing facility in Brisbane Australia in 2014.

Mergers and Acquisitions

In 2016 Luminex bought molecular microbiology and diagnostics firm Nanosphere in a $58 million transaction. The purchase adds Nanosphere's Verigene technology which complements Luminex's existing infectious disease portfolio.

Company Background

Luminex takes its name from the special laser beams that each microsphere passes through during the bioassay screening process. The lasers excite dyes inside and on the surface of the microspheres and the resulting fluorescence is measured in real time and analyzed by the system's software.

EXECUTIVES

President and Chief Executive Officer; Director, Patrick J. Balthrop, age 62, $513,674 total compensation

Senior Vice President Research and Development, Jeremy Bridge-Cook, age 49, $355,048 total compensation

Senior Vice President Corporate Development and Global Marketing, Russell W. Bradley, age 55, $282,705 total compensation

Vice President Manufacturing and Quality Surveillance, Steve Back

Senior Vice President Operations, Michael F. Pintek, age 49, $325,297 total compensation

Vice President Luminex Molecular Diagnostics, Nancy Krunic

Vice President Biodefense, Amy L. Altman

President and CEO and Director, Nachum Shamir

Sr V Pres Hr, Nancy Fairchild

Senior Vice President and General Counsel, Richard Rew

Vice President of Marketing, Eric Shapiro

Senior Vice President Of Global Manufacturing And Quality, Randy Myers

Chairman, G. Walter Loewenbaum, age 73

Auditors: Ernst & Young LLP

LOCATIONS

HQ: Luminex Corp
12212 Technology Blvd., Austin, TX 78727
Phone: 512 219-8020
Web: www.luminexcorp.com

PRODUCTS/OPERATIONS

2014 Revenues

	$ mil.	% of total
Assay revenue	87.6	39
Consumable sales	48.3	21
Royalty revenue	39.4	17
System sales	29.2	13
Service revenue	9.4	6
Other	13.1	4
Total	**227.0**	**100**

Selected Products

Assay Development Tools
Calibration and Control Microspheres
Clinical Diagnostic Assays
FLEXMAP 3D
Life Science Research Assays
Luminex LX 100/200 (LX Systems)
MagPlex Microspheres
MicroPlex Microspheres
SeroMAP Microspheres
xPONENT
xTAG Microspheres

Selected Acquisitions

COMPETITORS

Abbott Labs
Affymetrix
Beckman Coulter
Becton Dickinson
Celera
Cepheid
GE Healthcare
Gen-Probe
GenMark
Hologic

Illumina
Johnson & Johnson
Life Technologies Corporation
Orchid Cellmark
QIAGEN
Roche Diagnostics
Sequenom
Siemens Healthcare

HISTORICAL FINANCIALS

Company Type: Public

Income Statement

FYE: December 31

	REVENUE ($ mil.)	NET INCOME ($ mil.)	NET PROFIT MARGIN	EMPLOYEES
12/17	306.5	29.4	9.6%	896
12/16	270.6	13.8	5.1%	936
12/15	237.7	36.8	15.5%	797
12/14	226.9	39.0	17.2%	745
12/13	213.4	7.1	3.3%	731
Annual Growth	**9.5%**	**42.7%**	**—**	**5.2%**

2017 Year-End Financials

Debt ratio: —	No. of shares (mil.): 43.4
Return on equity: 6.9%	Dividends
Cash ($ mil.) 127.1	Yield: 0.0%
Current ratio: 4.96	Payout: 35.8%
Long-term debt ($ mil.): —	Market value ($ mil.): 855.0

	STOCK PRICE ($) FY Close	P/E High/Low	PER SHARE ($) Earnings	Dividends	Book Value
12/17	19.70	33 27	0.67	0.24	10.09
12/16	20.23	73 55	0.32	0.00	9.43
12/15	21.39	26 17	0.86	0.00	8.71
12/14	18.76	22 17	0.93	0.00	7.65
12/13	19.40	140 91	0.17	0.00	6.55
Annual Growth	**0.4%**	**— —**	**40.9%**	**—**	**11.4%**

Luna Innovations Inc

Luna Innovations is a research and development firm. The company makes practical use of cutting-edge technologies in the areas of molecular technology and sensing. Its molecular technology efforts focus on materials (including polymers reagents and nanomaterials) with enhanced performance characteristics; Luna has developed contrast agents for MRI testing nanomaterials used in solar cells and protective coatings. It has also created sensing technologies used in medical monitoring equipment as well as wireless and fiber-optic monitoring systems for defense and industrial instrumentation. In mid-2015 Luna Innovations merged with Advanced Photonix.

EXECUTIVES

Chairman, Richard W. (Rich) Roedel, age 66
Media Contact, Karin Clark
Interim CFO and Chief Commercialization Officer, Scott A. Graeff, age 49, $185,000 total compensation
CTO, Mark Froggatt, age 46, $158,750 total compensation
VP General Counsel and Secretary, Talfourd H. Kemper Jr., age 47
Vice President of Marketing, Geoffrey McCarty
President; Chief Executive Officer; Director, My Chung
Director, John B. Williamson III, age 61
Director, Edward G. Murphy, age 60
Director, N. Leigh Anderson, age 66
Director, Jonathan M. Cool, age 57
Director, Warner Dalhouse
Independent Director, Michael Wise
Auditors: GRANT THORNTON LLP

LOCATIONS

HQ: Luna Innovations Inc
301 First Street S.W., Suite 200, Roanoke, VA 24011
Phone: 540 769-8400
Web: www.lunainc.com

PRODUCTS/OPERATIONS

2015 Sales

	% of total
Products and licensing	69
Technology development	31
Total	**100**

Selected Products

Applied research & development
Fiber optic sensing
Fiber optic test & measurement
High speed optical components
Optoelectronic solutions
Terahertz solutions

COMPETITORS

3M	General Dynamics
Agilent Technologies	Leidos
Bayer HealthCare Pharmaceuticals Inc.	Lockheed Martin
	Robert Bosch
Dow Chemical	Viavi Solutions
DuPont	

HISTORICAL FINANCIALS

Company Type: Public

Income Statement

FYE: December 31

	REVENUE ($ mil.)	NET INCOME ($ mil.)	NET PROFIT MARGIN	EMPLOYEES
12/17	46.2	14.6	31.6%	198
12/16	59.2	(2.3)	—	245
12/15	44.0	2.3	5.3%	243
12/14	21.2	5.9	28.2%	113
12/13	22.0	(0.8)	—	138
Annual Growth	**20.3%**	—	—	**9.4%**

2017 Year-End Financials

Debt ratio: 3.8%	No. of shares (mil.): 27.2
Return on equity: 34.5%	Dividends
Cash ($ mil.): 36.9	Yield: —
Current ratio: 3.98	Payout: —
Long-term debt ($ mil.): 0.6	Market value ($ mil.): 66.0

	STOCK PRICE ($) FY Close	P/E High/Low		PER SHARE ($) Earnings	Dividends	Book Value
12/17	2.43	5	2	0.52	0.00	1.82
12/16	1.47	—	—	(0.09)	0.00	1.27
12/15	1.08	17	9	0.10	0.00	1.34
12/14	1.42	6	3	0.40	0.00	1.26
12/13	1.40	—	—	(0.06)	0.00	0.81
Annual Growth	**14.8%**			—	—	**22.4%**

Lydall, Inc.

Lydall's products help to beat the heat nix the noise and filter the rest. The company makes thermal and acoustical barriers automotive heat shields and insulation products that offer protection in extreme temperatures. Lydall's thermal and acoustical products are used by the appliance and automotive industries and in industrial kilns and furnaces. The company rounds out its offerings with industrial and commercial air and liquid filtration products in addition to energy storage close-out panels and felt manufacturing services and products. Export sales represent about 35% of the company's annual net sales.

Operations

Lydall's segments include Thermal/Acoustical Metals and Fibers (nearly 60% of sales) which produces noise and heat abatement products for automotive applications and Performance Materials (12%) which encompasses its filtration and industrial thermal insulation businesses. Its Industrial Filtration segment offers industrial non-woven felt media and filter bags.

Geographic Reach

The company has operations in Europe Asia and the US which accounted for about 70% of its revenue in 2015.

Sales and Marketing

Lydall's products are primarily sold directly to customers through an internal sales force and external sales representatives and distributed via common carrier. The majority of products are sold to original equipment manufacturers and tier-one suppliers. Sales to Ford Motor Company accounted for almost 20% of net sales in 2015.

Financial Performance

After revenues peaked at a record-setting $536 million in 2014 Lydall saw its revenues fall 2% to $525 million in 2015. The company's profits however more than doubled from $22 million in 2014 to $46 million in 2015 mainly due to a gain on sale of its Life Sciences Vital Fluids business and a decrease in selling product development and administrative expenses.

The revenue dip for 2015 was fueled by lower sales from its Performance Materials segment and due to the divestiture of its Life Sciences Vital Fluids business. Performance Materials segment sales also decreased due to lower demand for air filtration products and thermal insulation products particularly in Asia and North America. It also experienced lower demand for its water purification and life protection application products and for cryogenic insulation products serving the liquid natural gas market.

Strategy

For its growth strategy Lydall focuses on new product development geographic expansion into Asia and Europe acquisitions and the application of Lean Six Sigma initiatives. A major focus for the company in 2014 is the integration of its acquired companies and the introduction of Lean Six Sigma principles to the acquired businesses.

In early 2014 the company acquired the industrial filtration business from Andrew Industries Limited for $83 million. The acquisition enhanced Lydall's already strong position in the filtration and engineered materials markets.

EXECUTIVES

EVP CFO and President Lydall Thermal/Acoustical Solutions, Scott M. Deakin, age 52
President and CEO, Dale G. Barnhart, age 65, $522,600 total compensation
President Lydall Performance Materials, Paul Marold, age 57
CIO, Joseph M. (Joe) Tait
SVP General Counsel and Chief Administration Officer, Chad A. McDaniel, $238,135 total compensation
Vice President Corporate Development Investor Relations, David Glenn
VICE PRESIDENT HUMAN RESOURCES, Kerry Tehan
Vice President, Eric Winters
Chairman, W. Leslie Duffy, age 78
Auditors: PricewaterhouseCoopers LLP

LOCATIONS

HQ: Lydall, Inc.
One Colonial Road, Manchester, CT 06042
Phone: 860 646-1233   **Fax:** 860 646-4917
Web: www.lydall.com

PRODUCTS/OPERATIONS

2015 Sales

	$ mil.	% of total
Performance Materials Segment		
Filtration	62.7	11
Thermal Insulation	28.3	5
Life Sciences Filtration	10.5	2
Industrial Filtration Segment		
Industrial Filtration	139.1	26
Thermal/Acoustical Metals Segment		
Metal parts	141.1	26
Tooling	19.8	4
Thermal/Acoustical Fibers Segment		
Fiber parts	135.6	25
Tooling	3.2	1
Other Products and Services		
Life Sciences Vital Fluids	1.7	-
Eliminations and Other	(17.5)	-
Total	**524.5**	**100**

Selected Products

Performance Materials
Air Filtration
Liquid Filtration
High Temp. Insulation
Low Temp. Insulation
Energy Storage
Arioso for Gas Turbine
Solupor Venting Grade
HD ASHRAE
Industrial Filtration
Checkstatic
Felt Design & Specifying
Felt Manufacturing
Mate

COMPETITORS

CTA Acoustics	Pall Corporation
Dana	Specialty Products &
Donaldson Company	Insulation
Johns Manville	Tower International
Kaydon	Unifrax
Magna International	
Morgan Advanced	
Materials	

HISTORICAL FINANCIALS

Company Type: Public

Income Statement

FYE: December 31

	REVENUE ($ mil.)	NET INCOME ($ mil.)	NET PROFIT MARGIN	EMPLOYEES
12/17	698.4	49.3	7.1%	2,600
12/16	566.8	37.1	6.6%	2,700
12/15	524.5	46.2	8.8%	2,100
12/14	535.8	21.8	4.1%	2,100
12/13	397.9	19.1	4.8%	1,600
Annual Growth	15.1%	26.7%	—	12.9%

2017 Year-End Financials

Debt ratio: 13.7%	No. of shares (mil.): 17.3
Return on equity: 15.7%	Dividends
Cash ($ mil.): 59.8	Yield: —
Current ratio: 2.68	Payout: —
Long-term debt ($ mil.): 76.9	Market value ($ mil.): 880.0

	STOCK PRICE ($) FY Close	P/E High/Low		PER SHARE ($) Earnings	Dividends	Book Value
12/17	50.75	22	16	2.85	0.00	20.38
12/16	61.85	29	12	2.16	0.00	15.87
12/15	35.48	14	9	2.71	0.00	14.31
12/14	32.82	25	13	1.28	0.00	12.28
12/13	17.62	17	12	1.14	0.00	11.90
Annual Growth	30.3%			25.7%	—	14.4%

Lyon (William) Homes

William Lyon's is one of the largest home-builders in the West. That's where the homebuilder and its joint venture partners design and build single-family detached and attached houses. Indeed more than 70% of William Lyon Homes are sold in the states of California Washington and Oregon though homes are also sold in Nevada Colorado and Arizona. The builder targets entry-level and move-up buyers; its homes range from $110000 to $900000 and sold at an average price of $466300 each during 2015. William Lyon owns an additional 13500 development lots and with options to buy almost 4000 additional lots. Beyond building it assists with financing through William Lyon Mortgage. The builder went public in 2013.

Operations

The builder organizes its operations by region tied to its six largest markets: California (Orange Los Angeles Riverside Bernardino Alameda Contra Costa San Joaquin and Santa Clara counties); Oregon (Portland Metro); Washington (Seattle Metro); Nevada (Las Vegas Metro); Colorado (Denver Metro); and Arizona (Phoenix Metro).

Geographic Reach

William Lyon's largest state market is in California where it generated 37% of its sales during 2015. Its next largest were Oregon (19% of sales) Washington (16%) Nevada (12%) Colorado (10%) and Arizona (6%).

Sales and Marketing

The builder advertises online as well as through social media brochures and on billboards in strategic locations. Online it markets its products through email lists and interest lists as well as through its website and via sales force.

The company spent $61.54 million on sales and marketing to support growing sales during 2015 up from $45.9 million and $26.1 million in 2014 and 2013 respectively.

Financial Performance

William Lyon's sales have more than tripled since 2012 thanks to the strengthening US housing market. The builder has struggled to consistently grow its profits however as thin operating margins have been met with costly restructuring costs.

The builder's revenue jumped 23% to $1.11 billion during 2015 as its sales volumes rose 32% to 2314 home closings for the year despite its average home sale prices falling 5% to $466300 each. The bulk of the sales growth was driven by more closings in Washington and Oregon which stemmed from its acquisition of PNW Homes. Sales in Arizona and Colorado also rose by 17% and 7% during the year respectively while home sales in California fell by 25% offsetting much of the builder's top-line growth.

Strong revenue growth in 2015 drove William Lyon's net income up 28% to $57.34 million for the year. The builder's operations used 8% more cash than in 2014 or $172.91 million due to a decrease in accrued expenses and an increase in accounts payable both caused by the timing of payments.

Strategy

With entry-level first-time move-up and second-time move-up homebuyers in mind William Lyons continued in 2016 to build its wide range of housing types in the six core markets of Orange County Los Angeles the Inland Empire the San Francisco Bay area Phoenix Las Vegas Denver Seattle and Portland. The company hopes that these fast-growing and populous markets combined with the hot real estate market and plenty of land plot reserves (it held or had options to buy more than 17000 lots as of early 2016) will keep sales humming in the years ahead.

The builder also may acquire smaller home-builders to move into new geographic markets.

Mergers and Acquisitions

In August 2014 William Lyon expanded into the fast-growing Seattle and Portland home markets after purchasing Polygon Northwest Homes and its subsidiaries for $520 million. The acquisition formed the Washington and Oregon segments of William Lyon's operations.

Company Background

In 2011 the company filed for Chapter 11 bankruptcy but emerged the following year. The filing which listed some $600 million in liabilities included a pre-approved restructuring plan to raise some $85 million and reduce its debt by 37%. The Lyon family invested $25 million as part of the recapitalization plan in exchange for additional equity.

Like other homebuilders William Lyon suffered from declining sales in the economic downturn. Because of decreased home orders and high cancellation rates in all but its California market the company in 2008 slashed its workforce by about 25% and sold properties in 10 communities for about $90 million to raise cash. The company fared a bit better in 2009 as cancellations decreased and new home orders began picking up. William Lyon also cut the base prices of its homes and offered new incentives to keep sales up.

In 2010 sales continued to slump and new home orders slacked off at the end of the year after a federal tax credit for new homebuyers expired. Lyon Homes temporarily suspended development sales and marketing on certain projects. The company shifted its acquisitions on finished lots in stable markets.

EXECUTIVES

President Nevada Division, Mary J. Connelly, age 67, $225,000 total compensation
CEO, Matthew R. Zaist, age 43
SVP and CFO, Colin T. Severn, age 47
Regional President California, Brian W. Doyle
President Colorado Division, Giles Patterson
VP Information Technology, Tom Bui
President Southern California Division, Jon W. Robertson
President Northern California Division, Carl S. Morabito
President Arizona Division, Julie E. Collins
President Oregon Division, Fred Gast
President Washington Division, Derek Straight
Vice President, Gary Haddy
Vice President Warranty, Joe Whittemore
Vice President Construction, Dan George
Vice President Corporate Controller, Brian Profancik
Vice President, Bryan Cazier
Vice President General Counsel and Corporate Secretary, Jason Liljestrom
CORPORATE VICE PRESIDENT OF FINANCE, Jeffrey Deane
Chairman, William H. (Bill) Lyon, age 45
Board Member, Lynn Null Schell
Board Member, Michael Barr
Auditors: KPMG LLP

LOCATIONS

HQ: Lyon (William) Homes
  4695 MacArthur Court, 8th Floor, Newport Beach, CA 92660
Phone: 949 833-3600   Fax: 949 476-2178
Web: www.lyonhomes.com

PRODUCTS/OPERATIONS

2015 Sales

		% of total
Home Sales	1079.0	98
Construction services	25.1	2
Lots land and other sales	2.5	-
Total	1,106.6	100

COMPETITORS

Beazer Homes	KB Home
CalAtlantic	Lennar
Capital Pacific	M.D.C.
Corky McMillin	Meritage Homes
D.R. Horton	Toll Brothers

HISTORICAL FINANCIALS

Company Type: Public

Income Statement

FYE: December 31

	REVENUE ($ mil.)	NET INCOME ($ mil.)	NET PROFIT MARGIN	EMPLOYEES
12/17	1,796.5	48.1	2.7%	643
12/16	1,406.0	59.7	4.2%	591
12/15	1,106.5	57.3	5.2%	586
12/14	896.6	44.6	5.0%	585
12/13	572.5	129.1	22.6%	350
Annual Growth	33.1%	(21.9%)	—	16.4%

2017 Year-End Financials

Debt ratio: 49.9%	No. of shares (mil.): 37.9
Return on equity: 6.5%	Dividends
Cash ($ mil.): 182.7	Yield: —
Current ratio: 11.13	Payout: —
Long-term debt ($ mil.): 1,030.1	Market value ($ mil.): 1,104.0

	STOCK PRICE ($) FY Close	P/E High/Low		PER SHARE ($) Earnings	Dividends	Book Value
12/17	29.08	23	13	1.24	0.00	20.56
12/16	19.03	13	5	1.55	0.00	21.98
12/15	16.50	17	9	1.48	0.00	20.08
12/14	20.27	22	13	1.34	0.00	18.21
12/13	22.14	5	0	4.95	0.00	13.80
Annual Growth	7.1%	—	—	(29.3%)	—	10.5%

M/I Homes Inc

M/I Homes sells single-family detached homes to first-time move-up empty-nest and luxury buyers under the M/I Homes Showcase Homes and TriStone Homes names. It delivers more than 2200 homes a year at prices ranging from about $140000 to $1.2 million (averaging $346000) and sizes ranging from 1400 to 5500 sq. ft. M/I Homes also builds attached townhomes and condominiums in select markets. It caters to 14 markets throughout the Midwest Mid-Atlantic and South. Its M/I Financial mortgage banking subsidiary provides title and mortgage services. M/I Homes was founded in 1976 by Melvin and Irving Schottenstein.

Operations

Complementing its homebuilding activities (97% of sales) the company provides financing through its wholly-owned subsidiary M/I Financial Corp.

Geographic Reach

The company is based in Columbus Ohio and operates in Columbus and Cincinnati Ohio; Indianapolis Indiana; Chicago; Minneapolis/St. Paul Minnesota; Tampa and Orlando Florida; Austin Dallas/Fort Worth Houston and San Antonio Texas; Charlotte and Raleigh North Carolina; and the Virginia and Maryland suburbs of Washington DC.

M/I Homes' biggest market is the Midwest (35% of sales) followed by the Mid-Atlantic region (26%). The South including Texas accounts for 36% of sales.

Financial Performance

M/I Homes has achieved extraordinary growth over the years with revenues peaking at a record-setting $1.4 billion in 2015. Its profits also jumped 2% from 2014 to 2015. The company however has experienced five straight years of negative cash flow as consistently burns up cash for its operating activities.

The historic growth was fueled by increases across all its segments: Southern homebuilding (22%) Midwest homebuilding (18%) Mid-Atlantic homebuilding (8%) and financial services (19%). Most of these segments were helped by a spike in the average sales price of homes delivered an increase in the number of homes delivered (115 units) and a bump in land sales revenue.

Strategy

As the housing market gradually bounces back M/I has made a few changes to the new homes it builds. The company is designing the homes and the communities to reap higher profit margins. Its homes are all eco-friendly slightly smaller and in line with consumer demands.

The company focuses on investing in attractive land and new market opportunities and growth in current markets particularly newer Texas and Minneapolis/St. Paul markets. It also grows through acquisitions.

Mergers and Acquisitions

In 2015 M/I completed the acquisition of the residential homebuilding operations of Hans Hagen Homes a premier homebuilder in the Minneapolis/St. Paul market. The deal further cemented M/I Homes' geographic position in a healthy and dynamic housing market.

EXECUTIVES

EVP and CFO, Phillip G. Creek, age 65, $600,000 total compensation
Chairman President and CEO, Robert II. Schottenstein, age 65, $900,000 total compensation
EVP Chief Legal Officer and Secretary, J. Thomas (Tom) Mason, age 60, $450,000 total compensation
Region President Charlotte Cincinnati Columbus Orlando Raleigh Tampa and Washington D.C. Divisions, Fred J. Sikorski, age 63
Region President Austin Dallas Houston and San Antonio Divisions, Thomas W. Jacobs, age 52
Region President Chicago Indianapolis and Minneapolis/St. Paul Divisions, Ronald H. Martin, age 49
Vice President, David Parker
Division Vice President Controller, Audrey Cangialosi
Region Manager Vice President Mifc, Todd Miller
VICE PRESIDENT OF LAND DEVELOPMENT, Michael George
Division Vice President, Brad Nelson
Vice President Of Product Development, Daniel Omalley
Vice President of Purchasing, Kelly Cunningham
Senior Vice President Finance and Business Development Treasurer, Kevin Hake
Vice President Finance, Angie Alexander
Vice President Sales and Marketing, Desiree Davis
Vice President Operations, David Gipe
Vice President of Information Technology and Supply Chain, Peter Batchelder
Vice President Of Land Acquisition, Mark Connor
Vice President Of Operations, Gary Rae

Division Vice President, Paul D Stern
Executive Vice President Chief Legal Officer and Secretary, J T Mason
Vice President Purchasing, Kevin Markham
Vice President Secondary Marketing, Greg Otto
Vice President Of Land, Mathew Walker
Vice President Sales and Marketing, Van Nguyen
Regional Vice President Of Land, ED Suchora
VICE PRESIDENT OPERATIONS, Chad Tschetter
VICE PRESIDENT SALES AND MARKETING, Jaci Calhoun
Vice President of Construction, Tom Blair
Vice President of Purchasing, David CGriffin
Vice President Of National Accounts, Larry Sekely
Vice President Of Construction, Joseph Lucado
Auditors: DELOITTE & TOUCHE LLP

LOCATIONS

HQ: M/I Homes Inc
3 Easton Oval, Suite 500, Columbus, OH 43219
Phone: 614 418-8000   **Fax:** 614 418-8080
Web: www.mihomes.com

PRODUCTS/OPERATIONS

2015 Sales

	$ mil.	% of total
Southern Homebuilding	514.7	36
Midwest homebuilding	500.9	35
Mid-Atlantic homebuilding	366.8	26
Financial services	36.0	3
Total	**1,418.4**	**100**

Selected Markets

Charlotte NC
Chicago IL
Cincinnati OH
Columbus OH
Dayton OH
Houston TX
Indianapolis IN
Maryland
Orlando FL
Raleigh NC
San Antonio TX
Tampa FL
Virginia

COMPETITORS

Beazer Homes	Lennar
CalAtlantic	M.D.C.
Comstock Holding	NVR
D.R. Horton	Orleans Homebuilders
David Weekley Homes	PulteGroup
Dominion Homes	Rottlund
Drees Homes	Toll Brothers
Hovnanian Enterprises	WCI Communities
John Wieland Homes	Woodbridge Holdings
KB Home	

HISTORICAL FINANCIALS

Company Type: Public

Income Statement

FYE: December 31

	REVENUE ($ mil.)	NET INCOME ($ mil.)	NET PROFIT MARGIN	EMPLOYEES
12/17	1,961.9	72.0	3.7%	1,238
12/16	1,691.3	56.6	3.3%	1,138
12/15	1,418.4	51.7	3.6%	1,008
12/14	1,215.1	50.7	4.2%	905
12/13	1,036.7	151.4	14.6%	827
Annual Growth	17.3%	(16.9%)	—	10.6%

Debt ratio: 43.3%
Return on equity: 10.2%
Cash ($ mil.): 151.7
Current ratio: 10.91
Long-term debt ($ mil.): 807.7

No. of shares (mil.): 27.8
Dividends
  Yield: —
  Payout: —
Market value ($ mil.): 958.0

	STOCK PRICE ($) FY Close	P/E High/Low		PER SHARE ($) Earnings	Dividends	Book Value
12/17	34.40	14	9	2.26	0.00	26.83
12/16	25.18	13	7	1.84	0.00	26.51
12/15	21.92	14	10	1.68	0.00	24.20
12/14	22.96	14	10	1.65	0.00	22.20
12/13	25.45	5	3	5.24	0.00	20.23
Annual Growth	7.8%	—	—	(19.0%)	—	7.3%

Macquarie Infrastructure Corp

If you've flown in a small plane or had a cold drink of water in a building in Chicago you may have done business with Macquarie Infrastructure Company. Its Atlantic Aviation Services unit provides fixed-base operations (FBO) including fueling and aircraft storage services at about 60 US airports. Another unit Hawaii Gas is Hawaii's only government franchised gas company. It also has a stake in District Energy a firm that provides chilled water in Chicago and heating and cooling to a casino complex in Las Vegas. The company holds a 50% stake in International-Matex Tank Terminals. Australia-based Macquarie Bank's Macquarie Infrastructure Management (USA) manages Macquarie Infrastructure Company.

Operations

The company operates in three segments: Atlantic Aviation (70% of sales) Hawaii Gas (20%) and District Energy (5%). Atlantic Aviation offers fuel sales and other airport services including de-icing aircraft hangarage and other aviation services at more than 60 airports in the US.

Hawaii Gas offers distribution and sales of synthetic natural gas (SNG) and liquefied petroleum gas (LPG). Hawaii Gas operates through 1100 miles of underground piping and the segment has two primary businesses: utility and non-utility. The utility operations serve 35200 utility customers through localized pipeline distribution systems located on the islands of Oahu Hawaii Maui Kauai Molokai and Lanai. The non-utility business sells and distributes LPG via on-site tanks and portable gas cylinders to 33400 customers located in Oahu Hawaii Maui Kauai Molokai and Lanai.

Macquarie has a 50% interest in its District Energy segment which accrues revenues through monthly fixed contract charges and consumption revenue which relates to contractual rates applied to actual usage. It also generates financing and equipment lease revenue related to direct financing lease transactions and equipment leases to its various customers.

Financial Performance

Macquarie has enjoyed steady growth over the last three years. Its revenue jumped 5% in 2012 due to increases from all its segments. The Hawaii

Gas segment enjoyed increased volume of gas sold while District Energy's growth was driven by warmer average temperatures. Atlantic Aviation was helped by higher volume of general aviation fuel sold throughout 2012.

Macquarie's net income dipped 51% in 2012 due to higher operating expenses primarily related to a quarterly base management fee during the year. The company's cash flow increased by $120 million in 2012 as a result of additional cash derived from operating and as well as investing activities related to increased return of investment.

Strategy

The company aims to operate and grow its diversified portfolio of infrastructure businesses. Sticking to this strategy the company invested about $9 million in its two utility-scale solar photovoltaic power generation facilities (Tucson Project and Presidio Project) in late 2012 to increase its capacity to around 30 MW. In 2013 it increased the number of its solar plants to five and invested in these facilities to increase an aggregate generating capacity of 57 megawatts of wholesale electricity.

Macquarie also invests in additional storage capacity for further expansion. It intends to increase penetration of the residential government (primarily military) and tourism-related markets through investing and promoting Hawaii Gas's products and services and by promoting its attractiveness as a cleaner alternative to other energy sources in Hawaii.

Mergers and Acquisitions

Macquarie acquired the Bayonne Energy Center in New Jersey from Hess and ArcLight Capital in 2015. However in July 2018 it announced plans to sell the 644-MW gas-fired generation plant by the end of the year for close to $900 million. The company wants to use the majority of its proceeds from the sale to reduce its substantial debt and strengthen its balance sheet.

EXECUTIVES

Managing Director, Aaron Rubin
Auditors: KPMG LLP

LOCATIONS

HQ: Macquarie Infrastructure Corp
125 West 55th Street, New York, NY 10019
Phone: 212 231-1000
Web: www.macquarie.com/mic

PRODUCTS/OPERATIONS

Selected Businesses

Atlantic Aviation (aircraft parking de-icing refueling and terminal operations)
International-Matex Tank Terminals (50%; handling and storage of bulk liquid products)
Hawaii Gas (producer and distributor of synthetic natural gas and a distributor of propane gas on the six major islands of Hawaii)
District Energy (50.01%; provides chilled water under long-term contracts to approximately 100 buildings in Chicago and heating and cooling to a hotel/casino complex in Las Vegas)

COMPETITORS

ASIG	Kinder Morgan Energy
AmeriGas Partners	Partners
Encore FBO	Mercury Air Group
Jet Aviation	Million Air
Jetscape	Signature Flight
KaiserAir	Westway Group

HISTORICAL FINANCIALS

Company Type: Public

Income Statement

FYE: December 31

	REVENUE ($ mil.)	NET INCOME ($ mil.)	NET PROFIT MARGIN	EMPLOYEES
12/17	1,814.7	451.2	24.9%	1,100
12/16	1,651.7	156.3	9.5%	1,052
12/15	1,639.2	(108.5)	—	1,097
12/14	1,350.9	1,042.0	77.1%	3,218
12/13	1,041.0	31.2	3.0%	3,077
Annual Growth	14.9%	94.9%	—	(22.7%)

2017 Year-End Financials

Debt ratio: 44.7%
Return on equity: 14.7%
Cash ($ mil.): 47.1
Current ratio: 1.20
Long-term debt ($ mil.): 3,530.3

No. of shares (mil.): 84.7
Dividends
  Yield: 0.0%
  Payout: 105.8%
Market value ($ mil.): 5,440.0

	STOCK PRICE ($) FY Close	P/E High/Low		PER SHARE ($) Earnings	Dividends	Book Value
12/17	64.20	15	12	5.13	5.43	37.22
12/16	81.70	44	27	1.85	4.89	35.99
12/15	72.60	—	—	(1.39)	2.24	37.87
12/14	71.09	4	3	16.10	3.89	39.21
12/13	54.43	98	75	0.61	3.35	18.51
Annual Growth	4.2%	—	—	70.3%	12.8%	19.1%

Madison Square Garden Co (The) (New)

Auditors: KPMG LLP

LOCATIONS

HQ: Madison Square Garden Co (The) (New)
Two Penn Plaza, New York, NY 10121
Phone: 212 465-6000
Web: www.themadisonsquaregardencompany.com

HISTORICAL FINANCIALS

Company Type: Public

Income Statement

FYE: June 30

	REVENUE ($ mil.)	NET INCOME ($ mil.)	NET PROFIT MARGIN	EMPLOYEES
06/18	1,559.1	141.5	9.1%	11,700
06/17	1,318.4	(72.7)	—	13,000
06/16	1,115.3	(77.2)	—	8,900
06/15	1,071.5	(40.6)	—	8,364
06/14	913.6	(116.9)	—	9,000
Annual Growth	14.3%	—	—	6.8%

2018 Year-End Financials

Debt ratio: 2.8%
Return on equity: 5.7%
Cash ($ mil.): 1,225.6
Current ratio: 1.85
Long-term debt ($ mil.): 101.3

No. of shares (mil.): 23.6
Dividends
  Yield: —
  Payout: —
Market value ($ mil.): 7,341.0

	STOCK PRICE ($) FY Close	P/E High/Low		PER SHARE ($) Earnings	Dividends	Book Value
06/18	310.19	52	32	5.94	0.00	107.18
06/17	196.90	—	—	(3.05)	0.00	102.28
06/16	172.51	—	—	(3.12)	0.00	106.41
Annual Growth	34.1%	—	—	—	—	0.4%

Main Street Capital Corp

Main Street Capital doesn't care if its investments are on Main St. Manufacturing Blvd or Professional Services Pkwy.A just as long as they are not too big and are (preferably) located in the southwestern US. As an investment firm Main Street provides long-term debt and equity capital to lower middle-market companies with annual revenues between $10 million and $100 million. Its portfolio includes more than 40 active investments in traditional and niche companies in the manufacturing technology restaurant business services and other sectors. Main Street tends to partner with business owners and management and provides capitalA to support buyouts recapitalizations growth financings and acquisitions.

EXECUTIVES

Managing Director, Colton Braud
Auditors: Grant Thornton LLP

LOCATIONS

HQ: Main Street Capital Corp
1300 Post Oak Boulevard, 8th floor, Houston, TX 77056
Phone: 713 350-6000
Web: www.mainstcapital.com

COMPETITORS

American Capital	MCG Capital
Apollo Investment	Sentinel Capital
Ares Capital	Partners
Capital Southwest	WestView Capital
Castle Harlan	Partners

HISTORICAL FINANCIALS

Company Type: Public

Income Statement			FYE: December 31
	REVENUE ($ mil.)	NET INCOME ($ mil.)	NET PROFIT MARGIN	EMPLOYEES
12/17	205.7	135.3	65.8%	58
12/16	178.3	115.8	64.9%	57
12/15	164.5	107.0	65.1%	50
12/14	140.7	95.5	67.9%	38
12/13	116.5	75.4	64.7%	37
Annual Growth	15.3%	15.7%	—	11.9%

2017 Year-End Financials

Debt ratio: 35.1%
Return on equity: 10.4%
Cash ($ mil.): 51.5
Current ratio: 0.70
Long-term debt ($ mil.): 797.1

No. of shares (mil.): 58.6
Dividends
  Yield: 0.0%
  Payout: 116.7%
Market value ($ mil.): 2,331.0

	STOCK PRICE ($) FY Close	P/E High/Low	Earnings	PER SHARE ($) Dividends	Book Value
12/17	39.73	17 15	2.39	2.79	23.53
12/16	36.77	17 12	2.23	2.73	22.12
12/15	29.08	15 12	2.18	2.49	21.24
12/14	29.24	16 12	2.20	2.39	20.85
12/13	32.69	17 13	2.06	2.18	19.89
Annual Growth	5.0%	— —	3.8%	6.4%	4.3%

Malibu Boats Inc

LOCATIONS

HQ: Malibu Boats Inc
5075 Kimberly Way, Loudon, TN 37774
Phone: 865 458-5478
Web: www.malibuboats.com

HISTORICAL FINANCIALS

Company Type: Public

Income Statement			FYE: June 30
	REVENUE ($ mil.)	NET INCOME ($ mil.)	NET PROFIT MARGIN	EMPLOYEES
06/18	497.0	27.6	5.6%	1,345
06/17	281.9	28.3	10.1%	586
06/16	252.9	18.0	7.1%	540
06/15	228.6	14.6	6.4%	509
06/14	190.9	(4.6)	—	411
Annual Growth	27.0%	—		34.5%

2018 Year-End Financials

Debt ratio: 29.6%
Return on equity: 30.0%
Cash ($ mil.): 61.6
Current ratio: 2.05
Long-term debt ($ mil.): 108.4

No. of shares (mil.): 20.5
Dividends
  Yield: —
  Payout: —
Market value ($ mil.): 862.0

	STOCK PRICE ($) FY Close	P/E High/Low	Earnings	PER SHARE ($) Dividends	Book Value
06/18	41.94	33 18	1.36	0.00	6.54
06/17	25.87	16 8	1.58	0.00	2.74
06/16	12.08	21 11	1.00	0.00	0.77
06/15	20.09	26 18	0.93	0.00	(1.50)
06/14	20.10	— —	(0.42)	0.00	1.74
Annual Growth	20.2%	— —			39.2%

Malvern Bancorp Inc

EXECUTIVES

Vice Chairman Malvern Bancorp And Malvern Federal Savings Bank, John B Yerkes
Senior Vice President Chief, William Woolworth
Auditors: Baker Tilly Virchow Krause, LLP

LOCATIONS

HQ: Malvern Bancorp Inc
42 E. Lancaster Avenue, Paoli, PA 19301
Phone: 610 644-9400
Web: www.malvernfederal.com

HISTORICAL FINANCIALS

Company Type: Public

Income Statement			FYE: September 30
	ASSETS ($ mil.)	NET INCOME ($ mil.)	INCOME AS % OF ASSETS	EMPLOYEES
09/18	1,033.9	7.3	0.7%	85
09/17	1,046.0	5.8	0.6%	81
09/16	821.2	11.9	1.5%	83
09/15	655.6	3.7	0.6%	71
09/14	542.2	0.3	0.1%	93
Annual Growth	17.5%	118.1%	—	(2.2%)

2018 Year-End Financials

Return on assets: 0.7%
Return on equity: 6.8%
Long-term debt ($ mil.): —
No. of shares (mil.): 6.5
Sales ($ mil.) 43.3

Dividends
  Yield: —
  Payout: —
Market value ($ mil.): 158.0

	STOCK PRICE ($) FY Close	P/E High/Low	Earnings	PER SHARE ($) Dividends	Book Value
09/18	23.95	25 19	1.13	0.00	16.84
09/17	26.75	30 19	0.90	0.00	15.60
09/16	16.40	10 8	1.86	0.00	14.42
09/15	15.65	27 19	0.58	0.00	12.41
09/14	11.39	259203	0.05	0.00	11.71
Annual Growth	20.4%	—	—118.0%	—	9.5%

Mammoth Energy Services Inc

Auditors: GRANT THORNTON LLP

LOCATIONS

HQ: Mammoth Energy Services Inc
14201 Caliber Drive Suite 300, Oklahoma City, OK 73134
Phone: 405 608-6007
Web: www.mammothenergy.com

HISTORICAL FINANCIALS

Company Type: Public

Income Statement			FYE: December 31
	REVENUE ($ mil.)	NET INCOME ($ mil.)	NET PROFIT MARGIN	EMPLOYEES
12/17	691.5	58.9	8.5%	1,846
12/16	231.0	(88.4)	—	520
12/15	359.9	(27.2)	—	500
12/14	259.5	(2.0)	—	0
Annual Growth	38.6%	—		—

2017 Year-End Financials

Debt ratio: 11.5%
Return on equity: 13.8%
Cash ($ mil.): 5.6
Current ratio: 1.43
Long-term debt ($ mil.): 99.9

No. of shares (mil.): 44.5
Dividends
  Yield: —
  Payout: —
Market value ($ mil.): 875.0

	STOCK PRICE ($) FY Close	P/E High/Low	Earnings	PER SHARE ($) Dividends	Book Value
12/17	19.63	16 8	1.42	0.00	11.39
12/16	15.20	— —	(2.81)	0.00	9.09
12/15	0.00	— —	(0.91)	0.00	10.77
Annual Growth	—	— —		—	2.8%

Manhattan Associates, Inc.

Whether you're in New York or Kansas or points between or beyond Manhattan Associates keeps things moving with its supply chain management software and systems. The Atlanta-based company provides customers in retail distribution transportation and manufacturing with supply chain management software and related services. Its line of supply chain and inventory software includes warehouse transportation trading partner distributed order and reverse logistics management applications. Manhattan also offers performance management and radio-frequency identification tools designed to enhance the functionality of its other products and sells third-party hardware such as bar code scanners.

Operations

Manhattan Associates has five sources of revenue: services about 55% of sales maintenance 25% software licensing about 10% cloud subscriptions and hardware 10%.

The company's products run on major computing platforms such as Linux IBM System i and Microsoft?s .NET as well as on the major public cloud infrastructures.

Geographic Reach

In addition to the US Manhattan Associates has offices in Australia China France Germany India Japan the Netherlands Singapore and the UK. It has reseller agreements or third-party representatives in a host of other markets throughout Latin America Eastern Europe the Middle East South Africa and Asia.

Manhattan generates about 80% of sales from customers in North and Latin America; Europe the Middle East and Africa (EMEA) and the Asia/Pacific region contribute about 15% and more than 5% respectively.

Sales and Marketing

Manhattan primarily sells through its direct sales force but it has made efforts to broaden its approach through programs such as Manhattan Value Partner and Manhattan GeoPartner that enable joint sales and marketing activities with organizations such as Accenture Deloitte IBM and Microsoft.

The company?s customers are suppliers manufacturers distributors retailers and logistics providers in a variety of industries. Its five biggest customers account for less than 10% of Manhattan?s revenue. Customers include Abercrombie & Fitch PETCO American Eagle RH and The Container Store.

Financial Performance

Manhattan?s sales grew steadily over seven years to reach a high of more than $604 million in 2016 but sales slipped in 2017. Revenue was down 2% to about $595 million in 2017 from 2016 because of its transition to a subscription-based model in which revenue is recognized over time. The company also cited a weaker retail environment for lower sales. Cloud subscription revenue jumped 66% in 2017 from 2016 but it accounts for just 2% of the total. Maintenance and Hardware also rose during the year while revenue from Software Licenses and Services fell. Geo-

graphically sales were higher in Europe and Asia but lower in the Americas.

Manhattan?s net income also dropped in 2017 to about $116 million from $124 million in 2016 on the lower revenue.

The company ended 2017 with about $125 million in cash about $30 million more than it had at the close of 2016.

Strategy

Manhattan Associates is in the midst of moving customers to a subscription sales model of its cloud offerings as are most software providers. Over time the subscription model provides a steadier stream of revenue while sending software updates to customers. In 2017 the company introduced cloud-based Manhattan Active Omni an omnichannel operations platform that brings together several supply chain functions. While a small part of the company?s revenue the cloud business is growing quickly.

The transition to a fully functioning cloud model takes time however. The company expects that its combined license and cloud subscription revenue will decrease early in the transition because of the revenue recognition timing and smooth out over time. Slowdowns in licensing revenue could reverberate to slow maintenance revenue.

EXECUTIVES

President CEO and Director, Eddie Capel, age 56, $575,000 total compensation
SVP Americas, Robert G. (Bob) Howell, age 45, $289,000 total compensation
Interim CFO, Linda C. Pinne, age 44
SVP and CTO, Sanjeev Siotia
SVP Europe Middle East and Africa (EMEA), Henri Seroux
SVP and General Manager India, Usha Tirumala
Vice President, Chris Hine
Vice President, Stewart Gantt
Vice President Planning Forecasting, Jim Schwender
Vice President, Marvin Lee
Chairman, John J. Huntz, age 67
Auditors: Ernst & Young LLP

LOCATIONS

HQ: Manhattan Associates, Inc.
2300 Windy Ridge Parkway, Tenth Floor, Atlanta, GA 30339
Phone: 770 955-7070   **Fax:** 770 995-0302
Web: www.manh.com

PRODUCTS/OPERATIONS

2017 Sales

	$ mil.	% of total
Services	326.5	55
Maintenance	143.0	24
Software License	72.3	12
Hardware	43.1	7
Cloud Subscription	9.6	2
Total	**594.5**	**100**

Selected Services

Carrier Management
Distribution Management
Inventory Optimization
Mobile Supply Chain
Order Lifecycle Management
Planning and Forecasting
Supply Chain Event Management
Supply Chain Intelligence
Supply Chain Visibility
Total Cost to Serve
Transportation Lifecycle Management

COMPETITORS

CDC Supply Chain	JDA Software
Epicor Software	Oracle
HighJump	SAP
IBM	SAS Institute
Infor Global	Transentric

HISTORICAL FINANCIALS

Company Type: Public

Income Statement
FYE: December 31

	REVENUE ($ mil.)	NET INCOME ($ mil.)	NET PROFIT MARGIN	EMPLOYEES
12/17	594.6	116.4	19.6%	2,790
12/16	604.5	124.2	20.5%	3,020
12/15	556.3	103.4	18.6%	2,930
12/14	492.1	82.0	16.7%	2,770
12/13	414.5	67.3	16.2%	2,530
Annual Growth	**9.4%**	**14.7%**	**—**	**2.5%**

2017 Year-End Financials

Debt ratio: —
Return on equity: 67.6%
Cash ($ mil.): 125.5
Current ratio: 1.84
Long-term debt ($ mil.): —
No. of shares (mil.): 67.7
Dividends
  Yield: —
  Payout: —
Market value ($ mil.): 3,358.0

	STOCK PRICE ($) FY Close	P/E High/Low	PER SHARE ($) Earnings	Dividends	Book Value
12/17	49.54	33 24	1.68	0.00	2.58
12/16	53.03	39 26	1.72	0.00	2.41
12/15	66.17	55 27	1.40	0.00	2.69
12/14	40.72	114 26	1.08	0.00	2.46
12/13	117.48	139 69	0.86	0.00	2.38
Annual Growth	**(19.4%)**	**— —**	**18.2%**	**—**	**2.1%**

Marcus & Millichap Inc

If you've got several million burning a hole in your pocket or you're looking to unload that old skyscraper Marcus & Millichap can help. One of the largest commercial real estate brokers in the US (with about 75 offices) the firm focuses on investment brokerage and provides financing research and advisory services to both buyers and sellers. The company is organized into groups by property type including shopping centers apartments office and industrial buildings and distressed properties. Marcus & Millichap was one of the earliest brokerages to maintain a centralized database to link potential buyers and sellers. In 2013 the company went public raising $72 million which it will use for general corporate purposes.

IPOMarcus & Millichap went public in October 2013 with an offering 6 million shares priced at $12 each. The firm intends to use the $42.3 million in net proceeds for general corporate purposes including capital expenditures and working capital to expand its services and potential acquisitions of real estate businesses or companies. It did not receive any proceeds from the sale of shares by the selling stockholders.

Operations

Marcus & Millichap specializes in commercial real estate investment sales with more than 1300 brokers in 76 markets throughout the US and

Canada. The firm also offers property financing research and advisory services.

Financial Services

The firm closed more than 6600 transactions with a value of approximately $24 billion in 2013. Revenue increased 13% versus 2012 to $435.9 million. The rise in revenue was primarily due to increasing real estate brokerage commissions. Despite the double-digit increase in revenue net income declined 71% in 2013 versus 2012 to $8.2 million on rising operating expenses as a result of stock-based compensation charges in connection with the firm's 2013 IPO. Cash flow from operations has tracked the rise in revenue over the past three years rising steeply in 2013 to $96.9 million from $35.4 million in 2012.

Strategy

The brokerage firm focuses on private clients who account for more than 80% of US commercial property sales transactions annually. Its growth plan includes increasing its market share of the private clients segment in such areas as apartment retail office hospitality and senior housing. M&M is expending its presence in Canada with the opening of three offices there in 2014.

EXECUTIVES

Vice President Investments, Philip Saglimbeni
Associate Vice President Capital Markets, Farhan Kabani
Vice President Investments, Cliff David
Vice President National Director Retail, Bill Rose
Vice President Capital Markets, Danny Abergel
Auditors: Ernst & Young LLP

LOCATIONS

HQ: Marcus & Millichap Inc
23975 Park Sorrento, Suite 400, Calabasas, CA 91302
Phone: 818 212-2250
Web: www.marcusmillichap.com

PRODUCTS/OPERATIONS

2015 Sales

	$ mil.	% of total
Real estate brokerage commissions	632.6	92
Financing fees	42.6	6
Other	13.9	2
Total	**689.1**	**100**

Selected Specializations

Health care
Hospitality and golf
Land
Manufactured housing
Multi-family
Net-leased
Office and industrial
Retail
Self-storage
Seniors housing
Student housing
Special assets

COMPETITORS

Baird & Warner	Inland Group
CBRE Group	Johnson Capital
Cassidy Turley	Jones Lang LaSalle
Coldwell Banker	Lee & Associates
Colliers International	NorthMarq Capital
Corky McMillin	ONCOR
Cushman & Wakefield	Sperry Van Ness
Grandbridge	Trammell Crow Company
HFF	

HISTORICAL FINANCIALS

Company Type: Public

Income Statement

FYE: December 31

	REVENUE ($ mil.)	NET INCOME ($ mil.)	NET PROFIT MARGIN	EMPLOYEES
12/17	719.7	51.5	7.2%	2,593
12/16	717.4	64.6	9.0%	2,390
12/15	689.0	66.3	9.6%	2,243
12/14	572.1	49.5	8.7%	2,105
12/13	435.9	9.2	2.1%	1,841
Annual Growth	**13.4%**	**53.6%**	**—**	**8.9%**

2017 Year-End Financials

Debt ratio: 1.8%	No. of shares (mil.): 38.3
Return on equity: 17.9%	Dividends
Cash ($ mil.): 220.7	Yield: —
Current ratio: 3.85	Payout: —
Long-term debt ($ mil.): 7.6	Market value ($ mil.): 1,251.0

	STOCK PRICE ($) FY Close	P/E High/Low		PER SHARE ($) Earnings	Dividends	Book Value
12/17	32.61	25	18	1.32	0.00	8.21
12/16	26.72	18	11	1.66	0.00	6.83
12/15	29.14	31	17	1.69	0.00	5.05
12/14	33.25	27	11	1.27	0.00	3.16
12/13	14.90	63	55	0.24	0.00	1.71
Annual Growth	**21.6%**	**—**	**—**	**53.1%**	**—**	**48.1%**

Marcus Corp. (The)

With this company it's either showtime or bedtime. The Marcus Corporation operates movie theaters and hotels primarily in the Midwest. It owns or operates more than 55 theaters boasting some 680 screens in Iowa Illinois Minnesota Nebraska North Dakota Ohio and Wisconsin. Its Marcus Hotels subsidiary owns and operates more than 10 hotels and resorts in Illinois Missouri Oklahoma and Wisconsin; it also manages 10 hotels for third parties in a handful of US states. Other holdings also include Funset Boulevard a family entertainment center adjacent to one of its Wisconsin theatres. Chairman Stephen Marcus and his sister Diane Marcus Gershowitz together control more than 75% of the firm.

Operations

The Marcus Corporation owns and/or manages more than 5200 hotel rooms. Properties include the Pfister Hotel in downtown Milwaukee Wisconsin; the Four Points by Sheraton Chicago Downtown/Magnificent Mile; and the Hotel Phillips in Kansas City Missouri.

The company offers digital 3D systems at more than 35 of its movie theater properties. About three-fourths of its theater portfolio are megaplex theaters (12 or more screens). Marcus Corporation also offers its Big Screen Bistro in-theater dining concept at two locations.

In fiscal 2015 the company's Theatres segment generated 55% of revenue while the other 45% was generated by its Hotels/ Resorts segment.

Geographic Reach

The theater division has operations in Wisconsin Illinois Ohio Minnesota Iowa North Dakota and Nebraska and a family entertainment center in

Wisconsin. The hotels and resorts business has owned and operated hotels and resorts in Wisconsin Missouri Illinois and Oklahoma. It manages properties for third parties in Wisconsin Minnesota Ohio Texas Missouri Nevada and California.

Financial Performance

The company's revenue increased by $40 million in fiscal 2015 compared to the prior fiscal period. It reported about $488 million in revenue for fiscal 2015. Despite the increased revenue the company's net income decreased by $1 million in fiscal 2015 compared to fiscal 2014. The Marcus Corporation did claim a profit of $23.9 million in fiscal 2015 and net cash provided by operating activities increased by $14 million compared to fiscal 2014 levels.

Strategy

Marcus is working on upgrades at its theater facilities. It is adding special 70-foot-wide screens (called UltraScreens) to some locations and rolling out digital 3D cinema technology at its theaters. It is also introducing new food and beverage offerings at its theaters.

EXECUTIVES

CFO and Treasurer, Douglas A. Neis, age 59, $318,923 total compensation
President CEO and Director, Gregory S. Marcus, age 53, $522,307 total compensation
Senior Managing Director MCS Capital LLC, William H. Reynolds, age 68
EVP and President and CEO Marcus Theatres Corporation, Rolando B. Rodriguez, age 58
President Marcus Hotels and Resorts, Joseph S. Khairallah
CIO and VP Technology Marcus Theatres Corporation, Kim M. Lueck
Vice President of Revenue Strategy and Distribution, Linda Gulrajani
Vice President Of Selling Support Services, Ken Day
Vice President Of Sales, Michael Lindley
Vice President Real Estate, Katie Falvey
Vice President, Marie McSzkowski
Vice President Information Technology, Pete Helf
Vice President, Tom Kissinger
Senior Vice President Development Marcus Hotels and Resorts, Andrea Foster
Vice President of Human Resources, John E Murray
Chairman, Stephen H. Marcus, age 83
Board Member, Diane Gershowitz
Auditors: DELOITTE & TOUCHE LLP

LOCATIONS

HQ: Marcus Corp. (The)
100 East Wisconsin Avenue, Suite 1900, Milwaukee, WI 53202-4125
Phone: 414 905-1000   **Fax:** 414 905-2879
Web: www.marcuscorp.com

PRODUCTS/OPERATIONS

Selected Hotels

Beverly Garland's Holiday Inn (North Hollywood California)
Crowne Plaza-Northstar Hotel (Minneapolis)
Four Points by Sheraton Chicago Downtown
The Grand Geneva Resort & Spa (Lake Geneva Wisconsin)
Hilton Garden Inn Houston
Hilton Madison at Monona Terrace (Wisconsin)
The Hilton Milwaukee City Center (Wisconsin)
Hotel Mead (Wisconsin Rapids Wisconsin)
Hotel Phillips (Kansas City)

The Pfister Hotel (Milwaukee)
Timber Ridge Lodge (Lake Geneva Wisconsin)

Selected Movie Theaters
Century Cinema Fargo (North Dakota)
Chicago Heights Cinema (Illinois)
Duluth Cinema (Minnesota)
Eastgate Cinema Madison (Wisconsin)
Lincoln Grand Cinema (Nebraska)
Northtown Cinema Milwaukee (Wisconsin)
Orland Park Cinema (Illinois)

COMPETITORS

AMC Entertainment	Kerasotes ShowPlace
Carmike Cinemas	Kohler
Cinemark	Marriott
Heart of America	Nath Companies
Restaurants & Inns	Radisson Hotels
Hilton Worldwide	Ramada
Hostmark Hospitality	Regal Entertainment
Hyatt	Starwood Hotels &
IMAX	Resorts
InterContinental	Wyndham Destinations
Hotels	

HISTORICAL FINANCIALS

Company Type: Public

Income Statement

FYE: December 28

	REVENUE ($ mil.)	NET INCOME ($ mil.)	NET PROFIT MARGIN	EMPLOYEES
12/17	622.7	65.0	10.4%	7,800
12/16	543.8	37.9	7.0%	7,900
12/15*	324.2	23.5	7.3%	7,000
05/15	488.0	24.0	4.9%	7,100
05/14	447.9	25.0	5.6%	6,900
Annual Growth	8.6%	27.0%	—	3.1%

*Fiscal year change

2017 Year-End Financials

Debt ratio: 33.1%	No. of shares (mil.): 27.8
Return on equity: 15.6%	Dividends
Cash ($ mil.): 16.2	Yield: 1.8%
Current ratio: 0.48	Payout: 35.9%
Long-term debt ($ mil.): 318.1	Market value ($ mil.): 758.0

	STOCK PRICE ($) FY Close	P/E High/Low		PER SHARE ($) Earnings	Dividends	Book Value
12/17	27.20	14	10	2.29	0.50	15.98
12/16	31.55	23	13	1.36	0.45	14.10
12/15*	18.97	24	21	0.84	0.41	13.13
05/15	19.65	25	16	0.87	0.39	12.48
05/14	16.84	19	13	0.92	0.35	11.95
Annual Growth	12.7%	—	—	25.6%	9.3%	7.5%

*Fiscal year change

Marine Products Corp

A day on the water for you is a day at the office for Marine Products. The company builds recreational powerboats mainly though its Chaparral subsidiary. Its lineup includes fiberglass sterndrive and inboard deckboats cruisers and sport yachts ranging from 18 feet to 42 feet. Marine Products also makes a line of freshwater/saltwater sport fishing boats known for their "unsinkable hull" through subsidiary Robalo. Boats are sold to a network of about 230 independent dealers who then sell the lines to retail customers. The US generates the majority of the company's sales.

Geographic Reach

Headquartered at Atlanta the company sells its products to clients in Europe South America Asia Russia the Middle East and the US. Sales outside of the US accounted for 11% of its sales in 2015.

Sales and Marketing

Marine Products leverages a network of roughly 60 Chaparral dealers 25 Robalo dealers and 64 dealers selling both brands throughout the US. Oversees its boats are sold through some 85 international dealers.

Financial Performance

As the economy has gradually recovered Marine Products has achieved explosive growth over the years. Its total sales increased 21% from $171 million in 2014 to $207 million in 2015. Profits also surged 60% from $9 million in 2014 to $14 million in 2015. (Both these totals represented its highest amounts in at least eight years.)

The growth for 2015 was primarily due to a 23% increase in the number of boats sold. Unit sales increased due to higher sales of its Robalo outboard sport fishing boats as well as increased unit sales of its Chaparral Vortex jet boats and Suncoast outboards.

In addition to its trending revenue and net income Marine Products' operating cash flow surged by 51% from 2014 to 2015.

Strategy

With a health level of cash from operations and increasing production the company anticipates replenishing dealer inventories now normalizing from its historic low levels. Simultaneously it aims to enhance dealer offerings and spur retail purchases by manufacturing more models with standard features and fewer options.

Marine Products has recently launched new Chaparral and Robalo models: the Chaparral H2O Sport and Fish & Ski Boats and the Robalo R180 and R200. The new models are more affordable with a small number of standard features. They adhere to the company's strategy to produce lower-priced entry level models appealing to a value-conscious consumer.

EXECUTIVES

President CEO and Director, Richard A. Hubbell, age 74, $350,000 total compensation
EVP and President Chaparral Boats, James A. Lane, age 75, $250,000 total compensation
VP CFO and Treasurer, Ben M. Palmer, age 57, $175,000 total compensation
Senior Vice President Customer Relationship Ma, Ed French
Vice President Secretary and Director, Linda H Graham
Chairman, R. Randall Rollins, age 87
Auditors: GRANT THORNTON LLP

LOCATIONS

HQ: Marine Products Corp
  2801 Buford Highway, Suite 520, Atlanta, GA 30329
Phone: 404 321-7910
Web: www.marineproductscorp.com

PRODUCTS/OPERATIONS

Selected Products

Chaparral (family recreational cruiser and sport yachts)
  Premiere sport yachts (fiberglass sport yachts)
  Signature cruisers (fiberglass cruisers)
SSi sportboats (fiberglass closed deck runabouts)
SSX sportdecks (fiberglass bowrider crossover sportboats)
Sunesta Xtreme tow boats (fiberglass pleasure boats)
Robalo (outboard sport fishing boats)

COMPETITORS

Bombardier	Sea Fox Boats
Brunswick Corp.	Sea Ray Boats
Bénéteau	Sunseeker
Cigarette Racing Team	Taylor Made Group
Correct Craft	Viking Yacht
Duckworth Boat Works	Yamaha Motor
Fountain Powerboat	

HISTORICAL FINANCIALS

Company Type: Public

Income Statement

FYE: December 31

	REVENUE ($ mil.)	NET INCOME ($ mil.)	NET PROFIT MARGIN	EMPLOYEES
12/17	267.3	19.3	7.2%	891
12/16	241.3	16.7	6.9%	823
12/15	207.0	14.3	6.9%	767
12/14	171.0	8.9	5.2%	605
12/13	168.2	7.5	4.5%	651
Annual Growth	12.3%	26.5%	—	8.2%

2017 Year-End Financials

Debt ratio: —	No. of shares (mil.): 34.5
Return on equity: 28.5%	Dividends
Cash ($ mil.): 7.6	Yield: 0.0%
Current ratio: 2.80	Payout: 60.0%
Long-term debt ($ mil.): —	Market value ($ mil.): 440.0

	STOCK PRICE ($) FY Close	P/E High/Low		PER SHARE ($) Earnings	Dividends	Book Value
12/17	12.74	31	18	0.55	0.33	2.01
12/16	13.87	33	12	0.44	0.24	1.88
12/15	6.04	23	14	0.39	0.20	2.37
12/14	8.44	42	25	0.24	0.16	2.19
12/13	10.05	51	29	0.20	0.15	2.14
Annual Growth	6.1%	—	—	28.8%	21.8%	(1.5%)

MarineMax Inc

MarineMax aims to float your boat. The nation's largest recreational boat dealer has about 60 locations in around 16 states. Dealerships sell new and used pleasure boats fishing boats motor yachts ski boats and high-performance boats. Sales of new boats made by Brunswick including Sea Ray and Boston Whaler boats account for more than 40% of revenue. The company also sells boat engines trailers parts and accessories; arranges for financing and insurance; provides repair and maintenance; and offers boat brokerage and storage services. MarineMax is the exclusive dealer of Sea Ray in almost all the areas where it operates. Since its founding in 1998 MarineMax has acquired about 35 boat dealers.

Operations

MarineMax gets more than 70% of its revenue from the sale of brand new boats (average price: $195000). Used boat sales account for about 15%

with the remainder provider by its repair finance and insurance and brokerage sales.

Within the new boat category sales of Sea Ray and Boston Whaler craft (made by Brunswick) account for about 25% and about 15% of revenue respectively. New Azimut boats and yachts supply about 10% of the company?s revenue.

Geographic Reach

MarineMax is based in Florida (Clearwater) and the state accounts for more than half of its sales. The other 15 states in which it has retail locations are Alabama California Connecticut Florida Georgia Maryland Massachusetts Minnesota Missouri New Jersey New York North Carolina Ohio Oklahoma Rhode Island South Carolina and Texas. The company is also in the British Virgin Islands.

Sales and Marketing

MarineMax knows that nothing becomes a boat more than water and that?s why many of its retail spots are on waterfronts in popular destinations. To help get people to those locations the company uses its website email marketing and social media. It?s also a constant presence at boat shows throughout the country.

Financial Performance

A rising economic tide has helped MarineMax?s revenue increase 80% from 2014 through 2017. The company?s sales plunged during the Great Recession but have rebounded in the years since.

In 2017 the company?s sales rose 11% to just over $1 billion from 2016. Same store sales were up 5% in 2017 from incremental increases in new boat sales and increases in its other revenue sources such as brokerage sales storage services finance and insurance products and charter rentals pushed along by better economic conditions.

Net income rose about 4% to $23.5 million in 2017 from 2016. MarineMax held the line on most expenses but losses from Hurricane Irma forced sales general and administrative costs higher.

The company had about $42 million in cash at the end of 2017 up from about $39 million in 2016.

Strategy

Not to feel sorry for a business that sells yachts but the boating industry took a beating during the Great Recession. Annual sales averaged 309000 boats from 1990-2006 but slowed significantly after 2007 and 2008. (MarineMax closed 29 stores in 2009 alone). In 2016 about 188000 boats were sold industrywide but the trend line is rising.

Borrowing a page from the playbook of retailers like Home Depot MarineMax is trying to consolidate what has been a fragmented market dominated by local boat sellers. MarineMax has expanded through acquisitions making about 35 deals in its 20-year history.

The company also does more than sell boats. It trains the buyers on how to use them services them insures them and lends buyers money to buy them. It also charters boats to people who don?t own one. MarineMax has extended the brands it carries to more of its markets to provide more choice for customers.

Mergers and Acquisitions

MarineMax acquired Island Marine Center which serves the southern New Jersey market in 2017. Island Marine has locations in Ocean View and Somers Point New Jersey.

In another 2017 deal MarineMax acquired Hall Marine Group which had six locations in North Carolina South Carolina and Georgia.

In 2016 MarineMax bought Russo Marine a boat dealer with three locations in Massachusetts and Rhode Island.

EXECUTIVES

EVP CFO and Secretary, Michael H. (Mike) McLamb, age 53, $315,000 total compensation
Chairman President and CEO, William H. McGill, age 75, $550,000 total compensation
EVP Chief Legal Officer and Assistant Secretary, Paulee C. Day, age 49, $260,000 total compensation
EVP and Chief Revenue Officer, Charles A. (Chuck) Cashman, age 55, $200,000 total compensation
EVP and COO, William Brett McGill, age 49, $200,000 total compensation
Vice President East Operations, Chuck Cashman
Auditors: KPMG LLP

LOCATIONS

HQ: MarineMax Inc
2600 McCormick Drive, Suite 200, Clearwater, FL 33759
Phone: 727 531-1700
Web: www.MarineMax.com

PRODUCTS/OPERATIONS

2017 Sales

	$ mil.	% of total
New boat sales	747.0	70
Used boat sales	157.0	15
Maintenance repair & storage services	60.0	6
Marine Engines Related Marine Equipment and Boating Parts and Accessories	38.0	2
F&I Products	25.0	4
Brokerage Sales	20.0	2
Total	**1,052.0**	**100**

Selected Products & Trade Names

Motor Yachts
  Azimut
  Hatteras Motor Yachts
Convertibles
  Cabo
  Hatteras Convertibles
Pleasure Boats
  Meridian
  Sea Ray
Fishing Boats
  Boston Whaler
  Grady White
Ski Boats
  Axis
  Malibu

COMPETITORS

Bass Pro Shops	Lenco Marine
Coast Distribution	Wal-Mart
Defender Industries	West Marine
L.L. Bean	

HISTORICAL FINANCIALS

Company Type: Public

Income Statement   FYE: September 30

	REVENUE ($ mil.)	NET INCOME ($ mil.)	NET PROFIT MARGIN	EMPLOYEES
09/18	1,177.3	39.3	3.3%	1,573
09/17	1,052.3	23.5	2.2%	1,516
09/16	942.0	22.5	2.4%	1,422
09/15	751.3	48.2	6.4%	1,289
09/14	624.6	11.2	1.8%	1,228
Annual Growth	**17.2%**	**36.7%**	**—**	**6.4%**

2018 Year-End Financials

Debt ratio: 33.2%	No. of shares (mil.): 22.6
Return on equity: 12.0%	Dividends
Cash ($ mil.): 48.8	Yield: —
Current ratio: 1.63	Payout: —
Long-term debt ($ mil.): —	Market value ($ mil.): 482.0

	STOCK PRICE ($) FY Close	P/E High/Low		PER SHARE ($) Earnings	Dividends	Book Value
09/18	21.25	14	9	1.71	0.00	15.57
09/17	16.55	24	14	0.95	0.00	13.81
09/16	20.95	23	15	0.91	0.00	12.87
09/15	14.13	14	7	1.92	0.00	11.72
09/14	16.85	41	26	0.46	0.00	9.88
Annual Growth	**6.0%**	**—**	**—**	**38.9%**	**—**	**12.0%**

MarketAxess Holdings Inc.

A little creative spelling never got in the way of a good bond trade. MarketAxess offers an electronic multi-dealer platform for institutional traders buying and selling US corporate high-yield and emerging market bonds as well as Eurobonds. Participating broker-dealers include some of the world's largest such as BNP Paribas Citigroup Deutsche Bank Goldman Sachs and Merrill Lynch. In all MarketAxess serves more than 1000 investment firms mutual funds insurance companies pension funds and other institutional investors. The company also provides real-time corporate bond price information through its Corporate BondTicker service.

Operations

Nearly 85% of the company's revenue comes from monthly distribution fees and commissions for transactions executed on its platform between institutional investor and broker-dealer clients. About 10% of its revenue comes from its information and post-trade services from its Trax division (the trading name under Xtrakter Ltd.) which provides trade matching regulatory transaction reporting and market and reference data across a range of fixed income products. Less than 5% of its revenue comes from its technology products and services. MarketAxess had a staff of 303 employees at the end of 2014 with 187 of them based in teh US and the others mostly in the UK.

Geographic Reach

MarketAxess generates 85% of its revenue from the US while nearly all of the remainder comes from the UK. The company has office locations in the US UK Brazil and Singapore.

Sales and Marketing

To boost awareness of its brand and electronic trading platform MarketAxess uses advertising direct marketing promotional mailings and participates in industry conferences and media engagement. As an example it worked with The Wall Street Journal to make its Corporate BondTicker service the source of WSJ's information for its daily corporate bond and high-yield tables.

In the US high-grade corporate bond market more than 600 active institutional investors and 68 broker-dealers used MarketAxess' platform in

2014 including all of the top 20 broker-dealers as ranked by 2014 US corporate bond new-issue underwriting volume. The company's broker-dealer clients made up 96% of all underwriting activity for newly-issued corporate bonds in 2014.

Overall the firm spent $5.8 million on advertising in 2014 up 25% from $4.6 million spent in 2013.

Financial Performance

MarketAxess' revenues and profits have risen at a healthy clip over the past several years largely as the bond market has become more attractive to investors which has led to growth in both MarketAxess' commission income and information and post-trade services income.

The firm's revenue rose by 10% to $262.8 million in 2014 mostly thanks to commission income growth as trading activity in the bond market remained strong. Its revenue from its information and post-trade services also grew thanks to its 2013 acquisition of Xtrackter while favorable foreign currency exchange rates also added to the company's top-line growth.

Despite generating higher revenue in 2014 MarketAxess' net income dipped by 2% to $74.8 million for the year mostly because in 2013 it had enjoyed a $7.6 million (non-recurring) gain from its since-discontinued Greenline subsidiary. MarketAxess' operating cash levels jumped 21% to nearly $110 million in 2014 mostly as it generated higher cash earnings compared to the prior year.

Strategy

MarketAxess focuses on technology investments to expand its connectivity offerings for electronic transactions. Its main objective reiterated in 2015 is to "provide the leading global electronic trading platform for fixed-income securities connecting broker-dealers and institutional investors more easily and efficiently while offering a broad array of information trading and technology services to market participants across the trading cycle."

The strategy's key elements include: innovating and introducing new product offerings to the MarketAxess platform; leverage its existing client network to increase the number of potential counterparties and boost liquidity; continue to build on its existing service offerings to ensure that its platform is more full integrated into the workflow of its client base; and add new content and analytical capabilities to its Corporate BondTicker service.

The firm also fosters growth by entering strategic alliances or acquiring smaller marketplace firms to expand its service capabilities extend its market reach or bolsters its existing service expertise.

Mergers and Acquisitions

In February 2013 MarketAxess expanded its capacity when it acquired Xtrakter Limited a leading provider of regulatory transaction reporting financial market data and trade matching services to the European securities markets. The acquired company became MarketAxess' Trax division.

EXECUTIVES

Chairman President and CEO, Richard M. (Rick) McVey, age 59, $400,000 total compensation

CFO, Antonio L. (Tony) DeLise, age 56, $200,000 total compensation

CIO, Nicholas Themelis, age 55, $250,000 total compensation

Investor Relations, James N.B. (Jim) Rucker, $200,000 total compensation

Head of Marketing and Communications, Florencia Panizza

Head of US Sales, Kevin McPherson

Head Europe and Asia, Robert H. Urtheil
Vice President, Bill Barnett
Board Member, Steven Begleiter
Auditors: PricewaterhouseCoopers LLP

LOCATIONS

HQ: MarketAxess Holdings Inc.
299 Park Avenue, 10th Floor, New York, NY 10171
Phone: 212 813-6000   **Fax:** 212 813-6390
Web: www.marketaxess.com

PRODUCTS/OPERATIONS

2014 Sales

	$ mil.	% of total
Commissions	221.1	84
Information and post-trade services	31.5	12
Technology products and services	6.9	3
Investment income	0.5	-
Others	2.8	1
Total	**262.8**	**100**

Selected Mergers and Acquisitions

FY2012
Xtrakter Limited (undisclosed price; London UK; provider of regulatory transaction reporting)

COMPETITORS

BGC Partners	NEX
BondsOnline	TRADEBOOK
Cantor Fitzgerald	Tradeweb
GFI Group	Weeden
Interactive Brokers	
Intercontinental Exchange	

HISTORICAL FINANCIALS

Company Type: Public

Income Statement   FYE: December 31

	REVENUE ($ mil.)	NET INCOME ($ mil.)	NET PROFIT MARGIN	EMPLOYEES
12/17	397.4	148.0	37.3%	429
12/16	369.9	126.1	34.1%	383
12/15	303.1	96.0	31.7%	342
12/14	262.7	74.8	28.5%	303
12/13	238.7	76.0	31.8%	293
Annual Growth	13.6%	18.1%	—	10.0%

2017 Year-End Financials

Debt ratio: —	No. of shares (mil.): 37.6
Return on equity: 30.1%	Dividends
Cash ($ mil.): 167.0	Yield: 0.0%
Current ratio: 6.91	Payout: 33.9%
Long-term debt ($ mil.): —	Market value ($ mil.): 7,590.0

	STOCK PRICE ($) FY Close	P/E High/Low		PER SHARE ($) Earnings	Dividends	Book Value
12/17	201.75	52	37	3.89	1.32	13.68
12/16	146.92	51	30	3.34	1.04	12.47
12/15	111.59	44	26	2.55	0.80	10.44
12/14	71.71	36	23	2.03	0.64	8.96
12/13	66.93	34	17	2.01	1.82	8.23
Annual Growth	31.8%	—	—	17.9%	(7.7%)	13.6%

Marlin Business Services Corp

Marlin is hooked on equipment leasing. Marlin Business Services leases more than 100 categories of commercial equipment to about 68000 small and mid-sized businesses — and it provides the financing for the deals in part through its Marlin Business Bank subsidiary. The market is known in the equipment leasing field as the "small-ticket" segment. Copiers makes up about 30% of Marlin's lease portfolio but its customers also can get products as diverse as computer hardware and software security systems telecom equipment dental implant systems water filtration systems and restaurant equipment. The company primarily operates through its main subsidiary Marlin Leasing.

Operations

The "small-ticket" segment covers the leasing of equipment up to $250000 although Marlin's average equipment lease is about $14000 and runs 50 months (leases usually range from 36 to 60 months). Customers can opt to buy equipment at the end of the initial contracts. More than 95% of the company's transactions originate through almost 12000 independent commercial equipment dealers; Marlin also uses direct communications with customers and lease brokers. Financing is increasingly offered through Marlin Business Bank; in addition it has a close relationship with Wells Fargo's Capital Finance.

About three quarters of Marlin's revenue comes from interest it charges on equipment financing. Fee income accounts for 17% of revenue with insurance at 7%.

Geographic Reach

Although Marlin Leasing has customers in across the US its business follows population trends with California and Texas as its largest markets each accounting for between 9% and 13% of lease payments.

In addition it has offices in Colorado Georgia New Jersey New Hampshire Pennsylvania and Utah.

Sales and Marketing

Marlin uses both telephone direct sales and for strategic larger accounts a team of about 140 outside sales executives.

Financial Performance

Marlin's revenue ticked 1% higher to about $90 million in 2015 from 2014. In the low interest environment the company's interst income was flat while fee and insurance income revenues were higher.

The company's net income of about $16 million in 2015 was 17% lower than 2014's figure. The company had higher expenses to deal with the exits of the chief executive and financial officers while also paying for additional workers overall.

Cash flow from operations in 2015 slipped to about $27 million a 19% drop from 2014.

Strategy

In 2015 Marlin opened several new business channels added sales people and offered a working capital loan product. It also initiated a product called Funding Stream a flexible loan program of Marlin Business Bank.

Marlin prides itself on having a diverse portfolio while working to effectively manage credit risk. It

HISTORICAL FINANCIALS

Company Type: Public

Income Statement

FYE: September 30

	REVENUE ($ mil.)	NET INCOME ($ mil.)	NET PROFIT MARGIN	EMPLOYEES
09/18	1,602.5	107.3	6.7%	11,000
09/17	1,515.6	74.3	4.9%	11,000
09/16	1,480.4	66.7	4.5%	10,300
09/15	1,426.0	63.4	4.4%	10,300
09/14	1,106.6	43.6	3.9%	9,400
Annual Growth	9.7%	25.2%	—	4.0%

2018 Year-End Financials

Debt ratio: 40.4%	No. of shares (mil.): 32.0
Return on equity: 12.9%	Dividends
Cash ($ mil.): 41.5	Yield: 0.0%
Current ratio: 2.03	Payout: 22.5%
Long-term debt ($ mil.): 929.3	Market value ($ mil.): 1,609.0

	STOCK PRICE ($) FY Close	P/E High/Low		Earnings	PER SHARE ($) Dividends	Book Value
09/18	50.15	19	14	3.37	0.76	27.07
09/17	62.25	33	25	2.28	0.68	24.56
09/16	60.76	31	23	2.03	0.60	22.05
09/15	48.97	29	21	1.91	0.52	22.23
09/14	43.89	31	25	1.53	0.44	23.69
Annual Growth	3.4%	—	—	21.8%	14.6%	3.4%

Maui Land & Pineapple Co., Inc.

Aloha! Maui Land & Pineapple (ML&P) invites you to live and play on its Hawaiian island — Maui. Through its Kapalua Land Company subsidiary the company operates the 1650-acre Kapalua Resort on Maui's northwest coast. The resort includes a minority-owned Ritz-Carlton hotel as well as tennis and spa facilities residential homes and condos and shops and restaurants. ML&P also develops residential and commercial property on its 23000 acres surrounding the resort. Its Kapalua Realty Company is a general brokerage real estate firm located within the resort. The company additionally owns forest and nature preserves on the island. Formerly one of Hawaii's largest pineapple producers the company exited that business in 2009.

Revenues declined slightly in 2010 compared to 2009 because the company ceased to own The Kapalua Villas (vacation rental) and Kapalua Adventures (zip lines ropes course and other activities) choosing instead to lease those businesses to third party operators. However its net income soared to nearly $25 million up from a loss of more than $123 million. In 2010 ML&P gained on the sale of its Kapalua Plantation Golf Course as well as the termination of post-retirement plans for employees of discontinued operations. In addition due to the real estate crash and the subsequent decline in tourism the company lost considerable profits from its 51%-owned Bay Holdings in 2009. (Bay Holdings owns the Residences at

Kapalua Bay condos.) In order to cut costs ML&P eliminated more than 600 jobs in 2010 and 2009.

After David Cole resigned from his five-year stint as chairman and CEO at the end of 2008 the company split the functions appointing Warren Haruki (former president of GTE Hawaiian Tel and Verizon Hawaii) as chairman and Robert Webber as CEO. Months later Webber resigned. Haruki serves as chairman and interim CEO a position he has held since 2009.

Because of soaring oil and transportation costs ML&P exited the pineapple business in 2009 saying it could no longer sustain financial losses that threatened to destroy the company. It had grown pineapples on Maui for almost 100 years.

ML&P board member and AOL co-founder Steve Case owns more than 60% of the company. Through his Revolution LLC Case has a majority interest in Exclusive Resorts which has a 15% stake in Bay Holdings. Marriott International owns the remaining 34% of the condo project.

EXECUTIVES

Chairman and Interim CEO, Warren H. Haruki, age 63
President and COO, Ryan L. Churchill, $200,000 total compensation
CFO, Tim T. Esaki
Director, Walter A. Dods Jr., age 73
Director, Kent T. Lucien, age 62
Director, Stephen M. (Steve) Case
Director, Miles R. Gilburne, age 64
Director, David A. Heenan, age 75
Director, Fred E. Trotter III, age 84
Director, John H. Agee, age 66
Director, David C. Cole, age 62
Director, Duncan MacNaughton, age 72
Independent Director, Arthur Tokin
Auditors: Accuity LLP

LOCATIONS

HQ: Maui Land & Pineapple Co., Inc.
200 Village Road, Lahaina, Maui, HI 96761
Phone: 808 877-3351
Web: www.mauiland.com

COMPETITORS

Alexander & Baldwin	HTH Corporation
Barnwell Industries	Hilton Worldwide
Benchmark Hospitality	Outrigger Enterprises
Exclusive Resorts LLC	Sheraton Hotels
Four Seasons Hotels	

HISTORICAL FINANCIALS

Company Type: Public

Income Statement

FYE: December 31

	REVENUE ($ mil.)	NET INCOME ($ mil.)	NET PROFIT MARGIN	EMPLOYEES
12/17	24.3	10.9	44.7%	15
12/16	47.3	21.8	46.1%	17
12/15	22.7	6.8	29.9%	17
12/14	33.0	17.6	53.4%	17
12/13	15.2	(1.1)	—	19
Annual Growth	12.5%	—	—	(5.7%)

2017 Year-End Financials

Debt ratio: 2.7%	No. of shares (mil.): 19.0
Return on equity: 44.5%	Dividends
Cash ($ mil.): 1.0	Yield: —
Current ratio: 1.27	Payout: —
Long-term debt ($ mil.): 1.2	Market value ($ mil.): 329.0

	STOCK PRICE ($) FY Close	P/E High/Low		Earnings	PER SHARE ($) Dividends	Book Value
12/17	17.30	48	12	0.57	0.00	1.64
12/16	7.20	7	4	1.15	0.00	0.94
12/15	5.46	21	14	0.36	0.00	(0.58)
12/14	6.05	10	6	0.94	0.00	(0.81)
12/13	6.09	—	—	(0.06)	0.00	(1.45)
Annual Growth	29.8%	—	—	—		

MAXIMUS Inc.

MAXIMUS provides business services to help governments operate health and human services programs mostly at the state and national levels. The company?s health services segment offers outsourced program management and administrative services mainly to government agencies responsible for health and human services programs. MAXIMUS?s human services segment provides administrative and consulting support to welfare-to-work programs child support enforcement and higher education. A significant portion of the company?s revenue comes from the US federal government directly or indirectly.

Operations

MAXIMUS operates three segments: Health Services 60% of revenue and U.S. Federal Services and Human Services about 20% of revenue each.

MAXIMUS's Health Services segment offers outsourced program management and administrative services mainly to government agencies responsible for health and human services programs. These services support a variety of government health benefit programs including Medicaid the Children's Health Insurance Program (CHIP) and the Affordable Care Act (ACA) in the U.S. Health Insurance British Columbia in Canada and the Health Assessment Advisory Service (HAAS) contract in the UK.

The US Federal Services segment handles citizen engagement centers and support document and record management case management benefit appeals and IT services and support.

Its human services segment provides administrative and consulting support to welfare-to-work programs child support enforcement and higher education.

Geographic Reach

Headquartered in Virginia and operating through more than 400 offices MAXIMUS rings up more than 70% of its revenue from the US where the company has drawn clients from all 50 states. It also has won contracts in Australia Canada New Zealand Saudi Arabia and the UK.

Sales and Marketing

MAXIMUS's primary customers are government agencies mostly in the US (mostly state and federal agencies but some local governments as well) but also abroad. It typically contracts with government clients under four primary pricing arrangements namely performance-based cost-plus fixed-price and time-and-materials.

The company has a heavy concentration of revenue with four customers — the US Federal Government the UK Government the State of New York and the Australian Government — supplying about 55% of the total.

has a centralized collections department that assigns more experienced collectors to late-stage delinquent accounts and specialist collectors who focus on late fees property taxes bankruptcies and large balance accounts. While Marlin Business Bank is its primary funding source the company does have access to multiple funding sources.

EXECUTIVES

COO, Edward J. (Ed) Siciliano, age 56, $313,500 total compensation
SVP and CFO, W. Taylor Kamp, age 57, $111,919 total compensation
SVP Administration General Counsel and Secretary, Edward R. Dietz, age 43, $275,000 total compensation
CEO, Jeffrey A. Hilzinger
SVP and Chief Marketing Officer, Aswin Rajappa
Chairman, Lawrence J. (Larry) DeAngelo, age 51
Auditors: DELOITTE & TOUCHE LLP

LOCATIONS

HQ: Marlin Business Services Corp
300 Fellowship Road, Mount Laurel, NJ 08054
Phone: 888 479-9111
Web: www.marlincorp.com

PRODUCTS/OPERATIONS

2015 sales

	$ mil.	% of total
Interest	66.7	74
Fees	15.3	17
Insurance	5.9	7
Other	1.9	2
Total	**89.8**	**100**

COMPETITORS

American Express	KeyCorp
CalFirst	National Funding Inc
Citibank	Presidio Technology
Comerica	Capital
Deutsche Bank	Rabobank Group
HP Financial Services	Ricoh USA
IBM Global Financing	Wells Fargo
JPMorgan Chase	

HISTORICAL FINANCIALS

Company Type: Public

Income Statement

FYE: December 31

	REVENUE ($ mil.)	NET INCOME ($ mil.)	NET PROFIT MARGIN	EMPLOYEES
12/17	119.0	25.2	21.2%	330
12/16	100.0	17.2	17.3%	318
12/15	89.7	15.9	17.8%	314
12/14	88.7	19.3	21.8%	285
12/13	83.6	16.2	19.4%	285
Annual Growth	9.2%	11.7%	—	3.7%

2017 Year-End Financials

Debt ratio: —	No. of shares (mil.): 12.4
Return on equity: 14.7%	Dividends
Cash ($ mil.): 67.1	Yield: 0.0%
Current ratio: 0.12	Payout: 27.8%
Long-term debt ($ mil.): —	Market value ($ mil.): 279.0

Net income fell 56% to $131.6 million in 2017 as the company had higher costs of sales and operating expenses (primarily increased R&D expenses) related to its growing business.

The company ended 2017 with $315.5 million in net cash $7.3 million more than it had at the end of 2016. This was largely due to the decrease in net income. Operating activities provided $56.1 million in cash while investing activities used $47.9 million and financing activities used $4.1 million.

Strategy

Masimo's strategies for growth include expanding its presence in the pulse oximetry market getting its products into more types of patient care settings and selling more of its rainbow SET products and Root patient-monitoring products to hospitals and other care settings. The company's R&D efforts focus on novel products as well as improvement to existing products. It is expanding the applications of its rainbow products which measure multiple blood components at once; it is also adding products that reduce the invasiveness of testing and that provide remote monitoring and alarm capabilities.

To branch out beyond its traditionally targeted emergency and critical care setting markets Masimo is promoting existing products (and adding new products) to meet the general treatment needs of hospitals and non-hospital environments. For example the company is promoting its SET technology as ideal for use by home care agencies post-acute care hospitals and sleep diagnostic centers. It has also launched new handheld products that allow for fast and simple measurement of perimeters in a variety of care settings. The company expects moves such as these to greatly expand its presence in non-critical care markets.

Masimo also expands by entering new OEM licensing agreements; by widening agreements with wholesale distributors; and by making occasional acquisitions.

However the company is somewhat slow to breaking into new niches which has made it lose a bit of its market share to new competitors.

EXECUTIVES

Chairman and CEO, Joe E. Kiani, age 54, $883,518 total compensation
EVP and CIO, Yongsam Lee, age 54, $340,704 total compensation
President Worldwide OEM Business and Blood Management, Rick Fishel, age 60, $357,574 total compensation
EVP Business Development, Paul R. Jansen, age 47
COO, Anand Sampath, age 52, $369,277 total compensation
EVP Finance and CFO, Mark P. de Raad, age 58, $363,034 total compensation
EVP General Counsel and Corporate Secretary, Tom McClenahan, age 45
President Masimo Worldwide Sales Professional Services and Medical Affairs, Jon Coleman, age 54, $354,103 total compensation
VP Quality, Glenn Pohly
Regional Vice President, Michelle Hahn
Vice President Information Systems, Mark Brinton
Global Vice President Of Sales, Brad Snow
Senior Vice President, Dan Brothman
Executive Vice President, Raul Bennis
VP Business Development, Eli Kammerman
Vice President Oem Business, Nikolai Marinow
Vice President Global Government Affairs, Jim Bialick

Masimo Corp.

As important as the blood running through your veins is the oxygen it carries. Masimo knows that and makes tools that monitor arterial blood-oxygen saturation levels and pulse rates in patients. The company's product range which is based on Signal Extraction Technology (SET) offers pulse oximeters in both handheld and stand-alone (bedside) form. Product benefits include the provision of real-time information and elimination of signal interference such as patient movements. In addition to general product sales Masimo licenses SET-based products to dozens of medical equipment manufacturers including Philips Atom Mindray North America GE Medical Medtronic Spacelabs and Zoll.

Operations

Masimo's primary products include patient monitoring solutions sensor products and other devices and accessories such as adapter cables. The company also makes revenue on royalties.

Geographic Reach

While the US accounts for about two-thirds of its product sales Masimo is working to grow its operations in Africa Asia Australia Europe and the Middle East.

The company has locations in Switzerland Canada and Japan as well as two manufacturing facilities in Mexico.

Sales and Marketing

Masimo markets its products globally through direct sales representatives and distributors. Customers include hospitals alternative care entities and wholesalers. Two distributors Owens & Minor and Cardinal Health each account for more than 10% of annual sales.

The company has partnerships with several group purchasing organizations (GPOs) to facilitate increased direct sales of pulse oximetry products to hospitals.

Advertising costs for fiscal 2017 totaled $12.8 million compared to around $11 million in 2016.

Financial Performance

Masimo's revenues have been rising steadily for the past five years as product sales have grown. However net income has been more volatile rising significantly in 2016 due to a $270000 settlement award but falling back down the following year.

In 2017 revenue increased 15% to $798.1 million. Both product sales across all geographic segments and royalty income rose that year. The company's base of installed circuit boards and pulse oximeters nearly reached 1.6 million units a 6% increase for 2017. With that higher base sales of consumable and reusable sensor products also increased.

	STOCK PRICE ($) FY Close	P/E High/Low		Earnings	PER SHARE ($) Dividends	Book Value
12/17	22.40	15	10	2.01	0.56	14.43
12/16	20.90	16	10	1.38	0.56	12.91
12/15	16.06	17	10	1.25	2.53	12.10
12/14	20.53	19	11	1.49	0.47	13.55
12/13	25.20	22	15	1.25	2.42	12.55
Annual Growth	(2.9%)	—	—	12.6%	(30.6%)	3.6%

Regional Vice President Strategic Accounts, Jodie Pellerin
Regional Vice President Texas Region, Billy Clark
Auditors: GRANT THORNTON LLP

LOCATIONS

HQ: Masimo Corp.
52 Discovery, Irvine, CA 92618
Phone: 949 297-7000
Web: www.masimo.com

PRODUCTS/OPERATIONS

2017 Sales

	$ mil.	% of total
Products	741.3	93
Royalties	56.8	7
Total	**798.1**	**100**

COMPETITORS

Bio-logic
CAS Medical
Criticare
GE Healthcare
Medtronic

HISTORICAL FINANCIALS

Company Type: Public

Income Statement — FYE: December 30

	REVENUE ($ mil.)	NET INCOME ($ mil.)	NET PROFIT MARGIN	EMPLOYEES
12/17	798.1	131.6	16.5%	4,600
12/16*	694.6	300.6	43.3%	4,293
01/16	630.1	83.3	13.2%	3,700
01/15	586.6	72.5	12.4%	3,600
12/13	547.2	58.3	10.7%	3,139
Annual Growth	9.9%	22.5%	—	10.0%

*Fiscal year change

2017 Year-End Financials

Debt ratio: —
Return on equity: 20.8%
Cash ($ mil.): 315.3
Current ratio: 3.72
Long-term debt ($ mil.): —
No. of shares (mil.): 51.6
Dividends
Yield: —
Payout: —
Market value ($ mil.): 4,379.0

	STOCK PRICE ($) FY Close	P/E High/Low	PER SHARE ($) Earnings	Dividends	Book Value
12/17	84.80	41 26	2.36	0.00	13.69
12/16*	67.40	11 6	5.65	0.00	11.16
01/16	41.51	27 16	1.55	0.00	5.52
01/15	25.88	24 16	1.30	0.00	5.82
12/13	28.86	29 18	1.02	0.00	5.77
Annual Growth	30.9%	— —	23.3%	—	24.1%

*Fiscal year change

MasterCraft Boat Holdings Inc

Auditors: BDO USA, LLP

LOCATIONS

HQ: MasterCraft Boat Holdings Inc
100 Cherokee Cove Drive, Vonore, TN 37885
Phone: 423 884-2221
Web: www.mastercraft.com

HISTORICAL FINANCIALS

Company Type: Public

Income Statement — FYE: June 30

	REVENUE ($ mil.)	NET INCOME ($ mil.)	NET PROFIT MARGIN	EMPLOYEES
06/18	332.7	39.6	11.9%	882
06/17	228.6	19.5	8.6%	490
06/16	221.6	10.2	4.6%	510
06/15	214.3	5.5	2.6%	470
06/14	177.5	19.9	11.2%	475
Annual Growth	17.0%	18.8%	—	16.7%

2018 Year-End Financials

Debt ratio: 42.4%
Return on equity: 123.3%
Cash ($ mil.): 7.9
Current ratio: 0.73
Long-term debt ($ mil.): 70.0
No. of shares (mil.): 18.6
Dividends
Yield: —
Payout: —
Market value ($ mil.): 541.0

	STOCK PRICE ($) FY Close	P/E High/Low	PER SHARE ($) Earnings	Dividends	Book Value
06/18	28.95	15 8	2.12	0.00	2.81
06/17	19.55	19 10	1.05	0.00	0.63
06/16	11.05	28 18	0.56	4.30	(0.45)
Annual Growth	61.9%	— —	94.6%	—	—

Matador Resources Co

Auditors: KPMG LLP

LOCATIONS

HQ: Matador Resources Co
5400 LBJ Freeway, Suite 1500, Dallas, TX 75240
Phone: 972 371-5200
Web: www.matadorresources.com

HISTORICAL FINANCIALS

Company Type: Public

Income Statement — FYE: December 31

	REVENUE ($ mil.)	NET INCOME ($ mil.)	NET PROFIT MARGIN	EMPLOYEES
12/17	544.2	125.8	23.1%	217
12/16	264.4	(97.4)	—	165
12/15	316.1	(679.7)	—	151
12/14	431.0	110.7	25.7%	99
12/13	260.8	45.0	17.3%	66
Annual Growth	20.2%	29.3%	—	34.7%

2017 Year-End Financials

Debt ratio: 26.7%
Return on equity: 13.6%
Cash ($ mil.): 102.4
Current ratio: 0.91
Long-term debt ($ mil.): 574.0
No. of shares (mil.): 108.5
Dividends
Yield: —
Payout: —
Market value ($ mil.): 3,378.0

	STOCK PRICE ($) FY Close	P/E High/Low	PER SHARE ($) Earnings	Dividends	Book Value
12/17	31.13	25 17	1.23	0.00	10.66
12/16	25.76	— —	(1.07)	0.00	6.94
12/15	19.77	— —	(8.34)	0.00	5.70
12/14	20.23	19 9	1.56	0.00	11.81
12/13	18.64	31 10	0.77	0.00	8.67
Annual Growth	13.7%	— —	12.4%	—	5.3%

Match Group Inc

Auditors: Ernst & Young LLP

LOCATIONS

HQ: Match Group Inc
8750 North Central Expressway, Suite 1400, Dallas, TX 75231
Phone: 214 576-9352
Web: www.matchgroupinc.com

HISTORICAL FINANCIALS

Company Type: Public

Income Statement — FYE: December 31

	REVENUE ($ mil.)	NET INCOME ($ mil.)	NET PROFIT MARGIN	EMPLOYEES
12/17	1,330.6	350.1	26.3%	1,400
12/16	1,222.5	171.4	14.0%	5,100
12/15	1,020.4	120.3	11.8%	4,800
12/14	888.2	147.7	16.6%	4,800
12/13	803.0	125.0	15.6%	0
Annual Growth	13.5%	29.4%	—	—

2017 Year-End Financials

Debt ratio: 58.8%
Return on equity: 70.1%
Cash ($ mil.): 272.6
Current ratio: 1.40
Long-term debt ($ mil.): 1,252.7
No. of shares (mil.): 274.2
Dividends
Yield: —
Payout: —
Market value ($ mil.): 8,588.0

	STOCK PRICE ($) FY Close	P/E High/Low	PER SHARE ($) Earnings	Dividends	Book Value
12/17	31.31	24 12	1.18	0.00	1.83
12/16	17.10	29 13	0.64	0.00	1.94
12/15	13.55	22 19	0.65	0.00	1.12
Annual Growth	52.0%	— —	34.7%	—	27.6%

Matthews International Corp

Matthews International might not bury its competition but it can supply the casket and bronze marker. One of the nation's leading makers of cremation equipment and urns bronze memorials (including Elvis Presley's Graceland marker) metal and wood caskets and commemorative products (Baseball Hall of Fame plaques) Matthews also builds mausoleums. In addition it provides graphic imaging products and services for the consumer packaging and retail industries as well as merchandising services and marking and fulfillment systems. Matthews has operations in Asia Australia Canada and Europe but the US accounts for more than 60% of its sales.

Operations

Within its two major divisions — Memorialization and Brand Solutions — Matthews breaks its offerings down into six areas: cemetery products funeral home products cremation graphics imaging merchandising solutions and marking and fulfillment systems. Graphics imaging contributes the most to overall revenue some 35% with cemetery products and funeral home products each accounting for about 20%.

Geographic Reach

The US and Europe represent Matthews' largest markets accounting for more than 60% and about 35% of sales respectively. Other markets include Asia Australia and Canada. It has facilities in the US as well as in Austria Australia Belgium Canada China Germany Hong Kong Hungary Italy Malaysia Mexico the Netherlands Poland Singapore Sweden Turkey and the UK.

Sales and Marketing

The company's memorialization products are sold primarily to cemeteries memorial parks and funeral homes as well as corporations hospitals schools and other organizations. Brand solutions product and services are marketed to customers in the consumer packaged goods and retail industries.

Financial Performance

Matthews has seen sales rise in recent years. The company attributes the gains to higher sales volume within its Brand Solutions business and timely boosts from acquisitions. In 2014 revenue crossed the billion dollar mark up 12% to $1.1 billion. Although memorialization sales were down 2% as the number of casketed in-ground burials declines brand solutions sales powered by the mid-2014 acquisition of Schawk (which it renamed SGK LLC) were up a healthy 28%.

Net income and cash flow from operations however were both down as selling and administrative expenses rose significantly boosted by acquisition activity.

Strategy

Much of the company's recent growth has been an expansion of its brand solutions business which has grown from 45% of sales in 2012 to 54% in 2014. Matthews plans to extend those services globally (both organically and through acquisitions) so it can cater to multinational clients.

Mergers and Acquisitions

In 2014 Matthews made its largest acquisition to date with the purchase of Schawk (SGK). The deal valued at more than $570 million combines Matthews' brand solutions expertise in Europe with Schawk's experience in the US and Asia.

In mid-2015 the company purchased former rival casket and urn maker Aurora Casket Company for $214 million.

HISTORY

John Matthews began making stencils signs and steel stamps in 1850. Two of his sons joined his company in 1861; they renamed it Jas. H. Matthews Co. in 1894 after the youngest. The company developed the first vulcanized rubber printing plate in 1912 and began marking corrugated shipping containers. In 1927 it applied its plaque-making ability which it had been using for plaques to adorn buildings to make America's first flush bronze memorial plaque mounted in a Florida cemetery.

The company changed its name to Matthews International in 1976 to reflect its presence in other countries. Five years later it purchased the Sunland Memorial Park and Mortuary in Arizona to learn more about customers' needs. Matthews went public in 1994; sales continued to climb steadily.

In 1995 David Kelly joined the company as president and COO; he became CEO six months later and was elected chairman in 1996. That year Matthews sold its cemetery (3% of total revenues) and started expanding its product offerings and geographic markets through acquisitions beginning with its purchase of Industrial Equipment and Engineering Company in 1996. Acquisitions in 1997 and 1998 (such as Gibraltar Mausoleum Construction) expanded its graphics and memorial businesses. In 1999 the company acquired Europe's leading supplier of bronze memorialization products Caggiati SpA.

Matthews acquired The York Group the second-largest US casket maker in December 2001. A Federal Trade Commission inquiry regarding that acquisition was closed in late 2002 with no action taken.

Matthews boosted its marking products capabilities in July 2004 when it acquired Holjeron Corporation an Oregon-based industrial controls manufacturer. The same month Matthews acquired merchandising solutions provider Cloverleaf Group (formerly iDL and Big Red Rooster) to expand its presence in that market. In late 2004 the company purchased The InTouch Group a European reprographics firm. The next year Matthews expanded its Casket Division picking up Milso Industries to work alongside York.

In 2005 Matthews appointed group president David DeCarlo to the newly-created role of vice chairman and EVP Joseph Bartolacci as president and COO. In July the firm completed the acquisition of Milso Industries now a wholly-owned subsidiary of Matthews belonging to its casket division.

David Kelly remained as chairman and CEO. The next year Bartolacci replaced Kelly as CEO.

In May 2008 Matthews acquired a 78% stake in Saueressig GmbH & Co. a leading European provider of prepress and gravure printing forms based in Vreden Germany. Saueressig has manufacturing operations in Germany Poland and England. Saueressig operates as a subsidiary of the firm's Graphics Imaging Group. In December Matthews purchased a small European cremation equipment manufacturer.

In December 2009 the firm bought California-based United Memorial Products a leading supplier of granite memorial products burial vaults and caskets in the western US.

In April 2010 Matthews acquired Reynoldsville Casket Co. The Pennsylvania-based company makes and distributes caskets primarily in the Northeast.

EXECUTIVES

CFO and Secretary, Steven F. Nicola, age 57, $475,692 total compensation
EVP Strategy and Corporate Development, Brian J. Dunn, age 60, $374,365 total compensation
CTO and Director, Gregory S. (Greg) Babe, age 60
President and CEO, Joseph C. Bartolacci, age 57, $800,267 total compensation
President Environmental Solutions, Paul F. Rahill, age 60, $188,350 total compensation
Group President Memorialization, Steven D. Gackenbach, age 54, $380,827 total compensation
President SGK Brand Solutions, Gary R. Kohl
Vice President, Cindy Mills
Executive Vice President Strategic Initiatives, Joe Bozada
Vice President and General Manager, Michael Baklarz
VICE PRESIDENT GENERAL MANAGER, Terry Porter
Vice President, John Standard
Chairman, John D. Turner, age 72
Treasurer, Robert Marsh
Auditors: Ernst & Young LLP

LOCATIONS

HQ: Matthews International Corp
Two Northshore Center, Pittsburgh, PA 15212-5851
Phone: 412 442-8200
Web: www.matw.com

PRODUCTS/OPERATIONS

2014 Sales

	$ mil.	% of total
Memorialization		
Funeral home	234.6	21
Cremetery	222.0	20
Cremation	51.8	5
Brand Solutions		
Graphic Imaging	398.2	36
Marking and Fullfilment Systems	100.9	9
Merchandising Solutions	99.1	9
Total	**1,106.6**	**100**

Selected Products

Bronze
- Commemorative and identification plaques
- Crypt letters and plates
- Flower vases
- Flush bronze memorials
- Granite benches
- Mausoleums
- Statuary

Caskets
- Corrugated
- Metal
- Particle board
- Wood

Cremation
- Cremation gardens
- Cremation memorials and urns
- Cremation niche systems
- Crematories

Graphic Systems
- Imaging systems
- Prepress services
- Printing plates (bar codes logos identification)
- Rotary and flat cutting dies

Marking Products
- Cleaners
- Hand stamps
- Ink-jet printing systems
- Inks
- Laser-marking equipment
- Solvents

Merchandising Solutions
- Brand concept shops
- Custom packaging
- Custom store fixtures
- Graphic design
- Interactive kiosks
- Model development
- Permanent displays
- Promotional signage
- Prototyping
- Temporary displays

COMPETITORS

Batesville Casket
Cold Spring Granite
DIC Corporation
Eastman Kodak
International Imaging Materials
Rock of Ages
Service Corporation International
Wilbert

Financial Performance

MAXIMUS?s revenue trended steadily higher for four years until it dipped 2% in 2018 (ended September). The company?s income growth outpaced revenue increasing 10% a year since 2014.

Revenue was $2.4 billion in 2018 down about $59 million from 2017. The Health Services segment supplied 2% growth with help from State of New York contracts and improvement in performance in the HAAS contract in the UK. The company blamed a 12% revenue drop in the Federal Services unit on contracts that came to an end. Contracts that closed also contributed to a 3% decline in Human Services revenue.

Cost reductions and a tax benefit from the US Tax Cuts and Jobs Act pushed net income 5% higher to $220.8 million in 2018 from 2017.

MAXIMUS reported it had about $349 million in cash and equivalents at the end of 2018 about $120 million more than in 2017. Operating activities generated $134.5 million in 2018 while investing activities used $4.9 million and financing activities used $8.4 million.

In recent years MAXIMUS used cash flow from operations in fiscal years 2016 and 2017 to reduce debt which had been incurred with the acquisitions and its interest expenses.

Strategy

MAXIMUS pursues contracts with long-term and recurring revenue believing than an incumbent has a better chance of re-winning contracts. It also makes acquisitions to expand its services offering.

MAXIMUS?s 2018 acquisition of the citizen engagement centers of General Dynamics Information Technology unit provides greater size and scope to the company helping it compete with larger rivals. The deal enables greater economies of scale and brings technology and operational capabilities that could benefit other parts of the MAXIMUS portfolio. The scale makes MAXIMUS a more viable prime contractor to the US federal government and reduces the company?s need to partner with other companies to win contracts. The acquisition increases its competitiveness on procurement in the federal marketplace.

Two large-scale contracts included in the deal provide MAXIMUS with the contact center operations for the Centers for Medicare and Medicaid Services and operation support and citizen engagement centers for the 2020 US census.

The timing of contracts which can produce less revenue at beginning and end can make the company?s revenue uneven.

Mergers and Acquisitions

MAXIMUS paid $400 million buy General Dynamics Information Technology?s large-scale citizen-engagement centers in the US. The acquisition is expected to strengthen MAXIMUS?s position in the administration of federal government programs across the US.

Company Background

David Mastran who worked for the Department of Health Education and Welfare during the Nixon administration founded MAXIMUS in 1975. The company's name comes from its goal of maximizing US government efficiency. MAXIMUS went public in 1997.

The company has grown through acquisitions throughout its history continuing through 2018 (calendar year) when it acquired citizen engagement centers from General Dynamics Information Technology business for $400 million.

EXECUTIVES

Vice Chairman, Richard A. (Rich) Montoni, age 67, $725,000 total compensation
Chief of Human Capital, Mark S. Andrekovich, age 57, $395,000 total compensation
CFO and Treasurer, Richard J. Nadeau, $425,000 total compensation
CEO, Bruce L. Caswell, age 52, $487,500 total compensation
General Manager Human Services, Akbar Piloti, age 61, $410,000 total compensation
CIO, Kelly L. Clark
Vice President, Lisa Simmons
Senior Vice President, John Walz
Vice President, Viann Hardy
Vice President, Kelly Blaschke
Vice President, Nelson Clugston
Vice President UK Information Technology, Beverly Smith
Vice President Human Resources, Nick Figurelli
Vice President Technology Maximus Information, Kevan McCallum
Vice President, Adam Polatnick
Senior Vice President Global Human Resources, Catalina Murillo
Senior Vice President Technology Strategy and Solutions, Raj Parameswaran
Vice President, Jon Lemelin
Vice President Healthcare Services Business Develo, John Crouse
MPH Vice President Center For Health Literacy, Kinte Ibbott
Vice President, Tricia Belman
Vice President Information Security Management and Assurance, Vicki Cippus
VICE PRESIDENT, Fatima Mccasland
VICE PRESIDENT FINANCIAL SERVICE, Randall Phillips
Chairman, Peter B. Pond, age 73
Board Member, Russell Beliveau
Auditors: Ernst & Young LLP

LOCATIONS

HQ: MAXIMUS Inc.
1891 Metro Center Drive, Reston, VA 20190
Phone: 703 251-8500
Web: www.maximus.com

PRODUCTS/OPERATIONS

2018 Sales

	% of total
Health Services	59
US Federal Services	20
Human Services	21
Total	**100**

COMPETITORS

Accenture	IBM
Atos	LEIDOS INC.
CACI International	Oracle
Capita	SAP
Conduent	United Way
Goodwill Industries	

HISTORICAL FINANCIALS

Company Type: Public

Income Statement

FYE: September 30

	REVENUE ($ mil.)	NET INCOME ($ mil.)	NET PROFIT MARGIN	EMPLOYEES
09/18	2,392.2	220.7	9.2%	21,051
09/17	2,450.9	209.4	8.5%	20,400
09/16	2,403.3	178.3	7.4%	18,800
09/15	2,099.8	157.7	7.5%	17,000
09/14	1,700.9	145.4	8.6%	13,000
Annual Growth	8.9%	11.0%	—	12.8%

2018 Year-End Financials

Debt ratio: —	No. of shares (mil.): 64.3
Return on equity: 21.8%	Dividends
Cash ($ mil.): 349.2	Yield: 0.0%
Current ratio: 2.91	Payout: 5.3%
Long-term debt ($ mil.): —	Market value ($ mil.): 4,188.0

	STOCK PRICE ($) FY Close	P/E High/Low	PER SHARE ($) Earnings	Dividends	Book Value
09/18	65.06	21 18	3.35	0.18	16.84
09/17	64.50	20 14	3.17	0.18	14.43
09/16	56.56	26 17	2.69	0.18	11.48
09/15	59.56	29 16	2.35	0.18	9.36
09/14	40.13	23 18	2.11	0.18	8.35
Annual Growth	12.8%	— —	12.3%	(0.0%)	19.2%

MB Financial Inc

The "MB" in MB Financial doesn't stand for "Midsized Businesses" though that's its target market. The $16 billion-asset holding company owns MB Financial Bank which has about 80 branches in the Chicago area and one in Philadelphia. Commercial-related credits including mortgages operating loans lease financing and construction loans make up 85% of the bank's loan portfolio. In addition to serving small and middle-market businesses MB Financial provides retail banking and lending to consumers. The company also offers wealth management and trust services through its Cedar Hill Associates subsidiary and brokerage through Vision Investment Services. LaSalle Systems leases technology-related equipment to corporations.

Operations

MB Financial operates three main business segments: Banking which counts its deposit and lending activities; Leasing which originates leases and related services through subsidiaries LaSalle Systems Leasing Celtic Leasing Corp and MB Equipment Finance; and Mortgage Banking which originates and services residential mortgage loans to hold in its portfolio or list for sale to investors via retail or third party channels.

Broadly speaking about 54% of the bank's total revenue came from loan interest during 2015 while another 10% came from interest on its investment securities. The rest of its revenue came from mortgage banking revenue (13% of revenue) lease financing (9%) commercial deposits and treasury management fees (6%) trust and asset management fees (3%) card fees (2%) capital markets and international banking fees (1%) and other miscellaneous fee sources.

Geographic Reach

Beyond its 80 branches in Chicago and one branch in Philadelphia MB Financial boasts 39 mortgage retail offices in 18 states.

Sales and Marketing

MB Financial mostly targets small and middle market businesses and individuals. The bank spent $10.07 million on advertising during 2015 up 14% from the $8.85 million it spent in 2014.

Financial Performance

The bank's annual revenues have risen more than 65% since 2011 thanks to a combination of mortgage banking revenue growth and steady loan business growth driven by bank acquisitions. Its profits have quintupled over the same time period as a result.

MB Financial's revenue jumped 37% to $816 million during 2015 mostly driven by strong loan business and mortgage banking revenue growth both stemming from the full-year results of its 2014 acquisition of Taylor Capital.

Double-digit revenue growth in 2015 drove the bank's net income up 85% to $159 million for the year. MB Financial's operating cash levels climbed 23% to $205 million as cash earnings rose in 2015.

Strategy

MB Financial mainly pursues growth by acquiring banks and other financial companies to expand its branch network across its target geographies and boost its loan and deposit business. Other strategies for growth include expanding its private banking and asset managements operations as well as its fee-based business services including treasury management and leasing.

Mergers and Acquisitions

In mid-2016 MB Financial bought American Chartered Bancorp— along with its 15 American Chartered Bank branches in the Chicago-area $2.8 billion in assets and $2.2 billion in deposits -- in a deal valued at $449 million.

In December 2015 the company expanded its investment management and trust business after buying MSA along with its MainStreet and Cambium subsidiaries. MainStreet which boated $2.9 billion in assets under management (AUM) provided investment management services to the bank trust and independent trust markets while Cambium ($109 million in AUM) was a registered investment advisor that served affluent individuals and institutions.

In August 2014 MB Financial completed its $649-million acquisition of Rosemont Illinois-based Taylor Capital Group the holding company for Cole Taylor Bank (CTB). With $5.7 billion in assets and some 10 branches in the Chicago metro area CTB was merged with MB Financial Bank. Like its acquirer CTB is a commercial bank focused on the middle market.

Company Background

Taking advantage of the dozens of bank failures in 2009 MB Financial acquired Heritage Community Bank InBank Corus Bank and Benchmark Bank in separate FDIC-assisted transactions. In 2010 it acquired failed Chicago-area institutions Broadway Bank and New Century Bank in similar deals. Gains on these acquisitions helped the company's revenues (and profits) grow in 2010. Although the company didn't have the benefit of gains on acquisitions in 2011 (and revenues fell 20% to $493.7 million) profits continued to climb

that year growing 89% to $38.7 million largely due to a lowered provision for loan losses. Also that year the bank got millions of dollars of non-performing loans off of its books via a sale to Colony Capital.

EXECUTIVES

President and CEO, Mitchell S. Feiger, age 59, $895,308 total compensation

Chairman MB Financial Bank, Ronald D. Santo, age 75, $321,741 total compensation

EVP Credit Management MB Financial Bank, Mark A. Heckler, age 54, $293,077 total compensation

EVP Commercial Banking MB Financial Bank, Edward F. Milefchik, age 53

EVP MB Financial Bank; President MB Business Capital, Michael D. Sharkey, age 64, $456,923 total compensation

EVP and Chief Credit Officer, Michael J. Morton, age 55

President and CEO MB Financial Bank, Mark A. Hoppe, age 64, $726,923 total compensation

EVP Wealth Management Card Services Leasing and Indirect Lending, Jill E. York, age 54, $489,461 total compensation

VP MB Financial Inc. and EVP Administration MB Financial Bank, Rosemarie Bouman, age 61, $287,846 total compensation

EVP Commercial Banking, Lawrence G. Ryan, age 59

VP and CFO MB Financial Inc. and EVP COO and CFO MB Financial Bank N.A., Randall T. Conte, age 57, $451,731 total compensation

EVP Risk Management and Chief Risk Officer MB Financial Bank N.A., Brian J. Wildman, age 55, $292,846 total compensation

Vice President, Michael Scarsella

First Vice President, Priscilla Rodriguez

First Vice President, Mike Markovitz

Vice President Item Processing Manager, Veronica McGowan

Vice President Risk Management, Irene Remeniuk

Vice President, Kathy Grele

Senior Vice President and Division Manager Commercial Banking, Scott Mier

Assistant Vice President Commercial Bank, Nick Cox

First Vice President, Michael Lynch

Vice President Digital Marketing, Michelle Y Finch

Vice President Commercial Banking, Michael Salvador

Senior Vice President, Judy Hill

Vice President Compliance Manager, Kevin Osborn

Assistant Vice President Asset Manager, Brian Nagorsky

Senior Vice President and Division Manager, Jerry Kallio

Vice President, Rick J Chang

Assistant Vice President Employee Relations Office, Katie Drinan Allberry

Senior Vice President Managed Assets Division Mananger, Mary Alberts

Vice President Collateral Manager, Lisette Alamo

Vice President, Anthony Gattuso

Senior Vice President Finance Reporting Budgeting, John Francoeur

Senior Vice President, Jennifer Brogan

Vice President Business Banking, Robert Baitler

Vice President Business Banking, Jim Marshall

Assistant Vice President Marketing Communications Manager, Diane Shaughnessy

Senior Vice President, Greg Urban

Vice President Treasury Management Sales, Eloy Hodges

Vice President, Sandra Biske

Vice President Business Bankin, Steve Grabavoy

Vice President Quality Assurance Manager, Chris Hicks

Assistant Vice President Compensation, Cindy Katsikas

Vice President Business Banking, Sam Elhaj

Assistant Vice President Banking Center Manager, Galina Veksler

Vice President Marketing Manager, Megan Garr

Assistant Vice President, Brenda Allen

Senior Vice President and Division Head, Christina Bavery

Assistant Vice President Quality Control Manager, Margie Acevedo

First Vice President Chief Appraiser, Mitchell Zaveduk

Assistant Vice President Bsa Aml Loss Prevention Management, Michelle Mercer

Assistant Vice President Compensation And Benefits, Catherine Nacpil

Vice President of Managed Assets, Mike Pindak

Assistant Vice President Marketing And Crm Administrator, Cari Dam

Senior Vice President Division Head, Thomas Moran

Senior Vice President Lease Banking, Dennis Roesslein

First Vice President Regional Division M, Deborah Wheeler

Senior Vice President Lease Banking, Stewart Kapnick

Senior Vice President, Melissa Bleiweis

Vice President Commercial Banking, Dawn Lauderdale

Senior Vice President, Mitch Morgenstern

Assistant Vice President Accounting Manager, Patricia Basan

Senior Vice President Human Resources, Laura Entwistle

First Vice President, Thomas Carmody

Senior Vice President Operations, Pete Steger

Senior Vice President Overseeing Credit, Jennifer Rosenberg

Senior Vice President Corporate Controller, David Emerson

Senior Vice President, Adam Garrett

Senior Vice President Senior Audit Manager, Julie Greco

Vice President Senior Field Credit Officer, Brian Monson

Vice President Treasury Management Solutions Group, Jeffrey Malek

Vice President Treasury Management Solutions Group, Isela Calabrese

Senior Vice President CRA Fair Lending Program Manager, Mary Boetel

Assistant Vice President, Manal Sughayer

Vice President Banking Center Manager, Karen Franciere

Assistant Vice President Treas, Luke Chesick

Senior Vice President Field Risk Officer Enterprise Risk Management and Op Risk, Patricia K Bartler

Vice President Marketing, Debranne Santucci

Vice President Banking Center Manager, Enrique Arroyo

Senior Vice President, Eric Staczek

Vice President Banking Center Manager, Fran Barker

Assistant Vice President Operations, Jackie Schmitz

Senior Vice President, Lisa Gibbs

Assistant Vice President Customer Solutions Specialist, Lori Rottmuller

Senior Vice President, Martha Gaskin

Senior Vice President Commercial Banking, Matt Stefani

Senior Vice President, Mark Staunton

has a centralized collections department that assigns more experienced collectors to late-stage delinquent accounts and specialist collectors who focus on late fees property taxes bankruptcies and large balance accounts. While Marlin Business Bank is its primary funding source the company does have access to multiple funding sources.

EXECUTIVES

COO, Edward J. (Ed) Siciliano, age 56, $313,500 total compensation
SVP and CFO, W. Taylor Kamp, age 57, $111,919 total compensation
SVP Administration General Counsel and Secretary, Edward R. Dietz, age 43, $275,000 total compensation
CEO, Jeffrey A. Hilzinger
SVP and Chief Marketing Officer, Aswin Rajappa
Chairman, Lawrence J. (Larry) DeAngelo, age 51
Auditors: DELOITTE & TOUCHE LLP

LOCATIONS

HQ: Marlin Business Services Corp
300 Fellowship Road, Mount Laurel, NJ 08054
Phone: 888 479-9111
Web: www.marlincorp.com

PRODUCTS/OPERATIONS

2015 sales

	$ mil.	% of total
Interest	66.7	74
Fees	15.3	17
Insurance	5.9	7
Other	1.9	2
Total	**89.8**	**100**

COMPETITORS

American Express	KeyCorp
CalFirst	National Funding Inc
Citibank	Presidio Technology
Comerica	Capital
Deutsche Bank	Rabobank Group
HP Financial Services	Ricoh USA
IBM Global Financing	Wells Fargo
JPMorgan Chase	

HISTORICAL FINANCIALS

Company Type: Public

Income Statement

FYE: December 31

	REVENUE ($ mil.)	NET INCOME ($ mil.)	NET PROFIT MARGIN	EMPLOYEES
12/17	119.0	25.2	21.2%	330
12/16	100.0	17.2	17.3%	318
12/15	89.7	15.9	17.8%	314
12/14	88.7	19.3	21.8%	285
12/13	83.6	16.2	19.4%	285
Annual Growth	**9.2%**	**11.7%**	**—**	**3.7%**

2017 Year-End Financials

Debt ratio: —	No. of shares (mil.): 12.4
Return on equity: 14.7%	Dividends
Cash ($ mil.): 67.1	Yield: 0.0%
Current ratio: 0.12	Payout: 27.8%
Long-term debt ($ mil.): —	Market value ($ mil.): 279.0

	STOCK PRICE ($) FY Close	P/E High/Low		PER SHARE ($)		
				Earnings	Dividends	Book Value
12/17	22.40	15	10	2.01	0.56	14.43
12/16	20.90	16	10	1.38	0.56	12.91
12/15	16.06	17	10	1.25	2.53	12.10
12/14	20.53	19	11	1.49	0.47	13.55
12/13	25.20	22	15	1.25	2.42	12.55
Annual Growth	**(2.9%)**	**—**	**—**	**12.6%**	**(30.6%)**	**3.6%**

Masimo Corp.

As important as the blood running through your veins is the oxygen it carries. Masimo knows that and makes tools that monitor arterial blood-oxygen saturation levels and pulse rates in patients. The company's product range which is based on Signal Extraction Technology (SET) offers pulse oximeters in both handheld and stand-alone (bedside) form. Product benefits include the provision of real-time information and elimination of signal interference such as patient movements. In addition to general product sales Masimo licenses SET-based products to dozens of medical equipment manufacturers including Philips Atom Mindray North America GE Medical Medtronic Spacelabs and Zoll.

Operations

Masimo's primary products include patient monitoring solutions sensor products and other devices and accessories such as adapter cables. The company also makes revenue on royalties.

Geographic Reach

While the US accounts for about two-thirds of its product sales Masimo is working to grow its operations in Africa Asia Australia Europe and the Middle East.

The company has locations in Switzerland Canada and Japan as well as two manufacturing facilities in Mexico.

Sales and Marketing

Masimo markets its products globally through direct sales representatives and distributors. Customers include hospitals alternative care entities and wholesalers. Two distributors Owens & Minor and Cardinal Health each account for more than 10% of annual sales.

The company has partnerships with several group purchasing organizations (GPOs) to facilitate increased direct sales of pulse oximetry products to hospitals.

Advertising costs for fiscal 2017 totaled $12.8 million compared to around $11 million in 2016.

Financial Performance

Masimo's revenues have been rising steadily for the past five years as product sales have grown. However net income has been more volatile rising significantly in 2016 due to a $270000 settlement award but falling back down the following year.

In 2017 revenue increased 15% to $798.1 million. Both product sales across all geographic segments and royalty income rose that year. The company's base of installed circuit boards and pulse oximeters nearly reached 1.6 million units a 6% increase for 2017. With that higher base sales of consumable and reusable sensor products also increased.

Net income fell 56% to $131.6 million in 2017 as the company had higher costs of sales and operating expenses (primarily increased R&D expenses) related to its growing business.

The company ended 2017 with $315.5 million in net cash $7.3 million more than it had at the end of 2016. This was largely due to the decrease in net income. Operating activities provided $56.1 million in cash while investing activities used $47.9 million and financing activities used $4.1 million.

Strategy

Masimo's strategies for growth include expanding its presence in the pulse oximetry market getting its products into more types of patient care settings and selling more of its rainbow SET products and Root patient-monitoring products to hospitals and other care settings. The company's R&D efforts focus on novel products as well as improvement to existing products. It is expanding the applications of its rainbow products which measure multiple blood components at once; it is also adding products that reduce the invasiveness of testing and that provide remote monitoring and alarm capabilities.

To branch out beyond its traditionally targeted emergency and critical care setting markets Masimo is promoting existing products (and adding new products) to meet the general treatment needs of hospitals and non-hospital environments. For example the company is promoting its SET technology as ideal for use by home care agencies post-acute care hospitals and sleep diagnostic centers. It has also launched new handheld products that allow for fast and simple measurement of perimeters in a variety of care settings. The company expects moves such as these to greatly expand its presence in non-critical care markets.

Masimo also expands by entering new OEM licensing agreements; by widening agreements with wholesale distributors; and by making occasional acquisitions.

However the company is somewhat slow to breaking into new niches which has made it lose a bit of its market share to new competitors.

EXECUTIVES

Chairman and CEO, Joe E. Kiani, age 54, $883,518 total compensation
EVP and CIO, Yongsam Lee, age 54, $340,704 total compensation
President Worldwide OEM Business and Blood Management, Rick Fishel, age 60, $357,574 total compensation
EVP Business Development, Paul R. Jansen, age 47
COO, Anand Sampath, age 52, $369,277 total compensation
EVP Finance and CFO, Mark P. de Raad, age 58, $363,034 total compensation
EVP General Counsel and Corporate Secretary, Tom McClenahan, age 45
President Masimo Worldwide Sales Professional Services and Medical Affairs, Jon Coleman, age 54, $354,103 total compensation
VP Quality, Glenn Pohly
Regional Vice President, Michelle Hahn
Vice President Information Systems, Mark Brinton
Global Vice President Of Sales, Brad Snow
Senior Vice President, Dan Brothman
Executive Vice President, Raul Bennis
VP Business Development, Eli Kammerman
Vice President Oem Business, Nikolai Marinow
Vice President Global Government Affairs, Jim Bialick

Regional Vice President Strategic Accounts, Jodie Pellerin
Regional Vice President Texas Region, Billy Clark
Auditors: GRANT THORNTON LLP

LOCATIONS

HQ: Masimo Corp.
52 Discovery, Irvine, CA 92618
Phone: 949 297-7000
Web: www.masimo.com

PRODUCTS/OPERATIONS

2017 Sales

	$ mil.	% of total
Products	741.3	93
Royalties	56.8	7
Total	**798.1**	**100**

COMPETITORS

Bio-logic	GE Healthcare
CAS Medical	Medtronic
Criticare	

HISTORICAL FINANCIALS

Company Type: Public

Income Statement				FYE: December 30
	REVENUE ($ mil.)	NET INCOME ($ mil.)	NET PROFIT MARGIN	EMPLOYEES
12/17	798.1	131.6	16.5%	4,600
12/16*	694.6	300.6	43.3%	4,293
01/16	630.1	83.3	13.2%	3,700
01/15	586.6	72.5	12.4%	3,600
12/13	547.2	58.3	10.7%	3,139
Annual Growth	**9.9%**	**22.5%**	**—**	**10.0%**

*Fiscal year change

2017 Year-End Financials

Debt ratio: —	No. of shares (mil.): 51.6
Return on equity: 20.8%	Dividends
Cash ($ mil.): 315.3	Yield: —
Current ratio: 3.72	Payout: —
Long-term debt ($ mil.): —	Market value ($ mil.): 4,379.0

	STOCK PRICE ($) FY Close	P/E High/Low		PER SHARE ($) Earnings	Dividends	Book Value
12/17	84.80	41	26	2.36	0.00	13.69
12/16*	67.40	11	6	5.65	0.00	11.16
01/16	41.51	27	16	1.55	0.00	5.52
01/15	25.88	24	16	1.30	0.00	5.82
12/13	28.86	29	18	1.02	0.00	5.77
Annual Growth	**30.9%**	—	—	**23.3%**	—	**24.1%**

*Fiscal year change

MasterCraft Boat Holdings Inc

Auditors: BDO USA, LLP

LOCATIONS

HQ: MasterCraft Boat Holdings Inc
100 Cherokee Cove Drive, Vonore, TN 37885
Phone: 423 884-2221
Web: www.mastercraft.com

HISTORICAL FINANCIALS

Company Type: Public

Income Statement				FYE: June 30
	REVENUE ($ mil.)	NET INCOME ($ mil.)	NET PROFIT MARGIN	EMPLOYEES
06/18	332.7	39.6	11.9%	882
06/17	228.6	19.5	8.6%	490
06/16	221.6	10.2	4.6%	510
06/15	214.3	5.5	2.6%	470
06/14	177.5	19.9	11.2%	475
Annual Growth	**17.0%**	**18.8%**	**—**	**16.7%**

2018 Year-End Financials

Debt ratio: 42.4%	No. of shares (mil.): 18.6
Return on equity: 123.3%	Dividends
Cash ($ mil.): 7.9	Yield: —
Current ratio: 0.73	Payout: —
Long-term debt ($ mil.): 70.0	Market value ($ mil.): 541.0

	STOCK PRICE ($) FY Close	P/E High/Low		PER SHARE ($) Earnings	Dividends	Book Value
06/18	28.95	15	8	2.12	0.00	2.81
06/17	19.55	19	10	1.05	0.00	0.63
06/16	11.05	28	18	0.56	4.30	(0.45)
Annual Growth	**61.9%**	—	—	**94.6%**		

Matador Resources Co

Auditors: KPMG LLP

LOCATIONS

HQ: Matador Resources Co
5400 LBJ Freeway, Suite 1500, Dallas, TX 75240
Phone: 972 371-5200
Web: www.matadorresources.com

HISTORICAL FINANCIALS

Company Type: Public

Income Statement				FYE: December 31
	REVENUE ($ mil.)	NET INCOME ($ mil.)	NET PROFIT MARGIN	EMPLOYEES
12/17	544.2	125.8	23.1%	217
12/16	264.4	(97.4)	—	165
12/15	316.1	(679.7)	—	151
12/14	431.0	110.7	25.7%	99
12/13	260.8	45.0	17.3%	66
Annual Growth	**20.2%**	**29.3%**	**—**	**34.7%**

2017 Year-End Financials

Debt ratio: 26.7%	No. of shares (mil.): 108.5
Return on equity: 13.6%	Dividends
Cash ($ mil.): 102.4	Yield: —
Current ratio: 0.91	Payout: —
Long-term debt ($ mil.): 574.0	Market value ($ mil.): 3,378.0

	STOCK PRICE ($) FY Close	P/E High/Low		PER SHARE ($) Earnings	Dividends	Book Value
12/17	31.13	25	17	1.23	0.00	10.66
12/16	25.76	—	—	(1.07)	0.00	6.94
12/15	19.77	—	—	(8.34)	0.00	5.70
12/14	20.23	19	9	1.56	0.00	11.81
12/13	18.64	31	10	0.77	0.00	8.67
Annual Growth	**13.7%**	—	—	**12.4%**	—	**5.3%**

Match Group Inc

Auditors: Ernst & Young LLP

LOCATIONS

HQ: Match Group Inc
8750 North Central Expressway, Suite 1400, Dallas, TX 75231
Phone: 214 576-9352
Web: www.matchgroupinc.com

HISTORICAL FINANCIALS

Company Type: Public

Income Statement				FYE: December 31
	REVENUE ($ mil.)	NET INCOME ($ mil.)	NET PROFIT MARGIN	EMPLOYEES
12/17	1,330.6	350.1	26.3%	1,400
12/16	1,222.5	171.4	14.0%	5,100
12/15	1,020.4	120.3	11.8%	4,800
12/14	888.2	147.7	16.6%	4,800
12/13	803.0	125.0	15.6%	0
Annual Growth	**13.5%**	**29.4%**	**—**	

2017 Year-End Financials

Debt ratio: 58.8%	No. of shares (mil.): 274.2
Return on equity: 70.1%	Dividends
Cash ($ mil.): 272.6	Yield: —
Current ratio: 1.40	Payout: —
Long-term debt ($ mil.): 1,252.7	Market value ($ mil.): 8,588.0

	STOCK PRICE ($) FY Close	P/E High/Low		PER SHARE ($) Earnings	Dividends	Book Value
12/17	31.31	24	12	1.18	0.00	1.83
12/16	17.10	29	13	0.64	0.00	1.94
12/15	13.55	22	19	0.65	0.00	1.12
Annual Growth	**52.0%**	—	—	**34.7%**	—	**27.6%**

Matthews International Corp

Matthews International might not bury its competition but it can supply the casket and bronze marker. One of the nation's leading makers of cremation equipment and urns bronze memorials (including Elvis Presley's Graceland marker) metal and wood caskets and commemorative products (Baseball Hall of Fame plaques) Matthews also builds mausoleums. In addition it provides graphic imaging products and services for the consumer packaging and retail industries as well as merchandising services and marking and fulfillment systems. Matthews has operations in Asia Australia Canada and Europe but the US accounts for more than 60% of its sales.

Operations

Within its two major divisions — Memorialization and Brand Solutions — Matthews breaks its offerings down into six areas: cemetery products funeral home products cremation graphics imaging merchandising solutions and marking and fulfillment systems. Graphics imaging contributes the most to overall revenue some 35% with cemetery products and funeral home products each accounting for about 20%.

Geographic Reach

The US and Europe represent Matthews' largest markets accounting for more than 60% and about 35% of sales respectively. Other markets include Asia Australia and Canada. It has facilities in the US as well as in Austria Australia Belgium Canada China Germany Hong Kong Hungary Italy Malaysia Mexico the Netherlands Poland Singapore Sweden Turkey and the UK.

Sales and Marketing

The company's memorialization products are sold primarily to cemeteries memorial parks and funeral homes as well as corporations hospitals schools and other organizations. Brand solutions product and services are marketed to customers in the consumer packaged goods and retail industries.

Financial Performance

Matthews has seen sales rise in recent years. The company attributes the gains to higher sales volume within its Brand Solutions business and timely boosts from acquisitions. In 2014 revenue crossed the billion dollar mark up 12% to $1.1 billion. Although memorialization sales were down 2% as the number of casketed in-ground burials declines brand solutions sales powered by the mid-2014 acquisition of Schawk (which it renamed SGK LLC) were up a healthy 28%.

Net income and cash flow from operations however were both down as selling and administrative expenses rose significantly boosted by acquisition activity.

Strategy

Much of the company's recent growth has been an expansion of its brand solutions business which has grown from 45% of sales in 2012 to 54% in 2014. Matthews plans to extend those services globally (both organically and through acquisitions) so it can cater to multinational clients.

Mergers and Acquisitions

In 2014 Matthews made its largest acquisition to date with the purchase of Schawk (SGK). The deal valued at more than $570 million combines Matthews' brand solutions expertise in Europe with Schawk's experience in the US and Asia.

In mid-2015 the company purchased former rival casket and urn maker Aurora Casket Company for $214 million.

HISTORY

John Matthews began making stencils signs and steel stamps in 1850. Two of his sons joined his company in 1861; they renamed it Jas. H. Matthews Co. in 1894 after the youngest. The company developed the first vulcanized rubber printing plate in 1912 and began marking corrugated shipping containers. In 1927 it applied its plaque-making ability which it had been using for plaques to adorn buildings to make America's first flush bronze memorial plaque mounted in a Florida cemetery.

The company changed its name to Matthews International in 1976 to reflect its presence in other countries. Five years later it purchased the Sunland Memorial Park and Mortuary in Arizona to learn more about customers' needs. Matthews went public in 1994; sales continued to climb steadily.

In 1995 David Kelly joined the company as president and COO; he became CEO six months later and was elected chairman in 1996. That year

Matthews sold its cemetery (3% of total revenues) and started expanding its product offerings and geographic markets through acquisitions beginning with its purchase of Industrial Equipment and Engineering Company in 1996. Acquisitions in 1997 and 1998 (such as Gibraltar Mausoleum Construction) expanded its graphics and memorial businesses. In 1999 the company acquired Europe's leading supplier of bronze memorialization products Caggiati SpA.

Matthews acquired The York Group the second-largest US casket maker in December 2001. A Federal Trade Commission inquiry regarding that acquisition was closed in late 2002 with no action taken.

Matthews boosted its marking products capabilities in July 2004 when it acquired Holjeron Corporation an Oregon-based industrial controls manufacturer. The same month Matthews acquired merchandising solutions provider Cloverleaf Group (formerly iDL and Big Red Rooster) to expand its presence in that market. In late 2004 the company purchased The InTouch Group a European reprographics firm. The next year Matthews expanded its Casket Division picking up Milso Industries to work alongside York.

In 2005 Matthews appointed group president David DeCarlo to the newly-created role of vice chairman and EVP Joseph Bartolacci as president and COO. In July the firm completed the acquisition of Milso Industries now a wholly-owned subsidiary of Matthews belonging to its casket division.

David Kelly remained as chairman and CEO. The next year Bartolacci replaced Kelly as CEO.

In May 2008 Matthews acquired a 78% stake in Saueressig GmbH & Co. a leading European provider of prepress and gravure printing forms based in Vreden Germany. Saueressig has manufacturing operations in Germany Poland and England. Saueressig operates as a subsidiary of the firm's Graphics Imaging Group. In December Matthews purchased a small European cremation equipment manufacturer.

In December 2009 the firm bought California-based United Memorial Products a leading supplier of granite memorial products burial vaults and caskets in the western US.

In April 2010 Matthews acquired Reynoldsville Casket Co. The Pennsylvania-based company makes and distributes caskets primarily in the Northeast.

EXECUTIVES

CFO and Secretary, Steven F. Nicola, age 57, $475,692 total compensation
EVP Strategy and Corporate Development, Brian J. Dunn, age 60, $374,365 total compensation
CTO and Director, Gregory S. (Greg) Babe, age 60
President and CEO, Joseph C. Bartolacci, age 57, $800,267 total compensation
President Environmental Solutions, Paul F. Rahill, age 60, $188,350 total compensation
Group President Memorialization, Steven D. Gackenbach, age 54, $380,827 total compensation
President SGK Brand Solutions, Gary R. Kohl
Vice President, Cindy Mills
Executive Vice President Strategic Initiatives, Joe Bozada
Vice President and General Manager, Michael Baklarz
VICE PRESIDENT GENERAL MANAGER, Terry Porter

Vice President, John Standard
Chairman, John D. Turner, age 72
Treasurer, Robert Marsh
Auditors: Ernst & Young LLP

LOCATIONS

HQ: Matthews International Corp
Two Northshore Center, Pittsburgh, PA 15212-5851
Phone: 412 442-8200
Web: www.matw.com

PRODUCTS/OPERATIONS

2014 Sales

	$ mil.	% of total
Memorialization		
Funeral home	234.6	21
Cemetery	222.0	20
Cremation	51.8	5
Brand Solutions		
Graphic Imaging	398.2	36
Marking and Fullfilment Systems	100.9	9
Merchandising Solutions	99.1	9
Total	**1,106.6**	**100**

Selected Products

Bronze
  Commemorative and identification plaques
  Crypt letters and plates
  Flower vases
  Flush bronze memorials
  Granite benches
  Mausoleums
  Statuary
Caskets
  Corrugated
  Metal
  Particle board
  Wood
Cremation
  Cremation gardens
  Cremation memorials and urns
  Cremation niche systems
  Crematories
Graphic Systems
  Imaging systems
  Prepress services
  Printing plates (bar codes logos identification)
  Rotary and flat cutting dies
Marking Products
  Cleaners
  Hand stamps
  Ink-jet printing systems
  Inks
  Laser-marking equipment
  Solvents
Merchandising Solutions
  Brand concept shops
  Custom packaging
  Custom store fixtures
  Graphic design
  Interactive kiosks
  Model development
  Permanent displays
  Promotional signage
  Prototyping
  Temporary displays

COMPETITORS

Batesville Casket	Rock of Ages
Cold Spring Granite	Service Corporation
DIC Corporation	International
Eastman Kodak	Wilbert
International Imaging Materials	

HISTORICAL FINANCIALS

Company Type: Public

Income Statement

FYE: September 30

	REVENUE ($ mil.)	NET INCOME ($ mil.)	NET PROFIT MARGIN	EMPLOYEES
09/18	1,602.5	107.3	6.7%	11,000
09/17	1,515.6	74.3	4.9%	11,000
09/16	1,480.4	66.7	4.5%	10,300
09/15	1,426.0	63.4	4.4%	10,300
09/14	1,106.6	43.6	3.9%	9,400
Annual Growth	9.7%	25.2%	—	4.0%

2018 Year-End Financials

Debt ratio: 40.4%
Return on equity: 12.9%
Cash ($ mil.): 41.5
Current ratio: 2.03
Long-term debt ($ mil.): 929.3

No. of shares (mil.): 32.0
Dividends
  Yield: 0.0%
  Payout: 22.5%
Market value ($ mil.): 1,609.0

	STOCK PRICE ($) FY Close	P/E High/Low	PER SHARE ($) Earnings	Dividends	Book Value
09/18	50.15	19 14	3.37	0.76	27.07
09/17	62.25	33 25	2.28	0.68	24.56
09/16	60.76	31 23	2.03	0.60	22.05
09/15	48.97	29 21	1.91	0.52	22.23
09/14	43.89	31 25	1.53	0.44	23.69
Annual Growth	3.4%	— —	21.8%	14.6%	3.4%

Maui Land & Pineapple Co., Inc.

Aloha! Maui Land & Pineapple (ML&P) invites you to live and play on its Hawaiian island — Maui. Through its Kapalua Land Company subsidiary the company operates the 1650-acre Kapalua Resort on Maui's northwest coast. The resort includes a minority-owned Ritz-Carlton hotel as well as tennis and spa facilities residential homes and condos and shops and restaurants. ML&P also develops residential and commercial property on its 23000 acres surrounding the resort. Its Kapalua Realty Company is a general brokerage real estate firm located within the resort. The company additionally owns forest and nature preserves on the island. Formerly one of Hawaii's largest pineapple producers the company exited that business in 2009.

Revenues declined slightly in 2010 compared to 2009 because the company ceased to own The Kapalua Villas (vacation rental) and Kapalua Adventures (zip lines ropes course and other activities) choosing instead to lease those businesses to third party operators. However its net income soared to nearly $25 million up from a loss of more than $123 million. In 2010 ML&P gained on the sale of its Kapalua Plantation Golf Course as well as the termination of post-retirement plans for employees of discontinued operations. In addition due to the real estate crash and the subsequent decline in tourism the company lost considerable profits from its 51%-owned Bay Holdings in 2009. (Bay Holdings owns the Residences at

Kapalua Bay condos.) In order to cut costs ML&P eliminated more than 600 jobs in 2010 and 2009.

After David Cole resigned from his five-year stint as chairman and CEO at the end of 2008 the company split the functions appointing Warren Haruki (former president of GTE Hawaiian Tel and Verizon Hawaii) as chairman and Robert Webber as CEO. Months later Webber resigned. Haruki serves as chairman and interim CEO a position he has held since 2009.

Because of soaring oil and transportation costs ML&P exited the pineapple business in 2009 saying it could no longer sustain financial losses that threatened to destroy the company. It had grown pineapples on Maui for almost 100 years.

ML&P board member and AOL co-founder Steve Case owns more than 60% of the company. Through his Revolution LLC Case has a majority interest in Exclusive Resorts which has a 15% stake in Bay Holdings. Marriott International owns the remaining 34% of the condo project.

EXECUTIVES

Chairman and Interim CEO, Warren H. Haruki, age 63
President and COO, Ryan L. Churchill, $200,000 total compensation
CFO, Tim T. Esaki
Director, Walter A. Dods Jr., age 73
Director, Kent T. Lucien, age 62
Director, Stephen M. (Steve) Case
Director, Miles R. Gilburne, age 64
Director, David A. Heenan, age 75
Director, Fred E. Trotter III, age 84
Director, John H. Agee, age 66
Director, David C. Cole, age 62
Director, Duncan MacNaughton, age 72
Independent Director, Arthur Tokin
Auditors: Accuity LLP

LOCATIONS

HQ: Maui Land & Pineapple Co., Inc.
  200 Village Road, Lahaina, Maui, HI 96761
Phone: 808 877-3351
Web: www.mauiland.com

COMPETITORS

Alexander & Baldwin	HTH Corporation
Barnwell Industries	Hilton Worldwide
Benchmark Hospitality	Outrigger Enterprises
Exclusive Resorts LLC	Sheraton Hotels
Four Seasons Hotels	

HISTORICAL FINANCIALS

Company Type: Public

Income Statement

FYE: December 31

	REVENUE ($ mil.)	NET INCOME ($ mil.)	NET PROFIT MARGIN	EMPLOYEES
12/17	24.3	10.9	44.7%	15
12/16	47.3	21.8	46.1%	17
12/15	22.7	6.8	29.9%	17
12/14	33.0	17.6	53.4%	17
12/13	15.2	(1.1)	—	19
Annual Growth	12.5%	—		(5.7%)

2017 Year-End Financials

Debt ratio: 2.7%
Return on equity: 44.5%
Cash ($ mil.): 1.0
Current ratio: 1.27
Long-term debt ($ mil.): 1.2

No. of shares (mil.): 19.0
Dividends
  Yield: —
  Payout: —
Market value ($ mil.): 329.0

	STOCK PRICE ($) FY Close	P/E High/Low	PER SHARE ($) Earnings	Dividends	Book Value
12/17	17.30	48 12	0.57	0.00	1.64
12/16	7.20	7 4	1.15	0.00	0.94
12/15	5.46	21 14	0.36	0.00	(0.58)
12/14	6.05	10 6	0.94	0.00	(0.81)
12/13	6.09	— —	(0.06)	0.00	(1.45)
Annual Growth	29.8%	—	—	—	—

MAXIMUS Inc.

MAXIMUS provides business services to help governments operate health and human services programs mostly at the state and national levels. The company?s health services segment offers outsourced program management and administrative services mainly to government agencies responsible for health and human services programs. MAXIMUS?s human services segment provides administrative and consulting support to welfare-to-work programs child support enforcement and higher education. A significant portion of the company?s revenue comes from the US federal government directly or indirectly.

Operations
MAXIMUS operates three segments: Health Services 60% of revenue and U.S. Federal Services and Human Services about 20% of revenue each.

MAXIMUS's Health Services segment offers outsourced program management and administrative services mainly to government agencies responsible for health and human services programs. These services support a variety of government health benefit programs including Medicaid the Children's Health Insurance Program (CHIP) and the Affordable Care Act (ACA) in the U.S. Health Insurance British Columbia in Canada and the Health Assessment Advisory Service (HAAS) contract in the UK.

The US Federal Services segment handles citizen engagement centers and support document and record management case management benefit appeals and IT services and support.

Its human services segment provides administrative and consulting support to welfare-to-work programs child support enforcement and higher education.

Geographic Reach
Headquartered in Virginia and operating through more than 400 offices MAXIMUS rings up more than 70% of its revenue from the US where the company has drawn clients from all 50 states. It also has won contracts in Australia Canada New Zealand Saudi Arabia and the UK.

Sales and Marketing
MAXIMUS's primary customers are government agencies mostly in the US (mostly state and federal agencies but some local governments as well) but also abroad. It typically contracts with government clients under four primary pricing arrangements namely performance-based cost-plus fixed-price and time-and-materials.

The company has a heavy concentration of revenue with four customers — the US Federal Government the UK Government the State of New York and the Australian Government — supplying about 55% of the total.

Financial Performance

MAXIMUS?s revenue trended steadily higher for four years until it dipped 2% in 2018 (ended September). The company?s income growth outpaced revenue increasing 10% a year since 2014.

Revenue was $2.4 billion in 2018 down about $59 million from 2017. The Health Services segment supplied 2% growth with help from State of New York contracts and improvement in performance in the HAAS contract in the UK. The company blamed a 12% revenue drop in the Federal Services unit on contracts that came to an end. Contracts that closed also contributed to a 3% decline in Human Services revenue.

Cost reductions and a tax benefit from the US Tax Cuts and Jobs Act pushed net income 5% higher to $220.8 million in 2018 from 2017.

MAXIMUS reported it had about $349 million in cash and equivalents at the end of 2018 about $120 million more than in 2017. Operating activities generated $134.5 million in 2018 while investing activities used $4.9 million and financing activities used $8.4 million.

In recent years MAXIMUS used cash flow from operations in fiscal years 2016 and 2017 to reduce debt which had been incurred with the acquisitions and its interest expenses.

Strategy

MAXIMUS pursues contracts with long-term and recurring revenue believing than an incumbent has a better chance of re-winning contracts. It also makes acquisitions to expand its services offering.

MAXIMUS?s 2018 acquisition of the citizen engagement centers of General Dynamics Information Technology unit provides greater size and scope to the company helping it compete with larger rivals. The deal enables greater economies of scale and brings technology and operational capabilities that could benefit other parts of the MAXIMUS portfolio. The scale makes MAXIMUS a more viable prime contractor to the US federal government and reduces the company?s need to partner with other companies to win contracts. The acquisition increases its competitiveness on procurement in the federal marketplace.

Two large-scale contracts included in the deal provide MAXIMUS with the contact center operations for the Centers for Medicare and Medicaid Services and operation support and citizen engagement centers for the 2020 US census.

The timing of contracts which can produce less revenue at beginning and end can make the company?s revenue uneven.

Mergers and Acquisitions

MAXIMUS paid $400 million buy General Dynamics Information Technology?s large-scale citizen-engagement centers in the US. The acquisition is expected to strengthen MAXIMUS?s position in the administration of federal government programs across the US.

Company Background

David Mastran who worked for the Department of Health Education and Welfare during the Nixon administration founded MAXIMUS in 1975. The company's name comes from its goal of maximizing US government efficiency. MAXIMUS went public in 1997.

The company has grown through acquisitions throughout its history continuing through 2018 (calendar year) when it acquired citizen engagement centers from General Dynamics Information Technology business for $400 million.

EXECUTIVES

Vice Chairman, Richard A. (Rich) Montoni, age 67, $725,000 total compensation
Chief of Human Capital, Mark S. Andrekovich, age 57, $395,000 total compensation
CFO and Treasurer, Richard J. Nadeau, $425,000 total compensation
CEO, Bruce L. Caswell, age 52, $487,500 total compensation
General Manager Human Services, Akbar Piloti, age 61, $410,000 total compensation
CIO, Kelly L. Clark
Vice President, Lisa Simmons
Senior Vice President, John Walz
Vice President, Viann Hardy
Vice President, Kelly Blaschke
Vice President, Nelson Clugston
Vice President UK Information Technology, Beverly Smith
Vice President Human Resources, Nick Figurelli
Vice President Technology Maximus Information, Kevan McCallum
Vice President, Adam Polatnick
Senior Vice President Global Human Resources, Catalina Murillo
Senior Vice President Technology Strategy and Solutions, Raj Parameswaran
Vice President, Jon Lemelin
Vice President Healthcare Services Business Develo, John Crouse
MPH Vice President Center For Health Literacy, Kinte Ibbott
Vice President, Tricia Belman
Vice President Information Security Management and Assurance, Vicki Cippus
VICE PRESIDENT, Fatima Mccasland
VICE PRESIDENT FINANCIAL SERVICE, Randall Phillips
Chairman, Peter B. Pond, age 73
Board Member, Russell Beliveau
Auditors: Ernst & Young LLP

LOCATIONS

HQ: MAXIMUS Inc.
   1891 Metro Center Drive, Reston, VA 20190
Phone: 703 251-8500
Web: www.maximus.com

PRODUCTS/OPERATIONS

2018 Sales

	% of total
Health Services	59
US Federal Services	20
Human Services	21
Total	**100**

COMPETITORS

Accenture	IBM
Atos	LEIDOS INC.
CACI International	Oracle
Capita	SAP
Conduent	United Way
Goodwill Industries	

HISTORICAL FINANCIALS

Company Type: Public

Income Statement   FYE: September 30

	REVENUE ($ mil.)	NET INCOME ($ mil.)	NET PROFIT MARGIN	EMPLOYEES
09/18	2,392.2	220.7	9.2%	21,051
09/17	2,450.9	209.4	8.5%	20,400
09/16	2,403.3	178.3	7.4%	18,800
09/15	2,099.8	157.7	7.5%	17,000
09/14	1,700.9	145.4	8.6%	13,000
Annual Growth	8.9%	11.0%	—	12.8%

2018 Year-End Financials

Debt ratio: —	No. of shares (mil.): 64.3
Return on equity: 21.8%	Dividends
Cash ($ mil.): 349.2	Yield: 0.0%
Current ratio: 2.91	Payout: 5.3%
Long-term debt ($ mil.): —	Market value ($ mil.): 4,188.0

	STOCK PRICE ($) FY Close	P/E High/Low	PER SHARE ($) Earnings	Dividends	Book Value
09/18	65.06	21 18	3.35	0.18	16.84
09/17	64.50	20 14	3.17	0.18	14.43
09/16	56.56	26 17	2.69	0.18	11.48
09/15	59.56	29 16	2.35	0.18	9.36
09/14	40.13	23 18	2.11	0.18	8.35
Annual Growth	12.8%	— —	12.3%	(0.0%)	19.2%

MB Financial Inc

The "MB" in MB Financial doesn't stand for "Midsized Businesses" though that's its target market. The $16 billion-asset holding company owns MB Financial Bank which has about 80 branches in the Chicago area and one in Philadelphia. Commercial-related credits including mortgages operating loans lease financing and construction loans make up 85% of the bank's loan portfolio. In addition to serving small and middle-market businesses MB Financial provides retail banking and lending to consumers. The company also offers wealth management and trust services through its Cedar Hill Associates subsidiary and brokerage through Vision Investment Services. LaSalle Systems leases technology-related equipment to corporations.

Operations

MB Financial operates three main business segments: Banking which counts its deposit and lending activities; Leasing which originates leases and related services through subsidiaries LaSalle Systems Leasing Celtic Leasing Corp and MB Equipment Finance; and Mortgage Banking which originates and services residential mortgage loans to hold in its portfolio or list for sale to investors via retail or third party channels.

Broadly speaking about 54% of the bank's total revenue came from loan interest during 2015 while another 10% came from interest on its investment securities. The rest of its revenue came from mortgage banking revenue (13% of revenue) lease financing (9%) commercial deposits and treasury management fees (6%) trust and asset management fees (3%) card fees (2%) capital markets and international banking fees (1%) and other miscellaneous fee sources.

Geographic Reach

Beyond its 80 branches in Chicago and one branch in Philadelphia MB Financial boasts 39 mortgage retail offices in 18 states.

Sales and Marketing

MB Financial mostly targets small and middle market businesses and individuals. The bank spent $10.07 million on advertising during 2015 up 14% from the $8.85 million it spent in 2014.

Financial Performance

The bank's annual revenues have risen more than 65% since 2011 thanks to a combination of mortgage banking revenue growth and steady loan business growth driven by bank acquisitions. Its profits have quintupled over the same time period as a result.

MB Financial's revenue jumped 37% to $816 million during 2015 mostly driven by strong loan business and mortgage banking revenue growth both stemming from the full-year results of its 2014 acquisition of Taylor Capital.

Double-digit revenue growth in 2015 drove the bank's net income up 85% to $159 million for the year. MB Financial's operating cash levels climbed 23% to $205 million as cash earnings rose in 2015.

Strategy

MB Financial mainly pursues growth by acquiring banks and other financial companies to expand its branch network across its target geographies and boost its loan and deposit business. Other strategies for growth include expanding its private banking and asset managements operations as well as its fee-based business services including treasury management and leasing.

Mergers and Acquisitions

In mid-2016 MB Financial bought American Chartered Bancorp— along with its 15 American Chartered Bank branches in the Chicago-area $2.8 billion in assets and $2.2 billion in deposits -- in a deal valued at $449 million.

In December 2015 the company expanded its investment management and trust business after buying MSA along with its MainStreet and Cambium subsidiaries. MainStreet which boated $2.9 billion in assets under management (AUM) provided investment management services to the bank trust and independent trust markets while Cambium ($109 million in AUM) was a registered investment advisor that served affluent individuals and institutions.

In August 2014 MB Financial completed its $649-million acquisition of Rosemont Illinois-based Taylor Capital Group the holding company for Cole Taylor Bank (CTB). With $5.7 billion in assets and some 10 branches in the Chicago metro area CTB was merged with MB Financial Bank. Like its acquirer CTB is a commercial bank focused on the middle market.

Company Background

Taking advantage of the dozens of bank failures in 2009 MB Financial acquired Heritage Community Bank InBank Corus Bank and Benchmark Bank in separate FDIC-assisted transactions. In 2010 it acquired failed Chicago-area institutions Broadway Bank and New Century Bank in similar deals. Gains on these acquisitions helped the company's revenues (and profits) grow in 2010. Although the company didn't have the benefit of gains on acquisitions in 2011 (and revenues fell 20% to $493.7 million) profits continued to climb

that year growing 89% to $38.7 million largely due to a lowered provision for loan losses. Also that year the bank got millions of dollars of non-performing loans off of its books via a sale to Colony Capital.

EXECUTIVES

President and CEO, Mitchell S. Feiger, age 59, $895,308 total compensation

Chairman MB Financial Bank, Ronald D. Santo, age 75, $321,741 total compensation

EVP Credit Management MB Financial Bank, Mark A. Heckler, age 54, $293,077 total compensation

EVP Commercial Banking MB Financial Bank, Edward F. Milefchik, age 53

EVP MB Financial Bank; President MB Business Capital, Michael D. Sharkey, age 64, $456,923 total compensation

EVP and Chief Credit Officer, Michael J. Morton, age 55

President and CEO MB Financial Bank, Mark A. Hoppe, age 64, $726,923 total compensation

EVP Wealth Management Card Services Leasing and Indirect Lending, Jill E. York, age 54, $489,461 total compensation

VP MB Financial Inc. and EVP Administration MB Financial Bank, Rosemarie Bouman, age 61, $287,846 total compensation

EVP Commercial Banking, Lawrence G. Ryan, age 59

VP and CFO MB Financial Inc. and EVP COO and CFO MB Financial Bank N.A., Randall T. Conte, age 57, $451,731 total compensation

EVP Risk Management and Chief Risk Officer MB Financial Bank N.A., Brian J. Wildman, age 55, $292,846 total compensation

Vice President, Michael Scarsella

First Vice President, Priscilla Rodriguez

First Vice President, Mike Markovitz

Vice President Item Processing Manager, Veronica McGowan

Vice President Risk Management, Irene Remeniuk

Vice President, Kathy Grele

Senior Vice President and Division Manager Commercial Banking, Scott Mier

Assistant Vice President Commercial Bank, Nick Cox

First Vice President, Michael Lynch

Vice President Digital Marketing, Michelle Y Finch

Vice President Commercial Banking, Michael Salvador

Senior Vice President, Judy Hill

Vice President Compliance Manager, Kevin Osborn

Assistant Vice President Asset Manager, Brian Nagorsky

Senior Vice President and Division Manager, Jerry Kallio

Vice President, Rick J Chang

Assistant Vice President Employee Relations Office, Katie Drinan Allberry

Senior Vice President Managed Assets Division Mananger, Mary Alberts

Vice President Collateral Manager, Lisette Alamo

Vice President, Anthony Gattuso

Senior Vice President Finance Reporting Budgeting, John Francoeur

Senior Vice President, Jennifer Brogan

Vice President Business Banking, Robert Baitler

Vice President Business Banking, Jim Marshall

Assistant Vice President Marketing Communications Manager, Diane Shaughnessy

Senior Vice President, Greg Urban

Vice President Treasury Management Sales, Eloy Hodges

Vice President, Sandra Biske

Vice President Business Bankin, Steve Grabavoy

Vice President Quality Assurance Manager, Chris Hicks

Assistant Vice President Compensation, Cindy Katsikas

Vice President Business Banking, Sam Elhaj

Assistant Vice President Banking Center Manager, Galina Veksler

Vice President Marketing Manager, Megan Garr

Assistant Vice President, Brenda Allen

Senior Vice President and Division Head, Christina Bavery

Assistant Vice President Quality Control Manager, Margie Acevedo

First Vice President Chief Appraiser, Mitchell Zaveduk

Assistant Vice President Bsa Aml Loss Prevention Management, Michelle Mercer

Assistant Vice President Compensation And Benefits, Catherine Nacpil

Vice President of Managed Assets, Mike Pindak

Assistant Vice President Marketing And Crm Administrator, Cari Dam

Senior Vice President Division Head, Thomas Moran

Senior Vice President Lease Banking, Dennis Roesslein

First Vice President Regional Division M, Deborah Wheeler

Senior Vice President Lease Banking, Stewart Kapnick

Senior Vice President, Melissa Bleiweis

Vice President Commercial Banking, Dawn Lauderdale

Senior Vice President, Mitch Morgenstern

Assistant Vice President Accounting Manager, Patricia Basan

Senior Vice President Human Resources, Laura Entwistle

First Vice President, Thomas Carmody

Senior Vice President Operations, Pete Steger

Senior Vice President Overseeing Credit, Jennifer Rosenberg

Senior Vice President Corporate Controller, David Emerson

Senior Vice President, Adam Garrett

Senior Vice President Senior Audit Manager, Julie Greco

Vice President Senior Field Credit Officer, Brian Monson

Vice President Treasury Management Solutions Group, Jeffrey Malek

Vice President Treasury Management Solutions Group, Isela Calabrese

Senior Vice President CRA Fair Lending Program Manager, Mary Boetel

Assistant Vice President, Manal Sughayer

Vice President Banking Center Manager, Karen Franciere

Assistant Vice President Treas, Luke Chesick

Senior Vice President Field Risk Officer Enterprise Risk Management and Op Risk, Patricia K Bartler

Vice President Marketing, Debranne Santucci

Vice President Banking Center Manager, Enrique Arroyo

Senior Vice President, Eric Staczek

Vice President Banking Center Manager, Fran Barker

Assistant Vice President Operations, Jackie Schmitz

Senior Vice President, Lisa Gibbs

Assistant Vice President Customer Solutions Specialist, Lori Rottmuller

Senior Vice President, Martha Gaskin

Senior Vice President Commercial Banking, Matt Stefani

Senior Vice President, Mark Staunton

Senior Vice President, Jack Gracheck
Assistant Vice President Accounting Manager, Janis Griffin
Assistant Vice President Banking Center Manager, Casey Weaver
Assistant Vice President Commercial Banking, Andrea Bukacek
Senior Vice President, Timothy Carstens
Senior Vice President, Harold Chmiel
Senior Vice President documentation for MB Equipment Finance, Jeannie McManus
Vice President MB Community Development Corp., Ailisa Herrera
Assistant Vice President Retail Operations, Jennifer Stoll
Vice President Portfolio Management, William Bence
Vice President Risk and Policy Manager Financial Crimes Risk Management, Christoper Bagnall
Vice President Business Banking, Jennifer Cortese
Assistant Vice President Prepaid Product Manager, Denice Myszewski
Senior Vice President, Jon Spoerry
Senior Vice President, Bryan Orton
Senior Vice President, Raphael Shin
Vice President Asset Manager, Jean Thompson
Assistant Vice President, John Scardullo
Assistant Vice President Business Development Officer, Craig Tenuto
Senior Vice President, Chuck Gitles
First Vice President, Robert Thompson
Senior Vice President National Healthcare Finance, Sarah Willett
Vice President Commercial Banking, Elizabeth Riesche
Vice President Senior Project Manager, Lisa Brumbaugh
Senior Vice President, Steven Janson
Vice President, Harry Petruleas
Vice President Loss Mitigation, Michael van Ede
Vice President Business Banking, Steven Grabavoy
Senior Vice President Correspondent Banking, Thomas Wilson
Senior Vice President Manager Business Equipment Finance, Rob Bolo
Vice President Equipment Finance, Sean Holden
Vice President, Michael Connelly
Vice President Banking Center Manager, Deborah Manno
Chairman, Thomas H. Harvey, age 57
Executive Board Member, Matt Weberling
Vice Chairman, Bruce Taylor
Auditors: RSM US LLP

LOCATIONS

HQ: MB Financial Inc
800 West Madison Street, Chicago, IL 60607
Phone: 888 422-6562
Web: www.mbfinancial.com

PRODUCTS/OPERATIONS

2015 Sales

	$ mil.	% of total
Interest		
Loans	413.6	51
Investment securities	80.3	10
Other	0.3	-
Noninterest		
Mortgage banking	117.4	13
Lease financing net	76.6	9
Commercial deposit and treasury management fees	45.3	6
Trust and Asset management	23.5	3
Card fees	15.3	2
Consumer and other deposit service fees	13.3	2
Loan service fees	6.2	1
Others	24.5	3
Total	816.3	100

Selected Services

Business Banking
Commercial Banking
Personal Banking
Wealth Management

Selected Subsidiaries

MB Financial Bank N.A.
Ashland Management Agency Inc.
Cedar Hill Associates LLC (80%)
LaSalle Systems Leasing Inc.
LaSalle Business Solutions LLC
Melrose Equipment Company LLC
MB Deferred Exchange Corporation
MB Financial Center LLC
MB Financial Center Land Owner LLC
MB Financial Community Development Corporation
Vision Investment Services Inc.
Vision Insurance Services Inc.7

COMPETITORS

Bank of America	Northern Trust
Citigroup	PNC Financial
Fifth Third	PrivateBank
Harris	U.S. Bancorp
JPMorgan Chase	Wintrust Financial

HISTORICAL FINANCIALS

Company Type: Public

Income Statement   FYE: December 31

	ASSETS ($ mil.)	NET INCOME ($ mil.)	INCOME AS % OF ASSETS	EMPLOYEES
12/17	20,086.9	304.0	1.5%	3,574
12/16	19,302.3	174.1	0.9%	3,486
12/15	15,585.0	158.9	1.0%	2,980
12/14	14,602.1	86.1	0.6%	2,839
12/13	9,641.4	98.4	1.0%	1,775
Annual Growth	20.1%	32.6%	—	19.1%

2017 Year-End Financials

Return on assets: 1.5%	Dividends
Return on equity: 10.8%	Yield: 0.0%
Long-term debt ($ mil.): —	Payout: 23.5%
No. of shares (mil.): 83.9	Market value ($ mil.): 3,736.0
Sales ($ mil): 1,039.3	

	STOCK PRICE ($) FY Close	P/E High/Low		Earnings	PER SHARE ($) Dividends	Book Value
12/17	44.52	14	11	3.49	0.82	35.87
12/16	47.23	22	13	2.13	0.74	30.90
12/15	32.37	18	14	2.02	0.65	28.31
12/14	32.86	25	20	1.31	0.52	27.11
12/13	32.06	18	11	1.79	0.44	24.11
Annual Growth	8.6%	—	—	18.2%	16.8%	10.4%

MedEquities Realty Trust Inc

Auditors: KPMG LLP

LOCATIONS

HQ: MedEquities Realty Trust Inc
3100 West End Avenue, Suite 1000, Nashville, TN 37203
Phone: 615 627-4710
Web: www.medequities.com

HISTORICAL FINANCIALS

Company Type: Public

Income Statement   FYE: December 31

	REVENUE ($ mil.)	NET INCOME ($ mil.)	NET PROFIT MARGIN	EMPLOYEES
12/17	61.1	20.4	33.4%	12
12/16	49.3	11.0	22.4%	11
12/15	44.4	12.7	28.6%	11
12/14	5.4	0.0	0.4%	0
Annual Growth	123.9%	861.1%	—	—

2017 Year-End Financials

Debt ratio: 37.0%	No. of shares (mil.): 31.8
Return on equity: 5.7%	Dividends
Cash ($ mil.): 12.6	Yield: 0.0%
Current ratio: 4.72	Payout: 131.2%
Long-term debt ($ mil.): 215.5	Market value ($ mil.): 357.0

	STOCK PRICE ($) FY Close	P/E High/Low		Earnings	PER SHARE ($) Dividends	Book Value
12/17	11.22	20	16	0.64	0.84	11.11
12/16	11.10	—	—	(0.18)	0.63	11.20
12/15	0.00	—	—	0.42	0.85	23.74
Annual Growth (31.6%)	—	—	—	23.4%	(0.6%)	

Medical Properties Trust Inc

Hospitals trust Medical Properties to provide the leases under which their facilities operate. The self-advised real estate investment trust (REIT) invests in and owns more than 120 health care facilities including acute care hospitals inpatient rehabilitation hospitals and wellness centers in 25 US states and Germany. California and Texas combined account for nearly 50% of the REIT's annual revenue. It leases the facilities to more than 25 hospital operating companies under long-term triple-net leases where the tenant bears most of the operating costs. Prime Healthcare Services and Ernest Health are among the REIT's largest clients. Medical Properties Trust entered the European health care market in 2013.

Geographic Reach

Alabama-based Medical Properties Trust (MPT) has properties in 25 US states and Germany. The REIT has 32 properties in Texas and 14 in California representing about 24% and 26% of its revenue respectively. New Jersey is another important market for the firm accounting for about 7% of annual revenue.

Financial Performance

MPT reported $242.5 million in revenue in 2013 an increase of 20% versus 2012. Net income increased by 8% over the same period to $97 million. The REIT has experienced rapid revenue and profit growth in recent years as it portfolio of properties has grown and rents and other income increased. Annual escalation provisions in its leases have contributed to the growth of rental revenue. Cash flow increased by $73 million in 2013 over 2013 due to an increase in cash from financing activities. MPT has more than $3 billion in assets.

Strategy

The REIT is focused on expanding and diversifying its tenant roster both in terms of the types of hospitals it owns and location. To that end Medical Properties Trust entered the European market in late 2013 with the purchase of 11 rehabilitation facilities in Germany from RHM Klinik-und Altenheimbetriebe GmbH & Co. for ?184 million ($254.3 million) The REIT which is looking to expand in other markets beyond the US was attracted by Germany's strong economic position and the health care environment. Back home in the US the REIT has been investing heavily in acquisitions and other related investments in 2013 and 2012 amounting to about $655 million and $621.5 million respectively. Purchases included three general acute-care hospitals from IASIS Healthcare LLC as well as two acute-care hospitals in Kansas.

The firm owns a variety of health care related properties including acute care hospitals inpatient rehabilitation hospitals long-term acute care hospitals wellness centers medical office buildings and surgical facilities.

Mergers and Acquisitions

In 2016 MPT bought the real estate assets of nine hospitals operated by Steward Health Care in a $1.25 billion transaction; the deal included a $50 million investment in Steward as well a right of first refusal to buy future Steward facilities.The following year the REIT acquired 11 hospitals from IASIS Healthcare (which was then acquired by Steward) for $1.4 billion.

EXECUTIVES

EVP CFO and Director, R. Steven Hamner, age 61, $575,000 total compensation
Chairman President and CEO, Edward K. Aldag, age 54, $950,000 total compensation
EVP COO Treasurer and Secretary, Emmett E. McLean, age 62, $525,000 total compensation
Vice Chairman, William G. McKenzie, age 59
Auditors: PricewaterhouseCoopers LLP

LOCATIONS

HQ: Medical Properties Trust Inc
1000 Urban Center Drive, Suite 501, Birmingham, AL 35242
Phone: 205 969-3755 **Fax:** 205 969-3756
Web: www.medicalpropertiestrust.com

PRODUCTS/OPERATIONS

2015 Sales by Property Type

	% of total
General acute care hospitals	58
Rehabilitation hospitals	30
Long-term acute care hospitals	12
Wellness centers	-
Total	**100**

COMPETITORS

Extendicare	Omega Healthcare
HCP	Investors
Healthcare Realty	Physicians Realty
Trust	Universal Health
LTC Properties	Realty
National Health	Ventas
Investors	Welltower

HISTORICAL FINANCIALS
Company Type: Public

Income Statement
FYE: December 31

	REVENUE ($ mil.)	NET INCOME ($ mil.)	NET PROFIT MARGIN	EMPLOYEES
12/17	704.7	289.7	41.1%	66
12/16	541.1	225.0	41.6%	54
12/15	441.8	139.6	31.6%	50
12/14	312.5	50.5	16.2%	45
12/13	242.5	96.9	40.0%	38
Annual Growth	**30.6%**	**31.5%**	**—**	**14.8%**

2017 Year-End Financials

Debt ratio: 54.3%
Return on equity: 8.2%
Cash ($ mil.): 171.4
Current ratio: 1.90
Long-term debt ($ mil.): 4,898.6
No. of shares (mil.): 364.4
Dividends
Yield: 0.0%
Payout: 117.0%
Market value ($ mil.): 5,022.0

	STOCK PRICE ($) FY Close	P/E High/Low	PER SHARE ($) Earnings	Dividends	Book Value
12/17	13.78	17 15	0.82	0.96	10.48
12/16	12.30	18 11	0.86	0.91	10.13
12/15	11.51	24 17	0.63	0.88	8.88
12/14	13.78	49 42	0.29	0.84	8.00
12/13	12.22	27 18	0.63	0.81	8.33
Annual Growth	**3.0%**	**— —**	**6.8%**	**4.3%**	**5.9%**

Medidata Solutions, Inc.

Medidata Solutions has electronic remedies to help clinical trials run smoothly. Founded in 1999 the company offers cloud-based applications that help biotechnology pharmaceutical and other life sciences companies conduct clinical trials and related research. Its products include hosted software for administering and managing clinical trials electronic data capture applications study management applications and patient diaries. The company also offers a variety of professional services such as consulting implementation integration and maintenance. Medidata operates in more than 115 countries but most of its sales come from the US.

Geographic Reach

Medidata does most of its business in the US which accounted for more than 70% of the company's sales in 2014. Japan is the company's second-largest geographic market accounting for 10% of sales during the same period. Other key markets include the UK and Switzerland.

Sales and Marketing

The company markets its products primarily through a direct sales force across North America Europe and Asia; however it does leverage relationships with contract research organizations such as PAREXEL and Quintiles Transnational to make its software the foundation for outsourced services they provide. Medidata's top five customers including Johnson & Johnson Roche and AstraZeneca account for more than 25% of sales. Overall the company counts some 500 customers.

Financial Performance

Medidata continued its strong upward revenue trajectory in 2014 with sales increasing 21% year-over-year to $335 million. Current customers played a strong revenue role by renewing contracts and adding services. Net income fell 63% in 2014 to $6.1 billion because of a wire transaction loss (associated with a fraud against the company) and related investigation costs.

Strategy

Expanding its customer base is a key element of Medidata's strategy. It has grown from less than 100 customers in 2008 to about 500 by the end of 2014. Among the segments the company is targeting are midsized companies non-US geographies the medical device industry and academic research centers and government organizations. Medidata is also focused on expanding its product line including through acquisitions.

The works with a range of technology providers in order to offer options to its customers. Medidata's technology partners include Oracle Microsoft and Amazon Web Services.

Mergers and Acquisitions

In 2014 Medidata acquired Patient Profiles an early-stage US-based software company focused on data analytics in clinical trials. The acquisition provides Medidata a centralized statistical monitoring technology that it can use with its risk-based monitoring technology.

EXECUTIVES

EVP Human Resources, Eileen M. Schloss, age 64
Chairman and CEO, Tarek A. Sherif, age 56, $545,833 total compensation
Managing Director Asia-Pacific Region, Takeru Yamamoto
COO, Michael L. (Mike) Capone, age 51, $450,000 total compensation
President, Glen de Vries, age 45, $545,833 total compensation
EVP Product Development and CTO, Julie Iskow
CFO, Rouven Bergmann, age 45, $262,500 total compensation
EVP and General Counsel, Michael I. (Mike) Otner, age 47
EVP Sales, Michael Pray
EVP Professional Services, Daniel (Dan) Shannon
Vice President Application Strategy, Daniel Mudgett
Vice President Corporate Strategy, Shih-Yin Ho
Vice President Implementation Services, Les Taylor
Vice President Deputy General Counsel And Assistant Secretary, Kathryn Schneider
Vice President Human Resources Operations, Robyn Perry
Vice President Professional Services, Keta Lakdawala
Senior Vice President Corporate Development, Steven Goldberg
Vice President Sales and Partnerships, John Ohrn
Vice President Procurement, Rhonda Griscti
Vice President Corporate Marketing, Dianne Yurek
Vice President Sales Operations, Manish Bhatt
Vice President Global Enterprise Sales, Bob Erdle
Vice President Technology, Greg Owens
Senior Vice President and Deputy General, Brandon Ziegler
Vice President R and D APAC, Motohide Nishi
Vice President Global Strategic Solution Sales, Sefton Cohen
Vice President Global System Integrators, Tony Giaccio
Vice President Strategic Solution Sales Mid Market, James Hayden

Vice President Strategic Consulting Services,
Rajesh Patel
Senior Vice President Global Partners Business,
Renee Hart
Senior Vice President Enterprise Agreements,
Vladimir Lebedev
Senior Vice President Global Go To Market,
Michael Wendell
Executive Vice President And Chief Human Resources Officer (Chro), Jill Larsen
Auditors: Deloitte & Touche LLP

LOCATIONS

HQ: Medidata Solutions, Inc.
350 Hudson Street, 9th Floor, New York, NY 10014
Phone: 212 918-1800
Web: www.mdsol.com

PRODUCTS/OPERATIONS

2014 Sales

	$ mil.	% of total
Subscription	280.0	84
Professional services	55.1	16
Total	**335.1**	**100**

Selected Customers

Pharmaceutical
Abbott Laboratories
Astellas Pharma
AstraZeneca
Baxter International
Bayer HealthCare
Daiichi Sankyo
F. Hoffmann-La Roche
Johnson & Johnson
H. Lundbeck
Orion Corporation
Pfizer
Roche Holding
Shionogi & Co.
Takeda Pharmaceutical
Biotechnology
Amgen
Array BioPharma
Elan Pharmaceuticals
Genzyme Corporation
Gilead Sciences
Infinity Pharmaceuticals
Seattle Genetics
Medical Devices and Diagnostics
bioMérieux
Boston Scientific
DePuy International
Edwards Lifesciences
Contract Research Organizations
CMIC
EPS
ICON Clinical Research
INC Research
Kendle International
PRA International
Quintiles Transnational
Sumisho Computer Systems
Institutions
Ludwig Institute for Cancer Research
Northwestern University

COMPETITORS

Aptuit	MedNet Solutions
BioClinica	Merge Healthcare
DATATRAK International	Microsoft
DRS Data & Research	OmniComm
DrugLogic	Oracle
Liquent	Perceptive Informatics
M2S	eResearchTechnology

HISTORICAL FINANCIALS
Company Type: Public

Income Statement   FYE: December 31

	REVENUE ($ mil.)	NET INCOME ($ mil.)	NET PROFIT MARGIN	EMPLOYEES
12/17	545.5	44.3	8.1%	2,130
12/16	463.3	28.9	6.3%	1,424
12/15	392.5	13.1	3.4%	1,487
12/14	335.0	6.0	1.8%	1,077
12/13	276.8	16.6	6.0%	923
Annual Growth	**18.5%**	**27.8%**		**23.3%**

2017 Year-End Financials

Debt ratio: 35.4%
Return on equity: 9.8%
Cash ($ mil.): 484.2
Current ratio: 1.49
Long-term debt ($ mil.): 92.8

No. of shares (mil.): 58.6
Dividends
Yield: —
Payout: —
Market value ($ mil.): 3,714.0

	STOCK PRICE ($) FY Close	P/E High/Low	PER SHARE ($) Earnings	Dividends	Book Value
12/17	63.37	104 61	0.74	0.00	8.49
12/16	49.67	109 62	0.51	0.00	6.96
12/15	49.29	240153	0.23	0.00	5.05
12/14	47.75	563283	0.11	0.00	4.86
12/13	60.50	374119	0.31	0.00	4.21
Annual Growth	**1.2%**	**— —**	**24.3%**	**—**	**19.2%**

Medpace Holdings Inc

Auditors: DELOITTE & TOUCHE LLP

LOCATIONS

HQ: Medpace Holdings Inc
5375 Medpace Way, Cincinnati, OH 45227
Phone: 513 579-9911
Web: www.medpace.com

HISTORICAL FINANCIALS
Company Type: Public

Income Statement   FYE: December 31

	REVENUE ($ mil)	NET INCOME ($ mil)	NET PROFIT MARGIN	EMPLOYEES
12/17	436.1	39.1	9.0%	2,500
12/16	421.5	13.4	3.2%	2,500
12/15	359.0	(8.6)	—	2,300
12/14	248.5	(14.3)	—	1,700
Annual Growth	**20.6%**	**—**	**—**	**13.7%**

2017 Year-End Financials

Debt ratio: 23.3%
Return on equity: 7.0%
Cash ($ mil.): 26.4
Current ratio: 0.67
Long-term debt ($ mil.): 205.1

No. of shares (mil.): 35.4
Dividends
Yield: —
Payout: —
Market value ($ mil.): 1,286.0

	STOCK PRICE ($) FY Close	P/E High/Low	PER SHARE ($) Earnings	Dividends	Book Value
12/17	36.26	38 22	0.98	0.00	14.20
12/16	36.07	100 71	0.37	0.00	15.02
12/15	0.00	— —	(0.28)	0.00	12.67
Annual Growth	**—**	**— —**	**—**	**—**	**5.8%**

Mercantile Bank Corp.

Mercantile Bank Corporation is the holding company for Mercantile Bank of Michigan (formerly Mercantile Bank of West Michigan) which boasts assets of nearly $3 billion and operates more than 50 branches in central and western Michigan around Grand Rapids Holland and Lansing. The bank targets local consumers and businesses offering standard deposit services such as checking and savings accounts CDs IRAs and health savings accounts. Commercial loans make up more than three-fourths of the bank's loan portfolio. Outside of banking subsidiary Mercantile Insurance Center sells insurance products.

Operations

Mercantile Bank Corp. generated 82% of its total revenue from loan interest (including fees) in 2014 with securities interest contributing another 8% to total revenue. Service charges on deposit and sweep accounts and credit and debit card fees made up another 5% of Mercantile's total revenue while its mortgage banking income generated another 2%.

Sales and Marketing

Mercantile provides its banking services to businesses individuals and government organizations. Its commercial banking services mostly cater to small- to medium-sized businesses.

The company spent $1.315 million on advertising in 2014 compared to $1.113 million and $1.167 million in 2013 and 2012 respectively.

Financial Performance

Mercantile Bank Corp's revenues had been declining for a number of years as its loan business withered while profits have remained mostly flat.

The company had a breakout year in 2014 however after its historic acquisition of FirstBank Corp. The bank's revenue skyrocketed by 53% to $99.15 million (the highest level since 2009) mostly as the acquisition nearly doubled its loan assets and boosted its interest income on loans and securities by significant amounts. The bank's non-interest income also grew by 46% thanks to higher fee income across the board also resulting from the recent acquisition.

Higher revenue and a $3.2 million reduction in loan loss provisions with a stronger credit portfolio in 2014 also pushed the company's net income up by 2% to $17.33 million for the year. Mercantile's operating cash declined by 50% to $14.41 million due to changes in accrued interest and other liabilities during the year.

Strategy

Mercantile Bank Corporation has been growing its loan business and branch network reach through strategic acquisitions of smaller banks and bank branches. Its mid-2014 acquisition of Firstbank Corporation was perhaps the most effective to date as the purchase doubled its assets and boosted the size of its branch network nearly seven-fold from seven branches to a whopping 53.

Mergers and Acquisitions

In June 2014 Mercantile Bank Corp. purchased Firstbank Corp of Alma Michigan for a total purchase price of $173 million adding 46 branches and $1.3 billion in assets. The deal which made Mercantile the third-largest bank based in the state also expanded the bank's service offerings diversified its loan portfolio boosted its loan origination capacity and significantly extended its geographic footprint into Michigan's lower peninsula.

EXECUTIVES

SVP CFO and Treasurer Mercantile Bank Corporation and SVP and CFO Mercantile Bank of Michigan, Charles E. (Chuck) Christmas, age 52, $263,000 total compensation
President and CEO, Robert B. Kaminski, age 56, $315,000 total compensation
EVP Corporate Finance and Strategic Planning Mercantile Bank Corporation and Mercantile Bank of Michigan, Samuel G. Stone, age 73, $159,833 total compensation
Executive Vice President Corporate Banking, Robert Dewey
Vice President Electronic Banking, Shannon Tramontin
Senior Vice President Commercial Lending, Kevin Paul
Vice President Security, Paul Wegener
Vice President and Branch Manager, Cheri Stanton
Assistant Vice President Human Resources Specialist, Tina Van Valkenburg
Vice President Treasury Management, Joe Allen
Senior Vice President Retail Banking Director, Dave Miller
Senior Vice President Business Development Officer, Brian Talbot
Vice President Commercial Loan Officer, Jeff Hicks
Branch Manager Vice President, Andrea Spagnuolo
Vice President, Teresa Rupert
Assistant Vice President, Jennifer Harris
Senior Vice President, Mike Siminski
Mortgage Operations Manager Vice President, Lori Schafer
VICE PRESIDENT COMMERCIAL LENDER, Andrew Miedema
Assistant Vice President Human Resources Administrator, Kate Glover
Vice President of Commercial Lending, Bradley Wahr
Assistant Vice President Assistant Controller, Peggy Coutchie
Senior Vice President Information Systems Manager, Allen Smith
Assistant Vice President Commercial Loan Officer, Justin Horn
Vice President, Martin Smith
Executive Vice President Finance and Strategic Planning, Sam Stone
Vice President Corporate Banking, Bob Klimczak
Senior Vice President General Counsel and Risk Management Director, Bob Worthington
Vice President Treasury Sales Officer, Tim Ladd
Assistant Vice President Legal Documentation Risk Manager, William Franks
Senior Vice President Commercial Loan Officer, Cheryl Gaudard
Vice President, Betsy Mccue
Assistant Vice President Leonard Branch Manager, Daniel Zink
Senior Vice President, Michael Erfourth
Vice President, Jim Kloostra
Chairman, Michael H. Price, age 61
Auditors: BDO USA, LLP

LOCATIONS

HQ: Mercantile Bank Corp.
310 Leonard Street N.W., Grand Rapids, MI 49504
Phone: 616 406-3000
Web: www.mercbank.com

PRODUCTS/OPERATIONS

2014 Sales

	$ mil.	% of total
Interest income		
Loans and leases including fees	80.8	82
Securities taxable	6.4	6
Securities tax-exempt	1.6	2
Other	0.2	-
Noninterest income		
Service charges on accounts	2.6	3
Credit and debit card fees	2.5	2
Mortgage banking activities	1.7	2
Other	3.3	3
Total	**99.1**	**100**

COMPETITORS

Chemical Financial	Flagstar Bancorp
ChoiceOne Financial Services	Huntington Bancshares
Comerica	Independent Bank (MI)
Fifth Third	Macatawa Bank

HISTORICAL FINANCIALS

Company Type: Public

Income Statement

FYE: December 31

	ASSETS ($ mil.)	NET INCOME ($ mil.)	INCOME AS % OF ASSETS	EMPLOYEES
12/17	3,286.7	31.2	1.0%	701
12/16	3,082.5	31.9	1.0%	682
12/15	2,903.5	27.0	0.9%	701
12/14	2,893.3	17.3	0.6%	731
12/13	1,426.9	17.0	1.2%	268
Annual Growth	**23.2%**	**16.4%**	**—**	**27.2%**

2017 Year-End Financials

Return on assets: 0.9%
Return on equity: 8.8%
Long-term debt ($ mil.): —
No. of shares (mil.): 16.5
Sales ($ mil): 144.5

Dividends
Yield: 0.0%
Payout: 38.9%
Market value ($ mil.): 587.0

	STOCK PRICE ($) FY Close	P/E High/Low		PER SHARE ($) Earnings	Dividends	Book Value
12/17	35.37	20	15	1.90	0.74	22.05
12/16	37.70	19	11	1.96	1.16	20.76
12/15	24.54	16	12	1.62	0.58	20.41
12/14	21.02	19	15	1.28	2.48	19.33
12/13	21.58	11	8	1.95	0.45	17.54
Annual Growth	**13.1%**	**—**	**—**	**(0.6%)**	**13.2%**	**5.9%**

Mercury Systems Inc

Mercury Systems (formerly Mercury Computer Systems) delivers digital signals faster than a wing-footed messenger. The company makes real-time digital signal processing (DSP) systems for the homeland security military and aerospace and telecommunications markets. Its military systems process radar sonar and other signals. It also makes specialized electronics used in semiconductor wafer inspection and airport baggage screeners. Mercury Systems acts as a subcontractor to prime contractors such as Northrop Grumman and Raytheon.

Operations

Mercury Systems operates in two business segments: Mercury Commercial Electronics (MCE) 88% of revenue and Mercury Defense Systems (MDS) 12% of revenue. MCE provides specialized processing subsystems for defense and intelligence applications. Technologies and capabilities include embedded processing modules and subsystems RF and microwave multi-function assemblies and RF and microwave components.

MDS provides capabilities for systems used in electronic warfare (EW) electronic attack and electronic counter measure subsystems signal intelligence and radar environment test and simulation systems.

Geographic Reach

Mercury Systems has research and development centers and other facilities in the US (Alabama California Massachusetts New Hampshire New Jersey and Virginia) Japan and the UK. It generates more than 98% of sales from the US; Europe and the Asia-Pacific region each account for about 1%.

Sales and Marketing

Together Raytheon Northrop Grumman and Lockheed Martin account for more than 60% of revenue.

Financial Performance

Revenue jumped 12.5% in 2015 (ended June) to $234.8 million. In the previous two years revenue was stuck at about $208 million. Revenue in the MCE unit increased 18% in 2015 from projects such as the F-35 jet Patriot missile and the Surface Electronic Warfare Improvement Program (SEWIP).

Mercury posted a profit in 2014 $10.3 million for the first time in three years. Better sales combined with lower operating costs to produce the profit.

Strategy

After a series of acquisitions Mercury restructured some operations as part of integrating new units into the company. It cut about 70 jobs and closed four facilities relocating activities to its Advanced Microelectronics Center in Hudson New Hampshire. It also completed the first phase of the Chelmsford Massachusetts headquarters consolidation in 2014.

Mercury closed the sale of its Mercury Intelligence Systems in 2015. It sold the unit because it didn't fit into its core business.

As part of its investment in research and development the company opened the second of four planned innovation centers. The new center is at Mercury's Chelmsford headquarters.

Mergers and Acquisitions

Mercury Systems uses acquisitions to add products services and technical capabilities. In 2017 the company acquired Richland Technologies which develops safety-critical and high integrity systems software and hardware and safety-certification services for mission-critical applications. Richland also develops safety-certifiable embedded graphics software for commercial and military aerospace applications.

The Richland acquisition complements Mercury's 2016 purchase of Creative Electronic Systems which also develops technology for mission critical technology for aviation and aerospace applications. The deals set up Mercury as a provider of secure and safety-critical subsystems for aerospace and defense.

EXECUTIVES

President Mercury Commercial Electronics, Didier M.C. Thibaud, age 57, $324,198 total compensation
EVP CFO and Treasurer, Gerald M. (Gerry) Haines, age 55, $316,796 total compensation
President and CEO, Mark Aslett, age 50, $510,962 total compensation
VP Controller and Chief Accounting Officer, Charles A. Speicher, age 59, $219,750 total compensation
Chairman, Vincent Vitto, age 77
Auditors: KPMG LLP

LOCATIONS

HQ: Mercury Systems Inc
  50 Minuteman Road, Andover, MA 01810
Phone: 978 256-1300
Web: www.mrcy.com

PRODUCTS/OPERATIONS

2015 Sales

	$ mil.	% of total
Mercury Commercial Electronics	207.1	88
Mercury Defense Systems	27.4	12
Eliminations	0.3	-
Total	**234.8**	**100**

COMPETITORS

ADLINK Technology	GE Intelligent
Analog Devices	Platforms
Analogic	Kontron
Applied Signal	Pentek
CSP	RadiSys
Concurrent Computer	Spectrum Signal
DRS Technologies	Processing
Dedicated Computing	

HISTORICAL FINANCIALS

Company Type: Public

Income Statement

FYE: June 30

	REVENUE ($ mil.)	NET INCOME ($ mil.)	NET PROFIT MARGIN	EMPLOYEES
06/18	493.1	40.8	8.3%	1,320
06/17	408.5	24.8	6.1%	1,159
06/16	270.1	19.7	7.3%	965
06/15	234.8	10.3	4.4%	629
06/14	208.7	(11.4)	—	632
Annual Growth 24.0%		—	—	20.2%

2018 Year-End Financials

Debt ratio: 18.3%	No. of shares (mil.): 46.9
Return on equity: 5.4%	Dividends
Cash ($ mil.): 66.5	Yield: —
Current ratio: 4.63	Payout: —
Long-term debt ($ mil.): 195.0	Market value ($ mil.): 1,786.0

	STOCK PRICE ($) FY Close	P/E High/Low	PER SHARE ($) Earnings	Dividends	Book Value
06/18	38.06	61 36	0.86	0.00	16.45
06/17	42.09	71 37	0.58	0.00	15.67
06/16	24.86	42 24	0.56	0.00	12.23
06/15	14.64	55 33	0.31	0.00	10.75
06/14	11.34	— —	(0.37)	0.00	10.46
Annual Growth 35.4%		— —	—	—	12.0%

Meredith Corp

Meredith is a diversified media firm. The company publishes magazines special interest publications and books. Meredith's portfolio of more than 20 subscription magazines includes flagship title Better Homes and Gardens as well as Family Circle Ladies' Home Journal Parents Fitness and More . The company is also active in broadcasting with about a dozen network-affiliated TV stations across the US. Meredith additionally operates about 50 websites and some 50 mobile apps offers integrated marketing services and has a large consumer database.

HISTORY

Around the turn of the century Edwin Thomas (E. T.) Meredith's grandfather eschewed traditional gifts and gave his grandson a unique wedding present — a handful of $20 gold pieces enough to buy the grandfather's controlling interest in the Farmer's Tribune and a note instructing his grandson to "Sink or Swim" with the financially troubled publication. Meredith proceeded to revive the Farmer's Tribune and after he sold it in 1902 he used the profits to found Meredith Corporation and launch Successful Farming magazine.

Following a stint as Secretary of Agriculture under President Woodrow Wilson E. T. Meredith extended the company's publishing reach introducing Fruit Garden and Home in 1922. Two years later the publication became Better Homes and Gardens. E.T. Meredith died in 1928 but his company forged ahead moving into book publishing in 1930 with the first issue of Better Homes and Gardens Cook Book and branching into special interest publications in 1937.

After going public in 1946 Meredith wasted no time diversifying into the fledgling TV industry. It bought its first TV station (Syracuse New York's WHEN-TV) in 1948 followed by KPHO (Phoenix) in 1952 and Kansas City's KCTV in 1953.

Meredith launched a commercial printing business in 1957 and expanded its printing activities in 1969 by teaming with West Germany's Burda family to operate several US printing plants. With decades of home and family experience under its belt the company entered the real estate market in 1978 launching its Better Homes and Gardens franchised real estate business.

Accelerated expansion was the essence of Meredith's story in the 1980s. In addition to buying two more TV stations the company acquired Ladies' Home Journal from Family Media in 1986 and introduced Midwest Living and Traditional Home in 1987 and 1989 respectively.

Meredith reacted to an advertising slump in the early 1990s by paring down its holdings. Among its divestitures were its printing business (1990) two television stations (1993) a book club (1995) and its cable TV interests (1996). In 1997 it launched its syndicated Better Homes and Gardens TV show the same year William Kerr became CEO. Focusing on its core assets the company sold its Better Homes and Gardens real estate business to General Motors' GMAC Home Services in 1998.

In 1999 Meredith expanded its profile in cyberspace securing a deal with America Online (later AOL) to provide a variety of content to the Internet service. The company's 1999 purchase of Atlanta's TV station WGNX (changed to WGCL in a 2000 restructuring) brought the number of TV stations in its stable to one dozen. Meredith discontinued several publications (Family Money Antiques Extra Mature Outlook) and sold Golf for Women magazine in 2001. An advertising slump resulted in job reductions at the company. In mid-2001 the company hired a marketing company to better leverage its magazine brands.

In 2002 the company swapped its TV stations in Orlando (WOFL) and Ocala Florida (WOGX) for FOX Broadcasting 's KPTV in Portland Oregon. It also added to its magazine collection with its purchase of PRIMEDIA 's American Baby magazine group (American Baby Childbirth Espera) for $115 million. Executive committee chairman E. T. Meredith III — grandson of the company's founder — died in early 2003.

The company bought Michigan radio station WKNX-AM in 2004 with plans to change the call letters to WNEM-AM. In 2005 Meredith purchased the Parents Child Fitness and Family Circle magazines from Bertelsmann's Gruner + Jahr for $350 million. In 2006 president and COO Stephen Lacy succeeded Kerr as CEO. Later that year Meredith acquired the ReadyMade do-it-yourself lifestyle magazine. (It divested that title in 2011.)

The company closed the print edition of Child in 2007; the brand continues to exist online. Also in 2007 Meredith acquired four companies: online customer relationship marketing firm Genex interactive word-of-mouth marketing company New Media Strategies consumer health information search engine Healiea and Directive Corporation a provider of database strategy analytics and customer asset management services.

In 2008 it purchased Big Communications a healthcare marketing communications firm. The company also beefed up Meredith Integrated Marketing in 2008 with the acquisitions of Directive Corporation a specialized customer intelligence firm and Big Communications a healthcare marketing communications firm. Also that year the company sold WFLI a CW affiliate serving Chattanooga Tennessee.

The following year it closed its Country Home magazine. Meredith made the divestitures in order to cut costs and focus on growth areas such as digital and markerting activities. Also in 2009 the firm expanded its licensing operations through forming agreement with John Wiley & Sons to publish and distribute more books based on the Better Homes and Gardens imprint. Under the agreement Meredith creates book content while Wiley is responsible for publishing services such as layout and design printing sales and marketing distribution and inventory management.

In 2010 the company acquired mobile marketing firm The Hyperfactory in order to help develop mobile applications. Another digital acquisition in 2010 was Meredith's purchase of the Real Girls Media Network (RGM) a social content hub for women online. In 2011 it closed down its struggling home shelter title ReadyMade . Also that year it rebranded its Meredith Integrated Marketing business which became Meredith Xcelerated Marketing. In 2012 Meredith acquired AllRecipes.com from Reader's Digest for $175 million.

EXECUTIVES

Chief Development Officer General Counsel and Secretary, John S. Zieser, age 59, $659,616 total compensation

President Local Media Group, Paul Karpowicz, age 65, $719,616 total compensation

CFO, Joseph H. Ceryanec, age 57, $581,923 total compensation

Chairman and CEO, Stephen M. (Steve) Lacy, age 64, $993,270 total compensation

President and COO, Thomas H. (Tom) Harty, age 55, $750,577 total compensation

President National Media Group, Jon Werther, age 49

Senior Vice President Operations, Doug Olson

Vice President Research Solutions, Britta Cleveland

Vice President Retail Brand Licensing, Elise Contarsy

Executive Vice President Operations, Patrick McCreery

Vice President Of Information Systems, Heather Dooling

Senior Vice President Chief Technology Officer, Jack Goldenberg

Vice President of Strategic Sourcing and Production Operations, Charles Howell

Senior Vice President and GM, Melinda Lee

Vice Chairman, D. Mell Meredith Frazier, age 62

Treasurer, Kevin Wagner

Auditors: KPMG LLP

LOCATIONS

HQ: Meredith Corp
1716 Locust Street, Des Moines, IA 50309-3023
Phone: 515 284-3000
Web: www.meredith.com

PRODUCTS/OPERATIONS

2015 Sales

	$ mil.	% of total
Advertising	896.5	56
Circulation	313.8	20
Other	383.9	24
Total	**1,594.2**	**100**

2015 Sales

	$ mil.	% of total
National Media	1,059.9	66
Local Media	534.3	34
Total	**1,594.2**	**100**

Selected Magazines

American Baby (parenthood)
Better Homes and Gardens (home content)
Family Circle (women's content)
Fitness (women's content)
Ladies' Home Journal (women's content)
Midwest Living (regional travel and lifestyle)
More (aimed at women ages 40 and above)
Parents (parenthood)Siempre Mujer (Hispanic women's magazine)
Successful Farming (farm content)
Traditional Home (home decorating)
Wood (woodworking)

Selected TV Stations

KCTV (CBS; Kansas City MO)
KPHO (CBS Phoenix)
KPTV (FOX; Portland OR)
KVVU (FOX Las Vegas)
KSMO (MyNetworkTV Kansas City MO)
WFSB (CBS; Hartford/New Haven CT)
WGCL (CBS Atlanta)
WHNS (FOX; Greenville/Spartanburg/Asheville NC)
WNEM (CBS; Flint/Saginaw/Bay City MI)
WSMV (NBC; Nashville TN)
Other Operations
AllRecipes.com

Meredith Books
Meredith Interactive Media
Meredith Xcelerated Marketing

COMPETITORS

21st Century Fox	Hearst Corporation
ACME Communications	Lagard 're Active
Advance Publications	Martha Stewart Living
American Media	Media General
Dwell LLC	RELX Group
Dynamic Resource Group	Rodale
E. W. Scripps	TEGNA
Essence Communications	Time Inc.
F+W Media	Tribune Media
Farm Journal	Trusted Media Brands
Gruner + Jahr	

HISTORICAL FINANCIALS

Company Type: Public

Income Statement

FYE: June 30

	REVENUE ($ mil.)	NET INCOME ($ mil.)	NET PROFIT MARGIN	EMPLOYEES
06/18	2,247.4	99.4	4.4%	7,915
06/17	1,713.3	188.9	11.0%	3,620
06/16	1,649.6	33.9	2.1%	3,730
06/15	1,594.1	136.7	8.6%	3,825
06/14	1,468.7	113.5	7.7%	3,600
Annual Growth	**11.2%**	**(3.3%)**	**—**	**21.8%**

2018 Year-End Financials

Debt ratio: 46.6%	No. of shares (mil.): 44.9
Return on equity: 7.6%	Dividends
Cash ($ mil.): 437.6	Yield: 0.0%
Current ratio: 1.66	Payout: 144.9%
Long-term debt ($ mil.): 3,117.9	Market value ($ mil.): 2,290.0

	STOCK PRICE ($) FY Close	P/E High/Low		PER SHARE ($) Earnings	Dividends	Book Value
06/18	51.00	49	32	1.47	2.13	36.08
06/17	59.45	16	10	4.16	2.03	22.36
06/16	51.91	69	48	0.75	1.91	19.95
06/15	52.15	19	14	3.02	1.78	21.33
06/14	48.36	21	17	2.50	1.68	20.05
Annual Growth	**1.3%**	**—**	**—**	**(12.4%)**	**6.1%**	**15.8%**

Meridian Bancorp Inc

Meridian Bancorp is the holding company of East Boston Savings Bank which provides standard deposit and lending services to individuals and businesses in the greater Boston area. The bank writes single-family commercial and multi-family mortgages as well as construction and business loans and consumer loans. East Boston Savings operates about 30 branches in eastern Massachusetts. Mutual holding company Meridian Financial Services owns 59% of Meridian Bancorp.

Geographic Reach

Meridian Bancorp operates across the greater Boston metropolitan area in Essex Middlesex and Suffolk counties.

Operations

The bank has about $2.7 billion in assets; commercial real estate loans comprise 45% of its loan portfolio.

Meridian owns a 40% stake in Hampshire First Bank a New Hampshire-chartered bank established in 2006.

Sales and Marketing

Meridian has devoted more dollars to advertising in recent years. It spent $2.95 million in fiscal 2013 on advertising up from $2.54 million in 2012 and $2.45 million in 2011.

Financial Performance

Like many small banks that survived the Great Recession Meridian has grown steadily the last few years. In 2013 it reported an 8% increase in revenue from $106 million to $115 million due to increased loan payments as interest rates recovered. Net income grew 24% from $12 million to $15 million on the strength of higher revenue and changes in the company's bookkeeping. Cash from operations jumped to $28 million after the company sold some of its loans.

Strategy

As part of its growth strategy the bank has bolstered its commercial real estate and business loans as well as its construction loans. Previously residential mortgages represent the company's largest loan segment.

The bank also intends to grow through the opening of new branches and pursuing branch acquisitions. It has opened 14 new branches in upscale Boston neighborhoods in the last two years and acquired another six.

To further enable growth Meridian in 2014 announced that it will convert from a mutual company to a public corporation.

EXECUTIVES

CFO and Treasurer, Mark L. Abbate, age 63

SVP Consumer and Business Banking, Keith D. Armstrong

Chairman President and CEO Meridian Interstate Bancorp and East Boston Savings Bank, Richard J. Gavegnano, age 70, $311,400 total compensation

EVP Corporate Banking, Frank Romano

EVP Lending, John Migliozzi

EVP and COO, John A. Carroll

SVP Electronic Banking, Mary Hagen

SVP Retail Banking, James Morgan

SVP Residential Lending, Joseph Nash

Vice President, Michael Raftery

Auditors: Wolf & Company, P.C.

LOCATIONS

HQ: Meridian Bancorp Inc
67 Prospect Street, Peabody, MA 01960
Phone: 617 567-1500

PRODUCTS/OPERATIONS

2015 Sales

	$ mil.	% of total
Interest & dividend income		
Interest & fees on loans	118.6	87
Interest on debt securities	1.8	1
Dividends on equity securities	1.6	1
Others	1.3	1
Non-interest income		
Customer service fees	8.0	6
Gain on sales of securities net	2.4	2
Income from bank-owned life insurance	1.2	1
Loan fees	1.0	1
Mortgage banking gains & other income	0.5	-
Total	**136.4**	**100**

Selected Products & Services

Personal
Deposit Rates

Investments
Personal Checking
Personal Lending
Personal Online Banking
Retirement Services
Savings & CDs
Business
Business Checking
Business Lending
Business Online Banking
Business Retirement Services
Business Savings
Deposit Rates
Institutional Banking
Merchant Services
Commercial
Cash Management
Commercial Lending
Corporate Banking
Deposit Rates

COMPETITORS

Bank of America	Middlesex Savings
Cambridge Financial	Peoples Federal
Citizens Financial	Bancshares Inc.
Group	Sovereign Bank
Eastern Bank	TD Bank USA

HISTORICAL FINANCIALS

Company Type: Public

Income Statement   FYE: December 31

	ASSETS ($ mil.)	NET INCOME ($ mil.)	INCOME AS % OF ASSETS	EMPLOYEES
12/17	5,299.4	42.9	0.8%	538
12/16	4,436.0	34.1	0.8%	500
12/15	3,524.5	24.6	0.7%	488
12/14	3,278.5	22.3	0.7%	466
12/13	2,682.1	15.4	0.6%	455
Annual Growth 18.6%		29.2%	—	4.3%

2017 Year-End Financials

Return on assets: 0.8%
Return on equity: 6.8%
Long-term debt ($ mil.): —
No. of shares (mil.): 54.0
Sales ($ mil): 208.1

Dividends
Yield: 0.0%
Payout: 20.7%
Market value ($ mil.): 1,113.0

	STOCK PRICE ($) FY Close	P/E High/Low	PER SHARE ($) Earnings	Dividends	Book Value
12/17	20.60	25 19	0.82	0.17	11.96
12/16	18.90	29 19	0.65	0.12	11.33
12/15	14.10	31 24	0.46	0.06	10.72
12/14	11.22	27 24	0.42	0.00	10.56
Annual Growth 22.4%			— 25.0%	—	4.2%

Merit Medical Systems, Inc.

When it comes to medical devices this company believes its merits speak for themselves. Merit Medical Systems makes disposable medical products used during interventional and diagnostic cardiology radiology gastroenterology and pulmonary procedures. The company's products include catheters guide wires needles and tubing used in heart stent procedures pacemaker placement and angioplasties as well as products for endoscopy dialysis and other procedures. Merit Medical sells its products as stand-alone items or in custom-made kits to hospitals and other health care providers as well as to custom packagers and equipment makers worldwide.

Operations

Merit's largest operating segment — accounting for more than 95% of sales — is its cardiovascular division which makes cardiology and radiology devices for the diagnosis of arterial and vascular disease among other conditions. Offerings include stand-alone devices (which account for some 45% of revenues) custom procedure trays and kits inflation devices and catheters. It also includes embolotherapy products which use bioengineered microspheres to create targeted vascular occlusion (the blockage of blood vessels) and drug delivery.

Merit Medical's much smaller endoscopy segment makes devices for gastroenterology and pulmonary treatments including minimally invasive treatment of throat and biliary constriction from malignant tumors. The endoscopy operations are conducted through Merit Medical's Endotek subsidiary.

The company also conducts selected manufacturing of custom medical kits and components for third parties through its OEM division.

Geographic Reach

The US accounts for roughly 60% of Merit's total sales. China is the company's second-largest market bringing in another 10% of sales.

Merit Medical has manufacturing facilities in Ireland the US Mexico the Netherlands France Brazil Australia and Singapore. It has distribution centers in New Zealand India China the US Brazil the Netherlands Australia Canada Russia South Korea Mexico and Japan. The company has R&D facilities in the US Ireland France Singapore and the Netherlands. It has four sales offices in China and Hong Kong.

Sales and Marketing

Merit's marketing and sales efforts in the US and abroad are conducted through a direct sales force as well as through independent distributors and manufacturers. Products are marketed to hospital and clinic-based medical professionals in fields including cardiology radiology gastroenterology pulmonary medicine vascular surgery pain management and thoracic surgery.

The company also has direct or modified sales teams in Canada Europe Australia Brazil Russia Japan China Malaysia South Korea India and the United Arab Emirates.

Financial Performance

Merit Medical's revenues have been growing steadily for the past five years. Net income has generally been trending upward over the same period as the company works to balance costs with earnings. The firm is building up its international business which requires capital but it expects to increase profits because of those activities.

In 2017 revenue increased 21% to $727.9 million. Stand-alone cardiovascular product sales rose 44% that year while catheter sales rose 13% and endoscopy device sales grew 15%. Sales in China increased 22% driving up international sales.

Net income rose 37% to $27.5 million in 2017 thanks to the higher revenue but that gain was partially offset by higher expenses related to Merit's international expansion increased headcount and acquisitions.

The company ended 2017 with $32.3 million in net cash 68% more than it had at then end of 2016. Financing activities contributed $96.5 million in cash and operating activities contributed another $62.7 million. Investing activities primarily business acquisitions used $146.8 million.

Strategy

Though a sizable part of Merit Medical's strategy is growth by acquisition the company also invests about 7% of its annual income in R&D efforts. These activities help it develop new products but Merit is also focused on introducing existing products into new geographic markets.

The company has been transitioning much of its business model in international markets switching from outside distributors to direct sales operations.

Mergers and Acquisitions

Merit Medical acquired Cianna Medical in a deal valued at up to $200 million in 2018. Cianna Medical makes SAVI SCOUT the first US-approved wire-free radar breast tumor localization system for long-term implant capabilities. The system is awaiting approval in Europe.

Also in 2018 the company acquired the Achieve and other branded soft tissue core needle biopsy products from Becton Dickinson for $100 million. It then acquired most of the assets (including the ClariVein specialty infusion and occlusion catheter systems) of Massachusetts-based Vascular Insights for $40 million.

In 2017 Merit bought a custom procedure pack business in Australia from ITL Healthcare for $11.3 million. Also that year it purchased Osseon's vertebral augmentation product line for $6.8 million.

In early 2016 Merit Medical acquired the HeRO Graft product line for end-stage renal disease from CryoLife for $18.5 million. The HeRO Graft is a hemodialysis access graft used in patients who have catheter-dependent because of vein blockage.

EXECUTIVES

Chairman President and CEO, Fred P. Lampropoulos, age 69, $1,108,654 total compensation
President Merit Endotek, Darla R. Gill
President Merit Technology Group, Joseph (Joe) Wright
EVP Sales and Marketing, Justin Lampropoulos
CIO, Joseph Pierce
CFO, Bernard Birkett
COO, Ronald A. Frost, age 56, $317,500 total compensation
Vice President Business Development, George Frioux
Vice President Research and Development, Mark Ferguson
Vice President Manufacturing and Logistics, Gearoid Quinn
Executive Vice President Of Sales And Marketing, Marty Stephens
Vice President Us Sales, Conor Nolan
Vice President Research And Development, Chris Heine
Executive Vice President Global Intelligence And Security, Nico Walker
Auditors: DELOITTE & TOUCHE LLP

LOCATIONS

HQ: Merit Medical Systems, Inc.
1600 West Merit Parkway, South Jordan, UT 84095
Phone: 801 253-1600
Web: www.merit.com

PRODUCTS/OPERATIONS

2017 Sales by Segment

	$ mil.	% of total
Cardiovascular		
Stand-alone devices	275.4	38
Catheters	127.8	17
Custom kits & procedure trays	126.1	17
Inflation devices	79.9	11
Embolization devices	48.5	7
CRM/EP	41.9	6
Endoscopy	27.2	4
Total	**727.9**	**100**

Selected Products

Backstop (waste handling system)
BasixCOMPAK (inflation devices)
Blue Diamond (inflation devices)
Fountain (thrombolytic infusion catheters)
Medallion (specialty syringes)
Merit Disposal Depot (waste handling system)
Meritrans (disposable blood pressure transducer)
Monarch (inflation devices)
Prelude (sheath introducers)
ProGuide (chronic dialysis catheter)

COMPETITORS

3M	Cordis
Abbott Labs	Edwards Lifesciences
AngioDynamics	ICU Medical
B. Braun Medical	Medtronic
Becton Dickinson	Stryker
Boston Scientific	Teleflex
CONMED Corporation	Terumo
Cook Incorporated	

HISTORICAL FINANCIALS

Company Type: Public

Income Statement   FYE: December 31

	REVENUE ($ mil.)	NET INCOME ($ mil.)	NET PROFIT MARGIN	EMPLOYEES
12/17	727.8	27.5	3.8%	4,876
12/16	603.8	20.1	3.3%	4,150
12/15	542.1	23.8	4.4%	3,754
12/14	509.6	22.9	4.5%	3,105
12/13	449.0	16.5	3.7%	2,888
Annual Growth	12.8%	13.5%	—	14.0%

2017 Year-End Financials

Debt ratio: 25.0%
Return on equity: 4.6%
Cash ($ mil.): 32.3
Current ratio: 2.73
Long-term debt ($ mil.): 259.0
No. of shares (mil.): 50.2
Dividends
  Yield: —
  Payout: —
Market value ($ mil.): 2,171.0

	STOCK PRICE ($) FY Close	P/E High/Low	PER SHARE ($) Earnings	Dividends	Book Value
12/17	43.20	81 44	0.55	0.00	13.46
12/16	26.50	59 35	0.45	0.00	11.16
12/15	18.59	47 28	0.53	0.00	10.53
12/14	17.33	33 22	0.53	0.00	9.98
12/13	15.74	42 25	0.39	0.00	9.47
Annual Growth	28.7%	— —	9.0%	—	9.2%

Meritage Hospitality Group Inc

This company is really big on the beef in Michigan. Meritage Hospitality Group is a leading franchisee of Wendy's fast food hamburger restaurants with about 70 locations operating mostly in western and southern Michigan. The units franchised from Wendy's/Arby's Group offer a menu of burgers and other sandwiches fries and other items. In addition to its quick-service operations Meritage runs four franchised O'Charley's casual dining restaurants in Michigan near Grand Rapids and Detroit. The company was founded in 1986 as Thomas Edison Inns. The family of chairman Robert Schermer Sr. including CEO Robert Schermer Jr. controls Meritage.

Meritage expanded its restaurant estate in 2009 when the company acquired 20 Wendy's locations from Wendy's/Arby's in the Jacksonville Florida area. The deal also diversified Meritage's operations away from the Michigan market which was hit hard by the recession and credit collapse late in 2008.

The Schermer's led a group to take Meritage private in 2007 through a reverse stock split. The buyout was a cost-cutting move in response to increased reporting equipments enacted by the US Securities and Exchange Commission (SEC). Meritage had been a public company since 1986.

Thomas Edison Inns had previously operated a small number of Michigan resort inns. Schermer and partner Don Reynolds took control of the company in 1996; the business was renamed later that year.

EXECUTIVES

Vice President Facility Maintenance, Robert Potts
Auditors: Plante & Moran, PLLC

LOCATIONS

HQ: Meritage Hospitality Group Inc
45 Ottawa Avenue SW, Suite 600, Grand Rapids, MI 49503
Phone: 616 776-2600   **Fax:** 616 776-2776
Web: www.meritagehospitality.com

COMPETITORS

American Dairy Queen	McDonald's
B.R. Associates	Quality Dining
Burger King	Subway
Carrols	Tubby's
Hardee's	YUM!
Interfoods	

HISTORICAL FINANCIALS

Company Type: Public

Income Statement   FYE: December 31

	REVENUE ($ mil.)	NET INCOME ($ mil.)	NET PROFIT MARGIN	EMPLOYEES
12/17*	312.5	8.9	2.9%	6,800
01/17	235.7	6.4	2.7%	5,700
01/16	210.0	7.0	3.3%	5,100
12/14	160.2	2.7	1.7%	4,000
12/13	137.7	3.0	2.2%	3,300
Annual Growth	22.7%	30.9%	—	19.8%

*Fiscal year change

2017 Year-End Financials

Debt ratio: 60.8%
Return on equity: 27.8%
Cash ($ mil.): 12.9
Current ratio: 0.25
Long-term debt ($ mil.): 97.4
No. of shares (mil.): 6.1
Dividends
  Yield: 0.0%
  Payout: —
Market value ($ mil.): 123.0

	STOCK PRICE ($) FY Close	P/E High/Low	PER SHARE ($) Earnings	Dividends	Book Value
12/17*	20.00	— —	(0.00)	0.10	6.25
01/17	11.15	— —	(0.00)	0.07	4.37
01/16	11.25	— —	(0.00)	0.06	3.63
12/14	4.97	— —	(0.00)	0.03	2.32
12/13	4.30	— —	(0.00)	0.02	1.94
Annual Growth	46.9%	— —	—	49.5%	34.0%

*Fiscal year change

Merrill Lynch Life Insurance Co - Insurance Products

EXECUTIVES

Pres, Marilyn Carp
Auditors: PricewaterhouseCoopers LLP

LOCATIONS

HQ: Merrill Lynch Life Insurance Co - Insurance Products
4333 Edgewood Road, NE, Cedar Rapids, IA 52499-0001
Phone: 800 346-3677
Web: www.transamerica.com

HISTORICAL FINANCIALS

Company Type: Public

Income Statement   FYE: December 31

	ASSETS ($ mil.)	NET INCOME ($ mil.)	INCOME AS % OF ASSETS	EMPLOYEES
12/17	8,621.8	99.4	1.2%	0
12/16	8,670.2	(20.5)	—	0
12/15	9,165.9	13.6	0.1%	0
12/14	10,108.4	33.5	0.3%	0
12/13	10,555.8	(254.4)	—	0
Annual Growth	(4.9%)	—	—	—

2017 Year-End Financials

Return on assets: 1.1%
Return on equity: 9.2%
Long-term debt ($ mil.): —
No. of shares (mil.): 0.2
Sales ($ mil) 216.8
Dividends
  Yield: —
  Payout: 140.8%
Market value ($ mil.): —

Mesabi Trust

In the Iron Range of Mesabi the stockholders trust. Mesabi Trust collects royalties and bonuses from the sale of minerals that are shipped from

Northshore Mining's Silver Bay Minnesota facility. The mining company is a wholly owned subsidiary of Cliffs a supplier of iron ore products to the steel industry. Northshore Mining pays royalties to Mesabi Trust based on production and sales of crude ore pulled from the trust's property; it has curtailed its extraction efforts citing lack of demand. Independent consultants track production and sales for Mesabi Trust. Deutsche Bank Trust Company Americas is the corporate trustee of Mesabi Trust.

The company was formed in 1961 to hold the interests formerly owned by Mesabi Iron Company. Mesabi Trust's revenues are generated solely in the form of leasehold royalty income.

EXECUTIVES

Individual Trustee, Norman F. Sprague III, age 67
Individual Trustee, Richard G. Lareau, age 86
Individual Trustee, Robert C Berglund, age 68
Individual Trustee, James A. Ehrenberg, age 72
VP; Deutsche Bank Trust Company Americas, Kenneth R. Ring
Auditors: Baker Tilly Virchow Krause, LLP

LOCATIONS

HQ: Mesabi Trust
c/o Deutsche Bank Trust Company Americas, Trust & Agency Services, 60 Wall Street, 16th Floor, New York, NY 10005
Phone: 904 271-2520
Web: www.mesabi-trust.com

COMPETITORS

BHP Billiton   Rio Tinto Limited
Great Northern Iron
 Ore

HISTORICAL FINANCIALS

Company Type: Public

Income Statement   FYE: January 31

	REVENUE ($ mil.)	NET INCOME ($ mil.)	NET PROFIT MARGIN	EMPLOYEES
01/18	34.5	33.5	96.9%	0
01/17	10.7	9.6	89.5%	0
01/16	9.7	8.5	88.0%	0
01/15	26.0	24.7	95.0%	0
01/14	22.0	21.0	95.5%	0
Annual Growth	11.9%	12.3%	—	—

2018 Year-End Financials

Debt ratio: —
Return on equity: 323.4%
Cash ($ mil.): 0.3
Current ratio: 1.67
Long-term debt ($ mil.): —
No. of shares (mil.): 13.1
Dividends
 Yield: 10.2%
 Payout: 99.1%
Market value ($ mil.): 325.0

	STOCK PRICE ($) FY Close	P/E High/Low		PER SHARE ($) Earnings	Dividends	Book Value
01/18	24.80	12	5	2.55	2.53	0.80
01/17	13.70	19	5	0.73	0.64	0.78
01/16	4.40	27	5	0.65	0.09	0.69
01/15	17.08	12	9	1.89	1.84	0.12
01/14	20.09	15	11	1.61	1.62	0.08
Annual Growth	5.4%	—	—	12.3%	11.8%	80.8%

Meta Financial Group Inc

Delivering financial products and services to Iowa and South Dakota is the calling of Meta Financial Group. The group?s biggest component is MetaBank a 10-branch operation that offers standard banking solutions such as deposit accounts CDs home mortgages and student loans. Other subsidiaries provide prepaid card services insurance and a variety of tax related solutions. It holds a loan portfolio that exceeds $1 billion and deposits that surpass $3 billion.

Operations
Meta Financial Group operates two customer-facing business segments Banking and Payments and a supporting segment that includes corporate services and other sources of revenue. The Banking segment generates the majority of interest income and a small amount of non-interest income. The Payments unit is the opposite where non-interest income accounts for 90% of its overall revenue and interest income is less than 10% of its business.

The Banking unit doing business as MetaBank operates 10 branches in four key geographic markets: Central Iowa Storm Lake Iowa Brookings South Dakota and Sioux Falls South Dakota. It offers standard deposit products and services including checking and savings accounts. Its lending and investment activities are weighted towards real estate and real estate-related assets; commercial and multifamily residential mortgages comprise more than half of the bank's loan portfolio. It also writes single-family residential mortgages and business loans.

Meta Financial's bread and butter however is the bank's Meta Payment Systems (MPS) division which provides prepaid cards consumer credit and ATM sponsorship services nationwide under operating names of MPS Refund Advantage EPS Financial and SCS. The segment has grown primarily through acquisitions.

Geographic Reach
The MetaBank subsidiary of Sioux Falls SD-based Meta Financial Group operates mainly in Iowa and South Dakota. Its Payment segment includes subsidiaries that run business out of Dallas TX Newport Beach CA Louisville KY Easton PA and Hurst TX.

Financial Performance
Non-interest income from the Payments business grew more than 70% in the year to $166 million. Interest income from the Bank segment rose 37% to $52 million. Total revenue for 2017 was $265 million. The stellar growth is the result of acquisitions and organic growth ? the Bank unit acquired $134 million of private student loans in late 2016 and a further $73 million portfolio in late 2017. The Payment business grew its tax refund business 13-fold underwriting and originating $1.3 billion of refund advance loans for the 2017 tax season.

Net income in 2017 rose 33% to $45 million thanks to the significant upswing in Payments revenue including big growth in its tax business along with improvements in card fee income.

Strategy

Meta Financial Group is looking to boost is non-interest income business endeavors in the Payments division. It feels constrained in its banking business by the need to raise more capital before it can lend out more money from which it would generate interest income. Without the ability to raise more capital (or to raise it at an advantageous cost) the Group believes its efforts are better directed at growth that is not hindered by insufficient capital.

EXECUTIVES

Chairman and CEO Meta Financial Group and MetaBank, J. Tyler Haahr, age 55, $550,000 total compensation
EVP Sales and Operations MetaBank and Director Meta Financial Group (MFG) and MetaBank, Troy Moore, age 50, $252,350 total compensation
EVP Secretary Treasurer and CFO, David W. Leedom, age 64, $215,000 total compensation
President Meta Financial Group Inc. (MFG) and MetaBank and Division President Meta Payment System, Bradley C. (Brad) Hanson, age 54, $550,000 total compensation
EVP Meta Payment Systems, Scott Galit, age 48, $235,000 total compensation
EVP and CFO Meta Financial Group (MFG) and MetaBank, Glen W. Herrick, age 55, $255,000 total compensation
Vice Chairman Meta Financial Group (MFG) and MetaBank, Frederick V. (Fred) Moore, age 62
Board Member, Douglas Hajek
Auditors: Crowe LLP

LOCATIONS

HQ: Meta Financial Group Inc
 5501 South Broadband Lane, Sioux Falls, SD 57108
Phone: 605 782-1767
Web: www.metabank.com

COMPETITORS

Blackhawk Network   Great Western Bancorp
BofI   Green Dot
Citi Prepaid Services HF Financial
First National of   West Bancorporation
 Nebraska

HISTORICAL FINANCIALS

Company Type: Public

Income Statement   FYE: September 30

	ASSETS ($ mil.)	NET INCOME ($ mil.)	INCOME AS % OF ASSETS	EMPLOYEES
09/18	5,835.0	51.6	0.9%	1,219
09/17	5,228.3	44.9	0.9%	827
09/16	4,006.4	33.2	0.8%	672
09/15	2,529.7	18.0	0.7%	638
09/14	2,054.0	15.7	0.8%	453
Annual Growth	29.8%	34.6%	—	28.1%

2018 Year-End Financials

Return on assets: 0.9%
Return on equity: 8.7%
Long-term debt ($ mil.): —
No. of shares (mil.): 39.1
Sales ($ mil): 343.0
Dividends
 Yield: 0.0%
 Payout: 10.7%
Market value ($ mil.): 3,237.0

STOCK PRICE ($)		P/E	PER SHARE ($)		
	FY Close	High/Low	Earnings	Dividends	Book Value
09/18	82.65	70 46	1.67	0.18	19.00
09/17	78.40	66 39	1.61	0.17	15.05
09/16	60.61	47 28	1.31	0.17	13.10
09/15	41.77	59 36	0.89	0.17	11.08
09/14	35.26	54 41	0.84	0.17	9.44
Annual Growth 23.7%		— —	18.6%	0.9%	19.1%

Mid Penn Bancorp Inc

Mid Penn Bancorp is the holding company for Mid Penn Bank which operates more than a dozen branches in central Pennsylvania's Cumberland Dauphin Northumberland and Schuylkill counties. The bank offers full-service commercial banking insurance and trust services. Its deposit products include checking savings money market and NOW accounts. Commercial real estate construction and land development loans account for nearly 80% of the company's loan portfolio; the bank also writes residential mortgages and business agricultural and consumer loans. Mid Penn is a descendant of Millersburg Bank founded in 1868. Trust company CEDE & Co. owns about a third of Mid Penn Bancorp.

EXECUTIVES

SVP and Senior Credit Officer Mid Penn Bank, Randall L. Klinger, age 67
Secretary; VP and Corporate Secretary Mid Penn Bank, Cindy L. Wetzel, age 54
VP and Treasurer; SEVP and Northern Region President and COO Mid Penn Bank, Kevin W. Laudenslager, age 52, $108,983 total compensation
President CEO and Director Mid Penn Bancorp and Mid Penn Bank, Rory G. Ritrievi, age 52
Vice Chairman, William A. Specht III, age 54
Chairman, Robert C. Grubic, age 64
SVP and CFO Mid Penn Bank, Edward P. Williams
Senior Vice President and Chief Lending Officer of the Bank, Scott Micklewright
President CEO and Director Mid Penn Bancorp and Mid Penn Bank, Rory G. Ritrievi, age 52
Vice Chairman, William A. Specht III, age 54
Independent Director, Robert Abel
Independent Director, Steven Boyer
Auditors: BDO USA, LLP

LOCATIONS

HQ: Mid Penn Bancorp Inc
349 Union Street, Millersburg, PA 17061
Phone: 866 642-7736
Web: www.midpennbank.com

COMPETITORS

Fulton Financial
PNC Financial
Pennsylvania State Employees Credit Union

HISTORICAL FINANCIALS
Company Type: Public

Income Statement
FYE: December 31

	ASSETS ($ mil.)	NET INCOME ($ mil.)	INCOME AS % OF ASSETS	EMPLOYEES
12/17	1,170.3	7.0	0.6%	277
12/16	1,032.6	7.8	0.8%	257
12/15	931.7	6.5	0.7%	252
12/14	755.6	5.7	0.8%	203
12/13	713.1	4.9	0.7%	198
Annual Growth 13.2%		9.5%	—	8.8%

2017 Year-End Financials

Return on assets: 0.6%	Dividends
Return on equity: 9.7%	Yield: 0.0%
Long-term debt ($ mil.): —	Payout: 46.1%
No. of shares (mil.): 4.2	Market value ($ mil.): 140.0
Sales ($ mil): 49.5	

STOCK PRICE ($)		P/E	PER SHARE ($)		
	FY Close	High/Low	Earnings	Dividends	Book Value
12/17	33.10	21 14	1.67	0.77	17.85
12/16	23.83	13 8	1.85	0.68	16.65
12/15	16.10	12 10	1.47	0.54	16.58
12/14	15.55	11 9	1.53	0.45	16.90
12/13	14.34	11 7	1.32	0.25	15.14
Annual Growth 23.3%		— —	6.1%	32.5%	4.2%

Mid-America Apartment Communities Inc

For Mid-America Apartment Communities the Sunbelt is where it's at. Operating as MAA the firm is a self-administered self-managed real estate investment trust (REIT) that focuses solely on buying multifamily residences. MAA owns or has interests in approximately 79500 apartment units in 15 states primarily located in the West Southeast and south-central US. Its largest markets are California Florida Tennessee and Texas. MAA which has an average property occupancy rate of 95% targets large and midsized markets. MAA bought rival Colonial Properties in 2013 in an $8.6 billion deal. It is now buying Post Properties for $3.9 billion to become the nation's largest public apartment owner by unit number.

Strategy
Rather than developing new properties MAA prefers to buy and upgrade existing complexes increasing curb appeal to attract middle-income residents. Although MAA generally considers property management and maintenance its focus and strength it does invest in new properties with joint venture partners from time to time and anticipates that that will be a growing part of its strategy.

Multifamily investors have been leading the way in the slowly recovering property markets and MAA in particular has had strongly growing sales for at least a decade.

EXECUTIVES

Senior Vice President Director Physical Assets, Kevin Perkins
Vice President Director Risk Management, Doug Clark
Chairman President and CEO, H. Eric Bolton, age 61, $404,133 total compensation
SVP and Operations Director Central North and East Regions, Thomas L. (Tom) Grimes, $168,928 total compensation
EVP and CFO, Albert M. (Al) Campbell, age 51, $158,223 total compensation
SVP Management Information Systems, Shelton Barron
EXECUTIVE VICE PRESIDENT FOR DEVELOPMENT, Don Aldridge
Senior Vice President, Robert Donnelly
Regional Vice President, Jackie Melnick
VICE PRESIDENT DIRECTOR OF CAPITAL IMPROVEMENTS, Dennis Duke
REGIONAL VICE PRESIDENT, Gayle Mackovic
Senior Vice President Controller, Micah Holton
Executive Vice President and General Counsel, Robert DelPriore
Regional Vice President, Denise Bowers
Regional Vice President, Jon King
Vice President, David Schindler
Senior Vice President Transactions, Brad Hill
Vice President Human Resources, Melanie Carter
Regional Vice President, Cara Mober
Regional Vice President, Anna Lister
Executive Vice President and Chief Financial Officer, Al Campbell
Vice President Operations Coastal Region, Bob Donnelly
VICE PRESIDENT CONSTRUCTION, Kelly C Carter
SENIOR VICE PRESIDENT DIRECTOR OF INTENAL AUDIT, Larry C Davis
SENIOR VICE PRESIDENT, Charles Mcnamee
REGIONAL VICE PRESIDENT, Lynn Mcdaniel
Vice President Construction, Robert Scheller
Vice President Construction, Indrid Agaj
Board Member, Joe Fracchia
Board Member, David Stockert
Auditors: Ernst & Young LLP

LOCATIONS

HQ: Mid-America Apartment Communities Inc
6584 Poplar Avenue, Suite 500, Germantown, TN 38138
Phone: 901 682-6600   **Fax:** 901 682-6667
Web: www.maac.com

PRODUCTS/OPERATIONS

2015 sales

	$ mil.	% of total
Rental	952.2	91
Other property	90.6	9
Total	**1,042.8**	**100**

COMPETITORS

AMLI Residential	Camden Property
Apartment Investment and Management	Equity Residential
Berkshire Income Realty	Milestone Management
	Southern Management
	UDR

HISTORICAL FINANCIALS

Company Type: Public

Income Statement   FYE: December 31

	REVENUE ($ mil.)	NET INCOME ($ mil.)	NET PROFIT MARGIN	EMPLOYEES
12/17	1,528.9	328.3	21.5%	2,464
12/16	1,125.3	212.2	18.9%	2,528
12/15	1,042.7	332.2	31.9%	1,989
12/14	989.3	147.9	15.0%	2,090
12/13	634.7	115.2	18.2%	2,241
Annual Growth	24.6%	29.9%	—	2.4%

2017 Year-End Financials

Debt ratio: 39.1%	No. of shares (mil.): 113.6
Return on equity: 5.1%	Dividends
Cash ($ mil.): 10.7	Yield: 0.0%
Current ratio: —	Payout: 121.6%
Long-term debt ($ mil.): 4,502.0	Market value ($ mil.): 11,428.0

	STOCK PRICE ($) FY Close	P/E High/Low	PER SHARE ($) Earnings	Dividends	Book Value
12/17	100.56	39 33	2.86	3.48	55.88
12/16	97.92	41 31	2.69	3.28	56.50
12/15	90.81	21 16	4.41	3.08	39.79
12/14	74.68	39 31	1.97	2.92	38.48
12/13	60.74	33 26	2.25	2.78	39.45
Annual Growth	13.4%		6.2%	5.8%	9.1%

Middleby Corp

Founded in 1888 Middleby makes a slew of commercial and institutional foodservice equipment for restaurants retailers and hotels worldwide. Middleby operates through three segments: Commercial Foodservice Equipment Food Processing Equipment and Residential Kitchen Equipment. The largest Foodservice makes machines for most types of cooking and warming activities. Products are sold under some two dozen blue chip brands — Anets Blodgett Southbend and TurboChef among them. Food Processing makes cooking mixing slicing and packaging machines and Residential Kitchen makes ovens refrigerators dishwashers microwaves and other related products.

Operations

The company's mainstay Commercial Foodservice Equipment segment offers ovens ranges broilers fryers toasters coffee and tea brewers and other cooking equipment; it generates around 55% of total sales each year. Its Food Processing Equipment group (15% of sales) offers a slate of labor-saving products from batch ovens to mixing and slicing machines packaging and food safety equipment. Residential Kitchen (almost 30%) makes everything from ovens and refrigerators to dishwashers and microwaves. The group's manufacturing facilities often neighbor major food processors.

Geographic Reach

Middleby operates nearly 25 manufacturing facilities in the US and 20 internationally throughout the Americas Europe Asia and the Middle East. About 65% of its revenues come from the US and Canada. Europe and the Middle East account for nearly 25%.

Financial Performance

Middleby has enjoyed unprecedented growth over the last five years. Revenues rose by 24% from 1.8 billion in 2015 to peak at a record-setting #2.3 billion in 2016. The historic growth for 2016 was fueled by sales increases across all its segments: Commercial Foodservice (13%) Food Processing Equipment (15%) and Residential Kitchen (62%). The growth was primarily attributed to additional revenue from previous acquisitions.

Profits also surged 48% from $192 million in 2015 to $284 million in 2016 another company milestone. This was attributed to the record revenue growth coupled with a reduction in restructuring expenses. In addition to revenues and profits Middleby's operating cash flow has trended upward over the years jumping from $250 million in 2015 to $294 million in 2016.

Mergers and Acquisitions

Acquisitions have significantly added to Middleby's revenue stream and strengthened its competitive position as a one-stop-shop for such giants as Cracker Barrel McDonald's Olive Garden and Panda Express. Middleby in 2018 acquired M-TEK a manufacturer of Modified Atmosphere Packing (MAP) systems allowing the company to expand its packaging capabilities in its industrial food processing business.

In 2017 the company purchased Arkansas-based QualServ Solutions a global commercial kitchen design manufacturing engineering project management and equipment provider. QualServ has annual revenues of $100 million and the deal expanded Middleby's product offerings to include kitchen fabrication and allows it to provide integrated equipment products and services with its existing portfolio of brands and products.

EXECUTIVES

Chairman and CEO, Selim A. Bassoul, age 62, $1,000,000 total compensation
VP and CFO, Timothy J. (Tim) Fitzgerald, age 49, $575,000 total compensation
COO Commercial Foodservice, David Brewer, age 62, $400,000 total compensation
VICE PRESIDENT BUSINESS DEVELOPMENT, Jana Perkins
Vice President of Engineering, Steve Lombardo
Vice President Business Development, Gerard Giustino
Vice President of Government Sales, Jason Doonan
Vice President Business Development, Rob Carpenter
Auditors: Ernst & Young LLP

LOCATIONS

HQ: Middleby Corp
1400 Toastmaster Drive, Elgin, IL 60120
Phone: 847 741-3300
Web: www.middleby.com

PRODUCTS/OPERATIONS

2016 Sales

	$ mil.	% of total
Commercial Foodservice	1,267.0	56
Residential Kitchen	658.7	29
Food processing	342.2	15
Total	**2,267.9**	**100**

Selected Foodservice Brands

Anets
Beech
Blodgett
Bloomfield
BritanniaCarter-Hoffmann
Celfrost
Concordia
Cook
Tek
Desmon
Doyon
Southbend Selected Food Processing Equipment Brands
AlkarAuto-Bake
Armor Inox
BakerCozzini
Danfotech
Drake
Maurer-Atmos Gmb
HMP Equipment
Rapid
Pak

COMPETITORS

Dacor	Illinois Tool Works
Dover Corp.	Thermador Groupe
Electrolux	Vulcan-Hart
GEA Group	Welbilt
Hobart Corp.	

HISTORICAL FINANCIALS

Company Type: Public

Income Statement   FYE: December 30

	REVENUE ($ mil.)	NET INCOME ($ mil.)	NET PROFIT MARGIN	EMPLOYEES
12/17	2,335.5	298.1	12.8%	8,493
12/16*	2,267.8	284.2	12.5%	8,026
01/16	1,826.6	191.6	10.5%	7,800
01/15	1,636.5	193.3	11.8%	4,860
12/13	1,428.6	153.9	10.8%	4,491
Annual Growth	13.1%	18.0%	—	17.3%

*Fiscal year change

2017 Year-End Financials

Debt ratio: 30.8%	No. of shares (mil.): 55.7
Return on equity: 22.7%	Dividends
Cash ($ mil.): 89.6	Yield: —
Current ratio: 1.97	Payout: —
Long-term debt ($ mil.): 1,023.7	Market value ($ mil.): 7,521.0

	STOCK PRICE ($) FY Close	P/E High/Low	PER SHARE ($) Earnings	Dividends	Book Value
12/17	134.95	27 21	5.26	0.00	24.42
12/16*	128.81	29 16	4.98	0.00	21.99
01/16	107.87	37 28	3.36	0.00	20.36
01/15	99.04	88 21	3.40	0.00	17.58
12/13	242.50	89 46	2.74	0.00	14.61
Annual Growth	(13.6%)		17.7%	—	13.7%

*Fiscal year change

Middlefield Banc Corp.

Here's your cash stuck in the Middlefield Banc with you. The firm is the holding company for Middlefield Bank which has about 10 offices in northeast and central Ohio. The community bank offers standard deposit services such as checking and savings accounts CDs and IRAs. Investments insurance and brokerage services are offered through an agreement with UVEST a division of LPL Financial. Residential mortgage loans comprise more than 60% of the company's loan portfolio; commercial and industrial loans make up about 20%. The bank also offers commercial mortgages construction loans and consumer installment loans. Middlefield Banc is buying Liberty Bank which operates three branches in northeast Ohio.

EXECUTIVES

President and CEO Middlefield Banc and Middlefield Banking Company, Thomas G. Caldwell, age 58, $252,558 total compensation
SVP Operations and Administration Middlefield Banking Company, Teresa M. Hetrick, age 52
CFO and Treasurer; SVP and CFO Middlefield Banking Company, Donald L. Stacy, age 62, $139,735 total compensation
SVP and Senior Commercial Lender Middlefield Banking Company, Jay P. Giles, age 66, $117,013 total compensation
VP and Loan Administrator Middlefield Banking Company, Alfred F. Thompson Jr., age 56
EVP and COO Middlefield Banc and Middlefield Banking Company, James R. Heslop II, age 62, $203,012 total compensation
Chairman Middlefield Banc and Middlefield Banking Company, Richard T. Coyne, age 80
President and CEO Emerald Bank, James L. (Jim) Long
Auditors: S.R. Snodgrass, P.C.

LOCATIONS

HQ: Middlefield Banc Corp.
15985 East High Street, Middlefield, OH 44062-0035
Phone: 440 632-1666
Web: www.middlefieldbank.com

COMPETITORS

Cortland Bancorp	PVF Capital
Huntington Bancshares	U.S. Bancorp
PNC Financial	

HISTORICAL FINANCIALS

Company Type: Public

Income Statement

FYE: December 31

	ASSETS ($ mil.)	NET INCOME ($ mil.)	INCOME AS % OF ASSETS	EMPLOYEES
12/17	1,106.3	9.4	0.9%	190
12/16	787.8	6.4	0.8%	139
12/15	735.1	6.8	0.9%	143
12/14	677.5	7.1	1.1%	139
12/13	647.0	7.0	1.1%	125
Annual Growth	**14.3%**	**7.7%**	**—**	**11.0%**

2017 Year-End Financials

Return on assets: 1.0%
Return on equity: 9.6%
Long-term debt ($ mil.): —
No. of shares (mil.): 3.2
Sales ($ mil): 48.8
Dividends
Yield: 0.0%
Payout: 34.8%
Market value ($ mil.): 155.0

	STOCK PRICE ($) FY Close	P/E High/Low	PER SHARE ($) Earnings	Dividends	Book Value
12/17	48.20	17 12	3.10	1.08	37.25
12/16	38.70	13 10	3.03	1.08	34.00
12/15	32.40	10 8	3.39	1.07	33.19
12/14	33.61	10 7	3.50	1.04	31.12
12/13	26.00	10 7	3.47	1.04	26.31
Annual Growth	**16.7%**	**— —**	**(2.8%)**	**0.9%**	**9.1%**

Midland States Bancorp Inc

Born in rural Illinois Midland States Bancorp is now discovering banking life in new states. It is the $3 billion-asset holding company for Midland States Bank a community bank that operates more than 35 branches in central and northern Illinois and around 15 branches in the St. Louis metropolitan area. The bank offers traditional consumer and commercial banking products and services as well as merchant card services insurance and financial planning. Subsidiary Midland Wealth Management which boasts $1.2 billion-plus in assets under administration provides wealth management services while Heartland Business Credit offers commercial equipment leasing services. Midland States Bancorp went public in 2016.

IPO

The bank holding company raised $80.1 million in its initial public offering. It plans to contribute some $25 million to Midland States Bank and use the rest for general corporate purposes including possible acquisitions.

Operations

About 57% of Midland States Bancorp's total revenue came from loan interest during 2014 while another 17% came from interest income from investment securities. The rest came from wealth management fees (8% of revenue) deposit account service charges (3%) ATM and interchange revenue (3%) mortgage banking revenue (3%) merchant services revenue (1%) and nonrecurring gains on the sales of assets (around 8%).

Subsidiary Love Funding provides multifamily and healthcare facility FHA financing.

Geographic Reach

Midland has more than 80 branches and offices across the US with around 50 in Illinois and around the St. Louis metro area and the rest in California Colorado Florida Massachusetts North Carolina Ohio Tennessee and Texas.

Financial Performance

Midland States Bancorp's revenue climbed 3% to $93 million despite a decline in loan interest income during 2014 mostly thanks to profitable asset sales and other income.

Despite modest revenue growth in 2014 the bank's net income dove 67% to $3.2 billion as acquisition and integration expenses stemming from its late 2014 acquisition of Heartland ate up any revenue gains it had made. Excluding these nonrecurring items the bank's net income grew modestly.

Strategy

Midland States Bancorp has been pursuing an acquisition and branch expansion growth strategy since 2007 after it replaced its executive management and laid out a plan to expand Midland States Bank's presence in Illinois. Midland States Bank continues to focus on moving into suburban areas and other markets in Illinois and Missouri that have growing populations. During 2015 it opened a new branches in the St. Louis region (in Jennings) downtown Joliet and downtown Effingham areas as well as a wealth management office in downtown Decatur.

The company also planned in 2016 to continue building its fast-growing wealth management business which now makes up nearly 10% of its total revenue. Thanks to Midland's efforts the business' wealth management assets under administration have skyrocketed twelve-fold since 2008 growing from $95 million then to $1.19 billion at the end of 2014.

Mergers and Acquisitions

In February 2017 CEO Leon Holschbach signed a $175 million deal with rival Centrue Bank to merge. The two banks had been treading on each others' toes in Princeton Illinois.

In February 2016 Midland States Bank agreed to purchase $400 million in wealth management assets from Sterling National Bank which would boost its assets under administration by more than 30% to $1.6 billion. Sterling Bank had originally obtained the wealth management assets — which were mostly Special Needs and Settlement Trusts — after buying Hudson Valley Bank.

In December 2014 the bank acquired Heartland Bank as well as its $900 million in assets 13 Heartland Bank branches in the St. Louis metropolitan area four branches in Colorado and single locations in Joplin Missouri and Raleigh/Durham North Carolina.

Company Background

Between 2008 and 2010 the bank's branch locations grew from just a half-dozen in central Illinois and St. Louis to nearly 30 around the state and in the St. Louis metropolitan area. During that time the bank acquired the assets of Waterloo Bancshares and WestBridge in St. Louis AMCORE in northern Illinois and Strategic Capital in central Illinois. It also opened new locations in some of its faster-growing markets. As a result of its efforts Midland States Bancorp has watched its revenue and profits trend upward significantly from 2007 levels.

EXECUTIVES

Vice Chairman President and CEO, Leon J. Holschbach, age 65, $529,389 total compensation
EVP Midland States Bancorp and President Midland States Bank, Jeffrey G. Ludwig, age 46, $367,500 total compensation
EVP Banking, Jeffrey S. Medford
CFO Midland States Bancorp and Midland States Bank, Kevin L. Thompson
Senior Vice President Community Banking, Jeffrey Mefford
Vice President, Deanna Haught
Vice President Banking Center Manager, Karen Attwood
Vice President Mortgage Banking, Mark Widdicombe
Senior Vice President, Sharon Schaubert
Chairman, John M. Schultz, age 66
Auditors: Crowe Horwath LLP

HQ: Midland States Bancorp Inc
1201 Network Centre Drive, Effingham, IL 62401
Phone: 217 342-7321
Web: www.midlandsb.com

PRODUCTS/OPERATIONS

2014 Sales

	% of total
Interest income	
Loans	57
Investment Securities & others	17
Noninterest income	
Wealth management revenue	8
Service charges on deposit accounts	3
Mortgage banking revenue	3
Gain on sale of other assets	3
ATM and interchange revenue	3
Impairments	-
Other	6
Total	**100**

Selected Services

Bank By Phone
Bill Paying
Checking
Debit Card
Online Banking
Savings & CDs

COMPETITORS

Bank of America	Harris
Edward D. Jones	Mercantile Bancorp
Fifth Third	PNC Financial
First Mid-Illinois	U.S. Bancorp
Bancshares	

HISTORICAL FINANCIALS

Company Type: Public

Income Statement   FYE: December 31

	ASSETS ($ mil.)	NET INCOME ($ mil.)	INCOME AS % OF ASSETS	EMPLOYEES
12/17	4,412.7	16.0	0.4%	840
12/16	3,233.7	31.5	1.0%	715
12/15	2,884.8	24.3	0.8%	700
12/14	2,676.6	10.8	0.4%	0
12/13	0.0	14.5***************%	0
Annual Growth	—	2.6%	—	—

2017 Year-End Financials

Return on assets: 0.4%	Dividends
Return on equity: 4.1%	Yield: 0.0%
Long-term debt ($ mil.): —	Payout: 91.9%
No. of shares (mil.): 19.1	Market value ($ mil.): 621.0
Sales ($ mil): 212.4	

	STOCK PRICE ($) FY Close	P/E High/Low	PER SHARE ($) Earnings	Dividends	Book Value
12/17	32.48	40 33	0.87	0.80	23.51
12/16	36.18	17 9	2.17	0.36	20.78
Annual Growth	(10.2%)	—	(59.9%)	122.2%	13.1%

MidWestOne Financial Group, Inc.

This could be the saga of How the MidWest Was One . MidWest One Financial Group is the holding company for Midwest One Bank which operates about two dozen branches throughout central and east-central Iowa. The bank offers standard deposit products such as checking and savings accounts CDs and IRAs in addition to trust services credit cards insurance and brokerage and investment services. About two-thirds of MidWest One Financial's loan portfolio consists of real estate loans including residential and commercial mortgages and farmland and construction loans. Founded in 1983 MidWest One has total assets of $1.8 billion.

Geographic Reach

Headquartered in Iowa City Midwest One Bank has branches and loan production offices in 15 counties in central and east-central Iowa.

Financial Performance

The company reported net income of $18.6 million in 2013 a 13% increase over 2012. Earnings have been rising steadily while the bank's revenue has been trending downward. Indeed 2013's $80.8 million in revenue was 10% below 2012. Assets declined slightly over the same period as did deposits. (The bank is facing stiff competition for deposits from aggressive credit unions offering above market deposit rates.) However loans increased 5% year over year and the growth in loans combined with stable net interest margins of about 3.5% resulted in a modest uptick in net interest income. Non-interest income got a boost from the bank's wealth management division which posted a 7% revenue gain in 2013 versus 2012.

EXECUTIVES

President and CEO, Charles N. Funk, age 64, $422,000 total compensation
EVP Chief Lending Officer and Commercial Banking, Kent L. Jehle, age 58, $271,000 total compensation
VP and Chief Risk Officer, James M. Cantrell, $205,000 total compensation
COO, Kevin Kramer
SVP and CFO, Katie A. Lorenson, age 38, $206,231 total compensation
Senior Regional President, Mitchell W. Cook, age 54, $204,400 total compensation
Vice President Information Technology Managing Officer, Allen Schneider
Senior Vice President Loan Sales, Jason Swestka
Vice President Senior Loan Review Officer, Jeff Richards
Vice President Lpl Financial Advisor Located, John Evans
Vice President and Program Manager, Daniel Bailey
SENIOR VICE PRESIDENT TREASURY MANAGEMENT, Kevin Pleasant
Vice President, Janeen Benoy
VICE PRESIDENT MORTGAGE LOAN OPERATIONS, Linda A Nelson
SENIOR VICE PRESIDENT SMALL BUSINESS ADMINISTRATION, John Kimball
SECOND VICE PRESIDENT MORTGAGE BANKER, Kerri Higgins
VICE PRESIDENT COMMERCIAL LENDING, Andrew L Brust

SENIOR VICE PRESIDENT CREDIT ADMINISTRATION, Bob Blenkush
VICE PRESIDENT COMMERCIAL LENDING, Andrew Brust
Vice President Commercial Banking, Nick Raffensperger
Chairman, Kevin W. Monson, age 66
Auditors: RSM US LLP

LOCATIONS

HQ: MidWestOne Financial Group, Inc.
102 South Clinton Street, Iowa City, IA 52240
Phone: 319 356-5800
Web: www.midwestone.com

PRODUCTS/OPERATIONS

2015 Sales

	% of total
Interest Income	
Interest and fees on loans	71
Interest on investment securities	11
Other	1
Non-Interest Income	
Trust investment and insurance fees	5
Other service charges commissions and fees	5
Service charges and fees on deposit accounts	3
Mortgage origination and loan servicing fees	2
Other	2
Total	**100**

Selected Subsidiaries

MidWestOne Bank
MidWestOne Insurance Services Inc.
MidWestOne Statutory Trust II

COMPETITORS

Bank of the West	U.S. Bancorp
Hills Bancorporation	Wells Fargo
QCR Holdings	West Bancorporation

HISTORICAL FINANCIALS

Company Type: Public

Income Statement   FYE: December 31

	ASSETS ($ mil.)	NET INCOME ($ mil.)	INCOME AS % OF ASSETS	EMPLOYEES
12/17	3,212.2	18.7	0.6%	610
12/16	3,079.5	20.3	0.7%	587
12/15	2,979.9	25.1	0.8%	648
12/14	1,800.3	18.5	1.0%	374
12/13	1,755.2	18.6	1.1%	376
Annual Growth	16.3%	0.1%	—	12.9%

2017 Year-End Financials

Return on assets: 0.5%	Dividends
Return on equity: 5.7%	Yield: 0.0%
Long-term debt ($ mil.): —	Payout: 43.2%
No. of shares (mil.): 12.2	Market value ($ mil.): 410.0
Sales ($ mil): 141.6	

	STOCK PRICE ($) FY Close	P/E High/Low	PER SHARE ($) Earnings	Dividends	Book Value
12/17	33.53	25 21	1.55	0.67	27.85
12/16	37.60	22 14	1.78	0.64	26.71
12/15	30.41	14 12	2.42	0.60	25.96
12/14	28.81	13 10	2.19	0.58	23.07
12/13	27.20	13 9	2.18	0.50	20.99
Annual Growth	5.4%	—	(8.2%)	7.6%	7.3%

Miller Industries Inc. (TN)

This body builder wants to pump up your chassis. Miller Industries makes bodies for light- and heavy-duty wreckers along with car carriers and multi-vehicle trailers. It serves as the official recovery team at some of the NASCAR races (including Talladega) as well as the Indy 500 races. Miller makes its recovery and towing vehicles at plants in the US and Europe. Its multi-vehicle transport trailers can carry as many as eight vehicles and loads up to 75 tons. Miller Industries' US brand names include Century Challenger Champion Chevron Eagle Holmes Titan and Vulcan. The company's European brands are Jige (France) and Boniface (UK). Miller and rival Jerr-Dan dominate the US market for wrecker bodies.

Operations

Professional wrecker operators repossession and salvage companies comprise the light-duty wrecker market. Commercial vehicle operators and professional wreckers are served by the company's heavy-duty vehicles.

The company creates vehicles by bending steel and aluminum and welding the parts together to create a frame; hydraulic cylinders pumps winches and valves are attached to complete the carrier or wrecker body. The bodies are then attached to truck chassis made by third-party manufacturers such as Kenworth (a brand belonging to PACCAR) which is Miller's primary provider of truck chassis.

Miller has developed a wrecker that allows for damage-free towing of newer aerodynamic vehicles that are made of composite or lighter weight materials. The company boasts innovative technology which includes underlift parallel linkage and L-arms and the Vulcan "scoop" — these systems offer better lift-and-carry options that also protect cargo.

Geographic Reach

The company has six manufacturing facilities in France the UK and the US. These facilities reside in Ooltewah (Chattanooga) Tennessee; Hermitage Pennsylvania; Mercer Pennsylvania; and Greeneville Tennessee. It also has manufacturing operations at two facilities located in the Lorraine region of France and manufacturing operations in Norfolk England. North America accounted for 86% of Miller's revenue in 2015.

Sales and Marketing

Its products primarily are sold through independent distributors consisting of approximately 80 distributors in North America that serve all 50 states Canada and Mexico and other foreign markets.

Financial Performance

Miller experienced historic revenue growth in 2015 when revenues peaked at a record-setting $541 million. Profits also spiked by 7% to reach $16 million in 2015 and cash flow from operations skyrocketed by 102% during the year. The unprecedented growth for 2015 was fueled by a 17% rise in North American sales due to higher production levels based on the continued recovery of economic conditions and improving consumer sentiment.

Strategy

The company's involvement with professional racing increases the exposure of Miller's products and supports sales and marketing efforts. Additionally the company focuses on domestic and international trade shows where it partners with its independent distributors in promotions.

Miller grows its operations by enhancing its production capacity. It continues to expand its Pennsylvania manufacturing facility and it began to enhance the facilities at its Ooltewah Tennessee; and Greeneville Tennessee plants during 2016 and beyond.

Company Background

Headed by William Miller the Miller Group (which owned Challenger Wrecker and Holmes International) acquired the wrecking operations of Century Holdings in 1990 and formed the basis for Miller Industries. However Miller Industries wasn't officially created until 1994 when the Miller Group placed all of its wrecking and towing businesses under that nameplate. The company went public in 1995.

EXECUTIVES

EVP CFO and Treasurer, J. Vincent Mish, age 67, $225,009 total compensation
EVP Secretary and General Counsel, Frank Madonia, age 69, $225,009 total compensation
Co-CEO, Jeffrey I. (Jeff) Badgley, age 66, $450,017 total compensation
President and Co-CEO, William G. Miller, $175,007 total compensation
Vice President Of Heavy duty Sales, John Hawkins
Auditors: Elliott Davis, LLC

LOCATIONS

HQ: Miller Industries Inc. (TN)
8503 Hilltop Drive, Ooltewah, TN 37363
Phone: 423 238-4171   **Fax:** 423 238-5371
Web: www.millerind.com

PRODUCTS/OPERATIONS

Selected Products and Brands

Boniface (heavy-duty wreckers for the European market)
Century (wreckers car carriers)
Challenger (wreckers car carriers)
Champion (car carriers)
Chevron (wreckers car carriers towing and recovery equipment)
Eagle (light-duty wreckers)
Holmes (mid-priced wreckers and car carriers)
Jige (light- and heavy-duty wreckers and car carriers for the European market)
Miller (parts and accessories catalog)
SP Series (medium-duty wreckers & carriers)
Titan (multi-vehicle transport trailers)
Trailers (Titan T Series)
Vulcan (wreckers car carriers towing and recovery equipment)

COMPETITORS

Daimler Trucks North America
Jerr-Dan
Mitsubishi Fuso
Penske Truck Leasing
United Rentals

HISTORICAL FINANCIALS
Company Type: Public

Income Statement
FYE: December 31

	REVENUE ($ mil.)	NET INCOME ($ mil.)	NET PROFIT MARGIN	EMPLOYEES
12/17	615.1	23.0	3.7%	1,120
12/16	601.1	19.9	3.3%	1,103
12/15	540.9	15.9	3.0%	990
12/14	492.7	14.9	3.0%	890
12/13	404.1	9.2	2.3%	820
Annual Growth	11.1%	25.7%	—	8.1%

2017 Year-End Financials

Debt ratio: 3.3%
Return on equity: 11.8%
Cash ($ mil.): 21.9
Current ratio: 2.24
Long-term debt ($ mil.): 10.2
No. of shares (mil.): 11.3
Dividends
  Yield: 0.0%
  Payout: 35.6%
Market value ($ mil.): 294.0

	STOCK PRICE ($) FY Close	P/E High/Low		PER SHARE ($) Earnings	Dividends	Book Value
12/17	25.80	14	12	2.02	0.72	17.85
12/16	26.45	16	11	1.75	0.68	16.27
12/15	21.78	18	12	1.41	0.64	15.33
12/14	20.79	16	13	1.31	0.60	14.90
12/13	18.63	23	18	0.82	0.56	14.40
Annual Growth	8.5%	—	—	25.3%	6.5%	5.5%

Minerals Technologies, Inc.

Minerals Technologies one of the top producers of bentonite and precipitated calcium carbonate (PCC) supplies a broad range of specialty mineral and synthetic products to primarily the paper foundry steel construction environmental energy polymer and consumer products industries. With more than 1600 trademarks the company?s technologically advanced product lines include Fulfill New Yield Volclay Additrol Hotcrete and Lacam. Majority of company sales are generated in the US.

Operations

Minerals Technologies reports through four segments.

Performance Materials segment brings in 45% of sales. It is a leading supplier of bentonite chromite and leonardite as well as products for non-residential construction environmental and infrastructure projects.

Specialty Minerals segment (35% sales) produces PCC and quicklime. The segment also engages in mining of mineral ores and selling natural mineral products primarily limestone and talc.

The Refractories segment (below 20% of total sales) produces monolithic and shaped refractory materials provided services and sells application and measurement equipment calcium metal and metallurgical wire products used in the steel nonferrous metal and glass industries.

The Energy Services segment provides services for off-shore filtration and well testing to the worldwide oil and gas industry bringing in some 5% revenue.

Geographic Reach

Minerals Technologies has major customers across the US as well as 15 countries including Canada Brazil China India France and Brazil. It has operations in some 25 countries the major ones being the US Australia China Turkey and the UK. The US accounts for more than 50% of total sales followed by Europe (some 25%) and a rapidly growing Asia (currently 20%).

Sales and Marketing

Minerals Technologies has sales offices in Bethlehem Pennsylvania and Hoffman Estates Illinois and international centers located in India the UK Brazil and China. It relies on its worldwide direct sales force to market its products.

The company?s products are used principally in the paper building materials paint and coatings glass ceramic polymer food automotive pharmaceutical metal and glass and oil and gas industries.

Some of its registered products include acid-tolerant AT OPACARB Fulfill and New Yield catering to the paper industry; Volclay Additrol and Panther Creek for metal casting; and Hotcrete and Lacam for refractory products.

The Company also sells a range of PCC products to merchants in Adams Massachusetts and Lifford United Kingdom.

Financial Performance

In the last decade Minerals Technologies? sales has increased from $1.2 billion in 2008 to a peak of $1.8 billion in 2015 before reducing slightly in the following two. Net income has increased from $65 million in 2008 to just below $200 million 10 years later.

In 2017 company sales increase very slightly to $1.7 billion as Basic Minerals sales increased some 20% due to higher sales of chromite and drilling products.

Net income increased some $60 million to $195 million in 2017 over the year prior mostly from acquisition due to company restructuring measures as well as a $47 million tax benefit from tax reform.

Cash holdings increased from $189 million to $212 million. Operations provided $208 million while investments used up some $78 million. Investments claimed a further $118 million mostly repayment of long-term debt.

Strategy

Minerals Technologies went through a major consolidation in 2017 to increase efficiency?in last quarter the company spent more than $15 million in restructuring costs. It combined its Performance Materials and Construction Technologies segments into one as well as reorganized its Environmental and Building Products teams to accelerate the launch new products.

Thanks to increased local commercial leadership Asia has been a solid growth market to the company such as a shift to higher valued products in the foundry market of China and metalcasting products in India. Similarly pet care business in China grew twice as big in 2017. A 2018 acquisition of Sivomatic is going to make the company?s business more competitive in Europe as well.

Minerals Technologies also continues to dominate with advanced products. Its leading research in fields of inorganic chemistry crystallography and structural analysis allows the company to constantly introduce performance enhancing applications.

Its new product lines include Thixocarb PCC Vicality EMforce and Optibloc for the Processed Minerals and Specialty PCC product lines and the Additrol formulation a custom blend for ferrous and non-ferrous applications.

The company also recently introduced the satellite PCC plant concept of producing materials right next to operational paper mills to eliminate transport cost.

Yearly average CAPEX is holding below $25 million a year. It has kept expenditures low to pay of acquisition-related debt?in the last four years it has paid off some $600 million in debt.

However the company may face growth challenges if raw material prices keep increasing and energy costs climb higher. Moreover demands for the company?s products outstrips the facility capacities in India China and Thailand and infrastructure investment remains low.

Mergers and Acquisitions

In May 2018 Minerals Technologies acquired Sivomatic for an undisclosed sum. Sivomatic is a leader in premier clumping products (for pet litter) derived from bentonite. In 2017 it had sales of ?73 million.

EXECUTIVES

SVP General Counsel Secretary and VP Human Resources, Thomas J. Meek, age 60, $478,308 total compensation

CEO, Douglas T. (Doug) Dietrich, age 49, $1,025,000 total compensation

SVP and Managing Director Paper PCC, W. Rand Mendez, age 58

SVP and Director MTI Supply Chain, Douglas W. Mayger, age 60, $356,923 total compensation

COO Specialty Minerals and Refractories, D. J. Monagle, age 55, $486,921 total compensation

SVP and Managing Director Performance Materials, Gary L. Castagna, age 56, $467,789 total compensation

VP and Managing Director Minteq International Inc., Brett Argirakis

VP and Managing Director Energy Services, Andrew M. Jones, age 59

SVP Building Materials and Environment Products Construction Technologies, Thomas Stam

SVP Finance and Treasury and CFO, Matthew E. Garth

Vice President of Sales and Business Development, Joel Henley

Chairman, Duane R. Dunham, age 77

Auditors: KPMG LLP

LOCATIONS

HQ: Minerals Technologies, Inc.
622 Third Avenue, New York, NY 10017-6707
Phone: 212 878-1800
Web: www.mineralstech.com

PRODUCTS/OPERATIONS

2015 Sales

	$ mil.	% of total
Specialty minerals	624.6	35
Performance material	514.8	29
Refractories	295.9	16
Energy service segment	182.2	10
construction technologies segment	180.1	10
Total	**1,797.6**	**100**

2015 Sales

in million		% of sales
Product sales	1,615.4	90
Service revenue	182.2	10
Total	**1,797.6**	**100**

2015 Sales by Product

	% of total
Paper PC	23
Metalcasting	15
Refractory Products	13
Household Personal Care and Specialty Products	10
Energy Services	10
Building Materials and Other Products	6
Specialty PCC	4
Ground Calcium Carbonate	4
Metallurgical Products	4
Basic Minerals and Other Products	4
Environmental Products	4
Talc	3
Total	**100**

COMPETITORS

Ash Grove Cement	Saint-Gobain
BASF Catalysts	U.S. Lime & Minerals
Imerys	Vulcan Materials
Magneco/Metrel	
Martin Marietta	
Materials	

HISTORICAL FINANCIALS

Company Type: Public

Income Statement

	REVENUE ($ mil.)	NET INCOME ($ mil.)	NET PROFIT MARGIN	EMPLOYEES
12/17	1,675.7	195.1	11.6%	3,657
12/16	1,638.0	133.4	8.1%	3,583
12/15	1,797.6	107.9	6.0%	3,868
12/14	1,725.0	92.4	5.4%	4,464
12/13	1,018.1	80.3	7.9%	1,978
Annual Growth	**13.3%**	**24.8%**	**—**	**16.6%**

FYE: December 31

2017 Year-End Financials

Debt ratio: 32.6%	No. of shares (mil.): 35.3
Return on equity: 17.2%	Dividends
Cash ($ mil.): 212.2	Yield: 0.0%
Current ratio: 2.75	Payout: 3.6%
Long-term debt ($ mil.): 959.8	Market value ($ mil.): 2,436.0

	STOCK PRICE ($) FY Close	P/E High/Low		PER SHARE ($) Earnings	Dividends	Book Value
12/17	68.85	15	11	5.48	0.20	35.38
12/16	77.25	22	10	3.79	0.20	28.78
12/15	45.86	24	15	3.08	0.20	26.18
12/14	69.45	29	18	2.65	0.20	24.91
12/13	60.07	26	17	2.30	0.25	24.67
Annual Growth	**3.5%**	**—**	**—**	**24.2%**	**(5.4%)**	**9.4%**

MKS Instruments Inc

In case it's not clear from the name MKS Instruments makes instruments. In particular it makes systems that analyze and control gases during semiconductor manufacturing and other thin film industrial processes such as those used to make flat panel displays LEDs solar cells and data storage media. Top customers include chip equipment heavyweights Applied Materials and Lam Research. Other applications include medical equipment pharmaceutical manufacturing energy generation and environmental monitoring. MKS Instruments generates more than half its revenue from customers in the US. IN 2016 the company agreed to acquire laser company Newport Corp. for nearly $1 billion.

Operations

MKS groups its products into three categories: Instruments Control and Vacuum Products Power and Reactive Gas Products and Analytical Solutions. Instruments and Control Products account for half of the company's revenue with Power and Reactive Gas Products generating 43% of sales while Analytical Solutions brings in some 7% of sales. The company's Japanese and Korean subsidiaries are responsible for about one-fifth of sales.

Geographic Reach

The company has manufacturing plants in the US UK Germany Italy Korea China Israel and Mexico. It buys electronic mechanical and electrical components from other companies to assemble into its instruments. Customers based in the US account for 56% of sales followed by customers in Asia at 35% and European customers at 9%.

Sales and Marketing

MKS Instruments deploys a direct sales force operating in about a dozen countries. Applied Materials accounts for 18% of MKS Instruments' revenue with LAM Research accounting for 13%.

Financial Performance

MKS Instruments sales rose 4% in 2015 to $814 million from 2014. Overall revenue nearly tracked the 5% increases in revenue for the Instruments Control and Vacuum Products and the Power and Reactive Gas Products segments. An upturn in the global semiconductor sales cycle helped boost revenue. Sales were off 2% in the Analytical Solutions Products segment.

The company's net income rose 6% to $122 million in 2015 from 2014. The increase came from higher revenue and interest income. It also had lower selling general and administrative expenses.

MKS Instruments generated $138 million in cash in 2015 up from $102 million in 2014.

Mergers and Acquisitions

A large part of MKS Instruments' strategy involves acquisitions.

In 2018 MKS offered $1 billion to buy Electro Scientific Industries (ESI) in an all-cash deal. The amount surpasses the $980 million MKS paid for Newport Cop. in 2016. The ESI transaction approved by both boards would create a company with combined revenue of about $2.2 billion. MKS expects the deal to strengthen its offerings in the photonics and optics markets. ESI has worked with MKS in the printed circuit board market and expects continued collaboration. The deal approved by each company's board of directors could close in the first quarter of 2019.

The addition of Newport's laser business in 2016 provided MKS an entry into research health and life sciences markets.

In 2015 the company acquired Precisive a developer of optical analyzers based on Tunable Filter Spectroscopy (TFS) for $13 million for the process and environmental markets. The acquisition target in 2014 was Granville-Phillips a division of Brooks Automation Inc. That $86 million deal added to MKS Instruments' vacuum measurement and control instruments portfolio.

EXECUTIVES

President CEO and Director, Gerald G. Colella, age 61, $673,077 total compensation
VP CFO and Treasurer, Seth H. Bagshaw, age 58, $424,038 total compensation
SVP and COO, John T. C. Lee, age 55, $424,038 total compensation
SVP Global Operations, Brian C. Quirk, $339,423 total compensation
Vice President Global Applications Engineering, John Doherty
Vice President and General Manager, Philip Sullivan
Senior Vice President Global Sales, John Abrams
Senior Vice President, Jack Abrams
Vice President; General Manager ENI Products, Paul Eyerman
Chairman President and CEO, John R. Bertucci, age 78
Auditors: PricewaterhouseCoopers LLP

LOCATIONS

HQ: MKS Instruments Inc
  2 Tech Drive, Suite 201, Andover, MA 01810
Phone: 978 645-5500
Web: www.mksinst.com

PRODUCTS/OPERATIONS

2015 Sales by Products

	% of total
Instruments Control and Vacuum Products	50
Power and Reactive Gas Products	43
Analytical Solutions Products	7
Total	**100**

2015 Sales

	% of total
Advanced Manufacturing Capital Equipment	62
Asia Region Sales	19
Global Service	11
Other	8
Corporate Eliminations	-
Total	**100**

Selected Products

Instruments and Control Systems
  Pressure Measurement and Control Products
  Baratron®; Pressure Measurement Products
  Automatic Pressure and Vacuum Control Products
  Materials Delivery Products
  Flow Measurement and Control Products
  Gas Composition Analysis Products
  Mass Spectrometry-Based Gas Composition Analysis Instruments
  Fourier Transform Infra-Red (FTIR) Based Gas Composition Analysis Products
  Control and Information Technology Products
  Control Products
  Information Technology Products
Power and Reactive Gas Products
  Power Delivery Products
  Reactive Gas Generation Products
  Processing Thin Films
  Equipment Cleaning
Vacuum Products
  Vacuum Gauging Products
  Vacuum Valves Stainless Steel Components Process Solutions and Custom Stainless Steel Hardware
  Custom Manufactured Components

COMPETITORS

ATMI	INFICON
Advanced Energy Industries	KLA-Tencor
Arizona Instrument	L'Air Liquide
BW Technologies	Nova Measuring
Brooks Automation	Pall Corporation
CVD Equipment	Veeco Instruments
Ebara	WIKA
	Winton Products

Entegris
HORIBA
Hitachi
  High-Technologies

Company

HISTORICAL FINANCIALS

Company Type: Public

Income Statement

	REVENUE ($ mil.)	NET INCOME ($ mil.)	NET PROFIT MARGIN	EMPLOYEES
				FYE: December 31
12/17	1,915.9	339.1	17.7%	4,923
12/16	1,295.3	104.8	8.1%	4,667
12/15	813.5	122.3	15.0%	2,181
12/14	780.8	115.7	14.8%	2,371
12/13	669.4	35.7	5.3%	2,394
Annual Growth	**30.1%**	**75.5%**	**—**	**19.8%**

2017 Year-End Financials

Debt ratio: 16.2%	No. of shares (mil.): 54.3
Return on equity: 23.9%	Dividends
Cash ($ mil.): 333.7	Yield: 0.0%
Current ratio: 4.27	Payout: 11.4%
Long-term debt ($ mil.): 389.9	Market value ($ mil.): 5,137.0

	STOCK PRICE ($) FY Close	P/E High/Low		PER SHARE ($) Earnings	Dividends	Book Value
12/17	94.50	17	10	6.16	0.71	29.23
12/16	59.40	31	16	1.94	0.68	23.14
12/15	36.00	17	14	2.28	0.68	21.82
12/14	36.60	17	12	2.16	0.66	20.35
12/13	29.92	46	37	0.67	0.64	19.14
Annual Growth	**33.3%**	**—**	**—**	**74.1%**	**2.4%**	**11.2%**

Modine Manufacturing Co

Modine Manufacturing runs hot and cold but not when it comes to the products it makes for vehicles. Founded in 1916 the company designs and makes highly engineered heating and cooling systems and components for a range of customers worldwide: automotive OEMs agricultural and construction OEMs heating and cooling equipment OEMs construction contractors wholesalers of plumbing and heating equipment and fuel cell manufacturers. Products include heat transfer modules oil coolers radiators and vehicular air conditioning systems. With operations in some 14 countries and technical centers in the US and Germany more than half of Modine's revenues are generated outside of the US.

Geographic Reach

Modine maintains a geographic presence in Austria Brazil China Germany Hungary India Italy Japan Mexico the Netherlands South Africa South Korea the US. After the US (45% of total sales) other major markets include Germany (13%) Austria (8%) and Hungary (11%).

Sales and Marketing

Modine serves 10 main customers that generate 63% of its total revenue. These include such big names as BMW Caterpillar Daimler Deere & Company Denso Corporation Ford Motor Navistar

Volkswagen and Volvo. (In 2015 and 2014 Daimler and Volkswagen were the only customers that accounted for 10% or more of total sales.)

Financial Performance

Modine has experienced revenues increases the last two years with revenues rising 1% from $1.48 billion in 2014 to $1.5 billion in 2015. Its profits however nosedived by 83% from $130 million in 2014 to $22 million in 2015 largely due to the absence of income tax benefits.

The revenue growth for 2015 was fueled by a 25% spike in HVAC equipment sales and an 8% increase from both oil coolers and condensers. In addition Asia net sales increased in 2015 primarily due to new automotive program launches in China and higher sales across all markets in India.

Strategy

Modine's strategy for improved profitability includes diversifying its markets and customer base as well as partnering with customers in the development of new products and technologies. It is also focusing on emerging markets in China and India. The company plans to launch new automotive and commercial vehicle programs in 2016 which will complete the transition of its light assembly facility in Shanghai into an engine products-focused manufacturing facility.

In 2014 the company completed the acquisition of Barkell a custom air handling company located in the UK for roughly $8 million. The acquisition expanded both its product line and sales channel within the country.

EXECUTIVES

Regional VP Asia, Scott L. Bowser, age 54, $293,400 total compensation
President and CEO, Thomas A. (Tom) Burke, age 61, $740,000 total compensation
EVP and COO, Thomas F. (Tom) Marry, age 57, $350,000 total compensation
Regional Vice President - North America, Scott D. Wollenberg
VP Finance and CFO, Michael B. Lucareli, $322,000 total compensation
Regional Vice President - Europe, Holger Schwab
VP and CTO, Ralf Beck, age 57
VP Human Resources, Brian Agen
Vice President Corporate Controller and Tax, Mark Hudson
VICE PRESIDENT COMM AND INDUST SOLUTIONS, Dennis P Appel
VICE PRESIDENT COMM AND INDUST SOLUTIONS, Dennis Appel
Vice President, C Langer
Chairman, Gary L. Neale, age 79
Vice President Treasurer and Investor Relations, Kathleen T Powers
Auditors: PricewaterhouseCoopers LLP

LOCATIONS

HQ: Modine Manufacturing Co
1500 DeKoven Avenue, Racine, WI 53403
Phone: 262 636-1200   **Fax:** 262 636-1424
Web: www.modine.com

PRODUCTS/OPERATIONS

2015 Sales

	$ mil.	% of total
Original equipment		
Original equipment - Europe	578.2	38
Original equipment - North America	573.5	38
Original equipment - Asia	81.2	6
South America	93.9	6
Building HVAC	186.3	12
Adjustments	(16.7)	-
Total	**1,496.4**	**100**

2015 Sales by Product

	$ mil.	% of total
Modules/assemblies	367.5	25
Oil coolers	233.0	16
EGR coolers	183.5	12
Building HVAC	199.6	13
Charge-air coolers	148.9	10
Condensers	140.0	9
Radiators	124.8	8
Other	99.1	7
Total	**1,496.4**	**100**

2014 Sales by Product

	$ mil.	% of total
Modules/packages	379.9	25
Oil coolers	215.4	14
EGR coolers	172.5	12
Building HVAC	159.5	12
Charge-air coolers	157.0	11
Condensers	129.2	9
Radiators	129.0	8
Other	135.1	9
Total	**1,477.6**	**100**

COMPETITORS

Bergstrom Inc.	Greenheck
Blissfield	Honeywell
Manufacturing	International
C P Auto Products	Lennox
CalsonicKansei North	Luvata
America	Mestek
DENSO	Mobile Climate Control
Daikin	Red Dot Corporation
Dana	ThermaSys
Delphi Automotive	Thomas & Betts
Systems	Valeo
Emerson Electric	Visteon

HISTORICAL FINANCIALS

Company Type: Public

Income Statement

FYE: March 31

	REVENUE ($ mil.)	NET INCOME ($ mil.)	NET PROFIT MARGIN	EMPLOYEES
03/18	2,103.1	22.2	1.1%	11,700
03/17	1,503.0	14.2	0.9%	11,200
03/16	1,352.5	(1.6)	—	7,100
03/15	1,496.4	21.8	1.5%	6,900
03/14	1,477.6	130.4	8.8%	6,900
Annual Growth	**9.2%**	**(35.8%)**	**—**	**14.1%**

2018 Year-End Financials

Debt ratio: 30.4%
Return on equity: 4.9%
Cash ($ mil.): 39.3
Current ratio: 1.25
Long-term debt ($ mil.): 386.3

No. of shares (mil.): 50.5
Dividends
  Yield: —
  Payout: —
Market value ($ mil.): 1,068.0

	STOCK PRICE ($) FY Close	P/E High/Low		PER SHARE ($) Earnings	Dividends	Book Value
03/18	21.15	57	23	0.43	0.00	9.70
03/17	12.20	56	29	0.29	0.00	8.26
03/16	11.01	—	—	(0.03)	0.00	7.94
03/15	13.47	37	25	0.45	0.00	7.43
03/14	14.65	6	3	2.72	0.00	8.92
Annual Growth	**9.6%**	—	—	**(36.9%)**	**—**	**2.1%**

Moelis & Co

Auditors: DELOITTE & TOUCHE LLP

LOCATIONS

HQ: Moelis & Co
399 Park Avenue, 5th Floor, New York, NY 10022
Phone: 212 883-3800
Web: www.moelis.com

HISTORICAL FINANCIALS

Company Type: Public

Income Statement

FYE: December 31

	REVENUE ($ mil.)	NET INCOME ($ mil.)	NET PROFIT MARGIN	EMPLOYEES
12/17	684.6	29.4	4.3%	749
12/16	613.3	38.3	6.3%	645
12/15	551.8	33.1	6.0%	660
12/14	518.7	(3.0)	—	550
12/13	411.3	70.2	17.1%	470
Annual Growth	**13.6%**	**(19.6%)**	**—**	**12.4%**

2017 Year-End Financials

Debt ratio: —
Return on equity: 10.9%
Cash ($ mil.): 213.1
Current ratio: 0.81
Long-term debt ($ mil.): —

No. of shares (mil.): 53.3
Dividends
  Yield: 0.0%
  Payout: 317.9%
Market value ($ mil.): 2,588.0

	STOCK PRICE ($) FY Close	P/E High/Low		PER SHARE ($) Earnings	Dividends	Book Value
12/17	48.50	52	35	0.78	2.48	6.09
12/16	33.90	19	12	1.58	3.29	4.10
12/15	29.18	21	16	1.55	1.00	3.27
12/14	34.93	—	—	(0.19)	1.40	2.21
Annual Growth	**11.6%**	—	—	**—**	**21.0%**	**40.3%**

Monmouth Real Estate Investment Corp

Monmouth specializes in mammoth industrial properties particularly warehouses and distribution centers. The real estate investment trust (REIT) owns about 80 industrial buildings and a single New Jersey shopping center comprising some 10.7 million sq. ft. in more than 25 states mostly in the East and Midwest. Most are net-leased (in which tenants pay insurance taxes and maintenance costs) under long-term leases. The REIT's two largest tenants FedEx and Milwaukee Electric Tool together account for half of its revenue. The firm also invests in REIT securities. Founded in 1968 Monmouth is one of the oldest public equity REITs in the nation.

Geographic Reach

New Jersey-based Monmouth's properties are located in 27 states including Arizona Connecticut Florida Illinois Michigan New Jersey New York Ohio Pennsylvania Tennessee Texas and Wisconsin.

Sales and Marketing

FedEx is the REIT's single largest customer accounting for 44% of its leasable space.

Financial Performance

The industrial REIT's revenue increased 5% in fiscal 2013 (ended September) versus the prior year to $66.3 million due to an increase in rental and reimbursement revenues generated by its larger portfolio of properties. Net income grew 15% over the same period to $21 million. The firm's revenue and profits have increased steadily over the past four years as its portfolio increased in size.

Strategy

The REIT specializes in net-leased industrial properties subject to long-term leases primarily to investment grade tenants. It derives its income primarily from real estate rental operations. Monmouth owns all of its properties with the exception of two in New Jersey in which it holds a majority interest.

In 2013 the REIT acquired five industrial properties totaling approximately 1.1 million square feet with net-leased terms ranging from 10 to 20 years of which about 237000 square feet (or 21%) is leased to FedEx Ground Package System. The REIT paid about $73.9 million for the five sites which are located in Kansas Kentucky Oklahoma Pennsylvania and Texas. The firm intends to continue increasing its real estate investments in fiscal 2014 through acquisitions and the expansion of select properties.

EXECUTIVES

CFO, Kevin S. Miller, age 48, $239,663 total compensation
President and CEO, Michael P. Landy, age 57, $525,000 total compensation
General Counsel, Allison Nagelberg, age 54, $312,656 total compensation
Chairman, Eugene W. Landy, age 85
Auditors: PKF O'Connor Davies, LLP

LOCATIONS

HQ: Monmouth Real Estate Investment Corp
Juniper Business Plaza, 3499 Route 9 North, Suite 3-D, Freehold, NJ 07728
Phone: 732 577-9996
Web: www.mreic.com

PRODUCTS/OPERATIONS

2016 Sales

	$ mil.	% of total
Rental	81.6	86
Reimbursement	13.3	14
Total	**94.9**	**100**

COMPETITORS

Brandywine Realty	Mack-Cali
CenterPoint Properties	One Liberty Properties
First Industrial Realty	PS Business Parks
First Potomac Realty	Prologis

HISTORICAL FINANCIALS

Company Type: Public

Income Statement   FYE: September 30

	REVENUE ($ mil.)	NET INCOME ($ mil.)	NET PROFIT MARGIN	EMPLOYEES
09/18	139.3	56.0	40.2%	15
09/17	113.5	40.2	35.5%	15
09/16	94.9	32.4	34.2%	14
09/15	78.0	25.6	32.8%	15
09/14	65.8	19.8	30.1%	14
Annual Growth	**20.6%**	**29.6%**	**—**	**1.7%**

2018 Year-End Financials

Debt ratio: 52.2%	No. of shares (mil.): 81.5
Return on equity: 7.4%	Dividends
Cash ($ mil.): 9.3	Yield: 0.0%
Current ratio: 4.48	Payout: 138.7%
Long-term debt ($ mil.): 898.1	Market value ($ mil.): 1,363.0

	STOCK PRICE ($) FY Close	P/E High/Low	PER SHARE ($) Earnings	Dividends	Book Value
09/18	16.72	37 28	0.49	0.68	9.79
09/17	16.19	29 23	0.56	0.64	9.43
09/16	14.27	30 20	0.50	0.64	8.67
09/15	9.75	28 21	0.43	0.60	7.18
09/14	10.12	27 22	0.40	0.60	7.38
Annual Growth	**13.4%**	**— —**	**5.2%**	**3.2%**	**7.3%**

Monolithic Power Systems Inc

Monolithic Power Systems (MPS) sends out mixed signals and that's a good thing. The fabless semiconductor company offers mixed-signal and analog microchips — especially DC-to-DC converters for powering flat-panel TVs wireless communications equipment notebook computers set-top boxes and other consumer electronic devices. MPS outsources production of its chips to three silicon foundries in China. The company's products are incorporated into electronic gear from tech heavyweights such as Dell Hewlett-Packard Samsung Electronics and Sony. The company was founded in 1997.

Operations

MPS has two main business segments. Its DC-to-DC products convert and control voltages in electronics from cell phones to TVs to medical equipment. The DC-to-DC chips are monolithic in that they accounted for 90% of the company's sales in 2015. MPS's lighting control products are used to backlight LCD and LED screens. The segment was 10% of sales in 2015.

Geographic Reach

MPS is headquartered in San Jose California but most of its activities are in Asia. Production assembly and packaging and testing are done at facilities in China and Malaysia. The finished products don't have far to go since 90% of sales are in Asia; China is the company's biggest market with 64% of sales. MPS has sales offices in the US Europe Singapore Taiwan China Korea and Japan.

Sales and Marketing

The company sells through distributors value-added resellers and directly to original equipment manufacturers (OEMs) original design manufacturers (ODMs) and electronic manufacturing service (EMS) companies. Sales to its largest distributor accounted for about 24% of revenue in 2015 and another distributor accounted for 10% of revenue in 2015. The MPS sales process includes working with customers in the design and use of MPS chips in their products.

Financial Performance

MPS's revenue grew at a healthy rate in 2015 while net income was flat.

Sales rose 18% in the company's DC to DC segment leading to an 18% growth rate from 2014 to 2015. It combined more unit sales with higher average sale prices to reach $333 million in revenue in 2015 compared to $282 in 2014.

Net income however slipped about 1% to $35.1 million from $35.5 million. MPS increased research and development spending in 2015 and paid more taxes compared to 2014.

Cash flow from operations dipped to $69.7 million in 2015 from $74 million in 2014.

Strategy

MPS is working to diversify its customers moving away from consumer-dependent products and to industrial automotive and lighting markets. It also is developing new products aimed at those markets and has signed distributor agreements. One such product is a DC-to-DC conversion technology QSMod that improves system efficiency which was introduced in 2013.

MPS spends about 20% of revenue on R&D each year.

Mergers and Acquisitions

In 2014 MPS acquired Sensima Technology a developer of magnetic sensor technologies which will be combined with MPS technologies for automotive industrial and cloud computing. The purchase price includes an initial cash payment of about $12 million and a subsequent cash earn-out payment of up to $9 million based on meeting performance goals.

EXECUTIVES

Senior Vice President Design Engineering, Paul Ueunten
Chairman President and CEO, Michael R. Hsing, age 58, $448,000 total compensation
President - MPS Asia Operations, Deming Xiao, age 55, $340,000 total compensation
VP Strategic Corporate Development General Counsel and Secretary, Saria Tseng, age 47, $300,000 total compensation
SVP Worldwide Sales and Marketing, Maurice Sciammas, age 58, $300,000 total compensation
CFO, Bernie Blegen
Vice President, Eric Yang
Auditors: Deloitte & Touche LLP

LOCATIONS

HQ: Monolithic Power Systems Inc
4040 Lake Washington Blvd. NE, Suite 201, Kirkland, WA 98033
Phone: 425 296-9956
Web: www.monolithicpower.com

PRODUCTS/OPERATIONS

2011 Sales

	$ mil.	% of total
DC-to-DC converters	165.6	85
LCD backlight inverters	26.5	13
Audio amplifiers	4.4	2
Total	**196.5**	**100**

Selected Products

AC/DC Offline
  Bridge rectifier
  Controllers and regulators
  Synchronous rectifiers
Audio amplifiers
Backlighting solutions
  EL drivers
  White LED drivers (inductors and charge pumps)
Automotive
Battery chargers
  Cradle chargers
  Linear chargers
  Protection
  Switching chargers
Full-bridge and half-bridge power drivers
Isolated and transformer-based power supplies
Lighting and illumination
Low dropout (LDO) linear regulators
Motor drivers
  Brushless DC motor drivers
  Stepper DC motor drivers
Photo-flash chargers and drivers
Power Over Ethernet powered device (PD) solutions
  PD controllers
  PD identity
Precision analog
  Analog switches
  High-side current sense amplifiers
  Operational amplifiers
  Voltage reference
Supervisory circuits and voltage supervisors
Switching power supply regulators
  DC-DC (step-down)
  Controller
  Intelli-Phase (monolithic driver + MOSFET)
  Non-synchronous switcher
  Synchronous switcher
  DC-DC (step-up)
  Controller
  Energy storage and release management
  LNB power supply
  Non-synchronous switcher
  Synchronous switcher
USB and current-limit load switches

COMPETITORS

Analog Devices	O2Micro
Fairchild	ON Semiconductor
Semiconductor	Power Integrations
Intersil	ROHM
Linear Technology	Richtek Technology
Maxim Integrated	Corp.
Products	STMicroelectronics
Microchip Technology	Semtech
Microsemi	Texas Instruments

HISTORICAL FINANCIALS

Company Type: Public

Income Statement   FYE: December 31

	REVENUE ($ mil.)	NET INCOME ($ mil.)	NET PROFIT MARGIN	EMPLOYEES
12/17	470.9	65.2	13.8%	1,534
12/16	388.6	52.7	13.6%	1,417
12/15	333.0	35.1	10.6%	1,260
12/14	282.5	35.5	12.6%	1,178
12/13	238.0	22.9	9.6%	1,105
Annual Growth	18.6%	29.9%	—	8.5%

2017 Year-End Financials

Debt ratio: —	No. of shares (mil.): 41.6
Return on equity: 13.6%	Dividends
Cash ($ mil.): 82.7	Yield: 0.0%
Current ratio: 6.81	Payout: 53.3%
Long-term debt ($ mil.): —	Market value ($ mil.): 4,676.0

	STOCK PRICE ($) FY Close	P/E High/Low	PER SHARE ($) Earnings	Dividends	Book Value
12/17	112.36	80 52	1.50	0.80	12.54
12/16	81.93	66 43	1.26	0.80	10.57
12/15	63.71	77 51	0.86	0.80	9.29
12/14	49.74	55 34	0.89	0.45	8.92
12/13	34.66	56 34	0.59	0.00	8.45
Annual Growth	34.2%	— —	26.3%	—	10.4%

Monotype Imaging Holdings Inc

Monotype Imaging may be the one to thank if you're reading this whether it's on a portable electronic device or a printed page. With most sales going to device manufacturers (OEMs) the company's text imaging software is integrated into applications and embedded in electronics ranging from mobile phones to laser printers automotive displays and digital cameras as well as navigation tools set-top boxes and Internet of Things devices. Its applications manage compression scaling color and layout. Providing customers access to thousands of typefaces OEM sales are complemented by about 46% of revenue coming from licenses to creative professionals mostly commercial clients. Customers have included Apple Google Sony and Microsoft.

Operations

The US has grown as a percentage of total revenues contributing 55% of Monotype Imaging's revenues in 2015. The company does however expect international to continue to be a major percentage of total revenues. Since Asia is an underpenetrated region for Monotype Imaging it is a particularly attractive growth opportunity specifically in Chinese Japanese and Korean language markets for laser printers digital copiers and other devices.

Geographic Reach

Geographic recognition of revenue does not necessarily reflect the destination of Monotype Imaging's products as sales are attached to the subsidiary receiving the revenue. Sales by a US subsidiary to Korea-based customers for example are classified as US sales. The company's products are sold from offices in Germany Hong Kong Japan South Korea the UK and the US. Sales from Asia generally go to Asian customers while the other subsidiaries cover many different countries including the US.

The company's research and development operations are located in Woburn Massachusetts; Los Altos California; Boulder Colorado; Belfast Northern Ireland; Salford United Kingdom; Bad Homburg and Berlin Germany; Noida India; Hong Kong China; and Tokyo Japan.

Sales and Marketing

Although no customer accounts for more than 10% of sales Monotype Imaging's top ten clients account for about 40% of annual revenues. The company serves many of its target industries' leaders including e-book reader and tablet makers including Amazon and Kobo top automotive brands such as Chrysler Ford Honda and Hyundai laser printer manufacturers and phone makers. The company nearly doubled its advertising spending to $3.3 million in 2015 from $1.7 million in each of 2014 and 2013.

Financial Performance

Monotype Imaging has seen an upward trend in its revenues of the past few years. In 2015 it reported an 4% rise in revenues driven by a 14% increase in its Creative Professional revenue. OEM revenue fell 3% for the year.

Net income slipped 2% to $26 million in 2015 after several years of steady increases. The company had acquisition costs to deal with as well as higher advertising costs in 2015.

Cash flow from operations dropped to $53 million in 2015 from $61.5 million in 2014.

Strategy

At the center of Monotype Imaging's growth strategy is a focus on serving high growth consumer electronic devices such as smartphones tablets navigation devices and consumer appliances to name a few. It will however also stay focused on the slower-growth laser printer market where it holds a leadership position and sees a demand for customized driver applications such as language interpretation. The company also continues to value its creative professionals and consumer users. It has several Websites including fonts.com and linotype.com.

Monotype Imaging focuses particularly on digital marketing where it sees opportunities in HTML-5-based marketing campaigns.

In 2015 the company introduced new and remastered typefaces like Neue Haas Unica Kairos and Zapfino Arabic and the Eric Gill series. In 2014 the company expanded its Fonts.com Web Fonts inventory to include typefaces from the famous FontFont library.

Mergers and Acquisitions

Monotype Imaging in 2015 acquired Mark Boulton Design Ltd. a Web design studio based in the UK for $1.75 million. It expands Monotype Imaging's capability to provide web design and web publishing.

Another 2015 acquisition was of TextPride Inc. which operated under the name of Swyft Media for $12 million. The deal expanded monotype Imaging's services in the new and growing to branded mobile advertising.

In 2014 the company acquired Germany-based FontShop International GmbH a privately-held font distributor and its US subsidiary California-based FontShop International for $13 million. The deal supported the company's growth in international markets.

Company Background

In 2012 the company furthered its aspirations for both of its primary customer groups when it acquired major competitor Bitstream for $50 million. With that purchase Monotype Imaging gained the 62000 fonts on MyFonts.com font capabilities such as an identification service and font rendering and layout technologies fonts for embedded and mobile settings and 10 patents as well as 40 engineers and type designers at a facility in India. That year the company also acquired Design by Front Limited a privately held web strategy design and technology studio in Belfast Northern Ireland for $4.6 million.

In 2009 Monotype Imaging saw a chance to build on its strategy of expanding its offerings for OEM customers acquiring Planetweb for about $2 million. PlanetWeb provided user interface developer tools for consumer electronics manufacturers.

Monotype Imaging was formed when a group of investors including TA Associates acquired Agfa Monotype (then a subsidiary of Agfa) in 2004. The company does business as International Typeface Corporation or ITC in the US; Monotype Hong Kong and Monotype Japan in Asia; and Monotype UK and Linotype in Europe.

EXECUTIVES

Managing Director Monotype Imaging Ltd., John H. McCallum, age 62, $260,996 total compensation
VP; General Manager Creative Professional, Christopher J. (Chris) Roberts, age 52
President and CEO, Scott E. Landers, age 47, $308,550 total compensation
EVP Sales and Market Strategy, Ben Semmes
Managing Director Monotype Solutions India, Neeraj Gulati
Managing Director Monotype Imaging Hong Kong, Ricky Chun
VP; General Manager ISV and Strategic Accounts, Ira Mirochnick
SVP Engineering, Steven R. (Steve) Martin, $271,253 total compensation
VP; General Manager OEM, Joe Roberts
EVP and CFO, Anthony Callini, age 47
Vp Corp Mkt, Lisa Landa
Vice President Corporate Development, Daniel Gerron
Executive Vice President, Tony Callini
Board Member, Douglas Shaw
Chairman, Robert L. (Bob) Lentz
Board Member, Gay Gaddis
Auditors: DELOITTE & TOUCHE LLP

LOCATIONS

HQ: Monotype Imaging Holdings Inc
600 Unicorn Park Drive, Woburn, MA 01801
Phone: 781 970-6000
Web: www.monotypeimaging.com

PRODUCTS/OPERATIONS

2015 Sales

	$ mil.	% of total
OEM	104.3	54
Creative Professional	88.1	46
Total	**192.4**	**100**

Selected Customers

E-book readers
　Amazon
　Kobo
Digital TVs and set-top-boxes
　Sharp
　Toshiba
　TTE Technology
Mobile phones
　Motorola
　Nokia
　RIM
　Sony
　ZTE
Other
　Activision
　Gannett Company
　Google
　Microsoft
　Nintendo
　Ubisoft
　UBS
　TiVo
　Whirlpool

COMPETITORS

Adobe Systems　　　Quark
Extensis　　　　　　Xara

HISTORICAL FINANCIALS

Company Type: Public

Income Statement

FYE: December 31

	REVENUE ($ mil.)	NET INCOME ($ mil.)	NET PROFIT MARGIN	EMPLOYEES
12/17	235.7	11.5	4.9%	734
12/16	203.4	14.8	7.3%	762
12/15	192.4	26.2	13.6%	494
12/14	184.5	32.5	17.6%	435
12/13	166.6	31.0	18.7%	354
Annual Growth	**9.1%**	**(21.9%)**	**—**	**20.0%**

2017 Year-End Financials

Debt ratio: 17.6%
Return on equity: 3.5%
Cash ($ mil.): 82.8
Current ratio: 2.26
Long-term debt ($ mil.): 93.0
No. of shares (mil.): 41.7
Dividends
Yield: 0.0%
Payout: 167.4%
Market value ($ mil.): 1,005.0

	STOCK PRICE ($) FY Close	P/E High/Low		PER SHARE ($) Earnings	Dividends	Book Value
12/17	24.10	95	66	0.27	0.45	7.89
12/16	19.85	68	50	0.36	0.44	7.61
12/15	23.64	51	32	0.65	0.40	7.68
12/14	28.83	39	30	0.81	0.32	7.48
12/13	31.86	40	20	0.78	0.24	7.34
Annual Growth	**(6.7%)**	**—**	**—**	**(23.3%)**	**17.1%**	**1.8%**

Motorcar Parts of America Inc

Motorcar Parts of America (MPA) is always ready for a fresh start. The company manufactures remanufactures and distributes alternators and starters for cars and all-weight trucks. MPA sells the remanufactured products to retailers and warehouse distributors which sell to do-it-yourself (DIY) consumers and to repair shops (DIFM or do-it-for-me) primarily in the US and Canada. Some of its top customers include retail chains AutoZone (almost 50% of sales) Advance Genuine Parts Pep Boys and O'Reilly Automotive. Although most of MPA's products are sold under its customers' private labels (about 90%) the company does market alternators and starters with its Quality-Built Reliance and Xtreme brands.

Geographic Reach

The majority of MPA's remanufacturing operations are conducted at facilities in Mexico and Malaysia. The company sells products throughout the US and Canada with facilities located in California Mexico Malaysia and China. It has domestic administrative offices located in California and Tennessee and international administrative offices in Mexico Singapore Malaysia and Canada.

Sales and Marketing

The company sells products to the largest auto parts retail and traditional warehouse chains and to major automobile manufacturers for both its aftermarket programs and warranty replacement programs. It manages an aggregate network of 24000 retail outlets.

Financial Performance

The auto parts maker reported revenues increases of 22% from 2015 to 2016. The growth for 2016 was attributed to increases across all its product lines and also reflected the full year impact of additional sales from new products. This included its new rotating electrical business and its new remanufactured brake master cylinder product portfolio.

MPA's profits remained flat from 2015 to 2016 hovering around the $11 million mark for both years. The stagnation in 2016 was driven by a spike in general and administrative expenses related to insurance recoveries and by a litigation settlement from bankruptcy cases relating to a discontinued subsidiary.

The company's operating cash flow has fluctuated wildly over the last several years; after experiencing negative cash flow in 2015 MPA's posted positive cash flow of $15 million in 2016. This was the result of favorable inventory levels and accrued core payments made in fiscal 2016.

Strategy

While MPA has historically served the DIY market — which is popular in times of recession — it is also pursuing the DIFM market which it views as a growth opportunity. MPA is especially looking to sell to major automotive manufacturers for their aftermarket and warranty replacement programs. In order to serve the large producers MPA generally must enter into longer-term agreements which requires expending more working capital and building inventory through increased production.

To counteract costs associated with this strategy the company has relocated the vast majority of its US remanufacturing operations to offshore facilities. Approximately 99% of MPA's manufacturing now takes place in Malaysia and Mexico. It also operates a warehousing testing and distribution facility in Singapore.

Company Background

A former executive with auto parts maker Echlin (now part of Dana) Mel Marks founded Motorcar Parts & Accessories (MPA) in 1968. Initially MPA only distributed imported auto parts but in 1986 it expanded into remanufacturing through foreign affiliates. The next year the company began remanufacturing in the US. As the number of imported cars in the US grew so did MPA. The company went public in 1994.

EXECUTIVES

VP New Technologies, Steven Kratz, age 63, $350,000 total compensation
Chairman President and CEO, Selwyn Joffe, age 60, $700,000 total compensation
VP Secretary and General Counsel, Michael M. Umansky, age 76, $506,000 total compensation
CFO, David Lee, age 48, $262,192 total compensation
Chief Accounting Officer, Kevin Daly, age 58, $214,462 total compensation
SVP Under-the-car Product Lines and Chief Manufacturing Officer, Doug Schooner, age 48, $294,000 total compensation
SVP Under-the-hood Product Lines, Bryan Cain
Auditors: Ernst & Young LLP

HQ: Motorcar Parts of America Inc
2929 California Street, Torrance, CA 90503
Phone: 310 212-7910
Web: www.motorcarparts.com

PRODUCTS/OPERATIONS

Selected Subsidiaries
Motorcar Parts de Mexico S.A. de C.V.
Motorcar Parts of Canada
MVR Products Pte. Limited (Singapore)
Unijoh Sdn. Bhd. (Malaysia)

Selected Products
Alternators
Bearings
Brake Master Cylinders
Hub Assemblies
Starters

COMPETITORS

BERU	Prestolite Electric
Cardone Industries	Robert Bosch LLC
DENSO	Standard Motor
Federal-Mogul	Products
Fred Jones Enterprises	Steel City Products
Jasper Engines	Inc.
Keystone Automotive	Universal
Operations	Manufacturing

HISTORICAL FINANCIALS
Company Type: Public

Income Statement   FYE: March 31

	REVENUE ($ mil.)	NET INCOME ($ mil.)	NET PROFIT MARGIN	EMPLOYEES
03/18	428.0	16.3	3.8%	2,996
03/17	421.2	37.5	8.9%	2,817
03/16	368.9	10.5	2.9%	2,663
03/15	301.7	11.4	3.8%	2,362
03/14	258.6	107.3	41.5%	2,270
Annual Growth	13.4%	(37.6%)	—	7.2%

2018 Year-End Financials

Debt ratio: 14.3%	No. of shares (mil.): 18.8
Return on equity: 6.2%	Dividends
Cash ($ mil.): 13.0	Yield: —
Current ratio: 0.74	Payout: —
Long-term debt ($ mil.): 13.9	Market value ($ mil.): 405.0

	STOCK PRICE ($) FY Close	P/E High/Low	PER SHARE ($) Earnings	Dividends	Book Value
03/18	21.43	36 23	0.84	0.00	14.55
03/17	30.73	19 12	1.93	0.00	13.33
03/16	37.98	69 45	0.55	0.00	11.38
03/15	27.79	53 33	0.65	0.00	10.58
03/14	26.57	4 1	7.01	0.00	7.28
Annual Growth	(5.2%)	—	(41.2%)	—	18.9%

MTS Systems Corp

In this world nothing is certain but death and taxes — and those things tested by MTS Systems. The company produces testing systems that simulate repeated or harsh conditions to determine mechanical behavior of materials products and structures. Its systems are used worldwide in infrastructure markets from inspecting steel to locomotive rails. MTS caters to auto makers with road simulators while in aerospace its equipment tests aircraft fatigue. Services include maintenance and training. MTS also supplies industrial sensors to increase machine efficiency and safety. International customers generate more than two-thirds of the company's revenue.

Operations
MTS's test segment primarily offers products for the testing of ground vehicles (accounting for about 50% of the segment's revenue) and products for testing materials in industries that include power generation aerospace vehicles and bio-medicine (25% of the segment's revenue). Structure-testing products for aerospace wind energy structural engineering petroleum and other industries account for the remainder of the test segment's revenue.

The company's sensors which account for about 35% of sales are used in construction agriculture mining and manufacturing (35% of the segment's revenue) and industrial sensors (about 20% of the segment's revenue) are used in heavy industrial markets and energy and power generation. Systems sensors (accounting for 10% of the segment's revenue) consist of dynamic test measurement and sensing systems used to test model and monitor the behavior of structures and processes.

Geographic Reach
MTS based in Eden Prairie Minnesota has manufacturing plants in China Germany and the US (in Minnesota New York Utah Michigan and North Carolina). Other offices are located across Asia Europe and the Americas. The US generates about a third of sales Europe about 25% China 20% and Asia (excluding China) about 20%.

Sales and Marketing
MTS's test segment has sales staff in the US and sales and service subsidiaries in Canada China France Germany Italy India Japan Russia South Korea Spain Sweden and the UK. The sensor segment has direct field sales and service representatives throughout US and sales subsidiaries in Italy the UK France Germany China Japan Canada and Belgium. The company also sells through distributors.

Financial Performance
MTS followed two years of declining revenue with two years of rising revenue including a 21% jump in 2017 (ended October) from 2016. The leap to $788 million in revenue for 2017 came courtesy of the acquisition of PCB which boosted Sensor revenue more than 100%. The company highlighted strong demand for positional sensors particularly in the heavy industrial markets. Test revenue fell about 2% from year-to-year.

Net income slipped to about $25 million in 2017 from $27.5 million in 2016 because of higher operating expenses some related to the PCB deal and increased interest expense.

Cash and cash equivalents rose to about $109 million in 2017 from about $85 million in 2016 driven by about $35 million in depreciation and amortization $25 million of net income an increase in working capital of about $11 million and other factors.

Strategy
MTS Systems' acquisition of PCB Group helped position the company take advantage of the growing market for sensors. Just in 2017 (ended October) the acquisition more than doubled MTS's sensor sales. The increasing number of sensors used in automotive applications for electric and self-driving vehicle technologies is an opportunity for MTS. The company also sees growth in sensors for industrial hydraulics and in equipment ordered by the US Department of Defense.

Mergers and Acquisitions
In 2016 MTS acquired PCB Group a manufacturer of piezoelectric sensors and components used for vibration pressure and force measurement for $580 million. The acquisition of PCB expanded MTS's market position in sensors.

HISTORY

MTS Systems a spinoff of Research Incorporated was started in 1966 to make software so automakers could replicate test track conditions in the laboratory. MTS's first products measured auto body endurance. Donald Sullivan who became president in 1982 and CEO in 1987 pulled the company through a market slump in the early 1990s by steering it into the factory automation business. The move was initiated by the 1992 acquisition of small startup Custom Servo Motors a maker of compact powerful motors used to control fabrication and packaging motions in factory applications. Sullivan was named chairman in 1994 replacing company co-founder George Butzow.

To feed revenue momentum the company made some of its systems compatible with Microsoft's Windows NT environments and it tailored tools to specific customers. In 1996 the Japanese government bought a $23 million seismic simulator in the wake of the 1995 Hanshin earthquake. The company moved into the aerospace products market in 1997 creating titanium-based component subsidiary AeroMet. (MTS shut down AeroMet in late 2005 saying the unit could not achieve a sustainable business model.)

Sullivan stepped down as CEO in 1998 and was replaced by longtime Honeywell executive Sidney (Chip) Emery. MTS in 1999 bought engine design testing specialist DSP Technology. A drop in profits for the fiscal year partly the result of the purchase prompted MTS to restructure and lay off nearly 10% of its workforce.

In 2000 the company won a $37 million contract from the US Army to design manufacture and install an advanced roadway simulator. The next year MTS sold its electronic assembly operations to PEMSTAR and expanded its line of software products for the auto industry.

MTS sold its automation division in 2003 to Parker Hannifin.

The company signed an agreement with National Instruments in 2004 to cooperate on research and development of a low-cost framework for noise and vibration testing.

In 2005 MTS sold its Powertrain Technology (engine testing) division to A&D Co. Ltd. of Japan.

Chip Emery left the CEO's post in early 2008 and was succeeded by president/COO Laura Hamilton. Emery remained chairman until the end of fiscal 2008.In mid 2008 the company sold off its Nano Instruments business to Agilent Technologies. The deal marked MTS's exit from supplying nanoindentation systems and related equipment used in verifying structural integrity of semiconductor devices and coatings and thin films.

In late 2008 the company widened its pipeline to China. MTS acquired the assets of SANS Group a Chinese supplier of materials testing systems for nearly $44 million. The Shenzhen-based firm makes electromechanical and static-hydraulic testing machines among other products. The deal builds upon MTS' move to establish a wholly foreign-owned enterprise in Shanghai in 2007. A sales office was first opened in China in 1985.

EXECUTIVES

President and CEO, Jeffrey A. (Jeff) Graves, age 56, $647,500 total compensation
SVP and CIO, Mark D. Losee
President Material Test Systems, William C. Becker, age 64
President Vehicles and Structures Test Systems, Steven B. Harrison, age 52
SVP and CFO, Brian T. Ross, age 42
President MTS Sensors, David T. Hore, age 52, $125,000 total compensation
Senior Vice President Test, William E Bachrach
Vice President Market Development and Technology Vehicle Dynamics Division, Maurice Mergeay
Vice President, Kelly Donaldson
Vice President Sales, Kevin McQuillan
Vice President Customer Service And Support, J E Egerdal
Vice President Of Information Technology, Duane Fox
Chairman, David J. (Dave) Anderson, age 71
Board Member, David Johnson
Auditors: KPMG LLP

LOCATIONS

HQ: MTS Systems Corp
14000 Technology Drive, Eden Prairie, MN 55344
Phone: 952 937-4000
Web: www.mts.com

PRODUCTS/OPERATIONS

2017 Sales

	$ mil.	% of total
Test	504.1	64
Sensors	283.8	36
Total	**787.9**	**100**

2017 Sales

	$ mil.	% of total
Product	691.4	88
Service	96.5	12
Total	**787.9**	**100**

COMPETITORS

ACS Motion Control	Mechanical Technology
AMETEK	Moog
Aero Systems	OYO
Engineering	Pepperl+Fuchs
GE	PerkinElmer
HORIBA	Pure Technologies
Illinois Tool Works	Schmitt Industries
Instron	Tech/Ops Sevcon
JT3	

HISTORICAL FINANCIALS

Company Type: Public

Income Statement   FYE: September 29

	REVENUE ($ mil.)	NET INCOME ($ mil.)	NET PROFIT MARGIN	EMPLOYEES
09/18	778.0	61.3	7.9%	3,400
09/17*	787.9	25.0	3.2%	3,500
10/16	650.1	27.4	4.2%	3,500
10/15	563.9	45.4	8.1%	2,400
09/14	564.3	42.0	7.4%	2,180
Annual Growth	**8.4%**	**9.9%**	**—**	**11.8%**

*Fiscal year change

2018 Year-End Financials

Debt ratio: 34.0%
Return on equity: 13.5%
Cash ($ mil.): 71.8
Current ratio: 1.79
Long-term debt ($ mil.): 355.6
No. of shares (mil.): 17.8
Dividends
Yield: 0.0%
Payout: 37.7%
Market value ($ mil.): 978.0

	STOCK PRICE ($) FY Close	P/E High/Low	PER SHARE ($) Earnings	Dividends	Book Value
09/18	54.75	18 14	3.18	1.20	26.77
09/17*	53.45	45 32	1.31	1.20	24.14
10/16	46.03	40 25	1.70	1.20	24.33
10/15	57.73	25 18	3.00	1.20	17.29
09/14	68.74	27 23	2.73	1.20	17.00
Annual Growth	**(5.5%)**	**— —**	**3.9%**	**(0.0%)**	**12.0%**

*Fiscal year change

Multi-Color Corp.

Multi-Color Corporation's labels aren't just black and white and red all over. The company produces printed labels for product makers in markets such as home and personal care wine and spirit food and beverage and specialty consumer goods. Multi-Color serves customers in North and South America Europe the Asia/Pacific region and South Africa. The company prints and affixes heat transfer re-sealable shrink wrap pressure sensitive and other label types to glass and plastic containers. Multi-Color also offers gravure printing and injection in-mold labels. Over the years the company has counted Procter & Gamble and Miller Brewing among its biggest customers. Multi-Color traces its roots to 1916.

EXECUTIVES

VP CFO and Chief Accounting Officer, Sharon E. Birkett, age 51, $387,500 total compensation
COO Wine and Spirit Markets, David G. Buse, age 52
President CEO and Director, Vadis A. Rodato, age 57, $500,000 total compensation
COO Consumer Product Goods, Floyd E. Needham, age 49, $500,000 total compensation
National Account Manager, Hal Hunt
Chairman, Nigel A. Vinecombe, age 54
Auditors: Grant Thornton LLP

LOCATIONS

HQ: Multi-Color Corp.
4053 Clough Woods Dr., Batavia, OH 45103
Phone: 513 381-1480
Web: www.mcclabel.com

PRODUCTS/OPERATIONS

Selected Products and Services
Labels
Heat transfer
In-mold
Neck bands
Peel-away
Pressure sensitive
Re-sealable
Shrink sleeve

COMPETITORS

Fort Dearborn	Outlook Group
H. S. Crocker	WS Packaging Group

HISTORICAL FINANCIALS

Company Type: Public

Income Statement   FYE: March 31

	REVENUE ($ mil.)	NET INCOME ($ mil.)	NET PROFIT MARGIN	EMPLOYEES
03/18	1,300.9	71.9	5.5%	8,400
03/17	923.3	61.0	6.6%	5,450
03/16	870.8	47.7	5.5%	5,000
03/15	810.7	45.7	5.6%	3,550
03/14	706.4	28.2	4.0%	3,250
Annual Growth	**16.5%**	**26.4%**	**—**	**26.8%**

2018 Year-End Financials

Debt ratio: 55.0%
Return on equity: 12.6%
Cash ($ mil.): 67.7
Current ratio: 1.84
Long-term debt ($ mil.): 1,577.8
No. of shares (mil.): 20.4
Dividends
Yield: 0.0%
Payout: 5.1%
Market value ($ mil.): 1,350.0

	STOCK PRICE ($) FY Close	P/E High/Low	PER SHARE ($) Earnings	Dividends	Book Value
03/18	66.05	22 16	3.87	0.20	37.05
03/17	71.00	22 14	3.58	0.20	22.35
03/16	53.35	28 14	2.82	0.20	20.16
03/15	69.33	26 12	2.71	0.20	17.40
03/14	35.00	22 14	1.70	0.20	18.14
Annual Growth	**17.2%**	**— —**	**22.8%**	**(0.0%)**	**19.5%**

MVB Financial Corp

EXECUTIVES

Chief Executive Officer; President, Larry Nazza
Auditors: Dixon Hughes Goodman LLP

LOCATIONS

HQ: MVB Financial Corp
301 Virginia Avenue, Fairmont, WV 26554
Phone: 304 363-4800
Web: www.mvbbanking.com

HISTORICAL FINANCIALS

Company Type: Public

Income Statement
FYE: December 31

	ASSETS ($ mil.)	NET INCOME ($ mil.)	INCOME AS % OF ASSETS	EMPLOYEES
12/17	1,534.3	7.5	0.5%	0
12/16	1,418.8	12.9	0.9%	382
12/15	1,384.4	6.8	0.5%	371
12/14	1,110.4	2.0	0.2%	324
12/13	987.0	4.0	0.4%	274
Annual Growth	11.7%	17.2%	—	—

2017 Year-End Financials

Return on assets: 0.5%	Dividends
Return on equity: 5.1%	Yield: 0.0%
Long-term debt ($ mil.): —	Payout: 14.7%
No. of shares (mil.): 10.4	Market value ($ mil.): 210.0
Sales ($ mil): 97.3	

	STOCK PRICE ($) FY Close	P/E High/Low		PER SHARE ($) Earnings	Dividends	Book Value
12/17	20.10	29	18	0.68	0.10	14.38
12/16	12.80	10	7	1.31	0.08	14.57
12/15	13.10	20	16	0.76	0.08	14.23
12/14	14.99	164	65	0.22	0.08	13.71
12/13	33.20	66	40	0.57	0.08	12.28
Annual Growth	(11.8%)	—	—	4.5%	7.5%	4.0%

MYR Group Inc

MYR Group's work can be electrifying. The specialty contractor builds and maintains electric delivery infrastructure systems for utilities and commercial clients. MYR Group constructs transmission and distribution lines for the oil and gas power and telecommunications industries. The company also installs and maintains electrical wiring in commercial and industrial facilities and traffic and rail systems. The group operates nationwide through subsidiaries including The L.E. Myers Co. Harlan Electric Hawkeye Construction Sturgeon Electric MYR Transmission Services and Great Southwestern Construction. MYR's transmission and distribution segment accounts for about three-fourths of the group's revenues.

Operations

The company's Transmission & Distribution customers generated 74% of MYR Group's revenue in 2014. Its Commercial & Industrial segment brought in 26% of revenue in 2014.

Completed projects include the Cross Texas Transmission 345kV Transmission Line Project Spearville to Axtell 345kV Transmission Line (also known as the KETA Project) the Meadowbrook to Loudoun 500kV Transmission Line and Carson Substation to Suffolk Substation 500kV Transmission Lines.

Sales and Marketing

Transmission & Distribution customers include electric utilities private developers cooperatives and municipalities. Its Commercial & Industrial segment provides electrical contracting services to property owners and general contractors in the Western US.

Its top 10 customers accounted for nearly 50% of revenues in fiscal 2014; no single customer accounted for more than 10% of sales.

MYR Group has logged between $400000 and $500000 each year since 2010 on selling general and administrative expenses (which include advertising expenses).

Financial Performance

With the exception of a slight dip in 2013 revenue has been on the rise for the past five years. In 2014 it increased 5% to $944 million largely on growth in the Commercial & Industrial segment. That segment's services were generally in higher demand; improving economic conditions in its core markets of Colorado and Arizona also helped boost business.

Net income has risen for the past five years and in 2014 it increased 5% to $36.6 million thanks both to MYR's higher revenue and increased interest earnings. Cash flow from operations fell 42% to $44 million that year as more cash was used for accounts payable.

Strategy

MYR Group looks to grow organically or through strategic acquisitions and joint ventures. It aims to improve its competitive position in existing markets while also expanding into new geographic markets. The company has also dog-eared funds to invest in additional properties and equipment to support its strategy.

The Transmission & Distribution segment counts some 125 cooperatives electric utilities and municipalities as customers. The business stands to benefit from a continued emphasis on improving and upgrading the country's power supply and the increasing market for alternative energy. As wind and solar farm developments grow there is an increasing demand to link the farms to large power grids. MYR Group works on numerous wind farm projects each year. The company expects increased activity in that sector.

The company's Commercial & Industrial segment has a regional focus in Colorado and Arizona.

MYR Group maintains one of the largest fleets of vehicles in the US (some 5000 units) that can be mobilized for transmission and distribution work around the country. Because of this asset MYR Group often is called to restore power in the aftermath of hurricanes floods ice storms and other natural disasters. This is a relatively small part of the company's business though.

The group's strategy to take advantage of the growing need for infrastructure work includes seeking out possible acquisition targets or joint venture partners as well as expanding into new markets. It will also add to its fleet as it deems beneficial and has been spending tens of millions of dollars on new specialty equipment and tooling.

Company Background

MYR was founded in 1891 by Lewis Edward Myers who briefly worked as a salesman with Thomas Edison.

EXECUTIVES

SVP, William H. Green, age 74, $346,000 total compensation
President and CEO, Richard S. (Rick) Swartz, age 54, $376,500 total compensation
SVP CFO and Treasurer, Betty R. Johnson, age 59
SVP East and President L.E. Myers Co., Tod Cooper
Vice President Large Projects, Rick Pieper
Vice President Information Technology, Jean Luber
Vice President Human Resources, Doreen L Keller
VICE PRESIDENT, Kelley Lange
President and CEO, William A. (Bill) Koertner, age 68
Auditors: Crowe Horwath LLP

LOCATIONS

HQ: MYR Group Inc
1701 Golf Road, Suite 3-1012, Rolling Meadows, IL 60008
Phone: 847 290-1891
Web: www.myrgroup.com

PRODUCTS/OPERATIONS

2014 Sales by Segment

	% of total
Transmission & Distribution	74
Commercial & Industrial	26
Total	100

Selected Services

Electrical
  Commercial/Industrial
  Construction
  Design-build services
  Directional boring
  Emergency storm response
  Fiber optics
  Foundations & caissons
  Gas distribution
  Highway lighting
  Overhead distribution
  PCS/Cellular towers
  Preconstruction services
  Substation
  Telecommunications
  Traffic signals
  Transmission
  Underground distribution
Mechanical
  Boiler construction and maintenance
  Erection of piping systems
  General contracting
  In-house fabrication
  Instrumentation
  Maintenance
  Preconstruction services
  Retrofit to existing systems

Selected Subsidiaries

ComTel Technology Inc.
Great Southwestern Construction Inc.
Harlan Electric Company
Hawkeye Construction Inc.
Meyers International Inc.
MYR Transmission Services Inc.
MYRpower Inc.
The L.E. Myers Co.
Sturgeon Electric Company Inc.

COMPETITORS

Austin Industries	MDU Resources
Cupertino Electric	MasTec
Dycom	Mass Electric
EEI	Pike Corporation
EMCOR	Quanta Services
Goldfield	Siemens AG
Henkels & McCoy	Vario Construction
IES Holdings	Company
Kelso-Burnett	

HISTORICAL FINANCIALS
Company Type: Public

Income Statement FYE: December 31

	REVENUE ($ mil.)	NET INCOME ($ mil.)	NET PROFIT MARGIN	EMPLOYEES
12/17	1,403.3	21.1	1.5%	5,275
12/16	1,142.4	21.4	1.9%	4,600
12/15	1,061.6	27.3	2.6%	4,075
12/14	943.9	36.5	3.9%	3,650
12/13	902.7	34.7	3.9%	3,500
Annual Growth	11.7%	(11.7%)	—	10.8%

2017 Year-End Financials

Debt ratio: 13.6%
Return on equity: 7.6%
Cash ($ mil.): 5.3
Current ratio: 2.01
Long-term debt ($ mil.): 81.5

No. of shares (mil.): 16.4
Dividends
Yield: —
Payout: —
Market value ($ mil.): 588.0

	STOCK PRICE ($) FY Close	P/E High/Low	PER SHARE ($) Earnings	Dividends	Book Value
12/17	35.73	33 18	1.28	0.00	17.43
12/16	37.68	32 15	1.23	0.00	16.11
12/15	20.61	24 14	1.30	0.00	16.52
12/14	27.40	16 13	1.69	0.00	15.51
12/13	25.08	16 12	1.61	0.00	13.95
Annual Growth	9.3%	— —	(5.6%)	—	5.7%

Nanometrics, Inc.

Nanometrics works on a nano scale for electronics manufacturers that need their goods to measure up. The company provides thin-film metrology and inspection systems used by makers of precision electronic gear. These stand-alone integrated and tabletop measurement devices gauge the thickness and consistency of film materials used in making semiconductors LEDs data storage components and power management components. Its systems are used throughout the fabrication process from substrate manufacturing to advanced wafer-scale packaging. Top customers include Samsung Electronics Intel and SK Hynix. Nanometrics generates most of its sales in Asia.

Operations
Nanometrics gets about 60% of its revenue from its automated systems such as the Atlas series with integrated systems including the IMPULSE line accounting for about 15% and its materials characterization systems such as the RPMBlue less than 10%. The remaining revenue comes from the company's service operations. The company also offers software applications that include NanoDiffract and SpectraProbe.

The company makes most of its automated and integrated products at its factory and it send some work to third-party contractors.

Geographic Reach
Nanometrics is based in Milpitas California and it has field and support operations in China France Germany Israel Italy Japan South Korea Singapore and Taiwan.

The company's sales are concentrated in Asia with some 35% going to South Korea about 15% to Japan and more than 10% to China. The US accounts for nearly 15% of the company's revenue.

Nanometrics has a manufacturing operation in California and it uses uses contract manufacturers in China Israel Japan and the US for subassembly tasks.

Sales and Marketing
Customers include semiconductor manufacturers and equipment suppliers producers of high brightness-LEDs solar PVs data storage devices silicon wafers and photomasks. Its top three customers — Samsung Electronics Intel and Micron - together account for about 50% of sales.

Nanometrics sells its products through a direct sales force.

Financial Performance
Nanometrics has ridden a robust semiconductor industry to annual average increases of about 14% since 2013. The company beat the average with a 17% increase to more than $258 million in 2017 from 2016 as customers bought instruments for making 3D-NAND and DRAM chips. The Atlas III Nanometrics' newest version of its flagship line accounted for nearly two-thirds of the revenue increase.

Nanometrics reported a lower profit of $30 million in 2017 compared to $44 million in 2016 due to money set aside to comply with the US Tax Cuts and Jobs Act. Before taxes operating income in 2017 was about $43 million compared to $29 million the year before.

The company had $117 million in cash at the end of 2017 compared to $130 million in 2016. Cash from operations fell $25 million in 2017 from 2016 because of higher inventory levels and a higher accounts receivable balance due to record fourth quarter revenue in 2017.

Strategy
Nanometrics has released new versions of key products such as its Atlas metrology systems as the semiconductor industry looks for ways to make smaller and smaller chips. The Atlas III released in 2017 offers improved precision and higher throughput compared to the previous model. Sales of the system boosted Nanometrics' revenue in 2017 and the company expects the Atlas drive revenue in 2018.

The company has added software and analytics capabilities to its portfolio to generate more revenue and provide more services to customers. Its service revenue has increased as its base of installed products has grown.

With a higher percentage of its sales to customers in Asia Nanometrics is susceptible from disruptions if trade issues become a concern and tariffs are implemented.

Mergers and Acquisitions
In 2018 Nanometrics agreed to buy 4D Technology Corp. for about $40 million. The addition of 4D's interferometric measurement and inspection systems should bolster the offerings from Nanometrics while enabling the company to enter new markets. 4D is to become a business unit within Nanometrics when the deal closes probably by the end of 2018.

EXECUTIVES

CFO, Jeffrey (Jeff) Andreson, age 56
President CEO and Director, Timothy J. Stultz, age 70, $465,000 total compensation
SVP Strategic Marketing and Business Development, Kevin Heidrich, age 47
EVP Business Operations, S. Mark Borowicz, age 45
Senior Vice President Commercial Operations, Rollin Kocher
Senior Vice President, Mark Borowicz
Vice President Applications Engineering, Nagesh Avadhany
Vice President Safety, Michael Weber
Vice President Global Human Resources, Dawn Laplante
Vice President Information Technology, Marcy McKee
Vice President Engineering, Rodney Smedt
Vice President Global Operations, Michael Shaughnessy
Vice President Information Technology, Venkat Gopalakrishnan
VP Supply Chain, Ingo Riedl
Vice President Global Human Resources, Philip Ziman
Vice President Service, Randy Tully
Vice President Supply Chain Management, Shane Smith
Chairman, Bruce C. Rhine, age 60
Auditors: PricewaterhouseCoopers LLP

LOCATIONS

HQ: Nanometrics, Inc.
1550 Buckeye Drive, Milpitas, CA 95035
Phone: 408 545-6000
Web: www.nanometrics.com

PRODUCTS/OPERATIONS

2017 Sales

	$ mil.	% of total
Products		
Automated systems	151.4	59
Integrated System	42.2	16
Material characterization systems	21.3	17
Service	43.7	17
Total	**258.6**	**100**

COMPETITORS

ASM International	Qcept Technologies
Applied Materials	Rudolph Technologies
Bio-Rad Labs	SCREEN Holdings
KLA-Tencor	Tokyo Electron
Nova Measuring	Zygo

HISTORICAL FINANCIALS
Company Type: Public

Income Statement FYE: December 30

	REVENUE ($ mil.)	NET INCOME ($ mil.)	NET PROFIT MARGIN	EMPLOYEES
12/17	258.6	30.2	11.7%	592
12/16	221.1	44.0	19.9%	532
12/15	187.3	2.9	1.6%	518
12/14	166.4	(31.1)	—	525
12/13	144.3	(14.1)	—	536
Annual Growth	15.7%	—	—	2.5%

2017 Year-End Financials

Debt ratio: —
Return on equity: 11.9%
Cash ($ mil.): 117.0
Current ratio: 5.45
Long-term debt ($ mil.): —

No. of shares (mil.): 24.6
Dividends
Yield: —
Payout: —
Market value ($ mil.): 614.0

	STOCK PRICE ($)	P/E		PER SHARE ($)		
	FY Close	High/Low	Earnings	Dividends	Book Value
12/17	24.92	27 20	1.17	0.00	10.65
12/16	25.06	14 7	1.75	0.00	9.72
12/15	15.79	155 101	0.12	0.00	7.73
12/14	16.59	— —	(1.30)	0.00	7.54
12/13	18.61	— —	(0.61)	0.00	8.81
Annual Growth	7.6%	— —	—	—	4.9%

National Beverage Corp.

National Beverage works to quench America's thirst. The company makes and distributes the Shasta and Faygo brands of flavored soft drinks both of which were launched more than a century ago and come in multiple flavors to appeal to diverse consumer tastes. It also offers spring and flavored waters under the LaCroix and ClearFruit brands Everfresh and Mr. Pure juice and juice-added drinks Rip It energy drinks and Ohana lemonades and teas. Customers include national and regional grocers convenience stores and foodservice distributors. National Beverage operates a dozen facilities located across the US. Company chairman and CEO Nick Caporella owns 74% of the business.

Operations

National Beverage's operations consist of various subsidiaries that purchase raw materials (aluminum cans and plastic bottles corn syrup and juice concentrates) produce the concentrates and manufacture the finished products. In addition to its own brands National Beverage produces soft drinks under private label for certain retailers (who also market some National Beverage brands).

Its dozen bottling plants are situated near major US metropolitan areas enabling timely availability of products. The company also uses customers' warehouse facilities and its own delivery fleet to distribute the National Beverage lineup along with the delivery systems of independent distributors and wholesalers.

Geographic Reach

National Beverage develops manufactures markets and sells its flavored beverages nationwide. It is taking steps to expand distribution directly and through exporters to customers in Canada Mexico the Caribbean Latin America the Pacific Rim Asia Europe and the Middle East.

Sales and Marketing

National Beverage sells its products through an internal sales force as well as via specialized broker networks.

The firm distributes its products to convenience stores through its own direct-store delivery fleet and with help from independent distributors. The company's foodservice division distributes items to independent specialized distributors that serve hospitals schools military bases airlines hotels and foodservice wholesalers. National Beverage's take-home convenience and foodservice operations also leverage vending machines and glass-door coolers to market and promote their brands.

National Beverage spent $50.2 million on advertising in fiscal 2014 compared to $44.6 million in 2013 and $45.8 million 2012. Within the grocery store market National Beverage competes head-to-head with national cola giants but through regionally-focused marketing efforts which tend to be less costly than national campaigns.

Financial Performance

Revenue for National Beverage dropped 3% in fiscal 2014 to $641 million from 2013's $662 million. The company attributes the decline to a more than 7% volume decrease in sales of carbonated soft drinks thanks to unfavorable weather conditions and a drop in consumption of the drinks across the industry. Net income dropped 7% during the reporting period to more than $43 million from about $47 million. The 2014 revenue decrease combined with an increase in expenses such as advertising spurred the drop. Cash from operations rose $12 million to $52 million in 2014.

Strategy

Amid a nation where cola-flavored soft drinks account for about 50% of the soft drink sector's grocery market National Beverage colas account for less than 20% of the company's volume. Rather than concentrate on cola-consuming customers National Beverage has adopted a "fantasy of flavors" product strategy that caters to regional and ethnic (Hispanic) tastes. Indeed a number of brands such as Faygo's RedPop Moon Mist and Rock'n'Rye are positioned as local heroes. The strategy includes adding products in the rapidly growing functional drink category which targets consumers who are willing to pay more for beverages perceived to promote health and wellness. To this end its Power+ Brands target consumers who seek healthier and functional beverage alternatives. This collection of brands includes LaCroix LaCroix Curate Rip It Everfresh and Everfresh Premier Varietals.

Concurrently the company focuses on the convenience store market where flavors generate 56% of soft drink sales. Convenience stores including dollar stores gas stations and other smaller "up and down the street" businesses (the company's term) also provide top shelf visibility for its beverages at a higher selling price.

EXECUTIVES

EVP Finance, George R. Bracken, age 75
SVP Operational Guidance, Dean A. McCoy, age 62, $225,000 total compensation
President and Director, Joseph G. (Joe) Caporella, age 59, $650,000 total compensation
Chairman and CEO, Nick A. Caporella, age 83
EVP BevCo Sales, Dennis L. Thompson, $200,000 total compensation
Executive Vice President Strategic Sourcing, James Bolton
Senior Vice President Sales, Anthony Kibbey
Auditors: RSM US LLP

LOCATIONS

HQ: National Beverage Corp.
8100 SW Tenth Street, Suite 4000, Fort Lauderdale, FL 33324
Phone: 954 581-0922
Web: www.nationalbeverage.com

PRODUCTS/OPERATIONS

SELECTED BRANDS
LaCroix
Shasta Sparkling
Everfresh and Mr. Pure
Rip It

SELECTED SUBSIDIARIES
BevCo Sales Inc.
Big Shot Beverages Inc.
Everfresh Beverages Inc.
Faygo Beverages Inc.
National Beverage Vending Company
NewBevCo Inc.
NutraFizz Products Corp.
Shasta Beverages Inc.
Sundance Beverage Company

COMPETITORS

Big Red	Mondelez International
Chiquita Brands	Monster Beverage
Citrus World	Mountain Valley
Clearly Canadian	Naked Juice
Coca-Cola	National Grape
Cott	Cooperative
Crystal Rock Holdings	Nestlé Waters North
Danone Water	America
Dole Food	Ocean Spray
Dr Pepper Snapple	Odwalla
Group	PepsiCo
Eldorado Artesian	Red Bull
Springs	South Beach Beverage
Energy Brands	Sunkist
Fiji Water	Sunny Delight
Gatorade	Tropicana
Hornell Brewing	Welch's
Impulse Energy USA	Wet Planet Beverages
Jones Soda	

HISTORICAL FINANCIALS
Company Type: Public

Income Statement — FYE: April 28

	REVENUE ($ mil.)	NET INCOME ($ mil.)	NET PROFIT MARGIN	EMPLOYEES
04/18	975.7	149.7	15.3%	1,500
04/17	826.9	107.0	12.9%	1,300
04/16*	704.7	61.2	8.7%	1,200
05/15	645.8	49.3	7.6%	1,200
05/14	641.1	43.6	6.8%	1,200
Annual Growth	11.1%	36.1%	—	5.7%

*Fiscal year change

2018 Year-End Financials

Debt ratio: —	No. of shares (mil.): 46.6
Return on equity: 52.0%	Dividends
Cash ($ mil.): 189.8	Yield: 0.0%
Current ratio: 3.37	Payout: 47.0%
Long-term debt ($ mil.): —	Market value ($ mil.): 4,185.0

	STOCK PRICE ($)	P/E		PER SHARE ($)		
	FY Close	High/Low	Earnings	Dividends	Book Value
04/18	89.78	39 26	3.19	1.50	7.11
04/17	88.59	40 19	2.29	1.50	5.27
04/16*	46.74	37 16	1.31	0.00	4.43
05/15	22.42	25 16	1.05	0.00	3.19
05/14	19.21	24 16	0.92	0.00	2.29
Annual Growth	47.0%	— —	36.5%	—	32.7%

*Fiscal year change

National Commerce Corp

Auditors: Porter Keadle Moore, LLC

LOCATIONS

HQ: National Commerce Corp
600 Luckie Drive, Suite 350, Birmingham, AL 35223
Phone: 205 313-8100
Web: www.nationalbankofcommerce.com

HISTORICAL FINANCIALS

Company Type: Public

Income Statement

	ASSETS ($ mil.)	NET INCOME ($ mil.)	INCOME AS % OF ASSETS	EMPLOYEES
				FYE: December 31
12/17	2,737.6	20.0	0.7%	433
12/16	1,950.7	17.8	0.9%	297
12/15	1,763.3	9.6	0.5%	289
12/14	1,138.4	5.4	0.5%	235
12/13	791.7	4.0	0.5%	0
Annual Growth	36.4%	49.6%	—	—

2017 Year-End Financials

Return on assets: 0.8%	Dividends
Return on equity: 6.4%	Yield: —
Long-term debt ($ mil.): —	Payout: —
No. of shares (mil.): 14.7	Market value ($ mil.): 595.0
Sales ($ mil): 129.8	

	STOCK PRICE ($) FY Close	P/E High/Low	PER SHARE ($) Earnings	Dividends	Book Value
12/17	40.25	30 24	1.41	0.00	26.55
12/16	37.15	23 13	1.61	0.00	21.01
12/15	25.05	27 20	1.02	0.00	19.33
Annual Growth	26.8%	— —	17.6%	—	17.2%

National Health Investors, Inc.

National Health Investors has a financial investment in the nation's health. The real estate investment trust (REIT) owns or makes mortgage investments in health care properties primarily long-term care facilities. With more than 180 properties in over 30 states its holdings also include residences for people with developmental disabilities assisted-living complexes medical office buildings retirement centers and an acute care hospital. About one-third of National Health Investors' properties are leased to its largest tenant National HealthCare Corporation; half are leased to regional health care providers. A majority of the REIT's facilities are located in Florida Texas and Tennessee.

Operations

The company owned 183 facilities in 31 states in 2014 including 106 senior housing communities 71 skilled nursing facilities four hospitals and two medical office buildings.

As a REIT National Health generates nearly 95% of its business from rental income with the remainder of its revenue coming from investment income and interest income on mortgage or other notes. About 40% of the REIT's total revenue came from rental income from regional operators in 2014 while rental income from publicly-owned operators and privately-owned national chains contributed 26% and 29% to the REIT's total revenue. Smaller operators contributed the remainder.

Geographic Reach

Tennessee-based National Health Investors has most of its properties in the states of Florida Texas and Tennessee.

Sales and Marketing

National Health's three main operators (tenants) include: an affiliate of Holiday Retirement National HealthCare Corporation and Bickford Senior Living; each of which contributed more than 10% of the REIT's total revenue during 2014. Senior Living Communities began making lease payments on eight retirement communities during 2015 which would amount to more than 17% of National Health's total revenue during the year.

Some of National Health's other top tenants include: Brookdale Senior Living Fundamental Health Services Management and Legend Healthcare.

Financial Performance

National Health Investors' revenues and profits have been on the rise in recent years thanks to aggressive expansion from property acquisitions. The REIT's revenue spiked by 51% to a record $177.51 million in 2014 mostly thanks to a 57% increase in rental income stemming from nearly $749 million worth of new real estate investment properties.

Despite higher revenue in 2014 National's net income dipped by 4% to $103.05 million as depreciating expenses rose with new property acquisitions and due to higher interest expenses from the company's credit borrowings during the year.

The REIT's operating cash levels rose by 21% to $21.95 million after adjusting its earnings for (non-cash) depreciation and amortization expenses.

Strategy

National Health Investments typically expands its property portfolio — and therefore rental income — through strategic property acquisitions of senior housing communities and assisted living properties from real estate investors mortgage loans or in operations through structures allowed by RIDEA. The REIT typically takes a purchase-leaseback approach in which it acquires properties and leases them back to their previous operators. It also may provide mortgage and construction loans to operators who agree to lease the property once built.

The REIT on occasion also makes divestitures of under-performing rental properties to free up resources for further investments in higher-potential properties. In 2014 for example National Health sold three of its decades-old skilled nursing facilities in Texas which averaged 41 years in age and housed some 484 beds to an affiliate of Fundamental Long Term Care Holdings for a total of $18.49 million.

Mergers and Acquisitions

In 2014 NHI purchased eight senior housing communities for $476 million which would be leased to Senior Living Communities (SLC) and would continue to be managed by an SLC affiliate. Also that year it spent $42 million toward acquir-

ing an 105-unit assisted living community in Idaho as well as three skilled nursing facilities in Oregon with plans for a sale-leaseback arrangement from Prestige Senior Living; and another $18.1 million toward the purchase of a 101-unit assisted living and memory care community in Middleton Ohio through its joint venture with Bickford Senior Living.

In late 2013 the company purchased 25 independent-living properties which boasted 2841 units from Holiday Acquisition Holdings for a total of $491 million.

In April 2013 the REIT acquired a pair of skilled nursing facilities in Canton and Corinth Texas for $26.3 million. The purchase added a total of 254 beds to the REIT's portfolio.

In 2012 NHI acquired a 181-unit senior living campus in Loma Linda California for $12 million from Chancellor Health Care (CHC) thereby establishing a presence in Southern California. CHC would lease and continue to operate the facility.

EXECUTIVES

Chief Credit Officer, Kristin S. Gaines, age 47, $155,167 total compensation
EVP Investments and Chief Investment Officer, Kevin C. Pascoe, age 38, $150,000 total compensation
Chief Accounting Officer, Roger R. Hopkins, age 57, $286,841 total compensation
President CEO and Director, D. Eric Mendelsohn, age 56, $198,000 total compensation
EVP Finance, John L. Spaid, age 59
Chairman, W. Andrew (Andy) Adams, age 73
Auditors: BDO USA, LLP

LOCATIONS

HQ: National Health Investors, Inc.
222 Robert Rose Drive, Murfreesboro, TN 37129
Phone: 615 890-9100
Web: www.nhireit.com

PRODUCTS/OPERATIONS

2014 Sales

	$ mil.	% of total
Rental income	166.3	94
Interest income from mortgage and others	7.0	4
Investment income and other	4.2	2
Total	**177.5**	**100**

2014 Portfolio by Operations

	% of total
Regional	40
National Chain(Privately Owned)	28
Public	27
Small	5
Total	**100**

COMPETITORS

Cousins Properties	Omega Healthcare
HCP	Investors
Healthcare Realty	Senior Housing
Trust	Properties
LTC Properties	Ventas
Medical Properties	Welltower
Trust	

HISTORICAL FINANCIALS
Company Type: Public

Income Statement
FYE: December 31

	REVENUE ($ mil.)	NET INCOME ($ mil.)	NET PROFIT MARGIN	EMPLOYEES
12/17	278.6	159.3	57.2%	16
12/16	248.5	151.5	61.0%	15
12/15	228.9	148.8	65.0%	12
12/14	177.5	101.6	57.2%	12
12/13	117.8	106.1	90.1%	11
Annual Growth	24.0%	10.7%	—	9.8%

2017 Year-End Financials

Debt ratio: 45.0%
Return on equity: 12.5%
Cash ($ mil.): 3.0
Current ratio: 1.76
Long-term debt ($ mil.): 1,145.5

No. of shares (mil.): 41.5
Dividends
Yield: 0.0%
Payout: 98.1%
Market value ($ mil.): 3,131.0

	STOCK PRICE ($) FY Close	P/E High/Low	PER SHARE ($) Earnings	PER SHARE ($) Dividends	PER SHARE ($) Book Value
12/17	75.38	21 18	3.87	3.80	31.83
12/16	74.17	21 14	3.87	3.60	30.36
12/15	60.87	19 14	3.95	3.40	29.52
12/14	69.96	23 18	3.04	3.08	27.74
12/13	56.10	19 14	3.74	2.90	23.19
Annual Growth	7.7%	— —	0.9%	7.0%	8.2%

National Retail Properties Inc

For National Retail Properties good things come in big boxes. The self-administered real estate investment trust (REIT) acquires develops and manages freestanding retail properties in heavily traveled commercial and residential areas. Its portfolio includes more than 2250 properties with some 25 million sq. ft. of leasable space in almost all 50 states concentrated in Texas the Southeast and the Midwest. National Retail Properties also invests in mortgages operates some of its retail properties and develops properties to sell them later for a profit. More than 30% of its rental income comes from convenience store and restaurant operators with its top clients being Sunoco Mister Car Wash LA Fitness The Pantry and Camping World.

Operations
While some retail REITs own entire strip malls or shopping malls National Retail Properties keeps it simple with freestanding retail properties. National Retail Properties typically signs triple-net leases with initial terms of 15 to 20 years in which tenants are responsible for expenses such as taxes utilities repairs and maintenance.

Geographic Reach
National Retail Properties' largest markets are in Texas (20% of rental income in 2015) and Florida (9%). Other large markets include Ohio North Carolina Illinois Georgia Virginia Indiana Alabama and Tennessee which combined made up around one-third of its rental income during 2015.

Sales and Marketing
The trust's retail tenants include convenience stores and gas stations full-service and limited-service restaurants and other retailers. Its five largest tenants by rental base during 2015 included Sunoco (5.9% of rental income) Mister Car Wash (4.4%) LA Fitness (3.7%) The Pantry (3.6%) and Camping World (3.6%).

Other tenants include Stripes (Susser Holdings) 7-Eleven; restuarant tenants Applebee's Chili's Denny's Logan's Roadhouse Taco Bell and Wendys; and retailers Best Buy CarQuest and Pep Boys.

Financial Performance
National Retail Properties' annual revenues and profits have more than doubled since 2010 mainly as new property acquisitions have spurred higher rental income.

The REIT's revenue jumped 11% to $482.91 million during 2015 mostly as its rental income increased with the acquisition of 221 new properties spanning 2.42 million square feet.

Strong revenue growth in 2015 drove National Retail Properties' net income up 4% to $197.84 million. The REIT's operating cash levels climbed 15% to $341.09 million for the year as it collected more in cash-based rental income.

Strategy
Keeping a diversified tenant base in mind National Retail Properties mostly targets single-building retail real estate property located near local markets where its retail tenants trade. During 2015 it acquired 221 of such properties expanding its portfolio by more than 10% while selling just 19 properties with six more up for sale.

EXECUTIVES

EVP CFO and Treasurer, Kevin B. Habicht, age 58, $450,000 total compensation
President and CEO, Julian E. (Jay) Whitehurst, age 60, $525,000 total compensation
EVP and Chief Investment Officer, Paul E. Bayer, age 56, $365,000 total compensation
EVP and General Counsel, Christopher P. (Chris) Tessitore, age 50, $355,000 total compensation
EVP and Chief Acquisition Officer, Stephen A. Horn, age 46, $325,000 total compensation
Vice President Of Acquisitions, Josh Lewis
Vice President Underwriting, Matthew Sunderland
Vice President of Real Estate, Russell Shelton
Senior Vice President Asset Management, Kristin Furniss
Legal Secretary, Ivette Cordero
Vice President of Real Estate Underwriting, Matt Williams
Chairman, Robert C. Legler, age 74
Auditors: Ernst & Young LLP

LOCATIONS

HQ: National Retail Properties Inc
450 South Orange Avenue, Suite 900, Orlando, FL 32801
Phone: 407 265-7348   **Fax:** 407 423-2894
Web: www.nnnreit.com

COMPETITORS

Acadia Realty Trust	Kimco Realty
Brixmor	One Liberty Properties
DDR	Realty Income
Federal Realty Investment	Regency Centers

HISTORICAL FINANCIALS
Company Type: Public

Income Statement
FYE: December 31

	REVENUE ($ mil.)	NET INCOME ($ mil.)	NET PROFIT MARGIN	EMPLOYEES
12/17	584.9	264.9	45.3%	66
12/16	533.6	239.5	44.9%	65
12/15	482.9	197.8	41.0%	62
12/14	434.8	190.6	43.8%	64
12/13	392.3	160.1	40.8%	62
Annual Growth	10.5%	13.4%	—	1.6%

2017 Year-End Financials

Debt ratio: 39.3%
Return on equity: 6.8%
Cash ($ mil.): 1.3
Current ratio: 0.22
Long-term debt ($ mil.): 2,459.7

No. of shares (mil.): 153.5
Dividends
Yield: 0.0%
Payout: 128.2%
Market value ($ mil.): 6,624.0

	STOCK PRICE ($) FY Close	P/E High/Low	PER SHARE ($) Earnings	PER SHARE ($) Dividends	PER SHARE ($) Book Value
12/17	43.13	32 25	1.45	1.86	25.01
12/16	44.20	38 28	1.38	1.78	26.62
12/15	40.05	37 28	1.20	1.71	23.70
12/14	39.37	33 24	1.24	1.65	23.35
12/13	30.33	38 27	1.10	1.60	22.76
Annual Growth	9.2%	— —	7.2%	3.8%	2.4%

National Rural Utilities Cooperative Finance Corp

Cooperation may work wonders on Sesame Street but in the real world it takes money to pay the power bill. The National Rural Utilities Cooperative Finance Corporation provides financing and investment services for rural electrical and telephone projects throughout the US. The group is owned by some 1500 member electric utility and telecommunications systems. National Rural supplements the government loans that traditionally have fueled rural electric utilities by selling commercial paper medium-term notes and collateral trust bonds to fund its loan programs. National Rural was formed in 1969 by the National Rural Electric Cooperative Association a lobby representing the nation's electric co-ops.

Of the approximately 900 electric utility systems that are members of National Rural more than 90% are distribution systems and the rest are generation-and-transmission systems. The cooperative also serves more than 500 telecommunications providers through Rural Telephone Finance Cooperative. Other members of the group include state and regional associations and national associations of cooperatives.

In addition to its lending services the agency offers a number of investment options including securities commercial paper and money market funds designed to earn interest and dividends on members' long and short-term capital surpluses.

National Rural uses the income from its investment activities to lower the cost of funding.National Rural is governed by a 23-member board of directors that represents 10 geographically defined districts the electric cooperatives' national trade association and an at-large director.After losing nearly $70 million in 2009 the agency saw its net income rise dramatically. In fiscal 2012 though National Rural lost $148.8 million. Revenues that year slipped 11% to $996.8 million. The declines stemmed primarily from an increase in derivative losses (to $206 million) and an increase in loss on foreclosed asset operations (to $52 million) both indicative of weak economic recovery.The agency has been shying away from its lending to telecommunications projects which have seen unrest as competition heats up and the regulatory landscape shifts over the past five years. Instead it has increasingly focused on lending to electric systems which are typically residential projects and a necessity. Electric systems therefore carry much less risk as borrowers. National Rural's loan portfolio is more than 95% represented by power customers.In addition to sharpening its focus on its electric lending portfolio the agency has been broadening its funding sources beyond collateral trust bonds and commercial paper. Its funding programs now include the USDA's Guaranteed Underwriter Program and Farmer Mac notes and loans. National Rural also holds an agreement with KeyBank to whom it made its first loan sale in mid-2012.

EXECUTIVES

Vice President Capital Markets Relations, Ling Wang
Regional Vice President, Billy Kulwicki
Associate Vice President, Uzma Rahman
Auditors: KPMG LLP

LOCATIONS

HQ: National Rural Utilities Cooperative Finance Corp
20701 Cooperative Way, Dulles, VA 20166
Phone: 703 467-1800   **Fax:** 703 709-6779
Web: www.nrucfc.coop

PRODUCTS/OPERATIONS

Selected Subsidiaries and Affiliates
National Cooperative Services Corporation (financing for members and affiliated not-for-profit entities)
Rural Telephone Finance Cooperative (rural telecommunications lending)

HISTORICAL FINANCIALS

Company Type: Public

Income Statement   FYE: May 31

	REVENUE ($ mil.)	NET INCOME ($ mil.)	NET PROFIT MARGIN	EMPLOYEES
05/18	1,326.6	455.1	34.3%	254
05/17	1,149.5	309.9	27.0%	248
05/16	717.6	(49.6)	—	243
05/15	672.6	(19.0)	—	232
05/14	927.3	190.0	20.5%	221
Annual Growth	9.4%	24.4%	—	3.5%

2018 Year-End Financials

Debt ratio: 92.2%   No. of shares (mil.): —
Return on equity: 35.7%   Dividends
Cash ($ mil.): 231.0   Yield: —
Current ratio: 0.28   Payout: —
Long-term debt ($ mil.): 20,837.3   Market value ($ mil.): —

National Vision Holdings Inc

Auditors: DELOITTE & TOUCHE LLP

LOCATIONS

HQ: National Vision Holdings Inc
2435 Commerce Avenue, Building 2200, Duluth, GA 30096
Phone: 770 822-3600
Web: www.nationalvision.com

HISTORICAL FINANCIALS

Company Type: Public

Income Statement   FYE: December 30

	REVENUE ($ mil.)	NET INCOME ($ mil.)	NET PROFIT MARGIN	EMPLOYEES
12/17	1,375.3	45.8	3.3%	10,902
12/16*	1,196.2	14.7	1.2%	10,360
01/16	1,062.5	3.6	0.3%	0
01/15	735.6	(27.0)	—	0
Annual Growth	23.2%	—	—	—

*Fiscal year change

2017 Year-End Financials

Debt ratio: 35.9%   No. of shares (mil.): 74.6
Return on equity: 8.6%   Dividends
Cash ($ mil.): 4.2   Yield: —
Current ratio: 0.77   Payout: —
Long-term debt ($ mil.): 561.9   Market value ($ mil.): 3,032.0

	STOCK PRICE ($) FY Close	P/E High/Low	PER SHARE ($) Earnings	Dividends	Book Value
12/17	40.61	53 36	0.74	0.00	8.84
12/16*	0.00	— —	0.26	0.00	7.15
Annual Growth	—	—	—184.6%	—	23.6%

*Fiscal year change

Natural Grocers By Vitamin Cottage Inc

Natural Grocers by Vitamin Cottage is riding the wave of increased consumer interest in wellness and nutrition. The fast-growing company (both in sales and store count) operates about 140 stores in some 20 US states that sell natural and organic food including fresh produce meat frozen food and non-perishable bulk food; vitamins and dietary supplements; personal care products; pet care products; and books. The company uses United Natural Foods as its primary supplier and it also runs a bulk food repackaging facility and distribution center in its home state of Colorado. Founded by Margaret and Philip Isely in 1958 Natural Grocers by Vitamin Cottage is run by members of the Isely family.

Operations

The company's stores range in size from 5000 sq. ft. to 16000 sq. ft. (A typical new store averages 11000 sq. ft.) Each store offers about 21000 different natural and organic products and 6500 different dietary supplements.

Natural Grocers by Vitamin Cottage generates about two-thirds of its revenue from groceries with dietary supplements accounting for more than 20% and the remainder coming from body care pet care books and general merchandise.

Geographic Reach

Colorado is the company's home state and also its largest market with about a quarter of its stores. Other major markets for the company include Texas (home to about 15% of stores) as well as Arizona Oregon and Kansas.It operates a bulk food repackaging facility and distribution center in Colorado.

Sales and Marketing

Like other grocery retailers Natural Grocers by Vitamin Cottage advertises its weekly circular by mail and in local newspapers. The company plans to attract new customers through targeted marketing efforts such as distributing health-related newsletters and sponsoring health fairs and community wellness events. The chain devotes considerable marketing resources to educating customers on the benefits of natural and organic grocery products and dietary supplements. The company also occasionally relies on TV ads that are produced locally and primarily feature members of the founding Isely family.

Natural Grocers by Vitamin Cottage reported total advertising and marketing expenses for fiscal 2017 (ended September) of $10.7 million compared with $10.8 million the prior year.

Financial Performance

Natural Grocers has shown strong sales growth over the past five years as American consumers continue to focus on more natural healthy organic foods. Powered by new store openings the company?s revenue has jumped some 75% since 2013. Increased competition however has put pressure on margins resulting in reduced net income.

In fiscal 2017 (ended September) Natural Grocers reported revenue of $769 million up 9% from the prior year. New store openings (about 15 that year) led the growth and was more than enough to offset a less than 1% decline in comparable-store sales.

Amid Natural Grocers? consistent store growth salaries supplies and other store-level expenses have been rising more rapidly than revenue in recent years. The company?s operating margin fell more than a point in 2017 from 2.9% to 1.8% leading to net income of less than $7 million a 40% drop.

Cash at the end of 2017 was $6.5 million an increase of $2.5 million from the prior year. Cash from operations contributed $41 million to the coffers while investing activities used $38 million mainly for property and equipment used in the buildout of new stores. Financing activities added about $150000 as Natural Grocers borrowed and repaid about the same amount in debt (some $290 million).

Strategy

As part of its growth strategy Natural Grocers by Vitamin Cottage plans to continue expanding its store base although at a slower pace. After adding 23 and 14 new stores in fiscal years 2016 and 2017 respectively another 8-10 are planned in fiscal 2018. The stores are slated for Colorado Iowa Missouri Oregon Texas and Utah.

As it slows down new store openings the company plans to focus on improving same-store sales and other operating metrics. Amid an extremely competitive environment highlighted by Amazon's acquisition of Whole Foods Natural Grocers by Vitamin Cottage is hoping to distinguish itself with superior product standards while maintaining affordable prices. It also plans a new private label launch in 2018.

EXECUTIVES

CFO, Sandra M. Buffa, age 65, $320,000 total compensation
Chairman and Co-President, Kemper Isely, age 56, $607,800 total compensation
Co-President and Director, Zephyr Isely, age 69, $576,000 total compensation
EVP Corporate Secretary and Director, Heather Isely, age 52, $528,000 total compensation
EVP and Director, Elizabeth Isely, age 63, $480,000 total compensation
Auditors: KPMG LLP

LOCATIONS

HQ: Natural Grocers By Vitamin Cottage Inc
12612 West Alameda Parkway, Lakewood, CO 80228
Phone: 303 986-4600
Web: www.naturalgrocers.com

PRODUCTS/OPERATIONS

2017 Sales

	% of total
Grocery	67
Dietary supplements	22
Body care pet care and other	11
Total	**100**

COMPETITORS

ALDI	Sprouts
Blue Apron	Target Corporation
Costco Wholesale	Trader Joe's
Fresh Market	Vitacost
GNC	Vitamin Shoppe
H-E-B	Vitamin World
Kroger	Wal-Mart
Lidl	Whole Foods
Safeway	

HISTORICAL FINANCIALS

Company Type: Public

Income Statement — FYE: September 30

	REVENUE ($ mil.)	NET INCOME ($ mil.)	NET PROFIT MARGIN	EMPLOYEES
09/18	849.0	12.6	1.5%	3,598
09/17	769.0	6.8	0.9%	3,270
09/16	705.5	11.4	1.6%	3,074
09/15	624.6	16.2	2.6%	2,830
09/14	520.6	13.4	2.6%	2,346
Annual Growth	**13.0%**	**(1.5%)**	**—**	**11.3%**

2018 Year-End Financials

Debt ratio: 17.6%
Return on equity: 9.0%
Cash ($ mil.): 9.4
Current ratio: 1.39
Long-term debt ($ mil.): 53.6
No. of shares (mil.): 22.3
Dividends
Yield: —
Payout: —
Market value ($ mil.): 378.0

	STOCK PRICE ($) FY Close	P/E High/Low	PER SHARE ($) Earnings	Dividends	Book Value
09/18	16.89	34 8	0.56	0.00	6.56
09/17	5.58	44 18	0.31	0.00	5.96
09/16	11.16	50 21	0.51	0.00	5.64
09/15	22.69	44 22	0.72	0.00	5.13
09/14	16.28	73 29	0.60	0.00	4.40
Annual Growth	**0.9%**	**— —**	**(1.7%)**	**—**	**10.5%**

Natural Health Trends Corp.

When it comes to direct selling Natural Health Trends (NHT) was just born that way. The company through its subsidiaries sells products designed to enhance health happiness as well as beauty to a network of some 16000 independent distributors that use and/or resell the goods direct or through the Internet to consumers. Offerings are produced by third parties under the NHT Global brand (formerly Lexxus International). Core lines include skincare (trademark Skindulgence) sexual enhancement (Alura) and an energizing drink (Premium Noni Juice). NHT also sells herbal and dietary supplements for an array of complaints. Sales are generated primarily outside of North America; Hong Kong is the largest market.

Despite its reach into developing regions the company has suffered an accelerated decline in sales. Between 2005 through 2010 demand for NHT products plummeted in all markets where it has a presence except Russia. Nonetheless NHT's negative earnings have narrowed and cash from operations albeit generating a deficit are on the upswing.

The company attributes the slide in sales most significant in Hong Kong Taiwan and South Korea to a disappointing effort to recruit new members by lowering the cost of new member acquisition. In 2010 sales continued to be hurt by a decreasing number of active distributors coupled with dwindling fees from new memberships due to discounted promotions. The number of active distributors most of who are in Hong Kong has fallen more than 50% since 2008. Responding NHT has cut operating expenses as well as interest expense and focused its resources on Greater China (Hong Kong Taiwan and China) and Russia markets which are anticipated to grow.

To date although the company has failed to gain the required license for direct selling in China it has launched an e-commerce retail platform which provides an incentive for volume purchases. Hong Kong sales at risk too are largely dependent Chinese buyers who face the risk of violating their country's laws depending upon their interpretation and enforcement. Undeterred NHT has ramped up its training and public relations efforts to reinforce its position of complying with the law.

EXECUTIVES

President, Chris T. Sharng, age 54, $257,500 total compensation
Chief Financial Officer; Senior Vice President, Timothy S. Davidson, age 47, $160,000 total compensation
Director, Randall A. Mason, age 59
Auditors: Marcum LLP

LOCATIONS

HQ: Natural Health Trends Corp.
609 Deep Valley Drive, Suite 395, Rolling Hills Estates, CA 90274
Phone: 310 541-0888   **Fax:** 972 243-5428
Web: www.naturalhealthtrendscorp.com

PRODUCTS/OPERATIONS

Selected Products
Lifestyle
  Alura
  LaVie
  Twin Slim
  Valura
Skincare
  24K Renaissance Skin Rejuvenation Serum
  BioCell
  Skindulgence 30 Minute Non-Surgical Facelift
  Time Restore
Wellness and nutritional supplements
  Cluster X2
  EnerGin
  Essential Probiotics
  FibeRich
  Glucosamine 2200
  Premium Noni Juice
  ReStore
  TriFusion Max
  Triotein

COMPETITORS

Amway	Merck
Bactolac Pharmaceutical	Nature's Sunshine
Burt's Bees	Nu Skin
Chattem	Pfizer
Herbalife Ltd.	Reliv' International
Mannatech	USANA Health Sciences
Medicis Pharmaceutical	ViSalus
	Walgreen

HISTORICAL FINANCIALS

Company Type: Public

Income Statement — FYE: December 31

	REVENUE ($ mil.)	NET INCOME ($ mil.)	NET PROFIT MARGIN	EMPLOYEES
12/17	197.5	23.5	11.9%	149
12/16	287.7	55.0	19.1%	143
12/15	264.8	47.2	17.8%	133
12/14	124.5	20.3	16.3%	113
12/13	52.5	4.0	7.8%	99
Annual Growth	**39.3%**	**55.0%**	**—**	**10.8%**

2017 Year-End Financials

Debt ratio: —
Return on equity: 27.2%
Cash ($ mil.): 135.3
Current ratio: 3.61
Long-term debt ($ mil.): —
No. of shares (mil.): 11.3
Dividends
Yield: 0.0%
Payout: 72.7%
Market value ($ mil.): 172.0

STOCK PRICE ($)		P/E		PER SHARE ($)		
	FY Close	High/Low		Earnings	Dividends	Book Value
12/17	15.19	14	7	2.09	1.52	7.99
12/16	24.85	8	4	4.83	0.61	7.30
12/15	33.53	14	3	3.82	0.14	4.68
12/14	0.35	—	—	1.61	0.03	2.11
12/13	0.35	—	—	0.36	0.00	0.54
Annual Growth	156.7%	—	—	55.2%	—	96.5%

Nautilus Inc

Nautilus wants to pump you up. The company makes and markets cardio and strength-building fitness equipment for home use. Its products include home gyms free weights and benches treadmills exercise bikes and elliptical machines that are sold under the popular brand names Bowflex Nautilus Schwinn Fitness and Universal. Nautilus sells its fitness equipment directly to consumers through its variety of brand websites and catalogs as well as through TV commercials. The company also markets its gear through specialty retailers in the US and Canada. Nautilus exited the commercial fitness category in recent years so that it could focus entirely on providing gear that consumers can use at home.

Operations

The company operates its fitness equipment business through a pair of reportable segments. Its Direct segment (64% of revenue) sells products directly to consumers through TV advertising the Internet and catalogs. As part of its Retail segment (34%) Nautilus sells products through a network of third-party retailers that operate websites and stores located in the US and internationally.

Geographic Reach

Nautilus operates in the US and Canada with warehouse and distribution facilities located in Oregon and Ohio in the US and in Manitoba in Canada.

The US accounts for about 85% of revenue.

Sales and Marketing

Nautilus sells its products to fitness enthusiasts and to those who want to work out regularly. It sells through two sales channels: direct and retail.

In 2014 it spent about $42.6 million on advertising and expenses.

Financial Performance

Revenue which has been on a steady upward trajectory for five years rose 25% to $274 million in 2014 on the strength of new products. But net income which has fluctuated over the years was hit by spending on selling and marketing and plummeted 61% to $18.8 million

Strategy

Mostly because it had been largely unprofitable Nautilus opted to exit its commercial fitness business to focus on its core consumer fitness segment and the direct marketing model which have been key to its growth. The deep recession in the US had urged consumers to redirect spending to mostly essential goods and pushed commercial customers to cut back on equipment purchases.

EXECUTIVES

CEO and Director, Bruce M. Cazenave, age 63, $375,000 total compensation
COO, William B. McMahon, age 53, $250,000 total compensation
CFO, Sid Nayar
Vice President General Manager Direct, Robert O. (Rob) Murdock, $180,000 total compensation
Chairman, M. Carl Johnson
Auditors: KPMG LLP

LOCATIONS

HQ: Nautilus Inc
  17750 S.E. 6th Way, Vancouver, WA 98683
Phone: 360 859-2900
Web: www.nautilusinc.com

PRODUCTS/OPERATIONS

2014 Sales

	% of total
Direct	64
Retail	34
Royalty income	2
Total	100

Selected Brands

Bowflex
Nautilus
Schwinn Fitness
Universal

COMPETITORS

Amer Sports	ICON Health
Beachbody	Life Fitness
Cybex International	Precor
Dorel Industries	adidas
Escalade	

HISTORICAL FINANCIALS

Company Type: Public

Income Statement — FYE: December 31

	REVENUE ($ mil.)	NET INCOME ($ mil.)	NET PROFIT MARGIN	EMPLOYEES
12/17	406.1	26.2	6.5%	491
12/16	406.0	34.1	8.4%	469
12/15	335.7	26.6	7.9%	470
12/14	274.4	18.8	6.8%	340
12/13	218.8	47.9	21.9%	311
Annual Growth	16.7%	(14.0%)	—	12.1%

2017 Year-End Financials

Debt ratio: 14.7%
Return on equity: 15.4%
Cash ($ mil.): 85.2
Current ratio: 1.94
Long-term debt ($ mil.): 31.9
No. of shares (mil.): 30.3
Dividends
  Yield: —
  Payout: —
Market value ($ mil.): 405.0

	STOCK PRICE ($)	P/E		PER SHARE ($)		
	FY Close	High/Low		Earnings	Dividends	Book Value
12/17	13.35	23	14	0.85	0.00	5.91
12/16	18.50	23	14	1.09	0.00	5.22
12/15	16.72	27	17	0.84	0.00	4.10
12/14	15.18	25	13	0.59	0.00	3.54
12/13	8.43	6	2	1.52	0.00	2.94
Annual Growth	12.2%	—	—	(13.5%)	—	19.1%

Navigators Group Inc (The)

The Navigators Group writes specialty lines of insurance and reinsurance to clients whom it hopes are good navigators themselves. The company's various subsidiaries write marine liability and other lines of business primarily in the US and the UK. Its Navigators Insurance and Navigators Underwriting Agency (NUA) units specialize in ocean marine insurance including hull energy and cargo insurance as well as property insurance for inland marine and onshore energy concerns. Navigators Specialty primarily provides excess and surplus (high risk) lines. The firm's subsidiaries are also involved in professional liability especially directors' and officers' coverage as well as general liability for contractors. The Hartford Financial Services Group is buying Navigators for $2.1 billion.

Change in Company Type

In mid-2018 property/casualty insurer The Hartford agreed to buy Navigators adding international and specialty businesses to its operations. The deal will bring The Hartford a number of new lines of coverage as well as giving it a presence on the Lloyd's market.

Operations

In early 2015 Navigators realigned its reporting structure creating four primary segments that align with the types of coverage it writes: US Insurance International Insurance Global Reinsurance and Corporate.

Navigators' global product lines are distributed through a network of retail and wholesale brokers. In addition to its specialty property/casualty insurance and reinsurance policies the company and its subsidiaries provide catastrophe risk management services.

In the International Insurance segment NUA serves as a Lloyd's of London underwriting agency managing Lloyd's Syndicate 1221. The unit primarily underwrites marine and related lines of business along with offshore energy professional liability insurance and construction coverage for onshore energy businesses.

Geographic Reach

Outside its core markets of the US and the UK Navigators has operations in several European nations such as Belgium Denmark and Sweden mainly through NUA's activity on the European Lloyd's of London insurance exchange (via Lloyd's Syndicate 1221). The firm has also established offices in emerging markets such as Brazil and China.

Financial Performance

Navigators' revenue which has largely been on the rise for the past five years rose 12% to $1 billion in 2014 on higher net written premiums and investment income. Net written premiums increased 12.6% that year due to higher retention rates in the reinsurance business as well as growth in gross written property/casualty premiums.

Net income on the other hand has been more erratic than revenue. In 2014 it grew 50% to $95 million thanks primarily to Navigator's higher revenue. Cash flow from operations has been growing every year and in 2014 it rose 63% to $222 million.

Strategy

Navigators is focused on strengthening and controlling costs within its existing operations. At the same time Navigators is looking for opportunities to expand into new niche coverage areas and regions aiming for underserved commercial markets with high-value assets and low-frequency loss levels. In mid-2018 the company agreed to be acquired by US-based The Hartford Financial Services Group for $2.1 billion.

Mergers and Acquisitions

In late 2017 Navigators agreed to buy Belgian insurer ASCO-BDM which specializes in marine and industrial coverage. That purchase will further strengthen its operations in Europe

EXECUTIVES

President CEO and Director and Chair Navigators Insurance and Navigators Management, Stanley A. (Stan) Galanski, age 59, $1,000,000 total compensation

SVP and Chief Underwriting Officer, H. Clay Bassett, age 52, $525,000 total compensation

President and CEO Navigators Management Company Inc., Vincent C. Tizzio, age 51, $570,833 total compensation

President International Insurance, Michael J. Casella, age 57

President Navigators Specialty, Jeff L. Saunders, $412,500 total compensation

EVP and CFO, Ciro M. DeFalco, age 62, $780,833 total compensation

SVP and Chief Marketing Officer, LoriAnn V. Lowery-Biggers, age 51

Managing Director Asia, Jon Doherty

President Navigators Technical Risk, Patrick J. Milner

Assistant Vice President, Susan Natt

Vice President and Group Controller, George Iacono

East Coast Zonal Vice President Environmental Division, Paul Dastis

Assistant Vice President, Kathleen Boswell

Vice President, Andrew Dicob

Senior Vice President, David Stevenson

Assistant Vice President, Joshua Elmore

Senior Vice President, Linda Schultz

Vice President, David Crudo

Assistant Vice President, Jaime Rodriguez

VICE PRESIDENT, SPHR VACCARO

Vice President, Tracy Kiffer

Vice President Eastern and Central Regional Cargo Manager, Robert Ryan

Vice President E and S Primary Casualty, Jerry O'Neill

Senior Vice President Field Operations and NYC Branch Manager, James Hutchinson

Senior Vice President Communications, Dudley Alex

Chairman, Terence N. Deeks, age 78

Auditors: KPMG LLP

LOCATIONS

HQ: Navigators Group Inc (The)
400 Atlantic Street, Stamford, CT 06901
Phone: 203 905-6090
Web: www.navg.com

PRODUCTS/OPERATIONS

2014 Gross Written premiums

	% of total
Insurance companies	75
Lloyd's Operations	25
Total	**100**

2014 Sales

	$ mil
% of total	
Net earned premiums	91
Net investment income	7
Net realized gains	1
Others	1
Total	**100**

Selected Subsidiaries

Millennium Underwriting Ltd. (UK)
Navigators A/S (Denmark)
Navigators Corporate Underwriters Ltd. (UK)
Navigators Holdings (UK) Ltd.
Navigators Insurance Company
Navigators Management Company Inc.
Navigators Management (UK) Limited
Navigators NV (Belgium)
Navigators Specialty Insurance Company
Navigators Underwriting Agency Ltd. (UK)
Navigators Underwriting Limited (UK)
NUAL AB (Sweden)

Selected Products and Services

Commercial Surety
Standard Transactional
Non Standard Transactional
Account
Program
Energy and Engineering
Onshore Energy
Offshore Energy
Construction
Operational Engineering
Excess Casualty
Umbrella & Excess (Wholesale Brokerage)
Umbrella & Excess (Retail Agency)
Environmental Casualty
Contractors Pollution Liability
Site Pollution Legal Liability
NP3 sm General & Environmental Liability (Mfg. & Distributors)
NP4 sm General Environmental & Professional Liability (Env'l Consultants)
Environmental Excess
Inland Marine
Commercial Output Policy
Construction
Specialty
Transportation
Management Liability
Directors & Officers Liability
Employment Practices Liability
Fiduciary Liability
Crime Liability
Nonprofit D & O Liability
Marine
Bluewater Hull
Brownwater Hull
Cargo
Specie
Transportation
Marine & Energy Liability
War
Protection & Indemnity
Primary Casualty
General Liability
NAVIGATORS RE
Accident & Health
Agriculture
Latin American & Caribbean
Professional Liability Reinsurance
Property & Casualty
Life Sciences
Global Package Solutions
Commercial Auto
Professional Liability
Lawyers Professional Liability
Accountants Professional Liability
Miscellaneous Professional Liability
Insurance Agents & Brokers E&O
Technology Media & Cyber Liability
Design Professionals Liability
Real Estate Professionals E&O

COMPETITORS

AIG
AXA Corporate Solutions
Allianz
Amica Mutual
Arch Insurance Group
Aspen Insurance
Berkshire Hathaway
CNA Financial
Global Indemnity
ProSight Specialty Insurance Group
RLI
Safeco
Specialty Underwriters' Alliance
Travelers Companies
White Mountains Insurance Group
XL Group plc
Zurich American

HISTORICAL FINANCIALS

Company Type: Public

Income Statement

FYE: December 31

	ASSETS ($ mil.)	NET INCOME ($ mil.)	INCOME AS % OF ASSETS	EMPLOYEES
12/17	5,224.6	40.4	0.8%	732
12/16	4,814.0	82.7	1.7%	683
12/15	4,584.0	81.0	1.8%	675
12/14	4,464.1	95.3	2.1%	651
12/13	4,169.4	63.4	1.5%	596
Annual Growth	5.8%	(10.6%)	—	5.3%

2017 Year-End Financials

Return on assets: 0.8%	Dividends
Return on equity: 3.3%	Yield: 0.0%
Long-term debt ($ mil.): —	Payout: 16.6%
No. of shares (mil.): 29.5	Market value ($ mil.): 1,437.0
Sales ($ mil): 1,314.4	

	STOCK PRICE ($) FY Close	P/E High/Low	Earnings	PER SHARE ($) Dividends	Book Value
12/17	48.70	85 34	1.35	0.23	41.55
12/16	117.75	41 28	2.75	0.14	40.45
12/15	85.79	31 24	2.74	0.00	37.98
12/14	73.34	22 17	3.26	0.00	35.96
12/13	63.16	30 23	2.21	0.00	31.77
Annual Growth	(6.3%)	—	—(11.6%)	—	6.9%

NCI Building Systems, Inc.

NCI's buildings could be considered quite a "steel." NCI Building Systems also known as NCI Group engineers designs manufactures and distributes metal components (doors roofs walls and trim) and engineered building systems for nonresidential construction markets in North America. It sells its products to contractors developers and builders. The group also provides metal coil coating which is used by manufacturers of HVAC systems lighting fixtures and appliances. NCI has more than 40 manufacturing facilities in the US China and Mexico and operates distribution and sales offices in the US and Canada. Investment firm Clayton Dubilier & Rice owns NCI Group.

Operations

NCI operates three business segments. Its Metal Components segment which generated 50% of its total revenue during fiscal 2015 (ended November 1) makes and sells metal roof and wall systems as well as metal partitions trims doors and related accessories for use in industrial commercial institutional agricultural and rural markets.

The Engineered Building Systems segment (37% of revenue) makes structural members and heavy-gauge plate steel panels designed to reinforce a building's framing from the stresses of the roof and walls to the external load pressures. The group's Metal Coil Coating segment (13% of revenue) cleans treats and paints different types of flat-rolled metals. It also provides metal embossing and slitting services.

Geographic Reach

The Houston Texas-based group operates 42 manufacturing facilities in the US Mexico and China (as of early 2016) and has sales and distribution offices across the US and Canada. About 94% of its revenue came from sales in the US during 2015 while another 5% came from sales in Canada and less than 1% came from Mexico and other countries.

Sales and Marketing

The majority of NCI's engineered building systems are made through its authorized builder networks and are mostly sold to builders general contractors developers and end users working in the commercial industrial agricultural government and community markets (non-residential markets).

NCI's Metal Components business which targets the same markets sells to regional building manufacturers general contractors and subcontractors as well as to lumberyards and cooperative buying groups. The Metal Coil Coating segment sells its products mostly to original equipment manufacturer customers.

The group has been ramping up its advertising spend in recent years. It spent $8.6 million on advertising in fiscal 2015 (ended November 1) up from $7.6 million and $6.6 million in 2014 and 2013 respectively.

Financial Performance

NCI's annual revenues have risen more than 60% since 2011 as the construction and commercial real estate markets have boosted demand for its products. It's also come back from losses in 2011 and 2013 as it's managed to keep its operating and overhead costs in check.

The group's sales climbed 14% to $1.5 billion during fiscal 2015 (ended November 1 2015) mostly thanks to the Metal Components segment's acquisition of CENTRIA which also added increased tonnage sales volumes (specifically for single-skin products). The group's Metal Coil Coating segment sales declined 6% while Engineered Building Systems sales were down less than 1% for the year. Most of the sales growth came from the US where sales grew 17% while the rest came from double-digit sales growth in Mexico. Sales in Canada fell by 21%.

Strong revenue growth in FY2015 drove NCI's net income up 59% to $17.8 million. The group's operating cash levels more than tripled to $105 million in FY2015 mostly on strong cash earnings growth and positive working capital changes mainly related to a rise in accounts payable balances.

Strategy

With its eye toward a stronger market position and increased sales and profitability NCI Group planned in 2016 to push four main initiatives including: leveraging automation and supply chain efficiencies to become "one of the lowest cost producers"; pushing its Engineered Building Systems segment to provide a "total value building solution" for customers; grow its customer base to expand on its top position in the Metal Components business; and diversify its Metal Coil Coating segment's external customer base and national footprint with plans to become a low-cost producer and grow its non-construction sales as a supply chain partner to national manufacturers.

NCI also looks for opportunistic acquisitions that expand its service lines and bolster its market share.

Mergers and Acquisitions

In January 2015 NCI Building Systems strengthened its market position after purchasing Pennsylvania-based CENTRIA which made architectural insulated metal panel (IMP) wall and roof systems and provided coil coating services. The $245 million deal added CENTRIA's four manufacturing facilities in the US and another in China.

HISTORY

NCI Building Systems' founder Johnie Schulte Jr. began his career in the mid-1950s when he landed a job punching and shearing metal building pieces in Houston.

In 1984 he founded NCI. The enterprise made only metal building components until 1987 when it began making metal buildings. That year NCI had sales of about $2 million. The company went public in 1992 and a year later its sales had reached more than $130 million.

While competitors were shuttering plants in the soft market of the early 1990s NCI was buying companies — including its 1992 purchase of A&S Building Systems a metal building maker based in Caryville Tennessee. NCI later expanded its product line to include self-storage buildings.

It entered the market for roll-up steel overhead doors in 1995 when it bought Doors & Building Components (also a maker of interior steel parts) and started its own line of steel-frame homes.

The company continued to make acquisitions in 1996 picking up a metal stud plant in Texas from Alabama Metal Industries the equipment of Carlisle Engineered Metals and Mesco Metal Buildings. The next year it bought the rest of Carlisle including a manufacturing plant in Alabama and began a 51%-owned joint venture in Mexico to manufacture framing systems. NCI bought the US metal building components business of UK-based BTR in 1998 for $593 million doubling its size and adding painting and coating capabilities. The company spent 1999 integrating the large business.

NCI bought out Consolidated System's share in their DOUBLECOTE metal coil-coating joint venture for $26 million in 2000. Later that year NCI bought Midland Metals a maker of metal building components. The move strengthened NCI's presence in the Midwest.

In 2001 NCI sold its 50% interest in Midwest Metal Coatings to its joint venture partner. The company closed five manufacturing facilities during the first quarter of fiscal 2002. NCI launched into direct selling to the public by opening a series of NCI Metal Depot retail factory stores that offer commercial and residential metal components

(metal roof and wall panels light structural and tubing shapes and accessories) and a variety of small metal building packages (carports storage sheds and other metal buildings).

The company opened two retail stores in Texas in fiscal 2003. Also that year NCI entered the residential garage door market by acquiring Texas-based Able Manufacturing and Wholesale Garage Door Company for about $3.3 million. NCI shortened the company's name to Able Door Manufacturing. Able operates distribution centers in the Dallas Atlanta and Oklahoma City areas and Ontario California.

Founder president and CEO Johnie Schulte Jr. retired as an executive in November 2003 and retired as a director the next year; he was succeeded by A. R. Ginn. The following year NCI filed a suit against Schulte alleging he had violated non-competitive agreements. Schulte filed a countersuit; an undisclosed settlement was reached in 2005.

To expand its retail and builder distribution channels for its small engineered buildings NCI bought North Little Rock Arkansas-based Heritage Building Systems and Steelbuilding.com for approximately $30 million in 2004. NCI also acquired the 49% minority stake held by its partners in its manufacturing plant in Monterrey Mexico.

The next year NCI bought the intellectual property rights of metal building and components maker STEELOX Systems of Ohio gaining the patents and trademarks copyrights common law rights names logos websites and customer lists of the established (by more than 70 years) company.

In 2006 NCI paid $370 million in cash for metal buildings maker Robertson-Ceco Corporation and its Robertson Building Systems Ceco Building Systems Star Building Systems and Steelspec divisions. Late that year Ginn stepped down as CEO with president and COO Norm Chambers becoming president and CEO. The next year Chambers assumed the chairmanship. NCI also bought Garco Building Systems in 2007.

EXECUTIVES

EVP General Counsel and Corporate Secretary, Todd R. Moore, age 59, $357,477 total compensation
EVP CFO and Treasurer, Mark E. Johnson, age 52, $434,139 total compensation
President Group Manufacturing Segment, John L. Kuzdal, age 53, $393,231 total compensation
President and CEO, Donald R. (Don) Riley, age 55, $517,385 total compensation
VP and CIO, Albert K. Stolpe
Vice President Tax, Louis Walton
Vice President Finance and Chief Accounting Officer, Bradley S Little
Vice President, Fred Schubert
Vice President Supply Chain Management, Dan Ronchetto
Vice President Engineering, Stephen Heil
Vice President Of Finance Components Div, Mark Shearer
Vice President Finance, Chico Doughtie
Vice President Internal Audit, Sharla Ruland
Vice President Investor Relations, Darcey Matthews
Chairman, Norman C. (Norm) Chambers, age 69
Auditors: Grant Thornton LLP

LOCATIONS

HQ: NCI Building Systems, Inc.
5020 Weston Parkway, Suite 400, Cary, NC 27513
Phone:
Web: www.ncilp.com

PRODUCTS/OPERATIONS

2015 Sales by Segment

	$ mil.	% of total
Metal components	920.9	50
Engineered building systems 667.2		37
Metal coil coating	231.7	13
Adjustments	(256.1)	-
Total	**1,563.7**	**100**

Selected Brands

A&S
All American
American Building Components (ABC)
Ceco
Doors and Buildings Components (DBCI)
Garco
Heritage
IPS
MBCI
Metallic
Metal Coaters
Metal Depots
Metal Prep
Mesco
Mid-West Steel
Star
SteelBuilding.com
Steel Systems

Selected Subsidiaries

Building Systems de México S.A. de C.V.
NCI Group Inc.
Robertson Building Systems Limited (Canada)
Robertson-Ceco II Corporation
Steelbuilding.com Inc.

Selected Products and Services

Metal building components and complete buildings
  (carports utility buildings etc.)
Metal cladding and accessories
Mini-storage buildings
Modular offices
Roll-up doors partitions and panels

COMPETITORS

American Buildings	Gibraltar Industries
Berger Building	Horton Homes
Products	Johns Manville
Berlin Steel	Nucor
Butler Manufacturing	Overhead Door
Design Components	Varco Pruden Buildings
G-I Holdings	Williams Scotsman

HISTORICAL FINANCIALS

Company Type: Public

Income Statement | | | | FYE: October 28

	REVENUE ($ mil.)	NET INCOME ($ mil.)	NET PROFIT MARGIN	EMPLOYEES
10/18	2,000.5	63.1	3.2%	5,300
10/17	1,770.2	54.7	3.1%	5,300
10/16*	1,684.9	51.0	3.0%	5,500
11/15	1,563.6	17.8	1.1%	5,326
11/14	1,371.8	11.1	0.8%	4,556
Annual Growth	**9.9%**	**54.1%**		**3.9%**

*Fiscal year change

2018 Year-End Financials

Debt ratio: 36.7%	No. of shares (mil.): 66.2
Return on equity: 20.0%	Dividends
Cash ($ mil.): 54.2	Yield: —
Current ratio: 1.76	Payout: —
Long-term debt ($ mil.): 403.0	Market value ($ mil.): 824.0

	STOCK PRICE ($) FY Close	P/E High/Low	PER SHARE ($) Earnings	Dividends	Book Value
10/18	12.45	24 13	0.94	0.00	4.99
10/17	15.55	24 17	0.77	0.00	4.46
10/16*	14.40	25 13	0.70	0.00	3.97
11/15	10.46	83 41	0.24	0.00	3.67
11/14	19.87	141 97	0.15	0.00	3.35
Annual Growth	**(11.0%)**	**— —**	**58.2%**	**—**	**10.4%**

*Fiscal year change

Neogen Corp

Bacteriophobes have a friend in Neogen a maker of products for the food safety and animal health markets. Its food safety testing products are used by the food industry to make sure our edibles are clean unspoiled and free of toxins pathogens and allergens. In core markets in the Americas and Europe Neogen reaches end users (including dairies meat processors and animal feed producers) through a direct sales force; it uses distributors elsewhere. On the animal health front Neogen produces drugs vaccines diagnostics and instruments for the veterinary market; it also makes rat poisons and disinfectants used in animal production plants and diagnostic products for research laboratories.

Operations

Some of Neogen's best-selling food-safety testing products include its Reveal and Alert tests used by meat poultry and seafood processors to detect food-borne bacteria. Others include its Veratox Agre-Screen and Reveal tests which are used by grain producers to detect mycotoxins (toxins produced by fungi).

When it comes to animals lead products include PanaKare a digestive aid; RenaKare a supplement for potassium deficiency in cats and dogs; and the NeogenVet brand including Vita-15 and Liver 7 which are used for the treatment and prevention of nutritional deficiencies in horses. Sales in its Animal Safety unit account for more than half of Neogen's revenue.

Geographic Reach

Neogen's animal products are sold to distributors around the world as well as through farm supply retailers in North America. International sales of all of its products account for about 40% of Neogen's revenue.

The company has manufacturing plants in Michigan Kentucky Wisconsin North Carolina and Iowa as well as in Scotland.

Sales and Marketing

Neogen sells its products through a direct sales force in North America parts of Europe Mexico Brazil and China. Elsewhere it sells through independent distributors. The company has some 20000 customers.

Strategy

Though Neogen has primarily used acquisitions to achieve relatively rapid growth the company is also looking for organic growth over the longer term through new product introductions higher sales of existing products international expansion efforts (it has made strides in India and China as of late) and the formation of strategic alliances. Neogen has ongoing development projects for new

diagnostic tests and other complementary products for both the food safety and animal safety markets. The company also sees its over-the-counter animal health products as being particularly ripe for growth so it seeks to increase its line of rodenticides disinfectants instruments and horse care products.

Mergers and Acquisitions

In early 2019 Neogen acquired Canadian animal genomics laboratory Delta Genomics which specializes in beef and cattle testing. After that purchase the group operates five such labs around the world.

In 2018 Neogen acquired Virginia-based Livestock Genetic Services which provides evaluation and data management for cattle breeding groups. The deal boosted Neogen's in-house genetic evaluation abilities.

The prior year Neogen acquired Queensland Animal Genetics Laboratory (AGL) the largest animal genomics lab in Australia. That purchase expanded Neogen's genomics operations in the Asia/Pacific region. AGL provides services for region's large cattle market as well as the sheep goat alpaca and other markets. The lab was renamed GeneSeek Australasia.

EXECUTIVES

Vice President and Senior Research Director, Jennifer Rice
VP and CFO, Steven J. (Steve) Quinlan, age 55, $191,000 total compensation
VP Food Safety Operations, Edward L. Bradley, age 58, $167,000 total compensation
VP Animal Safety Operations, Terri A. Morrical, age 53, $165,000 total compensation
President and CEO, John E. Adent, age 50
Vice President Corporate Development, Jason Lilly
Chairman, James L. Herbert, age 78
Auditors: BDO USA, LLP

LOCATIONS

HQ: Neogen Corp
  620 Lesher Place, Lansing, MI 48912
Phone: 517 372-9200   **Fax:** 517 372-0108
Web: www.neogen.com

PRODUCTS/OPERATIONS

2015 Sales

	$ mil.	% of total
Animal safety	151.6	54
Food safety	131.5	46
Total	**283.1**	**100**

2015 Sales

	$ mil.	% of total
Food safety		
Natural toxins allergans drug residues	60.6	21
Dehydrated culture media & other	41.1	15
Bacterial & general sanitation	29.8	11
Animal safety		
Rodenticides insecticides & disinfectants	45.9	16
Animal care & other	35.0	12
Veterinary instruments & disposables	34.3	12
DNA testing	27.7	10
Life sciences & other	8.7	3
Total	**283.1**	**100**

Selected Products

Food safety
  AccuClean (detects proteins and sugars)
  AccuPoint (rapid sanitation test)
  AgriScreen (detects mycotoxins)
  Alert (detects food-borne bacteria food allergens)
  Beta Star (detects antibiotics in milk)

BioKits (detects allergens in food; also used for species identification)
GeneQuence (detects food-borne bacteria)
Reveal (detects food-borne bacteria food allergens ruminant by-products)
Soleris (detects spoilage organisms)
Veratox (detects mycotoxins food allergens)
Animal safety
AgTek (Kane) products (apparel accessories etc.)
BioSentry (chemicals)
CyKill (rodent control)
Di-Kill (rodent control)
ElectroJac (automated semen collection)
Havoc (rodenticide)
Ideal (animal health products and instruments)
NeogenVet (animal health products)
Prozap (rodenticide)
Ramik (rodenticide)
Rodex (rodenticide)
Squire (animal health products)

COMPETITORS

American Animal Health	Merck Animal Health
Bayer Animal Health	Merial
Celldex Therapeutics	Novartis
Ecolab	Orchid Cellmark
Eurofins Scientific	Pfizer
Hartz Mountain	Phibro Animal Health
Heska	Sdix
IDEXX Labs	Silliker
Life Technologies	Telesta
Corporation	Virbac Corporation
Merck	

HISTORICAL FINANCIALS

Company Type: Public

Income Statement

FYE: May 31

	REVENUE ($ mil.)	NET INCOME ($ mil.)	NET PROFIT MARGIN	EMPLOYEES
05/18	402.2	63.1	15.7%	1,546
05/17	361.5	43.7	12.1%	1,413
05/16	321.2	36.5	11.4%	1,235
05/15	283.0	33.5	11.8%	1,062
05/14	247.4	28.1	11.4%	926
Annual Growth	12.9%	22.4%	—	13.7%

2018 Year-End Financials

Debt ratio: —
Return on equity: 12.2%
Cash ($ mil.): 83.0
Current ratio: 9.71
Long-term debt ($ mil.): —

No. of shares (mil.): 51.7
Dividends
Yield: —
Payout: —
Market value ($ mil.): 3,917.0

	STOCK PRICE ($) FY Close	P/E High/Low	PER SHARE ($) Earnings	Dividends	Book Value
05/18	75.71	69 44	1.21	0.00	10.83
05/17	63.29	79 57	0.86	0.00	9.26
05/16	49.37	83 60	0.73	0.00	8.07
05/15	46.74	76 54	0.68	0.00	7.09
05/14	37.79	123 63	0.57	0.00	6.26
Annual Growth	19.0%	— —	20.7%	—	14.7%

NetScout Systems Inc

NetScout Systems products ride out on computer networks looking for trouble. The company?s monitoring appliances placed throughout a network allow administrators to collect information about traffic flow and to optimize application and network performance. NetScout?s nGenius Service Assurance Solution monitors systems ranging from VoIP communications to customer relationship management applications. NetScout sells directly and through resellers and distributors to corporate and government customers. The US supplies about 60% of revenue.

Operations

Products generate more than half of NetScout's sales with the rest coming from services. The Adaptive Service Intelligence (ASI) technology is the foundation of its flagship nGenius product. ASI converts network traffic data into "smart data" that companies can use for analysis.

The company procures parts from contractors and does the assembly and testing of products itself.

Geographic Reach

NetScout Systems is headquartered in Westford Massachusetts. It has offices in several US states and some two dozen countries throughout the world.

NetScout gets about 60% of revenue from the US about 20% from Europe and about 10% from Asia.

Sales and Marketing

NetScout sells through its own sales force and indirect channels. Its markets are enterprises telecommunications service providers and government agencies. No customer direct or indirect accounts for more than 10% of sales although Verizon did in the past.

Financial Performance

In its 2016 and 2017 fiscal years (ended March) NetScout?s revenue jumped to a high of $1.2 billion following its acquisition of Danaher?s communications business. However NetScout?s revenue slipped 15% in 2018 to $987 million from 2017. Product sales fell 26% in 2018 from 2017 because of lower revenue from a large tier-one service provider and lower-than expected orders for service assurance and DDoS offerings. Service revenue rose 3% because of an increase in maintenance contracts.

Net income rose to about $80 million in 2018 compared to $33 million in 2017 boosted by a $98 million tax benefit. NetScout had a loss of about $19 million before taxes in 2018 compared to income of $52 million before tax.

NetScout had about $448 million of cash cash equivalents and marketable securities at the end of 2018 down about $17 million from 2017. During the year it spent more than $500 million to repurchase shares about $16 million for capital expenditures and about $8 million for the acquisition of Efflux.

Strategy

The increasing amounts of data that flow through networks are right up NetScout?s alley. The company offers products and services that can corral data and help make sense of it. It further develops its products to help IT organizations sort through complex service delivery datacenter consolidation branch office consolidation and optimization to move applications to private and public clouds.

The acquisition of the communications of Danaher several years ago significantly expanded NetScout?s direct sales force with sales people who have expertise in targeting the enterprise service provider and government markets. NetScout intends to leverage that sales force to increase its presence in the enterprise and service provider markets.

NetScout found itself the victim of a reduction in spending by a large telecom provider as well as overall slowdown in telecom spending. Enterprise customers especially federal agency customers had delayed funding extending sales cycles and softening demand for some product lines.

Mergers and Acquisitions

In 2017 NetScout acquired Efflux for $8.6 million. Efflux?s technology detects analyzes and correlates threat activity within enterprise networks.

In 2016 NetScout bought Avvasi for $4.6 million. Avvasi?s technology allows service providers to measure improve and monetize video in networks.

HISTORY

The company acquired the assets and business of Quantiva a supplier of automated analytics software for application performance management for about $9 million in cash in 2006. The acquisition added technology that automates the process of detecting and diagnosing application performance problems before they impact critical business services.

In 2007 NetScout purchased competitor Network General developer of the Sniffer line of performance and security analysis tools for $206 million. NetScout which developed products based on Sniffer technology prior to the acquisition more than doubled its revenue with the purchase.

EXECUTIVES

SVP Services and CIO, Ken Boyd
SVP Product Operations, Michael Szabados, age 66, $275,000 total compensation
Chairman President and CEO, Anil K. Singhal, age 64, $325,000 total compensation
VP and CTO, Bruce Kelley
VP and General Manager Packet Flow Switch Business, Brian P. McCann, age 52
SVP and CFO, Jean A. Bua, age 59, $262,924 total compensation
VP Worldwide Marketing, Jim McNiel
Assistant Vice President Engineering, Rajeev Nadkarni
Vice President General Counsel Secretary, Jeff Levinson
Vice President Information Technology, Yingchao Zhang
Vice President International Channel Sales, Joseph Lenz
Senior Vice President Research And Development, Ashwani Singhal
Vice President Human Resources, Skip Maloney
Vice President of Sales Americas, Curt Tubbs
Vice President Sales Operations and Channels, James Ficaro
VP East Region, Greg Redmond
ASSISTANT VICE PRESIDENT SALES, Barry L Johnson
Assistant Vice President Telco, Eric Earhart
Board Member, Christopher Perretta
Board Member, James Lico
Auditors: PricewaterhouseCoopers LLP

LOCATIONS

HQ: NetScout Systems Inc
310 Littleton Road, Westford, MA 01886
Phone: 978 614-4000
Web: www.netscout.com

PRODUCTS/OPERATIONS

2018 Sales

	$ mil.	% of total
Product	546.1	55
Service	440.6	45
Total	**986.7**	**100**

COMPETITORS

Agilent Technologies	NIKSUN
Blue Coat	RADCOM
CA Inc.	Resonate Inc.
EMC	Riverbed Technology
HP	SolarWinds
IBM	TTI Team Telecom
InfoVista	Viavi Solutions
MedTel Services	

HISTORICAL FINANCIALS

Company Type: Public

Income Statement

FYE: March 31

	REVENUE ($ mil.)	NET INCOME ($ mil.)	NET PROFIT MARGIN	EMPLOYEES
03/18	986.7	79.8	8.1%	3,019
03/17	1,162.1	33.2	2.9%	3,113
03/16	955.4	(28.3)	—	3,144
03/15	453.6	61.1	13.5%	1,069
03/14	396.6	49.1	12.4%	1,021
Annual Growth	25.6%	12.9%		31.1%

2018 Year-End Financials

Debt ratio: 17.8%
Return on equity: 3.5%
Cash ($ mil.): 369.8
Current ratio: 1.82
Long-term debt ($ mil.): 600.0

No. of shares (mil.): 80.2
Dividends
Yield: —
Payout: —
Market value ($ mil.): 2,115.0

	STOCK PRICE ($) FY Close	P/E High/Low		PER SHARE ($) Earnings	Dividends	Book Value
03/18	26.35	42	28	0.90	0.00	25.77
03/17	37.95	107	59	0.36	0.00	26 47
03/16	22.97	—	—	(0.35)	0.00	25.97
03/15	43.85	32	21	1.47	0.00	10.68
03/14	37.58	33	18	1.17	0.00	9.94
Annual Growth	(8.5%)	—	—	(6.3%)	—	26.9%

New England Realty Associates L.P.

New England Realty Associates invests in develops operates and sells residential and commercial real estate primarily in the Boston area. The company's portfolio includes more than 2300 apartment and condominium units and about 85000 sq. ft. of commercial space that includes a shopping center and mixed-use properties. It also has a 50% stake in a portfolio of about 10 commercial properties. New England Realty Associates is managed by general partner NewReal which in turn is owned by company officers and brothers Ronald and Harold Brown. Harold Brown also owns The Hamilton Company which manages the partnership's properties.

EXECUTIVES

Treasurer and Director, Harold Brown, age 91
President and Director, Ronald Brown, age 80
Treasurer and Director, Harold Brown, age 91
President and Director, Ronald Brown, age 80
Director, Guilliaem Aertsen IV, age 68
Director, Conrad DiGregorio, age 89
Director, David A. Aloise, age 61
Director, Roberta D. Ornstein, age 66
Auditors: Miller Wachman LLP

LOCATIONS

HQ: New England Realty Associates L.P.
39 Brighton Avenue, Allston, MA 02134
Phone: 617 783-0039
Web: www.thehamiltoncompany.com

COMPETITORS

Apartment Investment and Management	Equity Residential
	Home Properties
Boston Capital	WinnCompanies

HISTORICAL FINANCIALS

Company Type: Public

Income Statement

FYE: December 31

	REVENUE ($ mil.)	NET INCOME ($ mil.)	NET PROFIT MARGIN	EMPLOYEES
12/17	52.8	6.9	13.1%	68
12/16	49.5	4.9	10.0%	0
12/15	45.4	3.7	8.3%	0
12/14	42.6	1.0	2.4%	0
12/13	38.3	5.6	14.7%	67
Annual Growth	8.3%	5.2%		0.4%

2017 Year-End Financials

Debt ratio: 110.3%
Return on equity: —
Cash ($ mil.): 7.2
Current ratio: 0.86
Long-term debt ($ mil.): 250.2

No. of shares (mil.): 0.1
Dividends
Yield: 0.0%
Payout: 3.8%
Market value ($ mil.): 9.0

	STOCK PRICE ($) FY Close	P/E High/Low		PER SHARE ($) Earnings	Dividends	Book Value
12/17 (283.92)	73.35	1	1	55.77	2.14	
12/16 (275.10)	60.90	2	1	39.62	1.80	
12/15 (245.75)	50.75	2	2	29.86	1.00	
12/14 (214.39)	48.75	7	6	7.96	1.00	
12/13 (168.73)	44.44	1	1	43.55	1.00	
Annual Growth	13.3%	—	—	6.4%	20.9%	—

New Mountain Finance Corp

Investment firm New Mountain Finance Corporation won't make its portfolio companies climb over too many hills for a loan. The affiliate of private equity firm New Mountain Capital makes investments of $10 million-$50 million in middle-market companies (those with annual revenues of less than $200 million). Its portfolio is made up of senior secured first-lien and second-lien term loans and subordinated debt. Organized as a business development company (BDC) New Mountain Finance pays little in income taxes as long as it distributes 90% of its profits back to shareholders. It is externally managed by New Mountain Finance Advisers BDC L.L.C. The company went public in 2011.

EXECUTIVES

Managing Director, Mathew Lori
Board Member, Alfred Hurley
Treasurer, David M Cordova
Board Member, Kurt Wolfgruber
Board Member, David Ogens
Auditors: DELOITTE & TOUCHE LLP

LOCATIONS

HQ: New Mountain Finance Corp
787 Seventh Avenue, 48th Floor, New York, NY 10019
Phone: 212 720-0300   **Fax:** 212 582-2277
Web: www.newmountainfinance.com

COMPETITORS

Apollo Investment	MVC Capital
Fifth Street Finance	Medley Capital
Gladstone Capital	PennantPark
Golub Capital BDC	Rand Capital
Harris & Harris	Saratoga Investment
Horizon Technology	Corp.
Finance	Solar Capital
KCAP Financial	THL Credit
MCG Capital	Triangle Capital

HISTORICAL FINANCIALS

Company Type: Public

Income Statement

FYE: December 31

	REVENUE ($ mil.)	NET INCOME ($ mil.)	NET PROFIT MARGIN	EMPLOYEES
12/17	197.8	102.2	51.7%	0
12/16	168.0	88.1	52.4%	0
12/15	153.8	82.5	53.6%	0
12/14	135.6	80.0	59.0%	0
12/13	90.8	50.5	55.6%	0
Annual Growth	21.5%	19.3%	—	—

2017 Year-End Financials

Debt ratio: 45.1%
Return on equity: 10.3%
Cash ($ mil.): 34.9
Current ratio: 3.26
Long-term debt ($ mil.): 869.5

No. of shares (mil.): 75.9
Dividends
Yield: 0.0%
Payout: 98.5%
Market value ($ mil.): 1,029.0

	STOCK PRICE ($) FY Close	P/E High/Low		PER SHARE ($) Earnings	Dividends	Book Value
12/17	13.55	10	9	1.38	1.36	13.63
12/16	14.10	8	6	1.60	1.36	13.46
12/15	13.02	28	22	0.55	1.36	13.08
12/14	14.94	14	13	1.10	1.48	13.83
12/13	15.04	—	—	(0.00)	1.48	(0.00)
Annual Growth	(2.6%)	—	—	—	(2.1%)	—

New Residential Investment Corp

EXECUTIVES

Ceo-pres, Kenneth Riis
Senior Vice President, Josh Denney
Auditors: Ernst & Young LLP

LOCATIONS

HQ: New Residential Investment Corp
1345 Avenue of the Americas, New York, NY 10105
Phone: 212 798-3150
Web: www.newresi.com

HISTORICAL FINANCIALS

Company Type: Public

Income Statement

FYE: December 31

	REVENUE ($ mil.)	NET INCOME ($ mil.)	NET PROFIT MARGIN	EMPLOYEES
12/17	2,151.8	957.5	44.5%	0
12/16	1,257.2	504.4	40.1%	0
12/15	687.1	268.6	39.1%	0
12/14	721.9	352.8	48.9%	0
12/13	328.5	265.9	80.9%	0
Annual Growth	60.0%	37.7%	—	—

2017 Year-End Financials

Debt ratio: 31.8%	No. of shares (mil.): 307.3
Return on equity: 24.0%	Dividends
Cash ($ mil.): 295.8	Yield: 0.1%
Current ratio: 0.20	Payout: 62.8%
Long-term debt ($ mil.): 7,084.3	Market value ($ mil.): 5,496.0

	STOCK PRICE ($) FY Close	P/E High/Low		PER SHARE ($) Earnings	Dividends	Book Value
12/17	17.88	6	5	3.15	1.98	15.26
12/16	15.72	8	5	2.12	1.84	13.00
12/15	12.16	13	8	1.32	1.75	12.13
12/14	12.77	5	2	2.53	0.38	11.28
12/13	6.68	3	3	2.06	0.99	10.00
Annual Growth	27.9%	—	—	11.2%	18.9%	11.1%

New Senior Investment Group Inc

Auditors: Ernst & Young LLP

LOCATIONS

HQ: New Senior Investment Group Inc
1345 Avenue of the Americas, New York, NY 10105
Phone: 212 479-3140

HISTORICAL FINANCIALS

Company Type: Public

Income Statement

FYE: December 31

	REVENUE ($ mil.)	NET INCOME ($ mil.)	NET PROFIT MARGIN	EMPLOYEES
12/17	449.1	12.2	2.7%	0
12/16	472.4	(72.2)	—	0
12/15	388.4	(82.4)	—	0
12/14	254.9	(46.4)	—	0
12/13	85.1	(30.0)	—	0
Annual Growth	51.6%	—	—	—

2017 Year-End Financials

Debt ratio: 76.0%	No. of shares (mil.): 82.1
Return on equity: 2.2%	Dividends
Cash ($ mil.): 137.3	Yield: 0.1%
Current ratio: 2.61	Payout: 693.3%
Long-term debt ($ mil.): 1,907.9	Market value ($ mil.): 621.0

	STOCK PRICE ($) FY Close	P/E High/Low		PER SHARE ($) Earnings	Dividends	Book Value
12/17	7.56	72	50	0.15	1.04	6.16
12/16	9.79	—	—	(0.88)	1.04	7.05
12/15	9.86	—	—	(1.08)	0.98	8.98
12/14	16.45	—	—	(0.70)	0.23	9.76
Annual Growth (22.8%) (14.2%)		—	—	—	65.4%	

New York Mortgage Trust Inc

New York Mortgage Trust is a self-advised real estate investment trust (REIT) that invests in mortgage-related real estate assets and some financial assets. It mostly invests in residential mortgage loans including multi-family commercial mortgage-backed securities (CMBS) distressed residential mortgage loans and direct financing to multi-family property owners through mezzanine loans and preferred equity investments. More than 60% of its revenue comes from interest on multi-family loans held in securitization trusts though the REIT's fortunes depend heavily on security gains and losses. New York Mortgage Trust was formed in 2003 and is headquartered in New York City.

Operations

New York Mortgage Trust generated about 62% of its total revenue from interest income from multi-family loans held in securitization trusts in 2014 while another 11% came from interest on its investment securities. About 22% of its revenue came from other income sources mostly related to realized gains on investment securities and related hedges realized gains on distressed residential mortgage loans and unrealized gains on its multi-family loans and debt held in securitization trusts. The company had a staff of 7 full-time employees at the end of 2014.

RiverBanc LLC; The Midway Group LP; and Headlands Asset Management LLC provide investment management services to the REIT with respect to certain of its targeted asset classes.

Financial Performance

New York Mortgage Trust's revenues and profits have been rising sharply in recent years mostly as the REIT has been generating higher interest income by acquiring more multi-family loan assets held in securitization trusts.

The REIT's revenue jumped 51% to $484.1 million in 2014 mostly thanks to a combination of higher interest income stemming from the company's continued purchase of more higher-yielding credit sensitive investments and a $52.8 million realized gain on investment securities and related hedges as the REIT sold certain multi-family CMBS securities.

Higher revenue in 2014 caused New York Mortgage Trust's net income to nearly double to $136.2 million. The company's operating cash levels fell by 30% to $37.6 million after adjusting its earnings for non-cash gains on its investments.

Strategy

New York Mortgage Trust's strategy for growth involves building a residential portfolio that includes elements of both interest rate and credit risk by focusing its investments on credit residential assets and leveraged residential mortgage-backed securities.

Starting in 2013 and continuing throughout 2014 the REIT had been "allocating new and re-invested capital to credit sensitive higher yielding investments and allocated less capital to its Agency RMBS portfolio which is lower yielding." These moves have boosted the company's interest income — and overall financial performance — in recent years.

EXECUTIVES

Chairman President and CEO, Steven R. Mumma, age 59, $533,333 total compensation
VP and Secretary, Nathan R. Reese, age 39, $260,000 total compensation
CFO, Kristine R. Nario, age 38, $225,000 total compensation
Auditors: GRANT THORNTON LLP

LOCATIONS

HQ: New York Mortgage Trust Inc
275 Madison Avenue, New York, NY 10016
Phone: 212 792-0107
Web: www.nymtrust.com

PRODUCTS/OPERATIONS

2014 Sales

	$ mil.	% of total
Interest income	378.8	78
Other income	105.2	22
Total	**484.0**	**100**

Selected Subsidiaries and Operations

Hypotheca Capital LLC
New York Mortgage Funding LLC
New York Mortgage Ownership Corporation
New York Mortgage Securities Corporation
New York Mortgage Securitization Trust 2012-1
New York Mortgage Servicing Corporation
New York Mortgage Trust 2005-1
New York Mortgage Trust 2005-2
New York Mortgage Trust 2005-3
NYM Preferred Trust I
NYM Preferred Trust II
NYMT Commercial LLC
NYMT Residential 2012-RP1 LLC
NYMT Residential Tax LLC
NYMT Residential LLC
NYMT-Midway LLC
RB Commercial Mortgage LLC
RB Commercial Trust Series 2012-RS1

COMPETITORS

Annaly Capital Management	Institutional Financial Markets
Anworth Mortgage Asset	MFA Financial
CIFC	Putnam Mortgage
Capstead Mortgage	Two Harbors
Drive Shack	iStar Financial Inc
Dynex Capital	
Impac Mortgage Holdings	

HISTORICAL FINANCIALS

Company Type: Public

Income Statement   FYE: December 31

	REVENUE ($ mil.)	NET INCOME ($ mil.)	NET PROFIT MARGIN	EMPLOYEES
12/17	439.3	91.9	20.9%	19
12/16	359.7	67.5	18.8%	19
12/15	384.0	78.0	20.3%	7
12/14	485.9	136.1	28.0%	7
12/13	322.2	68.9	21.4%	6
Annual Growth	8.1%	7.5%	—	33.4%

2017 Year-End Financials

Debt ratio: 91.2%
Return on equity: 10.1%
Cash ($ mil.): 95.1
Current ratio: 0.07
Long-term debt ($ mil.): 9,572.1

No. of shares (mil.): 111.9
Dividends
Yield: 0.1%
Payout: 121.2%
Market value ($ mil.): 690.0

	STOCK PRICE ($) FY Close	P/E High/Low	PER SHARE ($) Earnings	Dividends	Book Value
12/17	6.17	10 9	0.66	0.80	8.68
12/16	6.60	14 8	0.50	0.96	7.61
12/15	5.33	13 8	0.62	1.02	8.05
12/14	7.71	6 5	1.48	1.08	7.78
12/13	6.99	7 5	1.11	1.08	7.50
Annual Growth	(3.1%)	—	(12.2%)	(7.2%)	3.7%

NexPoint Residential Trust Inc

Auditors: KPMG LLP

LOCATIONS

HQ: NexPoint Residential Trust Inc
300 Crescent Court, Suite 700, Dallas, TX 75201
Phone: 972 628-4100
Web: www.nexpointliving.com

HISTORICAL FINANCIALS

Company Type: Public

Income Statement   FYE: December 31

	REVENUE ($ mil.)	NET INCOME ($ mil.)	NET PROFIT MARGIN	EMPLOYEES
12/17	144.2	53.3	37.0%	2
12/16	132.8	21.8	16.5%	2
12/15	117.6	(10.8)	—	0
12/14	43.1	(15.6)	—	0
12/13	0.3	(0.1)	—	0
Annual Growth	362.2%	—	—	—

2017 Year-End Financials

Debt ratio: 75.1%
Return on equity: 22.6%
Cash ($ mil.): 16.0
Current ratio: 1.64
Long-term debt ($ mil.): 784.2

No. of shares (mil.): 21.0
Dividends
Yield: 0.0%
Payout: 36.5%
Market value ($ mil.): 588.0

	STOCK PRICE ($) FY Close	P/E High/Low	PER SHARE ($) Earnings	Dividends	Book Value
12/17	27.94	12 9	2.49	0.91	11.38
12/16	22.34	22 10	1.03	0.84	11.00
12/15	13.09	— —	(0.51)	0.62	10.40
Annual Growth	46.1%	— —	—	21.3%	4.6%

Nexstar Media Group Inc

Star light star bright Nexstar Broadcasting wishes for you to tune in tonight. The company is a leading television station operator with more than 70 stations serving 40 small and midsized markets. Nexstar has duopolies (two or more stations) in many of its markets. Its portfolio includes more than a dozen affiliates each of the FOX and NBC networks as well as stations affiliated with ABC CBS The CW and MyNetworkTV. More than 15 of its TV stations are operated through local service agreements with Mission Broadcasting which owns those broadcast licenses. Private investment firm ABRY Partners owns a majority share in the company and controls 88% of the voting power.

Geographic Reach

Nexstar operates in dozens of US states. Most of the company's television stations are located in the Northeast Midwest and Southwest.

Sales and Marketing

Nexstar spend about $2 million on advertising and marketing promotions every year.

Strategy

Shared services agreements enable the Nexstar to provide sales news and other services to a second station in 66% of the markets where the company operates.

Mergers and Acquisitions

In 2018 Nexstar Media agreed to acquire storied media company Tribune Media for $4.1 billion in cash. The deal includes Tribune's more than 40 TV stations most notably the WGN America cable station and WPIX-TV New York KTLA-TV Los Angeles WGN-TV Chicago. Upon completion of its acquisition Nexstar will own more than 200 stations and extend its broadcasting footprint into major US markets like New York Los Angeles and Chicago.

EXECUTIVES

Chairman; President and CEO, Perry A. Sook, age 60, $1,191,539 total compensation
EVP and Co-COO, Timothy C. (Tim) Busch, age 55, $404,231 total compensation
EVP Co-COO, Brian Jones, age 58, $404,231 total compensation
SVP Regional Manager, Julie Pruett, age 55

EVP and CFO, Thomas E. (Tom) Carter, age 60, $423,654 total compensation
EVP Digital Media and Chief Revenue Officer, Thomas (Tom) O'Brien, age 56
SVP Regional Manager, William Sally
VP and Director Technology, Dione Rigsby
Vice President Controller and Secretary, Patrick Cusick
Vice President and General Manager, Albert Gutierrez
National Sales Manager, Kathleen Goble
Vice President, Bill Caudill
NATIONAL SALES MANAGER, Don Bradley
Auditors: PricewaterhouseCoopers LLP

LOCATIONS

HQ: Nexstar Media Group Inc
545 E. John Carpenter Freeway, Suite 700, Irving, TX 75062
Phone: 972 373-8800
Web: www.nexstar.tv

PRODUCTS/OPERATIONS

2016 Sales

	$ mil.	% of total
Broadcasting	1,040.7	94
Other	62.5	6
Total	1,103.2	100

List of Items
KAMR (NBC; Amarillo TX)
KARD (FOX; Monroe LA)
KARK (NBC; Little Rock AR)
KFDX (NBC; Wichita Falls TX)
KFTA (FOX; Ft. Smith-Fayetteville AR)
KLBK (CBS; Lubbock TX)
KLST (CBS; San Angelo TX)
KMID (ABC; Odessa-Midland TX)
KNWA (NBC; Ft. Smith-Fayetteville AR)
KSNF (NBC; Joplin MO)
KSVI (ABC; Billings MT)
KTAB (CBS; Abilene-Sweetwater TX)
KTAL (NBC; Shreveport LA)
WBRE (NBC; Wilkes Barre-Scranton PA)
WCIA (CBS, Champaign-Springfield IL)
WDHN (ABC; Dothan AL)
WFRV (CBS; Green Bay WI)
WFXV (FOX; Utica NY)
WHAG (NBC; Washington DC)
WJET (ABC; Erie PA)
WJMN (CBS; Marquette MI)
WMBD (CBS; Peoria-Bloomington IL)
WQRF (FOX; Rockford IL)
WROC (CBS; Rochester NY)
WTAJ (CBS; Johnstown-Altoona PA)
WTVW (FOX; Evansville IN)
WTWO (NBC; Terre Haute IN)

COMPETITORS

Allbritton Communications	LIN Media
Barrington Broadcasting	Local TV
Granite Broadcasting	Newport Television
Gray Television	Raycom Media
Hearst Television	TEGNA
	Tribune Media

Company Type: Public

Income Statement				FYE: December 31
	REVENUE ($ mil.)	NET INCOME ($ mil.)	NET PROFIT MARGIN	EMPLOYEES
12/17	2,431.9	475.0	19.5%	9,113
12/16	1,103.1	91.5	8.3%	4,527
12/15	896.3	77.6	8.7%	4,422
12/14	631.3	64.5	10.2%	3,464
12/13	502.3	(1.7)	—	3,222
Annual Growth	48.3%	—	—	29.7%

2017 Year-End Financials

Debt ratio: 58.3%
Return on equity: 54.6%
Cash ($ mil.): 115.6
Current ratio: 1.57
Long-term debt ($ mil.): 4,269.6

No. of shares (mil.): 45.9
Dividends
  Yield: 0.0%
  Payout: 11.9%
Market value ($ mil.): 3,595.0

	STOCK PRICE ($) FY Close	P/E High/Low		PER SHARE ($) Earnings	Dividends	Book Value
12/17	78.20	8	5	10.07	1.20	34.17
12/16	63.30	22	12	2.89	0.96	5.50
12/15	58.70	24	17	2.42	0.76	2.63
12/14	51.79	27	16	2.02	0.60	1.69
12/13	55.73	—	—	(0.06)	0.48	(0.43)
Annual Growth	8.8%	—	—	—	25.7%	—

NI Holdings Inc

Auditors: Mazars USA LLP

LOCATIONS

HQ: NI Holdings Inc
  1101 First Avenue North, Fargo, ND 58102
Phone: 701 298-4200
Web: www.nodakmutual.com

HISTORICAL FINANCIALS

Company Type: Public

Income Statement				FYE: December 31
	ASSETS ($ mil.)	NET INCOME ($ mil.)	INCOME AS % OF ASSETS	EMPLOYEES
12/17	376.9	15.9	4.2%	136
12/16	278.7	4.5	1.6%	129
12/15	258.6	17.4	6.7%	126
12/14	247.2	13.7	5.6%	0
Annual Growth	15.1%	5.1%	—	—

2017 Year-End Financials

Return on assets: 4.8%
Return on equity: 7.9%
Long-term debt ($ mil.): —
No. of shares (mil.): 22.3
Sales ($ mil): 189.1

Dividends
  Yield: —
  Payout: —
Market value ($ mil.): 379.0

	STOCK PRICE ($) FY Close	P/E High/Low		PER SHARE ($) Earnings	Dividends	Book Value
12/17	16.98	26	20	0.71	0.00	11.30
12/16	0.00	—	—	(0.00)	0.00	6.52
Annual Growth	—	—	—	—	—	73.4%

Nicolet Bankshares Inc

EXECUTIVES

Pres-ceo, Robert Atwell
Vice President Commercial Banking, Ken Glasheen
Auditors: Porter Keadle Moore, LLC

LOCATIONS

HQ: Nicolet Bankshares Inc
  111 North Washington Street, Green Bay, WI 54301
Phone: 920 430-1400
Web: www.nicoletbank.com

HISTORICAL FINANCIALS

Company Type: Public

Income Statement				FYE: December 31
	ASSETS ($ mil.)	NET INCOME ($ mil.)	INCOME AS % OF ASSETS	EMPLOYEES
12/17	2,932.4	33.1	1.1%	535
12/16	2,300.8	18.4	0.8%	480
12/15	1,214.4	11.4	0.9%	280
12/14	1,215.2	9.9	0.8%	280
12/13	1,198.8	16.1	1.3%	290
Annual Growth	25.1%	19.7%	—	16.5%

2017 Year-End Financials

Return on assets: 1.2%
Return on equity: 10.3%
Long-term debt ($ mil.): —
No. of shares (mil.): 9.8
Sales ($ mil): 143.8

Dividends
  Yield: —
  Payout: —
Market value ($ mil.): 537.0

	STOCK PRICE ($) FY Close	P/E High/Low		PER SHARE ($) Earnings	Dividends	Book Value
12/17	54.74	17	13	3.33	0.00	37.09
12/16	47.69	19	12	2.37	0.00	32.26
12/15	31.79	12	9	2.57	0.00	26.36
12/14	25.00	11	7	2.25	0.00	27.35
12/13	16.54	5	4	3.80	0.00	24.73
Annual Growth	34.9%	—	—	(3.2%)	—	10.7%

NMI Holdings Inc

NMI Holdings provides mortgage insurance through two primary subsids - National Mortgage Insurance Corp (NMIC) and National Mortgage Reinsurance Inc. One (Re One). NMIC is its primary insurance subsidiary approved to write coverage in all 50 states and Washington DC. Re One provides reinsurance to NMIC on insured loans with coverage levels in excess of 25%. The company also provides outsourced loan review services to mortgage loan originators through NMI Services. Mortgage insurance protects lenders and investors from default-related losses.

Operations

NMI Holdings offers primary mortgage insurance which provides protection on individual mortgage loans. Mortgages are insured on a case-by-case basis at the time of origination. The company previously offered pool insurance which covers the excess of loss on defaulted mortgages not covered under primary mortgage insurance. It didn't write any pool insurance in 2017 and doesn't expect to do much in that business line in the near future.

Geographic Reach

NMI Holdings gets all of its revenue in the US. Ten states account for more than half of its total risk-in-force (RIF) or the total dollar amount of claims it expects to receive during the year. California, Texas and Virginia account for about 15% 10% and 5% of RIF respectively.

Financial Performance

NIH's revenues have been climbing rapidly over the past five years but net income has been up and down. The company lost money in 2013 2014 and 2015 but was in the black in 2016 and 2017.

Revenue increased 47% to $178.6 million in 2017. Net premiums earned rose thanks to the company's growing insurance in-force. Investment income also rose that year.

Net income dropped 65% to $22.1 million in 2017 as operating expenses primarily insurance claims and claims expenses increased.

The company ended 2017 with $19.2 million in cash and cash equivalents 60% less than it had at the beginning of the year. Although operating cash flow provided $67.8 million cash from investments used $93.1 million.

Strategy

NMI Holdings is one of six private mortgage insurers operating in the US; the others are Arch Capital Essent Group Genworth Financial MGIC Investment Corporation and Radian Group. (Many others went out of business following the financial crisis of 2008.) However the company also competes with federal government agencies who filled the void left by private companies.

The company is working to increase its position in the private mortgage insurance market. It seeks to expand its customer base and strengthen its portfolio of high-quality assets largely through deepening its existing customer relationships.

EXECUTIVES

Chairman and CEO, Bradley M. (Brad) Shuster, age 63
EVP and Chief Risk Officer, Patrick L. Mathis, age 58
EVP and COO, Claudia J. Merkle
CFO, Glenn Farrell
EVP and General Counsel, William J. Leatherberry
Auditors: BDO USA, LLP

LOCATIONS

HQ: NMI Holdings Inc
  2100 Powell Street, Emeryville, CA 94608
Phone: 855 530-6642
Web: www.nationalmi.com

PRODUCTS/OPERATIONS

2017 Sales

	% of total
Net premiums earned	91
Net investment income	9
Net realized investment gains	-
Other	-
Total	**100**

COMPETITORS

Arch Capital	MGIC Investment
Essent Guaranty	Radian Group
Genworth Mortgage Insurance	

HISTORICAL FINANCIALS

Company Type: Public

Income Statement
FYE: December 31

	ASSETS ($ mil.)	NET INCOME ($ mil.)	INCOME AS % OF ASSETS	EMPLOYEES
12/17	894.8	22.0	2.5%	299
12/16	841.7	65.8	7.8%	276
12/15	662.4	(27.7)	—	243
12/14	463.2	(48.9)	—	189
12/13	481.2	(55.1)	—	141
Annual Growth	16.8%	—		20.7%

2017 Year-End Financials

Return on assets: 2.5%	Dividends
Return on equity: 4.4%	Yield: —
Long-term debt ($ mil.): —	Payout: —
No. of shares (mil.): 60.5	Market value ($ mil.): 1,029.0
Sales ($ mil): 182.7	

	STOCK PRICE ($) FY Close	P/E High/Low	PER SHARE ($) Earnings	Dividends	Book Value
12/17	17.00	48 27	0.35	0.00	8.41
12/16	10.65	10 4	1.08	0.00	8.07
12/15	6.77	— —	(0.47)	0.00	6.85
12/14	9.13	— —	(0.84)	0.00	7.31
12/13	12.73	— —	(0.99)	0.00	7.98
Annual Growth	7.5%	— —	—	—	1.3%

NN, Inc

Hardly an unknown or no name ("NN") supplier NN produces a slew of precision metal components and assemblies for a highly diverse global market. Operating through three manufacturing units NN makes precision steel balls and rollers for bearing makers; carmakers; drilling bit makers whose products extract water oil and gas and minerals; and OEMs of stainless steel valves and pumps. It also churns out precision bearing seals metal and plastic retainers for ball and roller bearings and molded plastic products for automotive electronic instrument and fluid control industries.

Operations

NN operates through three segments: autocam precision components (49% of sales) precision bearing components (39%) and precision engineered products (11%).

Geographic Reach

NN has 42 manufacturing plants in North America. International plants reside in China Slovakia Italy and the Netherlands. The US accounts for 49% of NN's total sales while Europe generates 26%. Asia is its third-largest segment representing 13% of sales.

Sales and Marketing

NN's top 10 customers which generate around 53% of sales includes SKF (almost 15%).

Financial Performance

NN enjoyed unprecedented growth in 2015 with revenues surging 37% to peak at a record-setting $667 million in 2015. The historic growth for 2015 was fueled by extraordinary increases from its precision engineered products (130%) and autocam precision components segments (85%). A large portion of this growth was attributed to additional revenue from previous acquisitions.

The company suffered a net loss of $7 million in 2015 mostly due to higher depreciation amortization and write-off costs related to the refinacing of its acquisitions. Cash flow was up by 9% in 2015 mostly due to favorable changes in accounts receivable inventories and other non-current assets.

Mergers and Acquisitions

Going forward NN looks to deploy cash generated from operations to grow organically as well as through business acquisitions in the global market for metal bearing and precision metal components.

In 2015 it bought Caprock Manufacturing and Caprock Enclosures a privately held plastic components supplier located in Lubbock Texas. Caprock serves multiple end markets including the aerospace medical and general industrial sectors. The company will become a part of its precision engineered products segment.

Also in 2015 NN also purchased Precision Engineered Products Holdings (PEP). PEP is a global manufacturer of highly engineered precision customized products serving the medical electrical automotive and aerospace end markets.

EXECUTIVES

President and CEO, Richard D. Holder, age 55, $596,154 total compensation
SVP Integration and Corporate Transformation, James R. (J.R.) Widders, age 62, $262,442 total compensation
CIO, Scott Weinstein
SVP; General Manager Precision Bearing Components Group, L. Jeff Manzagol, $312,341 total compensation
SVP; General Manager Autocam Precision Components Group, Warren Veltman, $324,266 total compensation
SVP and CFO, Thomas C. Burwell, age 50
SVP; General Manager Precision Engineered Products Group, John A. Manzi
Vice President Marketing, Robert Sams
Chairman, G. Ronald Morris, age 82
Auditors: PricewaterhouseCoopers LLP

LOCATIONS

HQ: NN, Inc
6210 Ardrey Kell Road, Charlotte, NC 28277
Phone: 980 264-4300
Web: www.nninc.com

PRODUCTS/OPERATIONS

2015 Sales

	$ mil.	% of total
Autocam bearing components	328.3	49
Precision bearing components	261.8	39
Precision Engineering products	77.2	12
Total	**667.3**	**100**

Selected Products

Metal bearing components
  Cylindrical rollers
  Metal retainers
  Precision steel balls
  Tapered rollers
Plastic & rubber components
  Bearing seals
  Plastic retainers
  Precision plastic components
Precision metal components
  Fluid control components & assemblies
  Highly engineered precision metal components
  Shafts

COMPETITORS

A. Berger Precision	Key Plastics
Amatsuji Steel Ball	Linamar Corp.
Applied Industrial Technologies	MinebeaMitsumi
Autocam	NAKANISHI MFG. CO. LTD.
Conbraco Industries	NSK
General Bearing	NTN
Hoover Precision Products	Nypro
JTEKT	SKF USA
Kaydon	Stanadyne
	Tsubaki Nakashima

HISTORICAL FINANCIALS

Company Type: Public

Income Statement
FYE: December 31

	REVENUE ($ mil.)	NET INCOME ($ mil.)	NET PROFIT MARGIN	EMPLOYEES
12/17	619.7	163.0	26.3%	4,407
12/16	833.4	7.9	1.0%	5,299
12/15	667.2	(7.4)	—	5,313
12/14	488.6	8.2	1.7%	4,220
12/13	373.2	17.1	4.6%	1,861
Annual Growth	13.5%	75.5%		24.1%

2017 Year-End Financials

Debt ratio: 54.7%	No. of shares (mil.): 27.5
Return on equity: 40.7%	Dividends
Cash ($ mil.): 224.4	Yield: 0.0%
Current ratio: 4.40	Payout: 4.7%
Long-term debt ($ mil.): 790.8	Market value ($ mil.): 761.0

	STOCK PRICE ($) FY Close	P/E High/Low	PER SHARE ($) Earnings	Dividends	Book Value
12/17	27.60	5 3	5.87	0.28	17.63
12/16	19.05	70 36	0.29	0.28	11.57
12/15	15.04	— —	(0.35)	0.28	11.69
12/14	20.56	65 37	0.45	0.28	9.15
12/13	20.19	21 8	1.00	0.18	8.66
Annual Growth	8.1%	— —	55.7%	11.7%	19.4%

Noble Midstream Partners LP

Auditors: KPMG LLP

LOCATIONS

HQ: Noble Midstream Partners LP
1001 Noble Energy Way, Houston, TX 77070
Phone: 281 872-3100
Web: www.NBLMidstream.com

HISTORICAL FINANCIALS

Company Type: Public

Income Statement
FYE: December 31

	REVENUE ($ mil.)	NET INCOME ($ mil.)	NET PROFIT MARGIN	EMPLOYEES
12/17	239.2	140.5	58.7%	143
12/16	160.7	85.5	53.2%	90
12/15	92.4	38.0	41.1%	80
12/14	5.8	(15.0)		0
Annual Growth	243.9%	—	—	—

2017 Year-End Financials

Debt ratio: 10.6% No. of shares (mil.): 39.6
Return on equity: 37.6% Dividends
Cash ($ mil.): 55.5 Yield: 0.0%
Current ratio: 0.75 Payout: 42.8%
Long-term debt ($ mil.): 88.1 Market value ($ mil.): 1,981.0

	STOCK PRICE ($) FY Close	P/E High/Low		PER SHARE ($) Earnings	Dividends	Book Value
12/17	50.00	13	9	4.10	1.76	11.99
12/16	36.00	43	29	0.89	0.00	8.54
12/15	0.00	—	—	(0.00)	0.00	(0.00)
Annual Growth	—			—	—	—

Northeast Bancorp (ME)

Northeast Bancorp is the holding company for Northeast Bank which operates about a dozen branches in western and southern Maine. Founded in 1872 the bank offers standard retail services such as checking and savings accounts NOW and money market accounts CDs and trust services as well as financial planning and brokerage. Residential mortgages account for about a third of all loans; commercial mortgages and consumer loans each make up about 25%. The bank also writes business and construction loans. Newly created investment entity FHB Formation acquired a 60% stake in Northeast Bancorp in 2010. The deal brought in $16 million in capital. The 2011 sale of insurance agency Varney added another $8.4 million.

Northeast Bank Insurance has acquired about a half-dozen insurance agencies since 2006. It now has more than a dozen offices in Maine and southern New Hampshire where the company hopes to expand further by opening bank branches.

Investment firms including Sandler O'Neill Asset Management Nichols Investment Management and regional bank investor Tontine Financial Partners collectively own about a third of Northeast Bancorp.

EXECUTIVES

Vice President, Scott Hudson
Senior Vice President Business Development, Jonathan Levirne
Senior Vice President Business Development, Brad Heritage
Auditors: RSM US LLP

LOCATIONS

HQ: Northeast Bancorp (ME)
 500 Canal Street, Lewiston, ME 04240
Phone: 207 786-3245
Web: www.northeastbank.com

COMPETITORS

Bar Harbor Bankshares	Norway Bancorp
Camden National	TD Bank USA
KeyCorp	The First Bancorp

HISTORICAL FINANCIALS

Company Type: Public

Income Statement FYE: June 30

	ASSETS ($ mil.)	NET INCOME ($ mil.)	INCOME AS % OF ASSETS	EMPLOYEES
06/18	1,157.7	16.1	1.4%	185
06/17	1,076.8	12.3	1.1%	195
06/16	986.1	7.6	0.8%	203
06/15	850.8	7.1	0.8%	191
06/14	761.9	2.6	0.4%	195
Annual Growth	11.0%	56.5%	—	(1.3%)

2018 Year-End Financials

Return on assets: 1.4% Dividends
Return on equity: 12.3% Yield: 0.0%
Long-term debt ($ mil.): — Payout: 2.2%
No. of shares (mil.): 8.9 Market value ($ mil.): 195.0
Sales ($ mil): 72.9

	STOCK PRICE ($) FY Close	P/E High/Low		PER SHARE ($) Earnings	Dividends	Book Value
06/18	21.80	16	11	1.77	0.04	15.49
06/17	20.35	15	8	1.38	0.04	13.90
06/16	11.25	15	12	0.80	0.04	12.51
06/15	9.95	14	12	0.72	0.04	11.77
06/14	9.57	42	35	0.26	0.28	11.05
Annual Growth	22.9%			61.5% (38.5%)		8.8%

Northeast Community Bancorp Inc

Northeast Community Bancorp is the holding company for Northeast Community Bank which serves consumers and businesses in the New York metropolitan area and Massachusetts. Through about a half-dozen branches the thrift offers traditional deposit services like checking and savings accounts as well as a variety of lending products such as commercial and multi-family real estate loans home equity construction and secured loans. While its deposit services are confined to New York and Massachusetts it markets its loan products throughout the northeastern US. The bank offers investment and financial planning services through Hayden Wealth Management. Northeast Community Bank's roots date back to 1934.

EXECUTIVES

EVP CFO and Director, Salvatore Randazzo, age 48, $173,265 total compensation
Chairman President and CEO, Kenneth A. Martinek, age 63, $273,837 total compensation
Chief Operating Officer; Executive Vice President; Chief Information Officer, Jose Collazo
Auditors: BDO USA, LLP

LOCATIONS

HQ: Northeast Community Bancorp Inc
 325 Hamilton Avenue, White Plains, NY 10601
Phone: 914 684-2500
Web: www.necommunitybank.com

COMPETITORS

Bank of America	New York Community
Citigroup	Bancorp
HSBC USA	TrustCo Bank Corp NY
JPMorgan Chase	Wells Fargo
KeyCorp	

HISTORICAL FINANCIALS

Company Type: Public

Income Statement FYE: December 31

	ASSETS ($ mil.)	NET INCOME ($ mil.)	INCOME AS % OF ASSETS	EMPLOYEES
12/17	814.8	8.0	1.0%	0
12/16	734.5	5.0	0.7%	0
12/15	593.6	2.3	0.4%	0
12/14	515.4	1.7	0.3%	96
12/13	458.2	1.1	0.2%	104
Annual Growth	15.5%	63.1%	—	—

2017 Year-End Financials

Return on assets: 1.0% Dividends
Return on equity: 7.1% Yield: 0.0%
Long-term debt ($ mil.): — Payout: 17.9%
No. of shares (mil.): 12.1 Market value ($ mil.): 123.0
Sales ($ mil): 39.5

	STOCK PRICE ($) FY Close	P/E High/Low		PER SHARE ($) Earnings	Dividends	Book Value
12/17	10.10	15	11	0.67	0.12	9.59
12/16	7.90	19	15	0.42	0.12	8.96
12/15	7.12	40	34	0.20	0.12	8.59
12/14	7.22	53	48	0.14	0.12	8.42
12/13	7.22	87	59	0.09	0.09	8.29
Annual Growth	8.8%			65.2%	7.5%	3.7%

Northern Technologies International Corp.

Northern Technologies International (NTIC) keeps rust away with its proprietary corrosion-inhibiting packaging. Its ZERUST product line features special packaging that emits corrosion-inhibiting molecules and compounds; the packaging comes in films and bags liquids and coatings rust removers and cleaners vapor capsules and pipe strips for residue-free protection of pipes thermal spray coatings and cathodic protection technologies. NTIC's customers include automotive electronics power generation and metal processing firms. The company makes about 85% of its sales in North America.

Operations

Most of the company's sales come from ZERUST but the company has expanded its product mix. Its new product development focus is on biodegradable polymer resins which it sells under its Natur-Tec brand. The company is hoping to tap into a growing market emerging as a result of lower petroleum prices and increased interest in environmentally friendly alternatives to traditional plastics.

Its Natur-Tec resins are manufactured out of combination of biodegradable polymers and organic materials. Specific products include compost and trash bags agricultural films and various consumer goods packaging.

Geographic Reach

Based in Minnesota the company sells its products in over 60 countries including countries in North America South America Europe Asia and the Middle East. It generates about 85% of sales from North America followed by 9% from Brazil and 3% each from India and China.

NTIC also maintains a manufacturing laboratory and warehouse space located in Beachwood Ohio. It also has warehousing agreements in place in California and Indiana.

Sales and Marketing

NTIC's marketing activities include advertising and direct mail campaigns and also trade shows and technical forums. Customers include universities and school districts and film extruders and injection molders that produce bio-based and compostable end products such as film bags and cutlery.

Financial Performance

NTIC achieved unprecedented growth in 2015 posting record-setting revenues of $30 million that year. ZERUST segment net sales increased by 9% in 2015 mainly due to increased demand for its products and services from existing customers and new customers as a result of its marketing effort in the oil and gas sector.

Natur-Tec segment sales also spiked by 44% in 2015 mainly due to higher finished product sales in North America and finished product sales through Natur-Tec India as a result of market penetration and the reach of its distribution network.

Strategy

The company is focused on growth in India on the heels of higher sales from its Natur-Tec India subsidiary in 2015. Pursuant to this in 2016 the company plans to target and convert additional manufacturers to the use of Natur-Tec sustainable packaging products and services.

EXECUTIVES

Marketing Manager New Technologies, Vineet Dalal, age 50
Chief Financial Officer; Vice President, David Bonczek
Chief Executive Officer; Director, Mario Rodriguez
Chairman, Pierre Chenu, age 80
Auditors: Baker Tilly Virchow Krause, LLP

LOCATIONS

HQ: Northern Technologies International Corp.
4201 Woodland Road, P.O. Box 69, Circle Pines, MN 55014
Phone: 763 225-6600
Web: www.ntic.com

PRODUCTS/OPERATIONS

2015 Sales

	$ mil.	% of total
ZERUST	26.0	86
Natur-Tec	4.3	14
Total	30.3	100

Selected Products

Corrosion Products Division (ZERUST products)
Bags
Bubble cushioning
Can Liners
Corrugated plastic and profile board
Corrugated solid fiber and chipboard
Cutlery
Dunnage trays and bins
Foam sheeting
Lawn and leaf bags
Pet waste collection bags
Pipe strips
Shrink film
Tube strips
Vapor capsules

Selected Solutions

Diffusers
Liquids and Coatings
Plastic and Paper Packaging
Rust Removers and Cleaners
Z-CIS Technical Services
ZERUST Corrosion Prevention Solutions
ZERUST Corrosion Prevention Solutions
ZERUST Flange Savers
ZERUST ReCAST-R VCI Dispensers
ZERUST ReCAST-SSB Solutions
ZERUST Zerion

COMPETITORS

AZZ Galvanizing	Menasha
Services	Pactiv
Coroplast	Praxair
Corrpro	Sealed Air Corp.

HISTORICAL FINANCIALS

Company Type: Public

Income Statement
FYE: August 31

	REVENUE ($ mil.)	NET INCOME ($ mil.)	NET PROFIT MARGIN	EMPLOYEES
08/18	51.4	6.7	13.0%	136
08/17	39.5	3.4	8.6%	71
08/16	32.9	(0.8)	—	121
08/15	30.3	1.7	5.9%	123
08/14	26.8	4.1	15.3%	91
Annual Growth	17.7%	13.0%	—	10.6%

2018 Year-End Financials

Debt ratio: —
Return on equity: 13.1%
Cash ($ mil.): 4.1
Current ratio: 3.95
Long-term debt ($ mil.): —
No. of shares (mil.): 4.5
Dividends
  Yield: 1.1%
  Payout: 27.9%
Market value ($ mil.): 165.0

	STOCK PRICE ($) FY Close	P/E High/Low	PER SHARE ($) Earnings	Dividends	Book Value
08/18	36.40	27 11	1.43	0.40	11.60
08/17	17.60	25 11	0.75	0.00	10.77
08/16	13.89	— —	(0.19)	0.00	9.82
08/15	15.58	60 38	0.38	0.00	9.89
08/14	20.71	25 17	0.90	0.00	10.16
Annual Growth	15.1%	— —	12.3%	—	3.6%

Northfield Bancorp Inc (DE)

Auditors: KPMG LLP

LOCATIONS

HQ: Northfield Bancorp Inc (DE)
581 Main Street, Woodbridge, NJ 07095
Phone: 732 499-7200
Web: www.eNorthfield.com

HISTORICAL FINANCIALS

Company Type: Public

Income Statement
FYE: December 31

	ASSETS ($ mil.)	NET INCOME ($ mil.)	INCOME AS % OF ASSETS	EMPLOYEES
12/17	3,991.4	24.7	0.6%	352
12/16	3,850.0	26.1	0.7%	366
12/15	3,202.5	19.5	0.6%	306
12/14	3,020.8	20.2	0.7%	321
12/13	2,702.7	19.1	0.7%	326
Annual Growth	10.2%	6.6%	—	1.9%

2017 Year-End Financials

Return on assets: 0.6%
Return on equity: 3.9%
Long-term debt ($ mil.): —
No. of shares (mil.): 48.8
Sales ($ mil): 144.5
Dividends
  Yield: 0.0%
  Payout: 64.1%
Market value ($ mil.): 834.0

	STOCK PRICE ($) FY Close	P/E High/Low	PER SHARE ($) Earnings	Dividends	Book Value
12/17	17.08	37 28	0.53	0.34	13.09
12/16	19.97	35 24	0.57	0.31	12.80
12/15	15.92	36 31	0.45	0.28	12.29
12/14	14.80	36 30	0.41	0.26	12.27
12/13	13.20	45 32	0.34	0.49	12.36
Annual Growth	6.7%	— —	11.7%	(8.7%)	1.4%

Northrim BancCorp Inc

Can you get banking services at the north rim of the world? Of course! Northrim BanCorp formed in 2001 to be the holding company for Northrim Bank provides a full range of commercial and retail banking services and products through some 10 banking offices in Alaska's Anchorage Fairbanks North Star and Matanuska Susitna counties. Division offices that provide short-term capital to customers also are located in Washington and Oregon. The bank offers standard deposit products including checking savings and money market accounts; CDs; and IRAs. It uses funds from deposits to write commercial loans (40% of loan portfolio) and real estate term loans (nearly 35%) as well as construction and consumer loans.

Northrim BanCorp also owns a stake in a handful of other businesses including Residential Mortgage Holding Company which originates loans from offices throughout Alaska. The company also owns about 50% of Northrim Benefits Group an insurance brokerage company. In 2006 Northrim purchased a 24% stake in Pacific Wealth Advisors an investment advisory trust and wealth management firm in Seattle. Elliott Cove another investment advisory serivce company also is in Northrim's portfolio.

In 2007 Northrim BanCorp acquired Alaska First Bank & Trust for more than $6 million. The deal did not include Alaska First's insurance subsidiary Hagen Insurance.

EXECUTIVES

Vice President Commercial Cash Management,
 Kimberly F Brewington
Auditors: Moss Adams LLP

LOCATIONS

HQ: Northrim BancCorp Inc
 3111 C Street, Anchorage, AK 99503
Phone: 907 562-0062

PRODUCTS/OPERATIONS

2007 Sales

	$ mil.	% of total
Interest		
Loans including fees	66.5	80
Securities	4.6	6
Other	2.0	2
Noninterest		
Service charges on deposit accounts	3.1	4
Purchased receivable income	2.5	3
Other	4.2	5
Total	**82.9**	**100**

COMPETITORS

Alaska Pacific Bancshares	First National Bank Alaska
Alaska USA	KeyCorp

HISTORICAL FINANCIALS

Company Type: Public

Income Statement   FYE: December 31

	ASSETS ($ mil.)	NET INCOME ($ mil.)	INCOME AS % OF ASSETS	EMPLOYEES
12/17	1,519.1	13.1	0.9%	429
12/16	1,526.5	14.4	0.9%	451
12/15	1,499.4	17.7	1.2%	441
12/14	1,449.3	17.4	1.2%	426
12/13	1,215.0	12.3	1.0%	269
Annual Growth	**5.7%**	**1.6%**	**—**	**12.4%**

2017 Year-End Financials

Return on assets: 0.8%	Dividends
Return on equity: 6.9%	Yield: 0.0%
Long-term debt ($ mil.): —	Payout: 45.7%
No. of shares (mil.): 6.8	Market value ($ mil.): 233.0
Sales ($ mil): 99.7	

	STOCK PRICE ($) FY Close	P/E High/Low	Earnings	PER SHARE ($) Dividends	Book Value
12/17	33.85	20 14	1.88	0.86	28.06
12/16	31.60	16 10	2.06	0.78	27.05
12/15	26.60	11 8	2.56	0.74	25.74
12/14	26.24	11 9	2.54	0.70	23.97
12/13	26.24	15 11	1.87	0.64	22.05
Annual Growth	**6.6%**	**— —**	**0.1%**	**7.7%**	**6.2%**

Novanta Inc

Novanta's business is laser focused. The company uses its expertise in laser and motion control technologies to design and manufacture sets of products that are geared to the medical and healthcare and advanced industrial markets. Sealed CO2 lasers ultrafast lasers and optical light engines are sold primarily to the industrial and scientific markets. Novanta supplies lasers optics encoders and air bearing spindles to the healthcare and medical markets as well as the aerospace market for high-precision cutting drilling marking and measuring. The company changed its name to Novanta from GSI Group in mid-2016. International customers account for about 60% of sales.

Operations

Novanta conducts business through three primary segments: Photonics (45% of net sales) Vision (35%) and Precision Motion (20%).

Photonics designs makes and sells photonics-based tools that include laser scanning and laser beam delivery instruments CO2 lasers continuous wave and ultrafast lasers and optical light engine products.

The Vision segment makes and sells a range of medical technologies including medical insufflators (tools for pumping powder or gas into a body cavity) pumps and related disposables; surgical displays and operating room integration technologies; optical data collection and machine vision technologies; radio frequency identification (RFID) technologies; thermal printers; spectrometry technologies; and embedded touch screens.

The Precision Motion segment?s products include optical encoders precision motor and motion control technology air bearing spindles and precision machines components.

Novanta operates through several trade names that include Cambridge Technology Lincoln Laser Synrad Laser Quantum WOM Reach Technology JADAK ThingMagic Photo Research Celera Motion Applimotion and Westwind.

Geographic Reach

Novanta based in Bedford Massachusetts operates from about 20 locations in Europe the Asia/Pacific and the US. Geographically the US generates Novanta's largest amount of sales (more than 40%) followed by Europe (about 30%) and China and other countries in the Asia/Pacific region (about 30%).

Sales and Marketing

Novanta sells its products worldwide through a direct sales force and through resellers or distributors who in turn sell to OEMs that integrate Novanta's products into their own systems. Novanta primarily customers are in the medical and advanced industrial markets.

Financial Performance

After several years of revenue increasing at about a 2% rate Novantós revenue jumped 35% in 2017 thanks largely to acquisitions made in the past two years. Each segment posted higher sales in 2017 leading to revenue of $521 million. Acquisitions boosted sales for the Photonics and Vision businesses while increased demand in the advanced industrial and medical markets pushed Precision Motion sales higher.

Net income rose to $61 million in 2017 from $22 million in 2016 from higher revenue and as the company kept expenses at or close to previous levels as a percentage of revenue.

Novanta had about $100 million in cash in 2017 up from some $68 million in 2016. The increase came from cash provided by operating activities and money borrowed under its revolving credit facility. The company spent money on the WOM ThingMagic and Laser Quantum acquisitions debt repayments and capital expenditures.

Strategy

Novanta's general strategy includes focusing on scanning products fiber lasers and medical components and building more business in emerging markets through creating more internal sales channels and developing relationships with external channel partners. Part of that strategy involves acquisitions and divesting non-core businesses. Novanta bought three companies in 2016 and 2016 which added more than $100 million in sales in 2017 while shutting down its line of Dome brand radiology products in 2016.

With about 60% of revenue from international customers Novanta runs the risk of getting caught in possible trade wars. China has been a particular target of the US government and that?s where Novanta has done increasing business through sales and production outsourcing.

Novantós push into medical markets has helped increase revenue but the continued uncertainty of the US Patient Protection and Affordable Care Act could interfere with that strategy by changing what health and medical institutions buy and how they do it.

Mergers and Acquisitions

INovanta boosted its products for the medical market through a series of acquisitions.

In 2017 Novanta acquired Germany-based World of Medicine GmbH a provider of medical insufflators (for blowing gas or powder into a body cavity) pumps and related disposables for OEMs for ?118.1 million.

Also in 2017 the company increased it ownership of Laser Quantum to more than 75% with the purchase of additional shares for ó25.5 million. Laser Quantum provides solid state continuous wave lasers femtosecond lasers and optical light engines to OEMs in the medical market.

The 2017 acquisition of ThingMagic for about $19 million added ultra-high frequency (UHF) radio frequency identification (RFID) modules and finished RFID readers to Novantós offerings for OEMs.

In 2016 Novanta bought California-based Reach Technology Inc. a provider of embedded touch screen technology products to OEMs for more than $9 million.

EXECUTIVES

CFO, Robert Buckley, age 44, $378,762 total compensation
CEO and Director, Matthijs Glastra, $410,955 total compensation
Corporate Vice President of Global Information Technology, Scott Rehner
Vice President of Marketing, Maura Fitzpatrick
Chairman, Stephen W. Bershad, age 76
Auditors: PricewaterhouseCoopers LLP

LOCATIONS

HQ: Novanta Inc
 125 Middlesex Turnpike, Bedford, MA 01730
Phone: 781 266-5700   **Fax:** 781 266-5114
Web: www.gsig.com

PRODUCTS/OPERATIONS

2017 sales

	$ mil.	% of total
Photonics	232.4	45
Vision	183.0	35
Precision Motion	105.8	20
Total	**521.2**	**100**

Selected Products and Brands
Laser products
  Lasers and laser-based systems (Synrad)
  Light and color measurement systems (Photo Research Inc.)
  Optics (The Optical Corporation)
  Scanners (Cambridge Technology)
Precision motion
  Encoders (MicroE Systems)
  Lasers (eCO2 Lasers Spectron Lasers)
  Optics (ExoTec Precision)
  Printed circuit board spindles (Westwind Air Bearings)
Medical technologies
Visualizations solutions
Imaging Informatics

COMPETITORS

Analogic	Newport Corp.
Blue Sky Research	OMRON
Coherent Inc.	Omron Electronics
CyberOptics	ProPhotonix
Cymer	Quantel
Electro Scientific	Renishaw
Industries	Spectra-Physics
HEIDENHAIN Corp.	Swatch
Hitachi	TOPCON
II-VI	TRUMPF
IPG Photonics	Virtek Vision
JMAR Technologies	Zygo

HISTORICAL FINANCIALS
Company Type: Public

Income Statement
FYE: December 31

	REVENUE ($ mil.)	NET INCOME ($ mil.)	NET PROFIT MARGIN	EMPLOYEES
12/17	521.2	60.0	11.5%	2,034
12/16	384.7	22.0	5.7%	1,269
12/15	373.6	35.6	9.5%	1,355
12/14	364.7	(24.2)		1,410
12/13	341.6	7.3	2.1%	1,287
Annual Growth	11.1%	69.3%	—	12.1%

2017 Year-End Financials

Debt ratio: 33.3%	No. of shares (mil.): 34.6
Return on equity: 21.0%	Dividends
Cash ($ mil.): 100.0	Yield: —
Current ratio: 2.93	Payout: —
Long-term debt ($ mil.): 233.4	Market value ($ mil.): 1,730.0

	STOCK PRICE ($) FY Close	P/E High/Low	PER SHARE ($) Earnings	Dividends	Book Value
12/17	50.00	48 18	1.13	0.00	9.01
12/16	21.00	34 19	0.63	0.00	7.51
12/15	13.62	15 12	1.02	0.00	7.12
12/14	14.72	— —	(0.70)	0.00	6.16
12/13	11.24	53 38	0.21	0.00	7.12
Annual Growth	45.2%	— —	52.3%	—	6.1%

NutriSystem Inc

Nutrisystem helps its customers trim their waistline morning noon and night. It promotes weight loss by selling prepared meals and grocery items that are delivered directly to US consumers. Customers order monthly food packages consisting of 28 days of portion-controlled items such as a breakfast lunch dinner and dessert supplemented with fruits and vegetables. It also offers individualized calorie plans one-on-one diet counseling behavior modification and exercise education and maintenance plans. Nutrisystem also sells its weight-management products through a partnership with TV marketer QVC (3% of revenue) and club retailers the likes of Costco. Tivity Health is buying Nutrisystem for $1.4 billion.

Change in Company Type

Tivity Health which owns the SilverSneakers fitness program agreed to buy Nutrisystem in late 2018. The two companies should complement one another in their combined efforts to help customers lose weight.

Operations
The Nutrisystem program is based 40-plus years of nutrition research and the science of the low Glycemic Index which promotes quality carbohydrates in the diet. Roughly 99% of Nurtisystem's revenue comes from its food item sales.

Geographic Reach
Pennsylvania-based Nutrisystem serves customers nationwide through its US office in Pennsylvania.

Sales and Marketing
About 90% of Nutrisystem's revenue is made from direct sales. The company is keenly aware of its target customer: a female approximately 50-years-old who weighs about 187 pounds. Customers on average want to lose 43 pounds. Its typical customers stay on a Nutrisystem program for up to 12 weeks losing up to 2 pounds per week.

To get its name in front of existing and potential customers Nutrisystem heavily markets its business. It uses direct response television online marketing direct mail print advertising and a variety of other direct marketing efforts. Indeed the company spent $107.7 million on marketing in 2014 compared to $95.8 million in 2013 and $111.1 million in 2012. Most of the increase in 2014 went toward media advertising.

The company markets weight loss programs through brick-and-mortar stores and their online counterparts. Happily for Nutrisystem warehouse retailer Costco has lived up to Nutrisystem's sales expectations. The diet company severs relationships with underperforming retailers.

Its client base is relatively concentrated among a few key members. In 2014 inventory purchases from two vendors made up 17% and 14% of sales respectively.

Financial Performance
After several years of sale declines Nutrisystem's revenue in 2014 rebounded by 12% to $403.08 million thanks to growth from new customers retail and on-program revenue. The company also benefited from a higher average sales prices. Sales from reactivation and QVC declined offsetting some of the company's potential top-line gains.

Higher revenue caused profit to spike for a second year with net income skyrocketing by 162% to $19.31 million in 2014. Operations provided $32.81 million or 7% less cash than in 2013 mostly because of an increase in receivables and timing of accrued payroll and benefits.

Strategy
Nutrisystem has been banking on its food retailing efforts to return to pre-recession revenue (which reached a high of $776.77 million in 2007). Looking to add another sales channel to boost its revenue Nutrisystem originally entered the retail market in 2012 expanding its client base to include prominent retailers such as Wal-Mart and Costco in the years since. In 2014 as a testament to its early success over a two year period retail sales accounted for 7% of Nutrisystem's total revenue.

Endorsements from highly renowned sources could help the company grow as well.

Also to improve revenue the company has overhauled its e-commerce platform enhanced its fresh-frozen foods introduced a Nutrisystem D program through its retail channel and created a Culinary Council that is working to update its food choices and improve taste.

EXECUTIVES
President and CEO, Dawn M. Zier, $650,000 total compensation
CFO, Michael P. (Mike) Monahan, $335,000 total compensation
Chairman, Michael J. Hagan, age 55
Auditors: KPMG LLP

LOCATIONS
HQ: NutriSystem Inc
  Fort Washington Executive Center, 600 Office Center Drive, Fort Washington, PA 19034
Phone: 215 706-5300
Web: www.nutrisystem.com

PRODUCTS/OPERATIONS

2014 Sales

	% of total
Direct	91
Retail	7
QVC	2
Total	**100**

Selected Food Programs
Men's Program
Men's Silver Program
My Plan
SUCCESS
Women's Diabetic Program
Women's Program
Women's Silver Program
Vegetarian

COMPETITORS

Atkins Nutritionals	PowerBar
Bally Total Fitness	Schiff Nutrition
ConAgra	International
HMG	Slim-Fast
Jenny Craig	Weight Watchers
Medifast	International
Nestlé	eDiets.com

HISTORICAL FINANCIALS
Company Type: Public

Income Statement
FYE: December 31

	REVENUE ($ mil.)	NET INCOME ($ mil.)	NET PROFIT MARGIN	EMPLOYEES
12/17	696.9	57.8	8.3%	606
12/16	545.4	35.4	6.5%	487
12/15	462.6	26.1	5.7%	451
12/14	403.0	19.3	4.8%	417
12/13	358.0	7.3	2.1%	430
Annual Growth	18.1%	67.4%	—	9.0%

Debt ratio: —
Return on equity: 50.2%
Cash ($ mil.): 24.6
Current ratio: 2.38
Long-term debt ($ mil.): —

No. of shares (mil.): 30.0
Dividends
  Yield: 0.0%
  Payout: 36.8%
Market value ($ mil.): 1,581.0

	STOCK PRICE ($) FY Close	P/E High/Low	PER SHARE ($) Earnings	Dividends	Book Value
12/17	52.60	33 17	1.90	0.70	4.52
12/16	34.65	31 15	1.19	0.70	3.18
12/15	21.64	34 19	0.89	0.70	2.39
12/14	19.55	30 21	0.66	0.70	1.93
12/13	16.44	79 28	0.25	0.70	1.82
Annual Growth	33.7%	— —	66.0%	(0.0%)	25.6%

Nuvasive Inc

When a back is seriously out of whack NuVasive has some options. The company makes and markets medical devices for the surgical treatment of spinal disorders. NuVasive's products are primarily used in spinal restoration and fusion surgeries. Its minimally disruptive Maximum Access Surgery (MAS) platform enables surgeons to access the spine from the side of the body instead of from the front or back helping them to avoid hitting nerves. NuVasive also features a line of biologic bone grafting materials — both allograft and synthetic — and has a cervical disc replacement system in development. The company sells its FDA-approved products through a network of exclusive sales agents supported by an in-house sales team.

Operations

NuVasive offers more than 80 products for procedures in the lumbar thoracic and cervical regions including the mesh plates screws and biological implants used with its MAS system. Its Osteocel product is an adult stem-cell bone graft used for bone regeneration in orthopedic procedures and at one point was the only commercially available stem-cell product in the US.

NuVasive's revenues primarily come from the sale of disposable materials and implants. The full system of software and instruments are loaned to hospitals for free as long as they keep ordering disposables and implants though a small portion of the company's revenues are from the sale of instruments and systems. Revenues from its monitoring services come from hospitals and are also billed through various payers.

Geographic Reach

NuVasive maintains a facility in California where it trains doctors in the use of its products. It ships its products directly to doctors overnight from a distribution facility in Tennessee; other US facilities are located in New Jersey Ohio and Maryland. International offices are located in Australia Brazil Germany Japan the Netherlands and the UK.

The US accounts for the majority of NuVasive's sales but the company is working to establish its products in Europe and Asia. The first hurdle is obtaining regulatory approval for all of the components in its platform for each country it seeks to enter.

Sales and Marketing

NuVasive sells its products through its own direct sales force and through exclusive distributors and independent sales agents.

Financial Performance

NuVasive's revenues have steadily increased as it has grown through increased product sales new product additions and acquisitions including a 19% jump to $962.1 million in fiscal 2016. That year's growth was driven by increased spinal hardware product sales which rose 20% and higher surgical support sales which rose 14%.

Net income has fluctuated in recent years. In 2016 it fell 44% to $37.1 million — despite the higher revenue — as operating expenses such as sales and marketing and R&D costs rose.

Strategy

NuVasive's goal is to make its products and services part of the standard procedure for minimally invasive surgery up and down the entire spine. The firm is focused on expanding the reach of its MAS platform through marketing and sales force efforts to increase market penetration. It also conducts research and development efforts to improve existing offerings to make them more adaptable for surgeons and hospitals.

R&D efforts create new products as well. As cervical disc replacement technology — the holy grail for spinal device makers — is advancing rapidly NuVasive has several cervical disc replacement devices in late-stage development.

Mergers and Acquisitions

In mid-2016 NuVasive acquired Biotronic NeuroNetwork which provides intraoperative neurophysiological monitoring services for $98 million. That deal which more than doubled NuVasive's neurophysiology footprint extended the operations of the company's newly established NuVasive Clinical Services division. That unit now provides monitoring services for more than 75000 cases each year.

Also that year the company acquired Ellipse Technologies which developed magnetic growing rod implant systems for $380 million; those products which eliminate the need for repeat surgeries as pediatric patients grow are now sold by NuVasive Specialized Orthopedics. In yet another deal it purchased the LessRay software suite which enhances image quality while helping health care providers manage radiation exposure.

In 2017 NuVasive agreed to buy SafePassage which provides intraoperative neurophysiological monitoring (IONM) services for an undisclosed amount. SafePassage will join its Clinical Services division; it will expand the company's IONM business into new markets especially on the East Coast.

EXECUTIVES

Chairman and CEO, Gregory T. Lucier
EVP Asia Pacific, Takaaki Tanaka
EVP Global Operations, Tyler P. Lipschultz
EVP International, Russell Powers
EVP Strategic Sales and Operations, Scott Durall
EVP Strategy Technology and Corporate Development, Matthew W. (Matt) Link, age 43, $375,000 total compensation
EVP Corporate Affairs and Human Resources, Carol Cox
CIO, Johnson Lai
EVP Global Process Transformation, Stephen Rozow, age 49
EVP and CFO, Rajesh J. (Raj) Asarpota
Vice President Global Surgeon Education, Ed Mayadag
Vice Chairman, Patrick (Pat) Miles
Auditors: Ernst & Young LLP

LOCATIONS

HQ: Nuvasive Inc
7475 Lusk Boulevard, San Diego, CA 92121
Phone: 858 909-1800   **Fax:** 800 475-9134
Web: www.nuvasive.com

PRODUCTS/OPERATIONS

2016 Sales

	% of total
Spinal Hardware	70
Surgical Support	30
Total	100

Selected Acquisitions

COMPETITORS

Alphatec Spine	Natus Medical
CareFusion	Orthofix
DePuy Spine	Stryker
Globus Medical	Synthes
Integra LifeSciences	Zimmer Biomet
Interpore	
Medtronic Sofamor Danek	

HISTORICAL FINANCIALS

Company Type: Public

Income Statement   FYE: December 31

	REVENUE ($ mil.)	NET INCOME ($ mil.)	NET PROFIT MARGIN	EMPLOYEES
12/17	1,029.5	83.0	8.1%	2,600
12/16	962.0	37.1	3.9%	2,200
12/15	811.1	66.2	8.2%	1,600
12/14	762.4	(16.7)	—	1,500
12/13	685.1	7.9	1.2%	1,358
Annual Growth	10.7%	80.0%	—	17.6%

2017 Year-End Financials

Debt ratio: 35.5%
Return on equity: 11.1%
Cash ($ mil.): 72.8
Current ratio: 3.48
Long-term debt ($ mil.): 582.9

No. of shares (mil.): 56.1
Dividends
  Yield: —
  Payout: —
Market value ($ mil.): 3,285.0

	STOCK PRICE ($) FY Close	P/E High/Low	PER SHARE ($) Earnings	Dividends	Book Value
12/17	58.49	50 31	1.50	0.00	14.16
12/16	67.36	92 53	0.69	0.00	12.59
12/15	54.11	41 31	1.26	0.00	13.21
12/14	47.16	— —	(0.36)	0.00	13.42
12/13	32.33	186 86	0.17	0.00	13.26
Annual Growth	16.0%	— —	72.3%	—	1.7%

NV5 Global Inc

NV5 Global wants the world to envy its engineering services. It offers infrastructure engineering support and consulting services as well as construction quality assurance and asset management. Customers include government agencies along with quasi-public and private firms in education health care and energy. NV5's enviable projects have included the international terminal at Philadelphia International Airport UC Santa Barbara's Marine Center the New Jersey Devils Arena San Diego's Manchester Grand Hyatt and a wind turbine manufacturing plant in Colorado. The company works from about 20 offices in California Colorado Florida New Jersey and Utah. It was formed in 2011 and filed to go public in 2013.

IPO

The company plans to use its anticipated $6.9 million in IPO proceeds for general corporate purposes including working capital sales and marketing and acquisitions.

Operations

NV5 divides its business into what it calls its five vertical offerings. They are- infrastructure engineering and support services; construction quality assurance; public and private consulting and outsourcing; asset management consulting; and occupational health safety and environmental consulting.

It has traditionally focused on the first two service verticals but is expanding into the others and plans to focus on those going forward.

Financial Performance

NV5's revenues have generally been increasing while its costs have held steady except for acquisitions. The company hasn't reported 2012 numbers yet but in 2011 it nearly doubled revenue and increased net income nearly tenfold. Nolte Associates acquired during 2010 contributed all of the company's revenue for 2011.

Strategy

Going forward NV5 intends to continue to focus on public sector clients which account for about 60% of revenue while working to grow its private sector accounts. It also plans to look for strategic acquisitions and invest in attracting training and retaining personnel.

Mergers and Acquisitions

In 2011 NV5 completed a reorganization to incorporate Nolte Associates acquired the previous year. In 2012 it purchased engineering firm Kaderabek (Kaco) for about $3.5 million.

EXECUTIVES

Director; EVP Strategic Growth NV5, Donald C. (Don) Alford, age 74, $240,000 total compensation
Chairman and CEO, Dickerson Wright, age 72, $400,000 total compensation
VP and CFO, Michael P. Rama, age 52, $178,077 total compensation
Executive Vice President and General Counsel, Richard Tong, age 50, $230,000 total compensation
President and COO, Alexander A. Hockman, age 61, $290,385 total compensation
Executive Vice President and Chief Administrative Officer, Mary Jo O'Brien, age 56
Vice President of Buildings Energy and Science, Amanda Weir
Auditors: DELOITTE & TOUCHE LLP

LOCATIONS

HQ: NV5 Global Inc
200 South Park Road, Suite 350, Hollywood, FL 33021
Phone: 954 495-2112
Web: www.nv5.com

COMPETITORS

AECOM
Amec Foster Wheeler
Bureau Veritas
Cardno
Intertek
Jacobs Engineering
TRC Companies
Terracon
Tetra Tech
The Kleinfelder Group Inc.
WS Atkins
Willdan Group

HISTORICAL FINANCIALS

Company Type: Public

Income Statement				FYE: December 30
	REVENUE ($ mil.)	NET INCOME ($ mil.)	NET PROFIT MARGIN	EMPLOYEES
12/17	333.0	24.0	7.2%	2,023
12/16	223.9	11.6	5.2%	1,532
12/15	154.6	8.4	5.5%	975
12/14	108.3	4.8	4.5%	649
12/13	68.2	2.7	4.0%	436
Annual Growth	48.6%	71.7%	—	46.8%

2017 Year-End Financials

Debt ratio: 22.4%
Return on equity: 14.6%
Cash ($ mil.): 18.7
Current ratio: 2.33
Long-term debt ($ mil.): 57.4

No. of shares (mil.): 10.8
Dividends
 Yield: —
 Payout: —
Market value ($ mil.): 587.0

	STOCK PRICE ($) FY Close	P/E High/Low	PER SHARE ($) Earnings	Dividends	Book Value
12/17	54.15	25 14	2.23	0.00	16.62
12/16	33.40	29 12	1.22	0.00	14.02
12/15	21.98	22 8	1.18	0.00	9.83
12/14	13.00	15 8	0.87	0.00	6.19
12/13	8.14	12 9	0.70	0.00	5.23
Annual Growth	60.6%	— —	33.6%	—	33.5%

Oak Valley Bancorp (Oakdale, CA)

Oak Valley Bancorp was formed in 2008 to be the holding company for Oak Valley Community Bank which serves individuals and local businesses through about 10 branches in California's Central Valley. Eastern Sierra Community Bank a division of Oak Valley has three locations. The banks provide standard deposit products such as savings checking and retirement accounts and CDs. Their lending activities consist of commercial real estate loans (more than half of their combined loan portfolio) and business real estate construction agricultural residential mortgage and consumer loans. Investment products and services are offered through an agreement with PrimeVest Financial Services.

EXECUTIVES

VP Business Development Officer, Barbara Ducey
Auditors: RSM US LLP

LOCATIONS

HQ: Oak Valley Bancorp (Oakdale, CA)
125 North Third Avenue, Oakdale, CA 95361
Phone: 209 848-2265
Web: www.ovcb.com

COMPETITORS

Bank of America
Bank of the West
Citibank
MUFG Americas Holdings
U.S. Bancorp
Wells Fargo
Westamerica

HISTORICAL FINANCIALS

Company Type: Public

Income Statement				FYE: December 31
	ASSETS ($ mil.)	NET INCOME ($ mil.)	INCOME AS % OF ASSETS	EMPLOYEES
12/17	1,034.8	9.0	0.9%	175
12/16	1,002.1	7.6	0.8%	169
12/15	897.0	4.9	0.5%	167
12/14	749.6	7.1	1.0%	157
12/13	671.8	5.8	0.9%	146
Annual Growth	11.4%	11.5%	—	4.6%

2017 Year-End Financials

Return on assets: 0.8%
Return on equity: 10.5%
Long-term debt ($ mil.): —
No. of shares (mil.): 8.1
Sales ($ mil): 41.2

Dividends
 Yield: 0.0%
 Payout: 22.1%
Market value ($ mil.): 158.0

	STOCK PRICE ($) FY Close	P/E High/Low	PER SHARE ($) Earnings	Dividends	Book Value
12/17	19.54	18 11	1.13	0.25	11.21
12/16	12.55	13 10	0.95	0.24	10.19
12/15	10.40	18 15	0.61	0.21	9.69
12/14	10.16	12 9	0.89	0.17	9.29
12/13	8.37	12 10	0.74	0.00	8.14
Annual Growth	23.6%	— —	11.2%	—	8.3%

Oaktree Capital Group LLC

Oaktree Capital Group knows money doesn't grow on trees but it often grows on alternative investments. The global investment manager specializes in credit and contrarian value-oriented investments such as distressed debt corporate debt convertible securities real estate private equity (or control investing) and listed equities. Founded in 1995 Oaktree Capital boasts $97 billion of assets under management on behalf of institutional investors such as pension funds corporations government entities universities endowments foundations and private clients. The firm has more than 15 offices in the US Asia and Europe.

Operations

Oaktree generates 97% of its revenue from management fees which represents the company's share of investors' profits in some of its funds. The remainder of its revenue comes from incentive income related to investment performance. Fluctuations in the market value of Oaktree's funds directly impact its revenue.

Nearly 40% of the firm's assets under management (AuM) were invested in corporate debt (with about a third of that in US high-yield bonds) in 2015 while another 43% of AuM were invested in distressed debt and control investing (private equity investments). The rest was invested in convertible securities (6%) real estate (9%) and listed equities particularly emerging markets equities (4%).

Geographic Reach

Los Angeles-based Oaktree serves clients globally through its offices in 17 major financial cities across 12 countries including London New York City Hong Kong Stamford Houston Tokyo Luxembourg Paris Frankfurt Singapore Seoul Beijing Amsterdam Dublin Dubai and Shanghai. About 75% of its investor inflows come from North America while nearly 15% comes from Europe and some 10% comes from Asia and Australia with Africa & the Middle East (2%) and South America (1%) accounting for the remainder.

Sales and Marketing

As of the end of 2015 the firm boasted a 55-person in-house global Marketing and Client Relations group dedicated to relationship management and sales client service or sales strategy based in Europe the Middle East the Asia-Pacific region and the Americas. The team was backed by a team of 48 marketing support portfolio analytics and client reporting-professionals.

During 2015 its client base consisted of 75 of the 100 largest US pension plans 434 corporations and/or their pension funds 370 university charitable and other endowments and foundations 16 sovereign wealth funds and some 300 other institutional investors not based in the US. About 12% of its AuM were made on behalf of high-net-worth individuals or sub-advisory relationships with mutual funds.

Financial Performance

Oaktree Capital's revenues have trended higher in recent years thanks to higher management fee income as its assets under management have swelled from less than $75 billion in 2011 to $97 billion in 2015. Its profits have been volatile however mostly as the firm sold off (realizations) a significant amount of its investments (particularly its crisis-era distressed debt funds) to distribute to its investors between 2011 through 2013 which led to high profits during those years.

The firm's revenue climbed 4% to $201.9 million in 2015 due to higher fees across the board including management fees and incentive income. A recent slide in net income accelerated in 2015 falling 56% to $71.4 million due to depreciation on investments relating to distressed debt senior loan high-yield bond and emerging markets equities funds. Cash from operations decreased by 78% to $934.3 million on the back of decreases in accounts payable and deferred tax assets.

Strategy

Oaktree Capital regularly adds to its funds and strategies offerings (mainly on its own but also through acquisitions) to attract new investors and their capital. The company also relies on strong investment performance from its teams to ensure its customers keep coming back. The company working on closing its first debt transaction in India.

Mergers and Acquisitions

In 2014 Oaktree Capital expanded its investment strategy offerings after purchasing investment management firm Highstar Capital for $31.4 million in cash. Highstar — which specialized in US energy infrastructure waste management and transportation — presented Oaktree with an opportunity to capitalize on aging infrastructure assets (including originating owning and operating such assets) in the US and the expansion of infrastructure for growing energy needs in the country and North America as a whole.

HISTORY

Oaktree Capital made headlines in 2007 when it became the first to use an exclusive institutional investment platform launched by Goldman Sachs in order to sell a stake in itself. Similar to an IPO the move allowed the company to raise funds to bankroll additional acquisitions yet still remain private. Oaktree Capital raised some $800 million by selling less than 15% of itself.

Also that year Oaktree Capital made its first foray into Taiwan with its acquisition of Fu Sheng Industrial. It acquired Pangaea Capital Management adding four locations in the Pacific Rim.

Utilizing its expertise in distressed assets Oaktree has helped to shepherd firms such as Aleris AdvancePierre Foods Dayton Superior Masonite and Townsquare Media out of bankruptcy since 2008 netting it significant stakes in those companies.

In other transactions involving distressed assets Oaktree formed a joint venture with Ryland Homes in 2009 to acquire residential real estate in the midst of the dismal housing market. The following year it teamed with homebuilder Toll Brothers to acquire about $1.7 billion in distressed loans once held by AmTrust Bank which was seized by the FDIC. With a group of investors including Anschutz and Starwood Capital the company bought the assets of resort operator Sea Island as part of that firm's bankruptcy restructuring.

Oaktree went public via an IPO in 2012 and planned to use proceeds for general corporate purposes and to buy out its limited partners. The company raised some $380.2 million in its initial public offering about 27% less than it sought to raise. The timing of the IPO probably didn't help as wary investors shied away from new public companies due to a slump in the markets.

EXECUTIVES

CEO and Director, Jay S. Wintrob, age 61
Managing Director and Head Credit Strategies,
  Scott L. Graves, age 47, $130,000 total compensation
Principal Head Yield Bond and Director, Sheldon M. Stone, age 65
Principal CFO and Director, David M. Kirchheimer, age 62
Managing Director and Portfolio Manager, Caleb S. Kramer, age 49
Managing Director and Global Head Marketing, Tony Harrington
Managing Director and CIO, Bob Frank
Co-Chairman President and Chief Investment Officer, Bruce A. Karsh, age 62
Co-Chairman, Howard S. Marks, age 72
Vice Chairman, John B. (Bob) Frank, age 62
Auditors: Ernst & Young LLP

LOCATIONS

HQ: Oaktree Capital Group LLC
  333 South Grand Avenue, 28th Floor, Los Angeles, CA 90071
Phone: 213 830-6300
Web: www.oaktreecapital.com

PRODUCTS/OPERATIONS

2016 Assets Under Management by Investment

	% of total
Corporate debt	40
Distressed debt	27
Control investments	15
Real estate	9
Convertible securities	5
Listed equities	4
Total	**100**

2016 Assets Under Management by Client

	% of total
Public funds	24
Corporate pensions	24
Corporations	9
Insurance companies	9
Sovereign wealth funds	8
Sub-advisory mutual funds	6
Endowments & foundations	6
Private clients	5
Funds of funds	4
Unions	3
Oaktree & other	2
Total	**100**

2016 Sales

	$ mil.	% of total
Management fees	774.6	69
Incentive income	351.1	31
Total	**1,125.7**	**100**

COMPETITORS

Angelo Gordon	Equity Group
Anschutz	Investments
Apollo Global	Heico Companies
Management	KPS Capital Partners
BBX Capital	Soros Fund Management
Clinton Group	TPG
Elliott Management	

HISTORICAL FINANCIALS

Company Type: Public

Income Statement

FYE: December 31

	REVENUE ($ mil.)	NET INCOME ($ mil.)	NET PROFIT MARGIN	EMPLOYEES
12/17	1,469.7	231.4	15.8%	930
12/16	1,125.7	194.7	17.3%	939
12/15	201.9	71.3	35.3%	924
12/14	193.8	126.2	65.1%	927
12/13	194.9	222.0	113.9%	809
Annual Growth	65.7%	1.1%	—	3.5%

2017 Year-End Financials

Debt ratio: 53.5%	No. of shares (mil.): 156.2
Return on equity: 27.6%	Dividends
Cash ($ mil.): 1,136.0	Yield: 0.0%
Current ratio: 1.21	Payout: 88.9%
Long-term debt ($ mil.): 4,828.2	Market value ($ mil.): 6,580.0

	STOCK PRICE ($) FY Close	P/E High/Low	PER SHARE ($) Earnings	Dividends	Book Value
12/17	42.10	13 11	3.61	3.21	5.56
12/16	37.50	16 12	3.11	2.25	5.21
12/15	47.72	39 32	1.45	2.10	4.77
12/14	51.83	21 15	2.97	3.15	3.58
12/13	58.84	9 7	6.35	4.71	3.14
Annual Growth	(8.0%)	— —	(13.2%)	(9.1%)	15.4%

OceanFirst Financial Corp

Ask the folks at OceanFirst Bank for a home loan and they might say "shore." The subsidiary of holding company OceanFirst Financial operates 25 branches in the coastal New Jersey counties of

Middlesex Monmouth and Ocean. The community-oriented bank caters to individuals and small to midsized businesses in the Jersey Shore area offering standard products such as checking and savings accounts CDs and IRAs. It uses funds from deposits mainly to invest in mortgages loans and securities. One- to four-family residential mortgages make up more than half of OceanFirst Financial's loan portfolio which also includes commercial real estate (about 30%) business construction and consumer loans.

Operations

The Bank's principal business is attracting deposits from the general public in the communities surrounding its branch offices and investing those deposits primarily in single-family owner-occupied residential mortgage loans and commercial real estate loans. It active subsidiaries include Ocean-First Services LLC OceanFirst REIT Holdings Inc. and 975 Holdings LLC.

Geographic Reach

OceanFirst has operations in the New Jersey counties of Middlesex Monmouth and Ocean.

Financial Performance

OceanFirst's revenues dropped by 4% in 2012 due to decrease in loans and mortgage-backed securities partially offset by higher revenues from investment securities and other.

Net income declined by 3% in 2012 due to an increase in provision for loan losses and non-interest expenses (higher professional fees).

Strategy

OceanFirst seeks to grow commercial loans receivable by offering commercial lending services to local businesses; grow core deposits through broader product offerings andbranch expansion; and increase non-interest income by expanding its fee-based products and services

Part of the company's strategy for growth in cludes expanding its fee-based offerings. The bank for example offers trust and asset management services. Company subsidiary OceanFirst Services sells mutual funds annuities and insurance products from third-party vendors. OceanFirst is also seeking opportunities to grow by opening new branch locations within its existing markets.

In 2013 the Bank opened a full service Financial Solutions Center in Red Bank New Jersey offering deposit lending and asset management services. It also opened an additional branch office in Jackson New Jersey.

Since 1995 OceanFirst has opened sixteen branch offices (twelve in Ocean County and four in Monmouth County).

Mergers and Acquisitions

In January 2016 OceanFirst Financial agreed to buy Cape Bancorp— along with its 22 branches in central and southern New Jersey counties $1.1 billion in loans and $1.3 billion in deposits — for $208.1 million. The deal would grow OceanFirst's total total assets by over 60% and nearly double the size of its branch network.

Company Background

OceanFirst Bank's employee stock option plan owns more than 10% of OceanFirst Financial's shares. The company's charitable foundation OceanFirst Foundation owns 7%.

The Bank was founded as a state-chartered building and loan association in 1902. It converted to a Federal savings and loan association in 1945 and became a Federally-chartered mutual savings bank in 1989.

EXECUTIVES

EVP and CFO, Michael J. Fitzpatrick, age 61, $285,577 total compensation
EVP and Chief Administrative Officer, Joseph R. Iantosca, age 56, $284,808 total compensation
EVP and Chief Lending Officer, Joseph J. Lebel, age 54, $284,808 total compensation
First SVP General Counsel and Corporate Secretary, Steven J. Tsimbinos, $252,798 total compensation
Chairman President and CEO, Christopher D. Maher, age 50, $566,346 total compensation
Vp Information Services, Elizabeth Alexander
Vice President Bank Counsel, Michele Hart
Assistant Vice President OceanFirst Bank, Karen Rack
Senior Vice President Director Of Human Resources, Gary Hett
Senior Vice President, Brad Fouss
Assistant Vice President Collections Department, Karen Farrell
Vice President Senior Marketing Officer Strategy, Lisa Natale
Auditors: KPMG LLP

LOCATIONS

HQ: OceanFirst Financial Corp
110 West Front Street, Red Bank, NJ 07701
Phone: 732 240-4500
Web: www.oceanfirst.com

PRODUCTS/OPERATIONS

2016 sales

	% of total
Interest Income	
Loans	80
Mortgage-backed securities	4
Investment securities & other	2
Non-interest	
Bankcard services revenue	3
Wealth management revenue	2
Fees & service charges	7
Loan Servicing income	-
Net gains on sales of loans	1
Net loss from other real estate operations	-
Income from Bank owned Life Insurance	1
Other	-
Total	**100**

COMPETITORS

Bank of America	PNC Financial
Cape Bancorp	Sovereign Bank
Citibank	TD Bank USA
Hudson City Bancorp	Valley National
Investors Bancorp	Bancorp
JPMorgan Chase	

HISTORICAL FINANCIALS

Company Type: Public

Income Statement — FYE: December 31

	ASSETS ($ mil.)	NET INCOME ($ mil.)	INCOME AS % OF ASSETS	EMPLOYEES
12/17	5,416.0	42.4	0.8%	684
12/16	5,167.0	23.0	0.4%	797
12/15	2,593.0	20.3	0.8%	393
12/14	2,356.7	19.9	0.8%	376
12/13	2,249.7	16.3	0.7%	409
Annual Growth	24.6%	27.0%	—	13.7%

2017 Year-End Financials

Return on assets: 0.8%	Dividends
Return on equity: 7.2%	Yield: 0.0%
Long-term debt ($ mil.): —	Payout: 46.8%
No. of shares (mil.): 32.6	Market value ($ mil.): 856.0
Sales ($ mil): 215.9	

	STOCK PRICE ($) FY Close	P/E High/Low		PER SHARE ($) Earnings	Dividends	Book Value
12/17	26.25	23	18	1.28	0.60	18.47
12/16	30.03	30	16	0.98	0.54	17.80
12/15	20.03	17	13	1.21	0.52	13.79
12/14	17.14	16	13	1.19	0.49	12.91
12/13	17.13	19	14	0.95	0.48	12.33
Annual Growth	11.3%	—	—	7.7%	5.7%	10.6%

Office Properties Income Trust

If Government Properties Income Trust had one request of Uncle Sam it would be this: "I want you to lease our properties." As a real estate investment trust (REIT) Government Properties Income Trust invests in properties that are leased to government tenants. It owns nearly 11 million sq. ft. of leasing space across more than 70 properties across the US. The company leases mostly to federal agencies (such as the FBI IRS and FDA) but it does lease to some state-run agencies and the United Nations as well. It also makes some equity investments. Government Properties Income Trust went public in 2009.

Geographic Reach

Although the company has has more than 70 properties in 31 states about 65% of its 2014 rental revenues came from the states of Maryland California the District of Columbia Virginia Georgia New York and Massachusetts.

Sales and Marketing

About two-thirds of its leaseable properties (and two-thirds of its square footage) were leased to US Government agencies in 2014 while about 25% were leased to 12 state governments. One of its properties was leased to the United Nations. Less than 5% of its square footage (or 3 properties) were leased to non-government tenants.

Financial Performance

Government Properties Income Trust's revenues and profits has been steadily rising over the past several years thanks to high occupancy rates and rental rate hikes made after property improvements and as the real estate market has strengthened.

The REIT's revenue jumped 11% to $251 million in 2014 mostly from added rental income from new property acquisitions made during and after 2013. Its average occupancy rates on comparable properties also rose also helping its top-line.

Higher revenue and strong cost controls in 2014 boosted Government Properties' net income by 4% to $56.5 million while its operating cash levels rose 21% to $131 million during the year on higher cash earnings.

Strategy

In addition to making property acquisitions to grow its rental revenue Government Properties Income Trust also makes tenant-requested improvements to allow it to charge higher rental rates and keep lease renewals high. It also takes property-improving requests from potential lessees to attract new tenant leases.

While it's kept roughly the same amount of properties for a number of years (between 70 and 80) Government Properties sometimes sells its under-performing properties to free up resources for better investments. In 2014 the REIT sold two of its properties based in Falls Church Virginia and Phoenix.

EXECUTIVES

Treasurer Chief Financial Officer, Mark L. Kleifges, age 57, $162,960 total compensation
President and COO, David M. Blackman, age 56, $162,960 total compensation
Auditors: Ernst & Young LLP

LOCATIONS

HQ: Office Properties Income Trust
Two Newton Place, 255 Washington Street, Suite 300, Newton, MA 02458-1634
Phone: 617 219-1440
Web: www.govreit.com

COMPETITORS

Boston Properties	First Potomac Realty
CapLease	Piedmont Office Realty
Corporate Office	Trust
Properties Trust	USFP Trust

HISTORICAL FINANCIALS

Company Type: Public

Income Statement — FYE: December 31

	REVENUE ($ mil.)	NET INCOME ($ mil.)	NET PROFIT MARGIN	EMPLOYEES
12/17	316.5	12.0	3.8%	0
12/16	258.1	57.8	22.4%	0
12/15	248.5	(209.9)	—	0
12/14	251.0	56.5	22.5%	0
12/13	226.9	54.6	24.1%	0
Annual Growth	8.7%	(31.4%)	—	—

2017 Year-End Financials

Debt ratio: 60.6%	No. of shares (mil.): 99.1
Return on equity: 1.0%	Dividends
Cash ($ mil.): 16.5	Yield: 0.0%
Current ratio: 0.29	Payout: 1,228.5%
Long-term debt ($ mil.): 2,061.9	Market value ($ mil.): 1,838.0

	STOCK PRICE ($) FY Close	P/E High/Low	PER SHARE ($) Earnings	Dividends	Book Value
12/17	18.54	164 125	0.14	1.72	13.62
12/16	19.07	30 16	0.81	1.72	13.14
12/15	15.87	— —	(2.97)	1.72	13.45
12/14	23.01	28 24	0.92	1.72	18.44
12/13	24.85	27 23	1.00	1.72	18.09
Annual Growth	(7.1%)	— —	(38.8%)	(0.0%)	(6.8%)

Old Line Bancshares Inc

Old Line Bancshares is the holding company for Old Line Bank serving consumers businesses and wealthy individuals in the Old Line State and in the Washington DC area. With some 20 branch offices and total assets in excess of $1.2 billion the bank offers standard retail products including deposit accounts CDs and credit cards. Commercial and industrial and commercial real estate loans make up 75% of the bank's loan portfolio though it also offers consumer loans and luxury boat financing. The company also owns 50% of real estate firm Pointer Ridge Office Investment.

Operations

About 81% of its revenue came from interest income on loans in 2014 while another 7% came from interest on securities (including mortgage-backed US government agency and municipal securities). About 4% of revenue was generated from service charges on deposit accounts 4% came from fees and commissions and 2% came from gains on the sales of its loans.

Geographic Reach

Old Line Bank more than 20 branches mostly in suburban Maryland (which includes Washington DC and suburbs and Southern Maryland) in the counties of Anne Arundel Calvert Charles Prince George's and St. Mary's.

Financial Performance

Old Line Bancshares' revenues and profits have been trending higher over the past several years mostly driven by strong loan business growth obtained through acquisitions and organically.The bank's revenue dipped by 3% to $51.6 million in 2014 despite loan growth during the year mostly as its non-interest income shrank due to a decline in gains from the sale of its loans and investment securities compared to the prior year.

Lower revenue and higher loan loss provisions from a less credit-worth loan portfolio in 2014 caused Old Line's net income to fall by 8% to $7.1 million. The company's operating cash levels declined by 35% to $10.2 million on lower cash earnings.

Strategy

Old Line Bancshares in 2015 laid out its short-term plans to collect on its non-accrual and past due loans and strategically selling its acquired loans and real-estate owned loans to boost its credit quality. It also expressed its strategy of extending its core banking services growing its fee income (especially in the low-interest environment) and embracing digital banking technologies such as online and mobile banking to reduce its spending on costly branch expansion plans.

Management also touted success in organically growing its loan and deposit business in Montgomery Prince George's Anne Arundel counties in Maryland during 2014.

The company sometimes grows its loan business and branch network by strategically acquiring banks in its primary markets. Its agreement to acquire Regal Bancorp for example would add three new banking locations to its network and $133.7 million in assets to its books — which would make it the third-largest commercial bank in Maryland by assets and the second-largest by branch network.

Mergers and Acquisitions

In August 2015 the company agreed to acquire Regal Bancorp including its Regal Bank & Trust subsidiary its three branches and assets of $133.7 million. The deal was expected to close in late 2015 or early 2016.

In May 2013 Old Line Bancshare closed on its $54.7-million purchase of WSB Holdings adding five Washington Savings Bank FSB branches and $310 million in assets.

Previously Old Line acquired Maryland Bankcorp in 2011 in a move that doubled its branch network and asset portfolio.

EXECUTIVES

Vice President, Erik Fridley
Auditors: Dixon Hughes Goodman LLP

LOCATIONS

HQ: Old Line Bancshares Inc
1525 Pointer Ridge Place, Bowie, MD 20716
Phone: 301 430-2500
Web: www.oldlinebank.com

COMPETITORS

BB&T	PNC Financial
Bank of America	Tri-County Financial
M&T Bank	

HISTORICAL FINANCIALS

Company Type: Public

Income Statement — FYE: December 31

	ASSETS ($ mil.)	NET INCOME ($ mil.)	INCOME AS % OF ASSETS	EMPLOYEES
12/17	2,105.6	15.9	0.8%	271
12/16	1,709.0	13.1	0.8%	234
12/15	1,510.0	10.4	0.7%	248
12/14	1,227.5	7.1	0.6%	228
12/13	1,167.2	7.8	0.7%	254
Annual Growth	15.9%	19.5%	—	1.6%

2017 Year-End Financials

Return on assets: 0.8%	Dividends
Return on equity: 8.9%	Yield: 0.0%
Long-term debt ($ mil.): —	Payout: 23.7%
No. of shares (mil.): 12.5	Market value ($ mil.): 368.0
Sales ($ mil): 81.4	

	STOCK PRICE ($) FY Close	P/E High/Low	PER SHARE ($) Earnings	Dividends	Book Value
12/17	29.44	22 17	1.35	0.32	16.61
12/16	23.98	21 14	1.20	0.24	13.81
12/15	17.57	19 15	0.97	0.21	13.31
12/14	15.82	27 21	0.65	0.18	12.51
12/13	14.50	17 13	0.86	0.16	11.71
Annual Growth	19.4%	— —	11.9%	18.9%	9.1%

Ollie's Bargain Outlet Holdings Inc

Auditors: KPMG LLP

LOCATIONS

HQ: Ollie's Bargain Outlet Holdings Inc
  6295 Allentown Boulevard, Suite 1, Harrisburg, PA 17112
Phone: 717 657-2300
Web: www.ollies.us

HISTORICAL FINANCIALS

Company Type: Public

Income Statement   FYE: February 3

	REVENUE ($ mil.)	NET INCOME ($ mil.)	NET PROFIT MARGIN	EMPLOYEES
02/18*	1,077.0	127.5	11.8%	6,700
01/17	890.3	59.7	6.7%	5,500
01/16	762.3	35.8	4.7%	5,000
01/15	637.9	26.9	4.2%	5,000
02/14	540.7	19.5	3.6%	0
Annual Growth	18.8%	59.9%	—	—

*Fiscal year change

2018 Year-End Financials

Debt ratio: 4.7%
Return on equity: 17.3%
Cash ($ mil.): 39.2
Current ratio: 2.22
Long-term debt ($ mil.): 38.8

No. of shares (mil.): 62.0
Dividends
  Yield: —
  Payout: —
Market value ($ mil.): 3,332.0

	STOCK PRICE ($) FY Close	P/E High/Low	Earnings	Dividends	Book Value
02/18*	53.75	28 14	1.96	0.00	12.85
01/17	29.35	33 19	0.96	0.00	10.72
01/16	22.35	33 23	0.64	1.01	9.56
Annual Growth	55.1%	—	75.0%	—	15.9%

*Fiscal year change

Omega Healthcare Investors, Inc.

Omega Healthcare Investors can put an end to the burdens of real-estate management. The self-administered real estate investment trust (REIT) invests in health care facilities throughout the US. It owns some 900 properties primarily long-term care facilities in more than 40 states. The REIT specializes in sales/leaseback transactions in which it purchases properties owned by health care providers and leases them back to those companies (thereby freeing the health care companies from the responsibilities of real estate management). The REIT's properties are operated by third-party health care operating companies including Genesis HealthCare System and CommuniCare Health Services.

Geographic Reach

The Maryland-based REITs largest markets are Florida Indiana and Ohio. Texas is another important market for the firm. Overall Omega Healthcare Investors has holdings in 41 states.

Sales and Marketing

The REIT's largest tenants include New Ark Investment Genesis Healthcare and CommuniCare Health Services which together represent about a third of its portfolio.

Financial Performance

Omega Healthcare Investors (OHI) reported revenue of $418.7 million in 2013 a 19% increase versus 2012. Driving the double-digit gain was rising rental income generated by investments made in 2013 and 2012. Net income grew 43% to $172.5 million on higher rental income. Both revenue and cash flow has increased steadily over the past four years and profitability has rebounded.

Strategy

The REIT is investing aggressively in the health care sector as demand for senior living facilities grows in tandem with the aging population and the real estate market makes a comeback. Indeed in 2013 the firm completed transactions totaling about $622 million in new investments. Its core portfolio consists of long-term lease and mortgage agreements. All of its leases are "triple-net" leases which require the tenants to pay all property related expenses. The REIT's mortgage revenue comes from fixed-rate loans. Omega Healthcare's geographically diverse portfolio comprises 476 skilled nursing facilities 18 assisted living locations and 11 specialty facilities such as rehabilitation hospitals. Its properties are operated by third parties.

Mergers and Acquisitions

In mid-2015 Omega acquired Aviv REIT in a deal valued at some $3 billion. The combined company is one of the largest REITs focused on skilled nursing facilities.

EXECUTIVES

CEO and Director, C. Taylor Pickett, age 56, $750,000 total compensation
COO, Daniel J. Booth, age 54, $485,000 total compensation
CFO, Robert O. Stephenson, age 54, $465,000 total compensation
Chief Accounting Officer, Michael D. Ritz, age 49, $320,000 total compensation
Chairman, Craig R. Callen, age 62
Auditors: Ernst & Young LLP

LOCATIONS

HQ: Omega Healthcare Investors, Inc.
  303 International Circle, Suite 200, Hunt Valley, MD 21030
Phone: 410 427-1700   **Fax:** 410 427-8800
Web: www.omegahealthcare.com

PRODUCTS/OPERATIONS

2015 Sales

	$ mil.	% of total
Rental income	606.0	81
Mortgage interest	68.9	9
Income from direct financing leases	59.9	8
Others	8.8	2
Total	**743.6**	**100**

COMPETITORS

G&L Realty Properties
HCP
Healthcare Realty Trust
LTC Properties
National Health Investors
Senior Housing Properties
Ventas
Welltower

HISTORICAL FINANCIALS

Company Type: Public

Income Statement   FYE: December 31

	REVENUE ($ mil.)	NET INCOME ($ mil.)	NET PROFIT MARGIN	EMPLOYEES
12/17	908.3	100.4	11.1%	59
12/16	900.8	366.4	40.7%	60
12/15	743.6	224.5	30.2%	58
12/14	504.7	221.3	43.9%	27
12/13	418.7	172.5	41.2%	25
Annual Growth	21.4%	(12.7%)	—	23.9%

2017 Year-End Financials

Debt ratio: 52.1%
Return on equity: 2.7%
Cash ($ mil.): 85.9
Current ratio: 21.19
Long-term debt ($ mil.): 4,572.1

No. of shares (mil.): 198.3
Dividends
  Yield: 0.0%
  Payout: 498.0%
Market value ($ mil.): 5,461.0

	STOCK PRICE ($) FY Close	P/E High/Low	Earnings	Dividends	Book Value
12/17	27.54	69 53	0.51	2.54	17.93
12/16	31.26	20 14	1.90	2.36	19.67
12/15	34.98	35 25	1.29	2.18	19.95
12/14	39.07	23 17	1.74	2.02	10.98
12/13	29.80	26 16	1.46	1.86	10.52
Annual Growth	(2.0%)	—	(23.1%)	8.1%	14.2%

Omnicell Inc

Omnicell wants to be indispensable when it comes to dispensing drugs. The company makes systems that automate delivery of drugs to patients in hospitals homes long-term care centers and other medical healthcare settings. Pharmacies and medical facilities use its mobile cabinets and workstations to automatically dispense doses of medication and surgical supplies to help reduce errors and increase patient safety. More than 4000 hospitals use automation and analytics products such as the Omnicell XT Automated Dispensing Cabinet and Singlepointe software. Omnicell's medications adherence products that include specific-count blister packs help patients take the drugs they're supposed to when they're supposed to.

Operations

Omnicell's Automation and Analytics segment more than 80% of revenue is organized around the design manufacturing sales and servicing of medication and supply dispensing systems pharmacy inventory management systems and related software. The company's products provide predictive analytics from its systems' employment of artificial intelligence and cloud computing. Omnicell deploys robotics systems as well.

Its Medication Adherence segment about 20% of sales includes the manufacturing and selling of consumable medication blister cards packaging equipment and ancillary products and services. These products manage medication administration outside the hospital and include products under the MTS SureMed and Omnicell brands.

Omnicell also makes money from servicing and supporting its products.

The company has parlayed the technology behind its medication-dispensing cabinets into other hospital products that keep track of inventory and supplies. It makes a secure dispensing system for anesthesia supplies used in the operating room as well as a barcode inventory management system for controlled substances.

Geographic Reach

Omnicell based in Mountain View California generates more than 85% of sales in the US with other sales to customers throughout the world. The company has research and development facilities in Mountain View Cranberry Woods Pennsylvania St. Petersburg Florida Raleigh North Carolina and Warrendale Pennsylvania in the US and overseas in Beijing Bochum Germany Lancing UK and Trieste Italy.

Sales and Marketing

Omnicell's sales force is organized by geographic region in the US and Canada. The company deploys a direct sales force for Non-Acute Care products in Australia. For other geographies the company's products are sold through distributors and resellers.

Its Automation and Analytics segment has more than 4000 customers while the Medication Adherence segment's products are used by more than 32000 institutional and retail pharmacies worldwide. Customers include Brigham and Women's Hospital the Cleveland Clinic King Faisal Specialist Hospital & Research Center and Carilion Clinic.

Financial Performance

Omnicell delivered 18% annual revenue growth over the past five years. In 2017 however growth slowed to 3% at $716 million from 2016. Automation and Analytics segment sales fell about $20 million due to the introduction of the new XT series of products in the fourth quarter of 2016. The Medication Adherence segment's sales increased in 2017 from 2016 with the help of the Ateb acquisition (in 2016) and the introduction of the VBM product series in late 2016. The installed customer base pushed service revenue 20% higher in 2017 from 2016.

The company's profit improved to more than $20 million in 2017 from less than $1 million in 2016 due to a $21.5 million tax benefit from the US Tax Cuts and Jobs Act. Before taxes in 2017 the company had a $900000 loss compared to a $1.9 million pre-tax loss in 2016.

Cash on hand stood at about $32 million for 2017 down about $22 million from 2016.

Strategy

Omnicell's growth strategy centers on developing new products and enhancing existing products. The company in 2018 released the XR2 Automated Central Pharmacy System and the IVX Workflow products which have greater automation for compounding and prepared intravenous (IV) treatments.

The company is also building its customer roster with gains among institutions new to automation while current customers have increased the pace at which they add other Omnicell products to their existing portfolios.

Omnicell has been adding to its product lineup through in-house research and development (R&D averages $55 million over three years) and acquisitions. The 2016 acquisition of Aesynt bolstered Omnicell's robotic and automation offerings.

Mergers and Acquisitions

In 2017 Omnicell acquired InPharmics a developer of medication-use process cost analytics and regulatory compliance systems for acute care hospital pharmacies. The InPharmics technology adds clinical and compliance analytics to Omnicell's Performance Center offering.

In 2016 Omnicell bought Aesynt a provider of central pharmacy robotics and IV compounding automation systems. The Aesynt products and services extended Omnicell's lineup.

Also in 2016 Omnicell acquired Ateb a provider of pharmacy-based patient care products and medication synchronization to independent and chain retail pharmacies a market in which Omnicell had no penetration. The company paired Ateb's Time My Meds product with Omnicell's SureMed medication adherence packaging.

EXECUTIVES

EVP International and Global Quality and Manufacturing, Robin G. (Rob) Seim, age 58, $302,769 total compensation

EVP; Chief Legal and Administrative Officer, Dan S. Johnston, age 54, $270,154 total compensation

Chairman President and CEO, Randall A. Lipps, age 60, $551,538 total compensation

EVP Sales and Marketing, J. Christopher (Chris) Drew, age 52, $322,462 total compensation

EVP Strategy and Business Development, Nhat H. Ngo, age 45, $273,539 total compensation

EVP and CFO, Peter Kuipers, age 46

EVP of Engineering, Jorge R. Taborga, age 58

EVP and Chief Legal and Administrative Officer, Daniel Johnston

Vice President Human Resources, Susan Moriconi

Vice President of Engineering, Chalapathi RAO

Vice President Field Operations, Pat Diresta

Vice President of Engineering, Nathaniel Moody

Vice President of Finance and Corporate Controller, Joe Spears

RVP, Bill Wingfield

Vice President Quality and Regulatory, David Vanella

VICE PRESIDENT MANUFACTURING, Corinne Augustine

Auditors: DELOITTE & TOUCHE LLP

LOCATIONS

HQ: Omnicell Inc
590 East Middlefield Road, Mountain View, CA 94043
Phone: 650 251-6100
Web: www.omnicell.com

PRODUCTS/OPERATIONS

2017 Sales

	$ mil.	% of total
United States	617.3	86
Foreign Countries	98.9	14
Total	**716.2**	**100**

2017 Sales

	$ mil.	% of total
Product revenue	506.2	71
Service and other revenue	210.0	29
Total	**716.2**	**100**

2017 Sales

	$ mil.	% of total
Automation and Analytics	590.4	82
Medication Adherence	125.8	18
Total	**716.2**	**100**

COMPETITORS

Allscripts	Ergotron
AmerisourceBergen	Infor Global

Becton Dickinson	McKesson
CareFusion	SciQuest
Cerner	Siemens Healthcare
Emerson Electric	Swisslog

HISTORICAL FINANCIALS

Company Type: Public

Income Statement   FYE: December 31

	REVENUE ($ mil.)	NET INCOME ($ mil.)	NET PROFIT MARGIN	EMPLOYEES
12/17	716.1	20.6	2.9%	2,350
12/16	692.6	0.6	0.1%	2,444
12/15	484.5	30.7	6.3%	1,451
12/14	440.9	30.5	6.9%	1,236
12/13	380.5	23.9	6.3%	1,134
Annual Growth	**17.1%**	**(3.7%)**	**—**	**20.0%**

2017 Year-End Financials

Debt ratio: 21.4%	No. of shares (mil.): 38.4
Return on equity: 4.3%	Dividends
Cash ($ mil.): 32.4	Yield: —
Current ratio: 1.73	Payout: —
Long-term debt ($ mil.): 194.9	Market value ($ mil.): 1,864.0

	STOCK PRICE ($) FY Close	P/E High/Low		PER SHARE ($) Earnings	Dividends	Book Value
12/17	48.50	99	58	0.53	0.00	13.46
12/16	33.90	2020	1272	0.02	0.00	11.78
12/15	31.08	47	31	0.84	0.00	11.30
12/14	33.12	39	29	0.83	0.00	10.89
12/13	25.53	37	22	0.67	0.00	9.97
Annual Growth	**17.4%**	**—**	**—**	**(5.7%)**	**—**	**7.8%**

One Liberty Properties, Inc.

One Liberty Properties may own the space where lovebirds shop for loveseats. Or bird food. The self-managed and self-administered real estate investment trust (REIT) invests in retail industrial and office properties throughout the US. It owns or co-owns over 100 properties totaling more than 8 million sq. ft. of space; more than half of its portfolio is leased to retailers including Haverty Furniture PetSmart and Giant Food Stores. The REIT also owns warehouses fitness centers and a movie theater. One Liberty Properties targets net-leased properties minimizing its responsibilities for taxes maintenance and other operating costs. The firm is controlled by the family of its chairman.

Operations

One Liberty owned 107 properties spanning 8.2 million sq. ft. of space across 30 states at the end of 2015. General retail properties generated 28% of its total rental revenue that year while furniture restaurant office supply and supermarket retail properties made up another 25%. Industrial properties accounted for 23% of rental revenue followed by flex properties (6%) health and fitness properties (5%) and other properties (12%).

Liberty owned five joint venture properties during 2015 representing an investment of approximately $11.4 million on its part. Most of the joint ventures are 50% owned by Liberty.

Geographic Reach

Liberty's properties are located in 30 US states with properties in Texas New York South Carolina Georgia and Pennsylvania generating more than 40% of its rental income during 2015.

Sales and Marketing

Liberty's largest tenant Haverty Furniture contributed 8% to the company's 2015 rental revenue while its next largest tenants made up another nearly 20% of its rental income and included LA Fitness Northern Tool Ferguson Enterprises and Office Depot. Other top tenants include national chains such as PetSmart TGI Fridays The Men's Wearhouse Barnes & Noble Walgreens and Whole Foods.

Financial Performance

One Liberty's revenues have risen more than 60% while its profits have nearly doubled since 2011 as new property acquisitions have driven rental income.

The REIT's revenue jumped 9% to $65.71 million during 2015 mostly as 16 new property acquisitions made in 2015 and 2014 drove additional rental income.

Despite strong revenue growth in 2015 One Liberty Property's net income dipped 7% to $20.52 million mainly because in 2014 it had made twice as much in real estate sales gains after selling one of its properties in Parsippany New Jersey. The REIT's operating cash levels climbed 7% to $33.92 million as cash-denominated earnings rose during the year.

Strategy

One Liberty Properties mostly acquires US properties in locations with attractive locations and demographics. The REIT targets long-term lease agreements that offer more predictable cash flows and stability in markets with rental rate fluctuations and real estate values. Following this strategy the firm is better able to secure long-term financing for more property investments. Also by seeking long-term agreements the REIT has successfully assembled a diversified portfolio with an occupancy rate exceeding 98% based on square footage for the past several years.

Beyond outright property acquisitions One Liberty also looks to invest in properties that can be repositioned or redeveloped national or regional tenant-anchored community shopping centers and properties that are ground leased to multi-family property operators.

Even though One Liberty Properties has been enjoying revenue growth from a growing tenant base the rapidly changing retail landscape presents challenges for Liberty as some of its tenants such as Office Depot and Barnes & Noble are facing increased pressure from online retailers such as Amazon.com and are closing stores as a result.

EXECUTIVES

SVP and CFO, David W. Kalish, age 71
EVP and COO, Lawrence G. Ricketts, age 41, $355,000 total compensation
President and CEO, Patrick J. Callan, age 56, $700,000 total compensation
Chiarman, Matthew J. Gould, age 59
Vice Chairman, Fredric H. Gould
Auditors: Ernst & Young LLP

LOCATIONS

HQ: One Liberty Properties, Inc.
60 Cutter Mill Road, Great Neck, NY 11021
Phone: 516 466-3100
Web: www.onelibertyproperties.com

PRODUCTS/OPERATIONS

2015 Sales

	$ mil.	% of total
Rental income net	58.9	90
Tenant reimbursements	3.9	6
Lease termination fees	2.9	4
Total	**65.7**	**100**

COMPETITORS

DDR	Realty Income
Gladstone Commercial	Spirit Realty Capital
Lexington Realty Trust	Vornado Realty
Liberty Property Trust	Weingarten Realty
Monmouth Real Estate	
National Retail Properties	

HISTORICAL FINANCIALS

Company Type: Public

Income Statement				FYE: December 31
	REVENUE ($ mil.)	NET INCOME ($ mil.)	NET PROFIT MARGIN	EMPLOYEES
12/17	75.9	24.1	31.8%	9
12/16	70.5	24.4	34.6%	8
12/15	65.7	20.5	31.2%	9
12/14	60.4	22.1	36.6%	9
12/13	50.9	17.8	35.1%	7
Annual Growth	**10.5%**	**7.8%**	**—**	**6.5%**

2017 Year-End Financials

Debt ratio: 54.1%
Return on equity: 8.2%
Cash ($ mil.): 13.7
Current ratio: 3.34
Long-term debt ($ mil.): 401.9
No. of shares (mil.): 18.2
Dividends
  Yield: 0.0%
  Payout: 135.9%
Market value ($ mil.): 473.0

	STOCK PRICE ($) FY Close	P/E High/Low	PER SHARE ($) Earnings	Dividends	Book Value
12/17	25.92	21 17	1.28	1.74	16.25
12/16	25.12	18 14	1.39	1.66	16.48
12/15	21.46	21 17	1.22	1.58	15.99
12/14	23.67	18 15	1.37	1.50	16.17
12/13	20.13	24 17	1.14	1.42	16.35
Annual Growth	**6.5%**	**— —**	**2.9%**	**5.2%**	**(0.2%)**

OP Bancorp

Auditors: Crowe Horwath LLP

LOCATIONS

HQ: OP Bancorp
1000 Wilshire Blvd., Suite 500, Los Angeles, CA 90017
Phone: 213 892-9999
Web: www.myopenbank.com

HISTORICAL FINANCIALS

Company Type: Public

Income Statement				FYE: December 31
	ASSETS ($ mil.)	NET INCOME ($ mil.)	INCOME AS % OF ASSETS	EMPLOYEES
12/17	901.0	9.2	1.0%	129
12/16	761.2	7.4	1.0%	0
12/15	617.3	5.9	1.0%	0
12/14	528.1	4.4	0.8%	0
12/13	342.2	4.9	1.4%	0
Annual Growth	**27.4%**	**16.9%**	**—**	**—**

2017 Year-End Financials

Return on assets: 1.1%
Return on equity: 10.6%
Long-term debt ($ mil.): —
No. of shares (mil.): 13.1
Sales ($ mil): 49.2
Dividends
  Yield: —
  Payout: —
Market value ($ mil.): 129.0

	STOCK PRICE ($) FY Close	P/E High/Low	PER SHARE ($) Earnings	Dividends	Book Value
12/17	9.80	15 10	0.66	0.00	6.94
12/16	7.70	14 10	0.53	0.00	6.30
12/15	6.55	15 12	0.46	0.00	5.71
12/14	7.10	— —	(0.00)	0.00	5.27
12/13	7.50	— —	(0.00)	0.00	4.31
Annual Growth	**6.9%**		**—**	**—**	**12.6%**

Opus Bank (Irvine, CA)

Auditors: KPMG LLP

LOCATIONS

HQ: Opus Bank (Irvine, CA)
19900 MacArthur Blvd., 12th Floor, Irvine, CA 92612
Phone: 949 250-9800
Web: www.opusbank.com

HISTORICAL FINANCIALS

Company Type: Public

Income Statement				FYE: December 31
	ASSETS ($ mil.)	NET INCOME ($ mil.)	INCOME AS % OF ASSETS	EMPLOYEES
12/17	7,486.8	47.6	0.6%	797
12/16	7,882.5	11.4	0.1%	835
12/15	6,649.8	59.9	0.9%	661
12/14	5,084.9	43.8	0.9%	585
12/13	3,738.8	143.1	3.8%	550
Annual Growth	**19.0%**	**(24.0%)**	**—**	**9.7%**

2017 Year-End Financials

Return on assets: 0.6%
Return on equity: 4.8%
Long-term debt ($ mil.): —
No. of shares (mil.): 35.9
Sales ($ mil): 308.3
Dividends
  Yield: —
  Payout: —
Market value ($ mil.): 980.0

	STOCK PRICE ($) FY Close	P/E High/Low	PER SHARE ($) Earnings	Dividends	Book Value
12/17	27.30	23 14	1.26	0.00	28.50
12/16	30.05	112 58	0.33	0.53	27.01
12/15	36.97	21 13	1.79	0.34	26.68
12/14	28.37	22 18	1.38	0.00	28.41
Annual Growth	**(1.3%)**	**— —**	**(3.0%)**	**—**	**0.1%**

OraSure Technologies Inc.

When it comes to diagnostic tests OraSure is certain it can deliver results. The oral specimen kits and other diagnostic tests developed by Ora-Sure Technologies are designed to detect drug use and certain infectious diseases namely HIV and hepatitis C. Its OraSure products use oral specimens rather than traditional blood or urine based methods to test for HIV. The Intercept line uses oral samples to test for marijuana cocaine opiates PCP and amphetamines. OraSure has also developed a rapid HIV blood diagnostic testing method and it has entered the genetic testing market through its DNAG subsidiary. OraSure sells its products in the US and internationally to health care facilities and medical laboratories.

Operations

Products include tests that detect antibodies to the HIV and HCV viruses and tests for drug abuse detection. OraSure operates in two primary segments: Its OSUR business (70% of revenue) develops manufactures and sells diagnostic products specimen collection devices and genetic testing devices. Meanwhile OraSure Technologies makes and sells enzyme immunoassay test kits and oral fluid collection devices for insurance laboratories; these products are used to assess the health and behavior of insurance applicants.

In addition to diagnostic tests and specimen kits OraSure's Histofreezer cryosurgical removal system treats a range of different types of skin lesions including plantar and genital warts and other common benign skin lesions. OraSure also sells an OTC wart remover under the Freeze n' Clear brand.

Geographic Reach

Only about 25% of OraSure's sales come from abroad but the company is expanding its international sales efforts. Subsidiary DNAG leases a 23500 sq. ft. facility in Ottawa Canada.

OraSure's products are available across North America South America Europe and Australia.

Sales and Marketing

OraSure uses direct agents collaborative partners and independent distributors to market its products in the US and abroad. Marketing techniques include trade shows distributor promotions and print advertisements. Customers include public health clinics hospitals pathology laboratory operators and doctors' offices.

In fiscal 2014 the company spent $6910 on advertising down from $17142 spent in 2013.

Financial Performance

The company's revenues have been steadily climbing for the past five years. Revenue increased 8% to $106 million in 2014 on higher sales especially of its Oragene molecular collection systems HCV detection products and cyrosurgical systems products. Additionally licensing and product development earnings rose due to OraSure's co-promotion agreement with AbbVie for the HCV line.

To date OraSure hasn't been profitable. Net losses declined 59% to $5 million in 2014 though due to the firm's higher revenue and lower marketing expenses. Cash flow from operations which had spiked in 2013 due to settlement payment from Roche declined marginally in 2014 to $7 mil-

lion. That decline was primarily due to an increase in inventory of its OraQuick HCV product as well as higher expenses.

Strategy

In addition to geographic expansion OraSure is also increasing its product offerings by developing diagnostic tests for other infectious diseases. In 2014 R&D activities were focused primarily on developing its next-generation Intercept i2 collection device testing a new rapid Ebola test using the OraQuick platform and support for its existing products.

OraSure's growth strategy also consists of pursuing additional FDA approvals and European registrations for its best-selling product lines OraQuick and Intercept. In partnership with Thermo Fisher it develops and supplies oral fluid drugs of abuse assays to be used with its Intercept i2 collection device. The company entered an agreement with AbbVie in 2014 to co-promote OraQuick in the US and abroad. Additionally OraSure Technologies and AbbVie joined together with the Healthy Trucking Association of America to educate truckers about the hepatitis C virus.

Additionally the company is starting to offer some existing products over-the-counter. It already sells some of its cryosurgical wart removal kits on an OTC basis in Central America and Europe.

Mergers and Acquisitions

To enter the molecular diagnostics market while keeping its emphasis on oral fluids OraSure acquired private Canadian firm DNA Genotek (DNAG) in 2011. In exchange for some $53 million OraSure obtained DNA Genotek and its oral fluid collection products including the Oragene DNA sample collection kit which is used in a range of settings including academic research labs and personal genetics testing.

EXECUTIVES

COO and CFO, Ronald H. Spair, age 62, $486,243 total compensation
SVP Finance Controller and Assistant Secretary, Mark L. Kuna, age 55, $356,826 total compensation
President and CEO, Douglas A. Michels, age 61, $619,054 total compensation
EVP Sales and Marketing, Anthony (Tony) Zezzo, age 64, $398,403 total compensation
SVP and General Manager Consumer Products, Kathleen Weber
SVP Research and Development and Chief Science Officer, Michael Reed
SVP and General Manager Molecular Collection Systems, Brian Smith
Vice President, Jill Thompson
Chairman, Stephen S. Tang, age 57
Auditors: KPMG LLP

LOCATIONS

HQ: OraSure Technologies Inc.
220 East First Street, Bethlehem, PA 18015
Phone: 610 882-1820
Web: www.orasure.com

PRODUCTS/OPERATIONS

2016 Sales

	$ mil.	% of total
OSUR	96.0	75
DNAG	32.2	25
Total	**128.2**	**100**

Selected Products

AUTO-LYTE (enzyme immunoassay tests for insurance lab drug testing)
Histofreezer (cryosurgical wart removal system)
Freeze 'n Clear Skin Clinic (wart remover)
Intercept (saliva-based substance abuse testing)
MICRO-PLATE (plasma screening immunoassay tests for drug testing)
Oragene (DNA tests)
OraQuick HCV (rapid antibody test)
OraQuick ADVANCE HIV-1/2 (blood sample HIV test)
OraSure HIV-1 (oral HIV test)
QED Saliva Alcohol Test
QuickFlu Rapid Flu A+B (influenza)
Pointts Wart Remover (Central America OTC cryosurgical wart treatment)
Scholl Freeze Verruca & Wart Remover (Europe OTC cryosurgical wart treatment)

COMPETITORS

ANSYS	Organics
Abbott Labs	Prestige Brands
AcuNetx	Psychemedics
Alere	Quest Diagnostics
Bio-Rad Labs	Quidel
Calypte Biomedical	Roche Diagnostics
Johnson & Johnson	Siemens Healthcare
Medtox Scientific	Trinity Biotech
Merck	eScreen
Olympus Corporation of the Americas	

HISTORICAL FINANCIALS

Company Type: Public

Income Statement

FYE: December 31

	REVENUE ($ mil.)	NET INCOME ($ mil.)	NET PROFIT MARGIN	EMPLOYEES
12/17	167.0	30.9	18.5%	377
12/16	128.2	19.7	15.4%	325
12/15	119.7	8.1	6.8%	326
12/14	106.4	(4.6)	—	320
12/13	98.9	(11.1)	—	293
Annual Growth	**14.0%**	**—**		**6.5%**

2017 Year-End Financials

Debt ratio: —	No. of shares (mil.): 60.6
Return on equity: 13.9%	Dividends
Cash ($ mil.): 71.0	Yield: —
Current ratio: 6.88	Payout: —
Long-term debt ($ mil.): —	Market value ($ mil.): 1,144.0

	STOCK PRICE ($) FY Close	P/E High/Low		PER SHARE ($) Earnings	Dividends	Book Value
12/17	18.86	44	16	0.51	0.00	4.25
12/16	8.78	27	15	0.35	0.00	3.32
12/15	6.44	75	32	0.14	0.00	2.86
12/14	10.14	—	—	(0.08)	0.00	2.82
12/13	6.29	—	—	(0.20)	0.00	2.90
Annual Growth	**31.6%**			**—**	**—**	**10.1%**

Orchids Paper Products Co. (DE)

Orchids Paper Products hopes to leave its end users smelling like a rose. The company makes bulk tissue paper and converts it into bathroom tissue paper napkins and paper towels for the consumer market. Most of the company's products are sold as private-label items by discount retailers;

Orchids Paper products also are sold under the company's Colortex and Velvet brands. Dollar General is Orchids Paper's largest customer; other big customers include Family Dollar and Wal-Mart. Orchids Paper sells most of its products within a 500-mile radius of its manufacturing plant in northeastern Oklahoma.

Operations

Orchids divides its business into two lines: converted products and parent rolls. Converted products account for 97% of its revenue and include paper towels bathroom tissue and paper napkins.

Sales and Marketing

The company sells its products to value retailers generally known as "dollar" stores grocery stores grocery wholesalers and cooperatives. Its sales efforts are focused on an area within 500 miles of its facility in northeast Oklahoma which includes Texas Oklahoma Kansas Missouri Arkansas Nebraska and Iowa.

Major customers include Dollar General (accounting for 40% of its converted product sales in 2014) Family Dollar (11%) and Wal-Mart (9%). In 2014 Orchids spent $292 million on advertising.

Financial Performance

Orchids has enjoyed several straight years of steady growth. Revenues jumped 23% from $116 million in 2013 to reach a millstone high of $143 million in 2014. The historic growth was attributed to a 26% spike in sales from converted products due to its efforts on new product development in the mid and premium tier markets. Additional revenue from a previous acquisition also contributed to the growth.

Orchids' profits however dropped 29% from $13 million in 2013 to $9 million in 2014 due to higher expenses and business costs. This was due to higher expenses related to an acquisition coupled with higher fiber costs and increased production expenses associated with its converting and paper production operations.

Strategy

Orchids has been focused on increasing efficiency by producing its own parent rolls which is the material processed into its other products such as tissue. The move is an effort to limit the the company's reliance on outside sources for parent rolls and the subsequent price fluctuations that have characterized that market in recent years.

Going forward the company plans to maximize production with its older equipment in a strategic move that deviates from typical paper product makers that have been shutting down older equipment. Orchids has also invested in new equipment. The result of these efforts will be an increase in capacity that the company hopes to sell through new channels namely grocery and drug store chains.

Throughout 2015 its specific focus was on the timely start-up of its new paper machine and new converting line in Oklahoma.

Mergers and Acquisitions

In order to enhance its West Coast operations Orchids in 2014 entered into a strategic alliance with Fabrica de Papel San Francisco. Based in Baja California Mexico Fabrica is a low-cost manufacturer of high-quality tissue paper products. As part of the alliance Orchids acquired Fabrica's US business including certain manufacturing assets and access to 18000 metric tons of capacity each year. Products are now produced at Fabrica's facility in Mexicali Mexico and shipped directly to Orchids' US customers.

EXECUTIVES

President and CEO, Jeffrey S. Schoen, age 57, $400,000 total compensation
CFO, Rodney D. Gloss, age 61
Chairman, Steven R. (Steve) Berlin, age 73
Auditors: HoganTaylor LLP

LOCATIONS

HQ: Orchids Paper Products Co. (DE)
4826 Hunt Street, Pryor, OK 74361
Phone: 918 825-0616
Web: www.orchidspaper.com

PRODUCTS/OPERATIONS

2014 Sales

	$ mil.	% of total
Converted product	138.4	97
Parent roll	4.3	3
Total	**142.7**	**100**

COMPETITORS

Advanced Airlaid Materials	Potlatch
Cascades Tissue Group	Roses Southwest Papers
Georgia-Pacific	SCA Tissue North America
Irving Tissue	Wausau Paper
Kimberly-Clark	

HISTORICAL FINANCIALS

Company Type: Public

Income Statement				FYE: December 31
	REVENUE ($ mil.)	NET INCOME ($ mil.)	NET PROFIT MARGIN	EMPLOYEES
12/17	162.4	6.6	4.1%	472
12/16	164.4	12.8	7.8%	406
12/15	168.4	13.5	8.0%	352
12/14	142.7	9.4	6.6%	313
12/13	116.3	13.3	11.4%	317
Annual Growth	8.7%	(15.9%)	—	10.5%

2017 Year-End Financials

Debt ratio: 48.8%	No. of shares (mil.): 10.6
Return on equity: 4.8%	Dividends
Cash ($ mil.): 3.8	Yield: 0.0%
Current ratio: 0.21	Payout: 54.6%
Long-term debt ($ mil.): 0.0	Market value ($ mil.): 137.0

	STOCK PRICE ($) FY Close	P/E High/Low		PER SHARE ($) Earnings	Dividends	Book Value
12/17	12.80	47	14	0.64	0.35	13.29
12/16	26.18	29	19	1.24	1.40	12.94
12/15	30.92	23	15	1.38	1.40	13.03
12/14	29.11	30	21	1.11	1.40	11.48
12/13	32.84	20	12	1.67	1.35	10.52
Annual Growth	(21.0%)	—	—	(21.3%)	(28.6%)	6.0%

Osiris Therapeutics Inc

Unlike the Eygptian god this Osiris seeks to keep people out of the afterlife. The biotech company researches develops and markets cellular regenerative drug candidates. It engages in stem cell research bioengineering and the development of tissue-based products. Its marketed products include treatments in the areas of orthopedics sports medicine and wound care Bone repair and regeneration allograft Bio4 is a viable bone matrix and alternative to autografts (the transfer of tissue from one part of the body to another). Other products include allograft Cartiform placental membrane Grafix skin allograft TruSkin and placental allograft Stravix.

Operations

Osiris focuses on developing products that promote the body's natural healing. The company's drugs are based upon human mesenchymal stem cells (MSCs). Harvested from adult donors MSCs can be grafted onto various human tissue. They then can differentiate themselves to become bone cartilage fat muscle tendon or other types of tissue. The company can produce up to 10000 treatments from one bone marrow donation and because the material is universally compatible it does not have to be matched for individual patients.

Sales and Marketing

The company utilizes a direct distribution and marketing team as well as a network of specialty distributors for certain markets. It partners with Stryker Corporation to distribute its orthopedics products and with Arthrex to distribute its sports medicine products.

Financial Performance

Revenue has been up and down for the past few years. After declines in 2011 and 2012 revenue increased in 2013 and 2014. In the latter year it more than doubled rising 146% to $60 million on sales of its biosurgery products (largely driven by the expansion of Osiris' sales and marketing departments).

However the company had a net loss of $1.8 million in 2015 as general administrative and selling expenses rose. This was the second net loss for Osiris since 2011. That loss led to a $3 million operating cash outflow (but this was an improvement over 2013 then the company had an outflow of $13.3 million).

Strategy

Osiris focuses on products in the areas of wound care sports medicine and orthopedics. In 2013 the company sold its therapeutics unit for $100 million; it is now concentrating on biosurgery products.

EXECUTIVES

President and CEO, Linda Palczuk
Chief Scientific Officer, Alla Danilkovitch
CFO, Linda Chang
Vice President Finance, Phillip Jacoby
Chairman, Peter Friedli
Auditors: Ernst & Young LLP

LOCATIONS

HQ: Osiris Therapeutics Inc
7015 Albert Einstein Drive, Columbia, MD 21046-1707
Phone: 443 545-1800
Web: www.osiris.com

PRODUCTS/OPERATIONS

Selected Products

BIO4—a bone allograft
Cartiform—a viable chondral allograft
Grafix—a cryopreserved placental membrane

COMPETITORS

Abbott Labs	Johnson & Johnson
Astellas Institute	MultiCell Technologies
Athersys	StemCells
Biogen	UCB
Cytori Therapeutics	Vericel
Geron	

HISTORICAL FINANCIALS

Company Type: Public

Income Statement — FYE: December 31

	REVENUE ($ mil.)	NET INCOME ($ mil.)	NET PROFIT MARGIN	EMPLOYEES
12/17	118.5	8.7	7.4%	350
12/16	109.3	(3.7)	—	0
12/15	79.7	(35.7)	—	0
12/14	59.8	(1.7)	—	217
12/13	24.3	41.6	171.3%	75
Annual Growth	48.6%	(32.2%)	—	47.0%

2017 Year-End Financials

Debt ratio: —	No. of shares (mil.): 34.5
Return on equity: 23.7%	Dividends
Cash ($ mil.): 27.8	Yield: —
Current ratio: 2.08	Payout: —
Long-term debt ($ mil.): —	Market value ($ mil.): 207.0

	STOCK PRICE ($) FY Close	P/E High/Low	Earnings	PER SHARE ($) Dividends	Book Value
12/17	6.00	28 11	0.25	0.00	1.20
12/16	4.91	— —	(0.11)	0.00	0.94
12/15	10.38	— —	(1.04)	0.20	1.06
12/14	15.99	— —	(0.05)	0.00	2.44
12/13	16.08	20 5	1.25	0.00	2.37
Annual Growth	(21.8%) (15.7%)	— —	(33.1%)	—	

OTC Markets Group Inc

EXECUTIVES

Pres-ceo, R C Coulson
Vice President Corporate Services, Bill Karsh
Assistant Vice President Senior Accountant, Jeff Jin
Vice President, Robert Power
Auditors: DELOITTE & TOUCHE LLP

LOCATIONS

HQ: OTC Markets Group Inc
304 Hudson Street, 3rd Floor, New York, NY 10013
Phone: 212 896-4400 **Fax:** 212 868-3848
Web: www.otcmarkets.com

HISTORICAL FINANCIALS

Company Type: Public

Income Statement — FYE: December 31

	REVENUE ($ mil.)	NET INCOME ($ mil.)	NET PROFIT MARGIN	EMPLOYEES
12/17	54.6	12.5	23.0%	90
12/16	50.8	10.5	20.7%	88
12/15	49.9	10.2	20.6%	89
12/14	42.2	7.8	18.7%	85
12/13	35.5	5.6	15.9%	81
Annual Growth	11.4%	22.2%	—	2.7%

2017 Year-End Financials

Debt ratio: —	No. of shares (mil.): 11.4
Return on equity: 85.7%	Dividends
Cash ($ mil.): 23.6	Yield: 0.0%
Current ratio: 1.53	Payout: 109.4%
Long-term debt ($ mil.): —	Market value ($ mil.): 332.0

	STOCK PRICE ($) FY Close	P/E High/Low	Earnings	PER SHARE ($) Dividends	Book Value
12/17	29.05	29 17	1.06	1.16	1.21
12/16	23.00	25 16	0.90	1.16	1.36
12/15	16.30	18 15	0.88	1.08	1.55
12/14	14.36	21 11	0.69	0.37	1.62
12/13	7.75	17 15	0.51	0.24	1.70
Annual Growth	39.1%	— —	20.1%	48.3%	(8.2%)

Pacific City Financial Corp

Auditors: Crowe LLP

LOCATIONS

HQ: Pacific City Financial Corp
3701 Wilshire Blvd., Suite 900, Los Angeles, CA 90010
Phone: 213 210-2000 **Fax:** 213 210-2032

HISTORICAL FINANCIALS

Company Type: Public

Income Statement — FYE: December 31

	ASSETS ($ mil.)	NET INCOME ($ mil.)	INCOME AS % OF ASSETS	EMPLOYEES
12/17	1,442.0	16.4	1.1%	228
12/16	1,226.6	14.0	1.1%	0
12/15	1,042.5	12.1	1.2%	0
12/14	893.9	11.8	1.3%	0
12/13	755.9	21.3	2.8%	0
Annual Growth	17.5%	(6.4%)	—	—

2017 Year-End Financials

Return on assets: 1.2%	Dividends
Return on equity: 12.1%	Yield: 0.0%
Long-term debt ($ mil.): —	Payout: 9.9%
No. of shares (mil.): 13.4	Market value ($ mil.): 208.0
Sales ($ mil): 79.1	

	STOCK PRICE ($) FY Close	P/E High/Low	Earnings	PER SHARE ($) Dividends	Book Value
12/17	15.50	13 10	1.21	0.12	10.60
12/16	13.00	12 9	1.11	0.11	9.48
12/15	12.85	15 12	1.02	0.07	8.26
12/14	12.38	14 4	1.00	0.00	7.31
12/13	4.00	3 1	1.83	0.00	6.87
Annual Growth	40.3%	— —	(9.9%)	—	11.4%

Pacific Mercantile Bancorp

Pacific Mercantile is banking on southern California businesses. Pacific Mercantile Bancorp is the holding company for Pacific Mercantile Bank which operates more than a dozen branches in southern California's Los Angeles Orange San Bernardino and San Diego counties. Serving area consumers and businesses the bank provides standard services including checking savings and money market accounts CDs and IRAs as well as online banking and bill payment. It uses deposits primarily to fund business loans including commercial mortgages which account for some 65% of the bank's loan portfolio. The bank also offers residential mortgages construction land development and consumer loans.

Financial Performance

Increases in non-interest income drove the Pacific Mercantile's total revenue up 34% in 2012. The bank's non-interest income included revenue earned from mortgage banking fees and proceeds from the sale of mortgage loans tied to its retail mortgage business as well as its wholesale mortgage business which it exited in 2012. Other non-interest income increases that year were attributable to gains from securities the bank sold. Pacific Mercantile's revenue increase was partially offset by a decline in interest income which was caused in part by lower interest rates set by the Fed.

EXECUTIVES

Vice President Relationship Manager, Randi Greenberg
Vice President Operations Manager, Jimmy Hornsby
Vice President Fair Lending Compliance Officer, Kimberly Valley
Assistant Vice President Senior Credit Analyst, Yulia Davydova
Senior Vice President Senior Credit Administrator, David Quizon
Vice President Post Closing, Jacqui Irvine
Senior Vice President Commercial Banking, Leila Rohani
Senior Vice President, Adrian Ward
Senior Vice President Relationship Manager, D'Ann Lungberg
Vice President Senior Relationship Manager, Mark Martinez
Vice President Senior Human Resources Generalist, Kathleen Wiesinger
Vice President Senior Relationship Manager, Peter Pacheco
Senior Vice President Asset Based Lending, Robert Parks
Vice President Corporate Finance, Chris Lieber
Avp Senior Credit Analyst, Scott Shimozawa
Senior Vice President Loan Operations, George Younes
Assistant Vice President Special Assets Department, Mike Kruthers
VICE PRESIDENT ASSISTANT CONTROLLER, Christopher Lopez
VICE PRESIDENT, Santos Janbeth
VICE PRESIDENT COMPLIANCE AND PRIVACY OFFICER, Maryann Hopp
Treasurer, Tom Stellar
Auditors: RSM US LLP

LOCATIONS

HQ: Pacific Mercantile Bancorp
  949 South Coast Drive, Suite 300, Costa Mesa, CA 92626
Phone: 714 438-2500   **Fax:** 714 438-1059
Web: www.pmbank.com

COMPETITORS

Bank of America	City National
Bank of the West	JPMorgan Chase
California Bank &	MUFG Americas Holdings
Trust	U.S. Bancorp
Citigroup	

HISTORICAL FINANCIALS

Company Type: Public

Income Statement   FYE: December 31

	ASSETS ($ mil.)	NET INCOME ($ mil.)	INCOME AS % OF ASSETS	EMPLOYEES
12/17	1,322.6	10.4	0.8%	168
12/16	1,140.6	(34.6)	—	169
12/15	1,062.3	12.4	1.2%	160
12/14	1,099.6	0.3	0.0%	168
12/13	996.5	(22.2)	—	245
Annual Growth	**7.3%**	—		**(9.0%)**

2017 Year-End Financials

Return on assets: 0.8%
Return on equity: 9.8%
Long-term debt ($ mil.): —
No. of shares (mil.): 23.2
Sales ($ mil): 55.9

Dividends
  Yield: —
  Payout: —
Market value ($ mil.): 203.0

	STOCK PRICE ($) FY Close	P/E High/Low	PER SHARE ($) Earnings	Dividends	Book Value
12/17	8.75	22 16	0.45	0.00	4.86
12/16	7.30	— —	(1.51)	0.00	4.33
12/15	7.13	14 12	0.53	0.00	5.87
12/14	7.04	— —	(0.04)	0.00	6.13
12/13	6 22	— —	(1.28)	0.00	6.02
Annual Growth	**8.9%**		—		**(5.2%)**

Pacific Premier Bancorp Inc

Auditors: Crowe Horwath LLP

LOCATIONS

HQ: Pacific Premier Bancorp Inc
  17901 Von Karman Avenue, Suite 1200, Irvine, CA 92614
Phone: 949 864-8000
Web: www.ppbi.com

HISTORICAL FINANCIALS

Company Type: Public

Income Statement   FYE: December 31

	ASSETS ($ mil.)	NET INCOME ($ mil.)	INCOME AS % OF ASSETS	EMPLOYEES
12/17	8,024.5	60.1	0.7%	846
12/16	4,036.3	40.1	1.0%	448
12/15	2,790.6	25.5	0.9%	335
12/14	2,038.9	16.6	0.8%	285
12/13	1,714.1	8.9	0.5%	231
Annual Growth	**47.1%**	**60.8%**	—	**38.3%**

2017 Year-End Financials

Return on assets: 1.0%
Return on equity: 7.0%
Long-term debt ($ mil.): —
No. of shares (mil.): 46.2
Sales ($ mil): 301.1

Dividends
  Yield: —
  Payout: —
Market value ($ mil.): 1,850.0

	STOCK PRICE ($) FY Close	P/E High/Low	PER SHARE ($) Earnings	Dividends	Book Value
12/17	40.00	26 20	1.56	0.00	26.86
12/16	35.35	24 13	1.46	0.00	16.54
12/15	21.25	20 12	1.19	0.00	13.86
12/14	17.33	18 14	0.96	0.00	11.81
12/13	15.74	28 18	0.54	0.00	10.52
Annual Growth	**26.3%**	— —	**30.4%**	—	**26.4%**

PacWest Bancorp

PacWest Bancorp is the holding company for Pacific Western Bank which operates about 80 branches mostly in southern and central California plus an additional branch in Durham North Carolina. The $21 billion-asset bank caters to small and midsized businesses and their owners and employees offering traditional deposit and loan products and services. Commercial real estate mortgages make up more than 30% of its loan portfolio while cash flow- and asset-based business loans make up another 40%. The bank also originates residential mortgage real estate construction and land loans venture capital equipment finance and consumer loans. PacWest offers investment services and international banking through agreements with correspondent banks.

Operations

Like other retail banks PacWest generates the bulk of its revenue from interest income. About 83% of its total revenue came from interest income on loans and leases during 2015 while another 7% came from interest income on investments. The rest of its revenue came from leased equipment income (3% of revenue) deposit account service charges (1%) other commissions and fees (3%) and other miscellaneous income sources.

The bank's Square 1 Bank Division caters to entrepreneurial businesses and their venture capital and private equity investors while its CapitalSource Division provides cash flow asset-based equipment and real estate loans and leases as well as treasury management services to established middle-market businesses across the country.

Geographic Reach

PWB's branches are located across California in Los Angeles Orange Riverside San Bernardino Santa Barbara San Diego San Francisco San Luis Obispo San Mateo and Ventura Counties. It also has a branch in Durham North Carolina.

Financial Performance

PacWest's acquisitions in 2014 and 2015 boosted its interest-earning loan asset balances more than three-fold which sent its revenues and profits soaring during those years.

The bank's revenue jumped 30% to $968.3 million during 2015 mostly as newly acquired loans from its CapitalSource boosted its interest income during the year.

Strong revenue growth coupled with lower acquisition integration and reorganization costs in 2015 drove PacWest's net income up 77% to $300 million. Its operating cash levels spiked 79% to $594 million with the rise in cash-denominated earnings.

Strategy

PacWest has grown its loan and deposit business as well as its branch network through acquisitions of California community banks and specialized financial services companies. It has made 28 acquisitions since 2000 with some of its most recent being the Square 1 acquisition in 2015 and the CapitalSource Inc. acquisition in 2014.

Mergers and Acquisitions

In October 2015 PacWest purchased $4.6 billion-asset Square 1 and its Square 1 Bank subsidiary for $849 million forming the Square 1 Bank Division of the Bank. The deal boosted its core deposits expanded its national lending platform and bolstered its presence in the technology and life-sciences markets.

In April 2014 the bank bought $10.7 billion-asset CapitalSource Inc. and its CapitalSource Bank (CSB) subsidiary.

In May 2013 PacWest acquired $1.7 billion-asset First California Financial Group operator of First California Bank for $237 million. The purchase added six branches (after consolidation) in Los Angeles Orange Riverside San Bernardino San Diego San Luis Obispo and Ventura Counties.

Company Background

During the economic downturn PacWest took advantage of a rash of bank failures through FDIC-assisted transactions. The acquired institutions were merged into Pacific Western Bank. Under the loss-sharing deals the FDIC agreed to reimburse PacWest for future losses tied to the acquisitions. In a 2012 non-FDIC-assisted deal PacWest bought American Perspective Bank adding two branches and a loan office in the Central Coast area.

EXECUTIVES

EVP and Director the Company and Pacific Western Bank, Daniel B. Platt, age 71, $52,500 total compensation

EVP and Chief Risk Officer, Suzanne R. Brennan, age 67, $165,000 total compensation

CEO, Matthew P. (Matt) Wagner, age 61, $754,167 total compensation

EVP and CFO Pacific Western Bank, Patrick J. (Pat) Rusnak, age 54

EVP and Chief Accounting Officer, Lynn M. Hopkins, age 50

EVP; Director Human Resources, Christopher D. Blake, age 58, $298,958 total compensation

EVP and Chief Credit Officer, Bryan M. Corsini, age 56, $375,624 total compensation

EVP; President CapitalSource, James J. (Jim) Pieczynski, age 55, $554,539 total compensation

EVP Operations and Systems, Mark Christian
EVP General Counsel and Corporate Secretary,
 Kori L. Ogrosky
**Senior Vice President Information Systems
 Manager,** Norma Lopez
Chairman, John M. Eggemeyer, age 72
Auditors: KPMG LLP

LOCATIONS

HQ: PacWest Bancorp
 9701 Wilshire Blvd., Suite 700, Beverly Hills, CA 90212
Phone: 310 887-8500
Web: www.pacwestbancorp.com

PRODUCTS/OPERATIONS

2015 Sales

	% of total
Interest income	
Loans and leases	87
Investment securities & other	7
Noninterest income	
Other commissions and fees	3
Leased equipment income	3
Service charges on deposit accounts	1
Other	3
FDIC loss sharing expense net	-
Total	**100**

Selected Mergers & Acquisitions

COMPETITORS

Bank of America	Rabobank America
CVB Financial	San Diego County
California Bank &	Credit Union
Trust	U.S. Bancorp
City National	Wells Fargo
JPMorgan Chase	Westamerica
MUFG Americas Holdings	

HISTORICAL FINANCIALS

Company Type: Public

Income Statement   FYE: December 31

	ASSETS ($ mil.)	NET INCOME ($ mil.)	INCOME AS % OF ASSETS	EMPLOYEES
12/17	24,994.8	357.8	1.4%	1,786
12/16	21,869.7	352.1	1.6%	1,669
12/15	21,288.4	299.6	1.4%	1,670
12/14	16,234.8	168.9	1.0%	1,443
12/13	6,533.3	45.1	0.7%	1,110
Annual Growth	**39.9%**	**67.8%**	**—**	**12.6%**

2017 Year-End Financials

Return on assets: 1.5%	Dividends
Return on equity: 7.5%	Yield: 0.0%
Long-term debt ($ mil.): —	Payout: 68.7%
No. of shares (mil.): 128.7	Market value ($ mil.): 6,491.0
Sales ($ mil): 1,181.0	

	STOCK PRICE ($) FY Close	P/E High/Low	PER SHARE ($) Earnings	Dividends	Book Value
12/17	50.40	20 15	2.91	2.00	38.65
12/16	54.44	19 10	2.90	2.00	36.93
12/15	43.10	17 14	2.79	2.00	36.22
12/14	45.46	25 20	1.92	1.25	34.04
12/13	42.22	40 23	1.08	1.00	17.66
Annual Growth	**4.5%**	**— —**	**28.1%**	**18.9%**	**21.6%**

Par Pacific Holdings Inc

Supplying oil and gas to Hawaii is par for the course for Par Pacific. The company owns and operates a 94000 barrels per day refinery with related logistics and a retail network across the major Hawaiian islands. It owns an equity investment in Laramie Energy LLC which has natural gas production and reserves located in the Piceance Basin of Colorado. In addition Par Pacific also transports markets and distributes crude oil from the Western US and Canada to refining hubs in the Midwest Gulf Coast East Coast and to Hawaii.

Operations

Par Pacific's business is organized into three primary operating segments: Refining Retail and Logistics.

Its refinery in Kapolei Hawaii produces ultra-low sulfur diesel gasoline jet fuel marine fuel and other associated refined products primarily for consumption in Hawaii. The Refining segment accounts for 80% of Par Pacific's total sales.

Its Retail outlets bring in around 15% of revenue and sell gasoline diesel and retail merchandise throughout the islands of Oahu Maui Hawaii and Kauai. Its retail network includes Tesoro Hele and "76" branded retail sites company-operated convenience stores sites operated in cooperation with 7-Eleven and other sites operated by third parties.

In the Logistics segment accounts for about 5% of sales and owns and operates terminals pipelines a single-point mooring and trucking operations to distribute refined products throughout Hawaii. It also operates a crude oil pipeline gather system in Wyoming and a refined products pipeline from Wyoming to a common carrier with access to Rapid City South Dakota.

In addition to the above Par Pacific has two other small segments: Taxadian and a Corporate segment. Taxadian sources markets transports and distributes crude oil and refined products in the US and Canada.

Sales and Marketing

Par Pacific's refining business sells refined products through its logistics network to wholesale and bulk customers and to its retail business. Wholesale customers include jobbers and other non-end users as well as 37 fueling stations where operations and consumer pricing are controlled by third parties. Bulk customers include utilities military bases marine vessels industrial end-users and exports. Logistics distributes products through its logistics network throughout the Island of Oahu as well as the neighboring islands of Maui Hawaii Molokai and Kauai.

Financial Performance

Par Pacific's revenue has fallen markedly since 2014 due to the oil price collapse.

In fiscal 2016 revenue fell a further 10% to $1.9 billion due to falls of $183.7 million and $91.4 million in third-party revenue in its refining and Texadian segments. Falls relating to the oil price were partially offset by revenue from the acquired Wyoming Refining business in mid-2016; Wyoming Refining contributed $169.6 million to total revenue.

Par Pacific lost $45.8 million in 2016 and increase on the $39.9 million lost the year before. The price of oil in 2016 remained below the profitability threshold while the deterioration in performance on prior year relates to the maintenance turnaround at its Hawaii refinery and poor global crack spreads (trading on oil and refined products differentials).

Cash from operations fell from $132.4 million in 2015 to a net cash usage of $23.9 million. The cash outflow relates mostly to the increase in net loss as well as cash usage for changes in operating assets and liabilities totaling $19.7 million.

Strategy

Par Pacific expands through acquisitions. It bolstered its Texardian segment by acquiring an 18000 barrel a day refinery in Wyoming and increased its ownership in Laramie Energy from 32.4% to 42.3%.

Mergers and Acquisitions

Par Pacific is set to acquire US Oil & Refining in 2019 for $358 million. This includes a 42000 barrel per day refinery a marine terminal a unit train-capable rail loading terminal and 2.9 million barrels of refined product and crude oil storage. The refinery and associated logistics system are strategically located in Tacoma Washington and currently serve the Pacific Northwest market. With the acquisition Pac Pacific will be able to better connect its existing assets in Hawaii Pacific Northwest and the Rockies with downstream services.

Company Background

As Delta Petroleum the company had built up heavy debts over several years and in 2011 it filed for Chapter 11 bankruptcy protection from which it emerged in 2012 as reorganized company with a new name Par Petroleum.

As part of the financial rescue operation investing company Laramie Energy II LLC and Par Petroleum merged their assets in Mesa and Garfield counties Colorado to form a new joint venture Piceance Energy LLC (33%-owned by Par Petroleum).

The slimmed down Par Petroleum jettisoned its contract drilling business sold numerous oil and gas assets and focused on oil and gas exploration and production in Colorado.

To raise cash in 2011 the company sold its 49.8% in contract driller DHS Holding for $500000. It also sold non-core exploration and production assets to Wapiti Oil & Gas for $43.2 million. (In 2010 it sold $130 million of other non-core assets in Colorado Nebraska Texas and Wyoming to Wapiti Oil & Gas). That year Delta Petroleum called in Morgan Stanley and Evercore Partners to help it evaluate strategic alternatives.

EXECUTIVES

President CEO and Director, William C. (Bill) Pate, age 54, $460,000 total compensation
Director Par Pacific Holdings Inc. and President and CEO Par Petroleum LLC, Joseph Israel, age 46, $460,000 total compensation
SVP and General Counsel, James Matthew (Matt) Vaughn, age 45, $340,000 total compensation
President Par Hawaii, Jim Yates, $219,231 total compensation
CFO, William (Will) Monteleone, age 34, $360,000 total compensation
President Par Hawaii Refining LLC, Thomas Weber
Vice President Environmental Health Safety and Operational Risk, Barry McFarland
Vice President Supply, Jeff Shaffer
Chairman, Melvyn N. Klein, age 75
Vice Chairman, Robert S. Silberman, age 60
Auditors: DELOITTE & TOUCHE LLP

LOCATIONS

HQ: Par Pacific Holdings Inc
   800 Gessner Road, Suite 875, Houston, TX 77024
Phone: 281 899-4800
Web: www.parpacific.com

PRODUCTS/OPERATIONS

2016 sales

	% of total
Refining	79
Retail	14
Logistics	5
Texadian	2
Corporate Eliminations and Other	-
Total	**100**

COMPETITORS

BP	Key Energy
Bill Barrett	Noble Energy
Cabot Oil & Gas	Occidental Oil and Gas
Chesapeake Energy	Occidental Petroleum
Chevron	Patterson-UTI Energy
Comstock Resources	Pioneer Natural
Denbury Resources	Resources
Devon Energy	Precision Drilling
Eden Energy	Range Resources
Ensco	Royal Dutch Shell
Exxon Mobil	Swift Energy
Falcon Oil & Gas	

HISTORICAL FINANCIALS

Company Type: Public

Income Statement   FYE: December 31

	REVENUE ($ mil.)	NET INCOME ($ mil.)	NET PROFIT MARGIN	EMPLOYEES
12/17	2,443.0	72.6	3.0%	905
12/16	1,865.0	(45.8)	—	863
12/15	2,066.3	(39.9)	—	744
12/14	3,108.0	(47.0)	—	577
12/13	886.0	(70.6)	—	536
Annual Growth	28.9%	—		14.0%

2017 Year-End Financials

Debt ratio: 28.6%
Return on equity: 17.7%
Cash ($ mil.): 118.3
Current ratio: 1.28
Long-term debt ($ mil.): 386.0

No. of shares (mil.): 45.7
Dividends
   Yield: —
   Payout: —
Market value ($ mil.): 883.0

	STOCK PRICE ($) FY Close	P/E High/Low		PER SHARE ($) Earnings	Dividends	Book Value
12/17	19.28	13	8	1.57	0.00	9.78
12/16	14.54	—	—	(1.08)	0.00	8.10
12/15	23.54	—	—	(1.06)	0.00	8.31
12/14	16.25	—	—	(1.44)	0.00	7.88
12/13	2.23	—	—	(3.57)	0.00	7.85
Annual Growth	71.5%		—	—	—	5.6%

Parade Technologies Ltd.

Auditors: PricewaterhouseCoopers

LOCATIONS

HQ: Parade Technologies Ltd.
   2720 Orchard Parkway, San Jose, CA 95134
Phone: 408 329-5540   **Fax:** 408 329-5541
Web: www.paradetech.com

HISTORICAL FINANCIALS

Company Type: Public

Income Statement   FYE: December 31

	REVENUE ($ mil.)	NET INCOME ($ mil.)	NET PROFIT MARGIN	EMPLOYEES
12/17	349.1	65.1	18.7%	0
12/16	281.4	41.9	14.9%	0
12/15	218.7	34.8	15.9%	393
12/14	196.6	38.7	19.7%	293
12/13	141.2	22.7	16.1%	264
Annual Growth	25.4%	30.1%	—	—

2017 Year-End Financials

Debt ratio: —
Return on equity: 24.3%
Cash ($ mil.): 160.6
Current ratio: 3.45
Long-term debt ($ mil.): —

No. of shares (mil.): 78.3
Dividends
   Yield: —
   Payout: 50.1%
Market value ($ mil.): —

Paramount Group Inc

Auditors: Deloitte & Touche LLP

LOCATIONS

HQ: Paramount Group Inc
   1633 Broadway, Suite 1801, New York, NY 10019
Phone: 212 237-3100
Web: www.paramount-group.com

HISTORICAL FINANCIALS

Company Type: Public

Income Statement   FYE: December 31

	REVENUE ($ mil.)	NET INCOME ($ mil.)	NET PROFIT MARGIN	EMPLOYEES
12/17	718.9	86.3	12.0%	327
12/16	683.3	(9.9)	—	334
12/15	662.4	(4.4)	—	319
12/14*	66.1	57.3	86.7%	219
11/14	227.3	21.5	9.5%	0
Annual Growth	33.3%	41.6%	—	—

*Fiscal year change

2017 Year-End Financials

Debt ratio: 39.7%
Return on equity: 2.1%
Cash ($ mil.): 279.4
Current ratio: 3.04
Long-term debt ($ mil.): 3,541.3

No. of shares (mil.): 240.4
Dividends
   Yield: 0.0%
   Payout: 102.7%
Market value ($ mil.): 3,811.0

	STOCK PRICE ($) FY Close	P/E High/Low		PER SHARE ($) Earnings	Dividends	Book Value
12/17	15.85	47	41	0.37	0.38	17.37
12/16	15.99	—	—	(0.05)	0.38	17.35
12/15	18.10	—	—	(0.02)	0.42	17.73
12/14*	18.59	70	67	0.27	0.00	18.44
11/14	18.43	—	—	(0.00)	0.00	(0.00)
Annual Growth	(3.7%)		—	—	—	—

*Fiscal year change

Parsley Energy Inc

Auditors: KPMG LLP

LOCATIONS

HQ: Parsley Energy Inc
   303 Colorado Street, Suite 3000, Austin, TX 78701
Phone: 737 704-2300
Web: www.parsleyenergy.com

HISTORICAL FINANCIALS

Company Type: Public

Income Statement   FYE: December 31

	REVENUE ($ mil.)	NET INCOME ($ mil.)	NET PROFIT MARGIN	EMPLOYEES
12/17	967.0	106.7	11.0%	460
12/16	457.7	(74.1)	—	298
12/15	266.0	(50.4)	—	212
12/14	301.7	23.4	7.8%	174
12/13	121.0	27.5	22.7%	98
Annual Growth	68.1%	40.4%	—	47.2%

2017 Year-End Financials

Debt ratio: 24.8%
Return on equity: 3.1%
Cash ($ mil.): 554.1
Current ratio: 1.50
Long-term debt ($ mil.): 2,179.5

No. of shares (mil.): 314.3
Dividends
   Yield: —
   Payout: —
Market value ($ mil.): 9,256.0

	STOCK PRICE ($) FY Close	P/E High/Low		PER SHARE ($) Earnings	Dividends	Book Value
12/17	29.44	84	54	0.42	0.00	14.99
12/16	35.24	—	—	(0.46)	0.00	10.07
12/15	18.45	—	—	(0.45)	0.00	7.49
12/14	15.96	60	27	0.42	0.00	5.61
Annual Growth	22.6%		—	(0.0%)	—	38.8%

Patrick Industries Inc

A recreational vehicle is just an empty motor home until Patrick Industries adds the finishing interior touches. The company makes and distributes a range of building materials and prefinished products primarily for the manufactured home (MH) and RV industries. Patrick Industries manufactures decorative paper and vinyl panels moldings countertops doors and cabinet and slotwall components. In addition to these the firm distributes roofing siding flooring drywall ceiling and wall panels household electronics electrical and plumbing supplies and adhesives. Founded in 1959 the company operates about two dozen production facilities distribution centers and warehouses in a dozen states.

Operations

Patrick Industries operates 43 manufacturing plants where it makes furniture shelving wall counter and cabinet products mouldings interior passage doors and slotwall panels and components among other products. Its manufacturing segment contributes about three-quarters of its annual revenue. The company also distributes prefinished wall and ceiling panels drywall and drywall finishing products. electronics. wiring electrical and plumbing products shower doors fireplaces and other miscellaneous products from five distribution facilities nationwide. Distribution accounts for about 22% of revenue.

Geographic Reach

Patrick Industries is based in Elkhart Indiana where a number of RV makers are clustered. The company operates facilities in 13 states including California Texas Illinois Pennsylvania Michigan and Oregon.

Sales and Marketing

Patrick Industries counts most of the major manufactured housing (MH) and RV manufacturers among its clientele but it also serves customers in the marine casegoods home furniture and the commercial furnishings and fixtures industries. The company has about 800 active customers of which two accounted for about 55% of its sales in 2015. The RV industry represented approximately 759% of the company's sales in 2015 while manufactured housing accounted for 14%. The industrial market represented the rest.

Financial Performance

Patrick Industries has been moving along for several years with robust revenue and profit gains.

The company's revenue jumped 25% higher in 2015 to $920 million from about $736 in 2014. Sales rose in its RV MH and Industrial markets. It was the sixth straight year of revenue gain for Patrick Industries. Acquisitions made in 2014 and 2015 made strong contributions to the revenue gain. The RV growth was tempered by a shift to more entry level and lower-priced models which lowered per-unit growth. The company passed along lower prices for some commodities used in manufacturing to its customers.

Profit at Patrick Industries popped up about 38% to reach $42 million in 2015 for $31 million in 2014 spurred by higher revenue.

The company reported stronger cash flow from operations at about $66 million in 2015 from about $46 million in 2014.

Strategy

Patrick Industries doesn't want to put all its eggs in one RV or MH. It's diversifying its product line to other industrial commercial and institutional markets and it's going it mainly through acquisitions.

Mergers and Acquisitions

In late 2017 Patrick Industries acquired Indiana Transport which provides transportation and logistics services to recreational vehicle OEMs (original equipment manufacturers) and dealers. The deal expands Patrick's operations into a complementary line of business and provides the company access to technologies and relationships that could spur growth.

In 2016 it acquired the Progressive Group a distributor and manufacturer's representative for major name brand electronics primarily in the auto and home electronics retail custom integration and commercial channels for $11 million.

Also in 2016 Patrick Industries bought Parkland Plastics Inc. — a maker of reclaimed polymer-based wall and ceiling panels floors molding and other products — for $25 million using secured credit. The company also acquired aluminum and steel products fabricator Mishawaka Sheet Metal in 2016 for about $14 million.

The previous year the company bought RV products manufacturer North American Forest Products Inc. which makes laminate and soft wood

panels moulding and other components for RVs. The acquisition was valued at $85 million also funded by secured credit. Other key 2015 acquisitions include fiberglass components manufacturers Structural Composites of Indiana Inc. and Better Way Partners LLC.

EXECUTIVES

President, Andy L. Nemeth, age 49, $271,730 total compensation
CEO, Todd M. Cleveland, age 50, $555,770 total compensation
VP Human Resources, Courtney A. Blosser, $203,537 total compensation
EVP Sales and Chief Sales Officer, Jeffrey M. Rodino, age 48, $276,517 total compensation
CFO, Joshua A. Boone, age 39
EVP Operations and COO, Kip B. Ellis, age 44
Vice President Sales And Marketing, Alan M Rzepka
Vice President Sales, Jimmy Ritchey
Chairman, Paul E. Hassler, age 71
Auditors: Crowe Horwath LLP

LOCATIONS

HQ: Patrick Industries Inc
107 West Franklin Street, P.O. Box 638, Elkhart, IN 46515
Phone: 574 294-7511
Web: www.patrickind.com

PRODUCTS/OPERATIONS

Selected Products:
Adorn
AIA Countertops
Better Way Products
Carrera Custom Painting
Charleston
Creative Wood Designs
Custom Vinyls
Décor Manufacturing
Foremost Fabricators
Frontline Manufacturing
Gravure Ink Praxis Group
Gustafson Lighting
Infinity GraphicsInte

	$ mil.	% of total
Manufacturing	720.4	78
Distribution	199.9	22
Total	**920.3**	**100**

2015 Sales by Customer Type

	% of total
RV industry	75
Manufactured housing	14
Industrial market	11
Total	**100**

COMPETITORS

Decorator Industries	Lowe's
Flexsteel	Quanex Building
HD Supply	Products
LCI Industries	Saint-Gobain
LaSalle Bristol	

HISTORICAL FINANCIALS
Company Type: Public

Income Statement
FYE: December 31

	REVENUE ($ mil.)	NET INCOME ($ mil.)	NET PROFIT MARGIN	EMPLOYEES
12/17	1,635.6	85.7	5.2%	6,721
12/16	1,221.8	55.5	4.5%	4,497
12/15	920.3	42.2	4.6%	3,542
12/14	735.7	30.6	4.2%	2,799
12/13	594.9	24.0	4.0%	2,387
Annual Growth	**28.8%**	**37.4%**	**—**	**29.5%**

2017 Year-End Financials

Debt ratio: 40.8%	No. of shares (mil.): 25.3
Return on equity: 30.8%	Dividends
Cash ($ mil.): 2.7	Yield: —
Current ratio: 2.01	Payout: —
Long-term debt ($ mil.): 338.1	Market value ($ mil.): 1,759.0

	STOCK PRICE ($) FY Close	P/E High/Low	Earnings	PER SHARE ($) Dividends	Book Value
12/17	69.45	29 17	3.48	0.00	14.63
12/16	76.30	32 12	2.43	0.00	8.07
12/15	43.50	35 19	1.81	0.00	5.65
12/14	43.98	37 22	1.28	0.00	4.42
12/13	28.93	34 12	0.99	0.00	3.46
Annual Growth	**24.5%**	**— —**	**36.9%**	**—**	**43.4%**

Paycom Software Inc

Auditors: GRANT THORNTON LLP

LOCATIONS

HQ: Paycom Software Inc
7501 W. Memorial Road, Oklahoma City, OK 73142
Phone: 405 722-6900
Web: www.paycom.com

HISTORICAL FINANCIALS
Company Type: Public

Income Statement
FYE: December 31

	REVENUE ($ mil.)	NET INCOME ($ mil.)	NET PROFIT MARGIN	EMPLOYEES
12/17	433.0	66.8	15.4%	2,548
12/16	329.1	43.8	13.3%	2,075
12/15	224.6	20.9	9.3%	1,461
12/14	150.9	5.6	3.8%	1,021
12/13	107.6	7.7	7.2%	840
Annual Growth	**41.6%**	**71.6%**	**—**	**32.0%**

2017 Year-End Financials

Debt ratio: 2.6%	No. of shares (mil.): 57.7
Return on equity: 53.0%	Dividends
Cash ($ mil.): 46.0	Yield: —
Current ratio: 1.01	Payout: —
Long-term debt ($ mil.): 34.4	Market value ($ mil.): 4,642.0

	STOCK PRICE ($) FY Close	P/E High/Low	Earnings	PER SHARE ($) Dividends	Book Value
12/17	80.33	74 38	1.13	0.00	2.34
12/16	45.49	69 30	0.74	0.00	2.03
12/15	37.63	124 63	0.36	0.00	1.72
12/14	26.33	261 113	0.11	0.00	1.38
Annual Growth	**45.0%**	**— —**	**117.4%**	**—**	**19.4%**

Paylocity Holding Corp

Auditors: KPMG LLP

LOCATIONS

HQ: Paylocity Holding Corp
1400 American Lane, Schaumburg, IL 60173
Phone: 847 463-3200
Web: www.paylocity.com

HISTORICAL FINANCIALS

Company Type: Public

Income Statement   FYE: June 30

	REVENUE ($ mil.)	NET INCOME ($ mil.)	NET PROFIT MARGIN	EMPLOYEES
06/18	377.5	38.6	10.2%	2,600
06/17	300.0	6.7	2.2%	2,115
06/16	230.7	(3.8)	—	1,800
06/15	152.7	(13.9)	—	1,320
06/14	108.6	(7.1)	—	968
Annual Growth	36.5%	—	—	28.0%

2018 Year-End Financials

Debt ratio: —   No. of shares (mil.): 52.7
Return on equity: 21.4%   Dividends
Cash ($ mil.): 137.1   Yield: —
Current ratio: 1.08   Payout: —
Long-term debt ($ mil.): —   Market value ($ mil.): 3,105.0

	STOCK PRICE ($) FY Close	P/E High/Low	PER SHARE ($) Earnings	Dividends	Book Value
06/18	58.86	86 58	0.70	0.00	4.03
06/17	45.18	378230	0.12	0.00	2.85
06/16	43.20	— —	(0.08)	0.00	2.34
06/15	35.05	— —	(0.28)	0.00	2.12
06/14	21.63	— —	(0.26)	0.00	1.84
Annual Growth	28.4%	— —	—	—	21.7%

PCSB Financial Corp

Auditors: Crowe Horwath LLP

LOCATIONS

HQ: PCSB Financial Corp
2651 Strang Blvd., Suite 100, Yorktown Heights, NY 10598
Phone: 914 248-7272
Web: www.pcsb.com

HISTORICAL FINANCIALS

Company Type: Public

Income Statement   FYE: June 30

	ASSETS ($ mil.)	NET INCOME ($ mil.)	INCOME AS % OF ASSETS	EMPLOYEES
06/18	1,480.1	6.6	0.4%	183
06/17	1,426.4	3.2	0.2%	184
06/16	1,262.0	2.9	0.2%	177
06/15	1,200.7	0.5	0.0%	0
Annual Growth	7.2%	135.1%	—	—

2018 Year-End Financials

Return on assets: 0.4%   Dividends
Return on equity: 2.3%   Yield: 0.0%
Long-term debt ($ mil.): —   Payout: 7.6%
No. of shares (mil.): 18.1   Market value ($ mil.): 361.0
Sales ($ mil): 50.4

	STOCK PRICE ($) FY Close	P/E High/Low	PER SHARE ($) Earnings	Dividends	Book Value
06/18	19.87	56 43	0.39	0.03	15.83
06/17	17.06	— —	(0.00)	0.00	15.41
06/16	0.00	— —	(0.00)	0.00	(0.00)
Annual Growth	—	—	—	—	—

Peapack-Gladstone Financial Corp.

Peapack-Gladstone Financial is the $3.4 billion-asset holding company for the near-century-old Peapack-Gladstone Bank which operates more than 20 branches in New Jersey's Hunterdon Morris Somerset Middlesex and Union counties. Founded in 1921 the bank provides traditional deposit accounts credit cards and loans to individuals and small businesses as well as trust and investment management services through its PGB Trust and Investments unit. Multifamily residential mortgages represent nearly 50% of the company's loan portfolio while commercial mortgages make up around 15%. The bank also originates construction consumer and business loans.

Operations

Peapack-Gladstone Financial operates two main divisions: Banking which offers traditional deposit and loan services merchant card services; and Wealth Management which boasts more than $3.3 billion in assets under administration (as of early 2016) and operates through PGB Trust and Investments which offers asset management services for individuals and institutions as well as personal trust services. More than 80% of the bank's total revenue came from interest income (mostly on its loans) during 2015 while 14% came from its wealth management fee income and 3% came from service charges and fees.

Multifamily residential mortgages represented nearly 50% of the company's loan portfolio at the end of 2015 while commercial mortgages made up another 15%. The rest of its portfolio was made up of construction consumer and business loans.

Geographic Reach

The bank's branches are located across New Jersey in Somerset Morris Hunterdon Middlesex and Union counties Its private banking and wealth management locations are located in Bedminster Morristown Princeton and Teaneck.

Sales and Marketing

The bank's commercial banking business serves business owners professionals retailers contractors and real estate investors. Its wealth management division serves individuals families foundations endowments trusts and estates.

Peapack-Gladstone has been ramping up its advertising spend in recent years. It spent $637000 on advertising during 2015 up from $594000 and $519000 in 2014 and 2013 respectively.

Financial Performance

Peapack-Gladstone's annual revenues and profits have swelled more than 60% since 2011 as its nearly tripled its loan assets to over $2.9 billion.

The bank's revenue jumped 27% to $122.86 million during 2015 mostly thanks to higher interest income as its loan assets grew by 30% with exceptional increases in its multifamily mortgage and commercial loan volumes. Peapack-Gladstone's wealth management division income grew 20% with increases in securities gains service charges and other non-interest income.

Strong revenue growth in 2015 drove Peapack-Gladstone's net income up 34% to $19.97 million. The bank's operating cash levels climbed 11% to $30.31 million thanks to a rise in cash-based earnings.

Strategy

Peapack-Gladstone Financial continued in 2016 to focus on: enhancing its risk management to keep its loan provisions at a minimum and its profits up; expanding its multi-family loans as well as its commercial real estate loans (to a lesser extent); growing its commercial and industrial (C&I) lending business through its private banking divisions; and expanding its wealth management business which now accounts for 15% of its annual revenue.

Mergers and Acquisitions

In May 2015 Peapack-Gladstone bolstered its wealth management division after buying Morristown-based Wealth Management Consultants LLC for $2.8 million. The deal boosted the bank's assets under advisement and administration to $3.5 billion.

EXECUTIVES

SEVP and CFO Peapack-Gladstone Financial and Peapack-Gladstone Bank, Jeffrey J. Carfora, age 60
EVP and COO, Robert A. (Bob) Plante, age 59
President and CEO Peapack-Gladstone Financial and Peapack-Gladstone Bank, Douglas L. Kennedy, age 59
EVP CIO and Head of Banking Services Peapack-Gladstone Bank, Kevin B. Runyon
SEVP Chief Strategy Officer and General Counsel, Finn M.W. Casperson, age 48
EVP and Head of Retail Banking Peapack-Gladstone Bank, Anthony V. Bilotta, age 58
EVP and Head of Commercial Real Estate Peapack-Gladstone Bank, Vincent A. Spero
SEVP and President Private Wealth Management, John P. Babcock
EVP and Chief Credit Officer Peapack-Gladstone Bank, Lisa Chalkan
EVP and Director Human Capital Peapack-Gladstone Bank, Philip Portantino
EVP and President Wealth Management Consultants Peapack-Gladstone Bank, Thomas J. Ross
EVP and Head of Commercial Banking Peapack-Gladstone Bank, Eric H. Waser
SVP and Head of Residential and Consumer Lending Peapack-Gladstone, Glenn R. Straffi
Vice President Senior Applications Software Specialist, Nancy Murphy
Senior Vice President, Charles Adornetto
Vice President Sales Distribution Leader, Dominic Sedicino
Vice President Senior Operations Officer, Sean Martin
Vice President And Trust Officer, Kim Czyzewski

Vice President, Glenn Carroll
Vice President Commercial Real Estate, Gavin C
  Wellington
Vice President Portfolio Manager, Sarah Krieger
Vice President, Timothy Doyle
ASSISTANT VICE PRESIDENT, Rachel Giarrusso
**Assistant Vice President And Senior Loan
  Administrator,** Ana Ribeiro
**Assistant Vice President And Senior Custody
  Officer,** Amanda Pullizzi
**Assistant Vice President And Mortgage
  Consultant,** Stephanie Chu
Chairman, F. Duffield (Duff) Meyercord, age 71
Auditors: Crowe Horwath LLP

LOCATIONS

HQ: Peapack-Gladstone Financial Corp.
  500 Hills Drive, Suite 300, Bedminster, NJ 07921-0700
Phone: 908 234-0700
Web: www.pgbank.com

PRODUCTS/OPERATIONS

2015 Sales

	$ mil.	% of total
Interest Income		
Loans including fees	94.3	77
Securities available for sale	4.6	4
Other	0.3	—
Other Income		
Wealth management fee income	17.0	14
Service charges and fees	3.3	3
Bank owned life insurance	1.3	1
Other Income	1.0	1
Other	1.1	-
Total	**122.9**	**100**

COMPETITORS

Bank of America	PNC Financial
Hudson City Bancorp	TD Bank USA
JPMorgan Chase	Valley National
MSB Financial	Bancorp

HISTORICAL FINANCIALS

Company Type: Public

Income Statement

FYE: December 31

	ASSETS ($ mil.)	NET INCOME ($ mil.)	INCOME AS % OF ASSETS	EMPLOYEES
12/17	4,260.5	36.5	0.9%	384
12/16	3,878.6	26.4	0.7%	338
12/15	3,364.6	19.9	0.6%	316
12/14	2,702.4	14.8	0.6%	306
12/13	1,966.9	9.2	0.5%	326
Annual Growth	**21.3%**	**40.9%**	**—**	**4.2%**

2017 Year-End Financials

Return on assets: 0.9%	Dividends
Return on equity: 10.0%	Yield: 0.0%
Long-term debt ($ mil.): —	Payout: 9.8%
No. of shares (mil.): 18.6	Market value ($ mil.): 652.0
Sales ($ mil): 173.3	

	STOCK PRICE ($) FY Close	P/E High/Low	PER SHARE ($) Earnings	Dividends	Book Value
12/17	35.02	18 14	2.03	0.20	21.68
12/16	30.88	20 10	1.60	0.20	18.79
12/15	20.62	18 14	1.29	0.20	17.16
12/14	18.56	18 14	1.22	0.20	15.99
12/13	19.10	20 14	1.01	0.20	14.48
Annual Growth	**16.4%**	**— —**	**19.1%**	**(0.0%)**	**10.6%**

Pebblebrook Hotel Trust

Pebblebrook Hotel Trust wants the term staycation to take a vacation. The self-managed real estate investment trust (REIT) acquires and manages upscale hotels in the US targeting mostly full-service and select-service luxury properties that don't need major renovation in major US gateway cities. The REIT owns more than 30 hotels (with 7400 rooms) across 11 states and has a 49% interest in six more hotels spanning nearly 1800 rooms through its Manhattan Collection joint venture. Nearly 70% of its revenue comes from room fees while the remainder comes from food and beverage services. Pebblebrook Hotel Trust is the brainchild of CEO Jon Bortz who also founded LaSalle Hotel Properties.

Geographic Reach

Pebblebrook Hotel Trust's properties are in major cities spread across 11 US states. Most are in California (in San Francisco Los Angeles and surrounding areas and San Diego) while most of the others are in Boston Bethesda Minneapolis Miami Nashville New York City Philadelphia Portland and Seattle.

Financial Performance

Pebblebrook's revenues and profits have skyrocketed over the past several years as it has expanded its property portfolio through acquisitions and has charged higher room rates as the economy has strengthened.

The REIT's revenue jumped 22% to $598.8 billion in 2014 mostly thanks to $81 million in new room revenue from its recently acquired properties. Its comparable property revenues added an additional $28.6 million in growth to its top-line thanks to strong performance in its West Coast properties from increases in ADR (average daily rate) and an increase in revenue from its Hotel Zetta (which had been closed in 2012 and part of 2013).

Higher revenue and higher equity earnings on its joint venture properties drove Pebblebrook's net income higher by 70% to $72.9 million. The REIT's operating cash levels rose by 50% to $161.3 million thanks to higher cash earnings.

Strategy

Pebblebrook Hotel Trust has been actively building up its hotel portfolio as the lodging industry has strengthened with the overall economy. The REIT targets hotel property investments in "major gateway urban markets" with high barriers-to-entry and "diverse sources of meeting and room night demand generators." It also sometimes targets investment opportunities in upscale resort destinations in south Florida and southern California. In addition Pebblebrook regularly renovates its properties to add value and be able to charge more revenue per room.

During 2014 the REIT spent $626.8 million to acquire six properties in target markets including: the Prescott Hotel in San Francisco; The Nines a Luxury Collection Hotel in Portland; The Westin Colonnade Coral Gables in Miami; the Revere Hotel Boston Common; and leasehold interests in both the Hotel Palomar Los Angeles-Westwood in Los Angeles and the Union Station Hotel Autograph Collection in Nashville.

Company Background

Pebblebrook had its initial public offering (IPO) in December 2009 raising more than $350 million. The REIT used the proceeds from the offering to buy properties to grow its portfolio which then consisted of around 10 hotels.

EXECUTIVES

Chairman President and CEO, Jon E. Bortz, age 61, $300,000 total compensation
EVP CFO Treasurer and Secretary, Raymond D. Martz, age 47, $250,000 total compensation
EVP and Chief Investment Officer, Thomas C. Fisher, $243,151 total compensation
Vice President Asset Management, Steve Coe
Vice President Acquisitions, Robin Kennedy
Vice President Asset Management, Wendy Heineke
Auditors: KPMG LLP

LOCATIONS

HQ: Pebblebrook Hotel Trust
  7315 Wisconsin Avenue, 1100 West, Bethesda, MD 20814
Phone: 240 507-1300
Web: www.pebblebrookhotels.com

PRODUCTS/OPERATIONS

2014 Sales

	$ mil.	% of total
Rooms	410.6	68
Food & beverage	148.1	25
Other	40.1	7
Total	**598.8**	**100**

Selected Properties

Argonaut Hotel (San Francisco)
DoubleTree by Hilton Bethesda- Washington DC
The Grand Hotel (Minneapolis)
InterContinental Buckhead Hotel (Atlanta)
Monaco Washington DC
Sheraton Delfina (Philadelphia)
Sir Francis Drake (San Francisco)
Skamania Lodge and Conference Center (Stevenson WA)

COMPETITORS

Ashford Hospitality Trust	Hersha Hospitality Hospitality Properties Trust
Chesapeake Lodging	
Condor Hospitality	Host Hotels & Resorts
DiamondRock Hospitality	Innkeepers USA
FelCor	MHI Hospitality
HMG/Courtland Properties	Strategic Hotels

HISTORICAL FINANCIALS

Company Type: Public

Income Statement

FYE: December 31

	REVENUE ($ mil.)	NET INCOME ($ mil.)	NET PROFIT MARGIN	EMPLOYEES
12/17	769.3	99.8	13.0%	28
12/16	816.4	73.7	9.0%	26
12/15	770.8	94.6	12.3%	27
12/14	598.7	72.8	12.2%	27
12/13	489.2	42.9	8.8%	24
Annual Growth	**12.0%**	**23.5%**	**—**	**3.9%**

2017 Year-End Financials

Debt ratio: 34.1%	No. of shares (mil.): 68.8
Return on equity: 6.4%	Dividends
Cash ($ mil.): 25.4	Yield: 0.0%
Current ratio: 0.31	Payout: 127.7%
Long-term debt ($ mil.): 885.2	Market value ($ mil.): 2,558.0

STOCK PRICE ($) FY Close	P/E High/Low	PER SHARE ($) Earnings	Dividends	Book Value
12/17	37.17	32 23	1.19	1.52	21.78
12/16	29.75	48 34	0.64	1.52	22.33
12/15	28.02	53 29	0.95	1.24	24.51
12/14	45.63	65 41	0.71	0.92	24.89
12/13	30.76	97 72	0.32	0.64	23.13
Annual Growth	4.8%	— —	38.9%	24.1%	(1.5%)

Pegasystems Inc

Pegasystems helps companies fly through business changes without being reined in by their old processes. The company provides a range of enterprise software applications that include customer relationship management business process management business rules management systems and more. The company's Pega Platform serves as the base for its software development and is licensed to customers for their development needs. Pegasystems targets companies in the financial services insurance and health care industries. Established in 1983 Pegasystems also offers cloud-based systems software maintenance consulting and training. International customers account for about 45% of the company's revenue.

Operations

Pegasystems offers a range of software and services with the goal of helping its customers serve their customers better. The foundation is the Pega Platform on which the company builds its applications. It also licenses the platform to customers who want to develop their own applications. The platform uses process models predictive analytics user experience designs decision logic and other tools to build applications.

Software licenses account for about 35% of revenue. Term licenses (recurring) account for 51% of license revenue while perpetual licenses account for the rest. Other revenue comes from maintenance and consulting and training services which account for about 30% each and cloud sales which supply about 5% of revenue.

Geographic Reach

Pegasystems is headquartered in Cambridge Massachusetts and has about 10 other offices across the US. The company also had locations around the world. The US accounts for more than 55% of sales; Europe including the UK makes up more than 25%; and the Asia/Pacific region brings in more than 10%.

Sales and Marketing

Pegasystems sells through its direct sales force as well as through distributors resellers and trade shows (including the PegaWorld user conference). Its target market is the Global 3000 and the company claims customers among the largest healthcare and insurance companies well as the biggest banks and communications service providers. It also has US government agencies on its client roster. Customers include JP Morgan Chase Aeon Anthem Talk Talk Sanofi Intel and Coca-Cola.

Pegasystems also teams up with major IT services and software providers to extend its reach. Its strategic partners include Accenture Capgemini Cognizant Infosys Mahindra Tata Consultancy Services Virtusa Atos Ernst & Young and Wipro.

Financial Performance

Pegasystems continued its decade of increasing revenue in 2017 when it posted about $840 million in sales a 12% rise from 2016. The company reported higher revenue from term licenses which grew 11% in 2017 from 2016. At the same time perpetual license revenue decreased 4%. Services revenue rose 23% on increases in consulting and training and cloud. Maintenance revenue was up 11%. Strong growth in Europe (up 41%) and the Asia/Pacific region (up 57%) added more money to the top line than did 11% growth in the US. Sales declined in the Americas outside the US and in the UK.

Net income rose 22% to about $33 million in 2017 from 2016. While Pegasystems spent more money on sales and marketing and research and development the percentages were the same year-to-year.

Cash from operations jumped to $158 million in 2017 from about $40 million in 2016 from net income and trade accounts receivable which were boosted by increased cash collections and the timing of billings.

Strategy

Pegasystems' strategy of gaining entre to a customer by selling one product or service and then selling more and more is well founded. The company's array of CRM BPM and other types of software gives it a well-stocked warehouse from which to draw.

Along with just about every other software company Pegasystems is shifting to the business model of selling subscriptions to its products and services as well as running software in the cloud. Each year recurring revenue accounts for a larger portion of the total. It rose to 51% in 2017 from 47% in 2016 and 40% in 2015.

Pegasystems has hired more sales people in recent years to deepen relationships with existing accounts and expand into new industries and geographical areas.

Mergers and Acquisitions

In 2016 Pegasystems acquired OpenSpan a privately held software provider of robotic process automation and workforce analytics software for about $50 million. Following the acquisition the company unified the Pega Robotic Automation with its Pega Platform for Case and Business Process Management and its CRM portfolio.

EXECUTIVES

SVP Human Resources, Jeff Yanagi
Chairman and CEO, Alan Trefler, age 62, $456,000 total compensation
SVP Engineering and Product Development, Michael R. (Mike) Pyle, age 63, $348,000 total compensation
SVP Global Customer Success, Douglas I. (Doug) Kra, age 55, $343,000 total compensation
SVP Corporate Development, Max Mayer, $255,000 total compensation
SVP Products, Kerim Akgonul
CFO and Chief Administrative Officer, Ken Stillwell
SVP and Chief Marketing Officer, Tom Libretto
Vice President Marketing, Dave Donelan
Area Vice President Sales, Jim Alcina
Board Member, Steven Kaplan
Auditors: Deloitte & Touche LLP

LOCATIONS

HQ: Pegasystems Inc
One Rogers Street, Cambridge, MA 02142-1209
Phone: 617 374-9600
Web: www.pega.com

PRODUCTS/OPERATIONS

2017 Sales

	$ mil.	% of total
Software licenses	288.3	34
Maintenance	244.3	29
Services	307.9	37
Total	**840.6**	**100**

Selected Software

PegaCloud
PegaCRM
Pega Decision Management
PegaRULES Process Commander
Solutions Frameworks

COMPETITORS

Appian	SAP
EMC	Software AG
Fair Isaac	SunGard
Guidewire Software	TIBCO Software
IBM	TriZetto
Microsoft Dynamics	Trintech
Oracle	salesforce.com
Progress Software	

HISTORICAL FINANCIALS

Company Type: Public

Income Statement   FYE: December 31

	REVENUE ($ mil.)	NET INCOME ($ mil.)	NET PROFIT MARGIN	EMPLOYEES
12/17	840.5	32.9	3.9%	4,237
12/16	750.2	26.9	3.6%	3,908
12/15	682.7	36.3	5.3%	3,333
12/14	590.0	33.2	5.6%	2,970
12/13	508.9	38.0	7.5%	2,627
Annual Growth	13.4%	(3.5%)	—	12.7%

2017 Year-End Financials

Debt ratio: —
Return on equity: 9.3%
Cash ($ mil.): 162.2
Current ratio: 1.58
Long-term debt ($ mil.): —
No. of shares (mil.): 78.0
Dividends
Yield: 0.0%
Payout: 30.0%
Market value ($ mil.): 3,682.0

STOCK PRICE ($) FY Close	P/E High/Low	PER SHARE ($) Earnings	Dividends	Book Value
12/17	47.15	148 83	0.40	0.12	4.75
12/16	36.00	105 59	0.34	0.12	4.39
12/15	27.50	64 41	0.46	0.12	4.22
12/14	20.77	112 36	0.42	0.11	3.86
12/13	49.18	102 45	0.49	0.06	3.56
Annual Growth	(1.0%)	— —	(4.9%)	18.9%	7.5%

Pendrell Corp

Pendrell is an asset management company of the intellectual property (IP) kind. It gathers up patents (it holds about 1200) and licenses them to technology companies thus receiving a cut when a technology is used. Its patent holdings center on technologies for tablets smart phones and other consumer electronics devices. Besides licensing IP Pendrell also develops technologies though none generate revenue yet. Companies that license IP from Pendrell include Casio Hitachi LG Electronics Microsoft Nokia Technicolor and Xerox.

Operations

The technologies in Pendrell's IP portfolio include digital rights management software wireless memory and storage audio/visual ephemeral content protection semiconductor mobility networking and biotechnology. Its holding include ContentGuard Helsinki Memory Technologies Ovidian Group and Provitro Biosciences.

Financial Performance

Pendrell's net income zoomed 224% higher in 2014 to $42.5 million from $13.1 million in 2013. The company made a number of licensing agreements in 2014 for memory and storage technologies in comparison to 2013 when it had no licensing revenue. Even with the big jump in revenue Pendrell still lost more money than it took in overall. Its loss was $51 million in 2014 a slightly lower loss than the $55 million lost in 2013.

EXECUTIVES

EVP Chief Strategy Officer and Director, R. Gerard (Gerry) Salemme, age 62
Chairman President and CEO, Benjamin G. (Ben) Wolff, age 47
Vice President and Corporate Counsel, Timothy M. Dozois, age 54
Vice President for Investor Relations and Public Relations for Pendrell formerly ICO Global Communications, Christopher Doherty
Vice President General Counsel Corporate Secretary, Robert Jaffe
Vice President Chief Financial Officer, Tom Neary
Vice President Chief Scientist, Robert G. Mechaley
Vice President Chief People Officer, Mark Fanning
Vice President Licensing for Pendrell Technologies, Mario Obeidat
Chief IP Officer, Joseph Siino
Director, Craig O. McCaw, age 66
Director, H. Brian Thompson, age 76
Director, Richard P. (Rick) Fox, age 69
Director, Nicolas Kauser, age 76
Director, Barry L. Rowan, age 58
Director, Stuart M. Sloan, age 72
EVP Chief Strategy Officer and Director, R. Gerard (Gerry) Salemme, age 62
Director, Richard P. Emerson, age 59
Auditors: Grant Thornton LLP

LOCATIONS

HQ: Pendrell Corp
2300 Carillon Point, Kirkland, WA 98033
Phone: 425 278-7100
Web: www.pendrell.com

COMPETITORS

ARM Holdings	MoSys
Acacia Research	Quarterhill
Aware Inc.	RPX
Bain & Company	Rambus
Boston Consulting	Rovi
MOSAID Technologies	

HISTORICAL FINANCIALS

Company Type: Public

Income Statement

FYE: December 31

	REVENUE ($ mil.)	NET INCOME ($ mil.)	NET PROFIT MARGIN	EMPLOYEES
12/17	42.7	19.0	44.6%	12
12/16	59.0	17.7	30.1%	14
12/15	43.5	(109.6)	—	16
12/14	42.5	(51.0)	—	57
12/13	13.1	(55.0)	—	73
Annual Growth 34.4%	—	—	(36.3%)

2017 Year-End Financials

Debt ratio: —	No. of shares (mil.): 0.0
Return on equity: 9.3%	Dividends
Cash ($ mil.): 184.4	Yield: 68.1%
Current ratio: 22.73	Payout: 16.6%
Long-term debt ($ mil.): —	Market value ($ mil.): 1.0

	STOCK PRICE ($) FY Close	P/E High/Low	Earnings	PER SHARE ($) Dividends	Book Value
12/17 211,964	575	0	018,555.003,080		
12/16 187,848	6.75	0 0	16,000	0	
12/15 168,270	0.50	—	—(102,500)	0	
12/14 266,679	1.38	—	—(47,500)	0	
12/13 304,855	2.01	—	—(52,500)	0	
Annual Growth 311.3%	—	—	—	(8.7%)	

PennyMac Financial Services Inc (New)

If you're thinking residential mortgage this company has more than a penny for your thoughts. The parent of investment management loan services and investment trust companies PennyMac Financial Services (PennyMac) focuses on the US residential mortgage market offering loans and investment management services. Through its Private National Mortgage Acceptance Company the company's PennyMac Loan Services (PLS) originates home loans in 45 states and DC and services loans in 49 states DC and the US Virgin Islands. PLS's counterpart PNMAC Capital Management acts as investment manager and advisor. The companies service and advise PennyMac Mortgage Investment Trust (PMT). PennyMac went public in 2013.

IPO

PennyMac hoped to raise $287.5 million in its IPO but investors responded with $199.9 million. The company plans to use the proceeds to fund growth of its mortgage business through Private National Mortgage Acceptance Company. It will also use the funds for general corporate purposes.

Operations

PennyMac's mortgage banking segment includes correspondent lending retail lending and loan servicing. The correspondent line includes conventional residential mortgages acquired by PMT as well as those guaranteed by FreddieMac FannieMae and other government agencies. The company has more than 140 approved sellers; in 2012 it had $13 billion in conventional loans and $8.4 billion in government-insured loans. Retail lending originates new prime residential conventional and government-backed mortgage loans for purchasing or refinancing homes. PennyMac uses the Internet and a call center rather than traditional branch locations for direct-to-consumer approach. The company's loan servicing business includes the back office work of loan administration collection and default activities. It serves PennyMac subsidiaries and other mortgage companies. The unit handles prime credit and distress loans under the prime servicing and special servicing headings respectively.

PennyMac's investment management segment operates as an investment manager through PNMAC Capital Management (PCM). PCM handles the $1.8 billion in combined assets from PMT and PennyMac's other investment funds. PMT is a publicly traded real estate investment trust (REIT).

Geographic Reach

While PennyMac serves nearly the entire US its portfolio is heavily weighted toward California (38%) Florida (5%) and Colorado (5%).

Financial Performance

The company's revenue has increased on the strength of gains in both the loan servicing and management segments. Other operating metrics include net assets under management total mortgage loans serviced and total mortgage loan production; all have increased in the last three years. PennyMac reported lower net income for 2012 due to amortization and impairment charges and higher spending on compensation. It sold and repurchased loans loans and earned interest on investments to more than double its cash flow for the same period.

Strategy

Since PennyMac was formed during the financial crisis it hasn't had to scramble and adapt like many of its competitors. As many mortgage shoppers turn away from large banks the company believes its poised to take advantage of growth and a lack of stringent regulations imposed on banks. For growth the company intends to focus on expanding its servicing business organically and through acquisitions increasing the number of loan sellers from which it purchases loans and leveraging its servicing portfolio to increase refinance and loan servicing opportunities.

EXECUTIVES

Senior Managing Director and Chief Enterprise Operations Officer, Anne D. McCallion, age 63
President and CEO, David A. Spector, age 55, $503,370 total compensation
President PennyMac Loan Services, Douglas E. (Doug) Jones, age 61, $325,000 total compensation
Senior Managing Director and Chief Risk Officer, David M. (Dave) Walker, age 62
Senior Managing Director and Chief Mortgage Operations Officer, Steve R. Bailey, age 56
Senior Managing Director and CFO, Andrew S. Chang, age 40
Senior Managing Director and Chief Capital Markets Officer, Vandad Fartaj, age 43
Senior Managing Director and Chief Administrative and Legal Officer, Jeffrey P. Grogin, age 57

Senior Managing Director and Chief Asset and Liability Management Officer, Daniel S. Perotti, age 37
Chairman, Stanford L. Kurland, age 65
Auditors: DELOITTE & TOUCHE LLP

LOCATIONS

HQ: PennyMac Financial Services Inc (New)
3043 Townsgate Road, Westlake Village, CA 91361
Phone: 818 224-7442
Web: www.pennymacusa.com

COMPETITORS

Bank of America	Quicken Loans
Citigroup	Stonegate Mortgage
JPMorgan Chase	U.S. Bancorp
Nationstar Mortgage	Wells Fargo
Ocwen Financial	

HISTORICAL FINANCIALS

Company Type: Public

Income Statement

FYE: December 31

	ASSETS ($ mil.)	NET INCOME ($ mil.)	INCOME AS % OF ASSETS	EMPLOYEES
12/17	7,368.0	100.7	1.4%	3,189
12/16	5,133.9	66.0	1.3%	3,038
12/15	3,505.2	47.2	1.3%	2,509
12/14	2,507.1	36.8	1.5%	1,816
12/13	1,584.4	14.4	0.9%	1,373
Annual Growth	**46.8%**	**62.6%**	**—**	**23.5%**

2017 Year-End Financials

Return on assets: 1.6%
Return on equity: 24.6%
Long-term debt ($ mil.): —
No. of shares (mil.): 23.5
Sales ($ mil): 1,099.9

Dividends
Yield: —
Payout: —
Market value ($ mil.): 526.0

	STOCK PRICE ($) FY Close	P/E High/Low		PER SHARE ($) Earnings	Dividends	Book Value
12/17	22.35	5	4	4.03	0.00	19.95
12/16	16.65	6	4	2.94	0.00	15.49
12/15	15.36	9	7	2.17	0.00	12.32
12/14	17.30	11	8	1.73	0.00	9.92
12/13	17.55	27	19	0.82	0.00	8.04
Annual Growth	**6.2%**	**—**	**—**	**48.9%**	**—**	**25.5%**

People's Utah Bancorp

Auditors: Tanner LLC

LOCATIONS

HQ: People's Utah Bancorp
1 East Main Street, American Fork, UT 84003
Phone: 801 642-3998
Web: www.PeoplesUtah.com

HISTORICAL FINANCIALS

Company Type: Public

Income Statement

FYE: December 31

	ASSETS ($ mil.)	NET INCOME ($ mil.)	INCOME AS % OF ASSETS	EMPLOYEES
12/17	2,123.5	19.8	0.9%	483
12/16	1,665.9	23.6	1.4%	430
12/15	1,555.9	19.6	1.3%	414
12/14	1,367.1	14.9	1.1%	367
12/13	1,299.1	11.8	0.9%	0
Annual Growth	**13.1%**	**13.7%**		

2017 Year-End Financials

Return on assets: 1.0%
Return on equity: 8.1%
Long-term debt ($ mil.): —
No. of shares (mil.): 18.5
Sales ($ mil): 100.5

Dividends
Yield: 0.0%
Payout: 31.4%
Market value ($ mil.): 561.0

	STOCK PRICE ($) FY Close	P/E High/Low		PER SHARE ($) Earnings	Dividends	Book Value
12/17	30.30	30	22	1.08	0.34	13.91
12/16	26.85	21	11	1.30	0.22	12.82
12/15	17.21	15	13	1.17	0.18	11.92
Annual Growth	**32.7%**	**—**	**—**	**(3.9%)**	**37.4%**	**8.0%**

Peoples Bancorp Inc (Marietta, OH)

Peoples Bancorp offers banking for the people by the people and of the people. The holding company owns Peoples Bank which has about 50 branches in rural and small urban markets in Ohio Kentucky and West Virginia. The bank offers traditional services such as checking and savings accounts CDs loans and trust services. Commercial and agricultural loans including those secured by commercial real estate account for the majority of the bank's lending activities. Its Peoples Financial Advisors division offers investment management services while Peoples Insurance sells life health and property/casualty coverage.

Operations
Credit cards and brokerage services are offered through third-party providers.

Financial Performance
The company's revenue increased from $103.7 million in fiscal 2012 up to $104.6 million for fiscal 2013. However despite the slight spike in annual revenue Peoples Bancorp's net income decreased from $29.9 million in fiscal 2012 down to $29 million for fiscal 2013.

The company's cash on hand decreased by about $1 million in fiscal 2013 compared to fiscal 2012 levels.

Strategy
Peoples Bancorp is looking to increase its revenue from service changes and other fees and commissions particularly from insurance and wealth management which are not reliant on fluctuating interest rate margins.

The company is also looking to strengthen its brand and build deeper relationships with its clients.

EXECUTIVES

EVP and Chief Administrative Officer Peoples Bancorp and EVP Chief Administrative Officer and CashierPeoples Bank N.A., Carol A. Schneeberger, age 61, $233,000 total compensation
EVP and Chief Commercial Lending Officer Peoples Bancorp and Peoples Bank N.A., Daniel K. (Dan) McGill, age 63, $250,000 total compensation
EVP and Chief Credit Officer Peoples Bancorp and Peoples Bank N.A., Timothy H. Kirtley, age 48, $221,500 total compensation
President CEO and Director Peoples Bancorp and Peoples Bank N.A., Charles W. Sulerzyski, age 60, $500,000 total compensation
EVP CFO and Treasurer Peoples Bancorp and Peoples Bank N.A., John C. Rogers, age 58, $26,136 total compensation
Vice President, Steven Nulter
Assistant Vice President Branch Market Manager, Candace Frump
Branch Market Manager Assistant Vice President, Peggy Scott-Morgan
Vice President and Controller, Jeffrey Baran
VICE PRESIDENT, Randy Barengo
Chairman Peoples Bancorp and Peoples Bank N.A., David L. Mead, age 63
Auditors: Ernst & Young LLP

LOCATIONS

HQ: Peoples Bancorp Inc (Marietta, OH)
138 Putnam Street, P.O. Box 738, Marietta, OH 45750
Phone: 740 373-3155
Web: www.peoplesbancorp.com

PRODUCTS/OPERATIONS

2016 Sales

	$ mil.	% of total
Interest Income:		
Interest and fees on loans	93.9	56
Interest and dividends on taxable investment securities	18.5	11
Interest on tax-exempt investment securities	3.2	2
Other Income:		
Insurance income	13.9	8
Deposit account service charges	10.7	6
Trust and investment income	10.5	6
Electronic banking income	10.3	6
Bank owned life insurance income	1.4	1
Mortgage banking income	1.3	1
Commercial loan swap fee income	1.0	1
Net gain on investment securities	0.9	1
Net loss on asset disposals and other transactions	(1.1)	-
Other	1.8	1
Total	**166.3**	**100**

COMPETITORS

1st West Virginia Bancorp	Huntington Bancshares
	Ohio Valley Banc
BB&T	U.S. Bancorp
Fifth Third	United Bankshares

HISTORICAL FINANCIALS

Company Type: Public

Income Statement

FYE: December 31

	ASSETS ($ mil.)	NET INCOME ($ mil.)	INCOME AS % OF ASSETS	EMPLOYEES
12/17	3,581.6	38.4	1.1%	774
12/16	3,432.3	31.1	0.9%	782
12/15	3,258.9	10.9	0.3%	817
12/14	2,567.7	16.6	0.6%	699
12/13	2,059.1	17.5	0.9%	546
Annual Growth	**14.8%**	**21.6%**	**—**	**9.1%**

2017 Year-End Financials

Return on assets: 1.1%
Return on equity: 8.6%
Long-term debt ($ mil.): —
No. of shares (mil.): 18.2
Sales ($ mil.): 182.1

Dividends
Yield: 0.0%
Payout: 40.0%
Market value ($ mil.): 595.0

	STOCK PRICE ($) FY Close	P/E High/Low	PER SHARE ($) Earnings	Dividends	Book Value
12/17	32.62	16 14	2.10	0.84	25.13
12/16	32.46	19 10	1.71	0.64	23.99
12/15	18.84	42 30	0.61	0.60	22.88
12/14	25.93	20 15	1.36	0.60	22.92
12/13	22.51	15 12	1.63	0.54	20.89
Annual Growth	9.7%	— —	6.5%	11.7%	4.7%

Peoples Financial Services Corp

Power to the Peoples Financial Services. The firm is the holding company for Peoples Security Bank and Trust Company (formerly Peoples National Bank) which operates about 25 branches across northeastern Pennsylvania and neighboring Broome County in New York. Established in 1905 the bank offers standard retail products and services including checking and savings accounts CDs and credit cards to local businesses and individuals. Commercial loans including mortgages construction loans and operating loans make up the greatest portion (40%) of the company's loan book followed by residential mortgages (25%) and consumer loans. The company's Peoples Advisors subsidiary provides investment and brokerage services.

Operations

About 80% of Peoples Financial Services' total revenue came from interest income (mostly on loans) in 2014 while the remainder comes from non-interest income. The bank had a staff of 354 full-time employees at the end of that year.

Geographic Reach

Scranton-based Peoples Security Bank has more than 25 branches across Northeastern Pennsylvania (in the Lackawanna Lehigh Luzerne Monroe Susquehanna Wayne and Wyoming counties) and Broome County in New York state.

Sales and Marketing

The company primarily makes loans to small- and medium-sized businesses. It spent $450 on advertising in 2014 up from $350 and $287 in 2013 and 2012 respectively.

Financial Performance

Peoples has struggled to consistently grow its revenues in recent years due to shrinking interest margins on loans amidst the low-interest environment. Its profits however have been rising thanks to lower interest expenses on deposits and declining loan loss provisions as its loan portfolio's credit quality has improved with higher property valuations in the strengthened economy.

The company enjoyed a breakout year in 2014 however as its revenue jumped 60% to a record $79.21 million mostly as its interest income swelled from new loan business from its 2013 acquisition

of Penseco Financial Services. Its service charge fees and commissions merchant services income and commission and fee income from fiduciary services also rose mostly as a result of the significant acquisition.

Higher revenue in 2014 allowed Peoples' net income to more than triple to a record $17.6 million while its operating cash levels more than doubled to $20.6 million on higher cash earnings for the year.

Strategy

Peoples Security Bank occasionally acquires smaller banks to extend its branch network across target markets while adding new loan and deposit business. Its late 2013 acquisition of Penseco Financial Services Corporation for example nearly doubled its loan and deposit business and more than doubled its branch network to 25 branches.

Mergers and Acquisitions

In November 2013 Peoples acquired Penseco Financial Services Corporation along with its Penn Security Bank and Trust subsidiary. The $155 million-deal doubled Peoples' branch network from 12 to 25 branches creating the largest community bank headquartered in Northeastern Pennsylvania.

EXECUTIVES

CEO and President, Alan W. Dakey, age 66
EVP and COO Peoples National Bank, Debra E. Dissinger, age 63, $110,000 total compensation
Director, Richard S. Lochen, age 54, $130,000 total compensation
Senior Vice President Chief Financial Officer, Scott Seasock
Vice President Commercial Lending, Diane Effting
Chairman, William E. Aubrey, age 55
Auditors: Baker Tilly Virchow Krause, LLP

LOCATIONS

HQ: Peoples Financial Services Corp
150 North Washington Avenue, Scranton, PA 18503
Phone: 570 346-7741
Web: www.psbt.com

PRODUCTS/OPERATIONS

2014 Sales

	$ mil.	% of total
Interest	64.0	81
Non-interest	15.2	19
Total	**79.2**	**100**

COMPETITORS

Citizens & Northern	HSBC USA
Citizens Financial Services	M&T Bank
Fidelity D & D	NBT Bancorp
First Keystone	Penns Woods Bancorp
First National Community Bancorp	

HISTORICAL FINANCIALS

Company Type: Public

Income Statement

FYE: December 31

	ASSETS ($ mil.)	NET INCOME ($ mil.)	INCOME AS % OF ASSETS	EMPLOYEES
12/17	2,169.0	18.4	0.9%	388
12/16	1,999.4	19.5	1.0%	364
12/15	1,819.0	17.7	1.0%	348
12/14	1,741.6	17.6	1.0%	354
12/13	1,688.2	5.7	0.3%	354
Annual Growth	6.5%	34.0%	—	2.3%

2017 Year-End Financials

Return on assets: 0.8%
Return on equity: 7.0%
Long-term debt ($ mil.): —
No. of shares (mil.): 7.4
Sales ($ mil.): 91.4

Dividends
Yield: 0.0%
Payout: 50.4%
Market value ($ mil.): 345.0

	STOCK PRICE ($) FY Close	P/E High/Low	PER SHARE ($) Earnings	Dividends	Book Value
12/17	46.58	20 16	2.50	1.26	35.82
12/16	48.70	19 13	2.65	1.24	34.71
12/15	38.08	21 15	2.36	1.24	33.57
12/14	49.68	23 16	2.34	1.24	32.69
12/13	38.00	33 25	1.21	0.92	31.62
Annual Growth	5.2%	— —	19.9%	8.2%	3.2%

PGT Innovations Inc

PGT helps Floridians weather their storms. The company makes and sells WinGuard and PremierVue impact-resistant doors and windows for the residential market. The energy-efficient customizable doors and windows are made of aluminum or vinyl with laminated glass and are designed to withstand hurricane-strength winds. PGT also makes Eze-Breeze porch enclosure panels and garage door screens SpectraGuard vinyl replacement windows and PGT Architectural Systems windows for high-rises. The company has two manufacturing facilities in Florida and North Carolina. PGT sells its products through some 1200 window distributors dealers and contractors in the Southeastern US Canada Central America and the Caribbean.

Operations

The company's manufacturing facility is located in North Venice Florida where it makes customized impact-resistant windows and doors.

Geographic Reach

Florida-based PGT rings up more than 95% of its sales in storm-prone areas of the US. Indeed Florida is the company's largest market representing the majority of its sales. Other markets include the southeastern Gulf Coast and coastal Mid-Atlantic regions of the US as well as the Caribbean Central America and Canada.

Sales and Marketing

The company distributes its products through multiple channels including about 1200 window distributors building supply distributors window replacement dealers and enclosure contractors. The residential new construction and home repair and remodeling end markets represented about 41% and 59% of its sales respectively during 2015.

PGT markets its products through print and web-based advertising consumer dealer and builder promotions and selling and collateral materials. It markets its products based on quality building code compliance outstanding service shorter lead times and on-time delivery utilizing its fleet of trucks and trailers.

Financial Performance

PGT has achieved unprecedented growth over the years with revenues peaking at a record-setting $390 million in 2015. The historic growth was due to a spike in the sale of impact-resistant window and door products in addition to non-impact window and door products. These product lines were helped by additional sales of WinGuard and Storefront products coupled with additional sales from a previous acquisition.

Net income surged by 44% to reach $24 million in 2015 mainly due to the steep rise in sales and profits to improvement in the housing market (both new home construction and remodels) and aggressive marketing of its WinGuard product line. Cash flow from operations has risen along with sales and profits jumping 46% during 2015.

Strategy

PGT is focused on its core market — Florida — where it's looking to gain market share through promotional activities. The company also has programs and partnerships with national accounts to increase sales. The firm is focused on growing in both the new construction and remodeling markets.

In 2015 it launched Vinyl WinGuard and EnergyVue its new line of vinyl impact-resistant and non-impact energy saving windows. The company intends for the product line to replace various existing lines of vinyl impact-resistant and energy saving windows.

PGT's prospects for growth rely in part on demand during adverse weather conditions and also on the enforcement of building codes that mandate the use of impact-resistant windows and doors. The company began to pioneer such products in the aftermath of Hurricane Andrew in 1992.

Mergers and Acquisitions

In 2016 PGT purchased WinDoor a provider of high-performance impact-resistant windows and doors for five-star resorts luxury high rise condominiums hotels and custom residential homes. The deal increased its penetration into the commercial and high-end fenestration markets and added a line of thermally-broken products and new sliding and swing door product lines.

In September 2014 PGT acquired CGI Windows & Doors Holdings of Miami a local rival for $111 million. With $45 million in annual sales CGI will continue manufacturing and selling its own brand of storm-resistant products and operate as a subsidiary of PGT. The purchase of CGI which was the company's first major acquisition strengthens PGT's product line and should help it compete against national suppliers. CGI is expected to add to earnings in 2015.

EXECUTIVES

Chairman and CEO, Rodney (Rod) Hershberger, age 61, $476,100 total compensation
President and COO, Jeffrey T. (Jeff) Jackson, age 52, $427,268 total compensation
VP and General Counsel, Mario Ferrucci, age 54, $233,155 total compensation

SVP and CFO, Bradley (Brad) West, age 48, $219,270 total compensation
VP; General Manager Glass Operations, Martin Bracamonte
VP and General Manager PGT Custom Windows+Doors, Bob Keller
Auditors: KPMG LLP

LOCATIONS

HQ: PGT Innovations Inc
1070 Technology Drive, North Venice, FL 34275
Phone: 941 480-1600
Web: www.pgtinnovations.com

PRODUCTS/OPERATIONS

2013 Sales

	$ mil.	% of total
Impact window and door products	183.4	77
Other window & door products	56.9	23
Total	**239.3**	**100**

COMPETITORS

Andersen Corporation	Quanex Building
Atrium	Products
JELD-WEN	Silver Line Building
Keller Manufacturing	Products
MI Windows and Doors	Simonton Windows Inc.
Nor-Dec	TRACO
Pella	

HISTORICAL FINANCIALS

Company Type: Public

Income Statement

FYE: December 30

	REVENUE ($ mil.)	NET INCOME ($ mil.)	NET PROFIT MARGIN	EMPLOYEES
12/17	511.0	39.8	7.8%	2,700
12/16*	458.5	23.7	5.2%	2,600
01/16	389.8	23.5	6.0%	2,300
01/15	306.3	16.4	5.4%	1,900
12/13	239.3	26.8	11.2%	1,400
Annual Growth	**20.9%**	**10.4%**	**—**	**17.8%**

*Fiscal year change

2017 Year-End Financials

Debt ratio: 47.0%	No. of shares (mil.): 49.8
Return on equity: 25.9%	Dividends
Cash ($ mil.): 34.0	Yield: —
Current ratio: 3.49	Payout: —
Long-term debt ($ mil.): 212.6	Market value ($ mil.): 839.0

	STOCK PRICE ($) FY Close	P/E High/Low	Earnings	PER SHARE ($) Dividends	Book Value
12/17	16.85	21 13	0.77	0.00	3.52
12/16*	11.45	25 18	0.47	0.00	2.69
01/16	11.39	33 17	0.47	0.00	2.19
01/15	9.76	35 21	0.33	0.00	1.55
12/13	10.01	21 8	0.51	0.00	1.05
Annual Growth	**13.9%**		**10.8%**	**—**	**35.4%**

*Fiscal year change

Phillips 66 Partners LP

How many ways can you break up an oil and gas company? The ConocoPhillips and Phillips 66 family of companies may be trying to find out.

Phillips 66 Partners is the mid-stream component owning and acquiring crude oil refined petroleum and natural gas liquids pipelines terminals and storage facilities in the US. The company has capacity for about 650 million barrels a day and its assets include 135 miles of pipeline terminals and docks connected to Phillips 66 refineries in Texas Louisiana and Illinois. Phillips 66 Partners earns revenue from fees it charges for transportation and storage of petroleum. In 2016 it announced plans to buy some pipelines and terminals from Phillips 66 for $1.3 billion.

IPO

The company plans to use its $378 million in IPO proceeds to repay debt and for general corporate purposes including possible future acquisitions.

Strategy

Going forward Phillips 66 Partners plans to provide its transportation and storage services to Phillips 66 and third parties. It also intends to pursue acquisitions through a right-of-first-refusal deal with Phillips 66 and through third parties.

Ownership

Phillips 66 owns all of Phillips 66 Partners pre-IPO.

Auditors: Ernst & Young LLP

LOCATIONS

HQ: Phillips 66 Partners LP
2331 CityWest Blvd., Houston, TX 77042
Phone: 855 283-9237
Web: www.phillips66partners.com

COMPETITORS

Buckeye Partners	Plains All American
EnLink Midstream	Pipeline
Partners	Sunoco Logistics
Energy Transfer	TransMontaigne
Enterprise Products	Williams Companies
K-Sea Transportation	
Kinder Morgan Energy	
Partners	

HISTORICAL FINANCIALS

Company Type: Public

Income Statement

FYE: December 31

	REVENUE ($ mil.)	NET INCOME ($ mil.)	NET PROFIT MARGIN	EMPLOYEES
12/17	1,169.0	524.0	44.8%	0
12/16	873.0	408.0	46.7%	0
12/15	348.1	194.2	55.8%	0
12/14	229.1	124.4	54.3%	0
12/13	106.8	60.7	56.8%	0
Annual Growth	**81.9%**	**71.4%**	**—**	**—**

2017 Year-End Financials

Debt ratio: 55.2%	No. of shares (mil.): 124.0
Return on equity: ***.***.*%	Dividends
Cash ($ mil.): 185.0	Yield: 0.0%
Current ratio: 1.71	Payout: 92.8%
Long-term debt ($ mil.): 2,920.0	Market value ($ mil.): 6,494.0

	STOCK PRICE ($) FY Close	P/E High/Low	Earnings	PER SHARE ($) Dividends	Book Value
12/17	52.35	22 17	2.59	2.41	17.42
12/16	48.64	29 20	2.20	1.98	14.32
12/15	61.40	24 14	3.26	1.54	4.63
12/14	68.93	27 12	2.93	1.12	0.94
12/13	37.93	48 37	0.80	0.15	7.99
Annual Growth	**8.4%**		**34.1%**	**98.5%**	**21.5%**

Physicians Realty Trust

Physicians Realty Trust doesn't make house calls. The real estate investment trust (REIT) owns and invests in doctor's offices and other health care properties that are leased to hospitals and medical groups. A self-managed REIT its portfolio consists of more than 25 medical office buildings in about a dozen states. Tenants include Fresenius Dialysis Hackley Hospital and Piedmont Hospital. Physicians Realty Trust was formed in 2013 with properties owned by investment bank B.C. Ziegler & Company. As a REIT it is exempt from paying federal income tax as long as it distributes 90% of profits back to shareholders. Physicians Realty Trust went public in 2013 raising $120 million.

IPO

Physicians Realty Trust went public in July 2013 with an offering that raised $120 million. The proceeds were used to purchase additional properties and retire debt.

Geographic Reach

Based in Milwaukee Physicians Realty Trust has properties in 13 states including Georgia Texas and Michigan.

Financial Performance

The healthcare properties REIT reported revenue of $16.8 million in 2013 an increase of 30% versus 2012. The double-digit gain was driven by increased rental revenue from eight properties that returned $3.6 million in 2013. Despite the sizable gain in revenue Physicians Realty Trust was unprofitable in 2013 posting a loss of nearly $1.7 million due to acquisition costs and interest expense.

Strategy

Post IPO the REIT has been aggressively purchasing additional health care properties. In March 2014 it acquired and leased back two long-term acute care hospitals located in Pittsburgh Pennsylvania and Fort Worth Texas. Also in 2014 it acquired the Eagles Landing Family Practice medical office buildings consisting of four properties in Georgia. It also bought a hospital and two medical office buildings in San Antonio Texas. The REIT's overall strategy is to invest in real estate tied to health care delivery such as medical offices buildings outpatient treatment facilities acute and post-acute care hospitals as well as other real estate related to the health care industry.

EXECUTIVES

EVP and Chief Investment Officer, John W. Sweet, $255,385 total compensation
President and CEO, John T. Thomas, $630,769 total compensation
SVP and Principal Accounting and Reporting Officer, John W. Lucey, $240,000 total compensation
SVP Asset and Investment Management, Mark D. Theine, $249,231 total compensation
EVP and CFO, Jeff Theiler, $375,000 total compensation
EVP Investments, D. Deeni Taylor
Chairman, Tommy G. Thompson
Auditors: Ernst & Young LLP

LOCATIONS

HQ: Physicians Realty Trust
309 N. Water Street, Suite 500, Milwaukee, WI 53202
Phone: 414 367-5600

COMPETITORS

HCP	Sabra Health Care
Healthcare Realty Trust	Tiptree
Legacy Healthcare	Universal Health Realty
Medical Properties Trust	Ventas
National Health Investors	Welltower

HISTORICAL FINANCIALS

Company Type: Public

Income Statement — FYE: December 31

	REVENUE ($ mil.)	NET INCOME ($ mil.)	NET PROFIT MARGIN	EMPLOYEES
12/17	343.5	38.1	11.1%	63
12/16	241.0	29.9	12.4%	41
12/15	129.4	11.7	9.1%	25
12/14	53.3	(4.0)	—	14
12/13	16.8	(1.6)	—	5
Annual Growth	112.7%	—	—	88.4%

2017 Year-End Financials

Debt ratio: 35.4%
Return on equity: 1.8%
Cash ($ mil.): 2.7
Current ratio: 0.23
Long-term debt ($ mil.): 1,477.4

No. of shares (mil.): 181.4
Dividends
  Yield: 0.0%
  Payout: 395.6%
Market value ($ mil.): 3,264.0

	STOCK PRICE ($) FY Close	P/E High/Low	PER SHARE ($) Earnings	Dividends	Book Value
12/17	17.99	95 75	0.23	0.91	13.63
12/16	18.96	100 72	0.22	0.90	12.79
12/15	16.86	119 94	0.15	0.90	11.76
12/14	16.60	— —	(0.12)	0.90	10.56
12/13	12.74	— —	(0.13)	0.18	9.85
Annual Growth	9.0%	— —	—	49.9%	8.5%

Pinnacle Financial Partners Inc

Pinnacle Financial Partners works to be at the top of the community banking mountain in central Tennessee. It's the holding company for Tennessee-based Pinnacle Bank which has grown to some 40 branches in the Nashville and Knoxville areas since its founding in 2000. Serving consumers and small- to mid-sized business the $9 billion financial institution provides standard services such as checking and savings accounts CDs credit cards and loans and mortgages. The company also offers investment and trust services through Pinnacle Asset Management while its insurance brokerage subsidiary Miller Loughry Beach specializes in property/casualty policies.Pinnacle agreed to merge with North Carolina-based BNC Bancorp in 2017.

Operations

Pinnacle Financial Partners' commercial and industrial loans and commercial real estate loans account for nearly 40% and 20% respectively of its total portfolio of loans.

As part of its primary services to both individual and commercial clients Tennessee-based subsidiary Pinnacle Bank provides core deposits including savings checking interest-bearing checking money market and certificate of deposit accounts.

The bank's lending products include commercial real estate and consumer loans to individuals and small- to medium-sized businesses and professional entities. Pinnacle Bank Partners also offers auto dealer finance services to certain automobile dealers and their customers. Additionally it offers Pinnacle-branded consumer credit cards to select clients.

Its convenience-centered products and services include 24-hour telephone and Internet banking debit and credit cards direct deposit and cash management services.

Geographic Reach

Based in Tennessee Pinnacle Financial Partners has become the second-largest bank holding company in the state with nearly 35 offices in eight Middle Tennessee counties and four Knoxville offices. It boasts locations in Nashville Knoxville Murfreesboro Dickson Ashland City Mt. Juliet Lebanon Franklin Brentwood Hendersonville Goodlettsville Smyrna and Shelbyville.

Sales and Marketing

Pinnacle Bank traditionally has obtained its deposits through personal solicitation by its officers and directors although it has used media advertising more in recent years due to its advertising and banking sponsorship with the Tennessee Titans NFL Football team. While it would prefer its customers to bank in person the institution allows customers to bank remotely.

Its marketing and other business development costs have risen in recent years: $4.13 million $3.639 million and $3.636 million in 2014 2013 and 2012 respectively.

Financial Performance

Pinnacle Financial Partners has enjoyed steady revenue and profit growth for the past several years thanks to positive loan growth. Revenue in 2014 rose by 9% to a record $258.77 million mostly to thanks to 9% growth in interest income from loans as the bank's loan assets grew by double digits. Pinnacle also saw double-digit growth in its fee income from service charges on deposit accounts as deposit balances grew and double-digit growth in its investment services income and trust fees as brokerage and trust account balances grew.

Higher revenue drove net income up by 22% to a record $70.47 million. Operations provided $95.06 million or 25% less cash than in 2013 primarily because the bank collected roughly $30 million less in proceeds from its mortgage loans held for sale than it did the year before.

Strategy

Pinnacle's goal is to become the dominant bank in its home market of the Southeast. In 2016 it acquired Avenue Financial Holdings for $200 million and followed up the acquisition by agreeing to merge with regional rival BNC Bancorp of North Carolina in 2017. Once the merger completes the combined company will be the biggest in the region.

Pinnacle Financial Partners been looking to diversify its revenue streams through strategic investments in recent years. In early 2015 for example Tennessee-based subsidiary Pinnacle Bank purchased a 30% membership interest in Bankers Healthcare Group LLC which makes term loans to healthcare professionals and practices for $75 million.

Primarily serving small- to medium-sized businesses in the Nashville and Knoxville areas the company in 2013 began extending its reach in its primary markets by opening its fourth full-service banking location in the Knoxville market in the Cedar Bluff area.

Mergers and Acquisitions

In 2017 Pinnacle agreed to merge with BNC Bancorp. The combined company will have assets of some $20 billion and a presence in four states and in 12 of the largest metropolitan markets in the Southeast.

In 2016 Pinnacle acquired Avenue Financial Holdings (holding company of Avenue Bank with five banking locations in Nashville); the transaction was valued at some $201.4 million. Avenue Bank will operate as a division of Pinnacle Bank for a few months after which the companies will combine operations.

EXECUTIVES

President and CEO, M. Terry Turner, age 62, $784,700 total compensation

EVP and Chief Administrative Officer, Hugh M. Queener, age 62, $376,700 total compensation

EVP and Senior Lending Officer; Manager Client Advisory Group Nashville, J. Edward (Ed) White, age 68, $145,000 total compensation

EVP and Director Assocaite and Client Experience, Joanne B. Jackson, age 61, $117,000 total compensation

CFO, Harold R. Carpenter, age 59, $376,700 total compensation

SVP and Manager Trust and Investment Advisory, Robert Newman

President Pinnacle Knoxville, Mike DiStefano

Chief Credit Officer; President Pinnacle Knoxville, J. Harvey White, $283,800 total compensation

EVP and Manager Pinnacle Asset Management, Gary Collier

SVP and Senior Credit Officer Real Estate, Mike Hendren

SVP and Senior Credit Officer, Tim Huestis

SVP and CIO, Randy Withrow

President and CEO PNFP Capital Markets, Roger Osborne

SVP and Manager Residential Mortgage Services, Ross Kinney

EVP and Area Executive Rutherford County, Bill Jones

Chief Investment Officer, Mac Johnston

SVP Small Business Banking, Chip Higgins

EVP and Financial Advisor, Jerry Hampton

President Pinnacle Memphis, Damon Bell

Senior Vice President, Bill Decamp

Senior Vice President and financial advisor in Nashville, Lynn Kendrick

Senior Vice President, Kay Mcalister

Senior Vice President, Rhonda Smith

Vice President, Tyane Powell

Senior Vice President, Kevin Marchetti

Senior Vice President Financial Advisor, Cynthia Oliva

Senior Vice President, Larry Kain

Senior Vice President Financial Advisor, Lynn Lassiter

Senior Vice President, Michael G Lindseth

Senior Vice President, David Edwards

Senior Vice President And Financial Advisor, Brande Thomas

Mortgage Advisor Senior Vice President, Jeff Mayfield

Senior Vice President, Eric Kruse

Senior Vice President, Gail Outland

Senior Vice President, Steve Uebelhor

Senior Vice President Mortgage Advisor, Chris Maultsby

Senior Vice President, Sarah Teague

Senior Vice President, Kirk Garrett

Senior Vice President, Mary Isham

Senior Vice President, Rex Jones

Senior Vice President, Ken Warren

Senior Vice President, William Diehl

Senior Vice President Financial Advisor, Kim Ciukowski

Vice President Automotive Finance, Jeff Rhodes

Vice President, Luciano Scala

Vice President, Shelly Donohoo

SENIOR VICE PRESIDENT, Todd Carter

Senior Vice President Business Banking Financial Advisor, Dennis Mitchell

Senior Vice President, Kim Jenny

Executive Vice President And Chief Financial Officerand#8230, Alan Haefele

Senior Vice President, Dale Floyd

Senior Vice President, Clark Cox

Senior Vice President And Financial Adviser In Commercial Real Estate, Thomas Vester

Senior Vice President, Lucy Foutch

Senior Vice President Lending, Roger Leitner

Vice President, Kevin Roddey

Executive Vice President and Senior credit Officer, Edward White

Vice President Administration, Beth Hobbs

Senior Vice President, Donna Taylor

Senior Vice President and Communications Director, Sarae Janes Lewis

Senior Vice President Financial Advisor, Keely Ritchie

Senior Vice President Financial Advisor, Stacey Richards

Senior Vice President, Bryan Bean

Senior Vice President and Financial Advisor, Ashley Preskenis

Senior Vice President and Financial Advisor, Nancy Benskin

Senior Vice President Credit Advisor, Stacey Fantom

Senior Vice President Credit Advisor, Kendria Northcutt

Senior Vice President, Sam King

SENIOR VICE PRESIDENT, Tom Dozier

Senior Vice President, Gina Scott

Senior Vice President and Trust Officer, Scott Lindsey

Senior Vice President, Ron Stinson

Senior Vice President, Tim Bewley

Senior Vice President, Jason Reierson

Senior Vice President, John Douglas

Senior Vice President Financial Advisor, Amy Campbell

Senior Vice President, Diane Jones

Senior Vice President, Steven Zimmerman

Vice President: Treasury Management Advisor, Joy Bowen

CMB Senior Vice President, Jeff Tucker

Senior Vice President Mortgage Advisor, Clint Porter

SENIOR VICE PRESIDENT, Andy Wright

Senior Vice President, Ryan Murphy

CTFA Senior Vice President Financial Advisor, Steve Scott

Senior Vice President and Mortgage Advisor, Donathan Cassidy

SENIOR VICE PRESIDENT MANAGING DIRECTOR, Nathan Kurita

Senior Vice President, Rick Nelson

Senior Vice President, Bruce Von Almen

Senior Vice President, Jimmy Moncrief

Executive Vice President Music and Entertainment, Andy Moats

Senior Vice President, Dan Neumann

Senior Vice President Mortgage Advisor, Todd Flynn

Vice President, Cheryl Plummer

Senior Vice President, Donna Edwards

Senior Vice President, Glenn Layne

Vp Sba Business Development Officer, Janet Matthew

Mortgage Adv Sor Vice President, Debbie Del Corro

Senior Vice President Area Executive, Eddie Blount

Assistant Vice President, Reilly Shahna

Vice Chairman, Ed C. Loughry, age 75

Chairman, Robert A. (Rob) McCabe, age 67

Board Member, Charles Brock

Board Member, David Ingram

Board Member, Marty Dickens

Board Member, Joseph Galante

Auditors: Crowe Horwath LLP

LOCATIONS

HQ: Pinnacle Financial Partners Inc
150 Third Avenue South, Suite 900, Nashville, TN 37201
Phone: 615 744-3700
Web: www.pnfp.com

PRODUCTS/OPERATIONS

2014 Revenue

	% of total
Interest Income	80
Non-interest Income	20
Total	**100**

Selected Subsidiaries

Pinnacle Advisory Services Inc.
Pinnacle Credit Enhancement Holdings Inc.
Pinnacle National Bank
    Miller & Loughry Inc. (dba Miller Loughry Beach)
    PFP Title Company
    Pinnacle Community Development Corporation
    Pinnacle Nashville Real Estate Inc.
    Pinnacle Rutherford Real Estate Inc.
    Pinnacle Rutherford Towers Inc.
    Pinnacle Service Company Inc.
PNFP Insurance Inc.

COMPETITORS

BB&T	Regions Financial
Bank of America	SunTrust
Fifth Third	U.S. Bancorp
First Horizon	

HISTORICAL FINANCIALS

Company Type: Public

Income Statement				FYE: December 31
	ASSETS ($ mil.)	NET INCOME ($ mil.)	INCOME AS % OF ASSETS	EMPLOYEES
12/17	22,205.7	173.9	0.8%	2,132
12/16	11,194.6	127.2	1.1%	1,180
12/15	8,715.4	95.5	1.1%	1,065
12/14	6,018.2	70.4	1.2%	767
12/13	5,563.7	57.7	1.0%	748
Annual Growth	**41.3%**	**31.8%**	**—**	**29.9%**

2017 Year-End Financials

Return on assets: 1.0%
Return on equity: 6.6%
Long-term debt ($ mil.): —
No. of shares (mil.): 77.7
Sales ($ mil.): 781.0

Dividends
Yield: 0.0%
Payout: 20.7%
Market value ($ mil.): 5,154.0

	STOCK PRICE ($) FY Close	P/E High/Low		PER SHARE ($) Earnings	Dividends	Book Value
12/17	66.30	26	21	2.70	0.56	47.70
12/16	69.30	24	15	2.91	0.56	32.28
12/15	51.36	22	14	2.52	0.48	28.25
12/14	39.54	20	15	2.01	0.32	22.46
12/13	32.53	20	11	1.67	0.08	20.55
Annual Growth	19.5%	—	—	12.8%	62.7%	23.4%

Planet Fitness Inc

Auditors: KPMG LLP

LOCATIONS

HQ: Planet Fitness Inc
4 Liberty Lane West, Hampton, NH 03842
Phone: 603 750-0001
Web: www.planetfitness.com

HISTORICAL FINANCIALS

Company Type: Public

Income Statement   FYE: December 31

	REVENUE ($ mil.)	NET INCOME ($ mil.)	NET PROFIT MARGIN	EMPLOYEES
12/17	429.9	33.1	7.7%	1,046
12/16	378.2	21.5	5.7%	963
12/15	330.5	18.5	5.6%	936
12/14	279.7	36.8	13.2%	842
12/13	211.0	25.4	12.1%	0
Annual Growth	19.5%	6.8%	—	—

2017 Year-End Financials

Debt ratio: 64.4%
Return on equity: ***.***.*%
Cash ($ mil.): 113.0
Current ratio: 1.58
Long-term debt ($ mil.): 696.5

No. of shares (mil.): 98.3
Dividends
Yield: —
Payout: —
Market value ($ mil.): 3,407.0

	STOCK PRICE ($) FY Close	P/E High/Low		PER SHARE ($) Earnings	Dividends	Book Value
12/17	34.63	83	44	0.42	0.00	(1.21)
12/16	20.10	49	27	0.50	2.78	(1.33)
12/15	15.63	174	136	0.11	0.00	(0.16)
Annual Growth	48.8%	—	—	95.4%	—	—

Plumas Bancorp Inc

Plumas Bancorp is the holding company for Plumas Bank which serves individuals and businesses in the northeastern corner of California from Lake Tahoe to the Oregon border. Through more than a dozen branches the bank offers deposit products such as checking savings and retirement accounts and certificates of deposit. Loans secured by real estate account for more than half of Plumas Bank's loan portfolio; combined commercial and agricultural loans make up about a quarter. The bank writes consumer loans as well. It also provides access to investment products and services such as financial planning mutual funds and annuities.

EXECUTIVES

Vice President SBA Underwriter, John Rash
Auditors: Vavrinek, Trine, Day & Co., LLP

LOCATIONS

HQ: Plumas Bancorp Inc
35 South Lindan Avenue, Quincy, CA 95971
Phone: 530 283-7305
Web: www.plumasbank.com

COMPETITORS

Bank of America	Scott Valley Bank
Bank of Commerce	TriCo Bancshares
Bank of the West	U.S. Bancorp
North Valley Bancorp	Wells Fargo

HISTORICAL FINANCIALS

Company Type: Public

Income Statement   FYE: December 31

	ASSETS ($ mil.)	NET INCOME ($ mil.)	INCOME AS % OF ASSETS	EMPLOYEES
12/17	745.4	8.1	1.1%	161
12/16	657.9	7.4	1.1%	155
12/15	599.2	5.8	1.0%	151
12/14	538.8	4.7	0.9%	155
12/13	515.7	3.4	0.7%	159
Annual Growth	9.6%	24.3%	—	0.3%

2017 Year-End Financials

Return on assets: 1.1%
Return on equity: 15.7%
Long-term debt ($ mil.): —
No. of shares (mil.): 5.0
Sales ($ mil.): 37.2

Dividends
Yield: 0.0%
Payout: 17.7%
Market value ($ mil.): 118.0

	STOCK PRICE ($) FY Close	P/E High/Low		PER SHARE ($) Earnings	Dividends	Book Value
12/17	23.20	14	10	1.58	0.28	11.00
12/16	19.00	12	5	1.47	0.10	9.80
12/15	8.68	8	6	1.15	0.00	8.79
12/14	7.99	8	6	0.95	0.00	7.60
12/13	6.22	9	4	0.75	0.00	6.39
Annual Growth	39.0%	—	—	20.5%	—	14.5%

Pope Resources LP

More earthly than divine Pope Resources owns or manages more than 150000 acres of timberland and development property in Washington. Its holdings include the 70000-acre Hood Canal and 44000-acre Columbia tree farms in Washington. It sells its Douglas fir and other timber products mainly in the US Japan China and Korea; Weyerhaeuser and Simpson Investment Company are major customers. Pope Resources also invests in and manages two timberland investment funds and provides investment management and consulting services to third-party timberland owners and managers in Washington Oregon and California. Its real estate unit acquires develops resells and rents residential and commercial real estate.

Pope Resources' fee timber segment also gains revenue by selling gravel and by leasing cellular communication towers.

The partnership's Olympic Property Group real estate operations relate to its nearly 3000-acre portfolio of higher-and-better-use properties that may be reforested developed for sale as improved property or sold in developed or undeveloped acreage tracts. The company's Rural Lifestyles projects allow it to resell fully logged plots that no longer have value for timber production. Its operations are focused on residential and commercial property in Port Gamble Kingston Bremerton and Gig Harbor.

In 2004 the company acquired 3300 acres of timberland in southwest Washington from Plum Creek Timber Company Inc. for $8.5 million; it also paid about $12 million to a private party for 1339 acres of timberland in western Washington. That year the company sold 426 acres in northern Kitsap County near Kingston Washington and agreed to extend to the county an option to acquire up to 360 additional acres of adjacent land (in one or two phases); the option will expire in July 2008.

In 2006 the company sold more than 200 acres of residential land for $12 million.

Pope Resources was spun off from Pope & Talbot in 1985 and the latter retains some control of the company through managing general partner Pope MGP Inc. Pope MGP is owned by Emily Andrews and Peter Pope (former chairman of Pope & Talbot) who own 12% and 7% respectively of Pope Resources.

EXECUTIVES

Vice President of Timberland Operations, Mike Mackelwich
Auditors: KPMG LLP

LOCATIONS

HQ: Pope Resources LP
19950 7th Avenue NE, Suite 200, Poulsbo, WA 98370
Phone: 360 697-6626   Fax: 360 697-1156
Web: www.poperesources.com

PRODUCTS/OPERATIONS

Selected Subsidiaries
Olympic Property Group
Olympic Resource Management

COMPETITORS

Hampton Affiliates	Potlatch
International Paper	Rayonier

HISTORICAL FINANCIALS

Company Type: Public

Income Statement   FYE: December 31

	REVENUE ($ mil.)	NET INCOME ($ mil.)	NET PROFIT MARGIN	EMPLOYEES
12/17	99.8	17.8	17.9%	70
12/16	80.4	5.9	7.4%	65
12/15	78.0	10.9	14.0%	66
12/14	87.4	12.4	14.2%	60
12/13	70.6	13.1	18.6%	58
Annual Growth	9.0%	8.0%	—	4.8%

2017 Year-End Financials

Debt ratio: 33.4%
Return on equity: —
Cash ($ mil.): 5.2
Current ratio: 1.85
Long-term debt ($ mil.): 127.3

No. of shares (mil.): 4.3
Dividends
  Yield: 0.0%
  Payout: 68.2%
Market value ($ mil.): 301.0

	STOCK PRICE ($) FY Close	P/E High/Low	PER SHARE ($) Earnings	Dividends	Book Value
12/17	69.74	19 16	4.10	2.80	14.97
12/16	66.32	52 39	1.35	2.80	13.70
12/15	64.07	28 23	2.51	2.70	15.01
12/14	63.63	25 22	2.82	2.50	14.99
12/13	67.00	24 19	2.96	2.00	15.88
Annual Growth	1.0%	— —	8.5%	8.8%	(1.5%)

PQ Group Holdings Inc

Auditors: PricewaterhouseCoopers LLP

LOCATIONS

HQ: PQ Group Holdings Inc
  300 Lindenwood Drive, Malvern, PA 19355
Phone: 610 651-4400
Web: www.pqcorp.com

HISTORICAL FINANCIALS

Company Type: Public

Income Statement   FYE: December 31

	REVENUE ($ mil.)	NET INCOME ($ mil.)	NET PROFIT MARGIN	EMPLOYEES
12/17	1,472.1	57.6	3.9%	3,149
12/16	1,064.1	(79.7)	—	2,949
12/15	388.8	11.4	2.9%	0
12/14	35.5	(22.0)	—	0
Annual Growth	246.0%	—	—	—

2017 Year-End Financials

Debt ratio: 50.5%
Return on equity: 4.3%
Cash ($ mil.): 66.2
Current ratio: 1.90
Long-term debt ($ mil.): 2,185.3

No. of shares (mil.): 135.2
Dividends
  Yield: —
  Payout: —
Market value ($ mil.): 2,225.0

	STOCK PRICE ($) FY Close	P/E High/Low	PER SHARE ($) Earnings	Dividends	Book Value
12/17	16.45	34 29	0.52	0.00	12.04
12/16	0.00	— —	(21.01)	0.00	8.35
Annual Growth	—		—	—	44.2%

PRA Health Sciences Inc

Auditors: DELOITTE & TOUCHE LLP

LOCATIONS

HQ: PRA Health Sciences Inc
  4130 ParkLake Avenue, Suite 400, Raleigh, NC 27612
Phone: 919 786-8200
Web: www.prahs.com

HISTORICAL FINANCIALS

Company Type: Public

Income Statement   FYE: December 31

	REVENUE ($ mil.)	NET INCOME ($ mil.)	NET PROFIT MARGIN	EMPLOYEES
12/17	2,259.3	86.9	3.8%	15,800
12/16	1,811.7	68.1	3.8%	13,000
12/15	1,613.8	81.7	5.1%	12,000
12/14	1,459.5	(35.7)	—	11,000
12/13	379.2	(39.9)	—	10,600
Annual Growth	56.2%	—		10.5%

2017 Year-End Financials

Debt ratio: 40.0%
Return on equity: 10.4%
Cash ($ mil.): 192.2
Current ratio: 0.90
Long-term debt ($ mil.): 1,225.4

No. of shares (mil.): 63.6
Dividends
  Yield: —
  Payout: —
Market value ($ mil.): 5,794.0

	STOCK PRICE ($) FY Close	P/E High/Low	PER SHARE ($) Earnings	Dividends	Book Value
12/17	91.07	66 39	1.32	0.00	14.63
12/16	55.12	52 34	1.06	0.00	11.84
12/15	45.27	36 17	1.29	0.00	11.66
12/14	24.22	— —	(0.83)	0.00	11.32
Annual Growth	55.5%	—	—	—	8.9%

Preferred Apartment Communities Inc.

Preferred Apartment Communities prefers to own retail properties with multifamily ones. The real estate investment trust (REIT) owns nearly 20 multifamily communities with 6100-plus units as well as some 20 grocery-anchored retail shopping centers with some 2 million sq. ft. of leasable space in major metro areas including Atlanta Austin Dallas Houston Nashville Orlando and Philadelphia. Its largest retail tenants include Publix Kroger and Tom Thumb. The REIT also buys senior mortgage loans or mezzanine debt and membership or partnership interests in multifamily properties. Preferred Apartment Communities was formed in 2009 and went public in 2011.

Operations

The REIT operates three business segments: Multifamily which made up 60% of its total revenue during 2015 and generates rental income from its 19 owned multifamily apartment communities; Financing (28% of revenue) which generates interest income from its investment portfolio of real estate loans bridge loans and other development financing-related instruments; and Retail (12% of revenue) which collects rental income from its portfolio of 14 grocery-anchored shopping centers.

Some of Preferred Apartment Communities' subsidiaries include: Preferred Residential Management Preferred Campus Management Main Street Apartment Homes New Market Properties LLC and Preferred Capital Securities.

Geographic Reach

Atlanta-based Preferred had properties in 24 cities across 11 states at the end of 2015 mostly in large metropolitan cities including major metro areas including Atlanta Austin Dallas Houston Nashville Orlando and Philadelphia.

Sales and Marketing

More than 50% of the REIT's retail portfolio (by gross leasable area or GLA) was occupied by grocery anchor tenants at the end of 2015 which included Publix (27% of GLA) Kroger (15%) Bi-Lo (5%) Tom Thumb of Safeway (3%) and The Fresh Market (2%).

Financial Performance

Preferred Apartment Communities' revenues have risen ten-fold since 2011 mostly as new property acquisitions have spurred higher rental income. The REIT's bottom line has been fluctuating between losses and profitable years despite consistently reporting operating income growth mainly as it's had to pay for growth-supporting financing costs.

The REIT's revenue nearly doubled to $109.3 million during 2015 mainly as to new multifamily property acquisitions continued to boost rental revenues. Retail revenue also quadrupled for the year on new property acquisitions while financing revenue grew by 41% as the REIT purchased 10 real estate loans and bridge loans.

Despite exceptional revenue growth in 2015 Preferred reported a loss of $2.43 million as it paid more in interest expenses on finances used to support its acquisitions. The REIT's operating cash levels more than doubled to $35.2 million as cash-denominated rental income rose during the year.

Strategy

Preferred Apartment Communities has been acquiring more retail properties in recent years to diversify beyond its core apartment holdings. The REIT prefers to buy properties in fast-growing metropolitan markets around the US which attract plenty of new renters and command higher rental prices over time as demand increases.

In late 2017 and early 2018 the company went on a buying spree. Between November and February it purchased in Atlanta a 310-unit multifamily community a class A office building and a grocery-anchored shopping center. It also bought a 265-unit multifamily facility in Jacksonville FL a 255-unit community in Richmond VA a student housing complex in Waco TX (near Baylor University) and a grocery-anchored shopping center in Naples FL.

In mid-2016 the REIT acquired another seven shopping centers (with some 650400 sq. ft. of rentable space) for $158 million

During 2015 Preferred bought nine multifamily communities — nearly doubling its existing multifamily portfolio — with 2810 units in Orlando Nashville San Antonio Charlotte Sarasota and Houston. Adding to its retail property portfolio that year it spent $88 million toward buying four grocery-anchored shopping centers with 585000 sq. ft. of GLA in the Atlanta Dallas and Chattanooga markets.

Company Background

Preferred Apartment Communities went public in 2011 raising some $45 million in its initial public offering somewhat less than the $75 million it was aiming for. Preferred used net proceeds from the offering to acquire new properties and place certain proceeds in interest-bearing short-term investments intended to help it qualify as a real estate investment trust (REIT).

CEO John A. Williams controls both Preferred Apartment Communities and its manager Preferred Apartment Advisors. Williams is also founder of US REIT Post Properties.

EXECUTIVES

Executive Vice President Chief Distribution
Officer, Albert Haworth
Executive Vice President Business Development,
Bonnie Shekarabi
VICE PRESIDENT, Susan Porter
Auditors: PricewaterhouseCoopers LLP

LOCATIONS

HQ: Preferred Apartment Communities Inc.
3284 Northside Parkway N.W., Suite 150, Atlanta, GA
30327
Phone: 770 818-4100
Web: www.pacapts.com

COMPETITORS

Apartment Investment and Management	Home Properties
	MAA
Equity Residential	Steadfast Companies
Essex Property Trust	UDR

HISTORICAL FINANCIALS

Company Type: Public

Income Statement   FYE: December 31

	REVENUE ($ mil.)	NET INCOME ($ mil.)	NET PROFIT MARGIN	EMPLOYEES
12/17	294.0	27.6	9.4%	0
12/16	200.1	(9.5)	—	0
12/15	109.3	(2.4)	—	0
12/14	56.5	2.0	3.7%	0
12/13	28.5	(3.9)	—	0
Annual Growth	79.2%	—	—	—

2017 Year-End Financials

Debt ratio: 56.2%	No. of shares (mil.): 38.5
Return on equity: 2.5%	Dividends
Cash ($ mil.): 21.0	Yield: 0.0%
Current ratio: 0.76	Payout: —
Long-term debt ($ mil.): 1,787.6	Market value ($ mil.): 781.0

	STOCK PRICE ($) FY Close	P/E High/Low	Earnings	PER SHARE ($) Dividends	Book Value
12/17	20.25	— —	(1.13)	0.94	33.08
12/16	14.91	— —	(2.11)	0.82	33.35
12/15	13.08	— —	(0.95)	0.73	22.98
12/14	9.10	— —	(0.31)	0.66	13.53
12/13	8.04	— —	(1.59)	0.61	10.76
Annual Growth	26.0%	— —	—	11.6%	32.4%

Preferred Bank (Los Angeles, CA)

Preferred Bank wants to be the bank of choice
of Chinese-Americans in Southern California. Employing a multilingual staff the bank provides international banking services to companies doing
business in the Asia/Pacific region. It targets middle-market businesses typically manufacturing
service distribution and real estate firms as well as
entrepreneurs professionals and high-net-worth
individuals through about a dozen branches in Los
Angeles Orange and San Francisco Counties. Pre-

ferred Bank offers standard deposit products such
as checking accounts savings money market and
NOW accounts. Specialized services include private
banking and international trade finance.

Geographic Reach
Preferred Bank markets its services in half a
dozen Southern Californian counties: Los Angeles
Orange Riverside San Bernardino San Francisco
and Ventura.

Financial Performance
In 2013 Preferred Bank reported about $72 mil-
lion in revenue up just more than 10% from the
prior year. The increase was solely from interest
income as non-interest income (a very small part
of overall revenue anyway) fell more than 40%.
The company saw growth in its loan portfolio that
year as well as overall deposit growth. Net income
fell 20% to $19 million; the decline was primarily
related to a boost in net income for 2012 because
of a $20 million income tax benefit (compared to
income tax expense of $12 million in 2013).

Strategy
Historically the company was focused on the
Chinese-American market and although it continues to cater to that clientele most of its current
customer base is from the diversified mainstream
market.

EXECUTIVES

EVP and CFO, Edward J. Czajka
President and COO, Wellington Chen, age 58
Chairman and CEO, Li Yu, age 77
Senior Vice President, Ted Hsu
Vice President, William Ko
Senior Vice President, Jim Belanic
Senior Vice President, John C Stipanov
Vice President, Debbie White
First Vice President, Madelyn Hayashi
Vice President, Barbara Gordon
Vice President, Craig Miller
First Vice President, Nancy Pepper
Assistant Vice President Compliance Officer,
Kristie Yang
Vice President, Elsa Chen
Vice President, Sofia Huang
Vice President Lending, Luey Couto
Senior Vice President, Ann Cheung
Vice President, Michael Nagai
Vice President, Wayne Chow
Vice President Human Resources Manager, Karen
Cangey
Vice President And Manager, Lupe Quintana
Vice President, Isabella LI
Vice President Internal Audit Manager, Carlo
Garcia
First Vice President, Philip Wong
Vice President Product Manager, John Wong
Executive Vice President Chief Credit Officer,
Jonathan Sigal
Vice Chairman, Clark Hsu
Auditors: Crowe Horwath LLP

LOCATIONS

HQ: Preferred Bank (Los Angeles, CA)
601 S. Figueroa Street, 29th Floor, Los Angeles, CA
90017
Phone: 213 891-1188
Web: www.preferredbank.com

PRODUCTS/OPERATIONS

2015 Sales

	% of total
Interest income	
Loans and leases	90
Investment securities available for sale	6
Federal funds sold	—
Non-interest income	
Fees and service charges on deposit accounts	1
Trade finance income	2
BOLI income	—
Other income	1
Total	**100**

COMPETITORS

Bank of America	City National
Bank of the West	East West Bancorp
Broadway Financial	Far East National Bank
Cathay General Bancorp	Hanmi Financial
Citigroup	MUFG Americas Holdings

HISTORICAL FINANCIALS

Company Type: Public

Income Statement   FYE: December 31

	ASSETS ($ mil.)	NET INCOME ($ mil.)	INCOME AS % OF ASSETS	EMPLOYEES
12/17	3,769.8	43.3	1.2%	238
12/16	3,221.6	36.3	1.1%	218
12/15	2,598.8	29.7	1.1%	205
12/14	2,054.1	24.5	1.2%	163
12/13	1,768.9	19.2	1.1%	148
Annual Growth	20.8%	22.6%	—	12.6%

2017 Year-End Financials

Return on assets: 1.2%	Dividends
Return on equity: 13.2%	Yield: 0.0%
Long-term debt ($ mil.): —	Payout: 25.6%
No. of shares (mil.): 15.1	Market value ($ mil.): 889.0
Sales ($ mil): 163.4	

	STOCK PRICE ($) FY Close	P/E High/Low	Earnings	PER SHARE ($) Dividends	Book Value
12/17	58.78	22 16	2.96	0.76	23.48
12/16	52.42	20 10	2.56	0.60	20.94
12/15	33.02	17 12	2.14	0.46	19.02
12/14	27.89	15 11	1.78	0.10	17.40
12/13	20.05	15 10	1.42	0.00	15.58
Annual Growth	30.9%	— —	20.2%	—	10.8%

Premier Inc

EXECUTIVES

Vice Chair of the Board, Charles E. Hart, age 66
President Chief Executive Officer and Director,
Susan D. DeVore, age 57
Chair of the Board, Richard J. (Rich) Statuto, age 59
SVP Corporate Development and Strategy, Terry
Linn
President Premier Insurance Management
Services, Robert L. Dowdy
Chief Medical Officer, Richard Bankowitz
Senior Vice President of Premier Performance
Partners, R. Wesley (Wes) Champion, age 50
Senior Vice President of Healthcare Informatics,
Keith J. Figlioli

Senior Vice President and Chief Financial Officer, Craig S. McKasson, age 49

senior Vice President people, Kelli Price

senior Vice President enterprise growth, Jennifer Arcudi

SVP Group Purchasing, John Biggers

Vice Chairman, Keith Pitts

senior Vice President member field services, Andy Brailo

President and chief mission officer, Alan R. Yordy

Chief Operating Officer, Michael J. (Mike) Alkire, age 53

Chief Sales Officer, Gary S. Long

President of Supply Chain Services, Durral R. Gilbert, age 50

Chief Marketing Officer, Chip Carter

Director, Michael D. Connelly

Director, Glenn D. Steele Jr., age 70

Director, James H. (Jim) Hinton

Director, William E. Mayer, age 74

Director, Mark A. Eustis, age 62

Director, Dennis Vonderfecht

Director, Francisco J. (Frank) Perez

Vice Chair of the Board, Charles E. Hart, age 66

President Chief Executive Officer and Director, Susan D. DeVore, age 57

Director, Sister Mary Jean Ryan

Director, Christine K. Cassel

Director, Lee Perlman

Director, Thomas J. Strauss

Director, Nick W. Turkal

Director, J. Thomas Jones

Auditors: Ernst & Young LLP

LOCATIONS

HQ: Premier Inc
13034 Ballantyne Corporate Place, Charlotte, NC 28277
Phone: 704 357-0022
Web: www.premierinc.com

COMPETITORS

Aetna	HealthTrust
Allscripts	MedAssets
CVS Caremark	Medline Industries
Deloitte & Touche	Novation
Express Scripts	Owens & Minor
Global Healthcare	PSS World Medical
Exchange	UnitedHealth Group

HISTORICAL FINANCIALS

Company Type: Public

Income Statement | | | | FYE: June 30

	REVENUE ($ mil.)	NET INCOME ($ mil.)	NET PROFIT MARGIN	EMPLOYEES
06/18	1,661.2	33.3	2.0%	2,200
06/17	1,454.6	113.4	7.8%	2,400
06/16	1,162.5	41.6	3.6%	2,100
06/15	1,007.0	38.7	3.8%	1,800
06/14	910.5	28.3	3.1%	1,600
Annual Growth	**16.2%**	**4.1%**	**—**	**8.3%**

2018 Year-End Financials

Debt ratio: 4.6%
Return on equity: ***,***.*%
Cash ($ mil.): 152.3
Current ratio: 0.95
Long-term debt ($ mil.): 6.9

No. of shares (mil.): 133.1
Dividends
Yield: —
Payout: —
Market value ($ mil.): 4,842.0

	STOCK PRICE ($) FY Close	P/E High/Low		PER SHARE ($) Earnings	Dividends	Book Value
06/18	36.38	10	8	1.36	0.00	11.22
06/17	36.00	23	19	1.51	0.00	10.60
06/16	32.70	2	2	1.33	0.00	8.34
06/15	38.46	—	—	(24.25)	0.00	6.68
06/14	29.00	—	—	(105.85)	0.00	5.35
Annual Growth	**5.8%**	—	—	—	—	**20.3%**

Prestige Consumer Healthcare Inc

Prestige Brands is a lifesaver in the business of resuscitating offloaded consumer brands. The company acquires develops and markets over-the-counter (OTC) drugs and household cleaning products. Its portfolio includes Chloraseptic Clear Eyes Comet Compound W Doctor's Nightguard Little Remedies PediaCare Murine Monistat New Skin and many other big-name brands. Prestige Brands contracts out manufacturing of its products which are sold through mass merchandisers and retail stores primarily in North America. The company was formed in 1996 to acquire and revitalize leading but neglected consumer brands divested by major consumer companies such as Procter & Gamble.

Operations

Prestige operates through three segments: North American OTC Healthcare International OTC Healthcare and Household Cleaning. Its around 30 core OTC brands which contribute some 90% of revenue include names that have stocked medicine cabinets for generations - Luden Efferdent Beano Debrox PediaCare Chloraseptic Compound W and Dramamine. Household cleaning brands Chore Boy Comet and Spic and Span have similar name recognition.

Instead of maintaining its own manufacturing facilities Prestige Brands contracts out product-making using third-party manufacturers and warehouse distribution partners to simplify its organizational structure.

Geographic Reach

Nearly all of Prestige Brands' sales come from North America (the US is the firm's largest single market bringing in nearly 90% of sales) but the company is working to increase international sales by licensing some brands to large multinational companies in desirable international markets. It has one such agreement for Comet in Eastern Europe. It also sells Clear Eyes Chloraseptic and Murine internationally. Prestige Brands which in 2016 generated 8% of sales outside North America has already designed and developed product packaging for specific international markets and is focused now on growing its distribution network to help increase its international penetration.

Sales and Marketing

Prestige Brands generates revenue by leveraging several distribution channels to get its products on store shelves and in consumers' hands. Mass merchandisers drug stores and grocery stores account for the largest percentages of sales at some 30% 20% and 20% of total revenue respectively. Other growing but smaller channels that Prestige Brands relies on include dollar stores and club stores.

Uber worldwide retailer Wal-Mart accounts for about a fifth of the company's total sales. Other notable customers include Walgreen CVS Target Dollar Tree Meijer Ahold and Kroger among others.

Prestige Brands develops extensive marketing programs for new and existing products.

Financial Performance

With the exception of 2014 when the company reported a 3% drop in revenue Prestige Brands has seen growing revenues for the past five years. In fiscal 2016 (ended March) sales rose 13% to $806.3 million primarily due to 16% growth in the North American OTC Healthcare segment. That growth was driven by the recent acquisitions of the Insight (2014) and DenTek (2016) brands.

Net income has also been on the rise. In fiscal 2016 it rose 28% to $99.9 million thanks to the higher revenue and lower operating expenses.

Strategy

The company's strategy lies in acquiring new brands and developing effective marketing programs for its existing products. Acquisitions are key to keeping its products portfolio fresh and it is constantly on the lookout for new additions to keep itself competitive. Its goal is to have 85% of its earnings from "invest for growth" brands and the remainder from "manage for cash" brands.

When Prestige Brands is evaluating a product for acquisition it takes a number of factors into consideration including the period of time the product has been in existence the product's market position (typically about three-quarters of the company's sales come from brands with a #1 or #2 market position) its recent and projected sales growth and its potential for product extensions. Prestige Brands looks to acquire products that can be remarketed with additional enhancements. It uses a similar technique when marketing existing products introducing enhancements and line extensions.

In 2016 Prestige Brands sold three non-core but established brands (New Skin Fiber Choice and PediaCare) to Moberg Pharma for $40 million. The deal fell in line with its strategy of maintaining a portfolio of primarily newer brands; the company plans to use funds from the deal to pay down debt. In a similar move later that year the company sold the Dermoplast brand to Moberg Pharma for $47.6 million.

Among the company's highest-valued brands are Monistat DenTek Clear Eyes and Chloroseptic. On the other hand such brands as Pediacare and Beano have slipped due to growing competition (but Prestige remains committed to their recovery).

Mergers and Acquisitions

Prestige Brands acquired specialty oral care products distributor DenTek for $225 million in early 2016. Later that year it agreed to buy C.B. Fleet which makes OTC enemas and laxatives as well as Summers Eve feminine products for $825 million.

Company Background

Prestige Brands was pieced together in 1996 from the parts of defunct manufacturer Medtech Labs (shampoos nail care products) The Spic & Span Company and Prestige Brands International (Comet cleaners and Clear Eyes eye drops).

In 2012 Prestige Brands completed its largest asset acquisition to date spending $660 million to gain a portfolio of 17 North American OTC brands from GlaxoSmith Kline (GSK). The purchases added brands that included leading pain relief (BC Goody's and Ecotrin) gastrointestinal (Beano Fiber Choice Gaviscon Phazyme and Tagamet) sleep aid (Sominex) ear wax remover (Debrox) and oral rinse (Gly-Oxide) brands. Also in 2012 the company received an unsolicited acquisition proposal from Mexican health products firm Genomma Lab Internacional. The Prestige Brands board of directors rejected the proposal as inadequate and not in the best interest of the firm.

EXECUTIVES

General Counsel and VP Business Development, Samuel C. (Sam) Cowley, age 56, $345,000 total compensation

SVP International, John F. Parkinson, age 65, $257,522 total compensation

SVP Science and Technology, Jean A. Boyko, age 59, $250,000 total compensation

EVP Sales and Marketing, Timothy J. Connors, age 51, $415,000 total compensation

President and CEO, Ronald M. (Ron) Lombardi, age 54, $450,000 total compensation

CFO, Christine (Chris) Sacco

Lead Director, Gary E. Costley, age 74

Auditors: PricewaterhouseCoopers LLP

LOCATIONS

HQ: Prestige Consumer Healthcare Inc
660 White Plains Road, Tarrytown, NY 10591
Phone: 914 524-6800
Web: www.prestigebrands.com

PRODUCTS/OPERATIONS

2016 Sales

	$ mil.	% of total
North American OTC Healthcare	657.9	82
Household Cleaning	90.6	11
International OTC Healthcare	57.7	7
Total	**806.2**	**100**

2016 Sales

	$ mil.	% of total
Women's Health	135.2	17
Analgesics	119.4	15
Cough & Cold	116.6	14
Eye & Ear Care	107.5	13
Gastrointestinal	94.6	12
Household Cleaning	90.6	11
Dermatologicals	85.1	11
Oral Care	51.1	6
Other OTC	6.1	1
Total	**806.2**	**100**

Selected Products

Over-the-counter
Clear Eyes
Chloraseptic
Clear Eyes
Compound W
The Doctor's NightGuard
The Doctor's Brushpicks
Dramamine
Ecotrin
Efferdent
Effergrip
Fiber Choice
Little Remedies
Luden's
Murine
NasalCrom
New-Skin
PediaCare

Phazyme
Sominex
Tagamet
Wartner
Household cleaning
Comet
Chore Boy
Spic and Span

COMPETITORS

3M	Henkel Corp.
Airborne Inc.	Hi-Tech Pharmacal
Bayer Consumer Care	Inter Parfums
Boulder Brands	Johnson & Johnson
Chattem	Lifetime Brands
Church & Dwight	McNeil Consumer
Clorox	Healthcare
Colgate-Palmolive	Merck
Combe	Mondelez International
Coty Inc.	Novartis Corporation
GlaxoSmithKline	Pfizer
Hain Celestial	Procter & Gamble
Helen of Troy	Reckitt Benckiser
HemCon Medical	USANA Health Sciences
Technologies	Zep Inc.

HISTORICAL FINANCIALS

Company Type: Public

Income Statement

FYE: March 31

	REVENUE ($ mil.)	NET INCOME ($ mil.)	NET PROFIT MARGIN	EMPLOYEES
03/18	1,041.1	339.5	32.6%	530
03/17	882.0	69.4	7.9%	530
03/16	806.2	99.9	12.4%	259
03/15	714.6	78.2	11.0%	187
03/14	601.8	72.6	12.1%	155
Annual Growth	**14.7%**	**47.1%**	**—**	**36.0%**

2018 Year-End Financials

Debt ratio: 53.0%	No. of shares (mil.): 53.0
Return on equity: 33.9%	Dividends
Cash ($ mil.): 32.5	Yield: —
Current ratio: 2.46	Payout: —
Long-term debt ($ mil.): 1,992.9	Market value ($ mil.): 1,789.0

	STOCK PRICE ($) FY Close	P/E High/Low	PER SHARE ($) Earnings	Dividends	Book Value
03/18	33.72	9 5	6.34	0.00	22.22
03/17	55.56	44 35	1.30	0.00	15.53
03/16	53.39	29 21	1.88	0.00	14.11
03/15	42.89	29 18	1.49	0.00	12.00
03/14	27.25	26 18	1.39	0.00	10.87
Annual Growth	**5.5%**	**— —**	**46.1%**	**—**	**19.6%**

Proto Labs Inc

Need a prototype pronto? Proto Labs can help with that. The industrial manufacturer creates custom parts in quick turnaround for prototype and short-run production. The company uses 3D CAD software to upload new parts designs and then its computer numerical control (CNC) process analyzes the design quotes a price and makes the parts. Proto Labs creates machined metal (Firstcut) and injection-molded plastic (Protomold) parts and can ship them the next business day. Its medical device electronics consumer products appliance

and automotive manufacturing customers use the parts for prototyping market evaluation and functional testing. The company was established in 1999 and went public in 2012.

Operations

Proto Labs makes the majority of its revenue (67%) from its Protomold segment (also called ProtoQuote) which typically produces prototype quantities of 25-100 custom injection-molded plastic parts. It saves the designs and molds from these parts and benefits when the customer returns sometimes requesting up to 10000 additional parts for short-run production.

The company's Firstcut segment (FirstQuote; nearly 29%) specializes in designing and cutting plastic and metal blocks but in smaller quantities. In addition to these segments Proto Labs inherited a new segment Fineline (4%) in 2014 with the acquisition of FineLine Prototyping. Fineline features an additive manufacturing product line often referred to as 3D printing which offers a variety of high-quality precision rapid prototyping services.

Geographic Reach

Proto Labs has manufacturing facilities in Japan the UK and the US; sales offices also reside in Italy. The US accounts for around 75% of its revenue each year.

Sales and Marketing

Proto Labs sells its products through an internal sales team in more than 50 countries. Customers include Avox Systems BOSS Products PHT Aerospace Micro Engineering IFM Efector OEM controls Lombard Medical and Gamesman Limited. In 2014 the company served 9840 existing and approximately 11710 new product developers and engineers.

Financial Performance

Proto Labs has grown significantly since it was founded as revenues and profits continue to climb to unprecedented heights. From 2013 to 2014 Pro Labs' revenues surged 28% from $163 million to $209 million and its net income increased by 18% from $35 million to $42 million. (Both these totals for 2014 represent historic milestones for the company.)

The growth for 2014 was driven by a 30% increase in US revenue a 24% rise in international revenue a 22% jump in Protomold revenue a 25% increase in Firstcut revenue and additional revenue from its new Fineline segment. The revenue increases were due to an uptick in the number of product developers and engineers served which were driven by the company's enhanced marketing activities.

Proto Labs' operating cash flows have increased consistently over the past five years. In 2014 it increased 18% to $57 million due to a surge in cash inflows from depreciation and amortization and income taxes.

Strategy

Its strategy includes increasing penetration within existing customer organization and in geographical markets it already operates (US Europe and Japan) moving into new geographic regions and expanding its parts range and manufacturing processes. Another important component of its strategy involves optimizing its 3D CAD and CNC technology in order to design parts faster and more efficiently.

Mergers and Acquisitions

Proto Labs added to its manufacturing services in 2014 through the $38 million acquisition of FineLine Prototyping a provider of stereolithography selective laser sintering and direct metal laser sintering services.

Company Background
Proto Labs began as The Protomold Company (molded plastic parts) but added CNC metal part machining its Firstcut business in 2007. In 2009 both branches began operating under the Proto Labs banner. It all started when founder and computer geek Lawrence Lukis started a desktop printer design business and was astounded at the long turnaround (weeks) and cost (thousands) for prototype parts. He turned his computer skills to solving the problem and found a way to completely automate the entire process and produce a part in a day for prices starting at $1500.

EXECUTIVES

EVP and CTO, Donald G. Krantz, age 63, $286,083 total compensation
President and CEO, Victoria M. (Vicki) Holt, age 60, $514,539 total compensation
CFO, John A. Way, $290,000 total compensation
VP and General Manager and Managing Director - Europe Middle East and Africa, John B. Tumelty, age 47, $189,268 total compensation
CTO, Rich Baker
VP and General Manager Americas, Robert Bodor, age 45, $249,323 total compensation
National Account Manager, Brandon Marcus
National Account Manager, Todd Martin
Vice President of Human Resour, Renee Conklin
Chairman, Lawrence J. Lukis, age 70
Auditors: Ernst & Young LLP

LOCATIONS

HQ: Proto Labs Inc
5540 Pioneer Creek Drive, Maple Plain, MN 55359
Phone: 763 479-3680
Web: www.protolabs.com

PRODUCTS/OPERATIONS

2013 Sales

	$ mil.	% of total
Protomold	115.1	71
Firstcut	48.0	29
Total	**163.1**	**100**

COMPETITORS

Ajax United Patterns and Molds	Materialise
	Richco
Anchor Mfg. Group	Total Plastics
Deswell	

HISTORICAL FINANCIALS

Company Type: Public

Income Statement   FYE: December 31

	REVENUE ($ mil.)	NET INCOME ($ mil.)	NET PROFIT MARGIN	EMPLOYEES
12/17	344.4	51.7	15.0%	2,266
12/16	298.0	42.7	14.3%	1,700
12/15	264.1	46.5	17.6%	1,549
12/14	209.5	41.6	19.9%	1,077
12/13	163.1	35.2	21.6%	749
Annual Growth	**20.6%**	**10.1%**	**—**	**31.9%**

2017 Year-End Financials

Debt ratio: 0.9%		No. of shares (mil.): 26.8	
Return on equity: 12.3%		Dividends	
Cash ($ mil.): 36.7		Yield: —	
Current ratio: 3.77		Payout: —	
Long-term debt ($ mil.): —		Market value ($ mil.): 2,763.0	

	STOCK PRICE ($) FY Close	P/E High/Low	Earnings	PER SHARE ($) Dividends	Book Value
12/17	103.00	55 25	1.93	0.00	17.19
12/16	51.35	50 27	1.61	0.00	14.33
12/15	63.69	44 32	1.77	0.00	12.51
12/14	67.16	53 36	1.60	0.00	10.28
12/13	71.18	63 27	1.36	0.00	8.28
Annual Growth	**9.7%**	**— —**	**9.1%**	**—**	**20.0%**

Providence Service Corp

Social services firm Providence Service Corporation operates through two primary segments: Non-Emergency Transportation Services (NET Services also known as LogistiCare) and Workforce Development Services (WD Services). Through these segments the company provides provide non-emergency transportation to people in home and community-based settings manages foster care systems provides correctional support such as probation supervision offers job training and provides substance abuse treatment. Providence operates in about 40 states and in about 10 countries abroad.

Operations
The majority of Providence's revenue comes from its NET Services segment (nearly 80%). NET's primary payers include state Medicaid programs local government agencies hospital systems and managed care organizations (MCOs). Its clients range from senior citizens and individuals with limited mobility to people with limited means of transportation and people with disabilities that prevent them from using conventional methods of transportation. (The segment does not provide rides with its own vehicles but coordinates with external transportation providers.) Most of the NET segment's income comes from state payer contracts that are three-to-five years long with renewal options; only about 15% of the segment's income is derived from fee-for-service contracts.

WD Services which includes subsidiary Ingeus accounts for about nearly a quarter of Providence's sales. It offers workforce development and offender rehabilitation services including employment placement apprenticeships employee assistance programs and some health-related services. Most of the segment's business comes from government entities seeking to reduce recidivism and unemployment rates. Ingeus operates in about a dozen countries.

Matrix Investment the smallest segment offers at-home comprehensive health assessments (CHAs) for Medicare Advantage health plans. These measure members' health social environment and medication risks for health plans. Provi-

dence sold a majority stake in Matrix Investment to Matrix Medical in late 2016.

The company has a network of some 5000 independent transportation providers including operators of wheelchair-equipped vehicles and ambulances.

For its CHA tests Providence has a nationwide network of approximately 1100 nurse practitioners.

Geographic Reach
Providence has operations in Australia Canada France Germany Poland Saudi Arabia South Korea Spain Sweden Switzerland the UK and the US. The US brings in the majority of revenue (about 80%) followed by the UK (around 15%).

Financial Performance After significantly rising in 2014 and 2015 (thanks largely to acquisitions completed) Providence's revenue fell 7% to $1.6 billion in 2016. This was primarily due to a 13% drop in WD Services income.

Net income spiked more than 300% in 2015 when the company sold its Human Services segment. It rose another 10% to $91.9 million in 2016.

Cash flow from operations which declined 76% in 2015 recovered the following year rising more than 200% to $41.5 million.

Strategy
Providence's primary form of growth was historically through acquisitions but those have become infrequent lately. When it does consider acquisition opportunities it looks to expand into adjacent markets as well as complementary service lines so that it can take advantage of its existing networks.

More recently the company has made strategic divestitures to hone its focus. In 2015 to strengthen its core business the company sold its Human Services business for $200 million. The following year Providence sold a majority stake in the recently acquired Matrix Medical Network to Frazier Healthcare Partners for an after-tax gain of $109.4 million.

NET Services is responding to changes in the non-emergency transportation industry by innovating through technology and improving processes (including coordinating with growing on-demand transportation networks) which should help lower costs and improve services.

WD Services works to secure contracts in various markets to further boost income. To that end it tracks legislation and funding trends and then targets locations with favorable funding opportunities. Its current areas of focus include improving its Reducing Reoffending Partnership in the UK and expanding into contiguous markets while growth areas include its UK youth and health programs.

EXECUTIVES

Interim CEO, Carter Pate
CFO, David Shackelton, age 32, $450,000 total compensation
CEO Matrix Medical Network, Walt Cooper
CEO Ingeus, Jack Sawyer
Chief Accounting Officer, William Severance, age 52, $277,568 total compensation
SVP Strategic Services, Matthew K. Umscheid, age 48, $350,000 total compensation
CEO LogistiCare Solutions LLC, Jeff Felton, age 56
Chairman, Christopher S. (Chris) Shackelton, age 38
Auditors: KPMG LLP

LOCATIONS

HQ: Providence Service Corp
700 Canal Street, Third Floor, Stamford, CT 06902
Phone: 203 307-2800   **Fax:** 520 747-6605
Web: www.prscholdings.com

PRODUCTS/OPERATIONS

2016 Sales

	$ mil.	% of total
NET Services	1,234.4	78
WD Services	344.4	22
Corporate and Other	0.1	-
Total	**1,578.9**	**100**

Selected Subsidiaries

Health Trans Inc.
LogistiCare Inc.
Provado Insurance Service Inc.
Red Top Transportation Inc.
Ingeus Investments Limited
Mission Providence Pty Ltd
PSC of Canada Exchange Corp.
Health Trans Inc.
Zodiac Training Limited

COMPETITORS

AMR	Mental Health Network
Acadian Ambulance	Res-Care
Service Inc.	Safe Ride Services
Devereux Foundation	Salvation Army
Hazelden Betty Ford	UBH

HISTORICAL FINANCIALS

Company Type: Public

Income Statement

	REVENUE ($ mil.)	NET INCOME ($ mil.)	NET PROFIT MARGIN	EMPLOYEES
12/17	1,623.8	53.3	3.3%	7,100
12/16	1,578.8	91.9	5.8%	7,590
12/15	1,695.4	83.7	4.9%	9,072
12/14	1,481.1	20.2	1.4%	13,700
12/13	1,122.6	19.4	1.7%	8,500
Annual Growth	**9.7%**	**28.7%**	**—**	**(4.4%)**

2017 Year-End Financials

Debt ratio: 0.4%
Return on equity: 13.4%
Cash ($ mil.): 95.3
Current ratio: 1.31
Long-term debt ($ mil.): 0.5

No. of shares (mil.): 13.3
Dividends
 Yield: —
 Payout: —
Market value ($ mil.): 792.0

	STOCK PRICE ($) FY Close	P/E High/Low	Earnings	Dividends	Book Value
12/17	59.34	20 12	3.06	0.00	31.15
12/16	38.05	11 7	5.07	0.00	27.29
12/15	46.92	13 8	4.30	0.00	24.08
12/14	36.44	35 18	1.35	0.00	13.96
12/13	25.72	21 11	1.41	0.00	10.63
Annual Growth	**23.2%**	**— —**	**21.4%**	**—**	**30.8%**

Provident Bancorp Inc

Auditors: Whittlesey & Hadley, P.C.

LOCATIONS

HQ: Provident Bancorp Inc
5 Market Street, Amesbury, MA 01913
Phone: 978 834-8555
Web: www.theprovidentbank.com

HISTORICAL FINANCIALS

Company Type: Public

Income Statement

FYE: December 31

	ASSETS ($ mil.)	NET INCOME ($ mil.)	INCOME AS % OF ASSETS	EMPLOYEES
12/17	902.2	7.9	0.9%	135
12/16	795.5	6.3	0.8%	128
12/15	743.4	3.8	0.5%	115
12/14	658.6	4.5	0.7%	116
12/13	624.6	4.0	0.6%	0
Annual Growth	**9.6%**	**18.5%**	**—**	**—**

2017 Year-End Financials

Return on assets: 0.9%
Return on equity: 7.0%
Long-term debt ($ mil.): —
No. of shares (mil.): 9.6
Sales ($ mil): 45.7

Dividends
 Yield: —
 Payout: —
Market value ($ mil.): 255.0

	STOCK PRICE ($) FY Close	P/E High/Low	Earnings	Dividends	Book Value
12/17	26.45	31 20	0.86	0.00	12.02
12/16	17.90	28 19	0.69	0.00	11.31
12/15	12.99	— —	(0.00)	0.00	10.68
Annual Growth	**42.7%**	**— —**	**—**	**—**	**6.1%**

Prudential Bancorp Inc (New)

Auditors: S.R. Snodgrass, P.C.

LOCATIONS

HQ: Prudential Bancorp Inc (New)
1834 West Oregon Avenue, Philadelphia, PA 19145
Phone: 215 755-1500
Web: www.prudentialsavingsbank.com

HISTORICAL FINANCIALS

Company Type: Public

Income Statement

FYE: September 30

	ASSETS ($ mil.)	NET INCOME ($ mil.)	INCOME AS % OF ASSETS	EMPLOYEES
09/18	1,081.1	7.0	0.7%	83
09/17	899.5	2.7	0.3%	87
09/16	559.4	2.7	0.5%	63
09/15	487.1	2.2	0.5%	71
09/14	525.4	1.7	0.3%	76
Annual Growth	**19.8%**	**41.1%**	**—**	**2.2%**

2018 Year-End Financials

Return on assets: 0.7%
Return on equity: 5.3%
Long-term debt ($ mil.): —
No. of shares (mil.): 8.9
Sales ($ mil): 37.3

Dividends
 Yield: 0.0%
 Payout: 89.7%
Market value ($ mil.): 156.0

	STOCK PRICE ($) FY Close	P/E High/Low	Earnings	Dividends	Book Value
09/18	17.31	25 21	0.78	0.70	14.29
09/17	18.53	57 44	0.32	0.12	15.12
09/16	14.48	43 38	0.36	0.12	14.17
09/15	14.41	56 44	0.26	0.27	13.85
09/14	12.23	61 52	0.19	0.06	13.56
Annual Growth	**9.1%**	**— —**	**42.3%**	**84.8%**	**1.3%**

Psychemedics Corp.

Beware of giving a lock of hair as a keepsake — it could end up at Psychemedics which provides drug testing services through the analysis of hair samples. Its tests which it markets under the brand name RIAH (or Radioimmunoassay of Hair) not only reveal that a substance has been consumed but also detect patterns of use over time; the tests look for cocaine marijuana PCP Ecstasy and opiates. The company's primary market is employers who use the service for pre-employment screening as well as random testing of current employees. Psychemedics also sells its service to hundreds of schools nationwide (and in some foreign countries) and offers a service to parents worried that their kids might be on drugs.

The company performs testing services at its lab in Culver City California. Its personal home testing service for parents (PDT-90) is sold on the Internet and through retailers.

In addition to its commercial markets Psychemedics provides services to researchers studying drug abuse in various populations.

EXECUTIVES

VP Laboratory Operations, Michael I. Schaffer, age 68, $223,148 total compensation
SVP and General Counsel, William R. Thistle, age 63, $281,092 total compensation
Chairman President and CEO, Raymond C. Kubacki Jr., age 68, $385,437 total compensation
VP Sales, James V. Dyke
VP and Controller, Neil L. Lerner
Director, Walter S. Tomenson Jr., age 66
Director, Fred J. Weinert, age 65
Director, Harry F. Connick, age 87
Auditors: BDO USA, LLP

LOCATIONS

HQ: Psychemedics Corp.
289 Great Road, Acton, MA 01720
Phone: 978 206-8220
Web: www.psychemedics.com

COMPETITORS

Bio-Reference Labs	LabCorp
Kroll Background	Medtox Scientific
America	Quest Diagnostics

HISTORICAL FINANCIALS

Company Type: Public

Income Statement

FYE: December 31

	REVENUE ($ mil.)	NET INCOME ($ mil.)	NET PROFIT MARGIN	EMPLOYEES
12/17	39.7	6.1	15.4%	231
12/16	38.9	6.6	17.1%	206
12/15	26.9	1.5	5.6%	154
12/14	29.2	3.2	11.0%	156
12/13	26.8	3.8	14.2%	151
Annual Growth	10.3%	12.6%	—	11.2%

2017 Year-End Financials

Debt ratio: 12.7%
Return on equity: —
Cash ($ mil.): 8.1
Current ratio: 3.28
Long-term debt ($ mil.): 2.4

No. of shares (mil.): 5.4
Dividends
Yield: 0.0%
Payout: 54.5%
Market value ($ mil.): 113.0

	STOCK PRICE ($) FY Close	P/E High/Low	PER SHARE ($) Earnings	Dividends	Book Value
12/17	20.56	24 15	1.10	0.60	3.39
12/16	24.68	20 6	1.22	0.60	2.86
12/15	10.14	63 35	0.28	0.60	2.15
12/14	15.15	31 22	0.60	0.60	2.39
12/13	14.69	20 15	0.72	0.60	2.31
Annual Growth	8.8%	— —	11.2%	(0.0%)	10.1%

Pzena Investment Management Inc

It takes money to make money and Pzena Investment Management has made plenty. The firm serves corporate institutional and high-net-worth individual clients in the US and abroad and has about $21 billion in assets under management. Through a dozen funds Pzena makes long-term investments in domestic and international companies — particularly financial services firms. Pzena also acts as a sub-investment adviser for about two dozen mutual funds and offshore funds. The firm is the sole managing member of its operating company Pzena Investment Management LLC. The employee-owned firm was founded by chairman and CEO Richard Pzena in 1995.

Financial Performance

A decline in management and performance fee revenue led to an 8% decline in the company's overall revenue between 2011 and 2012. The company's net income was up 14% in the same period due in large part to lower investment-related expenses.

Strategy

The company focuses on long-term investments made in US and global markets. It serves both US clients and non-US clients and has been expanding its non-US client base through targeted sales efforts.

EXECUTIVES

Chairman CEO and Co-Chief Investment Officer, Richard S. Pzena, age 59, $377,500 total compensation
President and Co-Chief Investment Officer, John P. Goetz, age 60, $377,500 total compensation
President and Head of Business Development and Client Service, William L. Lipsey, age 59, $377,500 total compensation
COO, Gary J. Bachman, age 50, $350,000 total compensation
EVP and Portfolio Manager Global Focused Value International (ex-US) Focused Value International (ex-US) Expanded Value Global Expanded Value and European Focused Value, Michael D. Peterson, age 53, $377,500 total compensation
Manager Financial Reporting, Jessica R. Doran
Auditors: PricewaterhouseCoopers LLP

LOCATIONS

HQ: Pzena Investment Management Inc
320 Park Avenue, New York, NY 10022
Phone: 212 355-1600
Web: www.pzena.com

COMPETITORS

AllianceBernstein
BlackRock
FMR
Morgan Stanley Investment Management
Principal Global
State Street

HISTORICAL FINANCIALS

Company Type: Public

Income Statement

FYE: December 31

	REVENUE ($ mil.)	NET INCOME ($ mil.)	NET PROFIT MARGIN	EMPLOYEES
12/17	141.3	6.9	4.9%	105
12/16	108.3	16.1	14.9%	100
12/15	116.6	7.6	6.6%	88
12/14	112.5	8.1	7.2%	81
12/13	95.7	6.6	7.0%	76
Annual Growth	10.2%	0.9%	—	8.4%

2017 Year-End Financials

Debt ratio: —
Return on equity: 22.7%
Cash ($ mil.): 63.4
Current ratio: 3.80
Long-term debt ($ mil.): —

No. of shares (mil.): 68.8
Dividends
Yield: 0.0%
Payout: 92.5%
Market value ($ mil.): 734.0

	STOCK PRICE ($) FY Close	P/E High/Low	PER SHARE ($) Earnings	Dividends	Book Value
12/17	10.67	30 21	0.40	0.37	0.47
12/16	11.11	11 6	0.58	0.41	0.42
12/15	8.60	21 14	0.50	0.41	0.27
12/14	9.46	19 13	0.53	0.35	0.28
12/13	11.76	21 9	0.45	0.25	0.25
Annual Growth	(2.4%)	— —	(2.9%)	10.3%	16.9%

QCR Holdings Inc

Quad City is muscling in on the community banking scene in the Midwest. QCR Holdings is the holding company for Quad City Bank & Trust Cedar Rapids Bank & Trust Rockford Bank & Trust and Community State Bank. Together the banks have about 20 offices serving the Quad City area of Illinois and Iowa as well as the communities of Cedar Rapids Iowa; Rockford Illinois; and Milwaukee. The banks offer traditional deposit products and services and concentrate their lending activities on local businesses: Commercial real estate loans make up about half of the loan portfolio; commercial loans and leases make up another third.

Operations

QCR Holdings' Bancard subsidiary provides credit card processing services; its majority-owned M2 Lease Funds leases machinery and equipment to commercial and industrial businesses.

Strategy

QCR Holdings has grown by launching operations in new geographic markets and then building upon them. It also expands through acquisitions. In mid-2016 the company acquired Iowa-based Community State Bank which operates some 10 branches in the Des Moines area.

EXECUTIVES

President and CEO, Douglas M. (Doug) Hultquist, age 63, $290,000 total compensation
Director; President and CEO Cedar Rapids Bank and Trust, Larry J. Helling, age 62, $251,899 total compensation
EVP and Chief Credit Officer, Dana L. Nichols
EVP COO and CFO, Todd A. Gipple, age 55, $251,899 total compensation
EVP Corporate Strategy Human Resources and Branding, Cathie Whiteside, $162,000 total compensation
President and CEO Rockford Bank and Trust, Thomas D. Budd, $172,000 total compensation
President and CEO Quad City Bank and Trust, John H. Anderson, $200,000 total compensation
EVP Deposit Operations and Information Services, John A. Rodriguez
SVP and CIO, Michael J. Wyffels
EVP and Chief Operations Officer, John R. McEvoy
President and CEO Community Bank and Trust, Stacey Bentley
President m2 Lease Funds, Richard W. Couch
Chairman and CEO m2 Lease Funds, John R. Engelbrecht
EVP and Chief Investment Officer, M. Randolph (Rand) Westlund
Vice President Operations Manager, Sherrie L Larson
Senior Vice President Director Of Hum, Jill Dekeyser
Vice President Controller, Jeri Vandervinne
Vice President And Controller, Nick Anderson
ASSISTANT VICE PRESIDENT MARKETING AND PUBLIC RELATIONS OFFICER, Stacey L Keller
ASSISTANT VICE PRESIDENT MARKETING AND PUBLIC RELATIONS OFFICER, Stacey Keller
Executive Vice President Corporate Strategy and Branding, S Whiteside
Chairman, Patrick S. (Pat) Baird, age 65
Vice Chairman of the Board, Marie Z Ziegler

Board Member, Michael Peterson
Auditors: RSM US LLP

LOCATIONS

HQ: QCR Holdings Inc
  3551 7th Street, Moline, IL 61265
Phone: 309 736-3580
Web: www.qcbt.com

PRODUCTS/OPERATIONS

2015 Sales

	$ mil.	% of total
Quad City Bank & Trust	52.8	46
Cedar Rapids Bank & Trust	37.5	32
Rockford Bank & Trust	14.8	13
Wealth Management	9.1	8
All other	0.7	1
Inter-company Eliminations	(0.4)	-
Total	**114.5**	**100**

COMPETITORS

Bank of America	First National of
Blackhawk Bancorp	Nebraska
First Business	MidWestOne
Financial	U.S. Bancorp
First Midwest Bancorp	

HISTORICAL FINANCIALS

Company Type: Public

Income Statement

FYE: December 31

	ASSETS ($ mil.)	NET INCOME ($ mil.)	INCOME AS % OF ASSETS	EMPLOYEES
12/17	3,982.6	35.7	0.9%	641
12/16	3,301.9	27.6	0.8%	572
12/15	2,593.2	16.9	0.7%	406
12/14	2,524.9	14.9	0.6%	409
12/13	2,394.9	14.9	0.6%	400
Annual Growth	**13.6%**	**24.3%**	**—**	**12.5%**

2017 Year-End Financials

Return on assets: 0.9%	Dividends
Return on equity: 11.1%	Yield: 0.0%
Long-term debt ($ mil.): —	Payout: 7.6%
No. of shares (mil.): 13.9	Market value ($ mil.): 596.0
Sales ($ mil): 166.0	

	STOCK PRICE ($) FY Close	P/E High/Low		PER SHARE ($) Earnings	Dividends	Book Value
12/17	42.85	18	15	2.61	0.20	25.38
12/16	43.30	20	10	2.17	0.16	21.82
12/15	24.29	15	11	1.61	0.08	19.21
12/14	17.86	10	10	1.72	0.08	18.12
12/13	17.03	8	6	2.08	0.08	18.72
Annual Growth	**25.9%**	**—**	**—**	**5.8%**	**25.7%**	**7.9%**

Qualys, Inc.

Qualys tries to calm customers' qualms about cybersecurity. Its QualysGuard Cloud Platform is a cloud security and compliance management software suite that automates security weakness detection and network security asset auditing. Qualys also remotely manages data security for clients on a contract basis. Its biggest product Vulnerability Management automates network auditing and vulnerability management across an organization. The company counts about 9300 customers in more than 100 countries. It reaches many customers through partnerships with managed service providers and consultants including Dell Technologies Fujitsu Insight Technologies Inc. Optiv and Verizon Communications Inc.

Operations

Security software from Qualys rests on its Qualys Cloud Platform on which the Qualys Cloud Suite of security software runs. The leading product Vulnerability Management which includes Continuous Monitoring Cloud Agent AssetView and ThreatPROTECT generates about three-quarters of the company's revenue.

Besides software Qualys makes security hardware devices which are made on contract by SYNNEX Corp. Qualys's cloud operations run through third-party data centers in the US Switzerland the Netherlands and India.

Geographic Reach

Qualys operates from five offices in the US and it conducts research and development in the US France India and the UK. It also has customer support centers in the US the UK and India. About half the company's employees work in the US and half in international operations. About 70% of revenue comes from customers in the US.

Sales and Marketing

Qualys's field sales team focuses on enterprises and organizations with more than 5000 employees. Its inside sales team makes calls to small and medium-sized businesses and other organizations with fewer than 5000 employees. The company makes a significant number of sales through channel partners including managed service providers value-added resellers and consulting firms. Partners include Deutsche Telekom AG Fujitsu Hewlett Packard Enterprise Insight Technologies Inc. Optiv Security Inc. SecureWorks Corp. and Verizon Communications Inc.

Qualys has customers in banking industrial and materials insurance consumer goods health care technology and telecommunications.

Financial Performance

Qualys has delivered robustly rising revenue since 2009 and profit has increased in the past three years to deliver profit margins of about 10%.

In 2016 revenue jumped 20% to about $198 million from about $164 million in 2015. About two-thirds of revenue growth came from existing customers while the rest came from customers added in 2016. Sales rose more than 20% in the US and internationally.

Net income also rose about 20% in 2016 to $19 million from $16 million in 2015. Qualys had higher expenses for personnel and research and development in 2016 but they remained about the same year-to-year as a percentage of revenue.

Cash flow from operating activities hit about $68 million in 2016 from $66 million in 2015. The cash was generated by net income and increases in deferred revenues of about $18 million as well as accrued liabilities non-cash items and stock-based compensation. Counting against cash from operations were the non-cash effect of excess tax benefits from stock based compensation an increase in prepaid expenses and an increase in accounts receivable.

Strategy

One way companies like Qualys grow is to partner with other software firms to incorporate their products for sales purposes. In late 2016 Qualys added Deutsche Telekom to its partner roster and the company said has other partners lined up. It also added managed managed security services providers (MSSP) to its cloud platform. Those partners bring customers to Qualys at a low acquisition cost and low overhead.

In 2016 Qualys introduced its Cloud Agent technology that made its Vulnerability Management and Policy Compliance applications run continuously and more effectively. Cloud Agent supports the Windows Linux and Mac operating systems and is embedded within Microsoft Azure. The company also introduced ThreatPROTECT which enables customers to integrate and correlate threat information natively.

To support those and to develop other new products Qualys expanded its engineering operations in India. Qualys operates about half of its engineering operations and customer support activities in India at rates favorable to its cost structure.

Further down its product pipeline Qualys is working on a project called Cloud 360 which focuses on cloud security.

Mergers and Acquisitions

Qualys bought Layered Insight in 2018 to add more security to its offerings. Layered Insight provides security to applications running on virtual container systems. Pairing the two companies products is to provide their customers with greater visibility and security. Qualys expects to integrate Layered Insight's offerings into its systems by the second half of 2018.

EXECUTIVES

VP General Counsel and Corporate Secretary, Bruce K. Posey, age 67, $250,000 total compensation
Chairman and CEO, Philippe F. Courtot, age 73, $350,000 total compensation
VP Corporate Development and Strategic Alliances, Amer S. Deeba, age 51, $250,000 total compensation
CTO, Wolfgang Kandek
EVP Worldwide Field Operations, Dan Barahona
Chief Product Officer, Sumedh S. Thakar, age 42, $260,417 total compensation
CFO, Melissa Fisher
Vice President Human Resources, Rima Touma-Bruno
Vice President Digital Marketing, Sonu Agarwal
Vice President Global Business Process and Applications, Grayson Williams
Vice President Global Cloud Operations and Devops, Syamla Bandla
VP Product Management Cloud Agent Platform, Chris Carlson
VICE PRESIDENT CHANNEL AND BUSINESS DEVELOPMENT, Michael Guglielmi
Board Member, Howard Schmidt
Board Member, Peter Pace
Board Member, Sandra Bergeron
Board Member, Kristi Rogers
Board Member, Todd Headley
Auditors: Grant Thornton LLP

LOCATIONS

HQ: Qualys, Inc.
  919 E. Hillsdale Boulevard, 4th Floor, Foster City, CA 94404
Phone: 650 801-6100
Web: www.qualys.com

COMPETITORS

Barracuda Networks	Microsoft
BeyondTrust	NetIQ
CA Inc.	Novell
Check Point Software	Symantec
Cisco Systems	Tenable Holdings
F5 Networks	Trend Micro
Fortinet	Trustwave Holdings
Foundstone	VeriSign
HP	Visionael
IBM	e-DMZ Security
Imperva	eEye Digital Security
McAfee	

HISTORICAL FINANCIALS
Company Type: Public

Income Statement — FYE: December 31

	REVENUE ($ mil.)	NET INCOME ($ mil.)	NET PROFIT MARGIN	EMPLOYEES
12/17	230.8	40.4	17.5%	869
12/16	197.9	19.2	9.7%	684
12/15	164.2	15.8	9.7%	510
12/14	133.5	30.2	22.6%	431
12/13	107.9	1.6	1.5%	406
Annual Growth	20.9%	123.4%	—	21.0%

2017 Year-End Financials

Debt ratio: —	No. of shares (mil.): 38.6
Return on equity: 13.4%	Dividends
Cash ($ mil.): 86.5	Yield: —
Current ratio: 2.23	Payout: —
Long-term debt ($ mil.): —	Market value ($ mil.): 2,291.0

	STOCK PRICE ($) FY Close	P/E High/Low	PER SHARE ($) Earnings	Dividends	Book Value
12/17	59.35	57 30	1.01	0.00	8.90
12/16	31.65	71 32	0.50	0.00	7.21
12/15	33.09	117 59	0.42	0.00	5.68
12/14	37.75	44 20	0.81	0.00	4.52
12/13	23.11	496215	0.05	0.00	3.19
Annual Growth	26.6%	—	—112.0%	—	29.3%

Quanex Building Products Corp

Quanex Building Products (QBP) makes engineered materials and components for OEMs of building products. Its Engineered Products and Aluminum Sheet Products operations serve the new home building and remodeling markets in North America and lesser so in Asia and Europe. QBP produces aluminum flat-rolled products used in exterior home trims screens and gutters. It also churns out window and door components insulating glass spacers solar panel sealants and extruded vinyl and composite framing material for fenestration OEMs. QBP generates around 80% of its total sales in the US.

Operations
QBP operates across three main segments. North American (NA) Engineered Components is focused on the fenestration market in North America and makes vinyl profiles insulating glass spac-

ers screens and other fenestration components. European Engineered (EU) Components is comprised of its UK-based vinyl extrusion business (vinyl profiles) and its European insulating glass business which makes insulating glass spacers. North American (NA) Cabinet Components is comprised solely of its North American cabinet door and components business.

Geographic Reach
QBP operates through roughly 35 manufacturing facilities located in 17 states in the US. Internationally it has one facility in Germany one in Mexico and two in the UK. The US accounts for about 80% of net sales.

Sales and Marketing
The company sells its components products and systems to national and regional OEMs through a direct sales force in North America and the UK supplemented with a limited use of distributors and independent sales agents.

Financial Performance
QBP has seen its revenues fluctuate over the years. After declining in 2015 revenues jumped 44% to reach $928 million in 2016. The growth was fueled by a 60% surge in sales from European Engineered (EU) Components which was aided by the previous international acquisition of HLP. Its NA Cabinet Components segment also achieved growth due to the 2015 acquisition of Woodcraft Industries.

The company however posted a net loss of almost $2 million during 2016 mostly due to an additional $37 million it paid on interest expenses. Its operating cash flow jumped from $67 million in 2015 to $86 million in 2016 mainly due to about $16 million it earned on debt discounts.

Strategy
QBP's growth strategy continues to orbit around North American new home construction and residential remodeling and replacement (R&R) activity. It has also improved its international presence with the 2015 purchase of HLP a provider of vinyl extruded products in the UK.

Mergers and Acquisitions
QBP is focusing on improving the energy efficiency durability and aesthetics of its window and door components through the use of acquisitions. In 2015 the company acquired Minnesota-based Woodcraft Industries a premier supplier of doors and components to leading original equipment manufacturers (OEMs) in the kitchen and bathroom cabinet industry for $246 million. The acquisition expanded QBP's position in the $3 billion kitchen and bath cabinet component industry.

Also in 2015 the company enhanced its international presence through the purchase of HLP one of the larger providers of vinyl extruded products in the UK in terms of volume shipped. The deal diversified QBP's client base as HLP's primary customers are smaller window fabricators as opposed to the larger OEMs that comprise a large portion of the North American market.

HISTORY

Quanex began as Michigan Seamless Tube in South Lyon Michigan in 1927. Led by William McMunn the company reworked used boiler and condenser tubes. Michigan Seamless Tube went public in 1965. In 1977 the company changed its name to Quanex and moved to Houston.

EXECUTIVES

Vice President Treasurer, Jairaj Chetnani
Chairman President and CEO, William C. (Bill) Griffiths, age 67, $780,050 total compensation
SVP General Counsel and Secretary, Kevin P. Delaney, age 57, $354,511 total compensation
SVP Finance and CFO, Brent L. Korb, age 46, $398,296 total compensation
President - Nichols Aluminum, D. Russ Brown
President and CEO Mikron Industries, F. Timothy (Tim) Reese
VP Investor Relations and Treasurer, Martin P. Ketelaar, age 52, $222,165 total compensation
VP and Controller, M. Dewayne Williams, age 47, $221,012 total compensation
COO, George Wilson
Vice President Marketing And Sales Operations, Kevin Connor
National Sales Manager, Michael Luccasen
Vice President Finance, Steven Vanhandel
Vice President Sales, Mike McGowan
Auditors: Grant Thornton LLP

LOCATIONS

HQ: Quanex Building Products Corp
1800 West Loop South, Suite 1500, Houston, TX 77027
Phone: 713 961-4600
Web: www.quanex.com

PRODUCTS/OPERATIONS

2016 sales

	$ mil.	% of total
NA Eng. Comp.	560.0	60
NA Cabinet Comp.	223.3	24
EU Eng. Comp.	150.2	16
Unallocated Corp. & Other	(5.4)	-
Total	**928.1**	**100**

Selected Subsidiaries and Products
Aluminum sheet products
  Nichols Aluminum (mill finished aluminum sheet coated aluminum sheet)
Engineered products
  Homeshield (fabricated window and door components)
  Mikron (vinyl and composite window and door products)
  Truseal (insulating glass sealant systems)

COMPETITORS

Aleris Corp.	MI Windows and Doors
Arconic	PGT Inc.
Century Aluminum	PPG Industries
Deceuninck	Patrick Industries
Gibraltar Industries	Royal Group
Kaiser Aluminum	Valmont Industries

HISTORICAL FINANCIALS
Company Type: Public

Income Statement — FYE: October 31

	REVENUE ($ mil.)	NET INCOME ($ mil.)	NET PROFIT MARGIN	EMPLOYEES
10/18	889.7	26.3	3.0%	3,818
10/17	866.5	18.6	2.2%	3,954
10/16	928.1	(1.8)	—	4,138
10/15	645.5	16.0	2.5%	2,693
10/14	595.3	29.2	4.9%	2,206
Annual Growth	10.6%	(2.6%)	—	14.7%

2018 Year-End Financials

Debt ratio: 28.3%
Return on equity: 6.5%
Cash ($ mil.): 29.0
Current ratio: 1.85
Long-term debt ($ mil.): 209.3

No. of shares (mil.): 33.3
Dividends
Yield: 1.3%
Payout: 26.6%
Market value ($ mil.): 494.0

	STOCK PRICE ($) FY Close	P/E High/Low	PER SHARE ($) Earnings	Dividends	Book Value
10/18	14.82	32 20	0.75	0.20	11.82
10/17	21.95	43 28	0.54	0.16	11.68
10/16	16.30	— —	(0.05)	0.16	10.75
10/15	18.87	47 37	0.47	0.16	11.64
10/14	20.02	27 22	0.78	0.16	11.62
Annual Growth	(7.2%)	— —	(1.0%)	5.7%	0.4%

Quantenna Communications Inc

Auditors: PricewaterhouseCoopers LLP

LOCATIONS

HQ: Quantenna Communications Inc
1704 Automation Parkway, San Jose, CA 95131
Phone: 669 209-5500
Web: www.quantenna.com

HISTORICAL FINANCIALS

Company Type: Public

Income Statement   FYE: December 31

	REVENUE ($ mil.)	NET INCOME ($ mil.)	NET PROFIT MARGIN	EMPLOYEES
12/17*	176.3	34.4	19.5%	380
01/17	129.0	(1.9)	—	325
12/15	83.7	(7.0)	—	303
12/14	66.8	(13.6)	—	0
Annual Growth	38.2%	—	—	—

*Fiscal year change

2017 Year-End Financials

Debt ratio: 1.8%
Return on equity: 22.2%
Cash ($ mil.): 118.6
Current ratio: 5.59
Long-term debt ($ mil.): —

No. of shares (mil.): 35.5
Dividends
Yield: —
Payout: —
Market value ($ mil.): 433.0

	STOCK PRICE ($) FY Close	P/E High/Low	PER SHARE ($) Earnings	Dividends	Book Value
12/17*	12.20	25 10	0.89	0.00	5.08
01/17	18.13	— —	(0.30)	0.00	3.89
12/15	0.00	— —	(9.16)	0.00	26.24
Annual Growth (56.0%)		— —	—	—	—

*Fiscal year change

QuinStreet, Inc.

QuinStreet connects companies with potential customers through the information superhighway. The online direct marketing company uses proprietary technologies to provide leads to companies. Clients use the leads as the targets of their direct marketing campaigns. As a sign of its confidence in its quality QuinStreet has adopted a pay-for-performance model of pricing in which customers are charged based on lead performance. Catering mainly to the education and financial services sectors its customers have included big organizations such as DeVry and ADT. QuinStreet has offices in the US Brazil and India. The company was founded in 1999.

Operations

QuinStreet?s two largest client verticals are financial services and education. Its financial services segment represented 62% of revenue in fiscal 2017. QuinStreet's education client vertical represented 24% of revenue in fiscal 2017 while the company's other client verticals consisting of home services business-to-business technology and medical represented the remainder of revenue.

Geographic Reach

QuinStreet's corporate headquarters are located in Foster City California with additional offices in the US Brazil and India. Nearly all of the company's revenues (98%) come from the US.

Sales and Marketing

QuinStreet generates revenue from fees earned through the delivery of qualified leads clicks inquiries calls customers and display advertisements.

Financial Performance

QuinStreet has enjoyed steady revenue growth year-over-year. The company reported $299 million in revenue for fiscal 2017 up from $297 million the previous fiscal year (an increase of $2.1 million or 1%).

QuinStreet's financial services segment revenue increased $29.6 million or 19% primarily due to an enhanced product set. The company's education client segment's revenue decreased by $18 million or 20% primarily due to a reduction in clients . Revenue from QuinStreet's other client verticals decreased $9.5 million or 18% primarily due to decreased client demand.

Despite the top line revenue growth in fiscal 2017 QuinStreet suffered a net loss of $12.2 million. The company has suffered net losses in the past several fiscal years as its expenses overshadow its revenue.

QuinStreet reported $18.5 billion in cash from operations at the end of fiscal 2017 up from $1 billion at the close of fiscal 2016. Cash provided by operating activities in fiscal 2017 included the net loss of $12.2 million which included a restructuring charge of $2.4 million offset by non-cash adjustments of $23 million. There was also a net increase in cash from changes in working capital of $7.8 million during fiscal 2017 compared to the prior fiscal period.

Strategy

Education and financial services remain QuinStreet's largest vertical markets bringing in the majority of its revenue. The company's growth strategy is to increase the number of verticals it serves while also entering new verticals. It does so primarily acquisitions and has spent the last few years snapping up marketing and media firms. Other industries served include of business-to-business technology home services and medical sectors.

QuinStreet believes marketing approaches are changing as budgets continue to shift from offline analog advertising media to digital advertising media and internet marketing.

EXECUTIVES

Chairman and CEO, Douglas (Doug) Valenti, age 59, $525,000 total compensation
CTO, Nina Bhanap, age 45, $362,000 total compensation
CFO, Gregory Wong, $262,771 total compensation
General Counsel and Head of Compliance and Corporate Development, Martin J. (Marty) Collins, $75,000 total compensation
Vice President Information Technology Operations, Suresh Kondamareddy
Vice President Operations, Ron Cramer
Auditors: PricewaterhouseCoopers LLP

LOCATIONS

HQ: QuinStreet, Inc.
950 Tower Lane, 6th Floor, Foster City, CA 94404
Phone: 650 578-7700
Web: www.quinstreet.com

PRODUCTS/OPERATIONS

Selected Industries Served
Financial services
Education
Business-to-business technology
Home services
Medical

COMPETITORS

About.com	Leaf Group Ltd.
Agency.com	Marchex
Aptimus	Monster Worldwide
Conversant	Proven Direct
DigitasLBi	Yahoo!
Google	

HISTORICAL FINANCIALS

Company Type: Public

Income Statement   FYE: June 30

	REVENUE ($ mil.)	NET INCOME ($ mil.)	NET PROFIT MARGIN	EMPLOYEES
06/18	404.3	15.9	3.9%	506
06/17	299.7	(12.2)	—	469
06/16	297.7	(19.4)	—	601
06/15	282.1	(20.0)	—	638
06/14	282.5	(146.4)	—	667
Annual Growth	9.4%	—	—	(6.7%)

2018 Year-End Financials

Debt ratio: —
Return on equity: 11.9%
Cash ($ mil.): 64.7
Current ratio: 2.02
Long-term debt ($ mil.): —

No. of shares (mil.): 48.1
Dividends
Yield: —
Payout: —
Market value ($ mil.): 611.0

	STOCK PRICE ($) FY Close	P/E High/Low	PER SHARE ($) Earnings	Dividends	Book Value
06/18	12.70	43 10	0.32	0.00	3.08
06/17	4.17	— —	(0.27)	0.00	2.60
06/16	3.55	— —	(0.43)	0.00	2.74
06/15	6.45	— —	(0.45)	0.00	3.04
06/14	5.51	— —	(3.36)	0.00	3.30
Annual Growth	23.2%	— —	—	—	(1.7%)

Radian Group, Inc.

Radian Group is glowing from a conflagration of private mortgage insurance claims. Through subsidiaries Radian Guaranty Radian Mortgage Assurance and Radian Insurance Radian Group provides traditional private mortgage insurance coverage to protect lenders from defaults by borrowers who put down a deposit of less than 20% when buying a home. Such coverage provides protection on individual loans and covers unpaid loan principal and delinquent interest. Its pool insurance covers limited exposure on groups of loans. Radian still insures municipal bonds written before 2008 through its financial guaranty business. Radian Group's customers include mortgage bankers commercial banks and savings institutions.

Operations

Radian operates in two segments: The mortgage insurance division offers credit-related insurance coverage primarily private mortgage insurance as well as risk services for lending agencies. These operations are primarily conducted through the Radian Guaranty subsidiary. The company also provides mortgage and real estate services through its principal services subsidiary Clayton as well as Green River Capital Red Bell Real Estate and ValuAmerica.

Meanwhile the financial guaranty segment — handled by the Radian Asset Assurance unit — insures a runoff portfolio of public finance and structured finance credits. The unit which no longer actively markets policies historically offered direct insurance or reinsurance for credit based risks as well as credit protection through default swaps and financial guaranty transactions.

During headier days the government encouraged lenders to turn more Americans into homeowners and Radian made a steady diet of insuring subprime mortgages. However that strategy meant that it was among the first to be hit and hit hard when the housing market imploded and mortgage defaults piled up.

Geographic Reach

Headquartered in Philadelphia Radian has offices across the US as well as in Hong Kong and in Bristol UK.

Sales and Marketing

The principal customers of Radian's mortgage insurance business are mortgage originators such as mortgage bankers mortgage brokers commercial banks savings institutions credit unions and community banks.

Financial Performance

In fiscal 2015 Radian's revenue climbed 11% to $1.2 billion due mainly to a 101% increase in revenue from the Services segment. It also recorded higher net premiums in the year. Net income dropped however by 70% to $286.9 million due to a large income tax benefit in the prior fiscal year. The company's cash position strengthened with cash from operating activities climbing to $15.5 million from a loss of $153.2 million in 2014.

Strategy

Radian is looking to expand the depth and breadth of its mortgage offering as the housing market in the US continues to strengthen.

Mergers and Acquisitions

In 2017 Radian consulting subsidiary Clayton Holdings acquired California-based ValuEscrow which continues to operate under its own brand name. The following year Radian acquired Independent Settlement Services a national appraisal and title management firm. That company will continue to operate under its current brand but will eventually transition to the Radian name.

HISTORY

Radian Group was born from the ashes of the 1987 stock crash and the rubble of the natural disasters of the early 1990s. Parent insurance company Reliance Group was deep in debt and desperately in need of cash. To raise money Reliance separated CMAC Investment (and operating subsidiary Commonwealth Mortgage Assurance) from subsidiary Commonwealth Land Title and took the company public in 1992.

In 1994 after two years of lackluster stock performance the board promoted CFO Frank Filipps (an American International Group veteran) to CEO. Filipps limited commissions to new policies rather than retained business. The pokey stock nosed up with some help from low interest rates and high numbers of new mortgage loans. Despite a raise in interest rates in 1995 the company continued to expand its market share.

In 1996 the company launched Prophet Score a new risk-assessment model that allowed CMAC to expand its coverage to include subprime loans. These measures jump-started sales to new highs in 1997 and 1998. Nevertheless CMAC (and its competitors) suffered in the market because of negative publicity: private mortgage (PMI) insurers were slammed for keeping quiet when borrowers' equity rose to 20% the point when PMI is usually considered unnecessary. In 1999 CMAC bought former rival Amerin and changed the name of the combined company to Radian Group.

Radian diversified its operations through the 2001 acquisition of credit-based insurance and financial services provider Enhance Financial (renamed Radian Reinsurance and later merged into Radian Asset Assurance Inc.) In 2002 Radian sold off the Enhance Consumer Services subsidiary.

In 2005 Filipps departed to join Clayton Holdings. Sanford Ibrahim was then named CEO.

The company expanded into Asia in 2005 through a partnership with Standard Chartered Bank (Hong Kong) with Radian as the exclusive provider of residential mortgage insurance to the lender. However the deal did not take root and Standard Chartered Bank yanked their contract in early 2008.

As the credit markets went into meltdown that year the company began pulling back on the riskiest of bonds (such as second-liens) by mid-2007 but by early 2008 its ratings had been lowered.

In response to the market troubles Radian stopped insuring certain types of higher-risk home loans and began working with existing mortgage services to help distressed borrowers modify their loan terms. The company's Radian Asset Assurance operations in the US and UK also stopped accepting new business as part of its general hunkering down to ride out the storm and in 2010 it put the UK unit into liquidation.

EXECUTIVES

CEO, Richard G. (Rick) Thornberry
President Radian Guaranty, Teresa A. Bryce Bazemore, age 58, $550,000 total compensation
EVP and CFO, J. Franklin (Frank) Hall, age 50, $400,000 total compensation
EVP and CIO, Richard I. (Rick) Altman, age 51
EVP and Chief Risk Officer, Derek V. Brummer, $415,000 total compensation
President Clayton Holdings, Jeff Tennyson
Senior Vice President and Deputy General Counsel, Glenn Davis
Assistant Vice President Corporate Accounting, Abigail Rodriguez
Vice President Strategic Services, Susan King
Director, Herbert Wender, age 81
Auditors: PricewaterhouseCoopers LLP

LOCATIONS

HQ: Radian Group, Inc.
1500 Market Street, Philadelphia, PA 19102
Phone: 215 231-1000
Web: www.radian.biz

PRODUCTS/OPERATIONS

2016 Revenues

	$ mil.	% of total
Net premiums earned—insurance	921.8	74
Services revenue	168.9	14
Net investment income	113.5	9
Net gains (losses) on investments and other financial instruments	30.8	3
Other income	3.5	-
Total	**1,238.5**	**100**

COMPETITORS

Assured Guaranty	Old Republic
Essent Guaranty	Triad Guaranty
Genworth Financial	US Department of
MGIC Investment	Veterans Affairs
National Mortgage	United Guaranty
Insurance	

HISTORICAL FINANCIALS

Company Type: Public

Income Statement

FYE: December 31

	ASSETS ($ mil.)	NET INCOME ($ mil.)	INCOME AS % OF ASSETS	EMPLOYEES
12/17	5,900.8	121.0	2.1%	1,887
12/16	5,863.1	308.2	5.3%	1,971
12/15	5,642.1	286.9	5.1%	1,881
12/14	6,859.9	959.5	14.0%	1,702
12/13	5,621.6	(196.9)	—	782
Annual Growth	1.2%	—	—	24.6%

2017 Year-End Financials

Return on assets: 2.0%	Dividends
Return on equity: 4.1%	Yield: 0.0%
Long-term debt ($ mil.): —	Payout: 1.8%
No. of shares (mil.): 215.8	Market value ($ mil.): 4,448.0
Sales ($ mil): 1,221.6	

	STOCK PRICE ($) FY Close	P/E High/Low		PER SHARE ($) Earnings	Dividends	Book Value
12/17	20.61	40	28	0.55	0.01	13.90
12/16	17.98	13	6	1.37	0.01	13.39
12/15	13.39	13	9	1.22	0.01	12.07
12/14	16.72	3	2	4.16	0.01	11.37
12/13	14.12	—	—	(1.18)	0.01	5.43
Annual Growth	9.9%	—	—	—	(0.0%)	26.5%

Radiant Logistics, Inc.

When companies need someone to transport their freight Radiant Logistics delivers. Operating through its Airgroup and Adcom Worldwide subsidiaries the company offers logistics services such as domestic and international air ocean and ground freight forwarding (Radiant purchases transportation capacity from carriers and resells to its customers). In addition Radiant provides supply chain management services such as warehousing order fulfillment and inventory management. Government and automotive sectors (e.g. US Transportation Command Ford and General Motors) make up the company's customer base. Radiant operates through more than 100 offices located throughout North America.

Since its inception in 2001 the company has been actively expanding its operations through acquisitions. In early 2012 it obtained ALBS Logistics a provider of domestic and international transportation and logistics services serving manufacturers distributors and retailers across North America. The deal allowed Radiant to gain an important strategic gateway location as ALBS is based in the New York/JFK airport.

The year before Radiant purchased DBA Distribution Services (conducting business as Distribution By Air or "DBA") a New Jersey-based transportation and logistics services company. The deal was valued at $12 million and expanded Radiant's markets in Newark New Jersey and Los Angeles.

Looking to increase its presence in the South in late 2011 Radiant acquired Laredo Texas-based Isla International for an estimated $15 million. Isla International provided logistics and transportation services between the US and Mexico. The new unit was named Mexico Gateway fitting into Radiant's global growth strategy.

Radiant expects that its future growth will come from additional acquisitions as well as through organic growth. In addition it hopes to expand its global operations; currently the company operates primarily within the North American market.

EXECUTIVES

Chairman and CEO, Bohn H. Crain, age 53, $325,000 total compensation
SVP Operations, E. Joseph (Joe) Bento
SVP and CFO, Todd E. Macomber, age 53, $200,000 total compensation
Chief Commercial Officer and COO Service By Air Inc. (SBA), Arnie Goldstein
Vice President Risk Management, Paul Kwiatkowski
Auditors: Peterson Sullivan LLP

LOCATIONS

HQ: Radiant Logistics, Inc.
405 114th Ave S.E., Bellevue, WA 98004
Phone: 425 943-4599   **Fax:** 425 462-0768
Web: www.radiantdelivers.com

COMPETITORS

AIT Worldwide Logistics	DHL
APL Logistics	Landstar System
CEVA Logistics	UPS Supply Chain Solutions

HISTORICAL FINANCIALS
Company Type: Public

Income Statement
FYE: June 30

	REVENUE ($ mil.)	NET INCOME ($ mil.)	NET PROFIT MARGIN	EMPLOYEES
06/18	842.4	10.1	1.2%	728
06/17	777.6	4.8	0.6%	758
06/16	782.5	(3.5)	—	640
06/15	502.6	5.8	1.2%	760
06/14	349.1	5.1	1.5%	300
Annual Growth	24.6%	18.8%		24.8%

2018 Year-End Financials

Debt ratio: 15.3%
Return on equity: 7.9%
Cash ($ mil.): 6.9
Current ratio: 1.32
Long-term debt ($ mil.): 43.2
No. of shares (mil.): 49.4
Dividends
  Yield: —
  Payout: —
Market value ($ mil.): 193.0

	STOCK PRICE ($) FY Close	P/E High/Low		PER SHARE ($) Earnings	Dividends	Book Value
06/18	3.91	33	21	0.16	0.00	2.70
06/17	5.38	107	41	0.06	0.00	2.51
06/16	3.00	—	—	(0.11)	0.00	2.44
06/15	7.31	72	27	0.10	0.00	1.98
06/14	3.09	28	15	0.11	0.00	1.19
Annual Growth	6.1%	—	—	9.8%	—	22.7%

RBB Bancorp

Auditors: Varinek, Trine, Day & Co., LLP

LOCATIONS

HQ: RBB Bancorp
660 S. Figueroa Street, Suite 1888, Los Angeles, CA 90017
Phone: 213 627-9888
Web: www.royalbusinessbankusa.com

HISTORICAL FINANCIALS
Company Type: Public

Income Statement
FYE: December 31

	ASSETS ($ mil.)	NET INCOME ($ mil.)	INCOME AS % OF ASSETS	EMPLOYEES
12/17	1,691.0	25.5	1.5%	203
12/16	1,395.5	19.0	1.4%	177
12/15	1,023.0	12.9	1.3%	0
12/14	0.0	10.4	-	0
Annual Growth	—	34.8%	—	—

2017 Year-End Financials

Return on assets: 1.6%
Return on equity: 11.4%
Long-term debt ($ mil.): —
No. of shares (mil.): 15.9
Sales ($ mil): 87.3
Dividends
  Yield: 0.0%
  Payout: 4.7%
Market value ($ mil.): 435.0

	STOCK PRICE ($) FY Close	P/E High/Low		PER SHARE ($) Earnings	Dividends	Book Value
12/17	27.37	15	12	1.68	0.08	16.67
12/16	0.00	—	—	1.39	0.20	14.16
Annual Growth	—	—	—	20.9%	(60.0%)	17.8%

RBC Bearings Inc

RBC Bearings keeps businesses on a roll. The company makes an array of plain roller and ball bearing products. It specializes in regulated bearings used by OEMs and their aftermarkets of commercial/military aircraft automobiles and commercial trucks industrial/agricultural machinery as well as air turbines. Targeting high-end markets its precision lineup satisfies thousands of applications from engine controls to radar systems mining tools and gear pumps. RBC's top customers include Boeing GE Lockheed Martin and the US Department of Defense. RBC Bearings has grown since 1919 to some 30 manufacturing facilities in Europe and North America.

Operations

RBC operates through four reportable business segments: Plain Bearings Engineered Products Roller Bearings and Ball Bearings. Plain Bearings represents 45% of total revenue and is used in aircraft controls helicopter rotors or in heavy mining and construction equipment.

Engineered Products consists of highly engineered hydraulics fasteners collets and precision components used in aerospace marine and industrial applications. Roller Bearings are anti-friction bearings that use rollers in place of balls. The company manufactures four basic types of roller bearings: heavy duty needle roller bearings with inner rings tapered roller bearings track rollers and aircraft roller bearings.

Ball Bearings makes four basic types of ball bearings: high precision aerospace airframe control thin section and commercial ball bearings which are used in high-speed rotational applications.

Geographic Reach

The company operates about 30 facilities in the US and has international operations in Canada Switzerland Mexico and Poland. RBC's warehouses reside in the Midwest Southwest and on the East and West coasts of the US as well as in France and Switzerland. The US is its largest market accounting for more than 85% of total sales.

Sales and Marketing

The company sells its products through a direct sales force located in North America Europe Asia and Latin America. It also utilizes marketing managers product managers customer service representatives product application engineers and a global network of industrial and aerospace distributors. The aerospace and defense markets account for more than 65% of total sales. Sales to its top 10 customers generate 33% of total sales.

Financial Performance

RBC has experienced unprecedented growth over the last few years. Its revenues climbed 34% $445 million in 2015 to $597 million in 2016. Profits also jumped 10% from $58 million in 2015 to $64 million in 2016. Both these totals represented historic milestones for the company.

The historic growth for 2016 was driven by an explosive 439% surge in sales from Engineered Products largely due to additional revenue from its Sargent acquisition. Through the purchase RBC enjoyed impressive growth within the aerospace and industrial markets. Related to these factors sales from the US sales also climbed by 29% in 2016.

From 2015 to 2016 the company's cash flow spiked from $72 million to $84 million mainly due to favorable changes in inventory.

Strategy

RBC has managed to increase its sales to the aftermarket. Bearings which are indispensable for a machine's operating efficiency periodically wear out which creates a second stream of replacement parts sales. During 2016 aftermarket sales of replacement parts for installed equipment accounted for nearly 45% of RBC's revenues. Aerospace and defense customers also promise a particularly reliable opportunity for replacement business.

Mergers and Acquisitions

The company makes acquisitions in order to further develop its offerings end-markets and geographic footprint. In early 2016 the company acquired Arizona-based Sargent an expert in precision-engineered products services and repairs for aircraft airframes and engines rotorcraft submarines and land vehicles for $500 million in cash. The deal enhanced RBC's product portfolio and engineering technologies and added exponentially to its Plain Bearings and Engineering Products segments.

Company Background

RBC Bearings is an amalgamation of companies merged and acquired. The company got its start in 1919 making ball bearings; by the 1940s it became the sole supplier for landing gear bearings on military aircraft made by Ford Motor Company. In 2005 the company jetted onto the public investor market.

EXECUTIVES

Chairman President and CEO, Michael J. Hartnett, age 71, $922,643 total compensation
VP; General Manager RBC Division, Richard J. Edwards, age 61, $306,000 total compensation
VP COO and CFO, Daniel A. (Dan) Bergeron, age 57, $370,000 total compensation
VP; General Manager Heim Bearings and Schaublin, Thomas C. Crainer, age 59, $314,000 total compensation
Vice President Sales, Karen De Mestrio
Auditors: Ernst & Young LLP

LOCATIONS

HQ: RBC Bearings Inc
One Tribology Center, Oxford, CT 06478
Phone: 203 267-7001
Web: www.rbcbearings.com

PRODUCTS/OPERATIONS

2016 Sales

	$ mil.	% of total
Plain	270.5	45
Engineered Products	161.3	27
Roller	112.0	19
Ball	53.7	9
Total	**597.5**	**100**

2016 Sales

	% of total
Aerospace market	66
Industrial market	34
Total	**100**

PRODUCTS
AEROSPACE
Airframe Control Ball Bearings
Airframe Control Needle Track Rollers
Ball Bearing Rod Ends
Gear Box and Engine and Roller Ball Bearings
Journal Bearings

Links and Assemblies
Machined Components
Radial Ball Bearings
Rod End Plain Bearings
Spherical Plain Bearings
Stud Type Track Roller Bearings
Swage Tubes and Control Rods
Thin Section Ball Bearings
INDUSTRIAL
Ball Bearings
Cam Followers
Collets/Toolholders
Heavy Duty Fleet Customers
Heavy Duty Needle Roller Bearings
Pins Rollers Shafts
Rod Ends
Self-Lubricating Bearings
Spherical Plain Bearings
Tapered/Tapered Thrust Roller Bearings
Thin Section Ball Bearings

COMPETITORS

Emerson Electric	Rexnord
General Bearing	SKF USA
Kaydon	Timken
MinebeaMitsumi	
NTN Bearing Corp. of America	

HISTORICAL FINANCIALS

Company Type: Public

Income Statement
FYE: March 31

	REVENUE ($ mil.)	NET INCOME ($ mil.)	NET PROFIT MARGIN	EMPLOYEES
03/18*	674.9	87.1	12.9%	3,466
04/17	615.3	70.6	11.5%	3,401
04/16	597.4	63.8	10.7%	3,277
03/15	445.2	58.2	13.1%	2,490
03/14	418.8	60.2	14 4%	2,361
Annual Growth	**12.7%**	**9.7%**	**—**	**10.1%**

*Fiscal year change

2018 Year-End Financials

Debt ratio: 15.1%	No. of shares (mil.): 24.1
Return on equity: 11.2%	Dividends
Cash ($ mil.): 54.1	Yield: —
Current ratio: 4.60	Payout: —
Long-term debt ($ mil.): 154.1	Market value ($ mil.): 2,994.0

	STOCK PRICE ($) FY Close	P/E High/Low	PER SHARE ($) Earnings	Dividends	Book Value
03/18*	124.20	37 25	3.58	0.00	34.62
04/17	97.09	32 23	2.97	0.00	29.77
04/16	73.65	28 20	2.72	0.00	26.37
03/15	75.58	30 21	2.49	2.00	23.49
03/14	62.97	27 18	2.59	0.00	23.20
Annual Growth	**18.5%**	**— —**	**8.4%**	**—**	**10.5%**

*Fiscal year change

Ready Capital Corp

ZAIS is a REIT that invests in RMBS. As a real estate investment trust ZAIS Financial aims to put its money in residential mortgage-backed securities primarily of the non-agency variety meaning ones that are not issued or guaranteed by such government-sponsored entities as Fannie Mae Freddie Mac and Ginnie Mae. The company also invests in such real estate and financial assets as mortgage servicing rights (MSRs) asset-backed securities (ABS) and commercial mortgage-backed securities (CMBS). Formed in mid-2011 the company now plans to merge with private REIT Sutherland Asset Management.

IPO

ZAIS is using proceeds from its IPO and additional borrowings to purchase target assets like residential mortgage-backed securities (RMBS). In the short term the company may also invest in interest-bearing money market funds.

Geographic Reach

New Jersey-based ZAIS operates its business across the US Europe and Asia.

Strategy

While ZAIS plans to invest in agency RMBS the firm is primarily focused on non-agency securities particularly ones that were originally rated in the highest category. It expects to eventually shift its attention to new loans. The company sees opportunity in the US housing market as well due to the bottoming out of home prices and a gradual recovery seemingly underway the increased role for private capital owing to legislative reform and the existence of a "mortgage gap" for qualified borrowers as the federal government's portion of mortgage origination subsidies.

Financial Performance

Real estate securities helped to boost ZAIS's 2012 interest income by $9 million. It also logged an $18 million change in unrealized gain/(loss) on real estate securities while it posted $20 million in net income during the same reporting period.

Company Background

Prior to the IPO ZAIS Financial was owned by global asset management firm ZAIS Group LLC. Christian Zugel was the latter's chief investment officer and ZAIS Financial's chairman.

Auditors: Deloitte & Touche LLP

LOCATIONS

HQ: Ready Capital Corp
1140 Avenue of the Americas, 7th Floor, New York, NY 10036
Phone: 212 257-4600
Web: www.sutherlandam.com

COMPETITORS

American Capital Agency Corp.	Five Oaks Hatteras Financial
Anworth Mortgage Asset	Invesco Mortgage
Capital Trust	Capital
Capstead Mortgage	MFA Financial
Drive Shack	Starwood Property

HISTORICAL FINANCIALS

Company Type: Public

Income Statement
FYE: December 31

	REVENUE ($ mil.)	NET INCOME ($ mil.)	NET PROFIT MARGIN	EMPLOYEES
12/17	211.4	43.2	20.5%	0
12/16	171.4	49.1	28.7%	0
12/15	72.7	(1.2)	—	246
12/14	65.2	26.7	41.0%	216
12/13	24.2	6.6	27.5%	0
Annual Growth	**71.8%**	**59.6%**		

2017 Year-End Financials

Debt ratio: 70.3%
Return on equity: 8.2%
Cash ($ mil.): 63.4
Current ratio: 1.95
Long-term debt ($ mil.): 1,775.6

No. of shares (mil.): 32.0
Dividends
Yield: 0.1%
Payout: 107.2%
Market value ($ mil.): 485.0

	STOCK PRICE ($) FY Close	P/E High/Low		PER SHARE ($) Earnings	Dividends	Book Value
12/17	15.15	12	9	1.38	1.48	16.75
12/16	13.45	8	7	1.85	1.55	16.80
12/15	15.08	—	—	(0.16)	1.60	19.98
12/14	17.25	6	5	3.08	1.60	21.73
12/13	16.03	23	17	0.92	2.12	19.98
Annual Growth	(1.4%)	—	—	10.7%	(8.6%)	(4.3%)

Realty Income Corp

Retail real estate is a reality for Realty Income Corporation. The self-administered real estate investment trust (REIT) acquires owns and manages primarily free-standing highly-occupied single-tenant properties which it leases to regional and national consumer retail and service chains. Realty Income owns more than 4320 (mostly retail) properties spanning some 71 million sq. ft. of leasable space across every US state except Hawaii though nearly half of the REIT's rental revenue comes from its properties in Texas California Florida Minnesota Georgia Illinois and Virginia. Realty Income's top five tenants include Walgreens FedEx Dollar General LA Fitness and Family Dollar.

Operations

Realty Income owned more than 4320 properties during 2014 nearly 79% of which were Retail and the rest being Industrial and distribution (10%) Office (nearly 7%) Manufacturing (2%) and Agricultural related properties. Subsidiary Crest Net owns properties which are held for sale rather than for long-term investment.

Geographic Reach

California-based Realty Income's largest markets include Texas California Florida Minnesota Georgia Illinois and Virginia. More than 10% of its rental revenue came from properties in California in 2014 while properties in Texas contributed another nearly 10%.

Sales and Marketing

Realty Income's occupancy rate has been above 96% every year since its 1969 founding; its properties were 98.4% occupied in 2014 with an average remaining lease term of 10.2 years.

Its tenants have included owners of restaurants convenience stores theaters child care providers automotive care centers health and fitness facilities grocery stores and drug stores. Realty Income's top five tenants — Walgreens FedEx Dollar General LA Fitness and Family Dollar — combined generated nearly 25% of its total revenue in 2014. About 10% of its client types were owners of convenience stores.

Financial Performance

Acquisitive Realty Income has doubled its revenues and profits since 2010 as it has expanded its property portfolio and has charged higher rental rates as the real estate market has strengthened.

The REIT's revenue jumped 20% to $933.5 million in 2014 mostly thanks to new rental revenue from its acquisition of 479 properties. Same-store rents on 2728 of its properties rose by 2% also helping drive the company's top line growth.

Higher revenue and higher gains on property sales in 2014 boosted Realty Income's net income by 10% to $271.9 million while the REIT's operating cash levels climbed 21% to $627.7 million on higher cash earnings.

Strategy

Realty Income's investment strategy reiterated in 2015 involves acting as a source of capital to regional and national tenants. As such it focuses on long-term sale-leaseback transactions in which the tenant is responsible for taxes and maintenance. And when considering its investment targets the REIT looks to acquire what its tenants consider important toward the successful operation of their businesses.

Realty Income has traditionally grown its revenue through high-quality property acquisitions (with above 96% occupancy rates and existing long-term lease arrangements). It often sells properties with the intent to reinvest the proceeds in new real estate with the potential for higher returns. During 2014 it invested $1.4 billion in over 500 new properties (including ones under development or expansion) spanning 9.8 million leasable sq. ft. across 42 states with an average occupancy rate of 100% and a lease term of 12.8 years.

Mergers and Acquisitions

In January 2013 Realty Income purchased fellow REIT American Realty Capital Trust adding more than 480 commercial properties to its portfolio.

EXECUTIVES

EVP General Counsel and Secretary, Michael R. Pfeiffer, age 57, $375,000 total compensation
SVP Research, Robert J. Israel, age 58
Vice President Asset Management, Jenette O'brien
EVP CFO and Treasurer, Paul M. Meurer, age 52, $400,000 total compensation
President CEO and Director, John P. Case, age 54, $800,000 total compensation
President and COO, Sumit Roy, age 48, $406,250 total compensation
VP Information Technology, Clint Schmucker
EVP and Chief Investment Officer, Neil Abraham
Associate Vice President Director Of Research, Scott Kohnen
Associate Vice President Controller, Jill Cossaboom
Vice President Human Resources, Shannon Kehle
Associate Vice President Acquisitions Director, Greg Smith
Chairman, Michael D. McKee
Auditors: KPMG LLP

LOCATIONS

HQ: Realty Income Corp
 11995 El Camino Real, San Diego, CA 92130
Phone: 858 284-5000
Web: www.realtyincome.com

PRODUCTS/OPERATIONS

2014 Properties

	No.	% rental revenue
Retail	4.1	79
Industrial and distribution	82.0	10
Office	44.0	7
Manufacturing	14.0	2
Agriculture	15.0	2
Total	**4,327.0**	**100**

2014 Sales

	% of total
Rental	96
Tenant reimbursement	4
Others	-
Total	**100**

COMPETITORS

Acadia Realty Trust
Capital Automotive
DDR
EPR Properties
Federal Realty Investment
Kimco Realty
National Retail Properties
One Liberty Properties
Regency Centers
Simon Property Group
The Blackstone Group
Weingarten Realty

HISTORICAL FINANCIALS

Company Type: Public

Income Statement				FYE: December 31
	REVENUE ($ mil.)	NET INCOME ($ mil.)	NET PROFIT MARGIN	EMPLOYEES
12/17	1,215.7	318.8	26.2%	152
12/16	1,103.1	315.5	28.6%	146
12/15	1,023.2	283.7	27.7%	132
12/14	933.5	270.6	29.0%	125
12/13	778.3	245.5	31.5%	116
Annual Growth	11.8%	6.7%	—	7.0%

2017 Year-End Financials

Debt ratio: 43.5%
Return on equity: 4.5%
Cash ($ mil.): 6.9
Current ratio: 0.44
Long-term debt ($ mil.): 6,111.4

No. of shares (mil.): 284.2
Dividends
Yield: 0.0%
Payout: 230.6%
Market value ($ mil.): 16,206.0

	STOCK PRICE ($) FY Close	P/E High/Low		PER SHARE ($) Earnings	Dividends	Book Value
12/17	57.02	57	48	1.10	2.54	25.94
12/16	57.48	64	45	1.13	2.40	26.01
12/15	51.63	51	40	1.09	2.28	26.08
12/14	47.71	48	36	1.04	2.19	24.96
12/13	37.33	52	35	1.06	2.18	25.96
Annual Growth	11.2%	—	—	0.9%	3.9%	(0.0%)

Regency Centers Corp

Regency Centers' bread and butter comes from grocery stores. A real estate investment trust (REIT) the firm owns manages and develops neighborhood shopping centers in about two dozen states and Washington DC many of them anchored by a Kroger Publix or Safeway supermarket. Other tenants include retailers restaurants and professional services firms. The REIT wholly owns or has interests in about 330 properties measuring more than 44 million sq. ft. of leaseable space. The REIT focuses on high-growth areas in states including California Florida Texas Georgia and Colorado home to the majority of its wholly-owned holdings.

Geographic Reach

Florida-based Regency Centers has grocery-anchored shopping centers in 23 states and the District of Columbia. California Florida and Texas account for more than 10% of the firm's operating income.

Sales and Marketing

Grocery giants Kroger Florida-based Publix and Safeway are the REIT's largest clients contributing 5% 4% and 3% of its annualized base rent respectively.

Financial Performance

Regency's revenue declined by nearly 2% in 2013 versus 2012 to $489 million. Net income soared 479% over the same period to $149.8 million. The decline in revenue reflects the sale of a 15-property portfolio in July 2012 that resulted in a decrease in recoveries from tenants and other income in 2013. The huge bump in net income was due to the gain on the sale of the properties.

Strategy

The REIT grows its shopping center portfolio through acquisitions of existing shopping centers and new development. New development is customer driven in that the REIT generally has an executed lease from the anchor tenant before it breaks ground. Since 2000 the company has developed some 215 properties and acquired more than 100 more though such activity slowed during the recession. With the US economy on the mend Regency is actively acquiring developing and redeveloping properties in high-growth and affluent areas. Indeed in April 2014 Regency opened a new shopping center in South Los Angeles called the Juanita Tate Marketplace. The new development is anchored by Hispanic grocery chain Gonzalez Market.

While the REIT wholly owns about two-thirds of its properties about 125 others are partially owned by Regency Centers through joint ventures with other institutional investors such as CalSTRS and USAA.

Mergers and Acquisitions

In March 2017 Equity One merged with and into Regency with Regency continuing as the surviving public company. The merger formed a combined company with a total market capitalization of approximately $16 billion.

EXECUTIVES

Managing Director Texas Southern California Cincinnati and Columbus, John S. Delatour, $350,000 total compensation

EVP Operations, James D. (Jim) Thompson, age 62, $395,000 total compensation

Chairman and CEO, Martin E. (Hap) Stein, age 65, $790,000 total compensation

Managing Director Pacific Northwest and Northern California, H. Craig Ramey

Managing Director East, Alan T. Roth

EVP and CFO, Lisa Palmer, age 50, $455,000 total compensation

SVP and CIO, Dale Johnston

Managing Director West, Dan M. (Mac) Chandler, age 50, $375,000 total compensation

Managing Director Chicago Minneapolis and Colorado, Nick Wibbenmeyer

Senior Vice President, Snowden Leftwich

Senior Vice President Transactions, Barry E Argalas

Vice President Construction, John Hayes

Vice President Regional Officer, John Hricko

Vice President Financial Services, Patrick Johnson

Vice President of Investments and Market Officer, Jack deVilliers

Vice President Regional Officer, Andre Koleszar

Vice President of Construction, Scott Wilson

Vice President Investments, Paul Maxwell

Senior Vice President, Peter Knoedler

Vice President, James Chiang

Senior Vice President for Strategic Planning and Development, Kimberly Duncan

Vice President, Andy Hofheimer

Senior Vice President Senior Market Officer, Doug Shaffer

Vice President of Financial Services, Laura Clark

Senior Vice President Senior Market Officer, Krista Di Iaconi

Vice President Finance, Chris Leavitt

Senior Vice President Senior Market Officer, Craig Ramey

Director of Nursing, Tracy Vick

Senior Vice President, Rafael Muniz

Vice Chairman COO, Mary Fiala

Auditors: KPMG LLP

LOCATIONS

HQ: Regency Centers Corp
One Independent Drive, Suite 114, Jacksonville, FL 32202
Phone: 904 598-7000
Web: www.regencycenters.com

PRODUCTS/OPERATIONS

2016 Sales

	$ mil.	% of total
Minimum rent	444.3	72
Recoveries from tenants & other income	140.6	23
Management acquisition & other fees	25.4	4
Percentage rent	4.1	1
Total	**614.4**	**100**

COMPETITORS

CBL & Associates Properties	Kimco Realty
Cousins Properties	Macerich
DDR	Vornado Realty
Federal Realty Investment	Weingarten Realty

HISTORICAL FINANCIALS

Company Type: Public

Income Statement

FYE: December 31

	REVENUE ($ mil.)	NET INCOME ($ mil.)	NET PROFIT MARGIN	EMPLOYEES
12/17	984.3	176.0	17.9%	446
12/16	614.3	164.9	26.8%	371
12/15	569.7	150.0	26.3%	371
12/14	537.9	187.3	34.8%	370
12/13	489.0	149.8	30.6%	363
Annual Growth	**19.1%**	**4.1%**	**—**	**5.3%**

2017 Year-End Financials

Debt ratio: 32.2%	No. of shares (mil.): 171.0
Return on equity: 3.7%	Dividends
Cash ($ mil.): 45.3	Yield: 0.0%
Current ratio: 0.16	Payout: 210.0%
Long-term debt ($ mil.): 3,594.9	Market value ($ mil.): 11,830.0

	STOCK PRICE ($) FY Close	P/E High/Low	PER SHARE ($) Earnings	Dividends	Book Value
12/17	69.18	72 59	1.00	2.10	39.14
12/16	68.95	60 46	1.42	2.00	24.88
12/15	68.12	51 42	1.36	1.94	21.22
12/14	63.78	36 26	1.80	1.88	20.35
12/13	46.30	42 33	1.40	1.85	20.05
Annual Growth	**10.6%**	**— —**	**(8.1%)**	**3.2%**	**18.2%**

Regional Management Corp

Regional Management is looking to give credit where credit is due. Consumer finance company Regional Management provides secured personal loans (up to $27500) auto loans and furniture and appliance loans to consumers who may otherwise have limited access to credit through banks and other traditional lenders. The company which operates under the Regional Finance RMC Financial Services Anchor Finance and Sun Finance banners among others has some 265 branch locations in eight states in the south and southwest. It also provides loans through pre-screened live check mailings auto dealerships and its e-commerce site. Founded in 1987 Regional Management went public via an IPO in 2012.

IPO

The company intends to use a portion of the proceeds from its March 2012 IPO ($63 million down from what the $80 million it expected) to repay debt and for general corporate purposes. It also plans to use some of the proceeds to make a one-time payment to pre-IPO owners to terminate a consulting agreement. Prior to the IPO private equity firm Palladium Equity Partners held a 48% stake in the company and Parallel 2005 Equity Fund held a 28% stake.

Operations

The consumer finance company makes small installment loans (ranging from $300 to $2500) large installment loans (between $2500 and $20000) and automobile purchase loans (up to $27500). It also makes loans to finance retail purchases of up to $7500 that are secured by the purchased item. Regional Management also sells insurance on its loans. Most of its loan activity consists of small installment and auto purchase loans.

Geographic Reach

South Carolina-based Regional Management makes loans in the Carolinas Texas Georgia Tennessee Alabama Oklahoma and New Mexico.

Financial Performance

In its first full year as a public company Regional Management reported sales of $170.6 million in 2013 an increase of 25% versus the prior year on rising interest and fee income. Net income grew 14% to $28.8 million over the same period. Indeed the finance company's sales and profits have been rising in lockstep since 2008 as the company opened new branches. In 2013 about 75% of the firm's loans were classified as current with 17% between 1 to 29 days delinquent.

Strategy

Regional Management targets non-prime and underbanked consumers who have limited access to credit from traditional channels such as banks and credit card companies. While the population of such customers has grown in recent years the supply of consumer credit to them has contracted presenting Regional Management with a growth market for its installment auto and retail purchase loans.

As a key component of its growth strategy Regional Management has been busy opening new branches in new and existing markets. Indeed the company's branch network has more than doubled in size from 117 branches in 2009 to about 265 in 2013. In 2013 the firm opened or acquired 43 new branches including its first branches in Georgia. Regional Management is eyeing several states outside its present footprint with favorable interest rate and regulatory climates such as Kentucky Louisiana Mississippi Missouri and Virginia. The company also plans to bolster its other lending channels including driving traffic to its e-commerce website through marketing and advertising initiatives and by leveraging search engine optimization technologies.

EXECUTIVES

EVP and CFO, Donald E. (Don) Thomas, age 59, $332,000 total compensation
CEO, Peter R. Knitzer, age 59, $221,557 total compensation
SVP and Chief Risk Officer, Daniel J. Taggart, age 45, $308,000 total compensation
VP General Counsel and Secretary, Brian J. Fisher, age 34, $230,000 total compensation
COO, John D. Schachtel
Vice President Auto Products, Brian Switalski
Chairman, Alvaro G. (Al) de Molina, age 60
Auditors: RSM US LLP

LOCATIONS

HQ: Regional Management Corp
979 Batesville Road, Suite B, Greer, SC 29651
Phone: 864 448-7000
Web: www.regionalmanagement.com

PRODUCTS/OPERATIONS

2015 Sales

	% of total
Interest and fee income	90
Insurance income net	5
Other	5
Total	**100**

COMPETITORS

1st Franklin Financial	DFC Global
Advance America	Nicholas Financial
Capital One Auto Finance	OneMain
	QC Holdings
Check 'n Go	World Acceptance
Check Into Cash	Xponential
Community Choice Financial	

HISTORICAL FINANCIALS

Company Type: Public

Income Statement   FYE: December 31

	ASSETS ($ mil.)	NET INCOME ($ mil.)	INCOME AS % OF ASSETS	EMPLOYEES
12/17	829.4	29.9	3.6%	1,448
12/16	712.2	24.0	3.4%	1,363
12/15	629.0	23.3	3.7%	1,421
12/14	530.2	14.8	2.8%	1,443
12/13	533.8	28.7	5.4%	1,117
Annual Growth	**11.6%**	**1.0%**	**—**	**6.7%**

2017 Year-End Financials

Return on assets: 3.8%	Dividends
Return on equity: 13.4%	Yield: —
Long-term debt ($ mil.): —	Payout: —
No. of shares (mil.): 11.6	Market value ($ mil.): 307.0
Sales ($ mil): 272.4	

	STOCK PRICE ($) FY Close	P/E High/Low		PER SHARE ($) Earnings	Dividends	Book Value
12/17	26.31	10	7	2.54	0.00	20.53
12/16	26.28	13	6	1.99	0.00	18.12
12/15	15.47	11	8	1.79	0.00	15.89
12/14	15.81	31	10	1.14	0.00	13.99
12/13	33.93	15	7	2.23	0.00	12.74
Annual Growth	**(6.2%)**	**—**	**—**	**3.3%**	**—**	**12.7%**

Reliant Bancorp Inc

Auditors: Maggart & Associates, P.C.

LOCATIONS

HQ: Reliant Bancorp Inc
1736 Carothers Parkway, Suite 100, Brentwood, TN 37027
Phone: 615 221-2020

HISTORICAL FINANCIALS

Company Type: Public

Income Statement   FYE: December 31

	ASSETS ($ mil.)	NET INCOME ($ mil.)	INCOME AS % OF ASSETS	EMPLOYEES
12/17	1,125.0	7.2	0.6%	168
12/16	911.9	8.9	1.0%	143
12/15	876.4	5.5	0.6%	226
12/14	295.7	2.1	0.7%	47
12/13	253.1	1.9	0.7%	0
Annual Growth	**45.2%**	**39.8%**	**—**	**—**

2017 Year-End Financials

Return on assets: 0.7%	Dividends
Return on equity: 5.8%	Yield: 0.0%
Long-term debt ($ mil.): —	Payout: 45.4%
No. of shares (mil.): 9.0	Market value ($ mil.): 232.0
Sales ($ mil): 46.1	

	STOCK PRICE ($) FY Close	P/E High/Low		PER SHARE ($) Earnings	Dividends	Book Value
12/17	25.64	29	24	0.88	0.40	15.51
12/16	21.51	19	11	1.16	0.20	13.75
12/15	13.71	17	15	0.86	0.20	13.29
12/14	13.00	18	14	0.69	0.40	11.74
12/13	10.90	18	15	0.62	0.20	11.10
Annual Growth	**23.8%**	**—**	**—**	**9.1%**	**18.9%**	**8.7%**

Renasant Corp

Those who are cognizant of their finances may want to do business with Renasant Corporation. The holding company owns Renasant Bank which serves consumers and local business through about 80 locations in Alabama Georgia Mississippi and Tennessee. The bank offers standard products such as checking and savings accounts CDs credit cards and loans and mortgages as well as trust retail brokerage and retirement plan services. Its loan portfolio is dominated by residential and commercial real estate loans. The bank also offers agricultural business construction and consumer loans and lease financing. Subsidiary Renasant Insurance sells personal and business coverage. Shareholders approved a merger with Metropolitan Bank in mid-2017.

Financial Performance

The company's revenue increased in fiscal 2013 compared to the prior year. It reported revenue of $252.6 million for fiscal 2013 up from $228 million in revenue for fiscal 2012.

Renasant's net income also went up in fiscal 2013 compared to the previous fiscal period. It reported net income of about $33.5 million for fiscal 2013 up from net income of $26.6 million in fiscal 2012.

The company's cash on hand decreased by about $24 million in fiscal 2013 compared to fiscal 2012 levels.

Strategy

Renasant has looked to diversify its loan portfolio. The bank has reduced its amount of loans for construction and land development — a sector that has been hit particularly hard — by tightening its underwriting standards.

It's also been growing through acquistions. In late 2014 for example Renasant purchased Heritage Financial Group in an all stock merger deal that amounted to $258 million. The move added $1.9 billion in assets $1.2 billion in loan assets and $1.3 billion in deposit assets to Renasant's collection. In addition the move significantly expanded the bank's geographic reach adding 48 banking mortgage and investment offices in Alabama Florida and Georgia. All told the deal made Renasant one of the largest community banks in the Southeast region of the United States.

Mergers and Acquisitions

In 2017 Renasant agreed to a $190 million merger with Metropolitan Bank.

EXECUTIVES

EVP, Stuart R. Johnson, age 65, $250,000 total compensation
Chairman President and CEO, E. Robinson (Robin) McGraw, age 71, $750,000 total compensation
EVP, James W. Gray, age 62, $230,000 total compensation
EVP and Director of Retail Banking Renasant Bank, C. Mitchell (Mitch) Waycaster, age 60, $450,000 total compensation
EVP, Mary J. Witt, age 59
EVP, W. Mark Williams, age 55
EVP, R. Rick Hart, age 70, $496,000 total compensation
EVP and General Counsel, Stephen M. Corban, age 63, $75,000 total compensation
EVP; President Eastern Region Renasant Bank, O. Leonard (Len) Dorminey, age 65, $213,285 total compensation
EVP and CFO, Kevin D. Chapman, age 43, $375,000 total compensation
EVP; President Western Region Renasant Bank, J. Scott Cochran, age 55
Assistant Vice President Branch Manager, Cathy Jarvis
Executive Vice President, Claude Springfield
Assistant Vice President, Kent Dees
Executive Vice President, Craig Gardella
Assistant Vice President Account Executive, Brian Gagel
Senior Vice President, Robert Hankins

Executive Vice President Credit Administration, Stuart Weise

Vice President, Jack Stuart

Vice President Relationship Officer, Danny Crabtree

Senior Vice President Commercial Banking, David Harwell

Senior Vice President, Jason McClimans

Division President Executive Vice President, Raymond Vannorman

Senior Vice President Small Business Advisor Lending, Melanie Brown

Senior Vice President Director of Senior Business Analyst Lending, John Daly

Executive Vice President, Patricia Reid

Vice President, Raakhi Phillips

Vice President, Randy Harris

First Vice President Associate Counsel, Jared Carrubba

Vice President, Brian Porter

Small Business Lending Division Manager Senior Vice President, Butch Lyle

Senior Vice President, Phil Smith

Auditors: Horne LLP

LOCATIONS

HQ: Renasant Corp
209 Troy Street, Tupelo, MS 38804-4827
Phone: 662 680-1001
Web: www.renasant.com

PRODUCTS/OPERATIONS

2015 Sales

	$ mil.	% of total
Interest income		
Loans	236.3	64
Securities	26.5	7
Other	0.2	-
Non-interest income		
Mortgage banking income	35.8	10
Service charges on deposit accounts	29.3	8
Fees and commissions	16.1	4
Wealth management	9.8	3
Other	17.3	4
Total	**371.3**	**100**

COMPETITORS

BBVA Compass Bancshares	First Horizon
BancorpSouth	Hancock Holding
Citizens Holding	Regions Financial
Citizens National Bank of Meridian	Trustmark

HISTORICAL FINANCIALS

Company Type: Public

Income Statement				FYE: December 31
	ASSETS ($ mil.)	NET INCOME ($ mil.)	INCOME AS % OF ASSETS	EMPLOYEES
12/17	9,829.9	92.1	0.9%	2,102
12/16	8,699.8	90.9	1.0%	1,965
12/15	7,926.5	68.0	0.9%	1,996
12/14	5,805.1	59.5	1.0%	1,471
12/13	5,746.2	33.4	0.6%	1,483
Annual Growth	**14.4%**	**28.8%**	**—**	**9.1%**

2017 Year-End Financials

Return on assets: 1.0%	Dividends
Return on equity: 6.7%	Yield: 0.0%
Long-term debt ($ mil.): —	Payout: 37.2%
No. of shares (mil.): 49.3	Market value ($ mil.): 2,017.0
Sales ($ mil): 506.8	

STOCK PRICE ($)		P/E		PER SHARE ($)		
	FY Close	High/Low		Earnings	Dividends	Book Value
12/17	40.89	23	19	1.96	0.73	30.72
12/16	42.22	20	14	2.17	0.71	27.81
12/15	34.41	20	14	1.88	0.68	25.73
12/14	28.93	17	14	1.88	0.68	22.56
12/13	31.46	26	15	1.22	0.68	21.21
Annual Growth	**6.8%**	**—**	**—**	**12.6%**	**1.8%**	**9.7%**

Repligen Corp.

Repligen supplies bio-engineered drug ingredients to the pharmaceutical industry. The company's bioprocessing business develops and commercializes proteins and other agents used in the production of biopharmaceuticals. Repligen is a major supplier of Protein A a recombinant protein used in the production of monoclonal antibodies and other biopharmaceutical manufacturing applications. Its product portfolio also includes filtration products and chromatography devices. Repligen's largest customer is GE Healthcare with which it has a multi-year supply agreement. The US accounts for about half of the company's total revenue.

Geographic Reach

Repligen is headquartered in Massachusetts. The company has manufacturing facilities in the US (Massachusetts California Nevada and Texas) Sweden Germany the Netherlands China India Korea and Japan. It has sales and distribution facilities in India China Korea the Netherlands and Japan.

The company's two largest single markets are the US which accounts for about 45% of revenue and Sweden which brings in another 20%.

Sales and Marketing

Repligen uses its own direct sales force and partners including GE Healthcare MilliporeSigma and Purolite to sell its products to life sciences and biopharma companies.

Financial Performance

Repligen's revenue have been generally rising for the past five years. Net income fell in 2014 but has been recovering since.

In 2017 revenue increased 35% to $141.2 million. Two factors drove that gain — higher sales of filtration and chromatography products and the added income from recently acquired firms Spectrum Laboratories Atoll and TangenX Technology.

Net income rose 143% to $28.4 million in 2017 thanks partly to the higher revenue that year but also thanks to a $21.1 income tax benefit.

The company ended 2017 with $173.8 million in net cash about $50 million more than it had at the end of 2016. Financing activities — largely the issuance of common stock — provided $129.3 million while operating activities provided another $17.5 million. Investing activities used $98.2 million.

Strategy

Historically Repligen did most of its business selling products to antibody purification companies who would then sell their products to the pharmaceutical sector. Now the company is increasingly selling products directly to pharmaceuticals and contract research organizations. In fact direct sales make up more than 60% of the firm's product revenue. This shift in strategy has been beneficial as R&D spending by pharmaceuticals continues to rise.

However Repligen is a relatively small contender in the bioprocessing field and several of its competitors enjoy brand name recognition greater access to large amounts of capital and even more experience developing innovative products. This makes the company somewhat vulnerable to such threats as lower prices for competing products. Additionally Repligen has certain key customers which are also competitors. The loss of one of those customers due to new competing products (or any number of reasons) could significantly impact the company's finances.

To counteract these challenges the company aims to deliver products that can address unmet needs in bioprocessing. It utilizes its internal development expertise with an eye toward getting its products to key customers early. By doing so Repligen products have the potential to serve as foundational elements in customers' processes. The firm is investing in its core proteins franchise as well as developing products to support its filtration and chromatography lines. In addition to developing products internally Repligen keeps an eye out for potential acquisition targets such as Spectrum Laboratories (2017) the purchase of which strengthened the company's filtration business.

The company is also working to expand its operations geographically especially in the US Europe and Asia.

Mergers and Acquisitions

In 2017 Repligen bought California-based Spectrum Laboratories for $359 million. Spectrum makes products that filter isolate purify and concentrate protein-based drugs as well as vaccines and cell therapies. That deal strengthened Repligen's filtration business and its position in the single-use and continuous manufacturing technologies sector.

In 2016 Repligen bought German manufacturer Atoll which makes MediaScout pre-packed chromatography columns used in the clinical manufacturing of biologic drugs. The deal was valued at $22.5 million. With that purchase the company expanded its pre-packed column chromatography portfolio into high throughput process development screening.

Later in 2016 the company acquired TangenX Technology Corporation from Novasep for $39 million. TangenX develops and markets tangential flow filtration (TFF) technologies including the single-use Sius which are used in the manufacturing of biopharmaceuticals.

EXECUTIVES

SVP Research and Development, James R. Rusche, age 65, $311,000 total compensation

VP Sales and Marketing, Stephen Tingley

VP Business Development, Howard Benjamin, $279,000 total compensation

President and CEO, Tony J. Hunt, $403,846 total compensation

CFO, Jon K. Snodgres, $330,000 total compensation

VP and Managing Director Repligen GmbH, Martin Reuter

Vice President Operations, Gustav Silfversparre

VP Human Resources, Kelly Capra

VP Research and Development, Ralf Kuriyel

Vice President Global Operations, Steve Curran

Chairman, Karen A. Dawes

Auditors: Ernst & Young LLP

LOCATIONS

HQ: Repligen Corp.
41 Seyon Street, Bldg. 1, Suite 100, Waltham, MA 02453
Phone: 781 250-0111 **Fax:** 781 250-0115
Web: www.repligen.com

PRODUCTS/OPERATIONS

2017 Sales

	$ mil.	% of total
Product revenue		
Protein products	54.0	38
Filtration products	49.0	35
Chromatography products	36.3	26
Other	1.8	1
Royalties & other	0.1	-
Total	**141.2**	**100**

COMPETITORS

Abbott Labs	Incyte
Asahi Kasei	NeuroNova
Bio-Rad Labs	PDL BioPharma
Danaher	

HISTORICAL FINANCIALS

Company Type: Public

Income Statement				FYE: December 31
	REVENUE ($ mil.)	NET INCOME ($ mil.)	NET PROFIT MARGIN	EMPLOYEES
12/17	141.2	28.3	20.1%	476
12/16	104.5	11.6	11.2%	236
12/15	83.5	9.3	11.2%	168
12/14	63.5	8.1	12.9%	136
12/13	68.1	16.0	23.6%	116
Annual Growth	20.0%	15.2%	—	42.3%

2017 Year-End Financials

Debt ratio: 13.3%
Return on equity: 7.4%
Cash ($ mil.): 173.7
Current ratio: 9.63
Long-term debt ($ mil.): 99.2
No. of shares (mil.): 43.5
Dividends
Yield: —
Payout: —
Market value ($ mil.): 1,581.0

	STOCK PRICE ($) FY Close	P/E High/Low	PER SHARE ($) Earnings	Dividends	Book Value
12/17	36.28	62 39	0.72	0.00	13.57
12/16	30.82	97 60	0.34	0.00	4.99
12/15	28.29	151 71	0.28	0.00	3.73
12/14	19.80	102 49	0.25	0.00	3.41
12/13	13.64	27 12	0.50	0.00	3.25
Annual Growth	27.7%	— —	9.5%	—	42.9%

Republic Bancorp, Inc. (KY)

As one of the top five bank holding companies based in Kentucky $4 billion-asset Republic Bancorp is the parent of Republic Bank & Trust (formerly First Commercial Bank) which offers deposit accounts loans and mortgages credit cards private banking and trust services through more than 30 branches in across Kentucky and around 10 more in southern Indiana Nashville Tampa and Cincin-

nati Ohio. About one-third of the bank's $3 billion-loan portfolio is tied to residential real estate while another 25% is made up of commercial real estate loans. Warehouse lines of credit home equity loans and commercial and industrial loans make up most of the rest. The company also offers short-term consumer loans and tax refund loans.

Operations

Republic Bancorp operates three "core banking" segments: Traditional Banking which generated more than 80% of the company's total profit during 2015; Warehouse (almost 20% of profit) and Mortgage Banking (less than 1%). Its Warehouse lending business offers short-term credit facilities secured by single-family residences to mortgage bankers nationwide. Its Republic Processing Group segment offers short-term consumer loans prepaid debit cards and tax refund loans.

The bank made 75% of its total revenue from interest income almost entirely from loans during 2015 though a small percentage came from taxed investments and Federal Home Loan Bank stock. The rest of its revenue came from net refund transfer fees from its Republic Processing Group segment (9% of revenue) deposit account service charges (7%) interchange fee income (4%) mortgage banking income (2%) and other miscellaneous income sources.

Subsidiary Republic Insurance Services (also known as the Captive) provides property and casualty insurance coverage to the company and eight other third-party insurance captives for which insurance may not be available or cost effective.

Geographic Reach

The company had 40 RB&T branches at the end of 2015 including 32 in Kentucky mostly in the Louisville Metro area and others in the Central Western and Northern parts of the state. It had 3 branches in southern Indiana (in Floyds Knobs Jeffersonville and New Albany); two branches in the Tampa Florida metro area; two branches in the Nashville Tennessee metro area; and one more in the Cincinnati Ohio metro area.

Sales and Marketing

Republic spent $3.16 million on marketing and development expenses during 2015 compared to $3.26 million and $3.11 million in 2014 and 2013 respectively.

Financial Performance

Republic Bancorp's revenues and profits have been trending higher since 2013 as its loan assets have risen more than 30% over the period.

The company's revenue climbed 9% to $190 million during 2015 mostly thanks to higher interest income as its loan assets grew by 9% to $3.33 billion with commercial loans (real estate and business loans) and residential mortgage loans and lines of credit driving most of the growth.

Strong revenue growth in 2015 drove Republic's net income up 22% to $35 million for the year. The company's operating cash levels nearly doubled to $50 million after adjusting its earnings for non-cash items related to mortgage loan sales and thanks to favorable working capital changes related to changes in other liabilities.

Strategy

Republic Bancorp is moving toward building its commercial loans business launching a Corporate Banking division in 2015 to originate commercial loans with amounts ranging from $2.5 million to $25 million to borrowers with the highest credit ratings in its existing geographic markets. It also acquires smaller community banks to expand into

new geographic markets while building its loan and deposit business.

Additionally Republic Bancorp has been moving into other revolving credit lines while also looking to take advantage of the rapidly growing prepaid card market. During 2015 for example it partnered with netSpend to become a pilot issuer of netSpend-branded prepaid cards; and partnered with ClearBalance to originate revolving lines of credit nationally for hospital receivables.

Mergers and Acquisitions

In October 2015 Republic Bancorp expanded its presence in Florida and grew its loan business after agreeing to buy $250 million-asset Cornerstone Bancorp along its four Cornerstone Community Bank branches in the Tampa Florida metro area $190 million in loans and $200 million in deposits. The deal was expected to be completed in the first half of 2016.

Company Background

In 2012 Republic Bancorp entered the Nashville and Minneapolis market through the FDIC-assisted acquisitions of the failed Tennessee Commerce Bank and First Commercial Bank respectively.

EXECUTIVES

Vice Chairman; President Republic Bank & Trust, A. Scott Trager, age 65, $350,000 total compensation
President and CEO; CEO Republic Bank & Trust, Steven E. (Steve) Trager, age 57, $353,000 total compensation
EVP CFO and Chief Accounting Officer Republic Bancorp and Republic Bank & Trust, Kevin Sipes, age 46, $281,500 total compensation
Vice President and Risk Manager, Bryan Hendrick
Senior Vice President, Steve Pieragowski
Assistant Vice President, Mike Long
Senior Vice President CRA Compliance Republic Bankand#8230, Nancy Presnell
Senior Vice President, Lisa Butcher
Assistant Vice President Technology Services Managerand#8230, Scott Estes
Assistant Vice President Finance Project Manager, Tim Wheatley
Vice President Retail Collections, Lori Forbes
Avp Banking Center Supervisor, Robin Verenna
Assistant Vice President Senior Business Development Officer, Kevin Herthel
Senior Vice President Private Banking, Sarah Johnson
Senior Vice President, David Buchanon
Vice President Client Relations Manager, David Carter
Vice President Director of Business Intelligence, Deb Reese
Vice President, Karen McGee
Vice President Senior Manager of Technology Services, Sean O'Mahoney
Assistant Vice President Managing Director, Brad Savko
Assistant Vice President, Amy Quinn
Vice President Mortgage Warehouse Lending, Tim Poole
Assistant Vice President Business Development Manager, Wende Cosby
Chairman, Bernard M. Trager, age 89
Auditors: Crowe Horwath LLP

LOCATIONS

HQ: Republic Bancorp, Inc. (KY)
601 West Market Street, Louisville, KY 40202
Phone: 502 584-3600
Web: www.republicbank.com

PRODUCTS/OPERATIONS

2015 Sales

	$ mil.	% of total
Interest		
Loans including fees	134.0	70
Taxable investment securities	7.0	4
Other	1.4	1
Noninterest		
Net refund transfer fees	17.4	9
Service charges on deposit accounts	13.0	7
Interchange fee income	8.4	4
Mortgage banking	4.4	2
Other	5.1	3
Adjustments	(0.3)	-
Total	**190.4**	**100**

Selected Services

Checking
Credit & Debit Cards
Internet & Mobile Banking
Lending
Private Banking & Wealth Management
Savings & Investing

COMPETITORS

BB&T	Home Federal
Bank of America	KeyCorp
Citizens First	PNC Financial
Community Trust	Stock Yards Bancorp
Fifth Third	U.S. Bancorp

HISTORICAL FINANCIALS

Company Type: Public

Income Statement
FYE: December 31

	ASSETS ($ mil.)	NET INCOME ($ mil.)	INCOME AS % OF ASSETS	EMPLOYEES
12/17	5,085.3	45.6	0.9%	1,009
12/16	4,816.3	46.0	1.0%	954
12/15	4,230.2	35.1	0.8%	799
12/14	3,747.0	28.7	0.8%	735
12/13	3,371.9	25.4	0.8%	750
Annual Growth	**10.8%**	**15.7%**	**—**	**7.7%**

2017 Year-End Financials

Return on assets: 0.9%	Dividends
Return on equity: 7.3%	Yield: 0.0%
Long-term debt ($ mil.): —	Payout: 39.5%
No. of shares (mil.): 20.8	Market value ($ mil.): 793.0
Sales ($ mil): 277.1	

	STOCK PRICE ($) FY Close	P/E High/Low	PER SHARE ($) Earnings	Dividends	Book Value
12/17	38.02	19 15	2.20	0.87	30.33
12/16	39.54	18 11	2.22	0.83	28.97
12/15	26.41	16 13	1.70	0.78	27.59
12/14	24.72	18 16	1.38	0.74	26.80
12/13	24.54	23 17	1.22	0.69	26.09
Annual Growth	**11.6%**	**— —**	**15.9%**	**5.8%**	**3.8%**

Republic First Bancorp, Inc.

Republic First Bancorp is the holding company for Republic Bank which serves the Greater Philadelphia area and southern New Jersey from more than 15 branches. Boasting over $1 billion in assets the bank targets individuals and small to midsized businesses offering standard deposit products including checking and savings accounts money market accounts IRAs and CDs. Commercial mortgages account for more than 70% of the company's loan portfolio which also includes consumer loans business loans and residential mortgages. Republic has been transitioning from a commercial bank into a major regional retail and commercial bank.

Operations

The bank's loan portfolio is made up of mostly commercial loans including commercial real estate loans construction and land development loans commercial and industrial loans as well as owner occupied real estate loans consumer-related loans and residential mortgages. As of 2015 each its commercial loans typically ranged from $250000 to $5 million though it sometimes lent up to its legal limit of $19.9 million.

About 72% of Republic First Bancorp's total revenue came from loan interest (including fees) in 2014 while another 11% came from interest and dividends on its taxable and tax-exempt investment securities. The rest of its revenue came from gains on sales of SBA loans (10%) loan advisory and servicing fees (3%) service fees on deposit accounts (3%) and other miscellaneous income sources. The bank had a staff of 235 full-time employees at the end of 2014.

Geographic Reach

Republic First boasts more than 15 branch offices in Pennsylvania (in Abington Ardmore Bala Cynwyd Plymout Meeting Media and Philadelphia) and New Jersey (in Berlin Cherry Hill Glassboro Haddonfield Marlton and Voorhees).

Sales and Marketing

The bank's commercial loans are mostly made to small and medium-sized businesses as well as professionals who need working capital financing for asset acquisitions or other financial services.

Republic First has been ramping up its advertising spend in recent years. It spent $597 thousand on advertising in 2014 compared to $447 thousand and $307 thousand in 2013 and 2012 respectively.

Financial Performance

The company has struggled to consistently grow its revenues in recent years due to shrinking interest margins on loans amidst the low-interest environment. Republic First has been steadily climbing out from prior years of losses (2013 2011 2010) however thanks to declining interest expenses and lower loan loss provisions as its loan portfolio's credit quality has improved with higher property valuations in the strengthened economy.

Republic First's revenue rose by 4% to $48.4 million in 2014 mostly thanks to an 8% jump in interest income as loan balances increased during the year. The bank's non-interest income fell on lower sales of SBA loans with fewer SBA loan originations which offset some of its top-line growth.

The company shot back into the black with a $2.4 million profit in 2014 (compared to a net loss of $3.5 million in 2013) mostly because in 2013 it had suffered a non-recurring $3.6 million loan loss on a bad loan as well as a non-recurring $1.9 million charge related to a legal settlement. Republic First's operating cash levels also skyrocketed to $9.7 million mostly on higher cash earnings.

Strategy

Republic Bank which had historically been known for its business and commercial lending has been focused on retail banking in the past few years and is working to become a major regional retail and commercial bank. As part of this strategy the bank has restructured its loan portfolio to reduce its emphasis on commercial real estate loans and has pursued a "retail-focused" strategy by offering customers "extended store hours absolutely free checking and coin counting more than 55000 surcharge ATMs and free VISA gift cards" according to the company's CEO letter included in the 2014 annual report.

The company has been expanding organically through new branch openings in recent years. In 2015 for example Republic Bank opened three new branches in South New Jersey in Berlin Marlton and Glassboro. In April of that year the company also sold $45 million in common stock through a private placement offering to cover its "aggressive expansion plans in 2015 and beyond."

EXECUTIVES

Vice President of Commercial Lending for South Jersey, John Lavin
Assistant Vice President Network Engineer, John Rudolph
Vice President Commercial Lender, Tom Waller
SVP HUMAN RESOURCES DIRECTOR, Janine Zangrilli
Executive Vice President and Chief Retail Officer of the Bank, Rhonda Costello
Assistant Vice President And Core Applications Administrator, Jared Kushner
Senior Vice President, Jay Neilon
Senior Vice President Senior Commercial Lender, Stephen McWilliams
Senior Vice President Of Sales, Katie Michaleski
Vice President Of Consumer Lending, Dan Charyna
VICE PRESIDENT AND REAL ESTATE ADMINISTRATION MANAGER, Eileen Echols
Vice President and Commercial Lending, Frederick A Marcell
Vice President Senior Business Development Officer, Judy Rosner
Senior Vice President, Brennan Charlene
ASSISTANT VICE PRESIDENT LOAN CLOSER SBA DIVISION, Camille Oldenburg
Auditors: BDO USA, LLP

LOCATIONS

HQ: Republic First Bancorp, Inc.
50 South 16th Street, Philadelphia, PA 19102
Phone: 215 735-4422
Web: www.myrepublicbank.com

PRODUCTS/OPERATIONS

2014 Sales

	$ mil.	% of total
Interest income		
Interest and fees on taxable loans	34.5	71
Interest and dividends on taxable investment securities	5.1	10
Interest and fees on tax-exempt loans	0.3	1
Interest and dividends on tax-exempt investment securities	0.3	1
Interest on federal funds sold and other interest -earning assets	0.1	0
Non interest		
Gain on sales of SBA loans	4.7	10
Loan advisory and servicing fees	1.4	3
Service fees on deposit accounts	1.2	3
Gain on sale of investment securities	0.4	1
Legal settlements	0.0	0
Other-than-temporary impairment	0.0	0
Portion recognized in other comprehensive income (before taxes)	(0.03)	0
Net impairment loss on investment securities	0.0	0
Bank owned life insurance income	0.0	0
Other non-interest income	0.1	0
Total	**48.5**	**100**

COMPETITORS

Bank of America	Sovereign Bank
Citizens Financial Group	Sun Bancorp (NJ)
	TD Bank USA
PNC Financial	TF Financial
Prudential Bancorp	Wells Fargo
Royal Bancshares	

HISTORICAL FINANCIALS

Company Type: Public

Income Statement   FYE: December 31

	ASSETS ($ mil.)	NET INCOME ($ mil.)	INCOME AS % OF ASSETS	EMPLOYEES
12/17	2,322.3	8.9	0.4%	448
12/16	1,923.9	4.9	0.3%	306
12/15	1,439.4	2.4	0.2%	277
12/14	1,214.6	2.4	0.2%	235
12/13	961.6	(3.4)	—	226
Annual Growth	24.7%	—	—	18.7%

2017 Year-End Financials

Return on assets: 0.4%	Dividends
Return on equity: 4.0%	Yield: —
Long-term debt ($ mil.): —	Payout: —
No. of shares (mil.): 56.9	Market value ($ mil.): 482.0
Sales ($ mil): 90.9	

	STOCK PRICE ($) FY Close	P/E High/Low	PER SHARE ($) Earnings	Dividends	Book Value
12/17	8.45	62 47	0.15	0.00	3.97
12/16	8.35	69 29	0.12	0.00	3.79
12/15	4.33	77 55	0.06	0.00	3.00
12/14	3.75	76 43	0.07	0.00	2.98
12/13	2.98	— —	(0.13)	0.00	2.41
Annual Growth	29.8%	— —	—	—	13.3%

ResMed Inc.

ResMed develops makes and distributes medical equipment used to diagnose and treat respiratory disorders that occur during sleep such as sleep apnea. Most of its products treat obstructive sleep apnea (OSA) a condition in which a patient's air flow is periodically obstructed causing multiple disruptions during sleep that can lead to daytime sleepiness and other conditions such as high blood pressure. Its products include air-flow generators face masks diagnostic products and accessories. ResMed sells directly and through distributors worldwide to home health equipment dealers sleep clinics and hospitals. ResMed was founded in Australia in 1989 by Peter C. Farrell who remains chairman.

Operations

ResMed's main products are continuous positive airway pressure (CPAP) systems that deliver pressurized air from an airflow generator through a nasal mask or pillow keeping the upper airway open during sleep. The company also makes variable positive airway pressure (VPAP) systems which operate on the same principle but deliver different air pressures for inhalation and exhalation.

Additionally ResMed provides business management software to medical equipment and home health providers.

Geographic Reach

ResMed manufactures its products primarily at its Australian facility though it has additional production plants in China Singapore Malaysia France and the US. The company also has R&D and office facilities in Australia China Germany Singapore and the US. It leases warehousing and distribution facilities in the US (2) the UK Germany France Switzerland Sweden Norway Japan and China.

The company's systems are sold in about 120 countries. The US accounts for nearly 60% of annual revenues.

Sales and Marketing

ResMed's products are sold through its own subsidiaries (mainly in the US Europe and the Asia/Pacific region) and through independent distributors and representatives. Marketing efforts target consumers and health care professionals sleep clinics hospitals home health care systems and third-party payors.

Financial Performance

ResMed's revenue has been trending upward in recent years as demand for its products has grown. In fact the number of people with sleep apnea worldwide is nearing 1 billion. Net income has been declining slowly though as the company spends money to produce and launch new products.

In fiscal 2018 (ended June) revenue increased 13% to $2.3 billion. That growth was primarily due to higher unit sales of devices masks and accessories but was partially offset by a decline in average selling prices. Product sales increased overall around the world.

Net income fell 8% to $315.6 million in 2018. The company had higher expenses that year as it built up its personnel numbers to boost its commercial activities and invested more heavily in R&D to create new products. It also incurred restructuring expenses topping $18 million which cut further into the bottom line.

The company ended 2018 with $188.7 million in cash and cash equivalents a steep decline from the $821.9 million it had at the end of 2017. This was largely due to financing activities (mostly repayment of borrowings) which used $1 billion in cash. Operating activities provided $505 million and investing activities used $101.8 million.

Strategy

ResMed is benefiting from the growing awareness in the medical community and among the general population of the dangers of sleep disordered breathing (SDB). These include chronic daytime fatigue (and the resulting loss of productivity) heart disease stroke type 2 diabetes depression and other conditions. With the number of people with sleep apnea nearing 1 billion around the world ResMed has strong motivation to get the word out. It targets special interest groups such as the American Heart Association and it has partnered with other organizations to conduct medical research.

The company is investing in R&D activities to facilitate the development of new diagnostic and treatment products. During 2017 it launched the AirFit N20 nasal and F20 full face masks as well as the AirMini the smallest CPAP device on the market. The following year it introduced the Mobi portable oxygen concentrator the QuietAir diffuser vent elbow for its CPAP full face masks and the AirFit F30 its first minimal-contact CPAP full face mask. Recent acquisitions have helped expand the company's product portfolio.

ResMed is also investing in sales and marketing activities to promote itself around the world. The company has its sights set on the growing market potential for SDB COPD and respiratory care products in China.

Mergers and Acquisitions

In 2019 Resmed bought digital therapeutics firm Propeller Health for $225 million. Propeller specializes in helping patients manage chronic obstructive pulmonary disease and asthma. It continues to operate as a standalone business.

In 2018 ResMed acquired HEALTHCAREfirst which provides cloud-based software for home health and hospice agencies for an undisclosed amount. It then bought MatrixCare a provider of software for long-term care providers for $750 million. The deals complement the company's Brightree operations acquired in 2016 for $802 million.

Also in 2016 ResMed acquired Inova Labs a Texas-based maker of oxygen therapy products. The acquisition expanded the company's ability to address the global COPD epidemic. It also expanded ResMed's respiratory care portfolio to include both portable and fixed oxygen concentrators.

HISTORY

ResMed was founded as ResCare in 1989 after Peter Farrell led a management buyout of Baxter Healthcare's respiratory technology unit. ResCare initially developed the SULLIVAN nasal CPAP systems (named after inventor Colin Sullivan) in Australia. In 1991 it introduced the Bubble Mask and the APD2 portable CPAP device. Three years later ResCare began marketing its first VPAP which applied different air pressures for inhalation and exhalation in the US.

In 1995 the company went public changing its name to ResMed (its former name was already taken by another medical company). Over the next two years ResMed expended a lot of oxygen in court suing rival Respironics for patent infringements; judgments in 1997 and 1998 found in favor of Respironics but ResMed made plans to appeal. In 1998 the firm received FDA approval to market its VPAP device as a critical-care treatment for lung diseases.

The firm's listing was switched from Nasdaq to the NYSE in 1999 to stabilize stock prices after court losses against Respironics; it also listed on the Australian Stock Exchange.

EXECUTIVES

Chief Executive Officer; Director, Michael J. Farrell, age 46, $511,211 total compensation
CFO, Brett Sandercock, age 51, $505,266 total compensation
President and Chief Operating Officer, Robert (Rob) Douglas, age 59, $588,780 total compensation
President; Europe, Anne Reiser
President SDB Strategic Business Unit, Don Darkin, age 65
President Americas, Jim Hollingshead, $379,846 total compensation
President Respiratory Care Strategic Business Unit, Geoff Neilson
President Asia-Pacific, Karen Borg
Chief Information Officer, Frank Lacagnina

President of ResMed ?s, Raj Sodhi
VP of Information Technology, Atul Thapar
Area Vice President of Sales, Greg Thurman
Vice President Finance, Mehul Joshi
National Account Manager, Tom Melby
Vice President Patient Interface, Andrew Price
Vice President Social Media Strategy, Gil Ben Dov
Vice President Marketing Americas, Jon Yerbury
Area Vice President, Bill Shoop
National Account Manager, Shawn Blackburn
Vice President Regional Sales Northeast And
  Canada, Tom Miller
Vice President Sales For The Americas, Thomas
  Miller
Vice President Of Sales Americas, Christopher Gray
Vice President Marketing, Kari Hall
Vice President Technology, Shelly Selvaraj
Vice President UK and European Partner
  Network, Ross Sommerville
Vice President Quality Assurance Americas, Dawn
  Haake
Vice President Global Tax, Pat Sammon
Vice President Business Development and
  Corporate Ventures, Grant Olsen
VICE PRESIDENT OPERATIONS AMERICAS,
  Ian Thomas
Founder and Executive Chairman, Peter C. Farrell,
  age 76
Board Member, Richard Sulpizio
Board of Director, Gary Pace
Board Member, Carol Burt
Board Member, Ronald Taylor
Auditors: KPMG LLP

LOCATIONS

HQ: ResMed Inc.
  9001 Spectrum Center Blvd., San Diego, CA 92123
Phone: 858 836-5000
Web: www.resmed.com

PRODUCTS/OPERATIONS

Selected Products
Accessories
  Astral external battery
  Chin restraint
  ClimateLineAir heated tube
  Gecko nasal pad
  SlimLine tubing
  Standard Trolley
Devices
  AirMini
  AirStart 10 CPAP
  Astral 100
  Astral 150
  Lumis 100 VPAP S
  Stellar 100
  Stellar 150
Humidifiers
  H4i
Masks
  AirFit N20 Classic
  AirFit P10
  AirTouch F20
  Mirage FX
  Pixi
  Quattro Air
Swift FX

COMPETITORS

Allied Healthcare Products
Cephalon
Cleveland Medical
FISHER & PAYKEL HEALTHCARE CORPORATION
  LIMITED
Lincare Holdings
Philips Electronics
SleepMed
Vanda
Vital Signs

HISTORICAL FINANCIALS

Company Type: Public

Income Statement   FYE: June 30

	REVENUE ($ mil.)	NET INCOME ($ mil.)	NET PROFIT MARGIN	EMPLOYEES
06/18	2,340.2	315.5	13.5%	5,940
06/17	2,066.7	342.2	16.6%	6,080
06/16	1,838.7	352.4	19.2%	5,250
06/15	1,678.9	352.8	21.0%	4,340
06/14	1,554.9	345.2	22.2%	4,100
Annual Growth	10.8%	(2.2%)	—	9.7%

2018 Year-End Financials

Debt ratio: 9.1%
Return on equity: 15.7%
Cash ($ mil.): 188.7
Current ratio: 2.08
Long-term debt ($ mil.): 269.9

No. of shares (mil.): 142.6
Dividends
  Yield: 0.0%
  Payout: 63.9%
Market value ($ mil.): 14,779.0

	STOCK PRICE ($) FY Close	P/E High/Low	PER SHARE ($) Earnings	Dividends	Book Value
06/18	103.58	49 33	2.19	1.40	14.43
06/17	77.87	33 24	2.40	1.32	13.79
06/16	63.23	26 20	2.49	1.20	12.05
06/15	56.37	30 18	2.47	1.12	11.30
06/14	50.63	23 17	2.39	1.00	12.53
Annual Growth	19.6%	— —	(2.2%)	8.8%	3.6%

Retail Opportunity Investments Corp

For this company opportunity knocking sounds a lot like a neighborhood shopping center. Retail Opportunity Investments (ROIC) true to its name invests in owns leases and manages shopping centers. It targets densely populated middle and upper class markets and looks for centers anchored by large grocery or drug stores. The self-managed real estate investment trust (REIT) owns more than 50 shopping centers comprising 5.5 million sq. ft. in Oregon Washington and California. It makes money from rent management expenses and mortgage interest. ROIC was formed in 2007 as an acquisition company. It purchased NRDC Capital Management in 2009 and took its current name in 2010.

Financial Performance

Increases in base rents drove ROIC's revenue up 45% in 2012 over 2011. The company saw its net income drop 18% during the same period due in part to high operating and depreciation and amortization expenses as well as to expenditures related to the company's headquarters relocation from New York to California.

Strategy

ROIC's strategy includes renovating its properties and making lease agreement adjustments to keep its occupancy rates high. The company occasionally bolsters its portfolio with acquisitions of properties in its target markets. Between fiscal 2011 and 2013 the company added nearly three dozen properties to its portfolio. While it has focused its investments along the West Coast (Cali-

fornia Washington and Oregon) ROIC is also eying properties in the Northeast.

Company Background

The company began operating in late 2009 and immediately commenced building out its portfolio purchasing a 95000-square-foot shopping center in Los Angeles County anchored by Rite Aid. In its second year it boosted its holdings after acquiring another dozen properties.

EXECUTIVES

CFO, Michael B. (Mike) Haines, age 56, $290,000 total compensation
President CEO and Director, Stuart A. Tanz, age 59, $775,000 total compensation
COO, Richard K. Schoebel, age 51, $340,000 total compensation
Chairman, Richard A. Baker, age 51
Board Member, Lee Neibart
Board Member, Laura Pomerantz
Auditors: Ernst & Young LLP

LOCATIONS

HQ: Retail Opportunity Investments Corp
  11250 El Camino Real, Suite 200, San Diego, CA 92130
Phone: 858 677-0900
Web: www.roireit.net

PRODUCTS/OPERATIONS

2015 Sales

	$ mil.	% of total
Base Rents	148.6	77
Recoveries from tenants other	44.1	23
Total	192.7	100

Selected Properties

California
  Claremont Center
  Deser Springs Marketplace
  Gateway Village
  Marketplace Del Rio
  Nimbus Winery Village
  Norwood Shopping Center
  Paramount Plaza
  Phillips Village
  Pinole Vista
  Pleasant Hill Marketplace
  Santa Ana Downtown Plaza
  Sycamore Creek
Oregon
  Cascade Summit
  Division Crossing
  Halsey Crossing
  Happy Valley Town Center
  Oregon City Point
  Wilsonville Old Town Square
Washington
  Crossroads
  Heritage Market Center
  Meridian Valley Plaza
  The Market at Lake Stevens
  Vancouver Market Center

COMPETITORS

Kimco Realty	Simon Property Group
Macerich	Vornado Realty
Regency Centers	Weingarten Realty

HISTORICAL FINANCIALS
Company Type: Public

Income Statement				FYE: December 31
	REVENUE ($ mil.)	NET INCOME ($ mil.)	NET PROFIT MARGIN	EMPLOYEES
12/17	273.2	38.4	14.1%	73
12/16	237.1	32.7	13.8%	71
12/15	192.7	23.8	12.4%	69
12/14	155.8	20.3	13.0%	65
12/13	111.2	33.8	30.4%	61
Annual Growth	25.2%	3.3%	—	4.6%

2017 Year-End Financials

Debt ratio: 48.9%
Return on equity: 3.2%
Cash ($ mil.): 11.5
Current ratio: 0.10
Long-term debt ($ mil.): 1,487.1

No. of shares (mil.): 112.3
Dividends
Yield: 0.0%
Payout: 214.2%
Market value ($ mil.): 2,241.0

	STOCK PRICE ($) FY Close	P/E High/Low		PER SHARE ($) Earnings	Dividends	Book Value
12/17	19.95	64	51	0.35	0.75	10.72
12/16	21.13	74	56	0.31	0.72	10.87
12/15	17.90	74	62	0.25	0.68	10.42
12/14	16.79	71	59	0.24	0.64	9.93
12/13	14.72	32	25	0.48	0.60	9.33
Annual Growth	7.9%	—	—	(7.6%)	5.7%	3.5%

REV Group Inc

Auditors: RSM US LLP

LOCATIONS

HQ: REV Group Inc
111 East Kilbourn Avenue, Suite 2600, Milwaukee, WI 53202
Phone: 414 290-0190
Web: www.revgroup.com

HISTORICAL FINANCIALS
Company Type: Public

Income Statement				FYE: October 31
	REVENUE ($ mil.)	NET INCOME ($ mil.)	NET PROFIT MARGIN	EMPLOYEES
10/18	2,381.3	13.0	0.5%	7,600
10/17	2,267.7	31.3	1.4%	7,800
10/16	1,926.0	30.1	1.6%	6,000
10/15	1,735.0	22.8	1.3%	0
10/14	1,721.1	1.4	0.1%	0
Annual Growth	8.5%	71.9%	—	—

2018 Year-End Financials

Debt ratio: 29.9%
Return on equity: 2.3%
Cash ($ mil.): 11.9
Current ratio: 2.02
Long-term debt ($ mil.): 420.6

No. of shares (mil.): 62.6
Dividends
Yield: 1.8%
Payout: 100.0%
Market value ($ mil.): 684.0

	STOCK PRICE ($) FY Close	P/E High/Low		PER SHARE ($) Earnings	Dividends	Book Value
10/18	10.91	164	52	0.20	0.20	8.48
10/17	25.80	59	46	0.50	0.15	8.92
Annual Growth	(57.7%)	—	—	(60.0%)	33.3%	(5.0%)

Rexford Industrial Realty Inc

Rexford Industrial Realty knows that there's more to business in Southern California than moviemaking and fashion. A real estate investment trust or REIT Rexford Industrial owns and manages a portfolio of nearly 70 industrial properties in Los Angeles County and surrounding areas. Its portfolio comprises about 7.6 million sq. ft. of warehouse distribution and light manufacturing space that's leased to small and midsized businesses. It manages 20 more properties — altogether comprising 1.2 million sq. ft. of rentable space. A self-administered and self-managed REIT Rexford Industrial was formed in 2013 from the assets of its predecessor. In mid-2013 the company went public.

IPO

Rexford Industrial intends to use a portion of the $224 million in proceeds to repay debt much of which is secured by various properties.

Operations

Rexford Industrial's portfolio spans several California counties including Los Angeles Orange Ventura San Bernadino Riverside and San Diego.

Financial Performance

Revenue rose for Rexford Industrial by 27% in fiscal 2012 to $34 million from 2011's $28 million thanks to increases in rental revenue and tenant reimbursements from rising occupancy rates and a boost in revenues from properties it acquired during both 2012 and 2011. Rexford Industrial logged 64% increases in revenue from management leasing and development services due to the additional third-party management fees.

Strategy

Rexford Industrial is seeking to acquire equity stakes and debt in stable and distressed industrial properties in infill markets (i.e. highly developed urban centers) in Los Angeles Orange San Diego and Ventura counties and the West Inland Empire to the east. The REIT is also looking to manage properties located in these same areas that are owned by third parties.

The REIT has been buying properties throughout Southern California particularly in the cities of Van Nuys and Tarzana as well as in Glenview Illinois. It looks to purchase both newer and older vintage properties as well as single (40% of its portfolio) and multi-tenant (60%) projects. The REIT invests in every category of industrial property. Tenants are typically small and medium-sized businesses that are tied to the Southern California economy. Rexford Industrial boasts an average tenant size of about 9000 sq. ft. Nearly 70% of its tenants occupy fewer than 50000 sq. ft. apiece.

EXECUTIVES

Co-CEO and Director, Howard Schwimmer, $495,000 total compensation
Co-CEO and Director, Michael S. Frankel, age 55, $495,000 total compensation
CFO, Adeel Khan, $315,000 total compensation
Vice President And Assistant General Counsel, Laura Mask
Chairman, Richard S. Ziman, age 75
Auditors: Ernst & Young LLP

LOCATIONS

HQ: Rexford Industrial Realty Inc
11620 Wilshire Boulevard, Suite 1000, Los Angeles, CA 90025
Phone: 310 966-1680
Web: www.rexfordindustrial.com

PRODUCTS/OPERATIONS

2015 Revenue

	$ mil.	% of total
Rental		
Rental Revenues	81.1	86
Tenant Reimbursements	10.5	11
Management Leasing & Development Services	0.6	1
Other Income	1.0	1
Interest Income	0.7	1
Total	**93.9**	**100**

Selected Property Categories

Core
Core Plus
First Mortgages Tied to Target Industrial Property
Value Add

COMPETITORS

Brandywine Realty	Prologis
Brandywine Realty	Prologis
PS Business Parks	Terreno Realty
PS Business Parks	Terreno Realty

HISTORICAL FINANCIALS
Company Type: Public

Income Statement				FYE: December 31
	REVENUE ($ mil.)	NET INCOME ($ mil.)	NET PROFIT MARGIN	EMPLOYEES
12/17	161.3	40.7	25.2%	98
12/16	126.1	25.1	19.9%	90
12/15	93.9	1.8	2.0%	70
12/14	66.5	0.9	1.3%	48
12/13	21.6	(0.6)	—	40
Annual Growth	65.3%	—	—	25.1%

2017 Year-End Financials

Debt ratio: 31.6%
Return on equity: 3.5%
Cash ($ mil.): 6.6
Current ratio: 0.14
Long-term debt ($ mil.): 668.9

No. of shares (mil.): 78.5
Dividends
Yield: 0.0%
Payout: 120.8%
Market value ($ mil.): 2,289.0

	STOCK PRICE ($) FY Close	P/E High/Low		PER SHARE ($) Earnings	Dividends	Book Value
12/17	29.16	66	45	0.48	0.58	17.07
12/16	23.19	65	43	0.36	0.54	14.13
12/15	16.36	556423		0.03	0.51	12.09
12/14	15.71	800642		0.02	0.48	11.89
12/13	13.20	—	—	(0.03)	0.21	11.98
Annual Growth	21.9%	—	—	—	28.9%	9.3%

RF Industries Ltd.

RF Industries (RFI) helps keep the world connected. The company's core business is conducted by its RF Connector division which makes coaxial connectors used in radio-frequency (RF) communications and computer networking equipment. Its

Neulink Division makes wireless digital transmission devices such as modems and antennas used to link wide-area computer networks and global positioning systems. Through its Bioconnect division RF Industries also makes cable assemblies including electric cabling and interconnect products used in medical monitoring applications. RF Industries operates from locations in California and Nevada; customers in the US account for more than 80% of sales.

Other divisions include Aviel Electronics which makes microwave and RF connectors for the aerospace and military electronics markets and Worswick Industries a retail supplier of connectors and coaxial cable assemblies for multimedia radio and other communications applications. Its OddCables.com unit part of the Worswick division stocks audio video computer and other cables for sale online. RadioMobile makes wireless mobile data systems for public safety utilities and transportation customers; software used in the systems is developed in-house.

Coaxial connectors and cable assemblies account for most of the company's sales and are used in wireless and digital communications applications such as cellular base stations cable and satellite TV systems global positioning systems test instruments and video surveillance systems. RF Industries also targets the factory automation hospital equipment military and industrial monitoring markets. In addition the company's Neulink division offers transceivers and amplifiers made by other manufacturers.

More than half of sales are made through distributors though RF Industries also sells directly to equipment manufacturers. It has used acquisitions in the past to bolstered its product portfolio and manufacturing capabilities. In 2011 the company bought Cables Unlimited for about $5.6 million in cash and stock. The purchase boosted RF Industries' interconnect and wiring product lines with fiber-optic cables connectors and wire harnesses. It also expanded its list of manufacturing customers and added a presence on the East Coast near some of its largest customers.

RF Industries also uses research development and engineering to develop new products often in collaboration with customers. The company offers a broad range of products both custom and proprietary and generally keeps significant inventory in stock.

EXECUTIVES

President CEO and Director, Howard F. Hill, age 76, $205,677 total compensation
Chief Operating Officer, George R. Marks, age 65
President; Chief Financial Officer; Corporate Secretary, James S. Doss, age 48, $102,402 total compensation
President and General Manager Radio Mobile Division, James Moore
President CEO and Director, Howard F. Hill, age 76
Director, Marvin H. Fink, age 80
Director, John R. Ehret, age 77
Director, Robert Jacobs, age 65
Director, William L. Reynolds, age 80
Independent Director, John Waterfield
Auditors: CohnReznick LLP

LOCATIONS

HQ: RF Industries Ltd.
7610 Miramar Road, Building 6000, San Diego, CA 92126
Phone: 858 549-6340
Web: www.rfindustries.com

PRODUCTS/OPERATIONS

Selected Products
Adapters
Antennas
Coaxial cable assemblies
Coaxial connectors
Disposable ECG cables
Electromechanical wiring harnesses
Hand tools
Radio-frequency (RF) data links
Receivers
Safety and snap leads
Wireless modems

COMPETITORS

ARRIS	Huber + Suhner Inc.
Amphenol	Molex
Champlain Cable	Moseley Associates
CommScope	TE Connectivity
General Cable	

HISTORICAL FINANCIALS
Company Type: Public

Income Statement				FYE: October 31
	REVENUE ($ mil.)	NET INCOME ($ mil.)	NET PROFIT MARGIN	EMPLOYEES
10/18	50.2	5.8	11.6%	186
10/17	30.9	0.3	1.2%	195
10/16	30.2	(4.0)	—	189
10/15	32.8	0.9	3.0%	226
10/14	23.1	1.4	6.2%	143
Annual Growth	21.4%	42.0%	—	6.8%

2018 Year-End Financials
Debt ratio: —
Return on equity: 23.8%
Cash ($ mil.): 16.3
Current ratio: 6.05
Long-term debt ($ mil.): —
No. of shares (mil.): 9.2
Dividends
Yield: 1.0%
Payout: 13.1%
Market value ($ mil.): 72.0

	STOCK PRICE ($) FY Close	P/E High/Low		PER SHARE ($) Earnings	Dividends	Book Value
10/18	7.76	19	4	0.61	0.08	2.99
10/17	2.45	68	35	0.04	0.08	2.41
10/16	1.75	—	—	(0.47)	0.13	2.42
10/15	4.51	40	33	0.11	0.28	3.03
10/14	4.53	80	25	0.16	0.28	3.13
Annual Growth	14.4%	—	—	39.7%	(26.9%)	(1.1%)

River Financial Corp

Auditors: Mauldin & Jenkins, LLC

LOCATIONS

HQ: River Financial Corp
2611 Legends Drive, Prattville, AL 36066
Phone: 334 290-1012
Web: www.riverbankandtrust.com

HISTORICAL FINANCIALS
Company Type: Public

Income Statement				FYE: December 31
	REVENUE ($ mil.)	NET INCOME ($ mil.)	NET PROFIT MARGIN	EMPLOYEES
12/17	38.4	8.3	21.6%	151
12/16	35.2	7.9	22.5%	134
12/15	19.2	2.3	12.3%	129
12/14	17.9	3.4	19.4%	0
Annual Growth	29.0%	33.6%	—	—

2017 Year-End Financials
Debt ratio: 1.8%
Return on equity: 9.6%
Cash ($ mil.): 15.5
Current ratio: 0.31
Long-term debt ($ mil.): 15.3
No. of shares (mil.): 5.1
Dividends
Yield: —
Payout: 15.6%
Market value ($ mil.): —

	STOCK PRICE ($) FY Close	P/E High/Low		PER SHARE ($) Earnings	Dividends	Book Value
12/17	0.00	—	—	1.60	0.25	17.64
Annual Growth	—	—	—	—	—	—

Riverview Bancorp, Inc.

Riverview Bancorp is the holding company for Riverview Community Bank which operates about 20 branches located primarily in the Columbia River Gorge area of Washington State and Oregon. Serving consumers and local businesses the bank offers such standard retail banking services as checking and savings accounts money market accounts NOW accounts and CDs. Commercial construction and commercial real estate loans account for nearly 90% of its lending portfolio which also includes residential mortgages residential construction loans and other consumer loans. Trust and investment services are provided through the company's Riverview Asset Management Corp. Riverview Community Bank was founded in 1923.

EXECUTIVES

Vice President Operations Support Manager, Anthony Hays
Vice President And Cash Management Officer Vice President Cash Management Officer, Diana Fitzpatrick
Vice President Trust Operations, Sue Barham
Vice President Special Assets, Greg Brown
Vice President, Michael Bell
Vice President Loan Officer, Jeff Allen
Vice President Business Development Officer, Farhad Dadkho
Board Member, Bess Wills
Auditors: Delap LLP

LOCATIONS

HQ: Riverview Bancorp, Inc.
900 Washington St., Ste. 900, Vancouver, WA 98660
Phone: 360 693-6650
Web: www.riverviewbank.com

COMPETITORS

Bank of America	Merchants Bancorp
Banner Corp	The Commerce Bank of
FS Bancorp	Oregon
Heritage Financial	U.S. Bancorp
JPMorgan Chase	Umpqua Holdings
KeyCorp	

HISTORICAL FINANCIALS

Company Type: Public

Income Statement — FYE: March 31

	ASSETS ($ mil.)	NET INCOME ($ mil.)	INCOME AS % OF ASSETS	EMPLOYEES
03/18	1,151.5	10.2	0.9%	258
03/17	1,133.9	7.4	0.7%	260
03/16	921.2	6.3	0.7%	229
03/15	858.7	4.4	0.5%	231
03/14	824.5	19.4	2.4%	219
Annual Growth	8.7%	(14.8%)	—	4.2%

2018 Year-End Financials

Return on assets: 0.9%
Return on equity: 8.9%
Long-term debt ($ mil.): —
No. of shares (mil.): 22.5
Sales ($ mil): 55.9

Dividends
Yield: 0.0%
Payout: 21.1%
Market value ($ mil.): 211.0

	STOCK PRICE ($) FY Close	P/E High/Low	PER SHARE ($) Earnings	Dividends	Book Value
03/18	9.34	22 14	0.45	0.10	5.18
03/17	7.15	24 13	0.33	0.08	4.94
03/16	4.20	18 15	0.28	0.06	4.81
03/15	4.50	24 17	0.20	0.01	4.62
03/14	3.43	4 3	0.87	0.00	4.36
Annual Growth	28.5%	—	(15.2%)	—	4.4%

RLJ Lodging Trust

Auditors: PricewaterhouseCoopers LLP

LOCATIONS

HQ: RLJ Lodging Trust
3 Bethesda Metro Center, Suite 1000, Bethesda, MD
20814
Phone: 301 280-7777
Web: www.rljlodgingtrust.com

HISTORICAL FINANCIALS

Company Type: Public

Income Statement — FYE: December 31

	REVENUE ($ mil.)	NET INCOME ($ mil.)	NET PROFIT MARGIN	EMPLOYEES
12/17	1,356.2	75.3	5.6%	99
12/16	1,160.0	200.3	17.3%	58
12/15	1,136.3	218.2	19.2%	56
12/14	1,109.2	135.4	12.2%	56
12/13	970.3	112.9	11.6%	53
Annual Growth	8.7%	(9.6%)	—	16.9%

2017 Year-End Financials

Debt ratio: 42.3%
Return on equity: 2.6%
Cash ($ mil.): 659.0
Current ratio: 2.33
Long-term debt ($ mil.): 2,880.4

No. of shares (mil.): 174.8
Dividends
Yield: 0.0%
Payout: 280.8%
Market value ($ mil.): 3,842.0

	STOCK PRICE ($) FY Close	P/E High/Low	PER SHARE ($) Earnings	Dividends	Book Value
12/17	21.97	53 41	0.47	1.32	20.29
12/16	24.49	15 11	1.61	1.32	17.87
12/15	21.63	21 13	1.68	1.32	17.51
12/14	33.53	32 23	1.06	1.04	17.89
12/13	24.32	27 20	0.95	0.86	17.35
Annual Growth	(2.5%)	—	(16.1%)	11.5%	4.0%

RMR Group Inc (The)

Auditors: Ernst & Young LLP

LOCATIONS

HQ: RMR Group Inc (The)
Two Newton Place, 255 Washington Street, Suite 300,
Newton, MA 02458-1634
Phone: 617 796-8230
Web: www.rmrgroup.com

HISTORICAL FINANCIALS

Company Type: Public

Income Statement — FYE: September 30

	REVENUE ($ mil.)	NET INCOME ($ mil.)	NET PROFIT MARGIN	EMPLOYEES
09/18	404.9	96.0	23.7%	52,600
09/17	271.7	42.2	15.6%	53,475
09/16	266.9	37.2	14.0%	52,450
09/15	192.9	7.3	3.8%	50,400
09/14	285.0	10.2	3.6%	400
Annual Growth	9.2%	74.8%	—	238.6%

2018 Year-End Financials

Debt ratio: —
Return on equity: 50.2%
Cash ($ mil.): 256.8
Current ratio: 10.46
Long-term debt ($ mil.): —

No. of shares (mil.): 31.2
Dividends
Yield: 0.0%
Payout: 16.8%
Market value ($ mil.): 2,898.0

	STOCK PRICE ($) FY Close	P/E High/Low	PER SHARE ($) Earnings	Dividends	Book Value
09/18	92.80	16 9	5.92	1.00	7.45
09/17	51.35	21 13	2.63	1.00	4.80
09/16	37.94	17 5	2.33	0.55	3.92
Annual Growth	56.4%	—	59.4%	34.9%	38.0%

Rogers Corp.

Rogers lives in a material world and it is a materials company. The company's specialty materials are used in a variety of electronic and consumer

---

products. Its products include printed circuit board laminates and polyester-based industrial laminates which are used in wireless communications systems including hand-held devices GPS and direct broadcast TV. Rogers' high-performance foams include urethane and silicone foams used for making vehicle gaskets and seals communication devices computers and footwear insoles. It also makes high-performance elastomer components sold to OEMs in various markets including ground transportation office equipment and consumer industries.

Operations

The company operates in three segments: High Performance Foams (polyurethane and silicone foam products sold to fabricators and OEMs); Printed Circuit Materials (circuit board laminate products for high frequency high performance applications to meet the demands of increasing speed complexity and power in analog digital and microwave equipment); and Power Electronics Solutions (Curamik Electronics Solutions and Power Distribution Systems). Curamik Electronics Solutions makes direct copper bonded ceramic substrate products used in the design of intelligent power management devices such as insulated gate bipolar transistor modules. Power Distribution Systems makes busbar power distribution products for manufacturers of high power electrical inverter and converter systems for use in mass transit and clean technology applications (such as electric vehicles solar farms and wind turbines).

Geographic Reach

A global player Rogers has operations in the US (Arizona Connecticut and Illinois) Europe (Belgium and Germany) and Asia (China Japan Singapore South Korea and Taiwan). In 2013 non-US based customers accounted for 78% of the company's total sales.

Sales and Marketing

Rogers sells through direct channels. It sold its products to 3000 customers worldwide in 2013. The company's largest customer accounted for 4% of sales.

Financial Performance

After experiencing a revenue dip in 2012 due to a drop in Curamik Electronics Solutions and Power Distribution Systems' revenues in fiscal 2013 Rogers' revenues grew by 8% due to the significantly improved performance of the restructured Power Electronics Solutions operating segment (20% up on 2012 as the result of higher sales of technology applications across a number of markets including hybrid and electric vehicles solar and wind applications and industrial motor drives). The Printed Circuit Materials segment was up by 14%. These increases were partially offset by a 6% drop in High Performance Foams net sales.

In 2013 the company's net income dropped by 45% due to higher operating expenses and higher income tax expenses.

That year the company's operating cash inflow increased to $78.01 million (from $40.04 million in 2012) due to a change in working capital as a result of cash generated from accounts payable and other accrued expenses and inventories.

Strategy

The company focuses on offering advanced high-tech products at competitive prices in markets around the globe. It also seeks to be close to its customers marketing its products through direct sales channels in concentrated areas within its three major geographic regions. Rogers pursues growth organically by expanding its product line and market share as well as growth through acquisitions.

Its current strategy for growth focuses on developing high-tech products for industries involved in the Internet mass transit and clean technology. The growth of mobile devices for example has driven sales of one of the company's latest product brand lines its PORON molded components. In addition to being used in mobile devices such as iPADs and iPhones the shock-absorbing material is also used in sports apparel to protect athletes from crashes. The company's busbar products are used primarily in power distribution systems for mass transit and clean technology. It manufactures these components under the RO-LINX brand name.

In 2014 the Advanced Circuit Materials Division launched ROG Mobile a free mobile app for Apple and Android devices. The new app allows users to access Rogers' calculators literature technical papers and the ability to order samples. That unit launched COOLSPAN Thermally & Electrically Conductive Adhesive Film a thermosetting epoxy based silver filled adhesive film used to bond circuit boards to heavy metal backplanes heat sink coins and RF module housings.

As part of company's long-term strategy in 2014 Rogers and Northeastern University established the Rogers Innovation Center at Northeastern's George J. Kostas Research Institute for Homeland Security in Burlington Massachusetts. The center conducts complementary research and development initiatives in advanced materials with a focus on early stage technical and commercial development of new high-tech materials products.

To improve operational efficiency in 2013 the management of the Curamik Electronic Solutions and Power Distribution Systems operations were combined under one segment (Power Electronics Solutions) and the former operating segments became product lines.

Mergers and Acquisitions

In 2014 the company agreed to acquire Arlon LLC from Handy & Harman Ltd. for $157 million. The deal adds Arlon's complementary capabilities and technologies in circuit materials and engineered silicones.

Company Background

In Asia it formed a strategic alliance with Hitachi Chemical in 2011 to provide high-speed digital printed circuit materials. The materials produced help meet the growing demand for increased speed in Internet data and video transmission.

In 2011 Rogers acquired Curamik Electronics a manufacturer of power electronic substrate products in Eschenbach Germany for $153 million. Curamik Electronics is a global leader for the development of direct copper bonded ceramic substrate products which are used in industrial motor drives wind and solar energy converters and hybrid electric vehicle drive systems. The acquisition enhanced Rogers' existing power electronic products portfolio.

In late 2011 Rogers ceased operations at its underperforming Thermal Management Solutions segment after failing to gain traction in the market and having problems with the manufacturing process. With the acquisition of Curamik Electronics in 2011 Rogers restructured its business segments to add Power Electronics Solutions as one of its three core strategic units along with High

Performance Foams and Printed Circuit Materials. Curamik Electronic Solutions and Power Distribution Systems comprise the Power Electronics Solutions business segment.

Rogers was founded in 1832 as a materials manufacturer for the textile industry by Peter Rogers.

EXECUTIVES

Vice President Sales And Marketing, Mario Kerr
SVP and CTO, Robert C. (Bob) Daigle, age 55, $320,016 total compensation
CFO, Janice E. Stipp, age 58
President and CEO, Bruce D. Hoechner, age 57, $490,773 total compensation
President Enterprise Business Unit, Nitin Kawale
VP Advanced Circuit Materials Division, Jeffrey M. Grudzien, age 56, $276,543 total compensation
VP High Performance Foams Division, John C. Quinn
VP Power Electronics Solutions; President Rogers Asia, Helen Zhang
Auditors: PricewaterhouseCoopers LLP

LOCATIONS

HQ: Rogers Corp.
2225 W. Chandler Blvd., Chandler, AZ 85224-6155
Phone: 480 917-6000
Web: www.rogerscorp.com

PRODUCTS/OPERATIONS

2016 Sales

	$ mil.	% of total
Advanced Connectivity Solutions	277.7	42
Elastomeric Material Solutions	203.2	31
Power Electronics Solutions	152.4	23
Other	23.0	4
Total	**656.3**	**100**

Selected Products and Brands

High Performance Foams
  Plate backing and mounts for printing plates (R/bak)
  Silicon foams and sponges (BISCO)
  Urethane and silicon foams for high-impact cushioning gaskets and seals portable communications devices computers (PORON)
Printed Circuit Materials
  Flexible circuit materials (R/flex)
  Printed circuit board materials (DUROID ULTRALAM)
Power Electronics Solutions
  Curamik Electronics Solutions
  Direct copper bonded (DCB) ceramic substrate products
  Power distribution systems
  Busbar products used in mass transit and clean technology (RO-LINX)
Other Polymer Products
  Elastomer rollers and belts (ENDUR)
  Floats for fuel-level sensors (NITROPHYL)

COMPETITORS

Hexcel	Kingboard
Honeywell Electronic Materials	Park Electrochemical
	Plexus
Insulectro	Vesuvius

HISTORICAL FINANCIALS

Company Type: Public

Income Statement

FYE: December 31

	REVENUE ($ mil.)	NET INCOME ($ mil.)	NET PROFIT MARGIN	EMPLOYEES
12/17	821.0	80.4	9.8%	3,400
12/16	656.3	48.2	7.4%	3,100
12/15	641.4	46.3	7.2%	2,800
12/14	610.9	52.8	8.7%	2,800
12/13	537.4	37.7	7.0%	2,500
Annual Growth	11.2%	20.8%	—	8.0%

2017 Year-End Financials

Debt ratio: 12.2%	No. of shares (mil.): 18.2
Return on equity: 11.4%	Dividends
Cash ($ mil.): 181.1	Yield: —
Current ratio: 3.99	Payout: —
Long-term debt ($ mil.): 136.8	Market value ($ mil.): 2,956.0

	STOCK PRICE ($) FY Close	P/E High/Low	PER SHARE ($) Earnings	Dividends	Book Value
12/17	161.92	38 17	4.34	0.00	41.99
12/16	76.81	29 16	2.65	0.00	35.28
12/15	51.57	33 18	2.48	0.00	32.55
12/14	81.44	28 18	2.83	0.00	31.62
12/13	61.50	29 18	2.13	0.00	31.11
Annual Growth	27.4%		— — 19.5%	—	7.8%

RPT Realty

Ramco-Gershenson Properties Trust makes no bones about horning in on the retail world. A self-administered real estate investment trust (REIT) it owns develops and manages a property portfolio of about 90 shopping centers in about a dozen states east of the Mississippi River. The REIT's properties contain approximately 20 million sq. ft. of leasable space in the Midwest mid-Atlantic and Southeast. Nearly all of its assets are community shopping centers in metropolitan areas anchored by grocery or big-box stores. The REIT also owns one enclosed regional mall and one single-tenant property and has a handful of projects under development.Michigan is the Ramco-Gershenson's largest market accounting more than than 40% of rental revenue; Florida accounts for more than 30%. The REIT's largest tenants include T.J. Maxx and Publix.Ramco-Gershenson often enters into joint ventures when acquiring properties though it made no new acquisitions in 2009 due to the economic environment.Members of the Gershenson family including president and CEO Dennis own about 15% of the REIT's outstanding shares; institutional investors hold more than 35%

EXECUTIVES

President CEO and Director, Dennis E. Gershenson, age 74, $600,000 total compensation
EVP, Frederick A. (Fred) Zantello, age 74, $291,225 total compensation
CFO, Geoffrey Bedrosian
Vice President of Investor Relations and Corporate Communications, Dawn Hendershot

Vice President Human Resources, Karen Childress-Newberger
Vice President Development Redevelopment, Peter Debenedicts
Chairman, Stephen R. Blank, age 72
Auditors: GRANT THORNTON LLP

LOCATIONS

HQ: RPT Realty
31500 Northwestern Highway, Suite 300, Farmington Hills, MI 48334
Phone: 248 350-9900   Fax: 248 350-9925
Web: www.rgpt.com

PRODUCTS/OPERATIONS

2015 Sales

	$ mil.	% of total
Minimum rents	183.2	73
Recoveries income from tenants	61.6	24
Management and other fee income	1.8	1
Percentage rent	0.5	-
Other income	4.7	2
Total	**251.8**	**100**

COMPETITORS

Agree Realty	Macerich
CBL & Associates Properties	Milestone Properties
DDR	Pennsylvania Real Estate
Federal Realty Investment	Regency Centers
GGP	Schottenstein
IRC Retail Centers	Tanger Factory Outlet
Kimco Realty	Taubman Centers
	Weingarten Realty

HISTORICAL FINANCIALS

Company Type: Public

Income Statement				FYE: December 31
	REVENUE ($ mil.)	NET INCOME ($ mil.)	NET PROFIT MARGIN	EMPLOYEES
12/17	265.0	69.0	26.1%	122
12/16	260.9	59.6	22.9%	117
12/15	251.7	65.1	25.9%	120
12/14	218.3	(2.3)	—	116
12/13	170.0	11.0	6.5%	108
Annual Growth	**11.7%**	**58.3%**	**—**	**3.1%**

2017 Year-End Financials

Debt ratio: 49.2%
Return on equity: 7.9%
Cash ($ mil.): 8.0
Current ratio: 0.81
Long-term debt ($ mil.): 1,000.2

No. of shares (mil.): 79.3
Dividends
Yield: 0.0%
Payout: 112.8%
Market value ($ mil.): 1,169.0

	STOCK PRICE ($) FY Close	P/E High/Low	PER SHARE ($) Earnings	Dividends	Book Value
12/17	14.73	22 15	0.78	0.88	10.89
12/16	16.58	31 24	0.66	0.86	10.98
12/15	16.61	27 20	0.73	0.82	11.17
12/14	18.74	— —	(0.14)	0.78	11.25
12/13	15.74	295222	0.06	0.71	11.55
Annual Growth	**(1.6%)**	**—**	**89.9%**	**5.5%**	**(1.5%)**

RTI Surgical, Inc.

When it comes to surgical implants RTI Surgical (formerly RTI Biologics) recommends the natural alternative. The firm develops products made from human and animal tissue that are used in orthopedic dental and other surgeries to repair fractures spinal disorders sports injuries breast reconstruction and other procedures. Using its BioCleanse Cancelle SP and Tutoplast processes the company sterilizes tissue — including bone tendons and skin — that is then used in surgeries. RTI Surgical sells its allografts (made from human tissue) and xenografts (made from animals) in the US and more than 50 countries around the globe. Its direct sales force targets the sports medicine and general orthopedic markets.

Operations

RTI Surgical's fastest-growing segment comes from products for sports medicine procedures which accounts for about 25% of sales. As customer demand for such products increase a good portion of RTI's research and product development capabilities are focused on expanding its offerings for sports medicine applications. The bone graft substitutes (BGS) and general orthopedic segment and the surgical specialties (breast hernia urology and ophthalmology) segments are also growing. However its revenues in its spine and dental divisions have fluctuated in recent years primarily due to lower sales levels by its key distributors in those segments.

Geographic Reach

RTI is headquartered in Florida where it also has two tissue processing facilities. It also processes tissue at a plant in Germany and has metal and synthetic implant manufacturing facilities in Michigan and North Carolina.

The US accounts for about 90% of the company's revenue but it does offer its products and services in nearly 50 nations.

Sales and Marketing

In addition to its direct sales efforts RTI has also forged a distribution network of agreements with other companies each targeting a specific product market. Its agreements include deals with Medtronic and Stryker to handle spine implants and with Zimmer to handle spine and dental implants. It uses its own representatives and independent distributors for its sports medicine and wound-repair products. International distribution is also handled by independent distributors.

Strategy

One of the challenges RTI faces is that it competes with not-for-profit allograft-processing firms for the limited supply of human tissue. In addition the biologic implant industry must comply with strict regulations and the company is dependent upon third parties to secure human tissue ethically. Finally other companies are busily working to develop synthetic tissues that may eventually eliminate the need for some of RTI's products. It deals with these challenges by pushing to ever expand its product portfolio.

The company also streamlines its holdings to focus on more profitable operations. In mid-2017 it sold its cardiothoracic closure business to A&E Advanced Closure Systems for $54 million in cash and up to $6 million in contingencies. It will funds from the sale to pay down debt.

Mergers and Acquisitions

As part of its ongoing efforts to expand its product portfolio RTI in 2013 purchased spinal implant and instrument maker Pioneer Surgical Technology for $126 million. The buy also brought Pioneer's distribution network under the RTI umbrella and caused the company to change its name from RTI Biologics to RTI Surgical.

EXECUTIVES

EVP and Chief Scientific Officer, Caroline A. Hartill, age 61, $348,148 total compensation
EVP RTI Surgical and President RTI Donor Service, Roger W. Rose, age 58, $338,394 total compensation
Medical Director, Lennox K. (Lenny) Archibald
Interim CEO, Robert P. (Rob) Jordheim, age 54, $350,215 total compensation
VP and General Manager North American Spine, Kevin D. Brandt
VP and General Manager International, Keith Pelatowski
VP and General Manager Tissue-Based Implants, Rick Robbins
VP US Operations, John N. Varela, age 51, $310,154 total compensation
Interim CFO, Wy Louw
Vice President Legal, Keith Koford
Vice President Sales, Rod Allen
Vice President Sales Tissue Based Implants, Jimmy Blanchard
Vice President of Corporate Accounts, Eric Baldwin
Vice President Human Resources, Paul Montague
Vice President of Finance and Controller, Johannes Louw
Vice Chairman, Peter F. Gearen, age 70
Chairman, Curtis M. (Curt) Selquist, age 73
Board Member, Christopher Sweeney
Auditors: DELOITTE & TOUCHE LLP

LOCATIONS

HQ: RTI Surgical, Inc.
11621 Research Circle, Alachua, FL 32615
Phone: 386 418-8888
Web: www.rtix.com

PRODUCTS/OPERATIONS

2015 Sales

	$ mil.	% of total
Tissue distribution		
Spine	77.0	27
Ortho fixation	55.6	20
Sports medicine	46.7	17
Bone graft substitutes & general orthopedic	42.3	15
Dental	23.6	8
Surgical specialties	23.5	8
Other revenues	13.6	5
Total	**282.3**	**100**

COMPETITORS

ApaTech	Interpore
BioMimetic	Johnson & Johnson
Biocoral	Medtronic
Cook Incorporated	ReGen Biologics
CryoLife	Synovis Life Technologies
Integra LifeSciences	

HISTORICAL FINANCIALS

Company Type: Public

Income Statement

FYE: December 31

	REVENUE ($ mil.)	NET INCOME ($ mil.)	NET PROFIT MARGIN	EMPLOYEES
12/17	279.5	6.2	2.2%	942
12/16	272.8	(14.4)	—	1,140
12/15	282.2	14.9	5.3%	1,169
12/14	262.8	2.7	1.0%	1,102
12/13	197.9	(17.8)	—	1,100
Annual Growth	9.0%	—	—	(3.8%)

2017 Year-End Financials

Debt ratio: 13.4%
Return on equity: 2.6%
Cash ($ mil.): 22.3
Current ratio: 3.50
Long-term debt ($ mil.): 42.0

No. of shares (mil.): 62.6
Dividends
Yield: —
Payout: —
Market value ($ mil.): 257.0

	STOCK PRICE ($) FY Close	P/E High/Low	Earnings	Dividends	Book Value
12/17	4.10	146 78	0.04	0.00	3.92
12/16	3.25	— —	(0.31)	0.00	3.85
12/15	3.97	36 18	0.20	0.00	4.11
12/14	5.20	— —	(0.01)	0.00	3.89
12/13	3.54	— —	(0.34)	0.00	3.87
Annual Growth	3.7%	— —	—	—	0.3%

Rudolph Technologies, Inc.

Rudolph Technologies' inspection and metrology systems lead the way to better yields for chip makers. To create semiconductors manufacturers deposit precise layers of conducting and insulating materials on silicon wafers. Rudolph's process control metrology equipment monitors these layers to ensure that the material doesn't get too thick or too thin. Its inspection equipment (around half of sales) looks for defects not obvious to the human eye such as tiny scratches or gouges in the surface of a silicon wafer. The company also makes a range of data analysis and process control software. Rudolph gets about two-thirds of sales from customers outside the US.

Operations

Inspection and metrology make up the biggest part of Rudolph's revenue about 63% combined. The company's data analysis and review business accounts for 13% of revenue with parts and service accounting for 18%. About 6% of revenue comes from its small lithography business.

Geographic Reach

Rudolph sells its products to semiconductor makers in 20 countries. US-based semiconductor companies account for 34% of the company's revenue followed by Taiwan 27%; Singapore 10%; and several countries with smaller percentages. Purchases from Asian manufacturers are 65% of revenue.

Sales and Marketing

The company deploys a direct sales customer service and application support staff in offices in the US Europe and Asia. Although Intel and STATS ChiPac Ltd. each accounted for more than 10% of Rudolph's sales in 2013 no customers had that distinction in 2014. Other customers have included Infineon Technologies and Samsung Semiconductor Intel Broadcom Limited and Taiwan Semiconductor Manufacturing.

Financial Performance

Rudolph's revenue increased 3% to $181.2 million in 2014 from $176.2 million in 2013. A rise in capital spending by back-end semiconductor manufacturers chiefly Rudolph's customers in advanced packaging boosted sales.

The company posted a net loss of $4.6 million in 2014 compared to net income of $3.5 million in 2013. The loss came from higher higher selling general and administrative expenses. The expenses were inflated by litigation expenses for final judgment awarded to Integrated Technology Corporation as well as higher share-based compensation expenses and restructuring charges.

Cash flow from operations decreased to $4.3 million in 2014 from $6.1 million in 2013.

Strategy

Rudolph maintains a variety of businesses related to semiconductor manufacturing to mitigate the impact of the cyclical nature of the industry and generate cash flow during downturns. Its lithography business is one way the company takes pressure off the main inspection and metrology businesses.

The company restructured in 2014 reducing its headcount 9% and closing a manufacturing facility in Mainz Germany. The operations of the Mainz plant were moved to Rudolph facilities in Snoqualmie Washington and Bloomington Minnesota.

Mergers and Acquisitions

Rudolph purchased Stella Alliance a Massachusetts-based semiconductor inspection technology intellectual property portfolio company in 2015. Stella Alliance owns patented illumination autofocus and image acquisition technology that enhances inspection techniques. The acquisition is to result in a new high-resolution inspection system from Rudolph in the second quarter of 2016. The acquired technology also extends Rudolph's inspection portfolio into growing unserved segments of microelectronic device manufacturing.

EXECUTIVES

SVP Finance and Administration CFO and Secretary, Steven R. Roth, age 57, $312,666 total compensation
CEO and Director, Michael P. Plisinski, age 48, $298,492 total compensation
VP and General Manager Data Analysis and Review Business Unit, Thomas Sonderman, age 54
VP and General Manager Lithography Systems Group, Richard B. Rogoff, age 51, $265,000 total compensation
VP Asia Operations, Cleon Chan, age 50
VP and General Manager Metrology Business Unit, Michael J. Colgan, age 55
VP and General Manager Display Products Lithography Business Unit and Chief Technical Officer Lithography Systems Group, Elvino da Silveira, age 58
VP and General Manager Inspection Business Unit, Michael F. Goodrich, age 48
Vice President And General Manager, Mike Colgan
Chairman, Thomas G. (Tom) Greig, age 70
Auditors: Ernst & Young LLP

LOCATIONS

HQ: Rudolph Technologies, Inc.
16 Jonspin Road, Wilmington, MA 01887
Phone: 978 253-6200
Web: www.rudolphtech.com

PRODUCTS/OPERATIONS

2014 Sales

	$ mil.	% of total
Systems		
Inspection	87.8	49
Metrology	24.6	14
Data analysis & review	24.0	13
Lithography	11.2	6
Parts	20.3	11
Services	13.3	7
Total	**181.2**	**100**

Selected Products

Data Analysis and Review Software
  ARTIST Software (real-time monitoring software)
  AutoShell Software (equipment automation software)
  ControlWORKS Software (process control software)
  Discover Software (yield enhancement and process management software)
  GateWay Software(diagnostic and communications software)
  Genesis Software (data acquisition and integration data mining parametric analysis)
  HarmonyASR (off-line defect review and classification)
  Process Sentinel Software (spatial process control system)
  ProcessWORKS (process control software)
  RecipeWORKS (recipe management software)
  TrackWORKS (preventive maintenance management software)
  TrueADC Software (automatic defect classification)
  Yield Optimizer (yield management and predictive modeling software)
Inspection and Test Systems
  AXi Series (defect inspection for various process steps)
  B30 Inspection Module (2D defect detection on wafer's backside)
  E30 Inspection Module (2D defect detection of wafer's edge)
  Explorer Inspection Cluster (multi-surface inspection tools)
  F30 Inspection Module (multiple resolution defect inspection)
  NSX Series (macro-defect inspection)
  PrecisionWoRx System (probe card test and analysis)
  ProbeWoRx System (probe card production metrology)
  Wafer Scanner Inspection System (2-D/3-D bump dimensional inspection 2-D bump and surface defect inspection)
  WaferWoRx System (probing process and tip analysis)
Metrology Systems
  MetaPULSE Systems (optical acoustic-based systems for opaque thin-film layers)
  S3000 System (transparent thin-film measurement systems)

COMPETITORS

Applied Materials	Nanometrics
Camtek	Nikon
Carl Zeiss	Nova Measuring
FEI	PANalytical
Hexagon AB	PDF Solutions
Hitachi	Qcept Technologies
High-Technologies	SCREEN Holdings
KLA-Tencor	

HISTORICAL FINANCIALS

Company Type: Public

Income Statement

FYE: December 31

	REVENUE ($ mil.)	NET INCOME ($ mil.)	NET PROFIT MARGIN	EMPLOYEES
12/17	255.1	32.9	12.9%	592
12/16	232.7	36.9	15.9%	579
12/15	221.6	17.9	8.1%	572
12/14	181.2	(4.6)	—	586
12/13	176.2	3.4	2.0%	615
Annual Growth	9.7%	75.6%	—	(0.9%)

2017 Year-End Financials

Debt ratio: —
Return on equity: 10.5%
Cash ($ mil.): 67.7
Current ratio: 7.61
Long-term debt ($ mil.): —

No. of shares (mil.): 31.6
Dividends
Yield: —
Payout: —
Market value ($ mil.): 755.0

	STOCK PRICE ($) FY Close	P/E High/Low		PER SHARE ($) Earnings	Dividends	Book Value
12/17	23.90	26	20	1.02	0.00	10.54
12/16	23.35	20	10	1.16	0.00	9.44
12/15	14.22	26	17	0.56	0.00	8.75
12/14	10.23	—	—	(0.14)	0.00	8.33
12/13	11.74	127	92	0.10	0.00	8.47
Annual Growth	19.4%		—	—	78.7%	—	5.6%

S & T Bancorp Inc (Indiana, PA)

S&T Bancorp is the bank holding company for S&T Bank which boasts nearly $5 billion in assets and serves customers from some 60 branch offices in western Pennsylvania. Targeting individuals and local businesses the bank offers such standard retail products as checking savings and money market accounts CDs and credit cards. Business loans including commercial mortgages make up more than 80% of the company's loan portfolio. The bank also originates residential mortgages construction loans and consumer loans. Through subsidiaries S&T Bank sells life disability and commercial property/casualty insurance provides investment management services and advises the Stewart Capital Mid Cap Fund.

Operations

S&T Bancorp operates through three main business segments: Community Banking which offers traditional banking services and commercial and consumer loans; Wealth Management which boasts $2 billion in assets under management and administration and provides brokerage services trust and custodial services and investment advisory for affluent individuals and institutions; and Insurance which offers commercial property and casualty insurance group life and health coverage employee benefit services and personal insurance products through S&T Insurance Group LLC.

Its S&T Bancholding subsidiary provides investment services in the Wealth Management segment while its Stewart Capital Advisors subsidiary provides investment advisory services in the segment.

Overall S&T Bancorp generated 72% of its total revenue from loan interest (including fees) in 2014 plus another 6% from interest on its investment securities. About 10% of its total revenue came from debit and credit card fees and deposit account service charges while wealth management fees and insurance fees made up 6% and 3% of total revenue that year respectively.

Geographic Reach

Headquartered in Indiana Pennsylvania S&T Bancorp boasts branches in a dozen counties in the state including: Allegheny Armstrong Blair Butler Cambria Centre Clarion Clearfield Indiana Jefferson Washington and Westmoreland counties. It also has loan production offices in northeast and central Ohio and in western New York.

Sales and Marketing

Targeting both individuals and local businesses S&T Bancorp spent $3.32 million on marketing in 2014 up from the $2.93 million and $3.21 million it spent in 2013 and 2012 respectively.

Financial Performance

S&T Bancorp's revenue has slowly declined in recent years due to shrinking interest margins on loans amidst the low-interest environment. The firm's profits however have been rising thanks to declining loan loss provisions as its loan portfolio's credit quality has improved with the strengthened economy.

Following several years of top-line declines the bank's revenue inched up by nearly 1% to $206.86 million in 2014. The rise was mostly thanks to higher interest income as overall earning-asset balances grew by nearly 7% during the year reflecting the bank's growing loan business and increased investment securities assets. Wealth Management fees also continued to grow rising by 6% during the year.

Higher revenue coupled with lower interest expenses on deposits and a $6.6 million reduction in loan loss provisions in 2014 drove S&T Bancorp's net income higher by 15% to $57.91 million. S&T's operating cash levels fell by 9% to $78.1 million for the year after adjusting its earnings for non-cash items mostly related to its net proceeds from sales of its mortgage loans originated-for-sale.

Strategy

S&T Bancorp reiterated in 2015 that its growth strategy is centered around organic growth in existing and new markets and growth through strategic acquisitions that introduce new lines of business. Its 2015 acquisition of Integrity Bancshares for example expanded S&T's footprint eastward across four counties in Pennsylvania and added millions of dollars worth of new loan business. Also that year the bank entered the western part of New York for the first time with the opening of a new loan production office in the region.

In late 2012 the bank extended its operations into its neighbor Ohio when it opened a handful of branches in Akron. That same year the bank acquired Mainline Bancorp and Gateway Bank of Pennsylvania bolstering its presence in its core western Pennsylvania market.

Mergers and Acquisitions

In March 2015 S&T Bancorp purchased Camp Hill-based Integrity Bancshares for $155 million adding $860 million in assets and eight branches expanding S&T's geographic footprint eastward into Cumberland Dauphin Lancaster and York counties in Pennsylvania. S&T added that the acquisition positioned the bank in high-growth markets within the state and added experienced members to the bank's loan team.

In 2012 the bank acquired Mainline Bancorp and Gateway Bank of Pennsylvania. Both transactions served to expand S&T's presence in western Pennsylvania.

EXECUTIVES

SVP Operations and Technology, David P. Ruddock, age 56, $265,000 total compensation
Executive Vice President, Tony E Kallsen
President and CEO S&T and S&T Bank, Todd D. Brice, age 55, $525,000 total compensation
EVP and Retail Banking Division Manager, Richard A. (Rich) Fiscus
SEVP and CFO, Mark Kochvar, age 57, $278,000 total compensation
SEVP and Chief Lending Officer, David G. Antolik, age 51, $302,000 total compensation
EVP and Chief Investment Officer Wealth Management, Malcolm E. Polley, age 55
SEVP Chief Risk Officer and Secretary, Ernest J. Draganza
EVP and Deputy Chief Credit Officer, William (Bill) Kametz
SEVP and Chief Credit Officer, Patrick Haberfield
SEVP and Chief Banking Officer, Rebecca Stapleton
EVP and Commercial Loan Officer, Steve Drahnak
EVP and Chief Audit Executive, LaDawn D. Yesho
EVP, David Richards
EVP Marketing Division Manager, Rob Jorgenson
EVP and CIO, Jim Mill
EVP and Manager, Robert Jogrenson
SEVP and Market Executive, Thomas J. Sposito
Market President Central Pennsylvania, Jordan Space
Market President Northeast Ohio, Steve Hendricks
Vice President Mortgage Underwriting Manager, Christine Rumbaugh
Vice President Marketing, Kelly Thomas
Vice President Credit Analysis Operation Manager, Dennis Scott
Vice President Marketing, Kelly Corrinne
Vice President Network Operations Manager, Ron Todd
Vice President Community Banking, Tammy Czyz
Vice President Regional Manager, Megan White
Vice President and Manager Benefits, Sandy Loperfito
Chairman S&T and S&T Bank, Charles G. Urtin
Vice Chairman S&T and S&T Bank, Christine J. Toretti, age 61
Auditors: Ernst & Young LLP

LOCATIONS

HQ: S & T Bancorp Inc (Indiana, PA)
800 Philadelphia Street, Indiana, PA 15701
Phone: 800 325-2265
Web: www.stbancorp.com

PRODUCTS/OPERATIONS

2014 Sales

	% of total
Interest	
Loans including fees	72
Investment securities & other	6
Noninterest	
Wealth management fees	6
Debit and credit card fees	5
Service charges on deposit accounts	5
Insurance fees	3
Others	3
Total	**100**

Selected Subsidiaries

9th Street Holdings Inc.
Commonwealth Trust Credit Life Insurance Company
(50%)
S&T Bank
  S&T Insurance Group LLC
  S&T-Evergreen Insurance LLC
  S&T Bancholdings Inc.
  S&T Professional Resources Group LLC
  S&T Settlement Services LLC
  Stewart Capital Advisors LLC

COMPETITORS

AmeriServ Financial	First Commonwealth
Citizens Financial	Financial
Group	Northwest Bancshares
F.N.B. (PA)	PNC Financial
Fidelity Bancorp (PA)	

HISTORICAL FINANCIALS

Company Type: Public

Income Statement				FYE: December 31
	ASSETS ($ mil.)	NET INCOME ($ mil.)	INCOME AS % OF ASSETS	EMPLOYEES
12/17	7,060.2	72.9	1.0%	1,080
12/16	6,943.0	71.3	1.0%	1,080
12/14	4,964.6	57.9	1.2%	945
12/13	4,533.1	50.5	1.1%	948
12/12	4,526.7	34.2	0.8%	1,027
Annual Growth	11.8%	20.9%	—	1.3%

2017 Year-End Financials

Return on assets: 1.0%
Return on equity: 8.4%
Long-term debt ($ mil.): —
No. of shares (mil.): 34.9
Sales ($ mil): 316.1
Dividends
  Yield: 0.0%
  Payout: 39.2%
Market value ($ mil.): 1,392.0

	STOCK PRICE ($) FY Close	P/E High/Low	PER SHARE ($) Earnings	Dividends	Book Value
12/17	39.81	21 16	2.09	0.82	25.28
12/16	39.04	19 11	2.05	0.77	24.12
12/14	29.81	16 11	1.95	0.68	20.42
12/13	25.31	15 10	1.70	0.61	19.21
12/12	18.07	20 13	1.18	0.60	18.08
Annual Growth	21.8%	— —	15.4%	8.1%	8.7%

Sabra Health Care REIT Inc

Sabra Health Care REIT doesn't mind a little healthy competition in the real estate sector. The company invests in income-producing health care facilities in the US. The REIT's investment portfolio includes about 180 properties most of which are skilled nursing/post-acute centers. It also invests in assisted living and independent living facilities and hospitals. Sabra's facilities house more than 18300 beds and are located in 35-plus states. Substantially all of the properties are leased to and operated by subsidiaries of Sun Healthcare Group which spun off its real estate assets to form Sabra Health Care REIT in 2010. In mid-2017 Sabra ac-

quired Care Capital Properties for approximately $2.1 billion more than doubling the REIT's size.

Operations

Sabra owned 180 real estate properties that were leased to operates and tenants under triple-net lease agreements during 2015 with nearly 60% of them being skilled nursing/transitional care facilities and most of the rest being senior housing facilities.

Geographic Reach

The REIT has licensed beds in 37 US states with its three largest markets being New Hampshire Texas and Connecticut.

Financial Performance

Sabra's annual revenues have almost tripled since 2011 as it has expanded its property portfolio through acquisitions and has charged higher rental rates as the real estate market has strengthened. Meanwhile it annual profits have risen more than five-fold as it's been able to keep a lid on its overhead costs.

The REIT's revenue jumped 30% to $238.86 million during 2015 mostly thanks to added rental income from newly acquired properties (acquired after January 1 2014).

Strong revenue growth in 2015 drove Sabra's net income up 69% to $79.41 million for the year. The REIT's operating cash levels climbed 42% to $121.1 million mostly as its cash earnings rose during the year.

Strategy

Sabra aims to profit from the aging of the US population and increasing life expectancy both of which are driving demand for long-term care services. The REIT is focused on growing its geographically diverse portfolio primarily through the purchase of senior housing and memory care facilities with a secondary emphasis on acquiring skilled nursing homes. In mid-2015 for example Sabra Health Care REIT agreed to buy four Maryland-based skilled nursing facilities — which specialized in transitional care and medically complex post-surgical ventilator and dialysis patients — consisting of 678 beds for $234 million.

EXECUTIVES

Chairman and CEO, Richard K. Matros, age 64, $725,000 total compensation
Chief Investment Officer, Talya Nevo-Hacohen, $350,000 total compensation
EVP and CFO, Harold W. Andrews, age 54, $350,000 total compensation
Chief Technology Officer, Galen Warren
Chief Operating Officer, Nick Cafferillo
Auditors: PricewaterhouseCoopers LLP

LOCATIONS

HQ: Sabra Health Care REIT Inc
18500 Von Karman Avenue, Suite 550, Irvine, CA 92612
Phone: 888 393-8248
Web: www.sabrahealth.com

PRODUCTS/OPERATIONS

2015 Sales

	$ mil.	% of total
Rental income	209.9	88
Interest and other income	25.5	11
Resident fees and services	3.5	1
Total	**238.9**	**100**

COMPETITORS

Extendicare	Omega Healthcare
HCP	Investors
Healthcare Realty	Senior Housing
Trust	Properties
LTC Properties	Ventas
National Health	Welltower
Investors	

HISTORICAL FINANCIALS

Company Type: Public

Income Statement				FYE: December 31
	REVENUE ($ mil.)	NET INCOME ($ mil.)	NET PROFIT MARGIN	EMPLOYEES
12/17	405.6	158.3	39.0%	61
12/16	260.5	70.2	27.0%	14
12/15	238.8	79.4	33.2%	13
12/14	183.5	46.9	25.6%	11
12/13	134.7	33.7	25.0%	9
Annual Growth	31.7%	47.2%	—	61.4%

2017 Year-End Financials

Debt ratio: 48.2%
Return on equity: 7.1%
Cash ($ mil.): 518.6
Current ratio: 7.38
Long-term debt ($ mil.): 3,394.4
No. of shares (mil.): 178.2
Dividends
  Yield: 0.0%
  Payout: 123.5%
Market value ($ mil.): 3,346.0

	STOCK PRICE ($) FY Close	P/E High/Low	PER SHARE ($) Earnings	Dividends	Book Value
12/17	18.77	21 13	1.40	1.73	19.26
12/16	24.42	29 16	0.92	1.67	15.56
12/15	20.23	31 17	1.11	1.60	16.17
12/14	30.37	39 31	0.78	1.51	15.95
12/13	26.14	46 31	0.68	1.36	11.86
Annual Growth	(7.9%)	— —	19.8%	6.2%	12.9%

Salisbury Bancorp, Inc.

Salisbury Bancorp has a stake in New England's financial market. The holding company owns the Salisbury Bank and Trust Company which operates seven branches in northwestern Connecticut southwestern Massachusetts and southeastern New York. With roots dating to 1848 the bank offers a variety of financial products and services including checking savings and money market accounts CDs credit cards and trust services. Residential real estate mortgages make up the largest portion of the bank's loan portfolio by far; commercial real estate construction land development business financial agricultural and consumer loans round out its lending activities.

EXECUTIVES

CFO and Chief Accounting Officer, B. Ian McMahon, age 57
SVP Compliance Officer and CTO Salisbury Bank and Trust, Todd M. Clinton, $89,604 total compensation
President CEO and Director, Richard J. Cantele Jr., age 57, $165,934 total compensation
Chairman, Michael A. Varet, age 75

Director Human Resources Salisbury Bank and
Trust, Doug Cahill
VP and Assistant Secretary, Lana J. Morrison
SVP Marketing Salisbury Bank and Trust
Company, Diane Farrell
VP Operations Salisbury Bank and Trust, Darrel S.
Long
VP Commercial Loan Officer Salisbury Bank and
Trust, Darren Piper
VP Mortgage Origination Salisbury Bank and
Trust, Amy Raymond
Branch Administrator Salibury Bank and Trust,
Spring J. Bagnall
Trust Officer Salisbury Bank and Trust, Meredith
Tiedemann
Branch Manager and Assistant Treasurer Sharon
Office, Linda F. Decker
Branch Manager and Retail Banking Officer
Canaan Office, Betsy R. Devino
Branch Manager South Egremont Office,
Georgann B. Farnum
Branch Manager Lakeville Office, Julie Gregory
Auditors: Baker Newman & Noyes LLC

LOCATIONS

HQ: Salisbury Bancorp, Inc.
5 Bissell Street, Lakeville, CT 06039
Phone: 860 435-9801
Web: www.salisburybank.com

COMPETITORS

Berkshire Hills	M&T Bank
Bancorp	TD Bank USA
KeyCorp	Webster Financial

HISTORICAL FINANCIALS

Company Type: Public

Income Statement   FYE: December 31

	ASSETS ($ mil.)	NET INCOME ($ mil.)	INCOME AS % OF ASSETS	EMPLOYEES
12/17	986.9	6.2	0.6%	194
12/16	935.3	6.6	0.7%	187
12/15	891.1	8.4	0.9%	188
12/14	855.4	2.5	0.3%	182
12/13	587.1	4.0	0.7%	147
Annual Growth	13.9%	11.3%	—	7.2%

2017 Year-End Financials

Return on assets: 0.6%	Dividends
Return on equity: 6.5%	Yield: 0.0%
Long-term debt ($ mil.): —	Payout: 50.0%
No. of shares (mil.): 2.7	Market value ($ mil.): 124.0
Sales ($ mil): 43.7	

	STOCK PRICE ($) FY Close	P/E High/Low	Earnings	PER SHARE ($) Dividends	Book Value
12/17	44.65	21 16	2.24	1.12	35.01
12/16	37.50	16 12	2.41	1.12	34.08
12/15	33.48	11 9	3.02	1.12	33.13
12/14	27.34	23 20	1.32	1.12	37.42
12/13	26.89	13 10	2.30	1.12	42.56
Annual Growth	13.5%	— —	(0.7%)	(0.0%)	(4.8%)

Sanchez Energy Corp.

The Sanchez family has been around South
Texas almost as long as the oil found in the Eagle
Ford Shale. Sanchez Energy is a spin off from
Sanchez Oil & Gas Corporation (SOG) a private
firm owned by the Sanchez family who trace their
family history back to the founding of Laredo in
1755. Sanchez Energy was formed in 2011 to take
over almost 39000 acres (about 60 sq. mi.) of land
in the oil-rich Eagle Ford Shale in South Texas. In
2013 it had 140000 net acres in the Eagle Ford
play and 40000 net acres in the Tuscaloosa Marine
Shale in Louisiana. It also has undeveloped
acreage in Montana. The company reported estimated proved reserves of in 21.2 million barrels of
oil equivalent in 2012.

Sales and Marketing
Three customers accounted for 97% of the company's revenues in 2012 (one for 66%).

Financial Performance
Sanchez Energy's revenue increased by 197%
in 2012 primarily due to the higher oil and natural
gas production and higher oil prices partially offset
by lower natural gas prices.

The company reported a net Loss of $16.2 mil-
lion (compared to net income of $2 million in
2011) due to increased operating costs.

Strategy
Supported by strong oil prices the company is
focused on developing oil shale plays in Texas and
Louisiana.

The company improved its liquidity with a $345
million midstream asset sale in 2015.

Mergers and Acquisitions
In 2017 Anadarko Petroleum agreed to sell its
South Texas oil-and-gas assets to Sanchez Energy
and Blackstone Group for $2.3 billion. The deal in-
cludes 155000 net acres located next to Sanchez
Energy's existing assets with 130 gross drilled but
uncompleted wells.

In 2013 the company acquired 43000 net acres
in the Eagle Ford Shale in South Texas from Hess
for $265 million. The assets Dimmit Frio LaSalle
and Zavala Counties included 50 gross wells producing 4500 barrels of oil equivalent per day. It
completed another Eagle Ford purchase the
Wycross acquisition for $230.1 million. That deal
added production of 2000 barrels of barrels of oil
equivalent per day.

Moving into a new area in 2013 the company
bought 40000 net undeveloped acres in the
Tuscaloosa Marine Shale.

Company Background
Sanchez Energy went public in 2011 with a
$203 million IPO.

Following the offering SOG subsidiary Sanchez
Energy Partners I (SEPI) transferred the acreage
assets to Sanchez Energy. SEP I began acquiring
leases in the Eagle Ford Shale area in 2008 the
same year Petrohawk Energy announced its discovery of the oil deposit. (Fortunately the Sanchez
businesses have a storied history with South Texas
and wasted no time buying land leases).

EXECUTIVES

CEO, Antonio R. (Tony) Sanchez, age 44, $650,000
total compensation
EVP and CFO, Howard J. Thill, age 60
SVP and COO, Christopher D. Heinson, age 35,
$250,000 total compensation
President, Eduardo A. Sanchez, age 38, $72,958 total
compensation
Vice President of Geoscience, William Satterfield
Chairman, A. R. (Tony) Sanchez, age 75
Auditors: KPMG LLP

LOCATIONS

HQ: Sanchez Energy Corp.
1000 Main Street, Suite 3000, Houston, TX 77002
Phone: 713 783-8000
Web: www.sanchezenergycorp.com

PRODUCTS/OPERATIONS

2015 sales

	% of total
Oil sales	65
Natural gas liquid sales	14
Natural gas sales	21
Total	100

COMPETITORS

Abraxas Petroleum	Comstock Resources
Alta Mesa Holdings	Freeport-McMoRan Oil &
Anadarko Petroleum	Gas LLC
Apache	Magnum Hunter
BP	Resources
Cabot Oil & Gas	Petrohawk Energy
Carrizo Oil & Gas	Repsol Oil & Gas
Chesapeake Energy	Rosetta Resources Inc.
Clayton Williams	SM Energy
Energy	Swift Energy

HISTORICAL FINANCIALS

Company Type: Public

Income Statement   FYE: December 31

	REVENUE ($ mil.)	NET INCOME ($ mil.)	NET PROFIT MARGIN	EMPLOYEES
12/17	740.3	43.1	5.8%	0
12/16	431.3	(256.9)	—	0
12/15	475.7	(1,454.6)	—	0
12/14	666.0	(21.7)	—	0
12/13	314.4	26.9	8.6%	0
Annual Growth	23.9%	12.6%		

2017 Year-End Financials

Debt ratio: 79.1%	No. of shares (mil.): 83.9
Return on equity: ***.***.*%	Dividends
Cash ($ mil.): 184.4	Yield: —
Current ratio: 0.76	Payout: —
Long-term debt ($ mil.): 1,930.6	Market value ($ mil.): 446.0

	STOCK PRICE ($) FY Close	P/E High/Low	Earnings	PER SHARE ($) Dividends	Book Value
12/17	5.31	— —	(0.46)	0.00	(0.50)
12/16	9.03	— —	(4.63)	0.00	(10.52)
12/15	4.31	— —	(25.70)	0.00	(7.37)
12/14	9.29	— —	(1.06)	0.00	17.06
12/13	24.51	137 78	0.22	0.00	18.49
Annual Growth	(31.8%)	— —			

Santa Cruz County Bank (CA)

Auditors: Crowe Horwath LLP

LOCATIONS

HQ: Santa Cruz County Bank (CA)
740 Front Street Ste 220, Santa Cruz, CA 95060
Phone: 831 457-5000
Web: www.sccountybank.com

HISTORICAL FINANCIALS

Company Type: Public

Income Statement — FYE: December 31

	ASSETS ($ mil.)	NET INCOME ($ mil.)	INCOME AS % OF ASSETS	EMPLOYEES
12/17	629.9	6.7	1.1%	0
12/16	588.2	6.4	1.1%	0
12/15	513.3	5.4	1.1%	0
12/14	459.7	4.3	1.0%	0
12/13	398.5	3.3	0.8%	0
Annual Growth	12.1%	19.5%	—	—

2017 Year-End Financials

Return on assets: 1.1%
Return on equity: 12.5%
Long-term debt ($ mil.): —
No. of shares (mil.): 2.4
Sales ($ mil): 29.6
Dividends
Yield: 0.0%
Payout: 6.7%
Market value ($ mil.): 119.0

	STOCK PRICE ($) FY Close	P/E High/Low		PER SHARE ($) Earnings	Dividends	Book Value
12/17	48.95	18	14	2.76	0.19	23.64
12/16	39.50	15	10	2.67	0.18	21.05
12/15	28.60	13	9	2.26	0.18	18.52
12/14	21.42	12	9	1.84	0.18	16.40
12/13	17.75	13	9	1.47	0.14	14.91
Annual Growth	28.9%	—	—	17.0%	8.1%	12.2%

Seacoast Banking Corp. of Florida

Seacoast Banking Corporation is the holding company for Seacoast National Bank. It operates some 50 branches in Florida with a concentration in four large city markets. Serving individuals and businesses the bank offers a range of financial products and services including deposit accounts credit cards trust services and private banking. Commercial and residential real estate loans make up most of the bank's lending activities; to a lesser extent it also originates business and consumer loans.

Operations

Seacoast Bank offers traditional banking products such as deposit accounts checking & savings accounts CDs business loans home mortgages and the like. It also makes available to its customers brokerage and annuity services along with insur-ance products. A division of the bank Seacoast Marine Finance specializes in boat loans which it typically originates itself and then sells into the secondary market.

Geographic Reach

Seacoast National Bank has some 50 branches in 14 counties across Florida stretching from Broward County north through the Treasure Coast and into Orlando and west to Okeechobee and surrounding counties. Its primary markets are Tampa Orlando Port St. Lucie and West Palm Beach/Ft. Lauderdale.

Financial Performance

Seacoast Banking Corporation has done well in recent years steadily growing interest income to nearly $200 million in 2017 up from a low of $70 million just four years prior. The bank registered positive earnings from 2013 forward albeit the results fluctuated wildly.

In 2017 interest income grew 30% to $192 million and non-interest income improved by 25% to $170 million. Its loan portfolio grew ? through organic means as well as via acquisitions ? by almost 30% against which it earned additional interest income. The bank?s average net interest margin rose 10 basis points to 3.73%.

Net income also lodged an excellent year increasing 48% from the prior year to $43 million. Although the company incurred an $8.6 million impairment of its deferred tax assets due to the change in US Federal tax law the increase in revenue along with a $15 million gain on the sale an investment it made in Visa company stock pushed up yearly earnings.

Cash at the end of the year was $109 million unchanged from 2016. Financing activities contributed $196 million mostly from an increase in deposits from acquisitions. Investing activities used $246 million in the process of buying and selling securities and originating new loans. Operating activities added $49 million.

Strategy

Seacoast Bank has grown mostly through acquisitions in recent years. Since 2014 it opened one new office and acquired 49 branches (19 of which were subsequently shuttered). Orlando has been a hot destination for it as it transformed its presence there just a few branches to the largest Florida-based bank in the market by 2017. The bank anticipates continued geographic growth in Florida through organic means but also through acquisition if the right opportunity arises as with the 2017 purchases of NorthStar Banking and Palm Beach Community Bank.

Although it caters to personal customers as well as business clients the focus on businesses has sparked significant growth in the associated loan portfolio. The company tends to commercial clients with revenues exceeding $5 million in specific industry verticals. It takes a comprehensive relationship approach by providing business treasury lending and wealth management services. The commercial loan portfolio grew nearly 300% between year-end 2013 and year-end 2017 from $632 million to $2.5 billion.

The bank significantly expanded its banking technology platform by introducing digital deposit capture on smartphones updating its mobile platforms for consumer and business customers and enhancing its ATM capabilities. Customers have taken to the online functionality and in 2017 the bank processed more digital transactions than it did through its physical branch network.

Mergers and Acquisitions

In 2017 Seacoast purchased NorthStar Banking Corporation adding more than $200 million in assets $170 million in deposits and nearly $140 million in loans to Seacoast?s balance sheet. In the same year it acquired Palm Beach Community Bank for some $70 million adding $270 million in loans and four bank branches to Seacoast?s operations.

EXECUTIVES

Chairman and CEO, Dennis S. (Denny) Hudson, age 62, $537,852 total compensation
EVP and Residential Lending Executive, Michael J. (Mike) Sonego
EVP and Commercial Banking Executive, Charles K. Cross, age 60, $273,333 total compensation
EVP and Chief Risk and Credit Officer, David D. Houdeshell, age 57, $262,500 total compensation
EVP Enterprise Services and Initiatives, Kathleen (Kathy) Cavicchioli
EVP and Chief Marketing Officer, Jeffery (Jeff) Lee
EVP Service and Operations, Jeffery (Jeff) Bray
EVP and Chief Human Resources Officer, Daniel G. (Dan) Chappell
CFO and Head of Strategy, Charles M. (Chuck) Shaffer, age 44, $248,333 total compensation
EVP Community Banking, Julie Kleffel
Vice President Cre, Debra Mairs
Assistant Vice President Relationship Manager, Frances Portalatin
Executive Vice President Chief Human Resources Officer, Dan Chappell
Executive Vice President, William Hahl
Vice President Financial Advisor, Carl Newton
Vice President Data Warehouse Manager, Mark Blanchette
Executive Vice President Wealth Management and The Private Bank at Seacoast, Tom Hall
Senior Vice President Risk Officer, Peter Lowery
Senior Vice President Residential Lending Production Manager, REINA RAMOS
AVP Banking Center Manager, Amber Shirk
Senior Vice President, Tom Popieski
Vice President, Travis Engebretsen
Vice President Business Banker, Stephen Markham
Vice President Relationship Manager III and Lending Officer, Cathy Roberts
Vice President Collections and Recovery Manager, Gary Albert
VICE PRESIDENT AND MARKET MANAGER, Lee Jeff
Board Member, Maryann Goebel
Board Member, Herbert Lurie
Board Member, Tim Huval
Auditors: Crowe Horwath LLP

LOCATIONS

HQ: Seacoast Banking Corp. of Florida
815 Colorado Avenue, Stuart, FL 34994
Phone: 772 287-4000
Web: www.seacoastbanking.com

PRODUCTS/OPERATIONS

Selected Services
Commercial and retail banking
Mortgage services
Wealth management

COMPETITORS

BB&T
BBX Capital
Bank of America
PNC Financial
Regions Financial
SunTrust

BankUnited
CenterState Banks
EverBank Financial

Suncoast Schools FCU
Wells Fargo

HISTORICAL FINANCIALS
Company Type: Public

Income Statement
FYE: December 31

	ASSETS ($ mil.)	NET INCOME ($ mil.)	INCOME AS % OF ASSETS	EMPLOYEES
12/17	5,810.1	42.8	0.7%	805
12/16	4,680.9	29.2	0.6%	725
12/15	3,534.7	22.1	0.6%	665
12/14	3,093.3	5.7	0.2%	579
12/13	2,268.9	51.9	2.3%	519
Annual Growth 26.5%		(4.7%)	—	11.6%

2017 Year-End Financials

Return on assets: 0.8%
Return on equity: 7.6%
Long-term debt ($ mil.): —
No. of shares (mil.): 46.9
Sales ($ mil): 250.0

Dividends
Yield: —
Payout: —
Market value ($ mil.): 1,183.0

	STOCK PRICE ($) FY Close	P/E High/Low		PER SHARE ($) Earnings	Dividends	Book Value
12/17	25.21	26	21	0.99	0.00	14.70
12/16	22.06	29	17	0.78	0.00	11.45
12/15	14.98	25	18	0.66	0.00	10.29
12/14	13.75	68	48	0.21	0.00	9.44
12/13	12.20	5	1	2.44	0.00	8.40
Annual Growth 19.9%		—	—	(20.2%)	—	15.0%

Senior Housing Properties Trust

Senior Housing Properties Trust (SHPT) offers those in their golden years a place to rest their weary bones. The real estate investment trust (REIT) owns some 375 health care-related properties in about 40 states and Washington DC. Its portfolio includes senior apartments independent and assisted living facilities nursing homes medical office buildings biotechnology laboratories rehabilitation hospitals and gymnasiums. Tenants such as Sunrise Senior Living and Brookdale Senior Living sign triple-net leases which require them not only to pay rent but to also pay operating expenses remove hazardous waste and carry insurance on their properties.

Operations
The REIT's portfolio includes some 265 senior living communities 100 medical office buildings and 10 wellness centers. Its holdings are valued at about $5.3 billion. SHPT is managed by Reit Management & Research LLC (RMR) a real estate management company founded in 1986 to manage public investments in real estate.

Geographic Reach
Massachusetts-based Senior Housing Properties Trust (SHPT) owns properties in 40 states and the District of Columbia. Major markets include Florida California and Texas although the REIT's property portfolio is geographically diverse.

Financial Performance
The health care REIT reported revenue of $761.4 million in 2013 an increase of 18% versus 2012. Net income rose 11% over the same period to $151.2 million. Driving the increase was the firm's managed senior living communities business which benefited from the acquisition of 12 communities since 2012. The REIT's medical office buildings (MOB) segment posted a gain due to increased rental income from 18 MOBs acquired partially offset by the sale of one MOB in 2012.

Cash generated from operations increased to $306.7 million in 2013 from $283.3 million in 2012 primarily due to a gain on the sale of a single senior living community and two rehabilitation hospitals over the course of the year.

Strategy
SHPT's business strategy is primarily focused on acquiring upscale senior living properties where the majority of residents pay rent through their own resources rather than through government programs. More recently the firm has diversified by purchasing medical office buildings (MOB). Indeed five years ago MOBs contributed just 5% of revenue with senior living communities contributing about 90%. In 2013 senior living accounted for about 70% of total revenue with MOBs contributing more than 25%. The REIT is continuing to grow its MOB holdings. SHPT's investment goals include acquiring additional properties for income and to a lesser extent their appreciation potential. The REIT is counting on the aging of the US population to increase demand for existing independent and assisted living communities nursing homes MOBs and other health care-related properties.

Mergers and Acquisitions
In May 2014 SHPT acquired the headquarters building of Vertex Pharmaceuticals in Boston for $1.1 billion. The purchase fit with the REIT's strategy of focusing on medical office buildings and private-pay (as opposed to government reimbursed) properties.

Company Background
SHPT was spun off from HRPT Properties Trust in 1999 when that REIT sold off its health facilities in order to focus on office and industrial properties.

EXECUTIVES

President and COO, David J. Hegarty, age 62, $203,490 total compensation
CFO and Treasurer, Richard W. Siede
Managing Trustee, Barry M. Portnoy, age 73
Managing Trustee, Adam D. Portnoy, age 48
Auditors: Ernst & Young LLP

LOCATIONS

HQ: Senior Housing Properties Trust
Two Newton Place, 255 Washington Street, Suite 300, Newton, MA 02458-1634
Phone: 617 796-8350   Fax: 617 796-8349
Web: www.snhreit.com

PRODUCTS/OPERATIONS

2015 Sales

	$ mil.	% of total
Managed Senior Living Communities	367.9	37
MOB's	356.6	36
Triple Net Senior Living Communities	256.0	25
All Other Operations	18.3	2
Total	**998.8**	**100**

2015 Sales

	$ mil.	% of total
Rental income	630.9	63
Residents fees and services	367.9	37
Total	**998.8**	**100**

COMPETITORS

Chartwell Seniors Housing
Extendicare
G & K Industries
HCP
Healthcare Realty Trust
LTC Properties

Legacy Healthcare
National Health Investors
Omega Healthcare Investors
Sabra Health Care
Ventas
Welltower

HISTORICAL FINANCIALS
Company Type: Public

Income Statement
FYE: December 31

	REVENUE ($ mil.)	NET INCOME ($ mil.)	NET PROFIT MARGIN	EMPLOYEES
12/17	1,074.8	147.6	13.7%	0
12/16	1,058.0	141.3	13.4%	0
12/15	998.7	123.9	12.4%	0
12/14	844.8	158.6	18.8%	0
12/13	761.4	151.1	19.9%	0
Annual Growth 9.0%		(0.6%)		

2017 Year-End Financials

Debt ratio: 50.3%
Return on equity: 4.6%
Cash ($ mil.): 31.2
Current ratio: 0.56
Long-term debt ($ mil.): 3,674.5

No. of shares (mil.): 237.6
Dividends
Yield: 0.0%
Payout: 251.6%
Market value ($ mil.): 4,551.0

	STOCK PRICE ($) FY Close	P/E High/Low		PER SHARE ($) Earnings	Dividends	Book Value
12/17	19.15	36	30	0.62	1.56	13.07
12/16	18.93	40	23	0.60	1.56	13.47
12/15	14.84	45	26	0.53	1.56	14.15
12/14	22.11	31	26	0.80	1.56	14.48
12/13	22.23	37	27	0.81	1.56	14.76
Annual Growth (3.7%)		—	—	(6.5%)	(0.0%)	(3.0%)

ServisFirst Bancshares Inc

ServisFirst Bancshares is a bank holding company for ServisFirst Bank a regional commercial bank with about a dozen branches located in Alabama and the Florida panhandle. The bank also has a loan office in Nashville. ServisFirst Bank targets privately-held businesses with $2 million to $250 million in annual sales as well as professionals and affluent customers. The bank focuses on traditional commercial banking services including loan origination deposits and electronic banking services such as online and mobile banking. Founded in 2005 by its chairman and CEO Thomas Broughton III the bank went public in 2014 with an offering valued at nearly $57 million.

IPO

ServisFirst Bancshares sold 625000 shares priced at $91 per share. Proceeds from the May 2014 IPO will be used to support the bank's growth plans both in Alabama and in other states.

Geographic Reach

Birmingham-based ServisFirst Bank has branches in Birmingham Huntsville Montgomery Mobile Dothan Pensacola and Nashville.

Financial Performance

The bank reported net income of $41.2 million in 2013 compared with $34 million in 2012. The increase was primarily due to an increase in net interest income which rose nearly 20% to $112.5 million. Noninterest income increased 4% to $10 million in 2013.

As of March 2014 the bank had total assets of approximately $3.6 billion total loans of $2.9 billion and total deposits of about $3.0 billion.

EXECUTIVES

President and CEO ServisFirst Bancshares and ServisFirst Bank, Thomas A. (Tom) Broughton, age 62, $350,000 total compensation

EVP and COO ServisFirst Bancshares and ServisFirst Bank, Clarence C. Pouncey, age 61, $263,000 total compensation

EVP CFO Treasurer and Secretary ServisFirst Bancshares and ServisFirst Bank, William M. Foshee, age 63, $230,000 total compensation

EVP ServisFirst Bancshares and President and CEO ServisFirst Bank of Huntsville, Andrew N. (Andy) Kattos, age 48

President and CEO ServisFirst Bank of Mobile, William (Bibb) Lamar, age 74

EVP ServisFirst Bancshares and President and CEO ServisFirst Bank of Montgomery, G. Carlton (Carl) Barker, age 63

EVP ServisFirst Bancshares and President and CEO ServisFirst Bank of Pensacola, Rex D. McKinney, age 55

EVP Correspondent Banking ServisFirst Bancshares and ServisFirst Bank, Rodney E. Rushing, age 60, $245,000 total compensation

SVP and Chief Credit Officer ServisFirst Bancshares and ServisFirst Bank, Don G. Owens, age 66, $187,200 total compensation

President and CEO ServisFirst Bank of Atlanta, Ken Barber

EVP and Chief Lending Officer, Doug Rehm

CEO ServisFirst Bank Dothan, B. Harrison Morris, age 41

Assistant Vice President of Private Banking of ServisFirst Bank, Ron Morrison

First Vice President, Lee McKinnon

Senior Vice President Commercial Lending, Chad Thomason

Vice President Commercial Banking, Jamie Osteen

Vice President, John Peacock

Senior Vice President, Michael Wood

Senior Vice President, Justin Fontenot

Vice President, Kiley Elmore

SENIOR VICE PRESIDENT PRIVATE BANKING, Patricia Griner

Vice President, Chris Blaze

Vice President Portfolio Manager, Gary Allen

FVP Commercial Banking, Cheryl Dunn

Assistant Vice President Branch Manager, Ron Leddon

SENIOR VICE PRESIDENT, Samantha S Curd

VICE PRESIDENT CREDIT OFFICER, Stacy B Suddeth

ASSISTANT VICE PRESIDENT CASH MANAGEMENT SERVICES, Loretta Shapiro

VICE PRESIDENT CREDIT OFFICER, Stacy Suddeth

Chairman ServisFirst Bancshares and ServisFirst Bank, Stanley M. (Skip) Brock, age 67

Auditors: Dixon Hughes Goodman LLP

LOCATIONS

HQ: ServisFirst Bancshares Inc
2500 Woodcrest Place, Birmingham, AL 35209
Phone: 205 949-0302
Web: www.servisfirstbank.com

COMPETITORS

Bank of America   Wells Fargo
Bank of the Ozarks

HISTORICAL FINANCIALS

Company Type: Public

Income Statement

FYE: December 31

	ASSETS ($ mil.)	NET INCOME ($ mil.)	INCOME AS % OF ASSETS	EMPLOYEES
12/17	7,082.3	93.0	1.3%	434
12/16	6,370.4	81.4	1.3%	420
12/15	5,095.5	63.5	1.2%	371
12/14	4,098.6	52.3	1.3%	298
12/13	3,520.7	41.6	1.2%	262
Annual Growth	19.1%	22.3%	—	13.4%

2017 Year-End Financials

Return on assets: 1.3%
Return on equity: 16.4%
Long-term debt ($ mil.): —
No. of shares (mil.): 52.9
Sales ($ mil): 281.8
Dividends
Yield: 0.0%
Payout: 11.6%
Market value ($ mil.): 2,199.0

	STOCK PRICE ($) FY Close	P/E High/Low	PER SHARE ($) Earnings	Dividends	Book Value
12/17	41.50	25 19	1.72	0.20	11.46
12/16	37.44	48 23	1.52	0.19	9.93
12/15	47.53	40 24	1.20	0.12	8.64
12/14	32.95	83 26	1.05	0.16	8.20
Annual Growth	8.0%	— —	18.1%	8.1%	11.8%

Shell Midstream Partners LP

Auditors: Ernst & Young LLP

LOCATIONS

HQ: Shell Midstream Partners LP
150 N. Dairy Ashford, Houston, TX 77079
Phone: 832 337-2034
Web: www.shellmidstreampartners.com

HISTORICAL FINANCIALS

Company Type: Public

Income Statement

FYE: December 31

	REVENUE ($ mil.)	NET INCOME ($ mil.)	NET PROFIT MARGIN	EMPLOYEES
12/17	470.1	295.3	62.8%	0
12/16	291.3	244.9	84.1%	0
12/15	326.5	167.1	51.2%	0
12/14	182.4	13.4	7.3%	0
12/13	91.6	36.5	39.8%	0
Annual Growth	50.5%	68.7%	—	—

2017 Year-End Financials

Debt ratio: 136.7%
Return on equity: —
Cash ($ mil.): 137.7
Current ratio: 3.71
Long-term debt ($ mil.): 1,868.3
No. of shares (mil.): 191.6
Dividends
Yield: 0.0%
Payout: 92.9%
Market value ($ mil.): 5,714.0

	STOCK PRICE ($) FY Close	P/E High/Low	PER SHARE ($) Earnings	Dividends	Book Value
12/17	29.82	27 20	1.28	1.19	(3.07)
12/16	29.09	32 20	1.32	0.97	0.54
12/15	41.52	42 22	1.16	0.67	0.64
12/14	40.98	395320	0.10	0.00	3.03
Annual Growth	(10.1%)	—	—133.9%	—	—

Shenandoah Telecommunications Co

If Virginia is for lovers Shenandoah Telecommunications must carry some interesting conversations. Through subsidiaries the company (which does business as Shentel) provides telecom services in the Shenandoah Valley and beyond. Shenandoah Telephone has more than 20500 access lines in service. As a Sprint affiliate subsidiary Shenandoah Personal Communications offers wireless services to more than 262000 customers. The company's cable TV unit serves about 115000 customers while about 13000 households subscribe to its dial-up and broadband Internet access.

Operations

Recognizing that the market for wireline service is shrinking from the rise of mobile phones as a primary phone and VoIP technology Shentel is now primarily a wireless provider. Some 56% of sales come from its being a Sprint affiliate. (It also offers prepaid wireless service from Sprint subsidiaries Virgin Mobile and Boost.) Cable services account for about 26% of sales and its wireline service (which includes Internet service) makes up the remaining 18%.

Geographic Reach

Shentel's wireless segment provides digital wireless service to a portion of a four-state area covering the region from Harrisburg York and Altoona Pennsylvania to Harrisonburg Virginia. Its wireline cable and Internet services are offered throughout Shenandoah County and portions of northwestern Augusta County Virginia.

Financial Performance

Overall sales grew 5% in 2015 to $342.5 million from 2014 due to increases prepaid subscribers and a higher average revenue per subscriber from a richer product mix. all segments grew in 2015 with the cable operation increasing 15%.

The rise in revenue fueled a 21% increase in profit to $40.8 million in 2015. Cash from operations was $120 million in 2015 compared to $115 million in 2014.

Strategy

In order to focus on its core communications offerings in 2013 the company sold off its Shentel Converged Services business that provided local and long distance voice video and Internet services to off-campus college student housing throughout the southeastern United States.

Mergers and Acquisitions

Shenandoah is buying NTELOS Holdings Corp. for some $208 million. The deal was agreed to in 2015 and was to be finalized in 2016. Shenandoah acquired the NTELOS' wireless network assets retail stores and nearly 300000 retail subscribers in the nTELOS western markets. Shentel will complete plans to close down nTELOS' Eastern markets. The acquisition doubles Shentel's wireless customer base expands its footprint in the Mid-Atlantic region and strengthens its partnership with Sprint.

In 2016 Shentel acquired Colane Cable a video Internet and home phone-service provider in West Virginia for $2.4 million. Colane's operations are adjacent to areas served by Shentel.

EXECUTIVES

SVP Wireless, William L. (Willy) Pirtle, age 59, $262,787 total compensation

Chairman President and CEO, Christopher E. (Chris) French, age 60, $559,602 total compensation

EVP and COO, Earle A. MacKenzie, age 66, $370,565 total compensation

VP Finance CFO and Treasurer, Adele M. Skolits, age 59, $292,977 total compensation

Director Information Technology, Richard A. Baughman, age 50

VP Wireline and Engineering, Edward H. McKay, age 45

SVP Cable, Thomas A. (Tom) Whitaker, age 57, $217,308 total compensation

Board Member, Dale S Lam

Auditors: KPMG LLP

LOCATIONS

HQ: Shenandoah Telecommunications Co
500 Shentel Way, Edinburg, VA 22824
Phone: 540 984-4141
Web: www.shentel.com

PRODUCTS/OPERATIONS

2015 Sales

	$ mil.	% of total
Wireless	208.8	56
Cable	97.6	26
Wireline	67.4	18
Adjustments	(31.4)	-
Total	**342.5**	**100**

Selected Services

Business telephone products
Cable TV
Cellular products and services
Centrex
Fiber-optic capacity
Internet access
ISDN
Local telephone access
Long-distance
Paging
Security systems

COMPETITORS

AT&T	Suddenlink
Aquis Communications Group	Communications
	T-Mobile USA

Comcast	Time Warner Cable
DISH Network	U.S. Cellular
EarthLink	Verizon
Lumos	Verizon Wireless Inc.

HISTORICAL FINANCIALS

Company Type: Public

Income Statement — FYE: December 31

	REVENUE ($ mil.)	NET INCOME ($ mil.)	NET PROFIT MARGIN	EMPLOYEES
12/17	611.9	66.3	10.8%	1,066
12/16	535.2	(0.9)	—	1,236
12/15	342.4	40.8	11.9%	730
12/14	326.9	33.8	10.4%	708
12/13	308.9	29.5	9.6%	682
Annual Growth	**18.6%**	**22.4%**	**—**	**11.8%**

2017 Year-End Financials

Debt ratio: 58.2%
Return on equity: 20.5%
Cash ($ mil.): 78.5
Current ratio: 1.26
Long-term debt ($ mil.): 757.5
No. of shares (mil.): 49.3
Dividends
Yield: 0.0%
Payout: 19.5%
Market value ($ mil.): 1,667.0

	STOCK PRICE ($) FY Close	P/E High/Low	Earnings	PER SHARE ($) Dividends	Book Value
12/17	33.80	30 19	1.33	0.26	7.10
12/16	27.30	— —	(0.02)	0.25	6.05
12/15	43.05	60 33	0.83	0.24	5.98
12/14	31.25	47 33	0.70	0.24	5.35
12/13	25.67	47 22	0.62	0.18	4.87
Annual Growth	**7.1%**	**— —**	**21.3%**	**9.6%**	**9.9%**

Shutterfly Inc

Whether or not you are the consummate shutterbug you can rely on Shutterfly for digital prints. An e-commerce company specializing in digital photo products and services for the consumer and professional photography markets the company offers customers the ability to upload share store and edit digital photos through its website. In addition to traditional 4-inch by 6-inch prints Shutterfly provides prints ranging from wallet-sized to jumbo enlargements. The company also offers personalized items including mugs photo books and calendars through its personalized products and services business segment. In 2012 Shutterfly acquired Kodak Imaging Network (doing business as KODAK Gallery).

EXECUTIVES

SVP and CFO, Michael W. (Mike) Pope, age 52, $75,551 total compensation

SVP and General Manager Consumer Businesses, Karl Wiley

President and CEO, Christopher (Chris) North

SVP and Chief Marketing Officer, John Boris

SVP and CTO, Satish Menon

SVP Operations, Dwayne Black, $318,667 total compensation

President Shutterfly Enterprise, Scott Arnold

Svp And Chief Human Resources Officer, Gautam Srivastava

Vice President And General Counsel, Jason Sebring

Chairman, William J. (Will) Lansing, age 59

Board Of Directors, Tayloe Stansbury

Auditors: PricewaterhouseCoopers LLP

LOCATIONS

HQ: Shutterfly Inc
2800 Bridge Parkway, Redwood City, CA 94065
Phone: 650 610-5200
Web: www.shutterflyinc.com

PRODUCTS/OPERATIONS

Selected Products and Services

Online Services
  Edit and enhance
  Organize
  Print
  Share
  Upload
Photo-Based Products
  Greeting cards
  Personalized calendars
  Photo books
  Stationery

COMPETITORS

123Greetings	Google
AG Interactive	LifePics
Adobe Systems	Rite Aid
CVS	Snapfish
Cimpress	Wal-Mart
Costco Wholesale	Walgreen
Facebook	Yahoo!

HISTORICAL FINANCIALS

Company Type: Public

Income Statement — FYE: December 31

	REVENUE ($ mil.)	NET INCOME ($ mil.)	NET PROFIT MARGIN	EMPLOYEES
12/17	1,190.2	30.0	2.5%	1,934
12/16	1,134.2	15.9	1.4%	2,084
12/15	1,059.4	(0.8)	—	2,016
12/14	921.5	(7.8)	—	1,812
12/13	783.6	9.2	1.2%	1,573
Annual Growth	**11.0%**	**34.2%**	**—**	**5.3%**

2017 Year-End Financials

Debt ratio: 46.1%
Return on equity: 5.4%
Cash ($ mil.): 489.8
Current ratio: 1.40
Long-term debt ($ mil.): 394.7
No. of shares (mil.): 32.3
Dividends
Yield: —
Payout: —
Market value ($ mil.): 1,607.0

	STOCK PRICE ($) FY Close	P/E High/Low	Earnings	PER SHARE ($) Dividends	Book Value
12/17	49.75	59 44	0.88	0.00	17.05
12/16	50.18	113 80	0.45	0.00	16.62
12/15	44.56	— —	(0.02)	0.00	17.43
12/14	41.70	— —	(0.20)	0.00	19.99
12/13	50.93	239 119	0.24	0.00	20.63
Annual Growth	**(0.6%)**	**— —**	**38.4%**	**—**	**(4.7%)**

Shutterstock Inc

Shutterstock brings the online marketplace mentality to the world of digital images illustrations and videos. Its 35000+ contributors have uploaded more than 19 millions bits of content perused by 550000 subscribers. The company's primary customers include marketing agencies media organizations and communications departments of businesses that subscribe to single downloads a set number of images or unlimited downloads for a month or a year; average cost per image is $3. Shutterstock's marketplace is available in 10 languages and 150 countries where its images are used for corporate communications websites ads and books and other published materials. Formed in 2007 the company went public in 2012.

IPO

The company plans to use its $76 million in IPO proceeds for general corporate purposes including possible acquisitions though nothing specific is in the works. Shutterstock had initially valued its IPO at $115 million.

Financial Performance

Shutterstock has seen its revenue grow steadily doubling between 2009 and 2011. Not only has the company's library and number of downloads grown during that time its revenue per download has also increased from $1.80 to $2.05.

Strategy

Going forward Shutterstock's growth strategies include increased localization of content to meet specific ethnic and culture media requirements and pursuing new content types as they become available. It also intends to move from mostly word-of-mouth to focused marketing in order to improve its penetration of both the small-to-medium-size business segment (a majority of sales) and large agencies and enterprises.

EXECUTIVES

CFO, Steven Berns, age 53, $144,231 total compensation
Chairman and CEO, Jonathan (Jon) Oringer, age 44, $1 total compensation
Chief Product Officer, Catherine Ulrich, $324,423 total compensation
CEO WebDAM, Jody Vandergriff
Vice President And General Counsel, Michael Lesser
Senior Vice President Technology, Dan McCormick
Vice President of Product, Nikki Kuritsky
Chief People Officer, Matthew Jagoda
Vice President Sales Operations and Development, Kate Pignata
Vice President Infrastructure and Data, Chris Coluzzi
Vice President, Anne Islan
Vice President Head Of Infrastructure, Rick Bohm
Board Member, Nina Fry
Auditors: PricewaterhouseCoopers LLP

LOCATIONS

HQ: Shutterstock Inc
350 Fifth Avenue, 21st Floor, New York, NY 10118
Phone: 646 710-3417
Web: www.shutterstock.com

COMPETITORS

AG Interactive	New York Times
Agence France-Presse	PR Newswire
Associated Press	Piksel
Cartoon Bank	Reuters
Corbis	Rex Features
Facebook	Sipa Press
Getty Images	The NewsMarket
Masterfile	Wazee Digital
National Geographic	Zuma Press

HISTORICAL FINANCIALS

Company Type: Public

Income Statement   FYE: December 31

	REVENUE ($ mil.)	NET INCOME ($ mil.)	NET PROFIT MARGIN	EMPLOYEES
12/17	557.1	16.7	3.0%	1,130
12/16	494.3	32.6	6.6%	858
12/15	425.1	19.5	4.6%	621
12/14	327.9	22.0	6.7%	512
12/13	235.5	26.4	11.2%	345
Annual Growth	**24.0%**	**(10.8%)**	**—**	**34.5%**

2017 Year-End Financials

Debt ratio: —
Return on equity: 5.5%
Cash ($ mil.): 253.4
Current ratio: 1.39
Long-term debt ($ mil.): —

No. of shares (mil.): 34.7
Dividends
Yield: —
Payout: —
Market value ($ mil.): 1,494.0

	STOCK PRICE ($) FY Close	P/E High/Low		PER SHARE ($) Earnings	Dividends	Book Value
12/17	43.03	114	66	0.47	0.00	9.06
12/16	47.52	70	28	0.91	0.00	8.23
12/15	32.34	137	52	0.54	0.00	8.09
12/14	69.10	163	99	0.61	0.00	7.06
12/13	83.63	109	31	0.77	0.00	5.21
Annual Growth	**(15.3%)**	**—**	**—**	**(11.6%)**	**—**	**14.9%**

Sierra Bancorp

Sierra Bancorp is the holding company for the nearly $2 billion-asset Bank of the Sierra which operates approximately 30 branches in Central California's San Joaquin Valley between (and including) Bakersfield and Fresno. The bank offers traditional deposit products and loans to individuals and small and mid-size businesses. About 70% of its loan portfolio is made up of real estate loans while another 15% is made up of mortgage warehouse loans and a further 10% is tied to commercial and industrial loans (including SBA loans and direct finance leases). The bank also issues agricultural loans and consumer loans.

Operations

Bank of the Sierra makes almost 80% of its revenue from interest income. About 64% of its total revenue came from interest income on loans and leases (including fees) during 2015 while another 14% came from interest income on taxed and tax-exempt securities. The rest of its revenue came from deposit account service charges (12% of revenue) checkcard fees (5%) and other non-interest income sources.

Geographic Reach

The Porterville California-based bank operates branches and offices mostly in the San Joaquin Valley in Porterville Arroyo Grande Atascadero Bakersfield California City Clovis Delano Dinuba Exeter Farmersville Fillmore Fresno Hanford Lindsay Oxnard Paso Robles Reedley San Luis Obispo Santa Clarita Santa Paula Selma Tehachapi Three Rivers Visalia and Tulare.

Sales and Marketing

Bank of the Sierra has been gradually increasing its advertising spend in recent years. It spent $2.3

million on advertising and promotion in 2015 up from $2.2 million and $1.9 million in 2014 and 2013 respectively.

Financial Performance

The bank's revenue has been steadily rising over the past few years mostly as bank acquisitions and organic loan business growth has spurred higher interest income. Meanwhile its profits have more than doubled since 2011 thanks to declining loan loss provisions as its loan portfolio's credit quality has improved with higher property valuations in the strengthened economy.

Sierra Bancorp's revenue jumped 13% to $80.4 million during 2015 thanks to higher interest income from continued double-digit loan asset growth led by a jump in mortgage warehouse lines from increased line utilization a first-quarter purchase of residential mortgage loans and strong organic growth in non-farm real estate and agricultural production loans. Deposit account service fees also grew thanks to organic deposit client growth.

Strong revenue growth and lower acquisition costs in 2015 drove the bank's net income up 19% to $18 million. Sierra's operating cash levels rose 4% to $29.78 million during the year as its cash-based earnings increased.

Strategy

While the Bank of Sierra has traditionally grown organically by opening around one new branch per year in the Central Valley it has more recently acquired small area banks and individual branches to bolster its deposit and loan business while expanding into untapped markets such as further south into the Santa Clara Valley.

Mergers and Acquisitions

In July 2016 the bank bought $145 million-asset Coast Bancorp and its Coast National Bank branches in San Luis Obispo Paso Robles Arroyo Grande and Atascadero California.

In November 2014 Sierra Bancorp bought $129 million-asset Santa Clara Valley Bank N.A. and its branches in Santa Paula Santa Clarita and Fillmore in California for $15 million. the deal expanded Sierra's reach outside of its traditional market for the first time more south into the Santa Clara Valley of California.

EXECUTIVES

EVP and CFO, Kenneth R. (Ken) Taylor, age 58, $242,500 total compensation
EVP and Chief Credit Officer, James F. (Jim) Gardunio, age 67, $197,600 total compensation
President and CEO, Kevin J. McPhaill, age 45, $185,000 total compensation
Senior Vice President Director of Marketing, Matthew Hessler
Assistant Vice President Senior Credit Analyst, Karen S Nishimura
Vice President Commercial Lending, Kiersten Alfieri
Assistant Vice President Operations Manager, Karlee Ramirez
Chairman, Morris A. Tharp, age 78
Auditors: Vavrinek, Trine, Day & Co., LLP

LOCATIONS

HQ: Sierra Bancorp
86 North Main Street, Porterville, CA 93257
Phone: 559 782-4900
Web: www.bankofthesierra.com

COMPETITORS

Bank of America	MUFG Americas Holdings
Bank of the West	United Security
Central Valley	Bancshares
Community Bancorp	Wells Fargo
Citibank	Westamerica
Comerica	Zions Bancorporation
JPMorgan Chase	

HISTORICAL FINANCIALS

Company Type: Public

Income Statement

FYE: December 31

	ASSETS ($ mil.)	NET INCOME ($ mil.)	INCOME AS % OF ASSETS	EMPLOYEES
12/17	2,340.3	19.5	0.8%	576
12/16	2,032.8	17.5	0.9%	497
12/15	1,796.5	18.0	1.0%	431
12/14	1,637.3	15.2	0.9%	437
12/13	1,410.2	13.3	0.9%	406
Annual Growth	13.5%	10.0%	—	9.1%

2017 Year-End Financials

Return on assets: 0.8%
Return on equity: 8.4%
Long-term debt ($ mil.): —
No. of shares (mil.): 15.2
Sales ($ mil): 102.7

Dividends
Yield: 0.0%
Payout: 41.1%
Market value ($ mil.): 404.0

	STOCK PRICE ($) FY Close	P/E High/Low	PER SHARE ($) Earnings	Dividends	Book Value
12/17	26.56	21 17	1.36	0.56	16.81
12/16	26.59	20 12	1.29	0.48	14.94
12/15	17.65	14 11	1.33	0.42	14.36
12/14	17.56	16 14	1.08	0.34	13.67
12/13	16.09	21 12	0.94	0.26	12.78
Annual Growth	13.3%	— —	9.7%	21.1%	7.1%

Signature Bank (New York, NY)

Signature Bank marks the spot where some professional New Yorkers bank. The institution provides customized banking and financial services to smaller private businesses their owners and their top executives through 30 branches across the New York metropolitan area including all five boroughs Long Island and affluent Westchester County. The bank's lending activities mainly entail real estate and business loans. Subsidiary Signature Securities offers wealth management financial planning brokerage services asset management and insurance while its Signature Financial subsidiary offers equipment financing and leasing. Founded in 2001 the bank now boasts assets of roughly $29 billion.

Operations

Mortgage loans including commercial real estate loans multifamily residential mortgages home loans and lines of credit and construction and land loans comprise the bulk of Signature Bank's loan portfolio (and much of its asset base as well).

The bank which staffed some 1010 employees at the end of 2014 generated 68% of its revenue from interest on loans and leases that year while 20% came from interest on its securities available-for-sale and 7% came from securities held-to-maturity. The remainder of its revenue came from fees and service charges (2%) and various other miscellaneous sources.

Geographic Reach

The bank's nearly 30 branch offices are mostly in the New York metropolitan area which includes Manhattan Brooklyn Westchester Long Island Queens the Bronx Staten Island and Connecticut.

Sales and Marketing

Signature Bank mostly serves privately-owned businesses their owners and senior managers (typically with a net worth between $500000 and $20 million).

Financial Performance

The company's revenues and profits have risen in recent years thanks to strong organic loan business growth and declining loan loss provisions as its loan portfolio's credit quality has improved with higher property valuations in the strengthened economy.

Signature's revenue jumped by 22% to a record $959.3 million in 2014 mostly as loan interest (on commercial loans mortgages and leases) and security interest income continued to grow as the bank built up its interest-earning assets during the year.

Higher revenue and a continued decline and loan loss provisions in 2014 boosted the bank's net income by 30% to a record $296.7 million. Signature's operating cash levels more than doubled to $421 million on higher cash earnings.

Strategy

Signature Bank has long targeted privately-held businesses that have fewer than 1000 employees and revenues of less than $200 million. Some of its target clients include real estate owners/companies law firms accounting firms entertainment business managers medical professionals retail establishments money management firms and nonprofit foundations.

The bank continues to expand its service lines particularly focusing on specialty financing to grow its business organically. In 2015 it planned to offer direct commercial vehicle financing through a network of approved commercial vehicle dealerships in New York's Tri-State area with loans targeting small and mid-size business borrowers looking to acquire commercial vehicles and fleets. Also that year it formed its Maryland-based Signature Public Funding Corp subsidiary to provide municipal finance and tax-exempt lending and leasing products to local state and federal government agencies nationwide.

Company Background

The bank's emphasis on personal service helped it to grow its deposit base and loan portfolio in 2011. During a time when many other banks struggled under the weight of bad loans in a bad economy Signature Bank achieved record earnings for the fourth consecutive year.

Founded in 2001 as an alternative to megabanks Signature Bank was spun off from Bank Hapoalim in 2004.

EXECUTIVES

Executive Vice President and Chief Credit Officer, Michael Merlo
President CEO and Director, Joseph J. DePaolo, $577,500 total compensation
SVP and CFO, Vito Susca
President CEO and Director, Michael G. O'Rourke
EVP, Kevin P. Bastuga
EVP, Bryan D. Duncan
VP Retail Operations Manager, Ella Riordan-Pacheco
Vice President, Michael Nicolosi
Vice President, John C Spagnuolo
Group Director Senior Vice President, Joseph Alexander
Senior Vice President Group Director, Gary Shulevich
Senior Vice President And Group Director, Leon Kratsberg
Senior Vice President Group Director, Lucy Mazany
Vice President, Phyllis Rosenfeld
Senior Lender Vice President, Eugene Cartin
Group Director Senior Vice President, Tamara Gavrielof
Group Director Senior Vice President, David Artis
Vice President, John Ricchezza
Vice President Private Banking, Sue Frick
Senior Vice President Group Director, Nicole Rospond
Vice President, Richard Wang
Senior Vice President, Meyer Eichler
Senior Vice President, Kerry Mach
Executive Vice President, Joseph Fantauzzi
Senior Vice President Group Director, Brian Hallinan
Vice President Director of Operations, Richard Pelcher
Vice President Senior Lender; Commercial Real Estate, Jay Byrne
Vice President and Associate Group Director, Matthew Cohen
Senior Vice President, Joann Demartino
Senior Vice President and Group Director, Peter Marra
Vice President, Joseph Fingerman
Group Director Senior Vice President, Kevin Hardiman
Group Director Senior Vice President, Nikki Rospond
Group Director Senior Vice President, Lawrence Blascovich
Senior Vice President Group Director, Larry Goldberg
Group Director Senior Vice President, Michael Page
Vice President Commercial Banking, Ross Thomson
Senior Vice President Group Director, Salvatore Costa
Senior Vice President and Group Director, Roseann Manos
Vice President of Real Estate, Aaron Greene
Vice President, Howard Green
Vice President Section Manager Continuous Process Improvements, Angela Izzo
Senior Vice President Group Director, Tom Rogers
Group Director Senior Vice President, Jason Birnbaum
Senior Vice President Group Director, Brian Mazzotta
Senior Vice President Group Director, Sandy Sapperstein
SVP GROUP DIRECTOR, Joe Festa
Vice President, John Barfuss
Vice President, Henry Lee
VP Executive Sales Officer, Stephanie Paysse
SVP, Maria Hegi
Group Director Senior Vice President, Marie Moreno
Group Director Senior Vice President, Avi Azuolay
Vice President Capital Markets, Rob Campbell

Group Director Senior Vice President, Nellie Teplinsky
Senior Client Advisor Vice President, Cora Licht
Vice President Equipment Finance And Leasing, Michael Walsh
Group Director Senior Vice President, William Mooney
Chairman and Director, Leonard S. Caronia
Auditors: KPMG LLP

LOCATIONS

HQ: Signature Bank (New York, NY)
565 Fifth Avenue, New York, NY 10017
Phone: 646 822-1500
Web: www.signatureny.com

PRODUCTS/OPERATIONS

2014 Sales

	$ mil.	% of total
Interest		
Loans net	655.6	68
Securities available for sale	193.6	20
Securities held to maturity	69.8	7
Other	5.3	1
Noninterest		
Fees & service charges	19.3	2
Commissions	10.6	1
Net gains on sales of loans	5.4	1
Net gains on sales of securities	5.3	-
Other	2.2	-
Adjustments	(7.8)	-
Total	**959.3**	**100**

COMPETITORS

Apple Bank for Savings	Herald National Bank
Astoria Financial	JPMorgan Chase
Bank Leumi USA	New York Community
Capital One	Bancorp
Citigroup	Safra Bank
HSBC USA	TD Bank USA

HISTORICAL FINANCIALS

Company Type: Public

Income Statement

FYE: December 31

	ASSETS ($ mil.)	NET INCOME ($ mil.)	INCOME AS % OF ASSETS	EMPLOYEES
12/17	43,117.7	387.2	0.9%	1,305
12/16	39,047.6	396.3	1.0%	1,218
12/15	33,450.5	373.0	1.1%	1,122
12/14	27,318.6	296.7	1.1%	1,010
12/13	22,376.6	228.7	1.0%	945
Annual Growth	**17.8%**	**14.1%**	**—**	**8.4%**

2017 Year-End Financials

Return on assets: 0.9%
Return on equity: 10.1%
Long-term debt ($ mil.): —
No. of shares (mil.): 54.9
Sales ($ mil): 1,506.2

Dividends
Yield: —
Payout: —
Market value ($ mil.): 7,546.0

	STOCK PRICE ($) FY Close	P/E High/Low		PER SHARE ($) Earnings	Dividends	Book Value
12/17	137.26	23	17	7.12	0.00	73.33
12/16	150.20	21	15	7.37	0.00	66.15
12/15	153.37	22	16	7.27	0.00	56.81
12/14	125.96	22	17	5.95	0.00	49.61
12/13	107.42	22	15	4.76	0.00	38.06
Annual Growth	**6.3%**			**10.6%**	**—**	**17.8%**

Silicon Laboratories Inc

Silicon Laboratories makes little translation machines. The company develops mixed-signal integrated circuits (ICs) which translate real-world analog signals (such as sound) into digital signals that can be processed by electronic products. Silicon Labs provides ICs used in set-top boxes game consoles portable electronics industrial monitoring and control devices and wireless handsets. Products include microcontrollers clocks and oscillators sensors and broadcast communications chips. Top customers include Cisco Huawei LG Electronics Pace Samsung Technicolor Varian Medical Systems and ZTE. About 85% of the company's sales come from customers outside the US.

Geographic Reach

Chinese companies make that country the biggest customer of Silicon Labs supplying 44% of sales. The US is the next biggest market at 15%. Other notable country markets are Taiwan 9% and South Korea 2%. The company has operations in the US China France Germany Hungary India Ireland Japan South Korea Singapore Taiwan and the UK.

Sales and Marketing

The company markets its products through a direct sales force and network of independent sales representatives and distributors. Silicon Lab's two largest customers are Edom Technology (20% of sales) and Avnet (12%). In 2014 the firm reported advertising costs of 1.7 million compared with $2 million and $1.7 million in 2013 and 2012.

Financial Performance

Silicon Labs reported 2014 revenue of $621 million a company record and a 7% increase from 2013. Net income however dropped 24% over the same period. The revenue rise was driven by market share gains and additional product revenue from the acquisition of Energy Micro. Unit volumes of products increased 5% while average selling prices were stable compared with 2013. While China continued to be the biggest market for Silicon Labs devices sales to US customers grew 31% in 2014. On the other hand sales in South Korea dropped 40%.

On the bottom line higher costs for research and development (up 9%) and sales and marketing (up 18%) ate into the company's profit.

Cash flow from operations came in at $137 million at the end of 2014 compared to $120 million at the close of 2013.

Strategy

Silicon Labs is betting on the Internet of Things for its future. Chips and sensors that translate real-world data — temperature sound light and more — for collection in digital databases are in the company's wheelhouse. Already devices it makes for that market account for about half of its revenue. The company has been building with an eye on the IoT with a series of acquisitions that include Ember Energy Micro and Bluegiga. Of course a number of other IC makers are rushing to make IoT devices and Silicon Labs is sure to run into formidable competition.

Silicon Labs turns to its labs to develop new IoT products as well as those for other markets. The company typically spends around a quarter of its annual sales on research and development. The company primarily relies on Taiwan Semiconductor Manufacturing to produce its ICs.

Mergers and Acquisitions

In 2015 Silicon Labs acquired Bluegiga Technologies Oy a privately held provider of short-range wireless connectivity hardware and software for the Inetnet of Things (IoT). Bluegiga's wireless portfolio includes ultra-low-power Bluetooth Smart Bluetooth Classic and Wi-Fi modules as well as software stacks development tools and software development kits (SDKs) for a range of applications in industrial automation consumer electronics audio automotive retail residential and health and fitness. This strategic acquisition significantly expands Silicon Labs' wireless hardware and software solutions for the IoT.

In July 2013 the company acquired Oslo Norway-based Energy Micro AS whose portfolio boasts the industry's most energy-efficient range of 32-bit microcontrollers. Silicon Labs paid $115 million up front for Energy Micro plus an additional $55 million later as deferred and "earn-out" consideration is the business grows as planned.

EXECUTIVES

President and Interim SVP Worldwide Sales, William G. (Bill) Bock, age 67, $375,000 total compensation
SVP and CFO, John C. Hollister, age 48, $321,154 total compensation
CEO, G. Tyson Tuttle, age 50, $513,462 total compensation
SVP and General Manager Infrastructure, Mark Thompson
SVP and General Manager Internet of Things (IoT), James Stansberry
SVP and CTO, Alessandro Piovaccari
SVP Worldwide Operations, Sandeep Kumar, age 53
Senior Vice President Worldwide Sales, Brandon Tolany
Senior Vice President Chief People Officer, Lori Knowlton
Vice President Accounting Certification Manager, Ed Sharp
Vice President Americas Sales, John Dixon
Chairman, Navdeep S. (Nav) Sooch, age 56
Board Member, Neil Kim
Board Member, Nina Richardson
Auditors: Ernst & Young LLP

LOCATIONS

HQ: Silicon Laboratories Inc
400 West Cesar Chavez, Austin, TX 78701
Phone: 512 416-8500
Web: www.silabs.com

PRODUCTS/OPERATIONS

Selected Products

Access products
ISOmodem embedded modems
Power over Ethernet (PoE) power source equipment and powered device ICs
ProSLIC analog subscriber line interface (short-haul for customer premise and long-haul for central office)
Broad-based products
Digital isolators
EZRadio short-range wireless transceivers
Human interface sensors (capacitive touch sensors infrared sensors)
Microcontrollers
Precision clocks and oscillators
Wireless receivers
Broadcast products
Radio receivers and transmitters
Video tuners and demodulators

COMPETITORS

Analog Devices	Maxim Integrated
Atmel	Products
Conexant Systems	Microchip Technology
Cypress Semiconductor	Microsemi
Dialog Semiconductor	NXP Semiconductors
Dover Corp.	Renesas Electronics
Epson	STMicroelectronics
IXYS	Semtech
Infineon Technologies	Skyworks
Integrated Device	Sony
Technology	Texas Instruments
MaxLinear	

HISTORICAL FINANCIALS

Company Type: Public

Income Statement   FYE: December 29

	REVENUE ($ mil.)	NET INCOME ($ mil.)	NET PROFIT MARGIN	EMPLOYEES
12/18	868.2	83.5	9.6%	1,505
12/17	768.8	47.0	6.1%	1,279
12/16*	697.6	61.4	8.8%	1,252
01/16	644.8	29.5	4.6%	1,199
01/15	620.7	38.0	6.1%	1,107
Annual Growth	8.8%	21.8%	—	8.0%

*Fiscal year change

2018 Year-End Financials

Debt ratio: 21.8%	No. of shares (mil.): 43.0
Return on equity: 8.3%	Dividends
Cash ($ mil.): 197.0	Yield: —
Current ratio: 5.71	Payout: —
Long-term debt ($ mil.): 354.7	Market value ($ mil.): 3,382.0

	STOCK PRICE ($) FY Close	P/E High/Low	PER SHARE ($) Earnings	Dividends	Book Value
12/18	78.50	56 38	1.90	0.00	24.77
12/17	88.30	87 58	1.09	0.00	22.32
12/16*	65.00	46 25	1.45	0.00	19.74
01/16	48.54	84 57	0.69	0.00	18.24
01/15	47.51	61 42	0.87	0.00	17.95
Annual Growth	13.4%	— —	21.6%	—	8.4%

*Fiscal year change

Simmons First National Corp

Simmons First National thinks it's only natural it should be one of the largest financial institutions in The Natural State. The $8.1 billion-asset holding company owns Simmons First National Bank and seven other community banks that bear the Simmons First Bank name and maintain local identities; together they operate around 150 branches throughout Arkansas and in Kansas Tennessee and Missouri. Serving consumers and area businesses the banks offer standard deposit products like checking and savings accounts IRAs and CDs. Lending activities mainly consist of commercial real estate loans single-family mortgages and consumer loans such as credit card and student loans.

Operations

In addition to Simmons First National Bank the company owns Simmons First Bank of Jonesboro Simmons First Bank of South Arkansas Simmons First Bank of Northwest Arkansas Simmons First Bank of Russellville Simmons First Bank of Searcy Simmons First Bank of El Dorado and Simmons First Bank of Hot Springs. Simmons First Trust Company a subsidiary of Simmons First National Bank provides trust and fiduciary services; Simmons First Investment Group offers broker-dealer services.

Like other retail banks Simmons makes the bulk of its money from interest income. About 65% of its total revenue came from loan interest during 2015 while another 8% came from interest on investment securities. The rest of its revenue came from service charges on deposit accounts (8% of revenue) debit and credit card fees (6%) mortgage lending income (3%) trust income (2%) investment banking income (1%) and other non-interest income sources.

Geographic Reach

The bank has around 150 branches mostly in Arkansas but also in Kansas Missouri and Tennessee.

Financial Performance

Simmons First National Bank's annual revenues and profits have been rising mostly thanks to new loan business from rapid bank expansion (mostly stemming from acquisitions).

The bank's revenue jumped 60% to $396.8 million during 2015 mostly thanks to 58% growth in legacy loans and growth in acquired loan business from the acquisitions of Liberty and Community First. Non-interest income grew 54% thanks to rising trust service charges deposit fees mortgage lending income all also tied to its recent acquisitions.

Revenue growth in 2015 more than doubled Simmons' net income to $74.36 million. The bank's operating cash levels spiked eight-fold to $88.7 million for the year thanks to a rise in cash-based earnings and favorable changes in working capital.

Strategy

Simmons tries to differentiate itself from smaller competitors by offering a wider array of products while striving to provide more personalized service than larger regional banks. The company also likes to acquire banks to grow its loan and deposit business while expanding into new geographic markets. Between 1990 and 2015 Simmons made 11 whole bank acquisitions and a handful of branch deals with other banks adding some 125 branches to its total branch network.

Mergers and Acquisitions

In September 2016 Simmons acquired Citizens National Bank a Tennessee-based bank with about 10 branch locations.

In October 2015 the company purchased Ozark Trust & Investment Corporation and its Trust Company of the Ozarks subsidiary adding $1 billion in new assets under management and 1300 clients to its wealth management business.

In February 2015 Simmons First National acquired $1.1 billion-asset Liberty Bancshares as well as Liberty Bank branches in southwest Missouri St. Louis and Kansas City. It also added Liberty's expertise in small business lending.

Also in February 2015 the bank bought $1.9 billion-asset Community First Bancshares and its First State Bank branches in Tennessee. Community First also added expertise in small business and consumer lending.

EXECUTIVES

EVP Organizational Development, Stephen C. Massanelli, age 62

Chairman and CEO, George A. Makris, age 61, $502,500 total compensation

SEVP CFO and Treasurer, Robert A. Fehlman, age 53, $306,614 total compensation

EVP and Central and Northeast Arkansas Regional Chairman Simmons First National Bank, Barry K. Ledbetter

President and Chief Credit Officer Simmons First National Bank, N. Craig Hunt

EVP and South Arkansas Regional Chairman Simmons First National Bank, Freddie G. Black

EVP Corporate Strategy and Performance and Secretary, Susan F. Smith, age 56

President Chief Banking Officer and Director, David L. Bartlett, age 66, $376,142 total compensation

EVP, Marty D. Casteel, age 66, $304,180 total compensation

EVP Controller Chief Accounting Officer and Investment Relations Officer, David W. Garner, age 48

EVP Marketing, Robert C. Dill, age 75, $179,393 total compensation

EVP and Chief Risk Officer, Tina M. Groves, age 48

EVP Technology and Operations Simmons First National Bank, Lisa W. Hunter

SVP and Marketing Director Simmons First National Bank, Amy W. Johnson

President El Dorado Community Bank, Robert L. Robinson

Chairman Russellville Community Chairman, Ronald B. (Ron) Jackson

President Hot Springs Community Bank, Steven W. (Steve) Trusty

President Conway Community Bank, Jason Culpepper

EVP and General Counsel, Patrick A. Burrow, age 64

EVP Specialty Lending Simmons First National Bank, Larry L. Bates

EVP and Tennessee Regional Chairman Simmons First National Bank, John C. Clark

EVP and Kansas and Missouri Regional Chairman Simmons First National Bank, Gary E. Metsger

Senior Vice President Commercial Loans, Rick Harris

Vice President and Personnel Manager, Leigh Cockrum

Vice President, Pam Lawshe

Vp Of Mortgage, Deana Powell

Assistant Vice President Loans, Esther Chapman

Senior Vice President Director Of Marketing And Communications, Elizabeth Machen

Vice President, Chad Pittillo

Vice President Loan Review Manager, David Coleman

Executive Vice President Operations, Glenda Tolson

Vice President, Zilpha Wilson

Senior Vice President, Adam Mitchell

Vice President And Commercial Loan Officer, John Craig

Vice President Administration, David Rushing

Vice President Equipment Finance, Michael Childers

Vice President And Officer, Cathy Brazeale

Vice President and Trust Officer, Joyce Green

Vice President Commercial Banking Relationship Manager, Dave Ruby

Vice President, Ed Stahlman

Vice President Commercial Lending, Wayne Wilson

Assistant Vice President and Investment Officer, Kelton Harrison

Vice President Finance, Joey Walters
Senior Vice President, Steve Landry
Assistant Vice President, Chris Rittelmeyer
Vice President Commercial Lending, Vernon Scott
Assistant Vice President Atm Operations, Karla Dial
VICE PRESIDENT FACILITIES MANAGEMENT, Anita Murrell
SENIOR VICE PRESIDENT, Bob Williams
Executive Vice President and Chief Information Officer of Company and Simmons First National Bank, Paul D Kanneman
VICE PRESIDENT FINANCIAL ADVISOR, James Watkins
SENIOR VICE PRESIDENT AND SENIOR CREDIT OFFICER, Stephen Landry
Board Member, Edward Drilling
Board Member, Eugene Hunt
Board Member, Christopher Kirkland
Board Member, Mark Doramus
Auditors: BKD, LLP

LOCATIONS

HQ: Simmons First National Corp
501 Main Street, Pine Bluff, AR 71601
Phone: 870 541-1000
Web: www.simmonsbank.com

PRODUCTS/OPERATIONS

2015 Sales

	% of total
Interest Income	
Loans	65
Investment securities	8
Others	-
Non-interest income	
Service charges on deposit accounts	8
Debit and credit card fees	6
Mortgage lending income	3
Trust income	2
Other service charges and fees	2
others	6
Net (loss) gain on assets covered by FDIC loss share agreements	-
Total	**100**

COMPETITORS

Arvest Bank	Bear State Financial
BOK Financial	Home BancShares
BancorpSouth	IBERIABANK
Bank of America	Regions Financial
Bank of the Ozarks	U.S. Bancorp

HISTORICAL FINANCIALS

Company Type: Public

Income Statement				FYE: December 31
	ASSETS ($ mil.)	NET INCOME ($ mil.)	INCOME AS % OF ASSETS	EMPLOYEES
12/17	15,055.8	92.9	0.6%	2,640
12/16	8,400.0	96.8	1.2%	1,875
12/15	7,559.6	74.3	1.0%	1,946
12/14	4,643.3	35.6	0.8%	1,331
12/13	4,383.1	23.2	0.5%	1,306
Annual Growth	**36.1%**	**41.4%**	**—**	**19.2%**

2017 Year-End Financials

Return on assets: 0.7%	Dividends
Return on equity: 5.7%	Yield: 0.0%
Long-term debt ($ mil.): —	Payout: 37.5%
No. of shares (mil.): 92.0	Market value ($ mil.): 5,255.0
Sales ($ mil) 533.7	

	STOCK PRICE ($)	P/E	PER SHARE ($)		
	FY Close	High/Low	Earnings	Dividends	Book Value
12/17	57.10	47 37	1.33	0.50	22.65
12/16	62.15	42 25	1.57	0.48	18.40
12/15	51.36	44 27	1.32	0.46	17.78
12/14	40.65	41 31	1.06	0.44	13.69
12/13	37.15	52 33	0.71	0.42	12.44
Annual Growth	**11.3%**	**— —**	**17.0%**	**4.5%**	**16.2%**

Simply Good Foods Company (The)

Auditors: Ernst & Young LLP

LOCATIONS

HQ: Simply Good Foods Company (The)
1225 17th Street, Suite 1000, Denver, CO 80202
Phone: 303 633-2840
Web: www.thesimplygoodfoodscompany.com

HISTORICAL FINANCIALS

Company Type: Public

Income Statement				FYE: August 25
	REVENUE ($ mil.)	NET INCOME ($ mil.)	NET PROFIT MARGIN	EMPLOYEES
08/18	431.4	70.4	16.3%	141
08/17*	56.3	0.4	0.8%	145
07/17	339.8	(2.4)	—	0
08/16	427.8	10.0	2.3%	141
08/15	252.9	(5.3)	—	0
Annual Growth	**14.3%**	**—**	**—**	**—**

*Fiscal year change

2018 Year-End Financials

Debt ratio: 19.6%	No. of shares (mil.): 70.6
Return on equity: 11.1%	Dividends
Cash ($ mil.): 111.9	Yield: —
Current ratio: 6.07	Payout: —
Long-term debt ($ mil.): 190.9	Market value ($ mil.): 1,269.0

	STOCK PRICE ($)	P/E	PER SHARE ($)		
	FY Close	High/Low	Earnings	Dividends	Book Value
08/18	17.98	18 11	0.96	0.00	9.53
08/17*	11.88	1223 1175	0.01	0.00	8.48
Annual Growth	**51.3%**	**— —**	**9500.0%**	**—**	**12.4%**

*Fiscal year change

Simpson Manufacturing Co., Inc. (DE)

Through its subsidiaries Simpson Manufacturing makes connectors and venting systems for the building remodeling and do-it-yourself industries. Subsidiary Simpson Strong-Tie (SST) makes more than 15000 types of standard and custom products that are used to connect and reinforce joints between wood concrete and masonry building components which the company markets globally and distributes through home centers and a network of contractor and dealer distributors. The company's products are sold primarily in Canada Europe Asia the US and the South Pacific.

Operations

Simpson divides its product lines across two main categories: wood construction (85% of net sales) and concrete construction (15%).

Geographic Reach

The company has around 20 manufacturing locations in Canada France Denmark Germany Switzerland Poland Portugal China the UK and the US. North America accounted for 85% of its revenue in 2015.

Sales and Marketing

Simpson sells its products through an extensive distribution system comprising dealer distributors supplying thousands of retail locations nationwide contractor distributors home centers lumber dealers manufacturers of engineered wood products and specialized contractors such as roof framers. SST markets its products to the residential construction light industrial and commercial construction remodeling and do-it-yourself (DIY) markets.

Financial Performance

The company's revenues climbed 6% from $752 million in 2014 to $794 million in 2015 its highest total in about seven years. The growth for 2015 was driven by a 10% spike in North America that were mostly due to an increase in sales volume and from acquisitions primarily within the US.

Profits also jumped 7% from $64 million in 2014 to $68 million in 2015. Simpson's operating cash flow has fluctuated the last two years; after declining sharply in 2014 cash flow skyrocketed by 70% during 2015.

Strategy

Simpson's long-term strategy has relied on capturing additional market share in both the wood construction and concrete construction product groups by continuing to invest in mobile and web applications for customers. It is also utilizing social media blog posts and videos to connect and engage with its customers and to help them do their jobs more efficiently.

In March 2015 the company closed sales offices in China Dubai and Thailand due to continued losses in these operations.

Mergers and Acquisitions

The company also makes relatively small acquisitions to grow its product lines. In late 2015 it purchased the two businesses of Blue Heron Enterprises and Fox Chase Enterprises for $3.4 million. Both companies manufactured and sold hidden deck clips and associated products and systems.

EXECUTIVES

VP, Jeffrey E. Mackenzie, age 57, $181,830 total compensation
President and CEO, Karen W. Colonias, age 61, $350,000 total compensation
CFO Treasurer and Secretary, Brian J. Magstadt, age 50, $243,337 total compensation
President North American Sales Simpson Strong-Tie Company, Roger Dankel, age 54, $166,455 total compensation
COO Simpson Strong-Tie Company Inc, Ricardo M. Arevalo, age 61, $191,276 total compensation

Chairman, Peter N. Louras, age 69
Vice Chairman, Thomas J. (Tom) Fitzmyers, age 78
Auditors: GRANT THORNTON LLP

LOCATIONS

HQ: Simpson Manufacturing Co., Inc. (DE)
  5956 W. Las Positas Blvd., Pleasanton, CA 94588
Phone: 925 560-9000   Fax: 925 833-1496
Web: www.simpsonmfg.com

PRODUCTS/OPERATIONS

2015 Sales

	% of total
Wood construction	85
Concrete construction	15
Other	-
Total	**100**

Selected Products

Simpson Strong-Tie
  Adhesives
  Mechanical anchors
  Powder-actuated tools
  Screw fastening systems
  Shearwalls
  Wood-to-concrete connectors
  Wood-to-masonry connectors
  Wood-to-wood connectors

Selected Subsidiaries

Simpson Strong-Tie Australia Inc.
Simpson Strong-Tie Canada Limited
Simpson Strong-Tie Company Inc.
Simpson Strong-Tie Europe EURL
Simpson Strong-Tie International Inc.
Simpson Strong-Tie Japan Inc.

COMPETITORS

Action Industries	MSC Industrial Direct
Anaheim Manufacturing	MacLean-Fogg
Boral	Masco
Dayton Superior	W rth Group
Kemco Systems	

HISTORICAL FINANCIALS

Company Type: Public

Income Statement

	REVENUE ($ mil.)	NET INCOME ($ mil.)	NET PROFIT MARGIN	EMPLOYEES	FYE: December 31
12/17	977.0	92.6	9.5%	2,902	
12/16	860.6	89.7	10.4%	2,647	
12/15	794.0	67.8	8.5%	2,498	
12/14	752.1	63.5	8.4%	2,434	
12/13	706.3	50.9	7.2%	2,295	
Annual Growth	8.4%	16.1%	—	6.0%	

2017 Year-End Financials

Debt ratio: 0.3%
Return on equity: 10.5%
Cash ($ mil.): 168.5
Current ratio: 4.28
Long-term debt ($ mil.): 2.6

No. of shares (mil.): 46.7
Dividends
  Yield: 0.0%
  Payout: 40.2%
Market value ($ mil.): 2,684.0

	STOCK PRICE ($) FY Close	P/E High/Low	PER SHARE ($) Earnings	Dividends	Book Value
12/17	57.41	31 21	1.94	0.78	18.93
12/16	43.75	26 16	1.86	0.68	18.25
12/15	34.15	28 23	1.38	0.60	17.64
12/14	34.60	28 22	1.29	0.53	17.63
12/13	36.73	35 27	1.05	0.38	17.27
Annual Growth	11.8%	— —	16.6%	20.1%	2.3%

Simulations Plus Inc.

Molecular modeling software plus applications to help individuals with disabilities equals Simulations Plus. The company is a leading provider of applications used by pharmaceutical researchers to model absorption rates for orally dosed drug compounds. Its Words+ subsidiary provides augmentative communication software and input devices that help people with disabilities use computers. Simulations Plus also provides educational software targeted to high school and college students through its FutureLab unit. Pharmaceutical giants GlaxoSmithKline and Roche are among its clients. CEO Walter Woltosz and his wife Virginia (a director) together own about 40% of the company.

In late 2005 the company acquired the assets of Bioreason for nearly $800000. Bioreason was a supplier of chemistry software to the biotech and pharmaceutical industries. The purchase followed another acquisition earlier in the year for the assets of Sage Informatics a company in the same market.

EXECUTIVES

CFO and Director Human Resources Facilities and Equipment; CFO Words+, Momoko A. Beran, age 64, $135,000 total compensation
Chairman President and CEO, Walter S. (Walt) Woltosz, age 71, $250,000 total compensation
President Words+, Jeffrey A. (Jeff) Dahlen, age 55, $100,000 total compensation
Investor Relations Director, Renee Bouche
Director Life Sciences, Robert D. Clark
Team Leader Discovery Informatics, David Miller
Manager Marketing and Sales, John DiBella
Secretary Treasurer and Director, Virginia E. Woltosz, age 63
Director, David Z. D'Argenio, age 65
Director, Richard R. Weiss, age 81
Director, H. Wayne Rosenberger, age 76
Independent Director, David DArgenio
Auditors: Rose, Snyder & Jacobs LLP

LOCATIONS

HQ: Simulations Plus Inc.
  42505 Tenth Street West, Lancaster, CA 93534-7059
Phone: 661 723-7723   Fax: 661 723-5524
Web: www.simulations-plus.com

PRODUCTS/OPERATIONS

Selected Products

Augmentative Communication Products
  Cyberlink
  E Z Keys for Windows
  Freedom 2000
  HeadMouse
  MessageMate
  SoftSwitch
  Talking Screen for Windows
  Tracker One
  TuffTalker
Educational Software
  Circuits for Physical Science
  Gravity for Physical Science
  Ideal Gas for Chemistry
  Optics for Physical Science
  Universal Gravitation for Physical Science
Pharmaceutical Applications
  GastroPlus
  QMPRchitect
  QMPRPlus

COMPETITORS

Cyprotex	Fonix
DynaVox	Nuance Communications
Entelos	

HISTORICAL FINANCIALS

Company Type: Public

Income Statement

	REVENUE ($ mil.)	NET INCOME ($ mil.)	NET PROFIT MARGIN	EMPLOYEES	FYE: August 31
08/18	29.6	8.9	30.1%	95	
08/17	24.1	5.7	24.0%	86	
08/16	19.9	4.9	24.8%	63	
08/15	18.3	3.8	21.0%	60	
08/14	11.4	3.0	26.4%	66	
Annual Growth	26.8%	31.1%	—	9.5%	

2018 Year-End Financials

Debt ratio: —
Return on equity: 30.9%
Cash ($ mil.): 9.4
Current ratio: 3.69
Long-term debt ($ mil.): —

No. of shares (mil.): 17.4
Dividends
  Yield: 1.1%
  Payout: 48.0%
Market value ($ mil.): 363.0

	STOCK PRICE ($) FY Close	P/E High/Low	PER SHARE ($) Earnings	Dividends	Book Value
08/18	20.85	46 28	0.50	0.24	1.83
08/17	14.50	47 25	0.33	0.20	1.49
08/16	8.62	39 23	0.29	0.20	1.32
08/15	6.75	30 25	0.23	0.20	1.15
08/14	6.72	37 25	0.18	0.19	0.94
Annual Growth	32.7%	— —	29.1%	6.0%	18.0%

SiteOne Landscape Supply Inc

Auditors: Deloitte & Touche LLP

LOCATIONS

HQ: SiteOne Landscape Supply Inc
  300 Colonial Center Parkway, Suite 600, Roswell, GA 30076
Phone: 470 277-7000
Web: www.siteonelandscapesupply.com

HISTORICAL FINANCIALS

Company Type: Public

Income Statement

	REVENUE ($ mil.)	NET INCOME ($ mil.)	NET PROFIT MARGIN	EMPLOYEES	FYE: December 31
12/17*	1,861.7	54.6	2.9%	3,800	
01/17	1,648.2	30.6	1.9%	3,300	
01/16	1,451.6	28.9	2.0%	2,850	
12/14	1,176.6	21.7	1.8%	0	
12/13	5.3	(9.5)	—	0	
Annual Growth	332.9%	—	—	—	

*Fiscal year change

2017 Year-End Financials

Debt ratio: 52.1%
Return on equity: 30.2%
Cash ($ mil.): 16.7
Current ratio: 2.92
Long-term debt ($ mil.): 466.9

No. of shares (mil.): 39.9
Dividends
  Yield: —
  Payout: —
Market value ($ mil.): 3,065.0

	STOCK PRICE ($) FY Close	P/E High/Low	PER SHARE ($) Earnings	Dividends	Book Value
12/17*	76.70	56 26	1.29	0.00	5.33
01/17	34.73	— —	(3.01)	0.00	3.76
Annual Growth	120.8%	— —	—	—	41.7%

*Fiscal year change

SJW Group

It is hard to water down SJW Group's contribution in quenching America's thirst. A holding company it owns public utility services that engage in the production storage purification distribution and retail sale of water. Its two main subsidiaries the San Jose Water Company and Canyon Lake Water Service Company (CLWSC) serves nearly 1.5 million residents in California and Texas through more than 270000 water connections. The SJW Land Company is a holder of some undeveloped land in Tennessee. In March 2018 the SJW Group announced plans of a “merger of equals” with the public utility Connecticut Water Service pending regulatory approval.

Operations

SJW Group owns three subsidiaries.

Public utility San Jose Water serves about one million Californians through some 230000 connections in the San Jose county. It also provides non-tariffed services (water system operations maintenance antenna site leases) under agreements with municipalities and other utilities. The utility's water supply comprises groundwater from wells surface water from watershed run-off and diversion reclaimed water and water purchased from third parties.

CLWSC the second subsidiary supplies water to 42000 Texans through 14000 connections in the growing region between the cities of San Antonio and Austin. Its water supply consists of groundwater from wells and purchased treated and raw water from a third party.

SJW Land Company owns undeveloped real estate property commercial and warehouse properties in Tennessee.

Geographic Reach

San Jose Water Company's water production system is in Santa Clara California. It owns 7000 acres of land a storage capacity of 2.2 billion-gallon reservoirs and 248 million gallons of distribution as well as about 2500 miles of transmission and distribution mains.

The CLWSC subsidiary has a 244 sq. mile service area located in the southern region of the Texas hill country in Comal and Blanco counties with 8200 surface acre reservoir (Canyon Lake). It also holds a contract for 2 billion gallons of untreated surface water and 235 million gallons of treated surface water from annually. Additionally the subsidiary owns and operates three surface water treatment plants (9 million gallons/d) 600 miles

of transmission and distribution mains and maintains 60 storage tanks.

SJW Land Company owns approximately 55 acres of property in the state of Tennessee.

Financial Performance

SJW Group revenue has shown an upward trajectory in the last decade climbing from $220 million in 2008 to $389 million in 2017. Net income has hovered around $22 million in the 2008-13 period before bumping up to about $50 million.

Revenue spiked 15% in 2017 primarily due to a higher rate approved for 2017 that brought in $41 million more compared to a year ago plus an increase of $15 million due to higher water usage.

Net income stood at $59 million a 12% climb reflecting higher rates and increased usage as well as $12 million in pre-tax gain on sale of equity interests in TWA.

SJW Group had only around $8 million in cash holdings at the end of 2017. Operations provided $101 million more than offset by $113 million going in investment activities and a further $5 million used in financing.

Strategy

To boost profits SJW is looking to merge with Connecticut Water Services. With $2.4 billion in assets the proposed merger would create the third largest investor-owned water utility in the US serving 1.5 million customers. But the Connecticut Public Utility Regulatory Authority rejected the proposal over possible negative effects on local ratepayers and the lack of Connecticut-based representation on SJW's board. The merger's fate remains uncertain.

Maintenance cost of aging assets is SJW's biggest challenge. It invested $140 million in 2017 ($800 million earmarked till 2023). While CLWSC has grown despite modest maintenance (customers doubled in a decade) San Jose Water requires major upgrades. Rapid infrastructure growth in the San Jose region from expanding tech companies has further strained supply.

SJW has sold its Texas Water Alliance Limited in late 2017 and SJW Land Company's sale of commercial assets in Los Angeles. But these proceeds will not be enough. In early 2018 San Jose Water requested rate increases to support more than $400 million for immediate operation needs.

Both California and Texas also face long-term water supply challenges. The company has spoken of the need for greater investment in customer education on responsible water use practices and implementing long-range water supply planning.

Company Background

The company has geographically diversified its regulated water operations moving into Central Texas (through the acquisition of Canyon Lake Water Service) in 2006. SJW acquired four water systems in Comal County (Texas) in 2011.

EXECUTIVES

VP Information Services San Jose Water, D. R. Drysdale, age 63
Chairman President and CEO SJW Corp. San Jose Water Company SJW Land Company and SJWTX Inc., W. Richard (Rich) Roth, age 66, $676,000 total compensation
VP Engineering San Jose Water Company, Craig S. Giordano
CFO and Treasurer, James P. Lynch, age 59, $403,000 total compensation
SVP Regulatory Affairs San Jose Water Company, Palle Jensen, age 58, $293,692 total compensation

Chief Administrative Officer San Jose Water Company, Andrew F. Walters, age 47, $316,862 total compensation
Auditors: KPMG LLP

LOCATIONS

HQ: SJW Group
  110 West Taylor Street, San Jose, CA 95110
Phone: 408 279-7800
Web: www.sjwgroup.com

PRODUCTS/OPERATIONS

2016 Sales

	$ mil.	% of total
Water utility services		
Regulated	326.6	96
Non-regulated	6.4	2
Real estate services	6.7	2
Total	**339.7**	**100**

Selected Subsidiaries and Affiliates

California Water Service Group (minority stake water utility)
San Jose Water Company (water utility)
SJW Land Company (parking facilities and commercial real estate)
SJWTX Inc. (Canyon Lake Water Service Company — water utility)
Texas Water Alliance Limited (water supply development)

COMPETITORS

American States Water	SouthWest Water
American Water	United Water Inc.
California Water Service	Veolia Water North America
Los Angeles Water and Power	

HISTORICAL FINANCIALS

Company Type: Public

Income Statement

FYE: December 31

	REVENUE ($ mil.)	NET INCOME ($ mil.)	NET PROFIT MARGIN	EMPLOYEES
12/17	389.2	59.2	15.2%	411
12/16	339.7	52.8	15.6%	406
12/15	305.0	37.8	12.4%	399
12/14	319.6	51.8	16.2%	395
12/13	276.8	22.3	8.1%	379
Annual Growth	8.9%	27.5%	—	2.0%

2017 Year-End Financials

Debt ratio: 31.2%
Return on equity: 13.3%
Cash ($ mil.): 7.8
Current ratio: 0.79
Long-term debt ($ mil.): 431.0

No. of shares (mil.): 20.5
Dividends
  Yield: 0.0%
  Payout: 36.3%
Market value ($ mil.): 1,310.0

	STOCK PRICE ($) FY Close	P/E High/Low	PER SHARE ($) Earnings	Dividends	Book Value
12/17	63.83	24 16	2.86	1.04	22.57
12/16	55.98	22 11	2.57	0.81	20.61
12/15	29.65	19 15	1.85	0.78	18.83
12/14	32.12	13 10	2.54	0.75	17.75
12/13	29.79	27 22	1.12	0.73	15.92
Annual Growth	21.0%	— —	26.4%	9.3%	9.1%

Sleep Number Corp

Select Comfort has got your number. The firm's line of Sleep Number beds which can carry hefty price tags use air-chamber technology to allow sleepers to adjust the firmness on each side of the mattress providing better sleep quality and addressing sleep-related problems such as lower back pain. Select Comfort also offers foundations frames pillows and a sofa bed. A leading bedding retailer in the US Select Comfort operates nearly 490 company-owned stores. The air-bed maker also sells through a company-operated call center its own website and on the QVC shopping channel. Select Comfort was founded in 1987 has grown to become one of the nation's leading bed makers and retailers.

Operations

The firm operates two manufacturing plants (South Carolina and Utah) which supply beds on a just-in-time basis to its retail stores.

Geographic Reach

Minneapolis-based Select Comfort operates company-owned retail stores in 48 US states. Its two largest markets are California and Texas which combined account for more than 20% of its store base. The mattress giant distributes its products in the US and Canada and in Alaska Hawaii and Australia through retail partners.

Sales and Marketing

Select Comfort increased its sales and marketing efforts in 2015 boosting spending to $550 million from $512 million in 2014 and $440 million in 2013. The company advertises on television radio and in print and is increasing its use of digital advertising. More than 90% of its sales are through its retail stores with the online channel bringing in 6% of revenue. Wholesale accounts for 2% of revenue.

Financial Performance

Select Comfort's sales increased 5% in 2015 compared with 2014 to $1.2 billion. Driving sales were higher comparable store sales as well as the addition of about 25 new retail stores. Net income slumped 26% over the same period falling to $50.5 million. The company had higher expenses in 2015 than in 2014 as it developed a new digital presence and installed an enterprise resource planning system.

Strategy

While Select Comfort began as a direct marketer of its unique air-filled mattresses over the years it has evolved into a multichannel retailer with company-owned stores in about 48 states. Retail store sales have grown to account for more than 90% of Select Comfort's total sales.

The company redesigned its website to engage customers with the Select Comfort brand and generate store traffic. The number of visitors to sleepnumber.com increased 51% in 2015 from 2014.

The installation of an enterprise resource planning system from SAP ran into trouble in late 2015 and early 2016. Stores sales fell customers experienced delivery delays and there were higher returns and order cancellations. Problems seem to have been ironed out in the first quarter of 2016.

Mergers and Acquisitions

In 2015 Select Comfort acquired BAM Labs Inc. a provider of biometric sensor and sleep monitoring for data-driven health and wellness. The acquisition broadens and deepens Select Comfort's electrical biomedical software and backend capabilities in providing sleep-related information to mattress customers.

EXECUTIVES

President and CEO, Shelly R. Ibach, age 59, $779,231 total compensation
SVP and CFO, David R. Callen, age 52, $383,618 total compensation
SVP and Chief Operations Supply Chain and Lean Officer, Suresh Krishna, age 49
SVP and Chief Product Officer, Annie L. Bloomquist, age 49, $354,728 total compensation
EVP Chief Sales and Service Officer, Andy P. Carlin, age 55, $354,728 total compensation
SVP and CIO, J. Hunter J. Saklad, age 49
SVP and Chief Legal and Risk Officer and Secretary, Mark A. Kimball, age 60
Vice President Consumer Insight and Strategy, Melissa Barra
Vice President Digital Engagement, Paul Riedel
Chairman, Jean-Michel Valette
Auditors: Deloitte & Touche LLP

LOCATIONS

HQ: Sleep Number Corp
1001 Third Avenue South, Minneapolis, MN 55404
Phone: 763 551-7000
Web: www.SleepNumber.com

PRODUCTS/OPERATIONS

2015 Sales

	% of total
Retail	92
Online and call center	6
Wholesale	2
Total	**100**

Selected Products

Bed frames
Foundations
Mattress pads
Mattresses
Pillows
Pillowtops
Sleep Number SofaBed

COMPETITORS

1800Mattress.com	Simmons
Mattress Firm	Spring Air
Serta	Tempur Sealy

HISTORICAL FINANCIALS

Company Type: Public

Income Statement

FYE: December 30

	REVENUE ($ mil.)	NET INCOME ($ mil.)	NET PROFIT MARGIN	EMPLOYEES
12/17	1,444.5	65.0	4.5%	4,099
12/16*	1,311.2	51.4	3.9%	3,768
01/16	1,213.7	50.5	4.2%	3,484
01/15	1,156.7	67.9	5.9%	3,149
12/13	960.1	60.0	6.3%	2,858
Annual Growth	**10.7%**	**2.0%**		**9.4%**

*Fiscal year change

2017 Year-End Financials

Debt ratio: 5.1%	No. of shares (mil.): 38.8
Return on equity: 52.3%	Dividends
Cash ($ mil.): 3.6	Yield: —
Current ratio: 0.50	Payout: —
Long-term debt ($ mil.): —	Market value ($ mil.): 1,459.0

	STOCK PRICE ($) FY Close	P/E High/Low		PER SHARE ($) Earnings	Dividends	Book Value
12/17	37.59	24	12	1.55	0.00	2.30
12/16*	22.62	25	14	1.10	0.00	3.68
01/16	21.41	35	21	0.97	0.00	4.50
01/15	26.87	22	12	1.25	0.00	4.87
12/13	21.22	26	16	1.08	0.00	4.10
Annual Growth 15.4% (13.5%)		—	—	**9.5%**		—

*Fiscal year change

Smart Sand Inc

Auditors: GRANT THORNTON LLP

LOCATIONS

HQ: Smart Sand Inc
1725 Hughes Landing Blvd, Suite 800, The Woodlands, TX 77380
Phone: 281 231-2660
Web: www.smartsand.com

HISTORICAL FINANCIALS

Company Type: Public

Income Statement

FYE: December 31

	REVENUE ($ mil.)	NET INCOME ($ mil.)	NET PROFIT MARGIN	EMPLOYEES
12/17	137.2	21.5	15.7%	198
12/16	59.2	10.3	17.5%	103
12/15	47.7	4.9	10.5%	97
12/14	68.1	7.5	11.1%	0
Annual Growth	**26.3%**	**41.8%**		—

2017 Year-End Financials

Debt ratio: 0.3%	No. of shares (mil.): 40.3
Return on equity: 12.9%	Dividends
Cash ($ mil.): 35.2	Yield: —
Current ratio: 2.10	Payout: —
Long-term debt ($ mil.): —	Market value ($ mil.): 350.0

	STOCK PRICE ($) FY Close	P/E High/Low		PER SHARE ($) Earnings	Dividends	Book Value
12/17	8.66	39	9	0.53	0.00	4.70
12/16	16.55	38	25	0.42	0.00	3.67
12/15	0.00	—	—	415.83	0.00	370.97
Annual Growth (88.7%)		—	—	**(96.4%)**		—

Somero Enterprises Inc

EXECUTIVES

Pres, Jack Cooney
Auditors: Whitley Penn LLP

LOCATIONS

HQ: Somero Enterprises Inc
14530 Global Parkway, Fort Myers, FL 33913
Phone: 239 210-6500   **Fax:** 239 210-6600
Web: www.somero.com

HISTORICAL FINANCIALS

Company Type: Public

Income Statement
FYE: December 31

	REVENUE ($ mil.)	NET INCOME ($ mil.)	NET PROFIT MARGIN	EMPLOYEES
12/17	85.6	18.4	21.5%	177
12/16	79.3	14.2	18.0%	178
12/15	70.2	11.5	16.4%	165
12/14	59.2	14.5	24.5%	165
12/13	45.0	5.3	11.9%	128
Annual Growth	17.4%	36.0%	—	8.4%

2017 Year-End Financials

Debt ratio: —
Return on equity: 38.3%
Cash ($ mil.): 19.0
Current ratio: 4.13
Long-term debt ($ mil.): —

No. of shares (mil.): 56.2
Dividends
Yield: —
Payout: 46.9%
Market value ($ mil.): —

Sorrento Therapeutics Inc

EXECUTIVES

Pres-ceo, Henry Ji
Auditors: DELOITTE & TOUCHE LLP

LOCATIONS

HQ: Sorrento Therapeutics Inc
4955 Directors Place, San Diego, CA 92121
Phone: 858 203-4100
Web: www.sorrentotherapeutics.com

HISTORICAL FINANCIALS

Company Type: Public

Income Statement
FYE: December 31

	REVENUE ($ mil.)	NET INCOME ($ mil.)	NET PROFIT MARGIN	EMPLOYEES
12/17	151.8	9.1	6.0%	162
12/16	8.1	(60.9)	—	175
12/15	4.5	(45.8)	—	112
12/14	3.8	(34.6)	—	84
12/13	0.4	(21.9)	—	73
Annual Growth	326.2%	—	—	22.1%

2017 Year-End Financials

Debt ratio: 1.2%
Return on equity: 6.5%
Cash ($ mil.): 20.4
Current ratio: 0.38
Long-term debt ($ mil.): 5.2

No. of shares (mil.): 82.9
Dividends
Yield: —
Payout: —
Market value ($ mil.): 315.0

	STOCK PRICE ($) FY Close	P/E High/Low		PER SHARE ($) Earnings	Dividends	Book Value
12/17	3.80	46	12	0.13	0.00	2.41
12/16	4.90	—	—	(1.21)	0.00	1.57
12/15	8.71	—	—	(1.24)	0.00	3.84
12/14	10.07	—	—	(1.30)	0.00	3.00
12/13	8.10	—	—	(1.46)	0.00	2.90
Annual Growth	(17.2%)		—	—	—	(4.6%)

South State Corp

South State Corporation (formerly First Financial Holdings) is the holding company for South State Bank (formerly South Carolina Bank and Trust and South Carolina Bank and Trust of the Piedmont both known as SCBT). The bank operates branches throughout the Palmetto state as well as in select counties in Georgia and North Carolina. Serving retail and business customers the banks provide deposit accounts loans and mortgages as well as trust and investment planning services. More than half of the firm's loan portfolio is devoted to commercial mortgages while consumer real estate loans make up more than a quarter. South State plans to merge with Southeastern Bank Financial parent of Georgia Bank & Trust.

Operations

Beyond its retail and commercial banking mortgage lending consumer finance and trust and investment businesses the bank operates registered investment advisors Minis & Co. and First Southeast 401K Fiduciaries as well as limited-purpose broker-dealer First Southeast Investor Services.

South State Corporation generated 70% of its total revenue from loan interest (including fees) in 2014 while another 4% came from interest income on investment securities. Service charges and Bankcard services income made up another 14% of total revenue while trust and investment services income and mortgage banking income each contributed roughly 4% during the year.

Geographic Reach

South State Corporation boasts nearly 130 branches across nearly 20 counties in South Carolina a handful of counties in North Carolina and about a dozen counties in the northeast and coastal regions of Georgia.

Financial Performance

South State Corporation's revenues and profits have been on the rise over the past few years mostly thanks to continued growth of its loan business and declining loan loss provisions as its loan portfolio's credit quality has improved with the strengthened economy.

The company's revenue jumped by 28% to $436.72 million in 2014 which was mostly driven by 20% growth in its loan interest income as its average loan asset balances swelled by a similar percentage. South State's non-interest income also swelled by 76% thanks to higher deposit account service charge bankcard service trust and investment service and mortgage banking fees from overall growth in the business through acquisitions and organic initiatives.

Higher revenue and controlled operating costs in 2014 drove the bank's net income higher by 53% to $75.44 million. South State's operating cash levels declined by 51% to $118.65 million for the year after adjusting its earnings for non-cash net sales proceeds from its mortgage loans held-for-sale and as the bank spent more cash toward its accrued income taxes.

Strategy

Though it does sometimes expand or relocate its existing branches to better position its locations for more growth South State Corporation has been mostly growing its loan business and branch network through strategic bank and branch acquisitions. Its 2015 acquisition of 13 branch locations

from Bank of America for example extended South State's reach into six new markets and three existing markets while adding millions of dollars worth of new loan business. Then in mid-2016 South State Corporation agreed to buy Southeastern Bank Financial the holding company of Georgia Bank & Trust (which also operates in South Carolina as Southern Bank & Trust). The combined company will operate more than 130 branches in Georgia and the Carolinas.

Mergers and Acquisitions

In 2015 South State Corporation agreed to purchase 12 South Carolina branches and one Georgia branch from Bank of America expanding its reach into six new markets. The acquired branches were located in Hartwell Georgia; as well as Florence Greenwood Orangeburg Sumter Newberry Batesburg-Leesville Abbeville and Hartsville in South Carolina.

Company Background

South State Corporation and South State Bank changed their names from First Financial Holdings and South Carolina Bank and Trust respectively in 2014. The change was designed to better promote the South State brand with customers.

EXECUTIVES

CEO, Robert R. Hill, age 51, $645,000 total compensation
Senior Vice President Director of Media, Donna Pullen
CFO and COO, John C. Pollok, age 52, $442,000 total compensation
Chief Banking Officer, John F. Windley, age 66, $315,000 total compensation
Chief Credit Officer and Chief Risk Officer, Joseph Burns, $295,000 total compensation
President, R. Wayne Hall, $203,405 total compensation
EVP and Corporate Secretary, William C. Bochette
Vice President, Reid Davis
Senior Vice President Technology, Ross Bagley
Senior Executive Vice President, Dane H Murray
Vice President, Stacy Cannon
Senior Vice President, Cathie Austin
Senior Vice President City Executive, Dave Starnes
SENIOR VICE PRESIDENT, Sheryl Ross
SENIOR VICE PRESIDENT DIRECTOR HUMAN RESOURCES ADMINISTRATION, Leslie Chaplin
Senior Vice President Assistant Corporate Counsel, Lindsey Livingston
Executive Vice President, Bill Bochette
VICE PRESIDENT MORTGAGE LOAN OFFICER, Nancy Batson
SENIOR VICE PRESIDENT TECHNOLOGY, Lee Fryland
Senior Vice President Director of Bank Operations, Robb Byrd
Vice President Commercial Lender, Candy Greene
Senior Vice President Commercial Banking Executive, Kevin Blackwood
ASSISTANT VICE PRESIDENT AND MORTGAGE ORIGINATOR, Stephanie Waters
Executive Vice President, Jim Mabry
Senior Vice President City Executive, Kevin Rourk
Vice President Deposit Operations Manager, Janet Smith
Senior Vice President Commercial Loan Administrator, Jeannette Perna
Senior Vice President Commercial Real Estate, Mike Greer
VICE PRESIDENT, Wayne Dowling
SENIOR VICE PRESIDENT, Morris Hardigree
VICE PRESIDENT, Doug Jacobs

VICE PRESIDENT MORTGAGE LENDING, Reece Wrenn
SENIOR VICE PRESIDENT AND RETAIL MARKET LEADER, Linda Potts
VICE PRESIDENT, Anne Lambert
COMMERCIAL BANKER VICE PRESIDENT, Kendall Myers
SENIOR VICE PRESIDENT, James Holden
Treasurer, Richard Mathis
Chairman, Robert R. Horger, age 67
Vice Chairman, Paula Harper Bethea
Board Member, Kevin Walker
Board Member, Cynthia Hartley
Board Member, Robert Demere
Auditors: Dixon Hughes Goodman LLP

LOCATIONS

HQ: South State Corp
520 Gervais Street, Columbia, SC 29201
Phone: 800 277-2175
Web: www.southstatebank.com

PRODUCTS/OPERATIONS

2011 Sales

	$ mil.	% of total
Interest		
Loans including fees	319.9	70
Investment securities	20.3	4
Other	1.8	-
Noninterest		
Service charges on deposit accounts	36.2	10
Bankcard services income	29.6	6
Trust and investment services income	18.3	4
Mortgage banking	16.2	4
Securities gains net -	0	
Amortization of FDIC indemnification asset	(21.9)	0
Other	16.2	4
Total	**436.7**	**100**

COMPETITORS

BB&T	Regions Financial
Bank of America	Security Federal
Bank of South Carolina	
First Citizens Bancorporation	

HISTORICAL FINANCIALS

Company Type: Public

Income Statement

FYE: December 31

	ASSETS ($ mil.)	NET INCOME ($ mil.)	INCOME AS % OF ASSETS	EMPLOYEES
12/17	14,466.5	87.5	0.6%	2,719
12/16	8,900.5	101.2	1.1%	2,055
12/15	8,557.3	99.4	1.2%	2,058
12/14	7,826.2	75.4	1.0%	2,081
12/13	7,931.5	49.2	0.6%	2,106
Annual Growth	**16.2%**	**15.5%**	**—**	**6.6%**

2017 Year-End Financials

Return on assets: 0.7%
Return on equity: 5.0%
Long-term debt ($ mil.): —
No. of shares (mil.): 36.7
Sales ($ mil): 575.1
Dividends
Yield: 0.0%
Payout: 45.0%
Market value ($ mil.): 3,204.0

	STOCK PRICE ($) FY Close	P/E High/Low	PER SHARE ($) Earnings	Dividends	Book Value
12/17	87.15	32 27	2.93	1.32	62.81
12/16	87.40	22 14	4.18	1.21	46.83
12/15	71.95	19 14	4.11	0.98	43.84
12/14	67.08	22 18	3.08	0.82	40.78
12/13	66.51	28 17	2.38	0.74	40.72
Annual Growth	**7.0%**	**— —**	**5.3%**	**15.6%**	**11.4%**

Southern First Bancshares, Inc.

Southern First Bancshares operates in two markets: Greenville South Carolina where it operates under the Greenville First Bank moniker and in Columbia South Carolina as Southern First Bank. Selling itself as a local alternative to larger institutions the company which has more than five bank branches targets individuals and small to midsized businesses. It offers traditional deposit services and products including checking accounts savings accounts and CDs. The banks use funds from deposits mainly to write commercial mortgages residential mortgages and commercial business loans.

EXECUTIVES

Senior Vice President, Shannon Smoak
Board Member, Rudolph Johnstone
Auditors: Elliott Davis Decosimo, LLC

LOCATIONS

HQ: Southern First Bancshares, Inc.
100 Verdae Boulevard, Suite 100, Greenville, SC 29606
Phone: 864 679-9000
Web: www.southernfirst.com

COMPETITORS

BB&T	Regions Financial
Bank of America	
First Citizens Bancorporation	

HISTORICAL FINANCIALS

Company Type: Public

Income Statement

FYE: December 31

	ASSETS ($ mil.)	NET INCOME ($ mil.)	INCOME AS % OF ASSETS	EMPLOYEES
12/17	1,624.6	13.0	0.8%	198
12/16	1,340.9	13.0	1.0%	179
12/15	1,217.2	10.1	0.8%	167
12/14	1,029.8	6.6	0.6%	155
12/13	890.8	5.1	0.6%	138
Annual Growth	**16.2%**	**26.3%**	**—**	**9.4%**

2017 Year-End Financials

Return on assets: 0.8%
Return on equity: 10.0%
Long-term debt ($ mil.): —
No. of shares (mil.): 7.3
Sales ($ mil): 70.5
Dividends
Yield: —
Payout: —
Market value ($ mil.): 303.0

	STOCK PRICE ($) FY Close	P/E High/Low	PER SHARE ($) Earnings	Dividends	Book Value
12/17	41.25	23 17	1.76	0.00	20.37
12/16	36.00	18 11	1.94	0.00	17.00
12/15	22.70	14 10	1.55	0.00	14.98
12/14	17.02	15 11	1.10	0.00	13.34
12/13	13.28	14 9	0.98	0.00	15.20
Annual Growth	**32.8%**	**— —**	**15.8%**	**—**	**7.6%**

Southern Missouri Bancorp, Inc.

Southern Missouri Bancorp is the holding company for Southern Bank (formerly Southern Missouri Bank and Trust) which serves local residents and businesses in southeastern Missouri and northeastern Arkansas through more than 10 branches. Residential mortgages account for the largest percentage of the bank's loan portfolio followed by commercial mortgages and business loans. Construction and consumer loans round out its lending activities. Deposit products include checking savings and money market accounts CDs and IRAs. The bank also offers financial planning and investment services. Originally chartered in 1887 Southern Bank acquired Arkansas-based Southern Bank of Commerce in 2009.

Jeffrey Gendell of Tontine Financial Partners owns more than 9% of Southern Missouri Bancorp; independent investor Donald Crandell owns more than 8%; employees own around 6%; and president CEO and director Greg Steffens more than 5%.

EXECUTIVES

Vice President, Mel Jackson
Vice President of Deposit Operations, Tiffany Beaton
Vice President, Kevin Alpe
Vice President Senior Commercial Loan Officer, Brock Fletcher
Senior Vice President Community Bank President, Chris Roberts
Auditors: BKD, LLP

LOCATIONS

HQ: Southern Missouri Bancorp, Inc.
2991 Oak Grove Road, Poplar Bluff, MO 63901
Phone: 573 778-1800
Web: www.bankwithsouthern.com

COMPETITORS

Bank of America	Regions Financial
Commerce Bancshares	U.S. Bancorp
IBERIABANK	UMB Financial

HISTORICAL FINANCIALS
Company Type: Public

Income Statement				FYE: June 30
	ASSETS ($ mil.)	NET INCOME ($ mil.)	INCOME AS % OF ASSETS	EMPLOYEES
06/18	1,886.1	20.9	1.1%	415
06/17	1,707.7	15.5	0.9%	390
06/16	1,403.9	14.8	1.1%	342
06/15	1,300.0	13.6	1.1%	327
06/14	1,021.4	10.0	1.0%	247
Annual Growth	16.6%	20.0%	—	13.9%

2018 Year-End Financials

Return on assets: 1.1%	Dividends
Return on equity: 11.2%	Yield: 0.0%
Long-term debt ($ mil.): —	Payout: 18.4%
No. of shares (mil.): 9.0	Market value ($ mil.): 351.0
Sales ($ mil) 91.0	

	STOCK PRICE ($) FY Close	P/E High/Low		PER SHARE ($) Earnings	Dividends	Book Value
06/18	39.02	17	13	2.39	0.44	22.31
06/17	32.26	18	11	2.07	0.40	20.15
06/16	23.53	12	9	1.98	0.36	16.94
06/15	18.85	22	10	1.79	0.34	17.88
06/14	35.69	25	17	1.46	0.32	16.63
Annual Growth	2.3%	—	—	13.2%	8.3%	7.6%

Southern Power Co

Southern Power provides power for the burgeoning population in the South. The company owns builds acquires and markets energy in the competitive wholesale supply business. It develops and operates independent power plants in the southeastern US. The company which is part of Southern Company's generation and energy marketing operations has more than 10500 MW of primarily fossil-fueled facilities generating capacity operating or under construction in Alabama California Florida Georgia Nevada North Carolina Texas and New Mexico. Southern Power's electricity output is marketed to wholesale customers in the region. It is growing by acquiring and developing solar power facilities.

Operations

The company is a wholesale energy provider serving electricity needs of municipalities electric cooperatives and investor-owned utilities. Southern Power and its subsidiaries owns and/or operates 35 facilities in nine states. Its renewable assets include biomass and solar.

Thanks to solar facilities under construction and the acquisitions of Calipatria Solar and Grant Wind as well as other capacity and energy contracts the Southern Power has an average of 75% of its available demonstrated capacity covered through 2020 and an average of 70% of its available demonstrated capacity covered through 2025.

Geographic Reach

Southern Power has operations Alabama California Florida Georgia Nevada New Mexico North Carolina Oklahoma and Texas.

Financial Performance

In fiscal 2015 Southern Power's net sales decreased by $111 million compared to 2014. Power purchase agreements (PPA) energy revenues declined due to lower energy prices driven by a drop in natural gas prices which was passed through in fuel revenues.

Wholesale revenues and non-affiliates revenues declined due to lower energy and capacity revenues.

In 2015 net income increased by 25% due to lower fuel expenses and purchased power partially offset by decreased sales.

Fuel expense decreased due to lower natural gas generation costs.

Purchased power expenses decreased primarily due to a drop in volume of KWhs purchased as well as a decrease associated with the average cost of purchased power.

Net cash provided by the operating activities increased by 66% due to higher income tax benefits received and higher revenues from new PPAs including solar PPAs.

Strategy

The company is expanding its regional generation portfolio (primarily with solar power plants) in order to boost its overall generating capacity to almost 10000 MW.

Mergers and Acquisitions

Growing its solar power assets in 2016 Southern Power acquired the 120-MW East Pecos solar facility (Southern Power's second solar project in Texas).

That year Southern Power and Turner Renewable Energy jointly bought the 20-MW Calipatria solar facility from Solar Frontier Americas. (Southern Power's 10th solar facility in California).

In 2015 Southern Power acquired a controlling interest in the 200-MW Garland solar facility under construction in California from Recurrent Energy a subsidiary of Canadian Solar Inc.

In 2014 Southern Power and Turner Renewable Energy acquired the largest solar facility in New Mexico the 50-MW Macho Springs Solar Facility. The Southern Power-Turner Renewable Energy partnership's seventh solar project and its second-largest overall the plant is expected to generate enough electricity to power more than 18000 homes.

EXECUTIVES

SVP and COO, John G. Trawick
Vice President Operations and Government Relations Chief Administrative Officer, Charlie Freeman
Vice President of Construction, Keith Russell
Auditors: DELOITTE & TOUCHE LLP

LOCATIONS

HQ: Southern Power Co
30 Ivan Allen Jr. Boulevard, N.W., Atlanta, GA 30308
Phone: 404 506-5000
Web: www.southerncompany.com

PRODUCTS/OPERATIONS

2015 Sales

	$ mil.	% of total
Wholesale revenues non-affiliates	964.0	69
Wholesale revenues affiliates	417.0	30
Other revenues	9.0	1
Total	**1,390.0**	**100**

COMPETITORS

AEP	Duke Energy
AEP	Duke Energy
AES	Entergy
AES	Entergy
Calpine	NextEra Energy
Calpine	NextEra Energy

HISTORICAL FINANCIALS
Company Type: Public

Income Statement				FYE: December 31
	REVENUE ($ mil.)	NET INCOME ($ mil.)	NET PROFIT MARGIN	EMPLOYEES
12/17	2,075.0	1,071.0	51.6%	541
12/16	1,577.0	338.0	21.4%	0
12/15	1,390.0	215.0	15.5%	0
12/14	1,501.2	172.3	11.5%	0
12/13	1,275.2	165.5	13.0%	0
Annual Growth	12.9%	59.5%	—	—

2017 Year-End Financials

Debt ratio: 38.4%	No. of shares (mil.): 0.0
Return on equity: 22.3%	Dividends
Cash ($ mil.): 129.0	Yield: —
Current ratio: 0.62	Payout: 29.6%
Long-term debt ($ mil.): 5,071.0	Market value ($ mil.): —

Southside Bancshares, Inc.

Southside Bancshares is the holding company for Southside Bank which boasts nearly 65 branches across East North and Central Texas with many around the cities of Tyler and Longview. About one-third of its branches are located in supermarkets (including Albertsons and Brookshire stores) and 40% are motor bank facilities. The bank provides traditional services such as savings money market and checking accounts CDs and other deposit products as well as trust and wealth management services. Real estate loans primarily residential mortgages make up about half of the company's loan portfolio which also includes business consumer and municipal loans. The bank has total assets exceeding $4.8 billion.

Operations

Southside generated 48% of its total revenue from loan interest in 2014 while interest income on taxable investment securities and mortgage-backed securities made up 16% and 19% respectively. About 9% of its revenue came from deposit service fees and another 2% came from trust income.

Geographic Reach

The bank's branches are located in East North and Central Texas. Its main markets are in East Texas the greater Fort Worth area and the greater Austin area. It is also an affiliate with more than 55000 foreign ATMs worldwide.

Sales and Marketing

Southside which staffed 813 employees at 2014's end serves individuals businesses municipal entities and non-profit organizations in local communities.

Financial Performance

Southside Bancshares' revenues and profits have been falling over the past several years despite consistent growth in loan and investment interest income mostly because the bank's gains on securities held-for-sale have declined.

The company's revenue dipped by 4% to $148.3 million in 2014 mostly due to a $5.6 million decline in gains on the sale of its AFS securities and a $2.8 million impairment of equity related to its investment in SFG Finance stemming from the sale of loans purchased by SFG and the repossessed assets.

Lower revenue and an uptick in loan loss provisions in 2014 caused Southside's net income to tumble 49% to $20.8 million for the year while its operating cash levels dipped by 6% to $56 million on lower cash earnings.

Strategy

Southside looks to acquire financial institutions to grow its loan business and expand its geographic reach outside of its existing markets. Its 2014 acquisition of OmniAmerican Bank alone helped boost its loan assets by more than 60% to $2.17 billion while adding 14 branches in a new market (Dallas/Fort Worth).

To grow its deposits and deepen its presence in the markets it serves the company has also been expanding its network of banking locations — both in-store and full-service branches.

Mergers and Acquisitions

In December 2014 the company acquired OmniAmerican Bank to boost its loan business and expand its footprint to the Dallas area. The deal added 14 full-service branches in the 12-county Dallas/Fort Worth metroplex and more than $763 million in new loan business.

EXECUTIVES

Senior Executive Vice President, Jeryl Story

President and CEO Southside Bancshares and Southside Bank, Lee R. Gibson, age 61, $493,325 total compensation

Regional President North Texas Southside Bank, Tim Carter, age 63

Regional President Central Texas Southside Bank, Peter M. Boyd, age 62, $435,510 total compensation

EVP and Chief Credit Officer Southside Bank, Earl W. (Bill) Clawater, age 64, $265,000 total compensation

EVP and Chief Analytics Officer Southside Bank and Company Secretary, Brian K. McCabe, age 57, $228,385 total compensation

Regional President East Texas Southside Bank, Tim Alexander, age 61

EVP and CFO, Julie N. Shamburger, age 55

Assistant Vice President, Julie A Brown

Vice President, Jeff Quesenberry

Vice President, Cindy Davis

Vice President Branch Manager, Tara Suttle

Executive Vice President, Debra Rutledge

Senior Vice President, Zelton Harvey

Vice President, Julie Hunter

Vice President Wealth Management, Nathan Kelley

VP Internal Audit, Misty de Wet

Vice President Business Services, Grant Williams

Vice Chairman, John R. (Bob) Garrett, age 65

Chairman, W.D. (Joe) Norton, age 81

Auditors: Ernst & Young LLP

LOCATIONS

HQ: Southside Bancshares, Inc.
1201 S. Beckham Avenue, Tyler, TX 75701
Phone: 903 531-7111
Web: www.southside.com

PRODUCTS/OPERATIONS

2014 Sales

	$ mil.	% of total
Interest		
Loans	70.6	48
Mortgage-backed & related securities	28.2	19
Investment securities	24.7	16
Other	0.3	-
Non-interest		
Deposit services	15.3	9
Gain on sale of securities	2.9	2
Trust income	3.1	2
Back owned life insurance income	1.4	1
Gain on sale of loans	0.3	-
Other	4.3	3
Adjustments	(2.8)	-
Total	**148.3**	**100**

COMPETITORS

Bank of America	Jacksonville Bancorp
Capital One	of Illinois
East Texas Financial	Regions Financial

HISTORICAL FINANCIALS

Company Type: Public

Income Statement — FYE: December 31

	ASSETS ($ mil.)	NET INCOME ($ mil.)	INCOME AS % OF ASSETS	EMPLOYEES
12/17	6,498.1	54.3	0.8%	855
12/16	5,563.7	49.3	0.9%	679
12/15	5,162.0	44.0	0.9%	683
12/14	4,807.2	20.8	0.4%	813
12/13	3,445.6	41.1	1.2%	640
Annual Growth	**17.2%**	**7.2%**	**—**	**7.5%**

2017 Year-End Financials

Return on assets: 0.9%
Return on equity: 8.5%
Long-term debt ($ mil.): —
No. of shares (mil.): 35.0
Sales ($ mil): 224.9

Dividends
Yield: 0.0%
Payout: 60.6%
Market value ($ mil.): 1,179.0

	STOCK PRICE ($) FY Close	P/E High/Low	PER SHARE ($) Earnings	Dividends	Book Value
12/17	33.68	21 17	1.81	1.10	21.55
12/16	37.67	21 11	1.81	0.96	17.71
12/15	24.02	19 15	1.61	0.92	16.25
12/14	28.91	36 26	0.96	0.84	15.61
12/13	27.34	15 10	1.94	0.76	12.21
Annual Growth	**5.4%**	**— —**	**(1.7%)**	**9.7%**	**15.3%**

Spark Energy Inc

Auditors: Ernst & Young LLP

LOCATIONS

HQ: Spark Energy Inc
12140 Wickchester Ln, Suite 100, Houston, TX 77079
Phone: 713 600-2600
Web: www.sparkenergy.com

HISTORICAL FINANCIALS

Company Type: Public

Income Statement — FYE: December 31

	REVENUE ($ mil.)	NET INCOME ($ mil.)	NET PROFIT MARGIN	EMPLOYEES
12/17	798.0	18.8	2.4%	176
12/16	546.7	14.4	2.6%	143
12/15	358.1	3.8	1.1%	189
12/14	322.8	(0.0)	—	146
12/13	317.0	31.4	9.9%	137
Annual Growth	**26.0%**	**(12.0%)**	**—**	**6.5%**

2017 Year-End Financials

Debt ratio: 29.6%
Return on equity: 35.0%
Cash ($ mil.): 29.4
Current ratio: 1.96
Long-term debt ($ mil.): 124.8

No. of shares (mil.): 34.6
Dividends
Yield: 0.0%
Payout: 60.9%
Market value ($ mil.): 429.0

	STOCK PRICE ($) FY Close	P/E High/Low	PER SHARE ($) Earnings	Dividends	Book Value
12/17	12.40	39 9	1.19	0.73	2.24
12/16	30.30	28 14	1.12	0.73	0.91
12/15	20.72	34 19	0.53	0.73	0.41
12/14	14.09	— —	(0.01)	0.12	0.31
Annual Growth	**(4.2%)**	**— —**	**—**	**82.0%**	**92.2%**

Spartan Motors, Inc.

Spartan Motors has built itself on the foundation of its chassis. Founded in 1975 Spartan Motors (through its core Spartan Chassis unit) makes custom chassis for fire trucks motor homes and other specialty vehicles including mine resistant and light armored vehicles for the US military. The company also manufactures emergency vehicles through Spartan USA which was formed with the 2016 merger of three subsidiaries: Crimson Fire Aerials Crimson Fire and Utilimaster. Other operations manufacture chassis and other products to customer specifications for use in the package delivery one-way truck rental bakery and snack delivery utility and linen and uniform rental sectors.

Operations

Spartan operates through three reportable segments: Emergency Response Vehicles (34% of sales) Delivery and Service Vehicles (41%) and Specialty Chassis and Vehicles (25%).

Geographic Reach

The company has facilities in Michigan Pennsylvania South Dakota and Indiana. Spartan markets its products throughout the US and Canada as well as select markets in South America and Asia.

Sales and Marketing

Spartan markets its products primarily through the direct contact of our sales department with OEMs dealers and end users to the recreational vehicle (RV) emergency response government services defense and delivery and service markets.

Financial Performance

Spartan's revenues reached $550 million in 2015 its highest total in at least six years. However the company has posted a net loss three out of the last four years. Its most recent loss of $17 million occurring in 2015 was largely the result of the payment of additional taxes and restructuring expenses and consolidation costs.

Specialty Chassis and Vehicles revenues in 2015 increased by 21% mainly due to additional demand in motor home chassis as a result of higher unit volume and a spike in other specialty vehicles revenues largely due to completion of an order for defense vehicles in 2015. The spike in revenues for 2015 was also fueled by an 8% increase in Delivery and Service Vehicles and a 1% increase in Emergency Response Vehicles.

Spartan's operating cash flow has fluctuated over the last few years; after declining in 2014 it surged by 98% in 2015 mostly due to a large spike in customer deposits throughout the year.

Strategy

To mitigate its losses Spartan has been streamlining its organizational structure. In 2015 its former Spartan Motors Chassis subsidiary (which operated its Charlotte Michigan location) and its former Crimson Fire Aerials subsidiary (which operated its Ephrata Pennsylvania location) were merged into Spartan USA. In early 2016 its former Utilimaster Corporation subsidiary (which operated its Bristol and Wakarusa Indiana locations) was also merged into Spartan USA.

Company Background

Spartan Motors was founded in 1975 by George Satykiol a former lead engineer at Chrysler's heavy truck division along with William Foster Jerry Geary and John Knox. Funded with second mortgages Spartan started by building chassis for customized fire trucks.

EXECUTIVES

Vice President Manufacturing, Art Dickes
President and CEO, Daryl M. Adams, age 57, $620,385 total compensation
President Specialty Vehicles, Steve Guillaume, age 50
CFO, Frederick (Rick) Sohm, age 48, $269,231 total compensation
President Spartan Emergency Response, John W. Slawson, age 52, $250,000 total compensation
President Fleet Vehicles and Services (FVS), Tom Ninneman
Vice President Of Ft Sales, Bill Foster
NATIONAL SALES MANAGER, Brian Connely
Chairman, James A. (Jim) Sharman, age 59
Board Member, Ron Harbour
Board Member, Richard R Current
Auditors: BDO USA, LLP

LOCATIONS

HQ: Spartan Motors, Inc.
1541 Reynolds Road, Charlotte, MI 48813
Phone: 517 543-6400
Web: www.SpartanMotors.com

PRODUCTS/OPERATIONS

2015 Sales

	$ mil.	% of total
Delivery and services vehicles	227.7	41
Emergency response vehicles	187.1	34
Specialty chassis and vehicles	135.6	25
Total	**550.4**	**100**

2015 Sales by market

	% of total
Emergency response vehicles	34
Aftermarket parts and assemblies	3
Defense vehicles	1
Delivery and service vehicles	41
Motor home chassis	19
Other vehicles	2
Total	**100**

Selected Products

Spartan Chassis
Assembly and component integration for military vehicles including Mine Resistant Ambush
Custom cabs and chassis for fire apparatusCustom chassis for Class A motorhomesProtected or MRAP program and Iraqi Light Armored Vehic
Classic Fire LLC
Crimson Fire Aerials Inc.
Crimson Fire Inc.
Spartan Motors Chassis Inc.
Utilimaster Corporation

COMPETITORS

Alamo Group	Mack Trucks
Collins Industries	Navistar International
Daimler	Oshkosh Truck
E-ONE	Pierce Manufacturing
Federal Signal	Supreme Industries
Ford Motor	Terex
Freightliner Custom Chassis	Thor Industries
	Volvo
LCI Industries	Winnebago

HISTORICAL FINANCIALS

Company Type: Public

Income Statement				FYE: December 31
	REVENUE ($ mil.)	NET INCOME ($ mil.)	NET PROFIT MARGIN	EMPLOYEES
12/17	707.1	15.9	2.3%	2,327
12/16	590.7	8.6	1.5%	2,340
12/15	550.4	(16.9)	—	1,900
12/14	506.7	1.1	0.2%	1,600
12/13	469.5	(5.9)	—	1,900
Annual Growth	**10.8%**	**—**	**—**	**5.2%**

2017 Year-End Financials

Debt ratio: 5.9%
Return on equity: 9.8%
Cash ($ mil.): 33.5
Current ratio: 1.81
Long-term debt ($ mil.): 17.9
No. of shares (mil.): 35.1
Dividends
  Yield: 0.0%
  Payout: 21.7%
Market value ($ mil.): 553.0

	STOCK PRICE ($) FY Close	P/E High/Low		PER SHARE ($) Earnings	Dividends	Book Value
12/17	15.75	38	14	0.46	0.10	4.81
12/16	9.25	39	11	0.25	0.10	4.47
12/15	3.11	—	—	(0.50)	0.10	4.35
12/14	5.26	226	143	0.03	0.10	4.95
12/13	6.70	—	—	(0.18)	0.10	5.01
Annual Growth	**23.8%**	—	—	**—**	**(0.0%)**	**(1.0%)**

Spirit Realty Capital Inc (New)

Auditors: Ernst & Young LLP

LOCATIONS

HQ: Spirit Realty Capital Inc (New)
2727 North Harwood Street, Suite 300, Dallas, TX 75201
Phone: 972 476-1900
Web: www.spiritrealty.com

HISTORICAL FINANCIALS

Company Type: Public

Income Statement				FYE: December 31
	REVENUE ($ mil.)	NET INCOME ($ mil.)	NET PROFIT MARGIN	EMPLOYEES
12/17	668.9	77.1	11.5%	87
12/16	685.9	97.4	14.2%	84
12/15	667.3	114.7	17.2%	71
12/14	602.8	(33.8)	—	73
12/13	419.4	1.6	0.4%	59
Annual Growth	**12.4%**	**160.4%**	**—**	**10.2%**

2017 Year-End Financials

Debt ratio: 50.1%
Return on equity: 2.2%
Cash ($ mil.): 8.8
Current ratio: 0.06
Long-term debt ($ mil.): 3,639.6
No. of shares (mil.): 89.7
Dividends
  Yield: 0.4%
  Payout: 450.0%
Market value ($ mil.): 770.0

	STOCK PRICE ($) FY Close	P/E High/Low		PER SHARE ($) Earnings	Dividends	Book Value
12/17	8.58	14	8	0.80	3.60	36.98
12/16	10.86	13	9	1.05	3.53	38.07
12/15	10.02	10	7	1.30	3.43	39.49
12/14	11.89	—	—	(0.45)	3.34	40.33
12/13	9.83	—	—	(0.00)	1.51	42.09
Annual Growth	**(3.3%)**	—	—	**—**	**24.3%**	**(3.2%)**

SRC Energy Inc

SRC Energy (formerly Synergy Resources) is on a quest to exploit the natural energy sources found in the Denver-Julesburg Basin (D-J Basin) which spans Colorado Kansas Nebraska and Wyoming. The company is exploring the Wattenberg Field a 50-mile area north of Denver rich with oil and gas deposits. SRC Energy reports proved reserves of about 239 billion cu. ft. of natural gas and 26.4 million barrels of oil and condensate. It has about 349000 net acres under lease with more than 420 producing wells. SRC Energy was founded in 2005 and began operations three years later.

Operations

SRC Energy is engaged in the acquisition development and production of crude oil and natural gas in and around the Denver-Julesburg Basin (D-J Basin) in Colorado and adjacent states one of the top liquids-rich oil and gas resource plays in the US.

The company is focused on the horizontal development of the Codell and Niobrara formations which are characterized by relatively high liquids content. Most of the company's producing wells are either in or adjacent to the Wattenberg Field (an area that covers the western flank of the D-J Basin predominantly in Weld County Colorado). The company operates more than 75% of its proved producing reserves.

Geographic Reach

All of the company's developed acreage is located in Colorado but it has substantial undeveloped acreage in Nebraska and smaller holdings in Kansas and Wyoming.

Sales and Marketing

SRC Energy sells crude oil production to local refineries and third-party marketers. For fiscal 2015 (August year end) the company had two major customers which represented 65% and 11% of its annual revenue.

Financial Performance

Note: In 2016 the company moved its fiscal year end from August to December.

SRC Energy's fiscal 2015 revenues rose 20% to $124.8 million primarily due to a 104% increase in production (which outpaced a 44% drop in oil prices and a 35% drop in gas prices). During the fiscal year the company added 48 net horizontal wells increasing its reserves producing wells and daily production totals.

Net income dropped from $28.9 million to $18 million in fiscal 2015 primarily due to higher costs related to the expansion of drilling and production activities outpacing revenue growth as the result of lower commodity prices.

Cash provided by operations rose from $74.9 million to $125.1 million in fiscal 2015 due to the operating contribution from new wells that were drilled and producing wells that were acquired.

Strategy

SRC Energy plans to continue its focus on the D-J Basin. All its current wells are in the Basin and its undeveloped holdings are either in or adjacent to the Basin. More that 98% of its planned 2016 drilling and completion expenditures are focused on the Wattenberg Field.

To raise cash in 2017 SRC Energy agreed to divest 10000 non-core D-J Basin acreage for $71 million.

Mergers and Acquisitions

In 2016 the company acquired Greeley Crescent from Noble Energy for certain assets (33100 net acres and 800 barrels of oil equivalent production in Weld County Colorado) in the Wattenberg Field for $505 million.

In 2015 SRC Energy bought 4300 net acres of oil and gas leasehold interests and related assets and net production of approximately 1200 barrels of oil equivalent per day in the Wattenberg Field from a private company for $85.2 million.

EXECUTIVES

CEO, Lynn A. Peterson, age 65, $150,000 total compensation

EVP Finance and CFO, James P. (Jimmy) Henderson, age 53, $8,654 total compensation

EVP Business Development, Craig D. Rasmuson, age 50, $264,584 total compensation

COO Operations, Michael J. Eberhard, age 60

COO Development, Nick A. Spence, age 59

VP Exploration, Tom Birmingham

VP Land, Matthew Miller

Auditors: Deloitte & Touche LLP

LOCATIONS

HQ: SRC Energy Inc
1675 Broadway, Suite 2600, Denver, CO 80202
Phone: 720 616-4300 **Fax:** 720 616-4301
Web: www.srcenergy.com

PRODUCTS/OPERATIONS

2013 Sales

	$ mil.	% of total
Oil	36.2	78
Gas	10.0	22
Total	**46.2**	**100**

COMPETITORS

Bill Barrett	PDC Energy
Cimarex	Par Pacific
Double Eagle Petroleum	Resolute Energy
Earthstone Energy	Whiting Petroleum
Gasco Energy	

HISTORICAL FINANCIALS

Company Type: Public

Income Statement   FYE: December 31

	REVENUE ($ mil.)	NET INCOME ($ mil.)	NET PROFIT MARGIN	EMPLOYEES
12/17	362.5	142.4	39.3%	122
12/16	107.1	(219.1)	—	96
12/15*	34.1	(122.9)	—	62
08/15	124.8	18.0	14.5%	36
08/14	104.2	28.8	27.7%	29
Annual Growth	**36.6%**	**49.1%**		**43.2%**

*Fiscal year change

2017 Year-End Financials

Debt ratio: 25.8%
Return on equity: 13.2%
Cash ($ mil.): 48.7
Current ratio: 0.79
Long-term debt ($ mil.): 538.1

No. of shares (mil.): 241.3
Dividends
Yield: —
Payout: —
Market value ($ mil.): 2,059.0

	STOCK PRICE ($) FY Close	P/E High/Low		PER SHARE ($) Earnings	Dividends	Book Value
12/17	8.53	14	9	0.69	0.00	5.42
12/16	8.91	—	—	(1.26)	0.00	4.19
12/15*	8.52	—	—	(1.14)	0.00	4.60
08/15	10.74	72	45	0.19	0.00	5.45
08/14	13.46	36	22	0.37	0.00	3.61
Annual Growth	**(10.8%)**	—	—	**16.9%**	—	**10.7%**

*Fiscal year change

SS&C Technologies Holdings Inc

SS&C Technologies helps its clients buy low and sell high and do some of it automatically. The company develops software for managing financial portfolios alternative investments (such as hedge funds) loans real estate equity back-office processing and securities trading and it provides consulting and outsourcing services. Its applications automate several financial functions. SS&C serves asset managers insurance companies banks corporate treasuries hedge funds and government agencies among others. Clients have included Boston Financial Management Certified Advisory Corp. Essex Financial. It has offices around the world. SS&C added significant heft in 2018 when it bought DST Systems for about $5.4 billion.

Operations

About two-thirds of SS&C's revenue comes from its software-enabled services with about 30% from maintenance fees and term licenses. The rest of revenue is split between professional services and perpetual licenses.

Geographic Reach

SS&C Technologies has about 30 offices across the US. It has international offices in Australia Canada the Cayman Islands Hong Kong India Ireland Malaysia Singapore the Netherlands and the UK. SS&C's biggest market is the US which accounts for nearly 75% of sales. Other revenue is from the UK Europe and Asia/Pacific and Japan.

Sales and Marketing

SS&C Technologies counts a diverse customer base of 13000 clients in the financial services industry. It uses a direct sales force to serve the complexity of the industry and meet the industry's regulatory and reporting requirements. For its property management software however the company uses a telemarketing staff.

Financial Performance

SS&C's revenue rose at an annual clip of 27% since 2013 as acquisition have helped stoke the top line. Revenue increased 13% to about $1.6 billion in 2017 from 2016 boosted by sales from the acquisitions of CommonWealth Fund Services in late 2017 and GFS Conifer and Citigroup AIS in 2016. The acquired companies helped increase revenue from hedge funds and other alternative investment clients.

Net income jumped 150% to about $329 million in 2017 from 2016 on higher revenue a slight decrease in operating expenses and a tax benefit.

The company's cash and cash equivalents fell to about $64 million in 2017 from about $118 million in 2016. The decrease was due to repayments of debt payment of dividends capital expenditures and cash paid for acquisitions.

Strategy

Acquisitions play a key role in SS&C's growth. Using what the company calls a methodically opportunistic strategy it has bought about 50 companies since 1995 that expanded its product and service offerings took it into new markets and added to its client base within the financial services industry. The company's appetite for acquisitions remains undiminished as it made one of its biggest deals for rival DST Systems. The $5.4 billion transaction added substantial revenue and expanded SS&C's offerings.

Several deals in 2016 and 2017 expanded SS&C's presence in the hedge fund market just as the hedge fund industry bounced back from slow growth which helped boost the company's revenue. Another slowdown in hedge fund growth or in the greater economy could reverberate to SS&C and reduce the rate of growth.

Looking to expand international revenue beyond a fifth of sales SS&C seeks to leverage its software products and software-enabled services for foreign markets. It also intends to use its current presence in the Asia/Pacific region to as a base for expansion there.

SS&C increased the products and services for fund administration which helps it draw more revenue from clients. A new offering called Fundhub is aimed at the middle office market.

Mergers and Acquisitions

In 2017 SS&C bought DST Systems for about $5.4 billion. The transaction significantly increased SS&C's scale boosting its revenue to from $1.6 billion to a combined $3.9 billion. The deal put SS&C in the US retirement and wealth management markets while adding more than 110 million investor positions across DST's client base. DST became a wholly owned SS&C subsidiary. Previously SS&C bought DST subsidiary DST Global Solutions.

In another 2018 acquisition SS&C bought Intralinks which develops a communications platform for private equity and hedge fund investors for $1.5 billion. Intralinks provides SS&C with a communications technology that facilitates collaboration between investors. Intralinks has more than 4000 clients including banks and corporations.

Also in 2018 SS&C acquired CACEIS North America the fund administration business of CACEIS based in Toronto and New York. CACEIS offers fund administration services and support. SS&C bought CACEIS North America from CACEIS the asset servicing banking group of Crédit Agricole.

In 2016 and 2017 SS&C made several acquisitions that increased its hedge fund client base. The company added CommonWealth Fund Services and Conifer Financial Services in 2017 following its 2016 deals for Wells Fargo's Global Funds Service and Citigroup's Alternative Investor Service. The total cost was about $490 million.

HISTORY

Early History

Former KPMG Peat Marwick (now KPMG International) executive William Stone founded Securities Software & Consulting in 1986. The company produced its first product in 1989 — a DOS-based portfolio management program geared toward large and medium-sized institutional investors — and called it CAMRA (complete asset management reporting and accounting).

SS&C introduced a Windows-based version of CAMRA in 1993. That year the company also introduced its first loan portfolio management product. SS&C acquired Chalke Inc. in 1995 and with it Chalke's PTS (profit testing system) economic modeling software for insurance companies.

The company went public as SS&C Technologies in 1996. The next year groups from New York and Connecticut filed a class-action suit claiming the company made misrepresentations in its prospectus (the case was dismissed in 1999). Also in 1997 SS&C acquired Dutch financial software company Mabel Systems and Shepro Braun Systems.

EXECUTIVES

President and COO, Normand A. (Norm) Boulanger, age 55, $550,000 total compensation
Chairman and CEO, William C. (Bill) Stone, age 62, $875,000 total compensation
SVP and General Manager Advent, David Peter F. (Pete) Hess, age 48
SVP and CFO, Patrick J. Pedonti, age 66, $350,000 total compensation

SVP and Chief Development Officer, Steve H. Kremidas
SVP and General Manager DBC, Richard Shalowitz
SVP and General Manager Treasury Banks and Credit Unions Business, Colleen Nelsen
VP and Managing Director SS&C Technologies Canada, Eric R. Rocks
SVP and General Manager, Thomas (Tom) McMackin
SVP General Counsel and Secretary, Paul G. Igoe, age 55, $260,000 total compensation
SVP Global Institutional Outsourcing, David N. (Dave) Reid
SVP and Managing Director Alternative Assets, Rahul Kanwar, $475,000 total compensation
Managing Director SS&C GlobeOp Canada, Henry Toy
Managing Director SS&C Technologies Asia Pacific, Phil Banas
SVP Enterprise Risk, James (Jim) Ramenda
SVP and General Manager Financial Markets Division, Bob Moitoso
SVP Institutional and Investment Management, Christy Bremner
SVP Institutional and Investment Management, J. Timothy (Tim) Reilly
CTO, Bob Schwartz
Managing Director and Head SS&C GlobeOp Asia, Nandini Sankar
Vice President of Technology, Nicol Sutherland
Auditors: PricewaterhouseCoopers LLP

LOCATIONS

HQ: SS&C Technologies Holdings Inc
80 Lamberton Road, Windsor, CT 06095
Phone: 860 298-4500
Web: www.ssctech.com

PRODUCTS/OPERATIONS

2017 Sales by Product Group

	$ mil.	% of total
Portfolio management/accounting	1,546.2	92
Loan management/accounting	60.8	4
Trading/treasury operations	33.1	2
Property management	17.2	1
Money market processing	8.4	0
Financial modeling	8.2	0
Training	1.4	-
Total	**1,675.3**	**100**

Sales 2017

	$ mil.	% of total
Software-enabled services	1,114.0	66
Maintenance and term licenses	463.7	28
Professional services	77.9	5
Perpetual licenses	19.7	1
Total	**1,675.3**	**100**

Selected Services

Application outsourcing and hosting
Consulting
Data conversion
Installation
Maintenance
Technical support
Training

Selected Software

AdvisorWare (portfolio management and investment accounting)
Antares (trade order management)
CAMRA (asset management reporting and accounting)
DBC (financial modeling)
Debt & Derivatives (comprehensive derivative and debt portfolio analysis)
PortPro (balance sheet and investment portfolio analysis and management)
SKYLINE II (property management accounting and reporting)
SS&C Wealth Management (wealth management)
TradeThru (trading and treasury operations)

COMPETITORS

BNY Mellon Asset Servicing
Charles River Systems
Charles Schwab
Citigroup
Envestnet
Fidelity National Information Services
Intuit
Orion Group
Raymond James Financial
StatPro Group
Yardi Systems

HISTORICAL FINANCIALS

Company Type: Public

Income Statement | | | | FYE: December 31

	REVENUE ($ mil.)	NET INCOME ($ mil.)	NET PROFIT MARGIN	EMPLOYEES
12/17	1,675.3	328.8	19.6%	8,287
12/16	1,481.4	131.0	8.8%	8,001
12/15	1,000.2	42.8	4.3%	6,089
12/14	767.8	131.1	17.1%	4,674
12/13	712.7	117.9	16.5%	4,194
Annual Growth	23.8%	29.2%	—	18.6%

2017 Year-End Financials

Debt ratio: 36.9%
Return on equity: 13.3%
Cash ($ mil.): 64.0
Current ratio: 0.81
Long-term debt ($ mil.): 2,007.3
No. of shares (mil.): 206.5
Dividends
  Yield: 0.0%
  Payout: 17.1%
Market value ($ mil.): 8,361.0

	STOCK PRICE ($) FY Close	P/E High/Low	PER SHARE ($) Earnings	Dividends	Book Value
12/17	40.48	26 18	1.55	0.27	13.01
12/16	28.60	105 41	0.64	0.25	11.12
12/15	68.27	317224	0.23	0.25	10.69
12/14	58.49	76 46	0.75	0.06	8.00
12/13	44.26	60 31	0.69	0.00	7.45
Annual Growth	(2.2%)	— —	22.4%	—	15.0%

STAG Industrial Inc

If STAG Industrial were to show up alone at a party it would likely be on the hunt for single tenants looking to lease industrial space. The self-managed and self-administered real estate investment trust (REIT) has built a business acquiring and managing single-tenant industrial properties located across more than 35 states. The company's portfolio consists primarily of 50 million sq. ft. of leasable warehouse distribution manufacturing and office space located in secondary markets. STAG conducts most of its business through its operating partner STAG Industrial Operating Partnership. The Massachusetts-based REIT went public in 2011.

Operations

STAG's property portfolio consists of 265 buildings spanning some 54 million sq. ft. across 37 states. More than 83% of its rental income comes from its warehouse/distribution building properties while some 10% comes from its light manufacturing building properties. The rest of its rental revenue comes from its flex-office buildings. Its properties are about 95% leased to a collective 227 tenants.

Key subsidiaries include STAG Industrial Operating Partnership STAG Industrial GP STAG Industrial Management STAG Industrial TRS and STAG Investments Holdings III among others.

Geographic Reach

Based in Massachusetts STAG owns and manages single-tenant industrial properties across 30-plus states. Nearly 40% of its rental income came from its properties in the states of North Carolina Ohio Illinois Pennsylvania and Texas.

Sales and Marketing

STAG made over 50% of its rental income from tenants out of five industries including: Automotive; Industrial Equipment Components & Metals; Containers & Packaging; Air Freight and Logistics; and Food and Beverages. While none of its tenants accounted for more than 3% of its total rental income its top five customers in 2014 included Deckers Outdoor Corporation Solo Cup Company International Paper Company Bank of America and Exel Logistics.

Financial Performance

STAG Industrial's revenues have nearly quadrupled since 2011 as it has expanded its property portfolio through acquisitions and has charged higher rental rates as the economy has strengthened. The REIT has also suffered losses in recent years mostly as its interest expenses on its long-term debt have been higher than its operating profits.

The REIT's revenue jumped 30% to a record $173.82 million in 2014 thanks to continued growth in rental income from newly acquired properties. STAG's same store rental revenue declined by less than 1% mostly due to vacancies and tenants downsizing their spaces. Same store occupancy rates declined by two percentage points to 92.7%.

Despite generating higher revenue in 2014 STAG suffered a $4 million loss during the year mostly due to a $20.5 million increase in depreciation and amortization expenses stemming from its acquired properties. Its interest expenses increased by $4.8 million as its debt levels grew also hurting the company's bottom line. STAG's operating cash levels grew by 17% to $96.7 million in 2014 mostly thanks to higher cash revenue stemming from its property acquisitions.

Strategy

STAG Industrial acquires direct and indirect ownership of industrial space in secondary markets across the US — including small cities and towns and suburban areas — to grow its rental revenue. STAG typically purchases individual Class B single-tenant industrial properties located in secondary markets nationwide with its purchase prices ranging from $5 million to $25 million.

During 2014 the REIT acquired 43 industrial buildings spanning 9.3 million sq. ft. for $425 million while its pipeline of potential acquisitions included some 85 industrial buildings exceeding $1.1 billion in value. In mid-2013 STAG acquired eight warehouse and distribution facilities located in Belvidere Illinois and two light manufacturing facilities located near Grand Rapids Michigan. Altogether the 10 properties comprise more than 1.1 million sq. ft.

Some of its other recent purchases include its late 2012 buy of a Massachusetts warehouse and distribution facility containing a total of 217000 sq. ft. and a Michigan light manufacturing and warehouse facility that comprises a total of 108000 sq. ft. (both deals for $13.4 million); a portfolio of 31 primarily single tenant industrial buildings (for about $129 million); and three industrial buildings containing a total of 518838 sq. ft. ($19.8 million).

Company Background

The company's CEO and founder Benjamin S. Butcher founded STAG Industrial's predecessor companies in 2003. Butcher and other investors formed STAG Industrial to consolidate the companies' assets under a REIT umbrella for tax purposes and to raise public funds.

EXECUTIVES

EVP and COO, Stephen C. Mecke, age 55, $309,000 total compensation
Chairman President and CEO, Benjamin S. Butcher, age 65, $515,000 total compensation
EVP and Director Real Estate Operations, David G. King, age 50, $272,950 total compensation
CFO, William R. Crooker
EVP General Counsel and Secretary, Jeffrey M. Sullivan
SVP Data Analytics and Technology, Peter S. Fearey
SVP and Regional Director East, David A. Barker
Auditors: PricewaterhouseCoopers LLP

LOCATIONS

HQ: STAG Industrial Inc
One Federal Street, 23rd Floor, Boston, MA 02110
Phone: 617 574-4777 **Fax:** 617 574-0052
Web: www.stagindustrial.com

PRODUCTS/OPERATIONS

2014 Sales

	$ mil.	% of total
Rental income	149.5	86
Tenant recoveries	23.6	14
Others	0.7	-
Total	**173.8**	**100**

COMPETITORS

First Industrial Realty	Monmouth Real Estate
	Prologis
Liberty Property Trust	Welsh Property Trust

HISTORICAL FINANCIALS

Company Type: Public

Income Statement   FYE: December 31

	REVENUE ($ mil.)	NET INCOME ($ mil.)	NET PROFIT MARGIN	EMPLOYEES
12/17	301.0	31.2	10.4%	72
12/16	250.2	34.5	13.8%	68
12/15	218.6	(29.4)	—	68
12/14	173.8	(4.0)	—	54
12/13	133.8	5.5	4.1%	44
Annual Growth	**22.5%**	**54.2%**	**—**	**13.1%**

2017 Year-End Financials

Debt ratio: 43.7%	No. of shares (mil.): 97.0
Return on equity: 2.6%	Dividends
Cash ($ mil.): 24.5	Yield: 0.0%
Current ratio: 0.82	Payout: 610.8%
Long-term debt ($ mil.): 1,173.7	Market value ($ mil.): 2,651.0

	STOCK PRICE ($) FY Close	P/E High/Low		PER SHARE ($) Earnings	Dividends	Book Value
12/17	27.33	120	95	0.23	1.41	14.01
12/16	23.87	88	52	0.29	1.39	12.78
12/15	18.45	—	—	(0.61)	1.37	12.05
12/14	24.50	—	—	(0.28)	1.29	13.41
12/13	20.39	—	—	(0.10)	1.20	13.47
Annual Growth	**7.6%**	**—**	**—**	**—**	**4.0%**	**1.0%**

Stamps.com Inc.

Stamps.com hopes its customers keep putting letters in the mail. Its PC Postage Service lets registered users who have downloaded Stamps.com software buy stamps online and print the postage directly onto envelopes and labels. Customers can order US Postal Service options such as registered mail certified mail and delivery confirmation as well as print custom stamps using virtually any image through its PhotoStamps.com website. Stamps.com charges a monthly fee for its service which is aimed at consumers home offices and small businesses. In addition customers can buy mailing labels scales and dedicated postage printers from Stamps.com. Postage fees are sent directly to the US Postal Service.

Operations

The company operates through the single segment of Internet Mailing and Shipping Services offering customized postage under the PhotoStamps and PictureItPostage brand names. Revenue from services accounted for 83% in 2015.

Sales and Marketing

Stamps.com taps several channels to market its business. It relies on affiliated channels direct mail direct sales offline marketing programs partnerships traditional media and online advertising. Its target niche customer continues to be small businesses individuals home offices mid-sized businesses and large enterprises. It services to more than 600000 customers.

Financial Performance

Stamps.com has experienced significant revenue growth over the years with revenues peaking at a record-setting $214 million in 2015. However it suffered its first net loss ($2.4 million) in at least 10 years in 2015. After rising for several straight years the company's operating cash flow declined by 11% during 2015.

The historic revenue growth for 2015 was fueled by substantial increases in services (53%) insurance (27%) customized postage (33%) and other (78%) revenue. Services increased due to a surge in annual average paid customers and an increase in annual average service revenue per paid customer. Product revenue increased due to additional sales of mailing and shipping labels and label printers as those businesses continued to grow their customer base. Other product lines grew through acquisitions.

Its net loss for 2015 was fueled by a surge in general and administrative expenses related to its ShipStation ShipWorks and Endicia acquisitions increases in headcount and expenses related to infrastructure investments.

Mergers and Acquisitions

Stamps.com also seeks add-on acquisitions to grow its business organically. In 2015 it obtained PSI Systems a California corporation doing business as Endicia. Endicia is a provider of high volume shipping technologies and services for shipping with the USPS and was purchased for $215 million in cash. The deal accelerated its high volume and e-commerce shipping capabilities.

Adding both new customers and a couple of brand names to its portfolio Stamps.com in 2014 acquired Austin Texas-based ShipStation for about $50 million in cash. The business offers monthly subscription-based e-commerce shipping software primarily under the ShipStation and Auctane brands.

Company Background

Stamps.com was founded as StampMaster in 1996. The company changed its name to Stamps.com in 1998 and went public the following year.

EXECUTIVES

Chairman and CEO, Kenneth (Ken) McBride, age 51, $595,833 total compensation
President, Kyle Huebner, age 48, $364,583 total compensation
VP Postal Technology and Affairs, J.P. Leon, $185,691 total compensation
Chief Product and Strategy Officer, John Clem, age 47, $287,083 total compensation
CTO, Michael Biswas, age 41, $279,167 total compensation
VP Information Technology, Michael Patchen
CFO, Jeff Carberry, age 44
Vice President, Leslie Loomans
SECRETARY, John W Owen
Auditors: Ernst & Young LLP

LOCATIONS

HQ: Stamps.com Inc.
1990 E. Grand Avenue, El Segundo, CA 90245
Phone: 310 482-5800
Web: www.stamps.com

PRODUCTS/OPERATIONS

SELECTED PRODUCTS & SERVICES:
USPS Mailing and Shipping Services
Multi-Carrier Shipping Services
Mailing and Shipping Integrations
Mailing & Shipping Supplies Stores
Branded Insurance
International

2015 Sales

	$ mil.	% of total
Service	176.6	83
Product	18.2	9
Insurance	11.7	5
Customized postage revenue	7.1	3
Other	0.4	-
Total	**214.0**	**100**

BRANDS
Stamps.com
Endicia
ShipStation
ShipWorks
PRODUCT CATEGORIES
Products
Small Office Mailers
Online Sellers
Warehouse Shippers
Corporate Postage Solutions
PhotoStamps
Supplies

COMPETITORS

Endicia	Pitney Bowes
FedEx	UPS
Neopost USA	US Postal Service
Newell Brands	eBay

HISTORICAL FINANCIALS
Company Type: Public

Income Statement FYE: December 31

	REVENUE ($ mil.)	NET INCOME ($ mil.)	NET PROFIT MARGIN	EMPLOYEES
12/17	468.7	150.6	32.1%	825
12/16	364.3	75.2	20.7%	700
12/15	213.9	(4.2)	—	600
12/14	147.2	36.8	25.0%	343
12/13	127.8	44.1	34.5%	250
Annual Growth	**38.4%**	**35.9%**	**—**	**34.8%**

2017 Year-End Financials

Debt ratio: 10.1%
Return on equity: 34.6%
Cash ($ mil.): 153.9
Current ratio: 2.35
Long-term debt ($ mil.): 60.6
No. of shares (mil.): 17.5
Dividends
Yield: —
Payout: —
Market value ($ mil.): 3,304.0

	STOCK PRICE ($) FY Close	P/E High/Low		PER SHARE ($) Earnings	Dividends	Book Value
12/17	188.00	26	12	8.19	0.00	28.33
12/16	114.65	28	16	4.12	0.00	22.06
12/15	109.61	—	—	(0.26)	0.00	14.31
12/14	47.99	22	13	2.25	0.00	12.82
12/13	42.10	17	8	2.71	0.00	10.61
Annual Growth	**45.4%**		**—** **—**	**31.8%**	**—**	**27.8%**

Starwood Property Trust Inc.

Starwood Property Trust hopes to shine brightly in the world of mortgages. A real estate investment trust (REIT) the company originates finances and manages US commercial and residential mortgage loans commercial mortgage-backed securities and other commercial real estate debt investments. It acquires discounted loans from failed banks and financial institutions some through the FDIC which typically auctions off large pools of loan portfolios. Starwood Property Trust is externally managed by SPT Management LLC an affiliate of Starwood Capital Group. As a REIT the trust is exempt from paying federal income tax so long as it distributes quarterly dividends to shareholders.

Financial Performance

Overall revenues grew 63% in 2012 to $327 million up from $201 million in 2011. The trust primarily earns money on interest income from mortgage-backed securities and loans.

Mergers and Acquisitions

In 2013 Starwood Property Trust bought LNR Property LLC a real estate investment finance management and development firm. The trust paid $862 million for LNR's US special servicer the US investment securities portfolio Archetype Mortgage Capital (now Starwood Mortgage Capital) Arche-type Financial Institution Services LNR Europe and 50% of LNR's interest in Auction.com.

Later that year it moved to spin off its single-family residential business as a new REIT named Starwood Waypoint Residential Trust. The trust which will be affiliated with Waypoint Homes will invest own and operate single-family rental homes and non-performing residential mortgage loans in the US.

EXECUTIVES

Chairman and CEO, Barry S. Sternlicht, age 56
EVP and Interim Principal Financial Officer, Jerome C. (Jerry) Silvey, age 58
COO and General Counsel, Andrew J. Sossen, age 39
President and Managing Director, Boyd W. Fellows
CFO, Stew Ward
Chief Credit Officer and Managing Director, Chris Tokarski
Lead Independent Director, Richard Bronson
Chief Originations Officer and Managing Director, Warren de Haan
Independent Director, Camille J. Douglas
Independent Director, Jeffrey DiModica
Independent Director, Strauss Zelnick
Auditors: DELOITTE & TOUCHE LLP

LOCATIONS

HQ: Starwood Property Trust Inc.
591 West Putnam Avenue, Greenwich, CT 06830
Phone: 203 422-7700
Web: www.starwoodpropertytrust.com

COMPETITORS

American Capital Agency Corp.	JER Investors Trust
Annaly Capital Management	MFA Financial
	PennyMac Mortgage
Arbor Realty Trust	Petra Real Estate
Colony Northstar	RAIT Financial Trust
Drive Shack	Realty Finance Corporation
Hatteras Financial	Redwood Trust
Invesco Mortgage Capital	Two Harbors
	iStar Financial Inc

HISTORICAL FINANCIALS
Company Type: Public

Income Statement FYE: December 31

	REVENUE ($ mil.)	NET INCOME ($ mil.)	NET PROFIT MARGIN	EMPLOYEES
12/17	879.8	400.7	45.5%	312
12/16	784.6	365.1	46.5%	340
12/15	735.8	450.7	61.2%	450
12/14	702.8	495.0	70.4%	468
12/13	565.7	305.0	53.9%	2
Annual Growth	**11.7%**	**7.1%**	**—**	**253.4%**

2017 Year-End Financials

Debt ratio: 12.6%
Return on equity: 8.9%
Cash ($ mil.): 369.4
Current ratio: 1.28
Long-term debt ($ mil.): 7,972.4
No. of shares (mil.): 261.3
Dividends
Yield: 0.0%
Payout: 126.3%
Market value ($ mil.): 5,580.0

STOCK PRICE ($)		P/E		PER SHARE ($)		
	FY Close	High/Low		Earnings	Dividends	Book Value
12/17	21.35	15	14	1.52	1.92	17.13
12/16	21.95	15	11	1.50	1.92	17.44
12/15	20.56	13	10	1.91	1.92	17.43
12/14	23.24	13	10	2.24	1.92	17.27
12/13	27.70	16	13	1.82	1.82	21.90
Annual Growth	(6.3%)	—	—	(4.4%)	1.3%	(6.0%)

Sterling Bancorp (DE)

Sterling Bancorp is the holding company for Sterling National Bank a community-based thrift operating dozens of offices in New York's Hudson Valley region and Greater New York City area. Founded in 1888 the bank attracts consumers and business clients by offering traditional deposit products such as checking and savings accounts and CDs. It uses funds from deposits to originate primarily real estate loans and mortgages. Sterling Bancorp which has assets of more than $7 billion was formerly Provident New York Bancorp; Provident acquired the former Sterling Bancorp in late 2013 and changed its name as well as the name of its banking subsidiary to Sterling.

Financial Performance

In fiscal 2013 Sterling Bancorp reported revenue of about $160 million up 9% from the prior year. The increase was primarily because of an 18% jump in loans that year (powered by commercial real estate and commercial and industrial loans) offset slightly by a decline in noninterest income.

Net income was also up in 2013 rising 27% to $25 million. Net cash from operations was down about 10% to $22.6 million.

Strategy

In 2016 Sterling sold its mortgage banking business which had seen declined earnings to Freedom Mortgage in New Jersey. Excluded from that deal were its mortgage warehouse lending operations a business arena it entered when other banks were leaving. The company is also selling its trust operations.

Mergers and Acquisitions

Sterling is focused on expanding in the greater New York metropolitan region and increasing the importance of its commercial banking operations. To that end in late 2013 it acquired the former Sterling Bancorp and took its name. The acquisition added the former Sterling's varied commercial and consumer lending products as well as its presence in the New York City area.

EXECUTIVES

Senior Vice President Business Intelligence, Patrick DeKenipp
Auditors: Crowe Horwath LLP

LOCATIONS

HQ: Sterling Bancorp (DE)
400 Rella Boulevard, Montebello, NY 10901
Phone: 845 369-8040
Web: www.sterlingbancorp.com

COMPETITORS

Capital One	JPMorgan Chase
Citibank	KeyCorp
HSBC USA	M&T Bank

HISTORICAL FINANCIALS

Company Type: Public

Income Statement

FYE: December 31

	ASSETS ($ mil.)	NET INCOME ($ mil.)	INCOME AS % OF ASSETS	EMPLOYEES
12/17	30,359.5	93.0	0.3%	2,076
12/16	14,178.4	139.9	1.0%	970
12/15	11,955.9	66.1	0.6%	1,089
12/14*	7,424.8	17.0	0.2%	829
09/14	7,337.3	27.6	0.4%	836
Annual Growth	42.6%	35.4%	—	25.5%

*Fiscal year change

2017 Year-End Financials

Return on assets: 0.4%
Return on equity: 3.0%
Long-term debt ($ mil.): —
No. of shares (mil.): 224.7
Sales ($ mil): 746.6

Dividends
Yield: 0.0%
Payout: 48.2%
Market value ($ mil.): 5,530.0

STOCK PRICE ($)		P/E		PER SHARE ($)		
	FY Close	High/Low		Earnings	Dividends	Book Value
12/17	24.60	45	36	0.58	0.28	18.86
12/16	23.40	23	13	1.07	0.28	13.72
12/15	16.22	29	22	0.60	0.28	12.81
12/14*	14.38	72	63	0.20	0.28	11.62
09/14	12.79	40	32	0.34	0.27	11.49
Annual Growth	17.8%	—	—	14.3%	0.9%	13.2%

*Fiscal year change

Sterling Construction Inc

Sterling Construction company specializes in the building reconstruction and repair of transportation and water infrastructure. It also works on specialty projects such as excavation shoring and drilling. The heavy civil construction company and its subsidiaries (Texas Sterling Construction Ralph L. Wadsworth Contractors RDI Foundation Drilling Myers and Sons Banicki Construction and Road and Highway Builders) primarily serve public sector clients throughout the Southwest and West. Transportation projects include excavation and asphalt paving as well as construction of bridges and rail systems. Water projects include work on sewers and storm drainage systems.

Geographic Reach

Houston-based Sterling Construction and its subsidiaries operate from offices in Texas California Arizona Utah and Nevada. The firm's major markets include Texas Utah and Nevada.

Financial Performance

The economic recession and prolonged recovery has taken its toll on Sterling Construction. The company reported a net loss of $297 million in 2012 following a loss of $36 million in 2011. The company attributed the losses which continued in 2013 primarily to additional write-downs on three large projects booked prior to 2012 in Texas that continue to have a negative impact on profitability. Sterling says it expects the projects to be substantially complete by mid-2014.

Revenue is improving however. In 2012 sales increased 26% compared with 2011 to $630.5 million driven by projects in in Arizona and California. Indeed 2012 marked the third consecutive year of rising sales for the firm. While the revenue picture is brighter profits are still expected to suffer as Sterling faces increased competitive pressure to bid low for construction projects.

Strategy

Sterling Construction and other companies that rely heavily on government highway work have been hurt buy Congress' inability to pass the Federal Highway Bill. Without new legislation new projects and funding for the work is uncertain. In response to the uncertain outlook Sterling refocused on project execution and conservative bidding. The company also sold some equipment in order to raise cash to upgrade its fleet.

Sterling Construction's long-term strategy is to expand its geographic footprint to attractive markets. The company also seeks to add to its construction capabilities. It has mostly used acquisitions to achieve those goals.

Increased competition has sent Sterling looking for work in new markets. As a result it has landed contracts in places such as Hawaii Montana Idaho and Louisiana. Sterling also expanded its operations in Texas to include El Paso and Corpus Christi. The company continues to seek opportunities in new markets in western southwestern and southeastern states. Sterling also is seeking to work on larger higher-margin design/build projects by entering joint ventures. One example is Ralph L. Wadsworth Contractors' joint venture with Fluor and two other companies to build a $1.2 billion project on I-15 in Utah.

Mergers and Acquisitions

In January 2013 the firm acquired the remaining 20% interest in Ralph L. Wadsworth Construction Co. from its management for $23.1 million. In 2011 Sterling expanded into Arizona and California with the acquisition of J. Banicki Construction. Also that year Sterling bought a 50% stake in California-based Myer & Sons Construction.

EXECUTIVES

VICE PRESIDENT SPECIAL PROJECTS, Joseph Malucci
Auditors: GRANT THORNTON LLP

LOCATIONS

HQ: Sterling Construction Inc
1800 Hughes Landing Blvd., The Woodlands, TX 77380
Phone: 281 214-0800
Web: www.strlco.com

PRODUCTS/OPERATIONS

Selected Subsidiaries
J. Banicki Construction Inc. (Banicki)
Myers and Sons Construction
Ralph L. Wadsworth Contractors LLC (RLW)
RDI Foundation Drilling (RDI)
Road and Highway Builders LLC (RHB)
Road and Highway Builders of California (RHBCa)
Texas Sterling Construction Co. (TSC)

COMPETITORS

Austin Industries	J.D. Abrams
Bechtel	McCarthy Building
Boh Bros Construction	Meadow Valley
Clyde Companies	Michael Baker
Fluor	Peter Kiewit Sons'
Furmanite	Williams Brothers
Holloman	Construction
Insituform	Zachry Inc.
Technologies	

HISTORICAL FINANCIALS

Company Type: Public

Income Statement
FYE: December 31

	REVENUE ($ mil.)	NET INCOME ($ mil.)	NET PROFIT MARGIN	EMPLOYEES
12/17	957.9	11.6	1.2%	1,740
12/16	690.1	(9.2)	—	1,684
12/15	623.6	(20.4)	—	1,565
12/14	672.2	(9.7)	—	1,799
12/13	556.2	(73.9)	—	1,655
Annual Growth	**14.6%**	**—**	**—**	**1.3%**

2017 Year-End Financials

Debt ratio: 19.4%	No. of shares (mil.): 27.0
Return on equity: 9.3%	Dividends
Cash ($ mil.): 83.9	Yield: —
Current ratio: 1.53	Payout: —
Long-term debt ($ mil.): 86.1	Market value ($ mil.): 440.0

	STOCK PRICE ($) FY Close	P/E High/Low	Earnings	PER SHARE ($) Dividends	Book Value
12/17	16.28	41 18	0.43	0.00	5.22
12/16	8.46	— —	(0.40)	0.00	4.30
12/15	6.08	— —	(2.02)	0.00	4.85
12/14	6.39	— —	(0.54)	0.00	7.11
12/13	11.73	— —	(4.91)	0.00	7.74
Annual Growth	**8.5%**	**— —**	**—**	**—**	**(9.4%)**

STORE Capital Corp

Auditors: Ernst & Young LLP

LOCATIONS

HQ: STORE Capital Corp
8377 East Hartford Drive, Suite 100, Scottsdale, AZ 85255
Phone: 480 256-1100
Web: www.storecapital.com

HISTORICAL FINANCIALS

Company Type: Public

Income Statement
FYE: December 31

	REVENUE ($ mil.)	NET INCOME ($ mil.)	NET PROFIT MARGIN	EMPLOYEES
12/17	452.8	162.0	35.8%	80
12/16	376.3	123.3	32.8%	68
12/15	284.7	83.7	29.4%	60
12/14	190.4	48.1	25.3%	50
12/13	108.9	26.3	24.2%	48
Annual Growth	**42.8%**	**57.5%**	**—**	**13.6%**

2017 Year-End Financials

Debt ratio: 44.0%	No. of shares (mil.): 193.7
Return on equity: 5.7%	Dividends
Cash ($ mil.): 42.9	Yield: 0.0%
Current ratio: 0.12	Payout: 133.3%
Long-term debt ($ mil.): 2,306.9	Market value ($ mil.): 5,046.0

	STOCK PRICE ($) FY Close	P/E High/Low	Earnings	PER SHARE ($) Dividends	Book Value
12/17	26.04	29 22	0.90	1.20	16.36
12/16	24.71	38 27	0.82	1.12	15.58
12/15	23.20	35 29	0.68	1.04	14.62
12/14	21.61	36 32	0.61	0.11	13.74
Annual Growth	**6.4%**	**— —**	**13.8%**	**119.2%**	**6.0%**

Summit Financial Group Inc

Summit Financial Group is at the peak of community banking in West Virginia and northern Virginia. The company owns Summit Community Bank which operates about 20 branches that offer standard retail banking fare such as deposit accounts loans and cash management services. Commercial real estate loans including land development and construction loans account for about 40% of Summit Financial Group's loan portfolio which also includes residential mortgages and a smaller percentage of business and consumer loans. The bank's Summit Insurance Services unit sells both commercial and personal coverage.

Summit Financial shut down its Summit Mortgage subsidiary in 2006 due to poor performance.

Summit Financial Group has twice put off plans to buy Virginia-based Greater Atlantic Financial. The firm originally arranged to buy the bank holding company in 2007 but terminated the deal a year later after Greater Atlantic suffered steep loan losses. Not long after the two companies reached a renewed agreement but that too was scuttled due to the economy.

EXECUTIVES

Senior Vice President And Chief Banking, Doug Mitchell
Senior Vice President Chief Banking Offi, Patty Owens
Senior Vice President Commercial Lending, Jason Hicks
Executive Vice President of Business Development, Jack Rossi
SENIOR VICE PRESIDENT AND TRUST OFFICER, Julie H Johnson
VICE PRESIDENT COMMERICAL LOANS, Anna B Abbey
VICE PRESIDENT OF MORTGAGE ORIGINATIONS, Oguz Sengul
VICE PRESIDENT COMMERICAL LOANS, Anna Abbey
SENIOR VICE PRESIDENT AND TRUST OFFICER, Julie Johnson
Senior Vice President Commercial Lending, Jim Rodgers
Board Member, Scott Bridgeforth
Auditors: Yount, Hyde & Barbour, P.C.

LOCATIONS

HQ: Summit Financial Group Inc
300 North Main Street, Moorefield, WV 26836
Phone: 304 530-1000
Web: www.summitfgi.com

COMPETITORS

Allegheny Bancshares	Highlands Bankshares
BB&T	Inc.
F & M Bank	SunTrust
Fauquier Bankshares	

HISTORICAL FINANCIALS

Company Type: Public

Income Statement
FYE: December 31

	ASSETS ($ mil.)	NET INCOME ($ mil.)	INCOME AS % OF ASSETS	EMPLOYEES
12/17	2,134.2	11.9	0.6%	349
12/16	1,758.6	17.3	1.0%	251
12/15	1,492.4	16.1	1.1%	231
12/14	1,443.5	11.3	0.8%	222
12/13	1,386.2	8.0	0.6%	224
Annual Growth	**11.4%**	**10.2%**	**—**	**11.7%**

2017 Year-End Financials

Return on assets: 0.6%	Dividends
Return on equity: 6.6%	Yield: 0.0%
Long-term debt ($ mil.): —	Payout: 44.0%
No. of shares (mil.): 12.3	Market value ($ mil.): 325.0
Sales ($ mil) 98.9	

	STOCK PRICE ($) FY Close	P/E High/Low	Earnings	PER SHARE ($) Dividends	Book Value
12/17	26.32	28 19	1.00	0.44	16.30
12/16	27.53	18 7	1.61	0.40	14.47
12/15	11.88	8 7	1.50	0.32	13.47
12/14	11.90	9 7	1.17	0.00	15.86
12/13	9.91	10 5	0.84	0.00	14.91
Annual Growth	**27.7%**	**— —**	**4.5%**	**—**	**2.3%**

Summit Hotel Properties Inc

From the southern states to the Mountain States Summit Hotel Properties has plenty of room for US travelers. Operating through its subsidiaries Summit Hotel is a self-advised real estate investment trust (REIT) that holds a portfolio of almost 90 midscale and upscale hotels with 11400-plus rooms across 24 states including major markets in western and southern states like Arizona California Colorado Idaho and Texas. More than 60% of its hotels operated under the Marriott International and Hilton brands during 2015 while the rest mostly operated under the Hyatt and Intercontinental Hotel brands. Summit Hotel was formed in 2010 and went public in 2011.

Operations

Summit's property portfolio consisted of 87 hotel properties with 11420 rooms in 24 states at the end of 2015. About 64% of the rooms were tied to the company's Marriott and Hilton branded properties while the rest of the rooms were tied to the Hyatt (22% of rooms) Intercontinental Hotel (11%) Carlson (less than 1%) and Starwood (less than 1%) brands.

Geographic Reach
Austin Texas-based Summit Hotel Properties has its hotel properties in 24 states including major markets in western and southern states like Arizona California Colorado Idaho and Texas.

Financial Performance
Summit Hotel Properties' annual revenues have more than tripled since 2011 as new property acquisitions have spurred additional room revenue over the years. The REIT's profits have also come back strong since losses in 2011 and 2012 as it's paid down its debt and kept a lid on rising operating costs.

The REIT's revenue jumped 15% to a record $463.4 million during 2015 with about two-thirds of the growth stemming added room revenue from 13 new hotel property acquisitions (with over 2000 rooms combined) made in 2014 and 2015. The rest of the growth came from same-store revenue growth of 8.3% which was driven by a 160 basis point occupancy rate increase and a 6% increase in same-store average daily rate (ADR) over the prior year's performance.

Strong revenue growth and a $66.6 million gain on 10 property sales in 2015 caused Summit's net income to skyrocket six-fold to a record $124.44 million. The REIT's operating cash levels climbed 29% to $132.2 million for the year thanks to a rise in cash earnings from room revenue.

Strategy
Summit Hotel continues to focus on acquiring premium-branded select-service hotels to grow its portfolio and boost its total room revenue. It also looks to bolster its portfolio's value through property renovation repositioning and asset management efforts. Summit believes that because its properties operate under multiple leading hotel brands in markets suited to the hospitality industry (near tourist attractions corporate headquarters conventions centers etc.) it is well-positioned to reap strong returns in the hotel industry for the foreseeable future.

The REIT has been acquiring properties in hot real estate markets in recent years. During 2015 for example it acquired seven hotel properties in growing cities such as Minneapolis Boston Baltimore Miami and Atlanta. In 2014 Summit bought six hotel properties in other strong real estate markets such as Houston Santa Barbara San Francisco and Austin TX.

Company Background
The company and its operating company Summit Hotel OP were formed in 2010 to acquire and operate the hotel portfolio of predecessor company Summit Hotel Properties LLC. It used the more than $250 million that it raised in its IPO to repay debt fund capital improvements at its properties and for general corporate purposes.

EXECUTIVES
EVP CFO and Treasurer, Greg A. Dowell, age 55, $360,000 total compensation
Chairman President and CEO, Daniel P. Hansen, age 49, $575,000 total compensation
EVP and COO, Craig J. Aniszewski, age 55, $375,000 total compensation

EVP General Counsel and Chief Risk Officer, Christopher R. Eng, age 47, $260,000 total compensation
Auditors: Ernst & Young LLP

LOCATIONS
HQ: Summit Hotel Properties Inc
13215 Bee Cave Parkway, Suite B-300, Austin, TX 78738
Phone: 512 538-2300
Web: www.shpreit.com

PRODUCTS/OPERATIONS

2015

	% of total
Room	94
Other hotel operations revenue	6
Total	**100**

COMPETITORS
Ashford Hospitality Trust
FelCor
Hospitality Properties Trust
Host Hotels & Resorts
LaSalle Hotel Properties

HISTORICAL FINANCIALS
Company Type: Public

Income Statement				FYE: December 31
	REVENUE ($ mil.)	NET INCOME ($ mil.)	NET PROFIT MARGIN	EMPLOYEES
12/17	515.3	99.2	19.3%	49
12/16	473.9	107.8	22.7%	44
12/15	463.4	124.4	26.8%	40
12/14	403.4	20.8	5.2%	39
12/13	298.9	5.8	2.0%	33
Annual Growth	**14.6%**	**102.7%**	**—**	**10.4%**

2017 Year-End Financials

Debt ratio: 39.2%
Return on equity: 8.6%
Cash ($ mil.): 36.5
Current ratio: 1.44
Long-term debt ($ mil.): 868.2
No. of shares (mil.): 104.2
Dividends
  Yield: 0.0%
  Payout: 85.1%
Market value ($ mil.): 1,588.0

	STOCK PRICE ($) FY Close	P/E High/Low		PER SHARE ($) Earnings	Dividends	Book Value
12/17	15.23	24	18	0.79	0.67	12.22
12/16	16.03	16	9	1.00	0.55	10.80
12/15	11.95	12	9	1.24	0.47	9.82
12/14	12.44	254	174	0.05	0.46	9.05
12/13	9.00	—	—	(0.12)	0.45	9.48
Annual Growth	**14.1%**	—	—	—	**10.6%**	**6.5%**

Summit Materials Inc

Auditors: KPMG LLP

LOCATIONS
HQ: Summit Materials Inc
1550 Wynkoop Street, 3rd Floor, Denver, CO 80202
Phone: 303 893-0012
Web: www.summit-materials.com

HISTORICAL FINANCIALS
Company Type: Public

Income Statement				FYE: December 30
	REVENUE ($ mil.)	NET INCOME ($ mil.)	NET PROFIT MARGIN	EMPLOYEES
12/17	1,932.5	125.8	6.5%	6,000
12/16*	1,626.0	46.1	2.8%	5,000
01/16	1,432.3	3.3	0.2%	4,300
12/14	1,204.2	(8.7)	—	3,990
12/13	916.2	(106.7)	—	0
Annual Growth	**20.5%**	**—**		**—**

*Fiscal year change

2017 Year-End Financials

Debt ratio: 47.9%
Return on equity: 12.0%
Cash ($ mil.): 383.5
Current ratio: 3.13
Long-term debt ($ mil.): 1,810.8
No. of shares (mil.): 110.3
Dividends
  Yield: —
  Payout: 35.7%
Market value ($ mil.): 3,469.0

	STOCK PRICE ($) FY Close	P/E High/Low		PER SHARE ($) Earnings	Dividends	Book Value
12/17	31.44	29	21	1.11	0.00	11.40
12/16*	23.79	47	26	0.52	0.00	8.65
01/16	20.04	40	25	0.50	0.00	5.16
Annual Growth	**25.3%**	—	—	**48.6%**	**—**	**48.7%**

*Fiscal year change

Summit Midstream Partners LP

Auditors: DELOITTE & TOUCHE LLP

LOCATIONS
HQ: Summit Midstream Partners LP
1790 Hughes Landing Blvd., Suite 500, The Woodlands, TX 77380
Phone: 832 413-4770
Web: www.summitmidstream.com

HISTORICAL FINANCIALS
Company Type: Public

Income Statement				FYE: December 31
	REVENUE ($ mil.)	NET INCOME ($ mil.)	NET PROFIT MARGIN	EMPLOYEES
12/17	488.7	85.6	17.5%	0
12/16	402.3	(38.1)	—	0
12/15	371.3	(186.8)	—	0
12/14	330.6	(21.1)	—	0
12/13	242.8	43.6	18.0%	0
Annual Growth	**19.1%**	**18.4%**	**—**	**—**

2017 Year-End Financials

Debt ratio: 36.3%
Return on equity: —
Cash ($ mil.): 1.4
Current ratio: 1.13
Long-term debt ($ mil.): 1,051.1
No. of shares (mil.): 74.5
Dividends
  Yield: 0.1%
  Payout: 234.6%
Market value ($ mil.): 1,529.0

STOCK PRICE ($) FY Close	P/E High/Low	PER SHARE ($) Earnings	Dividends	Book Value
12/17	20.50	27 19	0.98	2.30	18.63
12/16	25.15	— —	(0.71)	2.30	15.90
12/15	18.73	— —	(6.08)	2.27	14.51
12/14	38.00	— —	(0.93)	2.04	16.10
12/13	36.65	22 12	1.65	1.73	17.76
Annual Growth	(13.5%)	— —	(12.2%)	7.5%	1.2%

Sun Communities Inc

Sun Communities helps residents in the Sunshine State and around the US. The self-managed real estate investment trust (REIT) owns develops and operates manufactured housing communities (trailer and recreation vehicle parks) in nearly 30 states. Its portfolio includes more than 200 properties with nearly 80000 developed manufactured home and RV sites. Its Sun Home Services unit sells new and used homes for placement on its properties the majority of which are in Michigan Florida Indiana Texas and Ohio. Sun Communities also acquires at a discount and resells mobile homes that have been repossessed by lenders in its communities.

Operations

Sun Communities operates two lines of business: Real property and homes sales and rentals.

The Real Property business which generates roughly 75% of the company's total revenue owns operates and develops manufactured home (MH) and RV communities and is in the business of acquiring and expanding those communities to grow revenue.

The Home Sales and Rentals segment which operates under the company's Sun Home Services subsidiary sells manufactured homes and provides leasing services to consumers looking to live in their communities.

The company's properties have trained on-site property managers and maintenance personnel as well as such amenities as clubhouses laundry facilities and swimming pools. At the end of 2014 the company owned and operated 217 properties in 29 states including 183 manufactured housing communities 25 RV communities and 9 properties containing both manufactured housing and RV sites. That year Sun Homes Services had 10973 occupied leased homes in its portfolio and boasted an average renewal rate for residents in Sun Communities' rental program of 59%.

Geographic Reach

Sun Communities has nearly 220 properties across 29 states. Around 30% of these properties were in Michigan in 2014 while 17% were in Florida. Texas Indiana and Ohio each held 5% or more of the company's properties. About 20% of properties were in other states in the Northeast and the Southwest.

Sales and Marketing

Sun Communities spent $3.2 million on advertising in 2014 compared to $2.9 million and $2.5 million in 2013 and 2012 respectively.

Financial Performance

Sun Communities has enjoyed years of healthy revenue and profit growth thanks to aggressively property acquisitions and expansions with revenue nearly doubling over the past five years.

The company's revenue grew by 14% to $471.68 million in 2014 mostly thanks to a 14% increase in income from its Real Property segment as the REIT raised its rental rates by 3% during the year and continued to grow its occupied home sites. Rental home revenue also swelled by 20% as more residents took to the company's Rental Program and thanks to higher monthly rental rates. Home sales fell slightly for the company despite higher new home sales mostly as the company sold its pre-owned homes at lower prices during the year.

Higher revenue coupled with a $17.7 million gain on the sale of 10 MH properties in 2014 drove the REIT's net income up by 71% to a record $28.51 million while its operating cash rose by 16% to $133.32 million thanks to higher cash earnings.

Strategy

Sun Communities' main strategy toward growth has been to acquire highly-occupied and high-quality MH and RV communities with attractive amenities that support more potential occupancy and rent growth. Typically these are family or retirement communities with at least 200 home sites located near cities with populations exceeding 100000. In 2015 for example the REIT made two acquisitions totaling more than $1.5 billion (one was its largest acquisition ever) which spread its property portfolio business further into the fast-growing markets of Florida and Arizona.

Sun Communities' solid performance is in part due to increased demand from retiring adults a growing demographic. The company also points to its rental program as key to its success during the recession. Home rentals have become a popular and affordable alternative to customers.

Mergers and Acquisitions

In April 2015 the REIT completed its largest acquisition to date with the $1.3 billion-plus purchase of the Green Courte properties which spanned 59 MH communities across 19000 sites in the fast-growing markets of Florida and Arizona.

Additionally in early 2015 Sun Communities purchased seven large manufactured housing communities in the Orlando Florida area for $257 million which spanned 3150 manufactured housing sites (approximately 60% of these were in age-restricted communities) and were 96% occupied. Management believed that the purchase further strengthened its portfolio of high-quality communities particularly in age-restricted communities which it said were essential toward the REIT's sustained growth.

In early 2013 the company acquired ten RV communities (Gwynns Island RV Resort LLC Indian Creek RV Resort LLC Lake Laurie RV Resort LLC Newpoint RV Resort LLC Peters Pond RV Resort Inc. Seaport LLC Virginia Tent LLC Wagon Wheel Maine LLC Westward Ho RV Resort LLC and Wild Acres LLC) with 3700 sites in Connecticut Maine Massachusetts New Jersey Ohio Virginia and Wisconsin for $112.8 million.

In 2012 Sun Communities made seven acquisitions (which included 14 properties in total seven manufactured housing communities five RV communities and two communities containing both manufactured housing and RV communities. The acquisitions included Three Lakes RV Resort Blueberry Hill RV Resort and Grand Lake Estates located in Florida; Blazing Star RV Resort (260 sites located in San Antonio Texas); Northville Crossing Manufactured Home Community (756 sites in Northville Michigan); Rainbow RV Resort (500 sites in Frostproof Florida); four manufactured home communities (the Rudgate Acquisition Properties) in southeast Michigan and Palm Creek Golf & RV Resort (283 manufactured home sites 1580 RV sites and the expansion potential of 550 manufactured housing or 990 RV sites) in Casa Grande Arizona.

EXECUTIVES

Vice President Tax, J Han
Auditors: GRANT THORNTON LLP

LOCATIONS

HQ: Sun Communities Inc
27777 Franklin Rd., Suite 200, Southfield, MI 48034
Phone: 248 208-2500
Web: www.suncommunities.com

PRODUCTS/OPERATIONS

2014 Sales

	$ mil.	% of total
Real property income	357.7	77
Home sales	54.0	11
Home rentals	39.2	8
Interest and other	19.8	4
Brokerage commission and other income	1.0	-
Total	**471.7**	**100**

COMPETITORS

American Land Lease	Nobility Homes
Equity Lifestyle Properties	Outdoor Resorts
	UMH Properties
Hometown America	

HISTORICAL FINANCIALS

Company Type: Public

Income Statement — FYE: December 31

	REVENUE ($ mil.)	NET INCOME ($ mil.)	NET PROFIT MARGIN	EMPLOYEES
12/17	982.5	76.7	7.8%	2,727
12/16	833.7	31.3	3.8%	2,679
12/15	674.7	160.4	23.8%	1,790
12/14	471.6	31.4	6.7%	1,525
12/13	415.2	19.4	4.7%	1,236
Annual Growth	24.0%	41.0%	—	21.9%

2017 Year-End Financials

Debt ratio: 50.3%	No. of shares (mil.): 79.6
Return on equity: 3.0%	Dividends
Cash ($ mil.): 10.1	Yield: 0.0%
Current ratio: 0.25	Payout: 315.2%
Long-term debt ($ mil.): 3,037.9	Market value ($ mil.): 7,393.0

	STOCK PRICE ($) FY Close	P/E High/Low	PER SHARE ($) Earnings	Dividends	Book Value
12/17	92.78	112 90	0.85	2.68	33.15
12/16	76.61	302236	0.26	2.60	32.27
12/15	68.53	28 24	2.52	2.60	26.35
12/14	60.46	118 78	0.54	2.60	18.36
12/13	42.64	184129	0.31	2.52	10.53
Annual Growth	21.5%	— —	28.7%	1.6%	33.2%

Sun Hydraulics Corp.

It's not solar power that Sun Hydraulics delivers but fluid power. The company makes screw-in hydraulic cartridge valves and custom manifolds used to control speed force and motion in fluid power systems. Cartridge valves offer a general purpose floating design that is unique in pressure capacity reliability reduced size and installation. Sun Hydraulics' valves and manifolds are used in myriad industrial and mobile products including construction agricultural and utility equipment and to a lesser extent in machine tools and material handling equipment. The company operates through subsidiaries and distributors in the US UK Germany Korea China and India. The Americas represents almost 50% of sales.

Geographic Reach
Its products' worldwide manufacture and availability fuels the Floridian company's performance. Approximately 60% of sales are to customers outside of the US. About 20% of sales are buoyed by customers in the Asia/Pacific region.

Sales and Marketing
Sun's products are sold globally through a combination of wholly-owned companies representative sales offices and independent and authorized distributors. In addition to distributors the company sells directly to other companies within the hydraulics industry including competitors which incorporate its products into their hydraulic products or systems.

The company currently has 87 distributors 56 of which are located outside the US. In 2015 sales to Sun's largest distributor represented less than 6% of net sales.

Financial Performance
After achieving a milestone revenue total of $228 million in 2014 Sun saw its revenues drop 12% to $201 million in 2015. Profits also plunged from $44 million in 2014 to $33 million in 2015. The declines for 2015 were attributed to decreased sales across all its geographical segments including the Americas (13%) Europe (11%) and the Asia/Pacific (9%). This was fueled by lower demand for capital goods equipment coupled with unfavorable foreign exchange rates for the year.

Strategy
The company maintains a strategy of selectively expanding its core product two-thirds of which are sold for breadth of mobile equipment applications and the remainder for fixed-in-place or automation machinery applications. Emerging end markets include nontraditional sectors such as animatronics wind power solar power and amusement park rides.

EXECUTIVES

CFO, Tricia L. Fulton, age 51, $247,692 total compensation
Officer, Tim A. Twitty, age 51, $249,692 total compensation
Officer, Steven Hancox, age 57, $209,323 total compensation
Officer, Mark B. Bokorney, age 53, $176,539 total compensation
President and CEO, Wolfgang H. Dangel
Chairman, Philippe J. Lemaitre, age 68
Auditors: Grant Thornton LLP

LOCATIONS

HQ: Sun Hydraulics Corp.
1500 West University Parkway, Sarasota, FL 34243
Phone: 941 362-1200
Web: www.sunhydraulics.com

PRODUCTS/OPERATIONS

Selected Products
Integrated packages (using custom designed manifolds)
Screw-in hydraulic cartridge valves (electrically actuated and non-electrically actuated)
Standard manifolds

COMPETITORS

Actuant	Koch Enterprises
Bosch Rexroth Corp.	Parker-Hannifin
Dayco Products	Sauer-Danfoss
Jet Research	Servotronics
Development	Textron

HISTORICAL FINANCIALS
Company Type: Public

Income Statement
FYE: December 30

	REVENUE ($ mil.)	NET INCOME ($ mil.)	NET PROFIT MARGIN	EMPLOYEES
12/17	342.8	31.5	9.2%	1,150
12/16*	196.9	23.3	11.8%	1,100
01/16	200.7	33.1	16.5%	680
12/14	227.6	43.7	19.2%	719
12/13	205.2	37.9	18.5%	684
Annual Growth	13.7%	(4.5%)	—	13.9%

*Fiscal year change

2017 Year-End Financials

Debt ratio: 25.2%
Return on equity: 12.4%
Cash ($ mil.): 63.8
Current ratio: 3.20
Long-term debt ($ mil.): 116.0

No. of shares (mil.): 27.0
Dividends
  Yield: 0.0%
  Payout: 24.7%
Market value ($ mil.): 1,752.0

	STOCK PRICE ($) FY Close	P/E High/Low		PER SHARE ($) Earnings	Dividends	Book Value
12/17	64.69	56	29	1.17	0.29	10.07
12/16*	39.97	48	28	0.87	0.40	8.78
01/16	31.73	34	22	1.24	0.45	8.29
12/14	39.64	27	21	1.65	1.36	7.46
12/13	41.06	30	17	1.45	0.45	7.26
Annual Growth	12.0%	— —		(5.2%)	(10.4%)	8.5%

*Fiscal year change

Sunrun Inc

Auditors: Ernst & Young LLP

LOCATIONS

HQ: Sunrun Inc
595 Market Street, 29th Floor, San Francisco, CA 94105
Phone: 415 580-6900
Web: www.sunrun.com

HISTORICAL FINANCIALS
Company Type: Public

Income Statement
FYE: December 31

	REVENUE ($ mil.)	NET INCOME ($ mil.)	NET PROFIT MARGIN	EMPLOYEES
12/17	529.7	124.5	23.5%	3,260
12/16	453.9	91.6	20.2%	3,020
12/15	304.6	(28.2)	—	3,380
12/14	198.5	(70.8)	—	1,700
12/13	54.7	(1.2)	—	0
Annual Growth	76.4%	—	—	—

2017 Year-End Financials

Debt ratio: 36.9%
Return on equity: 16.7%
Cash ($ mil.): 202.5
Current ratio: 1.29
Long-term debt ($ mil.): 1,417.3

No. of shares (mil.): 107.3
Dividends
  Yield: —
  Payout: —
Market value ($ mil.): 633.0

	STOCK PRICE ($) FY Close	P/E High/Low		PER SHARE ($) Earnings	Dividends	Book Value
12/17	5.90	6	4	1.15	0.00	7.56
12/16	5.31	13	5	0.87	0.00	6.45
12/15	11.77	—	—	(0.96)	0.00	5.47
Annual Growth	(29.2%)	— —		—	—	17.6%

Superior Group of Companies Inc

Superior Uniform Group works to keep its business all sewn up. The company makes work clothing and accessories for US employees in several industries. The apparel firm designs makes and markets uniforms for employees in the medical and health fields as well as those who work in hotels fast food joints and other restaurants and public safety industrial and commercial markets. About half of its products are sold under the Fashion Seal brand. The company also makes and distributes specialty labels such as Martin's Worklon Blade and UniVogue. Chairman Gerald Benstock and his son CEO Michael run company which began as Superior Surgical Mfg. Co. in 1920.

Operations
The company operates its business through two reportable segments: Uniforms and Related Products (97% of sales) and Remote Staffing Solutions which includes The Office Gurus and TOG an affiliate firm that offers cost effective bilingual telemarketing and office support services.

Geographic Reach
From its headquarters in Florida Superior Uniform serves to outfit companies and customers nationwide boasting manufacturing operations overseas. Suppliers in Central American typically produce more than 50% of the company's products. It operates in El Salvador Costa Rica and the US through its The Office Gurus businesses and an affiliate entity in Belize added to its operations at the end of 2012.

Financial Performance
Due to a boost in market penetration Superior Uniform logged a 6% net sales increase in fiscal

2012 as compared to 2011 across its Uniforms and Related Products unit and 9% from its Remote Staffing Solutions. Net income for the same reporting period declined 27% due to the rising cost of goods sold — primarily related to cotton shortages in the Uniforms and Related Products business — and increasing payroll-related costs across the Remote Staffing Solutions segment.

Strategy

Demand for Superior's uniforms and service apparel largely depends on the health of the economy. The economic downturn in the US negatively impacted the uniform supplier's customers who closed locations reduced headcounts or eliminated uniforms to save money.

In addition to the challenging economic climate the dramatic rise in cotton prices has the potential to pinch Superior Uniform's profit margin. While the company has been able to compensate for its higher materials costs by raising prices it warns at times that gross margins could be negatively impacted.

Mergers and Acquisitions

In March 2016 Superior Uniform acquired BAMKO Inc. a Los Angeles-based merchandise sourcing and promotional products company. It acquired BAMKO and its China Brazil and England subsidiaries as well as an India affiliate for $15.8 million in cash. BAMKO's products complement Superior Uniform's; however the acquisition expands the company's presence in China and India particularly its branded merchandise and promotional product offerings. Superior Uniform operates BAMKO as a subsidiary.

EXECUTIVES

Vice President Marketing, Ron Klepner
EVP; President Fashion Seal Healthcare, Peter Benstock, age 56, $251,248 total compensation
CEO, Michael Benstock, age 62, $513,133 total compensation
COO CFO and Treasurer, Andrew D. Demott, age 54, $324,454 total compensation
VP Marketing and President Superior I.D., David Schechter
Vice President Sales Healthcare, Scott Delin
Chairperson, Sidney Kirschner, age 83
Assistant Treasurer, Jerry Chiovaro
Assistant Treasurer, Gerard Chiovaro
Auditors: Mayer Hoffman McCann P.C.

LOCATIONS

HQ: Superior Group of Companies Inc
10055 Seminole Boulevard, Seminole, FL 33772-2539
Phone: 727 397-9611
Web: www.superiorgroupofcompanies.com

PRODUCTS/OPERATIONS

2016 sales

	% of total
Uniforms and related products	82
Promotional Products	11
Remote staffing solutions	7
Inter-segment elimination	-
Total	**100**

Selected Brands

Blade
Fashion Seal
Fashion Seal Healthcare
Martin's
Worklon
UniVogue

COMPETITORS

ARAMARK	Convergys
Accenture	Fujitsu America
Alsco	G&K Services
Angelica Corporation	Sitel Worldwide
Broder Bros.	StarTek
Capgemini North America	Sykes Enterprises
	TeleTech
Cintas	UniFirst

HISTORICAL FINANCIALS

Company Type: Public

Income Statement

FYE: December 31

	REVENUE ($ mil.)	NET INCOME ($ mil.)	NET PROFIT MARGIN	EMPLOYEES
12/17	266.8	15.0	5.6%	2,280
12/16	252.6	14.6	5.8%	1,632
12/15	210.3	13.0	6.2%	1,278
12/14	196.2	11.3	5.8%	1,055
12/13	151.5	5.8	3.9%	973
Annual Growth	**15.2%**	**26.6%**	**—**	**23.7%**

2017 Year-End Financials

Debt ratio: 17.7%	No. of shares (mil.): 15.0
Return on equity: 12.7%	Dividends
Cash ($ mil.): 8.1	Yield: 0.0%
Current ratio: 3.31	Payout: 36.8%
Long-term debt ($ mil.): 32.9	Market value ($ mil.): 403.0

	STOCK PRICE ($) FY Close	P/E High/Low	Earnings	PER SHARE ($) Dividends	Book Value
12/17	26.71	27 16	0.99	0.37	8.29
12/16	19.62	20 14	0.98	0.34	7.62
12/15	16.98	40 17	0.90	0.32	6.66
12/14	29.37	35 17	0.82	0.29	5.95
12/13	15.48	35 22	0.46	0.34	5.52
Annual Growth	**14.6%**	**— —**	**21.1%**	**2.0%**	**10.7%**

Supernus Pharmaceuticals Inc

Supernus Pharmaceuticals wouldn't mind being a drug-maker superhero of sorts to epileptics. As a specialty pharmaceutical company Supernus develops treatments for epilepsy and other central nervous system disorders. It has two marketed products for treating epilepsy: Oxtellar XR and Trokendi XR. In addition it is developing a number of candidates to treat such ailments as attention deficit hyperactivity disorder (ADHD) impulsive aggression in patients with ADHD autism bipolar disorder schizophrenia depression and dementia. The company utilizes third-party commercial manufacturing organizations (CMOs) for all of its manufacturing.

Geographic Reach

Supernus Pharmaceuticals has its corporate office and laboratory space in Maryland.

Sales and Marketing

Supernus markets its products through more than 150 sales representatives and distributes them through wholesalers and pharmaceutical distributors. Supernus primarily targets neurologists to grow sales of its epilepsy franchise.

In 2015 advertising costs totaled $19.3 million up from $14.8 million in 2014 and $14.6 million in 2013.

Financial Performance

Supernus began earning product revenue in 2013 when it launched Oxtellar XR. The 2014 launch of Trokendi led to further gains in revenues. In 2015 revenue increased 18% to $144 million as more prescriptions of its two medications were issued.

Net income spiked in 2014 but declined 29% to $14 million the following year. This drop was related to increased sales and marketing spend for its two products as well as higher R&D costs for additional pre-clinical and clinical trials. Additionally Supernus was hit with tax expenses for the first time in 2015 which further cut into the bottom line. As of the end of 2015 the company had an accumulated deficit of some $144.6 million.

Cash flow from operations has risen sharply over the past couple of years. In 2015 it increased 315% to $32 million due to several factors including changes in accounts payable and an increase in cash provided by accrued sales deductions.

Strategy

Supernus is focused on growing its epilepsy franchise in the US and in getting its pipeline products on the market. It also has a licensing and royalty agreements with other firms which helps boost its overall earnings.

Mergers and Acquisitions

In 2018 Supernus agreed to buy privately held Biscayne Neurotherapeutics which is developing a treatment for epilepsy for an upfront payment of $15 million plus some $170 million in development and sales milestone payments. SPN-817 has been given the Orphan Drug designation in the US for the treatment of Dravet Syndrome a rare form of epilepsy in children.

EXECUTIVES

President CEO and Director, Jack A. Khattar, age 57, $523,403 total compensation
SVP Sales and Marketing, Victor Vaughn, age 60, $291,635 total compensation
SVP Intellectual Property and Chief Scientific Officer, Padmanabh P. Bhatt, age 61, $337,443 total compensation
VP Finance and CFO, Gregory S. Patrick, age 66, $330,470 total compensation
EVP Research and Development and Chief Medical Officer, Stefan K. F. Schwabe, age 66, $356,411 total compensation
Vice President Marketing, Stefan Antonsson
Chairman, Charles W. (Chuck) Newhall, age 73
Auditors: KPMG LLP

LOCATIONS

HQ: Supernus Pharmaceuticals Inc
1550 East Gude Drive, Rockville, MD 20850
Phone: 301 838-2500
Web: www.supernus.com

PRODUCTS/OPERATIONS

2015 Sales

	$ mil.	% of total
Net product sales	143.5	99
Revenue from royalty agreement -- Licensing revenue	0.9	1
Total	**144.4**	**100**

Selected Products
Oxtellar XR (marketed)
SPN-809(under trail)
SPN-810 (under trail)
SPN-812(under trail)
Trokendi XR (marketed)

COMPETITORS

Abbott Labs	Novartis Corporation
AstraZeneca	Noven Pharmaceuticals
Eisai Inc.	Shire
GlaxoSmithKline	UCB
Johnson & Johnson	Upsher-Smith
Mylan Pharmaceuticals	

HISTORICAL FINANCIALS

Company Type: Public

Income Statement   FYE: December 31

	REVENUE ($ mil.)	NET INCOME ($ mil.)	NET PROFIT MARGIN	EMPLOYEES
12/17	302.2	57.2	19.0%	422
12/16	215.0	91.2	42.4%	363
12/15	144.4	14.0	9.7%	344
12/14	122.0	19.8	16.3%	309
12/13	12.0	(92.2)	—	235
Annual Growth	123.9%	—	—	15.8%

2017 Year-End Financials

Debt ratio: —	No. of shares (mil.): 51.3
Return on equity: 24.9%	Dividends
Cash ($ mil.): 100.3	Yield: —
Current ratio: 1.86	Payout: —
Long-term debt ($ mil.): —	Market value ($ mil.): 2,045.0

	STOCK PRICE ($) FY Close	P/E High/Low	Earnings	PER SHARE ($) Dividends	Book Value
12/17	39.85	44 21	1.08	0.00	5.21
12/16	25.25	15 6	1.76	0.00	3.84
12/15	13.44	71 27	0.28	0.00	2.43
12/14	8.30	24 16	0.32	0.00	1.66
12/13	7.54	— —	(2.90)	0.00	0.84
Annual Growth	51.6%	— —	—	—	58.0%

SVB Financial Group

SVB Financial Group is the holding company for Silicon Valley Bank which serves emerging and established companies involved in technology life sciences and private equity and provides customized financing to entrepreneurs executives and investors in such industries. It also offers deposit accounts loans and international banking and plays matchmaker for young firms and private investors. SVB Financial also provides investment advisory brokerage and asset management services; and provides credit and banking services to wealthy individuals.

Operations

The company operates in three segments: Global Commercial Bank SVB Private Bank and SVB Capital.

Global Commercial Bank segment is comprised of Commercial Bank SVB Specialty Lending SVB Analytics and Debt Fund Investments. Commercial Bank serves commercial clients in the technology venture capital/private equity life science and cleantech industries. SVB Analytics provides equity valuation services to private companies and venture capital/private equity firms while Debt Fund Investments has investments in debt funds.

SVB Private Bank provides personal financial solutions for consumers while its capital arm SVB Capital focuses primarily on funds management.

As part of its lending activities Silicon Valley Bank sometimes pursues warrants to purchase equity stakes in its clients. About 80% of the bank's loan portfolio is dedicated to commercial loans with about half of those going to software and internet companies and another 25% of commercial loans going toward private equity or venture capital firms. Traditionally focused on up-and-coming firms the bank has implemented a strategy of courting larger later-stage clients.

Geographic Reach

SVB Financial has 28 offices in the US as well as seven branches in China India Israel and the UK.

Sales and Marketing

SVB Financial's clients are primarily venture capital and private equity professionals. Its customers include Active Power Coskata EnerNOC Joule and Solexant.

Financial Performance

SVB's revenue grew for its fifth straight year with revenue rising by 4% to $1.46 billion in 2014. Though nearly all income streams grew the main drivers of growth came from higher interest income from investment securities and loans as average deposit and loan balances grew respectively. A 130% boost in net gains on derivative instruments also contributed significantly to the company's top line.

Despite higher revenue net income reversed course in 2014 and fell by 12% to $478.72 million. The drop was mostly because SVB paid higher compensation and benefits as it gave its employees market-adjusted raises and hired 146 new staff members to support its product development operational sales advisory and commercial banking operations and initiatives.

Operations provided $255.52 million or 33% more cash than in 2013 mostly because more of its earnings were cash payments as opposed to 2013 when non-cash gains on investment securities made up a larger share of earnings. The company also enjoyed higher cash generation from foreign exchange spot contracts.

Strategy

SVB Financial Group has been focused on growing its loan business and assets to drive growth in recent years. Indeed in 2014 the company's loan assets grew by 32% to $14.4 billion while deposits grew 52% to $34.3 billion — both factors that led the company to record-high revenue by the end of the year.

It's also been selectively expanding and divesting its overseas operations to focus resources on profitable segments. In early 2015 subsidiary SVB Bank agreed to sell all of its outstanding stock in its non-banking financial subsidiary SVP India Finance Private Limited to Singapore-based investment firm Temasek. In 2012 the company opened a banking branch in the UK and started a joint venture bank in China.

Mergers and Acquisitions

In January 2019 SVB Financial Group acquired Boston-based Leerink Holdings the parent company of healthcare and life science investment bank Leerink Partners. SVB paid $280 million up front and created a retention pool for employees of $60 million to be paid over five years.

Company Background

Greg Becker who joined SVB Financial in 1993 was named the company's CEO in 2011. He succeeded Ken Wilcox who became chairman and is focused on the company's efforts to expand in China including a joint venture with Shanghai Pudong Development Bank.

HISTORY

Silicon Valley Bank was founded in 1983 by Roger Smith to provide banking services to tech startups in San Jose. The bank boomed along with tech companies during the 1980s lending to the likes of Cisco Systems.

In 1990 the bank spread east to Boston's burgeoning technology alley. It also expanded into residential and commercial real estate lending. The recession of 1989 to 1991 found Silicon Valley Bancshares with an overextended loan portfolio and in 1992 the bank booked a loss due to nonperforming loans; the next year it was put under federal supervision.

To rally stockholder confidence the company brought in new management and demoted Smith from chairman to vice chairman; he left the in 1995. The bank reduced its real estate lending and diversified into factoring foreign exchange and executive banking for venture capitalists and clients' upper management.

The 1995 IPO frenzy aided the company's turnaround. Silicon Valley cashed in on warrants it had taken as collateral from young companies. Regulatory supervision was lifted in 1996 and the bank soon opened offices in the Atlanta; Austin Texas; Boulder Colorado; Phoenix; and Seattle areas.

In 1999 Silicon Valley Bancshares created a website targeted at technology firms in need of financing employees office space and equipment. However nonperforming loans began to dog the bank once again affecting profits and bringing a regulatory request to boost capital reserves.

In 2000 despite being hammered by the high-tech stock selloff the company continued to expand opening offices in West Palm Beach Florida and North Carolina's Research Triangle and successfully capitalizing its first venture fund. The following year it bought tech-focused investment bank Alliant Partners (later renamed SVB Alliant) to broaden its service offerings.

Still licking its wounds from the tech bust the company ceased lending to the entertainment industry and to churches in 2002. Silicon Valley Bancshares changed its name to SVB Financial Services in 2005.

SVB Alliant struggled with losses for years and SVB Financial explored its options including spinning the unit off to management. It ultimately decided to shut down the division which ceased operations in 2008.

EXECUTIVES

COO, Michael L. Dreyer, age 54
COO, Bruce E. Wallace, age 53, $398,113 total compensation
President and CEO SVB Financial Group and Silicon Valley Bank, Gregory W. (Greg) Becker, age 51, $925,904 total compensation

Managing Director Accounting and Financial
Reporting, Michael R. (Mike) Descheneaux, age 51,
$602,308 total compensation
Head of Technology Banking, John D. China,
$498,385 total compensation
Head of Europe Middle East and Africa (EMEA)
and President UK Branch, Philip C. Cox, age 51
Chief Credit Officer Silicon Valley Bank, Marc C.
Cadieux, age 51, $447,308 total compensation
CFO, Daniel Beck
Chief Risk Officer, Laura Izurieta, age 57
CIO, Roger E. Leone, age 64
Vice President Market Manager, Lisa A Jung
Senior Vice President, Dave Bhagat
Vice President, Mark Harris
Vice President, Christopher Leary
Vice President Relationship Manager, Don Chandler
Vice President Relationship Manager, Anthony R
Raley
Vice President Manager Of Sales and Business
Product Management, Dennis Corbett
Vice President Relationship Manager Corporate
Technology, Phil Silvia
Vice President, Damarie Rodriguez
Vice President, Sam Subilia
Vice President and Foreign Exchange Trader,
Patrick Chin
Vice President Regional Director, Carmella
Montesdeoca
Vice President Corporate Finance, Andrea Jones
Senior Vice President and Senior Relationship
Manager, Matt Maloney
Vice President, Austin Badger
Vice President Software, Alex Choy
Senior Vice President, Andy Tsao
Vice President Relationship Manager, John Peck
Vice President, Benjermin Colombo
Vice President, Patrick Scheper
Vice President, Josh Dorsey
Vice President Foreign Exchange, Joseph Landers
Vice President Relationship Manager Cleantech,
Jordan Kanis
Vice President, Rob Walker
Vice President, Sarah Kwan
Vice President, Cody Nenadal
Vice President, Max Lautmann
Vice President, Dennis He
Vice President, Chelsea Hakso
Vice President Structured Finance, James Caron
Vice President Relationship Manager, Glenn
Marasigan
Vice President, Jennie Bartlett
Vice President, Chase Little
Vice President Corporate Finance, Matt Kelty
Vice President, Marc Neri
Vice President, Sean Thompson
Vice President, Michael Copty
Vice President Structured Finance, Derek Almeida
Vice President, Erin Angerer
Vice President, Tyler Dietrich
Vice President Early Stage Banking, Navid
Shahrestani
Vice President, Jordan Parcell
Vice President Wine Division, Dave Morrison
Vice President, Carly Kiser
Vice President, Aerin Lim
Vice President, AJ Fang
Vice President, Lindsey Guinn
Chairman SVB Financial Group and Silicon Valley
Bank, Roger F. Dunbar, age 72
Board Member, Eric A Benhamou
Assistant Secretary And Treasurer, Lori De Leon
Board Member, Mary Miller
Auditors: KPMG LLP

LOCATIONS

HQ: SVB Financial Group
   3003 Tasman Drive, Santa Clara, CA 95054-1191
Phone: 408 654-7400
Web: www.svb.com

PRODUCTS/OPERATIONS

2016 Sales

	$ mil.	% of total
Interest		
Loans	834.2	51
Investment securities	359.3	22
Noninterest		
Net gains on investment securities	51.7	3
Net gains on derivative instruments	48.6	3
Foreign exchange fees	104.2	6
Credit card fees	68.2	4
Deposit service charges	52.5	3
Lending related fees	33.4	2
Letters of credit	25.6	2
Client investment fees	32.2	2
Other	40.0	2
Total	**1,649.9**	**100**

Selected Subsidiaries and Affiliates

Silicon Valley Bank
SVB Analytics Inc.
SVB Asset Management
SVB Business Partners (Beijing) Co. Ltd.
SVB Business Partners (Shanghai) Co. Ltd.
SVB Global Financial Inc.
SVB Global Investors LLC
SVB Growth Investors LLC
SVB India Advisors Pvt. Ltd.
SVB Israel Advisors Ltd.
SVB Qualified Investors Fund LLC
SVB Real Estate Investment Trust
SVB Securities
SVB Strategic Investors LLC
SVB Strategic Investors Fund L.P.
Venture Investment Managers L.P.

COMPETITORS

Bank of America	Heritage Commerce
Citigroup	MUFG Americas Holdings
City National	U.S. Bancorp
Comerica	

HISTORICAL FINANCIALS

Company Type: Public

Income Statement   FYE: December 31

	ASSETS ($ mil.)	NET INCOME ($ mil.)	INCOME AS % OF ASSETS	EMPLOYEES
12/17	51,214.4	490.5	1.0%	2,438
12/16	44,683.6	382.6	0.9%	2,311
12/15	44,686.7	343.9	0.8%	2,089
12/14	39,344.6	263.9	0.7%	1,914
12/13	26,417.1	215.8	0.8%	1,704
Annual Growth	**18.0%**	**22.8%**	**—**	**9.4%**

2017 Year-End Financials

Return on assets: 1.0%
Return on equity: 12.5%
Long-term debt ($ mil.): —
No. of shares (mil.): 52.8
Sales ($ mil): 2,022.3
Dividends
   Yield: —
   Payout: —
Market value ($ mil.): 12,351.0

	STOCK PRICE ($) FY Close	P/E High/Low	Earnings	Dividends	Book Value
12/17	233.77	26 17	9.20	0.00	79.11
12/16	171.66	24 11	7.31	0.00	69.71
12/15	118.90	22 15	6.62	0.00	61.97
12/14	116.07	25 18	5.31	0.00	55.33
12/13	104.86	22 12	4.70	0.00	42.93
Annual Growth	**22.2%**	**— —**	**18.3%**	**—**	**16.5%**

Tabula Rasa HealthCare Inc

Auditors: KPMG LLP

LOCATIONS

HQ: Tabula Rasa HealthCare Inc
   228 Strawbridge Drive, Suite 100, Moorestown, NJ 08057
Phone: 866 648-2767
Web: www.tabularasahealthcare.com

HISTORICAL FINANCIALS

Company Type: Public

Income Statement   FYE: December 31

	REVENUE ($ mil.)	NET INCOME ($ mil.)	NET PROFIT MARGIN	EMPLOYEES
12/17	134.5	14.3	10.6%	536
12/16	94.0	(6.2)	—	241
12/15	70.0	(2.8)	—	204
12/14	48.4	(1.1)	—	0
Annual Growth	**40.6%**	**—**	**—**	**—**

2017 Year-End Financials

Debt ratio: 0.9%
Return on equity: 16.0%
Cash ($ mil.): 10.4
Current ratio: 1.21
Long-term debt ($ mil.): 0.7
No. of shares (mil.): 19.3
Dividends
   Yield: —
   Payout: —
Market value ($ mil.): 541.0

	STOCK PRICE ($) FY Close	P/E High/Low	Earnings	Dividends	Book Value
12/17	28.05	43 14	0.76	0.00	6.35
12/16	14.98	— —	(0.59)	0.00	3.37
12/15	0.00	— —	(2.97)	0.00	(0.58)
Annual Growth					

Tactile Systems Technology Inc

Auditors: GRANT THORNTON LLP

LOCATIONS

HQ: Tactile Systems Technology Inc
   1331 Tyler Street NE, Suite 200, Minneapolis, MN 55413
Phone: 612 355-5100
Web: www.tactilemedical.com

HISTORICAL FINANCIALS

Company Type: Public

Income Statement

FYE: December 31

	REVENUE ($ mil.)	NET INCOME ($ mil.)	NET PROFIT MARGIN	EMPLOYEES
12/17	109.2	5.8	5.4%	406
12/16	84.5	2.8	3.4%	335
12/15	62.8	1.3	2.2%	275
12/14	47.7	2.0	4.3%	0
Annual Growth	31.8%	41.4%	—	—

2017 Year-End Financials

Debt ratio: —	No. of shares (mil.): 17.8
Return on equity: 8.8%	Dividends
Cash ($ mil.): 23.9	Yield: —
Current ratio: 5.29	Payout: —
Long-term debt ($ mil.): —	Market value ($ mil.): 517.0

	STOCK PRICE ($) FY Close	P/E High/Low	PER SHARE ($) Earnings	Dividends	Book Value
12/17	28.98	108 44	0.31	0.00	4.08
12/16	16.41	112 62	0.15	0.00	3.54
12/15	0.00	— —	(0.15)	0.00	8.46
Annual Growth (30.6%)	—	— —	—	—	—

Teradyne, Inc.

Electronics makers concerned about quality and consistency can put their products through the Teradyne tests. The company is a leading supplier of automated test equipment and a maker of systems for testing semiconductors. Teradyne caters to electronics manufacturing services suppliers as well as OEMs who use its test systems to analyze complex electronics used in the computing consumer electronics military/aerospace and telecommunications industries. Customers include Apple government contractors and the US government. Teradyne has operations in Asia Europe and the Americas; but it generates the majority of sales from customers in Asia.

Operations

Teradyne operates through three segments - semiconductor tests wireless tests and systems tests. The semiconductor test group which accounts for almost 80% of sales includes the design manufacturing and marketing of semiconductor test products and services used both for wafer level and device package testing. The wireless and systems test group each account for 10% of sales. Wireless tests include products and services for smartphones tablets notebooks/laptops personal computer peripherals and other Wi-Fi and cellular enabled devices. The systems test group designs makes and sells testing products and services for military/aerospace instruments hard disk drive storage and circuit boards.

Geographic Reach

Teradyne conducts semiconductor test operations in all of its facilities which are located in China Costa Rica Japan the Philippines Taiwan and the US. Systems test facilities co-exist at the company's facilities at its headquarters and in China and Taiwan.

The company doesn't manufacture its own products but relies on subcontractors and outsourced contract manufacturers such as Flextronics in China to make its well-known FLEX and J750 products.

Its two biggest markets are Taiwan 30% of sales and China 18%. US customers account for 13% of sales.

Sales and Marketing

Teradyne primarily uses a direct sales force to sell its products; customers in Asia (the hub of the semiconductor industry) account for 80% of sales. In 2014 the company's three largest customers accounted for 21% of revenue.

Financial Performance

Sales grew 15% in 2014 to $1.6 billion up from $1.4 billion in 2013. Revenue rose 27% for semiconductor test and 6% for system test. The semiconductor test jump came from higher system-on-a-chip product volume. The increase in system test revenue was from higher volume in storage test and production board test activities. Profit fell 50% to $81 million due to an increase in operating expenses from goodwill impairment from the wireless test segment.

Cash flow from operations rose to $492 million in 2014 from $267 million in 2013.

Mergers and Acquisitions

In 2015 Teradyne bought Universal Robots for $285 million bolstering Teradyne's System and Wireless Test segment in a growing business. Universal Robots develops low-cost easy-to-deploy and easy-to-program robots that work side by side with production workers to improve quality and increase manufacturing efficiency. With Universal Robots on its roster Teradyne is targeting a bigger share of the $100 million collaborative robotics market which is growing at a fast clip.

In 2014 Teradyne acquired Avionics Interface Technologies a supplier of equipment for testing data communication connections for about $21 million. The purchase fits in with Teradyne's defense and aerospace line of bus test instrumentation for commercial and defense avionics systems. A

EXECUTIVES

Vice President Human Resources, Loren Eaton
Vice President US Sales Semiconductor Test Division, Bradford T Nelson
CFO and Treasurer, Gregory R. (Greg) Beecher, age 60, $479,251 total compensation
President CEO and Director, Mark E. Jagiela, age 57, $625,000 total compensation
VP General Counsel and Secretary, Charles J. (Charlie) Gray, age 57, $359,598 total compensation
President Systems Test Group, Walter G. Vahey, age 53, $300,000 total compensation
President LifePoint, Bradford B. (Brad) Robbins, age 60, $316,200 total compensation
VP SOC Marketing Semiconductor Test Division, Gregory Smith
President Universal Robots A/S (UR), J rgen von Hollen
Vice President Of Engineering, Mike Malone
Vice President of Engineering, Rick Burns
Vice President Business Development, Mark Kohalmy
Chairman, Roy A. Vallee, age 66
Board Member, Timothy Guertin
Board Member, Kee C Tay
Board Member, Edwin J Gillis
Board Member, Mercedes Johnson
Auditors: PricewaterhouseCoopers LLP

LOCATIONS

HQ: Teradyne, Inc.
600 Riverpark Drive, North Reading, MA 01864
Phone: 978 370-2700
Web: www.teradyne.com

PRODUCTS/OPERATIONS

2014 Sales

	$ mil.	% of total
Semiconductor test	1,300.8	79
Wireless test	184.5	11
Systems test	162.5	10
Total	1,647.8	100

2014 Sales

	$ mil.	% of total
Product	1,364.0	83
Service	283.8	17
Total	1,647.8	100

Selected Products

Semiconductor test systems
  Memory test
  Microcontroller test
  Mixed-signal test (A5 line)
  System-on-a-chip test
  Very large scale integration (VLSI) chip test
Circuit board test and inspection systems
  Automated optical inspection
  In-circuit and functional board test
  Software
Military and aerospace
  Spectrum CTS (avionics systems)
  VICTORY (boundary scan and fault diagnostic software)
Wireless test
  IQfact (chipset)
  IQflex (WLAN)
  IQxstream (multi-device tester for devices)

COMPETITORS

Advantest	Mitsui
Agilent Technologies	National Instruments
Anritsu	Orbotech
Camtek	Rohde & Schwarz
Cascade Microtech	Tektronix
FormFactor	Xcerra
Hitachi	Xyratex
High-Technologies	Yokogawa Electric
KLA-Tencor	

HISTORICAL FINANCIALS

Company Type: Public

Income Statement

FYE: December 31

	REVENUE ($ mil.)	NET INCOME ($ mil.)	NET PROFIT MARGIN	EMPLOYEES
12/17	2,136.6	257.6	12.1%	4,500
12/16	1,753.2	(43.4)	—	4,300
12/15	1,639.5	206.4	12.6%	4,100
12/14	1,647.8	81.2	4.9%	3,900
12/13	1,427.9	164.9	11.6%	3,800
Annual Growth	10.6%	11.8%	—	4.3%

2017 Year-End Financials

Debt ratio: 11.7%	No. of shares (mil.): 195.5
Return on equity: 13.6%	Dividends
Cash ($ mil.): 429.8	Yield: 0.0%
Current ratio: 5.00	Payout: 21.8%
Long-term debt ($ mil.): 365.9	Market value ($ mil.): 8,188.0

	STOCK PRICE ($) FY Close	P/E High/Low	Earnings	Dividends	Book Value
12/17	41.87	34 20	1.28	0.28	9.99
12/16	25.40	— —	(0.21)	0.24	9.18
12/15	20.67	22 17	0.97	0.24	9.65
12/14	19.79	52 40	0.37	0.18	9.60
12/13	17.62	22 17	0.70	0.00	10.35
Annual Growth	24.2%	— —	16.3%	—	(0.9%)

Terreno Realty Corp

Terreno Realty has its eyes set on acquiring industrial real estate. The real estate investment trust (REIT) invests in and operates industrial properties in major US coastal markets including Los Angeles San Francisco Bay Area Seattle Miami Northern New Jersey/New York City and Washington DC/Baltimore. The REIT typically invests in warehouse and distribution facilities flex buildings for light manufacturing and research and development and transportation and shipping centers. The company owns more than 125 buildings spanning 9.3 million square feet and two improved land parcels totaling 3.5 acres.

Operations

About 89% of Terreno Realty's property portfolio consisted of warehouse/distribution properties while flex buildings (including light industrial and R&D facilities) made up another 9%. Trans-shipment properties made up the rest.

Sales and Marketing

Some of Terreno Realty's tenants include FedEx Cepheid Northrop Grumman HD Smith Wholesale Drug Company Home Depot and the US government.

Financial Performance

Terreno Realty's revenues and profits have rising at a healthy clip in recent years as its rental income has increased with new property acquisitions.

The REIT's revenue rose by 51% to a record $68.9 million in 2014 thanks to new rental income from property acquisitions made in 2014 and 2013. Same-store revenue grew as well as it increased rental rates by 8% and as occupancy rates increased to 97.1% from 96.3% the year before.

Higher revenue in 2014 drove the REIT's net income higher by 61% to $10.7 million while its operating cash levels more than doubled to $29.3 million thanks to higher cash earnings.

Strategy

Terreno Realty seeks long-term earnings growth by increasing rents and operating income at its existing properties and by acquiring new properties in its six target geographic markets. In 2015 it spent on $115.5 million on properties in Washington DC while it also purchased properties in Annapolis Junction Maryland; Medley Florida; Union City California; Tukwila Washington; and Kent Washington. During 2014 it spent $235.7 million on 29 industrial buildings spanning 2.27 million sq. ft. and one improved land parcel (1.2 acres) growing its property portfolio's square footage by 33%.

In 2012 the company acquired 22 industrial buildings (containing almost 1.8 million square feet) for $180.9 million. Properties included Global Plaza in Sterling Virginia; Garfield in Commerce California; Caribbean in Sunnyvale California; and South Main in Carson California.

Company Background

The company took itself public in February 2010 in an effort to capitalize on a distressed market ripe with foreclosures and troubled loans. Portions of the net proceeds from its public offering were used to invest in interest-bearing short-term securities to help it gain REIT status.

EXECUTIVES

President, Michael A. (Mike) Coke, age 50, $541,667 total compensation
Chairman and CEO, W. Blake Baird, age 57, $541,667 total compensation
Executive Vice President Jaime J. Cannon, Andrew T. Burke
SVP and CFO, Jaime J. Cannon, $245,000 total compensation
Auditors: Ernst & Young LLP

LOCATIONS

HQ: Terreno Realty Corp
101 Montgomery Street, Suite 200, San Francisco, CA 94104
Phone: 415 655-4580
Web: www.terreno.com

PRODUCTS/OPERATIONS

2012 Sales

	$ mil.	% of total
Rental	24.5	78
Tenant expense reimbursements	6.7	22
Total	31.2	100

COMPETITORS

DCT Industrial Trust	Liberty Property Trust
Duke Realty	Mack-Cali
EastGroup Properties	Monmouth Real Estate
First Industrial	PS Business Parks
Realty	Prologis
First Potomac Realty	

HISTORICAL FINANCIALS

Company Type: Public

Income Statement				FYE: December 31
	REVENUE ($ mil.)	NET INCOME ($ mil.)	NET PROFIT MARGIN	EMPLOYEES
12/17	132.4	53.1	40.1%	22
12/16	108.4	15.1	13.9%	19
12/15	95.9	14.6	15.2%	18
12/14	68.8	10.7	15.6%	18
12/13	45.5	6.6	14.6%	15
Annual Growth	30.6%	68.2%	—	10.0%

2017 Year-End Financials

Debt ratio: 29.4%	No. of shares (mil.): 55.3
Return on equity: 5.7%	Dividends
Cash ($ mil.): 35.7	Yield: 0.0%
Current ratio: 0.76	Payout: 88.4%
Long-term debt ($ mil.): 461.6	Market value ($ mil.): 1,941.0

	STOCK PRICE ($) FY Close	P/E High/Low	Earnings	Dividends	Book Value
12/17	35.06	40 28	0.95	0.84	18.56
12/16	28.49	111 80	0.26	0.76	17.12
12/15	22.62	92 75	0.26	0.66	16.93
12/14	20.63	93 73	0.23	0.57	17.43
12/13	17.70	135 103	0.15	0.51	17.56
Annual Growth	18.6%	— —	58.6%	13.3%	1.4%

Texas Capital Bancshares Inc

Texas Capital Bancshares is the parent company of Texas Capital Bank with more than 10 branches in Austin Dallas Fort Worth Houston and San Antonio. The bank targets high-net-worth individuals and Texas-based businesses with more than $5 million in annual revenue with a focus on the real estate financial services transportation communications petrochemicals and mining sectors. Striving for personalized services for its clients the bank offers deposit accounts Visa credit cards commercial loans and mortgages equipment leasing wealth management and trust services. Its BankDirect division provides online banking services. Founded in 1998 Texas Capital Bancshares has about $11.7 billion in assets.

Financial Performance

The bank reported $488.6 million in revenue in 2013 an nearly 11% increase versus 2012. Net income was flat at about $121 million after posting three consecutive years of gains. Cash flow from operations continued its steep three year decline. The bank's total assets increased 11% from about $10.5 billion in 2012 to $11.7 billion in 2013. Total deposits increased 24% year over year to about $9.3 billion.

Strategy

Headquartered in Dallas Texas Capital Bank (TCB) believes that its Texas roots give it a competitive advantage over larger competitors that are headquartered out of state. Indeed TCB is gaining market share and is expanding by hiring experienced bankers and support staff. The bank is looking to grow within its main metropolitan markets but has also branched out beyond the borders of its home state. The bank has an Cayman Islands branch to offer offshore cash management and deposit products to it core clientele.

EXECUTIVES

President and CEO Texas Capital Bancshares Inc. President and CEO Texas Capital Bank, C. Keith Cargill, age 65, $825,000 total compensation
President Texas and Chief Lending Officer Texas Capital Bank, Vince A. Ackerson, age 61, $454,166 total compensation
Managing Director Regional and Specialty Banking Texas Capital Bank Austin Fort Worth and San Antonio and Commercial Real Estate and Builder Finance, Mark M. Johnson
EVP Austin Region Texas Capital Bank, Kerry L. Hall

Regional President Texas Capital Bank Dallas, Russell Hartsfield

Chief Risk Officer Texas Capital Bancshares Inc. and Texas Capital Bank, John D. Hudgens, age 62, $455,833 total compensation

Managing Director Specialty and Regional Banking Texas Capital Bank Dallas and Syndicated Finance Lender Finance Leasing and Financial Institutions, James D. (Jim) Recer

Regional Chairman Texas Capital Bank Houston, Bill Wilson

Regional President Texas Capital Bank San Antonio, David Pope

Managing Director Regional and Specialty Banking Texas Capital Bank Houston, John C. Sarvadi

Controller and Chief Accounting Officer Texas Capital Bancshares and CFO Texas Capital Bank, Julie L. Anderson, age 49, $355,000 total compensation

Regional Chairman Texas Capital Bank San Antonio, Shaun Kennedy

Regional Chairman Texas Capital Bank Fort Worth, Robin Hamilton

Regional President Texas Capital Bank Fort Worth, David Williams

EVP Builder Finance, Melissa Abel

EVP Asset Based Lending, Chris Capriotti

EVP Commercial Real Estate, Rob Delph

EVP Lender Finance, David Fricke

EVP Energy/Oil and Gas Syndicated Finance and Financial Institutions, Lester Keliher

EVP Financial Institutions, Peter Stringer

President Mortgage Finance, Gary Ort

EVP Technology Operations Enterprise Planning and Information Security Texas Capital Bank, Kirk Coleman

EVP SBA Lending, John Gannon

EVP Public Finance, Paul Howell

EVP Strategic Sales and Marketing, Greg Lewis

President Private Wealth Advisors, Alan L. Miller

Vice President Manager Credit Underwriting, Anthony Violi

Senior Vice President Compensation Director, Chris Gullo

Vice President, Lela Naggar

Vice President Deposit Operations, Leslie Marsh

Vice President in Commercial Banking Group, Guy Miller

Vice President of Information Technology Infrastructure, Randy Tiegs

Vice President Project Management, Allen Baumbach

Senior Vice President and Deposit Operation, Connie Couch

Vice President Corp Security and Investigations, Cary Wicker

Senior Vice President Risk Management Officer, Terry King

Vice President Fraud Investigator, Jamie Burud

Vice President Security, Neal Baker

Executive Vice President, Brent Johnston

Executive Vice President, Ronald Baker

Vice President Planning, Prasad Varma

Executive Vice President Human Resources and LD, Cara McDaniel

Senior Vice President Energy Banking Texas Capital Bank, Jonathan Gregory

Executive Vice President Director of Operations, James White

Senior Vice President and CRA Manager, Phil Aslin

Chairman, Larry L. Helm, age 70

Board Member, Elysia Ragusa

Board Member, James Browning

Auditors: Ernst & Young LLP

LOCATIONS

HQ: Texas Capital Bancshares Inc
2000 McKinney Avenue, Suite 700, Dallas, TX 75201
Phone: 214 932-6600
Web: www.texascapitalbank.com

PRODUCTS/OPERATIONS

2015 Sales

	% of total
Interest income	
Interest and fees on loans	92
Other	1
Non-interest income	
Brokered loan fees	3
Service charges on deposit accounts	1
Trust fee income	1
Swap fees	1
Other	1
Total	**100**

Selected Services

Association capital bank
Bankdirect
Business services
Mortgage business finance
Online services
Personal banking
Private wealth advisors
Treasury and liquidity

COMPETITORS

Amegy	Comerica
BBVA Compass Bancshares	Cullen/Frost Bankers
	JPMorgan Chase
BOK Financial	Prosperity Bancshares
Bank of America	Wells Fargo

HISTORICAL FINANCIALS

Company Type: Public

Income Statement
FYE: December 31

	ASSETS ($ mil.)	NET INCOME ($ mil.)	INCOME AS % OF ASSETS	EMPLOYEES
12/17	25,075.6	197.0	0.8%	1,564
12/16	21,697.1	155.1	0.7%	1,442
12/15	18,909.1	144.8	0.8%	1,329
12/14	15,899.9	136.3	0.9%	1,142
12/13	11,714.6	121.0	1.0%	1,016
Annual Growth	**21.0%**	**13.0%**	**—**	**11.4%**

2017 Year-End Financials

Return on assets: 0.8%
Return on equity: 9.3%
Long-term debt ($ mil.): —
No. of shares (mil.): 49.6
Sales ($ mil): 953.5

Dividends
  Yield: —
  Payout: —
Market value ($ mil.): 4,413.0

	STOCK PRICE ($) FY Close	P/E High/Low	PER SHARE ($) Earnings	Dividends	Book Value
12/17	88.90	25 19	3.73	0.00	44.37
12/16	78.40	26 10	3.11	0.00	40.59
12/15	49.42	21 14	2.91	0.00	35.39
12/14	54.33	23 17	2.88	0.00	32.45
12/13	62.20	22 14	2.72	0.00	26.72
Annual Growth	**9.3%**	**— —**	**8.2%**	**—**	**13.5%**

Texas Pacific Land Trust

Texas Pacific Land Trust was created to sell the Texas & Pacific Railway's land after its 1888 bankruptcy and yup they're still workin' on it. The trust began with the railroad's 3.5 million acres; today it is one of the largest private landowners in Texas with around 960000 acres in 20 counties. Texas Pacific Land Trust's sales come from oil and gas royalties (70% of sales) grazing leases easements and land sales. It has a perpetual oil and gas royalty interest under some 470000 acres in West Texas. About 8% of the trust's oil and gas royalties are from leases operated by Chevron U.S.A. Texas Pacific Land Trust uses the revenues from sales and royalties to buy and retire its own shares.The trust sold about 2200 acres of land in 2008 compared to some 1500 acres in 2007. While Texas Pacific Land Trust sold more acreage in 2008 the price per acre was less than a third of the price in 2007.Grazing leases are in effect on 99% of the trust's land.

EXECUTIVES

Co-General Agent CEO and Secretary, Tyler Glover, age 33

Co-General Agent and CFO, Robert J. Packer, age 49, $127,083 total compensation

Chairman, Maurice Meyer, age 83

Auditors: Lane Gorman Trubitt, PLLC

LOCATIONS

HQ: Texas Pacific Land Trust
1700 Pacific Avenue, Suite 2770, Dallas, TX 75201
Phone: 214 969-5530   **Fax:** 214 871-7139
Web: www.TPLTrust.com

PRODUCTS/OPERATIONS

2015 sales

		% of total
Easements and sundry income		40
Oil and gas royalties		31
Land sales	22.6	28
Grazing lease rentals	0.5	1
Interest income from notes receivable	0.0	-
Total	**79.4**	**100**

COMPETITORS

American Realty Investors	Koch Industries Inc.
	Permian Basin

HISTORICAL FINANCIALS

Company Type: Public

Income Statement
FYE: December 31

	REVENUE ($ mil.)	NET INCOME ($ mil.)	NET PROFIT MARGIN	EMPLOYEES
12/17	132.3	76.3	57.7%	32
12/16	59.9	37.2	62.2%	10
12/15	79.4	50.0	63.0%	8
12/14	55.2	34.7	63.0%	8
12/13	44.1	27.2	61.7%	8
Annual Growth	**31.6%**	**29.4%**	**—**	**41.4%**

2017 Year-End Financials

Debt ratio: —
Return on equity: —
Cash ($ mil.): 79.5
Current ratio: 2.05
Long-term debt ($ mil.): —

No. of shares (mil.): 7.8
Dividends
  Yield: 0.0%
  Payout: 13.8%
Market value ($ mil.): 3,493.0

	STOCK PRICE ($) FY Close	P/E High/Low	PER SHARE ($) Earnings	Dividends	Book Value
12/17	446.63	46 27	9.72	1.35	10.12
12/16	296.77	65 24	4.66	0.31	6.01
12/15	130.92	27 18	6.10	0.29	5.63
12/14	118.00	56 23	4.14	0.27	3.21
12/13	99.99	32 16	3.16	0.00	2.12
Annual Growth	45.4%	— —	32.4%	—	47.9%

Texas Roadhouse Inc

If people are getting rowdy at this roadhouse it must be because of the steaks ribs or the famous sweet yeast rolls. Texas Roadhouse operates a leading full-service restaurant chain with more than 515 company-owned and franchised locations in 49 states and four countries outside of the US. The Southwest-themed eateries serve a variety of hand-cut steaks ribs chicken pork chops and seafood entrees along with sandwiches chili starters and a variety of side dishes. The company also operates a small number of restaurants under the name Aspen Creek that specialize in hamburgers pasta entrees and pizza.

Operations

About 430 Texas Roadhouse locations are company-owned while the rest are franchised. The company gets nearly all of its revenue from company-owned and operated units. The company operated 16 of its locations as Bubbós 33 restaurants. Bubbós 33 is a family-friendly sports restaurant concept offering an assortment of wings sandwiches pizza and burgers chicken beef fish and other seafood. Bubbós 33 also offers an extensive selection of draft beer.

Geographic Reach

Although the chain is essentially nationwide now the bulk of Texas Roadhouse restaurants are located in the Midwest and Southeast. More than 50 of the company's restaurants are located in Texas and many units are located near interstate highways.

Sales and Marketing

Targeting the casual dining sector the Texas Roadhouse concept focuses on offering mid-priced menu items and a family-friendly dining atmosphere. The chain is primarily interested in serving the dinner segment offering its lunch menu only during the weekends. Its over-the-top Texas décor including such down home touches as jukeboxes and complimentary in-the-shell peanuts helps the chain distinguish itself in a crowded field of competitors that includes Logan's Roadhouse (owned by LRI Holdings) and Lone Star Steakhouse. Texas Roadhouse also faces stiff competition from industry heavyweights Chili's (Brinker International) and Outback Steakhouse (OSI Restaurant Partners).

Country singer Willie Nelson who is a partner in two restaurants located in Austin Texas serves as a celebrity spokesperson for Texas Roadhouse. The chain sponsors the popular artist's concert tours and each restaurant features "Willie's Corner" decorated with memorabilia.

Financial Performance

The company's revenue was $$1.99 billion in fiscal 2016 up from $1.81 billion in fiscal 2015. The increase compared to the previous fiscal period was largely the result of adding new units.

Texas Roadhouse's net income was $115.6 million in fiscal 2016 up from $96 million in fiscal 2015. The spike in net income was also driven by the increased amount of restaurant locations.

Cash flow from operations remained strong in fiscal 2016 and the company ended the year with $257 million in cash on hand up $30 million compared to fiscal 2015 levels.

Strategy

The chain relies on specially-priced value menu items and targets its marketing message toward cost-conscious families looking for affordable dining options. The company has continued its strategy of expanding its restaurant base and it plans to open 25 to 30 restaurants per year. The majority of the company's restaurant growth in 2017 was Texas Roadhouse restaurants with approximately six being Bubbós 33 restaurants.

Company Background

Founder and chairman Kent Taylor opened the first Texas Roadhouse in 1993. A veteran of the restaurant business he previously served with such chains as Bennigan's (formerly owned by Metromedia Company) Hooters and KFC.

EXECUTIVES

President and CFO, Scott M. Colosi, age 53, $400,000 total compensation
Chairman and CEO, W. Kent Taylor, age 62, $525,000 total compensation
General Counsel and Corporate Secretary, Celia P. Catlett, $200,000 total compensation
Vice President Training And People Development, James Scholz
Board Member, Dean Skinner
Auditors: KPMG LLP

LOCATIONS

HQ: Texas Roadhouse Inc
6040 Dutchmans Lane, Suite 200, Louisville, KY 40205
Phone: 502 426-9984
Web: www.texasroadhouse.com

COMPETITORS

Applebee's International	LRI Holdings
Brinker	Landry's
Buffets Inc	Lone Star Steakhouse
Carlson Restaurants	O'Charley's
Cracker Barrel	OSI Restaurant Partners
Darden	P.F. Chang's
Golden Corral	Ruby Tuesday
Hooters	
Ignite Restaurant Group	

HISTORICAL FINANCIALS

Company Type: Public

Income Statement
FYE: December 26

	REVENUE ($ mil.)	NET INCOME ($ mil.)	NET PROFIT MARGIN	EMPLOYEES
12/17	2,219.5	131.5	5.9%	56,300
12/16	1,990.7	115.6	5.8%	52,500
12/15	1,807.3	96.8	5.4%	47,900
12/14	1,582.1	87.0	5.5%	43,300
12/13	1,422.5	80.4	5.7%	45,700
Annual Growth	11.8%	13.1%	—	5.4%

2017 Year-End Financials

Debt ratio: 3.9%
Return on equity: 16.6%
Cash ($ mil.): 150.9
Current ratio: 0.78
Long-term debt ($ mil.): 51.9

No. of shares (mil.): 71.1
Dividends
  Yield: 1.5%
  Payout: 48.5%
Market value ($ mil.): 3,849.0

	STOCK PRICE ($) FY Close	P/E High/Low	PER SHARE ($) Earnings	Dividends	Book Value
12/17	54.08	30 22	1.84	0.84	11.79
12/16	49.56	31 21	1.63	0.76	10.62
12/15	36.06	30 24	1.37	0.68	9.55
12/14	33.78	27 19	1.23	0.60	8.73
12/13	27.80	25 15	1.13	0.48	8.35
Annual Growth	18.1%	— —	13.0%	15.0%	9.0%

The New Home Company Inc

The New Home Company (TNHC) is busy building new homes throughout the Golden State. Targeting first-time move-up move-down and luxury home buyers TNHC builds homes under The New Home Company brand name mostly in select growth markets in California (including San Francisco and Sacramento) and in Phoenix Arizona. Its home prices range from $300000 to $5 million and range in size from 800 sq. ft. to 5400 sq. ft. It also builds homes under its brand for third-party property owners. Since its founding in 2009 TNHC has delivered more 1400 homes since its inception via company projects unconsolidated joint ventures and fee building projects. The builder went public in early 2014.

Operations

TNHC operates two business segments: Homebuilding which generated 65% of its total revenue during 2015; and Fee Building (35% of revenue) which builds The New Home Company branded homes for a fee on behalf of independent third-party property owners. The builder typically takes between 24 to 48 months to build each home and 24 to 48 months to develop land after it acquires each accompanying land plot.

The company's average home sold for $1.9 million during 2015 while the average sales price of its joint venture project homes was $1.3 million.

Geographic Reach

TNHC mostly targets projects in select growth markets in California (including coastal Southern California San Francisco Bay area and Sacramento metro) and in greater Phoenix Arizona. More broadly it builds in Northern California (El Dorado Placer Yolo Marin San Mateo Santa Clara and Sacramento counties) Southern California (Orange Ventura San Diego and Los Angeles counties) and in the greater Phoenix Arizona area.

Sales and Marketing

The builder markets its homes through its website social media brochures direct mail and community-specific publications. Most of its home sales go through its own sales representatives.

TNHC has been ramping up its selling and marketing spend every year since 2012 to support growth. The homebuilder spent $8.94 million in 2015 up from $3.17 million and $1.77 million in 2014 and 2013 respectively.

Financial Performance

TNHC's annual revenues have skyrocketed tenfold since 2011 thanks to exceptional demand and rising housing prices in its target markets in California. While the builder suffered losses to support its growth in 2012 and 2011 its profits have been growing rapidly since then as the builder has kept a lid on rising operating costs.

The builder's sales nearly tripled to $430.1 million during 2015 mainly as delivery volumes increased 179% to 148 homes for the year and as the average home sold for 79% more or $1.9 million as the builder sold a larger portion of higher-priced homes in coastal Southern California where prices exceeded $2.7 million per delivery. While having a much smaller impact on the top-line growth TNHC's fee building income rose 60% on higher joint venture management fees and as construction activity in fee building communities picked up.

Exceptional revenue growth and stable operating costs in 2015 caused TNHC's net income to more than quadruple to $21.7 million for the year. The homebuilder used $32.3 million in cash during 2015 as it continued to build its real estate inventory though it used about one-third the amount of cash used in 2014 as it eased up on inventory building.

Strategy

The New Home Company remained in 2016 committed to acquiring land lots and building in its core metro areas of coastal Southern California the San Francisco Bay area and the greater Sacramento and Phoenix markets. The homebuilder also actively explored the possibility in expanding into the Southwestern and Pacific Northwest markets after its success in Phoenix in recent years.

Company Background

In January 2014 NHC filed a $113-million IPO with plans to use the proceeds to continue to acquire land develop lots and fund new and existing home-construction initiatives as well as other related purposes.

EXECUTIVES

Chairman and CEO, H. Lawrence (Larry) Webb, age 70, $519,231 total compensation
CFO, John M. Stephens, age 49
Chief Investment Officer, Thomas (Tom) Redwitz, age 63, $467,308 total compensation
President Northern California, Kevin Carson, age 58
COO, Leonard Miller
President Southern California, Andrew J. Jarvis, age 53
SVP and CIO, Paolo Benzan
Vice President, Mark Kawanami

Vice President, Kim Forbes
Vice President And Regional Manager, Rick Bianchi
Vice President Of Sales, Annie Charles
Vice President Operations, John Graham
Vice President Land Acq. and Forward Planning, AJ Jarvis
Auditors: Ernst & Young LLP

LOCATIONS

HQ: The New Home Company Inc
85 Enterprise, Suite 450, Aliso Viejo, CA 92656
Phone: 949 382-7800
Web: www.thenewhomecompany.com

PRODUCTS/OPERATIONS

2015 Revenue

	$ mil.	% of total
Home building	280.2	65
Fee building	149.9	35
Total	**430.1**	**100**

COMPETITORS

CalAtlantic	KB Home
D.R. Horton	Lennar
David Weekley Homes	PulteGroup
Hovnanian Enterprises	Toll Brothers
John Wieland Homes	William Lyon Homes

HISTORICAL FINANCIALS

Company Type: Public

Income Statement				FYE: December 31
	REVENUE ($ mil.)	NET INCOME ($ mil.)	NET PROFIT MARGIN	EMPLOYEES
12/17	751.1	17.1	2.3%	281
12/16	694.4	21.0	3.0%	289
12/15	430.1	21.6	5.0%	272
12/14	149.6	4.7	3.2%	234
12/13	83.2	6.7	8.1%	153
Annual Growth	73.3%	26.5%	—	16.4%

2017 Year-End Financials

Debt ratio: 49.4%
Return on equity: 6.7%
Cash ($ mil.): 123.5
Current ratio: 10.31
Long-term debt ($ mil.): 318.6
No. of shares (mil.): 20.8
Dividends
Yield: —
Payout: —
Market value ($ mil.): 262.0

	STOCK PRICE ($) FY Close	P/E High/Low		PER SHARE ($) Earnings	Dividends	Book Value
12/17	12.53	16	12	0.82	0.00	12.65
12/16	11.71	13	8	1.01	0.00	11.81
12/15	12.96	14	9	1.28	0.00	10.75
12/14	14.48	53	39	0.30	0.00	9.00
Annual Growth	(4.7%)	—	—	39.8%	—	12.0%

The Trade Desk Inc

Auditors: PricewaterhouseCoopers LLP

LOCATIONS

HQ: The Trade Desk Inc
42 N. Chestnut Street, Ventura, CA 93001
Phone: 805 585-3434
Web: www.thetradedesk.com

HISTORICAL FINANCIALS

Company Type: Public

Income Statement				FYE: December 31
	REVENUE ($ mil.)	NET INCOME ($ mil.)	NET PROFIT MARGIN	EMPLOYEES
12/17	308.2	101.6	33.0%	713
12/16	202.9	(6.2)	—	467
12/15	113.8	24.6	21.7%	387
12/14	44.5	0.0	0.0%	0
Annual Growth	90.6%	2628.8%	—	—

2017 Year-End Financials

Debt ratio: 3.3%
Return on equity: 49.5%
Cash ($ mil.): 155.9
Current ratio: 1.48
Long-term debt ($ mil.): 27.0
No. of shares (mil.): 41.6
Dividends
Yield: —
Payout: —
Market value ($ mil.): 1,904.0

	STOCK PRICE ($) FY Close	P/E High/Low		PER SHARE ($) Earnings	Dividends	Book Value
12/17	45.73	53	21	1.15	0.00	5.90
12/16	27.67	—	—	(1.46)	0.00	4.20
12/15	0.00	—	—	0.39	0.00	3.52
Annual Growth	—	—	—	71.7%	—	29.4%

Thomasville Bancshares, Inc.

EXECUTIVES

Vice President, Wylie Watt
Assistant Vice President, Allen Corbin
Auditors: Mauldin & Jenkins, LLC

LOCATIONS

HQ: Thomasville Bancshares, Inc.
301 North Broad Street, Thomasville, GA 31792
Phone: 229 226-3300

COMPETITORS

Ameris	SunTrust
Bank of America	Synovus
Capital City Bank	

HISTORICAL FINANCIALS

Company Type: Public

Income Statement				FYE: December 31
	ASSETS ($ mil.)	NET INCOME ($ mil.)	INCOME AS % OF ASSETS	EMPLOYEES
12/17	806.4	12.0	1.5%	0
12/16	780.2	11.8	1.5%	0
12/15	753.5	9.6	1.3%	0
12/14	650.2	8.4	1.3%	0
12/13	592.7	7.2	1.2%	0
Annual Growth	8.0%	13.6%	—	—

2017 Year-End Financials
Return on assets: 1.5%
Return on equity: 17.5%
Long-term debt ($ mil.): —
No. of shares (mil.): 5.9
Sales ($ mil): 45.4

Dividends
Yield: 0.0%
Payout: 54.6%
Market value ($ mil.): 238.0

	STOCK PRICE ($)	P/E	PER SHARE ($)		
	FY Close	High/Low	Earnings	Dividends	Book Value
12/17	40.00	20 17	1.83	1.00	12.05
12/16	35.00	18 14	1.81	0.85	11.10
12/15	28.75	18 16	1.48	0.75	9.96
12/14	29.50	29 15	1.30	0.65	9.14
12/13	28.25	32 18	1.14	1.20	8.35
Annual Growth	9.1%	— —	12.6%	(4.5%)	9.6%

Tile Shop Holdings Inc

Auditors: Ernst & Young LLP

LOCATIONS

HQ: Tile Shop Holdings Inc
14000 Carlson Parkway, Plymouth, MN 55441
Phone: 763 852-2950
Web: www.tileshop.com

HISTORICAL FINANCIALS
Company Type: Public

Income Statement				FYE: December 31
	REVENUE ($ mil.)	NET INCOME ($ mil.)	NET PROFIT MARGIN	EMPLOYEES
12/17	344.6	10.8	3.1%	1,634
12/16	324.1	18.4	5.7%	1,448
12/15	292.9	15.7	5.4%	1,410
12/14	257.1	10.5	4.1%	1,190
12/13	229.5	(35.6)	—	1,214
Annual Growth	10.7%	—	—	7.7%

2017 Year-End Financials
Debt ratio: 10.1%
Return on equity: 7.6%
Cash ($ mil.): 6.6
Current ratio: 1.70
Long-term debt ($ mil.): 18.7

No. of shares (mil.): 52.1
Dividends
Yield: 0.0%
Payout: 95.2%
Market value ($ mil.): 501.0

	STOCK PRICE ($)	P/E	PER SHARE ($)		
	FY Close	High/Low	Earnings	Dividends	Book Value
12/17	9.60	104 39	0.21	0.20	2.76
12/16	19.55	59 35	0.36	0.00	2.69
12/15	16.40	56 23	0.31	0.00	2.24
12/14	8.88	88 38	0.21	0.00	1.83
12/13	18.07	— —	(0.72)	0.00	1.56
Annual Growth	(14.6%)	— —	—	—	15.3%

Timberland Bancorp, Inc.

Located among the tall trees of the Pacific Northwest Timberland Bancorp is the holding company for Timberland Savings Bank which operates more than 20 branches in western Washington. The bank targets individuals and regional businesses offering checking savings and money market accounts and CDs. Timberland Savings Bank concentrates on real estate lending including commercial and residential mortgages multifamily residential loans and land develoment loans; it also writes business loans and other types of loans. Timberland Savings Bank was founded in 1915 as a savings and loan.

EXECUTIVES

Vice President Deposit Operations Regional Manager, Maria Meyer
Vice President Executive Admin. Secretary Appraisal Officer, Rexann Napoleon
Auditors: Delap LLP

LOCATIONS

HQ: Timberland Bancorp, Inc.
624 Simpson Avenue, Hoquiam, WA 98550
Phone: 360 533-4747
Web: www.timberlandbank.com

COMPETITORS

Bank of America	KeyCorp
Columbia Banking	Washington Federal
JPMorgan Chase	Wells Fargo

HISTORICAL FINANCIALS
Company Type: Public

Income Statement				FYE: September 30
	ASSETS ($ mil.)	NET INCOME ($ mil.)	INCOME AS % OF ASSETS	EMPLOYEES
09/18	1,018.2	16.7	1.6%	268
09/17	952.0	14.1	1.5%	274
09/16	891.3	10.1	1.1%	269
09/15	815.8	8.2	1.0%	253
09/14	745.5	5.8	0.8%	256
Annual Growth	8.1%	30.0%	—	1.2%

2018 Year-End Financials
Return on assets: 1.7%
Return on equity: 14.1%
Long-term debt ($ mil.): —
No. of shares (mil.): 7.4
Sales ($ mil): 54.3

Dividends
Yield: 0.0%
Payout: 27.0%
Market value ($ mil.): 231.0

	STOCK PRICE ($)	P/E	PER SHARE ($)		
	FY Close	High/Low	Earnings	Dividends	Book Value
09/18	31.24	17 12	2.22	0.60	16.84
09/17	31.34	16 8	1.92	0.50	15.08
09/16	15.75	11 7	1.43	0.37	13.95
09/15	10.89	10 8	1.17	0.24	12.76
09/14	10.54	14 10	0.80	0.16	11.75
Annual Growth	31.2%	— —	29.1%	39.2%	9.4%

TowneBank

Auditors: Dixon Hughes Goodman LLP

LOCATIONS

HQ: TowneBank
5716 High Street, Portsmouth, VA 23703
Phone: 757 638-7500
Web: www.townebank.com

HISTORICAL FINANCIALS
Company Type: Public

Income Statement				FYE: December 31
	ASSETS ($ mil.)	NET INCOME ($ mil.)	INCOME AS % OF ASSETS	EMPLOYEES
12/17	8,522.1	87.6	1.0%	2,727
12/16	7,973.9	67.2	0.8%	2,529
12/15	6,296.5	62.3	1.0%	1,903
12/14	4,982.4	42.1	0.8%	1,737
12/13	4,673.0	41.7	0.9%	1,741
Annual Growth	16.2%	20.4%	—	11.9%

2017 Year-End Financials
Return on assets: 1.0%
Return on equity: 7.9%
Long-term debt ($ mil.): —
No. of shares (mil.): 62.6
Sales ($ mil): 493.2

Dividends
Yield: 0.0%
Payout: 39.0%
Market value ($ mil.): 1,926.0

	STOCK PRICE ($)	P/E	PER SHARE ($)		
	FY Close	High/Low	Earnings	Dividends	Book Value
12/17	30.75	25 21	1.41	0.55	18.06
12/16	33.25	29 14	1.18	0.51	17.20
12/15	20.87	18 12	1.22	0.47	15.71
12/14	15.12	14 11	1.18	0.43	17.02
12/13	15.39	15 12	1.14	0.38	16.32
Annual Growth	18.9%	— —	5.5%	9.7%	2.6%

TPG RE Finance Trust Inc

Auditors: DELOITTE & TOUCHE LLP

LOCATIONS

HQ: TPG RE Finance Trust Inc
888 Seventh Avenue, 35th Floor, New York, NY 10106
Phone: 212 601-4700
Web: www.tpgrefinance.com

HISTORICAL FINANCIALS
Company Type: Public

Income Statement				FYE: December 31
	REVENUE ($ mil.)	NET INCOME ($ mil.)	NET PROFIT MARGIN	EMPLOYEES
12/17	200.6	94.3	47.0%	0
12/16	154.0	69.9	45.4%	0
12/15	128.7	59.3	46.1%	0
12/14	1.8	(8.2)	—	0
Annual Growth	377.1%	—	—	—

2017 Year-End Financials

Debt ratio: 63.0% No. of shares (mil.): 60.6
Return on equity: 8.6% Dividends
Cash ($ mil.): 75.0 Yield: 0.0%
Current ratio: 2.38 Payout: 40.8%
Long-term debt ($ mil.): 2,114.9 Market value ($ mil.): 1,155.0

	STOCK PRICE ($) FY Close	P/E High/Low	PER SHARE ($) Earnings	Dividends	Book Value
12/17	19.05	12 11	1.74	0.71	19.82
12/16	0.00	— —	2.09	1.99	24.75
Annual Growth (19.9%)	—		—	(16.7%)	(64.3%)

TPG Specialty Lending Inc

Auditors: KPMG LLP

LOCATIONS

HQ: TPG Specialty Lending Inc
301 Commerce Street, Suite 3300, Fort Worth, TX 76102
Phone: 817 871-4000 **Fax:** 817 871-4001
Web: www.tpgspecialtylending.com

HISTORICAL FINANCIALS
Company Type: Public

Income Statement   FYE: December 31

	ASSETS ($ mil.)	NET INCOME ($ mil.)	INCOME AS % OF ASSETS	EMPLOYEES
12/17	1,720.2	120.2	7.0%	0
12/16	1,675.5	107.3	6.4%	0
12/15	1,516.9	95.3	6.3%	0
12/14	1,303.7	104.4	8.0%	0
12/13	1,039.1	57.5	5.5%	0
Annual Growth	13.4%	20.3%	—	—

2017 Year-End Financials

Return on assets: 7.0% Dividends
Return on equity: 12.5% Yield: 0.0%
Long-term debt ($ mil.): — Payout: 94.0%
No. of shares (mil.): 60.2 Market value ($ mil.): 1,193.0
Sales ($ mil): 210.9

	STOCK PRICE ($) FY Close	P/E High/Low	PER SHARE ($) Earnings	Dividends	Book Value
12/17	19.80	12 10	1.86	1.75	16.09
12/16	18.68	10 8	1.83	1.56	15.95
12/15	16.22	16 14	1.18	1.56	15.15
12/14	16.82	14 9	1.68	1.53	15.53
Annual Growth	5.6%	— —	3.5%	4.6%	1.2%

TPI Composites Inc

Auditors: KPMG LLP

LOCATIONS

HQ: TPI Composites Inc
8501 North Scottsdale Road, Gainey Center II, Suite 100,
Scottsdale, AZ 85253
Phone: 480 305-8910
Web: www.tpicomposites.com

HISTORICAL FINANCIALS
Company Type: Public

Income Statement   FYE: December 31

	REVENUE ($ mil.)	NET INCOME ($ mil.)	NET PROFIT MARGIN	EMPLOYEES
12/17	930.2	43.6	4.7%	7,700
12/16	754.8	13.8	1.8%	6,700
12/15	585.8	7.6	1.3%	6,000
12/14	320.7	(6.6)	—	0
12/13	215.0	1.2	0.6%	0
Annual Growth	44.2%	141.8%		

2017 Year-End Financials

Debt ratio: 21.1% No. of shares (mil.): 34.0
Return on equity: 32.7% Dividends
Cash ($ mil.): 148.1 Yield: —
Current ratio: 1.34 Payout: —
Long-term debt ($ mil.): 85.8 Market value ($ mil.): 696.0

	STOCK PRICE ($) FY Close	P/E High/Low	PER SHARE ($) Earnings	Dividends	Book Value
12/17	20.46	19 12	1.25	0.00	4.72
12/16	16.04	47 28	0.48	0.00	3.16
Annual Growth	27.6%	—	—160.4%	—	49.5%

TransUnion

Auditors: Ernst & Young LLP

LOCATIONS

HQ: TransUnion
555 West Adams, Chicago, IL 60661
Phone: 312 985-2000
Web: www.transunion.com

HISTORICAL FINANCIALS
Company Type: Public

Income Statement   FYE: December 31

	REVENUE ($ mil.)	NET INCOME ($ mil.)	NET PROFIT MARGIN	EMPLOYEES
12/17	1,933.8	441.2	22.8%	5,100
12/16	1,704.9	120.6	7.1%	4,700
12/15	1,506.8	5.9	0.4%	4,200
12/14	1,304.7	(12.5)	—	4,200
12/13	1,183.2	(35.1)	—	0
Annual Growth	13.1%			

2017 Year-End Financials

Debt ratio: 48.1% No. of shares (mil.): 183.2
Return on equity: 28.5% Dividends
Cash ($ mil.): 115.8 Yield: —
Current ratio: 1.28 Payout: —
Long-term debt ($ mil.): 2,345.3 Market value ($ mil.): 10,069.0

	STOCK PRICE ($) FY Close	P/E High/Low	PER SHARE ($) Earnings	Dividends	Book Value
12/17	54.96	23 13	2.32	0.00	9.44
12/16	30.93	54 32	0.65	0.00	7.44
12/15	27.57	700580	0.04	0.00	6.75
Annual Growth	41.2%	—	—661.6%	—	18.2%

Trex Co Inc

Trex Company is all decked out with plenty of places to go. It's the world's largest maker of wood-alternative decking and railing products which are used in the construction of residential and commercial decks rails and trims. Marketed under the Trex name products resemble wood and have the workability of wood but require less long-term maintenance. The Trex Wood-Polymer composite is made of waste wood fibers and reclaimed plastic. Trex serves professional installation contractors and do-it-yourselfers through about 90 wholesale distribution centers which in turn sell to retailers including Home Depot and Lowe's. Trex products are available in more than 5500 locations primarily in the US and Canada.

Operations

Trex produces five principal decking products: Trex Transcend Trex Enhance Trex Select Trex Accents and Trex Escapes. Its two railing products include Trex Designer Series Railing and Trex Transcend Railing. The company's collection also includes Trex Transcend Porch Flooring and Railing System (a porch product) Trex Elevations (a steel deck framing system) Trex Seclusions (a fencing product) Trex DeckLighting (a deck lighting system) TrexTrim (a cellular PVC outdoor trim product) and Trex Hideaway (a hidden fastening system for specially grooved boards). Its newest product is polyethylene pellets made from recycled plastic that it sells to plastic bag sheet and film makers.

The company converts millions of pounds of recycled and reclaimed plastic and waste wood each year into Trex products. Its raw materials come from recovered plastic grocery bags plastic film and waste wood fiber. As part of its operations the company each year purchases about 300 million pounds of both used polyethylene and hardwood sawdust. It recycles more than 1.3 billion grocery retail bags annually.

Geographic Reach

Based in Virginia Trex has manufacturing facilities in Winchester Virginia and Fernley Nevada. It operates globally through international retailers.

Sales and Marketing

Trex serves both professional installers and those who prefer to do it themselves. Through some 90 wholesale distribution centers the company sells its products to big-box home improvement retailers including Lowe's and Home Depot. It markets its products as having "unmatched good looks and longevity" — products that "will never rot crack or splinter." Its wood is also the only composite lumber to be code-listed by the nation's three major building code agencies.

A majority of Trex's net sales come from its vast network of wholesale distributors. In 2014 Boise Cascade accounted for more than 10% of sales. The company has extended its reach by providing some of its lines to international retailers.

Financial Performance

Revenue has been climbing at Trex since 2010. In 2014 it grew 14% to $392 million from $342 the previous year. Stronger demand from existing customers and new distributors lead to higher sales volume though a revamped pricing strategy caused lower average prices per unit.

Profits have been growing since 2012 and the bump in revenue helped net income top $41.5 million in 2014 a 20% increase over 2013's $34.6 million. Cash from operations also grew by $45.21 million to hit $58.64 million.

Strategy

Trex generates most of its sales by selling Trex products to wholesale distributors who market to retail lumber outlets. While Trex sells to both homeowners and contractors it focuses on sales to contractors remodelers and homebuilders because their installations are generally larger and feature professional craftsmanship.

The company chooses to sell through a wholesale distribution network for its higher value products and contractor-oriented lumber yards and other retail outlets. Typically Trex appoints a distributor on a non-exclusive basis to distribute its products within a specific area. The distributor in general purchases its products at the sales price the day it ships to the distributor.

Home improvement stores purchase Trex products directly from the company and through wholesale distributors for special orders placed by consumers. In 2014 the company moved online when it began offering its outdoor lighting products through Amazon.com. Trex licensees were already selling the company's outdoor furniture pergolas and deck drainage systems on the retail site.

Trex works to bring new products to the marketplace. Through research and development Trex is interested in creating products that are durable low maintenance and easy to install such as its cellular PVC fire-resistant deck board and outdoor trim products (including mouldings and millwork). The company has built on its high-performance Trex Transcend collection with a range of railing options for all its customer segments. Research and development expenses in 2014 came in at $2.3 million down from $2.9 million the previous two years.

Company Background

Trex was formed in 1996 through a buyout of a division of Mobil Corporation. It went public in 1999.

EXECUTIVES

President and CEO, James E. Cline, age 67, $289,100 total compensation
VP Marketing, Adam D. Zambanini
VP and CFO, Bryan H. Fairbanks
VP Operations, Jay Scripter
Chairman, Ronald W. (Ron) Kaplan, age 67
Auditors: Ernst & Young LLP

LOCATIONS

HQ: Trex Co Inc
160 Exeter Drive, Winchester, VA 22603-8605
Phone: 540 542-6300
Web: www.trex.com

PRODUCTS/OPERATIONS

Selected Brands
Decking
  Trex Accents
  Trex Enhance
  Trex Escapes
  Trex Select
  Trex Transcend
Deck Lighting System
  Trex DeckLighting
Fencing
  Trex Seclusions
Hidden Fastening System
  Trex Hideaway
Porch
  Trex Transcend Porch Flooring & Railing System
PVC Outdoor Trim
  TrexTrim
Railing
  Trex Designer Series
  Trex Transcend
Steel Deck Framing System
  Trex Elevations

Selected Products
Decking
Fencing
Railing
Trim

COMPETITORS

Advanced Environmental Recycling	NEW Plastics
CPG International	TAMKO
CertainTeed	Tumac Lumber
Huttig Building Products	Universal Forest Products
Louisiana-Pacific	Weyerhaeuser

HISTORICAL FINANCIALS
Company Type: Public

Income Statement   FYE: December 31

	REVENUE ($ mil.)	NET INCOME ($ mil.)	NET PROFIT MARGIN	EMPLOYEES
12/17	565.1	95.1	16.8%	815
12/16	479.6	67.8	14.1%	830
12/15	440.8	48.1	10.9%	700
12/14	391.6	41.5	10.6%	630
12/13	342.5	34.6	10.1%	590
Annual Growth	13.3%	28.8%	—	8.4%

2017 Year-End Financials

Debt ratio: —	No. of shares (mil.): 58.8
Return on equity: 52.0%	Dividends
Cash ($ mil.): 30.5	Yield: —
Current ratio: 2.38	Payout: —
Long-term debt ($ mil.): —	Market value ($ mil.): 6,379.0

	STOCK PRICE ($) FY Close	P/E High/Low		PER SHARE ($) Earnings	Dividends	Book Value
12/17	108.39	73	39	1.61	0.00	3.93
12/16	64.40	61	28	1.15	0.00	2.28
12/15	38.04	74	42	0.76	0.00	1.88
12/14	42.58	129	41	0.64	0.00	1.77
12/13	79.53	158	72	0.51	0.00	1.59
Annual Growth	8.0%	—	—	33.6%	—	25.3%

Tribune Media Co

Its roots were in print journalism but the Tribune Media Company (formerly known as Tribune Company) has evolved to embrace virtually every aspect of modern media. Tribune Media currently owns 42 TV stations in more than 30 markets cable network WGN America and a 31% stake in the Food Network. In addition Tribune Media owns a number of online media properties Tribune Studios Tribune Digital Ventures WGN-Radio and a significant number of iconic real estate properties and strategic investments. In 2014 Tribune Company spun off its cornerstone newspaper publishing business into a newly formed company called Tribune Publishing (later renamed tronc) and changed the name of the TV radio and digital business to Tribune Media. In 2018 Texas-based Nexstar Media Group agreed to acquire Tribune Media in a deal valued at $4.1 billion.

Operations

Tribune Media Company has a diverse portfolio of television and digital properties. It produces news entertainment and sports programming. The company generates more than 70% of its total revenue from advertising.

Tribune Broadcasting's 42 owned or operated local television stations reach approximately 50 million households. Cable network WGN America reaches approximately 80 million households.

The company's digital network services operate through Antenna TV and through the operation and distribution of THIS TV both of which are digital networks that air in households nationally.

Tribune Studios is a development and production studio. The company's radio program services include WGN-AM a Chicago radio station.

Geographic Reach

Tribune Media Company operates in New York; Los Angeles; Chicago; Philadelphia; Dallas; Washington; Houston; Seattle; Miami; Denver; Cleveland; Sacramento; St. Louis; Portland; Indianapolis; San Diego; Hartford; Kansas City; Salt Lake City; Milwaukee; Oklahoma City; Norfolk; Harrisburg; Grand Rapids; Greensboro; New Orleans; Memphis; Richmond; Wilkes Barre; Des Moines; Huntsville; Ft. Smith and Davenport.

Sales and Marketing

Tribune Media Company spent $42 million on advertising in fiscal 2016.

Financial Performance

Tribune Media Company's revenue has been consistent in recent fiscal years. The company reported revenue of $1.95 billion for fiscal 2016 after reporting $2 billion in revenue for fiscal 2015 and $1.95 billion in revenue for fiscal 2014. The consistency is impressive considering the struggles of advertising and traditional media companies in the modern economy.

Tribune Media Company reported net income of $220 million in fiscal 2016. That was an improvement compared to the $262 million net loss the company suffered in the previous fiscal year.

The swing from a net loss to a profit led to the company ending fiscal 2016 with $284 million in cash from operations after ending fiscal 2015 with only about $25 million.

Strategy

In 2017 Tribune Media Company sold off its stake in job listing website CareerBuilder. The company has tried to focus on its most profitable lines of business. The advertising marketplace has become increasingly fragmented. Competition for audience share and advertising revenue is fierce. Tribune Media Company split off its newspaper business to prop up its bottom line.

EXECUTIVES

Interim CEO, Peter M. Kern, age 50
EVP Human Resources, Melanie Hughes, age 55
EVP and CFO, Chandler Bigelow, age 50, $700,000 total compensation
President and General Manager WGN Americas and Tribune Studios, Matthew (Matt) Cherniss, age 45
CTO, David Ulmer, age 62
EVP General Counsel Chief Strategy Officer and Corporate Secretary, Edward P. (Eddie) Lazarus, age 58, $750,000 total compensation
President Broadcast Media, Lawrence (Larry) Wert, age 61, $812,705 total compensation
President Distribution Tribune Broadcasting, Dana Zimmer
Chief Product Officer, Josh Gogswell
Vice President of Sales, Wayne Lown
Senior Vice President Digila Mobile, Andy Vogel
Senior Vice President Affiliate Sales And Marketing (Tribune Broadcasting), Kevin Connor
Chairman, Bruce A. Karsh, age 62
Auditors: PricewaterhouseCoopers LLP

LOCATIONS

HQ: Tribune Media Co
515 North State Street, Chicago, IL 60654
Phone: 646 563-8296
Web: www.tribune.com

PRODUCTS/OPERATIONS

2016 Sales

	% of total
Television and Entertainment	
Advertising	71
Re-transmission consent and carriage fees	23
Other	4
Others	2
Total	**100**

Selected Brands

Gracenote
Tribune Broadcasting
Tribune Studios
WGN America
WPIX
KTLA

COMPETITORS

21st Century Fox	McClatchy Company
A. H. Belo	MediaNews
ABC Inc.	NBC
CBS	New York Times
Chicago Reader	Sun-Times Media
Graham Holdings	Holdings
Hearst Newspapers	TEGNA
LIN Media	

HISTORICAL FINANCIALS
Company Type: Public

Income Statement
FYE: December 31

	REVENUE ($ mil.)	NET INCOME ($ mil.)	NET PROFIT MARGIN	EMPLOYEES
12/17	1,848.9	194.1	10.5%	6,000
12/16	1,947.9	14.2	0.7%	8,200
12/15	2,010.4	(319.9)	—	8,000
12/14	1,949.3	476.6	24.5%	7,600
12/13	1,147.2	241.5	21.1%	0
Annual Growth	**12.7%**	**(5.3%)**	**—**	**—**

2017 Year-End Financials

Debt ratio: 35.7%
Return on equity: 5.7%
Cash ($ mil.): 691.2
Current ratio: 1.98
Long-term debt ($ mil.): 2,919.1
No. of shares (mil.): 87.3
Dividends
Yield: 0.1%
Payout: 307.7%
Market value ($ mil.): 3,709.0

	STOCK PRICE ($) FY Close	P/E High/Low	Earnings	PER SHARE ($) Dividends	Book Value
12/17	42.47	19 13	2.20	6.77	36.84
12/16	34.98	252171	0.16	1.00	41.01
12/15	33.81	— —	(3.38)	7.48	41.43
12/14	59.94	19 12	4.75	0.00	53.47
12/13	77.60	32 20	2.41	0.00	52.90
Annual Growth	**(14.0%)**	**— —**	**(2.3%)**	**—**	**(8.6%)**

TriCo Bancshares (Chico, CA)

People looking for a community bank in California's Sacramento Valley can try TriCo. TriCo Bancshares is the holding company for Tri Counties Bank which serves customers through some 65 traditional and in-store branches in 23 counties in Northern and Central California. Founded in 1974 Tri Counties Bank provides a variety of deposit services including checking and savings accounts money market accounts and CDs. Most patrons are retail customers and small to midsized businesses. The bank primarily originates real estate mortgages which account for about 65% of its loan portfolio; consumer loans contribute about 25%. TriCo has agreed to acquire rival North Valley Bancorp.

Operations

In addition to its retail banking products and services the company provides wholesale banking and investment services; TriCo offers brokerage services through an arrangement with Raymond James Financial. The company does not provide trust or international banking services.

Geographic Reach

Based in Chico California Tri Counties Bank operates 66 branches (41 traditional branches and 25 in-store branches) in 23 counties in Northern and central California including Fresno Kern Mendocino Napa Sacramento and Yuba counties.

Financial Performance

In 2013 net interest income the company's primary source of revenue rose 0.6% compared with 2012 to $102.2 million. The slight increase in net interest income was mainly due to a decrease in average balance of other borrowings a shift in deposit balances from relatively high interest rate earning time deposits to noninterest-earning demand and savings deposits an increase in the average balance of investments securities and an increase in the average balance of loans; all of which were substantially offset by a decrease in the average yield on loans.

Strategy

The bank's growth has been fueled by acquisitions and the opening of new branches; it frequently opens branches within grocery stores or other retailers including Wal-Mart. TriCo in 2010 acquired the three branches of Granite Community Bank which had been seized by regulators. The transaction which also included most of the failed bank's assets and deposits was facilitated by the FDIC and includes a loss-sharing agreement with the agency. The following year TriCo acquired Citizens Bank of Northern California. The FDIC-assisted deal included seven branches. The acquisitions are part of TriCo's strategy of adding new customers.

Mergers and Acquisitions

TriCo in January 2014 announced plans to buy its rival in Northern California North Valley Bancorp (NVB) for about $178.4 million. NVB is the parent company of North Valley Bank which had about $918 million in assets and 22 commercial banking offices across eight Northern California counties at the end of 2013. At closing which is expected in the second or third quarter of 2014 NVB will be merged into Tri Counties Bank. The combined bank would have about $3.6 billion in assets.

EXECUTIVES

EVP and CFO TriCo Bancshares and Tri Counties Bank, Thomas J. (Tom) Reddish, age 58, $309,601 total compensation
EVP and Chief Credit Officer, Craig B. Carney, age 59, $274,932 total compensation
EVP Wholesale Banking, Richard B. O'Sullivan, age 61, $260,890 total compensation
President and CEO, Richard P. Smith, age 60, $549,846 total compensation
EVP and COO, John S. Fleshood, age 56
EVP and Chief Retail Banking Officer, Daniel K. (Dan) Bailey, age 49, $268,335 total compensation
SVP and CIO, Bruce Barnett
VICE PRESIDENT MARKETING DIRECTOR, Michael Murphy
Vice President Facilities Expansion MA, Chimene Sonsteng
Senior Vice President Special Assets Manager, Steve Macrae
Executive Vice President and Chief Retail Banking Officer, Dan Bailey
Vice President Direct Banking Manager, Kay Armstrong
Chairman, William J. Casey, age 73
Vice Chairman, Michael W. Koehnen, age 57
Board Member, Virginia Walker
Board Member, Martin Mariani
Board Member, Patrick Kilkenny
Auditors: Moss Adams LLP

LOCATIONS

HQ: TriCo Bancshares (Chico, CA)
63 Constitution Drive, Chico, CA 95973
Phone: 530 898-0300   **Fax:** 530 898-0310
Web: www.tcbk.com

PRODUCTS/OPERATIONS

2015 Sales

	$ mil.	% of total
Interest		
Loans including fees	131.8	64
Debt securities	26.8	13
Dividends	2.1	1
Other	0.7	-
Noninterest		
Service charges & fees	31.8	16
Commissions	3.4	2
Gain on sale of loans	3.1	1
Other	7.1	3
Total	**206.8**	**100**

Selected Services

Business debit cards
Business online banking
Business workshops
Cash management
Education savings and CDs
Loans and credits
Merchant services
Order checks
Overdraft services
Pension and retirement
Personal certificates of deposit
Personal checking
Personal savings and money market
Retirement savings and CDs

COMPETITORS

Bank of America	MUFG Americas Holdings
Bank of the West	PremierWest
Central Valley	Wells Fargo
Community Bancorp	Westamerica

HISTORICAL FINANCIALS

Company Type: Public

Income Statement   FYE: December 31

	ASSETS ($ mil.)	NET INCOME ($ mil.)	INCOME AS % OF ASSETS	EMPLOYEES
12/17	4,761.3	40.5	0.9%	1,023
12/16	4,517.9	44.8	1.0%	1,063
12/15	4,220.7	43.8	1.0%	1,011
12/14	3,916.4	26.1	0.7%	1,009
12/13	2,744.0	27.4	1.0%	794
Annual Growth	14.8%	10.3%	—	6.5%

2017 Year-End Financials

Return on assets: 0.8%	Dividends
Return on equity: 8.2%	Yield: 0.0%
Long-term debt ($ mil.): —	Payout: 37.9%
No. of shares (mil.): 22.9	Market value ($ mil.): 869.0
Sales ($ mil): 231.4	

	STOCK PRICE ($) FY Close	P/E High/Low	Earnings	Dividends	Book Value
12/17	37.86	25 19	1.74	0.66	22.03
12/16	34.18	18 12	1.94	0.60	20.87
12/15	27.44	15 12	1.91	0.52	19.85
12/14	24.70	19 15	1.46	0.44	18.41
12/13	28.37	17 9	1.69	0.42	15.61
Annual Growth	7.5%	— —	0.7%	12.0%	9.0%

TriState Capital Holdings Inc

TriState Capital Holdings has found its niche right in the middle of the banking industry. The holding company owns TriState Capital Bank a regional business bank that caters to midsized businesses or those annually earning between $5 million and $300 million. TriState Capital also offers private banking services nationally to high-net-worth individuals. Its loan portfolio consists of about 50% commercial loans 30% commercial real estate loans and 20% private banking-personal loans. The bank serves clients from branches in Cleveland; New Jersey; New York City Philadelphia and Pittsburgh. Altogether it has some $2 billion in assets. TriState Capital went public in mid-2013.

IPO

The company does not have any specific plans outlined for its proceeds but will likely use it for general corporate purposes which might include maintaining liquidity at the holding company providing equity capital to the bank to fund balance sheet growth and possibly investing in or acquiring wealth management businesses.

Strategy

The company's founders saw an opportunity in serving what they perceived was an underserved market — midsized businesses. Consolidation had left major national banks catering to individuals and large businesses while community banks served individuals and small businesses.

Company Background

TriState Capital was founded in 2007 by two banking industry executives — chairman and CEO James Getz who spent 20 years at Federated Investors and vice chairman William Schenck the former secretary of banking for Pennsylvania.

EXECUTIVES

Chairman President and CEO, James F. (Jim) Getz, $1,500,000 total compensation
President Commercial Banking, David A. Molnar
Vice Chairman and CFO, Mark L. Sullivan, $425,000 total compensation
Regional President New Jersey, Kenneth R. Orchard
Regional President New York, Thomas N. Gilmartin
Regional President Ohio, John D. Barrett
Regional President Eastern Pennsylvania, Joseph M. Finley
Regional President Western Pennsylvania, Vince Locher
President Private Bank Team, Charles C. Fawcett
President and CEO TriState Capital Bank, Brian S. Fetterolf
Senior Vice President Relationship Manager, Michael Blasko
Senior Vice President, Sheila Roberts
Senior Vice President, Debra Flinner
SENIOR VICE PRESIDENT, John Buglione
Vice Chairman, A. William (Bill) Schenck
Auditors: KPMG LLP

LOCATIONS

HQ: TriState Capital Holdings Inc
One Oxford Centre, 301 Grant Street, Suite 2700, Pittsburgh, PA 15219
Phone: 412 304-0304   **Fax:** 412 304-0391
Web: www.tristatecapitalbank.com

PRODUCTS/OPERATIONS

2015 Sales

	% of total
Interest income	
Loans	67
Investments	3
Interest-earning deposits	-
Noninterest income	
Investment management fees	25
Commitment and other fees	2
Other income	3
Total	**100**

COMPETITORS

Bank of America	HSBC Private Bank
Bank of New York	Herald National Bank
Mellon	JPMorgan Private Bank
Boston Private	Julius Baer
Brown Brothers	Lakeland Bancorp
Harriman	M&T Bank
Citigroup	Safra Bank
Citigroup Private Bank	U.S. Trust
First Republic (CA)	

HISTORICAL FINANCIALS

Company Type: Public

Income Statement   FYE: December 31

	ASSETS ($ mil.)	NET INCOME ($ mil.)	INCOME AS % OF ASSETS	EMPLOYEES
12/17	4,777.9	37.9	0.8%	230
12/16	3,930.4	28.6	0.7%	224
12/15	3,302.8	22.4	0.7%	192
12/14	2,846.8	15.9	0.6%	182
12/13	2,290.5	12.8	0.6%	129
Annual Growth	20.2%	31.1%	—	15.6%

2017 Year-End Financials

Return on assets: 0.8%	Dividends
Return on equity: 10.2%	Yield: —
Long-term debt ($ mil.): —	Payout: —
No. of shares (mil.): 28.5	Market value ($ mil.): 658.0
Sales ($ mil): 181.2	

	STOCK PRICE ($) FY Close	P/E High/Low	Earnings	Dividends	Book Value
12/17	23.00	18 15	1.32	0.00	13.61
12/16	22.10	22 11	1.01	0.00	12.38
12/15	13.99	18 12	0.80	0.00	11.62
12/14	10.24	26 16	0.55	0.00	10.88
12/13	11.86	29 24	0.49	0.00	10.25
Annual Growth	18.0%	— —	28.1%	—	7.4%

Triumph Bancorp Inc

Auditors: Crowe Horwath LLP

LOCATIONS

HQ: Triumph Bancorp Inc
12700 Park Central Drive, Suite 1700, Dallas, TX 75251
Phone: 214 365-6900
Web: www.triumphbancorp.com

HISTORICAL FINANCIALS
Company Type: Public

Income Statement — FYE: December 31

	ASSETS ($ mil.)	NET INCOME ($ mil.)	INCOME AS % OF ASSETS	EMPLOYEES
12/17	3,499.0	36.2	1.0%	820
12/16	2,641.0	20.7	0.8%	705
12/15	1,691.3	29.1	1.7%	500
12/14	1,447.9	17.7	1.2%	466
12/13	1,288.2	11.8	0.9%	463
Annual Growth	28.4%	32.3%	—	15.4%

2017 Year-End Financials

Return on assets: 1.1%
Return on equity: 10.6%
Long-term debt ($ mil.): —
No. of shares (mil.): 20.8
Sales ($ mil): 217.8
Dividends
Yield: —
Payout: —
Market value ($ mil.): 656.0

	STOCK PRICE ($) FY Close	P/E High/Low	Earnings	Dividends	Book Value
12/17	31.50	19 11	1.81	0.00	18.81
12/16	26.15	24 12	1.10	0.00	16.01
12/15	16.50	11 8	1.57	0.00	14.88
12/14	13.55	10 8	1.52	0.00	13.22
Annual Growth	32.5%	— —	6.0%	—	12.5%

Turning Point Brands Inc

Auditors: RSM US LLP

LOCATIONS

HQ: Turning Point Brands Inc
5201 Interchange Way, Louisville, KY 40229
Phone: 502 778-4421
Web: www.turningpointbrands.com

HISTORICAL FINANCIALS
Company Type: Public

Income Statement — FYE: December 31

	REVENUE ($ mil.)	NET INCOME ($ mil.)	NET PROFIT MARGIN	EMPLOYEES
12/17	285.7	20.2	7.1%	289
12/16	206.2	26.9	13.1%	286
12/15	197.2	9.1	4.6%	231
12/14	200.3	(29.4)	—	0
Annual Growth	12.6%	—	—	—

2017 Year-End Financials

Debt ratio: 71.5%
Return on equity: 46.2%
Cash ($ mil.): 2.6
Current ratio: 2.08
Long-term debt ($ mil.): 186.1
No. of shares (mil.): 19.2
Dividends
Yield: 0.0%
Payout: 3.8%
Market value ($ mil.): 406.0

	STOCK PRICE ($) FY Close	P/E High/Low	Earnings	Dividends	Book Value
12/17	21.13	20 12	1.04	0.04	2.78
12/16	12.25	10 4	1.49	0.00	1.85
12/15	0.00	— —	1.10	0.00	(11.34)
Annual Growth	—	— —	(2.8%)	—	—

Tyler Technologies, Inc.

Tyler Technologies doesn't want local governments tied up in red tape. The company provides software and services intended to help state and local government offices operate more efficiently. Specializing in applications for local governments and public schools Tyler's products include software for accounting and financial management filing court documents electronically tracking and managing court cases and automating appraisals and assessments. Other products include applications that allow citizens to access utility accounts or pay traffic fines online. Tyler complements its software with hosting support and maintenance services. The company counts more than 13000 government and school customers in all 50 states Canada the Caribbean and the UK.

Operations
The company divides its operations into two segments — enterprise software and appraisal and tax software. Enterprise software which accounts for 88% of sales provides local governments and schools with software and services for back-office functions such as financial management and courts and justice processes. Appraisal and tax software which makes up the other 11% of sales is used by local governments and taxing authorities to automate property appraisal and assessment including physical inspection data collection property valuation preparing tax rolls and arbitration.

The company's technology partners include Microsoft and ESRI.

Geographic Reach
Tyler Technologies operates from about 20 offices in the US and one in Canada.

Sales and Marketing
The company uses a direct sales force. It participates in government associations and attends annual meetings trade shows and educational events to attract new customers. Its customers are primarily county and municipal agencies school districts and other local government offices.

Financial Performance
Tyler Technologies has been on a tear in revenue growth and it continued in 2014. Revenue jumped 18% to $493 million because of growth throughout its offerings. It posted 40% growth in subscriptions 22% in software services and 20% growth in software licenses and royalties from current customers and new ones. A particular driver of subscription-based services revenue came from a contract with the Texas Office of Court Admin-

istration for the company's Odyssey File and Serve e-filing system. Overall local government spending loosened as economic conditions improved.

Tyler Technologies converted the revenue growth into a 59% increase in profit. It rose to $59 million in 2014 from $39 million in 2013.

Cash flow from operations also jumped rising to $123 million in 2014 from $66 million in 2013.

Strategy
In addition to acquisitions the company expands its software product line with new offerings and product upgrades including the Odyssey judicial case management system and public-use Internet portals that enable users to pay property taxes utility bills and complete other transactions electronically. The company is also looking to grow by selling new products and services to its existing customer base expanding its market focus to include larger customers and entering new geographic regions.

Mergers and Acquisitions
In early 2015 Tyler Technologies acquired 20% of Record Holdings an Australian company specializing in digitizing the spoken word in courts. Also in 2015 Tyler Technologies bought Brazos Technology Corp. a provider of mobile hand-held products used by law enforcement agencies for field accident reporting and electronically issuing citations. Toward the end of 2015 Tyler Technologies bought New World Systems Corp. a provider of public safety and financial products. Tyler Technologies paid $360 million in cash and about 2.1 million shares of Tyler's stock.

In 2014 the company acquired SoftCode Inc. which developed civil process automation software for county sheriffs' departments. The acquisition broadened Tyler Technologies' courts and justice product line.

Company Background
Formerly an auto parts and supplies company established in 1966 Tyler sold its chain of auto parts stores in 1999 and used acquisitions to transform itself into a provider of software for the local government and education markets.

EXECUTIVES

EVP CFO and Treasurer, Brian K. Miller, age 59, $323,000 total compensation
COO and Director; President MUNIS Division, John S. Marr, age 59, $512,000 total compensation
President, H. Lynn Moore, age 50, $323,000 total compensation
EVP and President Local Government Division, Dustin R. Womble, age 59, $430,000 total compensation
VP and CIO, Matthew (Matt) Bieri
President Courts and Justice Division, Jeff Puckett
VP and Chief Marketing Officer, Samantha Crosby
President Appraisal and Tax Division, Andrew D. Teed
President ERP and School Division, Christopher P. (Chris) Hepburn
President Justice Group, Bret Dixon
President Public Safety Division, Greg Sebastian
Vice President, Stefan Werdegar
Vice President, Mary Lavik
Vice President of Product Development, David Grossman
Vice President of Support Services, Mitchell Spence
Vice President Software Strategy and Development, Brian Leary
Vice President of EnerGov Operations, Mark Beverly
National Sales Manager, Brian Baker

Vice President Of East Division, Todd Cloutier
BOARD MEMBER PROJECT
IMPLEMENTATION MANAGER, Malcolm Logan
Auditors: Ernst & Young LLP

LOCATIONS

HQ: Tyler Technologies, Inc.
5101 Tennyson Parkway, Plano, TX 75024
Phone: 972 713-3700
Web: www.tylertech.com

PRODUCTS/OPERATIONS

2014 Sales

	% of total
Enterprise software	89
Appraisal & tax software	11
Corporate	-
Total	**100**

2014 Sales

	% of total
Maintenance	43
Software services	23
Subscriptions	18
Software licenses and royalties	10
Appraisal services	4
Hardware & other	2
Total	**100**

Selected Products

Appraisal and assessment software (property appraisal and assessment)
Criminal justice software (court case tracking and management)
Document management and recording software (image storage and retrieval)
Education software
Finance and accounting software
Law enforcement and corrections software (police dispatch records and jail management)
Municipal court software (case management)
Odyssey (case and court management)
Public Records and content management
Tax collections software (tax collections office operations)
Utility billing software (billing and collections)

Selected Services

Information technology and professional services
Maintenance
Outsourced property appraisals for tax jurisdictions

COMPETITORS

CACI International	Official Payments
Constellation Software	Holdings
DynTek	Oracle
HP Enterprise Services	SAP
IBM	SunGard
MAXIMUS	USTI
Manatron	Xerox

HISTORICAL FINANCIALS

Company Type: Public

Income Statement   FYE: December 31

	REVENUE ($ mil.)	NET INCOME ($ mil.)	NET PROFIT MARGIN	EMPLOYEES
12/17	840.6	163.9	19.5%	4,069
12/16	756.0	109.8	14.5%	3,831
12/15	591.0	64.8	11.0%	3,586
12/14	493.1	58.9	12.0%	2,856
12/13	416.6	39.1	9.4%	2,573
Annual Growth	**19.2%**	**43.1%**	**—**	**12.1%**

2017 Year-End Financials

Debt ratio: —   No. of shares (mil.): 37.8
Return on equity: 15.7%   Dividends
Cash ($ mil.): 185.9   Yield: —
Current ratio: 1.30   Payout: —
Long-term debt ($ mil.): —   Market value ($ mil.): 6,708.0

	STOCK PRICE ($) FY Close	P/E High/Low		PER SHARE ($) Earnings	Dividends	Book Value
12/17	177.05	42	33	4.18	0.00	30.81
12/16	142.77	58	40	2.82	0.00	24.90
12/15	174.32	95	55	1.77	0.00	23.35
12/14	109.44	64	42	1.66	0.00	10.07
12/13	102.13	85	39	1.13	0.00	7.50
Annual Growth	**14.7%**	**—**	**—**	**38.7%**	**—**	**42.4%**

U.S. Physical Therapy, Inc.

U.S. Physical Therapy (USPh) through its subsidiaries lends a hand to injured workers athletes and others in need of some TLC. With some 560 outpatient clinics in more than 40 states USPh provides physical therapy services for work-related and sports injuries trauma orthopedic conditions osteoarthritis treatment and post-surgical rehabilitation. The clinics operate under a number of local or regional brands including Red River Valley Physical Therapy and Pioneer Physical Therapy. USPh also operates 22 physical therapy facilities for third parties including physician groups and hospitals.

Operations

Most of USPh's clinics are joint ventures in which the company owns a majority stake and the licensed therapists/clinic managers own a minority stake. Other facilities are wholly owned by the company but are operated through profit-sharing agreements with physical therapists. The company also manages a handful of physician-owned and hospital-owned clinics on a contract basis.

USPh relies on its therapist-managers to maintain relationships with local physicians who refer patients to the clinics. Services are paid for by commercial health insurance managed care programs Medicare workers' compensation insurance or proceeds from personal injury cases.

Geographic Reach

USPh has clinics in 42 states. The company has a significant presence in Georgia Maryland Michigan Pennsylvania Tennessee Texas Virginia Washington and Wisconsin.

Sales and Marketing

The company markets its activities to orthopedic surgeons neurosurgeons podiatrists occupational medicine physicians and other physicians.

In 2015 commercial health insurance accounted for 28% of USPh's net patient revenue. This was followed by Medicare and Medicaid (25% of net patient revenue) managed care programs (23%) workers' compensation (18%) and other (6%).

Financial Performance

Revenues for USPh have continued to increase over the years as the company has expanded its network of clinics. In 2015 revenues increased 9%

to $331 million due to an increase in patient visits (3 million up from 2.8 million in 2014) at both new and mature clinics. The acquisition of additional clinics also boosted revenues.

Net income which had declined in 2012 and 2013 has risen over the past couple of years. In 2015 it increased 7% to $22 million thanks to the higher revenue but this was partially offset by an increase in clinic operating expenses. Cash flow from operations had been trending upward until 2015 when it fell 9% to $41 million. This decline was primarily due to a decrease in accounts payable and accrued expenses as well as an increase in cash used in accounts receivable.

Strategy

USPh grows by developing and acquiring new clinics throughout the US. In 2015 the company acquired a total of 21 clinics for some $21 million. It plans to continue buying and developing additional facilities as well as opening satellite clinics in suitable locations.

Along with developing new partnerships and opening new clinics USPh seeks to increase its market share by upping its patient volume through marketing campaigns and by adding new services. It also works to recruit and retain physical therapists that have strong relationships with referring physicians by offering competitive salaries and opportunities to own a stake in or share profits in the clinics where they work.

Mergers and Acquisitions

In 2017 USPh paid about $6.6 million for a 55% stake in a company that provides industrial clients with onsite injury prevention and rehabilitation performance optimization and ergonomic assessments. It purchased a 65% stake in a similar firm for $9 million in 2018.

The company has also grown through the purchase of clinical practices throughout the nation. In 2016 it acquired a 55% stake in an eight-clinic physical therapy practice for $14 million and a 60% stake in a 12-clinic group for $11.5 million. Early the following year the company bought a 70% stake in a 17-clinic physical therapy practice for $11.4 million and a 60% stake in a nine-clinic practice for $16.3 million.

EXECUTIVES

CFO, Lawrance W. (Larry) McAfee, age 63, $409,577 total compensation
CEO, Christopher J. (Chris) Reading, age 54, $558,730 total compensation
COO, Glenn McDowell, age 62, $363,942 total compensation
Vice President Of Marketing, Bill Johnston
Vice President, Darryl Gotwalt
Vice President, Don Ryan
Chairman, Jerald L. Pullins, age 76
Board Member, Mark Brookner
Board Member, Clayton K Trier
Board Member, Harry S Chapman
Auditors: GRANT THORNTON LLP

LOCATIONS

HQ: U.S. Physical Therapy, Inc.
1300 West Sam Houston Parkway South, Suite 300, Houston, TX 77042
Phone: 713 297-7000
Web: www.usph.com

PRODUCTS/OPERATIONS

2015 Sales

	$ mil.	% of total
Patient revenue		
Commercial insurance	91.8	28
Medicare/Medicaid	79.3	24
Managed care	73.5	22
Workers' compensation	60.1	18
Other patient revenue	19.5	6
Other	7.0	2
Total	**331.3**	**100**

COMPETITORS

Concentra
Five Star Senior Living
Physiotherapy Associates
RehabCare
Select Medical
Spaulding Rehabilitation Hospital
U.S. HealthWorks

HISTORICAL FINANCIALS

Company Type: Public

Income Statement   FYE: December 31

	REVENUE ($ mil.)	NET INCOME ($ mil.)	NET PROFIT MARGIN	EMPLOYEES
12/17	414.0	22.2	5.4%	4,300
12/16	356.5	20.5	5.8%	3,800
12/15	331.3	22.2	6.7%	3,400
12/14	305.0	20.8	6.8%	3,151
12/13	264.0	12.7	4.8%	2,805
Annual Growth	**11.9%**	**15.0%**	**—**	**11.3%**

2017 Year-End Financials

Debt ratio: 14.5%
Return on equity: 11.3%
Cash ($ mil.): 21.9
Current ratio: 1.95
Long-term debt ($ mil.): 56.7

No. of shares (mil.): 12.5
Dividends
  Yield: 0.0%
  Payout: 45.4%
Market value ($ mil.): 909.0

	STOCK PRICE ($) FY Close	P/E High/Low	Earnings	Dividends	Book Value
12/17	72.20	44 32	1.76	0.80	16.27
12/16	70.20	44 28	1.64	0.68	14.98
12/15	53.68	32 22	1.77	0.60	13.11
12/14	41.96	27 19	1.62	0.48	11.92
12/13	35.26	34 22	1.05	0.80	10.60
Annual Growth	**19.6%**	**—**	**13.8%**	**(0.0%)**	**11.3%**

Ubiquiti Networks Inc

Auditors: KPMG LLP

LOCATIONS

HQ: Ubiquiti Networks Inc
  685 Third Avenue, 27th Floor, New York, NY 10017
Phone: 646 780-7958
Web: www.ubnt.com

HISTORICAL FINANCIALS

Company Type: Public

Income Statement   FYE: June 30

	REVENUE ($ mil.)	NET INCOME ($ mil.)	NET PROFIT MARGIN	EMPLOYEES
06/18	1,016.8	196.2	19.3%	843
06/17	865.2	257.5	29.8%	725
06/16	666.4	213.6	32.1%	537
06/15	595.9	129.6	21.8%	435
06/14	572.4	176.9	30.9%	312
Annual Growth	**15.4%**	**2.6%**	**—**	**28.2%**

2018 Year-End Financials

Debt ratio: 47.4%
Return on equity: 42.7%
Cash ($ mil.): 666.6
Current ratio: 8.87
Long-term debt ($ mil.): 460.3

No. of shares (mil.): 74.0
Dividends
  Yield: —
  Payout: —
Market value ($ mil.): 6,275.0

	STOCK PRICE ($) FY Close	P/E High/Low	Earnings	Dividends	Book Value
06/18	84.72	35 20	2.51	0.00	4.26
06/17	51.97	20 12	3.09	0.00	7.50
06/16	38.66	16 11	2.49	0.00	5.39
06/15	31.92	34 18	1.45	0.17	4.83
06/14	45.19	28 9	1.97	0.00	3.80
Annual Growth	**17.0%**	**— —**	**6.2%**	**—**	**2.9%**

Ultimate Software Group, Inc.

The Ultimate Software Group helps manage a company's ultimate resource: its employees. Customers employ its cloud-based UltiPro software suite to manage hiring human resources compliance benefits enrollment payroll appraisals and time and attendance. The company does business in the US and Canada with customers that include Bloomin? Brands Red Roof Inn and Subway. It targets the communications finance health care retail technology and transportation industries. Founded in 1990 Ultimate holds more than 37 million people records in its HCM (human capital management) cloud. In 2019 Ultimate agreed to go private in an $11 billion buyout led by Hellman & Friedman.

Change in Company Type

Ultimate agreed to sell to an investment group led by private equity firm Hellman & Friedman for about $11 billion. The offer values the company at a 19% premium over the pre-bid stock price. Other investors include Blackstone Group LP GIC Pte Ltd. the Canada Pension Plan Investment Board and JMI Equity. After the transaction is completed expected in mid-2019 Ultimate would function as a private company under its current leadership. The company says that as a private entity it can move more quickly into new products and markets than as a publicly held company.

Operations

Ultimate Software Group?s UltiPro product helps its customers manage the employee life cycle from recruitment to retirement.

Subscriptions for the company cloud-based products called recurring revenue accounts for about 85% of revenue. That also covers support and maintenance revenue. Service revenue about 15% of sales comes from consulting to deploy Ultimate's software.

Geographic Reach

Florida-based Ultimate sells in the US and Canada. It hosts its 376 million people records in third-party data centers in Phoenix Atlanta Toronto and Vancouver.

Sales and Marketing

Ultimate markets its software through direct sales teams organized by geographic region. It boasts some 4100 customers across industries that include manufacturing food services sports technology finance and others. No customer accounts for 10% or more of sales.

Financial Performance

Ultimate has enjoyed consistent robust sales growth over the past five years when revenue rose at a 25% a year clip. In 2017 the company posted a 21% gain to about $941 million from 2016. Recurring revenue was up about 23% in 2017 from sales to customers of at least a year and service revenue rose about 8% for the year.

Ultimate?s net income fell about 50% to about $15 million for 2017 from 2016. The company blamed an $18 million increase in its federal taxes because of provisions of the US Tax Cuts and Jobs Act. Its income before taxes was $2.3 million higher in 2017 than 2016.

Ultimate?s cash and cash equivalents more than doubled to about $155 million in 2017 from 2016. The increase was due to cash provided by operations and proceeds from issuing shares to employees offset to a degree by cash purchases of property and equipment.

Strategy

Posting new sales highs each year Ultimate Software Group is poised to pass the $1 billion revenue mark in 2018. The company relies on introducing 2017 new features to existing product and new products; it increased research and development spending 20% in 2017 from 2016.

In 2017 the company added 360 new features to the UltiPro product. It also brought an artificial intelligence system called Xander that analyzes free-form text from employees? open-ended survey answers. It also deciphers 100 emotions workplace themes and the overall sentiment of an individual employee or group.

Ultimate has designed its product to tightly operate with technologies from Microsoft which has long held sway over corporate software through its Windows operating system and Office suite of productivity applications. Microsoft?s dominance has been threatened in recent years by offerings from Google and other companies. A move away from Microsoft in corporate America could put a dent in Ultimate?s sales and require it to retool its products.

Mergers and Acquisitions

In 2016 Ultimate acquired Kanjoya Inc. a workforce intelligence and analytics platform for about $20 million. With Kanjoya Ultimate released UltiPro Perception to help companies collect understand and act on employee feedback.

EXECUTIVES

Senior Vice President and Chief Enterprise Sales Officer, Greg Swick

EVP CFO and Treasurer, Mitchell K. (Mitch) Dauerman, age 60, $525,000 total compensation

Chairman President and CEO, Scott Scherr, age 65, $700,000 total compensation

Vice Chairman and COO, Marc D. Scherr, age 60, $625,000 total compensation

SVP and Chief Technology Officer, Adam Rogers, age 43, $571,000 total compensation

SVP Marketing, Jody Kaminsky, age 43

Vice President of Finance, Felecia Alvaro

Vice President and General Manager Workplace Operations, Julie Dodd

Vice President of Sales Middle Atlantic Division, Don Schaeffer

Vice President of Sales West Division, Craig Christoffersen

GM Vice President Business Unit Manager, Lee McDermott

Vice President, Michael Schaberl

Vice President Finance, Felicia A Alvaro

Vice President Sales Operations, Sherry Stein

Vp Project Management, Terry Hudak

Vice President Client Services, Brenda Jennings

Senior Vice president, John Phenicie

Vice President User Experience, Patanjali Venkatacharya

Vice President IT, Kelvin Tamayo Tamayo

Vice President of PR and Communications, Darlene Marcroft

Vice President Software Engineering at ULTIMATE Software GROUP, Stephen Reid

Vice President, Eamonn Caulfield

Vice President Talent, Laura Gentry

Vice President Sales Mid market, Kevin Robins

Senior Vice President, Greg Mcmullen

VP GOVERNANCERISKCOMPLIANCE, Robert Vetter

Vice President Human Resources, Kathleen Pai

Vice President General Manager East, Scott Fletcher

Vice President Payment Services, John Stauffer

Vice President Software Engineering, Steve Reid

Auditors: KPMG LLP

LOCATIONS

HQ: Ultimate Software Group, Inc.
2000 Ultimate Way, Weston, FL 33326
Phone: 954 331-7000
Web: www.ultimatesoftware.com

PRODUCTS/OPERATIONS

2017 Sales

	$ mil.	% of total
Recurring	802.3	85
Services	138.4	15
Total	**940.7**	**100**

COMPETITORS

ADP	Paylocity
Ceridian	Peoplefluent
Kronos	SAP
LAWSON	SPM Global Services
Oracle	Sage Software
Paychex	Workday Inc.

HISTORICAL FINANCIALS

Company Type: Public

Income Statement   FYE: December 31

	REVENUE ($ mil.)	NET INCOME ($ mil.)	NET PROFIT MARGIN	EMPLOYEES
12/17	940.7	14.0	1.5%	4,208
12/16	781.2	30.2	3.9%	3,747
12/15	618.0	22.7	3.7%	2,880
12/14	505.9	44.7	8.8%	2,354
12/13	410.4	25.5	6.2%	1,913
Annual Growth	**23.0%**	**(13.9%)**	**—**	**21.8%**

2017 Year-End Financials

Debt ratio: 0.7%	No. of shares (mil.): 30.1
Return on equity: 2.9%	Dividends
Cash ($ mil.): 155.6	Yield: —
Current ratio: 1.18	Payout: —
Long-term debt ($ mil.): 4.4	Market value ($ mil.): 6,575.0

	STOCK PRICE ($) FY Close	P/E High/Low		PER SHARE ($) Earnings	Dividends	Book Value
12/17	218.23	494	390	0.46	0.00	17.19
12/16	182.35	214	147	0.99	0.00	14.73
12/15	195.51	267	177	0.76	0.00	11.60
12/14	146.82	108	71	1.52	0.00	9.53
12/13	153.22	173	101	0.88	0.00	6.70
Annual Growth	**9.2%**	**—**	**—**	**(15.0%)**	**—**	**26.6%**

Ultra Clean Holdings Inc

Ultra Clean Holdings is a pure play in helping computer chip makers keep their manufacturing conditions pristine. The company which does business as Ultra Clean Technology (UCT) designs engineers manufactures and tests customized gas liquid and catalytic steam generation delivery systems used primarily in the production of semiconductors The company also provides third party manufacturing services. UCT has extended its know-how in the semiconductor industry to move into flat-panel display medical research and energy markets.The company's three biggest customers account for about 85% of revenue.

Operations

Ultra Clean Technology functions through wholly owned subsidiaries: Ultra Clean Technology Systems and Service Inc. AIT LLC Ultra Clean Micro-Electronics Equipment (Shanghai) Co. Ltd. Ultra Clean Asia Pacific Pte Ltd. Marchi and Miconex. The company places its factories near its customers' plants in the US and Asia because of the tight integration of UCT tools into its customers' processes.

The company?s products perform functions throughout a semiconductor fabrication plant. Products include gas delivery systems liquid delivery systems precision robotics and process modules.

Geographic Reach

Ultra Clean Technology has international operations in China Singapore the Philippines Austria the Czech Republic and in California Arizona and Texas in the US. Manufacturing is done at all locations while engineering functions are also conducted at its California headquarters in Hayward and Austin Texas. A bit more than half of the company's sales are made to customers headquartered in the US while the rest are to international customers.

Sales and Marketing

Ultra Clean Technology relies on a direct sales force of sales directors account managers and sales support staff to work closely with customers. The sales staff includes technical sales support and engineers stationed at customers' factories. After several round of consolidation in the semiconductor industry just three customers account for about 85% of UCT?s revenue. They are LAM Research (50%) Applied Materials (25%) and ASM (about 10%).

Financial Performance

The record of Ultra Clean Tech?s revenue and profit for the past decade reflects the ups-and-downs on the semiconductor industry. The company had an up year in 2016 posting stronger revenue and a profit after a loss in 2015.

The company?s sales increased 20% to about $563 million in 2016 from about $470 million in 2015. The company shipped more products in 2016 to meet higher customer demand. Its semiconductor-related business accounted for about 80% of the sales increase while the rest came from the flat panel medical and energy work it does. Sales to US customers dropped by half in 2016 while sales to foreign customers jumped 48%. The foreign sales increase was due to the Miconexacquisition of 2015 and the continuing shift of business to UCT?s Singapore operations by a US customer. Sales generated by UCT?s Singapore site have increased 220% from 2014 to 2016.

UCT flipped a $10 million loss in 2015 to a $10 million profit in 2016. The turnaround came from higher revenue in 2016 along with lower expenses as the company maintained a tight rein on costs and had a lower tax bill in 2015.

Cash flow from operations jumped to about $18 million in 2016 from about $926000 in 2015. Sources of cash were non-cash activities such as depreciation of equipment and leasehold improvements amortization of intangible assets as well as decreases in prepaid expenses and other and deferred tax assets net and increases in accounts payable and accrued compensation.

Strategy

Ultra Clean Tech?s rode more investment more capacity and stronger demand in the semiconductor industry to higher revenue and profit in 2016 and the company looks for the trend to continue in 2017. Semiconductor makers are racing to keep up with consumer demand for more electronics and that means more business for UCT.

Customers look to UCT for manufacturing capacity as they max out their production facilities as well as make equipment for new facilities. And the company?s expansion beyond clean technologies has enlarged its addressable market. The company expects demand for its flat-panel capabilities to grow as they did in 2016 when flat panel revenue doubled from 2015.

Mergers and Acquisitions

Ultra Clean Tech made two acquisitions in 2015 that expanded its product lineup and geographic foot print.

In August 2015 UCT acquired Miconex a Czech Republic-based provider of advanced precision fabrication of plastics for about $15 million. The acquisition expands company?s capabilities in specialty manufacturing processes the semiconductor equipment market and adjacent markets.

Also in 2015 UCT acquired Marchi a designer and manufacturer of specialty thermocouples heaters and temperature controllers for $30 million in cash. The acquisition expanded UCT's offerings.

EXECUTIVES

CEO, James P. (Jim) Scholhamer, age 52, $370,577 total compensation
SVP Asia, Lavi A. Lev, age 62, $247,199 total compensation
SVP Supply Chain Management and Machining Operations, Mark G. Bingaman, age 63, $271,314 total compensation
SVP Finance and Chief Accounting Officer, Sheri Brumm, age 48
SVP Engineering, Michael Henderson
Chairman, Clarence L. Granger, age 70
Auditors: Moss Adams LLP

LOCATIONS

HQ: Ultra Clean Holdings Inc
26462 Corporate Avenue, Hayward, CA 94545
Phone: 510 576-4400
Web: www.uct.com

COMPETITORS

ATMI	L'Air Liquide
Air Products	Matheson Tri-Gas
Allegro MicroSystems	Praxair
Ebara	Sanmina
Flextronics	Wolfe Engineering

HISTORICAL FINANCIALS

Company Type: Public

Income Statement				FYE: December 29
	REVENUE ($ mil.)	NET INCOME ($ mil.)	NET PROFIT MARGIN	EMPLOYEES
12/17	924.3	75.0	8.1%	2,747
12/16	562.7	10.0	1.8%	2,183
12/15	469.1	(10.7)	—	1,817
12/14	513.9	11.3	2.2%	1,546
12/13	444.0	10.4	2.3%	1,622
Annual Growth	20.1%	63.8%	—	14.1%

2017 Year-End Financials

Debt ratio: 9.2%
Return on equity: 29.1%
Cash ($ mil.): 68.3
Current ratio: 1.97
Long-term debt ($ mil.): 39.8
No. of shares (mil.): 33.6
Dividends
  Yield: —
  Payout: —
Market value ($ mil.): 777.0

	STOCK PRICE ($) FY Close	P/E High/Low		PER SHARE ($) Earnings	Dividends	Book Value
12/17	23.09	15	4	2.19	0.00	8.92
12/16	9.70	34	15	0.30	0.00	6.56
12/15	5.38	—	—	(0.34)	0.00	6.23
12/14	9.38	38	19	0.38	0.00	6.38
12/13	10.05	28	13	0.36	0.00	5.99
Annual Growth	23.1%	—	—	57.0%	—	10.5%

UMH Properties Inc

UMH Properties (formerly United Mobile Homes) is a real estate investment trust (REIT) that owns and manages more than 80 manufactured home communities containing approximately 14500 developed lots in New Jersey New York Ohio Pennsylvania and several other states. The company leases home sites to private homeowners on a monthly basis and rents a small number of homes to residents. Communities offer such amenities as swimming pools playgrounds and municipal water and sewer services. The REIT sells and finances manufactured homes through subsidiary UMH Sales and Finance and owns more than 800 acres of land for development. UMH Properties also invests in other REITs.

Geographic Reach
The New Jersey-based REIT owns lots in Indiana Michigan New Jersey New York Ohio Pennsylvania and Tennessee.

Financial Performance
The REIT's revenue has been growing along with its active acquisition schedule and swelling portfolio of properties. In 2013 revenue increased by nearly a third over 2012 to $62.2 million. Rental and related income increased 41% in 2013 to $53.5 million from about $38 million in 2012. The increase was due to acquisitions made in 2013 and 2012. UMH has been raising rental rates by approximately 2% to 6% annually at certain communities. Sales of manufactured homes fell from $8.8 million in 2012 to $8.7 million in 2013 on fewer homes sold.

Despite the substantial increase in revenue net income declined 10% in 2013 versus 2012 to $5.8 million on an increase in community operating expenses acquisition costs interest and other expenses. Cash flow from operations has been rising along with revenue.

Strategy
UMH has been growing by acquisitions and plans to continue making opportunistic investments particularly in energy-rich areas such as the Marcellus and Utica shale regions in the Northeast. In 2013 it acquired 10 manufactured home communities for a total of $67.5 million. The 10 all-age communities totaled 1854 sites and spanned approximately 400 acres. Five of the acquired properties are in Indiana four in Pennsylvania and one in Michigan. In 2012 the REIT bought more than 15 properties including 11 manufactured home communities from ARCPA Properties LLC for an aggregate purchase price of $28.3 million.

Mergers and Acquisitions
In March 2014 UMH closed on the purchase of eight Ohio manufactured home communities for about $25 million. The eight all-age communities contan a total of 1018 developed homesites situated on about 270 acres.

EXECUTIVES

President CEO and Director, Samuel A. Landy, age 57, $460,000 total compensation
VP CFO and Director, Anna T. Chew, age 59, $349,000 total compensation
General Counsel and Secretary, Craig Koster, $152,769 total compensation
Executive Vice President; Director, Michael Landy
Chairman, Eugene W. Landy, age 85
Auditors: PKF O'Connor Davies, LLP

LOCATIONS

HQ: UMH Properties Inc
Juniper Business Plaza, 3499 Route 9 North, Suite 3-C, Freehold, NJ 07728
Phone: 732 577-9997
Web: www.umh.com

PRODUCTS/OPERATIONS

2016 Sales

	$ mil.	% of total
Rental and Related Income	90.7	91
Sales of Manufactured Homes	8.5	9
Total	**99.2**	**100**

COMPETITORS

American Land Lease	Hometown America
Clayton Homes	Origen Financial
Equity Lifestyle Properties	Sun Communities

HISTORICAL FINANCIALS

Company Type: Public

Income Statement				FYE: December 31
	REVENUE ($ mil.)	NET INCOME ($ mil.)	NET PROFIT MARGIN	EMPLOYEES
12/17	112.6	12.6	11.2%	340
12/16	99.2	11.5	11.6%	330
12/15	81.5	2.1	2.6%	295
12/14	71.4	4.2	5.9%	260
12/13	62.2	5.8	9.4%	250
Annual Growth	16.0%	21.4%	—	8.0%

2017 Year-End Financials

Debt ratio: 47.2%
Return on equity: 3.4%
Cash ($ mil.): 23.2
Current ratio: 3.12
Long-term debt ($ mil.): 389.6
No. of shares (mil.): 35.4
Dividends
  Yield: 0.0%
  Payout: 184.6%
Market value ($ mil.): 529.0

	STOCK PRICE ($) FY Close	P/E High/Low		PER SHARE ($) Earnings	Dividends	Book Value
12/17	14.90	46	35	0.39	0.72	11.87
12/16	15.05	36	22	0.42	0.72	10.79
12/15	10.12	133	114	0.08	0.72	9.09
12/14	9.55	55	48	0.19	0.72	8.57
12/13	9.42	37	29	0.31	0.72	9.18
Annual Growth	12.1%	—	—	5.9%	(0.0%)	6.6%

Umpqua Holdings Corp

Umpqua Holdings thinks of itself not so much as a bank but rather a retailer that sells financial products. Consequently many of the company's 380-plus Umpqua Bank "stores" in northern California northern Nevada Idaho Oregon and Washington feature coffee bars and computer cafes. While customers sip Umpqua-branded coffee pay bills online attend a financial seminar catch a poetry reading or check out wares from local merchants staff members pitch deposit accounts mortgages loans life insurance investments and more. Subsidiary Umpqua Investments (formerly Strand Atkinson Williams & York) provides retail brokerage services through more than a dozen locations mostly inside Umpqua Bank branches.

Operations

Umpqua operates two business segments: Community Banking which made up 79% of the company's total revenue during 2015 and provides traditional banking services as well as wealth management and private banking services for wealthier individuals; and Home Lending (21% of revenue) which originates and sells residential mortgage loans.

The company makes more than 75% of its revenue from interest income. About 72% of its revenue came from loan interest (including fees) during 2015 with another 5% coming from interest on investment securities. The rest of its revenue came from residential mortgage banking revenue (9% of revenue) deposit account service charges (5%) brokerage revenue (2%) and other miscellaneous income streams.

Geographic Reach

Oregon-based Umpqua Bank has branches in Idaho Washington Oregon California and Northern Nevada. Umpqua Investments has offices in Portland Lake Oswego and Medford Oregon as well as Santa Rosa California.

Sales and Marketing

Umpqua Holdings promotes its brand through customer-facing channels public relations social media and community-based events. It spent $11.4 million on marketing to promote its brand during 2015 up from $9.5 million and $6.1 million in 2014 and 2013 respectively.

Financial Performance

The bank's annual revenues have doubled since 2011 as its loan and lease assets have tripled to $16.85 billion which has resulted in strong interest income growth. Exceptional revenue growth and effective cost controls have helped the bank's net income triple over the same period.

Umpqua Holdings' revenue jumped 20% to $1.21 billion during 2015 mostly as its earning assets (including loans investments and loans held for sale) swelled by 20% which led to higher interest income. The bank's non-interest income also rose 52% for the year mostly thanks to the 2014 acquisition of Sterling Financial with residential mortgage banking revenue brokerage commissions and deposit service charges all growing during the year.

Strong revenue growth in 2015 drove the bank's net income up 51% to $222.54 million for the year. Umpqua's operating cash levels climbed 5% to $376.74 million as earnings rose.

Strategy

Umpqua Bank's primary mission is to become the top community-oriented financial services firm in the Western US by strategically acquiring banks in new markets and building its brand by offering unique personal experience for customers entering its "store" branches. Its mid-2014 acquisition of Sterling Financial — the largest ever acquisition in Umpqua's history — successfully extended the bank's presence in Southern California Eastern Washington Eastern Oregon and Idaho.

The bank differentiates itself by encouraging clients to come into its stores instead of using impersonal interfaces like ATMs and electronic banking more cost-effective methods preferred by many of its competitors. The bank's "Next Generation" stores feature interactive touch-screen walls fresh fruit and cold drinks. It hopes the comfortable environment will inspire customers to use more of the bank's financial services.

Hoping to build upon its one-of-a-kind branch experiences Umpqua Bank in 2015 launched its Silicon Valley-based Pivotus Ventures Inc subsidiary to explore disruptive new bank technologies.

In 2016 Umpqua launched its corporate banking division which is dedicated to providing companies with access to such offerings as treasury management international banking debt capital markets and others.

Mergers and Acquisitions

In April 2014 Umpqua Bank acquired $10-billion-in-assets Sterling Financial Corp. headquartered in Spokane Washington. The largest merger in Umpqua's history created the West Coast's largest community bank with some $22 billion in assets and 394 stores across five states. The Sterling branches were rebranded as part of the $1.9 billion deal.

Company Background

Traditionally consumer focused Umpqua Bank established a business banking division in 2011 to court small and mid-sized business clients. That year it pursued deposit growth assembled new lending teams and added new stores in key metropolitan areas like Portland Oregon; Seattle; San Francisco; and California's Silicon Valley.

Umpqua Holdings established a wealth management division in 2009 and launched a trust services group the following year. It provided asset management services through an agreement with independent firm Ferguson Wellman Capital Management.

EXECUTIVES

Evp Wealth Management Umpqua Holdings And Umpqua Bank, Kelly Johnson
EVP Creative Strategies Group Umpqua Bank, Lani Hayward, age 51
EVP and Chief Lending Officer Umpqua Holdings Corp and Umpqua Bank, David F. (Dave) Shotwell, age 59
EVP CFO and Principal Financial Officer Umpqua Holdings and Umpqua Bank, Ronald L. (Ron) Farnsworth, age 48, $425,000 total compensation
EVP Treasurer and Principal Accounting Officer Umpqua Holdings and Umpqua Bank, Neal T. McLaughlin, age 50
EVP Corporate Communications Umpqua Bank, Eve Callahan, age 44
President CEO and Director, Cort O'Haver, age 55, $565,000 total compensation
EVP and Chief Auditor Umpqua Bank, Joel Brandenburg, age 55
EVP Enterprise Risk Management Umpqua Holdings Corp and Umpqua Bank, Gary F. Neal, age 63
EVP Associate Relations Umpqua Holdings Corp and Umpqua Bank, Sheri T. Burns, age 50
EVP Cultural Enhancement and Government Relations Umpqua Bank, Marty J. Dickinson, age 48
EVP General Counsel and Corporate Secretary Umpqua Holdings Corp and Umpqua Bank, Andrew H. Ognall, age 46, $300,000 total compensation
Vice President of Benefits, Jennifer Hollenbeck
Senior Vice President Data Processing, Bo Harrison
Vice President Rewards and Recognition, Sandy Hunt
Vice President Enterprise Risk Manager, Aretina Trepczyk
Vice President, Susan Jensen
Vice President, Marie Fidler
Executive Vice President Commerical Banking of the Company and the Bank, Cort Oahaver
Senior Vice President Credit Review Manager Commercial Banking, Jim Storvick
Senior Vice President International Banking Manager, Anthony Oriti
Vice President Commercial Banking Center Manager, Jamie Hudson
Chairman, Raymond P. (Ray) Davis, age 69
Vice Chairman, Bryan L. Timm, age 54
Auditors: DELOITTE & TOUCHE LLP

LOCATIONS

HQ: Umpqua Holdings Corp
One S.W. Columbia Street, Suite 1200, Portland, OR 97258
Phone: 503 727-4100
Web: www.umpquaholdingscorp.com

PRODUCTS/OPERATIONS

2015 Sales

	$ mil.	% of total
Interest		
Interest and fees on loans and leases	869.4	72
TaxableInterest and dividends investment securities	58.2	5
Other	2.2	-
Non-interest		
Mortgage banking	124.7	9
Service charges on deposit accounts	59.7	5
Brokerage	18.5	2
Gain on loan sales net	22.4	2
BOLI income	8.4	1
Gain on investment securities net	2.9	-
Other	46.3	4
Adjustments	(7.2)	-
Total	**1,205.5**	**100**

2015 Sales

	$ mil.	% of total
Community Banking	954.7	79
Home Lending	250.8	21
Total	**1,205.5**	**100**

COMPETITORS

Bank of America	KeyCorp
Bank of the West	U.S. Bancorp
Banner Corp	Washington Federal
Cascade Bancorp	Wells Fargo
Columbia Banking	

HISTORICAL FINANCIALS

Company Type: Public

Income Statement   FYE: December 31

	ASSETS ($ mil.)	NET INCOME ($ mil.)	INCOME AS % OF ASSETS	EMPLOYEES
12/17	25,741.4	246.0	1.0%	4,380
12/16	24,813.1	232.9	0.9%	4,295
12/15	23,387.2	222.5	1.0%	4,491
12/14	22,613.2	147.5	0.7%	4,569
12/13	11,636.1	98.3	0.8%	2,490
Annual Growth	22.0%	25.8%	—	15.2%

2017 Year-End Financials

Return on assets: 0.9%	Dividends
Return on equity: 6.2%	Yield: 0.0%
Long-term debt ($ mil.): —	Payout: 61.2%
No. of shares (mil.): 220.1	Market value ($ mil.): 4,579.0
Sales ($ mil): 1,215.3	

	STOCK PRICE ($)		P/E	PER SHARE ($)		
	FY Close		High/Low	Earnings	Dividends	Book Value
12/17	20.80		20 15	1.11	0.68	18.24
12/16	18.78		18 13	1.05	0.64	17.79
12/15	15.90		19 15	1.01	0.62	17.48
12/14	17.01		24 20	0.78	0.60	17.17
12/13	19.14		22 14	0.87	0.60	15.43
Annual Growth	2.1%		— —	6.3%	3.2%	4.3%

Union Bankshares Corp (New)

Union Bankshares (formerly Union First Market Bankshares) is the holding company for Union Bank & Trust which operates approximately 100 branches in central northern and coastal portions of Virginia. The bank offers standard services such as checking and savings accounts credit cards and certificates of deposit. Union Bank & Trust maintains a loan portfolio heavily weighted towards real estate: Commercial real estate loans make up more than 30% while one- to four-family residential mortgages and construction loans account for approximately 15% and 20% respectively. The bank also originates personal and business loans.

EXECUTIVES

EVP and Director of Mortgage and Wealth Management, Jeffrey W. Farrar, age 57
EVP Union Bankshares and Chief Retail Officer Union Bank & Trust, Elizabeth M. Bentley, age 57, $268,491 total compensation
EVP and Chief Risk Officer, David G. (Dave) Bilko, age 58
President and CEO Union Bankshares Corporation and CEO Union Bank & Trust, John C. Asbury, age 53
EVP and CFO, Robert M. (Rob) Gorman, age 59, $351,167 total compensation
EVP Union Bankshares and Chief Banking Officer Union Bank & Trust, D. Anthony (Tony) Peay, age 58, $348,997 total compensation
EVP and CIO, M. Dean Brown, age 53, $259,625 total compensation
SVP and Chief Marketing Officer, L. Duane Smith, age 51
EVP and Chief Human Resource Officer, Loreen A. LaGatta, age 49
EVP and President Union Bank & Trust, John G. Stallings, age 51
Vice President and Senior Branch Manager, Sherry Cillo
Assistant Vice President Branch Manager, Jody Hardy
Vice President, Norfleet Stallings
Vice President And Senior Market Manager, Cheryl Kirby
Senior Vice President, Craig Parrent
Senior Vice President Commercial Market Team Lead Union Bank And Trust Commercial Lending Division, Jay Baldwin
Vice Chairman Union Bankshares Corporation and Union Bank & Trust, G. William (Billy) Beale, age 68
Chairman, Raymond D. (Ray) Smoot, age 71
Auditors: Ernst & Young LLP

LOCATIONS

HQ: Union Bankshares Corp (New)
1051 East Cary Street, Suite 1200, Richmond, VA 23219
Phone: 804 633-5031
Web: www.bankatunion.com

PRODUCTS/OPERATIONS

2015 Sales

	$ mil.	% of total
Interest		
Loans including fees	247.5	72
Other	29.3	9
Noninterest		
Other service charges commission and fees	15.6	5
Service charges on deposit accounts	18.9	5
others	30.8	9
Adjustments	(0.3)	-
Total	**341.8**	**100**

Selected Subsidiaries

Union First Market Bank
Union Insurance Group LLC
Union Investment Services Inc.
Union Mortgage Group Inc.

COMPETITORS

BB&T	PNC Financial
Bank of America	Regions Financial
C&F Financial	SunTrust
Eastern Virginia Bankshares	TowneBank
JPMorgan Chase	Wells Fargo

HISTORICAL FINANCIALS

Company Type: Public

Income Statement — FYE: December 31

	ASSETS ($ mil.)	NET INCOME ($ mil.)	INCOME AS % OF ASSETS	EMPLOYEES
12/17	9,315.1	72.9	0.8%	1,149
12/16	8,426.7	77.4	0.9%	1,416
12/15	7,693.2	67.0	0.9%	1,422
12/14	7,359.1	52.5	0.7%	1,471
12/13	4,176.5	34.5	0.8%	1,025
Annual Growth	22.2%	20.6%	—	2.9%

2017 Year-End Financials

Return on assets: 0.8%
Return on equity: 7.1%
Long-term debt ($ mil.): —
No. of shares (mil.): 43.7
Sales ($ mil): 401.8
Dividends
Yield: 0.0%
Payout: 48.5%
Market value ($ mil.): 1,582.0

	STOCK PRICE ($)	P/E	PER SHARE ($)		
	FY Close	High/Low	Earnings	Dividends	Book Value
12/17	36.17	23 18	1.67	0.81	23.92
12/16	35.74	21 12	1.77	0.77	22.95
12/15	25.24	18 13	1.49	0.68	22.23
12/14	24.08	23 19	1.14	0.58	21.66
12/13	24.81	19 11	1.38	0.54	17.55
Annual Growth	9.9%	— —	4.9%	10.7%	8.1%

Unique Fabricating Inc

Auditors: Deloitte & Touche, LLP

LOCATIONS

HQ: Unique Fabricating Inc
800 Standard Parkway, Auburn Hills, MI 48326
Phone: 248 853-2333
Web: www.uniquefab.com

HISTORICAL FINANCIALS

Company Type: Public

Income Statement — FYE: December 31

	REVENUE ($ mil.)	NET INCOME ($ mil.)	NET PROFIT MARGIN	EMPLOYEES
12/17*	175.2	6.4	3.7%	1,130
01/17	170.4	6.6	3.9%	1,180
01/16	143.3	5.0	3.5%	916
01/15	126.4	4.4	3.5%	796
12/13	63.8	0.2	0.4%	0
Annual Growth	28.7%	125.2%	—	—
*Fiscal year change

2017 Year-End Financials

Debt ratio: 43.6%
Return on equity: 12.8%
Cash ($ mil.): 1.4
Current ratio: 2.51
Long-term debt ($ mil.): 49.7
No. of shares (mil.): 9.7
Dividends
Yield: 0.0%
Payout: 90.9%
Market value ($ mil.): 72.0

	STOCK PRICE ($)	P/E	PER SHARE ($)		
	FY Close	High/Low	Earnings	Dividends	Book Value
12/17*	7.42	22 11	0.66	0.60	5.21
01/17	14.60	22 13	0.68	0.60	5.15
01/16	12.36	23 18	0.60	0.30	5.01
Annual Growth	(22.5%)	— —	4.9% 41.4%		2.1%
*Fiscal year change

United American Healthcare Corp.

EXECUTIVES

National Account Manager, Beth Beamer
Vice President Of Sales, Joanne Shuey
Vice President Chief Actuary, MARY MURLEY
Auditors: Bravos & Associates, CPA's

LOCATIONS

HQ: United American Healthcare Corp.
303 East Wacker Drive, Suite 1040, Chicago, IL 60601
Phone: 313 393-4571
Web: www.uahc.com

COMPETITORS

CONMED Corporation	Stryker
Medtronic	Zimmer Biomet

HISTORICAL FINANCIALS

Company Type: Public

Income Statement — FYE: December 31

	REVENUE ($ mil.)	NET INCOME ($ mil.)	NET PROFIT MARGIN	EMPLOYEES
12/17	10.6	10.9	102.0%	0
12/16	8.8	1.4	15.9%	0
12/15	8.9	(0.8)	—	0
12/14	7.9	(13.9)	—	0
12/13	3.2	(0.7)	—	33
Annual Growth	34.8%	—	—	—

2017 Year-End Financials

Debt ratio: 15.1%
Return on equity: ***.***.*%
Cash ($ mil.): 0.7
Current ratio: 0.98
Long-term debt ($ mil.): 0.0
No. of shares (mil.): 145.9
Dividends
Yield: —
Payout: —
Market value ($ mil.): 74.0

	STOCK PRICE ($) FY Close	P/E High/Low		PER SHARE ($) Earnings	Dividends	Book Value
12/17	0.51	9	1	0.10	0.00	0.04
12/16	0.08	10	0	0.02	0.00	(0.15)
12/15	0.01	—	—	(0.02)	0.00	(0.17)
12/14	0.03	—	—	(0.71)	0.00	(0.35)
12/13	0.07	—	—	(0.04)	0.00	0.12
Annual Growth	64.3% (25.1%)			—	—	—

United Bankshares Inc

United Bankshares (no relation to Ohio's United Bancshares) keeps it together as the holding company for two subsidiaries doing business as United Bank (WV) and United Bank (VA). Combined the banks boast some $12 billion in assets and operate roughly 130 branches that serve West Virginia Virginia and Washington DC as well as nearby portions of Maryland Pennsylvania and Ohio. The branches offer traditional deposit trust and lending services with a focus on residential mortgages and commercial loans. United Bankshares also owns United Brokerage Services which provides investments asset management and financial planning in addition to brokerage services.

Operations

The company's loan portfolio is made up of commercial and construction commercial and residential real estate and consumer loans (including credit card and home equity loans).

United Bankshares generated 75% of its total revenue from interest and fees on loans in 2014 plus an additional 7% from interest and dividends on its investment securities. The company generated about 9% of its total revenue from deposit services fees and another 4% from trust and brokerage services fees.

Geographic Reach

United Bankshares boasts some 130 full-service branches including more than 55 across the state of West Virginia nearly 70 in the Shenendoah Valley region of Virginia and the Northern Virginia Maryland and Washington DC metro area and a handful of branches split between southwestern Pennsylvania and southeastern Ohio.

Sales and Marketing

The company spent $4.76 million on advertising in 2014 up from $3.78 million and $4.27 million spent in 2013 and 2012 respectively.

Financial Performance

United Bankshares' revenues and profits have trended higher over the past few years thanks to growth in its loan business from acquisitions increased trust and brokerage services fee income and declining interest expense on deposits amidst the low-interest environment.

The company's revenue jumped by nearly 34% to a record $499.50 million in 2014 mostly as its interest income spiked by 37% after its Virginia Commerce acquisition added new interest-earning assets and increased the average yields on its loans investments and security assets. United Bankshare's non-interest income also swelled by 22% thanks to higher income from fees from trust and brokerage services bankcard fees and merchant discounts and net gains on investment securities.

Higher revenue in 2014 boosted the company's profits by 52% to a record $129.89 million while the company's operating cash grew by 2% thanks to higher cash earnings.

Strategy

United Bankshares has historically expanded through small bank and branch acquisitions closing nearly 30 bank purchases in the past quarter-century. Its growth strategy has mainly been focused in on the Washington DC/suburban Maryland/northern Virginia market though its also expanded into Pennsylvania in recent years as well. In 2014 for example the company extended its reach into Washington DC while boosting its loan business by $2 billion after completing its largest-ever acquisition of Virginia Commerce Bancorp.

In 2016 the company agreed to buy Cardinal Financial which has some $4.2 billion in assets and operates 30 branches in Virginia Maryland and Washington DC.

Mergers and Acquisitions

In January 2014 United Bankshares acquired Arlington-based Virginia Commerce Bancorp for a total cost of $585.53 million. The deal expanded United's reach into the Washington DC metropolitan area and added $2.07 billion in new loan business and $2.02 billion in deposits.

Company Background

The 2011 acquisition of West Virginia-based Centra Financial Holdings gave United Bankshares its first branches in Pennsylvania and entry into the Pittsburgh market.

EXECUTIVES

EVP the Company and United Bank and WV, James B. Hayhurst, age 72, $225,000 total compensation
President, Richard M. Adams, age 50, $328,846 total compensation
COO, James J. Consagra, age 58, $334,462 total compensation
EVP and COO United Bank (VA), Craige L. Smith, age 66, $243,750 total compensation
EVP and CFO, W. Mark Tatterson, age 43
EVP, Darren K. Williams
Assistant Vice President Information Technology Audit Manager, Jason Moore
Vice President Internal Audit Manager, Steve Hizak
Assistant Vice President Corporate Security Officer, Rachel Wilson
Assistant Vice President and Corporate Security Officer, Erica Fowler
Auditors: Ernst & Young LLP

LOCATIONS

HQ: United Bankshares Inc
 300 United Center, 500 Virginia Street, East, Charleston, WV 25301
Phone: 304 424-8716
Web: www.ubsi-inc.com

PRODUCTS/OPERATIONS

2014 Sales

	$ mil.	% of total
Interest		
Loans including fees	383.7	75
Interest and dividends on securities	33.9	7
Other	0.9	-
Noninterest		
Fees from deposit services	42.4	9
Fees from trust & brokerage services	18.1	4
Other	28.9	5
Adjustment (losses)	(8.4)	-
Total	**499.5**	**100**

COMPETITORS

BB&T	JPMorgan Chase
Bank of America	M&T Bank
Burke & Herbert Bank	PNC Financial
Cardinal Financial	SunTrust
City Holding	United Bancorp
Fifth Third	Virginia Commerce
Fulton Financial	Bancorp
Huntington Bancshares	WesBanco

HISTORICAL FINANCIALS

Company Type: Public

Income Statement — FYE: December 31

	ASSETS ($ mil.)	NET INCOME ($ mil)	INCOME AS % OF ASSETS	EMPLOYEES
12/17	19,058.9	150.5	0.8%	2,381
12/16	14,508.8	147.0	1.0%	1,701
12/15	12,577.9	137.9	1.1%	1,701
12/14	12,328.8	129.8	1.1%	1,703
12/13	8,735.3	85.6	1.0%	1,528
Annual Growth	21.5%	15.2%	—	11.7%

2017 Year-End Financials

Return on assets: 0.9%
Return on equity: 5.5%
Long-term debt ($ mil.): —
No. of shares (mil.): 105.0
Sales ($ mil): 755.4
Dividends
Yield: 0.0%
Payout: 86.3%
Market value ($ mil.): 3,650.0

	STOCK PRICE ($) FY Close	P/E High/Low		PER SHARE ($) Earnings	Dividends	Book Value
12/17	34.75	30	21	1.54	1.33	30.85
12/16	46.25	25	16	1.99	1.32	27.59
12/15	36.99	22	17	1.98	1.29	24.61
12/14	37.45	20	15	1.92	1.28	23.90
12/13	31.45	19	14	1.70	1.25	20.66
Annual Growth	2.5%	—	—	(2.4%)	1.6%	10.5%

United Community Banks Inc (Blairsville, GA)

United Community Banks is the holding company for United Community Bank (UCB). UCB provides consumer and business banking products and services through nearly 150 branches across Georgia North Carolina Tennessee and South Carolina. Commercial loans including construction loans and mortgages account for the largest portion of UCB's loan portfolio (more than 50%); residential mortgages make up 30%. The company which boasts roughly $10 billion in assets also has a mortgage lending division and provides insurance through its United Community Insurance Services subsidiary (aka United Community Advisory Services).

Operations

The bank's retail mortgage lending division United Community Mortgage Services (UCMS) sells and services mortgages for Fannie Mae and Freddie Mac and provides fixed and adjustable-rate home mortgages. It also offers retail brokerage services through an affiliation with a third-party broker/dealer.

About 65% of UCB's total revenue came from loan interest (including fees) in 2014 while another 16% came from taxable investments. The rest of its revenue came from service charges and fees (10%) mortgage loan fees (2%) and brokerage fees (2%) among other sources.

Geographic Reach

UCB's nearly 105 branches are located in Georgia (in the north the Atlanta-Sandy Springs-Roswell metro area Gainsville metro area and coastal areas); western North Carolina; eastern and central Tennessee; and South Carolina (in the Greenville-Anderson-Mauldin metro area).

Sales and Marketing

The bank provides community banking services for individuals small businesses and corporations.

Financial Performance

UCB has struggled to consistently grow its revenues in recent years due to shrinking interest margins on loans amidst the low-interest environment. Its profits however have been rising thanks to declining loan loss provisions as its loan portfolio's credit quality has improved with higher property valuations in the strengthened economy.

The bank's revenue inched higher by 1% to $304 million in 2014 thanks to an increase in interest income stemming from strategic business growth initiatives designed to add new business lines and expand into new markets as well as balance sheet management and restructuring actions taken in the second quarter of the year.

Despite higher revenue in 2014 UCB's net income dove 75% to $67.6 million mostly because in 2013 it had received a non-recurring income tax benefit of $238 million stemming from reversal of a deferred tax valuation allowance. Not counting this item however the bank's profit before taxes nearly tripled during the year. UCB's operating cash levels dropped by 47% to $101.9 million in 2014 due to lower cash earnings.

Strategy

UCB has been concentrating on growing its small business lending business in recent years. In 2014 it made "significant investments" in its SBA business after acquiring Business Carolina which specialized in SBA and USDA lending.

It also continues to pursue bank acquisitions to expand its reach in its existing core markets and boost its loan and deposit business. Its acquisitions in 2015 and 2014 alone have added over $1 billion in new loan business and $1.3 billion in new deposits.

Mergers and Acquisitions

In 2016 United Community Banks expanded into key markets in coastal South Carolina after buying Mt. Pleasant-based Tidelands and its seven Tidelands Bank branches in the Charleston Myrtle Beach and Hilton Head areas.

In 2015 UCB bought Tennessee-based MoneyTree Corporation and its 10 First National Bank branches in east Tennessee. The deal added $425 million in assets $354 million in deposits and $253 million in new loan business to UCB's books.

In 2014 the company purchased Palmetto Bancshares and its Palmetto Bank branches expanding its footprint into "major" southeastern metro markets in Greenville and the Upstate South Carolina area. The deal also added $1.2 billion in assets $832 million in loans and $967 million in deposits.

Also in 2014 UCB purchased Columbia-based Business Carolina a commercial lender that specialized in SBA and USDA loans for $31.3 million in cash. The deal included $25 million in loans $6 million in other assets and substantially all of the company's employees.

EXECUTIVES

President of Specialized Lending, Richard W. Bradshaw, age 56
Chairman and CEO, Jimmy C. Tallent, age 65, $750,000 total compensation
SVP Retail Banking; Chairman United Community Bank Adairsville and Summerville, William M. (Bill) Gilbert, age 65, $308,334 total compensation
President and Director United Community Banks Inc. and President CEO and Director United Community Bank, H. Lynn Harton, age 56, $575,000 total compensation
EVP General Counsel and Chief Risk Officer, Bradley J. (Brad) Miller, age 47
EVP and Chief Credit Officer, Robert A. (Rob) Edwards, age 53, $305,000 total compensation
EVP and CFO United Community Banks Inc. and United Community Bank, Jefferson L. Harralson
Senior Vice President, Debbie Williams
Vice President, Casey Brogdon
Senior Vice President Commercial Lending, Don Fowler
Senior Vice President Commercial Banking, Jay Roper
Executive Vice President, Rick Rowland
Vice President, RONNEY DIXON
Senior Vice President Retail Credit Administration, Chuck Valerio
Avp Mortgage Loan Officer, Tabitha Helms
Assistant Vice President Incentive Marketing Manager, Diana White
Vice President, Omar Galan
Assistant Vice President, Ginger Kilman
Senior Vice President Director of Loan Operations, Dan Graham
Vice President Mortgage Banker, Angie Abston
Vice President Of Business Development And Marketing, Elaine Bell
Vice President Business Banking, Bert Durand
Assistant Vice President, Adam Born
Senior Vice President Commercial Lending, Sam Churchill
Senior Vice President, Donald Harris
Senior Vice President Corporate Services Support, Jeanette Garrett
Senior Vice President, Skip Swain
Senior Vice President, Zachary Welch
Vice President, Jane Callihan
Assistant Vice President Business Banking Underwriting, Eric Rivenbark
Senior Vice President Commercial Banking, Ben Walker
Senior Vice President, Phil Beaudette
Assistant Vice President, Rob Andrews
Vice President and Director Bank Security, Dennis Tarnowski
Senior Vice President, Alan Kumler
Senior Vice President Builder Finance, Scott Ernest
Senior Vice President Human Resources, Susie Hooper
Vice President, Darryl Meadows
Senior Vice President and Treasurer, Michael Burke
Vice President, Anne Wade
VICE PRESIDENT AND PRIVATE BANKER, Terra Winter
Senior Vice President, Jessie Marolis
Vice President, Wendy Martin
SENIOR VICE PRESIDENT SECONDARY MARKETING, Jim Mcevoy
Vice President Commercial Lender, Donna Clark
Vice President Relationship Manager, Tim Ash
Vice President Business Development Officer Senior Analyst Lending, David Brindley
Vice President Franchise Lending, Mike Stone
Senior Vice President United Community Bank, Dennis McBride
Senior Vice President, Jennifer Lawley
SENIOR VICE PRESIDENT, Sheila Stolorena
Vice President, David Ball
VICE PRESIDENT BRANCH MANAGER, Liz Bowen
SENIOR VICE PRESIDENT, Will Ferguson
VICE PRESIDENT, Sandra Brown
VICE PRESIDENT UNDERWRITING, Linda Durden
ASSISTANT VICE PRESIDENT AND MORTGAGE PROCESSING MANAGER, Nalann Moss
VICE PRESIDENT, Frank Scott
VICE PRESIDENT CORPORATE BANKING, James Boccardo
VICE PRESIDENT CUSTOMER CONTACT CENTER TEAM MANAGER SC, Jeanie Roberts
VICE PRESIDENT, Kirby Butler
Assistant Treasurer, Mitchell Bleske
Board Member, Kenneth Daniels
Board Member, David Wilkins
Board Member, David Shaver
Auditors: PricewaterhouseCoopers LLP

LOCATIONS

HQ: United Community Banks Inc (Blairsville, GA)
125 Highway 515 East, Blairsville, GA 30512
Phone: 706 781-2265
Web: www.ucbi.com

PRODUCTS/OPERATIONS

2011 Sales

	$ mil.	% of total
Interest		
Loans including fees	239.1	69
Taxable investment securities	55.2	16
Other	3.3	1

Noninterest		
Service charges & fees	29.1	8
Mortgage loans & related fees	5.4	2
Brokerage fees	3.0	1
Net securities gains	0.8	-
Other	12.3	3
Adjustment	(0.7)	-
Total	**347.5**	**100**

COMPETITORS

Atlantic Coast Financial	Peoples Bancorp (NC)
BB&T	Regions Financial
Bank of America	Southeastern Bank Financial
Bank of Oak Ridge	Southeastern Banking
Fidelity Southern	SunTrust
First Citizens BancShares	Synovus
Georgia Bancshares	WGNB
Georgia-Carolina Bancshares	

HISTORICAL FINANCIALS

Company Type: Public

Income Statement   FYE: December 31

	ASSETS ($ mil.)	NET INCOME ($ mil.)	INCOME AS % OF ASSETS	EMPLOYEES
12/17	11,915.4	67.8	0.6%	2,137
12/16	10,708.6	100.6	0.9%	1,916
12/15	9,626.1	71.5	0.7%	1,883
12/14	7,566.9	67.6	0.9%	1,506
12/13	7,425.4	273.1	3.7%	1,472
Annual Growth	**12.6%**	**(29.4%)**	**—**	**9.8%**

2017 Year-End Financials

Return on assets: 0.6%	Dividends
Return on equity: 5.7%	Yield: 0.0%
Long-term debt ($ mil.): —	Payout: 41.3%
No. of shares (mil.): 77.5	Market value ($ mil.): 2,183.0
Sales ($ mil): 477.9	

	STOCK PRICE ($) FY Close	P/E High/Low	PER SHARE ($) Earnings	Dividends	Book Value
12/17	28.14	33 27	0.92	0.38	16.80
12/16	29.62	21 11	1.40	0.30	15.17
12/15	19.49	20 15	1.09	0.22	14.24
12/14	18.94	18 14	1.11	0.11	12.27
12/13	17.75	4 2	4.44	0.00	13.39
Annual Growth	**12.2%**	**— —**	**(32.5%)**	**—**	**5.8%**

United Community Financial Corp. (OH)

This thrift wants to keep your savings and your loans united. United Community Financial is the holding company for The Home Savings and Loan Company of Youngstown Ohio a community bank with more than 30 full-service branches and about 10 loan production offices in Ohio and western Pennsylvania. Boasting nearly $2 billion in assets the bank offers traditional checking and savings accounts CDs retirement accounts investments and credit cards as well as a variety of loans. Residential mortgages account for over 60% of the company's loan portfolio while commercial and consumer loans split the remainder.

Operations

About 62% of United Community's total revenue came from loan interest (including fees) in 2014 while another 16% came from interest on its securities held for sale. The rest of its revenue came from fees on deposit accounts (6%) mortgage servicing fees (3%) non-deposit investment income 2%) and other miscellaneous income sources. The bank had a staff of 428 full-time employees at the end of 2014.

Geographic Reach

Youngstown Ohio-based United Community Financial boasts more than 30 branches across Ohio and western Pennsylvania. Its primary markets include Allegheny and Beaver counties in Pennsylvania and Ashland Columbiana Cuyahoga Erie Franklin Geauga Huron Lake Mahoning Portage Richland Stark Summit and Trumbull Counties in Ohio.

Sales and Marketing

The company spent $838 thousand on advertising in 2014 compared to $893 thousand and $778 thousand in 2013 and 2012 respectively.

Financial Performance

United Community Financial has struggled to grow its revenue in recent years as its interest income has fallen with lower interest rates and because it's had to sell of many of its non-performing loan assets to de-risk its loan portfolio. The group's profits however are on the mend as its de-risking measures have led to declining loan loss provisions.

The company's revenue fell by 9% to $77 million in 2014 mostly due to a combination of lower interest income after it sold off some of its investment securities a $2.1 million decline in gains from security sales and a $3.2 million drop in mortgage banking income due to a reduction in mortgage origination sales.

Despite revenue declines in 2014 United's net income grew five-fold to a record $50.2 million for the year mostly thanks to a $39.7 million income tax benefit related to a reversal of a previous year's bad loan allowance and thanks to continued declines in loan loss provisions. The company's operating cash levels fell sharply with operations using $2.8 million in 2014 after its earnings were adjusted for non-cash items related to its net proceeds from its loans held for sale.

Strategy

Home Savings mainly focuses on originating residential real estate loans security by real estate in its primary market area. United Community Financial has been working to build its capital and shed its riskier assets to get its business back on solid footing. Indeed while the bank suffered several years of heavy losses between 2008 and 2012 its de-risking measures made 2014 the company's most profitable year in its history.

Mergers and Acquisitions

United Community agreed to buy Ohio Legacy Corp holding company of the four-branch Premier Bank & Trust for $40.3 million. Ohio Legacy also operates a wealth management and trust division.

Company Background

In 2012 federal and state regulators lifted a cease-and-desist order that the bank had been operating under since 2008. In its place the company began operating under a consent order under which United Community Financial would need to submit a formal capital plan to the regulators. To satisfy targets under the consent order the bank sold about $115 million worth of bad assets in late 2012.

EXECUTIVES

CFO United Community Financial Corp. and EVP and CFO Home Savings and Loan, Timothy W. Esson, age 68, $216,577 total compensation

General Counsel and Secretary UCFC and EVP General Counsel and Secretary Home Savings and Loan, Jude J. Nohra, age 49, $248,871 total compensation

President CEO and Director United Community Financial Corp. and Home Savings and Loan, Gary M. Small, age 58, $412,885 total compensation

EVP and Head of Commercial Lending and Credit Administration Home Savings and Loan, Matthew T. Garrity, age 51, $251,007 total compensation

EVP Retail Banking Home Savings and Loan, Barbara J. Radis, age 49

SVP and CIO, Douglas Young

Vice President Human Resources, Cindy Cerimele

Vice President Finance, Anthony Dantuono

VP Systems, Mark S Stricklin

Chairman United Community Financial and Home Savings and Loan, Richard J. Schiraldi, age 63

Auditors: Crowe Horwath LLP

LOCATIONS

HQ: United Community Financial Corp. (OH)
275 West Federal Street, Youngstown, OH 44503-1203
Phone: 330 742-0500
Web: www.ucfconline.com

PRODUCTS/OPERATIONS

2014 Sales

	$ mil.	% of total
Interest	63.3	80
Non-interest	13.7	20
Total	**77.0**	**100**

COMPETITORS

Central Federal	PNC Financial
F.N.B. (PA)	PVF Capital
Farmers National	U.S. Bancorp
KeyCorp	

HISTORICAL FINANCIALS

Company Type: Public

Income Statement   FYE: December 31

	ASSETS ($ mil.)	NET INCOME ($ mil.)	INCOME AS % OF ASSETS	EMPLOYEES
12/17	2,649.9	21.7	0.8%	503
12/16	2,191.3	18.8	0.9%	442
12/15	1,987.9	16.2	0.8%	428
12/14	1,833.5	50.2	2.7%	428
12/13	1,737.8	10.0	0.6%	514
Annual Growth	**11.1%**	**21.4%**	**—**	**(0.5%)**

2017 Year-End Financials

Return on assets: 0.9%	Dividends
Return on equity: 8.0%	Yield: 0.0%
Long-term debt ($ mil.): —	Payout: 31.8%
No. of shares (mil.): 49.8	Market value ($ mil.): 455.0
Sales ($ mil): 118.7	

STOCK PRICE ($) FY Close	P/E High/Low	PER SHARE ($) Earnings	Dividends	Book Value
12/17	9.13	23 18	0.44	0.14	5.91
12/16	8.94	24 13	0.40	0.11	5.36
12/15	5.90	18 14	0.34	0.07	5.14
12/14	5.37	5 3	1.00	0.02	4.88
12/13	3.57	71 41	0.07	0.00	3.48
Annual Growth 26.5%		— 58.3%	— 14.2%

United Financial Bancorp Inc (New)

EXECUTIVES

Secretary Rockville Financial and Rockville Bank, Judy L. Keppner, age 57
SVP Human Resources and Organizational Development Rockville Bank, Richard J. Trachimowicz, age 61, $138,531 total compensation
SVP and CFO Rockville Financial SVP and CFO Rockville Bank, John T. Lund, age 45
President and CEO; President and CEO Rockville Bank, William H. W. Crawford IV
Senior Vice President Investor Relations, Marliese Shaw
Director, William J. (Bill) McGurk, age 74
Director, Michael A. Bars, age 60
Director, C. Perry Chilberg, age 67
Director, David A. Engelson, age 72
Director, Raymond H. Lefurge Jr., age 66
Director, Stuart E. Magdefrau, age 61
Director, Rosemarie Novello Papa, age 71
Director, Richard M. Tkacz, age 63
Auditors: Wolf & Company, P.C.

LOCATIONS

HQ: United Financial Bancorp Inc (New)
225 Asylum Street, Hartford, CT 06103
Phone: 860 291-3600
Web: www.bankatunited.com

COMPETITORS

Bank of America	RBS Citizens Financial
Citibank	Group
Liberty Bank	SI Financial
Naugatuck Valley	Sovereign Bank
Financial	TD Bank USA
New England Bancshares	United Financial
PSB Holdings Inc.	Bancorp
People's United	Webster Financial
Financial	Westfield Financial

HISTORICAL FINANCIALS

Company Type: Public

Income Statement   FYE: December 31

	ASSETS ($ mil.)	NET INCOME ($ mil.)	INCOME AS % OF ASSETS	EMPLOYEES
12/17	7,114.1	54.6	0.8%	813
12/16	6,599.5	49.6	0.8%	768
12/15	6,228.5	49.6	0.8%	732
12/14	5,476.8	6.7	0.1%	725
12/13	2,301.6	14.2	0.6%	358
Annual Growth 32.6%		40.0%	—	22.8%

United Insurance Holdings Corp

2017 Year-End Financials

Return on assets: 0.8%
Return on equity: 8.1%
Long-term debt ($ mil.): —
No. of shares (mil.): 51.0
Sales ($ mil.): 269.6

Dividends
Yield: 0.0%
Payout: 44.8%
Market value ($ mil.): 900.0

STOCK PRICE ($) FY Close	P/E High/Low	PER SHARE ($) Earnings	Dividends	Book Value
12/17	17.64	18 15	1.07	0.48	13.58
12/16	18.16	18 11	0.99	0.48	12.91
12/15	12.88	14 12	1.00	0.46	12.53
12/14	14.36	91 76	0.16	0.40	12.16
12/13	14.21	28 23	0.54	0.56	11.53
Annual Growth 5.6%		— 18.6%	(3.8%) 4.2%

United Insurance Holdings insures homeowners in the Sunshine State throughout the seasons even hurricane season. The company underwrites flood fire and homeowners insurance policies in Florida and provides property insurance for automotive service companies. It distributes its products through independent agents. United Insurance was founded in 1999 then underwent a reverse merger in 2008 when it bought the OTC-listed FMG Acquisition Corp. for $95 million ($25 million in cash and 8.75 million shares of stock.) The newly merged company has listed on the NASDAQ exchange.

EXECUTIVES

Chief Underwriting Officer, Paul DiFrancesco
CEO, John L. Forney, $800,000 total compensation
CFO, B. Bradford Martz, $300,000 total compensation
CIO, Andrew D. (Andy) Swenson, $210,000 total compensation
General Counsel and Chief Legal Officer, Kimberly Salmon
Chairman, Gregory C. Branch
Auditors: DELOITTE & TOUCHE LLP

LOCATIONS

HQ: United Insurance Holdings Corp
800 2nd Avenue S., St. Petersburg, FL 33701
Phone: 727 895-7737
Web: www.upcinsurance.com

PRODUCTS/OPERATIONS

2015 Sales

	% of total
Net premiums earned	94
Investment income	3
Net realized gains	-
Other revenue	3
Total	**100**

COMPETITORS

AAA Auto Club South	Federated National
Allstate	Holding
American National	HCI Group

Insurance
Bankers Financial
Citizens Property
Insurance

Liberty Mutual
State Farm
Universal Insurance
Holdings

HISTORICAL FINANCIALS

Company Type: Public

Income Statement   FYE: December 31

	ASSETS ($ mil.)	NET INCOME ($ mil.)	INCOME AS % OF ASSETS	EMPLOYEES
12/17	2,059.9	10.1	0.5%	210
12/16	999.6	5.7	0.6%	167
12/15	740.0	27.3	3.7%	120
12/14	584.1	41.0	7.0%	120
12/13	441.2	20.3	4.6%	90
Annual Growth 47.0%	(16.0%)	—	23.6%

2017 Year-End Financials

Return on assets: 0.6%
Return on equity: 2.6%
Long-term debt ($ mil.): —
No. of shares (mil.): 42.7
Sales ($ mil.): 654.4

Dividends
Yield: 0.0%
Payout: 88.8%
Market value ($ mil.): 737.0

STOCK PRICE ($) FY Close	P/E High/Low	PER SHARE ($) Earnings	Dividends	Book Value
12/17	17.25	65 49	0.27	0.24	12.56
12/16	15.14	73 40	0.26	0.23	11.15
12/15	17.10	22 10	1.28	0.20	11.11
12/14	21.95	11 6	2.05	0.16	9.75
12/13	14.08	11 4	1.26	0.15	6.64
Annual Growth 5.2%		— (32.0%) 12.5% 17.3%

United Security Bancshares (CA)

United Security Bancshares (unrelated to the Alabama-based corporation of the same name) is the holding company for United Security Bank which operates about 10 branches loan offices and financial services offices in central California's San Joaquin Valley. The bank attracts deposits from area businesses and individuals by offering checking and savings accounts NOW and money market accounts certificates of deposit and IRAs. In 2007 United Security Bancshares bought Legacy Bank which had a single branch in Campbell California. A year later the company purchased ICG Financial and then formed a wealth management consulting and insurance division USB Financial Services.

United Security Bank's lending activities primarily consist of a mix of real estate mortgages and construction loans (together these are more than half of the company's loan portfolio) and commercial and industrial loans (more than 30%). The bank also writes agricultural consumer and lease financing loans.

Directors and executive officers of United Security Bancshares own more than a quarter of the company.

EXECUTIVES

Chairman President and CEO United Security Bancshares and United Security Bank, Dennis R. Woods, age 68, $368,036 total compensation

EVP and Chief Administrative Officer United Security Bancshares and United Security Bank, Kenneth L. (Ken) Donahue, age 67, $145,414 total compensation

SVP and COO United Security Bancshares and United Security Bank, David L. (Dave) Eytcheson, age 75, $142,815 total compensation

Secretary and Director, Robert G. Bitter, age 77

Vice Chairman, Ronnie D. Miller, age 74

SVP and CFO United Security Bancshares and United Security Bank, Richard Shupe

Secretary and Director, Robert G. Bitter, age 77

Vice Chairman, Ronnie D. Miller, age 74

Independent Director, Stanley J. Cavalla, age 65

Independent Director, Tom Ellithorpe, age 73

Independent Director, Walter Reinhard, age 86

Independent Director, John Terzian, age 83

Independent Director, Michael T. (Mike) Woolf, age 60

Independent Director, Robert M. Mochizuki, age 67

Independent Director, Todd Henry

Auditors: Moss Adams LLP

LOCATIONS

HQ: United Security Bancshares (CA)
2126 Inyo Street, Fresno, CA 93721
Phone: 559 248-4943   **Fax:** 559 248-5088
Web: www.unitedsecuritybank.com

COMPETITORS

Bank of America
First Hawaiian
MUFG Americas Holdings

Sierra Bancorp
Westamerica
Zions Bancorporation

HISTORICAL FINANCIALS

Company Type: Public

Income Statement   FYE: December 31

	ASSETS ($ mil.)	NET INCOME ($ mil.)	INCOME AS % OF ASSETS	EMPLOYEES
12/17	805.8	8.6	1.1%	128
12/16	787.9	7.3	0.9%	132
12/15	725.6	6.8	0.9%	129
12/14	663.1	6.2	0.9%	132
12/13	635.9	7.2	1 1%	138
Annual Growth	**6.1%**	**4.4%**	**—**	**(1.9%)**

2017 Year-End Financials

Return on assets: 1.0%
Return on equity: 8.7%
Long-term debt ($ mil.): —
No. of shares (mil.): 16.8
Sales ($ mil): 37.2

Dividends
Yield: 0.0%
Payout: 33.3%
Market value ($ mil.): 186.0

	STOCK PRICE ($) FY Close	P/E High/Low	Earnings	Dividends	Book Value
12/17	11.00	22 14	0.51	0.17	6.00
12/16	7.75	19 11	0.44	0.00	5.73
12/15	5.35	14 12	0.40	0.00	5.31
12/14	5.46	16 13	0.37	0.00	4.91
12/13	4.92	13 6	0.43	0.00	4.54
Annual Growth	**22.3%**	**— —**	**4.3%**	**—**	**7.2%**

United States Brent Oil Fund L.P.

Auditors: Spicer Jeffries LLP

LOCATIONS

HQ: United States Brent Oil Fund L.P.
1850 Mt. Diablo Boulevard, Suite 640, Walnut Creek, CA 94596
Phone: 510 522-9600
Web: www.unitedstatesbrentoilfund.com

HISTORICAL FINANCIALS

Company Type: Public

Income Statement   FYE: December 31

	REVENUE ($ mil.)	NET INCOME ($ mil.)	NET PROFIT MARGIN	EMPLOYEES
12/17	16.3	15.4	94.5%	0
12/16	38.0	37.0	97.4%	0
12/15	42.8	(43.6)	101.9%	0
12/14	26.1	(26.4)	101.4%	0
12/13	2.6	2.2	85.0%	0
Annual Growth	**57.5%**	**61.7%**	**—**	**—**

2017 Year-End Financials

Debt ratio: —
Return on equity: —
Cash ($ mil.): 78.3
Current ratio: 25.19
Long-term debt ($ mil.): —

No. of shares (mil.): 5.2
Dividends
Yield: —
Payout: —
Market value ($ mil.): 94.0

	STOCK PRICE ($) FY Close	P/E High/Low	Earnings	Dividends	Book Value
12/17	18.10	8 5	2.24	0.00	18.18
12/16	15.68	4 2	4.49	0.00	15.70
12/15	12.24	— —	(9.02)	0.00	12.22
12/14	22.70	— —	(26.86)	0.00	22.39
12/13	44.54	38 17	2.35	0.00	43.81
Annual Growth	**(20.2%) (19.7%)**	**— —**	**(1.2%)**	**—**	**—**

United Therapeutics Corp

United Therapeutics hopes its products will be in vein. Its injectable drug Remodulin treats pulmonary hypertension which affects the blood vessels between the heart and lungs; it also treats cancer and viral illnesses. The product is marketed directly and through distributors in North America Europe and the Asia/Pacific region. Other hypertension treatments include Adcirca Tyvaso and Orenitram. The company's development pipeline includes additional treatments for cardiovascular disease as well as various cancers respiratory conditions and infectious diseases. United Therapeutics has divested its cardiac monitoring division.

Operations

Remodulin accounted for 43% of United Therapeutics' 2014 sales.

The company is also developing the antibody Unituxin (formerly Ch14.18) for the treatment of neuroblastoma under an agreement with the National Cancer Institute. It has been accepted for review in the US and Europe. United Therapeutics has additional early stage research programs and it regularly evaluates opportunities to license additional compounds for development.

United Therapeutics holds a license agreement with Ascendis Pharma to develop a self-injectable therapeutic alternative for pulmonary arterial hypertension (PAH) patients by applying Ascendis Pharma's TransCon technology platform to its treprostinil molecule. The agreement also gives United Therapeutics exclusive rights to develop prostacyclin prostacyclin analog and prostacyclin-related products for treating PAH using the TransCon technology as well as rights to commercialize any products developed from the collaboration on a global basis.

Geographic Reach

United Therapeutics' Remodulin is approved for sale throughout North America and Europe as well as in the Asia/Pacific region. Tyvaso Adcirca and Orenitram are only approved in the US. The company's home country accounts for 90% of revenues.

United Therapeutics owns an office building near London; it serves as its European headquarters. It also owns a warehouse in Germany.

Sales and Marketing

United Therapeutics distributes Remodulin Tyvaso and Orenitram throughout the US and Puerto Rico through two contracted specialty distributors — CVS Caremark and Accredo Health. It also distributes Remodulin in Canada through a specialty pharma wholesaler. It sells Adcirca to pharmaceutical wholesalers at a discount.

Strategy

United Therapeutics pursues growth by developing new drugs either through R&D or in partnership with other firms. In 2015 the FDA approved Unituxin in combination with GM-CSF interleukin-2 and 13-cis-retinoic acid for the treatment of pediatric patients with high-risk neuroblastoma. In 2014 United Therapeutics formed an alliance with DEKA Research & Development to develop a potential technology breakthrough in the subcutaneous delivery of Remodulin Injection to PAH patients.

Mergers and Acquisitions

In 2018 United Therapeutics acquired SteadyMed in a deal valued at up to $216 million. SteadyMed's lead product candidate Trevyent is a treatment for pulmonary arterial hypertension (PAH) which makes the company a potential competitor of United Therapeutics. (Most of its revenue comes from treatments for PAH.) Buying SteadyMed will curtail difficulties between the companies that have arisen around patent legalities.

EXECUTIVES

Chairman and CEO, Martine A. Rothblatt, age 63, $1,078,099 total compensation

EVP General Counsel and Corporate Secretary, Paul A. Mahon, age 55, $760,201 total compensation

CIO, Shola Oyewole

President and COO, Michael Benkowitz

CFO and Treasurer, James Edgemond, $380,146 total compensation

Senior Vice President Manufacturing Sterile Products and Biologic, Patrick Poisson

Vice Chairman, Christopher Patusky

Auditors: Ernst & Young LLP

LOCATIONS

HQ: United Therapeutics Corp
   1040 Spring Street, Silver Spring, MD 20910
Phone: 301 608-9292
Web: www.unither.com

PRODUCTS/OPERATIONS

2014 Sales

	$ mil.	% of total
Cardiovascular products		
Remodulin	553.7	43
Tyvasco	463.0	36
Adcirca	221.5	17
Orenitram	41.3	3
Other	9.0	1
Total	**1,288.5**	**100**

Selected Products

Marketed
  Remodulin (pulmonary arterial hypertension)
  Tyvaso (pulmonary arterial hypertension)
  Adcirca (pulmonary arterial hypertension)
  Orenitram (pulmonary arterial hypertension)
In Development
  8H9 MAb (metastatic brain cancer)
  Beraprost (cardiovascular disease)
  Miglustat and other Glycobiology Antiviral Agents
  (hepatitis C and other infectious diseases)
  IW001 (pulmonary disease)
  Treprostinil (oral form for pulmonary arterial
  hypertension and peripheral vascular disease)

Selected Subsidiaries

Lung Biotechnology Hong Kong Limited
Lung Biotechnology (Nanjing) Co. Ltd.
Lung LLC
Lung RX Ltd. (UK)
Revivicor Inc.
United Therapeutics Europe Ltd. (UK)
Unither Biotech Inc. (Canada)
Unither Pharma LLC
Unither Pharmaceuticals Inc.

COMPETITORS

Abbott Labs	Gilead Sciences
Actelion	GlaxoSmithKline
American HealthChoice	NIPPON SHINYAKU
Ark Therapeutics Group	CO.LTD.
AstraZeneca	Novartis
Bayer HealthCare	Pfizer
Pharmaceuticals	Sandoz
Eli Lilly	Teva

HISTORICAL FINANCIALS

Company Type: Public

Income Statement				FYE: December 31
	REVENUE ($ mil.)	NET INCOME ($ mil.)	NET PROFIT MARGIN	EMPLOYEES
12/17	1,725.3	417.9	24.2%	800
12/16	1,598.8	713.7	44.6%	750
12/15	1,465.7	651.6	44.5%	750
12/14	1,288.5	340.0	26.4%	740
12/13	1,116.9	174.5	15.6%	706
Annual Growth	**11.5%**	**24.4%**	**—**	**3.2%**

2017 Year-End Financials

Debt ratio: 8.6%
Return on equity: 20.9%
Cash ($ mil.): 705.1
Current ratio: 3.26
Long-term debt ($ mil.): 250.0

No. of shares (mil.): 43.2
Dividends
  Yield: —
  Payout: —
Market value ($ mil.): 6,397.0

	STOCK PRICE ($) FY Close	P/E High/Low		PER SHARE ($) Earnings	Dividends	Book Value
12/17	147.95	18	12	9.31	0.00	49.05
12/16	143.43	10	6	15.25	0.00	43.34
12/15	156.61	13	8	12.72	0.00	34.96
12/14	129.49	19	12	6.28	0.00	26.87
12/13	113.08	33	15	3.28	0.00	25.89
Annual Growth	**7.0%**	**—**	**—**	**29.8%**	**—**	**17.3%**

Unity Bancorp, Inc.

Unity Bancorp wants to keep you and your money united. The institution is the holding company for Unity Bank a commercial bank that serves small and midsized businesses as well as individual consumers through nearly 20 offices in north-central New Jersey and eastern Pennsylvania. Unity Bank's deposit products include checking savings money market and NOW accounts and CDs. Lending to businesses is the company's life blood: Commercial loans including Small Business Administration (SBA) and real estate loans account for about 60% of its loan portfolio which is rounded out by residential mortgage and consumer loans.

The bank was given nationwide lending authority by the SBA and expanded its lending to markets outside of its core Tri-State area market to include Florida North Carolina Virginia and Illinois. The company expects to generate more loans through new offices established in those states.

Chairman David Dallas and his brother director Robert Dallas are Unity Bancorp's largest individual shareholders owning about 15% of the company each.

EXECUTIVES

Vice President Branch Sales Manager, Sarika
 Sikand
Vice President, Alvita Ayers
Assistant Vice President, Vanessa Galante
Avp Relationship Manager, Tracy Tortorello
Board Member, Raj Patel
Auditors: RSM US LLP

LOCATIONS

HQ: Unity Bancorp, Inc.
   64 Old Highway 22, Clinton, NJ 08809
Phone: 908 730-7630
Web: www.unitybank.com

PRODUCTS/OPERATIONS

Selected Subsidiaries

Unity Bank
  Unity Financial Services Inc.
  Unity Investment Company Inc.

COMPETITORS

1st Constitution	Magyar Bancorp
Bancorp	Peapack-Gladstone
Amboy Bancorp	Financial
Bank of America	Roma Financial
Bank of New York	TD Bank USA
Mellon	TF Financial

Brunswick Bancorp	Valley National
Fox Chase Bancorp	Bancorp
Investors Bancorp	

HISTORICAL FINANCIALS

Company Type: Public

Income Statement				FYE: December 31
	ASSETS ($ mil.)	NET INCOME ($ mil.)	INCOME AS % OF ASSETS	EMPLOYEES
12/17	1,455.5	12.8	0.9%	208
12/16	1,189.9	13.2	1.1%	194
12/15	1,084.8	9.5	0.9%	173
12/14	1,008.7	6.4	0.6%	183
12/13	921.1	5.1	0.6%	178
Annual Growth	**12.1%**	**26.0%**	**—**	**4.0%**

2017 Year-End Financials

Return on assets: 0.9%
Return on equity: 11.4%
Long-term debt ($ mil.): —
No. of shares (mil.): 10.6
Sales ($ mil): 63.5

Dividends
  Yield: 0.0%
  Payout: 19.1%
Market value ($ mil.): 210.0

	STOCK PRICE ($) FY Close	P/E High/Low		PER SHARE ($) Earnings	Dividends	Book Value
12/17	19.75	17	13	1.20	0.23	11.13
12/16	15.70	12	7	1.38	0.17	10.15
12/15	12.47	12	9	1.02	0.13	8.46
12/14	9.43	14	10	0.74	0.09	7.60
12/13	7.66	16	12	0.48	0.03	6.86
Annual Growth	**26.7%**	**—**	**—**	**25.6%**	**70.4%**	**12.9%**

Universal Display Corp

Universal Display thinks the world should be flat and lit with its organic light-emitting diode (OLED) technologies and materials. With its own research and through sponsored research agreements with PPG Industries and several universities the company develops OLED technologies and materials which use less energy than other lighting technologies for screens from cell phones to large flat panel displays and solid-state lighting. Based in the US it has facilities in Europe and the Asia/Pacific region. Most of the company's revenue comes from sale to customers in Asia.

Operations

Universal Display's materials segment generates about 60% of its revenue while the rest comes from its royalty and licensing fees.

The company's Adesis subsidiary is a contract research organization that provides services to the OLED pharma biotech catalysis and other industries.

Third-party manufacturing contractors handle much of Universal Display's production.

Geographic Reach

About 95% of Universal Display's revenue comes from customers in Asia. Customers in South Korea account for more than 85% of the Universal Display's revenue with customers in China Japan and the US accounting for the rest. The company has offices in the US China Hong Kong Ireland Japan South Korea and Taiwan.

Sales and Marketing

Universal Display targets flat panel display manufacturers and makers of lighting products to license its technologies and buy its materials. Universal Display supplies manufacturers with materials in development to see how they might work in a product. It works with manufacturers to develop displays and lighting products using phosphorescent OLEDs which use much less power than OLEDs.

Contracts with the US Department of the Army and US Department of Energy fund research to develop next-generation OLED technologies for applications such as flexible displays and solid-state lighting. Leading customer Samsung Display accounts for more than 60% of its revenue. Other customers include LG Display Tohoku Pioneer Konica Minolta Samsung Display AU Optronics and BOE Technology.

Financial Performance

After three straight years of revenue of just under $200 million Universal Display's sales jumped to $335 million a 69% increase in 2017 from 2016. Sales of the company's phosphorescent emitter products jumped more than 100% to more than $198 million in 2017 from 2016 from higher demand for red and green phosphorescent emitters. Sales to all geographic markets rose in 2017 from 2016 punctuated by a 50% leap in South Korea.

Universal Display parlayed record revenue to record net income of about $104 million in 2017 compared to about $48 million in 2016.

The company had about $133 million in cash at the end of 2017 off about $6 million from the previous year. Free cash flow was a positive $103 million compared to a negative $23 million in 2016.

Strategy

Universal Display is geared to grow with the OLED market. OLEDs are used in 10% of consumer electronics displays and the company believes there's plenty of room for expansion. Apple used OLEDs for the first time in its iPhone X which the company believes augurs growth for the technology.

The company's research develops new emissive material systems and technologies including next-generation reds greens yellows and hosts. It also has made progress in its blue phosphorescent OLED technology. The color OLEDs use less energy a feature demanded by customers.

Universal Display extended its tight relationship with Samsung Display by reaching a new long-term agreement in 2018. The company also reached agreements with Sharp and executed pacts with new customers Japan Display and EverDisplay Optronics.

Mergers and Acquisitions

In 2016 Universal Display acquired Adesis Inc. a contract research organization specializing in organic and organometallic synthetic research development and commercialization for about $36 million. Adesis operates as wholly-owned subsidiary of Universal Display.

EXECUTIVES

President and CEO, Steven V. Abramson, age 66, $581,049 total compensation
EVP and CFO, Sidney D. Rosenblatt, age 70, $581,049 total compensation
Vice President Innovation And Strategy, Julie Brown
Chairman, Sherwin I. Seligsohn, age 82
Auditors: KPMG LLP

LOCATIONS

HQ: Universal Display Corp
375 Phillips Boulevard, Ewing, NJ 08618
Phone: 609 671-0980
Web: www.oled.com

PRODUCTS/OPERATIONS

2017 Sales

	$ mil.	% of total
Material sales	200.3	60
Royalty and license fees	126.5	38
Contract research services	8.8	2
Total	**335.6**	**100**

COMPETITORS

AU Optronics	Merck KGaA
BASF SE	Microvision
Dow Chemical	Pioneer Corporation
DuPont	Samsung Electronics
Eastman Kodak	Sony
Epson	Sumitomo Chemical
Fujitsu	Texas Instruments
Idemitsu Kosan	Toshiba
LG Display	eMagin

HISTORICAL FINANCIALS

Company Type: Public

Income Statement				FYE: December 31
	REVENUE ($ mil.)	NET INCOME ($ mil.)	NET PROFIT MARGIN	EMPLOYEES
12/17	335.6	103.8	31.0%	224
12/16	198.8	48.0	24.2%	203
12/15	191.0	14.6	7.7%	154
12/14	191.0	41.8	21.9%	145
12/13	146.6	74.0	50.5%	124
Annual Growth	23.0%	8.8%	—	15.9%

2017 Year-End Financials

Debt ratio: —	No. of shares (mil.): 47.1
Return on equity: 8.7%	Dividends
Cash ($ mil.): 132.8	Yield: 0.0%
Current ratio: 8.13	Payout: 5.5%
Long-term debt ($ mil.): —	Market value ($ mil.): 8,135.0

	STOCK PRICE ($) FY Close	P/E High/Low		PER SHARE ($) Earnings	Dividends	Book Value
12/17	172.65	87	19	2 18	0.12	13.99
12/16	56.30	72	41	1.02	0.00	11.26
12/15	54.44	181	84	0.31	0.00	9.98
12/14	27.75	42	25	0.90	0.00	9.82
12/13	34.36	24	16	1.59	0.00	9.21
Annual Growth	49.7%	—	—	8.2%	—	11.0%

Universal Insurance Holdings Inc

While some companies shy away from insuring homes in hurricane-prone Florida Universal Insurance Holdings is right at home there. Operating through its Universal Property & Casualty Insurance Company (UPCIC) and American Platinum Property and Casualty Insurance Company (APP-CIC) subsidiaries the company underwrites distributes and administers homeowners property and personal liability insurance. The company's additional subsidiaries process claims perform claims adjustments and property inspections provide administrative duties and negotiate reinsurance. All together the group services some 765000 insurance policies.

Operations

Universal Insurance is Florida's largest private residential homeowners' insurance provider by direct written premiums in-force with some 10% of the market share.

In addition to UPCIC and APPCIC the company owns Universal Risk Advisors (managing general agent) Universal Inspection Corporation (underwriting inspections) Universal Adjusting Corporation (claims processing) and Blue Atlantic Reinsurance (reinsurance intermediary).

Through Universal Insurance's Universal Direct platform consumers in all states the group operates in are able to directly purchase homeowners policies online without meeting an intermediary face-to-face.

Geographic Reach

Universal Insurance's UPCIC unit has taken its expertise in flood and wind coverage to other markets. While Florida remains its largest market it also operates in 15 other states: Alabama Delaware Florida Georgia Hawaii Indiana Maryland Massachusetts Michigan Minnesota New Hampshire New Jersey New York North Carolina Pennsylvania South Carolina and Virginia. Although not yet active in Illinois Iowa New Hampshire or West Virginia the company is licensed in those states.

APPCIC writes homeowners multi-peril insurance for homes worth more than $1 million in Florida.

Sales and Marketing

Universal Insurance distributes its products through a network of some 8800 independent agents. It also sells its policies through its online platform Universal Direct.

Financial Performance

Universal Insurance's revenues have been rising for the past five years. In 2017 revenue increased 10% to $751.9 million as net premiums earned rose 9% commissions rose 20% and net investment income rose 41%. Policy fees and other rev enue also grew in 2017. Direct premiums written increased 11% within Florida and 40% in other states.

With the higher revenue net income rose 8% to $106.9 million. Operating cash flow followed suit more than doubling to $245 million. Factors driving that growth included positive changes to unpaid losses and loss adjustment expenses net reinsurance payable and liabilities and accrued expenses.

Strategy

Universal Insurance has been rapidly and organically expanding its operations beyond Florida especially in states with underserved homeowners markets. It has also introduced new types of coverage such as fire commercial multi-peril and other liability. With this diversification the company is less vulnerable to the catastrophes that have been the bane of Florida insurers. However because it does the majority of its business in Florida Universal Insurance has been hit hard with property/casualty claims in certain years — including in 2017 with the appearance of Hurricane Irma.

Additionally the company has seen an increase in lawsuits against it including suits originating in South Florida. As other insurers shy away from Florida business Universal Insurance remains committed to the state and to offset rising claims has sought approval to raise its rates some 10% across most of South Florida.

Personal residential homeowners insurance is the company's bread and butter but Universal Insurance is increasingly diving into commercial policies particularly commercial residential coverage in Florida.

EXECUTIVES

Chairman and CEO, Sean P. Downes, age 48, $2,278,015 total compensation
COO, Stephen J. Donaghy, $802,514 total compensation
President and Chief Risk Officer, Jon W. Springer, age 48, $1,337,416 total compensation
CFO and Principal Accounting Officer, Frank C Wilcox, $350,000 total compensation
CIO, Kimberly Cooper, $196,923 total compensation
Vice President Marketing, David Ahern
Auditors: Plante & Moran, PLLC

LOCATIONS

HQ: Universal Insurance Holdings Inc
   1110 W. Commercial Blvd., Suite 100, Fort Lauderdale, FL 33309
Phone: 954 958-1200
Web: www.universalinsuranceholdings.com

PRODUCTS/OPERATIONS

2017 Sales

	$ mil.	% of total
Net premiums earned	688.8	92
Commissions	21.2	3
Policy fees	18.8	2
Net investment income	13.5	2
Net realized gains on investments	2.6	-
Other	7.0	1
Total	**751.9**	**100**

Selected Products and Services

Condominium policy
Dwelling coverage
Dwelling fire policy
Homeowners policy
Other structures coverage
Personal liability coverage
Personal property coverage
Renter's policy

COMPETITORS

Allstate
Citizens Property
   Insurance
Federated National
   Holding
HCI Group
Heritage Insurance
   Holdings

Liberty Mutual
Progressive
   Corporation
State Farm
Travelers Companies
USAA
United Insurance
   Holdings

HISTORICAL FINANCIALS

Company Type: Public

Income Statement

FYE: December 31

	ASSETS ($ mil.)	NET INCOME ($ mil.)	INCOME AS % OF ASSETS	EMPLOYEES
12/17	1,455.0	106.9	7.3%	558
12/16	1,060.0	99.4	9.4%	483
12/15	993.5	106.4	10.7%	392
12/14	911.7	72.9	8.0%	335
12/13	920.0	58.9	6.4%	300
Annual Growth	**12.1%**	**16.0%**	**—**	**16.8%**

2017 Year-End Financials

Return on assets: 8.5%
Return on equity: 26.3%
Long-term debt ($ mil.): —
No. of shares (mil.): 34.7
Sales ($ mil): 751.9

Dividends
   Yield: 0.0%
   Payout: 23.0%
Market value ($ mil.): 950.0

	STOCK PRICE ($) FY Close	P/E High/Low		PER SHARE ($) Earnings	Dividends	Book Value
12/17	27.35	9	5	2.99	0.69	12.67
12/16	28.40	10	6	2.79	0.69	10.59
12/15	23.18	12	6	2.97	0.63	8.35
12/14	20.45	10	5	2.08	0.55	6.24
12/13	14.48	9	3	1.56	0.49	4.97
Annual Growth	**17.2%**	**—**	**—**	**17.7%**	**8.9%**	**26.4%**

Univest Financial Corp

Univest Corporation of Pennsylvania will keep your money close to its vest. The holding company owns $3 billion-asset Univest Bank and Trust which serves the southeastern part of the Keystone State and the broader Mid-Atlantic region online and though 30 branches and provides standard retail and commercial banking services such as checking and savings accounts CDs IRAs and credit cards. Subsidiary Univest Capital provides small-ticket commercial financing while Univest Insurance offers personal and commercial coverage. Univest Investments which boasts some $3 billion in assets under management offers brokerage and investment advisory services.

Operations

Univest operates three main business segments: Banking which accounted for 79% of the company's total revenue during 2015 and provides traditional banking services to consumers businesses and government entities through Univest Bank and Trust; Wealth Management (12% of revenue) which offers investment advisory retirement plan trust municipal pension and broker/dealer services through Univest Investments; and Insurance (9% of revenue) which offers commercial and personal insurance lines as well as benefits and human resources consulting through Univest Insurance.

Broadly speaking Univest Corporation gets more than 60% of its revenue from interest income. About 61% of its total revenue came from loan interest (including fees on loans and leases) during 2015 while another 5% came from interest on its investment securities. The rest of its revenue came from insurance commissions and fees (8% of revenue) investment advisory commission and fee in-

come (7%) trust fee income (5%) deposit account service charges (3%) mortgage banking sales (3%) and other miscellaneous income sources.

More than 40% of the company's loan portfolio was made up of commercial real estate loans at the end of 2015 while another 23% of loan assets were made up of commercial loans that were financial or agricultural-related. The remainder of the portfolio was made up of loans tied to residential properties secured for business purposes (10% of loan assets) residential properties for personal purposes (8%) lease financings (7%) construction real estate loans (4%) and loans to individuals (less than 2%).

Geographic Reach

Souderton Pennsylvania-based Univest Corporation and its subsidiaries serve clients across the Mid-Atlantic region. The company has around 30 bank branches and nearly 20 offices in the Montgomery Bucks Philadelphia Chester Berks Lehigh and Delaware counties of Pennsylvania as well as in Calvert County in Maryland Camden County in New Jersey and Lee County in Florida.

Sales and Marketing

Univest Corporation serves individuals businesses municipalities and non-profit organizations. It spent $2.25 million on marketing and advertising during 2015 to reach these clients up from $1.88 million and $1.95 million in 2014 and 2013 respectively.

Financial Performance

The bank's revenues and profits have been trending higher over the past several years thanks to 50% loan asset growth and 50% non-interest revenue growth since 2011 along with a continued reduction in loan loss provisions as its loan portfolio's credit quality has improved with higher property valuations in the strengthened economy.

Univest Corporation's revenue jumped 24% to a record $154.41 million during 2015 mostly as 35% loan asset growth (loan balances swelled to $2.16 billion) stemming from its Valley Green Bank acquisition helped boost interest income. The company's non-interest income also rose 9% as its mortgage banking gains doubled during the year on higher volumes and as its insurance commissions and fee income rose 20% after acquiring Sterner Insurance in mid-2014.

Strong revenue growth in 2015 drove the company's net income up 23% to $27.27 million for the year. Univest Corporation's operating cash levels climbed 12% to $35.63 thanks to the rise in earnings.

Strategy

Univest Corporation has been expanding its service lines and building its loan and deposit businesses by strategically acquiring other banks and investment or insurance-related financial firms.

Mergers and Acquisitions

In December 2015 Univest Corporation agreed to buy Fox Chase Bancorp along with its $1.1 billion in assets $768 million in loans $765 million in deposits and several Fox Chase Bank branches in Pennsylvania and New Jersey for a price exceeding $240 million. The deal would also expand Univest's presence in Bucks Chester Philadelphia and Montgomery counties in Pennsylvania as well as into Atlantic and Cape May counties in New Jersey.

In January 2015 the company purchased Valley Green Bank as well as its three branches and two loan production offices in the greater Philadelphia market for $77 million.

In July 2014 Univest bolstered its Univest Insurance subsidiary after acquiring Sterner Insurance Associates a full-service insurance and consultative risk management firm that served individuals and businesses across the Lehigh Valley Berks Bucks and Montgomery counties.

In January 2014 flagship subsidiary Univest Bank and Trust Co. bought registered investment advisory firm Girard Partners Ltd. as well as its $500 million in assets under management. The deal boosted Univest's assets under management by 20% to a total of $3 billion after the acquisition.

EXECUTIVES

President Corporate Banking, Philip C. (Phil) Jackson, $250,000 total compensation

EVP and Chief Credit Officer Univest Corporation and Univest National Bank, Duane J. Brobst, $200,000 total compensation

President and CEO, Jeffrey M Schweitzer, $450,000 total compensation

SEVP and CFO, Michael S Keim, $270,000 total compensation

Senior Vice President Marketing Underwriting Manager, Maria Di Marco

Senior Vice President Retail Banking, Tony Dacosta

Senior Vice President Credit Administration, Tami Garber

Vice President, Lisa Hartley

Executive Vice President Chief Experience Officer and Director Corporate Planning, Annette Szygiel

Vice President Corporate Communications, Kim Detwiler

Senior Vice President Retail Banking, Anthony Dacosta

VICE PRESIDENT AREA MANAGER, Gregory Taber

Senior Vice President Director of Project Management and Information Technology Strategy, Margie Boutcher

SENIOR VICE PRESIDENT EMPLOYEE BENEFITS PRACTICE LEADER, Dennis Boyle

Vice President Commercial Real Estate Lending, Robert Castro

SVP Director Bank Systems, Jeffrey Groff

Vice President and Senior Benefits Consultant, Rick Mack

Vice President Relationship Manager, Nicholas Yelicanin

Vice President Commercial Lending, Andrew Leaman

EXECUTIVE VICE PRESIDENT AND GENERAL COUNSEL, Megan Santana

VICE PRESIDENT SMALL BUSINESS RELATIONSHIP MANAGER, Steven Walker

ASSISTANT VICE PRESIDENT FINANCE BUSINESS UNIT ANALYTICS, Mary Beth Osbeck

SENIOR VICE PRESIDENT AND SENIOR TRUST OFFICER, Matt Holliday

VICE PRESIDENT, John Powers

VICE PRESIDENT, David Henrich

VICE PRESIDENT COMMERCIAL LENDING, Ramzi Dagher

Chairman, William S. Aichele, age 67

Board Member, Mark Schlosser

Treasurer, Bill Shelley

Board Member, Glenn Moyer

Auditors: KPMG LLP

LOCATIONS

HQ: Univest Financial Corp
14 North Main Street, Souderton, PA 18964
Phone: 215 721-2400
Web: www.univest.net

PRODUCTS/OPERATIONS

2015 sales

	$ mil.	% of total
Banking	120.9	79
Wealth Management	18.9	12
Insurance	14.4	9
Other	0.3	-
Total	**154.5**	**100**

COMPETITORS

Citizens Financial Group	PNC Financial
	QNB Corp.
Fulton Financial	Royal Bancshares
Harleysville Savings	Sovereign Bank
M&T Bank	

HISTORICAL FINANCIALS

Company Type: Public

Income Statement

FYE: December 31

	ASSETS ($ mil.)	NET INCOME ($ mil.)	INCOME AS % OF ASSETS	EMPLOYEES
12/17	4,554.8	44.0	1.0%	855
12/16	4,230.5	19.5	0.5%	840
12/15	2,879.4	27.2	0.9%	717
12/14	2,235.3	22.2	1.0%	638
12/13	2,191.5	21.1	1.0%	612
Annual Growth	**20.1%**	**20.1%**	**—**	**8.7%**

2017 Year-End Financials

Return on assets: 1.0%	Dividends
Return on equity: 7.9%	Yield: 0.0%
Long-term debt ($ mil.): —	Payout: 48.7%
No. of shares (mil.): 29.3	Market value ($ mil.): 823.0
Sales ($ mil): 222.2	

	STOCK PRICE ($) FY Close	P/E High/Low	PER SHARE ($) Earnings	Dividends	Book Value
12/17	28.05	20 16	1.64	0.80	20.57
12/16	30.90	37 22	0.84	0.80	19.00
12/15	20.86	15 13	1.39	0.80	18.51
12/14	20.24	16 13	1.36	0.80	17.54
12/13	20.68	17 13	1.27	0.80	17.22
Annual Growth	**7.9%**	**— —**	**6.6%**	**(0.0%)**	**4.5%**

US Concrete Inc

When things get hard U.S. Concrete's products get even harder. The company produces ready-mixed concrete precast concrete and related materials and services for commercial residential and infrastructure construction projects. U.S. Concrete has a fleet of about 1360 mixer trucks and about 145 ready-mixed concrete concrete block and 10 aggregate plants. During 2015 the company produced some 7 million cu. yd. of concrete and more than 4.9 million tons of aggregates; concrete accounts for about 90% of the company's sales. U.S. Concrete concentrates on major markets such as California New Jersey/New York and Texas. In 2017 the company agreed to purchase Polaris Materials for CAD$309 million.

Operations

U.S. Concrete operates primarily through the two segments of ready-mixed concrete and aggre-gate products. It has a fleet of over 1360 owned and leased mixer trucks and over 1325 other rolling stock and vehicles. Ready-mixed concrete accounted for about 90% of the revenue in 2015.

Geographic Reach

The company operates principally in Texas California and New Jersey/New York with those markets representing approximately 40% 29% and 26% respectively in 2015. It provides its ready-mixed concrete and concrete-related products from its operations in north and west Texas; northern California; New Jersey; New York; Washington DC; and Oklahoma. In addition U.S. Concrete produces precast concrete products at one plant in Pennsylvania.

Sales and Marketing

The company's customers include contractors for commercial and industrial residential street and highway and other public works construction. Concrete product revenue by type of construction activity for 2015 was commercial and industrial (57%); residential (15%); and street highway and other public works (15%).

Financial Performance

U.S. Concrete saw its revenues jump 39% from $704 million in 2014 to a record-setting $975 million in 2015. Its profits also climbed 24% from $21 million in 2014 to $26 million in 2015 mainly due to an income tax benefit it earned. The historic revenues for 2015 were driven by growth in sales of ready-mixed concrete and additional revenue from acquisitions.

Mergers and Acquisitions

U.S. Concrete has achieved milestone revenues over the years in part by acquiring smaller operators — part of its continuous growth strategy.

In 2017 the company expanded its aggregates business with the acquisition of Leon River Aggregate Material LLC a Texas-based sand and gravel producer along with its state-of-the-art processing plant.

In 2016 U.S. Concrete acquired the assets of NYCON Supply Corp. a ready-mixed concrete producer headquartered in the Long Island City neighborhood of Queens New York. NYCON's premier location widened its footprint to serve the New York City market and expanded its regional customer base. Also in 2016 U.S. Concrete obtained the assets of Greco Brothers Concrete a ready mixed concrete producer located in Brooklyn New York. The deal is expected to offer new opportunities to service its expanded customer base optimize service efficiencies and enhance raw material purchasing savings.

EXECUTIVES

President CEO and Director, William J. (Bill) Sandbrook, age 60, $816,788 total compensation

VP Marketing and Sales, Wallace H. Johnson, age 70

VP and General Manager Central Concrete Supply Co. Inc., Jeff L. Davis, age 67, $245,400 total compensation

VP and General Manager Ingram Concrete, Jeffrey W. Roberts, age 51, $246,248 total compensation

Principal Accounting Officer, Kevin R. Kohutek, age 45, $260,250 total compensation

EVP South East Division, Niel L. Poulsen, age 64, $282,500 total compensation

SVP General Counsel and Corporate Secretary, Paul M. Jolas, age 53, $300,850 total compensation

SVP and COO, Ronnie Pruitt, age 47

Vice President Human Resources, Mark Peabody

Chairman, Eugene I. (Gene) Davis, age 63

Auditors: Ernst & Young LLP

LOCATIONS

HQ: US Concrete Inc
331 N. Main Street, Euless, TX 76039
Phone: 817 835-4105
Web: www.us-concrete.com

PRODUCTS/OPERATIONS

2015 Sales

	% of total
Ready-mixed concrete	90
Aggregates	6
Other products	4
Total	**100**

2015 Sales by Product

	% of total
Ready-mixed concrete	90
Aggregates	3
Aggregate distribution	3
Lime	2
Hauling	1
Building materials	1
Other	-
Total	**100**

2015 Sales by Market

	% of total
Residential construction	22
Street & highway construction & paving	20
Commercial & industrial construction	18
Other public works & infrastructure construction	40
Total	**100**

Selected Products

Aggregate
 Granite
 Sand
Concrete Masonry
 Cinder blocks
 Concrete blocks
Building Materials
 Color Products
 Fasteners
 Concrete Forms
 Hand Tools
 Liquid Products
 Lumber
 Power Tools
 Safety Gear and Products
 Sand & Rock
 Tools & Accessories
 Fiber
 Waterproofing Material
Ready-Mixed Concrete
 Site Set
 Site Fill
 Site Fresh
 Construct-Lite

COMPETITORS

Ash Grove Cement	Lattimore Materials
Buzzi Unicem USA	Lehigh Hanson
CEMEX	Oldcastle
Eagle Materials	Superior Ready Mix
Holcim (US)	TXI
Lafarge North America	

HISTORICAL FINANCIALS

Company Type: Public

Income Statement   FYE: December 31

	REVENUE ($ mil.)	NET INCOME ($ mil.)	NET PROFIT MARGIN	EMPLOYEES
12/17	1,336.0	25.5	1.9%	3,070
12/16	1,168.1	8.8	0.8%	643
12/15	974.7	25.5	2.6%	2,700
12/14	703.7	20.5	2.9%	2,144
12/13	615.0	(20.1)	—	1,786
Annual Growth	**21.4%**	—	—	**14.5%**

2017 Year-End Financials

Debt ratio: 54.3%
Return on equity: 10.8%
Cash ($ mil.): 22.5
Current ratio: 1.50
Long-term debt ($ mil.): 667.3

No. of shares (mil.): 16.6
Dividends
 Yield: —
 Payout: —
Market value ($ mil.): 1,393.0

	STOCK PRICE ($) FY Close	P/E High/Low	PER SHARE ($) Earnings	Dividends	Book Value
12/17	83.65	53 37	1.53	0.00	16.84
12/16	65.50	116 71	0.55	0.00	12.03
12/15	52.66	33 14	1.64	0.00	11.09
12/14	28.45	19 14	1.48	0.00	7.26
12/13	22.63	— —	(1.56)	0.00	5.97
Annual Growth	**38.7%**	— —	—	—	**29.6%**

US Ecology, Inc.

US Ecology helps keep a lid on hazardous waste industrial waste and low-level radioactive waste. The company provides hazardous and nonhazardous waste management at sites in the US Canada and Mexico. It operates a low-level radioactive waste facility in Washington State. The company does business with private waste companies state and federal agencies and a variety of industries. Customers include nuclear plants steel mills petrochemical facilities and academic and medical institutions. US Ecology retains interests in several non-operating waste disposal facilities.

Operations

US Ecology operates in two segments: Environmental Services (67% of sales) and Field & Industrial Services (33%).

The Environmental Services segment provides a range of hazardous material management services including transportation recycling treatment and disposal of hazardous and non-hazardous waste at company-owned landfill wastewater and other treatment facilities. The Field & Industrial Services segment provides packaging and collection of hazardous waste and total waste management programs at customer sites and through its 10-day transfer facilities.

Geographic Reach

The company has operations in the US Canada and Mexico. The US accounted for 93% of revenues in 2015.

US Ecology's fixed facilities include five Resource Conservation and Recovery Act of 1976 (RCRA) subtitle C hazardous waste landfills and one low-level radioactive waste regulated under the federal Atomic Energy Act for disposal (LLRW) landfill. These are located near Beatty Nevada; Richland Washington; Robstown Texas; Grand View Idaho; Detroit Michigan and Blainville Québec Canada.

The company also has waste treatment-only facilities (Ohio Michigan Illinois Pennsylvania Oklahoma Georgia Alabama Florida Michigan and North Carolina.

US Ecology's field and industrial waste management facilities are in Michigan New Jersey Georgia and Massachusetts.

Sales and Marketing

US Ecology's customers include oil refineries chemical production plants steel mills real estate developers waste brokers/aggregators serving small manufacturers and other industrial customers.

Financial Performance

The company 26% growth in 2015 (to $563 million) was primarily due to growth in both segments as a result of full year revenue from the EQ Holdings acquisition.

US Ecology's net income declined by 33% to $26 million in 2015 due to higher selling general and administrative expenses as a result of acquired EQ business. The growth in interest expenses was also due to higher outstanding debt levels and the related interest expenses related to the acquisition of EQ.

Operating cash flow increased by under 0.5% (to $71 million) due to a change in receivables and income taxes.

Strategy

The company focuses on expanding into new markets. It also offers new services in order to cross-sell or bundle services to drive incremental volume at its disposal facilities. (It aims to enhance treatment capabilities at its existing facilities to handle additional waste streams and increase throughput).

Also the company targets acquisitions to expand its disposal network customer base and geographic footprint.

In 2015 the company sold its Allstate Power Vac subsidiary engaged in the industrial services business to a private investor group for $58.8 million. Allstate was included in its Field and Industrial Services segment which the company acquired with the acquisition of EQ Holdings. Divesting Allstate allowed the company to concentrate on growing its core environmental services business while continuing to expand its complementary field services.

Mergers and Acquisitions

In 2014 the company acquired integrated environmental services company EQ Holdings for $460.9 million. The acquisition strengthened US Ecology's environmental services group and the field and industrial services segment.

EXECUTIVES

EVP Sales and Marketing, Steven D. (Steve) Welling, age 60, $255,923 total compensation
Facility Manager US Ecology Idaho, Simon G. Bell, age 48, $207,989 total compensation
Chairman President and CEO, Jeffrey R. (Jeff) Feeler, age 49, $296,904 total compensation
EVP CFO and Treasurer, Eric L. Gerratt, age 49, $198,662 total compensation
Auditors: DELOITTE & TOUCHE LLP

LOCATIONS

HQ: US Ecology, Inc.
101 S. Capitol Blvd., Suite 1000, Boise, ID 83702
Phone: 208 331-8400
Web: www.usecology.com

PRODUCTS/OPERATIONS

2016 Sales

	$ mil.	% of total
Environmental services	337.8	71
Field & Industrial services	139.9	29
Total	**477.7**	**100**

Selected Subsidiaries

EQ Holdings Inc.
Stablex Canada Inc
US Ecology Inc.
US Ecology Idaho Inc.
US Ecology Michigan Inc.
US Ecology Nevada Inc.
US Ecology Texas L.P.
US Ecology Washington Inc.

COMPETITORS

Clean Harbors	Stericycle
EnergySolutions	Valhi
Heritage Environmental Services	Veolia ES Technical Solutions
Perma-Fix Environmental	Waste Control Specialists
Safety-Kleen	Waste Management

HISTORICAL FINANCIALS

Company Type: Public

Income Statement

FYE: December 31

	REVENUE ($ mil.)	NET INCOME ($ mil.)	NET PROFIT MARGIN	EMPLOYEES
12/17	504.0	49.3	9.8%	1,550
12/16	477.6	34.2	7.2%	1,450
12/15	563.0	25.6	4.5%	1,400
12/14	447.4	38.2	8.5%	1,800
12/13	201.1	32.1	16.0%	458
Annual Growth	**25.8%**	**11.3%**	**—**	**35.6%**

2017 Year-End Financials

Debt ratio: 34.5%
Return on equity: 16.3%
Cash ($ mil.): 27.0
Current ratio: 2.23
Long-term debt ($ mil.): 277.0

No. of shares (mil.): 21.8
Dividends
Yield: 0.0%
Payout: 32.0%
Market value ($ mil.): 1,114.0

	STOCK PRICE ($) FY Close	P/E High/Low	PER SHARE ($) Earnings	Dividends	Book Value
12/17	51.00	25 20	2.25	0.72	14.83
12/16	49.15	31 19	1.57	0.72	12.86
12/15	36.44	45 30	1.18	0.72	11.78
12/14	40.12	29 19	1.77	0.72	11.62
12/13	37.10	22 13	1.72	0.72	10.76
Annual Growth	**8.3%**	**— —**	**6.9%**	**(0.0%)**	**8.4%**

US Silica Holdings, Inc.

Life's a beach for the sand-sellers at U.S. Silica. While the industrial mineral company got its start making sand-based glass and other products it is now known for providing its popular "frac sand"

product used by natural gas and oil producers in hydraulic fracturing a process to boost oil and gas production. Supplying customers in the US and Canada the company also provides silica and aplite for the glass foundry chemical and construction industries; and fine ground silica and kaolin clay used to make paint plastics and ceramics. Additionally U.S. Silica makes raw materials for solar panels. Beyond its main facility in West Virginia U S. Silica also has 17 plants in the East.

Operations

U.S. Silica operates two business segments: Oil & Gas Proppants which made up 67% of its total revenue during 2015 and provides fracturing sand ("frac sand") for pumping down oil and natural gas well to prop open rock fissures; and Industrial & Specialty Products (33% of revenue) which supplies more than 250 products and materials used in the container glass fiberglass and specialty glass industries among others. The mining company primarily sells its products under short-term price agreements or at prevailing market rates.

The company operated 17 production facilities across the US at the end of 2015 including eight industrial sand production plants and eight oil and gas sand production plants. U.S. Silica has been ranked as the second-largest producer of silica used in hydraulic fracturing in the US behind Unimin a unit of Belgium's Sibelco Group.

Geographic Reach

Frederick Maryland-based U.S. Silica has additional offices in Chicago Houston and Shanghai. Its production facilities are located across the US with many in energy-rich states such as Texas Oklahoma Pennsylvania and West Virginia.

Sales and Marketing

The company's two largest customers by revenue in 2015 included Schlumberger (which made up 13% of its total revenue that year) and Halliburton Company (12% of revenue). Some of its other big customers have included Nabors Industries Texas Specialty Sands Calfrac and C&J Energy Services among others.

Financial Performance

Buoyed by strong demand for "frac sand" which is in short supply U.S. Silica's sales and profits had tripled between 2011 and 2014. Oil price declines in 2015 however put a halt to its growth.

The company's sales tumbled 27% to $643 million during 2015 as the huge drop in oil prices led shale oil & gas producers to demand less of its frac sand product.

Sharp revenue declines in 2015 caused U.S. Silica's net income to plummet 90% to $11.87 million. Its operating cash levels dove 64% to $61.5 million for the year due to the steep fall in earnings.

Strategy

While plummeting oil prices in 2015 and early 2016 threatened many tied to the commodity U.S. Silica has been busy getting ready for the comeback. During 2015 it continued increasing its transload points building upon the 49 facilities it had strategically located in or near all of the major shale basins in the US.

It also continues to expand its Oil & Gas Proppants production capacity and product lines to grow its supply chain network. In 2014 the company launched its high-performance resin coated propant InnoProp Python RCS which was designed to boost oil and gas well production in a cost-effective and efficient manner.

If and when oil prices come back up the company expects its fortunes to continue rising along with the sharp increase in domestic shale oil and gas production which uses sand to break up rock underground to free-up fossil fuel in the Hydraulic fracturing process (aka fracking). Another area of promise for U.S. Silica is resin-coated sand which is also used in hydraulic fracturing.

Mergers and Acquisitions

In July 2014 U.S. Silica acquired Cadre Services a regional sand mining company in Voca Texas. The $98 million purchase expanded the company's geographic footprint and product offering in the fast-growing Permian Basin.

Two years later the company acquired New Birmingham's NBR Sand unit which has the capacity to produce more than 2 million tons of mesh and mesh silica sand.

Company Background

U.S. Silica in February 2012 sold 11.7 million shares at $17 per share the middle of the range estimated for the IPO. Golden Gate Capital which had acquired the mining firm in 2008 sold 8.8 million shares while U.S. Silica offered 2.9 million shares. The offering coincided with an increasing demand for frac sand. U.S. Silica used the proceeds to invest in its frac and resin-coated sands operations by upgrading its existing plants and building a new resin-coated sand facility in Illinois (completed in 2014).

U.S. Silica was formed by the merger of Pennsylvania Glass and Ottawa Silica in 1987.

EXECUTIVES

CFO, Donald A. Merril, age 53, $86,250 total compensation
VP and General Manager Oil & Gas, Don D. Weinheimer, $140,038 total compensation
President and CEO, Bryan A. Shinn, age 57, $383,333 total compensation
VP and General Manager Industrial and Specialties, John P. Blanchard
VP and COO, Mike Winkler
Vice President Supply Chain, Tony Fox
VICE PRESIDENT OF STRATEGY, Alan Schultz
VICE PRESIDENT OIL AND GAS, Billy Ray Smith
Auditors: Grant Thornton LLP

LOCATIONS

HQ: US Silica Holdings, Inc.
24275 Katy Freeway, Suite 600, Katy, TX 77494
Phone: 281 258-2170
Web: www.ussilica.com

PRODUCTS/OPERATIONS

2015 Sales

	$ mil.	% of total
Oil & gas Proppants	430.4	67
Industrial & specialty products	212.6	33
Total	**643.0**	**100**

Selected Products & Services

Aplite
Fine Ground Silica
FLORISIL®;
Ground Silica
Hydrous Kaolin
Kaolin
Oil & Gas Proppants
Recreational Silica
Testing Silica
Whole Grain Silica

COMPETITORS

Carmeuse Lime & Stone Inc.	Martin Marietta Materials
Emerge Energy	Reserve Industries
Fairmount Minerals	Unimin
Hi-Crush	Vulcan Materials
Martin Marietta Aggregates	

HISTORICAL FINANCIALS

Company Type: Public

Income Statement

FYE: December 31

	REVENUE ($ mil.)	NET INCOME ($ mil.)	NET PROFIT MARGIN	EMPLOYEES
12/17	1,240.8	145.2	11.7%	2,202
12/16	559.6	(41.0)	—	1,404
12/15	642.9	11.8	1.8%	996
12/14	876.7	121.5	13.9%	1,092
12/13	545.9	75.2	13.8%	844
Annual Growth	22.8%	17.9%	—	27.1%

2017 Year-End Financials

Debt ratio: 22.1%
Return on equity: 10.8%
Cash ($ mil.): 384.5
Current ratio: 3.29
Long-term debt ($ mil.): 506.7

No. of shares (mil.): 80.5
Dividends
 Yield: 0.0%
 Payout: 14.1%
Market value ($ mil.): 2,622.0

	STOCK PRICE ($) FY Close	P/E High/Low	PER SHARE ($) Earnings	Dividends	Book Value
12/17	32.56	34 14	1.77	0.25	17.34
12/16	56.68	— —	(0.63)	0.25	15.71
12/15	18.73	178 62	0.22	0.44	7.20
12/14	25.69	32 10	2.23	0.50	7.49
12/13	34.11	25 12	1.41	0.38	5.78
Annual Growth	(1.2%)	— —	5.8%	(9.6%)	31.6%

USA Compression Partners LP

Auditors: GRANT THORNTON LLP

LOCATIONS

HQ: USA Compression Partners LP
 100 Congress Avenue, Suite 450, Austin, TX 78701
Phone: 512 473-2662
Web: www.usacompression.com

HISTORICAL FINANCIALS

Company Type: Public

Income Statement

FYE: December 31

	REVENUE ($ mil.)	NET INCOME ($ mil.)	NET PROFIT MARGIN	EMPLOYEES
12/17	280.2	11.4	4.1%	426
12/16	265.9	12.9	4.9%	433
12/15	270.5	(154.2)	—	478
12/14	221.5	24.9	11.3%	457
12/13	152.9	11.0	7.2%	360
Annual Growth	16.3%	0.8%	—	4.3%

2017 Year-End Financials

Debt ratio: 52.4%
Return on equity: —
Cash ($ mil.): 0.0
Current ratio: 1.04
Long-term debt ($ mil.): 782.9

No. of shares (mil.): 62.1
Dividends
 Yield: 0.1%
 Payout: 1,312.5%
Market value ($ mil.): 1,029.0

	STOCK PRICE ($) FY Close	P/E High/Low	PER SHARE ($) Earnings	Dividends	Book Value
12/17	16.54	123 92	0.16	2.10	10.19
12/16	17.30	71 27	0.27	2.10	12.02
12/15	11.49	— —	(3.15)	2.08	13.65
12/14	16.59	47 25	0.60	1.98	18.51
12/13	26.80	83 54	0.32	1.25	18.44
Annual Growth	(11.4%)	— —	(15.9%)	13.9%	(13.8%)

USANA Health Sciences Inc

Health is a matter of science at USANA Health Sciences. The company makes nutritional personal care and weight management products selling them through a direct-sales network marketing system of some 290000 independent distributors or associates. USANA Health Sciences also sells directly to "preferred" customers who buy its products for personal use; it has some 275000 active preferred customers. USANA's associates operate throughout North America as well as the Asia/Pacific region. The company's product portfolio includes nutritional supplements and foods sold under the USANA brand and skin and hair care products marketed under the Celavive and Sensé labels. Chairman and founder Myron Wentz controls nearly half of USANA.

Operations

USANA manufactures all of its tablet products and its beauty products in-house. It also develops capsules drink mixes nutrition bars and personal care items.

Sales to associates or independent distributors represent about 60% of the company's total revenue. Preferred customers — those who buy products for their own personal use — account for the remainder of sales.

Geographic Reach

USANA divides its operations into two regions: North America/Europe and Asia/Pacific. Together those regions cover about 25 markets. The company has a European headquarters in Paris where the company manages growth in newer markets including Germany Italy Spain and Romania markets it entered in 2018. Greater China is the group's largest single market bringing in about half of total sales.

The company makes most of its products at its facilities in Utah.

Sales and Marketing

USANA intends to fight sagging sales by increasing brand awareness — for instance it introduced a new social sharing platform in 2018 — and acquiring more associates and preferred customers. Advertising expenses totaled $11503 in

2017 compared to $12266 in 2016 and $13766 in 2015.

Along with direct selling USANA sells its products in natural health food retail stores via mail order and the internet and in drug stores and supermarkets.

Financial Performance

USANA's revenue has been steadily climbing for the past five years thanks largely to growth in the Asia/Pacific region. Net income has been more turbulent though rising and falling as the company's spending varies.

Revenue increased a modest 4% to $1.05 billion in 2017; that increase was primarily due to growth in the Asia/Pacific region especially through its associate customers. Sales in South Korea rose 27% while sales in China rose 9%. This was partially offset by slight decline in North American sales.

Net income fell 38% to $62.5 million in 2017. A one-time charge of $30 million related to US tax reform hurt the company's bottom line that year.

USANA ended 2017 with $247.1 million in net cash an increase of more than 70% from the prior year. Operating activities provided $123.8 million while investing activities used $12.9 million and financing activities used $50.3 million.

Strategy

USANA is focused on growing its active customer base especially targeting preferred customers who buy its products for their own personal use. It is increasingly personalizing customer experiences to build loyalty and increase sales. However as with all direct selling companies USANA is heavily reliant on attracting and retaining customers. The company does face a high level of customer turnover each year which hampers earnings.

China is among its most important markets for future growth and the company is working to expand into new regions in that country. With China being its largest market though the company is vulnerable to possible regulatory changes in that country which could negatively impact its business there. Other target markets for growth include Australia New Zealand and the Philippines.

Sales in North America and Europe have been lagging so USANA is increasing its marketing efforts in those markets. It is sponsoring athletes and athletic teams to make its brand more familiar to the public. It also has a partnership with television personality Dr. Mehmet Oz of the Dr. Oz show.

The company boasts that it gleans the latest scientific findings to help in its product development activities. For example in early 2018 it launched the Celavive skincare product line based on its new Incelligence platform that delivers key phytonutrients to the body's cells. Once the Celavive roll-out is successful USANA plans to phase out its Sensé product line.

USANA is open to making acquisitions to expand its product portfolio and customer base.

EXECUTIVES

CFO and Chief Leadership Development Officer, Paul A. Jones, age 54, $348,042 total compensation
CEO and Director, Kevin G. Guest, age 55, $608,516 total compensation
President Asia, Deborah Woo, age 64, $592,305 total compensation

Chief Legal Officer and Corporate Secretary, James H. (Jim) Bramble, age 48, $388,032 total compensation
President and COO, Jim Brown, age 49
Chief Scientific Officer, Robert (Rob) Sinnott
EVP Field Development Americas and Chief Communications Officer, Daniel A. (Dan) Macuga, age 48
CIO, Walter Noot
Chairman, Myron W. Wentz, age 77
Auditors: KPMG LLP

LOCATIONS

HQ: USANA Health Sciences Inc
3838 West Parkway Blvd., Salt Lake City, UT 84120
Phone: 801 954-7100
Web: www.usanahealthsciences.com

COMPETITORS

AIM International	Melaleuca
AMS Health Sciences	Nature's Sunshine
Amazon Herb	Nu Skin
Amway	Reliv' International
GNC	Shaklee
Herbalife Ltd.	Sunrider
Mannatech	

HISTORICAL FINANCIALS

Company Type: Public

Income Statement   FYE: December 30

	REVENUE ($ mil.)	NET INCOME ($ mil.)	NET PROFIT MARGIN	EMPLOYEES
12/17	1,047.2	62.5	6.0%	1,810
12/16*	1,006.0	100.0	9.9%	1,788
01/16	918.5	94.6	10.3%	1,664
01/15	790.4	76.6	9.7%	1,527
12/13	718.1	79.0	11.0%	1,480
Annual Growth	9.9%	(5.7%)		5.2%

*Fiscal year change

2017 Year-End Financials

Debt ratio: —
Return on equity: 18.2%
Cash ($ mil.): 247.1
Current ratio: 2.41
Long-term debt ($ mil.): —
No. of shares (mil.): 24.0
Dividends
Yield: —
Payout: —
Market value ($ mil.): 1,779.0

	STOCK PRICE ($) FY Close	P/E High/Low		PER SHARE ($) Earnings	Dividends	Book Value
12/17	74.05	29	21	2.53	0.00	15.12
12/16*	61.20	36	14	3.99	0.00	13.29
01/16	127.75	47	26	3.59	0.00	11.24
01/15	102.28	41	20	2.80	0.00	9.11
12/13	77.72	32	11	2.78	0.00	9.38
Annual Growth	(1.2%)	—	—	(2.3%)	—	12.7%

*Fiscal year change

USD Partners LP

Auditors: BDO USA, LLP

LOCATIONS

HQ: USD Partners LP
811 Main Street, Suite 2800, Houston, TX 77002
Phone: 281 291-0510
Web: www.usdpartners.com

HISTORICAL FINANCIALS

Company Type: Public

Income Statement   FYE: December 31

	REVENUE ($ mil.)	NET INCOME ($ mil.)	NET PROFIT MARGIN	EMPLOYEES
12/17	111.3	22.2	19.9%	0
12/16	111.1	24.1	21.8%	0
12/15	81.7	17.6	21.6%	0
12/14	36.1	(7.6)	—	0
12/13	26.3	6.4	24.3%	0
Annual Growth	43.4%	36.5%		

2017 Year-End Financials

Debt ratio: 65.2%
Return on equity: —
Cash ($ mil.): 7.8
Current ratio: 0.85
Long-term debt ($ mil.): 200.6
No. of shares (mil.): 26.3
Dividends
Yield: 0.1%
Payout: 153.4%
Market value ($ mil.): 297.0

	STOCK PRICE ($) FY Close	P/E High/Low		PER SHARE ($) Earnings	Dividends	Book Value
12/17	11.25	19	11	0.88	1.35	2.78
12/16	15.80	15	5	1.06	1.25	2.02
12/15	7.24	18	7	0.83	1.11	2.16
12/14	14.17	—	—	(0.29)	0.00	1.91
Annual Growth	(7.4%)	—	—	—	—	13.4%

Vail Resorts Inc

Vail Resorts hopes the ski vacation business is all uphill. One of North America's leading ski resort operators Vail Resorts operates four mountain resorts in Colorado (Beaver Creek Breckenridge Mountain Resort Keystone Resort and Vail Mountain) and three in Lake Tahoe on the California/Nevada border (Heavenly Mountain Northstar-at-Tahoe and Kirkwood Mountain Resort). The resorts operate under the company's Mountain segment. Through its Lodging segment the firm owns or manages about 20 resorts in Canada Colorado Utah and Wyoming. It also operates seven golf courses. Vail Resorts also has a Real Estate Development segment that develops real estate in and around the company's resorts.

Operations

The company reports revenue in three business segments: Mountain (which accounts for about 80% of revenue per year) Lodging (which accounts for about 15% of revenue per year) and Real Estate.

Geographic Reach

In addition to its resorts in Western mountain states and Canada the company also owns a handful of ski resorts in the Midwest and one in Australia.

Sales and Marketing

The company promotes its resorts through a variety of targeted marketing and sales programs. These include customer relationship marketing (CRM) to targeted audiences promotional programs digital marketing via its websites (including social networking search marketing and display ads) loyalty programs that reward frequent guests and traditional media advertising such as targeted print TV and radio ads.

Vail Resorts has used partnerships as a way to promote its resorts. The company's partners have included American Express GoPro Hertz Nature Valley and Starbucks.

Vail Resorts spent $32.3 million on advertising expenses in fiscal 2016 up from $27.5 million in fiscal 2015.

Financial Performance

The company's revenue has been increasing year-over-year. It reported revenue of about $1.6 billion for fiscal 2016 up roughly $200 million compared to the previous fiscal period when Vail Resorts reported almost $1.4 billion in revenue. The spike in revenue was largely the result of increased revenue from the company's Mountain segment.

The increased total annual revenue in fiscal 2016 led to increased net income. The company reported net income of about $150 million for fiscal 2016 up from the roughly $115 million it claimed for net income the prior year.

Strategy

Peak operating season for Vail Resorts is of course ski season which lasts from mid-November through mid-April. The company's largest source of revenue is its Mountain segment which makes most of its money from the sale of lift tickets (including season passes). Lift tickets represent about 40% of the Mountain segment's net revenue.

In order to deal with challenges in the tourism and real estate markets Vail Resorts has also been diversifying into revenue streams beyond its core operations. Its Mountain News Corporation operates the online snow sports portal OnTheSnow.com and resort guide information provider MountainGetaway.com. Mountain News targets the skiers snowboarders and resort travelers who subscribe to its websites.

Like many of its rival ski operators the company has been focused on marketing its ski properties as year-round operations in an effort to avoid serious business declines during periods of unseasonable winters. Vail Resorts promotes the use of its resorts for summer activities such as mountain biking zip lines ropes courses golf tennis and fishing to woo warm-weather visitors.

The company invests around $10 million per year to make enhancements to the ski and ride experience for its guests.

Mergers and Acquisitions

Vail Resorts completed its acquisition of Whistler Blackcomb Holdings Inc. (Whistler Blackcomb) in late 2016 for about $1.1 billion. Whistler Blackcomb operates the Whistler Blackcomb resort a year round mountain resort.

HISTORY

Vail Mountain resort was first developed by New Hampshire native Pete Seibert and opened in 1962. In 1966 Seibert's Vail Associates went public and later bought Beaver Creek Mountain in 1971. But in 1976 a gondola accident killed four skiers (the worst US skiing accident at the time) and lawsuits forced Vail Associates to sell a controlling interest to Texas oil magnate Harry Bass for $13 million. A row with his children ousted Bass in 1984 and the next year Vail was bought for $130 million by businessman George Gillett.

Gillett Holdings declared bankruptcy in 1991 however and the next year it was acquired by Wall Street deal maker Leon Black's Apollo Advisors. Gillett was allowed to stay on as chairman of Vail but left in 1996. Norwegian Cruise Lines president

Adam Aron was named chairman and CEO that year (he departed in 2006). The company's acquisition of the Breckenridge Keystone and Arapahoe Basin resorts from Ralcorp in 1997 made it the nation's top ski resort company. (It later divested Arapahoe Basin at the request of the FTC.) Vail Resorts went public that year and later it acquired the Breckenridge Hilton the area's largest hotel and the 61-room Lodge at Vail.

In 1998 days after the company cleared trees to begin work on an ecologically disputed expansion at Vail Mountain multiple fires caused $12 million in damage and completely destroyed a restaurant ski patrol headquarters and a picnic area. Environmental group Earth Liberation Front claimed responsibility for the fires. Poor weather that winter added to the company's woes and it lost its top ranking to Canada's Intrawest.

The following year Vail bought three resorts in Grand Teton National Park at Jackson Hole Wyoming for $50 million from CSX Corp. As Internet marketing became increasingly important the company also bought Colorado ISP VailNet and Web services firm InterNetWorks. Early in 2000 Vail opened its contested Blue Sky Basin expansion. Later that year the company bought 51% of the Renaissance Resort and Spa (renamed Snake River Lodge and Spa) in Jackson Hole Wyoming.

As part of Vail's efforts to become less dependent on seasonality the firm in 2001 bought RockResorts International which operated 11 resort hotels across the US. Also that year it bought the 349-room Vail Marriott Mountain Resort from Host Marriott for $49.5 million. In 2002 the company acquired Heavenly Ski Resort located on the Nevada/California border for about $102 million.

The company sold its Vail Marriott Mountain Resort in 2005 to DiamondRock Hospitality for $62 million while retaining a management agreement to run the property through 2020. The following year chairman and CEO Aron decided that his ten year anniversary was a good time to call it quits and he did. Robert Katz was appointed CEO in 2006.

In 2008 Vail Resorts acquired CME a shuttle business that offers year-round ground transportation from Denver International Airport and Eagle County Airport to resorts in Vail Aspen and Summit County Colorado.

In 2010 the company added a sixth ski resort to its portfolio: Northstar-at-Tahoe. Vail Resorts acquired a long-term lease on the property — owned by CNL Lifestyle Properties (part of CNL Financial Group) — from Vail-based Booth Creek Ski Holdings for some $63 million. The purchase allowed Vail Resorts to move into the North Shore of Lake Tahoe. (Its other property in the area Heavenly Mountain is on the South Shore.)

Also in 2010 the company acquired Mountain News Corporation which operates the online snow sports portal OnTheSnow.com and resort guide information provider MountainGetaway.com. Vail Resorts made the purchase worth nearly $16 million to reach the nearly 400000 skiers snowboarders and resort travelers who subscribe to Mountain News' websites.

In 2012 the company expanded its resort holdings when it acquired Kirkwood Mountain Resort in Lake Tahoe California for about $18 million. Also that year OnTheSnow.com expanded through the purchase of Skiinfo.com.

In 2016 the company paid about $1.1 billion to acquire Whistler Blackcomb Holdings Inc.

EXECUTIVES

Senior Vice President General Counsel, Fiona Arnold
Director, Robert A. (Rob) Katz, age 51, $869,341 total compensation
EVP and CIO, Robert N. Urwiler
SVP and COO Vail Mountain Division, Christopher E. (Chris) Jarnot
EVP and CFO, Michael Z. Barkin, age 40, $399,900 total compensation
President Mountain Division, Patricia A. (Pat) Campbell, age 55, $390,000 total compensation
EVP and Chief People Officer, Mark R. Gasta
EVP General Counsel and Secretary, David T. Shapiro, age 48, $375,794 total compensation
EVP and Chief Marketing Officer, Kirsten A. Lynch, age 50, $399,900 total compensation
SVP and COO Hospitality, James C. O'Donnell
COO Retail, Greg Sullivan
Vice President Information Technology, Tim April
Vice President Assistant Controller, Wayne Wasechek
Vice President Public Affairs and Sustainability, Beth Ganz
Director of Government Relations, Brendan Mcguire
Vice President Of Marketing, John Wagnon
Vice President, David Reed
VICE PRESIDENT HUMAN RESOURCE OPERATIONS, Benjamin Novy
Vice President Finance, Flora Ferraro
VICE PRESIDENT HEALTH AND SAFETY, Ken Colonna
VICE PRESIDENT MOUNTAIN OPERATIONS, Joseph Walker
Board Member, Roland Hernandez
Auditors: PricewaterhouseCoopers LLP

LOCATIONS

HQ: Vail Resorts Inc
 390 Interlocken Crescent, Broomfield, CO 80021
Phone: 303 404-1800   **Fax:** 303 404-6415
Web: www.vailresorts.com

PRODUCTS/OPERATIONS

2016 Charts

	$ mil.	% of total
Mountain		
Lift tickets	658.0	41
Retail/rental	241.1	15
Ski school	143.2	9
Dining	121.0	8
Other	141.2	9
Lodging	274.6	17
Real Estate	22.1	1
Total	**1,601.2**	**100**

Selected Operations

Skiing
 Beaver Creek Resort (Colorado)
 Breckenridge Ski Resort (Colorado)
 Heavenly Mountain Resort (Lake Tahoe NV)
 Keystone Resort (Colorado)
 Vail Mountain (Colorado)
Resorts
 The Arrabelle at Vail Square (Colorado)
 Austria Haus Hotel (Vail CO)
 Breckenridge Mountain Lodge (Colorado)
 The Great Divide Lodge (Breckenridge CO)
 Hotel Jerome (Aspen CO)
 The Keystone Lodge (Colorado)
 The Landings St. Lucia (West Indies)
 The Lodge at Vail (Colorado)
 Mountain Thunder Lodge (Breckenridge CO)
 The Osprey at Beaver Creek (Colorado)
 The Pines Lodge (Beaver Creek CO)
 Ski Tip Lodge (Keystone CO)
 Snake River Lodge & Spa (Teton Village WY)
 Vail Marriott Mountain Resort & Spa (Colorado)
 Village Hotel (Breckenridge CO)
 Whistler Blackcomb (Whisler BC Canada)

COMPETITORS

Aspen Skiing	International Leisure
Booth Creek Ski	Mammoth Mountain
Holdings	Sinclair Oil
Boyne USA	Snowdance
Club Med	The Resort Company
Crested Butte	Winter Sports

HISTORICAL FINANCIALS

Company Type: Public

Income Statement

FYE: July 31

	REVENUE ($ mil.)	NET INCOME ($ mil.)	NET PROFIT MARGIN	EMPLOYEES
07/18	2,011.5	379.9	18.9%	33,300
07/17	1,907.2	210.5	11.0%	33,500
07/16	1,601.2	149.7	9.4%	27,000
07/15	1,399.9	114.7	8.2%	21,613
07/14	1,254.6	28.4	2.3%	23,000
Annual Growth	**12.5%**	**91.1%**	**—**	**9.7%**

2018 Year-End Financials

Debt ratio: 31.3%	No. of shares (mil.): 40.5
Return on equity: 24.0%	Dividends
Cash ($ mil.): 178.1	Yield: 1.8%
Current ratio: 0.91	Payout: 55.2%
Long-term debt ($ mil.): 1,234.2	Market value ($ mil.): 11,221.0

	STOCK PRICE ($) FY Close	P/E High/Low		PER SHARE ($) Earnings	Dividends	Book Value
07/18	276.87	31	22	9.13	5.05	39.22
07/17	210.76	40	27	5.22	3.73	39.20
07/16	143.07	35	25	4.01	2.87	24.17
07/15	109.69	35	23	3.07	2.08	23.73
07/14	75.50	100	82	0.77	1.25	22.67
Annual Growth	**38.4%**	**—**	**—**	**85.6%**	**41.9%**	**14.7%**

Vector Group Ltd

Vector Group is small potatoes next to Big Tobacco running a distant fourth in the US market. The holding company's Liggett and Vector Tobacco subsidiaries manufacture discount cigarettes under brands including Liggett Select Grand Prix Pyramid and Eve and several private-label brands of cigarettes for other companies including the USA brand. The company manufactures cigarettes in North Carolina and distributes them throughout the US. Vector Group's real estate unit New Valley owns about 70% stake in the New York City broker Douglas Elliman Realty. It's looking to acquire other properties. All of Vector Group's revenue is derived from the sale of discount cigarettes.

HISTORY

Former computer analyst Bennett LeBow founded Brooke Partners in 1980 (renamed Brooke Group in 1990) to acquire troubled companies and turn them around. Many of LeBow's early investments were in the computer industry. He eventually expanded into other areas including tobacco (with the purchase of Liggett in 1986).

Founded in 1822 by the Liggett family as a snuff maker and joined by George Myers in 1873 Liggett & Myers produced several popular cigarette brands including L&M and Chesterfield. Liggett slipped during the 1950s and 1960s by failing to exploit the market for filtered and low-tar cigarettes. Although Liggett launched a successful discount brand under LeBow (Pyramid) its US market share continued to dwindle.

Like Liggett many of LeBow's other businesses were slipping. In 1993 Western Union (bought in 1987 and renamed New Valley) and computer maker MAI Systems (bought in 1985) entered Chapter 11 bankruptcy. That year LeBow paid about $20 million to Brooke Group shareholders who sued a group of company officers who they believed were stripping assets and using the company for personal loans.

Frustrated in the US Brooke Group turned to developing new markets. In 1993 the company began a joint venture with Russian cigarette maker Ducat. In 1995 New Valley emerged from bankruptcy.

In 1997 the company made deals with 41 states regarding tobacco-related Medicaid payments. But most of Liggett's state deals were negated when in late 1998 it joined a $206 billion settlement hammered out with 46 states by its much larger rivals. As part of the deal Liggett did not have to chip in as long as its market share stayed below its 1997 level of 1.67%.

To cut debt Liggett sold its L&M Chesterfield and Lark brands to Philip Morris for $300 million in 1999. (The deal also kept Liggett's market share well below 1.67%.) Also in 1999 an Alabama court rejected an agreement that would have allowed Liggett to settle tobacco-related lawsuits with a limited fund. That year the US government filed a massive lawsuit against the Big Tobacco companies to recover health care costs and profits allegedly derived from fraud.

In 2000 the firm changed its name to Vector Group to remove the old name's stigma of sick-smoker lawsuits. The company said it would appeal a Florida's $790 million verdict against it. Later Vector Group sold its Liggett-Ducat subsidiary (Russia) to cigarette manufacturer Gallaher for $400 million. A Florida judge upheld the July 2000 verdict; meanwhile Vector angled for a global settlement of all punitive cases payable to a public health trust fund over a 30-year period.

The company along with Brown & Williamson Lorillard (Carolina Group) Philip Morris and R.J. Reynolds faced paying Florida smokers $145 billion after losing a lengthy court battle in 2000. Three years later a state appeals court threw out the case saying that the thousands of Florida smokers named in the case could not lump their complaints in a single lawsuit. That decision is now under review by the Florida Supreme Court.

In late 2001 Vector launched OMNI a reduced-carcinogen cigarette which received a lukewarm acceptance and hit a slow burn in sales. OMNI generated a disappointing $5.1 million in revenue for 70.7 million units. (Vector gave up on the product several years later.)

The next year the company created Liggett Vector Brands a new unit that combines the sales and marketing functions of its Liggett Group and Vec-

tor Tobacco subsidiaries. Vector also bought The Medallion Company a discount cigarette manufacturer (USA and Marlin brands) for $110 million.

Vector closed its Timberlake North Carolina production plant and laid off 150 workers in 2003. The company moved operations to a nearby cigarette plant in Mebane North Carolina.

Vector announced in August 2004 that it would sell its reduced-nicotine cigarette brand QUEST on the Internet beginning in 2005 and is seeking FDA approval to sell QUEST as a device for quitting smoking. (In 2009 the company decided against seeking FDA approval of Quest as a smoking cessation aide citing the significant time and expense involved in seeking it.) However it switched gears in November 2004 by putting an indefinite hold on a national rollout of QUEST. The company said a review of marketing data made such a move necessary. Vector laid off approximately 330 full-time and 135 part-time positions that December.

In March 2005 the company began supplying Montego deep-discount brand cigarettes exclusively to more than 2200 Circle K and Mac's convenience stores in the US. In November it entered into a similar deal with Sunoco which operates 800-plus Sonoco APlus convenience stores to make and supply Silver Eagle brand cigarettes to its stores.

Howard Lorber succeeded LeBow as CEO in 2006. Later that year Vector entered into a settlement with the Internal Revenue Service that called for the company to pay about $42 million related to a gain stemming from a 1998 and 1999 deal with Philip Morris.

To tap the popular and more politically correct smokeless tobacco market Vector launched Grand Prix-branded snus in May 2008. The pouched tobacco product is made in Sweden and rolls out in a trio of varieties.

EXECUTIVES

VP CFO and Treasurer, J. Bryant Kirkland, age 52, $425,000 total compensation
EVP, Richard J. (Dick) Lampen, age 64, $900,000 total compensation
President and CEO, Howard M. Lorber, age 69, $3,055,482 total compensation
President and CEO Liggett Group LLC and Liggett Vector Brands LLC, Ronald J. Bernstein, age 64, $908,719 total compensation
Chairman, Bennett S. LeBow, age 80
Auditors: Deloitte & Touche LLP

LOCATIONS

HQ: Vector Group Ltd
4400 Biscayne Boulevard, Miami, FL 33137
Phone: 305 579-8000
Web: www.vectorgroupltd.com

PRODUCTS/OPERATIONS

2016 Sales

	$ mil.	% of total
Tobacco	1,011.6	60
Real estate	680.1	40
E-Cigarettes	(0.8)	-
Total	**1,690.9**	**100**

Selected Cigarette Brands
Eve
Grand Prix
Liggett Select
Pyramid
USA

Selected Subsidiaries
Liggett Group LLC
Liggett Vector Brands LLC
New Valley LLC
Vector Tobacco Inc.
VGR Holing LLC

COMPETITORS

800-JR Cigar	Reynolds American
Century 21 Real Estate	Smokin Joes
Commonwealth Brands	Sotheby's
Philip Morris USA	International Realty
RE/MAX	

HISTORICAL FINANCIALS
Company Type: Public

Income Statement			FYE: December 31
	REVENUE ($ mil.)	NET INCOME ($ mil.)	NET PROFIT MARGIN	EMPLOYEES
12/17	1,807.4	84.5	4.7%	1,484
12/16	1,690.9	71.1	4.2%	1,425
12/15	1,657.2	59.2	3.6%	1,367
12/14	1,591.3	36.9	2.3%	1,090
12/13	1,056.2	38.9	3.7%	989
Annual Growth	**14.4%**	**21.4%**	**—**	**10.7%**

2017 Year-End Financials

Debt ratio: 92.4%	No. of shares (mil.): 141.0
Return on equity: ***,***.*%	Dividends
Cash ($ mil.): 301.3	Yield: 0.0%
Current ratio: 3.00	Payout: 274.5%
Long-term debt ($ mil.): 1,194.2	Market value ($ mil.): 3,157.0

	STOCK PRICE ($) FY Close	P/E High/Low	PER SHARE ($) Earnings	Dividends	Book Value
12/17	22.38	41 35	0.56	1.54	(2.93)
12/16	22.74	46 40	0.50	1.47	(2.36)
12/15	23.59	61 50	0.42	1.33	(1.51)
12/14	21.31	83 56	0.29	1.27	(0.41)
12/13	16.37	53 46	0.32	1.21	(0.76)
Annual Growth	**8.1%**	**— —**	**15.0%**	**6.3%**	**—**

Veeva Systems Inc

Veeva Systems is breathing new life into software for the health care industry. Its cloud-based software and mobile apps are used by pharmaceutical and biotechnology companies to manage critical business functions. Veeva Systems' customer relationship management software uses Salesforce's platform to manage sales and marketing functions. Its Veeva Vault provides content management and collaboration software for quality management in clinical trials and regulatory compliance for new drug submissions. Its software is used in 75 countries and available in more than 25 languages but North America is its largest market. Founded in 2007 Veeva Systems went public in 2013.

Operations
Veeva sells its products through subscriptions and they account for about three-quarters of its business. The rest comes from professional services it provides for installing and training on its software.

Geographic Reach

Veeva Systems operates from three offices in the US and one in Canada. It also has locations in China Japan and Spain. North America is its largest market accounting for 55% of sales. Europe makes up another 26% while customers in Asia account for about 20% of sales. Sales outside North American increased about 64% in 2015 (ended January).

The company runs its software on data centers in California Illinois and Virginia and Germany Japan and the UK.

Sales and Marketing

The company uses a direct sales force with representatives in more than a dozen countries. Veeva Systems counts about 275 customers including global pharmaceutical companies such as Bayer Boehringer Ingelheim Eli Lilly Gilead Sciences Merck and Novartis.

Financial Performance

Veeva Systems has posted big gains in revenue since 2011. Sales zoomed from $30 million in fiscal 2011 (year-end January) to $313 million in 2015. In addition it has been consistently profitable which is uncommon for a relatively new and growing company. Profit increased almost 50% in 2015. While the company has increased spending on research and development and sales and marketing revenue growth covered the higher spending and then some.

Strategy

The company makes 95% of sales from its Veeva CRM customer relationship management software but new products are also being developed. Its latest software offering is Veeva Network a customer master solution that creates and maintains healthcare provider and organization master data. Veeva Network also contains a proprietary database of people and companies in China and the US using data gathered from state federal and industry sources.

While Veeva Systems currently focuses on the life sciences industry specifically pharmaceutical and biotechnology companies it would like to expand to other specialized companies such as contract research organizations (CROs) and contract manufacturing organizations (CMOs).

Mergers and Acquisitions

In 2015 Veeva acquired Qforma CrowdLink a developer of key opinion leader (KOL) data and services for life sciences' brand medical and market access teams. Veeva introduced a product based on Qforma technology to help its customers get more sophisticated information for introducing products.

EXECUTIVES

Vice President Multichannel Strategy, Paul Shawah
Vice President Professional Services Europe, Will Larter
VICE PRESIDENT, Rebecca Silver
VICE PRESIDENT SOLUTION CONSULTING AND SALES ENGINEERING, Michael Longo
VICE PRESIDENT, Jennifer Goldsmith
VICE PRESIDENT CUSTOMER SUCCESS MANAGEMENT, Nate Gazaway
Vice President, John Lawrie
Vice President Commercial Strategy, Jan Van Den Burg
Vice President Finance and Corporate Controller, Michele Oconnor
Vice President Engineering, Dan Soble
Executive Vice President Global Sales, Alan Mateo

Vice President Sales Americas, Tom Darby
VICE PRESIDENT CORPORATE COMMUNICATIONS, Roger Villareal
Senior Vice President Global Customer Services, Frederic Lequient
Vice President Global Customer Support, Hind Roubos
VICE PRESIDENT GLOBAL SERVICES, James Kelling
Vice President Global Medical Strategy, Robert Groebel
Vice President Vault Edc, Richard Young
Vp Products, Stanley Wong
VICE PRESIDENT PRODUCT MANAGEMENT VAULT PLATFORM, Peter Thorson
VICE PRESIDENT CUSTOMER ARCHITECTURE, Doug Caldwell
Vice President, Rik Vanmol
Auditors: KPMG LLP

LOCATIONS

HQ: Veeva Systems Inc
4280 Hacienda Drive, Pleasanton, CA 94588
Phone: 925 452-6500   **Fax:** 925 452-6504
Web: www.veeva.com

PRODUCTS/OPERATIONS

2015 Sales

	% of total
Subscription fees	74
Professional services	26
Total	**100**

Selected Products

Veeva CRM (customer relationship management)
  Veeva CLM (closed-loop marketing)
  Veeva iRep (mobile app for Apple products)
  Veeva CRM Approved Email (tracks regulatory compliant emails between sales reps and physicians)
Veeva Vault (content management and collaboration software)
  Veeva Vault eTMF (document management for clinical trials)
  Veeva Vault Investigator Portal (secure file exchange for clinical trials)
  Veeva Vault MedComms (medical content management)
  Veeva Vault PromoMats (promotional materials management)
  Veeva Vault QualityDocs (quality management)
  Veeva Vault Submissions (document management for regulatory submissions)
Veeva Network (master software and data stewardship)
  Veeva Network Provider Database (proprietary database of people and companies in China and the US)
  Veeva Network Customer Master (cleanse and match people and company data)
  Veeva Network Data Stewardship Services (data management)

COMPETITORS

Advanced Health Media	Microsoft
Allscripts	Open Text
Computer Sciences Corp.	Oracle
	SDI Health
EMC	StayinFront
IMS Health	

HISTORICAL FINANCIALS

Company Type: Public

Income Statement

FYE: January 31

	REVENUE ($ mil.)	NET INCOME ($ mil.)	NET PROFIT MARGIN	EMPLOYEES
01/18	685.5	141.9	20.7%	2,171
01/17	544.0	68.8	12.6%	1,794
01/16	409.2	54.4	13.3%	1,474
01/15	313.2	40.3	12.9%	951
01/14	210.1	23.6	11.2%	725
Annual Growth	34.4%	56.6%	—	31.5%

2018 Year-End Financials

Debt ratio: —
Return on equity: 18.6%
Cash ($ mil.): 320.1
Current ratio: 3.20
Long-term debt ($ mil.): —
No. of shares (mil.): 142.0
Dividends
  Yield: —
  Payout: —
Market value ($ mil.): 8,930.0

	STOCK PRICE ($) FY Close	P/E High/Low	PER SHARE ($) Earnings	Dividends	Book Value
01/18	62.86	66 42	0.92	0.00	6.13
01/17	42.33	93 40	0.47	0.00	4.74
01/16	24.10	80 56	0.38	0.00	3.78
01/15	28.76	122 58	0.28	0.00	3.10
01/14	31.79	231 155	0.15	0.00	2.24
Annual Growth	18.6%	— —	57.4%	—	28.6%

VEREIT Inc

EXECUTIVES

Pres-coo-sec-treas, Edward M Weil
Executive Vice President, Glenn Kindred
Executive Vice President and Chief Financial Officer, Michael J Bartolotta
Senior Vice President Leasing, Brett Sheets
Vice President Application Development, Ninad Tambe
Senior Vice President Corporate Communications, John Bacon
Vice President Construction Operations, Bryan Frarey
Vice President, Jim Vlahos
Senior Vice President, Mark Selman
Vice President Acquisitions, Chelsey Ginder
Senior Vice President Tax, Benjamin Coleman
Senior Vice President, Christina Mayo
Vice President, Debbie Hester
Senior Vice President Head of Property Management, Karen Halpert
Vice President Technology Operations, Josh Ornstein
Senior Vice President, Thomas Falatko
Vice President Leasing, Sarah Nelson
Senior Vice President. Underwriting, Brian McGlynn
Senior Vice President Head of Real Estate Finance, David Mannion
Board Member, David Henry
Board Member, Eugene Pinover
Board Member, Julie Richardson
Board Member, Mark Ordan
Auditors: Deloitte & Touche LLP

LOCATIONS

HQ: VEREIT Inc
2325 E. Camelback Road, Suite 1100, Phoenix, AZ 85016
Phone: 800 606-3610
Web: www.ir.vereit.com

HISTORICAL FINANCIALS

Company Type: Public

Income Statement   FYE: December 31

	REVENUE ($ mil.)	NET INCOME ($ mil.)	NET PROFIT MARGIN	EMPLOYEES
12/17	1,252.2	31.8	2.5%	330
12/16	1,454.8	(195.8)	—	350
12/15	1,556.0	(316.3)	—	350
12/14	1,579.2	(977.1)	—	400
12/13	240.5	(406.5)	—	400
Annual Growth	**51.1%**	**—**	**—**	**(4.7%)**

2017 Year-End Financials

Debt ratio: 41.3%
Return on equity: 0.3%
Cash ($ mil.): 34.1
Current ratio: 0.19
Long-term debt ($ mil.): 6,073.4
No. of shares (mil.): 974.2
Dividends
  Yield: 0.0%
  Payout: —
Market value ($ mil.): 7,589.0

	STOCK PRICE ($) FY Close	P/E High/Low	Earnings	PER SHARE ($) Dividends	Book Value
12/17	7.79	— —	(0.04)	0.55	8.09
12/16	8.46	— —	(0.29)	0.55	8.67
12/15	7.92	— —	(0.43)	0.28	9.42
12/14	9.05	— —	(1.36)	1.08	10.11
12/13	12.85	— —	(2.36)	0.91	8.01
Annual Growth	**(11.8%)**	**— —**	**—**	**(11.8%)**	**0.3%**

Veritex Holdings Inc

Auditors: GRANT THORNTON LLP

LOCATIONS

HQ: Veritex Holdings Inc
8214 Westchester Drive, Suite 400, Dallas, TX 75225
Phone: 972 349-6200
Web: www.veritexbank.com

HISTORICAL FINANCIALS

Company Type: Public

Income Statement   FYE: December 31

	ASSETS ($ mil.)	NET INCOME ($ mil.)	INCOME AS % OF ASSETS	EMPLOYEES
12/17	2,945.5	15.1	0.5%	324
12/16	1,408.5	12.5	0.9%	171
12/15	1,039.6	8.7	0.8%	149
12/14	802.2	5.2	0.6%	125
12/13	664.9	3.4	0.5%	126
Annual Growth	**45.1%**	**45.2%**	**—**	**26.6%**

2017 Year-End Financials

Return on assets: 0.7%
Return on equity: 4.1%
Long-term debt ($ mil.): —
No. of shares (mil.): 24.1
Sales ($ mil) 87.1
Dividends
  Yield: —
  Payout: —
Market value ($ mil.): 665.0

	STOCK PRICE ($) FY Close	P/E High/Low	Earnings	Dividends	Book Value
12/17	27.59	36 30	0.80	0.00	20.28
12/16	26.71	23 11	1.13	0.00	15.73
12/15	16.21	20 15	0.84	0.00	12.33
12/14	14.17	23 18	0.72	0.00	11.96
Annual Growth	**24.9%**	**— —**	**3.6%**	**—**	**19.2%**

Versum Materials Inc

Auditors: KPMG LLP

LOCATIONS

HQ: Versum Materials Inc
8555 South River Parkway, Tempe, AZ 85284
Phone: 602 282-1000
Web: www.versummaterials.com

HISTORICAL FINANCIALS

Company Type: Public

Income Statement   FYE: September 30

	REVENUE ($ mil.)	NET INCOME ($ mil.)	NET PROFIT MARGIN	EMPLOYEES
09/18	1,372.3	197.5	14.4%	2,300
09/17	1,126.9	193.0	17.1%	2,200
09/16	970.1	212.0	21.9%	1,900
09/14	1,009.3	184.1	18.2%	1,900
09/14	942.5	123.6	13.1%	0
Annual Growth	**9.8%**	**12.4%**	**—**	**—**

2018 Year-End Financials

Debt ratio: 65.1%
Return on equity: 234.4%
Cash ($ mil.): 399.8
Current ratio: 4.33
Long-term debt ($ mil.): 974.2
No. of shares (mil.): 108.9
Dividends
  Yield: 0.0%
  Payout: 12.2%
Market value ($ mil.): 3,923.0

	STOCK PRICE ($) FY Close	P/E High/Low	Earnings	Dividends	Book Value
09/18	36.01	23 19	1.80	0.22	1.64
09/17	38.82	22 13	1.76	0.10	(0.09)
Annual Growth	**(7.2%)**	**— —**	**2.3%**	**120.0%**	**—**

Vertex Pharmaceuticals, Inc.

Vertex Pharmaceuticals aims to cure patients with previously incurable diseases. The biotechnology firm uses an integrated multidisciplinary approach — employing biophysics computer-based modeling and functional genomics — to speed up the discovery and development of new drugs. Its orphan drugs Kalydeco and Orkambi (launched in 2015) are used to treat cystic fibrosis; the firm is also seeking approval for the medications for other indications. Vertex has other drugs in development including additional treatments for cystic fibrosis as well as cancer pain and the flu. The firm's first drug the blockbuster hepatitis C treatment Incivek was discontinued in 2014 after Gilead's popular Sovaldi hit the market.

Operations

Vertex received FDA and European Commission approval for Orkambi in 2015. The company is in late-stage trials exploring the use of lumacaftor in combination with ivacaftor in children with cystic fibrosis. Other pipeline programs include VX-66 VX-371 VX-152 and VX-440.

Net product revenues represented some 60% of the company's revenue in 2015.

Geographic Reach

The company has R&D sites in the US Canada and the UK; it has commercial offices in Australia Canada France Germany Italy the Netherlands and Spain.

The US accounted for about three-fourths of Vertex's revenue in 2015 followed by Europe which accounted for about 20%.

Sales and Marketing

The firm markets its products to physicians through direct contact as well as through advertising mail-outs and public relations activities.Advertising expenses totaled $24.5 million in 2015 up from $16.2 million in 2014 and $19.6 million in 2013.

Vertex markets Kalydeco in the US on its own and it is working to gain approval for the drug in additional countries.

Its top customer Walgreen brings in about 20% of total revenue; CVS and Accredo are also large customers accounting for about 15% of earnings each.

Financial Performance

After launching Incivek in 2011 the company began earning product revenues which brought up total revenue exponentially. However lower demand for Incivek (in light of the competition provided by Gilead's Sovaldi) caused revenue to decline in 2013 and 2014. The launch of Orkambi and growing sales of Kalydeco brought revenue back up the following year: Revenue rose 78% to $1 billion.

Vertex entered the black for the first time in 2011 but the drop in demand (and ultimate discontinuation) of Incivek as well as increased R&D costs led to net losses in 2013 and 2014. However net loss decreased 25% to $556 million in 2015 thanks largely to the increase in revenue. As of the end of 2015 the company's accumulated deficit totaled $5.3 billion.

Cash flow from operations has followed revenue trends for the company. In 2015 it fell by 36% to $365 million.

Strategy

Vertex's key strategies for growth include expanding the number of products in its pipeline as well as establishing more collaborations with other research companies. For example in 2015 it established a collaboration with Parion Sciences to develop cystic fibrosis and other pulmonary disease treatments. Through the agreement Vertex has global development and commercial rights to Parion's ENaC inhibitors. The company also has a research collaboration with gene editing firm CRISPR Therapeutics to discover and develop potential new treatments.

In 2014 Vertex entered into a license and collaboration agreement with BioAxone to jointly develop VX-210 for the treatment of patients with spinal cord injuries. It also has an agreement with Janssen which holds the exclusive worldwide license to develop certain flu treatments.

HISTORY

In 1989 venture capitalist Kevin Kinsella wooed Joshua Boger away from his job as Director of Basic Chemistry at Merck's drug research laboratory to form Vertex Pharmaceuticals. With nearly $6 million in funding the company pursued "rational" drug design intended to cut the time and costs of bringing a drug to market. It aimed to produce drugs for diseases with large pools of sufferers. In 1990 the firm teamed with Chugai to develop immunosuppressants and went public the next year.

In 1993 the company began its HIV/AIDS collaboration with an entity that later became GlaxoSmithKline; buoyed by that and other agreements it posted its first profit. The next year Vertex opened an office in the UK. In 1995 it licensed Alpha Therapeutic to develop its hemoglobin-disorder drug in the Americas (the agreement ended in 1997 because of a long development curve).

As the century drew to a close Vertex focused on deals to boost its drug pipeline. In 1996 it licensed a G. D. Searle patent necessary to develop its HIV/AIDS treatments; three years later the FDA approved HIV therapy Agenerase. The firm clinched a number of potentially lucrative development deals with such companies as Eli Lilly (1997 for a hepatitis C program) and Novartis (2000 kinase inhibitors).

In 2001 the firm cut back on its development of an arthritis drug candidate to focus instead on kinase inhibitor treatments for other inflammatory conditions. That same year it bought Aurora Biosciences to bolster its drug pipeline and merged it into another subsidiary to form PanVera.

Two years later the company sold the subsidiary to Invitrogen (later called Life Technologies) keeping the instrumentation systems operations (renamed Aurora Instruments). Vertex also received good news in 2003: The FDA approved HIV therapy Lexiva a drug partnered with GlaxoSmithKline. In late 2003 the company spun off its Discovery Tools and Services unit for $101 million to concentrate on drug development.

The company entered collaborations with Mitsubishi Tanabe and Cystic Fibrosis Foundation Therapeutics Incorporation (CFFTI an affiliate of the Cystic Fibrosis Foundation) in 2004 on its hepatitis C and cystic fibrosis candidates. In 2006 Vertex added Janssen Therapeutica (a subsidiary of Johnson & Johnson) as a partner for the hepatitis C program.

Vertex sold royalty rights for its two co-discovered HIV drugs (Lexiva/Telzir and Agenerase) to development and marketing partner GlaxoSmithKline in 2008.

Founder and CEO Dr. Joshua Boger retired in 2009 but chose to stay on as a company director. Five-year board member (and former head of UK drug firm Shire plc) Matthew Emmens stepped up to replace Boger. The two worked together at Merck before Boger founded Vertex. Emmens himself retired in 2012 and was replaced by Jeffrey Leiden another board member and a former Abbott executive.

EXECUTIVES

Chairman President and CEO, Jeffrey M. (Jeff) Leiden, age 62, $1,297,692 total compensation
EVP and COO, Ian F. Smith, age 52, $701,796 total compensation
EVP Global Medicines Development and Medical Affairs and Chief Medical Officer, Jeffrey A. Chodakewitz, age 62, $615,231 total compensation
EVP Chief Regulatory Officer and Chief of Staff to the CEO, Amit K. Sachdev, age 50, $378,341 total compensation
EVP Global Research and Chief Scientific Officer, David Altshuler, age 53, $528,846 total compensation
EVP and Chief Commercial Officer, Stuart A. Arbuckle, $629,262 total compensation
SVP and CFO, Thomas (Tom) Graney, age 53
SVP and General Manager International Commercial Operations, Simon Bedson
EVP and Chief Legal and Administrative Officer, Michael Parini, age 43
Senior Vice President Of Clinical Deve, Robert Kauffman
Vice President Global Patient Safety, Henry Seto
Vice President Strategic Regulatory Intelligence, Federico Goodsaid
Lead Engineer Medical Director Global Patient Safety, Simon Tian
Vice President Chief Intellectual Property Counsel, Kerry Flynn
Vice President Finance, Santosh Shanbhag
Senior Vice President Human Resources, Sheila Clark
Medical Director, Philippe Kiefer
Medical Director, Stuart Pinkerton
Associate Medical Director, Yulia Green
Vice President Commercial Regulatory Affairs, Lynette Hopkinson
Vice President Corporate Legal, Omar White
VP Clinical Science, Mary-Lynn Fulton
Vice President Regulatory Advocacy and Policy, Annetta Beauregard
Vice President, David Gillen
Medical Director, Sam Moskowitz
Auditors: Ernst & Young LLP

LOCATIONS

HQ: Vertex Pharmaceuticals, Inc.
50 Northern Avenue, Boston, MA 02210
Phone: 617 341-6100
Web: www.vrtx.com

PRODUCTS/OPERATIONS

2015 Sales

	$ mil.	% of total
Product	1,000.3	97
Royalty	24.0	2
Collaborative	8.0	1
Total	**1,032.3**	**100**

Selected Products
Commercialized
Incivek (telaprevir also known as Incivo and Telavic; hepatitis C with Janssen and Mitsubishi Tanabe)
Kalydeco (formerly VX-770 cystic fibrosis)
In development
ALS-2158 (hepatitis C)
ALS-2200 (hepatitis C)
VX-222 (hepatitis C)
VX-509 (rheumatoid arthritis)
VX-661 (cystic fibrosis)
VX-765 (epilepsy)
VX-787 (influenza A infection)
VX-809 (cystic fibrosis)

COMPETITORS

Abbott Labs	Johnson & Johnson
Achillion	Merck
Amgen	Novartis
Boehringer Ingelheim	PTC Therapeutics
Bristol-Myers Squibb	Pfizer
Enanta	Roche Holding
Gilead Sciences	Sanofi
GlaxoSmithKline	

HISTORICAL FINANCIALS
Company Type: Public

Income Statement
FYE: December 31

	REVENUE ($ mil.)	NET INCOME ($ mil.)	NET PROFIT MARGIN	EMPLOYEES
12/17	2,488.6	263.4	10.6%	2,300
12/16	1,702.1	(112.0)	—	2,150
12/15	1,032.3	(556.3)	—	1,950
12/14	580.4	(738.5)	—	1,830
12/13	1,211.9	(445.0)	—	1,800
Annual Growth	19.7%	—	—	6.3%

2017 Year-End Financials

Debt ratio: 17.1%
Return on equity: 16.5%
Cash ($ mil.): 1,665.4
Current ratio: 3.28
Long-term debt ($ mil.): 583.9
No. of shares (mil.): 253.2
Dividends
Yield: —
Payout: —
Market value ($ mil.): 37,953.0

	STOCK PRICE ($) FY Close	P/E High/Low		PER SHARE ($) Earnings	Dividends	Book Value
12/17	149.86	157	71	1.04	0.00	8.01
12/16	73.67	—	—	(0.46)	0.00	4.66
12/15	125.83	—	—	(2.31)	0.00	3.82
12/14	118.80	—	—	(3.14)	0.00	4.45
12/13	74.30	—	—	(1.98)	0.00	5.80
Annual Growth	19.2%	—	—	—	—	8.4%

VICI Properties Inc

Auditors: Deloitte & Touche, LLP

LOCATIONS

HQ: VICI Properties Inc
430 Park Avenue, 8th Floor, New York, NY 10022
Phone: 646 949-4631
Web: www.viciproperties.com

HISTORICAL FINANCIALS
Company Type: Public

Income Statement
FYE: December 31

	REVENUE ($ mil.)	NET INCOME ($ mil.)	NET PROFIT MARGIN	EMPLOYEES
12/17	187.6	42.6	22.7%	140
12/16	18.7	0.0	—	140
12/15	18.0	0.0	0.0%	0
12/14	18.9	0.0	0.0%	0
Annual Growth	114.9%	2101.2%	—	—

2017 Year-End Financials

Debt ratio: 49.1%	No. of shares (mil.): 300.2
Return on equity: 1.7%	Dividends
Cash ($ mil.): 197.4	Yield: —
Current ratio: 6.14	Payout: —
Long-term debt ($ mil.): 4,785.7	Market value ($ mil.): 6,156.0

	STOCK PRICE ($) FY Close	P/E High/Low		Earnings	PER SHARE ($) Dividends	Book Value
12/17	20.50	111	95	0.19	0.00	15.62
12/16	0.00			(0.00)	0.00	(0.00)
Annual Growth	—			—	—	—

Viper Energy Partners LP

Auditors: GRANT THORNTON LLP

LOCATIONS

HQ: Viper Energy Partners LP
500 West Texas, Suite 1200, Midland, TX 79701
Phone: 432 221-7400
Web: www.viperenergy.com

HISTORICAL FINANCIALS

Company Type: Public

Income Statement				FYE: December 31
	REVENUE ($ mil.)	NET INCOME ($ mil.)	NET PROFIT MARGIN	EMPLOYEES
12/17	172.0	111.4	64.8%	0
12/16	79.1	(10.9)	—	0
12/15	74.8	24.4	32.6%	0
12/14	77.7	29.6	38.1%	0
12/13	14.9	2.9	19.9%	0
Annual Growth	84.1%	147.1%	—	—

2017 Year-End Financials

Debt ratio: 9.2%	No. of shares (mil.): 113.8
Return on equity: 15.2%	Dividends
Cash ($ mil.): 24.2	Yield: 0.0%
Current ratio: 9.85	Payout: 114.8%
Long-term debt ($ mil.): 93.5	Market value ($ mil.): 2,657.0

	STOCK PRICE ($) FY Close	P/E High/Low		Earnings	PER SHARE ($) Dividends	Book Value
12/17	23.33	22	14	1.07	1.23	8.03
12/16	16.00	—	—	(0.13)	0.77	6.24
12/15	13.96	69	44	0.31	0.86	6.21
12/14	18.13	118	50	0.29	0.25	6.72
Annual Growth	8.8%		—	—	54.5% 70.0%	6.1%

Vivint Solar Inc

Plumbing fixtures equipment and supplie

EXECUTIVES

Pres-ceo, Gregory S Butterfield

Vice President Information Technology, Nate Jensen
VICE PRESIDENT PUBLIC POLICY AND GOVERNMENT AFFAIRS, Erica Dahl
VICE PRESIDENT TREASURY AND INVESTOR RELATIONS, Rob Kain
VICE PRESIDENT RETAIL SALES, Trever Bybee
VICE PRESIDENT AND CORPORATE CONTROLLER, Gregory Steinkopf
Auditors: Ernst & Young LLP

LOCATIONS

HQ: Vivint Solar Inc
1800 West Ashton Blvd., Lehi, UT 84043
Phone: 877 404-4129
Web: www.vivintsolar.com

HISTORICAL FINANCIALS

Company Type: Public

Income Statement				FYE: December 31
	REVENUE ($ mil.)	NET INCOME ($ mil.)	NET PROFIT MARGIN	EMPLOYEES
12/17	268.0	209.1	78.0%	2,322
12/16	135.1	17.9	13.3%	3,001
12/15	64.1	13.0	20.4%	3,685
12/14	25.2	(28.8)	—	2,294
12/13	6.1	5.6	91.4%	2,288
Annual Growth	156.7%	146.8%	—	0.4%

2017 Year-End Financials

Debt ratio: 38.3%	No. of shares (mil.): 115.1
Return on equity: 31.2%	Dividends
Cash ($ mil.): 108.4	Yield: —
Current ratio: 1.10	Payout: —
Long-term debt ($ mil.): 927.5	Market value ($ mil.): 466.0

	STOCK PRICE ($) FY Close	P/E High/Low		Earnings	PER SHARE ($) Dividends	Book Value
12/17	4.05	3	1	1.77	0.00	6.79
12/16	2.55	59	13	0.16	0.00	5.05
12/15	9.56	132	61	0.12	0.00	4.87
12/14	9.22	—	—	(0.35)	0.00	4.54
Annual Growth	(24.0%)		—	—	—	14.3%

VSE Corp.

VSE brings military hand-me-downs back into fashion. The company provides engineering testing and logistics services for the US Army the US Navy and other government agencies on a contract basis. VSE operates through various subsidiaries and divisions that comprise its core federal group segment (engineering logistics communications and management services) and its international group (fleet maintenance and foreign military sales). Other segments include IT energy and management consulting (technical and consulting services for civilian government) and infrastructure (engineering and construction services). VSE generates about half of its revenues from the Department of Defense (DOD).

Operations

The company's Supply Chain Management Group provides sourcing acquisition scheduling transportation shipping logistics data management and other services to assist our clients with supply chain management efforts. This group consists of its Wheeler Bros. Inc. (WBI) subsidiary.

The company's federal group segment operates through divisions that are dedicated to serving major military customers. Its communications & engineering engineering & logistics field support services and systems engineering divisions manage various aspects of its logistics and engineering contracts with the US Army Army Reserves and Marine Corps. VSE Services International on the other hand provides engineering industrial logistics and foreign military sales services primarily to the US military through its GLOBAL and fleet maintenance divisions. The GLOBAL division reactivates old Navy ships for transfer to other countries.

Conversely VSE divides its work in its non-federal group and international segments between a handful of subsidiaries that serve mostly civilian government agencies. Its Energetics subsidiary part of the IT energy and management consulting segment serves agencies concerned with energy and environmental issues. Another IT consulting subsidiary Virginia-based G&B provides information technology services to various civilian-based government agencies. Subsidiary Akimeka LLC also offers services in these fields. The infrastructure group's ICRC unit offers diversified technical and management services to the US Department of Transportation and similar government agencies.

In 2013 Supply Chain accounted for 33% of VSE's revenues; International 31%; Federal 20%; and IT Energy and Management Consulting 16%.

Geographic Reach

VSE has operations in Arkansas California Colorado Florida Georgia Guam Hawaii Maryland Michigan Mississippi New Jersey North Carolina Oklahoma Oregon Pennsylvania South Carolina Texas Utah Virginia Wisconsin and Washington DC.

Sales and Marketing

The company's services are performed for the US government various federal civilian agencies and other clients. Its largest customers are the DOD and the USPS.

Supply Chain Management Group supplies vehicle parts for the USPS truck fleet and direct sales to other clients. International Group provides its services to the US Navy Department of Treasury Air Force Department of Justice and Bureau of Alcohol Tobacco Firearms and Explosives (ATF).

The Managed Inventory Program (supplying truck replacement parts for the USPS fleet) the Foreign Military Sales Program for the US Navy and its vehicle and equipment refurbishment work for the US Army Reserve are VSE's three largest revenue generators accounting for 30% 20% and 13% respectively of its 2013 revenues.

Financial Performance

The company has seen a continuous decline in revenues since 2009. Revenues dipped by 14% in 2013 due to a 33% decline in revenues from the Federal Group segment primarily due to the expiration of a contract to provide mechanical maintenance services for Mine Resistance Ambush Protected vehicles and systems in Kuwait and to a reduction in revenues from its vehicle and equipment refurbishment work for the US Army Reserve due to the interruption of contract coverage. International Group segment sales declined by 12% as the result a decline of $18 million in pass-through work provided on engineering and technical services task orders and to due to a lesser decline in revenues from CFT Program services. Also IT Energy and Management Consulting Group decreased by 21% due to a decrease in services performed due to contract expirations and a decline in services ordered by clients on continuing contracts. The drop was partially offset by increase in revenues from the Supply Chain Management thanks to a stronger year for Wheeler Brothers' Managed Inventory Program with USPS.

Net income increased by 7% in 2013 as the result of the absence of impairment of intangible assets and a decline in interest expense due to reductions in the level of borrowing (the company paid down its bank loan during 2013) and a less severe loss from discontinued operations.

Operating cash flow decreased by $3 million to $57 million in 2013 due to changes in the levels of operating assets and liabilities; a decrease of a $3.6 million in depreciation and amortization and other non-cash operating activities; and an increase of $1.6 million in cash provided by net income.

Strategy

For the company which offers very few of its services to commercial clients relying on government contracts can be a bit like walking a mine field. VSE often faces funding delays terminations and political moratoriums and is subject to fluctuations in demand from its core customers. In an effort to curtail vulnerabilities inherent to such fluctuations the company makes acquisitions of complementary businesses that help bring in new customers and expand its services.

During 2013 the company abandoned the construction management operations of its wholly owned subsidiary Integrated Concepts and Research Corporation (ICRC). ICRC participated in an arrangement to provide performance and payment bonding services for certain small business prime contractors associated with ICRC's construction management business. Under the arrangement ICRC received subcontractor work from the small business prime contractors in exchange for indemnifying the surety company in respect of the performance and payment bonds it provided for the small business prime contractors.

Company Background

In 2011 VSE acquired Wheeler Bros. Inc. (WBI) a supply chain management company for roughly $180 million. WBI provides vehicle parts primarily to the USPS and the DOD. The takeover added fleet management for the USPS and expanded VSE's supply chain service offerings to existing customers. WBI also helps the company compensate for lost business from the DOD as it undergoes budget adjustments. The previous year the company bolstered its G&B unit with the acquisition of Hawaii-based Akimeka for $38 million. Akimeka is a health services information technology consulting group that came with a strong US government client base.

Besides acquisitions the company has been pursuing growth by developing new contracts to succeed fading deals. Included among these new agreements is a 2011 award that will make up for lost work from the discontinued R2 contract.

VSE was established in Virginia in 1959 with three employees; its first contract provided the US Navy with a competitive bidding package for missile rocket motors.

EXECUTIVES

SVP and CFO, Thomas R. (Tom) Loftus, age 62, $311,610 total compensation
VP General Counsel and Secretary, Thomas M. Kiernan, $249,174 total compensation
President CEO COO and Director, Maurice A. Gauthier, age 70, $700,000 total compensation
President Energetics Inc. and Akimeka LLC, Nancy Margolis, age 62, $214,240 total compensation
President and COO Wheeler Bros. Inc., Chad Wheeler, age 43, $250,000 total compensation
President and COO VSE Aviation Inc., Paul W. Goffredi, age 60
President Federal Services Group, Joseph R. (JR) Brown, age 61
CIO, Matthew (Matt) Mullenix
Chairman, Clifford M. Kendall, age 87
Auditors: Ernst & Young LLP

LOCATIONS

HQ: VSE Corp.
6348 Walker Lane, Alexandria, VA 22310
Phone: 703 960-4600   **Fax:** 703 960-2688
Web: www.vsecorp.com

PRODUCTS/OPERATIONS

2016 sales

	$ mil.	% of total
Supply Chain Management Group	205.4	30
Aviation Group	133.4	19
Federal Services Group	306.1	44
IT Energy and Management consulting Group	46.7	7
Total	**691.7**	**100**

2016 sales

	$ mil.	% of total
U.S.Postal Service	181.2	26
DOD		
U.S.Navy	190.1	27
U.S.Army	139.7	20
U.S Air Force	3.4	1
Commercial		
Commercial Aviation	131.0	19
Other Commercial	10.7	2
Other Civilian Agencies		
Department of Energy	11.7	2
Social Security Administration	9.7	1
Other Government	13.9	2
Total	**691.7**	**100**

Selected Subsidiaries

Air Parts & Supply Co.
Akimeka LLC
CT Aerospace LLC
Energetics Incorporated
G&B Solutions Inc.
Integrated Concepts and Research Corporation
Kansas Aviation of Independence L.L.C.
Prime Turbines LLC
VSE Aviation Inc.
Wheeler Bros. Inc

Selected Projects

Energy conservation projects
Engineering support for military vehicles and combat trailers
Large-scale port engineering development and construction management
Life cycle support for ships
Logistics management support
Machinery condition analysis
Military equipment refurbishment and modification
Ship communication systems
Ship force crew training
Ship maintenance overhaul and follow-on technical support
Specification preparation for ship alterations

Selected Operating Units

Supply Chain Group

Acquisition Management
  Configuration Management
  Obsolescence Management
  Prototyping & Fabrication
  Logistics
  Reserve Engineering
Federal Group
  Communications and Engineering Division
  Engineering and Logistics Division
  Field Support Services Division
  Systems Engineering Division
International Group
  GLOBAL Division
  Fleet Maintenance Division (global field engineering and logistics)
IT Energy and Management Consulting Group
  Akimeka
  Energetics Incorporated
  G&B Solutions

COMPETITORS

Boeing	Lockheed Martin
Force Protection	Northrop Grumman
General Dynamics	Todd Shipyards

HISTORICAL FINANCIALS

Company Type: Public

Income Statement

FYE: December 31

	REVENUE ($ mil.)	NET INCOME ($ mil.)	NET PROFIT MARGIN	EMPLOYEES
12/17	760.1	39.1	5.1%	2,306
12/16	691.7	26.7	3.9%	2,523
12/15	533.9	24.9	4.7%	2,057
12/14	424.0	19.3	4.6%	1,589
12/13	471.6	22.8	4.8%	1,872
Annual Growth	**12.7%**	**14.4%**	—	**5.4%**

2017 Year-End Financials

Debt ratio: 30.7%	No. of shares (mil.): 10.8
Return on equity: 14.2%	Dividends
Cash ($ mil.): 0.6	Yield: 0.0%
Current ratio: 2.18	Payout: 7.2%
Long-term debt ($ mil.): 186.2	Market value ($ mil.): 525.0

	STOCK PRICE ($) FY Close	P/E High/Low		PER SHARE ($) Earnings	Dividends	Book Value
12/17	48.43	16	10	3.60	0.26	27.04
12/16	38.84	30	12	2.47	0.23	23.63
12/15	62.18	36	15	2.31	0.42	21.33
12/14	65.90	41	23	1.81	0.38	19.17
12/13	48.01	24	10	2.14	0.34	17.51
Annual Growth	**0.2%**	—	—	**13.9%**	**(6.5%)**	**11.5%**

W.P. Carey Inc

Need help managing your property portfolio? Keep calm and Carey on. W. P. Carey invests in and manages commercial real estate including office distribution retail and industrial facilities. The company owns more than 1000 properties mainly in the US and Europe and manages properties for several non-traded real estate investment trusts (REITs). Its management portfolio totals some $15 billion. W. P. Carey typically acquires properties and then leases them back to the sellers/occupants on a long-term basis. It also provides build-to-suit financing for investors worldwide. W. P. Carey is converting to a REIT a corporate structure that comes with tax benefits and more flexibilty in investing in real estate.

Geographic Reach
New York-based W. P. Carey owns some 1020 properties in 21 countries. The firm has offices in Dallas London Amsterdam Hong Kong and Shanghai. International investments account for about 31% of the REIT's annual revenue.

Financial Performance
Carey's revenue increased 31% in 2013 versus 2012 to $489.9 million. Revenue growth was spurred by additions to the firm's real estate portfolio made in 2012 including 19 self-storage properties. Net income rose 59% over the same period to $98.9 million due primarily to higher revenue and income from discontinued operations.

Strategy
Since 1979 the REIT has sponsored a series of 18 income-generating investment programs that invest primarily in commercial properties net leased to single tenants under the Corporate Property Associates or CPA brand name. In 2013 the firm managed four global active funds: CPA 16 CPA 17 and CPA 18. W.P. Carey looks to diversify its managed funds and make investments in properties that provide consistent long-term sources of income. Property diversity helps shield W.P. from being reliant on any single industry. A few of its recent investments include a hypermarket in Germany operated by Metro AG a newly-constructed office in Wales the new Siemens AS headquarters in Oslo Norway and a 302-room Hampton Inn & Suites/Homewood Suites by Hilton hotel in Denver's central business district.

In addition to making property investments the firm is focused on diversifying its asset management capabilities. W.P. Carey has launched a lodging-focused fund (Carey Watermark Investors). The new investment program is dedicated to investing in the lodging sector and made its first investments in 2011.

In late 2014 the firm made its first investment in Australia via a 20-year net-lease transaction with Inghams Enterprises Pty. Ltd. The $138 million deal included industrial and agricultural properties.

EXECUTIVES

Vice President, Zachary A Pasanen
First Vice President External Wholesaler, Greg Rushing
Auditors: PricewaterhouseCoopers LLP

LOCATIONS

HQ: W.P. Carey Inc
50 Rockefeller Plaza, New York, NY 10020
Phone: 212 492-1100
Web: www.wpcarey.com

PRODUCTS/OPERATIONS

2015 sales

	% of total
Real estate ownership	78
Investment management	22
Total	**100**

COMPETITORS

Brandywine Realty	Inland Group
CNL Financial	Jones Lang LaSalle
Crescent Real Estate	Lexington Realty Trust
Equity Office	Vornado Realty
First Industrial Realty	

HISTORICAL FINANCIALS
Company Type: Public

Income Statement — FYE: December 31

	REVENUE ($ mil.)	NET INCOME ($ mil.)	NET PROFIT MARGIN	EMPLOYEES
12/17	848.3	277.2	32.7%	207
12/16	941.5	267.7	28.4%	281
12/15	938.3	172.2	18.4%	314
12/14	906.1	239.8	26.5%	272
12/13	489.8	98.8	20.2%	251
Annual Growth	**14.7%**	**29.4%**	**—**	**(4.7%)**

2017 Year-End Financials

Debt ratio: 51.8%
Return on equity: 8.5%
Cash ($ mil.): 162.3
Current ratio: 0.72
Long-term debt ($ mil.): 4,265.2
No. of shares (mil.): 106.9
Dividends
Yield: 0.0%
Payout: 156.6%
Market value ($ mil.): 7,367.0

	STOCK PRICE ($) FY Close	P/E High/Low	PER SHARE ($) Earnings	Dividends	Book Value
12/17	68.90	28 23	2.56	4.01	29.86
12/16	59.09	29 21	2.49	3.93	31.06
12/15	59.00	45 35	1.61	3.83	32.81
12/14	70.10	30 24	2.39	3.69	36.05
12/13	61.35	55 36	1.41	3.50	27.90
Annual Growth	**2.9%**	**— —**	**16.1%**	**3.5%**	**1.7%**

Walker & Dunlop Inc

When it comes to its commercial real estate loans Walker & Dunlop has the government on its side. The company provides commercial real estate financial services — mainly multifamily loans for apartments health care properties and student housing — to real estate owners and developers across the US. It originates and sells its products (e.g. mortgages supplemental financing construction loans and mezzanine loans) primarily through government-sponsored enterprises (GSEs) like Fannie Mae and Freddie Mac as well as through HUD. To a lesser extent the company originates loans for insurance companies banks and institutional investors.

Operations
The company generates its revenue from five main revenue streams: mortgage banking (62% of total revenue) servicing fees (about 30%) warehouse interest (5%) escrow earnings (1%) and other (5%).

Geographic Reach
Walker & Dunlop operates through 26 offices across the country with locations residing in Atlanta; Chicago; Dallas; Ft. Lauderdale Florida; Irvine California; Nashville Tennessee; New Orleans; New York; Seattle; San Francisco; Needham Massachusetts; and Walnut Creek California.

Sales and Marketing
Walker & Dunlop originates and sells loans through the programs of the Federal National Mortgage Associatio n the Federal Home Loan Mortgage Corporation the Government National Mortgage Association and the Federal Housing Administration a division of the US Department of Housing and Urban Development.

Financial Performance
Walker & Dunlop has enjoyed record-setting revenue growth over the last few years. In 2014 revenue grew 13% to $360.8 million as all primary business categories saw growth. The largest category mortgage banking rose 9% that year on greater loan origination volume. Servicing fees revenue also rose 9% due to a larger average servicing portfolio.

Net income has also been on the rise as of late with the exception of 2012 when it took a slight dip. In 2014 profits rose 24% to $51.4 million largely due to the increased revenue. However Walker & Dunlop posted a cash outflow of $729.5 million that year (an improvement over the $836.9 million outflow posted in 2013) primarily due to changes in working capital.

Strategy
Walker & Dunlop has shaped its growth strategy around certain opportunities in the commercial real estate market on which it believes it can capitalize. It intends to invest in origination activities and products to meet the expected increase in demand for real estate financing. In addition Walker & Dunlop's focus on growing its services to health care facilities is centered on an expected rise in the demand for health care real estate loans. It hopes to serve an expected increased demand for such facilities as baby boomers reach retirement age. The company is also motivated by the fact that many commercial health care loans are sought after through GSE and HUD programs.

To further grow its loan origination and servicing operations Walker & Dunlop acquired certain assets of Johnson Capital Group for some $23.5 million in late 2014. That deal added 30 new loan originators to its capital markets team which the company intends to keep expanding in order to meet expected demand in the coming years. It also plans to open additional capital markets offices throughout the nation to increasingly tap into the commercial real estate market.

Company Background
Walker & Dunlop's relationship with government-related housing finance companies began in the late 1980s after it started originating underwriting and selling loans through Fannie Mae. In 2008 it began working with Freddie Mac and HUD after acquiring a loan servicing portfolio worth $5 billion from Column Guaranteed LLC. The acquisition served to widen Walker & Dunlop's revenue base and increase its sales volume.

EXECUTIVES

Chairman and CEO, William M. (Willy) Walker, age 52, $750,000 total compensation
Vice Chairman Capital Markets, Guy K. Johnson
EVP General Counsel and Secretary, Richard M. (Rich) Lucas, age 53, $400,000 total compensation
President, Howard W. Smith, age 59, $500,000 total compensation
EVP and Chief Credit Officer, Richard C. Warner, age 63, $400,000 total compensation
EVP and CFO, Stephen P. Theobald, $400,000 total compensation
EVP and Chief Production Officer Multifamily Finance, Donald P. King
EVP Proprietary Capital, Jeffrey M. (Jeff) Goodman
CTO, Bill Granger

EVP and Group Head FHA Finance, Michelle
  Warner
SVP Walker & Dunlop Investment Sales (WDIS),
  Rob Coleman
EVP and Managing Director Capital Markets,
  James Cope
CEO and Managing Director Walker & Dunlop
  Investment Sales, Greg Engler
Vice President, Michael Liefer
Assistant Vice President Team Leader, Kim Perrell
Vice President, Laura Beaton
Senior Vice President Asset Management, Michael
  Palmer
Vice President, Jody Rosenzweig
Vice President and Team Lead, Terry Haynes
Vice President Asset Management, Suzanne Collins
Vice President, Kimberly Riordan
Vice President, Kevin Walsh
Vice President, Tom Meunier
Senior Vice President, Dan Martin
Vice President Capital Markets, Demetrius Ware
VICE PRESIDENT LOAN SERVICING, Bob
  Watson
Assistant Vice President, Josh West
Senior Vice President, Patrick Dempsey
Assistant Vice President Capital Markets, Brad
  Cullumber
ASSISTANT VICE PRESIDENT, Nancy Mcgrade
ASSISTANT VICE PRESIDENT, Mary Hui
Vice President Closing, Veronica Veraldi
CCIM Assistant Vice President Real Estate
  Finance, Heather Olson
SENIOR VICE PRESIDENT, Brad Burns
SENIOR VICE PRESIDENT, Thomas Sigrist
SENIOR VICE PRESIDENT, Levi Brooker
Vice President, Anthea Martin
ASSISTANT VICE PRESIDENT, Chris King
Vice President, Veronica Langhofer
Vice President and Deputy Chief Underwriter
  HUD Underwriting, Charles Conkling
Assistant Vice President Manager, Judy DiRienzo
Assistant Vice President Real Estate Finance,
  Laura Woltanski
Executive Vice President and Managing Director
  Capital Markets, Jim Cope
Assistant Vice President Asset Management, Matt
  Sutton
Vice President Capital Markets, Tim Cotter
Senior Vice President, Jeff Kearns
Senior Vice President Capital Markets, Steven
  Hinds
Assistant Vice President Capital Markets, Mark
  Vinitsky
SENIOR VICE PRESIDENT, Craig Mueller
ASSISTANT VICE PRESIDENT, Riley Manke
ASSISTANT VICE PRESIDENT, Rob Buelow
VICE PRESIDENT CM, Ryan Chapman
ASSISTANT VICE PRESIDENT, Scott Oeser
SENIOR VICE PRESIDENT, By Cartmell
ASSISTANT VICE PRESIDENT, Jason Taylor
SENIOR VICE PRESIDENT, Keaton Merrell
SENIOR VICE PRESIDENT, Michael Presser
SENIOR VICE PRESIDENT, Aaron Rosenfeld
Vice President Marketing, Chris Zegal
Assistant Vice President Accounting, Judy
  Cockerham
Auditors: KPMG LLP

LOCATIONS

HQ: Walker & Dunlop Inc
  7501 Wisconsin Avenue, Suite 1200E, Bethesda, MD
  20814
Phone: 301 215-5500
Web: www.walkerdunlop.com

PRODUCTS/OPERATIONS

2014 Sales

	% of total
Gains from mortgage banking activities	62
Servicing fees	27
Net warehouse interest income	5
Escrow earnings & other interest income	1
Other	5
Total	**100**

Selected Products and Services

Capital Markets and Investment Services
Construction loans
Equity investments
FHA Finance
First mortgage loans
Healthcare Finance
Mezzanine loans
Multifamily Finance
Second trust loans
Supplemental financings
Underwriting

COMPETITORS

American Capital	MetLife
Arbor Commercial	NewStar Financial
CapitalSource	Ocwen Financial
Centerline Holding Co.	Pzena Investment
Deutsche Bank	Management
Deutsche Bank	Redwood Trust
Berkshire Mortgage	Walter Investment
Encore Capital Group	Management
HFF	Wells Fargo
Kennedy-Wilson	

HISTORICAL FINANCIALS

Company Type: Public

Income Statement

FYE: December 31

	REVENUE ($ mil.)	NET INCOME ($ mil.)	NET PROFIT MARGIN	EMPLOYEES
12/17	711.8	211.1	29.7%	623
12/16	575.2	113.9	19.8%	550
12/15	468.2	82.1	17.5%	504
12/14	360.7	51.4	14.3%	465
12/13	319.0	41.5	13.0%	402
Annual Growth	22.2%	50.2%	—	11.6%

2017 Year-End Financials

Debt ratio: 49.8%	No. of shares (mil.): 30.0
Return on equity: 29.7%	Dividends
Cash ($ mil.): 191.2	Yield: —
Current ratio: 1.45	Payout: —
Long-term debt ($ mil.): 1,101.6	Market value ($ mil.): 1,426.0

	STOCK PRICE ($) FY Close	P/E High/Low		PER SHARE ($) Earnings	Dividends	Book Value
12/17	47.50	8	4	6.56	0.00	26.97
12/16	31.20	8	5	3.65	0.00	20.65
12/15	28.81	12	6	2.65	0.00	16.56
12/14	17.54	11	8	1.58	0.00	13.62
12/13	16.17	18	10	1.21	0.00	11.85
Annual Growth	30.9%	—	—	52.6%	—	22.8%

Warrior Met Coal Inc

Auditors: Ernst & Young LLP

LOCATIONS

HQ: Warrior Met Coal Inc
  16243 Highway 216, Brookwood, AL 35444
Phone: 205 554-6150
Web: www.warriormetcoal.com

HISTORICAL FINANCIALS

Company Type: Public

Income Statement

FYE: December 31

	REVENUE ($ mil.)	NET INCOME ($ mil.)	NET PROFIT MARGIN	EMPLOYEES
12/17	1,169.0	455.0	38.9%	1,354
12/16*	297.6	(49.6)	—	1,130
03/16	71.3	(61.8)	—	0
12/15	544.7	(310.5)	—	0
Annual Growth	29.0%	—	—	—

*Fiscal year change

2017 Year-End Financials

Debt ratio: 35.1%	No. of shares (mil.): 53.2
Return on equity: 78.0%	Dividends
Cash ($ mil.): 35.4	Yield: 0.5%
Current ratio: 2.48	Payout: 131.7%
Long-term debt ($ mil.): 342.9	Market value ($ mil.): 1,340.0

	STOCK PRICE ($) FY Close	P/E High/Low		PER SHARE ($) Earnings	Dividends	Book Value
12/17	25.15	3	2	8.62	11.36	7.75
12/16*	0.00	—	—	(13.15)	0.00	(0.00)
Annual Growth	—	—	—	—	—	—

*Fiscal year change

Wells Fargo Real Estate Investment Corp

Auditors: KPMG LLP

LOCATIONS

HQ: Wells Fargo Real Estate Investment Corp
  90 South 7th Street, Minneapolis, MN 55402
Phone: 855 825-1437
Web: www.wellsfargo.com/invest_relations/filings

HISTORICAL FINANCIALS

Company Type: Public

Income Statement

FYE: December 31

	REVENUE ($ mil.)	NET INCOME ($ mil.)	NET PROFIT MARGIN	EMPLOYEES
12/17	1,353.0	1,218.6	90.1%	2
12/16	899.9	783.8	87.1%	2
12/15	680.8	645.9	94.9%	2
12/14	697.0	637.9	91.5%	2
12/13	298.8	257.4	86.1%	0
Annual Growth	45.9%	47.5%		—

2017 Year-End Financials

Debt ratio: 9.8%
Return on equity: 3.7%
Cash ($ mil.): —
Current ratio: —
Long-term debt ($ mil.): 3,551.4

No. of shares (mil.): 34.0
Dividends
  Yield: 0.0%
  Payout: 4.5%
Market value ($ mil.): 902.0

	STOCK PRICE ($) FY Close	P/E High/Low		PER SHARE ($) Earnings	Dividends	Book Value
12/17	26.49	1	1	35.27	1.59	951.03
12/16	25.17	1	1	37.75	1.59	951.15
12/15	26.16	1	1	48.71	1.69	962.24
12/14	25.35	1	1	49.37	46.74	957.87
Annual Growth (0.2%)	1.5%			—	—(10.6%)	(67.6%)

WesBanco Inc

WesBanco wants to be the "BesBanco" for its customers. The holding company owns WesBanco Bank which has about 210 branches in Indiana Kentucky Ohio Pennsylvania and West Virginia. In addition to providing traditional services such as deposits and loans the bank operates a wealth management department with offices in West Virginia and Ohio and some $4.7 billion of assets under management and custody including the company's proprietary WesMark mutual funds. Other units include brokerage firm WesBanco Securities and multi-line insurance provider WesBanco Insurance Services.

Operations

Commercial loans including real estate and operating loans account for more than half of of WesBanco's loan portfolio. Its retail portfolio mainly consists of home equity loans and deposit overdraft limits. The bank usually sells new residential mortgages that it originates into the secondary market. It plans to continue to grow its portfolio of commercial and industrial loans.

Strategy

WesBanco likes to purchase smaller banks to expand its reach into new geographic markets while bolstering its loan and deposit business. It's acquired more than 50 banks and financial services firms in the past 25 years.

Mergers and Acquisitions

In 2018 WesBanco acquired Kentucky-based Farmers Capital Bank Corporation for $429.8 million and West Virginia-based First Sentry Bancshares for $107.5 million.

In 2016 the company expanded into Kentucky and southern Indiana when it acquired Your Community Bank.

EXECUTIVES

EVP Treasury and Strategic Planning, Brent E. Richmond, age 55
SVP and Chief Credit Officer, Peter W. Jaworski, age 63, $212,101 total compensation
EVP and CFO, Robert H. Young, age 62, $269,363 total compensation
President and CEO, Todd F. Clossin, age 56, $466,923 total compensation
SVP Risk Management, Michael L. Perkins
EVP Retail Delivery, Lynn D. Asensio

EVP and Senior Operations Officer, Gregory A. Dugan
EVP Wealth Management, Jonathan D. Dargusch, age 60, $230,270 total compensation
EVP Human Resources Management, Anthony F. Pietranton
EVP and Chief Lending Officer, Jayson M. Zatta
Market President Kanawha Region, David L. Sayre
Vice President and Manager Human Resources, Sheri Clarke
Regional Vice President, Daniel Mooney
Assistant Vice President Mortgage CRA Officer, Lisa Werner
Senior Vice President Special Assets, Jodi Pagnanelli
Vice President, Tom Timmons
Vice President Commercial Real Estate, Traci Boeing
Assistant Vice President, Bruce Bandi
Vice President, Allen Retton
Vice President, Tom Medovic
Assistant Vice President Branch Operations, Beth Bussard
Senior Vice President Credit Risk Management, Edward Polli
Assistant Vice President Information Technology Services, W Terrance Naughton
Vice President Of Information Technology, Mike Robbins
Vice President Investments, Steve Kellas
Senior Vice President, Gregory Agresta
Banking Center Manager Assistant Vice President, Jodi McKnight
Senior Vice President Senior Lender, Bob Friend
Vice President and Loan Review Officer, Diane Todd
Senior Vice President and Senior Credit Officer, David Knuth
Vice President of Commercial Banking, Michael Mlstovich
Senior Vice President, Mike Lander
Assistant Vice President Branch Manager, Tom Wiggershaus
Banking Center Manager Assistant Vice President, Nicholas Beresh
Vice President Secondary Marketing Manager, Ryan Freimark
Senior Vice President Corporate Banking, Charles Wharton
Senior Vice President Enterprise Services, Jan Pattishall
Assistant Vice President, Anthony Habbit
Assistant Vice President, Dan Baxter
Senior Vice President, Dave Mendenhall
Vice President, Brent Dapper
Vice President, Michael Puzausky
Vice President, Mike Moore
Vice President, Nathan Schoetz
Assistant Vice President, Drew Correll
Vice President Business Banking, Maher-dickerson Stephanie
Vice President Commercial Banking Officer, Craig Kinslow
VICE PRESIDENT PRIVATE BANKER, Leslie D Witzel
VICE PRESIDENT AND COMMERCIAL BANKER, Michael Epperley
SENIOR VICE PRESIDENT AND SENIOR COMMERCIAL BANKER, Michael T Misich
VICE PRESIDENT COMMERCIAL LENDER, Robert E Krzeminski
VICE PRESIDENT TREASURY MANAGEMENT SALES, Stacy Graf
VICE PRESIDENT SENIOR TRUST OFFICER, Thomas D Barsody
VICE PRESIDENT, Thomas Nigon

VICE PRESIDENT COMMERCIAL LENDING, Kurt C Bevan
VICE PRESIDENT AND TECHNOLOGY SERVICES COORDINATOR, Stephanie Skivington
Vice President, Dave Klick
AVP and BCMBusiness Development WeSBanCO, Michelle Donaldson
VICE PRESIDENT SENIOR TRUST OFFICER, Thomas Barsody
Chairman, James C. (Jim) Gardill, age 72
Secretary, Cindy Dailer
Auditors: Ernst & Young LLP

LOCATIONS

HQ: WesBanco Inc
  1 Bank Plaza, Wheeling, WV 26003
Phone: 304 234-9000
Web: www.wesbanco.com

PRODUCTS/OPERATIONS

2016 Sales

	$ mil.	% of total
Interest and Dividend Income		
Loans including fees	227.0	61
Interest and dividends on securities	56.9	15
Other interest income	2.2	1
Non-Interest Income		
Trust fees	21.6	6
Service charges on deposits	18.3	5
Electronic banking fees	15.6	4
Net securities brokerage	6.4	2
Bank-owned life insurance	4.1	1
Net gains on sales of mortgage loans	2.5	1
Net securities gains	2.4	1
Net gain / (loss) on other real estate owned and other assets	0.8	-
others	9.8	3
Total	**367.6**	**100**

Selected Products and Services

Personal Banking
Internet Banking
Checking
Savings
Time Deposits
Debit Cards
Credit Cards
Loans
Mortgage Lending
Other Services
Business
Internet Banking
Checking
Savings
Time Deposits
Credit Cards
Loans
Treasury Management
Insurance Services
Wealth Management

COMPETITORS

1st West Virginia Bancorp	Huntington Bancshares
BB&T	Ohio Valley Banc
Bank of America	PNC Financial
Cheviot Financial	United Bancorp
City Holding	United Bankshares
First Community Bancshares	

Income Statement — FYE: December 31

	ASSETS ($ mil.)	NET INCOME ($ mil.)	INCOME AS % OF ASSETS	EMPLOYEES
12/17	9,816.1	94.4	1.0%	1,940
12/16	9,790.8	86.6	0.9%	1,928
12/15	8,470.3	80.7	1.0%	1,633
12/14	6,296.5	69.9	1.1%	1,448
12/13	6,144.7	63.9	1.0%	1,469
Annual Growth	12.4%	10.3%	—	7.2%

2017 Year-End Financials

Return on assets: 0.9%
Return on equity: 6.9%
Long-term debt ($ mil.): —
No. of shares (mil.): 44.0
Sales ($ mil): 421.2
Dividends
Yield: 0.0%
Payout: 48.6%
Market value ($ mil.): 1,790.0

	STOCK PRICE ($) FY Close	P/E High/Low	PER SHARE ($) Earnings	Dividends	Book Value
12/17	40.65	20 16	2.14	1.04	31.68
12/16	43.06	20 13	2.16	0.96	30.53
12/15	30.02	17 14	2.15	0.92	29.18
12/14	34.80	15 11	2.39	0.88	26.90
12/13	32.00	15 10	2.18	0.78	25.59
Annual Growth	6.2%	— —	(0.5%)	7.5%	5.5%

Western Alliance Bancorporation

Western Alliance Bancorporation and its flagship Western Alliance Bank (WAB) have an alliance with several bank brands in the West operating as the Alliance Bank of Arizona; Bank of Nevada; First Independent Bank (Nevada); as well as Bridge Bank and Torrey Pines Bank which are both located across California. Combined the banks operate nearly 50 branches that provide standard consumer and business deposit and loan products. About half of the Western Alliance's loan portfolio is made up of commercial and industrial loans while another 40% is made up of commercial real estate loans. It also makes land development loans and consumer residential mortgages and other lines of credit.

Operations

Western Alliance focuses on commercial lending. About 46% of the bank's loan portfolio consisted of commercial and industrial loans at the end of 2015 while another 39% was made up of commercial real estate loans. The bank also had construction and land development loans (10% of loan assets) residential mortgages (3%) commercial leases (1%) and consumer loans (less than 1%).

More than 90% of the bank's revenue comes from interest income. About 86% of its total revenue came from loan interest during 2015 while another 9% came from interest or dividends on investment securities. The remainder of its revenue came from service charges and fees (2% of rev-

enue) card income (1%) and other miscellaneous sources.

Geographic Reach

Western Alliance's 40 branches and seven loan offices are spread across Arizona Nevada and California as well as Boston Dallas and Reston Virginia. At the end of 2015 its loan business was concentrated in the Los Angeles San Francisco San Jose Phoenix Tuscon Reno and Las Vegas metropolitan areas.

Sales and Marketing

The bank serves local businesses real estate developers and investors not-for-profit organizations and consumers. It specializes in lending to such customers operating in the healthcare professional services manufacturing and distribution resorts and timeshares technology and startups municipalities and local governments non-profit and renewable energy markets. Some of its clients (as of early 2016) include Cutter Aviation FNF Construction Hollenbeck Palms New American Funding and Signature Healthcare Services.

Western Alliance spent $2.89 million on marketing in 2015 up from $2.30 million and $2.58 million in 2014 and 2013 respectively.

Financial Performance

Western Alliance's annual revenues have risen nearly 70% since 2011 as its loan business has swelled. Meanwhile the bank's annual profits have ballooned more than five-fold as its credit portfolio's credit quality has improved with higher property valuations in the strengthened economy.

The group's revenue jumped 26% to $555 million during 2015 mostly thanks to new loan business more than half of which was obtained from the Bridge Bank acquisition which spurred more interest income for the year. Non-interest income especially service charges and lending-related fees grew by double digits during the year also thanks to the acquisition as well as from more organic deposit business growth.

Strong revenue growth and a continued decline in credit loss provisions in 2015 drove Western Alliance's net income up by 31% to $194 million for the year. The company's operating cash levels climbed 30% to $213 million mostly thanks to the rise in cash earnings.

Strategy

Western Alliance Bancorporation looks to expand its branch network and selectively acquire other banks to boost its loan and deposit business and extend its geographic reach. The bank may also buy other financial services businesses to bolster its line of service offerings.

Mergers and Acquisitions

In June 2015 Western Alliance bought $13 billion-asset Bridge Capital Holdings along with its 48 Bridge Bank branches in California Arizona and Nevada in a deal worth about $425 million. The purchase brought expertise in technology and international banking among other areas and expands Western Alliance's market into Northern California.

EXECUTIVES

EVP and Chief Credit Officer, Robert R. (Bob) McAuslan, age 65
Chairman and CEO, Robert G. Sarver, age 57, $830,000 total compensation
EVP and CFO, Dale M. Gibbons, age 57, $400,000 total compensation

EVP Northern California Administration and President and CEO Bridge Bank division, Daniel P. (Dan) Myers, age 57, $212,885 total compensation
EVP Southern Nevada Administration and CEO Bank of Nevada Division, John Guedry
EVP and CIO, John P. Peckham
EVP California Administration and President Torrey Pines Bank, Gerald A. (Gary) Cady, age 63, $360,000 total compensation
EVP and Chief Risk Officer, Patricia A. Taylor
EVP and General Counsel, Randall S. Theisen
EVP and COO, Jim Haught
EVP Arizona Administration and CEO Alliance Bank of Arizona, Don Garner
Auditors: RSM US LLP

LOCATIONS

HQ: Western Alliance Bancorporation
One E. Washington Street, Suite 1400, Phoenix, AZ 85004
Phone: 602 389-3500
Web: www.westernalliancebancorporation.com

PRODUCTS/OPERATIONS

2015 Sales

	% of total
Interest income	
Loans including fees	86
Investment securities	7
Dividends	2
Other	-
Non-interest income	
Service charges and fees	2
Income from bank owned life insurance	1
Card income	1
Other	1
Total	100

Selected Services

Business Checking & Savings
Business Loans & Credit
Card Services
International Banking
Personal Banking
Treasury Management

COMPETITORS

Bank of America	PacWest Bancorp
Bank of the West	U.S. Bancorp
Desert Schools FCU	Wells Fargo
First Banks	Westamerica
MUFG Americas Holdings	Zions Bancorporation

HISTORICAL FINANCIALS
Company Type: Public

Income Statement — FYE: December 31

	ASSETS ($ mil.)	NET INCOME ($ mil.)	INCOME AS % OF ASSETS	EMPLOYEES
12/17	20,329.0	325.4	1.6%	1,725
12/16	17,200.8	259.8	1.5%	1,557
12/15	14,275.0	194.2	1.4%	1,446
12/14	10,600.5	147.9	1.4%	1,131
12/13	9,307.1	114.5	1.2%	1,051
Annual Growth	21.6%	29.8%	—	13.2%

2017 Year-End Financials

Return on assets: 1.7%
Return on equity: 15.8%
Long-term debt ($ mil.): —
No. of shares (mil.): 105.4
Sales ($ mil): 890.8
Dividends
Yield: —
Payout: —
Market value ($ mil.): 5,973.0

STOCK PRICE ($) FY Close	P/E High/Low		PER SHARE ($) Earnings	Dividends	Book Value
12/17	56.62	19 14	3.10	0.00	21.14
12/16	48.71	20 11	2.50	0.00	18.00
12/15	35.86	19 12	2.03	0.00	15.44
12/14	27.80	17 12	1.67	0.00	11.29
12/13	23.86	19 8	1.31	0.00	9.81
Annual Growth	24.1%	— —	24.0%	—	21.2%

Western Asset Mortgage Capital Corp

Auditors: PricewaterhouseCoopers LLP

LOCATIONS

HQ: Western Asset Mortgage Capital Corp
385 East Colorado Boulevard, Pasadena, CA 91101
Phone: 626 844-9400
Web: www.westernassetmcc.com

HISTORICAL FINANCIALS

Company Type: Public

Income Statement

FYE: December 31

	REVENUE ($ mil.)	NET INCOME ($ mil.)	NET PROFIT MARGIN	EMPLOYEES
12/17	177.6	85.1	47.9%	0
12/16	64.1	(25.0)	—	0
12/15	60.4	(9.4)	—	0
12/14	141.7	100.7	71.1%	1
12/13	4.4	(27.8)	—	1
Annual Growth	151.7%	—	—	—

2017 Year-End Financials

Debt ratio: 86.7%
Return on equity: 18.9%
Cash ($ mil.): 48.0
Current ratio: 0.05
Long-term debt ($ mil.): 108.7

No. of shares (mil.): 41.7
Dividends
  Yield: 0.1%
  Payout: 61.0%
Market value ($ mil.): 416.0

	STOCK PRICE ($) FY Close	P/E High/Low		PER SHARE ($) Earnings	Dividends	Book Value
12/17	9.95	5	5	2.03	1.24	11.15
12/16	10.07	—	—	(0.61)	1.38	10.27
12/15	10.22	—	—	(0.25)	2.49	12.21
12/14	14.70	6	5	2.67	2.74	14.94
12/13	14.88	—	—	(1.19)	5.10	15.27
Annual Growth	(9.6%)	—	—	—	(29.8%)	(7.6%)

Western Capital Resources Inc

EXECUTIVES

President, Mr John Quandahl
Auditors: KLJ & Associates, LLP

LOCATIONS

HQ: Western Capital Resources Inc
11550 "I" Street, Suite 150, Omaha, NE 68137
Phone: 402 551-8888

HISTORICAL FINANCIALS

Company Type: Public

Income Statement

FYE: December 31

	REVENUE ($ mil.)	NET INCOME ($ mil.)	NET PROFIT MARGIN	EMPLOYEES
12/17	121.5	36.2	29.9%	1,100
12/16	109.1	1.4	1.3%	780
12/15	76.4	3.5	4.6%	660
12/14	40.7	2.4	5.9%	390
12/13	32.8	1.6	4.9%	320
Annual Growth	38.6%	117.6%	—	36.2%

2017 Year-End Financials

Debt ratio: 0.9%
Return on equity: 74.3%
Cash ($ mil.): 53.5
Current ratio: 2.26
Long-term debt ($ mil.): 0.8

No. of shares (mil.): 9.3
Dividends
  Yield: 0.0%
  Payout: 2.5%
Market value ($ mil.): 45.0

	STOCK PRICE ($) FY Close	P/E High/Low		PER SHARE ($) Earnings	Dividends	Book Value
12/17	4.75	2	1	4.00	0.10	7.13
12/16	5.00	47	17	0.15	0.05	3.23
12/15	3.50	11	6	0.45	0.00	3.14
12/14	3.30	6	0	0.64	0.00	3.35
12/13	0.12	0	0	0.60	0.00	5.75
Annual Growth	150.8%	—	—	60.7%	—	5.5%

Western Gas Equity Partners LP

Western Gas Equity Partners LP (WGEP) is taking stock of a fellow energy concern. The entity formed in September 2012 as an investment vehicle for Western Gas Partners LP (WGP). WGEP's sole purpose is to buy a stake in WGP specifically a limited partner interest of almost 45% and a general partner interest of about 2%. As a shareholder of WGP the entity will receive cash distributions at the end of every fiscal quarter from WGP and as a limited partnership WGEP will distribute its profits back to its own shareholders. It will also be exempt from paying federal income taxes. WGEP filed an IPO seeking up to $362.25 million in November 2012 and plans to use the proceeds raised to begin buying shares in WGP.
Auditors: KPMG LLP

LOCATIONS

HQ: Western Gas Equity Partners LP
1201 Lake Robbins Drive, The Woodlands, TX 77380
Phone: 832 636-6000   **Fax:** 832 636-6001
Web: www.westerngas.com

PRODUCTS/OPERATIONS

2011 Sales

	$ mil.	% of total
Natural gas NGLs and condensate sales	502.4	61
Gathering processing & transporation of natural gas & NGLs	301.3	36
Equity income & other	19.6	3
Total	**823.3**	**100**

COMPETITORS

DCP Midstream Partners   ONEOK Partners
Dominion Questar   XTO Energy
Enbridge Energy
Kinder Morgan Energy
  Partners

HISTORICAL FINANCIALS

Company Type: Public

Income Statement

FYE: December 31

	REVENUE ($ mil.)	NET INCOME ($ mil.)	NET PROFIT MARGIN	EMPLOYEES
12/17	2,248.3	376.6	16.8%	0
12/16	1,804.2	345.7	19.2%	0
12/15	1,561.3	87.8	5.6%	0
12/14	1,273.7	221.9	17.4%	0
12/13	1,053.5	160.2	15.2%	0
Annual Growth	20.9%	23.8%	—	—

2017 Year-End Financials

Debt ratio: 43.5%
Return on equity: —
Cash ($ mil.): 79.5
Current ratio: 0.60
Long-term debt ($ mil.): 3,492.7

No. of shares (mil.): 218.9
Dividends
  Yield: 0.0%
  Payout: 117.3%
Market value ($ mil.): 8,136.0

	STOCK PRICE ($) FY Close	P/E High/Low		PER SHARE ($) Earnings	Dividends	Book Value
12/17	37.16	28	20	1.72	2.02	4.85
12/16	42.35	30	13	1.53	1.71	4.79
12/15	36.29	167	77	0.39	1.40	4.85
12/14	60.23	64	37	1.02	1.04	5.76
12/13	39.51	61	42	0.71	0.63	4.13
Annual Growth	(1.5%)	—	—	24.8%	34.0%	4.1%

Western Gas Partners LP

Western Gas Partners' style is to gather and go. The company gathers and transports natural gas for its largest customer andA parent Anadarko Petroleum andA delivers natural gasA and natural gas liquids (NGLs) to end-users.A ItA handles gathering processing and throughputA of aboutA 2.2 billion cu. ft. of gas a dayA throughA eleven naturalA gas gathering systemsA sevenA treating facilitiesA one natural gas liquids pipeline and one interstate pipeline (totaling more thanA 8820 miles acrossA Wyoming Utah Texas Oklahoma and Kansas). Operating principally under long-term contracts the company gathers natural gas from individual wells after which it is compressed treated and delivered to customers.

EXECUTIVES

Senior Vice President Chief Financial Officer, Benjamin M. (Ben) Fink, age 46

Chairman, Robert G. Gwin, age 53, $107,392 total compensation

Chief Operating Officer; Senior Vice President of Western Gas Holdings; LLC, Danny J. Rea, $65,699 total compensation

VP General Counsel and Corporate Secretary, Amanda M. McMillian, $48,011 total compensation

Investor Relations, Chris Campbell

President Chief Executive Officer, Donald R. Sinclair

Vice President; General Counsel; Corporate Secretary of Western Gas Holdings; LLC, Philip Peacock

Director, Robert K. (Bobby) Reeves Sr., age 57

Director, James R. (Jim) Crane, age 61

Director, Anthony R. (Tony) Chase, age 61

Director, Milton Carroll, age 65

Director, R. A. (Al) Walker, age 59

Director, David J. Tudor, age 56

Director, Charles A. (Chuck) Meloy Sr., age 56

SVP and COO, Danny J. Rea

President CEO and Director, Donald R. Sinclair

Auditors: KPMG LLP

LOCATIONS

HQ: Western Gas Partners LP
1201 Lake Robbins Drive, The Woodlands, TX 77380
Phone: 832 636-6000   **Fax:** 832 636-6001
Web: www.westerngas.com

COMPETITORS

DCP Midstream Partners	ONEOK Partners
Dominion Questar	Tallgrass Energy
Enbridge Energy	Partners
Kinder Morgan Energy	XTO Energy
Partners	

HISTORICAL FINANCIALS

Company Type: Public

Income Statement   FYE: December 31

	REVENUE ($ mil.)	NET INCOME ($ mil.)	NET PROFIT MARGIN	EMPLOYEES
12/17	2,333.5	567.4	24.3%	0
12/16	1,882.9	591.3	31.4%	0
12/15	1,632.6	(73.5)	—	0
12/14	1,331.6	376.5	28.3%	0
12/13	1,053.5	275.1	26.1%	0
Annual Growth	**22.0%**	**19.8%**	**—**	**—**

2017 Year-End Financials

Debt ratio: 43.2%
Return on equity: —
Cash ($ mil.): 78.8
Current ratio: 0.60
Long-term debt ($ mil.): 3,464.7

No. of shares (mil.): 168.4
Dividends
  Yield: 0.0%
  Payout: 271.5%
Market value ($ mil.): 8,100.0

	STOCK PRICE ($) FY Close	P/E High/Low	Earnings	Dividends	Book Value
12/17	48.09	51 33	1.30	3.53	23.21
12/16	58.76	35 15	1.74	3.29	27.96
12/15	47.53	— —	(1.95)	2.95	23.99
12/14	73.05	37 28	2.12	2.55	27.92
12/13	61.69	35 26	1.83	2.20	20.96
Annual Growth	**(6.0%)**	**— —**	**(8.2%)**	**12.5%**	**2.6%**

Western New England Bancorp Inc

Westfield Financial is the holding company for Westfield Bank which serves western Massachusetts' Hampden County and surrounding areas from more than 20 branch locations. Founded in 1853 the bank has traditionally been a community-oriented provider of retail deposit accounts and loans but it is placing more emphasis on serving commercial and industrial clients. Commercial real estate loans account for approximately 45% of the company's loan portfolio and business loans are more than 25%. The bank also makes a smaller number of consumer and home equity loans. In 2016 Westfield Financial merged with Chicopee Bancorp the holding company of Chicopee Savings Bank (another bank serving Hampden County).

Residential mortgages made up more than half of the company's loan portfolio in 2000; the following year the bank began referring home loan originations to a third-party provider and such loans now account for less than 20% of its portfolio.

EXECUTIVES

Vice President; Residential Loan Officer, Deborah McCarthy

ASSISTANT VICE PRESIDENT FINANCIAL SERVICES, Libiszewski Darlene

Auditors: Wolf & Company, P.C.

LOCATIONS

HQ: Western New England Bancorp Inc
141 Elm Street, Westfield, MA 01085
Phone: 413 568-1911
Web: www.westfieldbank.com

COMPETITORS

Bank of America	Sovereign Bank
Citizens Financial	TD Bank USA
Group	

HISTORICAL FINANCIALS

Company Type: Public

Income Statement   FYE: December 31

	ASSETS ($ mil.)	NET INCOME ($ mil.)	INCOME AS % OF ASSETS	EMPLOYEES
12/17	2,083.0	12.3	0.6%	317
12/16	2,076.0	4.8	0.2%	310
12/15	1,339.9	5.7	0.4%	195
12/14	1,320.1	6.1	0.5%	200
12/13	1,276.8	6.7	0.5%	201
Annual Growth	**13.0%**	**16.2%**	**—**	**12.1%**

2017 Year-End Financials

Return on assets: 0.5%
Return on equity: 5.0%
Long-term debt ($ mil.): —
No. of shares (mil.): 30.4
Sales ($ mil): 82.5

Dividends
  Yield: 0.0%
  Payout: 29.2%
Market value ($ mil.): 332.0

	STOCK PRICE ($) FY Close	P/E High/Low	Earnings	Dividends	Book Value
12/17	10.90	27 22	0.41	0.12	8.11
12/16	9.35	38 30	0.24	0.03	7.85
12/15	8.40	25 22	0.33	0.12	7.63
12/14	7.34	23 20	0.34	0.21	7.61
12/13	7.46	23 19	0.34	0.29	7.65
Annual Growth	**9.9%**	**— —**	**4.8%**	**(19.8%)**	**1.5%**

Westwood Holdings Group, Inc.

Westwood Holdings Group provides investment management services to institutions mutual funds and high-net-worth clients. The asset manager operates through its subsidiaries. Westwood Trust handles trust custody and account management for companies institutions and high-net-worth individuals. Westwood Management is the group's institutional investment management unit overseeing accounts for corporations municipalities and charitable organizations with at least $10 million in investable assets. The firm is also the administrator of the Westwood family of mutual funds WHG Funds. Westwood Holdings Group boasts around $21 billion in assets under management.

Operations

Westwood operates in two segments: Advisory and Trust. Advisory which contributed 78% to the company's total revenue during 2015 provides investment advisory services to individuals foundations corporate and public retirement plans endowments and the company's other divisions. The Trust segment (22% of revenue) includes trust and custodial services for institutions and high net worth individuals.

Geographic Reach

Dallas-based Westwood serves clients worldwide from offices in Toronto Boston Omaha and Houston. About 84% of its total revenue came from business in the US during 2015 while the rest came from Canada (7% of revenue) Europe (5%) Asia (3%) and Australia (1%).

Sales and Marketing

Westwood markets and sells its mutual funds through Investment advisory firms registered investment advisors select broker-dealers fund supermarkets financial intermediaries and other third-party financial institutions.

About 57% of Westwood's assets were managed on behalf of institutional investors during 2015 while the rest were on behalf of Private Wealth clients (26% of assets) and Mutual Fund clients (17% of assets).

Financial Performance

Thanks to a rising stock market and a growing investor base Westwood has almost nearly doubled its assets under management since 2011 — from $13 billion to roughly $20.8 billion at the end of 2015. As a result Westwood's annual revenues and profits have more than doubled over that time period.

Westwood's revenue jumped 16% to a record $130.9 million during 2015 thanks to 3% growth in assets under management coupled with higher advisory fee rates which boosted asset-based advisory fees by 12%. The firm's trust fees swelled by 40% for the year driven mainly by the firm's April 2015 acquisition of Woodway Financial Advisors.

Despite strong revenue growth in 2015 the asset manager's net income dipped less than 1% to $27.11 million as it spent more on new hires and incentive compensation costs to support the growth of its asset management and trust businesses. Westwood's operating cash levels more than doubled to $55.2 million mostly as it transferred cash from its investment accounts and working capital.

Strategy

Westwood regularly adds to its funds and strategies offerings — either on its own or through acquisitions of asset managers mutual funds or private wealth firms — to attract new investors and their capital. During 2015 Westwood introduced three new mutual funds bringing its total collection of mutual funds to 15. Its acquisition of Woodway Financial Advisors that year expanded the firm's reach into the private wealth market bringing its Private Wealth assets to 26% of its total assets under management (up from 21% during 2014).

The asset manager also continues to build its business beyond the US successfully adding new clients in the Netherlands and Japan in 2015.

Mergers and Acquisitions

In April 2015 Westwood Holdings expanded more into the Private Wealth asset management market after purchasing Woodway Financial Advisors along with its portfolio $1.6 billion in managed private wealth client assets. Woodway now operates as a Houston branch of subsidiary Westwood Trust.

Company Background

Westwood was founded in 1983 by chairman and CEO Susan Byrne. The company was spun off from investment bank and brokerage SWS Group in 2002.

EXECUTIVES

Senior Vice President On Priva, Dick Frazar
President and Chief Executive Officer, Brian O. Casey, age 54, $600,000 total compensation
President of Westwood Trust Dallas, Randall L. Root, age 57, $237,500 total compensation
EVP and Chief Investment Officer, Mark R. Freeman, age 51, $500,000 total compensation
CFO, Tiffany B. Kice
Chief Information Officer, Fabian Gomez
Executive Vice President, Kellie Stark
Vice President Portfolio Manager Research Analyst, Matthew Lockridge
Senior Vice President, Kristie Konstans
Senior Vice President, Nicholas Wilwerding
Senior Vice President, Kristie Leatherberry
Vice President Senior Performance Analyst CIPM, Kari Saenz
Assistant Vice President Marketing Strategist, Sheana Suek
Vice President National Accounts Director, Jonathan Dale
Vice President Mutual Fund and Managed Account Sales, Jeffrey Gubala
Assistant Vice President, Nick English
Vice President Institutional Sales and Client Service, Ciaran Spillane
Chairman, Susan M. Byrne, age 71
Auditors: Deloitte & Touche, LLP

LOCATIONS

HQ: Westwood Holdings Group, Inc.
200 Crescent Court, Suite 1200, Dallas, TX 75201
Phone: 214 756-6900
Web: www.westwoodgroup.com

PRODUCTS/OPERATIONS

2015 Sales

	% of total
Advisory fees	
Asset-based	76
Performance-based	2
Trust fees	22
Other	0
Total	**100**

2015 Assets under Management

	% of total
Institutional	57
Private Wealth	26
Mutual funds	17
Total	**100**

COMPETITORS

American Century	Neuberger Berman
Atalanta Sosnoff	Nuveen
Duncan-Hurst	Oak Associates
Eaton Vance	Putnam
FMR	T. Rowe Price
Franklin Templeton	US Global Investors
Martin Capital	W.P. Stewart
NFJ Investment	

HISTORICAL FINANCIALS

Company Type: Public

Income Statement				FYE: December 31
	REVENUE ($ mil.)	NET INCOME ($ mil.)	NET PROFIT MARGIN	EMPLOYEES
12/17	133.7	19.9	14.9%	181
12/16	123.0	22.6	18.4%	174
12/15	130.9	27.1	20.7%	168
12/14	113.2	27.2	24.1%	130
12/13	91.8	17.8	19.5%	106
Annual Growth	**9.9%**	**2.8%**	**—**	**14.3%**

2017 Year-End Financials

Debt ratio: —	No. of shares (mil.): 8.9
Return on equity: 13.2%	Dividends
Cash ($ mil.): 54.2	Yield: 0.0%
Current ratio: 4.38	Payout: 106.7%
Long-term debt ($ mil.): —	Market value ($ mil.): 589.0

	STOCK PRICE ($) FY Close	P/E High/Low	PER SHARE ($) Earnings	Dividends	Book Value
12/17	66.21	29 21	2.38	2.54	17.57
12/16	59.99	22 15	2.77	2.33	16.58
12/15	52.09	18 14	3.33	2.07	15.52
12/14	61.82	19 14	3.45	1.82	13.24
12/13	61.91	25 16	2.34	1.64	10.84
Annual Growth	**1.7%**	**— —**	**0.4%**	**11.6%**	**12.8%**

Wex Inc

WEX (formerly Wright Express) provides payment processing and information management services to commercial and government vehicle fleets through a network that tracks purchases made on fleet charge cards at more than 190000 fuel and vehicle maintenance facilities throughout the US Canada Australia New Zealand and Europe. The company provides clients with transaction data analysis tools and purchase control capabilities for every vehicle in their fleets. Data collected at the point of sale include expenditures lists of items purchased odometer readings and driver vehicle and vendor identification. WEX serves some 350000 fleets that collectively have a total of approximately 7.7 million vehicles.

Operations

The company's subsidiaries include fleet card provider Fleet One (acquired in 2012) Utah-based WEX Bank and Pacific Pride Services a fuel distributor network with more than 340 independent fuel franchisees. WEX also owns a majority stake (acquired in 2012) in UNIK S.A. a provider of payroll cards and processing services in Brazil.

Geographic Reach

Maine-based WEX rings up more than 85% of its sales in the US. Australia accounts for nearly 10% of annual sales. The company also has operations in Brazil and the UK. WEX has fuel and vehicle maintenance facilities throughout the North America Australia and New Zealand and Europe.

Financial Performance

WEX derives a significant portion of its revenue from charging a fee each time each time a client's driver uses his or her fleet card; the company processes more than 250 million such transactions annually.

WEX's sales have climbed steadily in recent years rising 125% since 2009. In 2013 the firm reported sales of $717.5 million an increase of 15% versus 2012. Increased revenue from its Fleet Payment business which accounts for about three-quarters of its total revenue higher fees and the acquisition of Fleet One in 2012 helped drive revenue gains. While consistently profitable WEX's net income growth has been erratic. Indeed net income rose 54% in 2013 versus 2012 after falling 27% in the previous annual comparison.

Strategy

WEX's closed-loop card network allow it access to both sides of every card transaction which provides it with usage data for its cardholder customer base as well as revenues from merchant fees charged. Its cards are accepted at more than 90% of service stations in the US and Australia and the company enjoys a leading market share of nearly 10% of all the fleet vehicles in the US. What's more there is room for growth for the firm as WEX estimates that a majority of fleets don't use fleet cards to manage fuel costs.

The company's growth strategy includes diversifying beyond its traditional domestic markets through acquisitions. Recent acquisitions outside the US have included companies in Brazil Australia and the UK.

Mergers and Acquisitions

In October 2013 UNIK S.A. acquired FastCred a provider of fleet card services to heavy truck operators in Brazil. About a year earlier WEX purchased Fleet One a provider of fleet cards to operators of heavy duty trucks and cars or light duty vehicles in the US and Canada. Previously WEX acquired CorporatePay a provider of prepaid virtual cards to the corporate travel industry in the UK for $27.5 million in May 2012 . Also in 2012 the company entered Brazil by acquiring a 51% stake in payroll card provider UNIK S.A. for nearly

$22 million. At home it purchased fuel card provider Fleet One in an all-cash deal that closed in late 2012. Previous purchases include the Australian fuel and prepaid card operations of Retail Decisions for $318 million in 2010 making it a major player in the fleet card sector there.

EXECUTIVES

CTO, David Cooper
President CEO and Director, Melissa D. Smith, age 49, $578,317 total compensation
SVP General Counsel and Corporate Secretary, Hilary A. Rapkin, age 51, $362,884 total compensation
SVP International, George W. Hogan, age 57, $318,308 total compensation
SVP and General Manager North American Fleet, Kenneth W. (Ken) Janosick, age 56, $320,000 total compensation
CFO, Roberto R. Simon, age 43
SVP and General Manager Virtual Payments, Jim Pratt
SVP and General Manager WEX Health, Jeff Young
SVP and General Manager EFS, Scott Phillips
Vice President Product Management (Acting), Wayne Arthur
Senior Vice President Sales Marketing, David Maxsiimc
Vice Chairman, Rowland T. (Row) Moriarty, age 71
Chairman, Michael E. Dubyak, age 67
Auditors: DELOITTE & TOUCHE LLP

LOCATIONS

HQ: Wex Inc
97 Darling Avenue, South Portland, ME 04106
Phone: 207 773-8171
Web: www.wexinc.com

PRODUCTS/OPERATIONS

2016 Sales

	$ mil.	% of total
Payment processing revenue	520.7	51
Account servicing revenue	211.0	21
Finance fee revenue	138.9	14
Other revenue	147.7	14
Total	**1,018.5**	**100**

COMPETITORS

Comdata   Retail Decisions
FleetCor   U.S. Bancorp
Multi Service

HISTORICAL FINANCIALS
Company Type: Public

Income Statement

	REVENUE ($ mil.)	NET INCOME ($ mil.)	NET PROFIT MARGIN	EMPLOYEES
				FYE: December 31
12/17	1,250.5	160.2	12.8%	3,300
12/16	1,018.4	60.6	6.0%	2,600
12/15	854.6	111.3	13.0%	2,265
12/14	817.6	202.2	24.7%	2,004
12/13	717.4	149.2	20.8%	1,431
Annual Growth	14.9%	1.8%	—	23.2%

2017 Year-End Financials

Debt ratio: 35.9%
Return on equity: 9.9%
Cash ($ mil.): 508.0
Current ratio: 1.31
Long-term debt ($ mil.): 2,424.9
No. of shares (mil.): 43.0
Dividends
  Yield: —
  Payout: —
Market value ($ mil.): 6,076.0

	STOCK PRICE ($) FY Close	P/E High/Low	PER SHARE ($) Earnings	Dividends	Book Value
12/17	141.23	38 26	3.72	0.00	39.78
12/16	111.60	78 39	1.48	0.00	34.95
12/15	88.40	45 32	2.62	0.00	27.96
12/14	98.92	23 15	5.18	0.00	27.26
12/13	99.03	26 18	3.82	0.00	23.16
Annual Growth	9.3%	— —	(0.7%)	—	14.5%

Whitestone REIT

Whitestone REIT is out to make a name for itself in real estate. The self-managed real estate investment trust owns leases and operates around 70 retail office and warehouse properties in Texas (Houston is the company's largest market) Illinois and Arizona totaling 6 million sq. ft. Whitestone focuses on what it calls community-centered properties or high-visibility properties in established or developing culturally diverse neighborhoods. It recruits retail grocery financial services and other tenants to its Whitestone branded commercial centers. Some of its top tenants include Safeway Dollar Tree Wells Fargo Walgreens University of Phoenix and Alamo Drafthouse.

Geographic Reach
Whitestone REIT had 70 commercial properties in three states at the end of 2015 including 30 properties in Houston Texas and 25 properties in the Phoenix metro area of Arizona. The rest of its properties were located in Dallas-Fort Worth (7 properties) Austin Texas (4) San Antonio (3) and Buffalo grove near Chicago Illinois (1).

Sales and Marketing
The REIT's tenant base is made up of a diverse mix of mostly retail clients with some banks and university clients sprinkled in. While none of Whitestone's tenants contributed more than 2.6% to its total revenue during 2015 its five largest tenants by revenue for the year included: Safeway Stores Bashas' Inc. Haggens Food & Pharmacy Wells Fargo & Company and Alamo Drafthouse Cinema.

Financial Performance
Whitestone REIT has tripled its revenues and boosted its profits sixfold since 2011 mostly as it has expanded its property portfolio through acquisitions and has raised its average rent per square foot by more than 40%.

The REIT's revenue jumped 29% to $93.4 million during 2015 mostly thanks to 12 new property acquisitions made from January 2014 through the end of 2015. Its "Same Store" comparable sales for existing properties grew during the year as its revenue rate per average leased square foot rose 4% to $17.28 per foot. Occupancy rates dipped slightly but remained mostly around 87%.

Despite strong revenue growth in 2015 Whitestone REIT's net income shrank 11% to $6.75 million for the year mostly because in 2014 it generated a non-recurring $1.9 million gain from property sales. The REIT's operating cash levels climbed 44% to $36.1 million during 2015 as its cash-based earnings increased.

Strategy

Whitestone REIT's strategically acquires commercial properties in high growth markets with densely populated and culturally diverse neighborhoods in and around Austin Chicago Dallas-Fort Worth Houston Phoenix and San Antonio.

During 2015 it targeted acquisitions of "neighborhood- or community- retail properties" near master planned communities such as Quinlan Crossing (for $37.5 million) and Parkside Village South ($32.5 million) in Austin Texas; a single-tenant 14600 sq. ft. property in Gilbert Tuscany Village ($1.7 million); and the 93500 sq. ft. Keller Place property in the Keller suburb of Ft. Worth Texas. In mid-2014 it added Heritage Trace Plaza in Fort Worth Texas to its portfolio. It acquired half a dozen or so properties in 2013 including Market Street at DC Ranch in Scottsdale Arizona and Headquarters Village Shopping Center in Plano Texas.

EXECUTIVES

Chairman and CEO, James C. Mastandrea, age 75, $400,000 total compensation
COO, John J. Dee, age 67, $205,289 total compensation
CFO, David K. Holeman, age 55, $250,000 total compensation
VP Acquisitions and Asset Management, Bradford D. Johnson, $184,616 total compensation
VP Product Strategy and Market Research, Christine J. Mastandrea, $154,231 total compensation
Auditors: Pannell Kerr Forster of Texas, P.C.

LOCATIONS

HQ: Whitestone REIT
2600 South Gessner, Suite 500, Houston, TX 77063
Phone: 713 827-9595   **Fax:** 713 465-8847
Web: www.whitestonereit.com

PRODUCTS/OPERATIONS

2015 Sales

	$ mil.	% of total
Rental	71.8	77
Other	21.6	23
Total	**93.4**	**100**

COMPETITORS

GGP   Simon Property Group
IRC Retail Centers   Weingarten Realty

HISTORICAL FINANCIALS
Company Type: Public

Income Statement

	REVENUE ($ mil.)	NET INCOME ($ mil.)	NET PROFIT MARGIN	EMPLOYEES
				FYE: December 31
12/17	125.9	8.3	6.6%	103
12/16	104.4	7.9	7.6%	106
12/15	93.4	6.7	7.2%	95
12/14	72.3	7.5	10.5%	81
12/13	62.1	3.7	6.1%	68
Annual Growth	19.3%	21.7%	—	10.9%

2017 Year-End Financials

Debt ratio: 61.5%
Return on equity: 2.7%
Cash ($ mil.): 7.8
Current ratio: 0.77
Long-term debt ($ mil.): 659.0
No. of shares (mil.): 39.2
Dividends
  Yield: 0.0%
  Payout: 518.1%
Market value ($ mil.): 565.0

STOCK PRICE ($) FY Close	P/E High/Low	PER SHARE ($) Earnings	Dividends	Book Value
12/17 14.41	68 51	0.22	1.14	9.14
12/16 14.38	62 38	0.26	1.24	9.08
12/15 12.01	65 44	0.24	1.14	9.00
12/14 15.11	47 40	0.32	1.14	9.20
12/13 13.37	85 61	0.20	1.14	9.84
Annual Growth 1.9%	— —	2.4%	(0.0%)	(1.8%)

Willdan Group Inc

Willdan Group can and will do what it takes to meet its customers' numerous engineering needs. The company has four operating service segments: engineering (Willdan Engineering) energy efficiency (Willdan Energy Solutions) public finance (Willdan Financial Services) and homeland security (Willdan Homeland Solutions). Clients include federal and local governments school districts public utilities and some private industries. Willdan focuses on small- to mid-sized clients that may fall below the radar of larger competitors. The company was founded in 1964.

Operations
Willdan Group's engineering services which account for about a third of revenues are provided by subsidiaries Willdan Engineering and Public Agency Resources. Its public finance subsidiary Willdan Financial Services offers consulting services to municipalities and other public entities; its offerings include economic impact analyses facility financing plans and special district formation.

Willdan Energy Solutions provides energy efficiency and sustainability services to companies and agencies seeking to implement environmental strategies for conservation. (The high-growth business was split off from the engineering operations to its own segment in 2011.) Another subsidiary Willdan Homeland Solutions helps cities counties and communities protect infrastructure and personnel against terrorist attacks and natural disasters. The unit offers public safety consulting and management consulting services.

Geographic Reach
Willdan serves clients located predominantly in New York and California. Other locations reside in Arizona; Florida; Texas; Washington; and Washington DC.

Sales and Marketing
Willdan serves about 750 clients. Two clients — the Consolidated Edison Company of New York and the City of Elk Grove — accounted for 21% and 10% of its total revenue in 2012 respectively.

Financial Performance
After two straight years of revenue growth and positive net income Willdan saw its revenues decline by 13% from $107 million in 2011 to $93 million in 2012. It also posted a net loss of $17 million for 2012.

The revenue decline was driven by a 21% dip in its energy efficiency segment resulting from a decrease in the direct installation of energy efficiency measures in New York and California and contract renewal delays from those populous states. Willdan was also hurt by revenue decreases from its Willdan Homeland Solutions operations during 2012.

Its net loss for 2012 was due to higher general and administrative expenses associated with a $15 million goodwill impairment charge it paid related to its energy efficiency segment.

Strategy
Willdan Group looks for opportunities in areas that have increased demand for services as well as population growth which will place strain on existing infrastructure and prompt the need for new structures or the rehabilitation of aging systems. Additionally the company stands to benefit from the heightened need for homeland security as several of the markets it serves have received federal funding for preparedness initiatives.

EXECUTIVES

Vice President, Ross Khiabani
Senior Vice President Business Development, Edward Saltzberg
Vice President, Joe Dauchy
VICE PRESIDENT COMPLIANCE, Corinne Bertrand
SENIOR VICE PRESIDENT, Joseph De Ladurantey
VICE PRESIDENT ENERGY PROJECT DEVELOPMENT, Arthur Vertner
VICE PRESIDENT OF OPERATIONS, David Daniel
Board of Directors, Chell Smith
Auditors: Crowe LLP

LOCATIONS

HQ: Willdan Group Inc
  2401 East Katella Avenue, Suite 300, Anaheim, CA 92806
Phone: 800 424-9144
Web: www.willdan.com

COMPETITORS

AECOM	Langdon Wilson
Bureau Veritas	Lime Energy
CH2M HILL	Michael Baker
Ernst & Young LLP	Parsons Brinckerhoff
HDR	Psomas
Harley Ellis Devereaux	RBF Consulting
ICF International	Stantec
Jacobs Engineering	TRC Companies
Kimley-Horn and Associates	Tetra Tech

HISTORICAL FINANCIALS
Company Type: Public

Income Statement
FYE: December 29

	REVENUE ($ mil.)	NET INCOME ($ mil.)	NET PROFIT MARGIN	EMPLOYEES
12/17	273.3	12.1	4.4%	882
12/16*	208.9	8.3	4.0%	831
01/16	135.1	4.2	3.2%	688
01/15	108.0	9.4	8.7%	637
12/13	85.5	2.6	3.1%	534
Annual Growth	33.7%	46.5%	—	13.4%

*Fiscal year change

2017 Year-End Financials

Debt ratio: 2.4%	No. of shares (mil.): 8.8
Return on equity: 20.1%	Dividends
Cash ($ mil.): 14.4	Yield: —
Current ratio: 1.48	Payout: —
Long-term debt ($ mil.): 2.6	Market value ($ mil.): 211.0

STOCK PRICE ($) FY Close	P/E High/Low	PER SHARE ($) Earnings	Dividends	Book Value
12/17 23.94	26 15	1.32	0.00	8.03
12/16* 22.59	26 7	0.97	0.00	5.98
01/16 8.38	30 15	0.52	0.00	4.76
01/15 14.50	15 4	1.22	0.00	3.98
12/13 4.91	15 6	0.35	0.00	2.74
Annual Growth 48.6%	— —	39.4%	—	30.8%

*Fiscal year change

Willis Lease Finance Corp.

Hey buddy got any spare Pratt & Whitneys? Willis Lease Finance buys and sells aircraft engines that it leases to commercial airlines air cargo carriers and maintenance/repair/overhaul organizations in some 30 countries. Its portfolio includes about 180 aircraft engines and related equipment made by Pratt & Whitney Rolls-Royce CFMI GE Aviation and International Aero. The engine models in the company's portfolio are used on popular Airbus and Boeing aircraft. The Willis Lease portfolio also includes four de Havilland DHC-8 commuter aircraft. Customers include Island Air Alaska Airlines American Airlines and Southwest Airlines. Almost 80% of the company's engines are leased and operated outside the US.

Operations
The company divides its revenue streams across three segments. Lease rent accounted for 64% of its total sales in 2012 while maintenance reserve generated 28%. The gain of sale on leased equipment and other operations contribute the remainder of revenue.

Geographic Reach
Willis Lease has operations in Africa Asia Canada Europe Mexico the Middle East and the US. The majority of lease revenue comes from Europe (37% of total lease revenue in 2012) Asia (20%) the US (12%) and South America (10%).

Financial Performance
After experiencing revenue and profit increases in 2011 Willis Lease suffered a 6% drop in net revenue and a massive 90% nosedive in profits during 2012. From 2011 to 2012 its revenues dipped from $157 million to $148 million while its profits slipped from $14.5 million to $1.5 million.

The decrease in revenues was attributed a 10% decline in lease rent revenues. This slump reflected lower portfolio utilization in 2012 and a decrease in the average size of the lease portfolio (which translated into a lower amount of equipment on lease). In addition the lower revenue translated to a decrease on the sale of leased equipment which was $5 million in 2012 compared with $11 million in 2011.

The plunge in profits was mainly due to a $15 million loss stemming from the extinguish of debt and derivative instruments.

Strategy
Growth in the spare engine leasing industry is contingent on the number of commercial aircraft in the market and the proportion of leased versus

owned engines. Willis Lease is on the flip-side of most companies during economic downturns because it offers cash-strapped businesses a more affordable route — to lease engines rather than buying or repairing them. The company explains that engine repairs can cost as much as $3 million while leasing an engine may cost only $80000.

With fluctuating fuel costs an airline can spend the difference between maintenance and leasing on the cost of fuel. Additionally industry experts estimate that approximately 36000 aircraft will be in flight in less than 20 years. Growth is expected in both established markets as well as emerging markets especially Asia which is showing extraordinary growth in both passenger and cargo traffic.

EXECUTIVES

Senior Vice President Chief Commercial Officer, Dan Coulcher

Vice President Business Development, George Voskresensky

Vice President Investment And Fleet Solutions, Nicholas Pittler

Senior Vice President And Chief Commercial Officer, Craig Welsh

Board Member, Hans Hunziker

Auditors: KPMG LLP

LOCATIONS

HQ: Willis Lease Finance Corp.
4700 Lyons Technology Parkway, Coconut Creek, FL 33073
Phone: 415 408-4700
Web: www.willislease.com

COMPETITORS

AAR Corp.	ILFC
AerCap	Jetscape
AeroCentury	Kellstrom Industries
Boeing Capital	
GE Capital Aviation Services	

HISTORICAL FINANCIALS

Company Type: Public

Income Statement

	REVENUE ($ mil.)	NET INCOME ($ mil.)	NET PROFIT MARGIN	EMPLOYEES
12/17	274.8	62.1	22.6%	155
12/16	207.2	14.0	6.8%	147
12/15	199.6	7.3	3.7%	104
12/14	174.2	7.2	4.2%	99
12/13	158.4	15.6	9.9%	89
Annual Growth	14.8%	41.2%	—	14.9%

2017 Year-End Financials

Debt ratio: 67.6%
Return on equity: 23.7%
Cash ($ mil.): 7.0
Current ratio: 0.66
Long-term debt ($ mil.): 1,085.4

No. of shares (mil.): 6.4
Dividends
Yield: —
Payout: —
Market value ($ mil.): 160.0

	STOCK PRICE ($) FY Close	P/E High/Low		PER SHARE ($) Earnings	Dividends	Book Value
12/17	24.97	3	2	9.69	0.00	48.04
12/16	25.58	13	8	2.05	0.00	33.74
12/15	20.10	23	16	0.92	0.00	27.86
12/14	21.90	27	18	0.89	0.00	25.98
12/13	17.36	9	6	1.89	0.00	25.31
Annual Growth	9.5%	—	—	50.5%	—	17.4%

Wingstop Inc

Auditors: Ernst & Young LLP

LOCATIONS

HQ: Wingstop Inc
5501 LBJ Freeway, 5th Floor, Dallas, TX 75240
Phone: 972 686-6500
Web: www.wingstop.com

HISTORICAL FINANCIALS

Company Type: Public

Income Statement

FYE: December 31

	REVENUE ($ mil.)	NET INCOME ($ mil.)	NET PROFIT MARGIN	EMPLOYEES
12/17	105.5	27.3	25.9%	530
12/16	91.3	15.4	16.9%	479
12/15	77.9	10.1	13.0%	428
12/14	67.4	8.9	13.3%	366
12/13	59.0	7.5	12.8%	0
Annual Growth	15.7%	38.0%	—	—

2017 Year-End Financials

Debt ratio: 111.2%
Return on equity: ***.***.*%
Cash ($ mil.): 4.0
Current ratio: 0.84
Long-term debt ($ mil.): 129.8

No. of shares (mil.): 29.0
Dividends
Yield: 0.0%
Payout: 15.0%
Market value ($ mil.): 1,134.0

	STOCK PRICE ($) FY Close	P/E High/Low		PER SHARE ($) Earnings	Dividends	Book Value
12/17	38.98	45	27	0.93	0.14	(1.66)
12/16	29.59	61	39	0.53	2.90	(2.60)
12/15	22.56	95	55	0.36	1.83	(0.34)
Annual Growth	31.4%	—	—	60.7%	(72.3%)	—

Winnebago Industries, Inc.

A pioneer in the world of recreational vehicles Winnebago Industries makes products intended to encourage exploration and outdoor escape. Almost all of the company's sales come from its motor homes and towables which are sold via independent dealers throughout the US and Canada under the Winnebago Adventurer Sightseer Suncruiser Sunova and Minnie Winnie brands among others. Winnebago Industries also sells RV parts and provides related services; in addition the company produces OEM parts for other RV manufacturers and for use in commercial vehicles. The company traces its roots back to the 1950s.

Operations

Winnebago divides its motor homes portfolio across three main product lines: Class A (conventional motor homes) Class B (panel-type vans) and Class C (motor homes built on van-type chassis).

Geographic Reach

Winnebago is based in Forest City Iowa. It owns facilities in Middlebury Forest City Lake Mills and Charles City Iowa; Junction City Oregon; Middlebury Indiana; and Burnsville Minnesota.

Sales and Marketing

The company markets its RVs on a wholesale basis to a diversified independent dealer network located throughout the US and to a limited extent in Canada. The RV dealer network in the US and Canada includes almost 300 motorized and 160 towable physical dealer locations with roughly 75 of these locations carrying both Winnebago motorized and towable products. FreedomRoads and La Mesa RV Center the company's chief dealers accounted for 17% and 13% of its total revenue in fiscal 2016 respectively.

Financial Performance

Winnebago posted $976 million in revenues in 2015 its highest total in about 10 years. Revenues dropped marginally to $975 million in 2016. Profits jumped 10% from $41 million in 2015 to $46 million in 2016.

Its recent growth was attributed to a 2% bump in motorized wholesale deliveries from 2015 to 2016. Towable net revenue also experienced growth of approximately 25% in 2016. Strong demand for its Class B and Class C products was partially offset by weaker demand in Class A products. Going forward Winnebagao anticipates continued strong demand in its Class B and C categories.

The modest revenue decline for 2016 was due mainly to other manufactured products revenues which decreased by $21 million. This was primarily due to the company's exit of its aluminum extrusion and bus businesses. Both of these operations have provided very low margins over the years.

Strategy

Winnebago's motorized production facilities are located in largely rural areas of northern Iowa. Although the unemployment rate in these areas is currently low the company has been working to extend its geographical scope to avoid depending upon labor strictly within this region.

In 2016 it purchased a production facility in Junction City Oregon from a former motorized RV producer. It is expanding some motor home manufacturing functions to Junction City in order to diversify its geographical locations. The new site also provides a West Coast service option for customers.

Mergers and Acquisitions

In potentially its largest deal to date Winnebago in late 2016 agreed to buy privately held Grand Design Recreational Vehicle Co a maker of towable recreational vehicles. The cash-and-stock deal valued at $500 million will give Winnebago a bigger foothold in the growing towables market and create a company with net revenue of about $1.4 billion.

Company Background

During a mid-1950s economic downturn furniture store owner John Hanson convinced Forest City officials to welcome a local subsidiary of California trailer maker Modernistic Industries. The company's first trailer rolled off the line in 1958. Hanson later bought the plant and in 1960 named the business Winnebago Industries after Forest City's home county. Winnebago Industries went public in 1966. Sales took off when the company offered less-expensive RVs than its competitors.

EXECUTIVES

President and CEO, Michael J. Happe, age 47, $338,461 total compensation
VP; President Grand Design RV, Donald J. Clark
VP; General Manager Towables Business, S. Scott Degnan, age 53, $309,614 total compensation
VP Information Technology and CIO, Jeff Kubacki, age 61
VP; General Manager Motorhome Business, Brian Hazelton, age 53
VP and CFO, Bryan Hughes, age 50
VP Operations, Chris West, age 46
Vice President Strategic Planning and Development, Ashis Bhattacharya
VICE PRESIDENT ADMINISTRATION, Bret A Woodson
Chairman, Robert M. (Bob) Chiusano, age 67
Auditors: DELOITTE & TOUCHE LLP

LOCATIONS

HQ: Winnebago Industries, Inc.
P.O. Box 152, Forest City, IA 50436
Phone: 641 585-3535   **Fax:** 641 585-6966
Web: www.winnebagoind.com

PRODUCTS/OPERATIONS

2016 Sales

	$ mil.	% of total
Motorhomes parts and service	875.0	90
Towables and parts	89.4	9
Other manufactured products	10.8	1
Total	**975.2**	**100**

Selected Products

ERA
  ERA
Itasca
  Cambria
  Ellipse
  Impulse
  Impulse Silver
  Meridian
  Meridian V Class
  Navion
  Navion IQ
  Reyo
  Suncruiser
  Sunova
  Sunstar
Winnebago
  Access
  Access Premier
  Adventurer
  Aspect
  Journey
  Journey Express
  Sightseer
  Tour
  Via
  View
  View Profile
  Vista

COMPETITORS

Airstream	Patrick Industries
Elixir Industries	Prevost Car
Featherlite	Rexhall Industries
Forest River	Skyline
Gulf Stream Coach	Supreme Industries
Jayco Inc.	TRIGANO
Keystone RV	Thor Industries
Motor Coach Industries	Tiffin Motorhomes
Newmar Corporation	

HISTORICAL FINANCIALS

Company Type: Public

Income Statement

FYE: August 25

	REVENUE ($ mil.)	NET INCOME ($ mil.)	NET PROFIT MARGIN	EMPLOYEES
08/18	2,016.8	102.3	5.1%	4,700
08/17	1,547.1	71.3	4.6%	4,060
08/16	975.2	45.5	4.7%	3,050
08/15	976.5	41.2	4.2%	2,900
08/14	945.1	45.0	4.8%	2,850
Annual Growth	**20.9%**	**22.8%**	**—**	**13.3%**

2018 Year-End Financials

Debt ratio: 27.7%
Return on equity: 21.0%
Cash ($ mil.): 2.3
Current ratio: 1.82
Long-term debt ($ mil.): 291.4
No. of shares (mil.): 31.5
Dividends
  Yield: 0.0%
  Payout: 12.4%
Market value ($ mil.): 1,176.0

	STOCK PRICE ($) FY Close	P/E High/Low		PER SHARE ($) Earnings	Dividends	Book Value
08/18	37.30	18	11	3.22	0.40	16.95
08/17	34.55	16	9	2.32	0.40	13.98
08/16	23.91	14	10	1.68	0.40	9.98
08/15	20.42	17	12	1.52	0.36	8.20
08/14	24.73	20	13	1.64	0.00	7.13
Annual Growth	**10.8%**	**—**	**—**	**18.4%**	**—**	**24.2%**

Wintrust Financial Corp (IL)

Wintrust Financial is a holding company for 15 subsidiary banks (mostly named after the individual communities they serve) with more than 150 branches primarily in the metropolitan Chicago and southern Wisconsin (including Milwaukee) markets. Boasting assets of more than $23 billion the banks offer personal and commercial banking wealth management and specialty lending services with business and commercial real estate loans making up 60% of the company's loan portfolio. Wintrust's banks target small business customers though some of Wintrust's banks also provide niche lending for homeowners associations medical practices franchisees and municipalities.

Operations

Wintrust operates three business segments: Community Banking which accounted for 77% of total revenue in 2015 and serves individuals and small businesses; Specialty Finance (13% of revenue) operating through First Insurance Funding and First Insurance Funding of Canada which provide financing for commercial insurance and life insurance premiums in the US and Canada respectively; and Wealth Management (10% of revenue) which offers financial planning and brokerage services through The Chicago Trust Company N.A. Wayne Hummer Investments LLC and Great Lakes Advisors LLC.

Wintrust makes more than 70% of its revenue from interest income. About 66% of its total revenue came from loan interest (including fees) during 2015 while another 6% came from interest on

investment securities. The rest of its revenue came from mortgage banking (12%) wealth management services (7%) deposit account service charges (3%) and other miscellaneous income sources.

Geographic Reach

Wintrust's banks operate more than 150 branches and 220-plus automatic teller machines mostly located in communities throughout the Chicago metropolitan area and southern Wisconsin. Its wealth management offices are in Chicago; Appleton Wisconsin; and Safety Harbor Florida. Its Wintrust Mortgage subsidiary has 55 locations in a dozen states while its insurance subsidiaries have locations in Northbrook Illinois; Jersey City; Long Island New York; Toronto; Mississauga Ontario; and Vancouver.

Sales and Marketing

The bank's customers include individuals small to mid-sized businesses local governmental units and institutional clients residing primarily in the banks' local service areas.

Wintrust has been ramping up its advertising spend in recent years. It spent $21.9 million on advertising during 2015 up from $13.6 million and $11.1 million in 2014 and 2013 respectively.

Financial Performance

Wintrust Financial's annual revenues have risen more than 40% since 2011 as its loan assets have swelled by nearly 70% with rapid branch expansion. Its annual profits have doubled over the same period.

The banking group's revenue jumped 12% to $990.1 million during 2015 mostly as its average loan balances grew by 15% for the year. Mortgage banking revenue increased 26% for the year thanks to higher origination volumes and purchases on a more favorable mortgage banking environment also helping buoy the company's top line growth.

Strong revenue growth in 2015 drove Wintrust's net income up 4% to $156.75 million despite a rise in acquisition-related professional and legal fees. The group's operating cash levels fell 82% to $37.95 million due to unfavorable working capital changes mainly tied to an increase in accrued interest receivable and other assets.

Strategy

Wintrust has developed its community-based banking franchise through rapid branch expansion stemming from either through new openings or small bank acquisitions. Indeed the bank's branch count has flourished by more than 50% since 2011 from 99 back then to 152 branches at the end of 2015.

Beyond branch expansion the company remains focused on making new loans especially of the commercial and commercial real estate type where opportunities that meet its underwriting standards exist.

Mergers and Acquisitions

In January 2016 Wintrust Financial expanded into Pewaukee Wisconsin after agreeing to buy Generations Bancorp and its Foundations Bank subsidiary. Later that year the company finalized the $33.5 million purchase of First Community Financial Corporation the holding company of First Community Bank (which operates two branches in Elgin Illinois).

In July 2015 the company purchased Community Financial Shares Inc. and its four Community Bank of Wheaton/Glen Ellyn bank branches in the respective communities they serve in Illinois for a total of $42.4 million.

Also in July 2015 the company bought $118 million-asset North Bank and its two branches in Chicago.

In April 2015 Wintrust acquired Suburban Illinois Bancorp and its 10 Suburban Bank & Trust Company (SBT) branches in Chicago and surrounding suburbs for $12.5 million. The SBT locations would operate under Wintrust's Hinsdale Bank & Trust Company subsidiary.

In January 2015 the bank group purchased $224 million-asset Delavan Bancshares Inc. and its Community Bank CBD subsidiary.

Company Background

In 2012 Wintrust expanded its premium funding business into Canada with the acquisition of Macquarie Premium Funding Inc which was a subsidiary of Macquarie Group. The deal marked Wintrust's first international venture.

EXECUTIVES

EVP Technology; President Wintrust Information Technology Services, Lloyd M. Bowden, age 65, $167,333 total compensation

SEVP COO and Treasurer, David A. Dykstra, age 58, $759,167 total compensation

President CEO and Director, Edward J. Wehmer, age 63, $1,100,000 total compensation

EVP and Regional Market Head, Frank J. Burke

EVP and Chief Credit Officer, Richard B. Murphy, age 59, $509,167 total compensation

EVP and Chief Administration Officer, Leona A. Gleason

SVP Finance, David L. Stoehr, age 59, $419,167 total compensation

EVP and Regional Market Head, Timothy S. (Tim) Crane, age 56

EVP Wealth Management, Thomas P. (Tom) Zidar

EVP General Counsel and Secretary, Lisa J. Pattis, $446,167 total compensation

EVP and Regional Market Head, David L. Larson

EVP and COO Wintrust Commercial Finance (WCF), Joseph F. Thompson

Vice President Compliance, Kellie Oostendorp

Executive Vice President, Paul Carlisle

Vice President, Tim Edwards

Executive Vice President, Ursula Moncau

Vice President Managed Assets Division, Sandy Durek

Vice President Loan Operations, Sharon Hiller

Vice President Managed Assets Division, Irene Calzadilla

Vice President, Philip Sheridan

Assistant Vice President Treasury Management, Judy Majon

Assistant Vice President Financial System Management, Marty Lavin

Vice President, Mary Koehler

Vice President Treasury Management, Elizabeth Krumrey

Assistant Vice President Tax, Michelle Serna

Assistant Vice President, Robert Murphy

Vice President, Sarah Withrow

Vice President Real Estate Services, Trey Meers

Senior Vice President, Darragh Griffin

Senior Vice President Business Development, Matt Gambs

Vice President Wintrust Commercial Banking, John Hills

Executive Vice President Commercial Banking, Jeffrey Steigelman

Vice President and Assistant General Counsel, Daniel Stolarsky

Senior Vice President Commercial Banking, Sean Dunn

Vice President, Sara Staniszewski

Senior Vice President, Ryan Witte

Vice President Tax, Mike Masterson

Vice President, Jon Swanson

Vice President Regulatory Reporting, Anita Chakravarthy

Assistant Vice President Treasury Management, Amy Gulotta

Vice President, Teresa Handley

Vice President Professional Practice Group, Jan Eriksen

Assistant Vice President Branch Management, Rick Butterly

Vice President, Caroline Gonos

Vice President, Zornitsa Titova

Vice President Managed Assets Division, Hany Morsy

Vice President Human Resources, Janet Huffman

Executive Vice President and Chief Credit Officer, Paul Hallauer

Vice President Operations Manager Private Banker, Nicole Cox

Executive Vice President, Matthew Doucet

Vice President, Scott Rofstad

Vice President, Nick Koricanac

Vice President Treasury Management, Tracy Zako

Vice President Assistant Controller, Dana French

Senior Vice President Sales, Steve Cusick

Vice President Executive, Sharon Moeller

Vice President of Business Banking, Miguel Gomez

Assistant Vice President Retail Digital Product Manager, Natalie Fedus

Senior Vice President, Allan Weel

Vice President, Jeffery Wolinski

Senior Vice President Information Services, Mike Nathan

Vice President Finance, Derek Ramsden

Assistant Vice President Branch Manager, Anthony Scott

Senior Vice President, Joe Gensor

Senior Vice President Sales, Tom Forbes

Vice President, Sharon Sagert

Vice President Risk, Tim Doran

Senior Vice President Treasury Management, Chris Lantman

Senior Vice President, Brian de la Houssaye

Assistant Vice President, Edward Semik

Vice President, Liz Deboni

Senior Vice President Commercial Real Estate, Daniel Lawlor

Vice President of Infrastructure, Bill Eisenstot

Vice President Branch Manager, Jerry Kochowicz

Vice President, Tara Fedorko

Senior Vice President, Dawn Mase

Assistant Vice President Commercial Real Estate, Lauren Barnard

Senior Vice President, Tom Carlson

Senior Vice President Risk Strategy and Analytics, Venkat Veeramani

Senior Vice President Of Commercial Banking, Lena Dawson

Chairman, Peter D. Crist, age 67

Auditors: Ernst & Young LLP

LOCATIONS

HQ: Wintrust Financial Corp (IL)
9700 W. Higgins Road, Suite 800, Rosemont, IL 60018
Phone: 847 939-9000   **Fax:** 847 615-4091
Web: www.wintrust.com

PRODUCTS/OPERATIONS

2015 Sales

	$ mil.	% of total
Interest		
Loans including fees	651.8	66
Securities	61.0	6
Other	5.6	-

Non-interest		
Mortgage banking	115.0	12
Wealth management	73.5	7
Service charges on deposit accounts	27.4	3
Fees from covered call options	15.4	2
Other	40.6	4
Trading (losses) gains net	(0.2)	-
Total	**990.1**	**100**

Selected Subsidiaries and Affiliates

Banking
Barrington Bank & Trust Company N.A.
Beverly Bank & Trust Company N.A.
Crystal Lake Bank & Trust Company N.A.
Hinsdale Bank & Trust Company
Lake Forest Bank & Trust Company
Libertyville Bank & Trust Company
North Shore Community Bank & Trust Company
Northbrook Bank & Trust Company
Old Plank Trail Community Bank N.A.
Schaumburg Bank & Trust Company N.A.
St. Charles Bank & Trust
State Bank of The Lakes
Town Bank
Village Bank & Trust
Wheaton Bank and Trust Company
Non-banking
Chicago Trust Company N.A.
First Insurance Funding Corporation
Great Lakes Advisors LLC
Tricom Inc. of Milwaukee
Wayne Hummer Asset Management Company
Wayne Hummer Investments LLC
Wayne Hummer Trust Company N.A.
Wintrust Information Technology Services Company
Wintrust Mortgage Corporation (formerly WestAmerica Mortgage Company)

COMPETITORS

Associated Banc-Corp	Harris
Bank of America	JPMorgan Chase
Citigroup	MB Financial
Citizens Financial Group	Northern Trust
	PrivateBank
Fifth Third	U.S. Bancorp
First Midwest Bancorp	

HISTORICAL FINANCIALS

Company Type: Public

Income Statement

FYE: December 31

	ASSETS ($ mil.)	NET INCOME ($ mil.)	INCOME AS % OF ASSETS	EMPLOYEES
12/17	27,915.9	257.6	0.9%	4,075
12/16	25,668.5	206.8	0.8%	3,878
12/15	22,917.1	156.7	0.7%	3,770
12/14	20,010.7	151.4	0.8%	3,491
12/13	18,097.7	137.2	0.8%	3,413
Annual Growth	**11.4%**	**17.1%**	**—**	**4.5%**

2017 Year-End Financials

Return on assets: 0.9%	Dividends
Return on equity: 9.0%	Yield: 0.0%
Long-term debt ($ mil.): —	Payout: 12.7%
No. of shares (mil.): 55.9	Market value ($ mil.): 4,610.0
Sales ($ mil): 1,265.9	

	STOCK PRICE ($) FY Close	P/E High/Low		PER SHARE ($) Earnings	Dividends	Book Value
12/17	82.37	19	14	4.40	0.56	53.19
12/16	72.57	19	10	3.66	0.48	51.96
12/15	48.52	18	14	2.93	0.44	48.62
12/14	46.76	16	14	2.98	0.40	44.22
12/13	46.12	14	10	2.75	0.18	41.21
Annual Growth	**15.6%**	**—**	**—**	**12.5%**	**32.8%**	**6.6%**

WisdomTree Investments, Inc.

Asset management firm WisdomTree Investments specializes in exchange-traded funds (ETFs). (ETFs are funds that track indexes such as the S&P 500 or DJIA.) Through subsidiaries WisdomTree Trust and WisdomTree Asset Management the company manages more than 90 ETFs that invest in domestic and international equities currencies fixed-income and alternatives. It provides an alternative to funds weighted by market capitalization by focusing on fundamentals such as earnings dividends and industry. Serving both individual and institutional investors fast-growing WisdomTree Investments has about $46 billion in ETF assets under management about 65% of which are tied to international hedged equities (as of early 2016).

Operations

The asset manager makes almost all of its income from ETF advisory fees which are tied to managed assets. About 60% of the company's assets under management (AUM) and 60% of revenues in 2015 were tied to two of its US listed ETFs: WisdomTree Europe Hedged Equity Fund (HEDJ) and WisdomTree Japan Hedged Equity Fund (DXJ).

Sales and Marketing

The firm distributes its ETFs through all major channels within the asset management industry including registered investment advisers wirehouses institutional investors private wealth managers and discount brokers. The firm features its research through its professional sales force online through its websitevia targeted emails to financial advisers and financial media outlets such as Barron's Pensions & Investments Investor's Business Daily CNBC and Bloomberg.

WisdomTree increased its advertising and marketing spend by 16% to $13.37 million in 2015 versus 2014 as it boosted television print and online advertising support.

Financial Performance

Thanks to rising financial markets and a growing investor base driven by the popularity of ETFs WisdomTree has more than tripled its assets under management (AUM) since 2011 — from $12.2 billion to $51.6 billion at the end of 2015 — which has led strong fee and advisory income growth over the past several years. Its revenues have more than quadrupled over that period while its profits have grown more than 26-fold.

WisdomTree's revenue spiked 63% to $298.94 million during 2015 as its AUM balances rose more than 30% mostly on higher inflows from new customer business.

Strong revenue growth in 2015 drove the asset manager's net income up 31% to $80 million. The company's operating cash levels climbed 88% to $155 million as its cash-based operating revenue rose during the year.

Strategy

WisdomTree is banking on the continued growing popularity of ETFs around the world to grow its asset-based business. While ETFs have been around since the early 1980s their low fees have made them increasingly popular to investors over the past decade.

This factor combined with appreciating financial markets have boosted WisdomTree's assets under management from just shy of $10 billion at the end of 2010 to $51.6 billion in at the end of 2015. Its ETF annual net inflows from investors have also skyrocketed from $3.1 billion to $16.9 billion over the same period. Overall as of early 2016 fast-growing WisdomTree ranked as the fifth-largest US ETF sponsor with an 8% inflow market share (up from the 11th largest in 2009).

The asset manager regularly adds to its ETF offerings and expands its global distribution network (on its own through partnerships or by acquiring smaller asset managers) to attract new investors and their capital. The company also relies on strong investment performance from its teams to ensure its customers keep coming back.

Mergers and Acquisitions

In January 2016 WisdomTree expanded its commodity-based fund offerings after acquiring GreenHaven Commodity Services LLC — along with its GreenHaven Continuous Commodity Index Fund and GreenHaven Coal Services LLC and GreenHaven Coal Fund (to be rebranded as The WisdomTree Continuous Commodity Index Fund (GCC) and the WisdomTree Coal Fund (TONS) respectively) — for $12 million.

In April 2014 the firm expanded its distribution network in Europe after acquiring a 75% majority investment in UK-based exchange-traded product (ETP) provider Boost ETP LLP. The provider was renamed WisdomTree Europe and lists 12 branded UCITS ETFs on the London Stock Exchange and other prominent exchanges across Europe. WisdomTree will acquire the remaining 25% stake in Boost by March 31 2018.

HISTORY

The son of onetime corporate raider Saul Steinberg Jonathan Steinberg won The Wall Street Journal 's investing contest multiple times while still in his 20s. He founded Financial Data Systems in 1985 and bought The Penny Stock Journal in 1988.

The company launched the Special Situations Report newsletter in 1989; the following year The Penny Stock Journal became Individual Investor. Financial Data Systems went public in 1991 and adopted the Individual Investor Group moniker in 1993. It branched into hedge funds in 1994 by creating Wisdom Tree fund.

In 1996 Individual Investor introduced Ticker magazine. It launched the Individual Investor Web site the next year. In 1998 Individual Investor dissolved the ailing Wisdom Tree hedge fund and bought InsiderTrader.com. It took a stake in VentureHighway.com in 1999.

With its financial picture looking bleak the company took minority stakes in ReverseAuction.com and Tradeworx.com in exchange for advertising in 2000. Later that year the company engaged investment banking firm The Jordan Edmiston Group to find alternatives for buttressing its drooping financial position. It also sold the InsiderTrader.com Web site to Edgar Online. In 2001 Individual Investor cut its staff by 20% and was delisted from the Nasdaq exchange. Later that year the company closed Individual Investor. The company then merged its Web site with the WallStreetCity.com site owned by INVESTools (now thinkorswim). In 2002 the company changed its name to Index Development Partners and sold its

print division including its newsletter Special Situations Report .

In 2005 the company changed its name to WisdomTree Investments and reinvented itself.

EXECUTIVES

CIO, A. David Yates
CEO and President, Jonathan L. (Jono) Steinberg, $230,000 total compensation
EVP Business and Legal Affairs and Chief Legal Officer, Peter M. Ziemba
EVP Finance and CFO, Amit Muni
EVP Operations and COO, Gregory Barton
EVP Head Sales and Chief Investment Strategist, Luciano Siracusano
CEO WisdomTree Japan K.K., Jesper Koll
Chairman, Michael H. Steinhardt
Vice Chairman, Bruce Lavine
Auditors: Ernst & Young LLP

LOCATIONS

HQ: WisdomTree Investments, Inc.
245 Park Avenue, 35th Floor, New York, NY 10167
Phone: 212 801-2080
Web: www.wisdomtree.com

PRODUCTS/OPERATIONS

Selected Products
U.S. Listed Products
Alternative Strategy ETFs
Commodity ETFs
Currency ETFs
Equity ETFs
Fixed Income ETFs
International Hedged Equity ETFs
Non-U.S. Listed Products
Boost Short and Leveraged ETPs
WisdomTree UCITS ETFs

COMPETITORS

American Century	Legg Mason
BlackRock	MassMutual
E*TRADE Financial	Putnam
FMR	T. Rowe Price
Franklin Templeton	TD Ameritrade
Invesco	The Vanguard Group

HISTORICAL FINANCIALS

Company Type: Public

Income Statement   FYE: December 31

	REVENUE ($ mil.)	NET INCOME ($ mil.)	NET PROFIT MARGIN	EMPLOYEES
12/17	237.4	27.2	11.5%	204
12/16	219.4	26.1	11.9%	209
12/15	298.9	80.0	26.8%	177
12/14	183.7	61.0	33.2%	124
12/13	149.4	51.5	34.5%	87
Annual Growth	12.3%	(14.8%)	—	23.7%

2017 Year-End Financials

Debt ratio: —	No. of shares (mil.): 137.0
Return on equity: 13.8%	Dividends
Cash ($ mil.): 54.1	Yield: 0.0%
Current ratio: 2.69	Payout: 160.0%
Long-term debt ($ mil.): —	Market value ($ mil.): 1,719.0

STOCK PRICE ($) FY Close	P/E High/Low	PER SHARE ($) Earnings	Dividends	Book Value
12/17	12.55	63 41	0.20	0.32	1.41
12/16	11.14	83 44	0.19	0.32	1.48
12/15	15.68	45 25	0.58	0.57	1.71
12/14	15.68	40 21	0.44	0.08	1.38
12/13	17.71	44 15	0.37	0.00	0.84
Annual Growth	(8.3%)	—	— (14.3%)	—	13.9%

World Wrestling Entertainment Inc

The action might be fake but the business of World Wrestling Entertainment (WWE) is very real. The company is a leading producer and promoter of wrestling matches for TV and live audiences with about 250 live events each year including more than 50 international matches. Its main programming includes Monday Night Raw a top US cable program on USA Network; Friday Night SmackDown on Syfy; and WWE NXT on its website. WWE also produces about 12 live pay-per-view programs licenses characters for merchandise and sells videos and DVDs showcasing more than 140 wrestling stars such as Rey Mysterio Triple H and The Undertaker. Two-time WWE world champion Vince McMahon has nearly 90% voting control of the company.

Operations

The company classifies its operations into four reportable segments: Media Division (consisting of WWE Network and pay-per-view Television Home Entertainment and Digital Media Segments) Live Events Segment Consumer Products Division (consisting of Licensing Venue Merchandise and WWEShop Segments) and WWE Studios Segment.

Warner Brothers Home Entertainment became the distributor of WWE's home entertainment products in 2015.

Geographic Reach

WWE programming is broadcast in more than 175 countries and 25 languages and reaches more than 650 million homes worldwide. The company is headquartered in Stamford Connecticut with offices in New York Los Angeles Miami Mexico City Dubai London Mumbai Shanghai Singapore Istanbul and Tokyo. In fiscal 2014 the company brought in more than 75% of its revenue from North America.

WWE's office in Miami Florida serves as its headquarters for all operations in Latin America. The launch of its Latin America office allowed WWE to build upon its success and demonstrated its commitment to growth in the region.

Sales and Marketing

During fiscal 2014 the company spent a little more than $30 million on advertising expenses.

WWE uses the Internet to promote its brands and to create a community experience among its fans. Its primary website WWE.com attracted an average of 20.7 million monthly unique visitors worldwide during 2014. WWE currently has regional websites spanning 50 countries worldwide

allowing fans to experience WWE in their native language with a concentration on local events and shows.

WWE's home entertainment titles are generally sold through retailers such as Wal-Mart and Best Buy and via subscription and iTunes Amazon and Netflix.

Financial Performance

The company reported $542.6 billion in revenue for fiscal 2014. That was an increase of $34.6 billion compared to the prior fiscal period. Despite more than $500 billion in revenue WWE suffered a net loss of $30 billion in fiscal 2014. That was actually an improvement of more than $32 billion compared to the net loss the company claimed in fiscal 2013.

Even with a net loss the company's cash flow from operations remained strong in fiscal 2014. The company ended the year with $54.6 billion in cash on hand which was an increase of more than $30 billion compared to fiscal 2013 levels.

Strategy

While WWE is a diversified entertainment and media company its livelihood all stems from the live wrestling matches it produces around the country. The live events including ticket sales and merchandise sold at the matches account for only a portion of WWE's sales but more importantly those matches the wrestlers and the passion of the fans gets turned into all the other revenue streams. From that core WWE is able to produce and promote its TV shows pay-per-view events video games DVDs and other products.

The strengthening of WWE's content distribution agreements is another of WWE's primary long-term growth drivers.

HISTORY

Jesse McMahon made a name for himself as a boxing promoter in the 1940s before switching to wrestling. His son Vincent joined him in the business and they founded the World Wide Wrestling Federation in 1963. The company operated in Northeastern cities such as New York Philadelphia and Washington DC remaining a regional operation until the early 1980s (it dropped Wide from its name in 1979).

Vince McMahon Jr. inherited control of the WWF from his sick father in 1982 changed its name to Titan Sports and focused on gaining national exposure. McMahon made wrestling hugely popular but angered promoters as well as some fans with his nontraditional ideas. He embraced the idea of wrestling as show business instead of sport involving celebrities such as Cyndi Lauper and Mr. T and pursued a presence on cable TV. McMahon also purchased or put out of business many regional promoters as he spread the business across the US.

In the mid-1980s McMahon hit the jackpot with a former bodybuilder named Terry Gene Bollea. Christened Hulk Hogan he quickly became lord of the ring making the cover of Sports Illustrated and performing for sellout crowds across the US. His likeness spawned toys clothing and a Saturday morning cartoon. Titan set a record for attracting the largest indoor crowd (more than 93000 fans packed Detroit's Pontiac Silverdome for Wrestlemania III) in 1987 and by the following year was selling $80 million in tickets annually.

Titan was body slammed in 1993 when competitor World Championship Wrestling (WCW formed in 1988 by Ted Turner to broadcast on his

TBS network) lured away several major stars including Hogan. Also that year the US government charged Titan with illegal distribution of steroids. The company was acquitted in 1994 but the bad press along with the star defections allowed WCW to take the ratings lead by 1996.

Titan's refashioning of the WWF with more violence and sexual innuendo unleashed a hailstorm of criticism but returned it to the top spot by mid-1998; meanwhile former WWF star Jesse "The Body" Ventura was elected governor of Minnesota. Titan was named a defendant in a wrongful death suit in 1999 filed by the family of wrestler Owen Hart who fell to his death during a pay-per-view event (the case was settled in 2000). The company also changed its name to World Wrestling Federation Entertainment (WWFE) and went public that year. The company later licensed the WWF name for a theme restaurant in New York City.

WWFE continued its bone-crunching ways in 2000 by launching XFL a professional football league that played in the winter following the NFL season. Still smarting from the loss of the NFL broadcast rights to CBS NBC bought half of the new league and broadcast the games on its network. The deal also gave NBC a 3% stake in WWF. The league was a disaster during its first season and it quickly folded. (The company repurchased NBC's shares in 2002.)

Later that year the firm bought the WWF New York Times Square Entertainment Complex from its licensee for $24.5 million. (It closed the location in 2003.) It also abandoned its broadcasting contract with USA Networks (now IAC/InterActiveCorp) in favor of a more lucrative deal with Viacom which also took a 3% stake in the company. (Viacom sold the stake back to the company in 2003.) In 2001 WWFE put a headlock on the wrestling world when it bought the WCW from Turner Broadcasting.

In 2002 WWE received the smackdown in a court battle with the World Wildlife Fund which claimed the company (formerly WWF) lifted the animal preservation group's initials. The company had to change its name from World Wrestling Federation Entertainment to World Wrestling Entertainment as part of a settlement.

After ending its partnership with Viacom's Spike TV in 2005 the WWE cut a deal with NBCUniversal to air Monday Night Raw on the USA Network and on Spanish-language network Telemundo. The following year after The WB and the UPN merged to form The CW Network WWE inked a deal with the upstart broadcaster to air Friday Night SmackDown . (The show moved to MyNetworkTV owned by News Corporation in 2008.) It also created a new show ECW: Extreme Championship Wrestling for NBCUniversal's SCI FI Channel (now Syfy).

The company inked a lucrative toy licensing partnership with Mattel in 2010.

EXECUTIVES

Vp Public Relations, Jim Brown
Vp Home Entertainment And Retail Marketing, Joel Satin
Chairman and CEO, Vincent K. (Vince) McMahon, age 73, $1,239,923 total compensation
EVP Global Sales and Partnerships, John S. Brody
EVP Television Production, Kevin Dunn, age 57, $859,904 total compensation
Chief Strategy and Financial Officer, George A. Barrios, age 52, $723,692 total compensation

Chief Brand Officer, Stephanie McMahon, age 41
EVP Talent Live Events and Creative, Paul Levesque, age 48, $573,269 total compensation
President WWE Studios, Michael Luisi, age 52
Svp Consumer Products, James Connelly
Vice President, Peggy Waldo
Senior Vice President Marketing And Communications, Brian Flinn
Evp-content, Lisa F Lee
VP, Larry Smith
Vice President Global Consumer Insights and Analytics, Donna Berzolla
Vice President of Creative WWE Network, Julie Sbuttoni
Vice President Talent Brand Management, Christopher Handy
Vice President Tv Programming, Jennifer Good
Executive Vice President, Brett Hart
VP Interactive Technology, Felipe Negron
Vice President Of Event Booking Global Touring, Denis Sullivan
Senior Vice President And General Manager Digital Media, Brian Kalinowski
Vice President Legal And Business Affairs, Scott Amann
Vice President Post Production, Nancy Hirami
Vice President E Commerce And Retail Marketing, John Bancroft
VICE PRESIDENT FINANCIAL REPORTING AND ACCOUNTING, Lisa Rundle
SVP TV and Network Operations, Tracey Arrowood
Vice President Of Digital Media Content, Joseph Bonsignore
VICE PRESIDENT TRAVEL AND EVENT PLANNING, Emma Rubinov
Board of Directors, Linda McMahon
Board of Directors, Stephanie Levesque
Board Member, Laureen E Ong
Auditors: DELOITTE & TOUCHE LLP

LOCATIONS

HQ: World Wrestling Entertainment Inc
1241 East Main Street, Stamford, CT 06902
Phone: 203 352-8600
Web: www.wwe.com

PRODUCTS/OPERATIONS

Selected Operations
Live and televised entertainment
  Live wrestling events
  Pay-per-view programming
  Television programming
  A.M. RAW (USA Network)
  Friday Night SmackDown (Syfy)
  Monday Night Raw (USA Network)
  WWE NXT (WWE.com)
  WWE Superstars (WGN America)
  WWE Classics On Demand (video on demand service)
Consumer products
  Home video
  Magazines
  Product licensing
Digital media
  WWE.com
  WWEShop
WWE Studios (film production)

COMPETITORS

Harlem Globetrotters	NASCAR
Live Nation	NBA
Entertainment	NFL
Major League Baseball	NHL

HISTORICAL FINANCIALS

Company Type: Public

Income Statement   FYE: December 31

	REVENUE ($ mil.)	NET INCOME ($ mil.)	NET PROFIT MARGIN	EMPLOYEES
12/17	800.9	32.6	4.1%	850
12/16	729.2	33.8	4.6%	870
12/15	658.7	24.1	3.7%	840
12/14	542.6	(30.0)	—	761
12/13	507.9	2.7	0.5%	762
Annual Growth	12.1%	85.4%	—	2.8%

2017 Year-End Financials

Debt ratio: 34.7%	No. of shares (mil.): 77.1
Return on equity: 13.2%	Dividends
Cash ($ mil.): 137.7	Yield: 0.0%
Current ratio: 2.83	Payout: 114.2%
Long-term debt ($ mil.): 208.8	Market value ($ mil.): 2,358.0

	STOCK PRICE ($) FY Close	P/E High/Low		PER SHARE ($) Earnings	Dividends	Book Value
12/17	30.58	77	42	0.42	0.48	3.28
12/16	18.40	48	33	0.44	0.48	3.14
12/15	17.84	72	31	0.32	0.48	2.76
12/14	12.34	—	—	(0.40)	0.48	2.73
12/13	16.58	415	197	0.04	0.48	3.54
Annual Growth	16.5%	—	—	80.0%	(0.0%)	(1.9%)

WSFS Financial Corp

WSFS isn't a radio station but it is tuned to the banking needs of Delaware. WSFS Financial is the holding company for Wilmington Savings Fund Society (WSFS Bank) a thrift with nearly $5 billion in assets and more than 75 branches mostly in Delaware and Pennsylvania. Founded in 1832 WSFS Bank attracts deposits from individuals and local businesses by offering standard products like checking and savings accounts CDs and IRAs. The bank uses funds primarily to lend to businesses: Commercial loans and mortgages account for about 85% of its loan portfolio. Bank subsidiaries Christiana Trust Cypress Capital Management and WSFS Wealth Investment provide trust and investment advisory services to wealthy clients and institutional investors.

Operations

Its Christiana Trust division boasts nearly $9 billion in assets under administration and provides investment fiduciary agency bankruptcy and commercial domicile services from offices in Delaware and Nevada.

The company's Cash Connect division operates more than 450 ATMs for WSFS Bank which boasts the largest branded ATM network in Delaware. The division also manages some $490 million of vault cash in approximately 15000 ATMs nationwide and provides online reporting and ATM cash management predictive cash ordering armored carrier management and ATM processing and equipment sales.

Overall the bank generated roughly 57% of its total revenue from interest and fees on loans in 2014 plus an additional 10% from interest on its mortgage-back and other investment securities.

About 7% of its total revenue came from wealth management income while mortgage banking income contributed another 2%. The majority of the remaining revenue came from credit/debit card and ATM income and deposit service charges.

Geographic Reach

WSFS Bank has 45 branches throughout Delaware nearly 10 branches in Pennsylvania one branch in Nevada and one in Virginia.

Financial Performance

WSFS Financial's revenues and profits have been trending higher in recent years thanks to sustained growth in its lending business organically and through acquisitions and thanks to declining loan loss provisions as its loan portfolio's credit quality has improved with the strengthened economy.

The company's revenue rose by 5% to $238.62 million in 2014 thanks to interest income growth mostly driven by increased loan business and higher securities interest; which stemmed from a combination of the bank's First Wyoming Financial Corporation acquisition improvements in its balance sheet mix and additional income from its reverse mortgage-related assets.

Higher revenue and a continued decline in loan loss provisions in 2014 pushed WSFS Financial's net income up by 15% to $53.73 million during the year while the company's operating cash levels jumped by 17% to $67.06 million thanks to higher cash earnings.

Strategy

WSFS Financial reiterated its long-term growth strategy in 2015 which included growing the bank's lending business boosting its Trust and Wealth Management group's assets under administration and expanding Cash Connect's ATM customer base and customer cross-sell.

Beyond utilizing its community-oriented and local commercial lending teams the company has been growing its loan business and its branch reach through strategic acquisitions of banks and bank branches in target markets with preference toward markets in southeastern Pennsylvania. Its 2014 acquisition of First Wyoming Financial Corp for example bolstered WSFS' presence in Kent county while strengthening its position as the one of Delaware's top independent community banks.

Mergers and Acquisitions

In mid-2018 WSFS Financial agreed to purchase Philadelphia-based Beneficial Bancorp in a deal worth $1.5 billion. The transaction will create the largest locally headquartered community bank in the Greater Delaware Valley region with about $13 billion in assets.

EXECUTIVES

Chairman President and CEO, Mark A. Turner, age 55, $639,336 total compensation
SVP and Corporate Auditor WSFS Financial and WSFS Bank, Thomas W. Kearney
EVP and Chief Retail Banking Officer, Richard M. (Rick) Wright, age 65, $337,173 total compensation
EVP and COO, Rodger Levenson, age 56, $348,721 total compensation
EVP and Chief Human Capital Officer, Peggy H. Eddens, age 62
EVP and Chief Wealth Officer, Paul D. Geraghty, $310,671 total compensation
EVP and CTO, S. James (Jim) Mazarakis, $337,173 total compensation
President Cash Connect, Tom Stevenson
CFO, Dominic Canuso

Vice President Retail Banking, Adrienne Hawes
Vice President, John Olsen
Senior Vice President Middle Market Team Leader, James Gise
Executive Vice President Human Resources, Robert Silwa
Assistant Vice President Network Services Director, Jason Berkowitz
Vice President Retail Office Manager, Patricia Frechette
Executive Vice President, Cynthia Cole
Executive Vice President and Chief Technology Officer, James Mazarakis
Vice President, Glen Outten
Assistant Vice President Small business Lender Retail Office Manager, Carol Brindle
Senior Vice President Commercial R E Lending, Joseph C Walker
Vice President, Joseph Murphy
Assistant Vice President Retail Office Manager, Mitra Saffarian-Toosi
Assistant Vice President Commercial Banking, Don Lee
Assistant Vice President, Paul Roughton
AVP Facilities Manager, Bill Hornung
Vice President Relationship Manager, Eric Light
Vice Chairman, Charles G. Cheleden, age 74
Board Member, David Turner
Board Member, Jennifer Davis
Auditors: KPMG LLP

LOCATIONS

HQ: WSFS Financial Corp
500 Delaware Avenue, Wilmington, DE 19801
Phone: 302 792-6000
Web: www.wsfsbank.com

PRODUCTS/OPERATIONS

2014 Sales

	$ mil.	% of total
Interest		
Loans including fees	137.0	57
Mortgage-backed securities	13.5	6
Investment securities	9.8	4
Noninterest		
Credit/debit card & ATM income	24.1	11
Deposit service charges	17.1	7
Wealth management income	17.4	7
Mortgage baning activities	4.0	2
Other	15.7	6
Total	**238.6**	**100**

COMPETITORS

Bank of America	M&T Bank
Citizens Financial Group	PNC Financial
Fulton Financial	Sovereign Bank
JPMorgan Chase	TD Bank USA
	The Bancorp

HISTORICAL FINANCIALS

Company Type: Public

Income Statement — FYE: December 31

	ASSETS ($ mil.)	NET INCOME ($ mil.)	INCOME AS % OF ASSETS	EMPLOYEES
12/17	6,999.5	50.2	0.7%	1,159
12/16	6,765.2	64.0	0.9%	1,116
12/15	5,585.9	53.5	1.0%	947
12/14	4,853.3	53.7	1.1%	841
12/13	4,515.7	46.8	1.0%	762
Annual Growth	**11.6%**	**1.7%**	**—**	**11.1%**

2017 Year-End Financials

Return on assets: 0.7% Dividends
Return on equity: 7.1% Yield: 0.0%
Long-term debt ($ mil.): — Payout: 19.2%
No. of shares (mil.): 31.4 Market value ($ mil.): 1,503.0
Sales ($ mil): 378.6

	STOCK PRICE ($) FY Close	P/E High/Low	PER SHARE ($) Earnings	Dividends	Book Value
12/17	47.85	33 27	1.56	0.30	23.05
12/16	46.35	22 13	2.06	0.25	21.90
12/15	32.36	42 13	1.85	0.31	19.50
12/14	76.89	40 33	1.93	0.17	17.34
12/13	77.53	46 25	1.69	0.16	14.35
Annual Growth	**(11.4%)**	**— —**	**(1.9%)**	**17.0%**	**12.6%**

Xenia Hotels & Resorts Inc

Auditors: KPMG LLP

LOCATIONS

HQ: Xenia Hotels & Resorts Inc
200 S. Orange Avenue, Suite 2700, Orlando, FL 32801
Phone: 407 246-8100
Web: www.xeniareit.com

HISTORICAL FINANCIALS

Company Type: Public

Income Statement — FYE: December 31

	REVENUE ($ mil.)	NET INCOME ($ mil.)	NET PROFIT MARGIN	EMPLOYEES
12/17	945.2	98.8	10.5%	51
12/16	950.1	85.8	9.0%	49
12/15	976.1	88.7	9.1%	47
12/14	926.6	109.8	11.8%	36
12/13	651.8	(51.4)	—	0
Annual Growth	**9.7%**	**—**	**—**	**—**

2017 Year-End Financials

Debt ratio: 42.4% No. of shares (mil.): 106.7
Return on equity: 6.0% Dividends
Cash ($ mil.): 71.8 Yield: 0.0%
Current ratio: 1.40 Payout: 119.5%
Long-term debt ($ mil.): 1,322.5 Market value ($ mil.): 2,304.0

	STOCK PRICE ($) FY Close	P/E High/Low	PER SHARE ($) Earnings	Dividends	Book Value
12/17	21.59	25 18	0.92	1.10	15.13
12/16	19.42	25 16	0.79	1.10	15.26
12/15	15.33	31 19	0.79	0.84	15.47
Annual Growth	**18.7%**	**— —**	**7.9%**	**14.7%**	**(1.1%)**

XOMA Corp

XOMA Corporation doesn't want to toil in anonymity. Instead the company pairs with larger drug firms to develop and market its products primarily monoclonal antibodies (biotech drugs based on cloned proteins). It's developing lead candidate gevokizumab with French drugmaker Servier. The firm partners on therapeutics for infectious disease inflammatory ailments and autoimmune conditions and receives royalties on drugs developed from licensing its technologies. XOMA has collaborative agreements with pharma companies Takeda Pharmaceutical and Novartis; it also has metabolic and oncology candidates.

Operations

In addition to gevokizumab which treats a rare inflammation-related eye condition the company's main pipeline products include its XMet series (XMet A S and D) of diabetes and other metabolic disease treatments.

Separate from its drug development XOMA has created tools to help other drug companies discover and make antibodies and other proteins. It licenses its proprietary bacterial cell expression (BCE) technology a process for discovering and selecting recombinant proteins for further development. More than 60 companies have signed licensing agreements for BCE technology and will pay development milestone payments and royalties on any antibodies covered by the licenses.

In 2013 contracts brought in about 70% of XOMA's revenue (Servier contributed about 56% of that) while the National Institutes of Health (NIH) which XOMA has worked with to find treatments for bioterrorism threat botulinum brought in 37%.

XOMA began selling its first product Aceon a high blood pressure drug purchased from Servier in 2012. But it sold the development and commercialization rights to drug maker Symplmed in mid-2013.

Financial Performance

As a development-stage company XOMA's revenues are directly tied to licensing R&D collaboration and royalty fees. It makes around $35 million per year in fees but it spends about $70 million on R&D each year. This trend will continue until the company has products to market. Its total accumulated deficit was $1 billion at the end of 2013.

Strategy

The cornerstone of XOMA's strategy is using its expertise in recombinant protein development and production to build a diverse portfolio of drug candidates in core therapeutic areas. In addition to advancing its lead drug candidate the firm plans to license or acquire new products to strengthen its internal development efforts as well as to form new partnerships and technology agreements with third parties. Once it has a product ready to market XOMA will use its own sales force in the US. It plans to license the two diabetes drugs in its XMet series while retaining full rights to third which treats a rare insulin-regulation condition.

In 2015 the company sold its biodefense program including its XOMA 3AB botulinum antibody being developed for NIH to Florida-based biopharmaceutical Nanotherapeutics. Early the following year it sold an antibody manufacturing pilot plant to Agenus.

EXECUTIVES

CEO and Director, James R. (Jim) Neal, $354,165 total compensation
Vice President Regulatory Affairs and Compliance, Daniel P Cafaro
EVP and Chief Scientific Officer, Patrick J. (Pat) Scannon, age 70, $417,104 total compensation
VP Human Resources and Information Technology, Charles C. (Chris) Wells, age 67, $324,744 total compensation
VP Finance and CFO, Thomas (Tom) Burns, $274,749 total compensation
Vice President Development, Kirk Johnson
Vice President Human Resources and Information Technology, Chris Wells
Chairman, W. Denman Van Ness, age 75
Auditors: DELOITTE & TOUCHE LLP

LOCATIONS

HQ: XOMA Corp
2200 Powell Street, Suite 310, Emeryville, CA 94608
Phone: 510 204-7200
Web: www.xoma.com

PRODUCTS/OPERATIONS

2016 Sales

	$ mil.	% of total
License & collaborative fees & royalties	3.3	59
Contract and other	2.3	41
Total	**5.6**	**100**

2016 Contract & Other Revenue

	$ mil.	% of total
The National Institute of Allergy and Infectious Diseases (NIAID)	1.1	48
Servier	0.6	26
Other	0.6	26
Total	**2.3**	**100**

Selected Pipeline Products

XOMA 358 - Congenital hyperinsulinism & Post-bariatric surgery hyperinsulinism
XOMA 129 - Short-acting reversal of drug-induced hypoglycemia
XOMA 213 - Various hyperprolactinemias
Anti-PTH1R - Hyperparathyroidism Malignancy induced hypercalcemia
Anti-IL-2 - Oncology anti-tumor immunity

COMPETITORS

AbbVie	Janssen Biotech
Abbott Labs	MedImmune
Alexion	Novartis
Pharmaceuticals	Pfizer
Amgen	Regeneron
Biogen	Pharmaceuticals
Daiichi Sankyo	SANTEN
PHARMACEUTICAL	
Eli Lilly	CO. LTD.
Emergent BioSolutions	Sobi
Genentech	Takeda Pharmaceutical
GlaxoSmithKline	pSivida

HISTORICAL FINANCIALS

Company Type: Public

Income Statement

FYE: December 31

	REVENUE ($ mil.)	NET INCOME ($ mil.)	NET PROFIT MARGIN	EMPLOYEES
12/17	52.6	14.6	27.7%	12
12/16	5.5	(53.5)	—	18
12/15	55.4	(20.6)	—	86
12/14	18.8	(38.3)	—	183
12/13	35.4	(124.0)	—	168
Annual Growth	**10.4%**	**—**	**—**	**(48.3%)**

2017 Year-End Financials

Debt ratio: 32.4%
Return on equity: ***,***.*%
Cash ($ mil.): 43.4
Current ratio: 5.95
Long-term debt ($ mil.): 14.5
No. of shares (mil.): 8.2
Dividends
  Yield: —
  Payout: —
Market value ($ mil.): 294.0

	STOCK PRICE ($) FY Close	P/E High/Low		PER SHARE ($) Earnings	Dividends	Book Value
12/17	35.60	49	5	0.73	0.00	0.70
12/16	4.22	—	—	(8.89)	0.00	(7.72)
12/15	1.33	—	—	(3.40)	0.00	(0.39)
12/14	3.59	—	—	(13.40)	0.00	0.53
12/13	6.73	—	—	(28.60)	0.00	(0.76)
Annual Growth	**51.7%**	**—**		**—**	**—**	**—**

Yelp Inc

If yelping doesn't sound like fun you may not be as hip as you think. Yelp offers user-generated reviews and information on local businesses and service providers through its website at Yelp.com and via its mobile app. Its content targets younger urban consumers and covers restaurants bars salons retailers doctors and museums. The site has a social media-friendly interface — users can create and maintain profiles (complete with friend networks and photos) where they can blog on experiences with businesses. Yelp has established a foothold in cities across the US Canada and Europe. The firm was founded in 2004 by former PayPal engineers Jeremy Stoppelman and Russel Simmons. It went public in 2012.

Operations

Yelp divides itself into three segments for reporting purposes: local advertising brand advertising and other services. Local advertising which contributed 85% of revenue in fiscal 2014 includes free and paid business listings for businesses of all sizes. Brand advertising which accounted for about 9% of total revenue during fiscal 2014 offers advertising for national brands in the automobile financial services logistics consumer goods and health and fitness industries. Other services contributed the remaining 6% of annual revenue in fiscal 2014.

Geographic Reach

Yelp has more than 70 million cumulative reviews of almost every type of local business available in about 30 countries. The company has been expanding globally. It now has sites in Austria Canada France Germany Ireland the Netherlands Spain and the UK.

The firm continues to strengthen its presence in markets throughout the US and has plans for expansion in Canada and Western Europe.

Yelp's sales force works from five primary locations: San Francisco California; Scottsdale Arizona; New York City: London UK; and Hamburg Germany. The company has an office in Dublin Ireland as well.

Financial Performance

Yelp has seen sizable growth in its revenue since fiscal 2010. During fiscal 2014 its revenue increased by 62% to $377.54 million compared to $232.99 million in fiscal 2013. The increase was primarily due to revenue growth related to the

company's local advertiser customer base as well as the development of relationships with brand advertising agencies.

Local advertising segment revenue increased by 65% in fiscal 2014 compared to the prior year. The spike was due to a significant increase in the number of customers purchasing local advertising plans as they expanded their sales force to reach more local businesses. Brand advertising segment revenue increased by 23% in fiscal 2014 compared to fiscal 2013. The increase was largely due to an increase in the average spend per brand advertiser.

After suffering a net loss for three straight fiscal years in fiscal 2014 Yelp posted net income of $36 million (compared to a net loss of $10 million in fiscal 2013).

In fiscal 2014 Yelp's operating cash inflow increased to $57.93 million compared to $21.43 million in fiscal 2013. The influx of cash came from profit for the current year and higher account payable and deferred revenue.

Strategy

The company is counting on a strategy of reaching more people for growth: As it adds users its content expands to cover more local businesses which in turn attracts more consumers and more advertisers. Yelp sees its local business accounts as an opportunity for growth as it generates revenue from only a small fraction of those businesses.

During 2014 Yelp formed a partnership with Yahoo! to use Yelp content to power Yahoo Search in the US.

Mergers and Acquisitions

As a part of its content expansion in 2014 Yelp acquired Restaurant Kritik a German review website and Cityvox a French review website. Yelp expects to migrate the content from those sites to the Yelp platform in 2015.

During fiscal 2013 Yelp acquired SeatMe for a price of about $12.7 million ($2.2 in cash and the rest in stock).

EXECUTIVES

CFO, Charles C. (Lanny) Baker, age 51
CEO, Jeremy Stoppelman, age 41, $1 total compensation
SVP Marketing, Andrea Rubin
COO, Joseph R. (Jed) Nachman, age 46, $325,000 total compensation
SVP Legal and User Operations General Counsel and Secretary, Laurence Wilson, age 46, $325,000 total compensation
CEO Yelp Eat24, Mike Ghaffary
VP Corporate Infrastructure, Todd Miner
Vice President New Markets, Miriam Warren
National Account Manager, Brian Low
National Sales Manager, Sarah Steele
Vice President, Cindy Mesaros
National Account Manager, Michelle Chin
Senior Vice President Business and Corporate Development, Chad Richard
Vice President Consumer Marketing, Brian Osborn
Vice President of Corporate Communications, Shannon Eis
NATIONAL SALES MANAGER, Michael Shu
Vice President Sales, John Garnin
NATIONAL ACCOUNT MANAGER, Jeff Lonski
National Account Manager, Maria Hyzy
Auditors: DELOITTE & TOUCHE LLP

LOCATIONS

HQ: Yelp Inc
140 New Montgomery Street, 9th Floor, San Francisco,
CA 94105
Phone: 415 908-3801
Web: www.yelp.com

PRODUCTS/OPERATIONS

2014 Sales

	$ mil.	% of total
Local advertisig	319.1	83
Brand advertising	34.5	12
Other	23.9	5
Total	**377.5**	**100**

2014 Reviewed Businesses

	% of total
Shopping	26
Restaurants	21
Home & local services	12
Beauty & fitness	10
Health	6
Auto	5
Nightlife	4
Travel & hotel	4
Other	12
Total	**100**

2014 Reviews

	% of total
Restaurants	40
Shopping	22
Nightlife	9
Beauty & fitness	8
Home & local services	6
Auto	3
Health	3
Travel & hotel	3
Other	6
Total	**100**

Selected Business Categories

Arts entertainment & events
Automotive
Beauty & fitness
Health
Hotel & travel
Nightlife
Restaurants
Shopping

COMPETITORS

AOL	MSN
Better Business	OpenTable
Bureaus	Restaurant.com
CityGrid Media	Time Out Group
Consumers Union	TripAdvisor
Facebook	Yahoo!
Google	Yellowbook
Groupon	Zagat
LivingSocial	craigslist

HISTORICAL FINANCIALS

Company Type: Public

Income Statement
FYE: December 31

	REVENUE ($ mil.)	NET INCOME ($ mil.)	NET PROFIT MARGIN	EMPLOYEES
12/17	846.8	152.8	18.1%	5,323
12/16	713.0	(4.6)	—	4,256
12/15	549.7	(32.9)	—	2,220
12/14	377.5	36.4	9.7%	2,711
12/13	232.9	(10.0)	—	1,984
Annual Growth	**38.1%**	**—**	**—**	**28.0%**

2017 Year-End Financials

Debt ratio: —
Return on equity: 16.0%
Cash ($ mil.): 547.8
Current ratio: 10.60
Long-term debt ($ mil.): —

No. of shares (mil.): 83.7
Dividends
Yield: —
Payout: —
Market value ($ mil.): 3,513.0

	STOCK PRICE ($) FY Close	P/E High/Low	PER SHARE ($) Earnings	PER SHARE ($) Dividends	PER SHARE ($) Book Value
12/17	41.96	25 15	1.75	0.00	13.13
12/16	38.13	— —	(0.06)	0.00	10.16
12/15	28.80	— —	(0.44)	0.00	9.13
12/14	54.73	192 98	0.48	0.00	8.07
12/13	68.95	— —	(0.15)	0.00	6.86
Annual Growth	**(11.7%)**	**— —**	**—**	**—**	**17.6%**

ZAGG Inc

ZAGG hopes to stand in the way when a little zig threatens to scratch your iPhone or iPad. Short for "Zealous About Great Gadgets" ZAGG designs makes and sells protective coverings and other products for electronic devices. Its flagship product invisibleSHIELD is a thin scratch-resistant polyurethane film covering that's custom cut to fit invisibly on the screens and displays of Apple iPhones and other smartphones tablets laptops GPS devices and watch faces. ZAGG also offers additional accessories including keyboards headphones for iPods and MP3 players and decorative cases for phones. It sells its products through retailers the likes of Best Buy and Wal-Mart mall kiosks and its own website.

Operations

The company's operations are divided into three segments. The largest accounting for about three-quarters of total sales is ZAGG which designs makes and distributes products including protective coverings keyboards keyboard cases earbuds mobile power devices and cleaning accessories for mobiles devices under the ZAGG brand. iFrogz accounts for about 25% of sales. It makes cases Near-Field Audio amplifying speakers earbuds and regular and gaming headphones for mobile devices. The company's HzO segment is engaged in the development of water blocking coating technologies for consumer and industrial applications. It had no revenue in 2012.

Geographic Reach

The US is ZAGG's largest market. accounting for about 85% of its sales. Europe contributes about 5% of sales with other countries representing the rest. The company's international arm is based in Shannon Ireland.

Sales and Marketing

ZAGG's biggest customer is consumer electronics chain Best Buy which accounts for about a third of its total sales. Next is retail-giant Wal-Mart Stores which accounts for about 10%. Historically the company has focused on distributing through sales channels like kiosk vendors and through its e-commerce site; however more recently it has brought in more and more income through retailers (including Target RadioShack and Staples) and wireless carriers (AT&T Sprint Verizon). Ultimately demand for its products has been driven by the growing popularity of iPads iPhones and other smartphones. (iPhone accessories are its biggest sellers.) The company sells throughout Europe and other global regions through international distributors.

Financial Performance

In 2012 ZAGG's sales exceeded $264 million a 48% jump versus 2011. Driving the heady increase was the 2011 purchase of iFrogz which contributed about $68 million in sales in 2012. Strong demand from wholesale customers the addition of new distribution partners and continued growth of invisibleSHIELD products coupled with increased sales of ZAGG's keyboards audio and case product lines also pumped up sales. 2012 marked the fourth year of accelerating sales for the company. Indeed over the past four years sales have increased by more than a factor of 10: from nearly $20 million in 2008 to $264 million in 2012.

After four years of steep increases net income fell 21% in 2012 compared with 2011. ZAGG attributed the decline to higher operating expenses. Also marketing advertising and promotion expenses rose as the company invested heavily for key product launches including the invisibleSHIELD HD invisibleSHIELD EXTREME and ZAGGkeys PRO among other new products.

Strategy

Going forward ZAGG hopes to keep its growth momentum swinging in an upward direction by expanding its sales channels to include more telecom companies like U.S. Cellular and retailers like Amazon.com. It has also been broadening its range of accessories for the mobile phone market by adding car chargers and power supplies to its product offerings. Other growth strategies include focusing its sales and marketing efforts on cross-selling accessories to customers that purchase its invisibleSHIELD products.

Mergers and Acquisitions

In a move that simultaneously broadened its brand and product portfolio and increases its retail reach ZAGG in mid-2011 acquired iFrogz a maker and distributor of protective cases headphones and earbuds and other accessories for smartphones tablets and other mobile devices under the iFrogz and EarPollution brands. ZAGG paid $50 million in cash acquired 4.4 million restricted shares of ZAGG common stock and assumed about $5 million in debt. Utah-based iFrogz which counts Wal-Mart Stores among its customers became a wholly-owned subsidiary of ZAGG.

EXECUTIVES

CEO, Randall L. Hales, $696,400 total compensation
CFO, Bradley J. Holiday, $128,461 total compensation
President, Brian Stech
President mophie and International, Chris Ahern
VP Operations, Marshall Clark
Vice President of Marketing, Brad Bell
National Sales Manager, Jordan Sagona
Vice President, Chris Paterson
Chairman, Cheryl A. Larabee
Auditors: KPMG LLP

LOCATIONS

HQ: ZAGG Inc
910 West Legacy Center Way, Suite 500, Midvale, UT 84047
Phone: 801 263-0699
Web: www.zagg.com

PRODUCTS/OPERATIONS

Selected Brands
EarPollution
iFrogz
invisibleSHIELD (film coatings)
ZAGGbuds (audio headphones)
ZAGGskins (cell phone cases and covers)
ZAGGsmartbuds (audio headphones)

COMPETITORS

Apple Inc.	Kyocera Communications
Bose	Motorola Mobility
Dooney & Bourke	Otterbox
Forward Industries	Plantronics

HISTORICAL FINANCIALS

Company Type: Public

Income Statement   FYE: December 31

	REVENUE ($ mil.)	NET INCOME ($ mil.)	NET PROFIT MARGIN	EMPLOYEES
12/17	519.5	15.1	2.9%	543
12/16	401.8	(15.5)	—	431
12/15	269.3	15.5	5.8%	234
12/14	261.5	10.4	4.0%	220
12/13	219.3	4.7	2.2%	201
Annual Growth	24.1%	33.2%	—	28.2%

2017 Year-End Financials

Debt ratio: 11.6%	No. of shares (mil.): 28.0
Return on equity: 11.9%	Dividends
Cash ($ mil.): 24.9	Yield: —
Current ratio: 1.23	Payout: —
Long-term debt ($ mil.): —	Market value ($ mil.): 517.0

	STOCK PRICE ($) FY Close	P/E High/Low	PER SHARE ($) Earnings	Dividends	Book Value
12/17	18.45	43 11	0.53	0.00	4.85
12/16	7.10	— —	(0.56)	0.00	4.19
12/15	10.94	23 11	0.54	0.00	4.74
12/14	6.79	20 11	0.34	0.00	4.36
12/13	4.35	49 23	0.15	0.00	4.08
Annual Growth	43.5%	— —	37.1%	—	4.4%

Hoover's Handbook of

Emerging Companies

2019

Index by Headquarters

ARE

Abu Dhabi
Etisalat W145
Emirates Telecommunications Group
 Company PJSC W137
First Abu Dhabi Bank PJSC W150
Abu Dhabi Islamic Bank W4

Dubai
Mashreqbank W234
Dubai Islamic Bank Ltd W130

AUS

Brisbane
Suncorp Group Ltd. W348

Docklands
Australia & New Zealand Banking
 Group Ltd W37

Melbourne
BHP Group Ltd W62
Rio Tinto Ltd W304
National Australia Bank Ltd. W250
Telstra Corp., Ltd. W361

Newstead
Bank of Queensland Ltd W50

Perth
Wesfarmers Ltd. W392

Sydney
Woolworths Group Ltd W396
Commonwealth Bank of Australia
 W104
Westpac Banking Corp W394
Caltex Australia Ltd. W78
QBE Insurance Group Ltd. W296
Macquarie Group Ltd W226
AMP Ltd. W25

AUT

Linz
voestalpine AG W389

Vienna
OMV AG (Austria) W275
Erste Group Bank AG W144
UNIQA Versicherungen AG (Austria)
 W384
BAWAG Group AG W56

BEL

Brussels
Ageas NV W11
Umicore SA W379
KBC Group NV W204

Dexia SA W127
Dexia Bank Belgium S.A. (Belgium)
 W127

Leuven
Anheuser-Busch InBev SA/NV W27

BHR

Manama
Ahli United Bank W12

BMU

Hamilton
Jardine Strategic Holdings Ltd
 (Bermuda) W196
Brookfield Business Partners LP W75

Pembroke
Athene Holding Ltd W36
Arch Capital Group Ltd W31

BRA

Rio de Janeiro
Petroleo Brasileiro SA W283
Vale SA W384

Sao Paulo
Itau Unibanco Holding S.A. W191
Banco Bradesco SA W41
JBS SA W196
Banco Santander Brasil SA W43
Ultrapar Participacoes SA W378
Ambev SA W24

CAN

Aurora
Magna International Inc W228

Brampton
Loblaw Companies Ltd W224

Calgary
Enbridge Inc W138
Suncor Energy Inc W347
Imperial Oil Ltd W183
Husky Energy Inc W176

Laval
Alimentation Couche-Tard Inc W20

Montreal
Power Corp. of Canada W293
Power Financial Corp W294
Bank of Montreal (Quebec) W49
Bombardier Inc. W68
National Bank of Canada W252
Laurentian Bank of Canada W216

Ottawa
Bank of Canada (Ottawa) W47

Quebec City
IA Financial Corp Inc W180

Stellarton
Empire Co Ltd W137

Toronto
Manufacturers Life Insurance Co.
 (Toronto, Canada) W231
Manulife Financial Corp W231
Royal Bank of Canada (Montreal,
 Quebec) W310
Toronto Dominion Bank W369
Brookfield Asset Management Inc
 W74
Weston (George) Ltd W393
Bank of Nova Scotia Halifax W49
ONEX Corp (Canada) W277
Sun Life Financial Inc W346
Canadian Imperial Bank Of Commerce
 (Toronto, Ontario) W79
Fairfax Financial Holdings Ltd W146

Verdun
BCE Inc W60

Winnipeg
Great-West Lifeco Inc W161
Great-West Life Assurance Co W161

CHE

Baar
Glencore PLC W159

Basel
Roche Holding Ltd W307
Novartis AG Basel W270
Baloise Holding AG W40

Jona
LafargeHolcim Ltd W214

Lausanne
Banque Cantonale Vaudoise W52

Schindellegi
Kuehne & Nagel International AG
 W212

Vevey
Nestle SA W257

Zug
Ferguson PLC W148

Zurich
Zurich Insurance Group AG W404
UBS Group AG W378
ABB Ltd W3
Chubb Ltd W97
Adecco Group AG W7
Credit Suisse Group AG W110

Swiss Life Holding AG W352

CHL

Santiago
Cementos Bio-Bio S.A. (Chile) W85
AntarChile S.A. (Chile) W27
Empresas COPEC SA W137
Cencosud SA W85
Corporacion Nacional del Cobre de
 Chile W108
Banco Santander Chile W43
Banco de Chile W41
Itau CorpBanca W191

CHN

Baoding
Great Wall Motor Co. Ltd. W160

Beijing
China Petroleum & Chemical Corp
 W93
PetroChina Co Ltd W283
Industrial and Commercial Bank of
 China Ltd W185
China Construction Bank Corp W89
Agricultural Bank of China W11
China Railway Group Ltd W93
China Railway Construction Corp Ltd
 W93
China Communications Constructions
 Group Ltd W89
JD.com, Inc. W196
China Shenhua Energy Co., Ltd. W94
Metallurgical Corp China Ltd W240
Aluminum Corp of China Ltd. W24
Huaneng Power International Inc
 W175
China Life Insurance Co Ltd W91
China National Building Material Co
 Ltd W91
Air China Ltd W13
New China Life Insurance Co Ltd
 W259
BOE Technology Group Co Ltd W67

Dalian
China Grand Automotive Services Co
 Ltd W90

Guangzhou
Poly Real Estate Group Co., Ltd.
 W291
China Southern Airlines Co Ltd W95

Hangzhou
Zhejiang Material Industrial Zhongda
 Yuantong Group Co., Ltd. W403

Lianyungang
Lianyungang Ideal Group Co Ltd
 W221

A = AMERICAN BUSINESS
E = EMERGING COMPANIES
P = PRIVATE COMPANIES
W = WORLD BUSINESS

Longyan
Zijin Mining Group Co Ltd W403

Nanchang
Jiangxi Copper Co., Ltd. W197

Nanjing
Suning Appliance Co., Ltd. W348

Qingdao
Qingdao Haier Co Ltd W297

Shanghai
SAIC Motor Corp Ltd W316
Shanghai Jinfeng Investment Co Ltd W325
Baoshan Iron & Steel Co Ltd W52
China United Network Communications Ltd W96
China Pacific Insurance (Group) Co., Ltd. W92
Shanghai Construction Group Co., Ltd. W325
Huayu Automotive Systems Company Ltd W175
Shanghai Pharmaceuticals Holding Co Ltd W325
China Eastern Airlines Corp., Ltd. W89
Sinopec Shanghai Petrochemical Co., Ltd. W332

Shenzhen
China Evergrande Group W90
China Vanke Co Ltd W96
Tencent Holdings Ltd. W362
Ping An Insurance (Group) Co of China Ltd. W287
Zte Corp. W403

Shijiazhuang
Hebei Iron & Steel Co Ltd W165

Tianjin
Tianjin Tianhai Investment Co Ltd W366

Weifang
Weichai Power Co Ltd W392

Wuhan
China Gezhouba Group Co., Ltd. W90

Xiamen
Xiamen C & D Inc W399
Xiamen Xiangyu Co Ltd W399
Xiamen International Trade Group Corp Ltd W399

Zhuhai
Gree Electric Appliances Inc Of Zhuhai W162

Zoucheng
Yanzhou Coal Mining Co Ltd W401

COL

Bogota
Ecopetrol SA W133

Envigado
Almacenes Exito S.A. W23

Medellin
BanColombia SA W45

CSK

Praha 1
Komercni Banka AS (Czech Republic) W208

DEU

Bad Homburg
Fresenius SE & Co KGaA W153
Fresenius Medical Care AG & Co KGaA W152

Berlin
Deutscher Sparkassen-und Giroverband e.V. (Germany, Fed. Rep.) W127
Deutsche Bahn AG W121

Bonn
Deutsche Telekom AG W126
Deutsche Post AG W124
Deutsche Postbank AG W125

Cologne
Rewe-Zentral AG (Germany, Fed. Rep.) W302
Gothaer Versicherungsbank VVaG (Germany, Fed. Rep.) W160

Darmstadt
Merck KGaA (Germany) W239

Duesseldorf
Ceconomy AG W84
Henkel AG & Co KGAA W167

Essen
RWE AG W314
ThyssenKrupp AG W365
E.ON SE W131
Hochtief AG W170
Brenntag AG, Muehleim/Ruhr W72

Frankfurt
Deutsche Lufthansa AG (Germany, Fed. Rep.) W123
Dekabank Deutsche Girozentrale W120

Frankfurt am Main
Deutsche Bank AG W122
Commerzbank AG W104
Landesbank Hessen-Thueringen Girozentrale (Helaba) (Germany, Fed. Rep.) W215
Landwirtschaftliche Rentenbank (Germany, Fed. Rep.) W216

Friedrichshafen
ZF Friedrichshafen AG (Germany) W402

Gerlingen-Schillerhoehe
Bosch (Robert) GmbH (Germany Fed. Rep.) W69

Guetersloh
Bertelsmann AG (Germany, Fed. Rep.) W61

Hamburg
Otto Versand (GmbH & Co.) (Germany, Fed. Rep.) W280
Marquard & Bahls AG (Germany) W233
Hamburger Sparkasse (Germany, Fed. Rep.) W164

Hannover
Talanx AG W356
Hannover Rueckversicherung SE W164

Hanover
Continental AG (Germany, Fed. Rep.) W107
TUI AG W375

Heidelberg
HeidelbergCement AG W166

Herzogenaurach
Adidas AG W7

Ingolstadt
AUDI AG W37

Karlsruhe
ENBW Energie Baden-Wuerttemberg AG W139

Leverkusen
Bayer AG W56
Covestro AG W109

Ludwigshafen
BASF SE W54

Munich
Allianz SE W22
Bayerische Motoren Werke AG W58
Siemens AG (Germany) W330
Linde AG (Germany, Fed. Rep.) W222
BAYWA Bayerische Warenvermittlung Landwirtschaftlicher Genossenschaften AG W59
Man SE W231
Bayerische Landesbank (Germany) W57
Muenchener Hypothekenbank EG (Germany, Fed. Rep.) W250

Stuttgart
Daimler AG W114
McKesson Europe AG W235
Landesbank Baden-Wurttemberg W215
Mahle GmbH (Germany) W230

Walldorf
SAP SE W318

Wiesbaden
Aareal Bank AG W2

Wolfsburg
Volkswagen AG W390

DNK

Bagsvaerd
Novo-Nordisk AS W270

Copenhagen K
A.P. Moller - Maersk A/S W1
Danske Bank A/S W117

Silkeborg
Jyske Bank A/S W201

ESP

Alicante
Banco De Sabadell SA W42

Barcelona
Naturgy Energy Group SA W256

Bilbao
Banco Bilbao Vizcaya Argentaria SA (BBVA) W41
Iberdrola SA W181

La Coruna
Industria De Diseno Textil (Inditex) SA W184

Madrid
Banco Santander SA (Spain) W44
Telefonica SA W360
Repsol S.A. W300
Aedas Homes SAU W9
ACS Actividades de Construccion y Servicios, S.A. W6
International Consolidated Airlines Group SA W188
Endesa S.A. W140
Ferrovial SA W149
Bankia S A W51
Bankinter, S.A. W51

FIN

Copenhagen
Danske Bank Plc W118

Espoo
Nokia Corp W266
Neste Oyj W256

Helsinki
Varma Mutual Pension Insurance Co W386

FRA

Bezons
Atos Origin W37

Boulogne-Billancourt
Carrefour S.A. W82
Renault S.A. (France) W300
Colas SA Boulogne W103

Clermont-Ferrand
Compagnie Generale des Etablissements Michelin SCA W106

Clichy
L'Oreal S.A. (France) W213

Courbevoie
Total SA W371
Engie SA W142
Compagnie de Saint-Gobain W106
Thales W364
Esso SA W145

Ergue-Gaberic
Financiere De L Odet SA (France) W149

Issy-les-Moulineaux
Sodexo W334

Montrouge
Credit Agricole SA W110

Nanterre
Faurecia SA (France) W147

Paris
AXA SA W39
BNP Paribas (France) W65
EDF Trading Ltd W133
Electricite de France W135
Societe Generale W334
CNP Assurances S.A. W102
Christian Dior SE W96
LVMH Moet Hennessy Louis Vuitton W225
Orange W278
Rallye S.A. Neuilly-Sur-Seine W298
Sanofi W318
Bouygues S.A. W71
Schlumberger Ltd W321
NATIXIS SA W255
Air France-KLM W14
Veolia Environnement W386
Danone W116

L'Air Liquide S.A. (France) W213
Valeo SA W385
Safran SA W315
Kering SA W204
SCOR S.E. (France) W323
Rexel S.A. W302
Capgemini SE W80
Vivendi W388

Paris La Defense
SUEZ SA W343

Puteaux
Bollore SA W68

Rueil-Malmaison
Peugeot SA W286
Vinci SA W386
Schneider Electric SE W321

Saint-Etienne
Casino Guichard Perrachon S.A. W83

Velizy-Villacoublay
Eiffage SA W134

GBR
Phoenix Group Holdings W287

Bradford
Morrison (Wm.) Supermarkets Plc W248

Brentford
GlaxoSmithKline Plc W157

Bristol
Imperial Brands PLC W183

Cambridge
AstraZeneca Plc W34

Chertsey
Compass Group PLC (United Kingdom) W106

Edinburgh
Standard Life Aberdeen PLC W341
Royal Bank of Scotland Group Plc W311

Glasgow
Clydesdale Bank PLC (United Kingdom) W101

London
BP PLC W72
Fiat Chrysler Automobiles NV W149
Prudential Plc W295
HSBC Holdings Plc W173
Aviva Plc (United Kingdom) W37
Unilever Plc (United Kingdom) W382
Lloyds Banking Group Plc W224
Legal & General Group PLC (United Kingdom) W217
BHP Group Plc W64
Rio Tinto Plc W305
J Sainsbury PLC W192
Barclays PLC W52
Barclays Bank Plc W52
LyondellBasell Industries NV W226
BT Group Plc W76
Lloyds Bank plc W224
British American Tobacco Plc (United Kingdom) W73
CNH Industrial NV W101
HSBC Bank Plc (United Kingdom) W173
Anglo American Plc (United Kingdom) W27
Rolls-Royce Holdings Plc W308
BAE Systems Plc W39
National Grid plc W253
WPP Plc (New) W396
Associated British Foods Plc W32

Johnson Matthey Plc (United Kingdom) W198
Bupa Finance plc W77
Kingfisher PLC W206
Diageo Plc W127
Liberty Global plc W221
Marks & Spencer Group PLC W233
Lewis (John) Plc (United Kingdom) W219
Lewis (John) Partnership Plc (United Kingdom) W219
Dixons Carphone PLC W129
Royal Mail Plc W314
Old Mutual Plc W274
National Westminster Bank Plc W255
TSB Banking Group Plc W375

Manchester
Co-operative Bank plc W103

Newbury
Vodafone Group Plc W388

Perth
SSE PLC W338

Slough
Reckitt Benckiser Group Plc W299

Southhampton
Carnival Plc W81

Welwyn Garden City
Tesco PLC (United Kingdom) W362

Windsor
Centrica Plc W86

GRC

Athens
National Bank Of Greece S A W252
Alpha Bank SA W23
Piraeus Bank SA W288
Eurobank Ergasias SA W145

HKG
China Mobile Limited W91
CITIC Ltd W100
Lenovo Group Ltd W218
China Unicom (Hong Kong) Ltd W95
Alibaba Group Holding Ltd W19
Jardine Matheson Holdings Ltd. W195
AIA Group Ltd. W12
Hongkong & Shanghai Banking Corp Ltd W173
Country Garden Holdings Co Ltd W109
CK Hutchison Holdings Ltd W100
Cnooc Ltd. W101
China Taiping Insurance Holding Co., Ltd. W95
WH Group Ltd W395
Standard Chartered Plc W339
China Overseas Land & Investment Ltd W92
BYD Co Ltd W77
Sun Art Retail Group Ltd. W346
China Resources Land Ltd W94
Geely Automobile Holdings Ltd W157
Boc Hong Kong Holdings Ltd W67
Hang Seng Bank Ltd. W164
Bank of East Asia Ltd. W47
Far East Horizon Ltd. W146
DBS Bank (Hong Kong) Limited W119

HUN

Budapest
MOL Magyar Olaj es Gazipari Reszvenytar W246

IDN

Jakarta
P.T. Astra International TBK W281
PT Bank Negara (Indonesia) W295

IND

Mumbai
Indian Oil Corp., Ltd. (India) W184
Reliance Industries Ltd W299
State Bank of India W341
Tata Motors Ltd W357
Tata Steel Ltd W358
Tata Consultancy Services Ltd W357
Larsen & Toubro Ltd W216
ICICI Bank Ltd (India) W181
Mahindra & Mahindra Ltd W230

IRL

Cork
Johnson Controls International plc W198

Dublin
Accenture plc W5
CRH Plc W112
Medtronic PLC W238
DCC Plc W119
Adient Plc W9
Allergan PLC W20
Aptiv PLC W28
Bank of Ireland Group plc W48
AIB Group PLC W13

Dublin 4
Eaton Corp plc W132

Swords
Ingersoll-Rand Plc W187

ISR

Petach Tikva
Teva Pharmaceutical Industries Ltd W362

Ramat Gan
Mizrahi Tefahot Bank Ltd W246

Tel-Aviv
Bank Hapoalim B.M. (Israel) W46
Bank Leumi Le-Israel B.M. W46
Israel Discount Bank Ltd. W190
FIBI Holdings Ltd. W149
First International Bank of Israel W150

ITA

Bologna
Unipol Gruppo SpA W383
UnipolSai Assicurazioni SpA W383

Milan
Telecom Italia SpA W358
Mediobanca Banca Di Credito Finanziario SpA W236

Milano
Unicredito SpA W380

Reggio Emilia
Credito Emiliano Spa Credem Reggio Emilia W111

Rome
Enel Societa Per Azioni W140
ENI S.p.A. W143

Torino
Intesa Sanpaolo S.P.A. W188

Trieste
Assicurazioni Generali S.p.A. W31

JPN

Aki-gun
Mazda Motor Corp. (Japan) W234

Chiba
Aeon Co. Ltd. (Japan) W10
Chiba Bank, Ltd W88
Keiyo Bank, Ltd. (The) (Japan) W204

Fukuoka
Kyushu Electric Power Co Inc W213

Fukushima
Toho Bank, Ltd. (The) W366

Gifu
Juroku Bank, Ltd. W200

Hamamatsu
Suzuki Motor Corp. (Japan) W350

Hino
Hino Motors, Ltd. W169

Iwata
Yamaha Motor Co Ltd W399

Kadoma
Panasonic Corp W281

Kanazawa
Hokkoku Bank, Ltd. (The) (Japan) W170

Kariya
Denso Corp. (Japan) W120
Aisin Seiki Co Ltd W16
Toyota Industries Corporation (Japan) W372

Kobe
Kobe Steel Ltd (Japan) W207
Kawasaki Heavy Industries Ltd (Japan) W203

Kofu
Yamanashi Chuo Bank, Ltd. (Japan) W400

Kyoto
Kyocera Corp W212
Nidec Corp W259
Bank of Kyoto Ltd (Japan) W48

Maebashi
Gunma Bank Ltd (The) W163

Matsue
San-In Godo Bank, Ltd. (The) (Japan) W318

Matsuyama
Iyo Bank, Ltd. (Japan) W192

Morioka
Bank of Iwate, Ltd. (The) (Japan) W48

Nagano
Hachijuni Bank, Ltd. (Japan) W163

Nagoya
Toyota Tsusho Corp W375
Chubu Electric Power Co., Inc. W98

A = AMERICAN BUSINESS
E = EMERGING COMPANIES
P = PRIVATE COMPANIES
W = WORLD BUSINESS

Suzuken Co Ltd W350
Central Japan Railway Co. W86
Bank of Nagoya, Ltd. W49

Nara
Nanto Bank, Ltd. W250

Numazu
Suruga Bank, Ltd. W350

Ogaki
Ogaki Kyoritsu Bank, Ltd. W274

Oita
Oita Bank Ltd (Japan) W274

Okayama
Chugoku Bank, Ltd. (The) W99

Osaka
Nippon Life Insurance Co. (Japan) W260
ITOCHU Corp (Japan) W192
Daiwa House Industry Co Ltd W115
Sumitomo Life Insurance Co. (Japan) W344
Kansai Electric Power Co., Inc. (Kansai Denryoku K. K.) (Japan) W202
Sumitomo Electric Industries, Ltd. (Japan) W344
Daikin Industries Ltd W113
Sekisui House, Ltd. (Japan) W323
Suntory Holdings Ltd W349
Kubota Corp. (Japan) W211
West Japan Railway Co W393

Otsu
Shiga Bank, Ltd. W326

Saitama
Musashino Bank, Ltd. W250

Sakai
Sharp Corp (Japan) W325

Sapporo
North Pacific Bank Ltd W270

Sendai
Tohoku Electric Power Co., Inc. (Japan) W366
77 Bank, Ltd. (The) (Japan) W1

Shizuoka
Shizuoka Bank Ltd (Japan) W329

Takamatsu
Hyakujushi Bank, Ltd. W176

Takasaki
Yamada Denki Co Ltd W399

Tokushima
Awa Bank, Ltd. W39

Tokyo
Honda Motor Co., Ltd.(Honda Giken Kogyo Kabushiki Kaisha) (Japan) W171
Japan Post Holdings Co Ltd W193
Nippon Telegraph & Telephone Corp (Japan) W263
JXTG Holdings Inc W200
Hitachi, Ltd. W169
SoftBank Group Corp W334
Sony Corp W337
Japan Post Insurance Co Ltd W194
Mitsubishi Corp W240
Marubeni Corp. W234
Dai-ichi Life Holdings Inc W113
Seven & i Holdings Co. Ltd. W324

Tokyo Electric Power Company Holdings Inc W368
Nippon Steel & Sumitomo Metal Corp W262
Tokio Marine Holdings Inc W367
MS&AD Insurance Group Holdings W249
KDDI Corp W204
Mitsui & Co., Ltd. W245
Sumitomo Corp. (Japan) W343
Mitsubishi UFJ Financial Group Inc W244
Sumitomo Mitsui Financial Group Inc Tokyo W345
NTT DoCoMo Inc W271
Mitsubishi Electric Corp W240
Toshiba Corp W371
Mitsubishi Heavy Industries Ltd W241
Fujitsu Ltd W156
Meiji Yasuda Life Insurance Co. W238
Canon, Inc. W80
Sompo Holdings Inc W336
Idemitsu Kosan Co Ltd W182
Mitsubishi Chemical Holdings Corp W240
JFE Holdings Inc W197
Bridgestone Corp (Japan) W73
Subaru Corporation W342
Medipal Holdings Corp W237
East Japan Railway Co. W132
Orix Corp W279
NEC Corp W256
Alfresa Holdings Corp Tokyo W19
Cosmo Energy Holdings Co Ltd W109
Mitsubishi Shokuhin Co., Ltd. W243
Komatsu Ltd W208
FUJIFILM Holdings Corp W155
Toray Industries, Inc. W369
Mitsubishi Motors Corp. (Japan) W243
Sumitomo Chemical Co., Ltd. W343
Nippon Yusen Kabushiki Kaisha W264
Recruit Holdings Co Ltd W299
NTT Data Corp W271
Isuzu Motors, Ltd. (Japan) W190
Ricoh Co Ltd W303
Nippon Steel & Sumikin Bussan Corp W261
Japan Post Bank Co Ltd W193
Asahi Kasei Corp W31
Fast Retailing Co., Ltd. W147
Japan Tobacco Inc. W194
Nippon Express Co Ltd W259
ANA Holdings Inc W26
Asahi Group Holdings Ltd. W31
Showa Shell Sekiyu K.K. W329
Obayashi Corp W272
T&D Holdings Inc W353
Bank of Japan W48
Kajima Corp. (Japan) W201
Sojitz Corp W335
Hanwa Co Ltd (Japan) W165
Tokyo Gas Co Ltd W369
Takeda Pharmaceutical Co Ltd W354
Kirin Holdings Co Ltd W206
Mitsui Fudosan Co Ltd W245
Lixil Group Corp W223
Mitsui OSK Lines Ltd W246
Mitsubishi Materials Corp. W242
IHI Corp W183
Taisei Corp W353
Daito Trust Construction Co., Ltd. W115
Yamato Holdings Co., Ltd. W400
Shimizu Corp. W326
Sony Life Insurance Co., Ltd. (Japan) W338
Sumitomo Mitsui Trust Holdings Inc W346

Sumitomo Mitsui Trust Bank Ltd W346
Nomura Holdings Inc W267
Fukoku Mutual Life Insurance Co (Japan) W156
Resona Holdings Inc Osaka W301
Shinsei Bank Ltd W328
Shoko Chukin Bank (The) (Japan) W329
Aozora Bank Ltd W28
Hiroshima Bank Ltd (The) (Japan) W169

Toyama
Hokuhoku Financial Group Inc W170

Toyota
Toyota Motor Corp W373

Tsu
Hyakugo Bank Ltd. (Japan) W176

Yokohama
Nissan Motor Co., Ltd. W264

KOR

Busan
BNK Financial Group Inc W65

Cheonan-si
Hyundai Pharmaceutical Co Ltd W179

Daegu
Korea Gas Corp. (South Korea) W210
DGB Financial Group Co Ltd W127

Icheon-si
SK Hynix Inc W332

Incheon
Hyundai Steel Co W180

Naju-si
Korea Electric Power Corp W210

Pohang-si
POSCO (South Korea) W291

Seongnam-si
KT Corp (Korea) W211

Seoul
Hyundai Motor Co., Ltd. W179
LG Electronics Inc W220
Kia Motors Corp. (South Korea) W205
Hanwha Corp W165
SK Innovation Co Ltd W333
Hyundai Mobis Co Ltd (South Korea) W178
Samsung Life Insurance Co Ltd W317
Samsung C&T Corp (New) W316
LG Display Co Ltd W219
LG Chem Ltd (New) W219
KB Financial Group, Inc. W203
Posco Daewoo Corp W293
Hanwha Life Insurance Co., Ltd. W165
Samsung Fire & Marine Insurance (South Korea) W317
Shinhan Financial Group Co. Ltd. W327
S-Oil Corp W315
Lotte Shopping Co Ltd W224
Doosan Corp. (Korea) W129
SK Telecom Co Ltd (South Korea) W333
CJ CheilJedang Corporation W100
Hyundai Glovis Co., Ltd. W177
GS Holdings Co., Ltd W162
E-MART Co Ltd W131
SK Networks Co Ltd W333

Hyundai Marine & Fire Insurance Co., Ltd. (South Korea) W178
Woori Bank (Korea) W396

Suwon-si
Samsung Electronics Co Ltd W317

Ulsan
Hyundai Heavy Industries Co Ltd W177

LBN

Beirut
Bank Audi SAL W46
Blom Bank SAL W65

LUX

Luxembourg
ArcelorMittal SA W29

MEX

Mexico City
Petroleos Mexicanos (Pemex) (Mexico) W285
America Movil SAB de CV W24
Wal-Mart de Mexico S.A.B. de C.V. W391
Grupo Financiero Banorte S.A. BDE C V W162

Monterrey
Fomento Economico Mexicano, S.A.B. de C.V. W151

San Pedro Garza Garcia
ALFA SAB de CV W18

MYS

Kuala Lumpur
Malayan Banking Berhad W230
CIMB Group Holdings Bhd W99
RHB Bank Berhad W303
Hong Leong Bank Berhad W173
AMMB Holdings BHD W25

NLD

Amsterdam
ING Groep NV W186
Heineken NV (Netherlands) W167
Heineken Holding NV (Netherlands) W167
X5 Retail Group NV W398
NN Group NV (Netherlands) W265
Koninklijke Philips NV W209

Diemen
Randstad NV W298

Leiden
Airbus SE W15

Rotterdam
Unilever N.V. W381

The Hague
Royal Dutch Shell Plc W313
AEGON NV W9

Zaandam
Koninklijke Ahold Delhaize NV W209

NOR

Fornebu
Telenor ASA W360

Lysaker
Storebrand ASA W342

Oslo
DNB ASA W129
Kommunalbanken A/S (Norway)
  W208

Stavanger
Equinor ASA W144

PER

Lima
CrediCorp Ltd. W109

PHL

Makati City
BDO Unibank Inc. W61
Bank of the Philippine Islands W51

POL

Plock
Polski Koncern Naftowy Orlen S.A.
  W291

Warsaw
Powszechny Zaklad Ubezpieczen SA
  W294
Bank Polska Kasa Opieki SA W51

PRT

Lisbon
EDP Energias de Portugal S.A. W133
Galp Energia, SGPS, SA W156

QAT

Doha
Qatar National Bank W296
Commercial Bank of Qatar W104
Qatar Islamic Bank W296

RUS

Krasnodar
Magnit PJSC W229

Moscow
PJSC Gazprom W288
Rosneft Oil Co OJSC (Moscow) W309
PJSC Lukoil W290
Sberbank Of Russia W320
PJSC Rosseti W291
Inter RAO UES PJSC W187
Transneft W375

St. Petersburg
Gazprom Neft PJSC W157
JSC VTB Bank W199

Tyumenskaya Oblast
Surgutneftegas PJSC W349

SAU

Riyadh
Saudi Basic Industries Corp - SABIC
  (Saudi Arabia) W320
Samba Financial Group W316
Saudi British Bank (The) W320

SGP

Flex Ltd W150
Oversea-Chinese Banking Corp. Ltd.
  (Singapore) W280
Olam International Ltd. W274
Jardine Cycle & Carriage Ltd W195
China Aviation Oil Singapore Corp Ltd
  W89
DBS Group Holdings Ltd. W119
United Overseas Bank Ltd. (Singapore)
  W384
Great Eastern Holdings Ltd
  (Singapore) W160

SWE

Gothenburg
Volvo Car Corp. (Sweden) W391

Stockholm
Telefonaktiebolaget LM Ericsson
  (Sweden) W359
Ericsson W144
Hennes & Mauritz AB W168
Skanska AB W333
Vattenfall AB W386
Nordea Bank ABp W268
AB Electrolux (Sweden) W2
Atlas Copco AB (Sweden) W36
Alecta pensionsforsakring, omsesidigt
  (Sweden) W18
Svenska Handelsbanken W351
Sveriges Riksbank (Sweden) W352

Sundbyberg
Swedbank AB W352

THA

Bangkok
PTT Public Co Ltd W295
Charoen Pokphand Foods Public Co.,
  Ltd. (Thailand) W88
C.P. All Public Co Ltd W78
Kasikornbank Public Co Ltd W202
Siam Commercial Bank Public Co Ltd
  (The) W330
Krung Thai Bank Public Co. Ltd.
  W211
Bangkok Bank Public Co., Ltd.
  (Thailand) W45
Bank of Ayudhya Public Co Ltd W46
Thanachart Capital Public Co Ltd
  W365

TUR

Istanbul
Turkiye Is Bankasi AS W377
Haci Omer Sabanci Holding AS W163
Turkiye Garanti Bankasi AS W376
AKBANK W17
Yapi Ve Kredi Bankasi AS W401

TWN

Hsinchu
Taiwan Semiconductor Manufacturing
  Co., Ltd. W354
Wistron Corp W395

New Taipei
Hon Hai Precision Industry Co Ltd
  W171

Taipei
Pegatron Corp W282
Compal Electronics Inc W106
Fubon Financial Holding Co Ltd
  W154
Inventec Corp W189
Asustek Computer, Inc. W35
Cathay Financial Holding Co W84
CTBC Financial Holdings Co Ltd
  W113
E Sun Financial Holdings Co Ltd
  W130

Taoyuan
Quanta Computer Inc W297

Yunlin County
Formosa Petrochemical Corp W152

ZAF

Johannesburg
Standard Bank Group Ltd W338
Absa Group Ltd (New) W4
Nedbank Group Ltd W256

Pretoria
South African Reserve Bank W338

Sandton
Investec Ltd W190

USA

ALABAMA

ANDALUSIA
Powersouth Energy Cooperative P436

AUBURN
Auburn University P50

BAY MINETTE
Baldwin County Board Of
  Education P54

BIRMINGHAM
Regions Financial Corp A699
Alabama Power Co A26
Protective Life Insurance Co A674
Proassurance Corp A669
Servisfirst Bancshares Inc A737 E366
National Commerce Corp A573 E292
Southern Nuclear Operating
  Company, Inc. P515
Mayer Electric Supply Company,
  Inc. P315
The Children's Hospital Of
  Alabama P571
The Southeastern Conference P605
University Of Alabama Health Services
  Foundation, P.c. P639
Consolidated Pipe & Supply Company,
  Inc. P140
Navigate Affordable Housing Partners,
  Inc P366
Spire Alabama Inc. P520
St. Vincent's Birmingham P537
Jefferson County Board Of
  Education P260
Brookwood Baptist Medical
  Center P86
Medical Properties Trust Inc E267
Servisfirst Bancshares Inc A737 E366
National Commerce Corp A573 E292
Diversified Gas & Oil Plc E108

BROOKWOOD
Warrior Met Coal Inc E432

DECATUR
Agri-afc, Llc P13

DOTHAN
Aaa Cooper Transportation P1
Houston County Healthcare
  Authority P242
Sunsouth Llc P548

HUNTSVILLE
The Health Care Authority Of The City
  Of Huntsville P584
Huntsville Hospital Health
  System P244
Dynetics, Inc. P170

MOBILE
Infirmary Health System, Inc. P248
University Of South Alabama P654
Mobile Infirmary Association P348
City Of Mobile P123
Providence Hospital P444

OPELIKA
East Alabama Health Care
  Authority P171

PRATTVILLE
River Financial Corp E357

SCOTTSBORO
American Associated Pharmacies P32

TUSCALOOSA
University Of Alabama P639
The Dch Health Care Authority P576
Century Health Alliance Joint
  Venture P108

ALASKA

ANCHORAGE
First National Bank Alaska A352
Northrim Banccorp Inc A601 E307
Chugach Alaska Corporation P120
Chenega Corporation P111
Southcentral Foundation P511
Wolf Creek Federal Services,
  Inc. P694
Northrim Banccorp Inc A601 E307

FAIRBANKS
University Of Alaska System P640
The Greater Fairbanks Community
  Hospital Foundation
  Incorporated P583

JUNEAU
Alaska Permanent Fund
  Corporation A28 P17
Sealaska Corporation P489

NOME
Bering Straits Native Corporation P69

SOLDOTNA
Central Peninsula General Hospital,
  Inc. P106

ARIZONA

CHANDLER
Chandler Regional Medical
  Center P109

A = AMERICAN BUSINESS
E = EMERGING COMPANIES
P = PRIVATE COMPANIES
W = WORLD BUSINESS

Chandler Unified School
District P109
Rogers Corp. E358

FLAGSTAFF
Flagstaff Medical Center, Inc. P194
Northern Arizona University P392

GILBERT
Gilbert Unified School District
41 P212

GLENDALE
Don Ford Sanderson Inc P164
Peoria Unified School District
No.11 P422

KINGMAN
Kingman Hospital, Inc. P276

MESA
Mesa Unified School District 4 P334

PHOENIX
Avnet Inc A93
Freeport-mcmoran Inc A367
Republic Services Inc A706
Southern Copper Corp A753
On Semiconductor Corp A619
Sprouts Farmers Market Inc A759
Western Alliance
Bancorporation A891 E434
Banner Health A110 P55
Shell Medical Plan P500
Tutor Perini Building Corp. P630
Phoenix Union High School District
No 210 P428
Paradise Valley Unified School
District P416
Estrella Banner Medical Center P187
Deer Valley School District 97 P157
Knight-swift Transportation Holdings
Inc E234
Vereit Inc E426
Grand Canyon Education Inc E179
Western Alliance
Bancorporation A891 E434
Cavco Industries Inc (de) E60
Cole Credit Property Trust Iv Inc E84

PRESCOTT
Davidson's, Inc. P154
Yavapai Community Hosp Assn P699

SCOTTSDALE
Magellan Health Inc. A524
Scottsdale Healthcare Corp. P487
Vitalant P670
Gha Technologies, Inc. P211
Godaddy Inc E179
Tpi Composites Inc E400
Healthcare Trust Of America Inc E189
Store Capital Corp E387

SUN CITY
Banner Health A110 P55

TEMPE
Insight Enterprises Inc. A454
Drivetime Automotive Group,
Inc. P165
Salt River Project Agricultural
Improvement And Power
District P477
Arizona State University P43
Sundt Construction, Inc. P546
Versum Materials Inc E427

TUCSON
The Sundt Companies Inc P605

Pima County P429
Tucson Unified School District P628
Northwest Hospital, Llc P397

YUMA
Yuma Regional Medical Center
Inc P701

ARKANSAS
BENTONVILLE
Walmart Inc A877

CONWAY
Home Bancshares Inc A424 E200

EL DORADO
Murphy Usa Inc A571

FAYETTEVILLE
Washington Regional Medical
System P676
Washington Regional Medical
Center P675

JONESBORO
St. Bernard's Hospital, Inc. P528
E. C. Barton & Company P171

LITTLE ROCK
Dillard's Inc. A266
Windstream Holdings Inc A902
Bank Ozk A106 E34
University Of Arkansas System P640
Arkansas Children's Hospital P44
Arkansas Electric Cooperatives,
Inc. P46
Arkansas Electric Cooperative
Corporation P45
St. Vincent Infirmary Medical
Center P537
Little Rock School District P292
Bank Ozk A106 E34

LOWELL
Hunt (j.b.) Transport Services,
Inc. A438

NORTH LITTLE ROCK
Comfort Systems Usa (arkansas),
Inc. P133

PINE BLUFF
Simmons First National Corp A742
E372

ROGERS
Ccf Brands Llc P101

SPRINGDALE
Tyson Foods Inc A834

STUTTGART
Riceland Foods, Inc. P460
Producers Rice Mill, Inc. P441

CALIFORNIA
AGOURA HILLS
American Homes 4 Rent E14

ALAMEDA
Exelixis Inc E137

ALHAMBRA
Alhambra Unified School District P22
Apollo Medical Holdings Inc E20

ALISO VIEJO
The New Home Company Inc E397

ANAHEIM
Anaheim Union High School Dist P38
Willdan Group Inc E439
Eaco Corp E110

APPLE VALLEY
St. Mary Medical Center P535

ARCADIA
Methodist Hospital Of Southern
California P335

BAKERSFIELD
Kern High School Dst P273
Jaco Oil Company P259
Bakersfield Memorial Hospital P53
Bakersfield City School District P53

BALDWIN PARK
Cedarwood-young Company P103

BEVERLY HILLS
Live Nation Entertainment Inc A516
Pacwest Bancorp A632 E321
Mgm Holdings Inc. P339
Cedars-sinai Medical Care
Foundation P102
Pacwest Bancorp A632 E321
Kennedy-wilson Holdings Inc E230

BRISBANE
Bi-rite Restaurant Supply Co.,
Inc. P73
Innoviva Inc E216
Cutera Inc E103

BURBANK
Disney (walt) Co. (the) A271

CALABASAS
Marcus & Millichap Inc E256

CALEXICO
Coppel Corporation P142

CARLSBAD
Homefed Corp. E201

CARMICHAEL
San Juan Unified School
District P480

CASTRO VALLEY
Eden Township Hospital District,
Inc P175

CERRITOS
First Choice Bancorp E152

CHICO
Trico Bancshares (chico, Ca) A829
E402

CHINO HILLS
Victory International Group, Llc P666

CHULA VISTA
Chg Foundation P112
Sweetwater Union High School
District P550
Sharp Chula Vista Medical
Center P497
Chula Vista Elementary School
District P120
Sharp Chula Vista Auxiliary Inc P497

CITRUS HEIGHTS
Deacon Holdings, Inc. P155

CITY OF INDUSTRY
Hacienda-la Puente Unified School
District P225

COLTON
Arrowhead Regional Medical
Center P46
Colton Joint Unified School
District P132

COMMERCE
Smart & Final Stores Inc A746

COMPTON
Compton Unified School
District P136

CORONA
Monster Beverage 1990
Corporation P351

COSTA MESA
Orange County Superintendent Of
Schools P408
Pacific Mercantile Bancorp E320

CUPERTINO
Apple Inc A69

DANVILLE
San Ramon Valley Unified School
District P480

DIAMOND BAR
South Coast Air Quality Management
District P510

DOWNEY
Los Angeles County Office Of
Education P296
Downey Unified School District P164

DUARTE
City Of Hope Medical
Foundation P123

DUBLIN
Ross Stores, Inc. A714

EAST PALO ALTO
Finjan Holdings Inc E148

EL SEGUNDO
A-mark Precious Metals, Inc A3
Mattel Inc A538
The Aerospace Corporation P564
Icrest International Llc P245
Stamps.com Inc. E384
Landmark Infrastructure Partners
Lp E239

ELK GROVE
Grove Elk Unified School
District P221

EMERYVILLE
Nmi Holdings Inc E304
Xoma Corp E446

ESCONDIDO
Henry Avocado Corporation P233

FAIRFIELD
Northbay Healthcare Group P391

FONTANA
Fontana Unified School District P199

FOSTER CITY
Gilead Sciences Inc A385
Quinstreet, Inc. E344
Qualys, Inc. E342

FOUNTAIN VALLEY
Memorial Health Services P323
Orange County Sanitation District
Financing Corporation P408

FREMONT
Synnex Corp A779
Lam Research Corp A501
Washington Township Healthcare
District P676
Ichor Holdings Ltd E211

FRESNO
Central Valley Community
Bancorp A183 E66
Fresno Community Hospital And
Medical Center P206

Community Hospitals Of Central
California P135
California's Valued Trust P91
Saint Agnes Medical Center P471
Central Valley Community
Bancorp A183 E66
United Security Bancshares (ca) E414

FULLERTON
St. Jude Hospital P532

GARDEN GROVE
Garden Grove Unified School
District P208

GLENDALE
Avery Dennison Corp A91

GOLETA
Deckers Outdoor Corp. E105
Inogen, Inc E217

GUADALUPE
Apio, Inc. P41

HAYWARD
Ultra Clean Holdings Inc E407

HEMET
Hemet Unified School District P233

IMPERIAL
Imperial Irrigation District P246

IRVINE
Opus Bank (irvine, Ca) A623 E317
Pacific Premier Bancorp Inc A630
E321
First Foundation Inc A346 E155
Pacific Premier Bank A630 P415
Newport Corporation P379
Irvine Unified School Distict P254
Pacific Premier Bank A630 P415
Corelogic Inc. E95
Masimo Corp. E261
Boot Barn Holdings Inc E45
Sabra Health Care Reit Inc E363
Calamp Corp E51
Opus Bank (irvine, Ca) A623 E317
Pacific Premier Bancorp Inc A630
E321
First Foundation Inc A346 E155

KENTFIELD
Marin General Hospital P307

KINGSBURG
Sun-maid Growers Of California P546

LA CANADA FLINTRIDGE
Allen Lund Company, Llc P25

LA JOLLA
The Scripps Research Institute P604

LA MESA
Grossmont Hospital Foundation P221

LA QUINTA
Desert Sands Unified School District
School Building Corporation P160

LAGUNA HILLS
Saddleback Memorial Medical
Center P471

LANCASTER
Antelope Valley Hospital, Inc. P40
Simulations Plus Inc. E374

LIVERMORE
Formfactor Inc E165

LODI
Farmers & Merchants Bancorp (lodi,
Ca) A316 E141
Pacific Coast Producers P414
Lodi Unified School District P293

Farmers & Merchants Bancorp (lodi,
Ca) A316 E141

LOMA LINDA
Loma Linda University Medical
Center P294

LONG BEACH
Molina Healthcare Inc A564
Farmers & Merchants Bank Of Long
Beach (ca) A317
Ta Chen International, Inc. P553
City Of Long Beach P123
Long Beach Memorial Medical
Center P295
St. Mary Medical Center P535

LOS ALTOS
The David And Lucile Packard
Foundation P576

LOS ANGELES
Aecom A15
Cbre Group Inc A172
Reliance Steel & Aluminum Co. A702
Kb Home A483
Mercury General Corp. A551
Hope Bancorp Inc A429 E204
Cathay General Bancorp A170
Hanmi Financial Corp. A400 E186
Preferred Bank (los Angeles, Ca) A666
E336
Rbb Bancorp A695 E346
Pacific City Financial Corp A629 E320
University Of Southern
California A859 P655
Rexford Industrial Realty, Inc. A707
P459
University Of Southern
California A859 P655
The Childrens Hospital Los
Angeles P571
Aids Healthcare Foundation P14
Los Angeles Department Of Water And
Power P297
Bergelectric Corp. P69
California Hospital Medical Center
Foundation P90
Loyola Marymount University P298
Cvr Nitrogen, Lp P149
Good Samaritan Hospital P213
Cha Hollywood Medical Center
Lp P108
Rexford Industrial Realty, Inc. A707
P459
W M Keck Foundation Inc P671
Korn Ferry E234
Air Lease Corp E7
Oaktree Capital Group Llc E311
Ares Management Corp E22
J2 Global Inc (new) E226
Houlihan Lokey Inc E206
Hudson Pacific Properties Inc E208
Kilroy Realty L.p. E232
Kilroy Realty Corp E232
Hope Bancorp Inc A429 E204
Hanmi Financial Corp. A400 E186
Preferred Bank (los Angeles, Ca) A666
E336
Rexford Industrial Realty Inc E356
Rbb Bancorp A695 E346
Pacific City Financial Corp A629 E320
Op Bancorp E317

LOS GATOS
Netflix Inc A580

LYNWOOD
St. Francis Medical Center P529

MADERA
Valley Children's Healthcare P662
Valley Children's Hospital P662

MALIBU
Pepperdine University P423

MANTECA
Manteca Unified School District P305

MARYSVILLE
Rideout Memorial Hospital P461

MENLO PARK
Facebook Inc A313
Robert Half International Inc. A710
Novo Construction, Inc. P400
Sri International P522
Hewlett, William And Flora
Foundation (inc) P236
Corcept Therapeutics Inc E94

MERCED
Mater Misericordiae Hospital P314

MILL VALLEY
Four Corners Property Trust
Inc E167

MILPITAS
Devcon Construction
Incorporated P161
Renesas Electronics America
Inc. P457
Silicon Graphics International
Corp. P502
Advantech Corporation P7
Lumentum Holdings Inc E249
Nanometrics, Inc. E290

MISSION VIEJO
Mission Hospital Regional Medical
Center Inc P345
Ensign Group Inc E124

MODESTO
Doctors Medical Center Of Modesto,
Inc. P163
Modesto City School District P348
Modesto Irrigation District (inc) P348

MONTEREY
Community Hospital Of The Monterey
Peninsula P134

MORENO VALLEY
Moreno Valley Unified School
District P352

MOUNTAIN VIEW
Alphabet Inc A36
Intuit Inc A465
Symantec Corp A777
Mozilla Foundation P356
Omnicell Inc E315
Ceva Inc E67
Chemocentryx, Inc. E72

NEWPORT BEACH
Chipotle Mexican Grill Inc A193
Hoag Memorial Hospital
Presbyterian P238
Smart Circle International Llc P505
Lyon (william) Homes E252
Kbs Strategic Opportunity Reit
Inc E229

NORCO
Corona-norco Unified School
District P143

NORTH HIGHLANDS
Twin Rivers Unified School
District P630

NOVATO
Bank Of Marin Bancorp A103
Hennessy Advisors Inc E193

OAKDALE
Oak Valley Bancorp (oakdale,
Ca) E311

OAKLAND
Clorox Co (the) A208
San Francisco Bay Area Rapid Transit
District P479
East Bay Municipal Utility District,
Water System P172
East Bay Municipal Utility District,
Wastewater System P172
E.l.f. Beauty Inc E110

ONTARIO
Cvb Financial Corp A247
Chaffey Joint Union High School
District P108
Ontario-montclair School
District P407

ORANGE
St. Joseph Hospital Of Orange P531
Orange County Transportation
Authority P409
Children's Hospital Of Orange
County P115
Chapman University P109
Roth Staffing Companies, L.p. P466
Sfpp, L.p. P495

OROVILLE
Oroville Hospital P410

PALM SPRINGS
Palm Springs Unified School
Dist. P415

PALMDALE
Palmdale School District P415

PALO ALTO
Hp Inc A435
Hewlett Packard Enterprise Co A418
Tesla Inc A798
Vmware Inc A875
Lucile Salter Packard Children's
Hospital At Stanford P300
Foodcomm International P200
Electric Power Research Institute,
Inc. P178
Sunlight Giving Foundation P547
Gordon E. And Betty I. Moore
Foundation P216

PASADENA
East West Bancorp, Inc E285 E113
California Institute Of
Technology P90
Pasadena Hospital Association,
Ltd. P419
Huntington Hospital P244
East West Bancorp, Inc A285 E113
Alexandria Real Estate Equities
Inc E9
Green Dot Corp E181
Western Asset Mortgage Capital
Corp E435

PERRIS
Val Verde Unified Sch Dis P662

PITTSBURG
Uss-posco Industries, A California
Joint Venture P661

PLACENTIA
Placentia-yorba Linda Unified School
District P430

PLEASANTON
Simpson Manufacturing Co., Inc.
(de) E373
Veeva Systems Inc E425
Ellie Mae Inc E118

A = AMERICAN BUSINESS
E = EMERGING COMPANIES
P = PRIVATE COMPANIES
W = WORLD BUSINESS

PLUMAS LAKE
Plumas Lake Elementary School
District A658 P431

POMONA
Pomona Unified School District P433
San Antonio Regional Hospital P479

PORTERVILLE
Sierra Bancorp A740 E369
R. M. Parks, Inc. P450
Sierra Bancorp A740 E369

POWAY
Cohu Inc E83

QUINCY
Plumas Bancorp Inc E334

REDDING
Mercy Home Services A California
Limited Partnership P330

REDWOOD CITY
Oracle Corp A624
Electronic Arts, Inc. A291
Shutterfly Inc E368

RIALTO
Rialto Unified School District P459

RICHMOND
West Contra Costa Unified School
District P681

RIVERSIDE
County Of Riverside P145
Riverside Unified School
District P462

ROLLING HILLS ESTATES
Natural Health Trends Corp. E295

ROSEMEAD
Edison International A290
Southern California Edison Co. A751

ROSEVILLE
Adventist Health System/west P7
Sutter Roseville Medical Center P549
Pride Industries P441

SACRAMENTO
State Of California A764 P540
Sutter Health A775 P548
State Of California A764 P540
Sutter Health A775 P548
Sacramento Municipal Utility
District P470
Alston Construction Company,
Inc. P28
Sacramento City Unified School
District P470
Alta California Regional Center,
Inc. P28

SALINAS
Salinas Valley Memorial Healthcare
Systems P476
Dynasty Farms, Inc. P170

SAN BERNARDINO
Inland Counties Regional Center,
Inc. P249

SAN CARLOS
Rudolph And Sletten, Inc. P467

SAN CLEMENTE
Icu Medical Inc E211
Caretrust Reit Inc E58

SAN DIEGO
Qualcomm Inc A684
Sempra Energy A735
Axos Financial Inc A94 E27
Axos Bank A94 P53
American Assets Trust, Inc. A44 P31
Sharp Healthcare P498
Scripps Health P487
Rady Children's Hospital And Health
Center P451
Sharp Memorial Hospital P499
Mercy Scripps Hospital P332
Rady Children's Hospital-san
Diego P451
Axos Bank A94 P53
Sharp Chula Vista Medical
Center P497
University Of San Diego P653
American Assets Trust, Inc. A44 P31
Coast Citrus Distributors P127
Resmed Inc. E354
Amn Healthcare Services Inc E17
Realty Income Corp E348
Encore Capital Group Inc E123
Nuvasive Inc E310
Axos Financial Inc A94 E27
Halozyme Therapeutics Inc E185
Retail Opportunity Investments
Corp E355
Sorrento Therapeutics Inc E377
Ligand Pharmaceuticals Inc E245
Rf Industries Ltd. E356

SAN FRANCISCO
Mckesson Corp A545
Wells Fargo & Co (new) A886
Visa Inc A874
Pg&e Corp (holding Co) A650
The Gap Inc A808
Federal Reserve Bank Of San
Francisco, Dist. No. 12 A324
Salesforce.com Inc A722
Schwab (charles) Corp (the) A728
Williams Sonoma Inc A900
Levi Strauss & Co. A509
First Republic Bank (san Francisco,
Ca) A353
Federal Home Loan Bank Of San
Francisco A322 E146
Lendingclub Corp A507
American Balanced Fund, Inc. A46
P32
The Irvine James Foundation A809
P586
Swinerton Builders P550
Schwab Charitable Fund P486
American Balanced Fund, Inc. A46
P32
Ilwu-pma Welfare Trust P246
University Of San Francisco Inc P654
Metropolitan Transportation
Commission P338
Mulesoft, Inc. P356
The Irvine James Foundation A809
P586
Digital Realty Trust Inc E107
Federal Home Loan Bank Of San
Francisco A322 E146
Yelp Inc E447
Sunrun Inc E390
Cai International Inc E50
Terreno Realty Corp E395

SAN JOSE
Cisco Systems Inc A198
Western Digital Corp A892
Paypal Holdings Inc A637
Ebay Inc. A287
Adobe Inc A11
Sanmina Corp A724
Heritage Commerce Corp A414 E194
Good Samaritan Hospital, L.p. P215

Santa Clara Valley Medical
Center P482
San Jose Medical Systems, L.p P479
San Jose Unified School District P480
Nimble Storage, Inc. P382
San Jose Water Company P480
Housing Authority Of The County Of
Santa Clara P241
Align Technology Inc E10
Sjw Group E375
Parade Technologies Ltd. E323
Quantenna Communications
Inc E344
Heritage Commerce Corp A414 E194

SAN JUAN CAPISTRANO
Capistrano Unified School
District P93
Emerald Expositions Events Inc E120

SAN LEANDRO
Energy Recovery Inc E124

SAN MATEO
Franklin Resources, Inc. A365
Tesla Energy Operations, Inc. P558
Essex Property Trust Inc E133

SAN PEDRO
Port Of Los Angeles P433

SAN RAFAEL
Westamerica Bancorporation A889

SAN RAMON
Chevron Corporation A191
Hill Physicians Medical Group,
Inc. P236

SANTA ANA
First American Financial Corp A334
Banc Of California Inc A97 E31
First American Trust Company A336
P194
Banc Of California Inc A97 E31

SANTA BARBARA
Direct Relief P162
Santa Barbara Cottage Hospital P482
Tri-counties Association For The
Developmentally Disabled, Inc. P623
Sansum Clinic P482
Appfolio Inc E20

SANTA CLARA
Intel Corp A455
Applied Materials, Inc. A70
Nvidia Corp A606
Advanced Micro Devices Inc A13
Agilent Technologies, Inc. A21
Svb Financial Group A776 E392
Avaya Holdings Corp. P52
President And Board Of Trustees Of
Santa Clara College P440
Robinson Oil Corporation P462
Santa Clara Unified School
District P482
Svb Financial Group A776 E392
Coherent Inc E82
Arista Networks Inc E23
Ambarella, Inc. E13

SANTA CRUZ
Dominican Hospital P163
Santa Cruz County Bank (ca) E365

SANTA MONICA
Activision Blizzard, Inc. A9
Ucla Medical Center P631
City Of Santa Monica P123
Douglas Emmett Inc E109
Entravision Communications
Corp. E129

SANTA PAULA
Calavo Growers, Inc. E52

SANTA ROSA
Luther Burbank Corp A521
Exchange Bank (santa Rosa, Ca) A307
Redwood Credit Union A697 P454
Santa Rosa Memorial Hospital
Inc P482
Sutter Santa Rosa Regional
Hospital P549
Redwood Credit Union A697 P454

SCOTTS VALLEY
Fox Factory Holding Corp E168

SOUTH SAN FRANCISCO
Core Mark Holding Co Inc A236

STANFORD
Leland Stanford Junior
University A506 P287
Stanford Health Care P538

STOCKTON
Stockton Unified School District P543
St. Josephs Medical Center Inc P532
University Of The Pacific P657

SUNNYVALE
Netapp, Inc. A580
Juniper Networks Inc A481
Hcl America Inc. P228
R.s. Hughes Company, Inc. P451
Fortinet Inc E165

SYLMAR
Tutor Perini Corp A832

THERMAL
Coachella Valley Unified School
District P127

THOUSAND OAKS
Amgen Inc A60
Los Robles Hospital & Medical
Center P297

TORRANCE
American Honda Finance
Corporation A51 P33
Harbor-ucla Medical Center P226
Torrance Unified School District P621
Motorcar Parts Of America Inc E286

TURLOCK
Yosemite Farm Credit, Aca A915 P700
Turlock Irrigation District P629
Yosemite Farm Credit, Aca A915 P700

TUSTIN
Humax Usa, Inc P243
Tustin Unified School District P630
Foundation Building Materials
Inc E167

UPLAND
San Antonio Regional Hospital P479

VALENCIA
Sunkist Growers, Inc. P547
Henry Mayo Newhall Memorial
Hospital P235

VAN NUYS
North La County Regional Center
Inc P387
Valley Presbyterian Hospital P663

VENTURA
Community Memorial Health
System P135
The Trade Desk Inc E398

VERNON
Lawrence Wholesale, Llc P284

VISALIA
Kaweah Delta Health Care
District P271
Visalia Unified School District P670

VISTA
Vista Unified School District Inc P670

WALNUT CREEK
John Muir Health P262
John Muir Physician Network P263
Central Garden & Pet Co E64
United States Brent Oil Fund
  L.p. E415

WATSONVILLE
Pajaro Valley Unified School
  District P415

WEST COVINA
Citrus Valley Medical Center,
  Inc. P122

WEST HOLLYWOOD
Cedars-sinai Medical Center P102

WESTLAKE VILLAGE
Pennymac Financial Services Inc
  (new) A641 E328
Ltc Properties, Inc. E249

WHEATLAND
Wheatland Union High School
  District A897 P687

WHITTIER
County Sanitation District No. 2 Of
  Los Angeles County P145

WOODLAND HILLS
B Riley Financial Inc E28

COLORADO

AURORA
University Of Colorado Health P641
Children's Hospital Colorado P113
Aurora Public Schools P52
Healthnotes Llc P231
Access Management Services, Llc P3

BOULDER
The Regents Of The University Of
  Colorado P601
Boulder Valley School District Re-
  2 P81

BROOMFIELD
Ball Corp A95
Whitewave Foods Company P689
Mwh Global, Inc. P360
Vail Resorts Inc E423

CENTENNIAL
Arrow Electronics, Inc. A76
Western States Fire Protection
  Company Inc P686

COLORADO SPRINGS
Compassion International Inc P136
Memorial Hospital Corporation P324
City Of Colorado Springs P122
Young Life P700
United States Olympic Committee
  Inc P636
Century Casinos Inc. E66

DENVER
Davita Inc A254
Dcp Midstream Lp A256
Western Union Co A893
Colorado Housing And Finance
  Authority A219 P131
Denver Health And Hospitals
  Authority Inc P159
Colorado State University
  System P132
St. Joseph Hospital, Inc. P531
Colorado Seminary P131
Mercy Housing, Inc. P331

Denver Board Of Water
  Commissioners P159
Colorado Housing And Finance
  Authority A219 P131
Summit Materials Inc E388
Antero Midstream Partners Lp E18
Coresite Realty Corp E96
Simply Good Foods Company
  (the) E373
Src Energy Inc E381
Hallador Energy Co E185
Farmland Partners Inc E142

ENGLEWOOD
Dish Network Corp A270
Qurate Retail Inc A688
Liberty Expedia Holdings Inc A510
Liberty Media Corp (de) A510
Catholic Health Initiatives A170 P99
Catholic Health Initiatives
  Colorado P101
American Furniture Warehouse Co
  Inc P32
Innospec Inc E215

FORT COLLINS
Poudre Valley Health Care, Inc. P435
Poudre School District P435

GOLDEN
Jefferson County School District No.
  R-1 P261

GRAND JUNCTION
St. Mary's Hospital & Medical Center,
  Inc. P536

GREELEY
Pilgrims Pride Corp. A653
Hensel Phelps Construction Co. P235
Ncmc Volunteers P368

GREENWOOD VILLAGE
Newmont Mining Corp (holding
  Co) A587
Great West Life & Annuity Insurance
  Co - Insurance Products A395
National Bank Holdings Corp A573
Cobank, Acb A214 P128
Air Methods Corporation P14
Xanterra Holding Corporation P697
Xanterra, Inc. P697
Parks Xanterra & Resorts Inc P418
Isec, Incorporated P254
Century Communities Inc E67

HIGHLANDS RANCH
Advanced Emissions Solutions Inc E5

LAKEWOOD
Rockies Express Pipeline Llc P464
Linnea Basey Cancer Resource
  Center P292
Alliance For Sustainable Energy,
  Llc P25
Natural Grocers By Vitamin Cottage
  Inc E294

LITTLETON
Stillwater Mining Company P543

LONGMONT
St. Vrain Valley School District Re-
  1j P538

LOVELAND
Medical Center Of The Rockies P321
Heska Corp. E196

PARKER
Parker Adventist Hospital P417

THORNTON
Adams 12 Five Star Schools P6

CONNECTICUT

BLOOMFIELD
Cigna Holding Co A194

BRIDGEPORT
People's United Financial Inc A643
Bridgeport Hospital P83
Fairfield Country Radiology A P189

CHESHIRE
Lane Industries Incorporated P282
The Lane Construction
  Corporation P589

DANBURY
Linde Plc A514

DARIEN
Genesee & Wyoming Inc. E171

FAIRFIELD
Save The Children Federation,
  Inc. P484

FARMINGTON
United Technologies Corp A853
Phalcon, Ltd. P425

GREENWICH
Xpo Logistics, Inc. A913
Berkley (wr) Corp A121
Greenwich Hospital P220
Interactive Brokers Group Inc E220
Starwood Property Trust Inc. E385

HAMDEN
Quinnipiac University P450

HARTFORD
Hartford Financial Services Group
  Inc. A405
Talcott Resolution Life Insurance
  Co A785
United Financial Bancorp Inc
  (new) A846 E414
Hartford Healthcare
  Corporation P227
Hartford Hospital P227
Eversource Energy Service
  Company P188
Saint Francis Hospital And Medical
  Center Foundation, Inc. P472
Connecticut State University
  System P139
Connecticut Children's Medical
  Center P138
United Financial Bancorp Inc
  (new) A846 E414

LAKEVILLE
Salisbury Bancorp, Inc. E363

MANCHESTER
Lydall, Inc. E251

NEW BRITAIN
Stanley Black & Decker Inc A761
Hospital Of Central Connecticut P240

NEW CANAAN
Bankwell Financial Group Inc A109
  E36

NEW HAVEN
Yale University P698
Yale-new Haven Hospital, Inc. P699
The United Illuminating
  Company P609
Yale New Haven Health Services
  Corporation P698

NEW LONDON
Lawrence + Memorial Hospital,
  Inc. P283

NORWALK
Booking Holdings Inc A138
Xerox Corp A911
Frontier Communications Corp A368
Emcor Group, Inc. A293
The Advanced Center For
  Rehabilitation Medicine Inc P564
The Norwalk Hospital
  Association P598
Factset Research Systems Inc. E140

NORWICH
The William W Backus Hospital P617

OLD GREENWICH
Ellington Residential Mortgaging Real
  Estate Investment Trust E119

ORANGE
Avangrid Inc A90

OXFORD
Rbc Bearings Inc E346

RIDGEFIELD
Chefs' Warehouse Inc (the) E70

SHELTON
Prudential Annuities Life Assurance
  Corp A675

STAMFORD
Charter Communications Inc
  (new) A187
Synchrony Financial A779
United Rentals Inc A850
Navigators Group Inc (the) A575
  E296
Equinor Marketing & Trading (us)
  Inc. A305 P185
Equinor Natural Gas Llc P185
Tudor Investment Corporation P628
Americares Foundation, Inc. P37
City Of Stamford P123
Providence Service Corp E339
Navigators Group Inc (the) A575
  E296
World Wrestling Entertainment
  Inc E444

STRATFORD
Northeast Medical Group, Inc. P391

UNCASVILLE
Mohegan Tribal Gaming
  Authority P348

WALLINGFORD
Amphenol Corp. A61

WATERBURY
Webster Financial Corp (waterbury,
  Conn) A882

WILLIMANTIC
Si Financial Group Inc (md) A740

WILTON
Blue Buffalo Pet Products, Inc. P76

WINDSOR
Ss&c Technologies Holdings Inc E382

DELAWARE

DOVER
Bayhealth Medical Center, Inc. P64
Chesapeake Utilities Corp. E74

LEWES
Beebe Medical Center, Inc. P67

NEWARK
Slm Corp. A745
University Of Delaware P641

A = AMERICAN BUSINESS
E = EMERGING COMPANIES
P = PRIVATE COMPANIES
W = WORLD BUSINESS

WILMINGTON
Chemours Co (the) A188
Navient Corp A574
Wsfs Financial Corp A907 E445
The Bancorp Inc A805
Balfour Beatty, Llc A95 P55
Wilmington Trust Company A901 P692
Balfour Beatty, Llc A95 P55
Alfred I.dupont Hospital For Children P22
Gannett Fleming Affiliates, Inc. P207
Wilmington Trust Company A901 P692
Interdigital Inc (pa) E221
Wsfs Financial Corp A907 E445

DISTRICT OF COLUMBIA

WASHINGTON
Federal Reserve System A325
Fannie Mae A315
Danaher Corp A252
Federal Agricultural Mortgage Corp A320 E142
Securities Investor Protection Corporation A733 P490
National Railroad Passenger Corporation P364
Wgl Holdings, Inc. P686
Aarp P1
Smithsonian Institution P505
The Georgetown University P582
Washington Hospital Center Corporation P674
Children's Hospital P113
Howard University (inc) P243
Medstar-georgetown Medical Center, Inc. P322
American University P37
Patient Access Network Foundation P420
Corporation For Public Broadcasting P143
The George Washington University Hospital P582
American Institutes For Research In The Behavioral Sciences P33
Securities Investor Protection Corporation A733 P490
Medical Faculty Associates, Inc. P321
Legal Services Corporation P286
American Foreign Service Protective Association P32
Aarp Foundation P2
World Wildlife Fund, Inc. P696
Network For Good, Inc. P370
Providence Hospital P444
Costar Group, Inc. E97
Cogent Communications Holdings, Inc. E80
Federal Agricultural Mortgage Corp A320 E142

FLORIDA

ALACHUA
Rti Surgical, Inc. E360

ALTAMONTE SPRINGS
Adventist Health System Sunbelt Healthcare Corporation A14 P7

BOCA RATON
Office Depot, Inc. A612
Johnson Controls Fire Protection Lp P267
Boca Raton Regional Hospital, Inc. P79
Florida Atlantic University P196
Geo Group Inc (the) (new) E174
Cross Country Healthcare Inc E100

BOYNTON BEACH
Bethesda Hospital, Inc. P71

BRADENTON
Beall's, Inc. P66
Manatee Memorial Hospital, L.p. P304

BRANDON
Galencare, Inc. P207

CLEARWATER
Tech Data Corp. A791
Heritage Insurance Holdings Inc A415
Morton Plant Hospital Association, Inc. P352
Marinemax Inc E258

COCONUT CREEK
Food For The Poor, Inc. P200
Willis Lease Finance Corp. E439

CORAL GABLES
Mastec Inc. (fl) A535
Dolphin Entertainment Inc E108

DADE CITY
Withlacoochee River Electric Cooperative Inc P694

DAVIE
Nova Southeastern University, Inc. P398

DAYTONA BEACH
Memorial Health Systems, Inc. P323
Brown & Brown Inc E46
Consolidated-tomoka Land Co. E91

DELRAY BEACH
Morse Operations, Inc. P352
Delray Medical Center, Inc. P159

DUNEDIN
Trustees Of Mease Hospital, Inc. P627

ESTERO
Hertz Global Holdings Inc (new) A416
The Hertz Corporation A809 P584

FORT LAUDERDALE
Autonation, Inc. A88
Universal Insurance Holdings Inc A857 E417
School Board Of Broward County, The (inc) P486
Broward County Public Schools P86
North Broward Hospital District P384
Broward General Medical Center P87
Suzano Pulp And Paper America, Inc P549
Signature Consultants Llc P501
Kemet Corp. E230
National Beverage Corp. E291
Bbx Capital Corp (new) E39
Universal Insurance Holdings Inc A857 E417

FORT MYERS
Lee County Electric Cooperative, Inc. P284
Gulf Coast Medical Centre Ltd P223
Somero Enterprises Inc E376

FORT PIERCE
Lawnwood Medical Center, Inc. P282

GAINESVILLE
University Of Florida P641
Shands Teaching Hospital And Clinics, Inc. P496
Florida Clinical Practice Association, Inc. P197
North Florida Regional Medical Center, Inc. P386

HIALEAH
Lifemark Hospitals Of Florida, Inc. P291

HOLLYWOOD
South Broward Hospital District P508
Heico Corp E192
Nv5 Global Inc E310

JACKSONVILLE
Csx Corp A242
Fidelity National Information Services Inc A329
Fidelity National Financial Inc A327
Jea P259
Crowley Holdings, Inc. P149
Baptist Health System, Inc. P57
Nemours Foundation P370
Duval County Public Schools P170
Southern Baptist Hospital Of Florida Inc. P512
Shands Jacksonville Healthcare, Inc. P496
Shands Jacksonville Medical Center, Inc. P496
Mayo Clinic Jacksonville (a Nonprofit Corporation) P317
The Stellar Companies Inc P605
St. Vincent's Medical Center, Inc. P538
Wounded Warrior Project, Inc. P697
Pavilion Health Services, Inc. P421
University Of Florida Jacksonville Physicians Inc P642
Miller Electric Company P343
Black Knight Inc E43
Regency Centers Corp E348

JUNO BEACH
Nextera Energy Inc A590
Florida Power & Light Co. A357

KEYSTONE HEIGHTS
Clay Electric Cooperative, Inc. P126

KISSIMMEE
The School District Of Osceola County Fl P603

LAKELAND
Publix Super Markets, Inc. A679 P448
Midflorida Federal Credit Union A560 P342
Publix Super Markets, Inc. A679 P448
Lakeland Regional Medical Center, Inc. P280
Midflorida Federal Credit Union A560 P342

LARGO
Largo Medical Center, Inc. P282

MAITLAND
Florida Hospital Medical Group, Inc. P198

MANGONIA PARK
St Mary's Medical Center P525

MELBOURNE
Harris Corp. A404

MIAMI
World Fuel Services Corp. A905
Lennar Corp A507
Ryder System, Inc. A717
The School Board Of Miami-dade County P602

Public Health Trust Of Miami Dade County P445
Baptist Hospital Of Miami, Inc. P59
Variety Children's Hospital P664
Kendall West Baptist Hospital Inc P271
Vector Group Ltd E424
Ladenburg Thalmann Financial Services Inc E236

MIAMI BEACH
Mount Sinai Medical Center Of Florida, Inc. P355

MIAMI LAKES
Bankunited Inc. A108 E35

MULBERRY
W.s. Badcock Corporation P672

NAPLES
Naples Community Hospital Inc P361
Beasley Broadcast Group Inc E40

NORTH VENICE
Pgt Innovations Inc E330

OCALA
Monroe Regional Health System P350
Marion Community Hospital Inc P307

ORLANDO
Darden Restaurants, Inc. A253
Wyndham Destinations Inc A908
The Orange County Public School District P599
Florida Municipal Power Agency P198
Campus Crusade For Christ Inc P92
Central Florida Expressway Authority P105
Greater Orlando Aviation Authority P220
Hilton Grand Vacations Inc E198
Xenia Hotels & Resorts Inc E446
National Retail Properties Inc E293
Gencor Industries Inc E170

PENSACOLA
Baptist Hospital, Inc. P59
Lakeview Center, Inc P281

ROCKLEDGE
Health First, Inc. P229

SAFETY HARBOR
Mease Countryside Ambulatory Care Center P320

SAINT PETERSBURG
Raymond James & Associates Inc A692 P454
Johns Hopkins All Children's Hospital, Inc. P264
St. Anthony's Hospital, Inc. P527

SARASOTA
Roper Technologies Inc A713
Sarasota County Public Hospital District P483
Sun Hydraulics Corp. E390

SEMINOLE
Superior Group Of Companies Inc E390

SOUTH MIAMI
Baptist Health South Florida, Inc. P57
South Miami Hospital, Inc. P510

ST. PETERSBURG
Jabil Inc A470
Raymond James Financial, Inc. A692
Duke Energy Florida Llc A282
United Insurance Holdings Corp A847 E414

STUART

Seacoast Banking Corp. Of Florida A731 E365
Martin Memorial Health Systems, Inc. P310
Martin Memorial Medical Center, Inc P310
Seacoast Banking Corp. Of Florida A731 E365

SUNRISE

Fednat Holding Co E146

TALLAHASSEE

Capital City Bank Group, Inc. A161
Florida Housing Finance Corp A357 P198
Tallahassee Memorial Healthcare, Inc. P554
Florida Housing Finance Corp A357 P198

TAMPA

Wellcare Health Plans Inc A884
Hillsborough County School District P237
County Of Hillsborough P144
H. Lee Moffitt Cancer Center And Research Institute, Inc. P225
Florida Health Sciences Center Inc P197
Seminole Electric Cooperative, Inc. P491
University Community Hospital, Inc. P637
Health Insurance Innovations Inc E188
Carter Validus Mission Critical Reit Inc E60

WEST PALM BEACH

The School District Of West Palm Beach County P603
Chatham Lodging Trust E69

WESTON

Ultimate Software Group, Inc. E406

WINTER HAVEN

Centerstate Bank Corp A181 E63
Winter Haven Hospital, Inc. P693
Centerstate Bank Corp A181 E63

GEORGIA

ACWORTH

Cobb County Public Schools P129

ALBANY

Phoebe Putney Memorial Hospital, Inc. P427

ALPHARETTA

National Christian Charitable P363
Colonial Pipeline Company P130
Jackson Healthcare, Llc P258
Plantation Pipe Line Company P431

ATHENS

University Of Georgia P642

ATLANTA

Home Depot Inc A425
United Parcel Service Inc A849
Delta Air Lines Inc (de) A261
Coca-cola Co (the) A215
Southern Company (the) A752
Genuine Parts Co. A380
Westrock Co A895
Pultegroup Inc A680
Suntrust Banks Inc A773
Veritiv Corp A869
Georgia Power Co A382

Federal Reserve Bank Of Atlanta, Dist. No. 6 A322
Ncr Corp A578
Intercontinental Exchange Inc A457
Hd Supply Holdings Inc A411
Fidelity Southern Corp A330 E147
Atlantic Capital Bancshares Inc A86
Board Of Regents Of The University System Of Georgia A135 P78
Lettie Pate Evans Foundation A509 P288
Board Of Regents Of The University System Of Georgia A135 P78
Heartland Payment Systems, Llc P232
Northside Hospital, Inc. P395
Action Capital Corporation P5
Grady Memorial Hospital Corporation P217
Logisticare Solutions, Llc P293
Fulton County Board Of Education P207
Earthlink Holdings, Llc P171
Piedmont Hospital, Inc. P428
Emory University Hospital Midtown P182
Municipal Electric Authority Of Georgia P358
Cooperative For Assistance And Relief Everywhere, Inc. (care) P141
Balfour Beatty Infrastructure, Inc. P55
Ntg Investment Partners, Inc P400
Georgia Tech Applied Research Corporation P211
Lettie Pate Evans Foundation A509 P288
Southern Power Co E379
Gray Television Inc E180
Manhattan Associates, Inc. E256
Cousins Properties Inc E98
Preferred Apartment Communities Inc. E335
Fidelity Southern Corp A330 E147
Marine Products Corp E258

AUGUSTA

Doctors Hospital Of Augusta, Llc P163

AUSTELL

Cobb Hospital, Inc. P129

BLAIRSVILLE

United Community Banks Inc (blairsville, Ga) A843 E412

BRUNSWICK

Map International (inc.) P305

CALHOUN

Mohawk Industries, Inc. A563

COLUMBUS

Aflac Inc A18
Total System Services, Inc. A822
Synovus Financial Corp A780
The Medical Center P591
Muscogee County School District P359

CONYERS

Pratt Corrugated Holdings, Inc. P437
Pratt Industries, Inc. P437

CUMMING

Forsyth County Board Of Education P201
Sawnee Electric Membership Corporation P485

DALLAS

Paulding County Board Of Education P421

DECATUR

Global Health Solutions Inc P213
County Of Dekalb P144
Dekalb Regional Health System, Inc. P158
Dekalb Medical Center, Inc. P157

DOUGLASVILLE

Douglas County Board Of Education P164

DULUTH

Agco Corp. A19
Asbury Automotive Group Inc A78
Primerica Inc A667
National Vision Holdings Inc E294

FAYETTEVILLE

Fayette Community Hospital, Inc. P192

GAINESVILLE

Northeast Georgia Medical Center, Inc. P391
Hall County Board Of Education P225

JEFFERSON

Jackson Electric Membership Corporation P258

JOHNS CREEK

Ebix Inc E115

JONESBORO

County Of Clayton P143

KENNESAW

Municipal Gas Authority Of Georgia P358

LAWRENCEVILLE

Gwinnett Hospital System, Inc. P224

MACON

The Medical Center Of Central Georgia Inc P591

MARIETTA

Cobb County Board Of Education P128
Kennestone Hospital Inc P272
The Conlan Company P575
Cobb Electric Membership Corporation P129
Wellstar Health System, Inc. P680
Kennestone Hospital At Windy Hill, Inc. P272

MCDONOUGH

Henry County Board Of Education P234

MILLEDGEVILLE

Baldwin County Board Of Education P54

MOULTRIE

Ameris Bancorp A57 E15

NORCROSS

Deutz Corporation P160
Venture Construction Company Inc P666

PEACHTREE CORNERS

Fleetcor Technologies Inc E162

PENDERGRASS

Takeuchi Mfg. (u.s.), Ltd. P554

PERRY

Houston County Board Of Education P242

RICHMOND HILL

The Sommers Company P605

ROME

Floyd Healthcare Management, Inc. P198

ROSWELL

Siteone Landscape Supply Inc E374

SAVANNAH

Memorial Health, Inc. P324
Savannah-chatham County Board Of Education P484
Savannah Health Services, Llc P484
Candler Hospital, Inc. P92

SMYRNA

Floor & Decor Holdings Inc E163

STATESBORO

Agsouth Farm Credit Aca A22 P13

SUWANEE

Gwinnett County Board Of Education P224

THOMASVILLE

Archbold Medical Center, Inc. P42
John D Archbold Memorial Hospital P262
Thomasville Bancshares, Inc. E398

TUCKER

Georgia Transmission Corporation P211

VALDOSTA

Hospital Authority Of Valdosta And Lowndes County, Georgia P240
South Georgia Medical Center P510

WEST POINT

Powertech America, Inc. P437
Powertech America Sales, Llc P436

HAWAII

HONOLULU

First Hawaiian Inc A347
Bank Of Hawaii Corp A102
Central Pacific Financial Corp A182
Territorial Bancorp Inc A798
Servco Pacific Inc. P493
The Queen's Health Systems P601
Suasin Cancer Care Inc. P544
University Of Hawaii P643
Trustees Of The Estate Of Bernice Pauahi Bishop P627
Kapiolani Medical Center For Women And Children P270
Housing Finance And Development Corp P242

MAUI

Maui Land & Pineapple Co., Inc. E264

WAIPAHU

Albert C. Kobayashi, Inc P19

IDAHO

BOISE

Albertsons Companies Inc A29
Micron Technology Inc. A559
St. Luke's Health System, Ltd. P534
Saint Alphonsus Regional Medical Center, Inc. P472
Employers Resource Management Company P183
Us Ecology, Inc. E420

COEUR D ALENE

Kootenai Hospital District P277

A = AMERICAN BUSINESS
E = EMERGING COMPANIES
P = PRIVATE COMPANIES
W = WORLD BUSINESS

GENESEE
Pacific Northwest Farmers
Cooperative Inc. P415

HAILEY
Power Engineers, Incorporated P436

IDAHO FALLS
Potandon Produce L.l.c. P435

MERIDIAN
Engineered Structures, Inc. P184
Joint School District 2 P268

ILLINOIS

ABBOTT PARK
Abbott Laboratories A4

ARLINGTON HEIGHTS
Northwest Community Hospital
Inc P396
Okaya (u.s.a.), Inc. P405
Township High School District
214 P622

AURORA
Old Second Bancorp., Inc. (aurora,
Ill.) A616
Cabot Microelectronics Corp E49

BATAVIA
Fermi Research Alliance, Llc P193

BLOOMINGTON
Growmark, Inc. A397 P221

BOLINGBROOK
Ulta Beauty Inc A836

BUFFALO GROVE
Produce Alliance, L.l.c. P441

BURR RIDGE
Bankfinancial Corp A107

CARBONDALE
Southern Illinois Healthcare
Enterprises, Inc. P513
Southern Illinois University Inc P513
Southern Illinois Healthcare E P512

CARMI
Martin & Bayley, Inc. P310

CHAMPAIGN
First Busey Corp A339 E150

CHICAGO
Boeing Co. (the) A135
Archer Daniels Midland Co. A73
United Continental Holdings
Inc A845
Exelon Corp A308
Lkq Corp A518
Cna Financial Corp A210
Conagra Brands Inc A229
Jones Lang Lasalle Inc A477
Donnelley (rr) & Sons Company A277
Motorola Solutions Inc A569
Old Republic International
Corp. A615
Northern Trust Corp A598
Telephone & Data Systems Inc A793
Federal Reserve Bank Of Chicago,
Dist. No. 7 A322
Hyatt Hotels Corp A444
Kemper Corp (de) A486
Mb Financial Inc A540 E265

First Midwest Bancorp, Inc.
(naperville, Il) A351 E158
Byline Bancorp Inc A156
Marquette National Corp (il) A529
Board Of Education Of City Of
Chicago A134 P78
The University Of Chicago P609
Rush University Medical Center P467
The University Of Chicago Medical
Center P610
Northwestern Memorial
Hospital P397
The Pepper Companies Inc P600
Pepper Construction Group, Llc P423
Metropolitan Water Reclamation
District Of Greater Chicago P338
Pepper Construction Company P422
Crowe Llp P149
Regional Transportation
Authority P456
Chicago Transit Authority P113
O'neil Industries, Inc. P401
Sinai Health System P504
Loyola University Of Chicago
Inc P299
De Paul University P155
Newark Electronics Corporation P378
North Advocate Side Health
Network P384
Chicago Park District P113
Chicago Community Trust P112
Rehabilitation Institute Of
Chicago P457
Presence Chicago Hospitals
Network P440
American Medical Association Inc P34
Cboe Global Markets Inc E62
Echo Global Logistics Inc E116
Transunion E400
Tribune Media Co E401
John Bean Technologies Corp E227
Littelfuse Inc E246
Mb Financial Inc A540 E265
Grubhub Inc E183
First Midwest Bancorp, Inc.
(naperville, Il) A351 E158
Cars.com Inc E60
Kaanapali Land Llc E228
United American Healthcare
Corp. E410

CRYSTAL LAKE
Centegra Health System
Foundation P103

DEERFIELD
Walgreens Boots Alliance Inc A876
Caterpillar Inc. A169
Mondelez International Inc A566
Baxter International Inc A112
Fortune Brands Home & Security,
Inc. A363
Scai Holdings, Llc P485
Terra Nitrogen Company, L.p. P558

DOWNERS GROVE
Univar Inc A856
Dover Corp A278
Invesco Db Commodity Index
Tracking Fund A466
Advocate Health Care Network A15
P9
Midwestern University P343

EFFINGHAM
Midland States Bancorp Inc A560
E278
Effingham Equity P176
Midland States Bancorp Inc A560
E278

ELGIN
Sherman Advocate Hospital P500

Middleby Corp E277

ELK GROVE VILLAGE
Alexian Brothers Medical Center
Inc P22

ELMHURST
Elmhurst Memorial Hospital
Inc P180

EVANSTON
Northwestern University P397
North Shore University Health
System P390
Rotary International P465

FREEPORT
Furst-mcness Company P207

GENEVA
Delnor-community Hospital P158

GLENVIEW
Illinois Tool Works, Inc. A449
Anixter International Inc A65

HARVEY
The Ingalls Memorial Hospital P585

HINSDALE
Adventist Midwest Health P8

HOFFMAN ESTATES
Sears Holdings Corp A732
St. Alexius Medical Center P526

JOLIET
Will County P691

KANKAKEE
Riverside Medical Center P462

LAKE FOREST
Grainger (w.w.) Inc. A392
Tenneco Inc A795
Packaging Corp Of America A631

LIBERTYVILLE
Brightstar Us, Inc. P83
Aldridge Electric, Inc. P20

LINCOLNSHIRE
Cdw Corp A176

LISLE
Navistar International Corp. A577

MATTOON
First Mid-illinois Bancshares
Inc A350 E157
Consolidated Communications
Holdings Inc E90
First Mid-illinois Bancshares
Inc A350 E157

METTAWA
Brunswick Corp. A150

MOLINE
Deere & Co. A259
Qcr Holdings Inc A683 E341

MORTON
Core Construction Group, Ltd. P142

NAPERVILLE
Edward-elmhurst Healthcare P176
Edward Hospital P176
Naperville Community Unit School
District 203 P361

NEW LENOX
Silver Cross Health System P503
Silver Cross Hospital And Medical
Centers P503

NORTH CHICAGO
Abbvie Inc A5

NORTHBROOK
Allstate Corp A32

OAK BROOK
Mcdonald's Corp A544
Treehouse Foods Inc A828
Ace Hardware Corporation A8 P4
Irc Retail Centers Llc A470 P253
Ace Hardware Corporation A8 P4
Irc Retail Centers Llc A470 P253

PALATINE
Township High School District 211
Foundation P622

PARIS
North American Lighting, Inc. P384

PARK RIDGE
Advocate Health And Hospitals
Corporation P8

PEORIA
Rli Corp A709
Osf Healthcare System P411

PLAINFIELD
Plainfield Community Consolidated
School District 202 P430

QUINCY
Blessing Hospital P75

RIVERWOODS
Discover Financial Services A268

ROCKFORD
Swedishamerican Hospital P550
Rockford, Board Of Education P464
Bea Javon Hospital P66

ROLLING MEADOWS
Gallagher (arthur J.) & Co. A370
Myr Group Inc E289

ROMEOVILLE
Valley View Community Unit School
District 365u P663

ROSEMONT
Us Foods Holding Corp A866
Wintrust Financial Corp (il) A903
E441
The Big Ten Conference Inc P566
Wintrust Financial Corp (il) A903
E441

SCHAUMBURG
Paylocity Holding Corp E325

SPRINGFIELD
Horace Mann Educators Corp. A430
Memorial Medical Center P324
Tom Lange Company, Inc. P620
Illinois Municipal Electric
Agency P246

TINLEY PARK
Panduit Corp. P415

URBANA
The Carle Foundation P568
Carle Foundation Hospital P95

VERNON HILLS
Graham Enterprise, Inc. P217

WESTCHESTER
Ingredion Inc A453

INDIANA

BLOOMINGTON
Trustees Of Indiana University P626
Indiana University Health
Bloomington, Inc. P248

CARMEL
Cno Financial Group Inc A212
Merchants Bancorp (indiana) A549
Midcontinent Independent System
Operator, Inc. P342

CLARKSVILLE
First Savings Financial Group
Inc E160

COLUMBUS
Cummins, Inc. A245

CORYDON
First Capital Inc. E151

CRAWFORDSVILLE
Ceres Solutions, Llp P108

DANVILLE
Hendricks County Hospital P233

DECATUR
Adams County Memorial Hospital P6

ELKHART
Thor Industries, Inc. A816
Lci Industries E240
Patrick Industries Inc E323

EVANSVILLE
Berry Global Group Inc A124
Onemain Holdings Inc A621
Old National Bancorp (evansville,
In) A613
Deaconess Health System, Inc. P155
Atlas World Group, Inc. P49
Deaconess Hospital Inc P156
Southern Indiana Gas & Electric
Company P514
St. Mary's Health, Inc. P535

FISHERS
First Internet Bancorp A348 E155

FORT WAYNE
Steel Dynamics Inc. A767
Do It Best Corp. P162
Petroleum Traders Corporation P425

GARY
The Methodist Hospitals Inc P592

INDIANAPOLIS
Anthem Inc A67
Lilly (eli) & Co A510
Simon Property Group, Inc. A743
Oneamerica Financial Partners,
Inc. A621 P407
The Finish Line Inc P579
Oneamerica Financial Partners,
Inc. A621 P407
National Collegiate Athletic
Association P363
Wabash Valley Power Association
Inc P672
Pepper Construction Company Of
Indiana, Llc P423
Protrans International, Inc. P443
Federal Home Loan Bank
Indianapolis E144
Kite Realty Group Trust E233

JASPER
German American Bancorp Inc A383
E175
Kimball Electronics Inc E232
German American Bancorp Inc A383
E175

LAFAYETTE
St Elifranciscan & Elizabeth
Health P524

LEBANON
Witham Memorial Hospital P694

MERRILLVILLE
Nisource Inc. (holding Co.) A593
Northern Indiana Public Service
Company P393

MICHIGAN CITY
Horizon Bancorp Inc A430 E204

MISHAWAKA
Franciscan Alliance, Inc. P202
Saint Joseph Regional Medical Center-
south Bend Campus Inc P473

MONON
Vanguard National Trailer
Corporation P664

MUNCIE
First Merchants Corp A349 E156
Mutualfirst Financial Inc A572
Mutualbank A572 P359
First Merchants Corp A349 E156

MUNSTER
Community Foundation Of Northwest
Indiana, Inc. P134
Munster Medical Research
Foundation, Inc P359

NEWBURGH
Energy Systems Group, Llc P183

PORTLAND
Indiana Fcc Inc P248

RICHMOND
Reid Hospital & Health Care Services,
Inc. P457
Reid Hospital Mso, Llc P457

SEYMOUR
Jackson County Schneck Memorial
Hospital P257

SOUTH BEND
1st Source Corp A1

TERRE HAUTE
First Financial Corp. (in) A346
Union Hospital, Inc. P633

VINCENNES
Good Samaritan Hospital P213

WARSAW
Zimmer Biomet Holdings Inc A917
Lakeland Financial Corp A500 E238

WEST LAFAYETTE
Purdue University P449

IOWA

AMES
Iowa State University Of Science And
Technology P253

ANKENY
Casey's General Stores, Inc. A167
Perishable Distributors Of Iowa,
Ltd. P424

CEDAR RAPIDS
United Fire Group, Inc. A846
Merrill Lynch Life Insurance Co -
Insurance Products A553 E274
St Luke's Methodist Hospital
Inc P525
Mercy Hospital, Cedar Rapids,
Iowa P331
Merrill Lynch Life Insurance Co -
Insurance Products A553 E274

COUNCIL BLUFFS
Future Foam, Inc. P207

DAVENPORT
Genesis Health System P210

DES MOINES
Principal Financial Group Inc A668
Federal Home Loan Bank Of Des
Moines A321 E145
Emc Insurance Group Inc. A292
Iowa Finance Authority A468 P252
Catholic Health Initiatives - Iowa,
Corp. P101
Central Iowa Hospital Corp P106
Iowa Finance Authority A468 P252
Federal Home Loan Bank Of Des
Moines A321 E145
Meredith Corp E271

DUBUQUE
Heartland Financial Usa, Inc.
(dubuque, Ia) A411 E191

FOREST CITY
Winnebago Industries, Inc. E440

GOLDFIELD
Gold-eagle Cooperative P213

HILLS
Hills Bancorporation A419

IOWA CITY
Midwestone Financial Group,
Inc. A562 E279
The University Of Iowa P611
University Of Iowa Hospitals And
Clinics P643
Act, Inc. P5
Midwestone Financial Group,
Inc. A562 E279

JOHNSTON
Dll Finance Llc A273 P162

MONTICELLO
Innovative Ag Services Co. P249

SIOUX CENTER
Farmers Cooperative Society P191

WATERLOO
Covenant Medical Center, Inc. P146

WEST BURLINGTON
Big River Resources, Llc. P73

WEST DES MOINES
American Equity Investment Life
Holding Co A47
Fbl Financial Group Inc A319
West Bancorporation, Inc. A888
Iowa Student Loan Liquidity
Corporation A468 P253
Iowa Health System P252
Heartland Co-op P231
Iowa Student Loan Liquidity
Corporation A468 P253

KANSAS

KANSAS CITY
Dairy Farmers Of America, Inc. A251
P150
Associated Wholesale Grocers,
Inc. A82 P48
Dairy Farmers Of America, Inc. A251
P150
Associated Wholesale Grocers,
Inc. A82 P48
The University Of Kansas
Hospital P612

LEAWOOD
Amc Entertainment Holdings
Inc. A40
Amc Entertainment Inc. P30

Tallgrass Pony Express Pipeline
Llc P555
Euronet Worldwide Inc. E134

MANHATTAN
Kansas State University P270

MERRIAM
Seaboard Corp. A730

MOUNDRIDGE
Mid-kansas Cooperative
Association P341
Team Marketing Alliance, Llc P556

OLATHE
Olathe Unified School District
233 P406

OVERLAND PARK
Sprint Corp (new) A759
Yrc Worldwide Inc A915
Black & Veatch Holding
Company P75
Bvh, Inc. P88
Npc Restaurant Holdings, Llc P400

SHAWNEE MISSION
Shawnee Mission Medical Center,
Inc. P499
Shawnee Mission School
District P500

TOPEKA
Capitol Federal Financial Inc A164
Stormont-vail Healthcare, Inc. P543
Federal Home Loan Bank
Topeka E146

WICHITA
Spirit Aerosystems Holdings Inc A758
Equity Bancshares Inc A305 E131
Unified School District 259 P633
Wesley Medical Center, Llc P681
Via Christi Hospitals Wichita,
Inc. P666
Wichita, City Of (inc) P691
Equity Bancshares Inc A305 E131

KENTUCKY

ASHLAND
King's Daughters Health System,
Inc. P276
Ashland Hospital Corporation P47

BOWLING GREEN
Bowling Green-warren County
Community Hospital
Corporation P81

ELIZABETHTOWN
The Hardin Memorial Hospital
Foundation Inc P584

FRANKLIN
Keystops, Llc P275

HENDERSON
Kenergy Corp. P271

HOPKINSVILLE
Grupo Antolin Kentucky, Inc. P222

LEXINGTON
Appalachian Regional Healthcare,
Inc. P41
Kentucky Medical Services
Foundation, Inc. P273

LOUISVILLE
Humana Inc. A437
Yum! Brands Inc A917
Republic Bancorp, Inc. (ky) A704
E352
Stock Yards Bancorp Inc A771

A = AMERICAN BUSINESS
E = EMERGING COMPANIES
P = PRIVATE COMPANIES
W = WORLD BUSINESS

Baptist Healthcare System, Inc. P58
Norton Hospitals, Inc P398
Jefferson County Board Of Education P260
Almost Family, Inc. P27
University Medical Center Inc P638
Texas Roadhouse Inc E397
Turning Point Brands Inc E404
Republic Bancorp, Inc. (ky) A704 E352

PARIS
Kentucky Bancshares Inc E231

PIKEVILLE
Community Trust Bancorp, Inc. A227
Pikeville Medical Center, Inc. P428

RUSSELL SPRINGS
Stephens Pipe & Steel, Llc P542

LOUISIANA

BATON ROUGE
Investar Holding Corp A467 E222
Franciscan Missionaries Of Our Lady Health System, Inc. P204
Our Lady Of The Lake Hospital, Inc. P412
Universities Of Louisiana System P637
Mmr Group, Inc. P347
Cajun Industries, Llc P89
Mmr Constructors, Inc. P347
Cajun Constructors, Llc P89
The Newtron Group L L C P598
Baton Rouge General Medical Center P63
Triad E&c Holdings, L.l.c. P624
Triad Electric & Controls Inc P624
Woman's Hospital Foundation Inc P695
Investar Holding Corp A467 E222

COVINGTON
Zen-noh Grain Corporation A917 P701
Consolidated Grain & Barge Company A234 P139
Zen-noh Grain Corporation A917 P701
Consolidated Grain & Barge Company A234 P139
Saint Tammany Parish School Board P476
Saint Tammany Parish Hospital Service District 1 P475

DERIDDER
Amerisafe Inc A58

DONALDSONVILLE
Ascension Parish Schools P47

HAMMOND
First Guaranty Bancshares, Inc. A347

JEANERETTE
M.a. Patout & Son Limited, L.l.c. P300

LAFAYETTE
Iberiabank Corp A445 E209
Midsouth Bancorp, Inc. A561
Home Bancorp Inc A424 E199
Lafayette General Health System, Inc. P279

Lafayette General Medical Center, Inc. P279
Lafayette Parish School Board P279
Our Lady Of Lourdes Regional Medical Center, Inc. P412
Iberiabank Corp A445 E209
Lhc Group Inc E244
Home Bancorp Inc A424 E199

LAKE CHARLES
Calcasieu Parish School Board P89
Southwest Louisiana Health Care System, Inc. P517

METAIRIE
East Jefferson General Hospital P173

MONROE
Centurylink Inc A184
Qwest Corp A689
Allied Building Stores, Inc. P26

NEW ORLEANS
Entergy Corp A299
Ochsner Health System P403
Entergy Services, Inc. P185
The Administrators Of The Tulane Educational Fund P563
Orleans Parish School District P410
Touro Infirmary P621
Children's Hospital P113

PINEVILLE
Crest Industries, Llc P148

PONCHATOULA
Hospital Service District 1 Of Tangipahoa Parish P241

RUSTON
Origin Bancorp Inc A624

SHREVEPORT
Willis-knighton Medical Center P692
Biomedical Research Foundation Of Northwest Louisiana P75
Caddo Parish School Board P89

MAINE

AUGUSTA
Maine Municipal Bond Bank A525 P303
Mainegeneral Medical Center P303
Maine Municipal Bond Bank A525 P303

BANGOR
Eastern Maine Medical Center P174

BAR HARBOR
Bar Harbor Bankshares A111 E37
The Jackson Laboratory P587
Bar Harbor Bankshares A111 E37

BREWER
Eastern Maine Healthcare Systems P173

CAMDEN
Camden National Corp. (me) A159 E54

DAMARISCOTTA
First Bancorp Inc (me) A337

LEWISTON
Northeast Bancorp (me) E306

ORONO
University Of Maine System P643

PITTSFIELD
Cianbro Corporation P121

PORTLAND
Maine Medical Center P302

Martin's Point Health Care, Inc. P311

SOUTH PORTLAND
Wex Inc E437

WATERVILLE
President And Trustees Of Colby College A667 P440

WESTBROOK
Idexx Laboratories, Inc. E212

YORK
York Hospital P700

MARYLAND

ANNAPOLIS
Anne Arundel Medical Center, Inc. P39
Hannon Armstrong Sustainable Infrastructure Capital Inc E187

BALTIMORE
Under Armour Inc A840
T Rowe Price Group Inc. A783
Johns Hopkins Health Sys Corp A474 P265
The Whiting-turner Contracting Company A813 P616
Johns Hopkins University A475 P266
Johns Hopkins Health Sys Corp A474 P265
The Whiting-turner Contracting Company A813 P616
Johns Hopkins University A475 P266
Johns Hopkins Hospital P266
Lifebridge Health, Inc. P290
University Of Maryland Medical System Corporation P644
Sinai Hospital Of Baltimore, Inc. P504
Mercy Health Services, Inc. P329
Johns Hopkins Bayview Medical Center, Inc. P265
Gbmc Healthcare, Inc. P208
Franklin Square Hospital Center, Inc. P204
Mercy Medical Center, Inc. P331
St. Agnes Healthcare, Inc. P526
Cowan Systems, Llc P147
Greater Baltimore Medical Center Land Corporation P219
The Union Memorial Hospital P608
Callisonrtkl Inc. P91
Howard Bancorp Inc E206

BEL AIR
County Of Harford P144
University Of Maryland Upper Chesapeak House Inc. P645
Upper Chesapeake Medical Center, Inc. P660

BETHESDA
Lockheed Martin Corp A519
Marriott International, Inc. A529
Host Hotels & Resorts Inc A434
Eagle Bancorp Inc (md) A284 E111
Rlj Lodging Trust E358
Pebblebrook Hotel Trust E326
Walker & Dunlop Inc E431
Enviva Partners Lp E129
Eagle Bancorp Inc (md) A284 E111

BOWIE
Old Line Bancshares Inc A613 E314
Inovalon Holdings Inc E218
Old Line Bancshares Inc A613 E314

COLUMBIA
Medstar Health, Inc. A547 P321
Maxim Healthcare Services, Inc. P314
Osiris Therapeutics Inc E319

CUMBERLAND
Western Maryland Health System Rehab P685
Western Maryland Health System P685

EASTON
University Of Maryland Shore Regional Health, Inc. P645

FREDERICK
Frederick Memorial Hospital, Inc. P205

GAITHERSBURG
Adventist Healthcare, Inc. P7
Emergent Biosolutions Inc E120

GLEN BURNIE
University Of Maryland Baltimore Washington Medical System, Inc. P644

GREENBELT
Sgt, Llc P495

HAGERSTOWN
Meritus Medical Center, Inc. P333
Washington County Board Of Education P674

HANOVER
Allegis Group, Inc. A31 P24
Aerotek, Inc. A17 P10
Allegis Group, Inc. A31 P24
Aerotek, Inc. A17 P10
Maryland Department Of Transportation P312
Teksystems, Inc. P557

HUGHESVILLE
Maryland Southern Electric Cooperative Inc P312

HUNT VALLEY
Mccormick & Co Inc A543
Omega Healthcare Investors, Inc. E315

LA PLATA
The Wills Group Inc P617
Charles County Board Of Education P110

LAUREL
Tower Federal Credit Union A823 P622
Washington Suburban Sanitary Commission (inc) P676
Tower Federal Credit Union A823 P622

OLNEY
Sandy Spring Bancorp Inc A724

ROCKVILLE
County Of Montgomery P144
Westat, Inc. P682
Grunley Construction Co., Inc. P222
Infinite Computer Solutions, Inc. P248
The Good Samaritan Hospital Of Md Inc P583
American Kidney Fund, Inc. P34
Choice Hotels International, Inc. E75
Argan Inc E22
Supernus Pharmaceuticals Inc E391

SILVER SPRING
Discovery Inc A268
United Therapeutics Corp E415

WALDORF
Community Financial Corp (the) A226

WESTMINSTER
Board Of Education Of Carroll
County P78

MASSACHUSETTS

ACTON
Psychemedics Corp. E340

ALLSTON
New England Realty Associates
L.p. E301

AMESBURY
Provident Bancorp Inc E340

ANDOVER
Mks Instruments Inc E281
Mercury Systems Inc E270
Casa Systems Inc E60

AUBURNDALE
Atrius Health, Inc. P49

BEDFORD
Irobot Corp E224
Novanta Inc E308
Anika Therapeutics Inc. E17

BELMONT
Bsb Bancorp Inc. (md) A152 E49

BEVERLY
Northeast Hospital Corporation P391
Atn International Inc E25
Axcelis Technologies Inc E27

BILLERICA
Idemia Identity & Security Usa
Llc P245
Entegris Inc E125

BOSTON
General Electric Co A374
State Street Corp. A765
Santander Holdings Usa Inc. A726
American Tower Corp (new) A54
Wayfair Inc A882
Safety Insurance Group, Inc. A721
Berkshire Hills Bancorp Inc A124 E40
Boston Private Financial Holdings,
Inc. A142
Brookline Bancorp Inc (de) A149
Partners Healthcare System,
Inc. A635 P418
City Of Boston P122
Suffolk Construction Company,
Inc. P545
The Massachusetts General
Hospital P590
University Of Massachusetts P645
The Brigham And Women's Hospital
Inc P567
Boston University P80
Beth Israel Deaconess Medical Center,
Inc. P71
Northeastern University P392
Boston Medical Center
Corporation P80
The Children's Hospital
Corporation P570
Massachusetts School Building
Authority P314
Dana-farber Cancer Institute,
Inc. P153
Massachusetts Port Authority P314
Tufts Medical Center, Inc. P628
Public Consulting Group, Inc. P445
Jsi Research And Training Institute,
Inc. P269
Faculty Practice Foundation Inc And
Affiliates P189

Harvard Private Capital Realty,
Inc. P228
Suffolk University P545
Cdm Constructors Inc. P102
Wellington Trust Co, Na P680
Childrens Hospital Pediatric
Associates, Inc. P118
Suffolk University P545
Vertex Pharmaceuticals, Inc. E427
Logmein Inc E248
Federal Home Loan Bank
Boston E143
Berkshire Hills Bancorp Inc A124 E40
Stag Industrial Inc E383

BRIDGEWATER
Callahan, Inc. P91

BROCKTON
Harborone Bancorp Inc A403 E188

BURLINGTON
Keurig Dr Pepper Inc A487
Lahey Clinic, Inc. P279
Lahey Clinic Hospital, Inc. P279
Lemaitre Vascular Inc E241

CAMBRIDGE
Biogen Inc A128
Cambridge Bancorp A158
Massachusetts Institute Of
Technology P313
The Charles Stark Draper Laboratory
Inc P568
The Broad Institute Inc P567
Mount Auburn Hospital P353
Pegasystems Inc E327

CHESTNUT HILL
Trustees Of Boston College P625

CHICOPEE
Consumer Product Distributors,
Inc. P140

CONCORD
Welch Foods Inc., A Cooperative P679

DANVERS
Abiomed, Inc. E2

FRAMINGHAM
Tjx Companies, Inc. A817

HANOVER
Independent Bank Corp (ma) A451

HINGHAM
Hingham Institution For
Savings A421 E198

HOLLISTON
Wayne J. Griffin Electric, Inc. P678

HYANNIS
Cape Cod Healthcare, Inc. P92
Cape Cod Hospital P93

LEXINGTON
Concert Pharmaceuticals Inc E89

LOWELL
Enterprise Bancorp, Inc. (ma) A300
E127
Circle Health, Inc. P121
Lowell General Hospital P298
Enterprise Bancorp, Inc. (ma) A300
E127

LYNNFIELD
Babcock Power Inc. P53

MARLBOROUGH
Boston Scientific Corp. A143

MAYNARD
Acacia Communications Inc E3

MEDFORD
Century Bancorp, Inc. A183
Management Sciences For Health,
Inc. P304

MIDDLEBORO
Ocean Spray Cranberries, Inc. P403

NATICK
Cognex Corp E81

NEWTON
Newton Wellesley Hospital Corp P380
Hospitality Properties Trust E205
Senior Housing Properties
Trust E366
Rmr Group Inc (the) E358
Office Properties Income Trust E313

NORTH READING
Teradyne, Inc. E394

NORWOOD
Analog Devices Inc A64
Blue Hills Bancorp Inc A134 E45

OXFORD
Ipg Photonics Corp E223

PEABODY
Meridian Bancorp Inc A553 E272

PITTSFIELD
Berkshire Medical Center, Inc. P69

QUINCY
J.jill Inc E226

SALEM
North Shore Medical Center,
Inc. P389

SOMERVILLE
Neighborhood Health Plan,
Incorporated P369
Trustees Of Tufts College P627

SOUTH WEYMOUTH
South Shore Hospital, Inc. P511

SPRINGFIELD
Eversource Energy A306
Baystate Health Inc. P65

TEWKSBURY
Covenant Health, Inc. P146

WALTHAM
Raytheon Co. A694
Thermo Fisher Scientific Inc A814
Global Partners Lp A387
Parexel International
Corporation P416
New England Power Company P371
Brandeis University P82
Bentley University P68
Care.com Inc E57
Repligen Corp. E351

WATERTOWN
Bright Horizons Family Solutions,
Inc E46
Enanta Pharmaceuticals Inc E122

WESTBOROUGH
Bj's Wholesale Club Holdings
Inc A129

WESTFIELD
Western New England Bancorp
Inc A893 E436

WESTFORD
Netscout Systems Inc E300
Kadant Inc E228

WILMINGTON
Charles River Laboratories
International Inc. E68

Rudolph Technologies, Inc. E361

WOBURN
Monotype Imaging Holdings Inc E285

WORCESTER
Hanover Insurance Group Inc A401
Umass Memorial Medical Center,
Inc. P632
Umass Memorial Community Medical
Group, Inc. P632
Worcester Polytechnic Institute P695
Umass Memorial Community
Hospitals, Inc. P632

MICHIGAN

ADA
Alticor Inc. A37 P28
Access Business Group Llc P3

ALLENDALE
Grand Valley State University P218

ANN ARBOR
Regents Of The University Of
Michigan A698 P455
Truven Holding Corp. P628

AUBURN HILLS
Borgwarner Inc A141
Commercial Contracting Group,
Inc. P133
Unique Fabricating Inc E410

BATTLE CREEK
Kellogg Co A484
W. K. Kellogg Foundation P672

BENTON HARBOR
Whirlpool Corp A897

BIRMINGHAM
Sanctus, Llc P481

BLOOMFIELD HILLS
Penske Automotive Group Inc A642
Agree Realty Corp. E6

CADILLAC
Wolverine Power Supply Cooperative,
Inc. P694

CANTON
Lotus International Company P297

CHARLOTTE
Spartan Motors, Inc. E380

DEARBORN
Ford Motor Co. (de) A361
Logistics Hollingsworth Group
Llc P294

DETROIT
General Motors Co A378
Dte Energy Co A280
Ally Financial Inc A35
American Axle & Manufacturing
Holdings Inc A45
Dte Electric Company A279
Chemical Financial Corp A187 E71
Henry Ford Health System A413 P234
Wayne State University P679
The Detroit Institute Of Arts P577
Pressure Vessel Service, Inc. P441
Wayne County Airport Authority P678
Total Health Care, Inc. P621
Chemical Financial Corp A187 E71

EAST LANSING
Michigan State University P341

FARMINGTON HILLS
Orleans International, Inc. P410
Botsford General Hospital P81

```
A = AMERICAN BUSINESS
E = EMERGING COMPANIES
P = PRIVATE COMPANIES
W = WORLD BUSINESS
```

Rpt Realty E359

FENTON
Fentura Financial Inc E147

FLINT
Hurley Medical Center P245
Mclaren Regional Medical
  Center P319

FRANKENMUTH
Star Of The West Milling
  Company P539

GRAND BLANC
Genesys Regional Medical
  Center P210

GRAND RAPIDS
Spartannash Co. A756
Mercantile Bank Corp. A548 E269
Independent Bank Corporation (ionia,
  Mi) A452
Spectrum Health System A758 P519
Spectrum Health Hospitals P519
Meritage Hospitality Group Inc E274
Mercantile Bank Corp. A548 E269

HILLSDALE
Cnb Community Bancorp Inc E79

HOLLAND
Macatawa Bank Corp. A523

JACKSON
Cms Energy Corp A209
Consumers Energy Co. A235
Alro Steel Corporation P27
W. A. Foote Memorial Hospital P671

KALAMAZOO
Stryker Corp A772
Bronson Health Care Group, Inc. P84
Bronson Methodist Hospital Inc P84
Borgess Medical Center P79

LANSING
Sparrow Health System P517
Lansing Board Of Water And
  Light P282
Ingham Regional Medical
  Center P249
Neogen Corp E299

LIVONIA
Masco Corp. A533
Aristeo Construction Company P43

MADISON HEIGHTS
Mcnaughton-mckay Electric Co. P320

MIDDLEVILLE
Hps Llc P243

MIDLAND
Dowdupont Inc A279
Midmichigan Medical Center-
  midland P343

MOUNT CLEMENS
Henry Ford Macomb Hospitals P235
Mount Clemens Regional Medical
  Center P354

MOUNT PLEASANT
American Mitsuba Corporation P35
Central Michigan University P106

MT. PLEASANT
Isabella Bank Corp A470

NORTHVILLE
Gentherm Inc E173

NOVI
Nhk International Corporation P381
International Transmission
  Company P252
Michigan Electric Transmission
  Company, Llc P340

PONTIAC
St. Joseph Mercy Oakland
  Foundation P531

PORT HURON
Semco Energy, Inc. P491

ROYAL OAK
Beaumont Health P66
William Beaumont Hospital P692
Barrick Enterprises, Inc. P61

SAGINAW
Covenant Medical Center, Inc. P146

SOUTHFIELD
Lear Corp. A503
Sterling Bancorp Inc (mi) A769
Federal-mogul Holdings Llc A326
  P193
Metaldyne Performance Group
  Inc. P335
Barton Malow Enterprises, Inc. P61
Barton Malow Company P61
Providence Hospital P444
Credit Acceptance Corp (mi) E99
Sun Communities Inc E389

TRAVERSE CITY
Munson Healthcare P358
Munson Medical Center P359

TROY
Kelly Services, Inc. A486
Flagstar Bancorp, Inc. A356

WARREN
St. John Hospital And Medical
  Center P529
St John Macomb-oakland
  Hospital P524

WYANDOTTE
Henry Ford Wyandotte Hospital P235

ZEELAND
Gentex Corp. E172

MINNESOTA

ANOKA
Anoka-hennepin School Dist No
  11 P40

AUSTIN
Hormel Foods Corp. A431

BAGLEY
Team Industries Holding
  Corporation P556

BLOOMINGTON
Bridgewater Bancshares Inc A145
Lamex Foods Inc. P281

BURNSVILLE
Ames Construction, Inc. P38

CIRCLE PINES
Northern Technologies International
  Corp. E306

DULUTH
Essentia Health P186
Smdc Medical Center P505
St. Luke's Hospital Of Duluth P534
St. Mary's Medical Center P536
Allete Inc. E11

EDEN PRAIRIE
Robinson (c.h.) Worldwide, Inc. A711
Alliance Pipeline L.p. A25
Mts Systems Corp E287

EDINA
Production Technologies, Inc. P442

GOLDEN VALLEY
Resideo Technologies Inc A707

HERMANTOWN
Miners Incorporated P344

INVER GROVE HEIGHTS
Chs Inc A194

LITCHFIELD
The First District Association P580

MANKATO
Mayo Clinic Health System-southwest
  Minnesota Region P316

MAPLE GROVE
Great River Energy P219
Independent School District 279 P247

MAPLE PLAIN
Proto Labs Inc E338

MEDINA
Polaris Industries Inc. A660

MINNEAPOLIS
Target Corp A787
Us Bancorp (de) A864
General Mills Inc A376
Ameriprise Financial Inc A55
Xcel Energy Inc A909
Riversource Life Insurance Co A709
Fairview Health Services A314 P190
Allina Health System P26
Cliftonlarsonallen Llp P127
Minneapolis Public School
  District P345
North Memorial Health Care P387
University Of Minnesota
  Physicians P646
National Marrow Donor Program
  Inc P363
Metropolitan Airports
  Commission P337
Sleep Number Corp E376
Wells Fargo Real Estate Investment
  Corp E432
Apogee Enterprises Inc E18
Bio-techne Corp E41
Tactile Systems Technology Inc E393

MINNETONKA
Unitedhealth Group Inc A854

PLYMOUTH
Mosaic Co (the) A569
Silver Bay Realty Trust Corp. P503
Tile Shop Holdings Inc E399

RENVILLE
Southern Minnesota Beet Sugar
  Cooperative P514

RICHFIELD
Best Buy Inc A125

ROCHESTER
Mayo Clinic Hospital-rochester A540
  P316
Saint Marys Hospital P474

ROSEMOUNT
Rosemount-apple Valley-eagan School
  Board P465

ROSEVILLE
Presbyterian Homes And
  Services P439

SAINT CLOUD
Coborn's, Incorporated P129
The Saint Cloud Hospital P602

SAINT PAUL
Saint Paul Regional Water
  Services A722 P474
Api Group Inc. P40
Hmo Minnesota P238
Independent School Dist 625 P247
Merrill Corporation P333

ST. PAUL
3m Co A1
Ecolab Inc A289
Patterson Companies Inc A636

TRUMAN
Watonwan Farm Service, Inc P677

WAYZATA
Tcf Financial Corp A789

WHEATON
Coop Wheaton-dumont Elevator
  Inc P141

WINONA
Fastenal Co. A318

MISSISSIPPI

GULFPORT
Hancock Whitney Corp A399

HATTIESBURG
First Bancshares Inc (ms) A338 E149
Cooperative Energy, A Mississippi
  Electric Cooperative P141
Forrest General Health Services,
  Inc. P201
First Bancshares Inc (ms) A338 E149

JACKSON
Trustmark Corp A831
St. Dominic-jackson Memorial
  Hospital P529
Entergy Operations, Inc. P184

MERIDIAN
Southern Pipe & Supply Company,
  Inc. P516

MISSISSIPPI STATE
Mississippi State University P346

NATCHEZ
Callon Petroleum Co. (de) E53

SOUTHAVEN
Baptist Memorial Hospital-desoto,
  Inc. P60

TUPELO
Bancorpsouth Bank (tupelo, Ms) A99
Renasant Corp A703 E350
North Mississippi Health Services,
  Inc. P388
North Mississippi Medical Center,
  Inc. P389
Renasant Corp A703 E350

UNIVERSITY
University Of Mississippi P646

MISSOURI

BRIDGETON
Daughters Of Charity Services Of St.
  Louis P154

CAPE GIRARDEAU
Francis Saint Medical Center P202
Southeast Missouri Hospital
  Association P511

CHESTERFIELD

Reinsurance Group Of America,
Inc. A701
Mercy Health A551 P327
Missouri Higher Education Loan
Authority A563 P346
Mercy Health A551 P327
St. Luke's Episcopal-presbyterian
Hospitals P533
Missouri Higher Education Loan
Authority A563 P346

CLAYTON

Olin Corp. A617
Enterprise Financial Services
Corp A301 E128

COLUMBIA

University Of Missouri System P647
Mfa Incorporated P338
M. F. A. Oil Company P300
University Of Missouri Health
Care P646
Missouri Joint Municipal Electric
Utility Commission P347
Boone Hospital Center P79

DES PERES

Jones Financial Companies Lllp A477

FARMINGTON

U. S. Tool Grinding, Inc. P630

FENTON

Maritz Holdings Inc. P307

GRANDVIEW

Nasb Financial Inc A572

JEFFERSON CITY

Hawthorn Bancshares Inc A408

JOPLIN

Freeman Health System P206
The Empire District Electric
Company P578

KANSAS CITY

Commerce Bancshares Inc A222
Umb Financial Corp A837
Kansas City Life Insurance Co (kansas
City, Mo) A482
J.e. Dunn Construction Group,
Inc. P257
J.e. Dunn Construction
Company P256
Dst Systems, Inc. P166
Saint Luke's Health System,
Inc. P473
Mercy Children's Hospital P327
Kcp&l Greater Missouri Operations
Company P271
Saint Luke's Hospital Of Kansas
City P474
Midwest Division - Rmc, Llc P343
Epr Properties E130
Corenergy Infrastructure Trust
Inc E95

NORTH KANSAS CITY

Cerner Corp. A185
North Kansas City Hospital P387

POPLAR BLUFF

Southern Missouri Bancorp,
Inc. A754 E378

SAINT JOSEPH

Heartland Health P231
Heartland Regional Medical
Center P232

SAINT LOUIS

Ascension Health Alliance A80 P47
Ssm Health Care Corporation A760
P523

World Wide Technology, Llc A906
P695
Ascension Health Alliance A80 P47
Ssm Health Care Corporation A760
P523
World Wide Technology, Llc A906
P695
Mccarthy Holdings, Inc. P318
Mccarthy Building Companies,
Inc. P317
The Washington University P615
Barnes-jewish Hospital P60
Alberici Corporation P18
Spire Missouri Inc. P520
Mercy Hospitals East
Communities P331
Alberici Group, Inc. P19
Alberici Constructors, Inc. P18
St Louis Children's Hospital P525
Missouri Baptist Medical Center P346
Special School District Of St. Louis
County P518
St. Anthony's Medical Center P527
Korte Construction Company P277
Metropolitan St. Louis Sewer
District P337
Ascension Health Welfare Benefits
Trust P47
Millman Lumber Company P344

SIKESTON

Food Giant Supermarkets, Inc. P200

SPRINGFIELD

O'reilly Automotive, Inc. A609
Great Southern Bancorp, Inc. A394
New Prime, Inc. P371
Mercy Hospital Springfield P330
City Utilities Of Springfield Mo P124
Src Holdings Corporation P522
Springfield School District R12 P522

ST. LOUIS

Centene Corp A179
Emerson Electric Co. A294
Graybar Electric Co., Inc. A393
Post Holdings Inc A662
Ameren Corp A42
Stifel Financial Corp A770
Cass Information Systems Inc. A168
Esco Technologies, Inc. E131

MONTANA

BILLINGS

First Interstate Bancsystem Inc A349
E155
Billings Clinic P74
St. Vincent Healthcare P537
First Interstate Bancsystem Inc A349
E155

GREAT FALLS

Benefis Hospitals, Inc P68
Benefis Health System, Inc P68

KALISPELL

Glacier Bancorp, Inc. A387 E176
Kalispell Regional Healthcare
System P269
Glacier Bancorp, Inc. A387 E176

LEWISTOWN

Sports, Inc. P521

MISSOULA

St Patrick Hospital Corporation P526
University Of Montana P647

SIDNEY

Upper Missouri G & T Electric Cooperative Inc P661

NEBRASKA

BOYS TOWN

Father Flanagan's Boys' Home P192

COLUMBUS

Nebraska Public Power District P369

LINCOLN

Nelnet Inc A579
Union Bank And Trust Company A840
P633
Board Of Regents Of The University Of
Nebraska P78
Bryan Health P87
Bryan Medical Center P87
University Of Nebraska
Foundation P648
Union Bank And Trust Company A840
P633

NORFOLK

Affiliated Foods Midwest Cooperative,
Inc. P10

OMAHA

Berkshire Hathaway Inc A122
Union Pacific Corp A841
Td Ameritrade Holding Corp A790
Farm Credit Services Of America,
Pca A316 P191
The Scoular Company P603
Ag Processing Inc A Cooperative P11
Hdr, Inc. P228
Hdr Engineering, Inc. P228
The Nebraska Medical Center P596
Omaha Public Power District P406
Farm Credit Services Of America,
Pca A316 P191
Sapp Bros., Inc. P483
Alegent Health- Bergan Mercy Health
System P21
Omaha Public Schools P406
Northern Natural Gas Company P394
Nebraska Methodist Hospital
Inc P369
Creighton Alegent Health P147
Hdr Architecture, Inc. P228
Childrens Hospital & Medical
Center P117
Creighton Alegent Clinic P147
The Susan Thompson Buffett
Foundation P606
Metropolitan Utilities District P338
Western Capital Resources Inc E435
Green Plains Partners Lp E183
America First Multifamily Investors
Lp E14

NEVADA

CARSON CITY

Carson Tahoe Regional
Healthcare P98

LAS VEGAS

Las Vegas Sands Corp A502
Mgm Resorts International A557
Wynn Resorts Ltd A909
Caesars Entertainment Corp A156
Clark County School District P125
County Of Clark P143
University Medical Center Of Southern
Nevada P639
Summerlin Hospital Medical Center,
Llc P545
Las Vegas Convention & Visitors
Authority P282
Spring Valley Hospital Medical
Center P521
Valley Health System Llc P663
Allegiant Travel Company E11

Live Ventures Inc E247

RENO

Employers Holdings Inc A296
Nevada System Of Higher
Education P370
Washoe County School District P677
Hometown Health Plan Inc P240
Eldorado Resorts Inc E118

NEW HAMPSHIRE

CONCORD

University System Of New
Hampshire P659
Concord Hospital, Inc. P137

HAMPTON

Planet Fitness Inc E334

HANOVER

Trustees Of Dartmouth College P626
Dartmouth College P154

LEBANON

Dartmouth-hitchcock Health P154

MANCHESTER

Allegro Microsystems, Llc P24
Elliot Health System P179
Elliot Hospital Of The City Of
Manchester P179

NASHUA

Southern New Hampshire Health
System, Inc. P515

NEW JERSEY

BAYONNE

Bcb Bancorp Inc A116 E39

BEDMINSTER

Peapack-gladstone Financial
Corp. A638 E325

BRANCHVILLE

Selective Insurance Group Inc A733

BRIDGEWATER

Brother International
Corporation P86

BURLINGTON

Burlington Stores Inc A154

CAMDEN

Campbell Soup Co A160
The Cooper Health System P576
Delaware River Port Authority P158
Our Lady Of Lourdes Medical Center,
Inc P411

CLINTON

Unity Bancorp, Inc. A855 E416

CRANBURY

1st Constitution Bancorp E2

EAST BRUNSWICK

Wipro, Llc P693

EAST HANOVER

Novartis Pharmaceuticals
Corporation A603 P399

EAST RUTHERFORD

Cambrex Corp E54

EDISON

Hmh Hospitals Corporation P237
The Community Hospital Group
Inc P575
Larsen & Toubro Infotech
Limited P282

A = AMERICAN BUSINESS
E = EMERGING COMPANIES
P = PRIVATE COMPANIES
W = WORLD BUSINESS

ELIZABETH
Trinitas Regional Medical
Center P624

ENGLEWOOD
Englewood Hospital And Medical
Center Foundation Inc. P184

ENGLEWOOD CLIFFS
Connectone Bancorp Inc (new) A231
E90

EWING
Universal Display Corp E416

FAIRFIELD
Kearny Financial Corp (md) A484
E229

FARMINGDALE
Cherry Hill Mortgage Investment
Corp E72

FLORHAM PARK
Conduent Inc A231

FORT LEE
Empire Resources, Inc. P182

FRANKLIN LAKES
Becton, Dickinson & Co A118

FREEHOLD
Centrastate Healthcare System
Inc P107
Monmouth Real Estate Investment
Corp E283
Umh Properties Inc E408

GLASSBORO
Rowan University P466

HAMILTON
First Bank (williamstown, Nj) A338
E149

HOBOKEN
Newell Brands Inc A586
Jarden Corporation A472 P259

ISELIN
Hexaware Technologies, Inc. P236

JERSEY CITY
Provident Financial Services Inc A675
Jersey City Medical Center (inc) P261

KENILWORTH
Merck & Co Inc A550

LAWRENCEVILLE
Lawrence Township School District
Inc A503 P284

LINDEN
Turtle & Hughes, Inc. P629

LITTLE FALLS
Cantel Medical Corp E55

LIVINGSTON
St Barnabas Medical Center
(inc) P524

LONG BRANCH
Monmouth Medical Center Inc. P349

LONG VALLEY
Frazier Industrial Company P205

MADISON
Realogy Group Llc A696
Realogy Holdings Corp A696

MAHWAH
Ascena Retail Group Inc A79

MONTVALE
Berry Global Films, Llc P70

MOORESTOWN
Tabula Rasa Healthcare Inc E393

MORRIS PLAINS
Honeywell International Inc A428

MOUNT LAUREL
Marlin Business Services Corp E260

NEPTUNE
Meridian Hospitals Corporation P332

NEW BRUNSWICK
Johnson & Johnson A476
Saint Peter's University Hospital,
Inc. P474

NEW GRETNA
Viking Yacht Company P666

NEWARK
Prudential Financial Inc A676
Public Service Enterprise Group
Inc A677
Newark Beth Israel Medical Center
Inc. P378

OAK RIDGE
Lakeland Bancorp, Inc. A499 E237

PARSIPPANY
Pbf Energy Inc A637
Avis Budget Group Inc A92
Zoetis Inc A920
B&g Foods Inc E29

PATERSON
St. Joseph's Hospital And Medical
Center P531
Paterson Public School District P420

PLAINSBORO
Integra Lifesciences Holdings
Corp E219

PRINCETON
Nrg Energy Inc A603
The Trustees Of Princeton
University P606
Educational Testing Service Inc P175

RED BANK
Oceanfirst Financial Corp A611 E312

RIDGEWOOD
The Valley Hospital Inc P614

ROSELAND
Automatic Data Processing Inc. A87

SECAUCUS
Quest Diagnostics, Inc. A687
Njmhmc Llc P382

SHORT HILLS
Investors Bancorp Inc (new) A467
E222

SOMERSET
Shi International Corp. A739 P500

SOUTH ORANGE
Seton Hall University P494

SUMMIT
Celgene Corp A177

TEANECK
Cognizant Technology Solutions
Corp. A216
Holy Name Medical Center, Inc. P239

TOMS RIVER
Community Medical Center,
Inc. P135

TOWNSHIP OF WASHINGTON
Oritani Financial Corp (de) A624

UNION
Bed, Bath & Beyond, Inc. A119

WAYNE
Valley National Bancorp (nj) A868

WEST ORANGE
Barnabas Health, Inc. P60

WHIPPANY
Stephen Gould Corporation P541

WOODBRIDGE
Northfield Bancorp Inc (de) A600
E307
New Jersey Turnpike Authority
Inc P371
Northfield Bancorp Inc (de) A600
E307

WOODCLIFF LAKE
Eagle Pharmaceuticals, Inc. E113

NEW MEXICO

ALBUQUERQUE
University Of New Mexico P648
Albuquerque Municipal School
District Number 12 P20

FARMINGTON
San Juan Regional Medical Center,
Inc. P480

SANTA FE
St. Vincent Hospital P537

NEW YORK

ALBANY
Sefcu Services, Llc A733 P491
St. Peter's Health Care Services P537
Albany Medical Center Hospital P18
Albany Medical Center P17
Albany Medical College P18
Sefcu Services, Llc A733 P491

AMHERST
Allied Motion Technologies Inc E13

ARMONK
International Business Machines
Corp A459

BALLSTON SPA
Stewart's Shops Corp. P543

BATAVIA
O-at-ka Milk Products Cooperative,
Incorporated P401

BAY SHORE
Southside Hospital P516

BINGHAMTON
United Health Services Hospital,
Inc. P634
Our Lady Of Lourdes Memorial
Hospital, Inc. P412

BRENTWOOD
Brentwood Union Free School
District P83

BRIDGEHAMPTON
Bridge Bancorp, Inc. (bridgehampton,
Ny) A145 E46

BRONX
Montefiore Medical Center P351
Bronxcare Health System P84
Lincoln Medical And Mental Health
Center P292
Fordham University P200
Wildlife Conservation Society P691
St. Barnabas Hospital P528

BRONXVILLE
Lawrence Newyork-presbyterian
Hospital P283

BROOKLYN
Dime Community Bancshares,
Inc A267
Newyork-presbyterian/brooklyn
Methodist P381
Maimonides Medical Center P301
The Brookdale Hospital Medical
Center P568
Brooklyn Hospital Center P85
Etsy Inc E134

BUFFALO
M & T Bank Corp A521
Erie County Medical Center
Corp. P186
Mercy Hospital Of Buffalo P330

CARLE PLACE
1-800 Flowers.com, Inc. E1

CATSKILL
Greene County Bancorp Inc E183

COOPERSTOWN
The Mary Imogene Bassett
Hospital P590

CORNING
Corning Inc A237

DEWITT
Community Bank System Inc A224
E87

EAST AURORA
Astronics Corp E24

EAST MEADOW
Nassau Health Care Corporation P362

ELMIRA
Chemung Financial Corp. A188
Ogden Arnot Medical Center P404

FARMINGDALE
Marjam Supply Co., Inc. P308

FARMINGVILLE
Town Of Brookhaven P622

FLUSHING
Newyork-presbyterian/queens P381

GETZVILLE
Columbus Mckinnon Corp. (ny) E86

GLEN HEAD
First Of Long Island Corp A352 E159

GLENS FALLS
Arrow Financial Corp. A77
Glens Falls Hospital P213

GLENVILLE
Trustco Bank Corp. (n.y.) A831

GREAT NECK
Brt Apartments Corp E47
One Liberty Properties, Inc. E316

GREENVALE
Long Island University P296

HAMBURG
Evans Bancorp, Inc. E135

HAUPPAUGE
County Of Suffolk P145

HICKSVILLE
National Grid Generation Llc P363

HUNTINGTON
Huntington Hospital Dolan Family
Health Center, Inc. P244

ITHACA
Tompkins Financial Corp A820
Tompkins Trust Company A821 P621
Cornell University P142
Tompkins Trust Company A821 P621

JAMAICA
The Jamaica Hospital P587

KINGSTON
Ulster County P631
Kingstone Companies Inc E233

LAGRANGEVILLE
Health Quest Systems, Inc. P230

LAKE RONKONKOMA
Sachem Central School District At
Holbrook P470

LARCHMONT
L & M Development Partners
Inc. P278

LONG ISLAND CITY
Altice Usa Inc A37
Jetblue Airways Corp A473

LYNBROOK
Biospecifics Technologies Corp. E42

MANHASSET
North Shore University Hospital P390

MELVILLE
Schein (henry) Inc A727
Comtech Telecommunications
Corp. E88

MENANDS
Health Research, Inc. P231

MIDDLETOWN
Orange Regional Medical Center P409

MONTEBELLO
Sterling Bancorp (de) A768 E386

NEW HAMPTON
Balchem Corp. E30

NEW HYDE PARK
Long Island Jewish Medical
Center P295

NEW YORK
Verizon Communications Inc A870
Jpmorgan Chase & Co A479
Citigroup Inc A202
Federal Reserve Bank Of New York,
Dist. No. 2 A323
Metlife Inc A554
Pfizer Inc A648
American International Group
Inc A52
Morgan Stanley A567
Goldman Sachs Group Inc A389
American Express Co. A48
Twenty-first Century Fox Inc A834
Philip Morris International Inc A651
Travelers Companies Inc (the) A826
Intl Fcstone Inc. A464
Macy's Inc A524
Icahn Enterprises Lp A447
Bristol-myers Squibb Co. A146
Bank Of New York Mellon Corp A104
Colgate-palmolive Co. A217
Omnicom Group, Inc. A618

Voya Financial Inc A876
Marsh & Mclennan Companies
Inc. A531
Loews Corp. A519
Cbs Corp A174
Lauder (estee) Cos., Inc. (the) A503
Arconic Inc A75
Viacom Inc A871
Axa Equitable Holdings Inc A94
Blackrock Inc A130
First Data Corp (new) A343
Consolidated Edison Inc A233
Consolidated Edison Co. Of New York,
Inc. A232
L3 Technologies Inc A498
Coty, Inc. A240
News Corp (new) A588
Pvh Corp A681
Interpublic Group Of Companies
Inc. A463
Foot Locker, Inc. A360
Blackstone Group Lp (the) A131
Nielsen Holdings Plc A592 P382
Abm Industries, Inc. A7
Alleghany Corp. A29
Assurant Inc A82
Ralph Lauren Corp A690
Hsbc Usa, Inc. A436
S&p Global Inc A720
Tapestry Inc A785
Sirius Xm Holdings Inc A745
Hess Corp A416
National General Holdings Corp A574
Cit Group Inc A200
Annaly Capital Management Inc A66
E*trade Financial Corp. A282
Federal Home Loan Bank New
York A321 E144
Signature Bank (new York, Ny) A741
E370
Ambac Financial Group, Inc. A39
Metropolitan Bank Holding
Corp A556
The Turner Corporation A812 P607
New York City Health And Hospitals
Corporation A581 P373
New York University A585 P376
Tata America International
Corporation A789 P555
Nielsen Holdings Plc A592 P382
The New York And Presbyterian
Hospital A810 P597
New York City Transit Authority A582
P374
Signature Financial Llc A742 P502
Bre Glacier L.p. A145 P82
The Ford Foundation A808 P581
Jewish Communal Fund A474 P262
New York Community Trust And
Community Funds Inc A584 P374
State Of New York Mortgage
Agency A765 P540
Nielsen Holdings Plc A592 P382
The Turner Corporation A812 P607
New York City Health And Hospitals
Corporation A581 P373
New York University A585 P376
Tata America International
Corporation A789 P555
Nielsen Holdings Plc A592 P382
The New York And Presbyterian
Hospital A810 P597
New York City Transit Authority A582
P374
Trammo, Inc. P623
Memorial Sloan-kettering Cancer
Center P325
Mount Sinai Hospitals Group,
Inc. P355
Triborough Bridge & Tunnel
Authority P624
Signature Financial Llc A742 P502

The Bloomberg Family Foundation
Inc P566
Newmark & Company Real Estate,
Inc. P378
Lhh Corporation P289
The Andrew W Mellon
Foundation P565
Lighthouse Guild International,
Inc. P292
Lenox Hill Hospital P288
Guildnet, Inc. P223
St Luke's-roosevelt Hospital
Center P525
New York City Economic Development
Corporation P372
International Rescue Committee,
Inc. P251
Catholic Medical Mission Board
Inc P101
United States Fund For Unicef P636
Bre Glacier L.p. A145 P82
The Associated Press P565
The Ford Foundation A808 P581
New York Blood Center, Inc. P372
Jewish Communal Fund A474 P262
Logicalis Us Holdings, Inc. P293
The New School P596
New York State Housing Finance
Agency P376
Pace University P414
Medecins Sans Frontieres U.s.a.,
Inc P320
The Metropolitan Museum Of
Art P594
The New York Public Library P598
Marcum Llp P306
Metropolitan Opera Association,
Inc. P337
American Friends Of Bar-ilan
University P32
Battery Park City Authority Inc P63
The American Jewish Joint
Distribution Committee Inc P565
New York Community Trust And
Community Funds Inc A584 P374
Surdna Foundation Inc P548
State Of New York Mortgage
Agency A765 P540
Federal Home Loan Bank New
York A321 E144
New Residential Investment
Corp E302
Macquarie Infrastructure Corp E254
Evercore Inc E135
Minerals Technologies, Inc. E280
Madison Square Garden Co (the)
(new) E254
Signature Bank (new York, Ny) A741
E370
Chimera Investment Corp E75
Ubiquiti Networks Inc E406
W.p. Carey Inc E430
Exlservice Holdings Inc E138
Paramount Group Inc E323
Empire State Realty Trust Inc E121
Empire State Realty Op Lp E121
Moelis & Co E283
Istar Inc E225
Shutterstock Inc E368
Medidata Solutions, Inc. E268
Blackstone Mortgage Trust Inc E44
New Senior Investment Group
Inc E302
New York Mortgage Trust Inc E302
Marketaxess Holdings Inc. E259
Apollo Commercial Real Estate
Finance Inc. E19
Global Net Lease Inc E178
Wisdomtree Investments, Inc. E443
Ready Capital Corp E347
Corporate Property Associates 18
Global Inc E97

Tpg Re Finance Trust Inc E399
New Mountain Finance Corp E301
Vici Properties Inc E428
Ag Mortgage Investment Trust Inc E6
Pzena Investment Management
Inc E341
Goldman Sachs Bdc Inc E179
Ares Commercial Real Estate
Corp E22
Otc Markets Group Inc E320
Mesabi Trust E275

NEWBURGH
Newburgh City School District P378

NORWICH
Nbt Bancorp. Inc. A577

OCEANSIDE
South Nassau Communities Hospital
Inc P510

PEARL RIVER
Orange And Rockland Utilities
Inc P408
Hudson Technologies Inc E209

PORT WASHINGTON
Shake-n-go Fashion, Inc. P495

POUGHKEEPSIE
Central Hudson Gas & Electric
Corporation P106

PURCHASE
Pepsico Inc A646
Mastercard Inc A536
Mbia Inc. A542

ROCHESTER
Rochester General Hospital Inc P463
Rochester Gas And Electric
Corporation P463
Rochester Institute Of Technology
(inc) P463
The Unity Hospital Of Rochester P609
Eastman Kodak Co. E114

RONKONKOMA
Perfume Center Of America Inc. P424

ROSLYN
St. Francis Hospital, Roslyn, New
York P529

RYE
Acadia Realty Trust E4

RYE BROOK
Xylem Inc A914

SARATOGA SPRINGS
Saratoga Hospital P484

SCHENECTADY
Mvp Health Plan, Inc. P360
Ellis Hospital P180

STATEN ISLAND
Key Food Stores Co-operative,
Inc. P275
Staten Island University
Hospital P540
Richmond Medical Center P461

SUFFERN
Good Samaritan Regional Medical
Center P216

SYRACUSE
Syracuse University P551
St. Joseph's Hospital Health
Center P532
Syracuse City School District P551
Crouse Health Hospital, Inc. P148
Petr-all Petroleum Consulting
Corp. P425
Carrols Restaurant Group Inc E59

A = AMERICAN BUSINESS
E = EMERGING COMPANIES
P = PRIVATE COMPANIES
W = WORLD BUSINESS

TARRYTOWN
Regeneron Pharmaceuticals, Inc. A697
Db Us Holding Corporation P155
Prestige Consumer Healthcare Inc E337

UNIONDALE
Flushing Financial Corp. A358
Long Island Power Authority P296
Utility Debt Securitization Authority P662
Arbor Realty Trust Inc E22

VALHALLA
Westchester County Health Care Corporation P683

VICTOR
Constellation Brands Inc A234

WARSAW
Financial Institutions Inc. A333

WEST ISLIP
Good Samaritan Hospital Medical Center P214

WEST NYACK
The Salvation Army P602

WESTBURY
New York Community Bancorp Inc. A583

WHITE PLAINS
New York Power Authority P375
White Plains Hospital Medical Center P688
Northeast Community Bancorp Inc E306
Frmo Corp. E169

WILLIAMSVILLE
Life Storage Inc E245

YORKTOWN HEIGHTS
Pcsb Financial Corp A638 E325

NORTH CAROLINA

ASHEVILLE
Hometrust Bancshares Inc A428 E202
Mission Health System, Inc. P345
Mission Hospital, Inc. P345
Hometrust Bancshares Inc A428 E202

BOONE
Samaritan's Purse P478

BURLINGTON
Laboratory Corporation Of America Holdings A498

CARY
Ply Gem Holdings, Inc. P432
Coc Properties, Inc. P130
Nci Building Systems, Inc. E297

CHAPEL HILL
University Of North Carolina Hospitals P649
University Of North Carolina At Chapel Hill P648
Strata Solar, Llc P544

CHARLOTTE
Bank Of America Corp A100
Duke Energy Corp A281
Nucor Corp. A604
Sonic Automotive, Inc. A748
Duke Energy Carolinas Llc A281
Brighthouse Financial Inc A146
Brighthouse Life Insurance Co - Insurance Products A146
The Charlotte-mecklenburg Hospital Authority A806 P569
Snyder's-lance, Inc. P507
Foundation For The Carolinas P202
The University Of North Carolina At Charlotte P612
Crowder Constructors, Inc. P148
Premier Inc E336
Nn, Inc E305
Lendingtree Inc (new) E242

CONCORD
Carolinas Medical Center Northeast P97

DURHAM
Iqvia Holdings Inc A468
Duke University Health System, Inc. P168
Research Triangle Institute Inc P458
Family Health International Inc P191
Durham Public Schools P170
Duke Regional Hospital P168
Accord Healthcare, Inc. P4

ELON
Elon University P181

FAYETTEVILLE
Cape Fear Valley Medical Center P93
Cumberland County Schools P149
Fayetteville Public Works Commission P192

FRANKLIN
Entegra Financial Corp A299

GASTONIA
Mann+hummel Filtration Technology Intermediate Holdings Inc. P305
Caromont Health, Inc. P97

GREENSBORO
The Moses H Cone Memorial Hospital Operating Corporation P595
The Fresh Market Inc P581
The Moses H Cone Memorial Hospital P594
Market America, Inc. P308
Market America Worldwide, Inc. P308

GREENVILLE
University Health Systems Of Eastern Carolina, Inc. P638
Pitt County Memorial Hospital, Incorporated P429
East Carolina Health Inc P173

HICKORY
Commscope Holding Co., Inc. A224
Alex Lee, Inc. P21

LEXINGTON
Lexington Medical Center P289

MONROE
Union County Board Of Education P633

MOORESVILLE
Lowe's Companies Inc A520

NEW BERN
Carolinaeast Medical Center P96

PINEHURST
Firsthealth Of The Carolinas, Inc. P194
Moore Regional Hospital, Inc. P352

RALEIGH
First Citizens Bancshares Inc (nc) A340 E152
Wakemed P673
North Carolina Electric Membership Corporation P385
Rex Hospital, Inc. P459
North Carolina Eastern Municipal Power Agency P385
Duke Health Raleigh Hospital Guild P167
Carolina North Housing Finance Agency P96
Nc State Investment Fund Inc P367
Pra Health Sciences Inc E335
First Citizens Bancshares Inc (nc) A340 E152

SOUTHERN PINES
First Bancorp (nc) A337

STATESVILLE
Energyunited Electric Membership Corporation P183

WILMINGTON
Live Oak Bancshares Inc A517 E247
Live Oak Banking Company A518 P292
Live Oak Bancshares Inc A517 E247

WINSTON SALEM
North Carolina Baptist Hospital P385
Wake Forest University P673

WINSTON-SALEM
Bb&t Corp. A114
Hanesbrands Inc A399

NORTH DAKOTA

BEULAH
Dakota Gasification Company Inc P151

BISMARCK
Basin Electric Power Cooperative P62
North Dakota University System Foundation P386
St. Alexius Medical Center P526

DEVILS LAKE
Western State Bank P686

FARGO
Sanford P481
North Dakota University System P386
Dakota Supply Group, Inc. P151
Innovis Health, Llc P249
Eide Bailly Llp P176
Ni Holdings Inc E304

GRAND FORKS
Alerus Financial Corp A29 E9
Altru Health System P29
Minnkota Power Cooperative, Inc. P345
University Of North Dakota P650
Alerus Financial Corp A29 E9

MINOT
Trinity Health P624
Spf Energy, Inc. P519

WEST FARGO
Clark Equipment Company P125

OHIO

AKRON
Goodyear Tire & Rubber Co. A391
Firstenergy Corp A354
Jersey Central Power & Light Company P261
Ohio Edison Company P404
West Penn Power Company P681
The Cleveland Electric Illuminating Company P574
Pennsylvania Electric Company P422
Metropolitan Edison Company P337
Childrens Hospital Medical Center Of Akron P117
American Transmission Systems, Incorporated P37

BATAVIA
Multi-color Corp. E288

BEREA
Ohio Turnpike And Infrastructure Commission P404

CANFIELD
Farmers National Banc Corp. (canfield,oh) A317 E141

CANTON
The Aultman Hospital P566
Mercy Medical Center, Inc. P331

CINCINNATI
Kroger Co (the) A495
Procter & Gamble Company (the) A670
Fifth Third Bancorp (cincinnati, Oh) A331
American Financial Group Inc A50
Cintas Corporation A197
Federal Home Loan Bank Of Cincinnati A321 E145
First Financial Bancorp (oh) A344
General Electric International, Inc. A375 P210
Mercy Health A551 P327
Western & Southern Financial Group, Inc. A890 P683
General Electric International, Inc. A375 P210
Mercy Health A551 P327
Western & Southern Financial Group, Inc. A890 P683
Uc Health, Llc. P631
Children's Hospital Medical Center P114
Messer Construction Co. P334
General Electric International Operations Company, Inc. P210
The Christ Hospital P571
University Of Cincinnati Medical Center, Llc P640
Cincinnati Public Schools P121
Bethesda, Inc. P72
Bethesda Hospital, Inc. P71
Good Samaritan Hospital Of Cincinnati P215
Novelart Manufacturing Company P399
Federal Home Loan Bank Of Cincinnati A321 E145
Medpace Holdings Inc E269

CLEVELAND
Sherwin-williams Co (the) A737
Parker Hannifin Corp A633
Keycorp A488
Tfs Financial Corp A805
The Cleveland Clinic Foundation A807 P573
Eaton Corporation A287 P174
The Cleveland Clinic Foundation A807 P573
Eaton Corporation A287 P174
The Metrohealth System P592
Case Western Reserve University P98
Metrohealth Medical Center P336

Cleveland Municipal School
  District P126
Fairview Hospital P190
Northeast Ohio Regional Sewer
  District P392
Southwest General Health
  Center P516

COLUMBUS
American Electric Power Co Inc A46
L Brands, Inc A496
Big Lots, Inc. A127
Huntington Bancshares Inc A439
State Auto Financial Corp. A763
Ohiohealth Corporation P405
Nationwide Children's Hospital P365
American Electric Power Service
  Corporation P32
Franklin County Board Of
  Commissioners P204
Mount Carmel Health System P353
American Municipal Power, Inc. P35
Columbus Public School
  District P133
Columbia Gas Of Ohio, Inc. P132
Mount Carmel Health System P353
Buckeye Power, Inc. P88
Mount Carmel Health Plan
  Medig P353
Aep Ohio Transmission Company,
  Inc P10
The Fishel Company P580
M/i Homes Inc E253
Installed Building Products Inc E218
Diamond Hill Investment Group
  Inc. E106

DAYTON
Kettering Adventist Healthcare P274
Miami Valley Hospital P339
The University Of Dayton P611
Premier Health Partners P439
Good Samaritan Hospital P213
Dayton Public School District P154

DEFIANCE
First Defiance Financial Corp A343
  E153

DUBLIN
Cardinal Health, Inc. A164

EAST LIVERPOOL
Ag Foundation P11

FAIRFIELD
Cincinnati Financial Corp. A195

FINDLAY
Marathon Petroleum Corp. A526

FREMONT
Croghan Bancshares, Inc. E100

GAHANNA
Heartland Banccorp E191

GALLIPOLIS
Holzer Health System P239

HUDSON
The American Endowment
  Foundation P565

KENT
Carter-jones Companies, Inc. P98

LANCASTER
Fairfield Medical Center P189
South Central Power Company
  Inc P509

LIMA
Mercy Health - St. Rita's Medical
  Center, Llc P329

MARIETTA
Peoples Bancorp Inc (marietta,
  Oh) A645 E329
Marietta Area Health Care Inc P306
Marietta Memorial Hospital Inc P306
Peoples Bancorp Inc (marietta,
  Oh) A645 E329

MASSILLON
Ojim, Inc. P405

MAUMEE
Dana Inc A252

MAYFIELD VILLAGE
Progressive Corp. (oh) A672

MEDINA
Rpm International Inc (de) A715

MIDDLEFIELD
Middlefield Banc Corp. E278

NEWARK
Park National Corp (newark,
  Oh) A633

NORTH CANTON
Diebold Nixdorf Inc A265

ORRVILLE
Smucker (j.m.) Co. A747

OXFORD
Miami University P339

PAINESVILLE
Lake Hospital System, Inc. P279

PERRYSBURG
Owens-illinois, Inc. A627

PORTSMOUTH
Southern Ohio Medical Center P516

RICHFIELD
Element14 Us Holdings Inc P179

SANDUSKY
Civista Bancshares Inc A208
Firelands Regional Health
  System P193

TOLEDO
Owens Corning A626
The University Of Toledo P612
Mercy Health St Vincent Med
  Llc P329
Toledo Public Schools P620

WALBRIDGE
The Rudolph/libbe Companies
  Inc P602
Rudolph Libbe Inc. P467

WARREN
Anderson And Dubose, Inc. P38

WEST CHESTER
Ak Steel Holding Corp. A25

WESTLAKE
Travelcenters Of America Llc A826

WILMINGTON
Air Transport Services Group, Inc. E8

YOUNGSTOWN
United Community Financial Corp.
  (oh) A844 E413

OKLAHOMA

ANADARKO
Western Farmers Electric
  Cooperative P684

CATOOSA
Cherokee Nation Businesses Llc P111

DURANT
Stephenson Wholesale Company,
  Inc. P542

NORMAN
Norman Regional Hospital
  Authority P383

OKLAHOMA CITY
Devon Energy Corp. A262
Chesapeake Energy Corp. A189
Bancfirst Corp. (oklahoma City,
  Okla) A98 E32
State Of Oklahoma A765 P540
Hobby Lobby Stores, Inc. A422 P238
State Of Oklahoma A765 P540
Hobby Lobby Stores, Inc. A422 P238
Express Services Inc P188
Integris Health, Inc. P250
Seventy Seven Energy Llc P494
Integris Baptist Medical Center,
  Inc. P249
Ssm Health Care Of Oklahoma,
  Inc. P523
Kirby - Smith Machinery, Inc. P276
Gulfport Energy Corp. E184
Mammoth Energy Services Inc E255
Paycom Software Inc E324
Bancfirst Corp. (oklahoma City,
  Okla) A98 E32

PRYOR
Orchids Paper Products Co. (de) E318

TAHLEQUAH
The Cherokee Nation P569

TULSA
Ngl Energy Partners Lp A590
Oneok Inc A622
Williams Cos Inc (the) A900
Bok Financial Corp A137
Oneok Partners, L.p. A623 P407
Saint Francis Hospital, Inc. P472
Magellan Pipeline Company,
  L.p. P301
T. D. Williamson, Inc. P552
Ahs Hillcrest Medical Center, Llc P13
Independent School District 1 Of
  Tulsa County P247
Explorer Pipeline Services
  Company P188
United States Beef Corporation P636

VINITA
Grand River Dam Authority P217

OREGON

BEAVERTON
Nike Inc A592
Beaverton School District P67
Great Ajax Corp E181

CORVALLIS
Samaritan Health Services, Inc. P478
Good Samaritan Hospital
  Corvallis P214

ESTACADA
Portland General Electric Comp P434

EUGENE
University Of Oregon P650
Eugene Water & Electric Board P187

MEDFORD
Lithia Motors Inc A515

PORTLAND
Pacificorp A630
Umpqua Holdings Corp A838 E408

Precision Castparts Corp. A665 P438
Oregon Health & Science
  University P409
Legacy Health P285
Careoregon, Inc. P94
Blount International, Inc. P75
Fortis Construction, Inc. P201
Legacy Emanuel Hospital & Health
  Center P284
Portland Public Schools P434
Familycare, Inc. P191
Portland State University P434
Portland Adventist Medical
  Center P434
Port Of Portland (inc) P433
Mercy Corps P327
Columbia Sportswear Co. E85
Umpqua Holdings Corp A838 E408

ROSEBURG
Mercy Medical Center, Inc. P331

SALEM
Salem Health P476
Salem-keizer School District 24j P476

WILSONVILLE
Mentor Graphics Corporation P326

PENNSYLVANIA

ABINGTON
Abington Memorial Hospital Inc P2

ALLENTOWN
Air Products & Chemicals Inc A23
Ppl Corp A664
Talen Energy Supply, Llc P554
Lehigh Valley Health Network,
  Inc. P286
School District Of The City Of
  Allentown P486

ALTOONA
Upmc Altoona P659

AUDUBON
Globus Medical Inc E178

BALA CYNWYD
Philadelphia Consolidated Holding
  Corp. A650 P426
Entercom Communications
  Corp E126
Hamilton Lane Inc E186

BENSALEM
Healthcare Services Group, Inc. E189

BETHLEHEM
St. Luke's Health Network, Inc. P533
Saint Luke's Hospital Of Bethlehem,
  Pennsylvania P474
St Luke's Hospital & Health Network
  Inc P525
Lehigh University P286
Orasure Technologies Inc. E318
Embassy Bancorp Inc E120

BRYN MAWR
Bryn Mawr Bank Corp A151 E48
Main Line Hospitals, Inc. P302
Aqua Pennsylvania, Inc. P42
Bryn Mawr Bank Corp A151 E48

CAMP HILL
Rite Aid Corp A708
Fleming Gannett Inc P195

CANONSBURG
Centimark Corporation P104
Cnx Midstream Partners Lp E80

CARMICHAELS
Cb Financial Services Inc E61

A = AMERICAN BUSINESS
E = EMERGING COMPANIES
P = PRIVATE COMPANIES
W = WORLD BUSINESS

CHAMBERSBURG
Summit Health P546
Chambersburg Hospital P109

CHESTERBROOK
Amerisourcebergen Corp. A59
The J G Wentworth Company P586

CLEARFIELD
Cnb Financial Corp. (clearfield, Pa) A211 E79

CORAOPOLIS
Dick's Sporting Goods, Inc A263

DANVILLE
Geisinger Health A372 P208
Geisinger Medical Center P209
The Geisinger Clinic P582
Geisinger System Services P209

DOUGLASSVILLE
Stv Group, Incorporated P544

DOWNINGTOWN
Dnb Financial Corp. E108

DOYLESTOWN
Central Bucks School District P105
Doylestown Hospital Health And Wellness Center, Inc. P164

DUNCANSVILLE
Value Drug Company P664

EMMAUS
Buckeye Pipe Line Company, L P P88

ERIE
Erie Indemnity Co. A305
Upmc Hamot P660

FORT WASHINGTON
Nutrisystem Inc E309

GETTYSBURG
Acnb Corp A9

GREENSBURG
Westmoreland Regional Hospital P686

HARRISBURG
Pennsylvania Housing Finance Agency A641 P422
Pennvest A641 P422
United Concordia Life And Health Insurance Company P634
County Of Dauphin P144
Pennsylvania Housing Finance Agency A641 P422
Pennvest A641 P422
Ollie's Bargain Outlet Holdings Inc E315
Hersha Hospitality Trust E195

HERSHEY
Hershey Company (the) A415
Pennsylvania - American Water Company P421
Milton Hershey School & School Trust P344

HORSHAM
Toll Brothers Inc. A818

INDIANA
First Commonwealth Financial Corp (indiana, Pa) A341
S & T Bancorp Inc (indiana, Pa) A719 E362

KENNETT SQUARE
Exelon Generation Co Llc A309
Genesis Healthcare Inc A379

KING OF PRUSSIA
Universal Health Services, Inc. A856
Ugi Corp. A835

LANCASTER
Fulton Financial Corp. (pa) A369
The Lancaster General Hospital P588

LANGHORNE
St. Mary Medical Center P535

MALVERN
Erm-na Holdings Corp. P186
Pq Group Holdings Inc E335
Cubesmart E101

MANHEIM
Worley & Obetz, Inc. P696

MARIETTA
Donegal Group Inc. A276

MEDIA
Elwyn P181

MILLERSBURG
Mid Penn Bancorp Inc E276

MOON TOWNSHIP
Calgon Carbon Corporation P89

NEWTOWN
Epam Systems, Inc. E130

PAOLI
Malvern Bancorp Inc E255

PEACH GLEN
Knouse Foods Cooperative, Inc. P276

PHILADELPHIA
Comcast Corp A220
Aramark A72
Radian Group, Inc. A689 E345
Beneficial Bancorp Inc A121
Republic First Bancorp, Inc. A705 E353
The Trustees Of The University Of Pennsylvania A811 P606
Thomas Jefferson University P618
The School District Of Philadelphia P603
Hospital Of The University Of Pennsylvania P241
Health Partners Plans, Inc. P230
Thomas Jefferson University Hospitals, Inc. P619
Drexel University P165
Community Behavioral Health P134
Albert Einstein Medical Center P20
The Pew Charitable Trusts P600
Aria Health P42
Five Below Inc E161
Radian Group, Inc. A689 E345
Lannett Co., Inc. E239
Fs Energy & Power Fund E169
Independence Realty Trust Inc E214
Republic First Bancorp, Inc. A705 E353
Prudential Bancorp Inc (new) E340

PITTSBURGH
Kraft Heinz Co (the) A494
Pnc Financial Services Group (the) A658
Ppg Industries Inc A663
United States Steel Corp. A852
Alcoa Corporation A29
Wesco International, Inc. A887
Fnb Corp A359 E164
Tristate Capital Holdings Inc A830 E403

University Of Pittsburgh Medical Center A858 P651
University Of Pittsburgh P651
Smmh Practice Plan, Inc. P507
Carnegie Mellon University P95
Duquesne Light Company P169
Magee-womens Hospital Of Upmc P301
Allegheny General Hospital Inc P23
Pittsburgh School District P430
Western Pennsylvania Hospital P685
Mercy Upmc P332
St. Clair Health Corporation P528
Upmc Passavant P660
Duquesne University Of The Holy Spirit P169
The Pittsburgh Foundation P601
Matthews International Corp E262
Federal Home Loan Bank Of Pittsburgh E145
Evoqua Water Technologies Corp E137
Fnb Corp A359 E164
Eqm Midstream Partners Lp E131
Tristate Capital Holdings Inc A830 E403

RADNOR
Lincoln National Corp. A512
Airgas, Inc. A24 P14
Main Line Health System P302

READING
Boscov's, Inc. P79
Ugi Utilities, Inc. P631
Redner's Markets, Inc. P454

SAXONBURG
Ii-vi Inc E213

SAYRE
The Robert Packer Hospital P602

SCRANTON
Peoples Financial Services Corp A646 E330

SEWICKLEY
Valley Medical Facilities, Inc. P663

SHIPPENSBURG
Orrstown Financial Services, Inc. A625

SOUDERTON
Univest Financial Corp A861 E418

STATE COLLEGE
Mount Nittany Medical Center P355
Eclipse Resources Corp E117

STROUDSBURG
Essa Bancorp Inc A306

UNIVERSITY PARK
The Pennsylvania State University A811 P600

UPPER CHICHESTER
Sunoco Pipeline L.p. P547

VILLANOVA
Villanova University In The State Of Pennsylvania P667

WARREN
Northwest Bancshares, Inc. (md) A602

WAYNE
The Judge Group Inc P588

WEST CHESTER
Accesslex Institute A8 P3
The Chester County Hospital P570
Accesslex Institute A8 P3

WILKES BARRE
Geisinger Wyoming Valley Medical Center P209

WILLIAMSPORT
Penns Woods Bancorp, Inc. (jersey Shore, Pa) A640
The Williamsport Hospital P617

WORCESTER
Allan Myers, Inc P23

WYOMISSING
Customers Bancorp Inc A246 E102
Gaming & Leisure Properties, Inc E170
Customers Bancorp Inc A246 E102

YARDLEY
Crown Holdings Inc A241

YORK
Codorus Valley Bancorp, Inc. A216 E80
York Hospital P700
Wellspan Medical Group (inc) P680
Engel Machinery Inc. P184
Codorus Valley Bancorp, Inc. A216 E80

PUERTO RICO

BAYAMON
C C 1 Limited Partnership P88

RIO GRANDE
Desarolladora Del Norte S E P160

SAN JUAN
Popular Inc. A661

TOA BAJA
Best Petroleum Corporation P70

RHODE ISLAND

KINGSTON
University Of Rhode Island P652

LINCOLN
Narragansett Electric Comp P362

PAWTUCKET
Hasbro, Inc. A407

PROVIDENCE
Textron Inc A803
United Natural Foods Inc. A847
Citizens Financial Group Inc (new) A205
State Of Rhode Island And Providence Plantations A765 P540
Gilbane Building Company A384 P212
State Of Rhode Island And Providence Plantations A765 P540
Gilbane Building Company A384 P212
Care New England Health System Inc P94
Women & Infants Hospital Of Rhode Island P695
Johnson & Wales University Inc P267

WARWICK
Plan International, Inc. P431
Kent County Memorial Hospital P272

WEST KINGSTON
Gordon Research Conferences Inc P217

WESTERLY
Washington Trust Bancorp, Inc. A880

WOONSOCKET
Cvs Health Corporation A249

SOUTH CAROLINA

ANDERSON
Anmed Health P39

CHARLESTON
Carolina Financial Corp (new) A167
E58
The Medical University Of South
Carolina P591
Carealliance Health Services P94
Roper Hospital, Inc. P465
Blackbaud, Inc. E43
Carolina Financial Corp (new) A167
E58

COLUMBIA
South State Corp A750 E377
Agfirst Farm Credit Bank A20 P12
Central Electric Power Cooperative,
Inc. P105
University Of South Carolina P655
Agfirst Farm Credit Bank A20 P12
Richland County School District
1 P461
South State Corp A750 E377

CONWAY
Horry County School District P240

FLORENCE
Mcleod Regional Medical Center Of
The Pee Dee, Inc. P319

FORT MILL
Domtar Corp A276

GREENVILLE
Southern First Bancshares, Inc. A753
E378

GREER
Regional Management Corp E349

HARTSVILLE
Sonoco Products Co. A749

LEXINGTON
Southeastern Freight Lines, Inc. P511
Lexington County School District No.
1. P289
First Community Corp (sc) E153

MONCKS CORNER
South Carolina Public Service
Authority (inc) P509

MYRTLE BEACH
Grand Strand Regional Medical
Center, Llc P218

SPARTANBURG
J M Smith Corporation P255
Security Group, Inc. P490
Security Finance Corporation Of
Spartanburg P490

SUMMERVILLE
Advanced Technology
International P6

SUMTER
Thompson Construction Group,
Inc. P620

WEST COLUMBIA
Lexington Medical Center P289

SOUTH DAKOTA

ABERDEEN
Dacotah Banks Inc. A251

Agtegra Cooperative P13

RAPID CITY
Regional Health, Inc. P456
Rapid City Regional Hospital,
Inc. P453

SIOUX FALLS
Great Western Bancorp Inc A395
E181
Meta Financial Group Inc A553 E275
Sanford Health P481
The Evangelical Lutheran Good
Samaritan Society P579
Great Western Bancorp Inc A395
E181
Meta Financial Group Inc A553 E275

TENNESSEE

BRENTWOOD
Delek Us Holdings Inc (new) A260
Tractor Supply Co. A824
Brookdale Senior Living Inc A148
Premise Health Holding Corp. P439
Reliant Bancorp Inc E350

CHATTANOOGA
Unum Group A862
Hamilton Chattanooga County
Hospital Authority P225
Emj Corporation P182
Electric Power Board Of
Chattanooga P177
Memorial Health Care System,
Inc. P323
Signal Energy, Llc P501
Parkridge Medical Center, Inc. P418

COLUMBIA
Maury Regional Hospital P314

COOKEVILLE
Averitt Express Incorporated P52
Averitt Express, Inc. P52

FRANKLIN
Community Health Systems,
Inc. A226
Franklin Financial Network Inc A364
E168
Clarcor Inc. P124
Franklin Financial Network Inc A364
E168

GERMANTOWN
Mid-america Apartment Communities
Inc E276

GOODLETTSVILLE
Dollar General Corp A273

GREENEVILLE
Forward Air Corp E166

JACKSON
Jackson-madison County General
Hospital District P258

JOHNSON CITY
Mountain States Health Alliance
Auxiliary, Inc. P356

KINGSPORT
Eastman Chemical Co A285

KNOXVILLE
Tennessee Valley Authority A797
Smartfinancial Inc A747
Scripps Networks Interactive,
Inc. P488
Regal Entertainment Group P455
Covenant Health P145
Phillips And Jordan,
Incorporated P426

Parkwest Medical Center P418

LEBANON
Wilson Bank Holding Co. A902

LOUDON
Malibu Boats Inc E255

MEMPHIS
Fedex Corp A326
International Paper Co A462
Autozone, Inc. A89
First Horizon National Corp A347
American Lebanese Syrian Associated
Charities, Inc. P34
Baptist Memorial Hospital P59
Monogram Food Solutions, Llc P350

MURFREESBORO
The Middle Tennessee Electric
Membership Corporation P594
National Health Investors, Inc. E292

NASHVILLE
Hca Healthcare Inc A409
Pinnacle Financial Partners Inc A654
E332
Fb Financial Corp A319 E142
Ryman Hospitality Properties,
Inc. A718 P468
Tennessee State School Bond
Authority A797 P557
The Vanderbilt University P615
Ryman Hospitality Properties,
Inc. A718 P468
Dialysis Clinic, Inc. P161
Lifeway Christian Resources Of The
Southern Baptist Convention P291
Thomas Saint Midtown Hospital P619
Executive Committee Of The
Southern Baptist Convention P188
Tennessee State School Bond
Authority A797 P557
Pinnacle Financial Partners Inc A654
E332
Fb Financial Corp A319 E142
Healthstream Inc E190
Medequities Realty Trust Inc E267

OOLTEWAH
Miller Industries Inc. (tn) E280

SPRINGFIELD
Hollingsworth Oil Co. Inc. P239

VONORE
Mastercraft Boat Holdings Inc E262

TEXAS

ABILENE
First Financial Bankshares, Inc. A345
E154
Hendrick Medical Center P233
First Financial Bankshares, Inc. A345
E154

ALVIN
Alvin Independent School
District P30

AMARILLO
Affiliated Foods, Inc. P11
Baptist St. Anthony's Hospital
Corporation P60
Amarillo Independent School
District P30

ARLINGTON
Horton (dr) Inc A433
Texas Health Resources A801 P561
Arlington Independent School District
(inc) P46

AUSTIN
National Western Life Group
Inc A574
Citizens, Inc. (austin, Tx) A206
State Of Texas A765 P540
Whole Foods Market, Inc. A898 P689
University Of Texas System A860 P656
Texas Permanent School Fund
Management Company, Inc. A803
P562
Texas County And District Retirement
System A801 P561
Farm Credit Bank Of Texas A316 P191
State Of Texas A765 P540
Whole Foods Market, Inc. A898 P689
University Of Texas System A860 P656
Texas Permanent School Fund
Management Company, Inc. A803
P562
Texas County And District Retirement
System A801 P561
Permanent University Fund P424
University Of Texas At Austin P656
Lower Colorado River Authority P298
Texas State University System P563
Attorney General, Texas P50
Farm Credit Bank Of Texas A316 P191
St David's South Austin Medical
Center P524
Southwest Key Programs, Inc. P516
Cirrus Logic Inc E77
Parsley Energy Inc E323
Silicon Laboratories Inc E371
Summit Hotel Properties Inc E387
Chuy's Holdings Inc E76
Luminex Corp E250
Usa Compression Partners Lp E422

BEAUMONT
Communitybank Of Texas National
Association A228 P136

CARROLLTON
The Brandt Companies Llc P567
Carrollton-farmers Branch
Independent School District P97

COLLEGE STATION
Texas A&m Foundation A800 P559

COLUMBUS
Drymalla Construction Company,
Inc. P166

CONROE
Conroe Independent School
District P139

DALLAS
At&t Inc A83
Energy Transfer Lp A297
Energy Transfer Operating Lp A298
Southwest Airlines Co A755
Tenet Healthcare Corp. A794
Kimberly-clark Corp. A490
Jacobs Engineering Group, Inc. A471
Texas Instruments Inc. A802
Hollyfrontier Corp A422
Sunoco Lp A773
Dean Foods Co. A257
Builders Firstsource Inc. A153
Santander Consumer Usa Holdings
Inc A726
Enlink Midstream Llc A299
Neiman Marcus Group Ltd Llc A578
Comerica, Inc. A220
Hilltop Holdings, Inc. A419 E197
Texas Capital Bancshares Inc A800
E395
Triumph Bancorp Inc A831 E404
Veritex Holdings Inc A869 E427
Baylor Scott & White Holdings A114
P64

A = AMERICAN BUSINESS
E = EMERGING COMPANIES
P = PRIVATE COMPANIES
W = WORLD BUSINESS

Spirit Realty Capital, Inc. A759 P520
Baylor Scott & White Holdings A114 P64
Balfour Beatty Construction Group, Inc. P54
Balfour Beatty Construction, Llc P54
Dallas County Hospital District P151
Baylor University Medical Center P65
Children's Medical Center Of Dallas P116
Spirit Realty Capital, Inc. A759 P520
Stevens Transport, Inc. P542
Southern Methodist University Inc P514
Methodist Hospitals Of Dallas Inc P336
Sharyland Utilities, L.p. P499
Copart Inc E93
Hilltop Holdings, Inc. A419 E197
Eagle Materials Inc E112
Match Group Inc E262
Dave & Busters Entertainment Inc E104
Howard Hughes Corp E207
Texas Capital Bancshares Inc A800 E395
Spirit Realty Capital Inc (new) E381
Hff Inc E196
Matador Resources Co E262
Holly Energy Partners Lp E199
Braemar Hotels & Resorts Inc E45
Cim Commercial Trust Corp E77
Triumph Bancorp Inc A831 E404
Nexpoint Residential Trust Inc E303
Infrareit Inc E215
Westwood Holdings Group, Inc. E436
Texas Pacific Land Trust E396
Wingstop Inc E440
Veritex Holdings Inc A869 E427
Capital Southwest Corp. E56

DECATUR
Decatur Hospital Authority P157

DEER PARK
Deer Park Refining Limited Partnership P157

DENTON
University Of North Texas System P650
Denton Independent School District P159

DFW AIRPORT
Dallas/fort Worth International Airport P152

EDINBURG
Doctors Hospital At Renaissance, Ltd. P162

EL PASO
El Paso Independent School District P177
El Paso County Hospital District P177
Ysleta Independent School District P700
Socorro Independent School District P508

EULESS
Us Concrete Inc E419

FLOWER MOUND
Ivie & Associates, Llc P255

FORT WORTH
American Airlines Group Inc A42
Burlington Northern & Santa Fe Railway Co. (the) A154
Tpg Specialty Lending Inc A824 E400
Bnsf Railway Company A134 P77
Fort Worth Independent School District P201
Cook Children's Medical Center P141
County Of Tarrant P145
Tarrant County Hospital District P555
Texas Christian University Inc P560
Baylor All Saints Medical Center P64
Cook Children's Health Plan P140
Cook Children's Physician Network P141
Firstcash Inc E160
Tpg Specialty Lending Inc A824 E400

FRISCO
Addus Homecare Corp E4

GALVESTON
American National Insurance Co. (galveston, Tx) A53

GARLAND
Garland Independent School District P208

GRAPEVINE
Gamestop Corp A371
Lonestar Freightliner Group, Llc P295

HALTOM CITY
Classic Star Group, Lp P126

HOUSTON
Phillips 66 A652
Sysco Corp A781
Conocophillips A232
Enterprise Products Partners L.p. A302
Plains Gp Holdings Lp A658
Plains All American Pipeline Lp A657
Halliburton Company A398
Baker Hughes, A Ge Company A95
Waste Management, Inc. (de) A881
Kinder Morgan Inc. A491
Occidental Petroleum Corp A610
Eog Resources, Inc. A303
Group 1 Automotive, Inc. A396
Centerpoint Energy, Inc A180
Quanta Services, Inc. A686
Targa Resources Corp A786
Westlake Chemical Corp A894
National Oilwell Varco Inc A574
Centerpoint Energy Resources Corp. A180
Apache Corp A68
Cheniere Energy Inc. A188
Marathon Oil Corp. A525
Stewart Information Services Corp A769
Prosperity Bancshares Inc. A673
Cadence Bancorporation A156 E50
Cbtx Inc A176
Allegiance Bancshares Inc A30 E11
Citgo Petroleum Corporation A202 P121
Telco Intercontinental Corp A793 P557
Memorial Hermann Health System A548 P324
Spectra Energy Corp A757 P518
Citgo Petroleum Corporation A202 P121
Telco Intercontinental Corp A793 P557
Memorial Hermann Health System A548 P324
Spectra Energy Corp A757 P518
Houston Methodist Hospital P243
Houston Independent School District P242
Chemium International Corp. P111
Midcoast Energy Partners, L.p. P342
Harris County Hospital District P226
Texas Children's Hospital P559
Methodist Health Care System P335
Texas Eastern Transmission, Lp P561
Texla Energy Management, Inc. P563
Cypress-fairbanks Independent School District P149
Plains Pipeline, L.p. P431
Community Health Choice, Inc. P134
Florida Gas Transmission Company, Llc P197
Anr Pipeline Company P40
Aldine Independent School District P20
Natural Gas Pipeline Company Of America Llc P366
S & B Engineers And Constructors, Ltd. P469
Enterprise Te Products Pipeline Company Llc P185
El Paso Natural Gas Company, L.l.c. P177
Southern Natural Gas Company, L.l.c. P515
University Of Houston System P643
Enterprise Crude Pipeline Llc P185
Mid-america Pipeline Company, Llc P341
Alief Independent School District P22
Algonquin Gas Transmission, Llc P22
U.s. Pipeline, Inc. P630
Spring Branch Independent School District (inc) P521
Enable Gas Transmission, Llc P183
Lone Star Ngl Pipeline Lp P294
Texas Aromatics, Lp P559
Waukesha-pearce Industries, Inc. P677
Phillips 66 Carrier Llc P426
Tmh Physician Organization P620
Spring Independent School District P521
Pearce Industries, Inc. P421
Ruby Pipeline, L.l.c. P466
Port Of Houston Authority P433
Colorado Interstate Gas Company Llc P131
Harmony Public Schools P226
Greater Houston Community Foundation P220
Selectransportation Resources Llc P491
Russell & Smith Ford, Inc. P468
Northern Border Pipeline Company P393
Nbl Permian Llc P367
Houston Methodist Hospital P243
Par Pacific Holdings Inc E322
Kraton Corp E235
Phillips 66 Partners Lp E331
Quanex Building Products Corp E343
Spark Energy Inc E380
Carrizo Oil & Gas, Inc. E58
Sanchez Energy Corp. E364
Hi-crush Partners Lp E197
Cadence Bancorporation A156 E50
Francesca's Holdings Corp E168
Shell Midstream Partners Lp E367
U.s. Physical Therapy, Inc. E405
Noble Midstream Partners Lp E305
Main Street Capital Corp E255
Whitestone Reit E438
Allegiance Bancshares Inc A30 E11
Usd Partners Lp E423
Evolution Petroleum Corp E136

HUMBLE
Humble Independent School District P243

IRVING
Exxon Mobil Corp A312
Fluor Corp. A358
Celanese Corp (de) A176
Pioneer Natural Resources Co A656
Vistra Energy Corp A875
Michaels Companies Inc A559
Commercial Metals Co. A224
Federal Home Loan Bank Of Dallas A321 E145
Christus Health International P118
Gruma Corporation P222
Nch Corporation P367
Jp Energy Partners Lp P268
Irving Independent School District Inc P254
Boy Scouts Of America P81
Nexstar Media Group Inc E303
Federal Home Loan Bank Of Dallas A321 E145

KATY
Katy Independent School District P271
Us Silica Holdings, Inc. E421

KILGORE
Martin Resource Management Corporation P311

KILLEEN
Killeen Independent School District P275

LA JOYA
La Joya Independent School District P278

LAREDO
International Bancshares Corp. A458
United Independent School District P635
City Of Laredo P123

LEAGUE CITY
The Clear Creek Independent School District P573

LEANDER
Leander Independent School District P284

LUBBOCK
Plains Cotton Cooperative Association P430
Pro Petroleum, Inc. P441
Covenant Health System P146
Lubbock County Hospital District P299
Lubbock Independent School District P300

MCKINNEY
Torchmark Corp A821
Independent Bank Group Inc. A452 E214
Mckinney Independent School District P318
Independent Bank Group Inc. A452 E214

MESQUITE
Mesquite Independent School District P334

MIDLAND
Diamondback Energy, Inc. E107
Viper Energy Partners Lp E429

MOUNT PLEASANT
Guaranty Bancshares Inc A397 E184

NACOGDOCHES
East Texas Electric Cooperative, Inc. P173

NEW BRAUNFELS
Rush Enterprises Inc. A716

ODESSA
Ector County Independent School
District P174

PASADENA
Pasadena Independent School
District P420

PFLUGERVILLE
Pflugerville Independent School
District P425

PHARR
Pharr San Juan-alamo Independent
School District P426

PLANO
Penney (j.c.) Co.,inc. (holding
Co.) A639
Toyota Motor Credit Corp. A824
Alliance Data Systems Corp. A31
Yum China Holdings Inc A916
Legacytexas Financial Group
Inc A504 E241
Plano Independent School
District P431
Fogo De Chao, Inc. P199
Texas Heart Hospital Of The
Southwest, L.l.p. P562
Integer Holdings Corp E218
At Home Group Inc E25
Tyler Technologies, Inc. E404
Legacytexas Financial Group
Inc A504 E241
Bg Staffing Inc E41

RICHARDSON
Richardson Independent School
District P460

ROSENBERG
Lamar Consolidated Independent
School District (inc) P281

ROUND ROCK
Dell Technologies Inc A261
Round Rock Independent School
District (inc) P466

SAN ANGELO
Shannon Medical Center P497

SAN ANTONIO
Valero Energy Corp A867
Iheartmedia Inc A448
Cullen/frost Bankers, Inc. A243
Bexar County Hospital District P72
Presidian Destinations, Ltd. P440
Northside Independent School
District P396
North East Independent School
District P386
San Antonio Independent School
District Fac P478
Christus Santa Rosa Health Care
Corporation P119
Southwest Research Institute
Inc P517
University Health System P637

SAN MARCOS
Texas State University P562

SHERMAN
W. Douglass Distributing, Ltd. P672

SPRING
Klein Independent School
District P276

SUGAR LAND
Cvr Energy Inc A248

Noble Holding (u.s.)
Corporation P382
Applied Optoelectronics Inc E20

TEMPLE
Mclane Company, Inc. A547 P318
Scott & White Memorial
Hospital P486

TEXARKANA
Truman Arnold Companies P624
E-z Mart Stores, Inc. P170
Christus Health Ark-la-tex P118

THE WOODLANDS
Anadarko Petroleum Corp A63
Huntsman Corp A443
Chevron Phillips Chemical Company
Llc A192 P111
Chevron Phillips Chemical Company
Lp A193 P112
Chevron Phillips Chemical Company
Llc A192 P111
Chevron Phillips Chemical Company
Lp A193 P112
Arena Energy, Lp P42
Western Gas Partners Lp E435
Western Gas Equity Partners Lp E435
Lgi Homes, Inc. E243
Sterling Construction Inc E386
Summit Midstream Partners Lp E388
Smart Sand Inc E376

TYLER
Southside Bancshares, Inc. A754
E379
Christus Trinity Mother Frances
Health System P120
Mother Frances Hospital Regional
Health Care Center P353
Southside Bancshares, Inc. A754
E379

VICTORIA
South Texas Electric Cooperative,
Inc. P511

WACO
Brazos Education Loan Authority,
Inc A145 P82
Baylor University P64
Providence Health Services Of
Waco P444
Brazos Education Loan Authority,
Inc A145 P82

WEBSTER
Clear Lake Regional Medical Center,
Inc. P126

WESLACO
Idea Public Schools P245

WEST LAKE HILLS
The Drees Company P577

WICHITA FALLS
United Regional Health Care System,
Inc. P635

WYLIE
North Texas Municipal Water
District P391

UTAH

AMERICAN FORK
People's Utah Bancorp A645 E329
Alpine School District P27
People's Utah Bancorp A645 E329

CENTERVILLE
Management & Training
Corporation P303

DRAPER
Ralph L. Wadsworth Construction
Company, Llc P452
Healthequity Inc E190

LEHI
Vivint Solar Inc E429

LOGAN
Utah State University P662

MIDVALE
Ally Bank A34 P27
Zagg Inc E448

PROVO
Brigham Young University P83

SALT LAKE CITY
Zions Bancorporation, N.a. A919
Intermountain Health Care Inc A457
P250
Alsco Inc. P28
R.c. Willey Home Furnishings P450
Granite School District P218
O. C. Tanner Recognition
Company P402
Western Governors University P685
Northern Utah Healthcare
Corporation P394
O. C. Tanner Company P401
Arnold Machinery Company P46
Kern River Gas Transmission
Company P274
Salt Lake City School District P477
Marlin Business Bank P309
Extra Space Storage Inc E139
Usana Health Sciences Inc E422
Control4 Corp E92

SANDY
Canyons School District P92
Utah Association Of Realtors P661

SOUTH JORDAN
Merit Medical Systems, Inc. E273

SPANISH FORK
Nebo School District. P368

ST GEORGE
Ihc Health Services, Inc. A448 P246

WEST JORDAN
Jordan School District P268

WEST VALLEY CITY
Utah Housing Corporation A866 P661

VERMONT

BURLINGTON
The University Of Vermont Health
Network Inc P613
The University Of Vermont Medical
Center Inc P613
University Of Vermont & State
Agricultural College P657

COLCHESTER
Green Mountain Power
Corporation P220

WINOOSKI
Vermont Student Assistance
Corporation P666

VIRGINIA

ALEXANDRIA
City Of Alexandria P122
Alexandria Inova Hospital P21
Good360 P216
Volunteers Of America, Inc. P671

Vse Corp. E429

ARLINGTON
Aes Corp. A17
The Nature Conservancy P595
Ceb Inc. P102
Public Broadcasting Service P445
Avalonbay Communities, Inc. E26
Chesapeake Lodging Trust E73
Arlington Asset Investment Corp E24

BLACKSBURG
Virginia Polytechnic Institute & State
University P668

BLUEFIELD
First Community Bankshares Inc
(va) A342

BROADLANDS
Loudoun County Public School
District P297

CHARLOTTESVILLE
Petersburg Motor Company Inc P424
University Of Virginia
Investment P658
Martha Jefferson Hospital P310

CHESAPEAKE
Dollar Tree Inc A273
Fincantieri Marine Systems North
America, Inc. A334 P193

CLOVERDALE
New River Electrical
Corporation P372

DANVILLE
American National Bankshares, Inc.
(danville, Va) A52

DULLES
National Rural Utilities Cooperative
Finance Corp E293

EDINBURG
Shenandoah Telecommunications
Co E367

FAIRFAX
Fairfax County Virginia A314 P189
Guest Services, Inc. P222
National Rifle Association Of
America P364
Fvcbankcorp Inc E170

FALLS CHURCH
General Dynamics Corp A373
Northrop Grumman Corp A601

FISHERSVILLE
Augusta Health Care, Inc. P51

FREDERICKSBURG
Rappahannock Electric
Cooperative P453
Washington Healthcare Physicians,
Mary P674

GLEN ALLEN
Markel Corp (holding Co) A527

HERNDON
Beacon Roofing Supply Inc A116
Tata Communications (america)
Inc. P556
Continental Building Products
Inc E92

LEESBURG
Loudoun Hospital Center P298

LYNCHBURG
Liberty University, Inc. P290
Centra Health, Inc. P104

A = AMERICAN BUSINESS
E = EMERGING COMPANIES
P = PRIVATE COMPANIES
W = WORLD BUSINESS

MANASSAS
Northern Virginia Electric
Cooperative P394

MARTINSVILLE
Carter Bank & Trust (martinsville,
Va) A167
Hooker Furniture Corp E203

MCLEAN
Freddie Mac A366
Capital One Financial Corp A162
Hilton Worldwide Holdings Inc A420
Booz Allen Hamilton Holding
Corp. A139
Southern National Bancorp Of
Virginia Inc A754
Gladstone Commercial Corp E177

MECHANICSVILLE
Owens & Minor, Inc. A625

NEWPORT NEWS
Huntington Ingalls Industries,
Inc. A442
Riverside Healthcare Association,
Inc. P461
Riverside Hospital, Inc. P462

NORFOLK
Norfolk Southern Corp. A596
Sentara Healthcare A736 P492
Sentara Hospitals - Norfolk P493
Virginia International Terminals,
Llc P668
Children's Hospital Of The Kings
Daughters Inc P116
Old Dominion University P406

PORTSMOUTH
Townebank A823 E399

RESTON
Leidos Holdings Inc A505
Nvr Inc. A607
Noblis, Inc. P383
Maximus Inc. E264

RICHMOND
Altria Group Inc A37
Performance Food Group Co A648
Carmax Inc. A166
Dominion Energy Inc (new) A274
Genworth Financial, Inc. (holding
Co) A381
Virginia Electric & Power Co. A873
Federal Reserve Bank Of Richmond,
Dist. No. 5 A324
Union Bankshares Corp (new) A841
E410
Virginia Housing Development
Authority A873 P668
Virginia College Building
Authority A872 P667
Vcu Health System Authority P665
Estes Express Lines, Inc. P186
Virginia Premier Health Plan,
Inc. P669
Virginia Commonwealth
University P668
Virginia Housing Development
Authority A873 P668
Virginia College Building
Authority A872 P667
Mcv Associated Physicians P320
University Of Richmond P653
Apple Hospitality Reit Inc E20

Union Bankshares Corp (new) A841
E410
Kinsale Capital Group Inc E233

ROANOKE
Advance Auto Parts Inc A12
Carilion Medical Center P95
The Branch Group Inc P567
Luna Innovations Inc E251

ROCKINGHAM
Sentara Rmh Medical Center P493

STAUNTON
Farm Credit Of The Virginias
Aca A316 P191

SUFFOLK
Bon Secours-maryview Health
Corporation P79

TIMBERVILLE
F & M Bank Corp. E139

TYSONS
Computer Sciences Corporation A228
P136
Alarm.com Holdings Inc E9

TYSONS CORNER
Alvarez Llc P30

VIENNA
Actionet, Inc. P6

VIRGINIA BEACH
Lifenet Health P291
The Christian Broadcasting Network
Inc P572
Armada Hoffler Properties Inc E24

WEST POINT
C & F Financial Corp. A156

WILLIAMSBURG
The College Of William & Mary P574

WINCHESTER
American Woodmark Corp. E15
Trex Co Inc E400

WASHINGTON

BELLEVUE
T-mobile Us Inc A785
Paccar Inc. A628
Expedia Group Inc A310
Overlake Hospital Association P413
Overlake Hospital Medical
Center P413
Radiant Logistics, Inc. E346

BOTHELL
Northshore School District P395

BREMERTON
Harrison Medical Center P226

CASHMERE
Cashmere Valley Bank Washington
(new) A168

EVERETT
Fortive Corp A363
Public Utility District 1 Of Snohomish
County P447
Everett Public Schools P187

FEDERAL WAY
Federal Way Public Schools P192

HOQUIAM
Timberland Bancorp, Inc. E399

ISSAQUAH
Costco Wholesale Corp A239
Naes Corporation P361
Issaquah School District 411 P255

KENT
Kent School District P273

KIRKLAND
King County Public Hospital District
2 P275
Monolithic Power Systems Inc E284
Pendrell Corp E327

MOUNT VERNON
Public Hospital District 1 Skagit
County P446

MOUNTLAKE TERRACE
Fs Bancorp Inc (washington) E169

OLYMPIA
Heritage Financial Corp (wa) A414
E194
Providence Health And Services P444
Heritage Financial Corp (wa) A414
E194

POULSBO
Pope Resources Lp E334

PUYALLUP
Puyallup School District P450

REDMOND
Microsoft Corporation A560

RENTON
Providence Health & Services A674
P444
Public Hospital District 1 Of King
County P446

RICHLAND
Kadlec Regional Medical Center P269

SEATTLE
Amazon.com Inc A38
Starbucks Corp. A762
Nordstrom, Inc. A595
Alaska Air Group, Inc. A27
Weyerhaeuser Co A895
Expeditors International Of
Washington, Inc. A311
Washington Federal Inc A879
Homestreet Inc A427 E201
University Of Washington Inc A861
P658
Swedish Health Services P549
The City Of Seattle-city Light
Department P572
Port Of Seattle P433
Ocean Beauty Seafoods Llc P402
Washington Teamsters Welfare
Trust P676
Northwest Hospital & Medical
Center P396
Homestreet Inc A427 E201
Aptevo Therapeutics Inc E21

SPOKANE
Spokane Public Schools P521

TACOMA
Columbia Banking System Inc A219
E84
Multicare Health System P357
Franciscan Health System P203
Tacoma Public Schools P553
Tacoma Public Utilities P553
Columbia Banking System Inc A219
E84

VANCOUVER
Public Utility District 1 Of Clark
County P446
Salmon Legacy Creek Hospital P477
Vancouver Public Schools P664
Barrett Business Services, Inc. E38
Nautilus Inc E296
Riverview Bancorp, Inc. E357

WALLA WALLA
Banner Corp. A109 E36

WENATCHEE
Public Utility District No. 1 Of Chelan
County P447
Wenatchee Valley Hospital P681
Central Washington Health Services
Association P107

YAKIMA
Yakima Valley Memorial Hospital
Association Inc P697

WEST VIRGINIA

BRIDGEPORT
United Hospital Center, Inc. P635

CHARLES TOWN
Jefferson County Board Of
Education P260

CHARLESTON
United Bankshares Inc A842 E411
City Holding Co. A207
Charleston Area Medical Center,
Inc. P110
United Bankshares Inc A842 E411

FAIRMONT
Mvb Financial Corp A572 E288
Monongahela Power Company P350
Mvb Financial Corp A572 E288

HUNTINGTON
Premier Financial Bancorp, Inc. A667
Cabell Huntington Hospital Inc P88
St. Mary's Medical Center P536
Steel Of West Virginia, Inc. P541
Swva, Inc. P551

MOOREFIELD
Summit Financial Group Inc A773
E387

MORGANTOWN
Virginia West University Foundation
Incorporated A873 P669
West Virginia United Health System,
Inc. P681
West Virginia University P682
Virginia West University Foundation
Incorporated A873 P669

WHEELING
Wesbanco Inc A886 E433
Wheeling Hospital, Inc. P688
Wheeling Power Company P688
Wesbanco Inc A886 E433

WISCONSIN

APPLETON
The Boldt Group Inc P567
Thedacare, Inc. P618

BARABOO
Nordic Group Of Companies
Ltd. P383

BEAVER DAM
United Cooperative P634

BROOKFIELD
Fiserv Inc A355
Community Care, Inc. P134

CLINTON
The Delong Co Inc P577

COTTAGE GROVE
Landmark Services Cooperative P281

FITCHBURG
Promega Corporation P443

FOND DU LAC
Agnesian Healthcare, Inc. P12

GLENDALE
Wheaton Franciscan Services,
  Inc. P687

GREEN BAY
Associated Banc-corp A80
Nicolet Bankshares Inc A592 E304
Krueger International, Inc. P277
Bellin Memorial Hospital, Inc. P68
Bellin Health Systems, Inc. P67
Aurora Baycare Medical Center P51
Green Bay Area Public School
  District P220
Nicolet Bankshares Inc A592 E304

GREENDALE
Goodwill Industries Of Southeastern
  Wisconsin, Inc. P216

JANESVILLE
Mercy Health System
  Corporation P329

KENOSHA
Kenosha Unified School District
  1 P272

LA CROSSE
Gundersen Lutheran Medical Center,
  Inc. P224
Gundersen Lutheran Health System,
  Inc. P223
Dairyland Power Cooperative P151

MADISON
First Business Financial Services,
  Inc. A339 E151
Wisconsin Housing And Economic
  Development Authority A905 P694
Wisconsin Alumni Research
  Foundation A905 P693
Madison Metropolitan School
  District P301
Meriter Hospital, Inc. P333
Wisconsin Housing And Economic
  Development Authority A905 P694
Wisconsin Alumni Research
  Foundation A905 P693
First Business Financial Services,
  Inc. A339 E151

MANITOWOC
Bank First National Corp A100 E34
County Bancorp, Inc. E98

MARSHFIELD
Marshfield Clinic, Inc. P309
Saint Joseph's Hospital Of Marshfield,
  Inc. P473

MENASHA
Faith Technologies, Inc. P190

MENOMONEE FALLS
Kohl's Corp. A492

MIDDLETON
University Of Wisconsin Medical
  Foundation, Inc. P659

MILWAUKEE
Manpowergroup Inc A525
Wec Energy Group Inc A883
Rockwell Automation, Inc. A712
Harley-davidson Inc A403
Mgic Investment Corp. (wi) A556
Johnson Controls, Inc. A477 P268
Aurora Health Care, Inc. A86 P52
Johnson Controls, Inc. A477 P268
Aurora Health Care, Inc. A86 P52

Aurora Health Care Metro, Inc P51
Milwaukee Public Schools (inc) P344
The Medical College Of Wisconsin
  Inc P591
Columbia St. Mary's Hospital
  Milwaukee, Inc. P133
Marquette University P309
Wheaton Franciscan P687
Froedtert And Community Health
  Inc P206
Rev Group Inc E356
Marcus Corp. (the) E257
Douglas Dynamics, Inc. E109
Physicians Realty Trust E332

MOUNT HOREB
Duluth Holdings Inc E110

OSHKOSH
Oshkosh Corp (new) A625

RACINE
Racine Unified School District P451
Modine Manufacturing Co E282

SUN PRAIRIE
Independent Pharmacy
  Cooperative P247

WAUKESHA
Prohealth Care Inc P442
American Transmission Company,
  Llc P36
Waukesha Memorial Hospital,
  Inc. P677
Cib Marine Bancshares Inc E76

WAUSAU
Aspirus, Inc. P48
Aspirus Wausau Hospital, Inc. P48

WAUWATOSA
Waterstone Financial Inc (md) A882

WYOMING

CHEYENNE
Memorial Hospital Of Laramie
  County P324

Index of Executives

A

A, Sun W287
Aadland, Todd A322
Aaefedt, Matthew A855
Aaholm, Sherry A. A246
Aai, Julie E47
Aakre, D Scott A432
Aardsma, Wayne P503
Aaron, Thomas J. (Tom) A227
Aaron, Kimberly P141
Aaron, Todd P542
Aaronian, Ray A328
Aarons, Miriam P69
Aarons, Brian P525
Aaronson, Daniel A323
Aaronson, Diane P298
Aarup-Andersen, Jacob W118
Aasland, Brent P249
Abad, Rafael Lopez A753
Abadie, Laurent W282
Abadir, Jeffrey A240
Abarca, Jose A647
Abate, Victor (Vic) A375
Abate, Joanne A863
Abbal, Frédéric W322
Abbamondi, Desa A899
Abbamondi, Desa P690
Abbaseh, Samimi A685
Abbasi, Masoud P402
Abbate, Mark L. A553
Abbate, Mark L. E272
Abbatecola, Vincent P. E209
Abbeele, Annick D. Van den P153
Abbene, David A532
Abbey, Jared A122
Abbey, Anna B A773
Abbey, Anna A773
Abbey, Anna B E387
Abbey, Anna E387
Abblett, Fred A332
Abbondi, Piero A20
Abbott, Greg A173
Abbott, Sarah A558
Abbott, Dean A701
Abbott, Greg A765
Abbott, James A919
Abbott, Karen P64
Abbott, Mary J P261
Abbott, Jody P387
Abbott, Greg P540
Abbott, Charles P541
Abbott, John W313
Abboud, John A484
Abboud, Andy A502
Abboud, Ali El A766
Abdallah, Chaouki T. P648
Abdelhafiz, Gada M P227
Abdella, Shelly A883
Abdo, John E. (Jack) E39
Abdoo, Elizabeth A. A434
Abdoo, Richard A594
Abdullah, Rao A398
Abdullah, Sakinah P505
Abdun-Nabi, Daniel J. E121

Abe, Toshinori W323
Abe, Makoto W330
Abel, Greg A123
Abel, Gregory E. (Greg) A630
Abel, Melissa A800
Abel, Anju P248
Abel, Nir W190
Abel, John E119
Abel, Robert E276
Abel, Melissa E396
Abel-Hodges, Cheryl A682
Abela, John A556
Abell, Charlie A68
Abellera, Philip A710
Abelli, Donna L. A451
Abello, Marc P A221
Abelman, David A708
Abelsen, James N P505
Abercrombie, Les P206
Abergel, Danny E257
Aberle, Jim P697
Abernathy, Cammy P642
Abernethy, Brian A3
Abhishek, Shukla A260
Abhold, Kathleen P446
Abhyankar, Vivek P324
Abichandani, Sanjay A22
Abington, Clay A562
Abish, Jeffrey D. (Jeff) P6
Abiteboul, Jean A189
Abji, Minaz B. A434
Able, Pamela P348
Ables, Grady L. A69
Ables, Dorothy M. A758
Ables, Dorothy M. P519
Abney, Jack A764
Abney, David P. A850
Aboaf, Eric A766
Abood, Steven A701
Aboody, Linda P325
Aboulafia, Joseph A105
Aboumrad, Daniel Hajj W25
Abraham, JJ A508
Abraham, Edward P673
Abraham, Neil E348
Abrahamson, Laura A16
Abrahamson, Tom P278
Abramczyk, Andrew A306
Abramowicz, Daniel A. A242
Abramowitz, Scott A441
Abramowitz, Bernard H P376
Abramowski, Dan A701
Abrams, Murray A163
Abrams, Mike A196
Abrams, Ed A460
Abrams, Ryan A905
Abrams, Ryan P693
Abrams, Mark E75
Abrams, John E282
Abrams, Jack E282
Abramson, Steven V. E417
Abregu, Martin A808
Abregu, Martin P581
Abrell, Lane P430
Abreu, Lorena P508

Abreu, Ant- - nio Manuel Barreto Pita de W134
Abreu, Rodrigo Modesto W359
Abshire, Kathy P116
Abshire, Kathryn P116
Abston, Tyson T A397
Abston, Chris A593
Abston, Angie A844
Abston, Angie E412
Abt, John E239
Abtew, Mulugeta A725
Abts, Joy A865
Abulaban, Majdi B. W29
Abutaleb, Sam A814
Abutaleb, Sam P616
Accardo, Joseph A678
Accogli, Giuseppe A113
Accordino, Daniel T. E60
Accum, Claude A. W346
Acereda, Alberto P175
Acerra, Peter P205
Acevedo, Margie A541
Acevedo, Debby P466
Acevedo, Margie E366
Ach, J. Wickliffe A345
Achary, Michael M. A399
Acharya, Guru A906
Achat, Catherine P144
Achkire, Debra A354
Achleitner, Paul W123
Achorn, Tina A402
Achrekar, Manoj A729
Achten, Dominik von W166
Acito, Paul A2
Acito, Paiul A3
Acito, Joe A332
Ackaret, Gary P268
Acker, Serge A691
Acker, H William P660
Ackerman, Michelle A34
Ackerman, Joel A255
Ackerman, Dean M A504
Ackerman, John P152
Ackerman, Melissa Melshenker P441
Ackerman, Lyle P499
Ackerman, Jeffrey (Jeff) P581
Ackerman, Thomas F. E69
Ackermann, Dan A295
Ackermann, Bryan E235
Ackerson, Vince A. A800
Ackerson, Vince A. E395
Ackley, John P255
Acklin, Bobbie A770
Ackroyd, Jim A9
Ackroyd, Jim P4
Acoca, Bernard A762
Acord, Suzette A866
Acord, Suzette P661
Acosta, Navia A583
Acosta, Philip A P508
Acosta, Manuel E166
Acosta-Trant, Ivette P59
Acott, Sarah A133
Acres, Harold R P146
Acton, Michael A724
Adachi, Mitsuo W116

Adadevoh, Dela P92
Adair, Bryan A460
Adair, Donald D P551
Adair, A. Jayson E94
Adali, Erhan W377
Adam, Tim A272
Adam, Rolf A454
Adam, Mary P47
Adam, Sharon P198
Adamczyk, Darius A429
Adame, Pedro A899
Adame, Theresa P22
Adame, Bonita P28
Adame, Pedro P690
Adamo, Christopher A105
Adamos, Tara A448
Adamoski, Rob E95
Adamovich, David P429
Adams, Dennis A34
Adams, Colby A59
Adams, Gregg T. A108
Adams, John A109
Adams, Kevin A167
Adams, Lisa A167
Adams, Kevin D A234
Adams, Melissa A244
Adams, Craig L. A308
Adams, Isaac A406
Adams, Thomas A419
Adams, Michael A441
Adams, Gregory A460
Adams, Beth A489
Adams, Vivian A513
Adams, Calvin A521
Adams, Romaneo A532
Adams, Jennifer A532
Adams, John A575
Adams, John A583
Adams, Scott A614
Adams, Cathryn A649
Adams, D. Scott A674
Adams, Wayne A701
Adams, William A725
Adams, Bobbie A769
Adams, Patricia (Trish) A788
Adams, Trish A788
Adams, Tim A795
Adams, Dian A795
Adams, Samantha A823
Adams, Leigh A838
Adams, Richard M. A843
Adams, Stan P7
Adams, John V P22
Adams, Michelle P28
Adams, James R. P73
Adams, Cathy P128
Adams, Kevin D P139
Adams, Louis P181
Adams, Hank P228
Adams, Gregory P239
Adams, William P260
Adams, Joe M P271
Adams, Lana P279
Adams, Martin L. P297
Adams, Joseph (Joe) P360
Adams, Nicole P464

A = AMERICAN BUSINESS
E = EMERGING COMPANIES
P = PRIVATE COMPANIES
W = WORLD BUSINESS

Adams, Dan P483
Adams, Jennifer P483
Adams, Bradley P515
Adams, Michele P521
Adams, Lawrence P525
Adams, Jason P537
Adams, Justin P596
Adams, Holly P608
Adams, Cecelia P620
Adams, Samantha P622
Adams, Mary Jane P638
Adams, Nancy D P685
Adams, Trevor W256
Adams, Robert J. E13
Adams, D. Rick E73
Adams, Keith E104
Adams, Kurt P. E163
Adams, W. Andrew (Andy) E292
Adams, Daryl M. E381
Adams, Richard M. E411
Adamson, Adam A129
Adamson, Ermil L. A277
Adamson, John A800
Adamson, Nancy P187
Adamson, John P559
Adamson, Mark E109
Aday, Daniel P218
Adcock, Beth A382
Adcock, Robert H. A425
Adcock, Andy W233
Adcock, Robert H. E201
Adda, Nathalie E122
Addiego, Gino A71
Addis, Jason P276
Addiscott, Lynn P637
Addison, Ann M. A505
Addison, John A667
Addison, David A724
Addison, Paul A404
Addison, Janine P630
Addotta, Sibylle A539
Adduci, Rich W255
Adee, Greg E195
Adelman, Fredie P506
Adelman, Jeffrey D. (Jeff) E226
Adelman, Jeff E226
Adelson, Sarah A323
Adelson, Sheldon G. A502
Aden, John A878
Adent, John E. E299
Adepeder, Suzanne P155
Aderholdt, Mary A718
Ades, Susan P506
Adian, Jim P678
Adiri, Ben-Zion (Benzi) W150
Adix, Kenneth P425
Adkerson, Richard C. A367
Adkins, Candace A58
Adkins, Rodney C A93
Adkins, Rodney A665
Adkins, Rodney A850
Adkins, Britni P408
Adkins, Dana P493
Adkins, Jim P571
Adkins, Greg P634
Adkins, Candace E16
Adkison, Jeffrey A478
Adkisson, Mike A782
Adler, Kim A34
Adler, Dean S A121
Adler, Paul F. A198
Adler, Dennis A691
Adler, Michael M. P355
Adler, Vitaly P688
Adome, Amy P498
Adonnino, Joseph P409
Adornato, Theodore C. (Ted) A756
Adornetto, Charles A639
Adornetto, Charles E325

Adrah, Robert P568
Adreani, Lou A766
Adusumilli, Venkat E166
Advani, Pratibha K P556
Adzema, Gregg D. E98
Afejuku, Ayo A565
Affrique, Antoine de Saint W381
Affronti, Michael A173
Afonso, Maria A647
Afwerke, Issac A722
Afwerke, Issac P474
Afzal, Tahira A489
Agaj, Indrid E276
Agar, Stephen W314
Agarwal, Anil A49
Agarwal, Anu A166
Agarwal, Pankaj A204
Agarwal, Achal A490
Agarwal, Manu A568
Agarwal, Parag A620
Agarwal, Naveen A676
Agarwal, Jai E19
Agarwal, Sonu E342
Agata, Shintaro W279
Agee, Philip A788
Agee, Nancy Howell P95
Agee, Krista P528
Agee, John H. E264
Agen, Brian E283
Agerup, Wenche W360
Aggarwal, Rohit A443
Aggarwal, Lokesh A767
Aggarwal, Nidhi P69
Aghajanian, Phil A103
Aghdami, Amanda N A163
Agiasotis, Kerry A893
Agner, Rebecca P385
Agnew, John A899
Agnew, John P690
Agochiya, Mihir A480
Agostaro, Russell P378
Agostino, Jason E117
Agrawal, Rajesh K. (Raj) A893
Agrawal, Gail B. P611
Agree, Jonathan P619
Agree, Joey E7
Agree, Richard E7
Agresta, Richard A734
Agresta, Gregory A886
Agresta, Gregory E433
Aguiar, Michael W. E216
Aguila, Percy R A109
Aguila, Percy R E36
Aguilar, Edgard Corrales A753
Aguilar, Mike A823
Aguilar, Ashley P91
Aguilar, Gayla P386
Aguilar, Jorge P470
Aguilar, Mike P622
Aguilar, Patrick R P637
Aguilar, Juan Antonio W25
Aguirre, Jean A532
Aguirre, Rodney E70
Agulnek, Barbara A406
Agurto, Tonya A272
Ahearn, Tracey A521
Ahearn, Brian P198
Ahee, Joseph A441
Ahern, R A324
Ahern, David A858
Ahern, Anthony J P88
Ahern, David E418
Ahern, Chris E448
Aherne, Sean A144
Aherne, Chris P357
Ahlgrimm, Marijo P34
Ahluwalia, Pradeep A767
Ahmad, Surabhi A56
Ahmad, Rosidah A456
Ahmadi, Hamid A685
Ahmed, Nadim A178
Ahmed, Riffat K A413
Ahmed, Sohail U. A456
Ahmed, Riffat K P234
Ahmed, Riaz E. W370

Ahmet, Byron A173
Ahn, Henry P488
Aho, Todd R A413
Aho, Todd R P234
Ahola, Orrin P129
Ahrabi-Nejad, Nadine P321
Ahrendt, Dale A484
Ahrendts, Angela A70
Ahrens, Chris P125
Ahrens, Jere M P185
Ahuja, Deepak A799
Ahuja, Seema S P637
Ai, Lin P642
Aiba, Yasunori W349
Aichele, William S. A862
Aichele, William S. E419
Aiguo, Lin W283
Aiken, Jason W. A374
Aiken, Donald B A539
Aiken, Scott A912
Aiken, Jefferson K. (Jeff) P287
Aili, Liu W91
Aing, Melissa A548
Aing, Melissa P324
Aini, Maria P618
Ainslie, Carolyn N. P606
Aiosa, Lisa A691
Air, David A. E171
Airhart, Jim P486
Aishman, Lisa P250
Aitken, Murray L. A469
Aizawa, Zengo W368
Aja, Cathy P545
Ajalla, Pius P382
Ajmani, Deep P398
Akalski, Frank J. A359
Akashi, Masaru W116
Akatsuka, Yo W268
Akbar, Mehrdad A878
Akers, Jeffery P404
Akers, Harlan P478
Akers-Pecht, Anna P610
Akgonul, Kerim E327
Akhtar, Muhammad A522
Akiba, Junichi W116
Akikawa, Tadashi W156
Akin, Bilal P226
Akin, Terry P594
Akin, David P640
Akins, Nicholas K. (Nick) A46
Akins, Nicholas K. (Nick) A47
Akins, D. Wayne A781
Akins, Nick P10
Akins, Nicholas K P32
Akiyama, Tomofumi W156
Akiyoshi, Mitsuru W234
Akpoguma, Andrea P68
Akrout, Chekib A14
Aksdal, Roy A163
Aksyutin, Oleg E. W289
Al-Amoudi, Omar A. W320
Al-Benyan, Yousef A. W320
Al-Ghamdi, Othman W315
Al-Ghanoudi, Ashirf P215
Al-Humaid, Abdulaziz S. W320
Al-Khudhair, Mariam A250
Al-Mady, Mohamed H. W320
Al-Maker, Awadh W320
Al-Mana, Khaled W320
Al-Naim, Najib Abdulaziz W322
Al-Ohali, Mosaed W320
Al-Rabeeah, Abdullah S. W320
Al-Saud, Saud bin Abdullah bin Thenayan W320
Al-Sheaibi, Fahad W320
Al-Zamel, Yousef W320
Alabsi, Samir Y P252
Alaix, Juan R. A921
Alam, Mahmood A649
Alama, Bernie A102
Alameddine, Ray A657
Alami, Maher P417
Alamo, Lisette A541
Alamo, Lisette E266
Alarhayem, Abdulqader P637

Alba, Alex P549
Alban, Carlos A6
Albanel, Christine W278
Albanese, Gerard A528
Albano, Charles A8
Albano, Charles P3
Alber, Laura J. A901
Alberici, John S P18
Alberici, John S P19
Alberry, Andrew P680
Albers, Carissa A223
Albers, Nancy P254
Albert, Don A288
Albert, Gary A732
Albert, Gary E365
Alberti, Harry P487
Alberto, Luis A628
Alberts, Mary A541
Alberts, Jim P271
Alberts, Mary E266
Albertson, Paul A582
Albertson, Marty A770
Albertson, Paul P373
Alberty, Carl E78
Albi, Chris A496
Albinson, Brock A87
Albornoz, Linda A49
Albouy, Laurent A682
Albrecht, Vicki A59
Albrecht, Geoffrey A687
Albrecht, Julie A750
Albrecht, Raymond P P341
Albrechtsen, John P. E125
Albright, Randolph A641
Albright, Steven A765
Albright, Brandy A857
Albright, Tenley P313
Albright, Jody P413
Albright, Glen P421
Albright, Randolph P422
Albright, Steven P540
Albright, John P. E92
Alburg, Kenneth A81
Albury, Beverly P92
Alcantar, Michael A244
Alcantar, Michael A446
Alcantar, Alberto P664
Alcantar, Michael E210
Alcina, Jim E327
Alcock, Charles R. P506
Alcorn, Karen P322
Aldag, Edward K. E268
Aldeborgh, John E. E27
Alden, John A850
Alder, Bob A265
Alderman, Mark A532
Alderman, Marian A832
Alderoty, Stuart A201
Aldersley, Stephen P464
Alderson, Christopher D. A783
Alderson, Art A878
Aldinger, Alan A659
Aldous, Hugh E216
Aldrich, Peter D P488
Aldrich, Sister Barbara P536
Aldrich, Bernard P. (Bernie) E19
Aldrich, Richard H. E89
Aldridge, David A58
Aldridge, Bryan P52
Aldridge, Susan C. P165
Aldridge, David E16
Aldridge, Don E276
Aldy, Sonya P680
Aleardi, Keith P A369
Alec, Pittman A881
Alekh, Kshitiz P685
Alekperov, Vagit Y. W290
Alekperova, Rena A97
Alekperova, Rena E32
Aleksov, Lynn A659
Aleman-Bermudez, Aurelio A336
Alemany, Ellen R. A201
Alesandro, Michael J P244
Alesci, Anne P106
Alesci, Megan A446

Alesci, Megan E210
Alessandrini, James A763
Alessandrini, Robert G. P588
Aletrakis, Timothy A359
Alex, Dudley A576
Alex, Dudley E297
Alexaitis, Irene P497
Alexander, Robert A56
Alexander, Susan H. A129
Alexander, Mark R. A161
Alexander, Robert M. A163
Alexander, Darrell A163
Alexander, Karin A193
Alexander, Rebecca A196
Alexander, Blair A221
Alexander, Aaron A223
Alexander, Bob A249
Alexander, Hank A298
Alexander, Paul A408
Alexander, Gaylord A413
Alexander, Tenzin A441
Alexander, Matthew A441
Alexander, Forbes I. J. A471
Alexander, Paul A490
Alexander, Nathan A568
Alexander, Elizabeth A611
Alexander, Sheila A614
Alexander, Craig H A641
Alexander, Joseph A741
Alexander, Robert A744
Alexander, Tim A754
Alexander, Stan A755
Alexander, Rhonda A782
Alexander, Carol A838
Alexander, Cory B. A855
Alexander, Bill A915
Alexander, Bruce K. A919
Alexander, Jackie P27
Alexander, Jim P167
Alexander, Tempie P170
Alexander, Barbara J P211
Alexander, Barbara P211
Alexander, Gaylord P234
Alexander, Wendy P279
Alexander, Sherrie P335
Alexander, James P349
Alexander, Rosemary P395
Alexander, Gene P397
Alexander, Craig H P422
Alexander, Kelly P518
Alexander, Pamala P633
Alexander, Jeffery P635
Alexander, Gordon P662
Alexander, Koler Dan W46
Alexander, Deborah M. W50
Alexander, Dana M. E18
Alexander, Janice E47
Alexander, Angie E253
Alexander, Elizabeth E313
Alexander, Joseph E370
Alexander, Tim E380
Alexandre, Patrick W14
Alexiou, Joy P482
Alfano, Nicholas (Nick) A289
Alff, Christopher E163
Alfieri, Kiersten A740
Alfieri, Laurie P551
Alfieri, Robert P676
ALFIERI, CLAUDIA W111
Alfieri, Kiersten E369
Alfonso, Rosa A49
Alfonso, Diana A204
Alford, William C. P76
Alford, Katherine P489
Alford, Barbara P554
Alford, Donald C. (Don) E311
Alger, Eugene K. A312
Alger, Robert P282
Alger, Robert E P589
Algoe, Eric P563
Alhadeff, Kathie P428
Alhand, Liz P226
Ali, Farah A113
Ali, Alam A570
Ali, Michael P126

Ali-ahmad, Walid A685
Aliabadi, Paymon A308
Alicea, Maria P83
Alicea, Marisa P155
Alicea, Jaime P551
Aligheri, Tim P258
Alimard, Kristina P658
Alires, Martin A165
Alkins, Brett P183
Alkire, Michael J. (Mike) E337
Allaire, Bella Loykhter A693
Allan, Chris A71
Allan, Donald (Don) A761
Allan, Don A761
Allard, Scott M. E11
Allavie, Kathy P462
Allberry, Katie Drinan A541
Allberry, Katie Drinan E266
Allbright, Justin A108
Allbright, Justin E36
Allcock, Nicole P511
Allegue, Raul A828
Allen, Hubert L. A5
Allen, Mary A A85
Allen, Blane A98
Allen, Kim A115
Allen, Andrew A129
Allen, Bertrand-Marc (Marc) A136
Allen, Lee A137
Allen, Thad W. A140
Allen, Tom A162
Allen, Lawren A163
Allen, Jerry A185
Allen, Julianne A201
Allen, Warren A201
Allen, Jeremy A223
Allen, James A244
Allen, Douglas A255
Allen, Wayne A258
Allen, Samuel R. (Sam) A259
Allen, Samuel R. (Sam) A260
Allen, Cynthia D A327
Allen, Gregory R. A344
Allen, Christopher A350
Allen, Miles A388
Allen, Jim A391
Allen, Chuck A400
Allen, Lori A406
Allen, Robert A458
Allen, Rob A458
Allen, Yorke A478
Allen, John A500
Allen, Jeffrey A537
Allen, Brenda A541
Allen, Joe A549
Allen, Walter A622
Allen, Stephen B A622
Allen, Adrienne A635
Allen, Daniel A693
Allen, Michael E. A703
Allen, Barbara A710
Allen, Gary A718
Allen, Patrick A727
Allen, Vanessa A733
Allen, Gary A737
Allen, Enna A744
Allen, Scott Allen Scott A774
Allen, Dennis A800
Allen, Jodi J A809
Allen, Jay A878
Allen, Etta A889
Allen, Dustin A920
Allen, Michael D. P14
Allen, Les P73
Allen, Jennifer P145
Allen, Christy P160
Allen, Michael P223
Allen, Melissa P235
Allen, Robert P251
Allen, Rob P251
Allen, Clay M P279
Allen, Linda P303
Allen, Kim P363
Allen, Steve P365
Allen, David J. P379

Allen, Chris P416
Allen, Adrienne P419
Allen, Mark P431
Allen, Robert P456
Allen, Zaruba P466
Allen, Becky P480
Allen, Janine P486
Allen, Kim P499
Allen, Shelly P538
Allen, Gloria P543
Allen, Dennis P559
Allen, Jodi J P584
Allen, Elizabeth Heller P593
Allen, Elizabeth P593
Allen, Richard D P602
Allen, Beth P630
Allen, Gary K. P647
Allen, Andrew T. P653
Allen, Andrew P680
Allen, Ken W125
Allen, Stephen W227
Allen, Blane E33
Allen, David R. (Dave) E149
Allen, Gregory R. E154
Allen, Christopher E156
Allen, John E237
Allen, Brenda E266
Allen, Joe E270
Allen, Jeff E357
Allen, Rod E360
Allen, Gary E367
Allensworth, Tami A439
Alles, Mark J. A178
Alleva, Frank A133
Alley, Alex A330
Alley, Sherri A384
Alley, C. Thomas (Tom) P179
Alley, Sherri E176
Alleyne, Stuart P296
Allie, Teresa P525
Allinson, Brooke A691
Alliod, Mark D A740
Allison, John W. A425
Allison, Linn A493
Allison, Lin A493
Allison, Lynn A493
Allison, Michael A612
Allison, Roy A644
Allison, Doug A647
Allison, Paul D. A693
Allison, Jeff A874
Allison, David P299
Allison, Debra P339
Allison, Lane P342
Allison, William P366
Allison, John P406
Allison, Diane M P598
Allison, John P633
Allison, Brian R. W161
Allison, Brad W176
Allison, R. Dirk E5
Allison, John W. E201
Allman, Keith J. A534
Allman, Dora P52
Allocca, Lori P510
Allocco, Steve A166
Allon, Wright A243
Alloway, Jay P270
Allport, Jeffrey P663
Allred, Matt A204
Allred, Paula A446
Allred, Paula E210
Allshouse, Scott A899
Allshouse, Scott P690
Allums, LaShaunda A784
Almanzor, Aj A449
Almario, Miyuki A183
Almaznaai, Hedar P119
Almeida, José E. (Joe) A113
Almeida, Derek A777
Almeida, Odilon A893
Almeida, Derek E393
Almen, Bruce Von A655
Almen, Bruce Von E333
Almendarez, Jerry P132

Almo, Charles P428
Almon, Robert C P414
Almond, Michelle A616
Almonte, Moises A659
Almoro, Lynn A49
Almquist, David C. (Dave) A380
Almy, Scott A. A504
Almy, Scott A. E241
Aloia, Sal A133
Aloise, David A. E301
Alonso, Jose A109
Alonso, Victor Ventimilla W321
Alonso, Jose E36
Alonzo, Leonicio P54
Alonzo, Jason P396
Aloysius, Chanda P511
Alpay, John M P93
Alpe, Kevin A754
Alpe, Kevin E378
Alper, Cenk W163
Alperin, Janice A P466
Alpert-Romm, Adria A269
Alsfine, Joel A78
Alsip, Bryan P73
Alsman, Floyd A384
Alsman, Floyd E176
Alspaugh, James A149
Alspaugh, Rick A182
Alspaugh, Rick E63
Alstine, Irene Van P254
Alston, Felecia P144
Altamimi, Yara P37
Altaras, June P550
Altendorf, Michael J. (Mike) P162
Altendorf, Mike P162
Alter, Timothy P467
Alterbaum, Jordan E117
Alters, Alan E226
Althauser, Chris A394
Althoff, Sven W164
Altig, David E. A322
Altman, Richard I. (Rick) A690
Altman, Stanley J. (Stan) A703
Altman, Dara F. A745
Altman, Alexandria P63
Altman, Roger C. E136
Altman, Amy L. E250
Altman, Richard I. (Rick) E345
Altmiller, Steve P389
Alton, Gregg H. A386
Altorelli, Richard K A122
Altozano, Angel Manuel Garcia W6
Altre-Kerber, Alison A489
Altrogge, Jeannine A59
Altschul, Larry A558
Altschul, Larry A909
Altschuler, Glenn C. P143
Altshuler, David E428
Altstadt, Dale A384
Altstadt, Dale E176
Alty, Kimberly A644
Alunan, Claudio P482
Alvarado, Jose A109
Alvarado, Elizabeth A221
Alvarado, Jennifer A459
Alvarado, Angelita P247
Alvarado, Esther P478
Alvarado, Rodrigo Huidobro W137
Alvarado, Jose E36
Alvarez, Miguel I. A628
Alvarez, Juan Carlos A726
Alvarez, Peter A869
Alvarez, Marc P30
Alvarez, Teresa P38
Alvarez, James M P127
Alvarez, Margarita P127
Alvarez, Erica P127
Alvarez, Nick P127
Alvarez, Carolina P296
Alvarez, Sorita P325
Alvarez, Felix P637
Alvarez, Felix P656
Alvarez, Jose Antonio W45
Alvarez, Luis W76

A = AMERICAN BUSINESS
E = EMERGING COMPANIES
P = PRIVATE COMPANIES
W = WORLD BUSINESS

Alvarez, Ernesto E175
Alvaro, Jay A281
Alvaro, Felecia E407
Alvaro, Felicia A E407
Alves, Nuno M. Pestana de
  Almeida W134
Alvey, Larry P184
Alvey, Jennifer P248
Alviti, Paulette R. A361
Alvstad, Frank A770
Alwan, Basil W266
Amaba, Jane A327
Amado, Evey A183
Amado, Mitchell J P213
Amado, Cristina P321
Amado, Mitchell P409
Amado, Evey E66
Amador, Richard A163
Amaez, Manuel P214
Amamiya, Masayoshi W48
Amanaganti, Raviner Reddy A200
Amann, Scott E445
Amaro, Luis A671
Amaro, Denise P241
Amat, Leonardo A187
Amat, Leonardo E71
Amato, Lisa A107
Amato, Elizabeth B. A854
Amato, David P125
Amato, Louis P P575
Amato, Lisa E34
Amaya, Jose P256
Amazan, Gaelle P243
Ambe, Kazushi W337
Amberg, Deborah A. (Deb) E12
Amberson, Susan A295
Amberson, James A499
Amble, Mike A330
Amble, Marcy A545
Ambler, Heather A683
Ambrecht, Kenneth A51
Ambrose, Julia A175
Ambrose, Steve A280
Ambrose, Steven A334
Ambrose, Curtis L A390
Ambrose, Allan A599
Ambrose, Kelly P295
Ambroseo, John R. E83
AMBROSIO, ARTIE A49
Ambrosio, Anthony G. A175
Ambrosio, Ken E140
Ambrosius, Jorg A766
Amel, Benjamin A144
Amelio, William J A93
Amelsberg, Andree A476
Amen, Darrell S. van A427
Amen, Darrell S. van E202
Amend, Chris A316
Amend, Michael A640
Amend, Kurt A695
Amend, Chris P191
Amend-Campbell, Debbie A329
Amendola, Paul P251
America, James P131
America, Ms Anna P247
Amerongen, Marcel V A177
Amerson, Leon T. (Timmy) A21
Amerson, Melissa A461
Amerson, Leon T. (Timmy) P12
Amerson-Allman, Aneidre A700
Ames, Marissa A109
Ames, Craig P87
Ames, Marissa E36
Amesquita, Carol A204
Amevor, Kwassi A841
Amevor, Kwassi P633
Amicarella, Ana E167
Amick, W. Michael A462
Amig, Eric A321

Amig, Eric E144
Amin, Minesh A599
Amin, Nick W38
Amine, James L. W111
Amir, Mohammad A235
Amirat, Cherif P586
Amirouche, Lamia A644
Amirpoor, Laurie A180
Ammann, Daniel (Dan) A378
Ammann, Vincent L. P687
Ammen, Michael E104
Ammons, Julie A169
Amon, Cristiano R. A685
Amorim, Paula W156
Amornkiatkajorn, Boobpha W296
Amoroso, Michael A133
Amoroso, Josephine A359
Amos, Daniel P. (Dan) A18
Amos, Paul S. A18
Amos, Sister Helen P331
Amos, John P699
Amosson, Brett A817
Amparan, Oscar L. A801
Amparan, Oscar L. P562
Ampaw, Rob A204
Amranand, Piyasvasti W296
Ams, Matt E98
Amstel, Hans P. van W7
Amstrong, C Micheal A474
Amstrong, C Micheal P265
Amstutz, Karen A524
Amundsen, Brad A81
Amundsen, Eric P197
An, Weizhe P338
An, Tong-Il W292
An, Min Soo W317
Ana, Coleen Santa A736
Ana, Coleen Santa P492
Analdo, Stephen F P421
Anand, Manish P228
Ananyev, Sergei A. W350
Anasinski, Adam A600
Anastasi, Shane A723
Anastasio, Kathryn A837
Anaya, Pedro A850
Anaya, Jose Antonio Gonzalez W285
Anbinder, Natalie A30
Ancher-Jensen, Henrik A22
Ancheta, Dan A103
Anda, Gabriela De P299
Andel, Steve Van A37
Andel, Steve Van P29
Anderman, Craig A13
Anderman, Sig E119
Anders, Mark A362
Anders, Bob A477
Anders, Dave A596
Anders, Bob P268
Andersen, Bryan A152
Andersen, Jill A178
Andersen, Ric A489
Andersen, Carl A874
Andersen, Travis P133
Andersen, Richard P687
Andersen, Tonny Thierry W118
Andersen, Ole G. W118
Andersen, Bryan E48
Anderskouv, Niels A803
Anderskow, Jerry A25
Anderskow, Jerry P15
Anderson, James R. (Jim) A14
Anderson, Shawn A34
Anderson, Peter A49
Anderson, Tracy A56
Anderson, Bradley A81
Anderson, Cari A94
Anderson, Neil A96
Anderson, Gaylin D. A97
Anderson, John A98
Anderson, Peter A109
Anderson, Terri A110
Anderson, Daniel A136
Anderson, Kristine Martin A140
Anderson, Shelia A219
Anderson, William A221

Anderson, Christopher A258
Anderson, James A260
Anderson, Robert A261
Anderson, Gerard M A280
Anderson, Melissa H. A281
Anderson, Fred A288
Anderson, Lars C. A332
Anderson, Michael A355
Anderson, Phyllis A438
Anderson, A. Scott A458
Anderson, William A470
Anderson, Suzanne A476
Anderson, Miles A478
Anderson, Kenneth A478
Anderson, Ian D. A492
Anderson, Carol S A531
Anderson, Traci K. A548
Anderson, Matthew A575
Anderson, Shawn A594
Anderson, Eric A607
Anderson, John C. A621
Anderson, Carol A644
Anderson, John H. A683
Anderson, Nick A684
Anderson, Willie A685
Anderson, Roger W A695
Anderson, Greg A714
Anderson, David A725
Anderson, Steven H. (Steve) A728
Anderson, Steve A729
Anderson, Dawn A770
Anderson, Frank A774
Anderson, Chris A774
Anderson, Julie L. A800
Anderson, Stephen A. (Steve) A803
Anderson, Sean A817
Anderson, Roy A833
Anderson, Kenneth A855
Anderson, Llewellyn C. A873
Anderson, Becky A878
Anderson, Bradbury H. (Brad) A881
Anderson, A. Scott (Scott) A919
Anderson, Howard A919
Anderson, Dave A920
Anderson, Warren P38
Anderson, Eric P48
Anderson, Cari P53
Anderson, Bill P66
Anderson, Lynn P81
Anderson, Gary P89
Anderson, Lois P93
Anderson, Terry P101
Anderson, Markham J J P106
Anderson, David P115
Anderson, Shelia P131
Anderson, Staci P135
Anderson, Diane P154
Anderson, Kerrii Brown P181
Anderson, C. Colt P200
Anderson, Barbara P203
Anderson, David G P207
Anderson, Laura P212
Anderson, Anjanette P218
Anderson, Michael R P227
Anderson, Bob P233
Anderson, Don P247
Anderson, Larry P250
Anderson, A. Scott P251
Anderson, William P254
Anderson, Ronnie K P276
Anderson, Steven P281
Anderson, Maureen P283
Anderson, Allyson P285
Anderson, Joseph P301
Anderson, Gregory A P309
Anderson, David P319
Anderson, Traci K. P321
Anderson, Patricia P337
Anderson, Fred P348
Anderson, Lynn P363
Anderson, Terry Sam P391
Anderson, Kirk P418
Anderson, Carole P446
Anderson, Richard A P474
Anderson, Terry D P474

Anderson, Gerald P485
Anderson, Richard A P525
Anderson, Amanda P573
Anderson, Brian T. P588
Anderson, Judy P603
Anderson, Audrey J. P615
Anderson, Gerri P619
Anderson, Llewellyn C. P668
Anderson, David P680
Anderson, Lee P686
Anderson, Jackie P686
Anderson, Stephanie P695
Anderson, William D. (Bill) W347
Anderson, Darby E5
Anderson, Gregory C. E11
Anderson, Gaylin D. E32
Anderson, John E33
Anderson, Peter E36
Anderson, Terri E37
Anderson, Anya E46
Anderson, Scott A. E78
Anderson, Eric E93
Anderson, Joel D. E162
Anderson, N. Leigh E251
Anderson, David J. (Dave) E288
Anderson, John H. E341
Anderson, Nick E341
Anderson, Julie L. E396
Andersson, Cornelia A133
Anderton, Amanda A227
Andes, John P521
Andino, Peter A460
Ando, Kenji W241
Ando, G-¶ran W271
Andrada, Marissa A763
Andrade, Juan C. W98
Andrade, Miguel Stilwell de W134
Andre, Sharon P310
Andre, Stephen St P481
Andreasen, Sheryl P66
Andrekovich, Mark S. E265
Andrekus, Brad A487
Andreo, Andy A390
Andreoli, Alain A419
Andreski, Lynne P525
Andreson, Jeffrey (Jeff) E290
Andreth, David A249
Andrew, Cooley A344
Andrew, Jim A647
Andrew, Adams A762
Andrew, Pam P412
Andrews, Nathan J. A304
Andrews, John A331
Andrews, Antoine A593
Andrews, Kirkland B. A604
Andrews, Mark A823
Andrews, Rob A844
Andrews, Richard P53
Andrews, Briggs P95
Andrews, Carol P187
Andrews, Mike P196
Andrews, Stephanie P248
Andrews, David P408
Andrews, Felicia P573
Andrews, Sue P590
Andrews, Teresa P627
Andrews, Michael P680
Andrews, Thomas J. E9
Andrews, Tom E9
Andrews, Michael E44
Andrews, Chip E98
Andrews, John E148
Andrews, Harold W. E363
Andrews, Rob E412
Andrietti, Bernadette A456
Andritsch, Stacie P688
Andrizzi, Flynn P238
Andro, Ronald P23
Andro, Ronald P644
Andronikakis, Spiros A. W24
Andrukicwicz, Marc A307
Andrus, Terry W. P172
Andrus, John E P548
Andux-Gonzalez, Carmen P271
Aneaknithi, Pipit W203

Anenberg, Vickie L. E101
Anesi, Joe P409
Anfinnsen, Tor Martin P186
Anfinson, Matt A158
Angehrn, Urban W405
Angel, Stephen F. (Steve) A514
Angel, Norma P123
Angel, Magda P221
Angelakis, Michael A282
Angelakis, Michael A419
Angelastro, Philip J. A619
Angelichio, Mick J. P588
Angelina, Michael A710
Angelini, Michael P. A402
Angelis, Yamynn De A248
Angell, Jan A3
Angell, Diana A308
Angelle, Marcia A562
Angelle, Tommy P279
Angelo, Paula A407
Angelo, Jesse A589
Angelo, Tami A912
Angelos, Vicky A390
Angelotti, Jim A173
Angerer, Erin A777
Angerer, Erin E393
Angle, Pam A115
Angle, Greg P297
Angle, Colin M. E225
Angleton, J Thomas P188
Angley, Ellen P188
Angley, James P376
Anglin, Kyle A163
Anglin, Robert P620
Angotta, Paul A105
Angotti, Liz A838
Angulo, Christine Stiltner P510
Anicetti, Richard A. (Rick) P581
Aniszewski, Craig J. E388
Ankeny, Tina P283
Anker, Sarah P622
Ankrum, Bob P334
Annamalai, Deva A919
Annan, Angela P601
Annas, Linda P149
Annecharico, Mary Alice A413
Annecharico, Mary Alice P234
Annello, Frank A865
Annese, Gretchen A149
Annis, John A616
Anonson, Chester A866
Ansari, Ansar A874
Ansari, Abid P304
Anschell, Jonathan H. A175
Anschutz, J Barron P102
Ansell, Jeffery D. (Jeff) A761
Ansley, William A850
Anson, Betty P529
Anstice, Martin B. A501
Ansusinha, Panop W202
Antal, James J. A182
Antal, James J. E63
Antell, James A578
Antes, John P346
Anthon, Allan P429
Anthony, Martin A298
Anthony, Vald A885
Anthony, David P318
Anthony, Rosemary P404
Anthony, Nicholas E90
Antill, Nicholas A659
Antinetti, David P348
Antishin, Dennis A912
Antkowiak, Patrick M. A602
Antolik, David G. A720
Antolik, David G. E362
Anton, John J P110
Anton, Michael E P110
Anton, Joseph P619
Antonace, William A177
Antonelli, Nicole A250
Antonelli, Pierluigi A550
Antonelli, Giovanni W383
Antonellis, Dan P545

Antoniades, Spiro B P645
Antoniello, Angela P392
Antonsson, Stefan E391
Antony, Ajitha P176
Antos, Cathy P622
Antosy, James A857
Antoun, Georges A199
Antrim, Michael A674
Antrim, Michael P444
Antrobus, Mike A513
Antunes, Lionel A353
Antunez, Jason P314
Anuk, Amy E123
Anvar, Saba A130
Anzaldua, Erika A313
Anzaldua, Ricardo A. A555
Aoki, Takeo W268
Aoun, Joseph E. P392
Aoyama, Gregg P275
Aoyama, Shinji W172
Ao'brien, Kathryn P155
Apatoff, Robert A33
Apatoff, Robert A34
Apel, Thomas G. A770
Apfalter, Guenther W229
Apgar, Don A823
Apicerno, Ken A815
Apikian, Jennik A272
Aplin, Teresa Broyles P178
Aplington, David P525
Apo, Todd E207
Apodaca, Rod A173
Apodaca, Aaron A546
Apodaca, Desiree P225
Apostle, Tony P450
Apostolou, Carrie A442
Appel, Ron A727
Appel, Frank W125
Appel, Dennis P E283
Appel, Dennis E283
Appelbaum, P. Stephen (Steve) A169
Appelbaum, Kristin A201
Apperson, Kevin P315
Applbaum, Hilda L A46
Applbaum, Hilda L P32
Apple, Robert E. (Bob) A536
Applebee, Tim A426
Appleberg, Brett A782
Appleby, Jarrett B. E107
Applegate, Beth A315
Applegate, Don P151
Applegate, Diane P516
Applegate, John S. P627
Applestein, Gary A478
Appleyard, Joseph P625
Applys, Carline P196
Appold, Stacy R P144
Appolito, Bob P672
Appolonia, Jack A25
Appolonia, Jack P15
April, Tim E424
Apte, Chaitanya A45
Apter, Ronald A407
Apuzzo, Michelle P699
Aquilina, Joanne P72
Aquilla, Dave A912
Aquino, Marlene A140
Aquino, Carmela P249
Arabia, Carmine A38
Arabie, Cheryl P476
Aragon-Hernandez, Olga A878
Araiza, Ron E52
Aramaki, Tomoyuki W213
Aramini, Diane A821
Aramini, Diane P621
Aran, Pete P472
Aranda, Marc P208
Aranha, Brian W30
Aratari, Thomas E140
Araujo, George A460
Aravena, Jose A738
Aravindakshan, Santhosh A555
Arbuckle, Barry P295
Arbuckle, Stuart A. E428
Arcalgud, Anil A289

Arce, Chris P161
Arch, Larry A724
Archambeau, Shellye A596
Archambeau, Dave P410
Archer, Pmp A10
Archer, Timothy M. (Tim) A501
Archer, Ed A725
Archer, Cynthia A A773
Archer, Dominick A836
Archer, Bradley A872
Archer, Donna P271
Archer, Kuan E182
Archibald, Nolan D. A443
Archibald, Sandra A861
Archibald, Norm P233
Archibald, Donna P622
Archibald, Sandra P658
Archibald, Lennox K. (Lenny) E360
Archila, Scott E1
Archuleta, Kimberly A204
Arcidiacono, Salvator A578
Arcudi, Jennifer E337
Arden, Lee A593
Arden, Allison P668
Ardezzone, Anthony A584
Ardisonne, Ron A88
Ardizzone, Ann A28
Ardoin, Elizabeth A. (Beth) A446
Ardoin, Beth A446
Ardoin, Elizabeth A. (Beth) E210
Ardoin, Beth E210
Arduini, Peter J. E220
Arebalos, Ish A215
Arellano, Luis R A728
Arellano, Margarita P563
Arellano, Augusto E136
Arena, Thomas A478
Arenas, Charles A490
Arendt, Brian A540
Arendt, Brian P316
Arenivas, Jesse A492
Arent, Thomas A898
Arevalo, Ricardo M. E373
Argalas, Barry E. E349
Argao, Selene A729
Argent, Heather A399
Argetsinger, Jenna A658
Argetsinger, Jenna P431
Argirakis, Brett E281
Argo, Laurie A303
Argodale, George A825
Argue, David P229
Arias, Pattie P127
Arief, Armand B. W384
Arieli, Yaniv E67
Arif, Abu A56
Arif, Hasan A767
Arifkhan, Oktay A871
Arihara, Masahiko W241
Arii, Carrie P451
Arima, Koji W121
Arinder, Jeff A262
Arinder, Matt P350
Arinelli, Wilmar A242
Ariqat, Ghassan A833
Arison, Micky W81
Ark, Jon Vander A707
Arkilahti, Nina W352
Arko, Johnathan A513
Arledge, David A. W138
Arler, Daniel (Dan) W3
Armater, Ann P230
Armbruster, Patrice A591
Armentrout, Sharon A782
Armentrout, Tracy A P400
Armes, Joseph B. (Joe) E57
Armfield, Jeff P509
Armin, Craig A795
Armini, Michael P392
Armogan, Nathan A158
Armour, Norm A892
Arms, William C P529
Armstrong, Duff A85
Armstrong, Robert A94
Armstrong, Sherry A188

Armstrong, Paula A322
Armstrong, Christopher A323
Armstrong, Steven A362
Armstrong, Ann K A456
Armstrong, Steven S A486
Armstrong, Keith D. A553
Armstrong, Scott A583
Armstrong, Ronald E. (Ron) A629
Armstrong, Greg L. A657
Armstrong, Greg L A658
Armstrong, Susie A685
Armstrong, Kay A830
Armstrong, Michael A872
Armstrong, Rebecca P27
Armstrong, Robert P53
Armstrong, Scott A. P153
Armstrong, Wayne P167
Armstrong, Christie P208
Armstrong, Darlene P217
Armstrong, Laura P302
Armstrong, Diane P404
Armstrong, Greg L P431
Armstrong, Katrina A. P590
Armstrong, Kelli P625
Armstrong, Philip W161
Armstrong, Keith D. E272
Armstrong, Kay E402
Arnault, Bernard W97
Arnault, Bernard W225
Arndt, Joann A272
Arndt, Kenneth A. A368
Arner, Steve P95
Arnesen, Finn A408
Arneson, Craig P444
Arnett, Haynes A136
Arnett, Gevan A213
Arnett, Christina P270
Arnett, Randal M P516
Arnn, Roger A314
Arnn, Roger P189
Arnold, Steve A82
Arnold, Scott A88
Arnold, Colleen A165
Arnold, Gary A247
Arnold, Chris A260
Arnold, Michael J. A367
Arnold, Christy A454
Arnold, Jeffrey A485
Arnold, Charles A555
Arnold, Steve A630
Arnold, Scott A685
Arnold, Timothy G. (Tim) A863
Arnold, Steve P49
Arnold, Jeff P161
Arnold, Kay K P185
Arnold, Gwen P318
Arnold, Melissa P345
Arnold, Bill P349
Arnold, Steve P415
Arnold, Kelly P536
Arnold, Gregory A. (Greg) P625
Arnold, Truman P625
Arnold, Gary E103
Arnold, John E173
Arnold, Scott E368
Arnold, Fiona E424
Arnow, Debra P117
Arntzen, Corry P521
Arnzen, Julie P511
Aroesty, Lindsay P601
Aromando, Nicholas A105
Aromando, Ada A131
Aron, Adam M. A41
Aronhalt, Steven P1
Aronis, George C. W24
Aronoff, Miriam P597
Aronow, David P594
Aronowitz, Scott A328
Aronsohn, Richard P79
Aronson, Tom A272
Aronson, Arnold A691
Aronson, Brian P638
Aronson, Stephen P653
Aronson, Michele E110
Arora, Deepak A49

A = AMERICAN BUSINESS
E = EMERGING COMPANIES
P = PRIVATE COMPANIES
W = WORLD BUSINESS

Arora, Amit A49
Arora, Sumeet A199
Arora, Ankush W265
Arous, Gérard Ben A585
Arous, Gérard Ben P377
Arquette, Andy E117
Arquines, Edwin P22
Arredondo, Omar A774
Arredondo, Marisela P254
Arrell, Sarah A788
Arribas, Ernesto Antoln P222
Arrico, Libby A160
Arrico, Libby E55
Arrighi, Theresa A115
Arrington, Adam P295
Arriola, Dennis V. A735
Arrowood, Tracey E445
Arrowsmith, Andrea A120
Arroyo, F. Thaddeus A84
Arroyo, Enrique A541
Arroyo, Jesus A729
Arroyo, Ana A810
Arroyo, Elena P393
Arroyo, Ana P597
Arroyo, Enrique E266
Arseneault, Michael A175
Arseneault, Jason A332
Arseneault, Tom W40
Arstark, Reid A727
Arterian, Hannah R A8
Arterian, Hannah R P3
Arters, Doug A463
Arthachinda, Nick A838
Arthur, Sarbah A40
Arthur, Vicki B. A750
Arthur, Gary A868
Arthur, Mark W180
Arthur, John W395
Arthur, Wayne E438
Arthurs, Mike P567
Arthurs, Timothy E139
Articolo, Glenn A P411
Artigas, Andrés W85
Artis, David A741
Artis, David E370
Artman, Michael P327
Arumugam, Magesh A101
Arumugam, Singaravelu P282
Arun, Anupam E123
Arunratana, Siripong W88
Arvanites, Seth A644
Arvin, Ann Margaret A507
Arvin, Ann Margaret P288
Arwari, Andy P95
Asaad, Bilal P196
Asada, Teruo W234
Asai, Eriko A375
Asakowicz, Steven M. E196
Asami, Hiroyasu W272
Asano, Kikuo W238
Asarch, Justin P651
Asarian, Armand P85
Asarpota, Rajesh J. (Raj) E310
Asbury, Stephanie A100
Asbury, Jeff A329
Asbury, John C. A841
Asbury, John C. E410
Asch, Barry P107
Ascher, John A691
Ascher, Michael C P624
Ascher-Topilski, Lilach W190
Asel, Keith A408
Asenkerschbaumer, Stefan W70
Asensio, Lynn D. A886
Asensio, Lynn D. E433
Ash, Shari A572
Ash, David A738
Ash, Tim A844
Ash, Christine P99

Ash, Shari P359
Ash, Tim E412
Ashbaugh, William M. (Bill) E57
Ashby, Michael A736
Ashby, Michael P492
Ashe, James T P306
Ashenbrenner, Fred A235
Ashenfelter, Craig E172
Asher, Linda A140
Asher, Andrew L. (Drew) A885
Ashida, Jun W326
Ashkenazy, Stewart A555
Ashlando, Ryan P316
Ashley, Richard W A5
Ashley, Anthony A492
Ashley, David A528
Ashley, Pamela A700
Ashley, Marion P145
Ashley, Marc P308
Ashley, Stanley W P567
Ashley, Steven W268
Ashline, Michael P81
Ashlock, Mark P434
Ashlyn, Sowell A475
Ashlyn, Sowell P266
Ashmawee, Viola A729
Ashmeade-Brown, Jamila P20
Ashtary, Mishel P35
Ashtiani, Kaihan A501
Ashton, Sam A330
Ashton, Martin A456
Ashue, Meghan A902
Ashue, Meghan P693
Ashworth, Ken A25
Ashworth, Richard M. A877
Ashworth, Ken P15
Asinas, Reuel P235
Ask, Carrie A509
Askew, Mike A461
Askew, James P108
Askew, Pam P252
Askuvich, Hallie A134
Askuvich, Hallie P78
Askvig, Delon A920
Askwig, Verna P452
Aslett, Mark E271
Aslin, Phil A800
Aslin, Judy P511
Aslin, Phil E396
Asmar, Joseph A532
Asnani, Manish A874
Asp, Jim P596
Aspinwall, Glenn A478
Asplund, Dale A. A851
Asrat, Mack P502
Assaf, Michal P227
Assaf, Ronald G. P399
Assaf, Samir W175
Assef, Eduardo A202
Assef, Eduardo P122
Asselberg, Mark A620
Assil, Jessica P400
Assoc, Rick P611
Asthana, Sandeep W347
Astle, Angela P694
Astle, Angie P694
Astroth, Joseph A888
Astrup, Michael P176
Aswall, Mark A724
ATAKA, TATEKI W170
Atalay, Hakan A682
Atarashi, Akira W326
Atcherman, S Jeffrey P335
Atcheson, Michael E89
Atchison, Pierre A725
Athanasakos, Nick A593
Athanasia, Dean C. A100
Athanasopoulos, Athanasios I. W24
Athanassopoulos, Theodoros I. W24
Athavale, Atul P228
Atherton, Brian A729
Athreya, Kartik A324
Athreya, Anand (Andy) A482
Atik, Mustafa Ata P226
Atiya, Sami W4

Atkins, Bruce A388
Atkins, Ron A461
Atkins, Patricia J P498
Atkinson, E Morrey A147
Atkinson, Ralph A412
Atkinson, Cliff A558
Atkinson, Heather A723
Atkinson, Tracy A766
Atkinson, Mike P6
Atkinson, Melissa P86
Atkinson, Linda P354
Atkinson, Kerry M P551
Atkinson, Ralph E192
Atsumi, Naoki W201
Attanasio, John B. P514
Attar, Rias A158
Attaway, John A. A679
Attaway, John A. A680
Attaway, John A. P448
Attea, Robert J. E245
Attig, Kelley A522
Attili, Srinivas A460
Attiyah, Abdullah Bin Khalifa Al W104
Attock, Julian A556
Attrill, Ed P161
Attwell, J Evans P226
Attwood, Karen A561
Attwood, Karen E278
Atwell, Joseph A96
Atwell, Kellie A272
Atwell, Robert A592
Atwell, William A883
Atwell, Robert E304
Au, Joseph A285
Au, Reynette A559
Au, Hoi-Yi V P466
Au, Joseph E114
Aubin, Michael D. P58
Aubrey, William E. A646
Aubrey, William E. E330
Aubry, Stephane A133
Aubry, Marc A894
Auchincloss, Thomas E89
Auclair, Bethany A696
Aucoin, Gary P186
Aucreman, Christine P353
Aud, Steve P567
Audiffred, Doug P318
Audiffred, J Douglas P318
Auel, John B P346
Aufderheide, Susan P449
Augdahl, Mark E19
Auger, Stephen A357
Auger, Cindy P72
Auger, Stephen P198
Augi, Tony A872
August, Gerald A314
August, Jim A676
August, Gerald P190
August-deWilde, Katherine A354
Auguste, Sandy A481
Augustine, Luke A165
Augustine, Mike A483
Augustine, Michael A873
Augustine, Michael P669
Augustine, Corinne E316
Augustino, Philip P182
Augustsson, Tommy A374
Augustyn-Fierg, Laurie A829
Auld, David V. A433
Aulds, Wesley P295
Aulph, Karen A339
Aulph, Karen E150
Aultmon, Gisela P420
Aunan, Erik A3
Aungst, Debra P450
Auque, Fran-§ois W16
Aurilio, Lisa P118
Auris, Jan-Dirk W168
Aurora, Dana A131
Ausberry, Sheila A221
Ausdemore, Steve P338
Ausere, Michael J P188
Ausloos, Jamie P12
Ausman, Gary A791

Austen, Karla P360
Austin, Adrienne A17
Austin, Karen A. A650
Austin, Earl C. (Duke) A686
Austin, Cathie A751
Austin, Kae P30
Austin, John P42
Austin, Greg P159
Austin, Timothy R. P169
Austin, Brenda P354
Austin, Joe P427
Austin, William P461
Austin, Jennifer P486
Austin, Aaron P504
Austin, Pam P521
Austin, Scott P575
Austin, John D. E70
Austin, Cathie E377
Auten, Dan A484
Autenried, Paul von A147
Auteri, Joseph P164
Autry, Matt A532
Autry, Daniel P262
Auxila, Paul P304
Auyeung, Rex A668
AuYeung, Benjamin E87
Auzenne, Scott A802
Auzenne, Terry P279
Auzenne, Scott P562
Avadhany, Nagesh E290
Avant, Keith A562
Aveiro, Stephanie P242
Avelenda, Saily A500
Avelenda, Saily E237
Avendano, Christopher E P193
Averbach, Rob A901
Averbach, Rob P692
Averett, Addison A788
Averill, Chris P422
Averill, Christopher P423
Averill, Chris P423
Averill, Christopher R P600
Avery, Linda A390
Avery, Meg A507
Avery, Emily P108
Avery, Jonathan P285
Avery, Meg P288
Avery, Sonja P300
Avila, Alejandro A725
Avila, José A. W108
Aviles, Alan D. A582
Aviles, Alan D. P373
Avis, Nancy P385
Aviv, Greer E96
Awad, Anwar A456
Awada, Hassan A240
Awadallah, Ehab A163
Awan, Faisal A493
Awasthi, Puneet A390
Awells, Rebecca P155
Axelson, David P365
Axford, Eric W348
Axtell, Tom P445
Axtman, Renee P29
Ayala, Patti A244
Ayala, Diana P225
Ayala, Joseph P459
Ayala, Patricia P700
AYATA, YUJIRO W176
Aycock, Angela W A221
Aydinli, - - brahim W377
Aye, Chris A691
Ayer, William S. (Bill) A861
Ayer, William S. (Bill) P658
Ayers, Stephen A723
Ayers, Alvita A855
Ayers, Joshua P275
Ayers, Mark P368
Ayers, Jonathan W. (Jon) E212
Ayers, Alvita E416
Ayla, Ahmet Fuat W18
Aylouche, Mounzer M A535
Aylouche, Mounzer M P312
Aylward, Kevin A530
Ayoub, Johnny A140

Ayre, David J. A592
Ayres, Maria A13
Ayscue, Charles F P346
Ayyar, Shekar A875
Azam, Iram P450
Azar, Sam A607
Azar, Mark A817
Azar, Robert B P398
Azarela, Michael (Mike) P545
Azeez, Sulaiman P292
Azinovic, Drago A652
Aziz, Mohammed S P333
Aznaurova, Lolitta P499
Aznavorian, Rosemarie A801
Aznavorian, Rosemarie P562
Azoulay, Salomon A648
Azoulay, Jack W286
Azuara, Katherine A113
Azuolay, Avi A741
Azuolay, Avi E370
Azzam, Ruba P610

B

Baatar, Bold W305
Baatar, Bold W306
Baba, Shinsuke W28
Babb, Ralph W. A221
Babb, Ovid A330
Babcock, John P. A639
Babcock, Calvin P59
Babcock, Terri P546
Babcock, John P. E325
Babe, Gregory S. (Greg) E263
Babel, Bryan A898
Babik, Amber A441
Babikian, Jeffrey C A173
Babineau, Thomas A141
Babington, Adam E A272
Babos, Constance P123
Babson, Stephen E86
Babst, Gordon P109
Babuscio, Mark P620
Baca, Bertha P53
Baccellieri, Cynthia P163
Bach, Paul D. A380
Bach, Allen W A823
Bach, Allen A823
Bach, Melody P428
Bach, Allen W P622
Bach, Allen P622
Bachaalani, Issam A218
Bachand, Kelly A314
Bachand, Kelly P189
Bachand, Deborah P303
Bache-Wiig, Ben P26
Bachelder, Stuart A255
Bachman, Robert J P182
Bachman, Mike P249
Bachman, Gary J. E341
Bachmann, Lisa M. A127
Bachmann, Steve A136
Bachmann, James (Jay) E92
Bachrach, William E E288
Bachus, Kevin E105
Bachus, Daniel E. (Dan) E180
Baciarelli, Renato P119
Bacigalupo, Richard J P456
Back, Tekla A647
Back, Rico W314
Back, Steve E250
Backman, Mats A87
Backous, Timothy P536
Backus, Marcia E. A611
Backus, Harroll (Hop) P1
Backus, Ann P567
Backus, John P635
Backus, William A. E31
Bacon, Graham W. A303
Bacon, Ashley A480
Bacon, James P301
Bacon, Julie P416
Bacon, John E426
Bacus, Lisa R. A195

Baczewski, Rosemary P409
Badar, Ruben A568
Badders, Matt A244
Bader, Jeffrey A559
Bader, Ashley P406
Badger, Austin A777
Badger, Stephen L P321
Badger, Haruka P461
Badger, Austin E393
Badgett, Loretta A774
Badgley, Jeffrey I. (Jeff) E280
Badi, Mohammed A49
Badin, Julio P319
Badowska, Eva P200
Badrinath, Vivek W389
Baehren, James W. (Jim) A628
Baek, Eugene A133
Baek, Seongho P436
Baen, Mona A769
Baer, Nick A478
Baer, Richard N. (Rich) A688
Baer, TimothyR A788
Baer, Tim A788
Baer, Donald A. (Don) P445
Baer, Marc E7
Baerlocher, Shawn A405
Baeseman, Jody P48
Baeslack, William A. (Bud) P98
Baez, Cindy P480
Baffa, Mitchel A583
Bagai, Pavan E138
Bagarozza, Vincent E90
Bagattini, Roy A509
Bagby, Carolyn L P88
Bagchi, Sam P336
Bagel-Trah, Simone W168
Baggs, David A243
Bagley, Chris A. A99
Bagley, Shannon A180
Bagley, Ross A751
Bagley, David A902
Bagley, David P464
Bagley, David P693
Bagley, Ross E377
Baglino, Drew A799
Baglivo, Mary L. P398
Bagnall, Christoper A542
Bagnall, Roger A585
Bagnall, Roger P377
Bagnall, Christoper E267
Bagnall, Spring J. E364
Bagnara, Alessandro A481
Bagnoli, Mark P. A108
Bagnoli, Mark P. E35
Bagshaw, Seth H. E282
Bague, Hugo W305
Bague, Hugo W306
Bagwell, Norman P. A137
Baham, Desiree P20
Bahl, Himani A101
Bahl, Tracy L. A250
Bahner, Craig A485
Bahno, Anthony A533
Bahou, Elie A165
Bahr, Wendy A199
Bahr, Antony M. A214
Bahr, John A489
Bahr, Antony M. P128
Bahra, Paul A333
Bai, Michael E7
Baier, Lucinda M. (Cindy) A148
Baier, Frank W A231
Baier, Henry A698
Baier, Robin P311
Baier, Henry P456
Baig, Mirza P181
Baijnauth, Cheryl P314
Bailey, Bob A27
Bailey, Richard A435
Bailey, Todd A441
Bailey, Todd A480
Bailey, Daniel A562
Bailey, Rosie A568
Bailey, Steve R. A642
Bailey, Daniel K. (Dan) A830

Bailey, Dan A830
Bailey, Brooke A877
Bailey, Reed A919
Bailey, Lisa P86
Bailey, Joanna P92
Bailey, David E. P127
Bailey, Brad P164
Bailey, David P227
Bailey, Jeff P248
Bailey, David P255
Bailey, Kelsey P292
Bailey, Morgan P295
Bailey, Marie P417
Bailey, Jeff P431
Bailey, Jared P440
Bailey, Don P458
Bailey, A. Robert D. W22
Bailey, David W184
Bailey, Daniel E279
Bailey, Steve R. E328
Bailey, Daniel K. (Dan) E402
Bailey, Dan E402
Bailie, Mark W312
Baillie, Thomas A861
Baillie, Thomas P658
Baillon-plot, Nathalie A649
Bailly, Jean-Philippe W204
Baine, Diane A101
Bains, Michael E111
Bainum, Stewart E75
Baio, Richard M. A122
Baiocchi, Sarah A180
Baiocchi, Carol A493
Bairathi, Anurag A402
Baird, Howard A51
Baird, Allison A143
Baird, Lisa A460
Baird, Alice A644
Baird, Edward A677
Baird, Patrick S. (Pat) A684
Baird, Ian A865
Baird, Jim P291
Baird, Bob I. W176
Baird, Patrick S. (Pat) E341
Baird, W. Blake E395
Baisiwala, Udai A507
Baisiwala, Udai P288
Baisley, David P96
Baitieh, Rami W82
Baitler, Robert A541
Baitler, Robert E266
Bajpay, Pari A85
Bajraktari, Leta A204
Bajus, Paul P559
Baker, Charles E. A96
Baker, Richard A100
Baker, Charles A105
Baker, Lloyd W. A110
Baker, Scott A111
Baker, Aj A158
Baker, Rodney A166
Baker, David A204
Baker, Mary Ellen A205
Baker, Vickie A212
Baker, Trishia A223
Baker, Wayne A244
Baker, Scott A250
Baker, Melissa A254
Baker, Douglas M. (Doug) A289
Baker, Peter A294
Baker, Sally W A366
Baker, Jeffrey R. A432
Baker, Paula A460
Baker, Dan A476
Baker, Delores A565
Baker, Charles A583
Baker, Judson A599
Baker, Jane M A685
Baker, Thomas P A754
Baker, Stephen W. (Steve) A758
Baker, Carolyn A767
Baker, Angela A775
Baker, Neal A800
Baker, Ronald A800
Baker, Todd A815

Baker, Douglas A863
Baker, Doug A863
Baker, Joe A901
Baker, Joseph A902
Baker, Jared A913
Baker, J Craig P32
Baker, Scott P56
Baker, Emily A P122
Baker, Karen P141
Baker, Nancy P143
Baker, Hannelore P145
Baker, Paula P206
Baker, Johnna P230
Baker, Karen P232
Baker, Donna P240
Baker, Ron P260
Baker, Alexander K P269
Baker, Kathy P324
Baker, Alun P333
Baker, John P341
Baker, Debbie P361
Baker, Deanna P366
Baker, Dorma P415
Baker, Kay P476
Baker, Denis P483
Baker, Gary E. P487
Baker, Dean P512
Baker, Stephen W. (Steve) P519
Baker, Scott P527
Baker, Shannon P565
Baker, Timothy P584
Baker, Joe P692
Baker, Joseph P693
Baker, Jeff W303
Baker, Lloyd W. E37
Baker, Mike E65
Baker, Charles J. E77
Baker, Vickie E79
Baker, Gordon E147
Baker, Rich E339
Baker, Richard A. E355
Baker, Neal E396
Baker, Ronald E396
Baker, Brian E404
Baker, Charles C. (Lanny) E447
Baker-Greene, Edward E140
Bakish, Robert M. (Bob) A871
Bakken, A. Christopher (Chris) A300
Bakken, Chris A300
Bakken, Mary P503
Baklarz, Michael E263
Bakmas, Marlana P305
Bakshi, Hemant W381
Bala, Aru A761
Balaban, David A61
Balaji, P. B. W357
Balas, Egon P96
Balasubramanian, Ruma A199
Balasubramanian, Mallathur P693
Balasubramaniyam, Sam A406
Balasubramaniyam, Thirugnanap A407
Balawajder, Charles G. A852
Balbosa, Suzanne P59
Balcer, Holly P94
Balcezak, Thomas J. P699
Baldeh, Bachi A724
Balderson, Diane A602
Balderston, Betty P286
Baldridge, Don A257
Baldridge, Bruce P162
Balduzzi, Michael A P185
Baldwin, James L A487
Baldwin, Jill A530
Baldwin, Robert H. A558
Baldwin, Larry A565
Baldwin, Dianne A670
Baldwin, Penny A685
Baldwin, Jay A841
Baldwin, Jessica P126
Baldwin, Jeremy P239
Baldwin, Darrell P300
Baldwin, Frances P322
Baldwin, Lawanda P344
Baldwin, Steve R. E184
Baldwin, Eric E360

A = AMERICAN BUSINESS
E = EMERGING COMPANIES
P = PRIVATE COMPANIES
W = WORLD BUSINESS

Baldwin, Jay E410
Baldzicki, Lisa A272
Bale, Rachel A537
Balena, Alfredo A313
Bales, Brian A. A707
Bales, John P425
Bales, Joyce P670
Balfour, Max A330
Bali, Adnan W377
Ball, John A1
Ball, Martin A107
Ball, Vicki A244
Ball, Susan M. A249
Ball, Mindy A441
Ball, Tracey A480
Ball, Cinde A597
Ball, Gail S. A806
Ball, David A844
Ball, John D. P83
Ball, Terry B. P83
Ball, Margaret P201
Ball, Jon W. P235
Ball, Charles P314
Ball, Johnny P510
Ball, Andrew J. (Andy) P545
Ball, Rob P630
Ball, Martin E35
Ball, David E412
Ballance, Robert E39
Ballao, George P19
Ballard, Eugene G. A122
Ballard, Shari L. A126
Ballard, Jerry A422
Ballard, Mark A698
Ballard, Bruce A795
Ballard, Jerry P239
Ballard, Dr Keith P247
Ballard, Nate P452
Ballard, Sue P552
Ballard, Jeff E208
Ballash, Adam P578
Ballek, Janet P640
Ballenger, Jeremy A173
Ballesteros, Walter P144
Ballew, Cathy A564
Ballinger, Kevin J. A144
Ballock, Steven P68
Ballou, Amanda P6
Ballweg, Sallyanne K. A353
Ballweg, Sallyanne K. E159
Balmuth, Michael A. A715
Balocco, Richard P480
Balog, Joseph P404
Balogun, Kelvin A215
Balos, Lee P129
Balousek, Jon A208
Balsamini, Patricia P60
Balseiro, Liana A201
Balser, Kathy A572
Balser, Jeffrey R. P615
Balsera, Manuel A56
Balthrop, Patrick J. E250
Baltimore, David P567
Balwanti, Anil P228
Balzano, Janice P207
Bamford, William A P602
Bamfordiii, William A P602
Bamisile, Ajoke P381
Bamonte, Rick A173
Bampton, Cal A330
Banales, Lori P28
Banas, Phil E383
Banati, Amit A485
Bancarz, Gloria P7
Banchoff, Tom P583
Bancroft, Charles A. A147
Bancroft, Glen P274
Bancroft, Philip V. W98
Bancroft, John E445

Band, Robert A833
Band, Robert P630
Banda, Jose P470
Bandas, Mark P615
Banday, Arshad H P81
Bandelaria, Becky A441
Bandemer, Martial A600
Bander, Halit A113
Bandi, Bruce A886
Bandi, Bruce E433
Bandla, Madhuri A221
Bandla, Syamla E342
Bando, Colin A784
Banducci, Bradford (Brad) W396
Bane, Julie A478
Banerjea, Atish A314
Banerjee, Gargi A390
Banerjee, Aunoy A766
Banerjee, Prith W322
Bang, Derek P149
Bang, Carl S. W347
Banga, Harjit A147
Banga, Ajaypal S. (Ajay) A537
Bangalore, Ganesh A476
Banic, Susanna A677
Banikarim, Maryam A445
Banis, R. Daniel A248
Banis, Robert Daniel A336
Banis, Robert Daniel P194
Banister, Brian A685
Baniszewski, Daniel P539
Bank, Belmont A152
Bank, Belmont E49
Bankens, Barbara I P89
Banko, Peter P537
Bankowitz, Richard E336
Banks, Tony A318
Banks, Lee C. A634
Banks, Maureen A635
Banks, Joseph A738
Banks, Mary P60
Banks, Gary P102
Banks, Maureen P419
Banks, Kenneth B P591
Banks, David P595
Banks, Jennifer J. E9
Banks, Heather E15
Bannach, Mike P686
Banner, Jon A647
Banner, Gerald P313
Bannigan, T A P431
Bannister, Clive C R W287
Bansal, Arun W360
Banta, Walter J A369
Banta, Walter A369
Banta, Dave E182
Banting, Anne A102
Bantz, Charles R. P449
Bantz, Charles R. P627
Bao, David A390
Bao-Lang, Chen W152
Baptist, Kevin A102
Baptista, Antonio P410
Baptiste, Ernest J. A582
Baptiste, Ernest J. P373
Bar-Adon, Eshel A94
Bar-Adon, Eshel A95
Bar-Adon, Eshel P53
Bar-Adon, Eshel E28
Bar-Niv, Erez E67
Baraddon, Cynthia A721
Barahona, Dan E342
Barak, Kathleen P361
Barak, Angela P565
Baraldi, Raymond L. P576
Baran, Jeffrey A645
Baran, Mark S P333
Baran, Jeffrey E329
Baranov, Vitaliy W157
Baratta, Joseph P. A132
Barba, James J. P17
Barba, James J P18
Barba, J. Brendan P70
Barbagallo, John A. A672
Barbar-tzadik, Smadar W150

Barbara, Santa P623
Barbari, Michael A351
Barbari, Michael E158
Barbarick, Steve K. A825
Barbarino, Christopher A500
Barbarino, Christopher E238
Barbato, Vincenzo P291
Barbeauld, Rob P131
Barbee, Stephanie A101
Barbee, Kenneth A. P165
Barbella, AL A465
Barber, Wayne A115
Barber, Timothy C. A312
Barber, Tim A441
Barber, Walter W472
Barber, Ken A737
Barber, James J. (Jim) A849
Barber, Russell P7
Barber, Mike P89
Barber, Dennis P142
Barber, Gary P339
Barber, Sandy P404
Barber, Gary P424
Barber, Jill P516
Barber, Chris B P528
Barber, Michael P570
Barber, Roger L P604
Barber, Ken E367
Barber-Tzadik, Smadar W149
Barbera, Vanesa A382
Barbera, John A665
Barbercheck, Richard S. A344
Barbero, Antonio A878
Barbier, Robert P P638
Barbier, Fran-§ois W151
Barbieri, Eric P331
Barbizet, Patricia W205
Barbo, William D. E69
Barbone, Ray A109
Barbone, Ray E36
Barbosa, Monisa A504
Barbosa, Lisa A682
Barbosa, Monisa E241
Barbour, Sondra A504
Barca, Robin P584
Barca, Chris E1
Barchan, Olexander P391
Barchi, Daniel P698
Barchus, Carl A585
Barchus, Carl P377
Barclay, Alyson S. E132
Bardazzi, Marco W143
Barden, Jamie A478
Barden, Sean T P674
Bardonnex, Elisa P670
Bardos, Kevin E248
Bardot, Rob A56
Bardowsky, Brandon P310
Bardusch, Robert J. A868
Bardwil, Steven A271
Barefoot, Becky A115
Bareford, Steven A324
Bareis, Janet A878
Barengo, Randy A645
Barengo, Randy E329
Barer, Sol J. W363
Baresich, Michael A35
Bareswill, Joseph R P148
Barfield, David P20
Barfield, Kelle J P185
Barfuss, John A741
Barfuss, John E370
Barger, James R A489
Barger, Dawn A537
Barger, Dennis L A734
Bargull, Raymond C P605
Barham, Sue E357
Baribault, Paul A272
Baribault, Melissa A407
Baribeau, Nathan B P24
Baril, Thierry W16
Barila, Martin A3
Barillari, Edward A85
Barinka, Tim A432
Bariquit, Teri A596

Barker, Greg A27
Barker, Michelle A115
Barker, Joanilla A350
Barker, Phyllis A410
Barker, Fran A541
Barker, Debra A578
Barker, G. Carlton (Carl) A737
Barker, Ellen L. A803
Barker, Kurtis A851
Barker, Shela P92
Barker, James P P144
Barker, Annalesa P420
Barker, Joanilla E156
Barker, Fran E266
Barker, G. Carlton (Carl) E367
Barker, David A. E384
Barkin, Michael Z. E424
Barkley, Michael A629
Barkley, Joe A693
Barkman, Gary P334
Barksdale, Kay A674
Barksdale, Kay P444
Barkstrom, Tina P344
Barlak, Paul M P179
Barlak, Paul M P378
Barley, Ronald A115
Barley, J Patrick P268
Barley, Teri P457
Barlow, Jeff D. A565
Barlow, Debra A827
Barlow, Chris A883
Barlowe, Jamie P613
Barnard, Ray F A358
Barnard, Tony A879
Barnard, Lauren A904
Barnard, Zorayma P198
Barnard, John P365
Barnard, Lauren E442
Barnecut-Kearns, Jason A912
Barner, Mark A80
Barner, Mark P47
Barner, Chyla P121
Barnes, Lynn A42
Barnes, Joseph A105
Barnes, Dave A264
Barnes, Robert B. (Bob) A459
Barnes, Emily A465
Barnes, Melissa Stapleton A511
Barnes, Melissa A511
Barnes, Janet A600
Barnes, Carrie A641
Barnes, John P. (Jack) A644
Barnes, Scot A744
Barnes, Garrett A920
Barnes, Thomas P72
Barnes, Deborah P116
Barnes, Lucinda P252
Barnes, David G. P360
Barnes, Kim P411
Barnes, Carrie P422
Barnes, Nancy P446
Barnes, Maureen P. P576
Barnes, Mike P670
Barnes, Susan L. P670
Barnett, Theresa A221
Barnett, June A678
Barnett, Hoyt R. (Barney) A679
Barnett, Hoyt R. (Barney) A680
Barnett, Bruce A830
Barnett, Rob A901
Barnett, Shawn P118
Barnett, Hoyt R. (Barney) P448
Barnett, Rob P692
Barnett, Timothy P699
Barnett, Bill E260
Barnett, Bruce E402
Barnette, Mary K A225
Barnette, Chris W P63
Barnette, Kimberly P111
Barnette, Mary K E88
Barnhart, Cynthia P313
Barnhart, Glenn P550
Barnhart, Dale G. E251
Barnhill, Jerry A257
Barnicle, Susan A489

Barns, Mitch A592
Barns, Mitch P382
Barnum, James A614
Barocas, Lauren P3
Baron, Harold P400
Baron, Chris P412
Baron, Nir W363
Barone, Vincent A738
Barone, Steve A901
Barone, Laura A901
Barone, Ed A902
Barone, Steve P692
Barone, Laura P692
Barone, Ed P693
Barouski, William A323
Barr, Simon A131
Barr, Scott A140
Barr, William A275
Barr, John A643
Barr, Sarah A883
Barr, Dan P252
Barr, Stan P293
Barr, Stephen P294
Barr, Michael E252
Barra, Mary T. A378
Barra, Mary T. A379
Barra, Ornella A877
Barra, Melissa E376
Barranco, David A40
Barrantes, Jane P440
Barras, Blake E175
Barraza, Hector A769
Barrentine, Curt A480
Barrera, John A318
Barrera, Benjelyn P451
Barreto, Karla E129
Barrett, Noel A113
Barrett, George S. A165
Barrett, Elizabeth A272
Barrett, Clay A384
Barrett, John A647
Barrett, Lausanne A674
Barrett, Geoffrey (Geoff) A682
Barrett, Genevieve A818
Barrett, John D. A830
Barrett, John F. A890
Barrett, Karin A P161
Barsont, Bradley K P212
Barrett, Christi P233
Barrett, Patricia P249
Barrett, David P279
Barrett, Mark P281
Barrett, Barbara M. P564
Barrett, John A. P613
Barrett, William P631
Barrett, John F. P684
Barrett, Rick E140
Barrett, Clay E176
Barrett, John D. E403
Barria, Jose P80
Barrick, Robert L P61
Barriere, Steve E216
Barriga, Guillermo P52
Barrila, Craig A648
Barrinson, Tom P470
Barrio, Vita A693
Barrios, Frank A101
Barrios, Marina P630
Barrios, Alfredo (Alf) W305
Barrios, Alfredo W306
Barrios, George A. E444
Barron, Eric J. A811
Barron, Paula A820
Barron, James A. (Andy) A878
Barron, Eric J. P600
Barron, Shelton E276
Barros, D. Benjamin P613
Barros, Daniel Feldmann W25
Barroso, Carlos J. A161
Barrow, Brett A700
Barrows, John A93
Barrows, Karen P464
Barrs, Craig A383
Barry, Corie S. A126
Barry, Ellen A163

Barry, George A417
Barry, Benjamin A457
Barry, Chris A616
Barry, Kyle A902
Barry, John M P64
Barry, Amy P310
Barry, Ellen P338
Barry, Don P493
Barry, Thomas E P514
Barry, John P653
Barry, Kyle P692
Bars, Michael A. E414
Barsanti, Amy P612
Barsby, Anna W249
Barselou, Mei A375
Barsody, Thomas D A886
Barsody, Thomas A886
Barsody, Thomas D E433
Barsody, Thomas E433
Barstad, Joanne P650
Bart, Kelly P315
Bartee, Chris A166
Bartek, David A520
Bartel, Tony D. A372
Bartel, Gregg A493
Bartel, Charles R. (Chuck) P169
Bartel, Trish P238
Bartel, Ricardo W43
Barter, Jim P115
Barter, Brian P429
Barth, Janet A120
Barth, Kevin A175
Barth, Kevin G. A223
Barth, Kevin G A483
Barth, Werner A652
Barth, Catherine P281
Bartholomew, Timothy J. E183
Bartler, Patricia K A541
Bartler, Patricia K E266
Bartlett, Laura A34
Bartlett, Thomas A. (Tom) A55
Bartlett, Tom A328
Bartlett, David L. A742
Bartlett, Jennie A777
Bartlett, Russ A804
Bartlett, Michael A815
Bartlett, Daniel J. (Dan) A878
Bartlett, Bryan P64
Bartlett, Danielle P377
Bartlett, David L. E372
Bartlett, Jennie E393
Bartman, Teresa A500
Bartman, Teresa E238
Barto, Nick A171
Barto, Nick P100
Bartol, Ian P406
Bartolacci, Joseph C. E263
Bartoli, Andrea P494
Bartolomei, Tom P361
Bartolotta, Peter G A93
Bartolotta, Michael J E426
Bartolucci, Tony A17
Bartolucci, Tony P10
Barton, Robert F. A44
Barton, Lisa M. A47
Barton, Richard B. A110
Barton, Patricia A441
Barton, Mary A461
Barton, Nina A494
Barton, Rich A581
Barton, Douglas P A625
Barton, Linda A700
Barton, Kurt A825
Barton, Liza P10
Barton, Robert F. P31
Barton, Michelle P43
Barton, Jacqueline K. P91
Barton, Randolph P364
Barton, Alan P404
Barton, Richard B. E37
Barton, Christopher J. E208
Barton, Gregory E443
Bartone, Michael A762
Bartosh, Robert J. P62
Bartsch, Matthew P550

Bartschat, Michael A477
Bartschat, Michael P268
Bartscht, Ben A204
Bartz, Carol A A200
Bartz, Lisa A671
Baruch, Wayne A813
Baruch, Wayne P608
Baruffi, Kumi Yamamoto A219
Baruffi, Kumi Yamamoto E84
Barwani, Gulamali P126
Barwani, Muradali P126
Barwell, Owen P25
Barwell, Michael P154
Barwood, Marlene A P261
Barycki, Elvera P295
Baryshnikov, Vladislav W157
Barzilay, Jonathan P445
Bas, Leo P208
Bas, Didem W377
Basan, Patricia A541
Basan, Patricia E266
Basch, Kenneth P99
Basch, Ken P99
Baschky, Linda P640
Bascom, Steven P357
Bascom-Erazmus, Sue A644
Bascope, Nicole P298
Basden, Daniel P111
Baselga, José P325
Baselice, Marsha P482
Baser, Didem Din- §er W377
Basey, Jim A412
Basey, Jim E192
Basford, Matt P455
Bashaw, Michael A899
Bashaw, Michael P690
Basher, Linda A204
Basilio, Karin A71
Basilio, Paulo A494
Basilio, Esther P532
Basinger, Tracy A324
Baske, Jim W30
Baskerville, Bob P488
Basnet, Gandhi P572
Basnett, Stan P451
Basney, Barbara A912
Basoglu, Mehmet P226
Bason, John G. W33
Basore, Louise A724

Basque, Louis A767
Basri, Hassan E31
Bass, Maureen A827
Bass, Scott A. P37
Bass, William L. P105
Bass, Justin P149
Bass, Theodore P496
Bass, Theodore P642
Bass, Patrick W365
Bassett, Lawton E. A57
Bassett, Therese M A93
Bassett, Julie A235
Bassett, David A238
Bassett, H. Clay A576
Bassett, Donal J P361
Bassett, Mary Beth P670
Bassett, Lawton E. E16
Bassett, William E98
Bassett, H. Clay E297
Bassham, Terry D P271
Basso, Maurizio W32
Bassoul, Selim A. E277
Basterrechea, Jose A52
Basterrechea, Jose P33
Bastian, Christine A200
Bastian, Edward H. (Ed) A261
Bastings, Arthur A269
Basto, Edgar W63
Bastug, Recep W377
Bastuga, Kevin P. A741
Bastuga, Kevin P. E370
Basu, Devjit A131
Basulto, Jose P508
Batal, Courtney P67
Batalla, Rachael P139

Batato, Magdi W258
Batch, Kristine A838
Batchelder, Eugene L. (Gene) A611
Batchelder, Peter E253
Batcheler, Colleen A230
Batcheler, Colleen A231
Batchelor, Steve A881
Batchelor, Cheryl P194
Batelaan, Richard A85
Bateman, Kevin P441
Bateman, Mark T. P471
Bateman, Christopher M P543
Bateman, Gray P594
Bates, Larry L. A742
Bates, Jonathan R. (Jon) P45
Bates, Crandall P55
Bates, Angela P201
Bates, Martin W P218
Bates, Peter W. P303
Bates, Melissa P314
Bates, Ruth P331
Bates, Douglas P332
Bates, Jim P478
Bates, Ondrea P671
Bates, Laurence W. W223
Bates, Larry L. E372
Batey, Alan S. A378
Bath, Chuck E106
Bathgate, Brian E69
BATHLOW, JACKIE P536
Bathlomay, William C P113
Batista, Wesley Mendon- §a A654
Batra, Udit W239
Batres, Grace A868
Batres, Francisco P136
Batson, Charles H. (Chuck) A340
Batson, Nancy A751
Batson, Charles H. (Chuck) E151
Batson, Nancy E377
Batt, Douglas A. P417
Battafarano, Greg A691
Battaglia, Alex A474
Battas, Sandy A837
Batteiger, Tamara P525
Batten, Brian A132
Battenfield, Keith P104
Battifarano, Leonard A532
Battle, LaDonna A885
Batts, Arnisha P475
Batulis, Scott P409
Batzri, Ilab W150
Bauche, Douglas N. A302
Bauche, Douglas N. E128
Baucum, Carlton E P243
Baude, Bruce K. A213
Bauder, Charles J A693
Bauder, Douglas R. A752
Baudouin, Richard E8
Bauer, Brett C. A125
Bauer, Michael P. (Mike) A364
Bauer, Tom A784
Bauer, Daniel (Dan) A813
Bauer, Kris B. A846
Bauer, Tyler P390
Bauer, Daniel (Dan) P616
Bauer, Sabine W8
Bauer, Fred T. E173
Bauerle, Gary P368
Bauerlein, Alison E217
Baugh, Mike P630
Baugh, Ben E29
Baughman, Michael A113
Baughman, Karen A119
Baughman, Brian A546
Baughman, Richard A. E368
Bauhofer, Scott A13
Baum, Don A691
Baum, Peter A869
Baum, Kristin P425
Baum, Shannon P512
Bauman, James L. (Jim) A2
Bauman, Rachael P254
BAUMANN, ULF A200
Baumann, Caroline P506
Baumann, Joseph P694

A = AMERICAN BUSINESS
E = EMERGING COMPANIES
P = PRIVATE COMPANIES
W = WORLD BUSINESS

Baumann, Werner W56
Baumbach, Denise A368
Baumbach, Allen A800
Baumbach, Allen E396
Baumgarden, Michelle E135
Baumgardner, Jeffrey P80
Baumgarner, Marsha A164
Baumgarten, Alan S P346
Baumgartl, Wolf-Dieter W356
Baumgartner, Michael A. P58
Baumgartner, Robert V. E42
Baumli, Heather A449
Bauters, Fred J P149
Bautista, Javier Velez P222
Bauwel, Chantal Van P80
Bavaro, Marguerite A677
Bavasi, Chris P195
Bavazls, Marcelo P46
Bavery, Christina A541
Bavery, Christina E266
Bavouset, Jim A508
Bavrica, Karime A85
Bawden, Lori P685
Bawol, Jeff A792
Baxley, Anthony A813
Baxley, Anthony P608
Baxter, Warner L. A42
Baxter, Dave A282
Baxter, Jay A700
Baxter, Joel D. A738
Baxter, Peter A744
Baxter, Jeffrey A814
Baxter, Dan A886
Baxter, Jack P178
Baxter, Warner L. P179
Baxter, Marlene P551
Baxter, Jeffrey P616
Baxter, Dan E433
Bay, Annell R A69
Bay, Ann A565
Bay, Lea P224
Bayardo, Jose A A574
Baybars, Ilker P96
Baye, Cheryl A105
Bayer, Terry P. A565
Bayer, Ronald K P406
Bayer, Paul E. E293
Bayless, Victoria W P39
Bayless, George P208
Bayless, Jack E59
Baylor, Denise A372
Baylor, Denise P208
Bays, Claudia A449
Bayt, Phil P672
Bazan, Dora A868
Bazan, Fernando E42
Bazata, Todd A51
Bazeley, Joe P339
Bazemore, Teresa A. Bryce A690
Bazemore, Teresa A. Bryce E345
Bazire, Nicolas W225
Bazoli, Giovanni W189
Bea, Javon R P329
Beabout, Brent A596
Beach, Glenn A677
Beach, Brian C. A782
Beacham, Renee A101
Beacham, Michael A254
Beacher, Bob A314
Beacher, Bob P190
Beachman, Michael P141
Beadie, William M P40
Beadie, William M P686
Beaghler, Mark A P135
Beal, Jamie A734
Beal, Steven P323
Beal, Graham W J P577
Beale, G. William (Billy) A841
Beale, G. William (Billy) E410

Bealer, Christopher A898
Bealke, David A339
Bealke, David E150
Beall, Brian A187
Beall, Patrick (Pat) A769
Beall, Brian E71
Beam, Chris T. A47
Beam, Don A115
Beam, Diane A344
Beam, Karen A520
Beam, Jesse A814
Beam, Jesse P616
Beam, Diane E154
Beaman, John P434
Beaman, Jamie P697
Beamer, Beth E410
Bean, Robert A555
Bean, Bryan A655
Bean, Todd A767
Bean, Heather A788
Bean, Ron P72
Bean, Darlene P174
Bean, James C. P392
Bean, Richard E P421
Bean, Brian P537
Bean, Paul W334
Bean, Byron E75
Bean, Bryan E333
Bear, John R. P342
Beard, Deanne A350
Beard, Robert F. (Bob) A836
Beard, Amy P86
Beard, Dave P164
Beard, Michelle P425
Beard, Cheryl P431
Beard, Kirk P460
Beard, Simon E10
Beard, Deanne E156
Beard, JW E212
Beardall, Brent J. A879
Bearden, Jay P157
Beardsley, Kimberly A260
Beardsley, Bruce A371
Beardsley, Kirk M. A596
Bearison, Daniel A619
Bearson, Kent A835
Beasley, Hunter P279
Beasley, Scott P563
Beasley, Christian P567
Beassie, Rhonda P563
Beato, Jacqueline A157
Beaton, Tiffany A754
Beaton, Tiffany E378
Beaton, Laura E432
Beattie, Joseph A543
Beattie, Hank E65
Beatty, Mark A129
Beatty, Jonathan A728
Beatty, Keith A850
Beatty, Vincent L. A879
Beatty, Robert W P11
Beatty, Ellen M. P564
Beaty, Julie A449
Beauchamp, Alexander A556
Beauchamp, Linda A726
Beauchamp, Philip K P627
Beauchant, Phil P352
Beauchemin, Bernard A833
Beaudette, Phil A844
Beaudette, Phil E412
Beaudoin, Edward P24
Beaudoin, Pierre W69
Beaulieu, Lauren A13
Beaulieu, Aaron P170
Beaumont, Glenn W138
Beauregard, Colleen A818
Beauregard, Tom A855
Beauregard, Annetta E428
Beaven, Peter W63
Beaven, Peter W64
Beaver, Steven A19
Beaver, Rick A838
Beavers, Bridget A101
Beavers, Nancy A814
Beavers, Nancy P616

Bebber, David L. Van A834
Beberness, Benjamin P447
Beccaccio, Peter A345
Becerra, Maria A331
Becerra, Xavier A764
Becerra, Enrique X A782
Becerra, Jose P291
Becerra, Xavier P540
Becerra, Maria E148
Bech, Douglas Y. E226
Bechar, Yossi W190
Becher, Michael A441
Bechler, Kent P143
Becht, Lambertus J. H. (Bart) A241
Becht, Gerd W121
Becht, Charles E. E160
Bechtel, Chuck A265
Bechtle, Mavis P593
Bechtol, Nancy P506
Beck, Neil A15
Beck, Andrew H. (Andy) A20
Beck, Gary L. A28
Beck, Lance A32
Beck, Gregory A234
Beck, Christophe A289
Beck, David E. (Dave) A324
Beck, Lita A352
Beck, Constance A369
Beck, Joe A416
Beck, Amy A440
Beck, Elisabeth A469
Beck, Hilda A474
Beck, Christopher A583
Beck, Jeff A734
Beck, Daniel A777
Beck, Chuck P67
Beck, Gretchen P96
Beck, Gregory P139
Beck, Hilda P262
Beck, Teresa P598
Beck, Mary P649
Beck, Ralf E283
Beck, Daniel E393
Beck-Codner, Iris W363
Becker, Randall A94
Becker, Tricia A101
Becker, Cathleen A133
Becker, Jen A330
Becker, Christopher A353
Becker, Dave A597
Becker, Collette A711
Becker, David A730
Becker, Yin C. A772
Becker, Gregory W. (Greg) A777
Becker, Russell P40
Becker, Randall P53
Becker, Rik P69
Becker, Ralph P241
Becker, Anne P292
Becker, Bernard P543
Becker, Douglas A P624
Becker, Jeff P656
Becker, Kendall P681
Becker, W. Marston (Marty) W297
Becker, Christopher E159
Becker, William C. E288
Becker, Gregory W. (Greg) E392
Beckett, Evelyn P135
Beckett, Kim P699
Beckford, Paulette P350
Beckford, Avril P680
Beckius, Larry P45
Beckley, Michael A530
Beckley, Jason A691
Beckman, Kim A196
Beckman, Lawrence P21
Beckman, Seth P169
Beckman, Joni P686
Beckman, Per W352
Beckmann, Dave A295
Beckmann, Kai W239
Beckmeyer, Laura P155
Beckom, Daria A878
Becks, Charles A829
Beckum, Renee P529

Beckwith, Patricia A313
Beckwith, Tina A556
Beckwith, Robert P113
Beckwitt, Richard (Rick) A508
Becoats, Eric P170
Bedard, Jim A195
Bedard, Terri P484
Beddes, Hallie A532
Bedford, Charles E. P595
Bedford, Kirk E172
Bedi, Singh P629
Bedine, Matthew A784
Bedingfield, Kenneth L. A602
Bednar, Tony P333
Bednarovsky, Jessica A791
Bedner, Marie P72
Bedoukian, Kristin E140
Bedros, Suzanne A865
Bedrosian, Arthur P. E239
Bedrosian, Geoffrey E359
Bedson, Simon E428
Bedwell, Patrick E166
Beebe, Ashley A167
Beebe, Robert A199
Beebe, Mike A425
Beebe, Jeffrey A500
Beebe, Mike A835
Beebe, Lynda P92
Beebe, Mike E201
Beebe, Jeffrey E237
Beecher, Bill A17
Beecher, Barbara P92
Beecher, Bradley P. P578
Beecher, Gregory R. (Greg) E394
Beechner, Christine P220
Beede, Byron A10
Beedle, Bernice A555
Beeken, Scott A51
Beekman, Todd A440
Beeler, Don P119
Beeler, Jason P324
Beem, Janel P610
Beeman, Thomas E. (Tom) P589
Beeman, Tom P619
Beene, Delwin P134
Beer, Lori A. A480
Beer, James A. A546
Beer, Sander De A649
Beer, Robert P200
Beer, Megan W26
Beer-christensen, Debbie A683
Beerman, Martin W. P117
Beers, Marlene A665
Beery, Joseph C. (Joe) A815
Beeson, James A195
Beeson, John N A901
Beeson, John N P692
Beeuwsaert, Dirk W143
Begam, Thomas A333
Begle, Curt L. A125
Begleiter, Steven E260
Begley, William J. A722
Behal, Raj P538
Behan, Katherine P43
Behm, Michael J. A698
Behm, Michael J. P456
Behm, Marcia P465
Behmer, Nancy A889
Behnke, Dennis L. A833
Behr, Dr. Giorgio W402
Behrens, David A. A53
Behrens, Matt P252
Behring, Alexandre (Alex) A494
Beidelman, Jason A643
Beih, Mohamed El A133
Beilby, Dione A658
Beilby, Dione P431
Beilock, Sian P610
Beine, Beverly P390
Beiser, Ryan A204
Beissel, Andy P25
Beiter, Stephanie P463
Beithon, Patricia A. E19
Bejaran, Americo A17
Bejarano, Joelle P273

Bekker, Petrus J. (Pirow) E72
Belak, Cynthia P A644
Belanger, Dave A442
Belanger, Patti P481
Belanic, Jim A667
Belanic, Jim E336
Belanoff, Joseph K. E95
Belasco, Kent S. A351
Belasco, Kent S. E158
Belcher, Patricia A131
Belcher, Jason A343
Belcher, Samuel L. A355
Belcher, Barry J P47
Belcourt, Tracey A364
Belda, Annmarie P654
Belden, Scott A827
Belden, Doug P131
Belekewicz, William D. A356
Belen, Andy A857
Beletti, Chris A235
Belford, Michael A815
Belfort, Michael A. P560
Belger, Brenda A. E5
Belgya, Mark R. A748
Belhouse, Brad A158
Belhumeur, Geaorge P480
Belikoff, Michael P544
Belisle, Jocelyn A761
Belitsky, Lee J. A264
Beliveau, Russell E265
Belk, Jeffrey K A685
Belknap, Gary P435
Bell, Patricia A A19
Bell, Thomas A136
Bell, Brad A221
Bell, Mike A238
Bell, Christine A310
Bell, Doug A384
Bell, Christie A446
Bell, Teri A478
Bell, Adam A537
Bell, George A555
Bell, Del A565
Bell, Thomas A597
Bell, David A654
Bell, Damon A655
Bell, Bonnie A801
Bell, Elaine A844
Bell, Matthew A863
Bell, Mary A888
Bell, Deborah A919
Bell, Douglas P74
Bell, Alastair P80
Bell, Sergeant P123
Bell, Eldrin P143
Bell, Kathy P284
Bell, Troy P291
Bell, Deborah P344
Bell, Greg P430
Bell, Joanne P482
Bell, Jeffery A P493
Bell, Brent P523
Bell, Jack P537
Bell, Bonnie P561
Bell, Kathy P612
Bell, Jeff W87
Bell, Doug E176
Bell, Christie E210
Bell, Damon E333
Bell, Michael E357
Bell, Elaine E412
Bell, Simon G. E420
Bell, Brad E448
Bellack, Janis P. A635
Bellack, Janis P. P419
Bellamy, Adrian D. P. A901
Bellamy, Steve E115
Bellanti, Tim A82
Bellanti, Tim P49
Belle, Marty A393
Bellemare, Alain M. W69
Bellenfant, William P353
Beller, Mark P40
Bellettini, Francesca W204
Bellinger, Delaney M. A443

Bellinger, Terry P404
Bellino, Daniel A56
Bellino, Nick A360
Bellino, Nick E164
Bello, Kathy P609
Belloma, Kevin A223
Bellon, Sophie W334
Bellone, Steven P145
Belloni, Aldo W223
Belloni, Antonio (Toni) W225
Bellos, Alex A901
Belman, Tricia E265
Belmonte, Lawrence A49
Belmore, Jane P301
Belochi, Franck A683
Belous, Scott A49
Below, Ellen A406
Belsher, Geoffrey (Geoff) W80
Belsito, Charlene E P632
Belt, Katrina P584
Belton, Paul P498
Beltran, Andrea P170
Beltran, Chris P661
Beltre, Milca A133
Beltr--n, Eduardo Navarro W137
Belzley, Cody P3
Bem, David S. A664
Bembry, Gary P59
Bembry, Gary L P281
Bemiller, Todd A902
Bemiller, Todd P693
Bemis, Mark A. A74
Ben, Mark P625
Bena, Steve A292
Benak, Timothy P94
Benali, Karim E3
Benavides, Jeffrey P226
Benavides, Dr Alda T P278
Benbow, Camilla P615
Bence, William A542
Bence, William E267
Bench, Marcey A452
Bench, Marcey E215
Benchaaboun, Mohamed E31
Bencher, Susan D A406
Benchoff, Nancy A390
Bencivenga, Carol P325
Benck, Jeffrey A461
Bender, Jim A88
Bender, Jens A204
Bender, Jason C. A353
Bender, Andria A765
Bender, M. Steven (Steve) A895
Bender, Judy P464
Bender, Andria P540
Bendickson, Marcus J P170
Bendler, Matt P11
Bendure, Richard E31
Beneby, Doyle N A310
Benedettini, Natalie E117
Benedetto, Ben Di A531
Benedetto, Florence Di A775
Benedetto, Florence Di P548
Benedicto, Dawn P22
Benedum, Mary A493
Benefield, Donna A604
Beneke, Andrea P646
Benenati, Susan V P665
Benet, Jay S. A827
Benfer, Michelle E248
Beng, Na Wu W280
Bengston, Robert A. A629
Benham, Stephanie A25
Benham, Barbara A440
Benham, Stephanie P15
Benhamou, Eric A A777
Benhamou, Eric A E393
Benincasa, Justin D. E26
Benioff, Marc A723
Benito, Michael E. A414
Benito, David Pastrana A733
Benito, Michael E. E194
Benjamin, Rachel A201
Benjamin, Andre A390
Benjamin, Lily A683

Benjamin, Gerald A. A727
Benjamin, Mike P552
Benjamin, Howard E351
Benkart, Brian A767
Benkowitz, Michael E415
Benn, Markham A459
Benn, David P. A775
Benn, David P. P548
Bennack, Frank A691
Bennack, Frank A. A810
Bennack, Frank A. P597
Bennet, Deborah P276
Bennett, Rick A2
Bennett, Douglas M. A110
Bennett, Sarah A204
Bennett, Lance J. A267
Bennett, Chuck A342
Bennett, Jonathan R. A406
Bennett, Robyn A460
Bennett, Judy A703
Bennett, Rick A838
Bennett, Terry A878
Bennett, James A905
Bennett, Thomas P30
Bennett, Susan P94
Bennett, Karen P148
Bennett, Chris P232
Bennett, Melanie P289
Bennett, W. Bradley (Brad) P315
Bennett, Greg P410
Bennett, John P668
Bennett, James P694
Bennett, Glenn W8
Bennett, Ricardo W85
Bennett, Brad W98
Bennett, Adam W105
Bennett, Douglas M. E37
Bennett, Kerry E213
Bennie, James P295
Benning, Rachel A537
Bennion, Richard W. H. (Rich) A427
Bennion, Richard W. H. (Rich) E202
Bennis, Raul E261
Bennorth, Kara P683
Benoist, Gilles W103
Benoit, Cole A115
Benoit, Garrett P347
Benoy, Janeen A562
Benoy, Janeen E279
Benrubi, Guy P642
Benscoter, Sam P553
Bense, Allan A383
Bensema, David J. P58
Bensignor, Laurence E. A284
Bensignor, Laurence E. E111
Bension, Ronald (Ron) A517
Benskin, Nancy A655
Benskin, Nancy E333
Benson, Don A129
Benson, Nigel A131
Benson, David C. A315
Benson, Ed A316
Benson, Barbara A323
Benson, Jodi A377
Benson, Mike A377
Benson, Jason A478
Benson, DEA A696
Benson, Marta H. A901
Benson, Ed P60
Benson, Cedric P60
Benson, Ed P191
Benson, Helen P282
Benson, Bruce P601
Benson, Lora J P606
Benson, Paul H. P611
Benson, Richard P669
Benson, Ellen P699
Benson, Jo-Dee M. E78
Benson, Jodee E78
Benson, Jo Dee E78
Benson, Melissa E144
Bensoussan, Albert W204
Benstock, Peter E391
Benstock, Michael E391
Bent, Dennis P89
Benter, Bob A673

Bentestuen, Trond W129
Benthuysen, Maureen Van P303
Bentine, John P36
Bentkover, Adam E193
Bentley, John A160
Bentley, Stacey A683
Bentley, Elizabeth M. A841
Bentley, Philip A878
Bentley, John E55
Bentley, Stacey E341
Bentley, Elizabeth M. E410
Bento, E. Joseph (Joe) E346
Benton, Joe P86
Benton, Cory P188
Benton, Brent P200
Benton, Jeff P239
Benton, David P282
Benton, Andrew K. P423
Benvenuto, Joe A729
Benvenuto, Joe P61
Benz, John A683
Benz, Gary P350
Benzan, Paolo E398
Benziger, Reenie A592
Benzin, Sandy A287
Benzin, Sandy P174
Benzon, Jennie A530
Bené, Thomas L. (Tom) A782
Beran, Momoko A. E374
Berard, Sarah A406
Berard, Patrick W303
Berardino, Peter A537
Berberian, Lance V. A499
Berce, Daniel E. (Dan) A378
Berce, Daniel E A24
Berchtold, Joe A517
Bercovici, Nancy A323
Berdahl, Robert M. (Bob) P5
Berdan, Barclay E. A801
Berdan, Barclay E. P562
Bereche, Alfred C P363
Berendji, Sacha W233
Berendsen, J A898
Berenis, Joseph P105
Berenzweig, Harold A801
Berenzweig, Harold P562
Berera, Anil A898
Beresford, Michael P339
Beresh, Nicholas A886
Beresh, Nicholas E433
Berg, Charles G. (Chuck) A255
Berg, Tracey L. A296
Berg, Mark S. A657
Berg, John P. von A658
Berg, John A658
Berg, James A802
Berg, Joel H. A861
Berg, Jessica P98
Berg, David P402
Berg, James P562
Berg, Alicia P610
Berg, Joel H. P658
Berg, James P697
Berg, Achim W62
Berg, William E138
Bergamini, Nancy A531
Bergan, Chad A251
Bergdorf, Mark A728
Berger, Larry L. A289
Berger, Jed A361
Berger, Lou A419
Berger, Joe A421
Berger, Hilary A691
Berger, Jan A774
Berger, Vince P6
Berger, Chadd P141
Berger, Anne P146
Berger, Lisa P179
Berger, Alan P642
Berger, Tom E2
Bergerand, Christophe W286
Bergeron, Kate A70
Bergeron, Sandra E342
Bergeron, Daniel A. (Dan) E347
Berges, James G A411

A = AMERICAN BUSINESS
E = EMERGING COMPANIES
P = PRIVATE COMPANIES
W = WORLD BUSINESS

Berges-Gonzalez, Orlando A336
Bergeson, Steven P26
Bergh, Charles V. (Chip) A436
Bergh, Charles V. (Chip) A509
Berghs, Jim A865
Berghuis, Peter P441
Bergin, Cynthia A160
Bergin, James P. A323
Bergin, Cynthia E55
Berglund, Bryn A175
Berglund, Robert C E275
Bergman, Barbara A247
Bergman, Stanley M. A727
Bergman, David E. A840
Bergman, Carol A P286
Bergman, Chris P572
Bergman, Jessica P613
Bergman, Barbara E102
Bergmann, Rouven E268
Berguist, Lauren P452
Bergqvist, Yonnie W352
Bergren, Carnan P448
Bergstrom, Timothy D. A883
Bergstr-¶m, Henrik A664
Bergthold, Michelle A599
Beri, Rajive A84
Beringer, Ken A25
Beringer, Ken P15
Berisford, John L. A721
Berk, Donald A599
Berkau, Barbara P413
Berkay, H Sinan P529
Berke, Ethan M P154
Berkey, Dennis D P695
Berkley, W. Robert (Rob) A122
Berkley, William R. (Bill) A122
Berkley, William R. (Bill) A585
Berkley, William R. (Bill) P377
Berkman, Bryan A532
Berkman, Charles S. E246
Berkowitz, Adam A677
Berkowitz, Jason A907
Berkowitz, Martin A P602
Berkowitz, Jason E446
Berlamino, Betty E A175
Berle, David P642
Berle, Dolf E105
Berlin, Steven D P67
Berlin, Barry N. E77
Berlin, Steven R. (Steve) E319
Berloe-Buch, Wendy A691
Berman, Ross A6
Berman, Walter S. A56
Berman, Glenn S P200
Berman, Natalie P370
Berman, Mandy E46
Bermel, Seth A354
Bermes, Brian A616
Bermudez, Sabrina A54
Bernabei, Alan J P105
Bernacki, Jeanette M P535
Bernad, Jason P484
Bernadett, Martha Molina A565
Bernal, Belinda A770
Bernal, Alejandro A921
Bernard, Loraine A513
Bernard, Michel A539
Bernard, Nicole A599
Bernard, Catherine A659
Bernard, Scott A708
Bernard, Edward C. A783
Bernard, Daniel W206
Bernardi, Nives P462
Bernardo, Gary A496
Bernardo, Terry P631
Bernardo, Thomas E75
Bernd, David L P493
Berndt, Wolfgang C. W276
Berne, Robert (Bob) A585

Berne, Robert (Bob) P377
Bernhard, Mary P470
Bernhardt, Tom A599
Bernhardt, John A645
Bernhardt, John P629
Bernhardt, Hans W216
Bernier, Danielle A683
Bernier, Jody P599
Bernier, Jean W20
Bernier, Gregg E138
Bernis, Valérie W143
Bernon, Alan J. A252
Bernon, Alan J. P150
Bernotat, Wulf H. W23
Berns, Jason A691
Berns, Steven E369
Bernstein, Daniel A201
Bernstein, Jay A204
Bernstein, Andrew A272
Bernstein, Barbara A480
Bernstein, Tracy A659
Bernstein, Mark J. A698
Bernstein, David A729
Bernstein, Stacey P6
Bernstein, Michael P446
Bernstein, Mark J. P456
Bernstein, David W81
Bernstein, Kenneth F. E4
Bernstein, H. Carol E50
Bernstein, Ronald J. E425
Bernsten, James R. A214
Bernsten, James R. P128
Beronio, David A414
Beronio, David E194
Berotti, John A813
Berotti, John P616
Berra, Steve A318
Berra, John A718
Berradia, Jamal A671
Berres, Matthew A478
Berretta, Joseph V A412
Berretta, Joseph V E192
Berrios, Anthony A37
Berroeta, I-±aki W389
Berry, Matt A173
Berry, Hussein A262
Berry, Dottie A327
Berry, John A328
Berry, Kay A345
Berry, Liz A402
Berry, Mary A532
Berry, Gene P A621
Berry, James D. A722
Berry, Chris A727
Berry, Bob A863
Berry, David T. P45
Berry, David P108
Berry, Bob P111
Berry, Richard E P149
Berry, Janice P159
Berry, Greg P163
Berry, Holly P181
Berry, Susan P225
Berry, Gene P P407
Berry, Oran P497
Berry, Martha P500
Berry, Dan P511
Berry, Ray P581
Berry, Pat P623
Berry, Jessica P641
Berry, Kay E154
Berryman, Kevin C. A472
Bersamin, Andrea P640
Bershad, Stephen W. A294
Bershad, Stephen W. E308
Bert, Dave A190
Bert, John Di W69
Berta, Jane P300
Bertelli, Luca W144
Bertero, Gerardo A892
Berthiaume, Lois A322
Berthaut, Chris A446
Berthaut, Chris E210
Berthiaume, Mark L. A402
Bertholf, Leigh P21

Bertholf, Lee P148
Bertholf, Leigh P323
Bertiere, Francois W72
Bertolami, Charles N. A585
Bertolami, Charles N. P377
Bertolet-Duff, Dianne A406
Bertoli, Jose A453
Bertoli, Tullio P622
Bertolissi, Mario W189
Bertolla, Fernando A723
Bertoluzzo, Paolo W389
Bertone, Steve A726
Bertoni, Diana A371
Bertram, Jack W314
Bertrand, Greg D. A782
Bertrand, Marc L P626
Bertrand, Corinne E439
Bertsch, Jan A141
Bertsch, Jan A. A628
Bertsch, Jennifer P356
Bertscha, Noreen A676
Bertucci, John R. E282
Berus, Robert A165
Berwick, Tracy A487
Berwick, Belinda A532
Berzolla, Donna E445
Besanko, Bruce H. A493
Beseda, Leslie A452
Beseda, Leslie E215
Beshah, Guenet A163
Beshar, Peter J. A532
Bespalov, Alexander D. W289
Bess, David A555
Bessant, Catherine P. (Cathy) A100
Besse, Eric A59
Bessette, Diane J A508
Bessette, Andy F. A827
Bessette, Stephen A880
Bessey, Kerry P325
Bessler, Christine P442
Bessner, Jessica P48
Best, C. Munroe A117
Best, Munroe A117
Best, Amy A309
Best, James A703
Besteman, Dan A905
Besteman, Dan P694
Betancourt, Sofia A877
Betat, Bruno P610
Bethea, Elizabeth A448
Bethea, Paula Harper A751
Bethea, Paula Harper E378
Bethel, Jeff A272
BETLESKY, SCOTT A402
Bettano, Carla P369
Betterly, Luke A901
Betterly, Luke P692
Bettinger, Douglas R. (Doug) A501
Bettinger, Walter W. (Walt) A728
Bettis, Shannon A446
Bettis, Shannon E210
Bettridge, Ellen A49
Betts, Wendy A599
Betts, Kristen P368
Betz, Paul P314
Betz, Robert P318
Beumee, Gary A734
Beurden, Ben van W313
Beute, Randy E173
Beutin, Brian A111
Beutin, Brian P56
Bevan, Frank A462
Bevan, Kurt C A886
Bevan, Kurt C E433
Bever, Mark P675
Beveridge, Roy A. A437
Beverly, Ken P42
Beverly, Mark E404
Bevers, Mark P676
Bevinamar, Kiran A204
Bewley, Tim A655
Bewley, Tim E333
Beyene, Merykokeb A877
Beyer, Gary J A221
Beyer, Ruth A. A666

Beyer, Ruth A. P438
Beylin, Eddie A869
Bezich, Louis S. P576
Bezjak, Rob A394
Bezold, Katie A890
Bezold, Katie P684
Bezos, Jeffrey P. (Jeff) A38
Bezrucik, Peter P134
Bhagat, Dave A777
Bhagat, Dave P393
Bhakhri, Sandeep A304
Bhalla, Amit A119
Bhalla, Anant A146
Bhalla, Ajay A537
Bhalla, Vikas E138
Bhanap, Nina E344
Bhangoo, Raj P91
Bhansali, Ameet A456
Bharatwaj, Shekar A218
Bhardwaj, Sunil S A493
Bhargava, Amit A534
Bhargava, Vinay A565
Bhasin, Puneet A881
Bhaskar, Bhavna A647
Bhat, Anirudha A204
Bhatia, Karan A375
Bhatia, Qamar S A429
Bhatia, Avi A496
Bhatia, Prashant A791
Bhatia, Manish A892
Bhatia, Suresh P217
Bhatnagar, Harsh A185
Bhatt, Kalpesh P236
Bhatt, Amit P533
Bhatt, Deepak P556
Bhatt, Manish E268
Bhatt, Padmanabh P. E391
Bhattacharjee, Manash A537
Bhattacharya, Ashis E441
Bhatti, Hammad A496
Bhavsar, Kelly A762
Bhimineni, Sarath P187
Bhojani, Ratna P313
Bhojwani, Gary C. A213
Bhojwani, Gary A432
Bhutani, Aman A311
Bial, Erica J P353
Biala, Gerry P485
Bialick, Jim E261
Bialosky, David L. (Dave) A391
Bianca, Joe Di A738
Bianchi, Dean P99
Bianchi, Christophe M. W355
Bianchi, Juan C. E134
Bianchi, Rick E398
Bianco, John A769
Bianco, Mary A847
Bianco, Annamarie P583
Biancuzzo, Anna A86
Biancuzzo, Anna P52
Bibic, Mirko W61
Bible, Daryl N. A115
Bible, Mitchell A798
Bickel, Michael A137
Bicker, Mark A345
Bickerstaff, Robert A201
Bickerstaff, Detra P680
Bickerton, Michael A602
Bickett, Brent B. A328
Bickham, Brandon P577
Bickham, W. Bradley E5
Bickley, Ian A785
Bickley, Craig P133
Bickley, Dana P396
Bicknell, Jim P343
Biddle, James E. E135
Bidkar, Prashant A101
Bidner, Michael A769
Bidwell, Victoria P198
Bieber, Martin A P529
Bieberich, Dennis P6
Biedenfeld, Mark A194
Biedermann, Wynn P329
Biegel, Joe A546
Biegen, Gregory A102

Biegen, Arm Gregory A102
Biegger, Dave A230
Biehl, Maureen A532
Biehl, Terry P188
Biehl, Clara P213
Biehl, Keith P660
Biehler, Jefry M P665
Bielan, Judith Q. E40
Bielar, James A84
Bielecki, John P303
Bielen, Richard J. A674
Bien, Marie A699
Bien, Marie P456
Bienert, Philip A84
Bienstock, Steven A155
Bienvenue, Patrick D. E201
Bier, Alan P224
Bieri, Matthew (Matt) E404
Biermann, Frederick P19
Biernbaum, Robert P357
Biewend, Susan P535
Bigelow, Roger P524
Bigelow, Teresa P550
Bigelow, Jason P699
Bigelow, Chandler E402
Biggers, Candi A674
Biggers, Edwin P423
Biggers, John E337
Biggs, Morgan A120
Biggs, M. Brett A878
Biggs, Ray P490
Biggs, Randy E87
Bigler, Barbara A15
Bigler, Barbara P9
Digley, Gail A480
Bigley, Jamie A674
Bigley, Linda P539
Bigos, Christopher A369
Biittner, Sallie P532
Bijun, Wu W109
Bike, Brent A244
Bilbrey, John P. (J.P.) A416
Bildstein, Cole P514
Bilecki, Frank A134
Bilecki, Frank P78
Bileddo, Anthony P275
Bilko, David G. (Dave) A841
Bilko, David G. (Dave) E410
Bill, Stumpf A762
Bill, Clark A878
Bill, Shreve A912
Billak, Ann A480
Biller, Frank E76
Billig, Chris P69
Billig, David P683
Billigmeier, Steven P532
Billing, Duncan J. A408
Billings, Will A906
Billings, Craig S. A909
Billings, Kimberly P64
Billings, Robert P282
Billings, Al P356
Billings, Eric F. E24
Billman, Diane A247
Billman, Diane E103
Billups, Ramsey A3
Billy, Joseph A677
Bilney, Jody L. A437
Bilotta, Anthony V. A639
Bilotta, Aj P139
Bilotta, Anthony V. E325
Bilotti-Peterson, Christine A402
Bilse, Gregory A133
Bilsland, Brent E185
Bily, Shirley A870
Bimson, Stephen A158
Bin, Mo W109
Bin, Ong Eng W280
Binaco, Juli A16
Binbasgil, Hakan W18
Bincoletto, Cintia A898
Bindelglass, David P83
Binder, Steven G. A432
Binder, Joel A616
Binder, Tim P358

Bing, Steven B P27
Bing, Deann P192
Bing, Shang W91
Bingaman, Jonathan A175
Bingaman, Peter A460
Bingaman, Christopher (Chris) E106
Bingaman, Mark G. E408
Bingham, Kim R. A170
Bingham, Rob A384
Bingham, Paula A817
Bingham, CORY P1
Bingham, Douglas P604
Bingham, Rob E176
Bingol, Selim A282
Bingold, Michael A359
Binick, Emily Goodman A49
Binkley, D Bruce P552
Binkowski, Chuck P61
Binks, Michael A649
Binnie, Alastair A147
Binnie, Lisa A402
Binns, Justin T. A738
Bino, Gil W149
Bintz, John P231
Bintz, William (Bill) E27
Binvel, Yannick E235
Binzer, Ann A196
Binzer, Greg P682
Biocini, Peter P451
Biondi, Paul A147
Biossat, William A446
Biossat, William E210
Birch, Robert F. A425
Birch, Murray P25
Birch, Mark P55
Birch, Sue P84
Birch, Robert F. E201
Bircher, Meredith P583
Bird, Roger M. A5
Bird, Dean A101
Bird, Kim A140
Bird, Chris A149
Bird, Stephen A203
Bird, Norm A222
Bird, Andy A272
Bird, Stefan A. A630
Bird, Kristin A835
Bird, Lauren A868
Bird, Michael P118
Bird, Erin P486
Bird, J. Richard W138
Bird, Graham R. W161
Birenbaum, Matthew H. (Matt) E26
Birkelbach, Don A800
Birkelbach, Don P559
Birkelo, Jeff A879
Birkenstock, Tim M P665
Birkenstock, Timothy P665
Birkett, Bernard A273
Birkett, Sharon E. E288
Birkholz, Shelly A406
Birkmeyer, David A850
Birla, Nita A390
Birling, Melissa A81
Birmingham, Martin K. A334
Birmingham, Tom E382
Birmingham-Byrd, Melody A281
Birnbaum, David A131
Birnbaum, Scott A175
Birnbaum, Jason A741
Birnbaum, Ing. Leonhard W131
Birnbaum, Jason E370
Birns, Ira M. A906
Biron, Ziv W190
Biros, Cathy P632
Birr, Ruthann P158
Birrell, Ryan E140
Birren, Susan J. P82
Birrittella, Buffy A691
Bisaccia, Lisa A250
Bisaro, Paul M. W22
Bischak, Valerie A872
Bischmann, Joanne M. A403
Bischofberger, Norbert W. A386
Bischoff, Michael A532

Bischoff, Richard P99
Bischoff, David P634
Bischoff, Werner W108
Bischoff, Manfred W114
Biscotti, John A671
Bisegna, Anthony C. A766
Bishar, John J. E22
Bisher, Jon P36
Bishop, Blake A173
Bishop, John A508
Bishop, Marissa A589
Bishop, Steven D. (Steve) A671
Bishop, Amy A801
Bishop, Rachel R. A829
Bishop, David P30
Bishop, William (Billy) P77
Bishop, Ken P111
Bishop, Deena P289
Bishop, Lisa P340
Bishop, Meghan P551
Bishop, Amy P561
Bishop, Nancy P584
Bishop, Tim W227
Bishop, Greg E93
Bishop, William A. (Andy) E185
Bisignano, Frank J A343
Biske, Sandra A541
Biske, Sandra E266
Bison, Michael A31
Bison, Michael P24
Bisselberg, Stephanie A26
Biswas, Michael E385
Bitler, Cathy P509
Bitter, Robert G. E415
Bitterman, Pincas P467
Bittner, Edward P634
Bittner, Elaine B. E74
Bitton, Francesca P654
Bitzer, Marc R. A898
Bixby, R. Philip A483
Bixby, Walter E. (Web) A483
Bixler, Tony P700
Bizzard, Kenneth A700
Bizzarri, Marco W204
Bjorkman, Karen S. P613
Bjornlie, Jennifer P435
Bjornsson, Kresten M. E183
Bjornstad, Geir P186
Blachere, Catherine A147
Black, Arthur Q A22
Black, Steve A199
Black, Willa A199
Black, Dennis A221
Black, Derrick A273
Black, Chris A364
Black, Tom A419
Black, Jon A707
Black, Ken A709
Black, Trevor A725
Black, Freddie G. A742
Black, Katy A795
Black, Mary A869
Black, Arthur Q P13
Black, Randolph P86
Black, Kim P145
Black, David P170
Black, Michele P325
Black, Douglas P346
Black, Kevin P664
Black, Keith E195
Black, Dwayne E368
Black, Freddie G. E372
Blackburn, Joey A13
Blackburn, Fred K. A140
Blackburn, Andy A199
Blackburn, Howard W A227
Blackburn, Stella A469
Blackburn, Randy A493
Blackburn, Richard A649
Blackburn, Lezlee A727
Blackburn, Shawn E355
Blacken, Linda A649
Blackford, David E. A919
Blackford, Michael W. (Woody) E86
Blackhurst, Janis L. (Jan) Jones A157

Blackhurst, Janis J A158
Blackhurst, Jan Jones A158
Blackley, R. Scott A163
Blackman, Scott A221
Blackman, David M. E314
Blackmore, Kevin P301
Blackmore, Milton C. (Bud) E216
Blackmun, Scott P636
Blackney, Kenneth S. P165
Blackstock, Chet P485
Blackwell, Jean A177
Blackwell, Patrick P163
Blackwood, Eric A640
Blackwood, Kevin A751
Blackwood, Kevin E377
Blades, Bill P108
Blades, Thomas W223
Blaha, Albert A456
Blain, Robert (Rob) A172
Blaine, Mitchell A173
Blair, Rainer M. A253
Blair, Gavin A402
Blair, Scott A503
Blair, Kevin S. A781
Blair, Scott A920
Blair, Chuck P104
Blair, Linda P145
Blair, Linda H P252
Blair, Bill P271
Blair, John P563
Blair, Carrie W347
Blair, Tom E253
Blais, Greg A591
Blais, Marc A914
Blaise, Timothy A254
Blaise, Michelle A309
Blajwas, Michael P379
Blake, Tony A111
Blake, Nancy A221
Blake, Francis S. (Frank) A262
Blake, Patrick J. (Pat) A546
Blake, Christopher D. A632
Blake, David M. A668
Blake, Lynn S. A766
Blake, Nicholas A775
Blake, Tony P56
Blake, Joe P132
Blake, M. Brian P165
Blake, M P165
Blake, Bonita P223
Blake, Woods P225
Blake, Desiree P235
Blake, Randy P249
Blake, Kim E44
Blake, Christopher D. E321
Blakelock, Sarah P139
Blakemore, Anthony A752
Blakemore, Michael P256
Blakemore, Dominic W107
Blakeney, John A223
Blakewood, Benjamin F. A21
Blakewood, Benjamin F. P12
Blakey, Marion C. P383
Blakey, Rachel P391
Blakey, Choling P624
Blalock, Clare A383
Blalock, H A774
Blalock, Anthony P412
Blanc, Richard A903
Blanc, Christian A914
Blanc, Jean-Louis W143
Blanc, Robert M. (Bobby) Le W277
Blanchard, James A187
Blanchard, Brent A511
Blanchard, Tyanna P126
Blanchard, Jack P212
Blanchard, Debra P313
Blanchard, Stephanie P315
Blanchard, Carol P345
Blanchard, David W383
Blanchard, James E71
Blanchard, Jimmy E360
Blanchard, John P. E421
Blanchette, Mark A731
Blanchette, Bob P179

A = AMERICAN BUSINESS
E = EMERGING COMPANIES
P = PRIVATE COMPANIES
W = WORLD BUSINESS

Blanchette, Mary P664
Blanchette, Mark E365
Blanckmeister, Carolyn A649
Blanco, Danielle A73
Blanco, Alex A289
Blanco, Jenny A480
Blanco, Esteban Lopez E129
Bland, Jeffry P311
Blane, September A463
Blank, Kyle A449
Blank, Dr Josef P155
Blank, Stephen R. E360
Blankenship, Charles P. (Chip) A76
Blankenship, Corry P126
Blankenship, Jeffrey P258
Blankenship, Teresa P289
Blankfein, Lloyd C. A389
Blankmeyer, Erik A791
Blanks, Richard H P471
Blanton, Vicki A58
Blanton, Hamilton A163
Blanton, Vicki E16
Blaschke, Kelly E265
Blasco, Salvador A685
Blascovich, Lawrence A741
Blascovich, Lawrence E370
Blase, William A. (Bill) A84
Blaser, Brian J. A5
Blasingame, David T. P615
Blasini, David P A163
Blaska, John P281
Blaske, Stephen A56
Blasko, Michael A830
Blasko, Brian P588
Blasko, Michael A403
Blatt, Michael P207
Blatt, Jim E119
Blatter, Steve A745
Blau, Cecile A. E160
Blaufuss, Mark P335
Blaug, Suzanne A61
Blauser, Caryn A489
Blaya, Michelle E182
Blaylark, Timothy P337
Blaylock, Isaac A738
Blaze, Chris A737
Blaze, Chris E367
Blazejewski, Steve A165
Blazek, Robert P181
Blazer, Robert A528
Blazquez, Nicholas B. (Nick) W128
Blazye, Andrew R. E163
Blecher, Mark A408
Bleck, Regina P583
Bledsoe, Matthew A700
Bleeker, Gary L. P229
Blegen, Bernie E284
Blehm, Julie P481
Bleisch, N. David A612
Bleiweis, Melissa A541
Bleiweis, Melissa E266
Bleming, Jim E189
Blenderman, Bill A340
Blenderman, Bill E151
Blendermann, Sarah P217
Blenkush, Bob A562
Blenkush, Bob E279
Blerman, Mike A795
Bleske, Mitchell A844
Bleske, Mitchell E412
Blevins, P. Rodney A275
Blew, Dave A678
Bley, Daniel H. A883
Bleyl, Steven A458
Bleyl, Steven P251
Bliev, Alexander A178
Bligh, Carrick A402
Bliley, Mike P291
Blinn, Richard P. (Dick) A380

Bliss, Tom E146
Blitzer, David S. A132
Blivice, Marni A133
Block, Robert A33
Block, Arthur R A220
Block, Keith G. A723
Block, Steven P385
Blocker, Jeffrey A521
Blocker, Adrian M. A896
Blocker, Douglas Lyle P332
Bloemer, Steven A223
Bloj, Ricardo W218
Blom, David P. P405
Blome, James W57
Blood, Blane P282
Bloom, Leah A6
Bloom, William A. (Bill) A406
Bloom, Alfred H. A585
Bloom, Alfred H. P377
Bloom, Mark W10
Bloomquist, Cathy P247
Bloomquist, Annie L. E376
Bloss, Jon A478
Blosser, Joel P669
Blosser, Courtney A. E324
Blotz, Gerald R. E38
Blount, Eddie A655
Blount, Sally E. P397
Blount, Eddie E333
Bloxam, Richard A478
Bludau, Laurence A227
Blue, Robert M. (Bob) A275
Blue, Robert M. A873
Blue, Dan P481
Blum, Jeffrey A270
Blum, Steven A406
Blum, Donald W. A675
Blum, Olivier W322
Blume, Kenneth A247
Blume, Brent A866
Blume, Kenneth E103
Blumenfeld, Stephen A390
Blumenfeld, Barry P303
Blumenfeld, Julian P308
Blumenstein, Penny P565
Blumenthal, Norman Norman
  Blumenthal P629
Blumer, David J. A130
Blunt, Chris A132
Blunt, Mary L. A736
Blunt, Mary L. P492
Blunt, Mary P522
Blute, Todd P80
Blute, Michael L. P590
Bly, Allan E13
Blye, Jeffrey A325
Blyth, Lesley A763
Blyth, Myrna P2
Bo, Yao W287
Bo, Yang W348
Bo-hyuk, Yim W328
Boada, Robert C A752
Boan, Johnny E230
Boardley, Mike P473
Boardman, Joseph H P364
Boas, Nancy A401
Boatner, Stephanie P201
Boatright, Nancy A103
Boatright, Michael A676
Boatwright, Peter P96
Boatwright, Matt E146
Bobb, Stevan B. A134
Bobb, Stevan B. A154
Bobb, Stevan B. P77
Bobba, Anna P526
Bobby, Michael P461
Bober, Andrea A537
Bober, Sharon A635
Bober, Sharon P419
Bobich, Robert P503
Bobitz, Ward E. A382
Bobko, Gary P70
Bobrowski, Paul M. P611
Boccaletti, Giulio P596
Boccardi, Paul A335

Boccardo, James A844
Boccardo, James E412
Bocchieri, Jill P215
Boccolini, Giovanni W189
Bochette, William C. A751
Bochette, Bill A751
Bochette, William C. E377
Bochette, Bill E377
Bochicchio, Leigh A538
Bocian, Pete P368
Bock, Dana P665
Bock, Kurt W. W55
Bock, William G. (Bill) E371
Bockhorst, Daniel E. A182
Bockhorst, Daniel E. E63
Bockstaele, Elisabeth Van P165
Bocock, Julie P247
Bodapati, Ramesh A199
Bodegraven, Donna Van P181
Boden, Alison L. P606
Bodi, Attila A253
Bodi, Dave A659
Bodine, Bruce A569
Bodine, Pam P522
Bodisch, Laurie A369
Bodnar, Michael P297
Bodor, David A644
Bodor, Robert E339
Boe, Ryan A565
Boeck, Karel Gerard De W288
Boedeker, Kenneth W. A304
Boehler, Mike A478
Boehlke, Robert A879
Boehm, Jonathan J. P167
Boehm, Donna P537
Boehme, Linda P517
Boehmer, Mark D A916
Boehnlein, Glenn A772
Boeing, Traci A886
Boeing, Traci E433
Boelstler, Doreen A221
Boelter, Mike P216
Boelter, Pat P216
Boelter, Ben E117
Boemer, Sally P590
Boening, Jon Van P53
Boer, A. Dick W209
Boeren, Leni W14
Boersma, Brad A332
Boersma, Wendy P671
Boerst, Karen P220
Boes, Steven E P192
Boes, Rev Steve P192
Boeshaar, Brad A837
Boeshans, Wade W. E13
Boetel, Mary A541
Boetel, Mary E266
Boettcher, Paul P176
Bogan, Joyce P354
Bogan, Richard P512
Bogan, Richard K. (Rick) E153
Bogati, Anil P431
Bogdanoff, Debra P145
Bogdanov, Vladimir L. W350
Bogdanovich, Peter P627
Boggetto, Brian A309
Boggs, Rod A556
Boggs, Darrell A607
Boggs, Gail P192
Boggs, Carolyn P201
Boggs, Scott P541
Boggs, Melissa E234
Bogh, Julie P477
Bogle, Jill P67
Bogler, John A. A97
Bogler, Carl P472
Bogler, John A. E32
Bogner, Phil P125
Bogosian, John A133
Bogosta, Charles E. (Chuck) A859
Bogosta, Charles E. (Chuck) P652
Boguski, Michael L. A670
Bohaboy, Scott A113
Bohacek, Cheryl P369
Bohall, Tim A906

Bohannon, Donald P518
Bohanon, Chris A320
Bohanon, Chris E143
Bohart, Christine P404
Bohaty, Brian R. A33
Bohbrink, Marshall A397
Bohbrink, Marshall P221
Bohen, Mark P66
Bohen, Sean W35
Bohl, Nicki A171
Bohl, Nicki P100
Bohl, Howard P634
Bohlen, Matthew A774
Bohlinger, Thomas A173
Bohm, Mark P324
Bohm, Rick E369
Bohn, William M. A81
Bohn, Don A476
Bohnenkamp, Martin P440
Bohnke, Jaime A602
Bohnsack, Gary A492
Bohuny, Bruce G A500
Bohuny, Bruce G E238
Boid, Jonathan P121
Boike, Brian D.J. A356
Boiko, Joan P415
Boillat, Pascal W123
Boim, Dave A565
Bois, Michel W103
Boisclair, Christine E89
Boisier, Pierre A119
Boisseau, Philippe W372
Boisvert, Laura A282
Boisvert, Gerry J P227
Boitano, Robert A330
Boitumelo, Patrick W306
Boivin, Daniel P337
Bojdak, Robert J. A522
Bokan, Mike Null A559
Bokar, Cathy A836
Boklund, Carl A725
Bokorney, Mark B. E390
Bol, Alexander A231
Bol, Roslynn A P449
Bol, Alexander A. E90
Boland, Kay P635
Bolata, Frank A113
Bolcshazy, Karin A264
Bold, William A685
Bolden, Kenyatta A677
Boldt, James R P330
Boldt, Oscar C P567
Boldt, Thomas J P567
Bolen, Brandon A518
Bolen, Brandon P293
Bolen, Michael D. (Mike) P318
Bolen, Michael D P318
Bolerdavis, Alicia A379
Boles, Glen P118
Boles, Karla P120
Boley, Joseph A521
Bolg, Julee P570
Bolgar, Paulo A113
Bolger, T Michael P591
Bolger, Rod W310
Bolhing, Sandra P511
Bolich, Barbara P521
Bolick, Kruti A774
Boling, M Todd P106
Bolis, Ken P508
Bolisay, Eric A784
Bollent, Jason A885
Bolling, Deborah P668
Bollinger, Kathy A111
Bollinger, Lee C. A323
Bollinger, Kathy P56
Bollini, Marco W144
Bolloré, Vincent W149
Bolloré, Vincent W388
Bolo, Rob A542
Bolo, Rob E267
Bologna, Matt A912
Bolor, Linda P90
Bolos, Maikel P627
Bols, Ivo A24

Bolt, Cynthia A723
Bolt, Carmen P518
Bolt, Jennifer E219
Bolten, Joshua A295
Bolton, C. Anderson (Andy) A242
Bolton, Karen A865
Bolton, Heidi P490
Bolton, Dave E219
Bolton, H. Eric E276
Bolton, James E291
Bolts, George A547
Bolts, George P319
Bolwerk, Dave A81
Boly, Sarah P67
Bolyard, Joseph P308
Bolze, Steve A375
Boman, P-or W352
Boman, Nancy E160
Bombara, Beth A. A406
Bombard, Tate P459
Bombardier, J. R. André W69
Bombassei, Jim A871
Bommarito, Bruce A158
Bommentre, Frank A247
Bommentre, Frank E103
Bommersbach, Todd P345
Bompard, Alexandre W82
Bona, Robin A175
Bonacci, Antoinette A195
Bonanni, Jim A165
Bonanni, Craig C. P138
Bonanno, Kelly A371
Bonanotte, Gino A. A570
Bonarti, Michael A A87
Bonasera, Jered P491
Bonavita, Salvatore P275
Bonck, Michael P203
Bonczek, John E107
Bonczek, David E307
Bond, Simon A464
Bond, Christine A535
Bond, Richard E A577
Bond, Richard A594
Bond, Robert W. (Bob) A634
Bond, Melody A698
Bond, Martine A766
Bond, Ray P55
Bond, Joseph P83
Bond, James P101
Bond, Christine P312
Bond, Melody P456
Bonderoff, Scott P590
Bondeson, Rusty A257
Bondi, Paolo W140
Bonds, Michael P. (Mike) A846
Bone, Ronald A546
Bone, Doug A780
Boned, Cecilia W67
Boneparth, Peter A493
Boneta, Vanessa A532
Bonfield, Andrew A169
Bonfield, Andrew R. J. W255
Bonfiglio, Joanne A95
Bonfiglio, Joanne P55
Bonfilio, Pj A56
Bongiorno, Anthony A175
Bongiorno, John A871
Bonham, David W146
Bonhomme, Thierry W278
Bonick, Martin J. A227
Boniface, William P144
Bonifacemesce, Carolyn A908
Bonilla, Fernando A570
Bonilla, Eduardo A693
Bonin, Deb P369
Bonini, Sheila P696
Bonke, Neil A725
Bonn, Nicholas T. (Nick) A766
Bonnafé, Jean-Laurent W66
Bonneau, Jacques Q. W98
Bonnefont, Yves W286
Bonnell, William W252
Bonner, Bill P143
Bonner, Andy P480
Bonner, Dr Jim P639

Bonner, Darryl E98
Bonnett, John W A413
Bonnett, John W P234
Bonnett, Anthony P433
Bonomi, Philip P467
Bonomo, Christine P397
Bonsall, Mark B. P478
Bonsignore, Joseph E445
Bontcheva, Milena A270
Bontempelli, Frederic E229
Bonvie, Catelin P313
Bonzani, Andrew A464
Boocock, Richard A24
Booker, Martin W. A62
Booker, Robert A855
Boom, Marc L P243
Boom, Marc L P620
Boomer, Stephen L. A344
Boomer, Stephen L. E154
Boomgarden, Barbara A336
Boomgarden, Barbara P194
Boon, Philip J. (Phil) E216
Boondoungprasert, Prasit W88
Boone, Elsie A244
Boone, Elwood B. (Bernie) A736
Boone, Matthew P242
Boone, Elwood B. (Bernie) P492
Boone, Torrence P580
Boone, Sam R. E47
Boone, Joshua A. E324
Boonnoon, Anek W88
Boor, Kathryn J. P143
Boor, Anthony W. (Tony) E44
Boor, William C. (Bill) E61
Boortz, Kevin A439
Boosalis, Mary H P439
Boose, Donna P164
Boosin, Greg A537
Boot, Mike P435
Boote, John A173
Booth, William A163
Booth, Susan A724
Booth, Becky P101
Booth, Andrew P218
Booth, Sheryl P594
Booth, Kenneth S. E99
Booth, Lewis E174
Booth, Daniel J. E315
Boothe, Cebert A105
Boothe, Dorrett A108
Boothe, Steven A784
Boothe, Dorrett E35
Boots, James A441
Bootsma, Pieter W14
Boozan, Tim A546
Boozang, Kathleen M. P494
Boozer, Leslie P199
Bor, Chris A483
Boragine, Ellie A49
Borak, Andrew A871
Boras, Stephen A332
Borba, George A. A248
Borchardt, Randall A866
Borcherding, Tricia A213
Borchers, Bradford D. A621
Borchers, Susan C. A703
Borches, Elizabeth M P424
Borches, Peter P424
Borches, Pete P424
Borcke, Wulff-Erik von A6
Borda, Oscar W25
Borde, David A300
Bordeaux, Tom A85
Bordelon, Brian P624
Borden, Ian A545
Borden, Jane P93
Borden, Edward A644
Borden, Paul J. E201
Bordenave, Philippe W66
Borders, Charlie P276
Borders, Denise Glyn P522
Bordes, Michael P. (Mike) A294
Borelli, Janet A872
Boren, Kevin P333
Borenstein, Gerald P216
Borer, Mark A257

Borer, Francis E P425
Borg, Karen E354
Borgard, Lawrence P36
Borgen, Thomas F. W118
Borges, Steven D. (Steve) A471
Borgklint, Per G. W360
Borglund, Patricia P24
Borgmann, Kevin S. A163
Borgne, Gilles Le W286
Borgstrom, Marna P. P698
Borgstrom, Marna P. P699
Boris, John E368
Borisenko, David P237
Borisenko, Natalia W289
Borja, Paul D. A356
Borkowski, Tim A318
Born, Adam A844
Born, Adam E412
Bornemann, Frank A774
Bornhorst, Donald A262
Bornhurst, Don A262
Bornibus, Francois W218
Bornmann, David E. A679
Bornmann, David E. A680
Bornmann, David E. P448
Bornstein, Ethan S. E206
Boronat, Brian A328
Borota, Holly P282
Boroughs, Timothy A. W98
Borovsky, Daniel P418
Borowicz, S. Mark E290
Borowicz, Mark E290
Borowiecki, Jeff A180
Borque, Suzonne E244
Borrego, Susan E. A698
Borrego, Susan E. P456
Borrero, Luz P44
Borro, Douglas A707
Borror, Ron P19
Borschuk, Richard P208
Borsello, Fabrice A893
Borso, Stefan A729
Borst, Walter G A577
Borthwick, Erika P666
Borton, Chad M. A332
Bortz, Jon E. E326
Boruff, Brian E. E44
Borum, Andrea A693
Borwankar, Satish B. W357
Boryla, Stephanie A837
Borzi, James A119
Bosanko, Ed P677
Bosch, Scott P226
Boschelli, John M. A487
Boschini, Victor J. P560
Bosco, Paul A199
Bosco, Teresa A221
Bosco, Sara Yang A295
Boscov, Albert P79
Bose, Robert A40
Bose, Supratim A144
Boshart, Shelli P108
Boshoff, Chris A649
Bosi, Benoit A677
Bosio, Dave P48
Bosler, Richard E26
Bosley, Katharine A644
Bosley, Marvenia P133
Bosma, Laura A480
Bosma, Will P356
Bosma, Brad E173
Bosmat, Hana Ben Zvi W46
Bosowski, Edward M. (Ed) E92
Bosque, Angelita Del A478
Boss, R Daniel A303
Boss, Jane P93
Bosselmann, Rainer H. E23
Bossert, Bryan A260
Bossidy, Lawrence A. (Larry) E41
Bosso, Leonard A583
Bost, Philippe A10
Bost, Melton C A456
Boster, Barry A438
Bostic, Raphael W. A322
Bostic, Jennifer P175

Bostock, Nathan M. W312
Boston, Steve A26
Bostrom, Robert A366
Bostrom, Brent A397
Bostrom, Brent P221
Bostwick, Tony P188
Bosway, William T. A279
Boswell, Kathleen A576
Boswell, Nicole A920
Boswell, Donna A. P673
Boswell, Kathleen E297
Boswood, Mike P628
Bosworth, Jim P130
Bosworth-Deluca, Annette P449
Botbol, Michel A691
Bothe, Albert A372
Bothe, Albert P208
Bothe, Jason P281
Bothner, Joan P114
Bothwell, Peter A406
Botifoll, Jordi A199
Botker, Maria P481
Botnick, Alex A175
Boto, D August P188
Botsford, Tom A56
Bott, Richard E172
Botta, G. Andrea A189
Botte, Jeff A818
Botti, Jean J. W16
Bottinelli, Jaime Soler W85
Bottoms, Derek W A426
Botts, Pat A572
Botts, Pat P359
Bot-n, Ana P. W45
Bouboulis, Panagiota A105
Bouc, Herve Le W72
Bouc, Hervé Le W104
Bouch, Gary A327
Bouchard, Anthony B P102
Bouchard, Alain W20
Bouche, Renee E374
Boucher, Harold A219
Boucher, Tim A752
Boucher, Harold E84
Bouchereau, Sabine SE A108
Bouchereau, Valerie A375
Bouchereau, Sabine SE E35
Bouchiat, Pascal W364
Boudewyns, Tom A855
Boudreau, Thomas M A406
Boudreaux, Gail K. A67
Boudreaux, Gail K. A68
Boudreaux, Greg A353
Boudreaux, Susie A446
Boudreaux, Bryan A878
Boudreaux, Susie E210
Bough, John P578
Bouillon, Patty P692
Boukaya, Michael E67
Boulanger, Steve E57
Boulanger, Normand A. (Norm) E383
Boulos, Paul F. P361
Boulware, Omar M. P676
Bouman, Rosemarie A541
Bouman, Rosemarie E266
Bounds, Hank M. P78
Bounsy, Ryan A649
Bouongiono, Michael P302
Bourdeau, Gayle A A769
Bourdier, Maryanne A195
Bourgeois, Glenn P47
Bourgeois, Darlene P279
Bourgeois, Meagan L P347
Bourgeois, Eugene J. (Gene) P563
Bourget, Christine Potter A817
Bourgon, Jocelyne W180
Bourke, Catherine A322
Bourke, Greg P200
Bourla, Albert A648
Bourne, Robert W A69
Bourque, Robert H. A242
Bourque, Lessette P571
Bourque, Michael P625
Boursier, Jean-Marc W343
Bousbib, Ari A469

A = AMERICAN BUSINESS
E = EMERGING COMPANIES
P = PRIVATE BUSINESS
W = WORLD BUSINESS

Bousquet-Chavanne, Patrick W233
Boutcher, Margie A862
Boutcher, Margie E419
Boutros, Ekran P336
Boutros, Akram P336
Boutros, Akram P593
Boutte, Tracie A300
Bouvier, Laura A530
Bouvin, Anders W352
Bouygues, Olivier W72
Bouygues, Martin W72
Bouée, Pierre-Olivier W111
Bove, Joyce A584
Bove, Lane P299
Bove, Joyce P374
Bover, J P664
Bowden, James A366
Bowden, Daniel A736
Bowden, Bryson A838
Bowden, Lloyd M. A904
Bowden, Sherri P233
Bowden, Daniel P492
Bowden, Lloyd M. E442
Bowe, Dan A683
Bowe, Edwin P273
Bowen, John A122
Bowen, Richard A313
Bowen, Michelle A330
Bowen, Cara A528
Bowen, Joy A655
Bowen, Maggie A838
Bowen, Liz A844
Bowen, Arthur N. (Art) A873
Bowen, Jenny P13
Bowen, Deanna P201
Bowen, Tim P250
Bowen, John J. P267
Bowen, José A. P514
Bowen, Arthur N. (Art) P668
Bowen, Joy E333
Bowen, Liz E412
Bower, Huw S. A151
Bower, Joseph B. A212
Bower, Robert C. A851
Bower, Eric P99
Bower, Joseph B. E79
Bowerman, James A565
Bowers, William A27
Bowers, Ann A70
Bowers, Douglas H. (Doug) A97
Bowers, Matthew A158
Bowers, Christopher D. A179
Bowers, Paul A383
Bowers, David A518
Bowers, Ed A558
Bowers, Elizabeth A605
Bowers, Mike A760
Bowers, Jeff A838
Bowers, David G P116
Bowers, Stuart S. P167
Bowers, Mike P523
Bowers, Brian J. E24
Bowers, Douglas H. (Doug) E32
Bowers, Denise E276
Bowersox, Dennis A388
Bowersox, Jim A508
Bowes, Timothy E. (Tim) A45
Bowes, Warren A101
Bowes, Ken P188
Bowie, Paul J. A31
Bowie, Paul J. P24
Bowks, Derek P165
Bowlby, Jeffrey L. A670
Bowler, Rodney M P234
Bowles, Crandall A260
Bowles, Ryan P218
Bowles, Jack W74
Bowling, Brian A322
Bowling, Chuck A558

Bowling, Jamie P13
Bowling, Douglas P94
Bowling, Stuart P307
Bowling, Charlene E203
Bowman, Gina A249
Bowman, Richard A407
Bowman, Christopher A481
Bowman, Jeff A546
Bowman, Stephen B. (Biff) A599
Bowman, William A634
Bowman, Helen Y. P165
Bowman, Elaine P601
Bowman, David T. P671
Bowman, Katy P694
BowmanCHI, Alan A171
BowmanCHI, Alan P100
Bowry, Oran A662
Bowser, Scott L. E283
Bowshier, Terrence A764
Box, Laurie A838
Boxer, Mark L. A194
Boyaji, Brian A644
Boyanton, Bobby P66
Boyce, Jill A748
Boyce, David S. A820
Boyce, Kevin L P204
Boyce, Jane E19
Boyd, Norman A20
Boyd, Jeffery H. (Jeff) A139
Boyd, Alison A245
Boyd, Skiles A280
Boyd, John J. A304
Boyd, Jeff A521
Boyd, Peter M. A754
Boyd, Greg A774
Boyd, Robert A920
Boyd, Terry P133
Boyd, Suzanna P279
Boyd, David P342
Boyd, Michael P497
Boyd, Chris P497
Boyd, Chris P498
Boyd, Ken E300
Boyd, Peter M. E380
Boyden, Tracey A649
Boydston, James A730
Boydstun, Donnie P636
Boyer, Gregg A113
Boyer, Jason A223
Boyer, Jeffrey A702
Boyer, Jennifer Yi P5
Boyer, Ryan P158
Boyer, John W. P610
Boyer, Greg P663
Boyer, Jean-Michel W67
Boyer, Bradley S. (Brad) E15
Boyer, Steven E276
Boyet, Bo P6
Boyette, Richard P70
Boyette, Scott P368
Boykas, Paul A647
Boyken, James W A460
Boykin, Frank H. A563
Boykin, William P47
Boykins, Lamont A56
Boyko, Jean A. E338
Boylan, Laura A651
Boylan, Laura P426
Boylan, Peter C P472
Boylan, William J. E90
Boyle, Amy A56
Boyle, Hugh F. A97
Boyle, Robert A260
Boyle, Jim A269
Boyle, Blair A272
Boyle, Chris A366
Boyle, Kevin A546
Boyle, Terence A596
Boyle, Ed A597
Royle, David P A625
Boyle, David A625
Boyle, Debbie A644
Boyle, Patti A724
Boyle, Stephen J. (Steve) A791
Boyle, Dennis A862

Boyle, Ray A878
Boyle, Tom A912
Boyle, Kathy P160
Boyle, Brian P432
Boyle, Jodell J P478
Boyle, Jodell P478
Boyle, Hugh F. E32
Boyle, Timothy P. (Tim) E86
Boyle, Joseph P. (Joe) E86
Boyle, Gertrude (Gert) E86
Boyle, Dennis E419
Boyles, Andrew A102
Boyles, Kathryn A390
Boyles, Kevin A739
Boyles, Jonathan A746
Boyles, Kevin P501
Boyles, Lavender P685
Boyles, Peter W. W175
Boynton, Kimberly P148
Boynton, Andrew C. P625
Bozada, Joe E263
Bozek, Kathy A81
Bozek, Steven A744
Bozeman, Keith P557
Bozgo, Paul A133
Bozzi, Bryan A875
Bozzoli, Carlo W141
Braak, Cindy A530
Braathen, Kjerstin W129
Braatz, Jay P155
Brabant, Steven A173
Brabec-Lagrange, Claire W143
Brabham, Dave P269
Brabson, Charles A303
Braca, Greg W370
Bracamonte, Martin E331
Brace, George A427
Brace, George E202
Bracher, Paul H. A244
Bracher, Candido Botelho W191
Brachet, Anne W14
Bracken, Andrew A458
Bracken, Andrew P251
Bracken, Charles H. R. (Charlie) W222
Bracken, George R. E291
Brackenbury, Katie A133
Brackin, D. Wayne P57
Bracy, Kevin A439
Brad, Morgan P562
Bradac, Joe A878
Bradbury, Greg A744
Braden, Scott A547
Brader, Andy P73
Bradfoot, Melody A234
Bradfoot, Melody P139
Bradford, Mark D. A614
Bradford, Megan P339
Bradford, Tegan P547
Bradham, Sue A735
Bradley, W. Bennett A115
Bradley, Michael A178
Bradley, William E. (Bill) A185
Bradley, Jen A223
Bradley, John A480
Bradley, David A775
Bradley, Scott A788
Bradley, Kevin P. A852
Bradley, Patrick A899
Bradley, Tim P20
Bradley, Martin P20
Bradley, Alan P198
Bradley, Constance (Connie) P230
Bradley, Tonya P266
Bradley, Megan P275
Bradley, Wendy P282
Bradley, Carol P285
Bradley, Russell P335
Bradley, Dana P398
Bradley, Larry D P425
Bradley, Walter P446
Bradley, Jeanell P510
Bradley, David P548
Bradley, W S P622
Bradley, William L P675
Bradley, Patrick P690

Bradley, Allen E170
Bradley, Keith E220
Bradley, Russell W. E250
Bradley, Edward L. E299
Bradley, Don E303
Bradshaw, Steven G. (Steve) A137
Bradshaw, Jami A350
Bradshaw, Jim A496
Bradshaw, Richard W. A844
Bradshaw, Jami E156
Bradshaw, Richard W. E412
Bradvica, Michael A16
Bradway, Robert A. (Bob) A61
Bradwell, Hollis (Terry) P2
Brady, James A163
Brady, Deanna T. A432
Brady, Amy G. A489
Brady, Robert T. (Bob) A522
Brady, Elizabeth S. (Beth) A668
Brady, Kevin A767
Brady, Christian M. M. A811
Brady, Robin P462
Brady, Patrick P549
Brady, Christian M. M. P600
Brady, Lawrence P621
Brady, Janet M E65
Braemer, Richard A819
Bragdon, Peter J. E86
Brager, David A. A248
Bragg, Chris A107
Bragg, Dorry A328
Bragg, Michelle A637
Bragg, Michael B. A861
Bragg, Alisha P125
Bragg, Amy P649
Bragg, Michael B. P658
Bragg, Chris E34
Brahma, Harihar A204
Brailo, Andy E337
Braithwaite, Robert P238
Brake, Tonya A663
Brake, Gene P87
Brakeville, Barry A838
Brakman, Steven A729
Bral, Maciek A272
Bramble, James H. (Jim) E423
Bramlage, Stephen P. (Steve) A73
Bramlett, Cara A195
Bramlett, E Chandler P248
Bramman, Anne L. A596
Branagan, Lynn P551
Branca, Fred A537
Branch, Rich A461
Branch, Rodney A677
Branch, Gregory C. A847
Branch, Carole P525
Branch, Gregory C. E414
Brand, Meir A36
Brand, Dennis L. A98
Brand, Tina A869
Brand, Jeffrey S. P654
Brand, Christian W215
Brand, Dennis L. E33
Brandano, Janice A184
Brandano, Anthony P53
Brandel, Dan A173
Brandenberg, Frank G. E230
Brandenburg, Jennifer A375
Brandenburg, Joel A839
Brandenburg, Julie P561
Brandenburg, Joel E409
Branderiz, Eric A799
Brandgaard, Jesper W271
Brandner, James P13
Brandom, Jessica A81
Brandon, Joseph P. A30
Brandon, Mark A110
Brandon, Ira A221
Brandon, John A321
Brandon, David P252
Brandon, Hughey P490
Brandon, Mark E37
Brandon, John E144
Brandow, Peter B. P455
Brands, Andrew D. W161

Brandt, Kathleen A243
Brandt, Pam A260
Brandt, James A. A521
Brandt, Bryan K A625
Brandt, Louise P26
Brandt, Douglas P231
Brandt, Gayle P260
Brandt, Paul P559
Brandt, Kristen E149
Brandt, Kevin D. E360
Brandwene, Robert A175
Branham, Winter P239
Branion, Andrew W50
Brannan, Joseph A513
Brannan, Andrew E78
Brannemo, Tomas A914
Brannen, James P. (Jim) A319
Brannen, Charlie P242
Brannock, Christine P594
Branon, Bethany A863
Branscum, John E89
Branstetter, Shawn A784
Brantley, Todd A353
Brantley, John P105
Brantley, Adrienne P371
Brantley, Chris P586
Branz, Sandra A406
Braskamp, Steve A163
Brasteter, Christine M P466
Braswell, Sandra A115
Braswell, Ray P159
Bratcher, Melanie P242
Bratman, Fred A851
Bratspies, Steve A878
Bratt, Mikael A87
Bratz, Valmor A461
Braucht, Millie P542
Braud, Colton E255
Braude, Katie P296
Brauer, Stephen F. P616
Brault, Tom P68
Braun, Bill A96
Braun, Randall L. A384
Braun, Ray P99
Braun, Robert P145
Braun, Joel E4
Braun, Donald G E146
Braun, Michael H. E147
Braun, Randall L. E176
Braunagel, Pat P276
Braunstein, Louis A323
Brautigan, Bernard (Bernie) A715
Braveman, Peter P102
Braveman, Carla P179
Braverman, Alan N. A271
Bravo, Eduardo A403
Bravo, Giovanna P599
Brawley, Darin P136
Braxton, David A774
Bray, Derek A624
Bray, Jeffery (Jeff) A731
Bray, Dee L P543
Bray, Jeffery (Jeff) E365
Brayboy, Regina P P668
Brazeale, Cathy A743
Brazeale, Cathy E372
Brazil, Ben W227
Brda, Bruce W. A570
Bready, Bruce A500
Bready, Cameron M P252
Bready, Cameron M P340
Bready, Bruce E237
Breakefield, Xandra A635
Breakefield, Xandra P419
Breakey, Mark D. A212
Breakey, Mark D. E79
Breaux, Holly A492
Breber, Pierre R. A192
Brecher, Nancy A644
Breci, Jeff P338
Brecker, Nicholas L. A67
Breckon, Curt A555
Bredar, Randall P256
Bredin, Kristin P518
Bredow, Eugene J. A608

Bree, Joseph A865
Breeding, Louis A478
Breeman, Steven A500
Breeman, Steven E237
Breen, Timothy P. (Tim) A381
Breen, Margaret P135
Breen, Lisa P298
Breen, Jennifer P701
Breeton, Gary A343
Brega, Jo--o Carlos A898
Bregier, Fabrice W16
Breheny, James P691
Brehm, Jim A272
Breidenbach, Jesse P481
Breier, Barbara P563
Breig, J Scott A814
Breig, J Scott P616
Breight, Matthew A221
Breitenbach, Ellen P664
Breitenstein, Kurt A624
Brekelmans, Harry W313
Brekke, Scott A395
Brekke, Liz P30
Brekke, Sigve W360
Breland, Martin A823
Breland, Martin P622
Brell, Mark A244
Bremm, Dirk W55
Bremner, John A758
Bremner, John P519
Bremner, Christy E383
Brendis, Janet A371
Brendle, Jim A120
Breneman, Jill P421
Brennan, James J. A108
Brennan, Thomas A136
Brennan, Daniel J. (Dan) A144
Brennan, Troyen A. A250
Brennan, Kevin F. A372
Brennan, Suzanne R. A632
Brennan, Patrick A672
Brennan, Brian A784
Brennan, John P37
Brennan, Kevin F. P208
Brennan, Murray F. P325
Brennan, Maire P325
Brennan, Jim P361
Brennan, Paul W P449
Brennan, James P477
Brennan, Tara E70
Brennan, Thomas E158
Brennan, Suzanne R. E321
Brenneman, Bryan P184
Brenner, Timothy L. A577
Brenner, Dean A685
Brenner, Alena A718
Brenner, Glen A818
Brenner, Howard I P173
Brenner, Catherine W26
Brenner, Hans-Dieter W215
Brensinger, Donald A709
Brent, Jacques A362
Brenton, Flint A199
Breon, Richard C A758
Breon, Richard C P519
Bres, Thomas A. (Tom) P518
Brescia, Lauren A133
Bresky, Steven J. A730
Breslau, Carol P331
Breslaw, Ralph P72
Breslawski, James P. A727
Breslin, Karena A235
Breslin, David A354
Breslin, Susan P157
Breslin, Sean J. E26
Breslin, Christopher M. E108
Breslow, Jeffrey R P143
Bresnahan, Rodney A826
Bresnahan, Linda K P97
Bresnahan, Linda P97
Bress, Tracy A520
Bresser, Ron P183
Bressler, Allan A175
Bressler, Richard J. A448
Bressman, Jeremy P379

Brest, Paul P236
Brestovan, Peter A644
Breter, Greg A863
Brett, Kate P697
Brett, John L. W30
Bretton, Lise P498
Breuillac, Arnaud W372
Breux, Ken Le A599
Breves, Christine S. A852
Brewer, Allen M. A359
Brewer, Russell A507
Brewer, Dominic A585
Brewer, Ann A774
Brewer, Janet J. A798
Brewer, Kelley P250
Brewer, Russell P288
Brewer, Crissenda P307
Brewer, Tracy P366
Brewer, Dominic P377
Brewer, Christie P457
Brewer, Melanie P639
Brewer, Kevin J. E27
Brewer, David P616
Brewington, Kimberly F A601
Brewington, Kimberly F E308
Brewster, John A56
Brewster, James P7
Brewster, Judy P30
Brewton, Angela P281
Brexler, James P164
Brezden, Alexander A133
Brezski, Richard J. E222
Briand, Jeffrey A906
Briantais, Yves A218
Bricco, Brenda P482
Brice, Todd D. A720
Brice, Todd D. E362
Bricker, Jodi A809
Bricker, Tim P109
Bricker, J. Douglas P169
Brickley, David A813
Brickley, David P616
Brickman, David M. A366
Bricmont, Angela P159
Bridarolli, Shelley A142
Bride, Thomas Y Mc P224
Bridel, David A860
Bridel, David P656
Bridelli, Guido A131
Bridenbaugh, Carl A355
Bridge, Tracy B. A181
Bridge-Cook, Jeremy E250
Bridgeforth, Scott A773
Bridgeforth, Scott E387
Bridger, Chet A522
Bridges, Terri A446
Bridges, Linda A591
Bridges, John A678
Bridges, Katherine P105
Bridges, Laura P158
Bridges, Kay P261
Bridges, Anita P352
Bridges, Susan A P490
Bridges, Terri E210
Bridgham, Jerry A. P58
Bridgmon, Jessica P69
Bridleman, Dan A484
Brien, Jack O' P535
Brienza, David A147
Brier, Jeff A16
Brier, Alex P297
Briesemeister, Eric P252
Brigden, John A199
Briggs, Ashlea A98
Briggs, Troy A614
Briggs, Brian A658
Briggs, Larry A695
Briggs, Brent A920
Briggs, Brian P431
Briggs, Carol P521
Briggs, Jeanne P699
Briggs, Andy W38
Briggs, Ashlea E33
Bright, Christopher A51
Bright, Tobias A136

Bright, Vonette Z P92
Brightly, Teresa A774
Brightman, Donna P674
Brightwell, Jeffrey A298
Brightwell, Jeff A298
Briglia, Jennifer A865
Brigman, Vince A501
Brignoni, Gregory P296
Brill, Scott A788
Brilli, Richard J. P365
Brimhall, Matt A620
Brimmer, Stephanie E8
Brinberg, Simeon E47
Brinckerhoff, Ron A792
Brindle, Carol A907
Brindle, Lou A P660
Brindle, Carol E446
Brindley, David A844
Brindley, David E412
Bringe, Chad A183
Bringe, Chad E66
Brink, Diane A461
Brink, Evert Van Den A767
Brink, James P590
Brinker, Mark A647
Brinkerhoff, Bruce A208
Brinkerhoff, Robert L P148
Brinkley, Ruth W. A171
Brinkley, Cynthia J. (Cindy) A179
Brinkley, Ruth W. P100
Brinkley, Kevin A430
Brinkley, David L. E216
Brinkworth, Heather P486
Brinner, Scott A693
Brinton, Geraldine R. A775
Brinton, Geraldine R. P548
Brinton, Mark E261
Briscoe, Debi A137
Briscoe, James P92
Brisendine, Chad P525
Brislin, Harry P248
Brisse, Thomas M P354
Brister, Anthony P143
Bristor, Jacqueline A115
Bristow, Peter M. A341
Bristow, Peter M. E152
Britell, Jenne K. A851
Brito, Art A101
Brito, Michael A250
Britsch, Sheryl A322
Britt, Scott A51
Britt, Debbie P192
Britt, Stuart P385
Britt, Douglas (Doug) W151
Brittain, Kevin A164
Brittain, James F A358
Brittain, Max P396
Brittingham, Randall A514
Britto, Maria P115
Britton, Paula A254
Britton, Carl A346
Britton, William P22
Britton, Barry P66
Britton, Lynn P330
Brletic, Mat P670
Broaddus, Alfred A528
Broadway, Robert P72
Brobst, Barbara E A625
Brobst, Duane J. A862
Brobst, Duane J. E419
Brocato, Melissa A185
Brocheton, Bruno A272
Brochick, George A642
Brock, Charisse A230
Brock, Charles A655
Brock, Cheryl A707
Brock, Stanley M. (Skip) A737
Brock, Wendy A865
Brock, Kyle P213
Brock, Thomas W. P503
Brock, Gary P562
Brock, Jeffrey E99
Brock, Charles E333
Brock, Stanley M. (Skip) E367
Brockman, Dawn A56

A = AMERICAN BUSINESS
E = EMERGING COMPANIES
P = PRIVATE COMPANIES
W = WORLD BUSINESS

Brockman, Henry A364
Brockman, W Luke P183
Brockmann, Paige A101
Brockmann, Manfred A869
Brockmann, Jan W3
Brockway, Larry A852
Broderick, Craig W. A389
Broderick, John P406
Broderick, Chris P434
Brodet, David W46
Brodie, Troy D. A890
Brodie, Troy D. P684
Brodrick, Anita A190
Brodsky, Noah A908
Brodsky, Harry P392
Brodsky, William J P397
Brodsky, Stephen P414
Brodsky, Victor E233
Brody, Sharon S A677
Brody, Robert C. (Bob) A827
Brody, Paul J. E221
Brody, John S. E444
Broeder, Karen P537
Broek, Jacques van den W299
Broerman, Robert A. (Rob) A736
Broerman, Robert A. (Rob) P492
Broermann, Robert A P493
Brogan, John J A116
Brogan, Jennifer A541
Brogan, Debbie A620
Brogan, Mike A818
Brogan, Joseph E39
Brogan, Jennifer E266
Brogden, Sue-ellen P680
Brogdon, Casey A844
Brogdon, Georgia P P224
Brogdon, Casey E412
Broholm, Aaron A748
Brok, Martin A762
Bromagen, Ellen J. A323
Broman, Craig P602
Bromley, Craig R. W232
Bromstad, Marc A700
Bronchetti, Jayson A513
Bronczek, David J. A327
Bronet, Frances P651
Bronner, James P. A122
Brons-Poulsen, Peter A218
Bronsdon, Phillip A185
Bronson, David L. A807
Bronson, David L. P574
Bronson, Richard E385
Brook, Melissa P340
Brookbanks, Richard A272
Brooke, Gayle A452
Brooker, Levi E432
Brookes, Andy A5
Brookins, Patty A308
Brookman, Vanessa A872
Brookner, Mark E405
Brooks, Paulette A101
Brooks, Mark J. A179
Brooks, Brian P. A315
Brooks, Jessica A439
Brooks, Josh A449
Brooks, David R. A452
Brooks, Daniel W. A452
Brooks, Wendell M. A456
Brooks, Charles T. A487
Brooks, Ashley T. A518
Brooks, Raymond L. A527
Brooks, Michele A555
Brooks, Bill A575
Brooks, Rebekah A589
Brooks, Byron A647
Brooks, Mary A693
Brooks, Brian A700
Brooks, Nancy Schwartz A782
Brooks, Andy A784

Brooks, Espen S. A813
Brooks, George A850
Brooks, Tony A913
Brooks, Chris P13
Brooks, Ben P123
Brooks, Eve P131
Brooks, Roy P145
Brooks, Darian P158
Brooks, James P164
Brooks, Dawn P199
Brooks, Paula P204
Brooks, David P218
Brooks, Carrie P247
Brooks, S P320
Brooks, Roby P334
Brooks, Rebecca P345
Brooks, D Ick P411
Brooks, Timothy P484
Brooks, Deborah P556
Brooks, Deanne P594
Brooks, Espen S. P616
Brooks, Margaret P649
Brooks, David A E45
Brooks, David R. E214
Brooks, Daniel W. E215
Brooks-Williams, Denise A413
Brooks-Williams, Denise P234
Brooks-Williams, Denise P235
Brookshire, Jackie P33
Brookshire, William A. P469
Broom, Charles A316
Broom, John P359
Broom, Charles E141
Broome, Tol A115
Broome, Richard D. A157
Broomfield, Robert A855
Brophy, Joseph A402
Brophy, Joe A677
Brophy, Scott A865
Brophy, Beth P245
Bros, Warner E226
Broseker, Bob A555
Brosnahan, Maria A163
Brosnan, David J. (Dave) A211
Brosnan, Michael W153
Bross, Richard A A432
Brossart, Tim A910
Brost, Mike P260
Brost, Arin E213
Brothers, Robert A81
Brothers, Grace A213
Brothers, Lisa A350
Brothers, Norm A850
Brothers, James P611
Brothers, Lisa E156
Brothman, Phillip E135
Brothman, Dan E261
Brotman, Adam A763
Brotman, Donna P122
Brotzki, Bernard Ben A898
Brouaux, Marie-No- «lle W82
Brough, Rob A919
Broughman, Wade D P462
Broughton, Thomas A. (Tom) A737
Broughton, Thomas A. (Tom) E367
Brouillard, Rheo A A740
Broumidis, Haris W389
Broun, Elizabeth (Betsy) P506
Broussard, Paul A228
Broussard, Bruce D. A437
Broussard, Paul P136
Broussard, Eva P279
Brow, Betty A102
Brower, Chris A244
Browerick, John P406
Brown, Greg A16
Brown, Ken A16
Brown, Jeffrey J A34
Brown, Jeffrey J. (JB) A35
Brown, Bradley A35
Brown, Judy Gawlik A61
Brown, Eric A73
Brown, Carale A73
Brown, Jim A78
Brown, Vernon A115

Brown, Liz A115
Brown, Cj A133
Brown, Ian A139
Brown, James C. A142
Brown, Danielle A151
Brown, Heather A155
Brown, William A177
Brown, Debra A201
Brown, Tom A201
Brown, Pam A205
Brown, Adriane A238
Brown, William E. A267
Brown, Wendy A272
Brown, Darrell A289
Brown, Marcus V. A300
Brown, Douglas A309
Brown, Gregory Q. (Greg) A323
Brown, Jill A327
Brown, Marianne C. A330
Brown, Rod A332
Brown, Trish A335
Brown, David D. A343
Brown, Jennifer A368
Brown, Brandon A390
Brown, Julie T A395
Brown, James S. (Jim) A398
Brown, William M. (Bill) A405
Brown, Angie A410
Brown, Manuel L A413
Brown, Doug A433
Brown, Keith A439
Brown, Bruce A441
Brown, Michael J. (Mike) A446
Brown, Ken A446
Brown, Michelle A449
Brown, Mike A458
Brown, Natasha A478
Brown, Desiree A481
Brown, Alice A484
Brown, David A489
Brown, David A546
Brown, Tim A555
Brown, Gregory Q. (Greg) A570
Brown, Robert A583
Brown, Lynne A585
Brown, Donald E. A594
Brown, Jennifer Jackson A596
Brown, Holly A599
Brown, Keegan A607
Brown, Oscar A611
Brown, Teresa A614
Brown, Diana A614
Brown, Bartholomew A621
Brown, Brien H. A622
Brown, Leeann A641
Brown, Tara A649
Brown, Vicki A659
Brown, Dan A698
Brown, Melanie A704
Brown, Diane A709
Brown, Thomas L. A710
Brown, Gerald A718
Brown, Rafe A723
Brown, Kevin A733
Brown, Susan L A734
Brown, Maryam A735
Brown, Julie A A754
Brown, William A758
Brown, Joel E. A764
Brown, Patrick A765
Brown, Marc P. A766
Brown, Melanie A780
Brown, Adam A784
Brown, Bernard A788
Brown, Diann A802
Brown, Chuck A820
Brown, M. Dean A841
Brown, Sandra A844
Brown, Barbara A878
Brown, Mike A879
BROWN, MIKE A894
Brown, Erin A898
Brown, Michael A906
Brown, Michael D. A908
Brown, Jimmy A912

Brown, Greg A912
Brown, Doug P22
Brown, Jeffrey J P27
Brown, Cynthia P35
Brown, Benji P52
Brown, William A. P58
Brown, Jennifer P61
Brown, Jerald P69
Brown, David P74
Brown, Robert P80
Brown, Ellen P81
Brown, Rodney J. P83
Brown, Melissa P84
Brown, Richard A P95
Brown, Hannah P109
Brown, Mike P117
Brown, Austin P144
Brown, Michael P144
Brown, Doris P155
Brown, Shawn P166
Brown, Terry P170
Brown, Judy P173
Brown, Marcus V P185
Brown, Lewis P185
Brown, Marilyn P204
Brown, Gradyne P208
Brown, Susan P220
Brown, Sonya P222
Brown, Ed P224
Brown, Jim P225
Brown, Alev P226
Brown, Manuel L P234
Brown, Crystal P243
Brown, Amy P250
Brown, Jeff P250
Brown, Mike P251
Brown, James D P275
Brown, George J P285
Brown, Kevin P297
Brown, Diona P323
Brown, Melissa A. P342
Brown, Henry K P343
Brown, Daniel P343
Brown, Leonard P368
Brown, Lynne P377
Brown, Michael P379
Brown, Nancy P383
Brown, Rodger P388
Brown, Darnell P392
Brown, Kathleen P406
Brown, Bartholomew P407
Brown, Whitney P414
Brown, Leeann P422
Brown, Kevin P428
Brown, Geoff P428
Brown, Janine P428
Brown, Patrick P430
Brown, Travis P435
Brown, Tony McLean P445
Brown, Carolyn P450
Brown, Dan P456
Brown, Carole P456
Brown, William P460
Brown, Carolyn P465
Brown, Robin B. P488
Brown, James P498
Brown, W P509
Brown, Cindy P516
Brown, Howard P525
Brown, Lance P528
Brown, Mary W P532
Brown, Patrick P540
Brown, Anita P548
Brown, Shermece P550
Brown, Diann P562
Brown, Daniel A. P563
Brown, Stephanie P565
Brown, Tony P567
Brown, Michelle P584
Brown, Michael W P584
Brown, Vance M P590
Brown, David FM P590
Brown, Charlie P611
Brown, Kim P617

Brown, Jay P631
Brown, Maurice P633
Brown, Stevie-Joe P636
Brown, Adam P670
Brown, Bill P675
Brown, Laurie P680
Brown, Billy E P694
Brown, Billy P694
Brown, Charles W61
Brown, Gary W. W80
Brown, Michael W. T. (Mike) W256
Brown, Jason W297
Brown, Jim W312
Brown, Andrew W313
Brown, Randolph B. (Randy) W346
Brown, Celia E1
Brown, Roger H E46
Brown, Kevin E46
Brown, J. Powell E47
Brown, P E47
Brown, J. Hyatt E47
Brown, Marc L E52
Brown, William E. (Bill) E65
Brown, Michael J. (Mike) E134
Brown, Robin D. E153
Brown, Kelly E167
Brown, Craig E169
Brown, David A. E172
Brown, Michael J. (Mike) E210
Brown, Ken E210
Brown, Richard E236
Brown, Toya E244
Brown, Harold E301
Brown, Ronald E301
Brown, Harold E301
Brown, Ronald E301
Brown, D. Russ E343
Brown, Melanie E351
Brown, Greg E357
Brown, Julie A E380
Brown, M. Dean E410
Brown, Sandra E412
Brown, Julie E417
Brown, Jim E423
Brown, Joseph R. (JR) E430
Brown, Jim E444
Brownawell, Neil A216
Brownawell, Neil E80
Browne, Diane A73
Browne, Robert P. (Bob) A599
Browne, Robert A697
Browne, Paul T. A795
Browne, Colin A840
Browne, Robert P454
Browne, Mike E52
Browne, Michael A. (Mike) E52
Brownell, Nora A758
Brownell, Diane P233
Brownell, Jayne P339
Brownell, Nora P519
Brownie, Susan P496
Browning, Nicholas A440
Browning, Bill A483
Browning, James A800
Browning, Michael A814
Browning, Jay D. A867
Browning, Deborah P115
Browning, Matthew P233
Browning, Benita P292
Browning, Michael P616
Browning, James E396
Brownlow, William P503
Broxton, Sonnie A782
Broyles, Rhonda A788
Broz, Steven A. (Steve) A672
Brozyna, Roman A201
BRUBAKER, REBECCA P493
Brubaker, Terry Lee E178
Bruce, Howard A374
Bruce, Kofi A377
Bruce, Carrie A697
Bruce, Jim A850
Bruce, Harry A861
Bruce, Carrie P454
Bruce, Harry P658

Bruce, Sally W26
Bruch, Lucas P478
Bruchhaus, Karl P89
Bruder, David A405
Brudermuller, Martin W55
Brudnick, Richard A129
Brudnicki, Gary P683
Brudzynski, Daniel A280
Bruegenhemke, Kathleen A408
Bruen, Phil A555
Bruff, Edward P146
Bruggeman, Todd A481
Bruhin, Joseph D. (Joe) A235
Bruhmuller, Arthur A556
Bruhn, Carl A318
Bruhn, Michelle P481
Bruin, Teresa P218
Brumbaugh, Lisa A542
Brumbaugh, Lisa E267
Brumley, Blake P561
Brumm, Sheri E408
Brummer, Derek V. A690
Brummer, Derek V. E345
Brummerhoff, Leigh A530
Brummet, Dean P94
Brumsted, John P613
Brumsted, John R. P614
Brundage, Barry A221
Brundage, Stephen A314
Brundage, Adam A493
Brundage, Stephen P189
Brundige, Liz P449
Brundige, Cynthia P523
Brundige, Mary Lourdes P660
Brune, Donna A674
Brune, Rhonda P6
Bruneau, Brian A556
Brunel, Patrick A652
Brunelle, Fletch H A558
Brunelle, Renee P415
Brunengraber, Henri P99
Bruner, Andrea A422
Bruner, William P98
Bruner, Andrea P239
Brungess, Barbara A59
Bruni, Daniel J. A759
Brunick, Brett A790
Bruninga, Keith P467
Brunk, John A219
Brunk, John E84
Brunn, Carsten W57
Brunngraber, Eric H. A169
Bruno, Marc A73
Bruno, James E. A852
Bruno, John P P531
BRUNO, RICCARDO W111
Brunovsky, Megan P613
Bruns, Timothy D. A487
Brunschwig, Serge W97
Brunson, Janice A869
Brunton, Patty E226
Brus, David A866
Brusadelli, Maurizio A567
Bruss, John A15
Bruss, John P9
Brust, Andrew L A562
Brust, Andrew A562
Brust, Andrew L E279
Brust, Andrew E279
Bruton, Steve A725
Brutto, Daniel A782
Bruun, Ed P518
Bruza, John M P599
Bruzzichesi, Gina A93
Bryan, Cary A199
Bryan, J. Randolph A446
Bryan, Glynis A. A454
Bryan, Vincent A828
Bryan, Mark H P159
Bryan, Carl P272
Bryan, David J P279
Bryan, Lawana P391
Bryan, Gary P554
Bryan, Mona P584
Bryan, Kenneth P674

Bryan, Elizabeth W78
Bryan, Jason E15
Bryan, J. Randolph E210
Bryant, Daniel J A37
Bryant, Jennifer A48
Bryant, Christian A81
Bryant, Joy A136
Bryant, Steve A295
Bryant, Diane M. A456
Bryant, Andy D. A456
Bryant, John A. A485
Bryant, Andy D A456
Bryant, John J A625
Bryant, Kim A729
Bryant, Mike A850
Bryant, Frederick M P198
Bryant, Linda P207
Bryant, Phil P258
Bryant, Mary P259
Bryant, Kevin E P271
Bryant, Bill P620
Bryant, Jennings P639
Bryar, Alex P297
Bryars, William P639
Bryce, Maria A348
Bryce, Maria E155
Brycz, Kim A379
Brydon, Paul P440
Bryke, Christine P71
Bryner, Adam A216
Bryner, Adam E80
Bryson, Philip A530
Brzezinski, Robert A489
Br- - ckner, Martin L. E134
Brüngger, Renata Jungo W114
Bsirske, Frank W315
Bua, Jean A. E300
Buabbud, George E224
Buafo, Charles P591
Buccilli, Lynn A522
Buchanan, Travis A164
Buchanan, John D. A221
Buchanan, David A331
Buchanan, Stephen G. (Steve) A719
Buchanan, Ashley A878
Buchanan, Kenneth (Ken) P152
Buchanan, Angela P292
Buchanan, Stephen G. (Steve) P468
Buchanan, Jamie P659
Buchanan, Malcolm W312
Buchanan, David E148
Buchanan, Kent A405
Buchanon, David A705
Buchanon, David E352
Buchband, Richard D A525
Buchbinder, David K P115
Buchenau, Blaine P201
Bucher, Tyla A408
Buchert, Mark A340
Buchert, Mark E151
Buchholtz, Brian P345
Buchholtz, Christopher P458
Buchholz, Jane P96
Buchmeier, Peter A199
Buchner, Renee A902
Buchner, Renee P692
Bucholtz, Barbara K P552
Buchwald, Hyman A914
Buck, Robert R. A117
Buck, Michele G. A416
Buck, John D. A637
Buck, Carrie P430
Buckalew, Steve A397
Buckalew, John A402
Buckalew, Steve P221
Buckelew, Donna P346
Buckelew, Alan B. W81
Buckheit, Scott A160
Buckheit, Scott E55
Buckholtz, Fred J P244
Buckhout, Pam P233
Buckingham, Lisa M. A512
Buckingham, Phil P628
Buckiso, David A342
Buckiso, Scott D. A852

Buckius, Richard O. P449
Buckles, Eileen A272
Buckley, John A250
Buckley, John A449
Buckley, John A478
Buckley, Raegan A532
Buckley, Richard E A677
Buckley, Michael C. A711
Buckley, Guy G. A758
Buckley, George W. A762
Buckley, Mary P354
Buckley, John L. P432
Buckley, Gerard J. P464
Buckley, Guy G. P519
Buckley, Adam P. P614
Buckley, Owen P653
Buckley, Robert E308
Buckminster, Douglas E. A49
Bucknell, Constance A578
Buckner, Phillip A56
Buckner, Sue A677
Buckner, Connie P699
Bucko, James A644
Buco, Glen A724
Buczko, Brian A446
Buczko, Brian E210
Budakian-kinsella, Maryalice A744
Budd, Thomas D. A683
Budd, Thomas D. E341
Bude, Michael A223
Budesilich, Casey A809
Budesilich, Casey P586
Budraitis, Alyssa A. A24
Budroe, James A663
Budziak, Christopher J P235
Budzinski, Jeff A294
Budzinski, A James P129
Budzinski, Jim P680
Budzynski, Joseph A. P671
Bueche, Keirstin P204
Buechel, Jason A899
Buechel, Jason P690
Buechler, Mark A81
Buechse, Oliver A81
Buehler, Charlie A902
Buehler, Ralf P179
Buehler, Charlie P692
Buehrer, Jeffrey P193
Buelow, Dawn A532
Buelow, Rob E432
Buenaseda, Jude A585
Buenaseda, Jude P377
Buendia, Robin A487
Buer, Gene P. E86
Buergel, Erich P326
Buergler, William A190
Bueschen, Anton P639
Buescher, John P318
Buescher, Charles P318
Buese, Nancy K. A588
Buesinger, Robert F. A895
Buffa, Damiano A133
Buffa, Sandra M. E295
Buffalo, Bill A158
Buffett, Warren E. A123
Buffi, Cindy A817
Buffie, Craig A. A489
Buffington, John P480
Buffon, Mike A850
Buffoni, Chris A505
Buffy, Birrittella A691
Bugatto, David J. A30
Bugayong, Manuel A565
Bugbee, Dawn P220
Bugh, Frank A693
Bugher, Daniel P514
Buglione, John A830
Buglione, John E403
Buhay, Rene A375
Buhl, Reinhard W402
Buhnerkempe, Bonnie A292
Buhr, Jeffrey L. A1
Buhrer, Laura A308
Buhrmann, Dan A173
Bui, Dzung A460

A = AMERICAN BUSINESS
E = EMERGING COMPANIES
P = PRIVATE COMPANIES
W = WORLD BUSINESS

Bui, Greg A592
Bui, Tom E252
Bui-Thompson, Nancy P470
Buie, Derrick A774
Buijs, Peter P142
Buisson, Steve A115
Buitrago, Gus A359
Bujol, Warren A446
Bujol, Warren E210
Bukacek, Andrea A542
Bukacek, Andrea E267
Bukzin, David P306
Bula, Patrice W258
Bulakul, Surong W295
Bulanda, Mark J. A295
Bulander, Rolf W70
Bulanov, Alexander N. W350
Bulatovic, Milisav M P441
Bulawa, Bryan F. A303
Bulawa, Bryan F P341
Bulcke, Paul W258
Bulfin, Joey P525
Bulfin, John E175
Bull, Mick P466
Bull, Kenneth R. E162
Bullard, James B. A325
Bullard, Gregory A685
Bullen, Derrik A555
Buller, Katja A129
Buller, David P89
Buller, Mark P308
Buller, James P308
Bullington, Amy P88
Bullock, Shawn A81
Bullock, Brian H. A301
Bullock, Diana P178
Bullock, David P397
Bullock, Brian H. E127
Bullock, John E189
Bullwinkle, David E. E115
Bulmer, William H A676
Bulpin, Andrew A550
Bulpitt, Amy P530
Bultman, Gary A501
Bulus, Domingos H. G. A514
Bumgarner, David L. A207
Bunch, Tara A70
Bunch, Lonnie G. P506
Bundschuh, John A644
Bundschuh, Russell G. W98
Bundy, Michael P92
Bung-ju, Kwon W163
Bunger, Steven G. E61
Bunimovich, Vitaliy P338
Bunk, Craig A459
Bunker, Jeff A272
Bunn, Willard E77
Bunnell, Ronald R. (Ron) A111
Bunnell, Ronald R. (Ron) P56
Bunnell, Craig A. P153
Bunte, Brent A465
Bunting, Theodore H. (Theo) A300
Bunting, Chris A555
Bunton, Kris P560
Buntyn, Diane P242
Bunyard, Heather A375
Bunyard, Steve P405
BUONAURA, VINCENZO
  CALANDRA W111
Buonaura, Vincenzo Calandra W380
Buonforte, Jeffrey J. A500
Buonforte, Jeffrey J. E237
Buquicchio, Gerard A693
Buran, John R. A359
Burba, Deron P506
Burbick, Kevin A622
Burbules, Debbie A P660
Burch, Vivian P84
Burch, Lisa P516

Burch, Stephen A. P644
Burch, Brian E230
Burchett, Claudia P516
Burchette, Mary A865
Burchfield, Carol A181
Burchfield, David A729
Burchfield, Bobby R. P673
Burchill, Todd P252
Burchinal, Charles A548
Burchinal, Charles P321
Burckhart, Camille A661
Burd, Travis A140
Burdakin, David C. E227
Burdalski, Dan A158
Burdeau, Leo P133
Burdett, H W P577
Burdic, Charles A201
Burdick, Don A240
Burdick, Kevin L. A622
Burdick, Kenneth A. (Ken) A885
Burdiek, Michael J. E51
Burdiss, Paul E. A919
Burdjalov, Vladimir A807
Burdjalov, Vladimir P574
Burdolski, Jane P499
Burdsall, Rick A22
Buresti, Francesco W141
Burfitt, Gregory H P101
Burg, Jan Van Den E426
Burgard, Louis-Roch W387
Burgdorfer, Stuart B. A497
Burge, Debbie A671
Burge, Taylor P642
Burger, Mark A58
Burger, Karen P330
Burgess, Robert O A187
Burgess, Brian A746
Burgess, Brittni P188
Burgess, Robert O E71
BurgessJr, Robert A187
BurgessJr, Robert E71
Burget, Mark P596
Burghart, Julia E146
Burgher, Cedric W. A611
Burghouts, Koen A647
Burgis, David A34
Burik, Jeff A223
Burk, Michael A323
Burkart, John F. E133
Burke, Michael S. (Mike) A16
Burke, Ed A25
Burke, James T. A103
Burke, Sean A143
Burke, Zane M. A186
Burke, Stephen B A220
Burke, George J A225
Burke, Kevin A232
Burke, Kevin G. A276
Burke, Kevin G. A277
Burke, Roger A309
Burke, Joan A. A340
Burke, Brian A351
Burke, Ken A366
Burke, Patrick J. (Pat) A437
Burke, Sean A467
Burke, Edward J. (E.J.) A489
Burke, Debra A500
Burke, Geoffrey A568
Burke, William A. (Bill) A586
Burke, James J. (Jim) A591
Burke, John A599
Burke, Richard A599
Burke, Heather A724
Burke, Jason A729
Burke, Gene A736
Burke, Michael A844
Burke, Shannon A871
Burke, Phillip A878
Burke, Frank J. A904
Burke, Sean A917
Burke, Ed P15
Burke, Michael W P19
Burke, Jo-Ann P116
Burke, Edmund J. (Ned) P167
Burke, Timothy J. (Tim) P406

Burke, Thomas M. P472
Burke, James F. P487
Burke, Gene P492
Burke, Janice P618
Burke, John D. P625
Burke, Debbie P645
Burke, James P692
Burke, Sean P701
Burke, Patrick J. (Pat) W175
Burke, Michael W225
Burke, George J E88
Burke, Joan A. E151
Burke, Brian E158
Burke, Sean E223
Burke, Phil E226
Burke, Debra E238
Burke, Thomas A. (Tom) E283
Burke, Andrew T. E395
Burke, Michael E412
Burke, Frank J. E442
Burkert, Bart E180
Burket, Robert P433
Burkett, Steven P225
Burkhardt, Susan A133
Burkhardt, Thomas E P611
Burkhart, Megan D. A221
Burkhart, James R. P197
Burkholder, Robert P618
Burky, Kay A369
Burlage, David P. A214
Burlage, David P. P128
Burlando, Fabrizio A537
Burleigh, Clarence A105
Burleson, Russ P512
Burleson, Tamera P664
Burlingame, Pam A441
Burlingame, Holly P395
Burlog, Chris A851
Burlyaeva, Anna P636
Burman, Darryl M. A396
Burmaster, Brad P294
Burmester, Mark A P369
Burnell, James A912
Burnell, Jody P413
Burnett, Matt A173
Burnett, Bonnie P21
Burnett, Don P143
Burnett, Bonnie P148
Burnett, Mark P339
Burnett, Kevin M P546
Burnett, Kevin M P605
Burnett, Brian D. P647
Burnette, Roger A770
Burnette, Don P143
Burnette, Peg P160
Burnette, James Michael P192
Burney, David C. E25
Burnham, Jerry A449
Burnham, Roy A813
Burnham, Roy P608
Burnich, Jeffrey A775
Burnich, Jeffrey P548
Burnip, Douglas A863
Burnison, Gary D. E235
Burnley, Maureen P320
Burns, Nisha A A6
Burns, Layne A108
Burns, Scott A115
Burns, Ned A173
Burns, William S A231
Burns, Austin A244
Burns, Jim A248
Burns, John A255
Burns, Jennifer J. A324
Burns, Mark L. A374
Burns, Nellson D. A423
Burns, Nelson A423
Burns, Gail A448
Burns, Randolph A628
Burns, Gay A701
Burns, Maribeth A748
Burns, Joseph A751
Burns, Michelle A763
Burns, Sheri T. A839
Burns, Michael A850

Burns, Dennis A920
Burns, Glenn P54
Burns, Gail P246
Burns, Mandy P334
Burns, Patricia P346
Burns, Robert P400
Burns, Bobby P400
Burns, Robert P510
Burns, James P625
Burns, Jacqueline P642
Burns, Jon P. P644
Burns, Margaret P644
Burns, William J. E101
Burns, Bob E213
Burns, Joseph E377
Burns, Rick E394
Burns, Sheri T. E409
Burns, Brad E432
Burns, Thomas (Tom) E447
Burnside, John A21
Burnside, John P12
Burpee, Steve P466
Burrage, Patricia P86
Burrell, Carol P391
Burridge, Graham A272
Burrier, Vicki A255
Burrill, Dean P237
Burrin, Stephen E P564
Burris, Joseph P310
Burris, J Michael P310
Burris, Marie E123
Burriss, Steve P459
Burritt, David B. (Dave) A852
Burroughs, Michael A383
Burroughs, Phil A405
Burroughs, Philip A870
Burroughs, Margaret T P113
Burrow, Lynne M. A159
Burrow, Holden A532
Burrow, Patrick A. A742
Burrow, Patrick A. E372
Burrowes, Todd A254
Burrows, Clifford (Cliff) A762
Burrows, Richard W74
Burrus, Daniel P518
Bursey, Robert A644
Bursey, Robert C A645
Burson, Arthur A550
Burson, Michael L P121
Burt, Kathleen A390
Burt, Brady T. A633
Burt, Jeff A788
Burt, Stacey P67
Burt, Linda K P369
Burt, Larry P588
Burt, Suzie P662
Burt, Richard L. E89
Burt, Carol E355
Burtelson, Lee A450
Burtis, Andy A546
Burton, Melody A19
Burton, Brian A105
Burton, Laura A175
Burton, Lynn A198
Burton, Mary A699
Burton, Travis A833
Burton, Becky A866
Burton, Lavarne P34
Burton, Steven L P88
Burton, Mary P331
Burton, Corinne P371
Burton, Mary P456
Burton, Carol P486
Burton, Pam P658
Burton, Donald W. E57
Burton, Spencer E125
Burton, Peter E127
Burton, Andrew E248
Burts, Rob A781
Burud, Jamie A800
Burud, Jamie E396
Burvall, Pether W352
Burvill, Martin A870
Burwell, Thomas C. E305
Burzik, Catherine A119

Busacca, Brian P259
Busannagari, Chandra A766
Busbee, Perry (Chip) P680
Busby, Paul A878
Buscaglia, Nick A522
Buscemi, Stephanie A723
Buscemi, James R. E209
Busch, Pat A738
Busch, Steve P337
Busch, Roland W331
Busch, Timothy C. (Tim) E303
Busche, Michael A758
Busche, Michael P519
Buschman, John E. P494
Buschmeyer, Stephen A833
Buschner, Dave E117
Buse, David G. E288
Busey, Ricky A158
Bush, Julie A49
Bush, James A369
Bush, Stephanie A406
Bush, Mary A531
Bush, Antoinette (Toni) A589
Bush, Wesley G. (Wes) A602
Bush, Frederick S Steve P22
Bush, Valerie P42
Bush, Denny P344
Bush, Stephen P486
Bush, William L P519
Bushkin, Nancy E57
Bushman, Julie L. A2
Bushman, Karl P528
Bushnell, Rebecca W. A812
Bushnell, Rebecca W. P607
Bushong, Todd P13
Busk, Douglas E99
Buskey, Michael T. (Mike) A372
Buss, Jessica E. A764
Bussard, Beth A886
Bussard, Beth E433
Busse, Keith E. A768
Busse, Thomas A855
Bussel, Marina P417
Bussell, Brent A461
Bussells, Walter P260
Busson, Donald A140
Bussy, Jean-Franois P136
Bustad, Marius A574
Bustamante, Jose-Luis A358
Bustamante, Jolito A504
Buster, Bob P145
Bustos, Cassie P318
Buswell, Michelle A407
Butala, Reema A204
Butch, Jennifer A811
Butch, Jennifer P600
Butcher, Art A144
Butcher, Lisa A705
Butcher, Thomas P218
Butcher, Craig P400
Butcher, Lisa E352
Butcher, Benjamin S. E384
Butchko, Jason A804
Butier, Mitchell R. A91
Butkovich, Joe A175
Butkus, Sean A390
Butler, Charl L. A21
Butler, AL A160
Butler, John A210
Butler, Marsha A218
Butler, John M. A236
Butler, Keith G. A281
Butler, Bill A295
Butler, Gregory B. A307
Butler, Calvin G. A308
Butler, Ronald D. (Ron) A345
Butler, Maurice A446
Butler, Mark A471
Butler, Brad A702
Butler, Jessica A724
Butler, Yeng A767
Butler, Shelly A774
Butler, Amy A815
Butler, Eric L. A842
Butler, Kirby A844

Butler, Pat A894
Butler, Charl L. P12
Butler, Lisa P30
Butler, Gary P. P81
Butler, Lori P86
Butler, Malcolm P107
Butler, Rosr P139
Butler, Steve P163
Butler, David P217
Butler, John P289
Butler, Kelly P354
Butler, Drew P402
Butler, Linda P459
Butler, Barbara P598
Butler, P. Barry P611
Butler, Gerard W98
Butler, AL E55
Butler, Jason E97
Butler, Ronald D. (Ron) E154
Butler, Maurice E210
Butler, Richard D. E247
Butler, Kirby E412
Butram, Jackie P449
Butschek, Gunter W16
Butschek, Guenter W357
Butte, Grease P261
Butterfield, Stephen F. (Steve) A579
Butterfield, Tom A790
Butterfield, Cleon A866
Butterfield, Cleon P661
Butterfield, Gregory S E429
Butterly, Rick A904
Butterly, Rick E442
Butterworth, Liam W29
Butto, Joseph A820
Buttrick, Tony A356
Buttry, Jill P156
Butts, Mary P466
Butz, Genelle P97
Butzer, Marc A898
Buxton, Stephanie P191
Buyon, Ethan A323
Buytenhuys, Sheldon A723
Buzby, Timothy L. (Tim) A320
Buzby, Timothy L. (Tim) E143
Buzzell, Mark A362
Byard, Kim P222
Byard, Sarah P646
Bybee, Brian A730
Bybee, Trever E429
Byck, David P484
Byerly, Kurt A677
Byers, Jay A192
Byers, Allison A244
Byers, Carol P433
Byerwalter, Mariann P522
Byham, Richard P217
Bykoned, Margo P550
Bylen, Hans Van W168
Bynum, Shaun P104
Bynum, Cherlyn P241
Byrd, Stacy A182
Byrd, Daryl G. A446
Byrd, Jerry A643
Byrd, Vince A748
Byrd, Heath R. A749
Byrd, Robb A751
Byrd, Lu P74
Byrd, William D P261
Byrd, Dr Cyndy P407
Byrd, Linda P498
Byrd, Mark P679
Byrd, Stacy E63
Byrd, Daryl G. E210
Byrd, Robb E377
Byrne, Charles M A2
Byrne, Alice A33
Byrne, Alice A34
Byrne, Marianne A195
Byrne, Mike A599
Byrne, Mike A649
Byrne, Margaret A677
Byrne, Kevin A693
Byrne, Jay A741
Byrne, Jolene P77

Byrne, Barbara P176
Byrne, Bobbie P176
Byrne, Jolene P484
Byrne, Peter E52
Byrne, Jay E370
Byrne, Susan M. E437
Byrnes, Terry A158
Byrnes, James J. A820
Byrnes, James A823
Byrnes, James P621
Byron, Charles A101
Byron, Christina L P331
Byrwa, Joy A332
Bytner, Mark A460
Byunn, Jay A136
B-⊃te, Oliver W23
Bédier, Jér-´me W82
Béharel, Fran-§ois W299
Bénacin, Philippe W388
Bézard, Yannick W286
Büchele, Wolfgang W239
Bücker, Michael W58

C

C, Sr Margaret Tuley D P330
Caamano, John A177
Cab, Sandy A192
Caballero, Juan A774
Caban, John A817
Cabaniss, Taylor A685
Cabbil, Nathan A707
Cabezuela, Zaide P508
Cable, Carol A137
Cabral, Anna A575
Cabrera, Ramon A204
Cabrera, Juan P177
Cabrera, Maria P510
Caccamo, Frank A671
Cacciola, Tony P284
Caccioppo, Denise P79
Caccivio, James C. A766
Caceres, R. Louis (Lou) A724
Caceres, Lou A724
Cadavona, Karen A752
Cadena, Adrian A244
Cadena, Christine A272
Cadet, Bair P568
Cadieux, Marc C. A777
Cadieux, Melissa P174
Cadieux, Marc C. E393
Cadigan, Catherine P200
Cadile, Ben P305
Cadiz, Bruce J A136
Cadogan, Jenelle A101
Cadwallader, Brian J A477
Cadwallader, Barry P108
Cadwallader, Brian J P268
Cady, Gerald A. (Gary) A891
Cady, Gerald A. (Gary) E434
Cafarella, Julie Dawoodjee P149
Cafaro, Daniel P E447
Cafferillo, Nick E363
Caffery, David A678
Caffrey, Robert A85
Caffrey, Aisling P652
Caffrey, Elise E225
Cafiso, Giovanni A786
Caforio, Giovanni A147
Cafritz, Diane A166
Cage, Jeff A448
Cagle, Lorita A101
Cagle, Kevin A446
Cagle, Rebecca P388
Cagle, Kevin E210
Cahill, Dennis A105
Cahill, John T. A494
Cahill, Thomas P115
Cahill, Sr Helen P204
Cahill, Teresa P380
Cahill, Joseph P511
Cahill, Gerald R. (Gerry) W81
Cahill, Antony W251
Cahill, Doug E364

Cahillane, Steven A. (Steve) A485
Cahir, B.P. (Bart) W184
Cahlstadt, Timothy A522
Cahuzac, Antoine W136
Cai, Yibai A204
Cai, Xiangrong A406
Cai, Jianjiang W13
Cai-Lee, Wendy A285
Cai-Lee, Wendy E114
Caillier, Craig P300
Cain, Michael S A244
Cain, Christopher A449
Cain, Kelli P101
Cain, Nada P250
Cain, Bryan E286
Caine, Patrice W364
Caines, Brett A518
Caines, Brett P292
Caiola, Vincent P282
Cairns, Paul A292
Cairns, Ann A537
Cairns, Terri P465
Cairns, Gordon M. W396
Cajigas, Veronica A269
Calabrese, Kevin J A98
Calabrese, Vincent J. A360
Calabrese, Isela A541
Calabrese, Michael P89
Calabrese, Kevin J E33
Calabrese, Vincent J. E164
Calabrese, Isela E266
Calaiacova, Karen P330
Calanga, Jack A556
Calantzopoulos, André A652
Calba, Kerry P68
Calbert, Michael M A273
Calbert, Robert (Bo) P318
Calbone, Kathie P250
Calbone, Angelo G P484
Calbow, Brenda A149
Calcagnino, Adrienne P134
Calcaterra, Ronald J P105
Calcote, Colby A832
Caldart, Gilberto A537
Calder, Todd P546
Calderon, Fredy A109
Calderon, Fabricio A204
Calderon, Fredy E36
Calderon, Stanley J. E76
Calderone, Matthew A140
Caldwell, John E. A14
Caldwell, David A162
Caldwell, William J. A430
Caldwell, Melody A449
Caldwell, Christopher A572
Caldwell, Angie L A596
Caldwell, Kirbyjon A604
Caldwell, Christopher (Chris) A780
Caldwell, Michael R A782
Caldwell, Troy A813
Caldwell, Jay P92
Caldwell, Pete P241
Caldwell, Brian P462
Caldwell, Troy P616
Caldwell, Thomas G. E278
Caldwell, Doug E426
Calegari, Michael P440
Calhoun, J Pat A22
Calhoun, David L. (Dave) A132
Calhoun, David L A169
Calhoun, J Pat P13
Calhoun, Bill P230
Calhoun, Rochelle P606
Calhoun, Jaci E253
Cali, Jim A485
Calise, Michele M A624
Calkin, Mark A51
Calkins, Steve A612
Call, Barbara A225
Call, Chad A919
Call, Dawn P304
Call, Barbara E88
Callaghan, James P203
Callagy, Catherine P376
Callahan, Tim A19

A = AMERICAN BUSINESS
E = EMERGING COMPANIES
P = PRIVATE COMPANIES
W = WORLD BUSINESS

Callahan, Michael A120
Callahan, Don A203
Callahan, Daniel D. A223
Callahan, Donald A390
Callahan, Jeanne A442
Callahan, Brian A449
Callahan, Dan A614
Callahan, Patrick K. (Pat) A672
Callahan, Lorri A677
Callahan, Matt A681
Callahan, Paul A683
Callahan, Andrew P. (Andy) A834
Callahan, Eve A839
Callahan, Emily P34
Callahan, Patrick P91
Callahan, Tim P91
Callahan, Sean P101
Callahan, Mark P201
Callahan, Clara A. P618
Callahan, Eve E409
Callan, Patrick J. E317
Callaway, Antone A509
Callaway, Stephanie A850
Callaway, Antone P288
Calle, Esteban A115
Callecod, David P279
Callen, Anne A15
Callen, Anne P9
Callen, Craig R. E315
Callen, David R. E376
Callender, Scott A335
Callender, Adam A775
Callender, Chris P126
Callicott, Bevan A165
Callihan, Margaret L. A774
Callihan, Jane A844
Callihan, Jane E412
Callini, Anthony E286
Callini, Tony E286
Callis, Gaynor P461
Callis, David C P551
Callison, Tim P450
Callison, Marilyn P450
Callow, Shauna P338
Calmes, Mark E A74
Calp, Steffney P680
Caltagirone, Francesco G. W32
Calverley, David A478
Calvin, John C P149
Calvo, Raul A449
Calzadilla, Irene A904
Calzadilla, Irene E442
Cama, Domenick A. A467
Cama, Domenick A. E223
Camarillo, Linda P563
Camber, Susan A861
Camber, Susan P658
Cambern, Morgan A152
Cambern, Morgan E49
Cambra, Malcolm P458
Cambre, Linda P425
Camens, Mark P319
Cameron, Michael A3
Cameron, Michael A478
Cameron, Richard A607
Cameron, Christine A790
Cameron, Jennifer P113
Cameron, Donna P279
Cameron, J Nicholas P594
Cameron, Michael A. W348
Camilleri, Louis C. A652
Camillo, Dominic A721
Cammaker, Shelly A294
Cammarota, Karen P124
Cammer, Martin P302
Cammisecra, Antonio W141
Camp, Anne Van P506
Camp, Bryan P525
Camp, Jim P669

Campagnolo, Elise P391
Campana, Mark A517
Campanella, Edward J. A78
Campanello, Russell J. (Russ) E225
Campano, John A810
Campano, John P597
Campbell, Jeffrey C. (Jeff) A48
Campbell, Michael P. A83
Campbell, Mary A137
Campbell, Scott A157
Campbell, Joanne T. A160
Campbell, Mark A. A169
Campbell, Roger A. A239
Campbell, Kimberly A260
Campbell, Bruce L. A269
Campbell, Rebecca A272
Campbell, Gary A279
Campbell, Tabitha A328
Campbell, Jimmy A399
Campbell, Kristin A. A421
Campbell, Ann-Marie A426
Campbell, Ann A426
Campbell, Claude A513
Campbell, Alan A620
Campbell, Amy A655
Campbell, Ben G A711
Campbell, Gary A738
Campbell, Mike A738
Campbell, Rob A741
Campbell, David A744
Campbell, Todd A748
Campbell, Claire A774
Campbell, Stuart A878
Campbell, Steven A892
Campbell, Barbara A917
Campbell, Julie P6
Campbell, Sabrina V P32
Campbell, Stephen P98
Campbell, Christopher P102
Campbell, John P125
Campbell, Robert P178
Campbell, H Scott P181
Campbell, Tammy P192
Campbell, Karlene P210
Campbell, Brittany P221
Campbell, Curt P256
Campbell, Peter P286
Campbell, Bobby P318
Campbell, Laure P353
Campbell, Annette P361
Campbell, James P410
Campbell, Lisa P425
Campbell, Rick P455
Campbell, Donald P474
Campbell, Lisa P484
Campbell, Margaret H P524
Campbell, Daniel P535
Campbell, Suzannah P537
Campbell, Coleen P538
Campbell, Dusty P556
Campbell, Carol P561
Campbell, Thomas P P594
Campbell, Danny P624
Campbell, Anne P625
Campbell, Ballard C P627
Campbell, Marianne P677
Campbell, Barbara P701
Campbell, Norie C. W370
Campbell, R. Perry E15
Campbell, Joanne T. E55
Campbell, Bruce A. E167
Campbell, Albert M. (Al) E276
Campbell, Al E276
Campbell, Amy E333
Campbell, Rob E370
Campbell, Patricia A. (Pat) E424
Campbell, Chris E436
Camperi, Marcelo F. P654
Campion, Andrew (Andy) A592
Campion, Andy A592
Campion, Ken P539
Campisi, David J. (Dave) A127
Campisi, Vince A854
Campobasso, Deb P247
Campopiano, Peter P480

Campos, Deb A164
Campos, Angela P121
Campos, Anna P275
Campos, Micaela P628
Campot, Peter P545
Camps, Josep Pique i W16
Camus, Julie A873
Camus, Julie P668
Can, Alp A764
Can, Charles Mc P259
Canaday, Charles T. A52
Canafax, Daniel M. E217
Canavan, Dana E47
Canavera, Glen P361
Cancelloni, Frank A682
Cancelmi, Daniel J. (Dan) A794
Cancino, Diane P123
Candee, Chris A493
Canden, Hugh P187
Canderson, Jane P22
Candio, Christine P533
Cane, Michael A155
Caneer, Mary E98
Canel, Brad A229
Canel, Brad P137
Caner, Mark E. A890
Caner, Mark E. P684
Canestrari, Ken A817
Cangemi, Thomas R. (Tom) A583
Cangey, Karen A667
Cangey, Karen E336
Cangialosi, Audrey E253
Cangir, Christine A133
Caniglia, Jim A837
Canizales, Carlos P479
Canizales, Cesar P550
Canjar, Greg P686
Cankat, Burc A218
Cannady, Ed P46
Cannatelli, Len A813
Cannatelli, Brian A912
Cannatelli, Len P616
Cannell, Robert P701
Cannella, Carol P610
Canney, Jacqueline P. (Jacqui) A878
Canney, Jacqui A878
Cannici, Joe P338
Canning, Daniel A893
Canning, John J P P5
Canning, Lori P486
Cannon, Mary A2
Cannon, Marc A88
Cannon, Anita A101
Cannon, Ed A131
Cannon, Maria A199
Cannon, Dylan A200
Cannon, Leoline A252
Cannon, Darren A316
Cannon, John A366
Cannon, Eric A406
Cannon, Alexander (Alex) A682
Cannon, Stacy A761
CANNON, NORMAN P99
Cannon, Marivette P101
Cannon, Darren P191
Cannon, Michael R. P615
Cannon, Tyrone H. P654
Cannon, Chris P654
Cannon, Janis E75
Cannon, Stacy E377
Cannon, Jaime J. E395
Cano, Lorraine P243
Canose, Jeffrey L. A801
Canose, Jeffrey L. P562
Canova, Frank A869
Cantarell, Luis W258
Cantele, Richard J. E363
Cantera, Jose Garcia W45
Canterberry, Fred A476
Cantillon, Maria A766
Cantley, J Stott P306
Cantone, Vincent P333
Cantone, Fabienne Freymond W52
Cantor, Nancy A458
Cantor, Richard P216

Cantor, Nancy P251
Cantow, Don P326
Cantrell, Gary L. A471
Cantrell, James M. A562
Cantrell, Jane P234
Cantrell, David P571
Cantrell, James M. E279
Cantu, Dave A166
Cantu, Ernesto Torres A204
Cantu, Haydee P8
Cantu, Becky P134
Cantu, Blanca P278
Cantu, Ronaldo P426
Cantuniar, Niculae W304
Cantwell, Richard A199
Cantwell, David A478
Cantwell, Robert C. (Bob) E29
Canty, Kristi P327
Canup, Steven C. (Steve) A97
Canup, Ed A162
Canup, Steven C. (Steve) E32
Canuso, Dominic A907
Canuso, Dominic E445
Canuto, Myriam P624
Canzoneri, Mike A113
Cao, Tuqiang A199
Cao, Thinh P225
Cao, Peixi W175
Caoagas, Rachelle A698
Caoagas, Rachelle P456
Caparros, Alain W302
Capatides, Michael G. W80
Capek, John M. A4
Capek, Thomas A238
Capel, Lance A329
Capel, Eddie E256
Capellas, Michael A200
Capellas, Michael D. W151
Capello, Jeffrey D. (Jeff) A129
Capener, John T P551
Capers, Jacquelyn A101
Capers, Laynglyn A850
Caperton, Donna P670
Capetillo, Carlos A221
Caplan, Deborah H. A590
Caples, Michille P78
Capobianco, Marie-Claire W66
Capodanno, Jim A556
Capodici, Lisa A165
Capone, Linda P279
Capone, Michael L. (Mike) E268
Caponecchi, Kevin J. E134
Caporella, Joseph G. (Joe) E291
Caporella, Nick A. E291
Caposio, Sondra P294
Capossela, Christopher C A560
Capozzola, Peter A78
Capozzoli, Robert A675
Cappaert, William P593
Cappareli, Peter P575
Capparelli, Alejandro A712
Cappel, Markus J. E72
Cappelanti-Wolf, Amy A778
Capps, Allen C P22
Capps, Britni P408
Capra, Kelly E351
Capriotti, Chris A800
Capriotti, Chris E396
Capron, Christopher P52
Captain, Keith A277
Capuano, Anthony G. (Tony) A530
Capuano, Terry P287
Caputo, Marco A141
Caputo, Melissa A223
Caputo, Lisa M. A827
Caputo, Anthony M P39
Caputo, Michael J. P592
Caputo, Michael P. (Mike) P616
Capuzzi, Mike A34
Cara, Jose A649
Cara, Anne P498
Caraballo, Barbara A448
Caracino, Anthony E107
Carafiol, Dennis A744
Caragher, Nick A913

Caram, Meredith A84
Carapella, Victor A351
Carapella, Victor E158
Caras, Matthew A112
Caras, Matthew E38
Caravella, Louis P190
Caraway, Troy P252
Carbajal, José Antonio
  Fern--ndez W152
Carbary, Sherry A136
Carbary, Wendy M A698
Carbary, Wendy M P456
Carbaugh, John A105
Carberry, Jeff E385
Carbo, Angelique A734
Carbone, A A375
Carbone, Peter A603
Carbone, A P210
Carbone, Raymond (Ray) P315
Carbone, Jamie P332
Carbone, Peter P399
Carbone, Davide P525
Carboni, Michael A56
Carcache, Sonia A795
Carchedi, Francis (Frank) E97
Card, Isa V E78
Cardella, Jennifer A872
Cardenas, Ricardo (Rick) A254
Cardenas, Alberto de A536
Cardenas, Diana A866
Cardenas, Jesse P379
Cardenas, Sergio P440
Cardenas, Diana P446
Carder, Bryce A111
Carder, Bryce P56
Carder, John P334
Cardillo, James A629
Cardinal, Greg A384
Cardinal, Tim A674
Cardinal, Tony P521
Cardinal, Greg E176
Cardno, Brian A96
Cardona, Jocelyn P554
Cardone, Mark S. E90
Cardoso, Teresa P271
Caresani, Louis A865
Caret, Leanne G. A136
Caret, Robert L. P645
Carew, Thomas J. A585
Carew, Patrick J. P263
Carew, Thomas J. P377
Carey, Karen E A231
Carey, K Kristann A235
Carey, Matthew A. (Matt) A426
Carey, Matt A426
Carey, Albert A426
Carey, Thomas A619
Carey, Albert P. (Al) A647
Carey, Anthony A766
Carey, David R A785
Carey, Chase A834
Carey, Pat A873
Carey, Timothy S P63
Carey, Ann P189
Carey, Ann P538
Carey, Mark P631
Carey, Pat P668
Carey, James H. E8
Carfora, Jeffrey J. A639
Carfora, Jeffrey J. E325
Cargile, Richard A257
Cargile, Charles F. (Chuck) P379
Cargill, Jon A422
Cargill, Robyn A522
Cargill, C. Keith A800
Cargill, Jon P239
Cargill, C. Keith E395
Carhill, Norm A496
Carignan, Tom A837
CARINCI, WILLIAM A390
Carino, Vernice P245
Carkin, Mark A103
Carl, Ryan A3
Carl, David A82
Carl, Holowaty A702

Carl, David P49
Carleena, Scammon P255
Carleton, Mark D. A688
Carleton, Jay A764
Carli, Maurizio A875
Carlin, Andy P. E376
Carlino, Rosario A218
Carlino, Anthony P60
Carlisle, Paul A904
Carlisle, Jennifer P45
Carlisle, Paul E442
Carlo, Francesca Di W141
Carloss, Angie P105
Carls, Clara P8
Carlson, Jan A87
Carlson, Carl M. A149
Carlson, Chante A182
Carlson, W. Erik A270
Carlson, Richard A308
Carlson, Gabriel A539
Carlson, Gabe A539
Carlson, J.D. A643
Carlson, LeRoy T. (Ted) A794
Carlson, Walter C. D. A794
Carlson, Prudence A794
Carlson, Chris A813
Carlson, Stephen A857
Carlson, Jennie P. A865
Carlson, Tom A904
Carlson, Steven A920
Carlson, Kerry P29
Carlson, Jonathan P99
Carlson, Jeri P192
Carlson, Bob P381
Carlson, Edward P359
Carlson, Spencer P398
Carlson, Lesley P452
Carlson, Lori P466
Carlson, John A. P474
Carlson, Amanda J P536
Carlson, Carolyn P589
Carlson, Chris P616
Carlson, Thomas P681
Carlson, Chante E63
Carlson, Randy E78
Carlson, Chris E342
Carlson, Tom E442
Carlston, Wayne P402
Carlstrom, Dale P247
Carlton, Mark A725
Carlucci, Carl P. P643
Carmack, Aaron A426
Carmack, Timothy W P300
Carman, Amy A782
Carmichael, Brendan A223
Carmichael, Greg D. A332
Carmichael, Amanda A912
Carminati, Catherine A59
Carmody, Daniel A195
Carmody, Christine M. (Chris) A307
Carmody, Kevin A390
Carmody, Cora L. A472
Carmody, Thomas A541
Carmody, Thomas E266
Carmona, Keith P430
Carmouche, Sue P260
Carnahan, Justina P422
Carnaroli, Craig R. A812
Carnaroli, Craig R. P607
Carnegie-Brown, Bruce N. W45
Carneiro, Marcia A101
Carnell, Scott W36
Carnes, Jeff A399
Carney, James A204
Carney, James A461
Carney, Craig B. A830
Carney, Mary Ellen A865
Carney, Craig B. E402
Carnifax, Rod A635
Carnifax, Rod P419
Caro, Jennifer A647
Caro, Jodi J A836
Carobolante, Francesco A685
Carol, Vanslyke A67
Carolan, Edward L. (Ed) A161

Carolan, Milou A602
Carolan, Susan P155
Carole, Hackett P620
Carolis, Donna De P165
Carollo, Bill P566
Caron, James A777
Caron, William L. P303
Caron, Mike P425
Caron, Steve E75
Caron, James E393
Caronia, Leonard S. A741
Caronia, Leonard S. E371
Carotenuto, Michael A159
Caroti, Stefano E106
Carow, Bryan A865
Carp, Marilyn A553
Carp, Jeffrey N. A766
Carp, Marilyn E274
Carpenter, Wesley A85
Carpenter, Scott A115
Carpenter, Kaye A244
Carpenter, Matt A493
Carpenter, James J. A583
Carpenter, Bruce A607
Carpenter, Harold R. A655
Carpenter, Jonathan A733
Carpenter, Will A767
Carpenter, Lonny J. A772
Carpenter, Benjamin A865
Carpenter, Andrew A874
Carpenter, Don A881
Carpenter, Angie M P145
Carpenter, Barbara P148
Carpenter, Stan P563
Carpenter, Rick P636
Carpenter, Thomas P699
Carpenter, Cathy Penton P700
Carpenter, Rob E277
Carpenter, Harold R. E333
Carpenterjr, Robert A659
Carper, Patricia A814
Carper, Howell P. (Hal) A834
Carper, Patricia P616
Carpini, Michael X. Delli A812
Carpini, Michael X. Delli P607
Carpio, Anne P192
Carr, Gregory A56
Carr, Chris A173
Carr, Muneera S. A221
Carr, Bryan A438
Carr, Jim A649
Carr, Brenda A654
Carr, Chris A762
Carr, Dan A827
Carr, Eddie P123
Carr, John P151
Carr, Larry P223
Carr, Robert O P232
Carr, Deborah P409
Carr, Roger W40
Carr, Jeff W209
Carranza, Ricardo A460
Carrasco, Enrique P478
Carrasco, Jorge P573
Carrasquillo, Jose A725
Carraway, Leslie P317
Carre, Eric A398
Carreno, Tony A916
Carreno, Anthony A916
Carrera, Bill P245
Carrero, Franklin A163
Carretta, Robert P349
Carrick, Stephanie A530
Carrico, Stephen J. (Steve) P235
Carrier, Patrick B P119
Carrig, John A A232
Carrigan, James P286
Carrigan, Lee P403
Carrillo, Sue A701
Carrillo, Juan P415
Carrillo, Alicia P635
Carrington, Michael P544
Carri--n, Richard L. A661
Carroll, Milton A181
Carroll, Barry A221

Carroll, Thomas M. A278
Carroll, James A351
Carroll, Elizabeth A359
Carroll, Kevin A397
Carroll, Christopher F. A464
Carroll, Pamela A476
Carroll, Teresa S A486
Carroll, Paul A528
Carroll, Jay A536
Carroll, Kevin A537
Carroll, John A. A553
Carroll, Glenn A639
Carroll, Rhonda L. A673
Carroll, Dan A681
Carroll, Johnnie A865
Carroll, Scott A878
Carroll, Mark P23
Carroll, Allen P94
Carroll, Deborah P107
Carroll, William P123
Carroll, Kevin P132
Carroll, John P200
Carroll, Kevin P221
Carroll, Andrew W P225
Carroll, Amy P300
Carroll, Jim P332
Carroll, Mary P338
Carroll, Christopher P512
Carroll, Kathleen P566
Carroll, Kim P569
Carroll, Jeff P569
Carroll, Shannon P700
Carroll, James E159
Carroll, Robert E207
Carroll, John A. E272
Carroll, Glenn E326
Carroll, Milton E436
Carrubba, Jared A704
Carrubba, Jared E351
Carruth, Mary A513
Carruthers, Susan A244
Carruthers, Troy A493
Carruthers, Scott P14
Carson, David A56
Carson, Candace F A375
Carson, Joe A482
Carson, Brian M. A563
Carson, John C. A693
Carson, Candace F P210
Carson, Lane P475
Carson, Kevin E398
Carstens, Timothy A542
Carstens, Earl P182
Carstens, Timothy E267
Cartagena, Eduardo P297
Carte, Lori P449
Carter, Laurent A147
Carter, Cyndi A165
Carter, Pamela A246
Carter, Peter W. A261
Carter, Robert B. (Rob) A327
Carter, Briggett A339
Carter, Racheal A345
Carter, Ian R. A421
Carter, Chris A501
Carter, Anita A565
Carter, Chris A591
Carter, Charles J. (Jack) A631
Carter, Jack A631
Carter, Scott Carter Scott A638
Carter, Aron M. A640
Carter, George P. A645
Carter, Todd A655
Carter, Chrystah A658
Carter, Mary Randolph A691
Carter, Andrea A691
Carter, David A705
Carter, Ron A728
Carter, Mark A752
Carter, Tim A785
Carter, J Braxton A785
Carter, Lugeion Y A810
Carter, Dave A854
Carter, Lisa P47
Carter, Mitzi P108

A = AMERICAN BUSINESS
E = EMERGING COMPANIES
P = PRIVATE COMPANIES
W = WORLD BUSINESS

Carter, Keith P158
Carter, Paul P179
Carter, Ella P243
Carter, Donald E P273
Carter, Don P273
Carter, Ellen P298
Carter, David P331
Carter, Paige P356
Carter, Debra P368
Carter, Jim P433
Carter, Jeri P435
Carter, Gregory P483
Carter, Lonnie N. P509
Carter, Michael P516
Carter, Richard P573
Carter, Belinda P584
Carter, Lugeion Y P597
Carter, Donna P617
Carter, Julien P628
Carter, Jimmy P636
Carter, Matthew W103
Carter, Bob W374
Carter, Nicole E74
Carter, Bruce L.A. E122
Carter, Briggett E150
Carter, Racheal E154
Carter, Melanie E276
Carter, Kelly C E276
Carter, Thomas E. (Tom) E303
Carter, Todd E333
Carter, Chip E337
Carter, David E352
Carter, Tim E380
Carter-Robertson, Kira P518
Carter-Thompson, Tiffani A241
Carthew, Geoffrey P361
Cartier, Guillaume W243
Cartin, Eugene A741
Cartin, Eugene E370
Cartmell, By E432
Carton, Maeve W112
Cartwright, Kay P457
Carty, Douglas A916
Carugno, Paola A P292
Caruselle, Nicholas P541
Caruso, Dominic J. A476
Caruso, Christopher R. A664
Caruso, Kelly A788
Caruso, Michael P506
Caruso, Dave P543
Carvajal, Taylor A133
Carvajal, Maria Elisa A218
Carvajal, Oscar Von Chrismar W43
Carvalho, Sheila A481
Carvalho, Damon P212
Carvalho, Luiz Nelson Guedes de W284
Carvallo, Jorge P96
Carvelli, Joe P561
Carver, Bill A439
Carver, Bridget A474
Carver, Carla E A663
Carver, Bridget P265
Carver, Deb P701
Carver, Cathryn W251
Carwein, Vicky L. P449
Carwein, Vicky L. P627
Carwell, Mark P137
Cary, Glen A120
Cary, Bill A366
Cary, John P461
Cary, James P644
Caryer, Steve P135
Casale, Mike A701
Casalegno, Gina P96
Casanova, Pascal W214
Casarez, Timothy W P40
Casas, Jaime R. P367
Casasanta, Dan A141
Casassa, David A103

Casati, Gianfranco W5
Casazza, Louise A532
Casazza, Peter P69
Casazza, Elizabeth P148
Casbon, Scott A350
Casbon, Scott E157
Cascino, Laura A262
Cascione, Dina A353
Cascione, Dina E159
Case, Ken A865
Case, Edward B P457
Case, Thomas S P546
Case, Thomas S P605
Case, Thurman K. E78
Case, Stephen M. (Steve) E264
Case, John P. E348
Case-Wirth, Jill P680
Casella, Michael J. A576
Casella, Michael J. E297
Caselli, Mike A316
Caselli, Mike E141
Casello, Mario P450
Casente, Salvador P179
Cases, Juan Santamaria W6
Casey, Donald M. (Don) A165
Casey, Sharon A180
Casey, Sean A333
Casey, John P. A374
Casey, Pauline A408
Casey, Cathal A649
Casey, Donald J. (Don) A696
Casey, William J. A830
Casey, Lois P91
Casey, Helen P226
Casey, Margaret P692
Casey, William J. E402
Casey, Brian O. E437
Cash, Ryan A163
Cash, W. Larry A227
Cash, Linda A362
Cash, Jordan P250
Cashaw, Brad A258
Cashen, Susan K. E93
Cashill, Robert M. A467
Cashill, Robert M. E223
Cashin, Amanda E9
Cashion, John A478
Cashman, George D. A201
Cashman, Charles A. (Chuck) E259
Cashman, Chuck E259
Cashton, Michael A408
Casimiro, Michael A555
Casinelli, Lisa P425
Casino, Alfred A441
Caslin, Cindy A371
Cason, Randall A914
Cason, Randy P537
Casparino, Michael J. A644
Casper, Patricia A101
Casper, Marc N. A815
Casper, Steve E163
Casperson, Finn M.W. A639
Casperson, Finn M.W. E325
Cassaday, John M A782
Cassandra, Frank A556
Cassandra, Williams A585
Cassandra, Williams P377
Cassano, Richard A25
Cassano, Richard P15
Casseb, George A228
Casseb, George P136
Cassebaum, Mark A691
Cassel, Kerry P186
Cassel, Kari P497
Cassel, Brian P644
Cassel, Mat-as Domeyko W137
Cassel, Christine K. E337
Cassell, Jack C. P37
Cassella, James V. (Jim) E89
Casselman, Richard A644
Cassels, Bill P108
Cassels, W. T. (Tobin) P512
Cassels, W. T. P512
Cassels, Bill P577
Cassidy, Shawn A328

Cassidy, Jennifer A644
Cassidy, Donathan A655
Cassidy, Rick W354
Cassidy, Donathan E333
Cassilly, Joseph P660
Cassimy, Barbara P294
Cassin, Joe A881
Cast, Mike A164
Cast, Stacey P382
Cast, William R. P627
Casta, Shannon A709
Castagna, Eugene A. (Gene) A120
Castagna, Gary L. E281
Castaneda, Rodrigo A131
Castaneda, Amanda A614
Castaneda, Hugo P119
Castaneda, Luis P237
Castano, Robert P516
Castanon, Adrian A700
Castanon, Paul A795
Casteel, Marty D. A742
Casteel, Camille P109
Casteel, Marty D. P372
Castellaneta, Andrew A619
Castellano, John A221
Castellano, Federico A461
Castellano, Ilia A555
Castellano, Gail A583
Castellano, Jerry P410
Castellanos, Javier C A898
Castellucci, Paul A398
Castell--, Juan L. Pier A521
Casten, Peter G P577
Castille, Philip P643
Castillo, Eloise A417
Castillo, Consuelo Del P102
Castillo, Mona P113
Castillo, Hugo Del P211
Castillo, Alberto P245
Castillo, Raul P294
Castillo, Kimberly P497
Castillo-Cullather, Melanie P627
Castleberry, Jean A774
Castleberry, Chris A863
Castleberry, Deana P416
Castman, Rich A105
Casto, David P307
Caston, Kim P460
Castor, Richard L. (Rich) A380
Castoral, Roger A131
Castrejana, Josie P294
Castro, Jerry A329
Castro, Cheryl A537
Castro, Marco A537
Castro, Lorraine A857
Castro, Robert A862
Castro, Marie A869
Castro, Ricardo P251
Castro, Mercedes P583
Castro, Vince E47
Castro, Christopher E81
Castro, Robert E419
Casula, Roberto W144
Caswell, Darren A16
Caswell, Angie A476
Caswell, Jeff A835
Caswell, Jim P273
Caswell, Bruce L. E265
Catalano, Jamie A204
Catalano, David A A552
Catalano, Mark J. A907
Catalano, David A P328
Catalano, Robert P525
Catalano, Mark J. P696
Catalfo, R O A448
Catani, Steven A476
Catanzariti, Joe A508
Catapano, Michael A115
Catha, Connie P403
Cathcart, David A788
Catherman, Betty P441
Cathey, James A685
Catik, Ali M. A833
Catino, David A410
Catlender, Katie P369

Catlett, Celia P. E397
Catmull, Lori P368
Catoir, Christophe W7
Catran, Ricardo Isaac W379
Catsicas, Stefan W258
Catt, Michael S P466
Cattaneo, Flavio W359
Cattarusa, Sandy P480
Catton, Mark W312
Catz, Safra A A624
Cauce, Ana Mari A861
Cauce, Ana Mari P658
Caudill, Larry A396
Caudill, Anthony P663
Caudill, Bill E303
Caudullo, AL A693
Caughey, Andrew P671
Caughman, S Wright P182
Cauley, Shannon P54
Caulfield, Eamonn E407
Caumeil, Lori A774
Cauthon, Denise E146
Cauthron, Nazaneen P118
Cava, Vincent La A56
Cavalier, Rodney P627
Cavaliere, Joseph W. A586
Cavalla, Stanley J. E415
Cavallaro, Michele A329
Cavallo-Miller, Linda P529
Cavallucci, Eugene A405
Cavanagh, Lisa A120
Cavanagh, Michael J A220
Cavanagh, Brandy P449
Cavanagh, Shawn P. E54
Cavanaugh, David A644
Cavanaugh, Alison P379
Cavanaugh, Steven M. P613
Cavaness, Joel D. A370
Cave, Michael J. (Mike) A403
Cave, George H. (Sonny) A620
Cavellier, Jim A222
Cavender, Jack A207
Caveney, John E. (Jack) P416
Cavey, Brian A214
Cavey, Brian P128
Cavicchioli, Kathleen (Kathy) A731
Cavicchioli, Kathleen (Kathy) E365
Cavileer, Jamie A774
Cavinder, Greg A774
Cawley, Timothy P. A233
Cawley, Joseph A240
Cawley, Christopher A520
Cawley, Patrick J. P592
Caylor, Mark A. A602
Caylor, Gordon P370
Cayson, Patrick A700
Cazar, Jorge L. W98
Cazares, Sara L P543
Cazenave, Bruce M. E296
Cazer, David A136
Cazier, Bryan E252
Cazurra, Alvaro C P655
Cbet, John P403
Ccrn, Joscelyn P226
Cctc, Jennifer P300
Ceberio, Ernest A677
Cebrun, Hearold L P459
Cecchi, Joseph L. P648
Cecconi, John A173
Cecere, Andrew A865
Cecil, Coleen A478
Cecilia, Manuel Manrique W300
Cecoltan, Sergiu A537
Ceiley, Glen F. E111
Celepcikay, Oner Ulvi P226
Celestin, Angela A621
Celi, Ivo E86
Cella, Peter L A193
Cella, Peter L P112
Cellars, Kevin A678
Cellucci, Annemarie P302
Cely, Monte A84
Ceman, Jamie P109
Centa, Sandy A115
Centeno, Betsy P227

Centiva, Andres F Costas- P639
Ceragioli, Teresa P624
Cerda, Christian E225
Cerepak, Brad M. A279
Cerilli, Brian P104
Cerimele, Cindy A845
Cerimele, Cindy E413
Cerio, Shelly A607
Cerise, Frederick P. (Fred) P152
Cerna, Hector J. A459
Cerniglia, Gregg A330
Cerniglia, Linda P298
Cernugel, Carol A530
Cerone, Luciano A375
Cerone, Phyllis P396
Cerritelli, John P378
Cervantes, Leonard A449
Cervantes, Conley A795
Ceryanec, Joseph H. E272
Cesareo, Kerry P696
Cesario, Christina A770
Cesarz, Mike A546
Cesco, Craig P480
Chesheshyan, Emelina P251
Cevillano, Brenda P88
Cevis, Eric A870
CFRE, June E44
CGriffin, David E253
Cha, Michael A221
Cha, Sam Ho P437
Chabino, Doug P301
Chablani, Somesh A330
Chabot, René W180
Chack, Dennis M. A355
Chack, Karen H P282
Chacko, Jacob P51
Chacon, Hector A834
Chac--n, Chanda Cashen P560
Chac--n, Oscar Pe- ±a W25
Chad, Purdy P188
Chadbourne, Elizabeth P311
Chaddha, Shashi P189
Chaden, Caryn P155
Chadha, Sanjeev A647
Chadwell, Jeffrey A350
Chadwell, Jeffrey E157
Chadwich, Jerry P223
Chadwick, Edward G. (Ed) A413
Chadwick, David T A667
Chadwick, Edward G. (Ed) P234
Chae, Michael S. A132
Chae, Sharlene A183
Chae, Min P482
Chaffee, Dudley P401
Chaffee, Taylor P402
Chaffin, Paul B. A289
Chaffin, Patrick A719
Chaffin, Patrick P468
Chaffinch, Randy A670
Chaffins, Randall A242
Chagnon, Michael L. A505
Chahal, Courtney I A408
Chahin, Jaime P563
Chahrour, Chaker A375
Chaimengyew, David A417
Chain, Leon P42
Chaisson, Mary P145
Chakrabarti, Prabal A322
Chakraborty, Prabal A144
Chakravarthi, Sarita A734
Chakravarthy, Anita A904
Chakravarthy, Anita E442
Chalanick, Brett A133
Chalasani, Anitha A17
Chalifoux, Martha P294
Chalkan, Lisa A639
Chalkan, Lisa E325
Challenger, Brett A214
Challenger, Brett P128
Challon-Kemoun, Adeline W14
Chalons-Browne, Roland W. W331
Chaloux, Debra A863
Chaltraw, William P662
Chalut, Sylvain W47
Chambas, Corey A. A340

Chambas, Corey A. E151
Chamberlain, John W. A44
Chamberlain, Doug A200
Chamberlain, Rebecca A369
Chamberlain, Karen A. A890
Chamberlain, John W. P31
Chamberlain, April B. P336
Chamberlain, Karen A. P684
Chambers, Margaret W. (Megan) A142
Chambers, Diana A355
Chambers, Bradley S. A548
Chambers, Brian D. A627
Chambers, Elizabeth G. (Libby) A893
Chambers, H D P22
Chambers, Bradley S. P321
CHAMBERS, MARGARET P418
Chambers, Yohna P560
Chambers, Bill E140
Chambers, Norman C. (Norm) E298
Champ, Matt A165
Champion, Larry P216
Champion, Bret A P276
Champion, Bret P276
Champion, Bret A P284
Champion, R. Wesley (Wes) E336
Champlin, Ryan P141
Chan, Owen A199
Chan, Donna A204
Chan, Quay A257
Chan, Stephen A390
Chan, Garrett A508
Chan, Eric A539
Chan, Eugene A584
Chan, Kok-kheong A725
Chan, Jeanne A729
Chan, Kenyon S. A861
Chan, Kurt A892
Chan, Eugene P376
Chan, Hayley P449
Chan, Neville P496
Chan, Kenyon S. P658
Chan, Dennis W154
Chan, Eric W195
Chan, Cleon E361
Chana, Surjit A460
Chance, Diane A496
Chance, Kenneth B. P98
Chance, Mary P144
Chance, Linda P208
Chancellor, James P260
Chancy, Mark A. A774
Chand, Sujeet A712
Chandel, Nitin A874
Chandler, David A117
Chandler, John A207
Chandler, Willy A564
Chandler, Don A777
Chandler, Catherine A902
Chandler, Ryan R P193
Chandler, Jason P224
Chandler, Willis P632
Chandler, Catherine P692
Chandler, Dan M. (Mac) E349
Chandler, Don E393
Chandoha, Marie A. A728
Chandok, Vijay W181
Chandra, Sumeer A435
Chandra, Gautam P687
Chandramowli, Niranjan A324
Chandrani, Mic A49
Chandrasekaran, Ramakrishnan A217
Chandrasekaran, Rajiv A763
Chandrasekaran, Natarajan
    (Chandra) W357
Chandrasekaran, Natarajan
    (Chandra) W358
Chandrasekhar, Arun A456
Chandrasekher, Anand A685
Chandrashekar, Siram A525
Chandwani, Manesh A201
Chane, E-J A111
Chane, E-J P56
Chanen, Daniel P344
Chang, Shen A49
Chang, Tim A102

Chang, Daniel A133
Chang, Jennifer A133
Chang, Michael M Y A170
Chang, Chris A254
Chang, Renee A285
Chang, Peter A354
Chang, Rick J A541
Chang, Evans A599
Chang, Ann A607
Chang, Timothy A629
Chang, Andrew S. A642
Chang, Chienchung A685
Chang, Owen P132
Chang, Brian S P158
Chang, Rosemarie P270
Chang, Brian P332
Chang, Florence P357
Chang, Derek P488
Chang, Daphne P538
Chang, James P553
Chang, Andrew P553
Chang, Lay Nam P669
Chang, Fa-Te W84
Chang, In-Hwa W292
Chang, Morris W354
Chang, Pierce E8
Chang, Renee E114
Chang, Rick J E266
Chang, Linda E319
Chang, Andrew S. E328
Chang-goo, Lee W328
Changshun, Wang W95
Channamsetty, Vijay P298
Channavi, Omar A671
Chanter, Keith A294
Chao, Patrick A16
Chao, Sue A285
Chao, Yvonne A770
Chao, Albert A895
Chao, James Y. A895
Chao, Jon P191
Chao, Gong W12
Chao, Sue E114
Chao, Chimin J. E153
Chapa, Phillip P157
Chapa, Ram--n A. Leal W18
Chapanar, Marilyn A391
Chapek, Robert (Bob) A271
Chapin, Libby A332
Chapin, David A478
Chapin, Susan P521
Chaplin, Leslie A751
Chaplin, Leslie E377
Chapman, Christopher P A8
Chapman, Susan A607
Chapman, Ryan A133
Chapman, Jan A158
Chapman, Steven M. (Steve) A246
Chapman, Christopher A. A265
Chapman, Rhonda A341
Chapman, Martin A446
Chapman, Kevin D. A704
Chapman, Esther A742
Chapman, Paul A809
Chapman, Ken A827
Chapman, Pier A871
Chapman, Timothy M. A873
Chapman, Christopher P P3
Chapman, Martha P53
Chapman, Janet P60
Chapman, Dr John E P97
Chapman, Robert P179
Chapman, Diana P307
Chapman, Larry P474
Chapman, Carl L P514
Chapman, Catherine A P612
Chapman, Timothy M. P668
Chapman, Adrian P. P687
Chapman, Barbara W105
Chapman, David W180
Chapman, Laurence A. E107
Chapman, Rhonda E153
Chapman, Martin E210
Chapman, Kevin D. E350
Chapman, Esther E372

Chapman, Harry S E405
Chapman, Ryan E432
Chappell, Daniel G. (Dan) A731
Chappell, Dan A731
Chappell, George P444
Chappell, Brent P. E249
Chappell, Daniel G. (Dan) E365
Chappell, Dan E365
Chapple, Scott P410
Chappuis, Cameron P279
Chaput, Paul A173
Chaput, Steve E107
Charalambous, Ioannis A. A611
Charalampidis, Damianos I. W24
Charalampidis, Damianos W253
Charbonneau, Tracy A406
Charbonneau, Ed A685
Charbonneau, Laura P66
Chard, David P514
Charest, Laurie A205
Charest, Yvon W180
Charette, Scott P29
Charette, Gary C P40
Chargois, Trevor A526
Charity, Alicia A56
Charlat, Martin P488
Charlene, Brennan A706
Charlene, Brennan E353
Charles, Ronald A180
Charles, John P313
Charles, Timothy L P331
Charles, Kerwin P610
Charles, Doug E235
Charles, Annie E398
Charlton, R. Scott A782
Charmatz, Jeff A105
Charneski, Brian S. A414
Charneski, Brian S. E195
Charney, Eugene A532
Charo, Israel E72
Charoenanusorn, Apiphan W330
Charon, Maria A175
Charos, Rae P532
Charron, Jeffrey A774
Charron, Kenneth E172
Charsha, Dianne P576
Charton, Daryl A2
Charuchinda, Nuttachat W295
Charvat, Peter P602
Charyna, Dan A706
Charyna, Dan E353
Chasalow, Eric P82
Chase, William J. A6
Chase, Amy A16
Chase, Robin A272
Chase, Jonathan A334
Chase, Marc A449
Chase, Stephan A530
Chase, P. Kevin A735
Chase, Arlo A765
Chase, Christine A855
Chase, Dan P295
Chase, Pam P449
Chase, Arlo P540
Chase, Brian E144
Chase, Anthony R. (Tony) E436
Chasney, Laura P784
Chastain, Stephen A478
Chastain, Clayton A700
Chastain, Douglas A912
Chastulik, Cindy A149
Chatfield, Chris A350
Chatfield, Chris E156
Chatillon, Jean-Baptiste de W286
Chatman, Mary P484
Chatt, Theresa A539
Chatterjee, Koushik W358
Chattopadhyay, Sanat A550
Chau, Celia A131
Chaubal, Prasad A480
Chaudhary, Anurag A607
Chaudhry, Jawad A467
Chaudhry, Jawad E223
Chauhan, Ranveer S. W274
Chaussade, Jean-Louis W143

A = AMERICAN BUSINESS
E = EMERGING COMPANIES
P = PRIVATE COMPANIES
W = WORLD BUSINESS

Chaussade, Jean-Louis W343
Chausse, Jean W346
Chauvin, Stephen A659
Chauvin, Kathy P204
Chauvin, Robert F. (Bob) P267
Chauvin, Mark R. W370
Chavanne, Patrick B A503
Chavez, Joann A280
Chavez, R. Martin A389
Chavez, Mauricio A546
Chavez, Don A602
Chavez, Earl A697
Chavez, Lori P3
Chavez, Jennifer P161
Chavez, Isabel P407
Chavez, Earl P454
Chavez, Victor W364
Chavez, Pablo E8
Chavis, Eva A328
Chawla, Sona A493
Chawla, Sanjay A695
Chawla, Ashish P693
Chaya, Mary P617
Chea, Jun A489
Chean, Kevin A555
Cheap, Richard A. A440
Chearavanont, Dhanin W78
Chearavanont, Dhanin W88
Cheatham, J. Douglas A616
Cheatham, Ollie P372
Cheatham, Gabriele P601
Cheatman, Lora C P271
Cheatwood, Chris J. A657
Checketts, John A474
Checketts, Robert S P274
Checketts, Lannie P472
Checketts, Lannie P624
Checki, Terrence J. A323
Cheek, Bruce D. A47
Cheek, Deana A115
Cheek, Patty A850
Cheek, Kayla P201
Cheema, Amy A691
Cheeseman, Michael A398
Cheesewright, David A878
Chelala, Peter A871
Cheleden, Charles G. A908
Cheleden, Charles G. E446
Chelewski, Tom A446
Chelewski, Tom E210
Chelin, Julie A219
Chelin, Julie P131
Chella, Augie A406
Chellappan, Sriram P364
Chelminiak, Lee A635
Chelminiak, Lee P419
Chelminski, Piotr W291
Chelton, Scott A. P167
Chen, Donald A74
Chen, Sophie A133
Chen, Kuohsin A133
Chen, Heng W. A170
Chen, Lucia A204
Chen, Larry A352
Chen, Charles A532
Chen, Mei A550
Chen, Simone A556
Chen, Wellington A667
Chen, Elsa A667
Chen, Patgun A691
Chen, George A725
Chen, Ming A729
Chen, Emily A780
Chen, James A799
Chen, Linda A909
Chen, Heidi C. A921
Chen, Ashley W. P6
Chen, Eric P7
Chen, Jennifer P237

Chen, Shiming P268
Chen, Chunguang P378
Chen, Hanmei P466
Chen, Kevin P610
Chen, Grace W84
Chen, Tsu-Pei W84
Chen, Yusheng W89
Chen, James W113
Chen, Yong Jin W113
Chen, James Y.G. W113
Chen, Ching Chuan W113
Chen, Steve T.H. W154
Chen, Jida W403
Chen, Jie E7
Chen, Elizabeth C E18
Chen, Pehong E166
Chen, Wellington E336
Chen, Elsa E336
Cheney, Andrew B. (Andy) A57
Cheney, John A508
Cheney, Bradley P621
Cheney, Andrew B. (Andy) E16
Cheng, Nicole A222
Cheng, Andrew A386
Cheng, Marn K. A571
Cheng, Adelia P38
Cheng, Dr Rita P393
Cheng, Pam W35
Cheng, Jack T.K. W113
Cheng, Peng-Yuan W154
Cheng, Michael E140
Chengat, Vipindas P687
Chenore, Elizabeth A350
Chenore, Elizabeth E157
Chenoweth, Inge P307
Chenoweth, Susan E119
Chenu, Pierre E307
Cheong, Tony W160
Cheong, Wee Ee W384
Chepurnoy, Oleg W375
Cherbakov, Luba A460
Cherecwich, Peter B. A599
Cherepanov, Vsevolod W289
Cheriyan, Anil A774
Chermak, Jerome P398
Chernault, Daniel L P468
Cherner, Anatoly W157
Chernets, Natalie P618
Cherniss, Matthew (Matt) E402
Cheroux, Roch W343
Cherry, Thomas F A156
Cherry, Kimberley C. (Kim) A348
Cherry, Pedro A383
Cherry, Don J. A387
Cherry, Ruthie B Cook A774
Cherry, Richard A434
Cherry, Melody P517
Cherry, Don J. E177
Chertoff, Michael P383
Cherukuri, Deepak E123
Chery, Sulexan A40
Chery, Don A387
Chery, Don E177
Cheshire, Bryan P632
Cheshire, Ian W54
Chesick, Luke A541
Chesick, Luke E266
Chesler, Randall M. (Randy) A387
Chesler, Randall M. (Randy) E177
Chesley, Yonnie A410
Chesley, Philip P458
Chesney, John A693
Chesnut, Jeff A32
Chesnutt, Jim P410
Chessare, John B P208
Chessare, John P219
Chester, Nicholas P421
Chestnutt, Roy H. A870
Chetnani, Jairaj E343
Cheung, Nina A105
Cheung, Annie A460
Cheung, Jim A517
Cheung, Kathy A530
Cheung, Ann A667
Cheung, Sue A729

Cheung, Keith P231
Cheung, Christine P375
Cheung, Ramsey P538
Cheung, Sylvia E18
Cheung, Ann E336
Chevalier, John T A671
Chevalier, Karen A774
Chevardi-¨re, Patrick de La W372
Chevrette, John P75
Chew, Simon A131
Chew, Anna T. E408
Chewens, Michael J. A577
ChFC, Brooke A54
Chhean, Forster P631
Chhibbar, Vishal E138
Chi, David A69
Chi, Kung Yeung (Ann) Yun W67
Chia, Donny A568
Chiang, Ellen A285
Chiang, Hwai Hai (HH) A471
Chiang, Ellen E114
Chiang, James E349
Chiappetta, Mark E225
Chiappone, Charles A480
Chiappone, Michael P528
Chiarella, Jerry A670
Chiarello, Guy A343
Chiarini, Alberto W144
Chiaromonte, Jeannie A101
Chiasson, Becky A182
Chiasson, Becky E63
Chicas, Carlos P93
Chiccino, Peter (Pete) A806
Chichester, David A763
Chick, Wesley A795
Chick, Phillip P611
Chico, Michael Chico Michael A599
Chico, Jerry E101
Chicoine, Gerry A85
Chicoine, Jerry L. A319
Chih-Hsiang, Lin (Thompson) E21
Chikaraishi, Koichi W264
Chikhale, Caroline L. (Cece) E249
Chilante, Diane P568
Chilberg, C. Perry E414
Child, Jeffrey S. (Jeff) P450
Child, Curtis P450
Child, William H. (Bill) P450
Childers, Terry A207
Childers, Cecil A674
Childers, Michael A743
Childers, Robert P246
Childers, Bob P246
Childers, Dexter P551
Childers, Steven L. (Steve) E91
Childers, Michael E372
Childress, Scott A850
Childress, Brian P421
Childress-Newberger, Karen E360
Childs, Torrance A143
Childs, Jeffrey J A836
Childs, Kleta P184
Childs, Michelle P321
Childs, Craig P339
Childs, Bobby P591
Chiles, Kisha P60
Chiles, Thomas P625
Chilewitz, Mark A480
Chillemi, John A604
Chillo, Laura A863
Chilson, Scott A476
Chilson, Greg A710
Chilton, Jim A136
Chilwan, Adnan W130
Chimene, Kim P397
Chin, Marc A131
Chin, Mary A204
Chin, David A767
Chin, Patrick A777
Chin, Helen P548
Chin, Brian W111
Chin, Kee Min W195
Chin, Frederick V. F. W384
Chin, Eric E9
Chin, Michael E158

Chin, Patrick E393
Chin, Michelle E447
China, John D. A777
China, John D. E393
Chindemi, Craig P310
Chinea, Manuel A661
Ching, K.C. (Glenn) A183
Ching, Patrick D P493
Chinigo, Chin A438
Chinn, Michael A. (Mike) A721
Chinn, Terri P536
Chinniah, Nim P397
Chintamaneni, Ramakrishna Prasad A217
Chiocco, Leslie A619
Chioccola, Frank A786
Chiodi, Kim A890
Chiodi, Kim P684
Chiolan, Robert A130
Chiovaro, Jerry E391
Chiovaro, Gerard E391
Chiovatero, Georgia P503
Chipollini, Jose P101
Chirachanakul, Prasert A390
Chirakitcharern, Paisan W88
Chirico, Emanuel A264
Chirico, Emanuel (Manny) A682
Chirolas, William A555
Chisholm, Cheryl A339
Chisholm, Timothy A417
Chisholm, Moody L. A458
Chisholm, Ron A671
Chisholm, Bill P167
Chisholm, Moody L. P251
Chisholm, Cheryl E150
Chisholm-krosnicki, Christine A881
Chisler, Matt P635
Chisolm, Moody P538
Chistik, Alexis A204
Chiszar, Vicky A P282
Chitester, Todd A101
Chithran, Payyanadan V P184
Chiu, Diana A22
Chiu, Lisa P98
Chiu, Melissa P506
Chiu, Edward P688
Chiusano, Robert M. (Bob) E441
Chivavibul, Somsak A575
Chivily, Christine A109
Chivinski, Beth Ann L. A369
Chizmar, Naomi A115
Chlebicki, Marilee A362
Chmiel, Harold A542
Chmiel, Harold E267
Cho, Ho A178
Cho, SungHwan A447
Cho, Pat P172
Cho, Pat P173
Cho, Jessica P495
Cho, Chung-Myong W292
Choakpichitchai, Prapoj W88
Choate, Elizabeth A235
Chock, Lindsay A390
Chodak, Paul A46
Chodakewitz, Jeffrey A. E428
Choe, Yong A709
Choeff, Sonya A693
Choi, Justin C. A66
Choi, Byung U A133
Choi, Eunmoo A429
Choi, Augustine M.K. P143
Choi, Kyung Hee P239
Choi, Hyung-Seok W220
Choi, Eunmoo E204
Chojnowski, Daniel P311
Chokron, Jeni A107
Chokron, Jeni E35
Cholley, Jeff A441
Chomienne, Kathleen A375
Chon, Hyoung A173
Chong, Jack A19
Chong, Min A24
Chong, James A430
Chong, James E204
Chonko, Marcie A807

Chonko, Marcie P574
Choo, Douglas A556
Choo, Kangsoo W210
Choo, Vincent W280
Choong, Wong Kim W384
Choowatanapakorn, Somkuan W88
Chopey, Stephen A765
Chopey, Stephen P540
Chopp, Robin P526
Choppelas, Alison A175
Chopra, Robin K A358
Chopra, Rahul A589
Chopra, Ekta A809
Chopra, Saurabh A874
Chopra, Raj P428
Chopra, Ekta P586
Chor, Ting Sik P517
Chornohos, Chris A478
Chosy, James L. A865
Chotiner, Alan P159
Chotsuparach, Praderm W88
Chou, John G. A59
Chou, Ken A354
Chou, Shang P313
Choudhury, Shafi P292
Choudry, Tauseef P361
Choufuku, Yasuhiro W237
Chouraqui, Fabrice A603
Chouraqui, Fabrice P399
Choutka, Michael J. P235
Chovanec, Tony A303
Chow, Donald S. A170
Chow, Jonathan A517
Chow, David A620
Chow, Jean A648
Chow, Wayne A667
Chow, Marjorie P642
Chow, Wayne E336
Chowdhury, Ashfaque A913
Choy, Alex A777
Choy, Alex E393
Chrest, Travis P511
Chris, Fjellstad P586
Chrisbacher, Scott A96
Chrislaw, Cathy P577
Chrisman, George P514
Chrismar, Oscar E. Von W43
Chrisostomidis, Vasilios P632
Christ, John A190
Christakos, Bretta A182
Christakos, Bretta E63
Christanday, Geoffrey E3
Christanto, Jevri A762
Christekos, Vincent P233
Christen, Amy A199
Christensen, Michelle A127
Christensen, Rich A329
Christensen, Wesley J. A622
Christensen, Scott A833
Christensen, William P25
Christensen, Gwendolyn P51
Christensen, John P78
Christensen, Mylia P94
Christensen, Dianne P268
Christensen, Marc P. P514
Christensen, Christopher R. E125
Christensen, Roy E. E125
Christensen, Kent E139
Christenson, Patty P22
Christenson, Greg S. P689
Christian, David A. A275
Christian, Mark A632
Christian, Douglas A683
Christian, Dan P1
Christian, Timothy P216
Christian, Ronald E P514
Christian, Carol P538
Christian, John P682
Christian, Ralf W331
Christian, Mark E322
Christiana, Charles A677
Christiansen, Karen P206
Christiansen, Dave P341
Christiansen, Amira P550
Christiansen, Douglas L. P615

Christiansen, Jeppe W271
Christianson, David P537
Christianson, Mathias J P602
Christie, William T. A323
Christino, Grace P315
Christman, Kelli A837
Christman, Laura P568
Christmann, John J. A69
Christmas, Charles E. (Chuck) A549
Christmas, Bernard P669
Christmas, Charles E. (Chuck) E270
Christodoulou, Petros W253
Christodoulou, Nikos W253
Christoff, Renee A784
Christoff, Paul W323
Christoffersen, Craig E407
Christofferson, Carla J. A16
Christoforo, John P71
Christoph, Janna P166
Christophe, Pierrot A375
Christophe, Pierrot P210
Christophe, Scott P402
Christopher, Norman C. P118
Christopher, Rugg P121
Christopher, Gail C P672
Christopher, Joe E190
Christopoulos, James P415
Christou, Lorri E75
Christoun, Kevin P272
Christy, Charles D. A331
Christy, Lisa R A344
Christy, James A675
Christy, Scott E94
Christy, Charles D. E148
Christy, Lisa R E154
Chriszt, Michael A322
Chronister, Ronnie P170
Chrystal, Curtis A412
Chrystal, Curtis E192
Chrystie, Dale A327
Chu, Roberta A102
Chu, Gary A377
Chu, Joshua A429
Chu, Sophia A480
Chu, Christine A517
Chu, Stephanie A639
Chu, Tom A682
Chu, Edward P462
Chu, William W113
Chu, Joshua E204
Chu, Stephanie E326
Chua, Nicolas P610
Chubb, Jack P637
Chucri, Theresa P334
Chugh, Davinder W30
Chui, William A725
Chuisano, Joe A870
Chulick, Michele P116
Chulos, Nicholas J. A351
Chulos, Nicholas J. E158
Chum, Muni A109
Chum, Muni E36
Chumbley, Bud P48
Chumley, Robert J. (Rob) A571
Chun, Conrad A136
Chun, Gregory H. (Greg) P320
Chun, Ricky E286
Chun-Soo, Han W205
Chung, John A247
Chung, Michael H. K. A286
Chung, Felix A532
Chung, Kwang J A629
Chung, Yoon (Michael) A634
Chung, Jin A683
Chung, Paul W. A787
Chung, Alexander N P68
Chung, Chui P218
Chung, David P227
Chung, William P359
Chung, Melody P517
Chung, John E103
Chung, My E251
Chung-Yao, Li (Ford) E21
Chunko, Andrew T. E171
Chunyan, Wang W89

Chupina, Yulia G. W321
Church, John R. A377
Church, Jason A676
Church, Tracy P227
Church, Craig P529
Churchill, Sam A844
Churchill, Arthur L P231
Churchill, Gary P424
Churchill, Brian P530
Churchill, Laurie A. E242
Churchill, Ryan L. E264
Churchill, Sam E412
Churchman, Calvin A691
Churchwell, Kevin P570
Chuslo, Steven L. (Steve) E188
Chute, Tammie P546
Chutima, Sarunthorn W330
Chvez, Dr Jess H P466
Ch-`vre, Claude W164
Chéreau, Xavier W286
Ciaccia, Julius P392
Ciaccio, Teresa P462
Ciamillo, Rich A537
Ciampa, Dominick A584
Ciana, Meredith A677
Cianchette, Charlie P121
Cianciolo, Maura A818
Ciccarone, Rachel P212
Cicconi, Fiona W35
Cicero, Richard P280
Cichocki, Andrew R. (Andy) A25
Cichocki, Andrew R. (Andy) P15
Cichon, Monica A489
Cichowski, Lorraine P566
Ciello, Ronald Del P329
Cigarroa, Francisco G. A860
Cigarroa, Francisco G. P656
Cilento, Robert A502
Cillo, Sherry A841
Cillo, Sherry E410
Cimbri, Carlo W383
Cimmino, Dom A85
Cincera, Matthew Matt A262
Cinco-abela, Tracy A687
Cincotta, Tiffany A5
Cincotta, Tiffany A6
Cindric, Lucy A878
Cintra, George E219
Ciongoli, Adam G. A161
Cippus, Vicki E265
Ciraulo, Richard A175
Cirelli, Jean-Fran-§ois W143
Cirillo, Mary A200
Cirillo, Janice A901
Cirillo, Janice P692
Cirincione, Thomas A441
Cirino, Eileen P279
Cirin-, Luciano W32
Ciriza, Gloria P120
Ciroli, James K. A356
Ciserani, Giovanni A671
Ciskowski, Michael S. (Mike) A867
Cisneros, Zada A244
Cisneros, Tamara A877
Cisrik, James A303
Citrano, Jim A115
Citrano, John A. A152
Citrano, John A. E49
Ciukowski, Kim A655
Ciukowski, Kim E333
Ciulla, John R. A883
Ciullo, Richard A407
Civgin, Don A33
Civil, Timothy F A647
Clabaugh, Samuel F. P577
Clabby, Joseph S. (Joe) W98
Clack, Alan A175
Clacko, Phil A452
Cladouhos, Sherry A387
Cladouhos, Sherry E177
Clair, Ewan St A323
Clair, Joyce St. A599
Clair, Joyce St A599
Clair, Anne St A902
Clair, Bernadette St P359

Clair, Anne St P692
Clamp, Luke P289
Clancy, Rick A221
Clancy, John P. (Jack) A301
Clancy, Kevin P191
Clancy, Makkie P340
Clancy, Edward (Ed) W98
Clancy, John P. (Jack) E127
Clanton, Mike A182
Clanton, Lori P354
Clanton, Mike E63
Clapp, Dale A350
Clapp, Dale E156
Clapp, Gerald Wayne E160
Clappin, James P. A238
Clardy, David P242
Clarfeld, Richard P413
Clark, Matt A16
Clark, James B A47
Clark, James A47
Clark, Greg A47
Clark, Gina K. A59
Clark, Stacey A101
Clark, Frank A134
Clark, Robert A187
Clark, Patrick A204
Clark, Ginny A235
Clark, James A250
Clark, Scott A284
Clark, Kimberly A323
Clark, Hunter A323
Clark, Heather A329
Clark, Mark A355
Clark, David A377
Clark, Jeff A434
Clark, Neil S A441
Clark, Scott A449
Clark, Ed A458
Clark, Wade A478
Clark, Michael A518
Clark, Morris A526
Clark, Ron A547
Clark, Jeff A600
Clark, Richard A607
Clark, Todd C. A614
Clark, Jenny A614
Clark, Christopher A701
Clark, Jessica A726
Clark, Bernard J. A728
Clark, John C. A742
Clark, Gregory (Greg) A778
Clark, Terri L A782
Clark, Cathy A792
Clark, Joan S. A801
Clark, Mary A817
Clark, Judy A829
Clark, Cathy A838
Clark, Donna A844
Clark, Rhonda A850
Clark, Terry M. A855
Clark, James A890
Clark, Blair A898
Clark, Don A899
Clark, Mary Lynn A908
Clark, Christopher B. (Chris) A910
Clark, Frank P78
Clark, Jeffrey P139
Clark, Talisa R P144
Clark, Christopher P172
Clark, Randy P174
Clark, Dedra P200
Clark, R. Mel P250
Clark, Ed P251
Clark, Linda P268
Clark, Jeffrey P269
Clark, Jeff P269
Clark, Karri P276
Clark, Colby P305
Clark, Ron P319
Clark, Mark T P337
Clark, Susan P339
Clark, Carrie P340
Clark, Greg P361
Clark, Steven P380
Clark, Kathy P385

A = AMERICAN BUSINESS
E = EMERGING COMPANIES
P = PRIVATE COMPANIES
W = WORLD BUSINESS

Clark, Terri P406
Clark, Jennifer P407
Clark, Lonnie P418
Clark, Mark T P422
Clark, Edward Stuart P439
Clark, Debra V P445
Clark, Tim P467
Clark, Joseph T. (Joe) P485
Clark, Virginia B. (Ginny) P506
Clark, Kathy P528
Clark, Patricia P551
Clark, Joan S. P562
Clark, Tara P568
Clark, Mark T P574
Clark, Gary P593
Clark, Laverne P598
Clark, Erin P611
Clark, Carol P646
Clark, Mark P662
Clark, Nigel P682
Clark, James P684
Clark, Don P690
Clark, Kevin P. W29
Clark, Richard B. (Ric) W75
Clark, Robert E71
Clark, Scott E111
Clark, Jonathan C. E123
Clark, Bill E162
Clark, Kathy E182
Clark, Jennifer B. E206
Clark, Karin E251
Clark, Billy E262
Clark, Kelly L. E265
Clark, Doug E276
Clark, Laura E349
Clark, John C. E372
Clark, Robert D. E374
Clark, Donna E412
Clark, Sheila E428
Clark, Donald J. E441
Clark, Marshall E448
Clarke, Dean A51
Clarke, Michael B A78
Clarke, Peter A313
Clarke, Sandra A441
Clarke, Troy A A577
Clarke, Jeanne A682
Clarke, David A691
Clarke, Andrew C A711
Clarke, Sheri A886
Clarke, Stephen L P39
Clarke, Sharon M P461
Clarke, Cyril P669
Clarke, Peter W146
Clarke, Tracy W340
Clarke, Jeffrey J. (Jeff) E115
Clarke, Ronald F. (Ron) E163
Clarke, Thomas J. (Tom) E247
Clarke, Sheri E433
Clarkson, Thomas F. A33
Clarkson, Frances E P646
Clasen, Sebasti--n Gil W137
Class, Becky P347
Clatterbuck, Janice E. A324
Clatterbuck, Michelle A466
Claus, Charles A693
Clausen, Linda P81
Clautics, Douglas P302
Clavelle, Joanne P487
Clawater, Earl W. (Bill) A754
Clawater, Earl W. (Bill) E380
Claxon, Christi A422
Claxon, Christi P239
Clay, Shonda A322
Clay, Justin A578
Clay, Reed A765
Clay, Lori A801
Clay, Reed P50
Clay, Sharon Ten P127

Clay, Judy P428
Clay, Robert P485
Clay, Amy P487
Clay, Reed P540
Clay, Lori P562
Claybrook, Robert A120
Claypool, Pamela J. (Pam) A25
Claypool, Pamela J. (Pam) P15
Claypool, Forrest P113
Claypool, Blain P538
Clayton, Chris A214
Clayton, Chris P128
Clayton, James B. (Jim) P489
Clayton, Annette K. W322
Cleare, Christy A324
Cleary, James F. (Jim) A59
Cleary, Michael A136
Cleary, Mike A201
Cleary, Don A530
Cleary, Jim A647
Cleary, Gerard P2
Cleary, James J P177
Cleary, James J P466
Cleaver, Chuck P310
Clebsch, Bill A507
Clebsch, Bill P288
Cleek, Don A286
Cleghorn, Jayme A56
Cleland, Richard C P186
Clem, Mike A20
Clem, John E385
Clem-Haniff, Jennifer P381
Clemens, Martin A165
Clemens, John A235
Clemens, Chris A335
Clemens, Paul F. A351
Clemens, Peter P485
Clemens, Laurie P663
Clemens, Reinhard W126
Clemens, Paul F. E158
Clemensen, Hal P13
Clement, Mark P463
Clement, Richard W. P648
Clement-Holmes, Linda A196
Clement-Holmes, Linda W. A671
Clemente, Paul P68
Clementi, Erich A460
Clements, Dennis A78
Clements, Anne A724
Clements, Janet A838
Clements, Doug P452
Cleminson, Ian P. E216
Clemmensen, Christopher N. E117
Clemmensen, Chris E117
Clemons, Jeffrey A115
Clemons, Garrett A591
Clemons, Laticia P530
Clemons, George W52
Clemson, Conrad A199
Clennan, Sharri Mc P359
Clermont, Ralph A169
Cleveland, Colleen A250
Cleveland, Brian K. A703
Cleveland, Laura A902
Cleveland, Karrie P74
Cleveland, Laura P692
Cleveland, Britta E272
Cleveland, Todd M. E324
Cleymaet, James A296
Clickner, Kathryn A697
Clickner, Kathryn P454
Cliff, Suzy A775
Cliff, Suzy P548
Clifford, Scott S. A394
Clifford, Todd A644
Clifford, Paul R. A738
Clifford, John P. A827
Clifford, Laurae A909
Clifford, Lynn P652
Clifford, Peter G. E56
Clift, Armando P271
Clift, Ruth P411
Clifton, Toby A100
Clifton, Nicole A850
Clifton, Karmar P99

Clifton, Mark A. P522
Cline, Natalie H P207
Cline, Candy P624
Cline, James E. E401
Clingenpeel, Chris A784
Clinton, Tim A51
Clinton, Angeline A282
Clinton, Shaun A801
Clinton, Brenden P339
Clinton, Shaun P562
Clinton, Malissia P564
Clinton, Todd M. E363
Clithero, David A408
Cloer, Michael G. A851
Cloninger, Kriss A18
Clontz, Jerry L. A496
Clontz, Tim P595
Clontz, Steven T. (Terry) E222
Cloonan, Annmarie P189
Clopton, George A691
Clore, Sharon P480
Close, Kevin A546
Close, Brett P537
Closs, Diane A788
Clossin, Todd F. A886
Clossin, Todd F. E433
Closter, Harold A. P506
Clothier, Kevin C A242
Cloud, Andrew A902
Cloud, Mike P256
Cloud, Carol P299
Cloud, Andrew P692
Clough, G Wayne P211
Clough, Jeanette G P353
Clouse, Anne P250
Cloutier, Paul A. A108
Cloutier, Jean W146
Cloutier, Todd E405
Clouzard, Pascal W82
Clowers, Jennifer P412
Cloyd, Mark A115
Cluff, Tad A828
Clugston, Nelson E265
Clure, Gail D Mc P672
Clute, Daniel A855
Clutter, Cathy P642
Clyde, R. Andrew A571
Clymer, Karen P449
Clymo, Eileen P539
Cmes, Brody P390
Coad, Scott A893
Coady, Shawn W. A591
Coaker, Emily P584
Coakley, John P134
Coate, Alexander P172
Coates, Steve A105
Coates, Robert S A307
Coates, Spencer A200
Coates, Eddye P332
Coats, Sylvia A101
Coats, Brian A480
Coats, Sam P152
Coats, William E182
Cobau, Ed P246
Cobb, Gerald A173
Cobb, Sue P303
Cobb, Jay P544
Cobb, Steven D. P611
Cobb, Clif P664
Cobb, D. Keith E39
Cobb, Russ E44
Cobbs, Bob P623
Coben, Lawrence S. A604
Cobine, Stew P627
Coble, Fred A693
Coborn, Chris P130
Cobos, Vicki P225
Coburn, George F P309
Coccagno, James A. P90
Coccagno, Jim P90
Cochran, George A487
Cochran, Larry A670
Cochran, Dan A691
Cochran, Scott D. A701
Cochran, J. Scott A704

Cochran, Barbara A865
Cochran, Greg P148
Cochran, Karen P472
Cochran, Barry S. P577
Cochran, Cory P627
Cochran, J. Scott E350
Cochrane, Lisad A34
Cochrane, Marie A513
Cochrane, John Gregory P363
Cochrane, Andy P387
Cochrell, Patty P227
Cockcroft, Adrian A38
Cockerham, Judy E432
Cockrell, Kevin P26
Cockrell, Phillip P613
Cockrum, Leigh A742
Cockrum, Leigh E372
Cocks, Chris A408
Coco, Cedric T. A148
Coco, Denae P121
Coco, Jeffrey P621
Coco, Eric P624
Cocorullo, L Mark P310
Coder, Forrest David A155
Codispoti, Pam A49
Codkind, Gregory P109
Codner, Nancy P78
Codsi, Jean-marc A288
Cody, WM A223
Cody, William M. (Bill) A672
Cody, Bill Cody Bill A764
Cody, Kenneth P68
Cody, Thomas G. P115
Coe, Nicholas P.M. (Nick) A497
Coe, Patrick K A763
Coe, Susan P645
Coe, Steve E326
Coel, David P510
Coen, Bill P339
Coffell, Shannon P42
Coffey, Timothy P. A67
Coffey, Douglas A857
Coffey, Philip (Phil) W395
Coffman, Vance A3
Coffman, Kyle P343
Coffman, Joan P475
Coffman, Doug P635
Cofré, Daniel Rodr-guez W152
Cogan, Brian A101
Cogdill, Matthew P289
Cogdill, Richard A. (Rick) P604
Coggin, Bill P470
Cogliano, Michael A766
Cohan, Pablo A537
Cohen, Sharon A3
Cohen, Barry A78
Cohen, Gary M. A119
Cohen, Jalie A180
Cohen, David L A220
Cohen, Julian A235
Cohen, Darren A390
Cohen, Cory A484
Cohen, Harvey A517
Cohen, Elisa A585
Cohen, Sharon A600
Cohen, Jon R. A687
Cohen, Don A727
Cohen, Matthew A741
Cohen, Amanda A744
Cohen, Faye A774
Cohen, Andre A785
Cohen, Ira A786
Cohen, Daniel G. A806
Cohen, David L. A812
Cohen, Pinchas A860
Cohen, Mark A871
Cohen, Jack S A872
Cohen, Stephanie P22
Cohen, Carol P34
Cohen, Dennis P145
Cohen, Paula Marantz P165
Cohen, Caitlin P224
Cohen, David I. P302
Cohen, Elisa P377
Cohen, Bruce P378

Cohen, Jay P501
Cohen, David L. P607
Cohen, Gary P636
Cohen, Pinchas P656
Cohen, Dan W46
Cohen, David W105
Cohen, Nathan G. E77
Cohen, Jason E165
Cohen, Sefton E268
Cohen, Matthew E370
Cohill, Mike A775
Cohill, Mike P548
Cohn, Leslie A95
Cohn, Marc A556
Cohn, Arthur A649
Cohn, Leslie P55
Cohodes, Jeffery D. A599
Coia, Gerald A740
Cojbasic, Ivana A330
Coke, Michael A. (Mike) E395
Coker, R. Howard A750
Coker, Daniel R. E174
Cokyuksel, Aysun A163
Colaianni, Jim A478
Colaizzi, Meredith P301
Colalillo, Anna P19
Colandrea, Joe P200
Colanero, Stephen A. A41
Colangelo, Carmon P616
Colao, Vittorio A. W389
Colarusso, Alice A49
Colberg, Alan B. A83
Colbert, Theodore (Ted) A136
Colbert, Charles E A917
Colbert, Tom P482
Colbert, Charles E P701
Colburn, Susan A85
Colby, Ruth P503
Coldiron, Jenny P208
Coldiron, Den Ellen P638
Coldwell, Michael A322
Coldwell, Sue E169
Cole, Daniel F A42
Cole, Russell G. A149
Cole, David D. A185
Cole, Dave A185
Cole, Michael A332
Cole, Kenneth G. A534
Cole, Jason A556
Cole, Jody A644
Cole, David D A689
Cole, Brad A693
Cole, David A850
Cole, Martin A894
Cole, Cynthia A907
Cole, Amanda P13
Cole, Beth V. P83
Cole, Charles T. P94
Cole, Rischa P172
Cole, Chris P256
Cole, George P275
Cole, Bennie L P396
Cole, Randy P404
Cole, Mr Cliff P421
Cole, Johnnetta B. P506
Cole, David P591
Cole, Jeffrey P598
Cole, Randy P677
Cole, Jay P682
Cole, Michael W61
Cole, Hart E9
Cole, Lecil E. (Lee) E52
Cole, Jason E163
Cole, Matthew J. E247
Cole, David C. E264
Cole, Cynthia E446
Coleal, David M. W69
Colella, Andrea ellis A659
Colella, Thomas A878
Colella, Carmine P352
Colella, Gerald G. E282
Coleman, Casey A85
Coleman, Jay A248
Coleman, Russell F. A258
Coleman, Kelli A272

Coleman, Kenny A383
Coleman, Gary A406
Coleman, Scott A439
Coleman, Brian A448
Coleman, Jay A489
Coleman, Laura A583
Coleman, Donna A597
Coleman, David A742
Coleman, Kirk A800
Coleman, Gary L. A822
Coleman, Chris A855
Coleman, John P172
Coleman, Lewis W P216
Coleman, Chris P225
Coleman, Sabrina P236
Coleman, Mark P290
Coleman, Willi P658
Coleman, Michael J. W98
Coleman, Liam W103
Coleman, Jonathan E97
Coleman, Victor J. E208
Coleman, Brian F. E209
Coleman, Glenn E220
Coleman, Jon E261
Coleman, David E372
Coleman, Kirk E396
Coleman, Benjamin E426
Coleman, Rob E432
Colenda, Christopher P681
Coles, Allen P461
Colestock, Richard E A663
Coletti, Janet M. A522
Coletti, Larry P617
Coley, Peter A774
Colgan, Meegan A691
Colgan, Kevin P611
Colgan, Michael J. E361
Colgan, Mike E361
Colhoun, Dan P147
Colin, Mark A2
Colin, William A729
Colisto, Nicholas R. A914
Colistra, David A460
Colla, Chris E29
Collar, Gary L. A20
Collard, Steve P66
Collazo, Cynthia P123
Collazo, Jose E306
College, Eugene A316
College, Eugene P191
Colleran, Donald F A327
Collett, Tiffany P318
Collett, Raquel P605
Collette, Barbara A616
Colli, Alison A406
Colli, Michael P109
Collias, Art P104
Collie, Henry A512
Collier, Marcus A374
Collier, Erin A449
Collier, Dirk A476
Collier, Gary A655
Collier, Stephanie A674
Collier, Bradley W P260
Collier, John P314
Collier, Joe P441
Collier, Mary Sue P638
Collier, Christopher E. (Chris) W151
Collier, Gary E333
Collignon, David P6
Collings, Stacey P22
Collingsworth, J M P341
Collins, Melissa A1
Collins, Barbara A103
Collins, Bill A136
Collins, Whitley A173
Collins, William C. A187
Collins, Darryl A223
Collins, Jim A247
Collins, Jonathan M A252
Collins, Chris A261
Collins, Jodi A291
Collins, Martha A296
Collins, Ellis A314
Collins, Randy A374

Collins, Anitra A463
Collins, Gary S. A616
Collins, Christian A643
Collins, Daniel A701
Collins, Tomago A707
Collins, Patty A774
Collins, Dave A835
Collins, Steve A838
Collins, Joshua L. (Josh) P76
Collins, Courtney P88
Collins, Lance R. P143
Collins, Gregory F P183
Collins, Linn P245
Collins, Tommy H. P469
Collins, James P528
Collins, Bill P603
Collins, Liam P606
Collins, Rose P622
Collins, Michael F. P645
Collins, James E. E39
Collins, William C. E71
Collins, Jim E102
Collins, Julie E. E252
Collins, Martin J. (Marty) E344
Collins, Suzanne E432
Collis, Steven H. A59
Collischan, Michael A878
Collopy, Fred P99
Collura, Corren P545
Colman, Robin A288
Colmenares, Juan A270
Colmers, John A475
Colmers, John P266
Colombo, Russell A. (Russ) A103
Colombo, William J. (Bill) A264
Colombo, Mark J A327
Colombo, Beatrice A649
Colombo, Benjermin A777
Colombo, Costantino (Chris) P313
Colombo, Benjermin E393
Colon, Tara A84
Colon, Bill A115
Colondres, Jose A782
Colones, Robert L P319
Colonges, Guillaume de W82
Colonias, Karen W. E373
Colonna, Jerome P67
Colonna, Nicholas E231
Colonna, Ken E424
Colosi, Scott M. E397
Colpo, Charles C. A626
Colsman, Peggy A192
Colsman, Peggy P112
Coltart, Catherine A599
Colton, Sabine P456
Coltrane, Scott P651
Colucci, Eugene P220
Colucciello, Michael P440
Coluzzi, Chris E369
Colvin, Jeff A17
Colvin, Jason A537
Colvin, Donald A620
Colvin, Shelley A644
Colvin, John A693
Colvin, Jeff P10
Colvin, Kent P51
Colvin, Karen E106
Colwell, Chad A902
Colwell, Gale R P692
Colwill, Karen A277
Comas, Daniel L. A253
Comay, Josh A175
Combs, Al A599
Combs, Robert P356
Combs, Joseph D. P615
Comeaux, Preston P429
Comegys, Glenn P125
Comey, Kimberly P628
Comisar, David A175
Comitale, Jim A709
Comizzoli, Pierre P506
Commerford, Jack A136
Commons, David A420
Commons, David E198
Comnenus, Maurizia Angelo W237

Compton, Brian A131
Compton, Bob A251
Compton, Richard A607
Compton, Lisa A763
Compton, Kris P30
Compton, Carol P110
Compton, James M P141
Compton, Rocky P537
Compton, Paul W52
Compton, Paul W54
Comstock, Steve A175
Comstock, Karolyn P546
Comyn, Matt W105
Conahan, Danielle P244
Conatser, Vivienne A537
Conaway, Mary Ann A212
Conaway, Greg E59
Conaway, Mary Ann E79
Concannon, William F. (Bill) A172
Concannon, Michael (Mike) A406
Concannon, Chris E62
Conceicao, Cassio P502
Concordia, Elizabeth B. A859
Concordia, Elizabeth B. P652
Condegni, Anthony A87
Condia, Anthony P631
Condoleo, Edward A16
Condon, Gene A744
Condon, Robert P430
Condon, Michael A. P514
Condon, Liam W56
Condong, Carlo A481
Condran, Georgina A369
Condron, Robert P300
Condron, Gary D P575
Condry, Sterling Kirk A137
Cone, Steve P1
Cone, Jason P321
Coney, Jason A523
Confare, Amy P51
Conforti, James E. A775
Conforti, James E. P548
Cong, Lin A607
Congdon, Lesley P225
Conger, William A115
Conger, Harry M. (Red) A367
Conger, Ann A724
Conger, Rick P92
Congiusti, Robert E54
Congleton, Brian A85
Congoran, Thomas M. P50
Conidi, Francesco A729
Conklin, Patrick A671
Conklin, George S. P119
Conklin, Rasa P192
Conklin, Corey D P660
Conklin, Renee E339
Conkling, Charles E432
Conley, Ann P68
Conley, John P256
Conley, Amber P334
Conley, Karen P380
Conley, Gregory R. E197
Conley, Melinda S. E236
Conlon, Christopher E4
Conlon, Matt E56
Conn, Iain C. W87
Conn, Mitzi P. E53
Connatser, Gayle A505
Connell, Jesse A292
Connell, Hope Holding A341
Connell, Bruce A528
Connell, Pryor P262
Connell, Hope Holding E153
Connelly, Anthony A272
Connelly, James M. A413
Connelly, Deirdre A513
Connelly, Michael A542
Connelly, Michael D A552
Connelly, James M. P234
Connelly, Michael D P328
Connelly, Ryan H. E242
Connelly, Mary J. E252
Connelly, Michael E267
Connelly, Michael D. E337

A = AMERICAN BUSINESS
E = EMERGING COMPANIES
P = PRIVATE COMPANIES
W = WORLD BUSINESS

Connelly, James E445
Connelly, Michael P378
Connely, Brian E381
Conner, Peter J. A110
Conner, Raymond L. (Ray) A136
Conner, Brad L. A205
Conner, Jack W. A414
Conner, Anne A823
Conner, David E. A847
Conner, Thomas O P338
Conner, Mark P626
Conner, Peter J. E37
Conner, Jack W. E194
Connery, Raymond A105
Connery, Brian A644
Conness, Jason E182
Connett, Rick A56
Connick, Harry F. E340
Connolly, Thomas A59
Connolly, Sean M. A230
Connolly, Sean M. A231
Connolly, Joy A585
Connolly, Landon P104
Connolly, James W P213
Connolly, Joy P377
Connolly, Debbie P423
Connolly, Adrian L P524
Connolly, Brian P692
Connolly, Edward T. W176
Connolly, Patrick E. (Pat) W334
Connolly, M. Colin E98
Connor, Mark A143
Connor, Mitch A199
Connor, Tom A272
Connor, Kevin A481
Connor, Frank T. A804
Connor, Martin P. (Marty) A819
Connor, Richard P512
Connor, David P538
Connor, Daniel P670
Connor, Sue P682
Connor, Roger W158
Connor, Dean A. W347
Connor, Mark E253
Connor, Kevin E343
Connor, Kevin E402
Connors, Timothy A628
Connors, John A634
Connors, Bryon A767
Connors, Michael L. P92
Connors, Alfred F. P593
Connors, Timothy J. E338
Conophy, Thomas M. (Tom) A88
Conover, David A492
Conover, Jeffrey W A599
Conover, Bob A676
Conrad, William A513
Conrad, Scott V P551
Conrad, Jeffrey A P672
Conrado, Eduardo F. A570
Conroy, Donal A70
Conroy, Alexandre A119
Conroy, Courtney A175
Conroy, Nancy A823
Conroy, Joanne P279
Conroy, John D P425
Cons, Ricardo W3
Consagra, James J. A843
Consagra, James J. E411
Considine, William H. (Bill) P118
Considine, Timothy M. E201
Consiglio, Gayle P319
Consolino, Joseph E. (Jeff) A51
Consolino, Cathi P358
Constand, George T A252
Constant, Jean-Paul W206
Constantine, Tom A94
Constantine, Thomas A95
Constantine, Tom P53

Constantine, Thomas E28
Constantino, Tawnya A458
Constantino, Chris A582
Constantino, Tawnya P251
Constantino, Chris P373
Contakes, Chris P601
Contarsy, Elise E272
Conte, Randall T. A541
Conte, John A888
Conte, Randall T. E266
Conterno, Enrique A. A511
Conti, Maryann P221
Continenza, James V. (Jim) P333
Continenza, James V. (Jim) E115
Contis, David J. A744
Contreras, Jaime A4
Contreras, Claudia P443
Contreras, Sharon P551
Contreras-Soto, Alex P446
Contrerasn, Sharon P551
Converse, Lou A872
Convit, Rafael P675
Conway, Kevin A59
Conway, Trish A122
Conway, John W. A242
Conway, Karen A353
Conway, William A. A413
Conway, Dennis A441
Conway, Corrie A531
Conway, Michael A659
Conway, Michael A763
Conway, Jeffrey D. A766
Conway, Karen A869
Conway, Christopher L. P125
Conway, William A. P234
Conyers, Al P385
Cook, James A25
Cook, Randy A85
Cook, James A101
Cook, David A105
Cook, Derek A130
Cook, Ian M. A218
Cook, Thomas A223
Cook, Jennifer A395
Cook, Sari A402
Cook, Jay A460
Cook, Bill A480
Cook, Brent A493
Cook, Mitchell W. A562
Cook, Chris A572
Cook, Helen A614
Cook, Sandy A670
Cook, Dee A693
Cook, BettyL A698
Cook, Stephen R. (Steve) A745
Cook, Rachel A818
Cook, James P15
Cook, Jason P27
Cook, Richard P40
Cook, Maura P110
Cook, Kenn P143
Cook, Jodi P166
Cook, Stephen P170
Cook, Jonathan P218
Cook, Paul P249
Cook, Marie P284
Cook, Colleen P307
Cook, Christopher D P310
Cook, Will P332
Cook, Chris P359
Cook, Mike P395
Cook, Troy D P400
Cook, John P421
Cook, Robert P433
Cook, BettyL P456
Cook, Randy P570
Cook, Cindy P579
Cook, Jeffry P583
Cook, Kathryn E40
Cook, Mitchell W. E279
Cooke, Alan A492
Cooke, Dennis C. A718
Cooke, Bob A818
Cooke, Gary A903
Cooke, Patricia P575

Cookman, Tobin A620
Cookman, Duwayne P556
Cookson, Teresa A558
Cool, Mariane P664
Cool, Jonathan M. E251
Cooley, Kem P384
Coombe, Gary A671
Coombe, Robert D. (Bob) P132
Coombs, Cary A919
Coombs, Paul D. E31
Coonan, Kevin A103
Coonan, Marty A518
Cooney, Devon A729
Cooney, Dave P184
Cooney, Jack E376
Coonrod, Julie P648
Coons, Kenneth A480
Coons, Rick P672
Cooper, Michael A13
Cooper, Mark A17
Cooper, Ross D. A117
Cooper, Mark A153
Cooper, Debra A180
Cooper, Pamela A196
Cooper, Allen A231
Cooper, Benjamin A355
Cooper, Michael A372
Cooper, Edith W. A389
Cooper, David A399
Cooper, Angus A446
Cooper, John A509
Cooper, Ellen A512
Cooper, Steven A591
Cooper, Michael A654
Cooper, Don A669
Cooper, Chris A701
Cooper, Laurie A769
Cooper, Julie A774
Cooper, Frederick A819
Cooper, Kimberly A858
Cooper, Samantha A871
Cooper, Troy A. A913
Cooper, Mark P10
Cooper, Dennis P34
Cooper, Mark A. P104
Cooper, Gary P111
Cooper, Debbie P122
Cooper, Dorothy P146
Cooper, Pat P279
Cooper, John P288
Cooper, David P348
Cooper, Malcolm Charles P363
Cooper, Scott P395
Cooper, Scott P528
Cooper, Shelby S P590
Cooper, Robin P602
Cooper, Christopher J. P613
Cooper, Simon W340
Cooper, Brad W395
Cooper, Beth W. E74
Cooper, Buzz E178
Cooper, Angus E210
Cooper, Tod E289
Cooper, Walt E339
Cooper, Kimberly E418
Cooper, David E438
Cooper-Boone, Deborah P201
Cooperstein, Marci A175
Coopmans, Baptiest W222
Coore, Becky P668
Copa, Gail A182
Copa, Gail E63
Cope, Bud A901
Cope, George A. W61
Cope, James E432
Cope, Jim E432
Copeland, Scott A98
Copeland, John G. A99
Copeland, Jananne A A169
Copeland, Reed A249
Copeland, Rex A. A395
Copeland, R. Dallis (Roy) A781
Copeland, Jon P32
Copeland, Robert P43
Copeland, Byron P170

Copeland, Briand P218
Copeland, Brian P218
Copeland, William P222
Copeland, Darwinda P323
Copeland, Scott E33
Copelin, Bill A439
Copello, Corinne E A596
Copenhaver, Kaila P201
Copher, Ron J. A387
Copher, Ron J. E177
Copier, Judy A449
Copper, Donna A15
Copper, Donna P9
Coppey, Pierre W387
Coppock, Alisa A438
Coppola, Matthew A869
Copsey, Andrew W352
Copty, Michael A777
Copty, Michael E393
Corace, Robert E130
Coradi, Robert G A625
Coradine, Sedare A810
Coradine, Sedare P597
Corasanti, Joseph J. (Joe) E214
Corban, Stephen M. A704
Corban, Stephen M. E350
Corbat, Michael L. A203
Corbett, John A182
Corbett, Dennis A777
Corbett, Thomas A344
Corbett, Shirley P585
Corbett, S. Mark W161
Corbett, John E63
Corbett, Dennis E393
Corbin, John A440
Corbin, Janet P223
Corbin, Lee Anne P225
Corbin, Arthur C P358
Corbin, Allen E398
Corbo, Michael A. (Mike) A218
Corbridge, Nancy P413
Corbusier, Drue A266
Corcione, Gina P222
Corcoran, Mary A402
Cordani, David M. A194
Cordani, David A377
Cordano, Michael D. A892
Cordaro, Ron A187
Cordaro, Ron E71
Cordeaux, Kellie A343
Cordero, Paul M A624
Cordero, Ivette E293
Cordidan, Amanda P132
Cordova, David M E301
Corell, Kemp P412
Corey, Gloria A85
Corey, Toby P559
Corey, Barbara P680
Corirossi, David A703
Corkel, Lisa Mc P628
Corleto, Jose A685
Corleto-mena, Jose A685
Corlett, David A255
Corley, Kathryn McNamara A268
Corley, John A911
Corley, Steve P160
Corley, Vic P295
Corley, Clay P295
Corley, Craig P297
Cormier, Joanne A93
Cormier, Philip M P391
Cormier, Peter P396
Corn, R. E. (Ron) A192
Corn, Ron A193
Corn, R. E. (Ron) P112
Corn, Ron P112
Cornejo, Agustin P637
Cornelious, Derrick A105
Cornelius, Marcus A173
Cornelius, Laura A475
Cornelius, Laura P266
Cornelius, Daniel P292
Cornell, Catherine A221
Cornell, Kevin A221
Cornell, Brian C. A788

Cornell, Steve A894
Cornell, Brian C A917
Cornew, Kenneth W. (Ken) A308
Cornia, Silvano A564
Cornia, Gary C. P83
Cornish, Thomas M. A108
Cornish, Thomas M. E35
Cornuelle, Valerie P91
Cornum, Curt A454
Cornwall, Kevin A247
Cornwall, Kevin E103
Corominas, Armando P105
Corona, George S A486
Corr, Patrick A175
Corr, Steven P105
Corr, Edwin G P306
Corr, Jonathan H. E119
Corradetti, Laura A600
CORRADI, ENRICO W111
Corrado, Richard F. (Rich) E8
Corral, Armida P352
Corrato, Joe A677
Correa, Jaime A701
Correani, Andrea A593
Correiro, Valerie A241
Correll, Drew A886
Correll, Craig P337
Correll, Drew E433
Corrigan, Frank A568
Corrigan, Peter W P244
Corrigan, George M P510
Corrigan, Ann P587
Corrinne, Kelly A720
Corrinne, Kelly E362
Corro, Debbie Del A655
Corro, Debbie Del E333
Corry, David M P290
Corsini, Bryan M. A632
Corsini, Bryan M. E321
Corso, Salvatore A902
Corso, Salvatore P692
Corson, B. W. A313
Corson, Brad A313
Cortes, Fermin P135
Cortes, Antonio R. W231
Cortese, Jennifer A542
Cortese, Jennifer E267
Cortez, Juan A351
Cortez, Juan E158
Cortina, Ignacio A A625
Cortina, Albert P293
Cortés-V--zquez, Lorraine P1
Corum, Bethany H. (Beth) A162
Corvin, Paul P314
Corvino, Frank A P220
Corvino, Frank A. P698
Corwin, Steven J. (Steve) A810
Corwin, Steven J. (Steve) P597
Cory, Nick A368
Cory, Barry P521
Cosby, Wende A705
Cosby, Wende E352
Coscia, Anthony R P364
Cosco, Jim A419
Cosentino, Luca W144
Cosenza, Mark Cosenza Mark A388
Cosenzo, Donna P225
Cosey, Cathy A700
Cosgriff, Sue A769
Cosgrove, Delos M. (Toby) A807
Cosgrove, Toby P190
Cosgrove, Delos P190
Cosgrove, Norma P406
Cosgrove, Delos M. (Toby) P574
Cosman, James M. A149
Cosner, Robbie A25
Cosner, Robbie P15
Cossaboom, Jill E348
Cosset, Yael A496
Cosslett, Andy W206
Costa, Mark J. A286
Costa, Roland A324
Costa, Alan Null A734
Costa, Salvatore A741
Costa, James M. A790

Costa, Robert A798
Costa, Patricio Tapia W27
Costa, Ant--nio Fernando Melo Martins da W134
Costa, José Carlos da Silva W156
Costa, Salvatore E370
Costallos, Joann P284
Costanzo, Sherry A901
Costanzo, Ronald P164
Costanzo, Sherry P692
Costella, Margaret F P589
Costello, Michael A208
Costello, Christopher A227
Costello, Sue A322
Costello, Thomas A375
Costello, Meg A635
Costello, Rhonda A706
Costello, Meg P419
Costello, Joseph G P456
Costello, Rhonda E353
Costides, Nick A850
Costigan, Conor W120
Costley, Gary E. E338
Costopoulos, Spyro A158
Cote, David M. (Dave) A429
Cote, Mike P282
Cote, Brian P486
Cote, Bryce E248
Coterillo, Fernando Julio Arias W181
Cothran, April A332
Cotner, Kimberly P560
Coto, Patricia Raquel Hevia W25
Cotran, Paul R P279
Cott, Sharon H P594
Cotta, Rick E212
Cotter, Martin A65
Cotter, Edward P700
Cotter, Dick A723
Cotter, Tim E432
Cottington, Eric M. P325
Cottle, William P404
Cotto, Jared A81
Cotton, Charles A449
Cottrell, Karen P575
Cottrill, Mark A873
Cottrill, Mark P669
Couch, Drew A96
Couch, Richard W. A683
Couch, Brett D. A700
Couch, David deS. (Dave) A756
Couch, Connie A800
Couch, Terrell P218
Couch, Richard W. E341
Couch, Connie E396
Coudrelle, Laurent A607
Coughlan, Ian M. A909
Coughlin, Thomas M A116
Coughlin, Ron A435
Coughlin, Margaret P570
Coughlin, Thomas M. E39
Coughlin, John S. E163
Couglin, John E163
Coulcher, Dan E440
Coulson, R C E320
Coultas, Tonya P583
Coulter, Anne Marie A221
Coulter, Cuan A766
Coulter, John P627
Counihan, Kevin J. A179
Counsell, Jeffrey A173
Countouriotis, Athena E186
Counts, John A782
Coupe, Nick A379
Coupe, Mike W193
Coupland, Richard A707
Courant, Paul N. A698
Courant, Paul N. P456
Coureil, Hervé W322
Coursey, Donna A724
Coursey, Kenneth E8
Courtney, Tom A408
Courtney, Robert A744
Courtney, Rob A744
Courtney, Matthew A763
Courtney, Ann A863

Courtois, Vanessa A115
Courtois, Jean-Philippe A560
Courtois, Frédéric de W32
Courtot, Philippe F. E342
Courtright, Joanne A406
Courtright, Ann A912
Courville, Isabelle W217
Couse, Anthony A478
Cousino, Mark A280
Cousins, Mike A313
Cousins, Jill P669
Cousins, Richard J. W107
Coutchie, Peggy A549
Coutchie, Peggy E270
Coutee, Vince P2
Couto, Luey A667
Couto, Luey E336
Coutu, Pat A205
Couture, Sirena P630
Covella, Robert P70
Covert, Michael H. A171
Covert, Charlie A850
Covert, Michael H. P100
Covington, J. Curtis A320
Covington, Curt A320
Covington, Carol A691
Covington, J. Curtis E143
Covington, Curt E143
Covino, Greg A129
Covre, André W379
Cowan, Chad A518
Cowans, Sabrina P560
Coward, Thomas H A22
Coward, Robert A912
Coward, Thomas H P13
Cowart, Loy D A22
Cowart, Loy D P13
Cowart, Jay A430
Cowell, Andrew M. P458
Cowell, Treva P542
Cowger, David L P660
Cowhig, Michael T. A586
Cowles, James C. A203
Cowles, Darby P268
Cowley, Daron A458
Cowley, Daron P251
Cowley, Samuel C. (Sam) E338
Cowling, Malcolm P148
Cowman, Craig A165
Cowper, Matthew E40
Cox, Daniel A109
Cox, Ed A164
Cox, Kevin A166
Cox, Denise A200
Cox, Shawn A284
Cox, Mark K. A286
Cox, Christopher K. (Chris) A314
Cox, B. Guille A346
Cox, Rhydian H. A437
Cox, Clay A439
Cox, Nick A541
Cox, Morna A574
Cox, John A602
Cox, Michael A607
Cox, Clark A655
Cox, Matthew A758
Cox, Philip C. A777
Cox, Keith A780
Cox, John A818
Cox, Tom A850
Cox, John A878
Cox, Wayne A878
Cox, Nicole A904
Cox, Karen P6
Cox, Julie P95
Cox, Cyd P143
Cox, Terence C P228
Cox, Terry P228
Cox, Terence C. (Terry) P229
Cox, Terri P308
Cox, Sonja P312
Cox, Karen P327
Cox, Judy P352
Cox, George P363
Cox, Russell F P398

Cox, Matthew P519
Cox, Michael E P626
Cox, Diana P677
Cox, John J. E9
Cox, Daniel E36
Cox, Stacy E100
Cox, Shawn E111
Cox, Nick E266
Cox, Carol E310
Cox, Clark E333
Cox, Philip C. E393
Cox, Nicole E442
Coxall, Dan P114
Coy, Jeffrey W A625
Coy, Thomas P206
Coyle, Michael J. A412
Coyle, Lori A734
Coyle, Michael J. E192
Coyne, Patrick A323
Coyne, Keith A390
Coyne, Richard T. E278
Coyner, Sheri A67
Cozad, Stacy A758
Cozart, Kevin M P334
Cozza, Keith A447
Cozzolino, Christina A621
Cozzolino, Brian P364
Cozzolino, Christina P407
Cozzone, Robert D. A451
Cpa, Ronnie Vagnone A479
Crabbe, Amy A351
Crabbe, Amy E158
Crabtree, Stephen A693
Crabtree, Danny A704
Crabtree, Monte A P125
Crabtree, Monte P125
Crabtree, Cynthia P163
Crabtree, Dave P543
Crabtree, Danny E351
Cracchiolo, James M. (Jim) A56
Cracolici, Frank P525
Crader, Scott P191
Craft, Deborah A49
Craft, Frank A671
Craft, Robert A784
Craft, John P275
Crafter, Lochiel A766
Cragg, John A642
Craig, Kim A396
Craig, Marian A521
Craig, Jeffrey A528
Craig, Jonathan M. A728
Craig, John A743
Craig, Gloria A832
Craig, David P144
Craig, Curtis P188
Craig, Jacqueline P314
Craig, Taylor P501
Craig, Larry P632
Craig, Andr--nico Luksic W41
Craig, John E372
Crain, Robert B. A20
Crain, Jackie A475
Crain, Jackie P266
Crain, Bohn H. E346
Craine, Barry A56
Craine, Randy A153
Craine, Eric A837
Craine, Lori P660
Crainer, Thomas C. E347
Crainich, Karen P450
Craker, Robin P634
Crame, Glenn A634
Cramer, Errol A33
Cramer, Kathy A672
Cramer, Karen P395
Cramer, James R. (Jim) P487
Cramer, Joann P546
Cramer, David P634
Cramer, Ralf W108
Cramer, Stuart E231
Cramer, Ron E344
Cramper, Flo P154
Crampton, Kevin P243
Crandall, Brett A133

A = AMERICAN BUSINESS	
E = EMERGING COMPANIES	
P = PRIVATE COMPANIES	
W = WORLD BUSINESS	

Crandall, Theodore D. (Ted) A712
Crandall, Janice A870
Crandall, Debbie P258
Crane, Stephen A. A292
Crane, Christopher M. (Chris) A308
Crane, Christopher M A310
Crane, Cindy A. A630
Crane, Timothy S. (Tim) A904
Crane, James R. (Jim) E436
Crane, Timothy S. (Tim) E442
Cranfill, Ben P528
Cranford, Cheryl A137
Craparo, John A493
Crapps, Michael C. (Mike) E153
Crapse, Charles A478
Crater, Ann A201
Craven, Juile A432
Craven, Katherine P314
Craven, Anthony P346
Craven, Jeri P421
Craven, Dennis M. E69
Cravey, Lynn A330
Crawford, Frederick J. (Fred) A18
Crawford, Kermit A34
Crawford, Victor L. A73
Crawford, Stan A115
Crawford, Stephen S. (Steve) A163
Crawford, Rhonda A262
Crawford, Stephen G. (Steve) A286
Crawford, Mark A308
Crawford, James C. A337
Crawford, Kelly A489
Crawford, James A526
Crawford, Bruce A619
Crawford, Kermit R. A708
Crawford, Charles A727
Crawford, Charlie A727
Crawford, Peter A728
Crawford, David A766
Crawford, Courtney P196
Crawford, Michael P237
Crawford, Kevin P292
Crawford, Kathy P500
Cray, Charlesetta Mc P640
Creach, Rod P61
Creagh, Gerard (Gerry) E75
Creamer, Michele A550
Creamons, Joe E158
Creanza, Tony A500
Creanza, Tony E238
Creatura, Nick A211
Creaturo, Craig A. E214
Credle, Eric P. A337
Creech, Dennis A417
Creech, Matt A513
Creech, Lorry P154
Creed, Greg A917
Creedon, Michael A13
Creek, Phillip G. E253
Creery, Thomas G. A423
Creevy, William P80
Cregg, Daniel J. (Dan) A678
Creighton, Cheryl A878
Crenshaw, William E. (Ed) A679
Crenshaw, William E. (Ed) A680
Crenshaw, William E. (Ed) P448
Creque, Patricia P80
Cresap, Jennifer P481
Crescenzo, Giovanni De A178
Cresci, Robert J. E226
Crespo, Kate M A693
Crespo-almond, Evelyn A272
Crespy, Steven A. P6
Cressman, Jonathan A677
Cresswell, Alex W364
Crest, Jerome P316
Creus, Jose Oliu W42
Crews, Mark A27
Crews, Kenneth A602

Cribbs, Kevin A342
Crider, Abby P315
Criger, Sara P26
Crighton, Andy A677
Crigler, Forest A369
Crimmins, John A155
Crimmins, Timothy P. A644
Crimmins, Thomas P. E29
Crines, James T A918
Cripe, Kimberly P115
Cripps, Tony W175
Crisafulli, Susan P284
Crisci, Robert A714
Crisci, Kristin P2
Criscione, David A38
Crisman, Michael A622
Crisp, Scott P355
Crispo, Carol A600
Criss, Shannon P612
Crist, Peter D. A904
Crist, Peter D. E442
Cristman, Jim A202
Cristman, Jim P122
Cristoforo, Albert J. (Jerry) A766
Crites, James M. (Jim) P152
Crites, Mark P164
Crnkovich, Sean A532
Crocco, M. Scott A24
Crocco, Banner P187
Croce, Michael J. A772
Crocitto, Linda A40
Crockett, Joan A34
Crockett, Shawn P101
Crockett, Brenda P268
Crockett, Thomas P445
Croessmann, Philip P361
Croft, Bryan P103
Crofts, Sharon M. A102
Crofts, Sharon M. A103
Croll, David D. P143
Crombleholme, Timothy M. P114
Cromer, Roy P536
Cromer, Fred S. W69
Cromme, Gerhard W331
Cron, Robert P70
Cronan, Michael P159
Crone, Seth A105
Crone, Laura A456
Cronen, John A865
Cronen, Paul A869
Croney, Michael P268
Croney, Barbara P478
Cronin, James A695
Cronin, Gina A902
Cronin, Gina P692
Cronister, Becky J P5
Cronk, Gary A729
Crooke, Robert B. A456
Crooker, William R. E384
Croom, Marshall A. A520
Cropp, Doug P281
Cros, Christophe W343
Crosbie, Debbie W101
Crosby, Ryan A134
Crosby, Michael J. A906
Crosby, Ryan P78
Crosby, Michael P509
Crosby, Samantha E404
Cross, Jeffrey A47
Cross, Karen A58
Cross, Don A81
Cross, Charles K. A731
Cross, Jeffrey D P32
Cross, Coleen P208
Cross, Stephen P211
Cross, Kim P406
Cross, Frank P542
Cross, Charles E. (Charlie) P654
Cross, Karen E16
Cross, Charles K. E365
Crosswhite, Mark A27
Croston, J. Kevin P387
Croteau, Daniel A413
Croteau, Daniel P234
Crotteau, Susan P648

Crotty, David A784
Crouch, M. Andrew (Drew) A96
Crouch, Andrew A96
Crouch, Tami A339
Crouch, Jacob A350
Crouch, Kaye A902
Crouch, Dustin P440
Crouch, Kaye P693
Crouch, Robert P. (Bob) W7
Crouch, Tami E150
Crouch, Jacob E157
Crouchley, G. Eric A277
Crougthers, Troy A493
Crouse, Dianne A669
Crouse, Carol P110
Crouse, John E265
Crouser, Mark A95
Crouser, Mark P54
Crouser, Mark P55
Croushore, Susan P572
Crout, Steve A685
Crout, Megan P420
Crout, Randy P420
Crouter, Ann C. (Nan) A811
Crouter, Ann C. (Nan) P600
Crouther, Marilyn A419
Crow, M. Chad A153
Crow, John A196
Crow, Scott A314
Crow, Jeff A324
Crow, Timothy M. (Tim) A426
Crow, Stan A602
Crow, Michael M. P44
Crow, Stewart P51
Crow, Scott P190
Crow, Cameron P680
Crowder, Clara A539
Crowder, Carolyn P69
Crowder, Otis A P148
Crowder, William T P148
Crowder, Andy P488
Crowe, Richard A140
Crowe, Tim A160
Crowe, Mike A218
Crowe, Maria A511
Crowe, Carl A878
Crowe, Bill A916
Crowe, Tim E55
Crowell, Wyatt E A437
Crowell, Eric P106
Crowell, Eric P252
Crowell, Keri E185
Crowley, Larry A109
Crowley, JD A175
Crowley, F. Michael A528
Crowley, Margaret A557
Crowley, Michael A846
Crowley, Richard D. (Rick) P458
Crowley, Larry E36
Crown, Timothy A. (Tim) A454
Crown, Brian P453
Crownover, Shannon P596
Crowson, Niel P171
Crowther, Chip P72
Croxton, Kristen A163
Crozier, Barry A95
Crozier, Barry P55
Crozier, Susan P306
Cruce, Andrea A180
Crudo, David A576
Crudo, David E297
Crudup, Carlton P2
Cruikshank, J. David A105
Cruise, Bill P213
Crum, Bill A441
Crum, Jared A507
Crum, Jared P288
Crumby, Douglas P69
Crummy, Kevin A. E110
Crump, Darlene A175
Crump, Julie A452
Crump, Susan A563
Crump, Scott A734
Crump, Susan P346
Crump, Julie E215

Crumpton, Henry A. E23
Crutcher, Emily A478
Crutcher, Brian T. A803
Crutchfield, Joe P184
Cruz, Alex A168
Cruz, Edia A204
Cruz, Julie A240
Cruz, Sergio A490
Cruz, Michael P60
Cruz, Alberto De La P88
Cruz, Rosa De La P88
Cruz, Roberto de la P152
Cruz, Dimitri J P184
Cruz, Liza De La P528
Cruz, Scott De La P601
Cruz, Clairissa P619
Cruz, Paulo P676
Cruz, Jo--o Manuel Ver-ssimo Marques da W134
Cruz, A.B. E121
Cruzan, Jeff P250
Cryan, John W123
Cryer, Edward P361
Crystal, Enid A131
Crystal, Richard P580
Crépin, Frédéric R. W388
Csapo, Peter P. P14
Cseh, Bela W247
Csoma, Stephan W379
Csonger, Rob A607
Ctp, Jim Donohue A221
Cubbage, Gary C. A140
Cubbon, Henry W120
Cubias, Carlos A850
Cuccias, Brian A442
Cucco, Wayne A54
Cuchara, Lisa P450
Cuddihy, Robert A476
Cuddy, Christopher M. (Chris) A74
Cude, Roger A438
Cudkowicz, Merit Ester P590
Cudmore, Tony W63
Cudmore, Tony W64
Cue, Eduardo H. (Eddy) A70
Cue, Eddy A70
Cuellar, Lissa P422
Cuervo, Larry A399
Cuervo, Carlos A906
Cuevas, Disnalda A163
Cuevas, Jason A383
Cuevas, Arturo P184
Cuffe, Michael S. A410
Cugini, Dominic A489
Cuiksa, Wendy P449
Cukrowski, Walter P319
Culbert, John P155
Culbertson, Darian A32
Culbertson, Leslie S. A456
Culbreath, John P427
Culbreth, M. Scott E15
Culhaci, Hayri W18
Culham, Harry W80
Culhane, Michael A366
Cullari, Lynne A537
Cullen, Thomas A. (Tom) A270
Cullen, Susan A359
Cullen, William A405
Cullen, John A A478
Cullen, Michael R P69
Cullen, Michael P511
Cullimore, Philip E115
Cullinane, Charles A767
Culling, Robert (Doug) A736
Culling, Robert (Doug) P492
Culloch, Cathy Mc P484
Cullumber, Brad E432
Culnan, Mary Beth P537
Culp, John A474
Culp, Patricia A500
Culp, Susan P406
Culp, Patricia E238
Culpepper, Jason A742
Culpepper, Lee A878
Culpepper, Karen P198

Culpepper, Jason E372
Culver, Curt S. A557
Culver, John A762
Culver, Regina A769
Culwell, Curtis P208
Cumbaa, Charlie E44
Cumbaa, Charles E44
Cumberledge, George A823
Cumberledge, George P622
Cumming, Christine M. A323
Cumming, Ian M. E201
Cummings, Sean J. A403
Cummings, Charles R A420
Cummings, Kevin A467
Cummings, Sean A480
Cummings, Bob A480
Cummings, Jerilin A857
Cummings, Anita M P113
Cummings, Heather P276
Cummings, Bruce D. P283
Cummings, Gary P482
Cummings, Lori P521
Cummings, Sue W370
Cummings, Charles R E198
Cummings, Kevin E223
Cummins, Chris A28
Cummins, Michael A738
Cummins, Hugh S. (Beau) A774
Cummins, Chris P17
Cummiskey, Chris A383
Cummisky, Olivia A900
Cune, Bill A238
Cuneo, Jack A145
Cuneo, Jack P82
Cunfer, Todd A416
Cunha, Paulo Guliherme Aguiar W379
Cuningham, David P543
Cunliffe, Adam E172
Cunney, Michael A528
Cunningham, Lisa A81
Cunningham, Benjamin A131
Cunningham, David L. A327
Cunningham, Brenda A484
Cunningham, William H. A513
Cunningham, James A657
Cunningham, Everett V. A687
Cunningham, Mike P26
Cunningham, Larry P120
Cunningham, Jennifer P286
Cunningham, Christopher P392
Cunningham, John P645
Cunningham, Jodi P663
Cunningham, Phil P679
Cunningham, John H. E9
Cunningham, Jim E44
Cunningham, Jeff E190
Cunningham, Kelly E253
Cunnion, Bill A901
Cunnion, Bill P692
Cupp, Ronnie P575
Cupps, Nancy P301
Cupps, Donald L. P647
Curcio, Michael J. A283
Curd, Samantha S A737
Curd, Samantha S E367
Cure, David A885
Cure, Carlos W133
Curl, Kim P421
Curleigh, James A509
Curley, Michael A353
Curley, Shannon A478
Curley, Abby A691
Curley, Robert M. E41
Curnow, Randy A552
Curnow, Randy P328
Curoe, Tim A788
Curphy, Rona A111
Curphy, Rona P56
Curran, Terrie A178
Curran, Martin J. (Marty) A238
Curran, Teresa M. A324
Curran, Joe A532
Curran, Michael J. A548
Curran, Shawn A809
Curran, Michael J. P321

Curran, Jennifer P342
Curran, Michael J. P342
Curran, Greg P630
Curran, David W395
Curran, John J. E82
Curran, Steve E351
Currarino, Giancarlo A628
Curren, John A729
Currens, Bill A281
Current, Pam P183
Current, Richard R E381
Currey, Robert J. (Bob) E91
Currie, Calvin A780
Currie, Kenne A788
Currie, Dean W. P90
Currie, Phyllis P342
Currie, Scott P343
Currie, Theresa L. (Teri) W370
Currie, Gordon A.M. W394
Currington, Karen A185
Curry, Margaret A260
Curry, John A480
Curry, Janet P118
Curry, Robert P122
Curry, Denise P135
Curry, Wanda C P184
Curry, Maridee P320
Curry, Susan J. P611
Curry, Jeffrey T P686
Curry-Briggs, Doreen P39
Curtin, Jim A96
Curtin, Mike A835
Curtis, Barbara A97
Curtis, Michelle A112
Curtis, Mark D. A353
Curtis, Lynda D. A582
Curtis, Scott A. A693
Curtis, Marilyn P202
Curtis, Lynda D. P373
Curtis, Barbara E32
Curtis, Michelle E38
Curtis, Mark D. E159
Curtis, Dave E172
Curtis, Chase S. E226
Curtiss, Rick A644
Curtiss, Lisa A691
Curwin, Ronald A120
Cush, Tom A691
Cush, Thomas A691
Cusher, Andrew P631
Cushing, Robert B. (Bob) A13
Cushing, Laura A520
Cushing, Robert P18
Cushing, Donald E146
Cushman, Bob A300
Cushman, Deann A546
Cushman, Audrey P314
Cusick, Bob A725
Cusick, Steve A904
Cusick, Betty P356
Cusick, Thomas B. E86
Cusick, Patrick E303
Cusick, Steve E442
Cussen, Laura A480
Custer, Timothy R. A69
Custer, Scott A518
Custer, Scott P292
Custodio, William A898
Cutietta, Robert A. A860
Cutietta, Robert A. P656
Cutino, Camille G. E51
Cutler, Alexander A287
Cutler, Scott A288
Cutler, Juanita P99
Cutler, Alexander P174
Cutliff, Scott A692
Cutliff, Scott P454
Cutlip, Robert G. E178
Cutt, Timothy J. (Tim) W64
Cutter, David W128
Cutting, Tim A744
Cuyk, Ryun Van A81
Cuyler, Justin M P445
Cuzzi, Gregory A670
Cwalina, Marianne P82

Cwikla, Kelly P412
Cwynar, Mark A707
Cygan, James P48
Cymrot, Andrew A531
Cyndi, Framme P188
Cynthia, Chambers A823
Cyphers, Randy A149
Cyphers, Sue P225
Cyphert, Mark J. A674
Cyr, Alaina P562
Cyr, Carole P603
Cyr, Steven E18
Czajka, Edward J. A667
Czajka, Edward J. E336
Czajkowski, Tom A127
Czajkowski, Andrew P238
Czarnecki, Kevin A375
Czarnecki, Walter P A643
Czarnecky, Greg A728
Czartoski, Timothy A476
Czerniejewski, Stacy P651
Czeschin, Frank E160
Czumak, Michael P325
Czyz, Danielle A599
Czyz, Tammy A720
Czyz, Annemarie P532
Czyz, Tammy P362
Czyzewski, Kim A639
Czyzewski, Kim E325

D

D, Pedro Cazabon M P403
D, Gregory A Franklin Ed P630
D, Eric Dickson M P632
Dabagia, Robert C. A431
Dabagia, Robert C. E205
Dabbs, Lorrie P243
Dabelic, Claudio A730
Dabner, Mike A200
Daboval, Wendy A192
Dach, Leslie A A878
Dacko, Michael A81
Daco, Katherine A133
DaCorsi, Mike A913
Dacosta, Tony A862
Dacosta, Anthony A862
Dacosta, Tony E419
Dacosta, Anthony E419
Dacunha, Kathleen A258
Dacus, Scott A748
Dadalt, Peter J P652
Dadey, Bryan P613
Dadic, Paul P461
Dadkho, Farhad E357
Daehnke, Arno W339
Daeihagh, Pirouz P385
Daffey, Michael D. A389
Daffron, Eric P242
Daga, Shobna A155
Daghe, Noelle A214
Daghe, Noelle P128
Dagher, Ramzi A862
Dagher, Ramzi E419
Dahan, René W209
Dahl, Craig R. A789
Dahl, Robert P440
Dahl, Erica E429
Dahlberg, Janet A461
Dahlen, Jeffrey A. (Jeff) E374
Dahlheimer, Tim P40
Dahling, James D P116
Dahlmann, David S. (Dave) A342
Dahlstrom, Richard (Rick) P320
Dahnert, Wolfgang F P51
Dahua, Shi W94
Dahut, Karen M. A140
Dai, Xiao-ping A178
Daici, Silvia P184
Daigle, Robert C. (Bob) E359
Daigler, Christa A522
Dailer, Cindy A886
Dailer, Cindy E433
Dailey, Aimee A67

Dailey, John P489
Dailey, John R. (Jack) P506
Dailey, Jeffrey J. (Jeff) W405
Daiss, Ann A383
Dakey, Alan W. A646
Dakey, Alan W. E330
Dalal, Amit A599
Dalal, Vineet E307
Dalcin, Paolo A854
Dale, Jeffery F. A746
Dale, Jeffrey A746
Dale, Michael A919
Dale, Nancy P298
Dale, Ken P566
Dale, Jonathan E437
Dalecki, Cristin A390
Daleo, Robert D. (Bob) P200
Daley, Kevin A417
Daley, Dorian E A624
Daley, Elizabeth M. A860
Daley, Elizabeth M. P656
Dalgleish, Glen A139
Dalgleish, Glen A241
Dalhouse, Warner E251
Dalia, Randall A460
Dall, Trisha A448
Dallago, Lou A648
Dallaire, Seth A38
Dallala, Daniel P96
Dallam, Thomas A420
Dallam, Thomas A198
Dallara, Ron A544
Dalrymple, Christopher K. A30
Dalrymple, Jeff A912
DalSanto, Robert J. A890
DalSanto, Robert J. P684
Dalton, Hector A2
Dalton, Brett A56
Dalton, Gregory W. A112
Dalton, Michelle A165
Dalton, Alexandra A260
Dalton, Bary A324
Dalton, Lashawn A489
Dalton, James A628
Dalton, Mark A644
Dalton, James T. A698
Dalton, Justin A782
Dalton, Ellie A810
Dalton, Jessica P26
Dalton, William P225
Dalton, Lisa P361
Dalton, James T. P456
Dalton, Ellie P597
Dalton, Mark F. P615
Dalton, Gregory W. E38
Daly, Jim A115
Daly, Brendan P. A117
Daly, James A307
Daly, Andrew A406
Daly, Bill A454
Daly, Colleen A489
Daly, Tom A522
Daly, David M. A678
Daly, John A704
Daly, Ronald E. P2
Daly, Christine P147
Daly, Ashley P327
Daly, Marilyn P369
Daly, Audrey P676
Daly, Michael P. E41
Daly, Kevin E286
Daly, John E351
Dam, Cari A541
Dam, Anders Christian W201
Dam, Cari E266
Damanaki, Maria P596
Damashek, Yumiko E50
Damassa, Joe A461
Damato, Tim A81
Dambach, Michael A129
Dambrosio, Nancy A131
Dameron, Jeffrey C P110
Damico, Jennifer A649
Damiris, George J. A423
Damme, Niek Jan Van W126

A = AMERICAN BUSINESS	
E = EMERGING COMPANIES	
P = PRIVATE COMPANIES	
W = WORLD BUSINESS	

Dammon, Robert M. P96
Damore, Joseph P346
Damrongchietanon, Prasopsuk W202
Damschroder, Patricia P613
Dan, Brian A13
Dan, James R. A15
Dan, Munson A377
Dan, Chad A448
Dan, James R. P9
Dan, Foster P255
Dan, Joe P444
Dana, Michal Carmi W46
Dana, Michael W277
Danch, Stephen M P660
Danchak, Richard A728
Dandy, April P624
Daneau, Guy W180
Danes, Mike A82
Danes, Mike P49
Dang, Doan A247
Dang, Kimberly A. (Kim) A492
Dang, Thanh P391
Dang, Minh P602
Dang, Doan E103
Dangel, Wolfgang H. E390
Dangerfield, Clyde R P212
Danie, Mark A644
Daniel, James R. A98
Daniel, Marvin A201
Daniel, William K. (Dan) A253
Daniel, Jane A308
Daniel, John M. A348
Daniel, Becky A802
Daniel, Chuck P39
Daniel, Karen L P75
Daniel, Bobby P88
Daniel, Karen L P88
Daniel, Patricia P168
Daniel, Biediger P194
Daniel, Becky P242
Daniel, Jacob P274
Daniel, Tammy P421
Daniel, Becky P562
Daniel, Charles P668
Daniel, James R. E33
Daniel, David E439
Daniels, J. Todd A19
Daniels, Cheryl A49
Daniels, Alan A49
Daniels, Jon G. A166
Daniels, Bill A182
Daniels, Nancy A269
Daniels, Scott A452
Daniels, Ronald J. (Ron) A475
Daniels, Matthew A513
Daniels, Brady A597
Daniels, Tamika A724
Daniels, Christina A766
Daniels, Peter A817
Daniels, Kenneth A844
Daniels, Erik A865
Daniels, Jodie P101
Daniels, Stephen P114
Daniels, Clive P141
Daniels, Ronald J. (Ron) P266
Daniels, Mitchell E. (Mitch) P449
Daniels, Mark P521
Daniels, Ikeisha P610
Daniels, Bobbi P646
Daniels, Bill E63
Daniels, Scott E215
Daniels, Kenneth E412
Danielson, Jean P21
Danilewitz, Dale A59
Danilkovitch, Alla E319
Dankel, Roger E373
Dankner, Wayne P417
Danley, Derek A565
Danmeter, Debbie A244

Dannaher, Michelle A449
Dannenfeldt, Thomas W126
Danner, Nicole A318
Danner, Rosalin A721
Danner, Dean P48
Dannewitz, Charles V. (Chuck) A792
Dannov, David M. A730
Dansermsuk, Sukhawat W88
Dantani, Shigeki W336
Dantuono, Anthony A845
Dantuono, Anthony E413
Dantzler, Rhonda D A221
Danza, Franck P290
Danziger, Kay P281
Dao, Mark P356
Daochai, Predee W202
DaPaah, Janine A328
Dapeer, Jonathan E9
Daponte, Ken A130
Dapper, Brent A886
Dapper, Brent E433
Daprile, Joseph R P179
Daprile, Jospeh R P378
DAquila, Richard P698
Darby, Maria A140
Darby, Tom E426
Darcy, Larissa A112
Darcy, Mike A229
Darcy, Mike P137
Darcy, Larissa E38
Dardano, Raymond P309
Darden, J. Matthew A822
Darendinger, Steve A199
Dargan, Susan A766
DArgenio, David E374
Dargie, John A355
Dargusch, Jonathan D. A886
Dargusch, Jonathan D. E433
Darin, Bob A250
Dark, Dana P594
Darkatsh, Sam A693
Darkin, Don E354
Darkow, Grant P79
Darlene, Libiszewski A893
Darlene, Libiszewski E436
Darling, Michael A390
Darling, Joseph G. E18
Darlington, Angela W38
Darmon, Marc W364
Darnall, Alexander P526
Darne, Michael A530
Darnell, Lindsay P13
Darnley, Patricia A179
Darnow, Tamara A489
Darrenkamp, Kevin A519
Darricarrére, Yves-Louis W372
Darrington, Jim A458
Darrington, Jim P251
Darrow, Bruce P355
Darrow, Betsy E183
Darsey, James R. A605
Darsey, Larry P694
Dart, Richard C. P160
Daruwala, Zarin W181
Daruwala, Zarin W340
Darwin, Brett A885
Das, Sushanto A436
Das, Saroj A774
Das, Tuhin P325
Dasbach, Angie A249
Dasgupta, Tuhin A105
Dash, Michael A173
DaSilva, Kevin A695
DaSilva, Jack A813
DaSilva, Jack P616
Daskin, Patricia A691
Dasta, Vince P167
Dastis, Paul A576
Dastis, Paul E297
Dastugue, Michael P. A878
Datema, Craig A37
Datema, Craig P29
Dato, Sandra A163
Datta, Falguni A85
Daubner, Thomas P620

Dauch, David C. A45
Dauchy, Joe E439
Dauer, Daniel M P406
Dauerman, Mitchell K. (Mitch) E407
Dauger, Jean-Marie W143
Daugherty, Michael A330
Daugherty, John A501
Daugherty, Gary A611
Daugherty, Paul W5
Daughters, Shelly A800
Daughters, Shelly P559
Daughtrey, Tana A192
Daukas, Galan A644
Daulton, Howard A308
Daum, John P627
Daum, Martin W114
Daumer, Bill A85
Daurio, Jennifer A214
Daurio, Jennifer P128
Daurio, Nancy P302
Dauterive, F Ralph P403
Dave, Uday A250
Dave, Naimesh P125
Davenport, Rodney A32
Davenport, Bobby A115
Davenport, Joel W A196
Davenport, J. Mays A504
Davenport, Nancy A555
Davenport, Ronald A821
Davenport, DeWitt P92
Davenport, Mel P435
Davenport, Christopher P548
Davenport, Ronald P621
Davenport, Mary P666
Davenport, Mely P697
Davenport, J. Mays E241
Davern, Alexander E78
Davert, Marshall P361
Daveu, Marie Claire W204
Davey, Deirdre A56
Davey, James E. (Jim) A406
Davi, Philip A163
David, Dustin A64
David, Cathy A330
David, Harmon A405
David, Rose Marie A427
David, Scott B. A783
David, Richard A912
David, Glenn C. A921
David, Prabu P341
David, Laurent W66
David, Caio Ibrahim W191
David, Rose Marie E202
David, Cliff E257
David-Borha, Sola W339
Davidar, David D. E179
Davidman, Jeff A261
Davidoff, Ravin P80
Davids, Jody R. A647
Davidson, Bruce A182
Davidson, Benjamin A406
Davidson, Jonathan A482
Davidson, Wendy A485
Davidson, William A916
Davidson, Curt P18
Davidson, Richard P P106
Davidson, Robert G P331
Davidson, Lisa P356
Davidson, Sherwin P434
Davidson, Brian P536
Davidson, Catherine P571
Davidson, Gary P588
Davidson, Bruce E63
Davidson, Timothy S. E295
Davidsson, Peter A898
Davidtz, Judy A94
Davidtz, Judy P53
Davies, Richard A586
Davies, Pamela A750
Davies, John A752
Davies, Bill A885
Davies, Neal P333
Davies, Howard J. W312
Davies, John E41
Davila, Diana P242

Davis, Julia K. A18
Davis, James C. (Jim) A31
Davis, Chris A81
Davis, Helene B A103
Davis, Robert A115
Davis, John A115
Davis, Cindy A120
Davis, Darryl W. A136
Davis, Erica A149
Davis, J. Kimbrough (Kim) A162
Davis, Kim A162
Davis, Shelby A163
Davis, John A166
Davis, Kurt A175
Davis, John A196
Davis, Patrick A204
Davis, Patricia A207
Davis, Pat A207
Davis, Darrin A221
Davis, Shantel A243
Davis, Betty A244
Davis, Mike A244
Davis, Georgetta A280
Davis, Debby A327
Davis, Chad A330
Davis, Kathie A333
Davis, Lou J. A341
Davis, Sharon L. A344
Davis, Claude E. A344
Davis, Alicia Boler A378
Davis, Stephen J. A408
Davis, Jana J. A410
Davis, Jeffery Chad A428
Davis, Pau A438
Davis, John R. A446
Davis, Steven A448
Davis, Douglas L. (Doug) A456
Davis, Reginald A493
Davis, Ryan A497
Davis, Robert M. A550
Davis, Russ A558
Davis, Jeff A563
Davis, Will A572
Davis, Owen A584
Davis, Ian A611
Davis, Erika T. A626
Davis, Timothy Paul A638
Davis, Jeffrey (Jeff) A640
Davis, Scott A647
Davis, Randy A659
Davis, Donna A677
Davis, George S. A685
Davis, James E. A687
Davis, Glenn A690
Davis, Pam A700
Davis, Dan A723
Davis, Steven D. A735
Davis, Jonathan S. A736
Davis, Reid A751
Davis, Cindy A754
Davis, Mike A770
Davis, Nancy B. A772
Davis, Lanette A774
Davis, Mary A774
Davis, Laverne A780
Davis, Tim A782
Davis, Clarence A794
Davis, Dr Eddie J A800
Davis, Robert D. (Bob) A820
Davis, Raymond P. (Ray) A839
Davis, Raymond A857
Davis, Leslie C. A859
Davis, Wade C. A871
Davis, Stephanie A885
Davis, Mike A890
Davis, Jennifer A908
Davis, Ashley P3
Davis, Heather P6
Davis, Steve P8
Davis, Yolanda P11
Davis, James C. (Jim) P24
Davis, Elizabeth P64
Davis, Tommye Lou P64
Davis, Ray P66
Davis, Mary P68

Davis, Jonathan G. P82
Davis, Jason P89
Davis, Brandon P96
Davis, Pamela Bowles P98
Davis, Richard P106
Davis, Carolyn P118
Davis, Scott P120
Davis, Richard K P126
Davis, Dr Kent P157
Davis, Adora P170
Davis, Pamela P176
Davis, Brian P176
Davis, Ricky P178
Davis, Pamela P181
Davis, Joanne P196
Davis, Matt P199
Davis, Chris P234
Davis, Mary Jane P240
Davis, Steven P246
Davis, Shirley P247
Davis, Dawn P260
Davis, Beth P292
Davis, Cory P300
Davis, Auston P300
Davis, Leslie C P301
Davis, Jonathan S. P336
Davis, Tim P345
Davis, Don P345
Davis, Craig P352
Davis, Kenneth L P355
Davis, Eric P359
Davis, Will P359
Davis, Jed P368
Davis, Kay P368
Davis, Owen P376
Davis, Mathew P386
Davis, Richard E. P399
Davis, Alphonse G P410
Davis, Elaine P P420
Davis, Quincy P465
Davis, David P470
DAVIS, CHERYL P473
Davis, Jonathan S. P492
Davis, Anne P498
Davis, Steve P503
Davis, Kenneth P509
Davis, Dr Eddie J P559
Davis, Myra P560
Davis, Shawn P560
Davis, Dawn P565
Davis, Joan S. P576
Davis, Greg P579
Davis, Jeff P590
Davis, Ladeva P603
Davis, Debra A. P613
Davis, John P618
Davis, Michael P625
Davis, Bo P636
Davis, Jennifer P641
Davis, Leslie C. P652
Davis, Tyler P658
Davis, Deborah P665
Davis, A. Jack P669
Davis, Traci P677
Davis, Mike P684
Davis, Glenn P694
Davis, Darrell W20
Davis, Gareth W148
Davis, Lisa W331
Davis, Sarah R. W394
Davis, John B. E41
Davis, Todd E75
Davis, Mike E107
Davis, Terri E119
Davis, Lou J. E153
Davis, Sharon L. E154
Davis, Blake E175
Davis, John R. E210
Davis, Robert T. E220
Davis, Desiree E253
Davis, Larry C E276
Davis, Glenn E345
Davis, Reid E377
Davis, Cindy E380
Davis, Raymond P. (Ray) E409

Davis, Jeff L. E419
Davis, Eugene I. (Gene) E419
Davis, Jennifer E446
Davis-Smith, Amy A782
Davison, J Scott A621
Davison, Paul J A678
Davison, Corey A795
Davison, J Scott P407
Davisson, Robert J. A738
Davoren, Peter J A813
Davoren, Peter J P608
Davoren, Peter J. W6
Davy, Alan P455
Davy, Alan W74
Davydova, Yulia E320
Dawes, Christopher A507
Dawes, Christopher P288
Dawes, Christopher P300
Dawes, Karen A. E351
Dawley, Mary P50
Dawson, Mike A366
Dawson, Mark A398
Dawson, Suzanne A493
Dawson, Jane D A565
Dawson, Pat D. A618
Dawson, Lena A904
Dawson, Michelle P136
Dawson, Jeff E216
Dawson, Lena E442
Day, Craig A160
Day, Diane A329
Day, Thomas R. A432
Day, Samantha A468
Day, Zane A496
Day, Kate A556
Day, Diana A735
Day, J. Randal A748
Day, J Randal A748
Day, William B. (Bill) A782
Day, Janet A807
Day, Monica A832
Day, Sarah A903
Day, Mike A920
Day, Sarah P171
Day, Tracy P233
Day, Samantha P252
Day, Kim P330
Day, Debbie P357
Day, John P437
Day, Lynn Carmen P462
Day, Janet P574
Day, James H P625
Day, Howard P671
Day, Bill P677
Day, Anthony W348
Day, Craig E55
Day, Ken E257
Day, Paulee C. E259
Dayal, Gaurov A760
Dayal, Gaurov P523
Dayon, Alexandre (Alex) A723
Days, Karen P365
DC, Sister Bernice Coreil A80
DC, Sister Maureen McGuire A80
DC, Sister Bernice Coreil P47
DC, Sister Maureen McGuire P47
DDS, Will Daniels P68
DDS, L Kenneth Heuler P115
DDS, Daniel D Louie P226
DDS, Duane Voshell P525
DDS, Maurice Gregory P545
De, Maurilio A200
De, Kathy A272
De, Arlette P14
Deacon, Mary Ann A500
Deacon, Steven D P155
Deacon, Mary Ann E238
Deakin, Neil A693
Deakin, Scott M. E251
Deal, Casey A. (Stan) A136
Deal, Helena A417
Deal, Gale P97
Deal, Philip P141
Deal, Bradley P467
Dealy, Richard P. (Rich) A657

Deambrogio, Roberto W141
Dean, Robert A173
Dean, John C. A183
Dean, Clay A350
Dean, Robert A573
Dean, Judy A584
Dean, Andrea A710
Dean, Edward P53
Dean, James D P75
Dean, Kathy P163
Dean, Doug P179
Dean, Campbell P214
Dean, Ronald E P242
Dean, Patti P291
Dean, Linda P357
Dean, Pam P385
Dean, Morre P417
Dean, Alan J. E62
Dean, Deborah E101
Dean, Clay E157
Dean, Alison E225
Dean-Hammel, Bridget A131
Deane, Jeffrey E252
Deangelo, Joseph J A411
DeAngelo, Lawrence J. (Larry) E261
Deanhardt, Jill A115
Deardorff, Kevin L. A500
Deardorff, Kevin L. E238
Dearman, Paul A131
Dearmond, Carolyn A333
Dearth, Randall S. (Randy) P90
Deason, Richard A505
Deaton, Craig A912
Deaver, W. Scott A92
Deaver, Scott A93
Deaver, Russell A158
Deaver, Lori E233
Deaver, Jim P233
Deavers, Michael P243
DeBatty, Jill A500
DeBatty, Jill E238
Debenedetti, Pablo G. P606
Debenedictis, Nicholas P42
Debenedicts, Peter E360
Debergalis, Joseph P365
Debertin, Jay A194
Deblaere, Johan G. (Jo) W5
Deblasi, Michael P179
Debnam, Henry A405
Debo, Michael A187
Debo, Michael E71
DeBoer, Bryan B. A515
DeBoer, Mark A515
DeBoer, Sidney B. (Sid) A515
Deboer, Dave P191
Debolt, Mary Kay A468
Debolt, Mary Kay P253
Debon, Marie-Ange W343
Deboni, Liz A904
Deboni, Liz E442
Deborah, Pine P68
Debord, Wes A332
deBrauwere, Daniel A659
DeBruce, Paul A325
Debruin, Christopher P545
Debruyne, Luc W158
Decamp, Bill A655
Decamp, Bill E333
DeCarlo, Michelle A513
Decastro, Victoria P115
Dechant, Suzanne A763
Decher, Peter A842
Dechiro, Carlo V A758
Dechiro, Carlo V P519
Dechow, Joe P359
Deck, Richard A682
Deck, Brian A. E227
Deckard, Vicki A738
Decker, Daniel A. A149
Decker, Casey A319
Decker, Edward P. (Ted) A426
Decker, Julie A701
Decker, Patrick K. A914
Decker, Andrea P329
Decker, Jeff E17

Decker, Linda F. E364
Decknatel, Patty P602
DeClaris, Wade N. A906
Declas, Jean-Luc A913
Decleene, Judy P220
Decock, Tracy A659
Decoeur, Dan P694
DeCoeur, Daniel P694
Decolli, Chris A3
DeConinck, Louis H. W180
Decorte, Raymond P173
Decraene, Dave A350
Decraene, Stefaan W66
Decraene, Dave E157
Dedeke, Brian P188
Dedicoat, Chris A199
Dedinsky, John G. A634
Dedominicis, Kim A784
Dee, Steven A593
Dee, Timothy P416
Dee, Tim P416
Dee, John J. E438
Deeba, Amer S. E342
Deeds, Thomas A165
Deegan, Matt A235
Deeks, Terence N. A576
Deeks, Terence N. E297
Deering, Michael P296
Dees, Kent A704
Dees, Chuck A881
Dees, Kent E350
DeFalco, Ciro M. A576
DeFalco, Ciro M. E297
DeFazio, Gary A119
Defeis, Nicholas A676
Defenbaugh, Raymond E P73
Definis, Karen A130
Defoe, John A723
Defoggia, James A659
Defontnouvelle, Patrick A325
Deford, Meghan P196
Deforest, Roger P662
DeFranco, James (Jim) A270
DeFrank, Jay P68
DeFreese, Susan A446
DeFreese, Susan E210
DeFreitas, Shannie A109
DeFreitas, Shannie E36
Defusco, Richard P648
Degen, Paul P622
Degenhart, Elmar W108
Degges, Paul A797
Degges, Paul P557
Degier, Vanessa P482
Degina, Anthony P282
DeGiorgio, Kenneth D. A335
Degnan, S. Scott E441
DeGregorio, Ronald J. (Ron) A308
Deguzman, Arvin P205
Dehaan, Jan P223
Dehart, Jeanette P433
Dehaven, Judy A175
Dehaven, Michael P525
Dehaze, Alain W7
Deherrera, Brandy A919
Dehinde, Babatunde A478
Dehm, Pam P279
Dehner, Torsten A20
Dehner, Marlene P35
Dehring, Tim A594
Deigl, Jeffrey A33
Deignan, Kathleen P606
Dein, Brian P6
Deinish, Donna A474
Deinish, Donna P265
Deir, Kevin A101
Deir, Yvonne E96
Deis, Ron A453
Deitch, Sally A795
Deitch, Mark P290
Deith, Harry E153
Deitrick, James A902
Deitrick, James P693
Deitz, Robert A73
Deiure, Giovannella E242

A = AMERICAN BUSINESS
E = EMERGING COMPANIES
P = PRIVATE COMPANIES
W = WORLD BUSINESS

DeJong, Nick A67
Dejurnett, Mikki A502
Dekay, Sam A105
Dekel, Eitan E68
Deken, Paul P185
DeKenipp, Patrick A768
DeKenipp, Patrick E386
Dekeyser, Jill A684
Dekeyser, Paul P361
Dekeyser, Jill E341
Dekker, Karen A56
Dekker, Wout W299
Dekkers, Marijn W383
Delabriere, Yann W148
Delacruz, Cedric A406
Delafuente, Laura A478
Delagardelle, Pam P252
Delagi, R. Gregory (Greg) A803
Delagi, Greg A803
Delahoyde, Aaron P87
Delahunt, Susan A184
Delancey, Virginia P398
Delaney, John A143
Delaney, Steve A173
Delaney, BradleyBrad A196
Delaney, Bradley A196
Delaney, Chris A391
Delaney, Donald A476
Delaney, Thomas A. (Tom) A585
Delaney, Peter H A693
DeLaney, William J. (Bill) A782
Delaney, Thomas A. (Tom) P377
Delaney, Michelle Anne P506
Delaney, Annie P551
Delaney, Mary P683
Delaney, Kevin P. E343
Delanghe, Suzana P5
Delano, Laurie A. P579
Delany, Jim P566
Delarge, Steven P. W223
Delarosa, Dolly P497
Delatorre, Xavier P700
Delatour, John S. A349
Delaunay, Sophie P320
DeLawder, C. Daniel (Dan) A633
Delawder, Bruce A814
Delawder, Bruce P616
Delay, Jeffrey A659
Delay, Emmanuel W286
Delduchetto, Thomas A577
Delellis, Michael A683
Deleon, Marcos A475
Deleon, Marcos P266
Delessio, Linda P210
Delfassy, Gilles A620
Delgado, Joaquin A2
Delgado, Mercedes P184
Delgado, Karyn C P473
Delgatti, Michael W. E203
Delghiaccio, Brian A707
Delgiudice, Tim A695
Delhomme, Jake A562
Delie, Vincent J. (Vince) A360
Delie, Vincent J. (Vince) E164
DeLillo, Kevin A13
Delin, Scott E391
Delio, Anthony P. (Tony) A453
DeLise, Antonio L. (Tony) E260
Delkoski, Mike A3
Dell, Joseph E. A212
Dell, Michael S. A875
Dell, Joseph E. E79
Della-Rodolfa, Carolyn P164
Dellacroce, Peter A727
Dellafosse, Mack P89
Dellaglio, Vincent A131
Dellantonia, Dean A691
Dellaquila, Frank J. A295
Dellaripa, David A785

Dellocono, John A. P107
Dellows, Chary P695
Dell'Osso, Domenic J. (Nick) A190
Delnero, Dan P663
DeLoach, Thomas C. A78
DeLoach, Harris E. A750
DeLoach, Scott A906
Deloach, Darlene P518
Delong, David P577
Delong, William C P577
Delong, Charles R P577
Delong, Mary Lou P625
DeLongchamps, Peter C. A396
Delorenz, Don A912
DeLorenzo, Michael A56
DeLorenzo, Marc A165
DeLorenzo, Rhonda A359
Delorimier, John A438
Delorme, Philippe W322
Delp, Robert D. (Rob) A918
Delph, Rob A800
Delph, Rob E396
DelPriore, Robert E276
Delpropoto, Zachary A413
Delpropoto, Zachary P234
Delsol, Sheryl P493
Deltenre, Ingrid W52
Deluca, Catherine A163
DeLuca, Richard R. A550
Deluca, Donna P231
Deluca, Vince P293
Delucia, Gayle P224
DeLuise, James A204
Deluke, Linda A733
Deluke, Linda P491
Delvecchio, Christopher P360
Delventhal, Brad P602
Delzingaro, Mike A915
Delzotto, Paul A78
Demakas, Michael P318
Demange, Vincent W303
Demarchis, John A659
DeMarco, David S. (Dave) A78
Demarcus, Mark A428
Demarcus, W Mark A428
DeMaria, Jacqueline M. A892
Demarie, Noreen A108
Demartino, Joann A741
Demartino, Joann E370
Demas, Sandra A73
Demasi, Deena A871
Demastus, Jerry A277
DeMatteo, Daniel A. A372
DeMay, Brian A877
Dembitz, Terry A892
Demchak, William S. (Bill) A659
Demchak, Robert A744
DeMeester, Chris E162
Demel, Herbert W229
Demello, David P4
Demere, Robert A751
Demere, Robert E378
Demers, Andrew A204
Demeter, Chris A109
Demeter, Chris E36
Demetriou, Steven J. A472
DeMichiei, Robert A. A859
DeMichiei, Robert A. P652
Demild, Brian A369
Deming, Peggy P73
Demircan, Ugur P226
Demirmen, Okan A100
Demirovski, Fluturi P456
Demita, Tab A332
Demme, Kendra P86
Demmerle, Stefan A141
Demmings, Keith W. A83
Demoleas, John P P541
Demonbreun, Jamie P445
Demont, Melanie A56
Demont, Adam A81
Demosthenous, Barbara P248
Demott, Andrew D. E391
Demple, Bruce P217
Dempsey, Maureen A68

Dempsey, Joan A. A140
Dempsey, Patrick E432
Dempster, Graham Wayne W256
Demski, David M. (Dave) E178
Demuro, Jerry W40
Denahan, A. Alexandra E75
Denamur, Mike A478
Denault, Leo P. A300
Denault, Leo P P185
Denbaum, Larry A105
Denbina, David A163
denBoer, Marten P155
Denby, Farrell A130
Denby, Kristy A221
Deneau, Robin P610
Denehy, William A441
DeNezza, Matthew R. E118
Deng, Kenny P7
Dengg, Robb A458
Dengg, Robb P251
Denham, Heather A260
Denham, Amber P638
Denham, David P688
Denholm, David J. A485
Deni, Rob A141
Deninger, Matthew P314
Denisco, Thomas M P277
Denise, McEnaney P343
Denison, Kurtis A644
Denison, Jessica P577
Denker, Claude H. (Bud) A642
Denman, John A748
Denmark, Caitlin P140
Dennehy, Stacey A868
Denner, Volkmar W70
Denney, Josh E302
Dennis, Bruce A136
Dennis, Crystal A222
Dennis, Ott A324
Dennis, Brian A493
Dennis, Greg A770
Dennis, Jennifer A154
Dennis, Roger J. P165
Dennis, Everette E. P398
Dennis, Jason E140
Dennis, Thomas (Tom) St. E165
Dennis-Buss, Susan A195
Dennison, Kay P40
Dennison, Mike W151
Denny, Jd A438
Denoya, Dave A869
Denoyel, Eric A375
Dent, Pamela A366
Dent, Mary J. E182
Denti, Aldo A476
Denton, David M. (Dave) A250
Denton, Bill A449
Dentone, Kristin P482
Denuzzio, Catherine P241
Deo, Rajat P241
Depail, Jean-Claude W143
Depalma, David A478
DePaolo, Joseph J. A741
Depaolo, Joseph J A742
Depaolo, Joseph J P502
DePaolo, Joseph J. A741
Depauw, Annette P335
DePauw, Karen P. P669
DePiano, Frank P398
Depies, Dan P216
DePinto, Joseph I. A165
DePinto, Joseph M. (Joe) W324
Depler, Thomas A A208
Depodesta, Shannon P450
Depowski, Robert A480
Depratter, Darrin P630
Deprey, Matthew A269
Depriest, Derryl A408
Depriest, Steve P554
Deptula, George P532
Deputy, Christine F. A596
Derba, Laura A899
Derba, Laura P690
Derby, Cindy P525
Deren, Kevin A767

Derita, Nancy P530
DeRito, John A. A207
Derizans, Richard A537
Derksen, Brian A622
Dermanuelian, Nareg A204
Dermody, Michael A105
Dermody, Christopher R. P159
Dermott, Frank X Mc P371
Dern, Jeff P441
Derner, Patty A556
Dernoncourt, Jean-Baptiste W82
Deroche, Lynne A530
DeRocher, McKensie A180
DeRosa, Mike A360
Derosa, Rebecca P64
DeRosa, Mike E164
Deroy, Joseph P P184
Derpinghaus, Patrick J. A81
Derr, Michael A766
Derr, David P421
Derr, James P525
Derr, Gary P658
Derrick, Brian P326
Derrico, Georgia S A754
DeRue, Scott A698
DeRue, Scott P456
Dery, William E147
Deryckere, Bernard P. J. P689
Desai, Bobby A371
Desalvo, Tom A733
DeSanctis, Anthony A102
DeSantis, Caitlin A390
Desantis, Mark A648
Desart, Amy P346
Descalzi, Claudio W143
Deschamps, Ignacio (Nacho) W50
Descheneaux, Michael R. (Mike) A777
Descheneaux, Michael R. (Mike) E393
Desear, Vernon P304
Deserio, Stacy A178
Deshaies, Roger P614
Deshon, Michelle A489
Deshpande, Jayant K. P45
Deshpande, Alok E182
deSilva, Peter A791
Desimas, Danny P271
Desire, Jean-Luc A796
Desisto, Donna P483
Desjardins, Fran- §ois W217
Desmarais, Brian A764
Desmarais, Michael A871
Desmarais, Brian P540
Desmarais, André R. W293
Desmarais, Paul W293
Desmarais, André R. W294
Desmarais, Paul W294
Desmaris, Thierry P102
Desmartis, Charles W82
Desmond, Marcia A171
Desmond, James A703
Desmond, Michael A769
Desmond, Marcia P100
Desoer, Barbara J. A203
Desorbo, Louis A180
Desormeaux, Joseph A375
Desormeaux, Joseph P210
DeSousa, Dennis E. A394
Desouza, Jackie P343
Despain, Daniel E117
Despeaux, Kimberly H P185
Desse, Zeleke K P644
Deste, Dario A334
Deste, Dario P193
DeStefano, Joseph (Joe) A388
Destefano, Joe A388
DeStefano, Lisa A426
DeStefano, Joanne M. P143
Destler, William W. (Bill) P464
Detchemendy, Brian A42
Detering, David P518
Dettelbach, Michael P82
Dettmar, Jackie A564
Dettmer, Brad A908
Detwiler, Kim A862

Detwiler, Kim E419
Deuel, Jeffrey J. (Jeff) A414
Deuel, Jeffrey J. (Jeff) E195
Deuprey, Charleen A102
Deuser, Susan P525
Deutsch, William J. A108
Deutsch, Clayton G. (Clay) A142
Deutsch, Donald A624
Deutsch, Jonathan P165
Deutsch, Esther W190
Dev, Raj P559
Devadar, Julie E146
Devader, Julie E146
Devaney, Edward A250
Devaraju, Ramasamy W195
Devarajulu, Krishna A865
DeVard, Jerri L. A612
DeVaughn, Michael D. P674
Devault, David V. A880
Deveau, David R P131
Deveau, Pat P500
Devendran, Anand A817
Dever, Robert E P516
Deveson, Gregory S. (Greg) A45
Devienne, Frederic A20
Devilbiss, Lisamarie A480
deVilliers, Jack E349
DeVinck, Steven Q. (Steve) E13
Devine, Jeff A199
Devine, Marty A258
Devine, Michael P. A267
Devine, Catherine A476
Devine, Dennis A. A489
Devine, David P366
Devine, Jamie P461
Devine-Pride, Anne A792
Devino, Dale P613
Devino, Betsy R. E364
Devita, Maria V P290
Devito, Bryan A888
Devleeschouwer, James P441
Devlin, Jason A131
Devoe, Clint A164
Devon, Susan P282
Devoney, William P176
DeVoney, Michael P629
DeVore, Susan D. E336
DeVore, Susan D. E337
DeVos, Doug A37
DeVos, Doug P29
Devoy, Mike A614
Devries, Douglas A260
Devries, Michelle P592
Dewaard, Roelant A362
Dewald, Julius P398
Dewar, Patrick M A519
Dewar, Marvin P497
Dewerff, Mike P252
Dewese, Susan P208
Dewey, Robert A549
Dewey, Shelley A592
Dewey, Barbara I. A811
Dewey, Duane A. A832
Dewey, Susan F. A873
Dewey, Steve P233
Dewey, Barbara I. P600
Dewey, Susan F. P668
Dewey, Robert E270
Dewhurst, Moray P. A357
DeWilder, Dean E117
Dewitt, Erin A562
Dewitt, Stephanie P136
DeWolfe, Richard B. W232
Dewyngaert, Heidi S A109
Dexian, Chen W287
Dey, Eric R. E163
Deyo, Ronnie A478
Deyoung, Robert A247
Deyoung, Linda P194
Deyoung, Robert E102
Dez, Germ N Berm P139
Dezenzo, Rosemarie A721
Dhandapani, Chandra A173
Dharmadhikary, Rahul P125
Dhillon, Janet L. A155

Dhiman, Sushil A725
Dhingra, Ajay A912
Dhulia, Sanjay A101
Dial, Karla A743
Dial, Roger P620
Dial, Karla E373
Diallo, Aboubacar O P431
Dialto, Margaret P541
Diamante, Catherine P622
Diamond, Lee A173
Diamond, Mark C A413
Diamond, Arym A723
Diamond, Gene P203
Diamond, Mark C P234
Diamond, Margae P486
Diamond, Lester P529
Diamond, Victoria P632
Diamond, Larry J. E9
Diamond, Jeremy E75
Diamond, Ben E190
Dias, Jose A649
Dias, André Pires de Oliveira W379
Diaz, Fernando A96
Diaz, Guillermo A199
Diaz, Carlos A379
Diaz, Pedro A446
Diaz, Jose Antonio A764
Diaz, Octavio J. (Tavi) A795
Diaz, Linda A869
Diaz, Gerardo P14
Diaz, Juana P226
Diaz, Dawn P237
Diaz, Gina C P291
Diaz, Ulises E P371
Diaz, Rose P390
Diaz, Lizette P407
Diaz, Jesse P427
Diaz, Jose Antonio P540
Diaz, Jorge E P602
Diaz, Pedro E210
DiBella, John E374
Dibenedetto, Tony A869
DiBianca, Susanne A723
Dibona, Gail P91
Dibrell, Henry P271
DiCamillo, Gary T A898
Dicandilo, Michael A59
Dicarlo, Barbara P564
DiCaro, Daniel P. P396
Dicenso, Frank A59
Dicerchio, Richard A240
DiChiaro, Steven J. (Steve) A822
DiCicco, Sean A158
Dicicco, Aimee L A327
DiCicco, Wendy F. E214
DiCiurcio, John A. W6
Dick, Joseph A187
Dick, Russell A. P489
Dick, Joseph E71
Dickens, Marty A655
Dickens, Dave P92
Dickens, Marty E333
Dickenson, Bill A371
Dickenson, James P260
Dickenson, Drew P444
Dickenson, Larry P567
Dicker, Derek A560
Dickerson, Gary E. A71
Dickerson, Rita A361
Dickerson, John C. P298
Dickerson, Staci P498
Dickes, Art E381
Dickey, Bill A282
Dickey, Tine A328
Dickie, Robert W405
Dickinson, Laurie A489
Dickinson, Paul A505
Dickinson, Marty J. A839
Dickinson, Marty J. E409
Dickman, Susan F A474
Dickman, Randy A532
Dickman, Susan F P262
Dickman, Angie P457
Dicks, Cindy A668
Dickseski, Jerri Fuller A442

Dickson, Tom A111
Dickson, Steve A262
Dickson, Jenny A532
Dickson, Richard A539
Dickson, Joe A548
Dickson, Chuck A548
Dickson, Tom P56
Dickson, Kevin P191
Dickson, Joe P324
Dickson, Chuck P324
Dickson, Eric P632
Dickson, James M. (Jim) W137
Dicob, Andrew A576
Dicob, Andrew E297
Dicosola, Robert A616
Dictenberg, Jaime A872
Dicus, John B. A164
Diddee, Anu P279
Didier, Bridgett P335
Dieck, Eugenie P583
Dieckmann, Anita P233
Diederich, Kirsten P386
Diedwardo, Christine P279
Diefenderfer, William M. A575
Diefenderfer, William M. E102
Diefenthaler, Aaron P. A710
Diegel, Robert J A247
Diegel, Robert J E103
Diehl, William A655
Diehl, Kristine A893
Diehl, Valerie P101
Diehl, William E333
Diehl-boyle, Constance A85
Diehm, Russell C P79
Dieker, Sharon P75
Diekmann, Michael W55
Diekmann, Michael W223
Diercks, Dwight A607
Dierks, Sara P296
Diermeier, Daniel P610
Diesch, John H P149
Diess, Herbert W390
Dieter, Claus W140
Dietrich, Martin A. A578
Dietrich, Paul A710
Dietrich, Peter T. A752
Dietrich, Tyler A777
Dietrich, Charlie P254
Dietrich, William P651
Dietrich, Douglas T. (Doug) E281
Dietrich, Tyler E393
Dietsch, Johannes W57
Dietsche, Jim P67
Dietsche, Jim P68
Dietz, Brett A484
Dietz, Robert J P207
Dietz, Diane P566
Dietz, Steve E123
Dietz, Edward R. E261
Dietzen, Joseph A889
Diez, John J. A718
DiFerdinando, John E166
Diffley, Bryan P296
Difinizio, Antoinette A584
DiFrancesco, Paul A847
DiFrancesco, Paul E414
DiFranco, Dimitra A584
Difranco, Albert P99
DiGaetani, Mark A201
Digenova, Michele A691
Diggelmann, Roland W307
Diggins, Patty P228
Dighe, Prafad P532
DiGrande, Sebastian A809
DiGregorio, Conrad E301
Diguilio, Ralph A443
Dijk, Carol Van P343
Diker, Charles M. E56
Dilan, Jose P376
Dilger, Jason A449
Dilger, John A540
Dilger, John P316
Dill, Robert C. A742
Dill, Robert C. E372
Dillard, James E A37

Dillard, Maria A85
Dillard, Mike A266
Dillard, Alex A266
Dillard, William (Bill) A266
Dillard, Michael A698
Dillard, Evan P201
Dillard, Michael P456
Diller, Barry A311
Diller, Ed A449
Diller, Lisa R. P153
Dillingham, Frederick E147
Dillon, David A3
Dillon, Michael A. (Mike) A11
Dillon, Larry G A156
Dillon, Julie A218
Dillon, Donna A228
Dillon, Mary A763
Dillon, Mary N A836
Dillon, Daniel P44
Dillon, Donna P136
Dillon, Danel P318
Dillon, Eileen P353
Dillon, Lynn P410
Dillon, Deborah P567
Dillon, Tom P601
Dillon, Roderick H. (Ric) E106
Dillow, April P674
Dilorenzo, Marybeth A503
Dilorenzo, Christina A513
DiLorenzo, Dennis A585
Dilorenzo, Marybeth P284
DiLorenzo, Dennis P377
Dilts-Skaggs, Mary P516
Dilucchio, Laura P207
Dilworth, Robert A763
Dimarco, Tony P99
Dimarco, Dana P420
DiMarco, Bret M. E83
Dimaria, Dina A696
Dimas, Constantine A520
Dimas, Michelle P123
Dimauro, Bernice P695
Dimech, Johnpaul W334
Dimicelli, Thomas A478
Dimino, Sal A120
Dimmick, Ruth P20
Dimock, Rodney C. E41
DiModica, Jeffrey E385
Dimon, James (Jamie) A480
Dimond, Soni E40
Dimopoulos, Dimitrios G. W253
Dinan, Susan P414
Dinapoli, Leonard A533
DiNapoli, Mark L. P545
DiNapoli, Michael (Mike) P545
DiNapoli, Mike P545
Dincman, Tolga A162
Dindigal, Anil A723
DiNello, Alessandro P. A356
Dines, Dauna A98
Dines, Dauna E33
Ding, Yanzhang W90
Ding, Guangmu W401
Dingemans, Simon W158
Dinger, Stephanie A841
Dinger, Stephanie P633
Dingess, Cheryl A865
Dingle, Rick A607
Dingle, David K. W81
Dinh, Viet D A834
Dinh, Mark P338
Dinicola, Peter P465
Dinis, Filipe W47
Dinjian, Randy A402
Dinn, Colin R. W330
Dinnage, Susanna A269
Dinner, Larry A173
Dinnie, Holly P65
Dinsel, Doug P167
Dinshaw, Behram M. A827
Dinsmore, Walter A133
Dinsmore, Richard A334
Dinsmore, Richard P193
Dintzis, Suzanne P533
Dinwiddie, Lucy A231

A = AMERICAN BUSINESS
E = EMERGING COMPANIES
P = PRIVATE COMPANIES
W = WORLD BUSINESS

Din- Şer, Suzan Sabanci W18
Din- Şer, Haluk W163
Diokno, Ananias P692
Dion, Jeffrey P. (Jeff) P380
Dionisio, Mike A263
Dionne, Michael P605
Diorio, Philip A221
DiPalma, Greg A913
DiPaola, Steve A868
Dipasquale, Jeff A750
Dipetrio, Kenneth A129
DiPhillips, Lucius A288
DiPietro, Kenneth A. (Ken) A129
Dippolito, Tom A267
DiPrima, Natasha P398
Dircks, Thomas C. E101
Direnzo, Patrick A247
Direnzo, Patrick E103
Diresta, Pat E316
DiRienzo, Judy E432
Dirks, Douglas D. A296
Dirkschneider, Kathryn A A695
Dirmyer, Richard P464
Dirrane, Michael J A535
Dirrane, Michael J P312
DiRusso, Lonny R. A716
Disanti, Joseph A108
Disanti, Joseph E36
DiSanto, Edmund (Ed) A55
Disanto, Salvatore A691
Disanto, Phil E1
Dishaw, Michael P61
Dishman, William M. A772
Dishman, Roy P456
DiSilvestro, Anthony P. A161
Disney, Ed A137
Dispensa, James V A134
Dispensa, James V P78
Dissinger, Debra E. A646
Dissinger, Debra E. E330
Distasio, Lynne A555
Distaso, John C. A657
Distefano, Michael A133
DiStefano, Jim A522
Distefano, Kerry A537
DiStefano, Mike A655
DiStefano, Michael E235
DiStefano, Mike E333
Distelrath, James W. E147
Ditkoff, James A253
Ditmore, Jim W118
Ditocco, Phyllis A136
DiTondo, Michelle A558
Dittemore, Karen P231
Dittenber, Jody P106
Dittgen, Juergen A693
Dittmer, Robert P631
Diven, Cathy P64
DiVittorio, Thomas (Tom) A380
Divoky, David P676
Divol, Roxane A778
Dixon, Gordon A54
Dixon, Gregory A212
Dixon, Donna A677
Dixon, Jamie A677
DIXON, RONNEY A844
Dixon, Kenneth (Ken) A870
Dixon, Jonathan P197
Dixon, Mike P369
Dixon, George P404
Dixon, Regina E P536
Dixon, Brenda P638
Dixon, Mary A P691
Dixon, Mark W341
Dixon, Gregory E79
Dixon, John E371
Dixon, Bret E404
DIXON, RONNEY E412
Dixon-Williams, Sherrie P593

Djafari, Lisa A448
Djalali, Chaden P611
Dlouhy, Thomas A701
Do, Beth A291
Do, Kristopher A329
Do, Orlando Chapa P141
Doak, Mark A22
Doan, Dan L. A614
Doan, Brittany P22
Dobbe, Steven A53
Dobbelaere, Arthur G P343
Dobber, Hugh W35
Dobbins, R. Helm A52
Dobbins, John A903
Dobbins, John P171
Dobbins, Dick P490
Dobbs, Dennis A210
Dobbs, Stephen A246
Dobbs, Fred C P406
Dobbs, Donald P P589
Dobkin, Arkadiy E130
Dobranski, Edward J. A353
Dobrauc, Christian A591
Dobrinski, Everett M. A214
Dobrinski, Everett M. P128
Dobson, Caroline A343
Dobson, James P188
Dockendorff, Charles A144
Dockerty, Karen A180
Dockery, Mike A196
Docter, Judith M. A81
Docter, Judy A81
Dodd, Jay A140
Dodd, David A382
Dodd, Layne A446
Dodd, Lynn A446
Dodd, Susan P476
Dodd, Amanda P568
Dodd, Layne E210
Dodd, Lynn E210
Dodd, Julie E407
Dodderer, Arnold D A773
Dodds, Jeffrey A814
Dodds, Vince P331
Dodds, David P386
Dodds, Larry P434
Dodds, Jeffrey P616
Dodds, Alexander W247
Dodenhoff, Steven W. A454
Dodge, R. Stanton A270
Dodge, Richard E. P399
Dodig, Victor W80
Dods, Walter A. E264
Dodson, LaRae A185
Dodson, Marti A386
Dodson, Derek P418
Doebele, Luke A34
Doebler, Carl P227
Doehner, Tamara P369
Doerfler, Max A163
Doerger, Brian A288
Doering, Tracey E P620
Doerr, David M. P14
Doessel, Johnathan A294
Doggett, John P148
Doghramji, Karl P618
Dogra, Anil P133
Doherty, William J. A62
Doherty, Michael A246
Doherty, Jon A576
Doherty, Margaret A677
Doherty, Catherine T. A687
Doherty, John E282
Doherty, Jon E297
Doherty, Christopher E328
Dohle, Markus W62
Dohnalek, David A136
Dohzen, Shirley P564
DOI, NOBUHIRO W49
Doig, David P113
Doig, John W50
Dokken, Erik E101
Dolak, Lisa P552
Dolan, Paula D. A334
Dolan, Joseph P A500

Dolan, Janet A828
Dolan, Terrance R. (Terry) A865
Dolan, Amanda P19
Dolan, Kelly P23
Dolan, Paul G P68
Dolan, John P165
Dolan, Jill S. P606
Dolan, Joseph P E237
Dolbec, Brad A163
Dolce, Diane A163
Dolce, Jeff A419
Dolinski, Maria A105
Doll, Barbara P441
Doll, Cynthia P650
Dollison, Nicole P582
Dolly, Lisa A105
Dolph, Stephen J A73
Dolph, Laura P624
Dolsten, Mikael A648
Domanico, Ronald J A411
Domanico, Lee P477
Dombowsky, Shawn A214
Dombowsky, Shawn P128
Dombrowski, Anthony P8
Dombrowski, Joseph P120
Domene, Doug A430
Domenick, Joseph A817
Dominach, Sandy A235
Domingue, Holly P412
Dominguez, Letty A244
Dominguez, Joseph A309
Dominguez, Alexus A449
Dominguez, Maria P635
Dominiak, Christophe A252
Dominick, Jay P606
Domit, Carlos Slim W25
Domit, Patrick Slim W25
Domnisch, Michaele P275
Domski, Dave P621
Donado, Yvette P175
Donaghue, Jason M P530
Donaghy, Stephen J. A858
Donaghy, Sean T. E116
Donaghy, Stephen J. E418
Donahoe, Keith A244
Donahue, Brian D. A225
Donahue, Timothy J. A242
Donahue, Hugh O A367
Donahue, Paul D. A381
Donahue, Kieran A530
Donahue, Joseph A531
Donahue, Robert A644
Donahue, Michael P174
Donahue, Tom P187
Donahue, James A. E83
Donahue, Brian D. E88
Donahue, Kenneth L. (Ken) E415
Donald, Kirkland A300
Donald, Andrew A677
Donald, Kennedy P28
Donald, Bruce Mc P83
Donald, Gwen Mc P172
Donald, Arnold W. W81
Donald, Ian W258
Donaldson, Melinda A136
Donaldson, Michael P. A304
Donaldson, Lisel A786
Donaldson, Michelle A886
Donaldson, Allison P42
Donaldson, Marcia P66
Donaldson, Cynthia Cafasso P391
Donaldson, David P631
Donaldson, Kelly E288
Donaldson, Michelle E433
Donaldson-reitz, Gayle E47
Donarski, Dave A865
Donas, Paul A56
Donato, Donna A49
Donato, Thomas A712
Donatone, Lorna C. W334
Donatoni, Anthony P42
Donatsch, Reto W52
Doncarlos, Stephen H P226
Dondanville, Ted J. A248
Donder, Daniel J P344

Dondero, Cort J. E171
Donegan, Mark A666
Donegan, Mark P438
Donelan, Amanda A851
Donelan, Stephen P355
Donelan, Dave E327
Dong, Hanh A322
Dong, Brian A390
Dong, Christopher P612
Dong, Ren Ji W95
Dong, Hyunsoo W130
Dong, Mingzhu W162
Dongjin, Wang W283
Dongsheng, Wang W68
Donham, Julie A384
Donham, Julie E176
Donica, Kimberly A556
Donigian, John A727
Donlevie, John C E126
Donley, Jeffrey P98
Donley, Michael B. P564
Donlin, Paul E75
Donne, France E90
Donnell, Steve A316
Donnell, Patrick O P109
Donnell, Cathy Mc P115
Donnell, Steve P191
Donnellan, James A555
Donnellan, Kevin P1
Donnelly, Kyla M A131
Donnelly, Eileen A487
Donnelly, Michael J. (Mike) A496
Donnelly, Patrick L. A745
Donnelly, Scott C. A804
Donnelly, Lorra A866
Donnelly, Michael A874
Donnelly, Sean A914
Donnelly, Gloria F. P165
Donnelly, Thomas P333
Donnelly, Robert E276
Donnelly, Bob E276
Donner, Fred R. A827
Donnet, Philippe W32
Donofrio, Paul M. A100
Donofrio, Nicholas A461
Donoghue, Tom A564
Donohoo, Shelly A655
Donohoo, Shelly E333
Donohue, Martin A192
Donohue, Jessica A766
Donohue, Sean P. P152
Donohue, Madeline P275
Donohue, Peter M. P667
Donovan, John M. A84
Donovan, John A133
Donovan, Timothy R. (Tim) A157
Donovan, Susan A353
Donovan, Paul P71
Donovan, Jerry P211
Donovan, Darren P395
Donovan, Thomas C. (Tom) P416
Donovan, Tom P416
Donovan, Nate P435
Donovan, Mike P489
Donovan, R. Nowell P560
Donovan, Susan P596
Donovan, Susan E159
Doo, Lim Ah W274
Doolan, Pat A313
Doolan, James L P78
Dooley, Meta A171
Dooley, Meta P100
Dooley, Bill P137
Dooley, Jack P167
Dooley, Brad P431
Dooley, David M P652
Dooley, John E. P669
Dooling, Heather E272
Doonan, Jason E277
Doordan, Martin L P39
Doot, Martin A15
Doot, Martin P9
Dopson, Nicole P648
Dor, Sigal A180
Dora, Lou P357

Dorado, Louis A127
Doramus, Mark A743
Doramus, Mark E373
Doran, James A13
Doran, Tim A904
Doran, Brian J P220
Doran, Jessica R. E341
Doran, Tim E442
Dorchester, Wendy P295
Dorer, Benno A208
Dorff, Jill P449
Dorflinger, Connie P646
Dorfner, Mike P463
Dorian, Michelle P570
Dorig, Rolf W7
Doris, Mark P516
Dority, Matt A223
Dorkofikis, Constantinos R. W24
Dorle, Tom P595
Dorman, Kevin A51
Dorman, David W. (Dave) A250
Dorman, Kevin P33
Dorminey, O. Leonard (Len) A704
Dorminey, O. Leonard (Len) E350
Dormitzer, Philip A649
Dormo, Cindy P118
Dormois, John C P353
Dorn, Andrew A334
Dorn, Michael A865
Dornak, Eric A3
Dornbirer, Dave A214
Dornbirer, Dave P128
Dornbush, Darwin C. E39
Dorne, Eric A. A848
Dorofeev, Dmitry W398
Dorph, Martin S. A585
Dorph, Martin S. P377
Dorrance, Robert E. (Bob) W370
Dorris, Jim A851
Dorroh, Tina P639
Dorsey, Tonya A19
Dorsey, Josh A777
Dorsey, Harry P427
Dorsey, Josh E393
Dorto, Joseph P668
Dorton, Gary A669
Dorward-King, Elaine A588
Dosch, Theodore A. (Ted) A66
Dosch, Eric J A347
Doshi, Gunjan A103
Doshi, Tejas A584
Doshi, Krupali A644
Dosi, Abhishek A775
Dosi, Abhishek P548
Doss, Sheryl A272
Doss, James S. E357
Dossani, Imran P630
Dost, Nancy A446
Dost, Nancy E210
Dostal, Drew A111
Dostal, Drew P56
Doster, Jeffrey S. E190
Dotson, Marsha A58
Dotson, Judith H. (Judi) A140
Dotson, Judy A140
Dotson, Tony P47
Dotson, Marsha E16
Dottori-Attanasio, Laura W80
Dotts, Kevin P293
Doty, Wendy L P164
Doty, William S P514
Dotzenrath, Anja W131
Doubenmier, Joni P282
Doucet, Matthew A904
Doucet, Matthew E442
Doucette, Elmer P174
Doucette, Jami P439
Doucette, Mike J P462
Doud, Art A372
Doud, Terri A784
Doudna, Dave P131
Douds, Haley A163
Doug, Longman P255
Dougherty, Robert A. A25
Dougherty, Edward A105

Dougherty, Michael A432
Dougherty, Michael D. A660
Dougherty, Robert A. P15
Dougherty, James P53
Dougherty, Kevin P. W346
Doughtie, Chico E298
Doughty, Susan P64
Douglas, Kevin A6
Douglas, Janice A131
Douglas, Jana A133
Douglas, J. Alexander M. (Sandy) A215
Douglas, Sean A443
Douglas, John A655
Douglas, Laurie Z. A679
Douglas, Laurie Z. A680
Douglas, Keith A813
Douglas, Amy P51
Douglas, Joanne P157
Douglas, Lena P216
Douglas, Emelda J P220
Douglas, Laurie Z. P448
Douglas, Bill W P462
Douglas, Derek P610
Douglas, Keith P616
Douglas, David P664
Douglas, Steven J. (Steve) W75
Douglas, Paul C. W370
Douglas, John E333
Douglas, Robert (Rob) E354
Douglas, Camille J. E385
Douglass, Dorothy A572
Douglass, Stephen B P92
Douglass, Travis L P230
Douglass, Scott R P641
Douglass, William P P672
Douglass, Brad P672
Douglass, Joan P672
Douma, Roberta A166
Doumas, Michael A913
Dountio, Benjamin P431
Dourlias, George A912
Doustdar, Maziar Mike W271
Dov, Gil Ben E355
Dovdavany, Ruth A649
Dove, Timothy L. (Tim) A657
Dove, Reid P1
Dove, Cindy P175
Dove, Marianne P281
Dovey, Stephen A513
Dow, Susan P174
Dow, Agata P235
Dowd, David A247
Dowd, Lacey P551
Dowd, A Joseph P688
Dowd, David E103
Dowdell, Joanne A589
Dowdell, Robert (Bob) A673
Dowdle, Jeffrey A. (Jeff) A693
Dowdle, Jon P686
Dowdy, Robert L. E336
Dowe, Kim P214
Dowe, Val P272
Dowell, Britt A700
Dowell, Greg A. E388
Dower, David P37
Dowidar, Hatem W389
Dowler, Lynette A280
Dowling, Steve A70
Dowling, Victoria A371
Dowling, Carol A513
Dowling, Wayne A751
Dowling, Courtney A865
Dowling, Jeannette P78
Dowling, Michael J P244
Dowling, Casandra P292
Dowling, Dennis P390
Dowling, Caroline W151
Dowling, Wayne E377
Downe, William A525
Downe, Andrew J. W227
Downes, Sean P. A858
Downes, Terry P489
Downes, Sean P. E418
Downey, Todd A186
Downey, Patti A461

Downey, Rusty P54
Downey, William B P462
Downey, Roger W385
Downie, Bryan A790
Downing, Troy A13
Downing, Forrest A51
Downing, Marjorie A644
Downing, Mark A. P458
Downing, Helen Dean P484
Downing, Steve E173
Downs, Christopher Y. (Chris) A152
Downs, Ryan A288
Downs, Jeff A616
Downs, Mike A782
Downs, Mary P618
Downs, Hugh P636
Downs, Yvette P676
Downs, Linda S. E47
Downs, Christopher Y. (Chris) E49
Downs, Jordan E65
Doying, Richard P342
Doyle, James A25
Doyle, John D A80
Doyle, Fred A96
Doyle, Scott E. A181
Doyle, Donald A196
Doyle, Maria A353
Doyle, Dorothy A406
Doyle, John Q. A532
Doyle, John A532
Doyle, Timothy A639
Doyle, John A651
Doyle, Joseph A790
Doyle, James P15
Doyle, John D P47
Doyle, Johnna P132
Doyle, James P155
Doyle, Bob P155
Doyle, John P174
Doyle, James P181
Doyle, Brian P334
Doyle, John P426
Doyle, David P455
Doyle, Monica P619
Doyle, Kevin P629
Doyle, Noreen W111
Doyle, Michael E127
Doyle, Maria E159
Doyle, Brian W. E252
Doyle, Timothy E326
Dozier, C. Michael A629
Dozier, Tom A655
Dozier, Luann P563
Dozier, Tom E333
Dozois, Timothy M. E328
Do--mo, Daniel W322
Draa, Mark A748
Draganza, Ernest J. A720
Draganza, Ernest J. E362
Dragisich, Dominic E. E75
Drago, John P. A722
Drago, Barbara A790
Dragone, Domingos A761
Drahnak, Steve A720
Drahnak, Steve E362
Drake, Shelley A522
Drake, George A622
Drake, Tonya E225
Dransfield, Gary W348
Drapcho, Connie P676
Draper, Suzie A458
Draper, Scott A878
Draper, Suzie P251
Draper, Kimbra P348
Drass, M. Joy A548
Drass, M. Joy P321
Draughn, James B. (Jim) A227
Draut, Eric A487
Dravenstott, Rob A270
Dravenstott, John A489
Draves, Brad A725
Draves, Denise P48
Drayer, Keith A727
Drazkowski, William J. A318
Drazkowski, Bill A318

Dreal, John Van P476
Drebin, Jeffrey A. P325
Dredla, Daniel P498
Drees, Kirk A195
Drees, Ralph P578
Drees, David P578
Drees, Joachim W231
Drefs, Cheryl A764
Drefs, Cheryl P540
Dreier, Gregory A244
Dreiling, Ben P105
Drell, Persis S. A507
Drell, Persis S. P288
Drengler, Kathy P48
Drennan, Attendee A515
Drennen, Chris A693
Drescher, Lucinda P532
Dressel, David A131
Drew, Brian A73
Drew, Alton A314
Drew, Theresa A902
Drew, Joel P93
Drew, Denise P135
Drew, Alton P189
Drew, Rhonda P395
Drew, Theresa P693
Drew, J. Christopher (Chris) E316
Drewel, Michael A235
Drexler, Blake S A109
Drexler, Andrew A640
Dreyer, Andr A701
Dreyer, Michael L. A777
Dreyer, Michael L. E392
Drezek, Maria P567
Dries, Susan P214
Driessen, Jack A3
Driggers, Timothy K. A304
Driggers, Mark A742
Driggers, Mark P502
Driggs, Terry A710
Drilling, Edward A743
Drilling, Edward E373
Drillings, Robert M P376
Drimmie, Doreen P281
Drinan, Beth A34
Dring, Dan A829
Driscoll, Jennifer A163
Driscoll, Dan A332
Driscoll, Jennifer A599
Driscoll, Deborah P230
Driscoll, Brian J. P507
Driver, Darienne A344
Driver, Jeff P538
Drone, Marilyn P535
Drop, Jeffrey S. A171
Drop, Jeffrey S. P100
Drossaert, Wim P361
Drouin, Joseph L. A681
Drozdetski, Eugene A131
Drucker, Dennis P352
Drue, Jennifer P292
Druga, Gregory M P222
Drum, Jason A13
Drum, James A583
Drum, Craig E167
Drumm, Ann P313
Drummond, Brad C. A73
Drummond, Joseph P629
Drury, Scott D. A735
Drusin, Lewis A584
Drusin, Lewis P376
Druten, Robert J. E131
Druzbik, James R. A396
Dryden, Jennifer A599
Dryden, Ken P442
Drysdale, D. R. E375
Dsa, Roy A441
Duane, Mandy A190
Duane, Francis K. (Ken) A682
Duane, Dianne P480
Duarte, Joel P296
Duato, Joaquin A476
Duban, Heike P100
Dubauskas, Keith A693
Dubay, Christopher P57

A = AMERICAN BUSINESS
E = EMERGING COMPANIES
P = PRIVATE COMPANIES
W = WORLD BUSINESS

Dubczak, Roman W80
Dube, Sandeep A262
Dube, Joyce P474
Duberstein, Kenneth A315
Dubik, Nikolay N. W289
Dubin, Adam P8
Dubin, James M P223
Dubin, James M P292
Dubler, Josh E189
Dublin, Ardenia P20
Duboff, H A556
Dubois, Steve A712
Dubois, Benjamin P290
Dubois, Rick P383
Dubois, James P455
DuBois, Raymond N. P591
Dubreuil, Brian A677
Dubreuil, Stéphane W161
Dubridge, Samanntha A419
Dubuche, Karl Von P626
Dubuisson, Betty A555
Dubuque, Bethany A644
Dubyak, Meghan P583
Dubyak, Michael E. E438
Dubé, Richard W. (Dick) A614
Duc, Bernard le W61
Duca, Devika Del A105
Duca, Michael A. A159
Ducey, Scott A710
Ducey, Barbara E311
Ducham, Dennis E101
DuCharme, L. D. A313
Duchatellier, Christophe W7
Duchossois, Craig J. P611
Duchscher, Rob P465
Duck, Barbara F. A115
Duck, Kevin A166
Ducker, Michael L. A327
Duckett, W. David (Dave) A658
Duckett, Gregg P60
Duckworth, David A513
Duckworth, Robert A774
Ducré, Henri W143
Duda, David A P462
Dudas, John A164
Duden, Whitney P650
Dudevoir, Tracie P389
Dudik, Dale A327
Dudish, Sherry P224
Dudkin, Gregory N. A665
Dudley, William C. A323
Dudley, William C. A325
Dudley, Kelly A336
Dudley, Michael M. A736
Dudley, Kelly P194
Dudley, Warren P327
Dudley, Michael M. P492
Dudonis, Chris A40
Dudseemaytha, Surasak W203
Duerk, Jeffrey P98
Duerksen, Craig A223
Duersch, Taylor A878
Dueser, F. Scott A345
Dueser, F. Scott E154
Due-±as, Luis Cabra W300
Dufala, George D. (Chip) A487
Duff, Christopher A133
Duff, Sam A504
Duff, Michael A507
Duff, Scott K A574
Duff, Michael P288
Duff, Sam E241
Duffany, Dennis A375
Duffelen, Mark A912
Duffenbach, Chris A318
Duffie, Kent A530
Duffin, N. W. A313
Duffle, Denise A98
Duffle, Denise E33

Duffus, Robert A644
Duffy, Jack A85
Duffy, James J. (Jim) A201
Duffy, Mark A231
Duffy, Robert L. A405
Duffy, Liam A533
Duffy, Shannon A723
Duffy, Merry P363
Duffy, Dorothy P576
Duffy, Matthew P681
Duffy, David W101
Duffy, Brian W319
Duffy, W. Leslie E251
Dufour, Pierre A25
Dufour, Gregory A. (Greg) A160
Dufour, Pierre P15
Dufour, Victoria P530
Dufour, Gregory A. (Greg) E55
Dufresne, Maryse P355
Dufresne, Richard W394
Dufétel, Céline A784
Dugal, Martin P625
Dugan, Candy A109
Dugan, Gregory A. A886
Dugan, John P173
Dugan, Candy E36
Dugan, Melissa E86
Dugan, Gregory A. E433
Dugar, Pankaj A435
Dugarte, Colleen A489
Dugas, Tiffany A729
Dugdale, Jeff S A685
Dugenske, John A33
Dugent, Paul P187
Duggan, Christopher A478
Duggan, Conor A700
Duggan, Scott P581
Duggan, Frank W3
Dugger, Philip E175
Dugger, Tom E190
Duggirala, Rajeev A56
Duhamel, Philippe W364
Duhe, Thomas G P300
Duhn, Brian A600
Duke, Jennifer A489
Duke, Daniel A658
Duke, Timothy R. (Tim) A768
Duke, Beth M P116
Duke, Timothy R P541
Duke, Timothy R P551
Duke, Lee M. P589
Duke, Dennis E276
Dukeman, Van A. A339
Dukeman, Van A. E150
Dukes, Jw A58
Dukes, Jw E16
Dukshtein, Mark P568
Dulac, Fabienne W278
Dull, Ken A277
Dumais, Lynn A A146
Dumais, Michael R. (Mike) A854
Dumas, José Tom--s Guzm--n W27
Dumelle, Peter A108
Dumelle, Peter E35
Dumont, Patrick A502
Dumont, Serge A619
Dumora, Renaud W67
Dunagin, Martin A417
Dunaway, William J. (Bill) A465
Dunaway, Barry C. A748
Dunaway, Heather A782
Dunaway, Mike P315
Dunaway, Julie P637
Dunbar, Timothy M. (Tim) A668
Dunbar, Roger F. A777
Dunbar, Sandra P613
Dunbar, Roger F. E393
Duncan, George L. A301
Duncan, Buell A460
Duncan, Bryan A479
Duncan, Aaron A539
Duncan, David A564
Duncan, Lizzy A578
Duncan, Evans S A659
Duncan, Philip J A671

Duncan, Bryan D. A741
Duncan, Dana A770
Duncan, Michele A855
Duncan, Jim P74
Duncan, Gary P200
Duncan, Colleen P410
Duncan, Thomas M P439
Duncan, Terri P449
Duncan, Jon P489
Duncan, Michael P570
Duncan, Colleen P623
Duncan, George L. E127
Duncan, Kimberly E349
Duncan, Bryan D. E370
Dunderman, Carmela P145
Dung, Vu A635
Dung, Vu P419
Dungan, David P226
Dungan, Jefferson (Jeff) E93
Dunham, Mark A685
Dunham, Kara P106
Dunham, David P314
Dunham, Duane R. E281
Dunigan-wernke, Jennifer A332
Dunion, Amy P617
Dunkel, Drew P249
Dunkle, Stephen P582
Dunlaevy, Williar E41
Dunlap, James E. (Jim) A440
Dunlap, Michael S. (Mike) A579
Dunlap, Stan A723
Dunlap, David L. P94
Dunlap, Edward B. P104
Dunlap, Timothy M. P104
Dunlap, Ray P455
Dunlap, David L P465
Dunlap, Alice P521
Dunlap, Joe W. W180
Dunlavy, Justin P344
Dunleavy, Michael F A242
Dunleavy, J.K. W199
Dunley, Pamela P181
Dunn, Ann A57
Dunn, Gary S. A97
Dunn, Stacey A A182
Dunn, Kenneth A185
Dunn, Allison A214
Dunn, Dan A221
Dunn, Kenneth E. A304
Dunn, Jordan A335
Dunn, Marc A371
Dunn, Patrick A A417
Dunn, Cind M A438
Dunn, Tom A478
Dunn, Russell A500
Dunn, Michael G. A630
Dunn, Martin A729
Dunn, Cheryl A737
Dunn, Bradford A818
Dunn, Sheila A850
Dunn, Bryan C. A890
Dunn, Sean A904
Dunn, Bernardine P22
Dunn, Mary P80
Dunn, Carolyn P106
Dunn, Allison P128
Dunn, Jim P152
Dunn, Cindy P218
Dunn, William H P256
Dunn, Steve P256
Dunn, William H. (Bill) P257
Dunn, Stephen D. (Steve) P257
Dunn, Micheal P274
Dunn, Steve P354
Dunn, Gregory W. (Greg) P455
Dunn, Todd P464
Dunn, Janice P473
Dunn, George P510
Dunn, John P567
Dunn, Bryan C. P684
Dunn, Ann E16
Dunn, Gary S. E32
Dunn, Stacey A E63
Dunn, Colin E69
Dunn, Steve E226

Dunn, Peter E235
Dunn, Russell E237
Dunn, Brian J. E263
Dunn, Cheryl E367
Dunn, Sean E442
Dunn, Kevin E444
Dunn-Krause, Debbie P298
Dunne, Viola A130
Dunne, Melanie A533
Dunne, Jessica A539
Dunne, Ronan A870
Dunnett, Donalda P108
Dunning, Joe A238
Dunning, Tara P52
Dunoyer, Marc W34
Dunsmore, Kathy A115
Dunson, Tom A350
Dunson, Tom E156
Dunston, S. Cary E15
Dunton, Shirby P668
Dunwoody, Ann A707
Duong, Julie A97
Duong, Tran Ba W195
Duong, Julie E32
Dupal, Leslie P685
Dupaul, Stephanie P653
DuPilka, Cynthia E183
Dupiton, Lynore P362
Duplaix, Jean Marc W204
Dupler, Scott A441
Dupont, Michael R P371
Duprat, Pierre-Christophe A74
Dupre, Charles E P425
Dupree, Yvonne P34
Dupree, Tj E213
Duprez, Debra A817
Dupuie, Bill P43
Dupuis, Mike A683
Durall, Scott E310
Duran, Laura P177
Duran, Maria C P391
Duran, Julie P417
Durand, Bob A82
Durand, Bert A844
Durand, Bob P49
Durand, Michelle P247
Durand, Bert E412
Durant, Luke A607
Durant, Romules P620
Durant, Alison E248
Durante, Nicandro W74
Durbin, Sean A514
Durbin, Patrick M. A815
Durburg, Jack A172
Durden, Linda A844
Durden, Linda E412
Durek, Sandy A904
Durek, Sandy E442
Duren, Darla Van P188
Durfey, Jim A44
Durfey, Steve A323
Durfey, Jim P31
Durham, George A136
Durham, Adam A770
Durham, Bill A795
Durham, Mikel A835
Durham, Michelle P290
Durkee, Matthew K. A577
Durkee, Jeff A767
Durkin, Dennis A10
Durkin, James W. (Jim) A370
Durkin, Christopher P421
Durkovic, Svelana P420
Durmick, Koye P221
Durn, Daniel (Dan) A71
Durocher, Philip A218
Durocher, Stephen A676
Durr, Paul P498
Durrans, Jan A95
Durrans, Jan E28
Durrence, Neiciee A34
Dusenbery, Jack P147
Duseux, Francis W145
Dushinske, John T P274
Dusseault, Wendi E101

Dussert, Bertrand A913
Dussling, William J P622
Dustzadeh, Justin A874
Dutcher, Jason E117
Dutertre, Jey A520
Duthinh, Vuong P211
Dutkowsky, Robert M. A792
Dutra, Kasey P681
Dutt, Shilpa A322
Dutta, Soumitra P143
Dutton, Richard J A208
Dutton, Rob A263
Duty, Earnie P276
Duty, Denise P323
Duva, Judith P411
Duval, John P665
Duvvur, Amarendra A6
Duvvuri, Kumar A131
Duvvuri, Vikas A857
Duzer, William Van P660
Dvm, Prem Paul P87
Dvorak, Adam P567
Dvorchak, Steve A612
Dvorken, Rachel P504
Dvorkin, Victor E130
Dwight, Craig M. A431
Dwight, Craig M. E205
Dworkin, Aaron A698
Dworkin, Steve A744
Dworkin, Darren P102
Dworkin, Jack H. P107
Dworkin, Paul H. P138
Dworkin, James B. P449
Dworkin, Aaron P456
Dwyer, Anita A351
Dwyer, James E. (Jim) A663
Dwyer, Maria F. A766
Dwyer, Jay P67
Dwyer, Thomas L. G. P267
Dwyer, Anita E158
Dyck, Earl A25
Dyck, Earl P15
Dyckes, Jason A101
Dye, John R. A893
Dyer, Jay A165
Dyer, Chris A784
Dyer, Jonathon A894
Dyer, William B. E75
Dyess, Diane P60
Dyhrberg, Stephanie A863
Dyk, Nick Van A272
Dyke, Concetta Van A120
Dyke, Daniel Van A540
Dyke, Frank J. (Jeff) A749
Dyke, David P87
Dyke, Daniel Van P316
Dyke, Jill Van P630
Dyke, James V. E340
Dykens, Jeff P92
Dykes, Melissa P260
Dykes, Mary H. P427
Dykes, Archie R. E22
Dykstra, Scott A308
Dykstra, David A. A904
Dykstra, David A. E442
Dyro, Ralph J P75
Dyro, Ralph J P88
Dyslin, Nancy A2
Dyslin, Bradley E. A18
Dyukov, Alexander V. W157
Dzambo, Chris P455
Dzanis, Marie A599
Dziadzio, Richard S. A83
Dziak, Donna A323
Dzielak, Robert A311
Dzierzbinski, Danusia P251
Dziorny, Stanley A359
Dziwis, Carolyn P593
D'Agnese, Luca W141
D'Agostino, Thomas P A358
D'Agostino, John A693
D'Alessandri, Robert P681
D'Alessandro, Carl A405
D'Alimonte, Christa A. A871
D'Ambrose, Michael A74

D'Ambrosio, Lou A461
D'Amelio, Frank A. A648
D'Amico, Maty Jo P173
D'Amore, Robert R. (Bob) A644
D'Amore, Diana A676
D'andrea, Elena A537
D'Angelo, Franco A158
D'Angelo, Scott A364
D'Angelo, Larry E248
D'Angelo, Lawrence E248
D'Aniello, Gianluca P566
D'Anna, F Christopher A303
d'Apice, Leon E116
D'Appolonia, Kathleen A659
D'Aquila, Richard P698
D'Aquila, Richard P699
d'Archirafi, Francesco Vanni A203
D'Arezzo, Gloria A912
D'Argenio, David Z. E374
D'Arrigo, Daniel J. A558
D'Ascoli, Fred P372
d'Esparbes, Eric E217
d'Estaing, Antoine Giscard W83
d'Estais, Jacques W66
D'Lugos, Steve A85
D'Ouville, Paul A599
D'Souza, Francisco A217
D-az, Eduardo P506
Düren, Aydin W377

E

Eade-Viele, Carol P22
Eagels, Patricia P482
Eagles, Paul A874
Ealet, Isabelle A389
Ealy, Carleton A463
Eames, Tyler A644
Eames, Tristyn A729
Eames, Andy P521
Earhart, Cynthia C. (Cindy) A597
Earhart, Eric E300
Earl, Phillip A10
Earl, Joe P461
Earl, Nancy P498
Earl, Ashlee M P567
Earley, Jean McNicholas A105
Earley, Steve A919
Earley, Franklin P P668
Early, Betsy P493
Early, Johnnie L. P613
Earnest, Julie P155
Earnest, Morgan G. (Jerry) E131
Earnshaw, Bill A685
Earnshaw, William A685
Earp, Sandra A81
Easley, Ed A508
Easley, Stephen T P271
Eason, J. Cliff A702
Eason, David P478
Easter, Mona P595
Easter, Anita B. E153
Easterbrook, Stephen J. (Steve) A545
Easterlin, Edward E. P406
Easterling, William E. A811
Easterling, William E. P600
Easterwood, Scott A786
Eastin, David A591
Eastman, Laura A331
Eastman, Stephen L. A661
Eastman, Laura E148
Easton, Kelly P521
Easton, Diana P525
Eaton, Mary Jo A173
Eaton, Dave A861
Eaton, Roger A917
Eaton, Dave P658
Eaton, Rachel E244
Eaton, Loren E394
Ebanks, Leroy A592
Ebbrecht, Dave E172
Ebbs, Brian A607
Ebel, Gregory L. (Greg) A758
Ebel, Gregory L. (Greg) P519

Ebenal, Shelley D P583
Ebenhoeh, Allisssa A699
Ebenhoeh, Allisssa P456
Eber, Bob A837
Eberhard, Ed A195
Eberhard, Karin A329
Eberhard, Michael J. E382
Eberhardt, Jack A591
Eberhart, Dan P454
Eberhart, Paul P660
Eberling, Carl E123
Eberly, Carolyn A79
Eberly, Jeff P165
Ebermann, Wolfgang A454
Ebers, Kevin H A122
Ebert, Horst A391
Eberts, F. Samuel A499
Eberwein, Elise R. A43
Ebken, Stephanie P115
Ebner, R. M. A313
Ebrahimi, Fariborz P52
Eby, Tom A559
EBY, Douglas P511
Eccher, James L. A616
Eccles, Colin D. A883
Eccleshare, C. William A448
Echeverri, Diana P481
Echiverri, Henry C P176
Echols, Jimmie A620
Echols, Eileen A706
Echols, Lee P395
Echols, Eileen E353
Eck, Robert J. (Bob) A66
Eck, Robert A718
Eck, Shane P342
Eck, Chris P579
Eckart, Samuel E160
Eckel, Ryan A264
Eckel, Scott A729
Eckel, Robert A. (Bob) P245
Eckel, Jeffrey W. E188
Eckels, Dan P675
Eckels, Dan P676
Ecker, Kraig A907
Ecker, Jeffrey Lawrence (Jeff) P590
Ecker, Kraig P696
Eckert, Matthew P52
Eckert, Barbara P390
Eckert, Robert A497
Eckhart, Bradley A691
Eckhart, Brad P579
Eckhart, Gloria P620
Eckhoff, Heidi P601
Eckle, Ryan A264
Eckweiler, Karl A594
Edd, Edward A Sussman P164
Edd, Gary Orsinger P164
Edd, Ed Potter P164
Eddens, Peggy H. A907
Eddens, Peggy H. E445
Eddinger, Ronnie P80
Eddins, Brad A801
Eddins, Brad P561
Eddowes, Geoffrey W. P589
Eddy, Ashley A558
Eddy, Geno P219
Ede, Michael van A542
Ede, Michael van E267
Edel, Karsten A141
Edel, John A201
Edelman, Ann P3
Edelson, David B. A520
Edelstein, Justin A204
Edelstein, Jeffrey P P565
Edema, Douglas P518
Edens, Wesley R. (Wes) A621
Edens, Stacey P196
Eder, Noelle A163
Eder, Wolfgang W389
Edgar, Robert V A584
Edgar, Robert A584
Edgar, Ted P183
Edgar, Robert V P374
Edgar, Robert P374
Edgar, James E163

Edge, Judy A327
Edge, Jillian P299
Edge, Tom P512
Edgell, Eleonore A699
Edgell, Eleonore P456
Edgemond, James E415
Edgett, Paul W. A171
Edgett, Paul W. P100
Edgmond, Wanda A223
Edicola, Mike A113
Edin, Ebru Dildar W377
Edlund, Monte G. A443
Edlund, Todd E126
Edminster, Susan P12
Edmondson, Emanuel A183
Edmonson, W P188
Edmunds, Coleman A88
Edmunds, Coleman A89
Edmunds, Karen P686
Edney, Jerry A82
Edney, Jerry P49
Edridge, Thomas A532
Edsall, Tom A200
Edson, David A131
Edson, Kent A251
Edward, Cheryl P45
Edwards, Bill A17
Edwards, Jon S. A57
Edwards, Nate A85
Edwards, Jeff A93
Edwards, Peter G. A177
Edwards, Angela A347
Edwards, Patricia L. A304
Edwards, Jennifer A328
Edwards, John A333
Edwards, Thomas H. A431
Edwards, Bill A446
Edwards, Tom A460
Edwards, Crystal A503
Edwards, Dennis A530
Edwards, Zalise A546
Edwards, Kurt A578
Edwards, Trevor A. A592
Edwards, Darren A642
Edwards, David A655
Edwards, Donna A655
Edwards, Teresa L. (Terrie) A736
Edwards, Terrie A736
Edwards, Robert A788
Edwards, Bryan A838
Edwards, Robert A. (Rob) A844
Edwards, Tim A904
Edwards, Cheryl P45
Edwards, Glendia P51
Edwards, Steven L P75
Edwards, Steve L P88
Edwards, Michael P99
Edwards, Lisa P109
Edwards, Mary Ann P135
Edwards, Cecil P248
Edwards, Bill P256
Edwards, Crystal P284
Edwards, Gordon P285
Edwards, Lyndon P294
Edwards, Marcie L. P297
Edwards, Brady P298
Edwards, Janet P417
Edwards, Pearse P433
Edwards, Susan P442
Edwards, Gerry P458
Edwards, Rebecca P464
Edwards, C H P490
Edwards, Clarence P490
Edwards, Teresa L. (Terrie) P492
Edwards, Terrie P492
Edwards, Chris P651
Edwards, Sherman P682
Edwards, Jon S. E16
Edwards, Karen K. E22
Edwards, Mac E40
Edwards, Angela E103
Edwards, Thomas H. E205
Edwards, Bill E210
Edwards, Jeffrey w. E218

A = AMERICAN BUSINESS
E = EMERGING COMPANIES
P = PRIVATE COMPANIES
W = WORLD BUSINESS

Edwards, David E333
Edwards, Donna E333
Edwards, Richard J. E347
Edwards, Robert A. (Rob) E412
Edwards, Tim E442
Edwin, Prince A919
Effinger, Jason E181
Effting, Diane A646
Effting, Diane E330
Efird, Nina A331
Efird, Shannon A521
Efird, Nina E148
Efraimov, Angelina P565
Eftink, Mike A671
Egan, Anne A568
Egan, Beth A738
Egan, Scott A815
Egan, Tom A898
Egan, Karen P174
Egashira, Toshiaki W249
Egashira, Tetsuya W400
Ege, Fred P371
Eger, Paul P446
Egerdal, J E E288
Eggar, Justin A34
Eggemeyer, John M. A632
Eggemeyer, John M. E322
Egger, Jason A489
Eggers, Bill A721
Eggert, Mark A180
Eggli, Doug A416
Eghert, David P402
Egidi, Kenneth P422
Egl, Ed A881
Eglen, Richard A238
Eglinton, Mia A478
Egloff, Doug P368
Egloff, German W41
Egsieker, Erik P434
Ehara, George S P551
Ehele, Stephen A56
Ehlers, Michael D. (Mike) A129
Ehlert, Carey P591
Ehlinger, Jon D P166
Ehlinger, Forrest G P227
Ehlinger, Robert E239
Ehrenberg, Tommy A272
Ehrenberg, James A. E275
Ehrenpreis, Ira A799
Ehret, Michael A476
Ehret, John R. E357
Ehrhart, Brandon A270
Ehrler, Richard P414
Ehrlich, Whitney A131
Ehrlich, Robert P312
Ehrling, Marie W269
Ehrman, Larry P300
Ehrmann, Jean P449
Ehrmann, Jacques W82
Ehst, Richard A. A247
Ehst, Richard A. E102
Eibensteiner, Herbert W389
Eibling, David A565
Eichelberger, Mitch A193
Eichelberger, Mitch P112
Eichenberger, Matt A685
Eichenseer, Tim E165
Eichhorn, Barbara P549
Eichler, Adam A677
Eichler, Meyer A741
Eichler, Meyer E370
Eichorn, Mark A568
Eichorn, Marvin P356
Eick, Aaron P451
Eickenhorst, Thorsten A129
Eickholt, Jochen W331
Eidam, Jo Ellen P6
Eidelson, Steven A537
Eidson, Dennis A757

Eikenberg, Charles D. A504
Eikenberg, Charles D. E241
Eiland, Mattie P514
Eilberg, Herb E4
Eiler, Justin P458
Einseln, Matt A16
Eipper, D P6
Eippert, Debbie A244
Eis, Shannon E447
Eisbart, Benjamin A768
Eisen, Robert A353
Eisen, Julie A763
Eisen, Robert E159
Eisenbarth, Jeff A93
Eisenberg, Paul R. A61
Eisenberg, Warren A120
Eisenberg, Steven D. A291
Eisenberg, Stacey A449
Eisenberg, Glenn A. A499
Eisenbrandt, Peter P301
Eisenkraft, James P355
Eisenmann, Bob A489
Eisenstot, Bill A904
Eisenstot, Bill E442
Eisgruber, Christopher L. P606
Eismann, Charles A626
Eisman, Robert B. A40
Eisner, Paul A405
Eisner, Wesley A484
Eissinger, Robin A158
Ejaz, Hassan P606
Ekarius, Michele A101
Ekholm, B- ¶rje E. W360
Ekici, Tuncay A649
Ekinci, Murat A265
Ekman, Eric W269
Ektarian, Victoria A25
Ektarian, Victoria P15
Ekvall, Susan A180
El-Bayoumi, Jehan P321
El-Hibri, Fuad E121
Elachi, Charles P90
Elam, Lisa A162
Elam, Travis P521
Elamine, A K P511
Elbaghdady, Heba P431
Elbaum, Richard P103
Elberfeld, Adrienne P576
Elbers, Pieter W14
Elbert, Robert A838
Elborne, Cy A727
Elcar, Per W352
Eldayrie, Elias G. P642
Elder, Mark A235
Elder, Richard M. A338
Elder, Rick A338
Elder, Mike P281
Elder, Thomas J. E100
Elderkin, Greg A758
Elderkin, Greg P519
Eldern, Leonard Van A915
Eldern, Leonard Van P700
Eldredge, Derrek P300
Eldridge, Thomas A503
Eldridge, Thomas P284
Eldridge, Kristin P446
Elenio, Paul E22
Eleser, Karen A163
Eleswarpu, Lakshmi A136
Elfering, Steve P435
Elgart, Natalie A241
Elgin, Jeff A163
Elgohary, Nivin A214
Elgohary, Nivin P128
Elhaj, Sam A541
Elhaj, Sam E266
Elia, Lois A15
Elia, Nancy A109
Elia, Lois P9
Elia, Maryellen P237
Elia, Nancy E36
Elias, Richard P429
Eliasen, Mark A28
Eliasson, Karin A87

Eliasson, Fred A243
Elices, Simone P561
Elich, Michael L. (Mike) E38
Eliecagary, Aline A729
Eline, William G. (Bill) A634
Eling, Greg A198
Elisha, Audrey E46
Elix, Andrew A461
Elizondo, Geraldine P435
Elizondo, Carlos José Garc- a
  Moreno W25
Eljaiek, Lester A736
Eljaiek, Lester P492
Elkeles, Tamar A685
Elkin, Ilyas A607
Elkin, Jim P624
Elkins, Beth P348
Elkins, Carla P480
Elko, Kristin A861
Elko, Kristin P658
Ellard, Craig A162
Ellard, Beth P2
Ellehuus, Christoffer P102
Ellen, Martin M A487
Ellen, Jonathan M. P264
Ellenbogen, Marc A36
Eller, Jeff P7
Eller, Carl P484
Eller, Mike P516
Ellerbrook, Niel C P514
Ellinghausen, James R. (Jim) A681
Ellingsen, Catharine D. A707
Ellington, Kim A A350
Ellington, Debbie A463
Ellington, Chris P649
Ellington, Kim A E156
Elliot, John A207
Elliot, Douglas G. (Doug) A406
Elliot, Charles P549
Elliott, Geraldine T A121
Elliott, Todd A177
Elliott, Roz A257
Elliott, Anita C A273
Elliott, Robin N. A339
Elliott, Laura A441
Elliott, Mike A474
Elliott, Gerri A482
Elliott, Joseph C. A611
Elliott, Tommy A614
Elliott, Steven G A665
Elliott, Douglas G A667
Elliott, Brett P350
Elliott, Julie P415
Elliott, Bob P501
Elliott, Bruce P591
Elliott, Robin N. E150
Elliott, Marc G. E170
Elliott, E. J. (Mike) E170
Elliott, Marc G. E170
Elliott, Jay P. E218
Ellis, Mike A61
Ellis, Chris A140
Ellis, Craig A332
Ellis, Natalie A361
Ellis, Lance A508
Ellis, Andrew A712
Ellis, Jacque A744
Ellis, James G. A860
Ellis, Matthew D. (Matt) A870
Ellis, Andrea Shaffer P115
Ellis, Jeremiah P192
Ellis, John W P208
Ellis, Keith P271
Ellis, Suzanne P318
Ellis, Karen P329
Ellis, Karen P460
Ellis, Nancy P486
Ellis, John P601
Ellis, Mary P633
Ellis, James G. P656
Ellis, J. Thad E98
Ellis, Thad E98
Ellis, Kip B. E324
Ellison, Dave A101
Ellison, James A115

Ellison, P K A207
Ellison, Brian A466
Ellison, Seth M. A509
Ellison, Lawrence J A624
Ellison, Marvin R. A640
Ellison, Lois P3
Ellison, Greg P148
Ellithorpe, Tom E415
Ells, M. Steven (Steve) A193
Ells, Tom A476
Ellspermann, Caroline J. A614
Ellspermann, Kenneth J. A614
Ellsworth, Kathryn P210
Elmin, Henrik W36
Elming, Gregory B. (Greg) A668
Elmo, Kim A9
Elmore, Joshua A576
Elmore, Kiley A737
Elmore, John R. A865
Elmore, Joshua E297
Elmore, Kiley E367
Elmoslemany, Rehab A500
Elmoslemany, Rehab E238
Elmquist, David A480
Elnashai, Amr S. A811
Elnashai, Amr S. P600
Elnicky, Rob A522
Eloranta, Jorma W257
Elrich, Marc P144
Elrod, James K P692
Elsabrout, Kerri P688
Elsawaf, Ahmad A659
ElSawy, Amr A. P383
Elsbrock, Natalie P115
Elser, Jeffrey A355
Elser, Chrisanna A412
Elser, Chrisanna E192
Elsner, Deanie A485
Elson, Clifford P360
Elstad, Rob A56
Elste, Mark E77
Elster, Nanette P299
Elstrott, John B. A899
Elstrott, John B. P690
Eltonhead, Tricia A332
Eltz, Amanda P168
Elvekrog, John P577
Elwell, William A406
Elwood, Rob A668
Elwyn, Tashtego S. (Tash) A693
Ely, Lisa P478
Emami, Azita A861
Emami, Azita P658
Embree, Tracy A. A246
Embry, Kevin P144
Emel, Lisa A238
Emel, Aaron A838
Emelonye, Ken A877
Emerick, Joyce P685
Emerson, Frances A260
Emerson, Neil A265
Emerson, Bertrand M A474
Emerson, David A541
Emerson, Bertrand M P265
Emerson, Rob P518
Emerson, David A266
Emerson, Richard P. E328
Emery, Jean A384
Emery, Tom A644
Emery, Sidney W E13
Emery, Jean E176
Emiris, Ioannis M. W24
Emmans, John P92
Emmerich, I. Robert (Bob) A342
Emmerich, Matthew J. A661
Emmert, Mark A P363
Emmett, Nicholas A489
Emmett, Dan A. E110
Emmons, George A489
Emmons, Christopher W. P303
Emmons, John E65
Empey, Matt A701
Empey, Dennis P40
Empey, Dennis P624
Empson, Douglas A838

Emptage, William A56
Emrich, Richard P398
Enbody, Justin E231
Encarnacion, Beverly P627
Encelewski, Greg P511
Endacott, Dorothy P648
Enders, Thomas (Tom) W16
Endersby, Jeff A16
Endo, Melanie A133
Endres, Helmut A20
Endres, Jeff A440
Endresen, Heather A97
Endresen, William D. A427
Endresen, William D. E202
Eney, Alexander P278
Eng, Ilene A49
Eng, Steve A115
Eng, Sharon A204
Eng, Bland P207
Eng, Nelson P528
Eng, Christopher R. E388
Engblom, Stephen A16
Engebretsen, Travis A731
Engebretsen, Travis E365
Engel, Robert B. A214
Engel, Jody A375
Engel, Randy A588
Engel, Albert L. A868
Engel, John J. A888
Engel, Robert B. P128
Engel, Mary P247
Engel, Heather P464
Engel, Sandra P480
Engel, Hans-Ulrich W55
Engel, Marc W383
Engelbrecht, John R. A683
Engelbrecht, John R. E341
Engelby, Katy P363
Engelen, Peter W376
Engelhard, Bob A857
Engelhardt, Fredrik A180
Engelhardt, Mark A432
Engelhart, James A837
Engels, Leeanne A195
Engels, Trevor A827
Engels, Kerry P51
Engelson, David A. E414
Engelstoft, Morten H. W1
Engerer, Jill A350
Engerer, Jill E157
England, Jan A115
England, Donna M A280
Engle, Bridget E. A105
Engle, Pam A149
Engle, Barry A378
Englebright, Jane D. A410
Englehardt, Scott A693
Engler, Grace P235
Engler, Greg E432
Englert, Mitch A162
Englert, Brian A344
Englert, Brad P656
Engles, Gregg L. P689
English, Jim A330
English, James A387
English, Dominick A508
English, Shaileen A648
English, Steven E. A764
English, Rebecca A784
English, Alison P80
English, Kathy P117
English, Hopeton P291
English, James E177
English, Nick E437
Englund, Melissa P601
Engrav, Mary A565
Engskov, Kris A763
Engstrom, Kathryn A795
Engstrom, Mark E189
Enloe, Truett A192
Enloe, John A282
Enneking, Brian E123
Ennis, Ed A58
Ennis, Daniel G. A475
Ennis, Robert A589

Ennis, Daniel G. P266
Ennis, Patti P497
Ennis, Mitch P627
Ennis, Karen P674
Ennis, Niall W120
Enos, Deborah C. A635
Enos, Deborah C. P419
Enriquez, Javier P118
Enriquez, Alexandra P352
Ensign, Michele A558
Enslin, Robert (Rob) W319
Enterline, Larry L. E168
Entwisle, Beverly J P626
Entwistle, Laura A541
Entwistle, David P538
Entwistle, Laura E266
Epelman, Marina A698
Epelman, Marina P456
Epler, Alan A264
Epley, George A871
Epmeier, Bruce E P156
Epperlein, Susann A691
Epperley, Michael A886
Epperley, Michael E433
Epps, Mike A673
Epps, Barry L. A703
Epps, Jeremy A851
Epsilanty, Alexandra P552
Epstein, Mark A685
Epstein, Janet A728
Epstein, Irving R. P82
Epstein, Norman P P546
Eran, Oded W46
Erb, David B. A446
Erb, David B. E210
Erbil, Ali Fuat W377
Erdle, Bob E268
Erdman, Seth A246
Erdman, David A533
Erdmann, CherylL A699
Erdmann, Bryan P223
Erdmann, CherylL P456
Erdoes, Mary Callahan A480
Erekson, O. Homer P560
Erel, Hüsnü W377
Eremenko, Paul A854
Eremia, Alex P79
Erfourth, Michael A549
Erfourth, Michael E270
Ergen, Charles W. (Charlie) A270
Erickson, Randall J. A81
Erickson, Wendy A244
Erickson, Mona A332
Erickson, Peter C. A377
Erickson, Karen A546
Erickson, Andrew A766
Erickson, Sue P333
Erickson, Andrew P552
Erickson, Tina P593
Erickson, Mike E213
Erickson-King, Chris P357
Ericson, Brady D. A141
Ericson, Brent A397
Ericson, Brent P221
Ericson, Magnus W352
Erika, Hofmann A635
Erika, Hofmann P419
Eriksen, Jim A522
Eriksen, Jan A904
Eriksen, Jan E442
Erikson, Lynn A676
Eris, Christine A537
Erkan, Hafize Gaye (Gaye) A353
Erlandson, Daniel A441
Erlinger, James H. (Jim) A469
Erlinger, Joe A545
Erman, Tim A295
Ermatinger, William R. (Bill) A442
Ermatinger, Bill A442
Ermis, Tommy P511
ERMOLD, SHAWNA A851
Ernest, Scott A591
Ernest, Scott A. A804
Ernest, Scott A844
Ernest, Scott E412

Ernie, Barry P514
Ernst, David A819
Ernst, Barrie W. A847
Ernst, Cindi A917
Ernst, Cindi P701
Erny, Michelle A480
Erokhin, Vladimir P. W350
Erokhin, Yuri E224
Erpenbeck, Donald A P361
Errichetti, Ann A15
Errichetti, Ann P9
Errotabere, Leeann P670
Ersek, Hikmet A893
Erskine, Arthur P350
Erskine, Alistair P582
Ertel, Elizabeth A196
Ertzeid, Ottar W129
Ervin, Bryan A214
Ervin, Bryan P128
Ervin, Teri P174
Ervin, Susan P451
Erwin, Robert A857
Erwin, Tami A870
Erwin, Duane P48
Erwin, Steven P87
Erwin, Terry P307
Erzen, Rob A371
Erün, G-¶khan W377
Esaki, Tim T. E264
Esamann, Douglas F. (Doug) A281
Esarte, Marty A878
Escallon, Alvaro Jaramillo W41
Escaravage, Jason A140
Escarraman, Luz A481
Escarrer, Gabriel P160
Escatel, Martin A782
Esch, Steve P139
Eschete, Marlise P475
Escobar, Mike A34
Escobar, Daniel P508
Escobedo, Dr Francisco P120
Escoffery, Shawn P548
Escontrela, Luis A538
Escover, Norman P361
Escudero, Lucimar A188
Escuyer, Vincent P231
Esernio, Anthony W370
Esfahani, Sy A558
Esham, Pat P457
Eshee, Denver P501
Eshelbrenner, Adam A813
Eshelbrenner, Adam P616
Eshghi, Fleur P200
Eshleman, Denise P621
Eskew, Michael A34
Eskow, Alan D. A868
Esparza, Lisa A177
Esparza, Ryan P258
Esparza, Alma P430
Espeland, Curtis E. (Curt) A286
Espeseth, Katherine P178
Espey-English, Patricia P682
Espey-English, Patti P683
Espich, Samuel P301
Espich, Dan P425
Espindola, Bill A308
Espinosa, Jonathan A195
Espinosa, Alejandro A382
Espinosa, Rafael W133
Espinoza, Aurora P420
Espinoza, Jose P508
Esplin, J. Kimo A443
Esplin, J Kimo A443
ESPLIN, DEBRA A458
ESPLIN, DEBRA P251
Esposito, Chris A351
Esposito, Mike A389
Esposito, Tom A522
Esposito, Orlando C. A659
Esposito, Michael A765
Esposito, Michael P540
Esposito, Sonia P603
Esposito, Chris E158
Esquith, Stephen L. (Steve) P341
Esquivel, Orcar P120

Esrock, Brett P444
Essawi, Tarik A164
Esselman, Tom A56
Essenberg, Janice P67
Esser, Richard W P277
Esser, Manfred W302
Essert, Henry A556
Essex, Susan A244
Essex, James A890
Essex, James P684
Essig, Marshall A214
Essig, Marshall P128
Essig, Stuart M. E220
Essl, Gerald J. (Gerry) E112
Essman, Christian P99
Esson, Margo A56
Esson, Timothy W. A845
Esson, Timothy W. E413
Estabrook, David A354
Estabrook, James B. A399
Estabrook, Crystal P106
Estampes, Jerome A241
Estavillo, Roxanne P233
Esteban, Carmen A427
Esteban, A. Gabriel P155
Esteban, Carmen E202
Estep, Greg W274
Estes, Kim A149
Estes, Teri A204
Estes, William A322
Estes, Scott A705
Estes, Rob W. P187
Estes, Melinda L. P473
Estes, Scott E352
Esteves, Eduardo A685
Estevez, Carlos A649
Esther, Chet A397
Esther, Chet P221
Estock, Andrew A317
Estock, Andrew E142
Estrada, Betty P480
Estrada, Cindy P557
Estrella, Guilherme W284
Etchemendy, John W. A507
Etchemendy, John W. P288
Etcheverry, Marcia P244
Etesse, Gerald P238
Etheridge, Don P363
Ethridge, Mary A700
Ethridge, O. E153
Etim, Linda P247
Etoh, Kimihiro W48
Etorrez, Alex P425
Etre, Kathy Armijo P537
Etten, Peter Van P168
Etter, Carl J. P488
Ettinger, Michael A727
Ettl, Robert P228
Etzel, Tom A920
Eubank, G Manly A167
Eubanks, Brent A517
Eubanks, Clifford P184
Eubanks, Clay P554
Eudy, John D. E133
Eui-Sun, Chung W179
Eulate, Borja Prado W140
Eulau, Robert K. (Bob) A725
Euler, Jeff A327
Eulich, John S. A302
Eulich, John S. E128
Eun-Yeon, Hwang W292
Eung-sik, Kim W163
Eusden, Alan A238
Eustis, Mark A. E337
Euteneuer, Joseph J. (Joe) A539
Evangel, Lori M. A382
Evangelista, Paul A. A184
Evangelista, W. Scott A469
Evans, Nicholas A113
Evans, Steve A190
Evans, Dan A221
Evans, Charisse A261
Evans, Charles L. (Charlie) A323
Evans, Charles L. (Charlie) A325
Evans, Darliene A336

A = AMERICAN BUSINESS
E = EMERGING COMPANIES
P = PRIVATE COMPANIES
W = WORLD BUSINESS

Evans, Mark A343
Evans, Christopher A380
Evans, Gerald W. A400
Evans, Godfrey B. A427
Evans, Aicha S. A456
Evans, Thomas A487
Evans, Katrina M. (Trina) A489
Evans, Jimmy A532
Evans, Stephen R. T. A548
Evans, Ed A556
Evans, Lance A558
Evans, John A562
Evans, Terry A597
Evans, Keenan A620
Evans, Jane A635
Evans, Richard D. A647
Evans, John A681
Evans, Philip L A693
Evans, Todd A693
Evans, Joseph A693
Evans, James A693
Evans, Norman A725
Evans, Deanna A727
Evans, Stuart A729
Evans, Maura A766
Evans, J. Eric A795
Evans, V. Lynn A798
Evans, Craig A810
Evans, Karen A814
Evans, Malcolm A838
Evans, Jack B. A847
Evans, Robert P69
Evans, Brian K. P83
Evans, Doug P111
Evans, Sandra P129
Evans, Wallace P161
Evans, Crystal P182
Evans, Darliene P194
Evans, Cindy P246
Evans, Jeremy S P277
Evans, Kari P300
Evans, Gail P303
Evans, Stephen R. T. P321
Evans, Susan P326
Evans, Jane P419
Evans, Donnie W P420
Evans, Peggy P493
Evans, Scott P498
Evans, James P509
Evans, Craig P597
Evans, Richard P602
Evans, Karen P616
Evans, Robert P624
Evans, Arthur T P640
Evans, Mariah P677
Evans, Sara E8
Evans, Gregory E. E59
Evans, Stephen E78
Evans, William E144
Evans, Bruce R E163
Evans, Brian R. E175
Evans, Godfrey B. E202
Evans, John E279
Evanson, Brynn L. A640
Evanson, Jeff K A799
Evanson, Paul J P350
Evatt, Chris A345
Evatt, Chris E154
Eveland, Callie P176
Eveland, Dan P176
Evelhoch, Jeffrey A550
Evenson, Jeffrey A238
Evenzwig, Michael A555
Everett, Lenny A204
Everett, Ethan A452
Everett, Roger A658
Everett, Nora M. A668
Everett, Bryan A708
Everett, Judy P220

Everett, Greg P334
Everett, Ethan E215
Everling, Jeffrey A496
Evernham, Scott J. A614
Evers, Alison A769
Everson, Monty P256
Everson, Dawn P305
Everson, Mike P337
Eversz, Woody A871
Eves, David L. A910
Evitts, Beth P680
Evola, Peter J A73
Ewald, Sandra P51
Ewaldsson, Ulf W360
Ewert, Brian H P309
Ewert, Phil P478
Ewig, Randall G. A401
Ewig, Randall G. E187
Ewing, Christopher A231
Ewing, Clay W. A384
Ewing, Jane A878
Ewing, Marilyn E P249
Ewing, Clay W. E176
Ewing, Robert E244
Exnicios, Joseph S. A399
Exposito, Patricia A530
Exshaw, Christian W80
Exton, Martha A180
Ey, Nick A360
Ey, Nick E164
Eyeington, Thomas P508
Eyerman, Paul E282
Eyl, Steven M. (Steve) E196
Eyl, Steve E196
Eyler, David A602
Eyre, Brik V. A113
Eysenbach, Ted P542
Eytcheson, David L. (Dave) E415
Eze-Nliam, Chete P97
Ezer, Dorit Ben P115
Ezrol, Harvey A461

F

Fabara, Paul D. A49
Faber, Emmanuel W117
Fabian, Bruce A201
Fabrey, Robert P480
Fabricant, David A772
Fabris, Sabrina A532
Facchin, Claudio W4
Facciabene, Grace P528
Facer, Burnett A920
Fache, Jameson Smith P101
Fache, Joseph Winick P225
Fache, Gregory P496
Facheris, Maurizio A6
Factor, Saul P255
Fadem, Steve P566
Fadool, Joseph F. A141
Faehnle, Stephen T P233
Fafoglia, Nick A223
Fagan, John A693
Fagan, Mary P452
Fagan, Tiffani P472
Fagan, Shiraz M. P488
Fagen, Richard E. (Rich) P90
Fagen, Elizabeth C P628
Fagerstrom, Brad A855
Fagg, Jenny W80
Fagnoule, Dominique W252
Fague, Philip E A625
Fague, Philip P109
Faherty, Sean A406
Fahey, Mike A173
Fahey, Paul A599
Fahey, Walter J. P302
Fahim, Shafei P51
Fahle, Susan P120
Fahrig, Siegmund A532
Fai, Lee Wai W384
Faile, Ann E244
Failla, Lisa A47
Failor, Courtney M P637

Fails, Karl R A773
Fails, Don P557
Fain, Eric S. A4
Fain, Kathy P584
Faintuch, Amir A456
Fair, Jeffrey A32
Fair, Joyce A272
Fair, Sonia P22
Fair, James P610
Fairbairn, Robert W. (Rob) A130
Fairbank, Richard D. (Rich) A163
Fairbank, Randall A906
Fairbanks, Cheryl A902
Fairbanks, Donald P347
Fairbanks, Cheryl P692
Fairbanks, Bryan H. E401
Fairbrother, Priscilla A864
Fairchild, Larry A316
Fairchild, Larry P191
Fairchild, Pat P269
Fairchild, Nancy E250
Faircloth, Michael E. A400
Faircloth, David A460
Fairhurst, David A545
Fairless, Justin P14
Fairley, Mark A468
Fairley, Mark A252
Fairley, Kimberly P635
Fairweather, George R. A877
Fairweather, Annmarie A908
Faison, Lauren P554
Faisst, Georg A682
Faith, Mark E P568
Faith, David M. P604
Fajardo, Natasha A P271
Fakhoury, Marwan P440
Fakhry, Robert A131
Fakult, James V. A355
Falaguerra, Robert J. (Bob) P472
Falatko, Thomas E426
Falb, Mark C. A412
Falb, Mark C. E192
Falcone, Bryan A241
Falcone, Joseph C. P679
Falduto, Catherine P613
Fale, Mr Robert P12
Faleskin, Greg A616
Falgoust, Stephen A658
Falk, Thomas J. (Tom) A490
Falk, Christian A508
Falkin, Bruce A105
Falkner, Keon P58
Falkowitz, Mary A810
Falkowitz, Mary P597
Falkowski, David A250
Fall, Clinton P580
Fallen, Kelly A115
Faller, Marcia R. E17
Fallin, Jonathan A390
Fallon, James A223
Fallon, William C. (Bill) A542
Fallon, James A622
Fallon, Jeanne M. P92
Fallon, David J. P125
Fallon, Shawna P498
Fallon, Lynnette C. E27
Falotico, Joy A362
Falsey, Ann M P589
Falstad, Daniel T P184
Falvey, Katie E257
Falzon, Robert M. A676
Falzon, Michael A676
Famiglietti, Michael A643
Famiglietti, Robin A746
Fan, Chunying A101
Fan, Jiansheng P666
Fanchar, Brent P480
Fancher, Judy P225
Fanelli, Arcangelo A199
Faneuil, Edward J. A388
Fang, AJ A777
Fang, Bin P225
Fang, Zhang Zi W95
Fang, AJ E393
Fang-ming, Lu W171

Fangmann, Ruth A865
Fann, George H. E153
Fanning, Thomas A. (Tom) A322
Fanning, Chris A372
Fanning, Chris P208
Fanning, Robert W P408
Fanning, Mark E328
Fanqiu, Meng W89
Fantauzzi, Joseph A741
Fantauzzi, Joseph E370
Fantom, Stacey A655
Fantom, Stacey E333
Fantorno, Carla P553
Faraca-bond, Lynn A407
Farah, Jean Claude A893
Farah, Pedro W392
Farahvash, Pooya A49
Farber, Jeffrey M. (Jeff) A402
Farber, Nancy P676
Farber, William E239
Farber, Jeffrey K. E239
Farbes, Hubert A. P160
Fargo, Thomas B. A442
Farhangpour, Amir P399
Farhat, Jerry A16
Faria, Ami A380
Farida, Jaber P597
Faries, Stan A616
Farineau, Don A315
Farkas, Chris P237
Farland, Kenn Mc P345
Farleigh, Corinne P218
Farley, Jack A281
Farley, James D. (Jim) A362
Farley, Jim A362
Farley, Dan A766
Farley, Joseph M P93
Farley, Randy P136
Farley, Leigh P334
Farley, Joshua P658
Farmer, Scott A125
Farmer, Scott D. A198
Farmer, Curtis C. A221
Farmer, Dennis A397
Farmer, Dom A685
Farmer, Marc A838
Farmer, Dennis P221
Farmer, Michael P274
Farmer, Pam P694
Farnan, Patrick A333
Farnay, Matt A382
Farner, David M. A859
Farner, David M. P652
Farnin, Paul A165
Farnsworth, Bryan D. A432
Farnsworth, Ronald L. (Ron) A839
Farnsworth, Ronald L. (Ron) E409
Farnum, Marissa P175
Farnum, Georgann B. E364
Farr, David N. A295
Farr, Paul A P554
Farrall, Ann A599
Farrand, Stephen A550
Farrant, M. A. A313
Farrant, Malcolm A313
Farrar, Rick A691
Farrar, Jeffrey W. A841
Farrar, Jeffrey W. E410
Farrell, Lynn A73
Farrell, Peter A105
Farrell, Warren A152
Farrell, Thomas F. A275
Farrell, Todd A508
Farrell, William J. (Bill) A522
Farrell, Karen A611
Farrell, David A691
Farrell, Tj A729
Farrell, William A810
Farrell, Breege A. A863
Farrell, Scott A865
Farrell, Lori Ann P123
Farrell, Benny P300
Farrell, Edward P303
Farrell, William P597
Farrell, Mary C. P699

Farrell, Garry W227
Farrell, Joanne W305
Farrell, Joanne W306
Farrell, Warren E49
Farrell, James E54
Farrell, Glenn E304
Farrell, Karen E313
Farrell, Michael J. E354
Farrell, Peter C. E355
Farrell, Diane E364
Farrelly, Joseph E163
Farren, John P565
Farrier, Joe P368
Farrimond, Katherine P386
Farrington, Duane A631
Farrington, Shannon P439
Farrington, Craig E97
Farris, J. Matt A433
Farris, Kristofer M. A703
Farris, Joseph A857
Farris, Bain J P531
Farrow, Joan P391
Farrukh, Abdallah P40
Farry, Paul A173
Farstad, Jeffrey P520
Fartaj, Vandad A642
Fartaj, Vandad E328
Farthing, Gary A56
Farthing, Dana A441
Fasano, Rebecca A136
Fasano, Gerard A. (Gerry) A505
Fash, Boni P682
Fasman, Ken P587
Fasolo, Peter M. A476
Fassezke, Michael P539
Fassig, Gerry E96
Fath, Mike A158
Fath, Noella P40
Fathers, Bill A875
Fatovic, Robert D. A718
Fattore, Charles A278
Fattori, Ruth A647
Faubus, Todd A763
Faucette, Charleen P570
Fauchet, Philippe P615
Faujour, Olivier A377
Faul, Mark A813
Faul, Mark P616
Faulk, George A556
Faulkner, Tammy A272
Faulkner, Nigel A783
Faulkner, Mark P59
Faulkner, Archimedes P334
Faury, Guillaume W16
Fauth, David A. (Dave) A769
Favela, Nelson P407
Faver, Robert A837
Favinger, Debra A272
Favors, Gary P121
Favre, Michel W148
Favuzza, Steven P P609
Fawcett, John J. A201
Fawcett, Matthew K A580
Fawcett, Charles C. A830
Fawcett, Karen W340
Fawcett, Charles C. E403
Fawthrop, Kit A814
Fawthrop, Kit P616
Fawver, John A647
Faxon, David P567
Fay, Laura A607
Fayad, Walid A140
Fazio, Carl A56
Fazio, Denise A659
Fazio, Giulio W141
Fazzino, Tabitha P603
Fearey, Peter S. E384
Fearon, Richard A287
Fearon, Richard P174
Feast, Kenneth A530
Feathers, Eric A346
Febriyanti, Vera A398
Febvre, Christophe P435
Fechushak, John A262
Feczko, Peter J A413

Feczko, Peter J P234
Feddersen, Marci P57
Fedele, Jerry P79
Fedele, Jerry J P685
Fedele, Christopher E220
Fedeli, Frank P123
Federico, Anthony J. A833
Federighi, Craig A70
Fedorko, Tara A904
Fedorko, Tara E442
Fedronas, Eileen A872
Fedus, Natalie A904
Fedus, Natalie E442
Fedyszyn, Karen A9
Fedyszyn, Karen P4
Feehan, William A448
Feeler, Jeffrey R. (Jeff) E420
Feeney, Brian J. A184
Feeney, Connie A500
Feeney, Joan A677
Feeney, Paul M. P70
Feeney, Mark P151
Feeney, Connie E237
Feenstra, Gregory A84
Feeny, Edwin A803
Feffer, David P549
Feffer, Daniel P549
Fefferman, Liza Burnett A872
Fegley, Michael P148
Feher, William A294
Fehlman, Robert A. A742
Fehlman, Robert A. E372
Fehring, Mark A885
Feidt, William P364
Feierman, Dennis P302
Feigelson, Sharon A221
Feiger, Mitchell S. A541
Feiger, Mitchell S. E266
Feighery, Kate A585
Feighery, Kate P377
Feight, R. Preston A629
Feigin, Michael M. E26
Fein, David A309
Fein, Steven P18
Fein, Alan P567
Feinauer, Jonathan A919
Feinberg, David M. A46
Feinberg, David M. A47
Feinberg, David T. A372
Feinberg, Hill A. A420
Feinberg, Jeremy A537
Feinberg, David A. P153
Feinberg, David T. P208
Feinberg, David P631
Feinberg, Hill A. E198
Feiner, Robert A P425
Feiner, Barbara A. P615
Feinftein, Eric P47
Feinstein, Leonard (Lenny) A120
Feinstein, Fariah A480
Feitt, Ted A555
Fejer, Paul A417
Fejes, Balazs E130
Felan, N A228
Felan, N P136
Felber, Andy A173
Felcht, Utz-Hellmuth W121
Feld, John P489
Felder, Ron A697
Felder, Ron P454
Feldgreber, Rob P441
Feldhaus, Peter W365
Feldman, Ivan S A37
Feldman, Michael (Mike) A911
Feldman, Amy A918
Feleccia, Annie A339
Feleccia, Annie E150
Felenstein, Craig A269
Felice, Gregorio de W189
Feliciano, Hector A565
Felis, Sandra L. P614
Felix, Natalie A342
Felix, Ruth P451
Felix, Diana P538
Felke, Magnus A685

Felkey, Tana P613
Felkins, Jay A177
Felkner, Joseph P59
Felkner, Joseph (Joe) P230
Fellahi, Khalid A893
Felletter, John E22
Fellinger, Robert E. (Bob) P188
Fellman, Ted A693
Fellows, Melissa A81
Fellows, Steven P482
Fellows, Boyd W. E385
Fellure, Diana A85
Feltner, Michael P423
Felton, Jerry A850
Felton, Jeff P293
Felton, Tom P318
Felton, Jeff E339
Felts, Revis A521
Feltz, Lorianne A306
Feltz, Paul P314
Fendley, Tom P259
Fendrich, Amy A438
Fenech, Josie A221
Feng, Larry A691
Fenley, Michelle P333
Fennell, Laura A. A466
Fennell, Charles J P532
Fennell, George E213
Fennimore, Judy A530
Fenster, Jeanne A406
Fenstermacher, Scott E190
Fenstermaker, William H. A446
Fenstermaker, Barbara P486
Fenstermaker, William H. E210
Fenton, Andrew A921
Fenves, Gregory L. P656
Fenwick, Sandra L. P570
Fenzel, Paul P256
Fenzl, Paul P256
Feragne, Mark A P24
Ferando, Jim A111
Ferando, Jim P56
Ferber, Scott A160
Ferbert, Dal E247
Ferch, Wayne P7
Ferdig, Larry A568
Ferdon, Kandice P115
Ferdschneider, Marcy A585
Ferdschneider, Marcy P377
Ferebee, Julie P415
Ferencz, Steven M. P104
Feret, Peter A489
Fergan, Tim A333
Fergenbaum, David A408
Ferguson, Roy C. A98
Ferguson, Kelly A115
Ferguson, T. Ritson A172
Ferguson, Jim A327
Ferguson, Tim A330
Ferguson, Brad A343
Ferguson, Roger A377
Ferguson, Greg A490
Ferguson, Mike A546
Ferguson, Elpida A584
Ferguson, James A599
Ferguson, John R. A802
Ferguson, Rhonda S. A842
Ferguson, Will A844
Ferguson, Chris P165
Ferguson, Terra P176
Ferguson, Dwight P216
Ferguson, Joel I. P341
Ferguson, Dean P393
Ferguson, Jeff P518
Ferguson, John R. P562
Ferguson, Roy C. E33
Ferguson, Mark E273
Ferguson, Will E412
Ferguson-McHugh, Mary L. A671
Feria, Sandy P81
Ferketish, Gene B P651
Fermo, Anthony A163
Fernandes, Paulo A537
Fernandes, Al P629
Fernandez, Carlos A204

Fernandez, Varsovia A247
Fernandez, Martin Benedict A295
Fernandez, Jeff A438
Fernandez, Connie A446
Fernandez, Andre J A578
Fernandez, Manny A874
Fernandez, Nicole P390
Fernandez, Aurelio M. P508
Fernandez, Tracey P535
Fernandez, Carlos P650
Fernandez, Jacob P670
Fernandez, Daniel W82
Fernandez, Ramon W278
Fernandez, Freddy E51
Fernandez, Varsovia E103
Fernandez, Gene E140
Fernandez, Madeline E182
Fernandez, Connie E210
Fernandez-vasin, Jennifer A454
Fernando, Emil P216
Ferndinand, Norma P589
Ferniany, Will P639
Fernicola, Robert A478
Fernitz, Dan A478
Fern--ndez, José Luis A469
Fern--ndez, V-ctor Turpaud W137
Ferraiuolo, Caroline P79
Ferrando, Jonathan A88
Ferrante, Matt A120
Ferrara, Diana A441
Ferrara, Albert A852
Ferrari, Mauro P335
Ferraro, Joseph A. (Joe) A92
Ferraro, John A651
Ferraro, Paul A695
Ferraro, John P426
Ferraro, Flora E424
Ferree, Gregory M. A752
Ferree, Greg A752
Ferree, John N. P487
Ferreira, Chris A478
Ferreira, Daniel P556
Ferreira, Jose (Joe) E76
Ferreira-Golino, Cathy A644
Ferreiro, Jorge A175
Ferrell, Chad A53
Ferrell, Lee A54
Ferrell, Malcolm A163
Ferrell, Ashley P52
Ferrer, Maria A446
Ferrer, Jorge A500
Ferrer, Javier D. A661
Ferrer, Fernando A. P138
Ferrer, Antonio Garc-a W6
Ferrer, Maria E210
Ferrer, Jorge E237
Ferreri, Anthony C P541
Ferrero, Bruce P663
Ferretti, Richard A503
Ferrie, John A696
Ferriola, John J. A605
Ferris, Rick A196
Ferris, Steve A733
Ferris, Steve P491
Ferrise, Sam P125
Ferriss, Stephen A A726
Ferro, Anthony A81
Ferrucci, Mario E331
Ferrufino, Jimena P111
Ferry, Thomas P22
Ferry, Michael J. E41
Ferr--n, Javier W128
Fesen, Michael A587
Fesko, Frankie P134
Fesko, Frankie L P359
Fessler, Richard D P519
Festa, Stephen V. A296
Festa, Joe A741
Festa, Joe E370
Festerling, Ryan A493
Festervand, Terry A206
Fetsko, Francis M. A820
Fett, Brian P212
Fetterly-Bush, Shelly A820
Fetterolf, Brian S. A830

A = AMERICAN BUSINESS		
E = EMERGING COMPANIES		
P = PRIVATE COMPANIES		
W = WORLD BUSINESS		

Fetterolf, Brian S. E403
Fettig, Jeff M. A898
Fetto, Julie A807
Fetto, Julie P574
Fetzer, Ryan A330
Feuerlicht, Samuel P214
Feuerstein, Jeff A537
Feuge, Ladonna P685
Fewell, Amy A218
Fey, Michael A778
Feygin, David A144
Feynberg, Mikhail P363
Ffolkes, Marie A24
Fiala, Mary E349
Fiatte, Traci L. W299
Ficalora, Joseph R. A583
Ficaro, James E300
Fichadia, Ashok A842
Fichera, Michael A589
Fichtel, Howard P363
Fiddelke, Michael A788
Fiddler, Troy P537
Fidler, John A489
Fidler, Marie A839
Fidler, Josh P301
Fidler, Marie E409
Fiedler, Stacy A654
Fiedorek, R. Mark A758
Fiedorek, R. Mark P519
Field, Doug A70
Field, James M. A260
Field, Catherine A437
Field, Brock P34
Field, Ben P238
Field, Juan P402
Field, David J. E126
Field, Joseph M. E127
Fielding, Linda P160
Fields, Dave A173
Fields, Felicia J A362
Fields, Bruce A465
Fields, Danielle A532
Fields, David P36
Fields, Sarah P387
Fields, Mike P399
Fields, Billy P434
Fields, Dana P439
Fields, Deborah P641
Fields, Randolph H. E171
Fienup, Chris A693
Fierke, Carol A. A698
Fierke, Carol A. P456
Fietzer, Deanna A221
Fifarek, Kelly E163
Fife, Brady A49
Fifer, Joseph J P519
Fifick, Anne A677
Figer, Rich A875
Figge, Cherie A838
Fighs, Charles P508
Figley, Mark A489
Figlioli, Keith J. E336
Figliuolo, Steve A356
Figueredo, Jorge L. A546
Figueroa, Patricia A76
Figueroa, George A565
Figueroa, John A703
Figueroa, Mildred P623
Figueroa, Laureano P654
Figurelli, Nick E265
Fihla, Kenny W339
Fikaris, George A201
Fike, Sherri A96
Fike, Ruthita J. P294
Fikiet, Jim P91
Fikry, Christopher A687
Fiksdahl, Liv W129
Fikucki, Mark A402
Filaretos, Spyros N. W23

Filbin, Michael E A728
Filby, Steven J P194
Filcek, Rodney R A252
Files, John P577
Filho, Benjamin M. Baptista W30
Filho, Alfredo Egydio Arruda
  Villela W191
Filho, Pedro Jorge W379
Filho, Leocadio Antunes de
  Almeida W379
Filho, Lucio de Castro Andrade W379
Filiberto, Cosmo P189
Filipov, Douglas P95
Filippone, Chris P135
Filipski, Kevin A649
Filizetti, Gary P161
Filler, Cheryl P134
Fillippo, Thomas A. E108
Fillmore, Randall A565
Film, George P566
Filosa, Kirsten A131
Filosa, Ronald P296
Filton, Steve G. A857
Filtz, Joe P104
Finan, Irial A215
Finan, John J P204
Finberg, Robert P632
Finch, Mary E. A16
Finch, Felesha A446
Finch, Michelle Y A541
Finch, Eric P231
Finch, Kathleen P489
Finch, Duncan W217
Finch, Steven A. (Steve) W232
Finch, Felesha E210
Finch, Michelle Y E266
Fincher, C. Anderson A279
Fincher, Murray A832
Findlay, D. Cameron A74
Findlay, Thomas A115
Findlay, David M. A500
Findlay, David W268
Findlay, David M. E238
Findley, Mary A345
Findley, Mary P152
Findley, Peggy P257
Fine, Peter S. A111
Fine, Greg A371
Fine, Sharon A599
Fine, Rick A729
Fine, Kim P17
Fine, Peter S. P56
Fine, Michael H P462
Finedore, Marleen P217
Finelli, Frederick P675
Finer, Jeffrey T. E217
Finestone, Mark A. A90
Finger, Jennifer A889
Fingerman, Joseph A741
Fingerman, Joseph E370
Finholt, Thomas A. A698
Finholt, Thomas A. P456
Fini, Salvatore De A52
Finigan, Barbara A408
Finis, Mario P361
Finissi, Mike A594
Fink, Laurence D. (Larry) A130
Fink, Charles A300
Fink, Chris A332
Fink, Nicholas I. A364
Fink, Mary A476
Fink, Anne A647
Fink, Josh A838
Fink, Martin A892
Fink, Andrew P353
Fink, Michael P482
Fink, Marvin H. E357
Fink, Benjamin M. (Ben) E436
Finkel, Lynn A93
Finkelstein, David L. A66
Finkelstein, Stuart A537
Finkelstein, Jeffery A P241
Finkenbiner, Joy P211
Finklea, Jody P198
Finks, Jay A249

Finley, Tammy M. A13
Finley, John G. A132
Finley, Brett A364
Finley, Joseph M. A830
Finley, Teresa M. A850
Finley, Wayne P144
Finley, Christina P286
Finley, Rebecca S. P618
Finley, Joseph M. E403
Finn, Bradley A354
Finn, Tim A446
Finn, Thomas M. A671
Finn, Michael A855
Finn, Ruth A A869
Finn, Rita P204
Finn, William A. P509
Finn, Tim E210
Finnegan, John A85
Finnegan, Daniel J. A139
Finnegan, Mike A517
Finnegan, Deb A599
Finnegan, Chris P694
Finneran, John G. A163
Finnerty, Kyle A204
Finney, Michele A794
Finnie, Halana P204
Finnin, Jeffrey S. (Jeff) E96
Fioravanti, Mark A719
Fioravanti, Mark P468
Fiore, Thomas A158
Fiore, Paul G A744
Fiorentino, Karen P626
Fiorentino, Paolo W380
Fiorenzo, V James P660
Fiori, Kevin P547
Fiorilli, Matthew A120
Fiorina, Carly A216
Fiorito, Elizabeth P233
Fipps, Paul A840
Firestone, Marc S. A652
Firestone, James A912
Firman, Julie P513
First, Robert P392
Fisackerly, Haley R. A300
Fischer, Jean-Luc A218
Fischer, Robert A247
Fischer, Stanley A325
Fischer, Andrew A478
Fischer, Thomas J. (Tom) A508
Fischer, John E. A618
Fischer, Mark D. A682
Fischer, Avery A691
Fischer, Corinna A691
Fischer, Anthony J. (Tony) A837
Fischer, George J. A870
Fischer, Michael R. (Mike) P55
Fischer, Steven P71
Fischer, John A P262
Fischer, Orive E P306
Fischer, Jim P358
Fischer, Alex P365
Fischer, Susan P378
Fischer, Jennifer P413
Fischer, William P611
Fischer, Bill P611
Fischer, Sam W128
Fischer, David B. E31
Fischer, Timothy E101
Fischer, Robert E103
Fischer-Kinney, Julie P613
Fischmann, Joan A323
Fischvogt, Pam A246
Fisco, Bob A489
Fiscus, Richard A. (Rich) A720
Fiscus, Richard A. (Rich) E362
Fish, Frederick A231
Fish, Mike A406
Fish, Patrick A489
Fish, Kathleen B. (Kathy) A671
Fish, James C. (Jim) A881
Fish, Eric P257
Fish, Mark P360
Fish, John F. P545
Fish, John F. P626
Fish, Ted P675

Fish, Frederick E90
Fishbach, Mitchell P283
Fishbein, Daniel R. W347
Fishburn, Amy P537
Fishel, Rick E261
Fisher, Michael A19
Fisher, Daniel W. A96
Fisher, Scott A115
Fisher, Joe A221
Fisher, Stephen (Steve) A288
Fisher, Sherri R A422
Fisher, Douglas W. (Doug) A456
Fisher, John A463
Fisher, Nick A476
Fisher, Debby A493
Fisher, James A513
Fisher, James A530
Fisher, Jeff A607
Fisher, Gary A644
Fisher, Steve A736
Fisher, Jean A784
Fisher, Robert J. (Bob) A809
Fisher, John (Scott) A851
Fisher, Eric A867
Fisher, Marlise G. A879
Fisher, Mary A881
Fisher, Mary A902
Fisher, Stephanie D. A916
Fisher, Veronica P28
Fisher, John P106
Fisher, Michael P115
Fisher, Jill P163
Fisher, Scott P187
Fisher, Seth P210
Fisher, Sherri R P239
Fisher, Morris P303
Fisher, Nancy P336
Fisher, Lisa A P409
Fisher, Michelle P428
Fisher, Steve P492
Fisher, Scott W. P555
Fisher, David E. P590
Fisher, Jennifer P682
Fisher, Mary P692
Fisher, J. Bradley (Brad) E59
Fisher, Jeffrey H. E69
Fisher, Tammy E122
Fisher, Jill E140
Fisher, Thomas C. E326
Fisher, Melissa E342
Fisher, Brian J. E350
Fishman, Eric A417
Fishman, Robert A698
Fishman, Robert E P361
Fishman, Matthew E. P369
Fishman, Robert P456
Fishman, Robert S. E95
Fisk, George A505
Fisk, George E241
Fissinger, Jeannie E189
Fitch, Deborah A225
Fitch, Karl A635
Fitch, Karl P419
Fitch, Carl P681
Fitch, Deborah E88
Fithian, David B. P610
Fitschen, Jürgen W123
Fitterling, James A187
Fitterling, James E71
Fitts, Tina A313
Fitts, Dave A647
Fitts, Michael A. A812
Fitts, Michael A. P607
Fitz, Chris A700
Fitz, Grant A912
Fitz, Stefan W194
Fitzgerald, Timothy A105
Fitzgerald, Joseph M. (Joe) A144
Fitzgerald, Susan A196
Fitzgerald, Paula A235
Fitzgerald, Patrick A327
Fitzgerald, Bill A410
Fitzgerald, Michelle A556
Fitzgerald, Kathleen A678
Fitzgerald, Jay A683

FitzGerald, Scott R. A766
Fitzgerald, Ashley P22
Fitzgerald, Timothy P209
Fitzgerald, Jacqui P271
Fitzgerald, Paul J. P654
Fitzgerald, Laarry P685
Fitzgerald, Gale E101
Fitzgerald, Timothy J. (Tim) E277
Fitzgibbons, Michael A A622
Fitzgibbons, Michael A A623
Fitzgibbons, Carol A P249
Fitzgibbons, Carol P249
Fitzgibbons, Michael A P407
Fitzgibbons, Timothy P P632
Fitzmaurice, Michael A535
Fitzmaurice, Michael P312
Fitzmyers, Thomas J. (Tom) E374
Fitzpatrick, Brian A131
Fitzpatrick, Maggie A309
Fitzpatrick, Michael J. A611
FitzPatrick, Daniel M. (Dan) A883
Fitzpatrick, Sean P538
Fitzpatrick, M. Louise P667
FitzPatrick, Mark T. W295
Fitzpatrick, Francis J. (Frank) E31
Fitzpatrick, Alex E117
Fitzpatrick, Maura E308
Fitzpatrick, Michael J. E313
Fitzpatrick, Diana E357
Fitzsimmons, Ellen A42
Fitzsimons, Brooks A85
Fitzsimons, Patricia Sue P699
Fixer, Mike A406
Fixmer, Lee A193
Fixmer, Lee P112
Flach, Christian W234
Flack, Kerry A34
Flack, Cheryl A599
Flacke, Jennifer A158
Flagg, Ronald P286
Flaherty, Janice A417
Flaherty, Thomas A678
Flaherty, Kevin P435
Flaherty, Karen P515
Flaherty, Michael E213
Flaherty-Oxler, Karen P589
Flaks, Jeffrey A P227
Flanagan, Michael A85
Flanagan, Bill A597
Flanagan, Patrick A744
Flanagan, Kevin A900
Flanagan, J. Kelly P83
Flanagan, Lyn P354
Flanagan, Joseph F. (Joe) E219
Flanders, Cynthia E23
Flanders, Paul R. E60
Flanigan, John A17
Flanigan, Dan A332
Flanigan, Terri A885
Flanigan, John P10
Flanigan, Kevin P343
Flannery, John L. A375
Flannery, Matthew J. A851
Flannery, Robert P659
Flannery, David A. E149
Flappan, Bob A84
Flathers, Kristina P370
Flatt, J. Bruce W75
Flavin, Karen P23
Flaws, Brandan P671
Flax, Sherri P642
Flaxman, Jon E. A435
Fleagle, Steve R. P611
Fleckenstein, Michele A122
Fleece, Joseph (Jay) P264
Fleece, Eli P635
Fleet, Peter A362
Fleishman, Joel A691
Flemer, Ann P338
Fleming, Paul A98
Fleming, Michael A136
Fleming, Denise Russell A136
Fleming, Christine A599
Fleming, Mark A616
Fleming, Paul A766

Fleming, Russ P46
Fleming, Paul P139
Fleming, Eric P155
Fleming, John P563
Fleming, Scott P582
Fleming, Rita P640
Fleming, Paul E33
Flemming, Mark P96
Flescher, Mark A765
Flescher, Mark P540
Fleshood, John S. A830
Fleshood, John S. E402
Fletcher, Leslie A A221
Fletcher, Cedric A593
Fletcher, Whitney A729
Fletcher, Brock A754
Fletcher, J. Kevin A884
Fletcher, John P. A903
Fletcher, John P171
Fletcher, Brock E378
Fletcher, Scott E407
Fletterich, Michael W239
Fleury, Gustave A585
Fleury, Lynda A863
Fleury, Gustave P377
Fleury, Alison P498
Flewelling, Brian A489
Flick, Barbara A80
Flick, Barbara P47
Flickinger, Kenneth E P570
Flinn, James A173
Flinn, Brian E445
Flinner, Debra A830
Flinner, Debra E403
Flinois, Xavier P417
Flint, John W175
Flintjer, Erin P434
Flinton, David A914
Fliss, Jon A136
Flitman, David E P350
Flivo, Michael P605
Flod, Stacy Y P170
Flood, Michael G A412
Flood, Michael A412
Flood, Gary J. A537
Flood, John P249
Flood, Arlene P324
Flood, Michael G E192
Flood, Michael E192
Flood-Shaffer, Kellie P555
Florance, Andrew C. E97
Florence, Jared P156
Florence, Cristian W43
Flores, Juan A84
Flores, Debbie A111
Flores, Jana A168
Flores, Gabriel A178
Flores, Debra A. A736
Flores, Joshuah P. A851
Flores, Debbie P56
Flores, Monica P123
Flores, Barbara P140
Flores, Chris P245
Flores, Richard P291
Flores, Hector P464
Flores, Dr Steven P466
Flores, Donny P482
Flores, Debra A. P492
Flores, William V. (Bill) P643
Flores, Nidia E20
Florey, Reinhard W276
Flori, Lou A669
Florida, John P594
Florin, Daniel P. (Dan) A918
Floris, Karla A474
Floris, Karla P262
Florness, Daniel L. (Dan) A318
Flory, Kevin A607
Flournoy, Shirley P549
Flow, Donald E. P673
Flowe, Aaron A426
Flower, Karl A710
Flowers, Randy A202
Flowers, Garry W A358
Flowers, Randy P122

Flowers, Debbie P170
Flowers, Jeff P428
Flowers, BJ P499
Flowers, David P591
Floyd, Dennis A136
Floyd, H. Charles (Chuck) A444
Floyd, Dale A655
Floyd, David K. A772
Floyd, Julie P273
Floyd, Richard B P500
Floyd, Gary P555
Floyd, Krissy P583
Floyd, Dale E333
Flueckiger, Joe A207
Flueckiger, Russ P6
Flugstad, Daniel A405
Fluhler, Stephan H. A349
Fluhler, Stephan H. E156
Fluke, Brad E78
Flum, Joshua (Josh) A250
Flury, L. Richard E53
Flynn, Philip B. (Phil) A81
Flynn, Paul G. A303
Flynn, Jim A400
Flynn, Thomas L. A412
Flynn, Todd A655
Flynn, Michael A683
Flynn, Lynn A683
Flynn, Pamela A691
Flynn, William A707
Flynn, Robert A785
Flynn, Daniel A846
Flynn, Marilyn L. A860
Flynn, Elizabeth A883
Flynn, Dennis P41
Flynn, Erin P434
Flynn, Marilyn L. P656
Flynn, Mike E65
Flynn, Paul E173
Flynn, Thomas L. E192
Flynn, Todd E333
Flynn, Kerry E428
Flynt, John A439
Fodor, Darrin A644
Fodor, Troy P246
Foehr, Matthew W. E246
Foellmer, Frank P551
Fogarty, Steve A218
Fogarty, Tim A235
Fogarty, John P71
Fogarty, Cathy P290
Fogarty, Kevin M. E236
Fogel, David A56
Fogel, Glenn D. A139
Fogel, Arthur A517
Fogg, David H A374
Fogg, Bryan A691
Fogle, Natalie A102
Fogliato, Franco E86
Foglio, Neil A250
Foight, Debbie P202
Fojo, Carlos A733
Fojtasek, Georgia P671
Fojut, John A493
Fojut, Jack A493
Fok, Canning K. N. W176
Foley, John A153
Foley, Michael E. A283
Foley, Beth A307
Foley, William A316
Foley, William P. (Bill) A329
Foley, Shannon A439
Foley, Brendan M. A544
Foley, Patrick M A621
Foley, Jim A659
Foley, Joseph R. (Joe) A863
Foley, William P191
Foley, Patrick M P407
Foley, Cathy P437
Foley, Pamela P480
Foley, Marie P494
Foley, D Sue P602
Foley, Henry C. (Hank) P647
Foley, Brad P651
Foley, John W295

Foley, Michael W360
Foley, Mike W405
Folgado, Nicolas P111
Foli, Elsie P299
Folks, John P396
Folland, Jeffrey P345
Follen, William P283
Follens, Geert W36
Follett, Ray A255
Folliard, Thomas J. (Tom) A166
Folse, William P476
Folsom, Suzanne R. A852
Folster, Brent A160
Folster, Brent E55
Fomby, Rod A795
Fondell, Andrew P106
Fong, Ivan A3
Fong, Sylvia A490
Fong, Peter L. P588
Fonseca, Lidia A687
Font, Juan E96
Fontaine, Michael A766
Fontaine, April A818
Fontaine, Keith P227
Fontaine, Jean-Louis W69
Fontanez, Carmen A180
Fontenot, Teri A58
Fontenot, Justin A737
Fontenot, Teri G. P695
Fontenot, Justin E367
Foo, Chok-Pin P305
Foo, Peter M. T. W384
Foody, Paul A881
Fook, Hou Wey W119
Foos, Jason P602
Foot, Jim A103
Foote, James M. A243
Foraker, Randy P. A98
Foraker, John M. A377
Foraker, Randy P. E33
Foran, Bob A16
Foran, Margaret A676
Foran, Gregory S. (Greg) A878
Forbes, Glenn A432
Forbes, Lori A705
Forbes, Jeff S P184
Forbes, Paul P363
Forbes, Stephen J. W80
Forbes, Lori E352
Forbes, Kim E398
Forbes, Tom E442
Forbis, Chris P157
Force, Glenn A901
Force, Glenn P692
Ford, Robert B. A4
Ford, Mary A51
Ford, Thomas V A105
Ford, Michael A136
Ford, William C. (Bill) A362
Ford, Gerald J. A367
Ford, Brett A395
Ford, Jeremy B. A420
Ford, Gerald J. A420
Ford, Kevin A480
Ford, Fred A552
Ford, Jim A592
Ford, Aaron A678
Ford, Karen A691
Ford, Darrell L. A912
Ford, Meg P135
Ford, Denise P282
Ford, Lauren P321
Ford, Fred P328
Ford, Gary P335
Ford, Bob P468
Ford, Connie P468
Ford, Patrick P542
Ford, Gerald R P636
Ford, Michael W297
Ford, Marlon E94
Ford, Jeremy B. E198
Ford, Gerald J. E198
Ford, W. Sean E248
Ford, W E248
Forde, Deborah A810

A = AMERICAN BUSINESS
E = EMERGING COMPANIES
P = PRIVATE COMPANIES
W = WORLD BUSINESS

Forde, Terry P8
Forde, Deborah P597
Fordham, Pam P603
Fore, Delbert A303
Fore, Henrietta A377
Foreman, Kelly A919
Foreman, Jeff P255
Foreman, Jennifer P355
Foreman, Ken P455
Foreman, Anne E175
Forese, James A. (Jim) A203
Forese, Laura L. A810
Forese, Laura L. P597
Foresman, Stephen E189
Forest, Catherine A507
Forest, Catherine P288
Forestier, Jean-Pierre W364
Foret, Nathan A56
Foret, Mickey A262
Forger, James (Jim) P341
Forgette, Steve A817
Forgey, Warren P257
Forillo, Nick A533
Foris, Nico P223
Forkish, Jennifer A158
Forkosh, Garry P276
Forlenza, Vincent A. (Vince) A119
Forman, James A607
Forman, Susan A729
Forman, Keith B P149
Forman, Eric C. E97
Formella, Nancy P71
Forney, John L. A847
Forney, John L. E414
Forrest, Terry A59
Forrest, Scott A292
Forrest, Frank R. A332
Forrest, Michael A456
Forrest, John A478
Forrest, Stephen A698
Forrest, Mark P413
Forrest, Stephen A456
Forrest, Nelson P512
Forrester, Craig A196
Fors, Rudy A865
Forse, Jay A478
Forshee, Ryan A330
Forst, Israel A723
Forstner, Jim P157
Forsyte, Carol E8
Forsyth, John A113
Forsyth, Michael P653
Forsythe, Claire A316
Forsythe, Claire E141
Fort, Bob A736
Fort, Bob P492
Fort, Lydia E101
Forte, Jacquelynn A285
Forte, Karen P181
Forte, Jacquelynn E114
Forthman, Michael A P208
Fortier, William J A767
Fortin, Mary Jane B. A33
Fortin, Raymond D. A774
Fortino, Nickolas A607
Fortner, Craig A348
Fortner, Jack L. P648
Fortner, Craig E155
Fortnum, Debbie P579
Fortuna, David A865
Fortunas, Paula P554
Fortunato, Kim Fremont A161
Fortunato, Joseph A759
Fortunato, Ralph P273
Fortunato, Steve E29
Fortunato-diaz, Annette A182
Fortunato-diaz, Annette E63
Fortwangler, Robert P90
Forward, Bill A658

Forziati, Gina A130
Fosberg, Andy A173
Foschi, Pier Luigi W81
Foshee, William M. A737
Foshee, Kevin P32
Foshee, William M. E367
Fosina, Michael J P283
Foskett, Jennifer P413
Foss, Eric J. A73
Foss, Eric A195
Foss, Mark P151
Foss, Donald A. E99
Foss, Evelyn E212
Fossati, Massimiliano W380
Fossen, Cymbre Van A340
Fossen, Cymbre Van E151
Fossett, Sheryl P311
Fossett, Diana P383
Fossum, Jeff A140
Foster, Sarah A105
Foster, Mireya A109
Foster, Jesse G. A110
Foster, Nancy A201
Foster, James A208
Foster, Sara E. A223
Foster, David A287
Foster, Michael A327
Foster, Colleen A332
Foster, Holly M. A344
Foster, Daphne H. A388
Foster, Jon M. A410
Foster, Mark A460
Foster, Bill A461
Foster, Ray A659
Foster, Mike A701
Foster, Mark A767
Foster, Boyd E A773
Foster, Larry A818
Foster, Paul L. A860
Foster, Gordon K P53
Foster, Julie P92
Foster, Chris P101
Foster, Bob P123
Foster, Robert G P123
Foster, Andrew P124
Foster, Pam P141
Foster, Scott P143
Foster, David P174
Foster, Chandra P176
Foster, Terri P233
Foster, Paul D. P258
Foster, Robin P327
Foster, Susan P355
Foster, June P449
Foster, Robert F P507
Foster, Eric P551
Foster, Fran P593
Foster, Richard P598
Foster, Randall P604
Foster, Paul L. P656
Foster, Richard M P672
Foster, Mireya E36
Foster, Jesse G. E37
Foster, James C. E69
Foster, Andrea E257
Foster, Bill E381
Foti, Kevin C. A514
Foti, Joe P309
Foti, Alessandro W380
Fotiades, George L. E56
Fouad, Mag A281
Fouberg, Robert A251
Fougere, Richard A152
Fougere, Barry C. E26
Fougere, Richard E49
Foulke, Elvia P122
Foulkes, David M. A151
Foulkes, Helena B. A250
Foulston, Matthew J. A829
Fountain, David B. A281
Fountas, Nikos E134
Fouque, Jorge Andueza W27
Fourmas, Tom A489
Fournier, Martha A129
Fournier, Dave P400

Fournier, Joseph P632
Fournier, Dominique E236
Fouss, Brad A611
Fouss, Brad E313
Foust, Donald R. (Don) A916
Foutch, Lucy A655
Foutch, Lucy E333
Fouty, Dennis P643
Fowinkle, Ron A85
Fowke, Benjamin G. S. (Ben) A910
Fowle, John A402
Fowler, Bryan A280
Fowler, W. Randall (Randy) A303
Fowler, Terry A565
Fowler, Maggie A760
Fowler, Erica A843
Fowler, Don A844
Fowler, Tom A898
Fowler, Charles D. (Chuck) P99
Fowler, W Randall P185
Fowler, Bob P187
Fowler, W Randall P341
Fowler, James C P400
Fowler, Jim P400
Fowler, Maggie P523
Fowler, Mike P627
Fowler, J. B. W199
Fowler, Mike E127
Fowler, Erica E411
Fowler, Don E412
Fowles, Mike A443
Fox, Gregory C. A134
Fox, Gregory C. A154
Fox, Joseph A177
Fox, Matt A232
Fox, Matthew A295
Fox, James M A314
Fox, John A348
Fox, Sheldon J. A405
Fox, Debra A406
Fox, Brian J. A412
Fox, John A715
Fox, Brian A766
Fox, Hannah P52
Fox, Gregory C. P77
Fox, Carl P149
Fox, John T P182
Fox, James M P190
Fox, Rebecca P271
Fox, Jamie P371
Fox, Leona P402
Fox, Billie J P439
Fox, Tricia P531
Fox, Andrew P613
Fox, Susan P688
Fox, Brett M. W75
Fox, Jim E127
Fox, Brian J. E192
Fox, Duane E288
Fox, Richard P. (Rick) E328
Fox, Tony E421
Fox-Martin, Adaire W319
Foy, Denise P35
Foy, Stanford P543
Foye, Brian A254
Foyles, Kirsten A337
Fracchia, Joe E276
Fraczkiewicz, Robert J A388
Fradkin, Steven L. (Steve) A599
Frady, Brandon P395
Fraenkel, Martin A721
Fraga, Francisco A161
Fraga, Amanda A517
Fraga, Victor P315
Fragale, Peter A582
Fragale, Peter P373
Fragie, Jack A546
Fragkiadakis, Leonidas W253
Fragnoli, Stephen P133
Frahm, Monty A602
Frahm, Terry P231
Frain, Michael A583
Frakes, Rebeka P449
Fraley, Alton P271
Fralick, Tracy A221

Fralick, Julie P549
Fralix, Jason A58
Fralix, Jason E16
Framarin, Debbie E65
Frame, Randall A. A355
Framke, Gregory A. (Greg) W232
Frampton, Marcus A28
Frampton, Marcus P17
Frampton, Frank P477
France, Nena La P694
Franceschini, Luca W143
Franchak, Jen P339
Franciere, Karen A541
Franciere, Karen E266
Francioli, Richard W387
Francione, Brian A817
Francis, Tom A109
Francis, Laith A221
Francis, Shaun J. A357
Francis, Scott A532
Francis, Julian A627
Francis, Margaret A723
Francis, Hannah A766
Francis, Robert E. (Bob) A768
Francis, Francine P118
Francis, Robert P165
Francis, Gerald P181
Francis, Robert P284
Francis, Pauline P466
Francis, John P524
Francis, Tom E36
Francis, James L. E73
Francisco, Pamela A580
Francisco, Larry A594
Francisco, Michelle A855
Franck, John M P207
Franco, Joe A173
Franco, Luisa A338
Franco, Joseph A472
Franco, Patty A700
Franco, Ashley E116
Franco, Luisa E149
Francoeur, John A541
Francoeur, John E266
Francois, Larry P395
Franey, Bill A101
Franey, Henry J. P644
Franey, Hank P644
Frangetis, Dimitris W253
Frank, Janet D. (Jan) A30
Frank, Brian A33
Frank, Elizabeth A41
Frank, Joel A173
Frank, Malcolm A217
Frank, Terry A244
Frank, Billy A348
Frank, Aaron A354
Frank, Matthew A502
Frank, Larry A677
Frank, Joshua A782
Frank, Ben A807
Frank, Maxine A810
Frank, Ryan A866
Frank, Edward H. (Ed) P96
Frank, Chris P133
Frank, Kevin P155
Frank, Isabelle P200
Frank, Ben P574
Frank, Maxine P597
Frank, James S. (Jim) P611
Frank, Robert G. P648
Frank, Howard S. W81
Frank, Malcolm E140
Frank, Thomas A. J. E221
Frank, Bob E312
Frank, John B. (Bob) E312
Frank-lightfoot, Lorraine P358
Franke, Jerold P. A884
Franke, Mark A907
Franke, Don A919
Franke, Mark P696
Frankel, Kenneth A120
Frankel, Michael S. A708
Frankel, Bonnie P155

Frankel, Michael S. P459
Frankel, Adam B. E136
Frankel, Michael S. E356
Franklin, Ken A56
Franklin, Nicholas S. (Nick) A484
Franklin, Jerry A645
Franklin, Sarah A723
Franklin, Claudia A872
Franklin, Jeanne P81
Franklin, William H. P258
Franklin, Tamara P489
Franklin, Gregory A P630
Franklin, John P700
Franklin, William E. E94
Franks, Brent J. A73
Franks, Holly A272
Franks, William A549
Franks, Dennis P308
Franks, William E270
Franssen, Rhonda P681
Frantsi, Kimberley P22
Frantz, Dana A122
Frantz, Thom A346
Frantz, Darrell A734
Frantz, T K P93
Frantz, Rita A. P611
Franz, Paul S A806
Franz, Paul S P569
Franz, Christoph W307
Franzetta, Mary P528
Franzino, Michael E235
Franzoni, Kasey A644
Franzoni, Greg A784
Frarev, Bryan E426
Frary, Greg A826
Frascotti, Johnathan A. (John) A408
Fraser, Jim A97
Fraser, Jane A203
Fraser, Stephen A696
Fraser, John A782
Fraser, Ronald A868
Fraser, John M P369
Fraser, Karen P465
Fraser, Edward P516
Fraser, Mike W63
Fraser, Jim E32
Frasier, Edie A162
Fratamico, John J. A505
Fratanduono, Sal A163
Frates, Caton A240
Fratini, Adrienne P307
Fratus, Mark A767
Fraumann, Timothy A881
Frawley, Caroline A323
Frawley, Connie A537
Frayha, Najla A864
Frazar, Dick E437
Frazer, Tom A872
Frazier, Larry D A395
Frazier, Seth A413
Frazier, Spencer A439
Frazier, Kenneth C. (Ken) A550
Frazier, Donald P205
Frazier, Seth P234
Frazier, I P293
Frazier, Jennifer P318
Frazier, Royda P444
Frazier, D. Mell Meredith E272
Frazier-Flores, Charlene P3
Frazis, George W395
Frear, David J. A745
Frease, Gina A81
Frechette, Patricia A907
Frechette, Patricia E446
Frecker, Richard J A809
Frecker, Richard J P584
Freddino, Robert A729
Fredell, Thomas P333
Frederic, Dingemans P556
Frederick, Marc A173
Frederick, Brian A257
Frederick, Ben P42
Frederick, Dwayne P243
Fredericks, David A96
Fredericks, Mark J A500

Fredericks, Raymond P568
Fredericks, Mark J E238
Frederickson, Trevor A175
Frederickson, Philip A300
Frederiksen, Renee A774
Frederiksen, Derik P489
Fredin, Steven (Steve) A87
Free, Laura A582
Free, Laura P373
FREEBORN, TIM A515
Freebourn, Richard E47
Freed, Brian W. A69
Freed, Dan P91
Freed, Stuart P107
Freed, Todd P256
Freed, Dean P326
Freedman, Paul L A17
Freedman, Jill A476
Freedman, Stephen P200
Freedman, Jamie W34
Freehof, Leonard P521
Freel, John A599
Freeland, Richard J. (Rich) A246
Freeland, Cary P92
Freeland, Kristie P452
Freeman, Cathy S. A99
Freeman, Mark A115
Freeman, Mark A125
Freeman, Britt A135
Freeman, Marla A223
Freeman, Bruce A311
Freeman, Mark A489
Freeman, Charles A547
Freeman, Dexter A044
Freeman, Angela K A711
Freeman, Charlie A753
Freeman, Thomas E. (Tom) A774
Freeman, Sharon A774
Freeman, John A902
Freeman, Britt P78
Freeman, Joshua P101
Freeman, Dennis M. P313
Freeman, Charles P319
Freeman, Amy P331
Freeman, Marcus P385
Freeman, Todd P400
Freeman, Richard P498
Freeman, Daniel P535
Freeman, Jerri P591
Freeman, Jim P633
Freeman, Dan P641
Freeman, Richard E165
Freeman, Charlie E379
Freeman, Mark R. E437
Freeman-Resc, Pamela R P378
Freeny, Jennifer P695
Freer, Rudell S P296
Freguia, Luigi A875
Frehse, Todd A458
Frehse, Todd P251
Frei, Reto A390
Frei, Theresa A775
Frei, Theresa P548
Freiberg, Aubrey P292
Freidig, Jan A103
Freilich, Helen A785
Freimark, Ryan A886
Freimark, Ryan E433
Freitag, Randal J. A512
Freitag, Lee R A600
Freitag, Ragan P691
Freitas, Mike P549
Freitas, Humberto W385
Freixe, Laurent W258
Freker, Michael A677
Frelka, Greg A728
Fremier, Andrew B P338
French, Tracy M. A425
French, Jim A805
French, Dana A904
French, April P82
French, Brian P207
French, David P276
French, Constance P410
French, Richard P547

French, Donna P674
French, Hadley Mack P692
French, David E1
French, Tracy M. E201
French, Ed E258
French, Christopher E. (Chris) E368
French, Dana E442
Frenkiel, Paul A805
Frent, Marty A155
Frenzel, Robert C. (Bob) A910
Frenzel, Adam P281
Frenzel, Michael W376
Frese, Calvin W. (Cal) A172
Frese, Brian A847
Frese, Mark W85
Fresher, Brian A406
Freter, Glen E123
Fretwell, Roger P206
Fretz, Sujata P292
Freund, Charles R. E163
Freund, Lothar P. E236
Frevert, Myrl P79
Frew, Bill A272
Frey, Charles A298
Frey, Chris A546
Frey, Fredric A615
Frey, Michelle P337
Frey, Pamela P533
Frey, Julie P546
Frey, Karl E226
Freyling, Sylvia A328
Freymuller, Robert P545
Freyne, Colm J. W346
Freytas, Denise A105
Frias, James D. (Jim) A605
Frias, Yanela C A675
Frick, Cynthia A531
Frick, Cindy A531
Frick, Sue A741
Frick, Sue E370
Fricke, David A800
Fricke, David E396
Frickle, T A387
Frickle, T E177
Friday, Denise P35
Fridley, Erik A613
Fridley, Erik E314
Fried, Arthur P541
Fried, David W297
Friedland, Matthew P642
Friedlander, Benjamin A131
Friedli, Peter E319
Friedlos, Steve W103
Friedman, Jeffrey A204
Friedman, Richard A. A389
Friedman, Leonard A480
Friedman, John A481
Friedman, Howard A494
Friedman, Howard H. A670
Friedman, Joel A682
Friedman, Paula J. A760
Friedman, Michael A765
Friedman, Seth A874
Friedman, Jack P410
Friedman, Stephen J P414
Friedman, Wayne P495
Friedman, Paula J. P523
Friedman, Michael P540
Friedman, Jeremy A. E219
Friedmann, John A597
Friedrich, Amy C. A668
Friemel, Jake A221
Friend, Mark A366
Friend, Matthew A874
Friend, Bob A886
Friend, Katherine P45
Friend, Gwyn P155
Friend, Bob E433
Frierson, Henry T. P642
Fries, Rick P23
Fries, James P154
Fries, Michael T. (Mike) W222
Friesen, Ernie A395
Frieske, William A599
Frieson, Donald E A878

Friess, Robert A71
Frigeria, Vincent A678
Frillman, Fred A204
Friman, Maija-Liisa W257
Frioux, George E273
Frisbee, Kimberly P45
Frisch, Ann A582
Frisch, Scott P2
Frisch, Steven M. P17
Frisch, Greg P141
Frisch, Ann P373
Frisch, Melissa P644
Frishman, Arik W190
Frisk, Patrik A840
Friske, Rena A163
Frissora, Mark P. A157
Frist, Matthew J. P169
Frist, Robert A. E190
Friston, Paul W233
Friton, Frederick P178
Fritsch, Wayne A869
Fritsch, Steven P694
Fritts, William A213
Fritz, Connie A168
Fritz, Wendy A264
Fritz, Lance M. A842
Fritz, James S. P58
Fritz, Susan M. P78
Fritz, Peggy P621
Frock, Charles T P352
Froehlich, Melissa A530
Froehlich, Patti P204
Froehn, Ulli A141
Froggatt, Mark E251
Fromknecht, Greg A295
Fromm, Daniel A314
Fromm, Daniel P190
Fron, David A700
Fronheiser, Jason A333
Fronk, Bill A268
Fronk, Chris A599
Frons, Marc A589
Frontz, Marilyn A6
Frontz, Arlene A641
Frontz, Arlene P422
Frooman, Thomas E. A198
Frossmo, Kristin A596
Frost, G. Janelle A58
Frost, Jim A73
Frost, Christopher A103
Frost, Brian A222
Frost, Robert A225
Frost, Patrick B. (Pat) A244
Frost, Tom A244
Frost, Jack A388
Frost, Jack A833
Frost, James A. (Jack) A833
Frost, Frances P132
Frost, Robert E88
Frost, Dawn E91
Frost, Phillip E237
Frost, Ronald A. E273
Frounfelter, Danette P686
Frownfelter, Carl P249
Fruehauf, Richard A852
Fruhwirth, Paul A195
Frumkin, Theodore E. (Ted) A759
Frumkin, Howard A861
Frumkin, Howard P658
Frump, Candace A645
Frump, Candace E329
Frustaci, Dominick E219
Fry, James A. A916
Fry, John A. P165
Fry, Lindsay P521
Fry, Matthew E26
Fry, Nina E369
Frye, Craig A115
Frye, Sue A244
Frye, Arthur A478
Frye, Hadassah P88
Frye, Chris P455
Fryett, Terry W50
Fryfogle, James A658
Frykhammar, Jan W360

A = AMERICAN BUSINESS
E = EMERGING COMPANIES
P = PRIVATE COMPANIES
W = WORLD BUSINESS

Fryland, Lee A751
Fryland, Lee E377
Frymoyer, Valarry A342
FSA, Robert A407
Fu, Jia-Lin E140
Fubini, David A505
Fucci, John T. E232
Fucheck, Dawn M P378
Fuchs, Rainer A129
Fuchs, Jim A322
Fuchs, Mary Ann P168
Fuchs, W. Kent P642
Fudge, Duncan A568
Fuente, Maria Eugenia de la W43
Fuentes-Rivera, Virginia A565
Fuerst, Edward A570
Fuerst, James P68
Fuerstenberg, Jeffrey P299
Fueston, Cecil P318
Fugale, Stephen W. P667
Fugger, Edward F. P689
Fugina, Annette A555
Fugui, Xu W283
Fuhrmann, Roy P337
Fujibayashi, Kiyotaka W245
Fujie, Naofumi W17
Fujikura, Masato W336
Fujimoto, Coleen A102
Fujimoto, Masayoshi W336
Fujino, Michimasa W172
Fujino, Shinji W263
Fujisaki, Catherine A102
Fujita, Minoru W116
Fujita, Katsuyuki W116
FUJIWARA, ICHIRO W49
Fujiwara, Hiroaki W208
Fujiwara, Kiyoshi W235
Fukasawa, Yuji W132
Fukuda, Makoto W28
Fukuhara, Kazuyuki W235
Fukui, Soichi W242
Fukuichi, Tokuo W374
Fukunaga, Mark H P493
Fukunaga, Eric P493
Fulcher, Penny P239
Fulchi, Anthony A109
Fulchi, Anthony E36
Fulchino, Jay A767
Fulk, Sue A452
Fulkerson, Mike A530
Fulkerson, Debra A614
Fulkerson, Ed A728
Fulkerson, William J. P168
Fuller, Mark A10
Fuller, Sherrika A130
Fuller, Lynn B. A412
Fuller, Wilford H. (Will) A512
Fuller, Bryan A537
Fuller, Julie A593
Fuller, Jake A647
Fuller, Jim A725
Fuller, Rodger D. A750
Fuller, Anthony A878
Fuller, Jacqui A905
Fuller, Darren A906
Fuller, Robert A915
Fuller, Jim P358
Fuller, Joe P455
Fuller, Jacqui P693
Fuller, Robert P700
Fuller, Lynn B. E192
Fullington, Shelby P218
Fullum, Jane P172
Fulmer, James W. (Jim) A820
Fulsom, Melvin A835
Fulton, Howard A49
Fulton, Marshall A109
Fulton, Peter A445
Fulton, Mark P303

Fulton, Barbara P434
Fulton, Michael P500
Fulton, Marshall E36
Fulton, Tricia L. E390
Fulton, Mary-Lynn E428
Fults, Sarah A558
Fumagali, Oscar J P83
Funaoka, Akihiko W245
Funato, Takashi W241
Funayama, Norio W329
Fund, Steven L. A456
Funderburk, William W. P297
Funk, Dan A82
Funk, Charles N. A562
Funk, Dan P49
Funk, Robert A. P188
Funk, Charles N. E279
Fuoss, Cheryl P284
Fuqua, Barbara A480
Fuqua, Stacy A614
Fuqua, Leon P157
Fura, Embry A222
Furberg, Petter-Borre W360
Furby, David W98
Furey, Adrian A918
Furlong, Fred A324
Furlong, Bryan A700
Furlong, Dale P126
Furman, Maria D. P645
Furner, John A878
Furnish, Kyle P210
Furniss, Kristin E293
Furnstahl, Lawrence J. P410
Furr, William B. A420
Furr, Richard C P372
Furr, William B. E198
Furst, Frank E P207
Furst, Martha P207
Furtek, Kathryn A599
Furuichi, Takeshi W261
Furukawa, Shinya W373
Furuto, Gordon P643
Furuya, Katsumasa W156
Furuya, Kazuki W324
Fusco, Jack A. A189
Fusco, Joseph A532
Fusco, Art P105
Fusco, Andrew P385
Fushen, Li W95
Fushitani, Kiyoshi W279
Fusillo, Robert A878
Fuson, Micah P41
Fuson, Greg P491
Fussell, Stephen R. (Steve) A4
Futamiya, Masaya W337
Fybel, Gary G. P488
Fynan, Tamara J. A748
Fyodorov, Igor Y. W289
Fyodorov, Pavel W310
Félix, José Antônio Guaraldi W25

G

Gabanna, Louis W104
Gabbard, Brian A73
Gabbard, Brian A96
Gabbert, John A195
Gabel, Karen A738
Gabel, Timothy J. (Tim) P458
Gaber, Kerry A434
Gaber, Sharon L. P613
Gable, Deborah A56
Gable, Steve A368
Gable, Debra P161
Gabler, Donna P602
Gabriel, Gerry A313
Gabriel, Jim A390
Gabriel, Stuart A484
Gabriel, Pierre A558
Gabriel, Christina A877
Gabriel, Kaigham (Ken) P568
Gabriel, Yves W72
Gabriele, Jennifer A204
Gabriele, Gary A. P667

Gabrielson, Rick A521
Gabrys, Gerard T. P223
Gachot, Robert A628
Gack, Bruce A496
Gackenbach, Steven D. E263
Gadberry, Kirk P384
Gadberry, Laura J P525
Gaddes, Kathy H. A59
Gaddi, Peter A195
Gaddis, Byron J. A666
Gaddis, Byron J. P438
Gaddis, Gay E286
Gadekar, Aparna P519
Gaden, Nancy P80
Gaden, Kevin M P246
Gadol, Boris A583
Gadow, Julie P550
Gadzinski, Norman P361
Gaemperle, Chantal W225
Gaeta, Mary P83
Gaetz, Beth A120
Gaffney, Dan A105
Gaffney, Paul J. A264
Gaffney, James A774
Gaffney, Kathy A819
Gaffney, Jessica A823
Gaffney, Kevin A835
Gagala, Ryan A600
Gagat, Diane A522
Gage, E. Dean A206
Gage, Douglas A260
Gage, Marlyss J. A827
Gage, Steve P171
Gage, Timothy M. E61
Gagel, Brian A704
Gagel, Brian E350
Gagey, Frédéric W14
Gagliano, Joe A49
Gagliano, Vincent J. A58
Gagliano, Mario A648
Gagliardi, Frank A190
Gagliardi, Nick R P351
Gagliardotto, David A131
Gagnet, Spencer A163
Gagnon, Paula A109
GAGNON, BRENDA A196
Gagnon, Blaire O P652
Gagnon, Martin W252
Gagnon, Paula E36
Gagua, Irina P215
Gaherty, John B. A240
Gaidis, Shawn P443
Gain, Tom A907
Gain, Tom P696
Gainer, Tracy A445
Gaines, Bennett L. A355
Gaines, Teresa A374
Gaines, Patricia A807
Gaines, Ellen P40
Gaines, Patricia P574
Gaines, Kristin S. E292
Gairing, Peter A693
Gaiter, Jatrice Martel P671
Gaither, Kevin A749
Gaizutis, Jennifer A807
Gaizutis, Jennifer P574
Galan, Omar A844
Galan, Omar E412
Galano, Deborah A537
Galanski, Stanley A. (Stan) A576
Galanski, Stanley A. (Stan) E297
Galante, Joseph A655
Galante, Vanessa A855
Galante, Joseph E333
Galante, Vanessa E416
Galanti, Richard A. A240
Galapati, Venkatrama R P592
Galarza, Maria P392
Galasso, Mario E168
Galat, Amy P397
Galatali, Saltik W18
Galati, Jim P630
Galbraith, John F P101
Galbraith, Katie P168
Galdieri, Lou P320

Gale, Steven A599
Gale, Fournier J. (Boots) A700
Gale, Barry E144
Galel, Susan A507
Galel, Susan P288
Gales, Amy H. A214
Gales, Amy H. P128
Galhotra, A. Kumar A362
Galiana, Judith A2
Galifi, Vincent J. W229
Galik, Milan E221
Galin, Tomi A227
Galinat, Walter W239
Galindo, Sergio A628
Galindo, Thomas A630
Galindo, Esther A898
Galindo, Susan P386
Galindo, Thomas P415
Galioto, Sal A445
Galipeau, Michelle P571
Galipeau, Linda W299
Galit, Scott A554
Galit, Scott E275
Gall, David W251
Gallagher, Philip R A93
Gallagher, Patricia A105
Gallagher, John A119
Gallagher, Lorraine A163
Gallagher, Francis A317
Gallagher, J. Patrick (Pat) A370
Gallagher, Thomas J. (Tom) A371
Gallagher, J. Patrick (Pat) A371
Gallagher, Thomas C. (Tom) A381
Gallagher, Edward R A578
Gallagher, Marie A647
Gallagher, Linda A837
Gallagher, Karen Symms A860
Gallagher, Joe P18
Gallagher, Duncan P. P26
Gallagher, Kelly P38
Gallagher, Kevin P96
Gallagher, Sally P115
Gallagher, Elizabeth P176
Gallagher, Rick P371
Gallagher, Sandra P410
Gallagher, Brian P652
Gallagher, Stephen J. P654
Gallagher, Karen Symms P656
Gallagher, James D. (Jim) W232
Gallagher, Maurice J. (Maury) E11
Gallagher, Kathy E44
Gallagher, Francis E142
Gallagher, Timothy J. E171
Gallaher, Lynne P663
Gallary, John D P167
Gallas, Carla A A557
Gallatin, David P686
Galle, Rich P433
Galle, Jean-Lo- c W364
Gallego, Alex P482
Gallegos, Ed A180
Gallegos, Nadine P293
Gallegos, Paula P330
Gallegos, James P514
Gallentine, Bennie A674
Galler, Jennifer A131
Galles, Betsy P465
Gallett, Scott D. A141
Galletti, Michael E89
Galli, Guido A818
Galligan, Matthew E. (Matt) A201
Galligan, E B P433
Gallik, Diana P110
Gallik, Mary P280
Gallimore, Alec D. A698
Gallimore, Alec D. P456
Gallina, John E. A67
Gallo, Laurene (Laurie) A140
Gallo, Silvina A649
Gallo, A. C. A899
Gallo, A. C. P690
Gallo, Livio W141
Gallois, Louis W286
Gallop, Melanie A683
Galloway, Ian A52

Galloway, Walter A221
Galloway, Heather C. P563
Galloway, Scott E197
Gallucci, Chris A647
Callup, Ross W P382
Galovic, Robert A530
Galpin, Susan A620
Galsnte, Alena A782
Galson, Steven A61
Galuppi, Barb A371
Galuppo, Gail A. A18
Galusha, Rachel A489
Galvan, David A537
Galvan, Nina P332
Galvan, Roxann P456
Galvan, Johnna P694
Galvan, Martin P. E239
Galvez, Jean-Marc A125
Galvez, Michelle A131
Galvez, Jose D. Bogas W140
Galvin, William A. (Bill) A66
Galvin, Dana A247
Galvin, Anthony A786
Galvin, Suzanne A866
Galvin, Sue P235
Galvin, William J P298
Galvin, Carroll P316
Galvin, Dana E103
Gamache, Michelle A644
Gambhir, Vandana P329
Gamble, Rob Gamble Rob A34
Gamble, Pat A173
Gamble, Daniel A528
Gamble, Kevin A920
Gamble, Patrick P640
Gamboa, Ivan A905
Gamboa, Ivan P694
Gamboa, Arturo Natho W137
Gamborena, Ana A560
Gambrell, Todd A51
Gambs, Matt A904
Gambs, Matt F442
Gamewell, William A223
Gamez, Yenisel A163
Gamis, Mark A140
Gammiere, Tom P488
Gammieri, Jerry A44
Gammieri, Jerry P31
Ganatra, Manish A56
Ganatra, Gigi A596
Gancarczyk, Ken A484
Gander, John A537
Gandhi, Mihir A101
Gandhi, Apoorva N A530
Gandhi, Shyama A565
Gandhi, Paresh P172
Gandhi, Sanjeev W55
Gandolfo, Joanne A677
Ganeev, Oleg W321
Gangemi, Joseph D. E90
Ganger, Sonja P358
Gangestad, Nicholas C. A2
Gangloff, Christine P466
Gangone, Lynn P132
Gangwal, Rakesh A166
Ganley, Kevin P653
Gann, John W A423
Gann, Cecilia A439
Gannfors, John W. A612
Gannon, John A204
Gannon, Stephen T. (Steve) A205
Gannon, Carrie A390
Gannon, John A800
Gannon, Pam P313
Gannon, John E396
Gannotta, Rick P167
Gannotta, Richard J P397
Ganser, Michael A199
Gant, Beth A584
Ganti, Ravi A309
Ganti, Surya A685
Ganti, Andrew A857
Gantman, Alex A685
Gantner, Diane A81
Gantt, Jim P129

Gantt, Stewart E256
Ganz, Beth E424
Ganzlin, Karen A791
Gao, Dennis E247
Gapontsev, Valentin P. E224
Garafola, Lana A550
Garafola, Rachael P486
Garantiva, Fabian A107
Garantiva, Fabian E35
Garanzini, Michael J. P299
Garber, David A332
Garber, Tami A862
Garber, Ken P35
Garber, Sam P95
Garber, Tami E419
Garbin, Daniel A659
Garca, Joel P278
Garceau, Eric De A565
Garcia, Philip A58
Garcia, Charles A81
Garcia, James P A102
Garcia, James A102
Garcia, Faye A103
Garcia, Honey A103
Garcia, Luis A131
Garcia, Lindsay A158
Garcia, Ignacio A246
Garcia, Tami A272
Garcia, Grace A417
Garcia, Guillermo A459
Garcia, Arlene A460
Garcia, Carlo A667
Garcia, Cisco A681
Garcia, Victor A710
Garcia, Art A. A718
Garcia, Eddie A757
Garcia, Jo A770
Garcia, Kelly P A782
Garcia, Clifford P19
Garcia, Roland P58
Garcia, George P81
Garcia, Julian P87
Garcia, Michael P109
Garcia, Robert P123
Garcia, Claudia P134
Garcia, Joseph P163
Garcia, Ernest C P166
Garcia, Tommy P278
Garcia, Mar'ja P297
Garcia, Ace P299
Garcia, Norma P408
Garcia, Hector P418
Garcia, Carlos A458
Garcia, Robert P470
Garcia, Richard P480
Garcia, Al P491
Garcia, Henry P498
Garcia, David P676
Garcia, Perla P681
Garcia, Felix W117
Garcia, Victor M. E51
Garcia, Richard G. E74
Garcia, Mike E193
Garcia, Carlo E336
Garcia-Barbon, Jennifer A109
Garcia-Barbon, Jennifer E36
Garcia-Velez, Calixto A336
Garc-a, Federico Reyes W152
Garde, Sameer A199
Gardella, Craig A704
Gardella, Craig E350
Gardial, Sarah Fisher P611
Gardill, James C. (Jim) A886
Gardill, James C. (Jim) E433
Gardiner, Roger A390
Gardiner, Mary P653
Gardiner, Sandra A. E104
Gardiner, Nathaniel S. E122
Gardner, Kent C. A117
Gardner, Charles A175
Gardner, Jeffrey R A333
Gardner, Jeremy A479
Gardner, Steven R A630
Gardner, Rich A685
Gardner, Tom A723

Gardner, Jim A737
Gardner, Jonathan A763
Gardner, Dan A901
Gardner, Patrick P27
Gardner, Edward P160
Gardner, Linda P220
Gardner, Elizabeth P279
Gardner, Jean P333
Gardner, Joseph J. P342
Gardner, Thomas R P350
Gardner, Steven R P415
Gardner, Alan P661
Gardner, James P677
Gardner, Dan P692
Gardner, Paul W348
Gardunio, James F. (Jim) A740
Gardunio, James F. (Jim) E369
Garell, Tyler P400
Garfield, David R. A728
Garfinkle, Andrew A143
Garfinkle, Marni A677
Garg, Rahul A144
Garger, Stavros A691
Gargiulo, Joe A869
Gargiulo, Joe P514
Garibay, Alma P459
Garijo, Belén W239
Garimella, Suresh P449
Garippa, James P333
Garland, Lorie A115
Garland, Katherine A362
Garland, Greg C. A653
Garland, Kim A764
Garland, Greg C P426
Garland, Ann P653
Garma-Fernandez, Emilio A693
Garnadt, Karl U. W124
Garner, Sharon A54
Garner, Megan A103
Garner, Curtis (Curt) A193
Garner, Denise A208
Garner, Ed A351
Garner, David W. A742
Garner, Steven A821
Garner, Don A891
Garner, Stephen A912
Garner, Cicero P5
Garner, Brenda P472
Garner, Steven P621
Garner, Katherine W347
Garner, Ed E158
Garner, David W. E372
Garner, Don E434
Garnett, David A408
Garnett, Muscoe A478
Garnett, Chris A546
Garnett, Valerie P339
Garnett, Sherman W. P341
Garnick, Murray R A37
Garnier, Thierry W82
Garnin, John E447
Garofalo, Jill A555
Garofalo, Martin (Marty) A589
Garofalo, Ana P589
Garoff, Stephen P96
Garozzo, Scott A818
Garr, Megan A541
Garr, Megan E266
Garrabants, Greg A94
Garrabants, Greg P53
Garrabrants, Gregory A95
Garrabrants, Gregory E28
Garratt, John W A273
Garrett, Mark S. A11
Garrett, Sheri A149
Garrett, John A302
Garrett, Valerie A339
Garrett, Rob A350
Garrett, Adam A541
Garrett, Kirk A655
Garrett, John R. (Bob) A755
Garrett, Susan A802
Garrett, Jeanette A844
Garrett, Patrick P8
Garrett, Bobi P25

Garrett, Jimmy P78
Garrett, James H. P96
Garrett, Melinda P242
Garrett, Amy P363
Garrett, Terry M P372
Garrett, Russell P512
Garrett, Alan H P535
Garrett, Susan P562
Garrett, John E128
Garrett, Valerie E150
Garrett, Rob E157
Garrett, Adam E266
Garrett, Kirk E333
Garrett, John R. (Bob) E380
Garrett, Jeanette E412
Garrigan, Allison A375
Garrigues, Bernard M. A883
Garrigues, Gretchen H. W232
Garringer, Jesse A727
Garrison, Dave A260
Garrison, Nickole A902
Garrison, Denise P45
Garrison, Ashley P207
Garrison, Lori P386
Garrison, Sue P503
Garrison, Karen P521
Garrison, Andrea P537
Garrison, Mitchell P681
Garrison, Nickole P693
Garrity, Francis A120
Garrity, Catherine A204
Garrity, Matthew T. A845
Garrity, Matthew T. E413
Garry, Katy A785
Garske, Steve P277
Garsys, Lucia P144
Garth, Matthew E. E281
Gartland, Mike A484
Gartner, Steven A173
Gartner, James J. (Jim) A227
Gartner, Cherie A229
Gartner, Cherie P137
Cartner, Timr P443
Garvell, James R P8
Garver, David P599
Garverick, Larry A640
Garvey, Maureen A335
Garvey, Patrick P138
Garvey, Kim P138
Garvey, Randy P424
Garvey, James P536
Garvin, Robert M. (Bert) A884
Garvin, Jean P506
Garvin, Michele P570
Garwood, Robert P491
Gary, Steven P186
Gary, Ashlee P301
Garza, Bernardo De La A459
Garza, Mario J A565
Garza, Mario A565
Garza, Molly P199
Garza, Alfonso P384
Garza, Ed P478
Garza, Victoria P517
Garza, - - lvaro Fern- -ndez W18
Garza, Alfonso Garza W152
Gasbarra, Gary P611
Gascho, Dwith P243
Gasho, Thomas A644
Gasior, F. Morgan A108
Gaskey, Dustin A329
Gaskill, Logan A558
Gaskin, Martha A541
Gaskin, David P542
Gaskin, Martha E266
Gaskins, Tommy A899
Gaskins, Sherman L. P104
Gaskins, Tommy P690
Gaspard, Jessica A204
Gasparotto, James M A512
Gasparovic, John J. A141
Gasparovic, John J. A142
Gasper, Jim P104
Gasper, David P134
Gasper, Karen P528

A = AMERICAN BUSINESS
E = EMERGING COMPANIES
P = PRIVATE COMPANIES
W = WORLD BUSINESS

Gass, Michelle A493
Gass, Rhonda O. A761
Gass, Kevin P424
Gassen, Michael W29
Gasser, Ronald D. P367
Gast, Debbie A86
Gast, Debbie P52
Gast, Fred E252
Gasta, Mark R. E424
Gaston, Octavia P411
Gates, David A82
Gates, S A247
Gates, Dennis A556
Gates, Tim A899
Gates, David P49
Gates, Leigh Anne P64
Gates, Robert M. P81
Gates, John P223
Gates, Anne P250
Gates, W. Gary P406
Gates, Robert P557
Gates, S E103
Gates, Cathleen Schreiner E119
Gathing, Ayo A565
Gatliff, Peggy P395
Gaton, Jim P355
Gattas, Eileen P622
Gattle, William H. (Bill) A405
Gatto, Pamela A. P230
Gatto, Joseph C. E53
Gattullo, Barbara P461
Gattuso, Anthony A541
Gattuso, Anthony E266
Gatz, Ronald F. P579
Gauba, Gary A185
Gaubert, Glenda A562
Gaudard, Cheryl A549
Gaudard, Cheryl E270
Gaudet, Gordon J. A734
Gaudiosi, Monica M. A836
Gauger, George A335
Gaughen, Robert H. A421
Gaughen, Robert H. E199
Gaul, John P21
Gault, James S. (Jim) A371
Gault, Jeffrey M. (Jeff) E19
Gaus, Gregory J P343
Gause, Garry A794
Gause, Garry P86
Gausman, Loren A782
Gautam, Rajeev A429
Gauthier, Eugene A390
Gauthier, Joyce V P446
Gauthier, Daniel W166
Gauthier, -%oric W303
Gauthier, Maurice A. E430
Gauvin, Judy A790
Gavazzi, Alberto W128
Gavegnano, Richard J. A553
Gavegnano, Richard J. E272
Gavel, Anne A855
Gavell, Stefan M. A766
Gavelle, Jean-Luc A62
Gavenchak, Genie A589
Gavens, Mark R. P102
Gavigan, John A344
Gavin, Gary A463
Gavin, Michael E. A500
Gavin, Lawrence E87
Gavin, Tim E140
Gavin, Michael E. E238
Gavrielof, Tamara A741
Gavrielof, Tamara E370
Gavrilenya, Alexey E163
Gavulic, Melanie P245
Gaw, Turner A109
Gaw, Turner E36
Gawinski, Michelle M P567
Gawne, Berc P572

Gawron, Mark A405
Gay, Jonathan A481
Gay, Gregory A865
Gay, Al P329
Gay, Andrew P361
Gayar, Hesham P319
Gaye, Omar A899
Gaye, Omar P690
Gayer, Sandy P568
Gayman, Jeffrey S A625
Gayne, William P675
Gayner, Thomas S. A528
Gaytan, Bolivia P428
Gazarik, Michael A96
Gazaway, Brad A. P487
Gazaway, Nate E426
Gazdic, Mike A780
Gcabashe, Thulani W339
Gdowski, Christopher E P6
Geagea, Joseph C. (Joe) A192
Gean, Tom A878
Gearen, Peter F. E360
Gearhart, Jeffrey J. (Jeff) A878
Gearheart, Lisa A247
Gearheart, Lisa E103
Gearig, Wayne P20
Gearing, Kathy A774
Geary, William C. A66
Geary, Michael J A375
Geary, Tommy A419
Geary, Eileen A677
Geary, Michael J P210
Geatens, Fran A550
Gebauer, Peter R. E242
Gebb, Luke A49
Gebben, Steven P167
Gebremedhin, Girmay P391
Geckle, Geraldine A857
Geczik, Tom A305
Geczik, Tom P185
Geddes, John A898
Geddes, Paul W312
Gedir, Roksana Grazyna Ciurysek W51
Geduldig, Courtney A721
Gee, Kevin A133
Gee, Jessica A375
Gee, Patrick A828
Gee, E Gordon P682
Geekie, Matthew W. A394
Geer, Stacey K A667
Geers, Denise A452
Gefert, Jerry P401
Gegerson, Kelly A446
Gegerson, Kelly E210
Geha, Raif P118
Gehlen, Greg E9
Gehman, William A A167
Gehring, John F. A230
Gehrke, Terry A868
Gehrke, Cory P66
Gehrlich, Tom P422
Geibel, John P699
Geier, Peter A345
Geier, Ross A449
Geiersbach, Rik A136
Geiger, Alan A98
Geiger, Jeffrey S. A374
Geiger, Brooks A864
Geiger, Philippa P93
Geiger, Stacy P247
Geiger, Eric P291
Geiger, Alan E33
Geinosky, Sarah P610
Geir, Bill A196
Geiselman, Melissa P315
Geisler, Linda P107
Geisler, Karen P353
Geiss, Cindy P48
Geist, Stephen (Steve) W80
Gelbard, Wendy P464
Gelbcke, Alex A796
Gelber, David P324
Geldzahler, Seth A120
Gelfond, Larry A484
Gellart, Kathleen P186

Gelle, James A489
Geller, David A16
Geller, Jeff A550
Geller, Warren P184
Geller, Michael P565
Geller, J-¶rg M. E69
Gellerstedt, Lawrence L. E98
Gellert, Steve P677
Gelles, Richard A812
Gelles, Richard P607
Gelman, Jack A476
Gelman, Mesh A763
Gelman, Luba A869
Gelman, Lawrence P162
Gelsinger, Patrick P. (Pat) A875
Gelsomin, Lynn A83
Gelwix, Steve A266
Gembler, Dawn P386
Gemignani, Gino J. A813
Gemignani, Gino J. P616
Genco, Renee A474
Genco, Renee P265
Genden, Eric A355
Gendler, Gordon A837
Gendreau, Donna A406
Generale, Paul P119
Generous, Robin A406
Genestar, Thierry W104
Geng, Tan Wan W95
Genis, Arnaud P. A627
Geniviva, John A238
Gennaro, Susan P625
Geno, Sharon P671
Genola, Gabriele Galateri di W32
Genovesi, Diane A480
Gensler, Melanie A449
Genso, Gueitiro Matsuo W385
Gensor, Joe E442
Genter, Kathy P53
Gentile, Emily A49
Gentile, Richard A151
Gentile, Bob A685
Gentile, Thomas C A758
Gentile, Richard E48
Gentry, Art A225
Gentry, Michael A736
Gentry, Greg A867
Gentry, Michael P492
Gentry, Art E88
Gentry, Brad E146
Gentry, Laura E407
Gentsch, Benjamin W323
Gentzkow, Paul F. A711
Gentzler, Rollie A432
Genzink, Larry A758
Genzink, Larry P519
Gen-§, Onur W377
Georgacopoulos, Demetrios A295
George, David C. (Dave) A254
George, Ester L. A325
George, Anton H Tony A346
George, Tito A390
George, Martin (Marty) St. A474
George, Martin St A474
George, Tina A500
George, Al St A685
George, RCraig A774
George, Keith P20
George, Boyd L. P21
George, Brian P21
George, Dennis St P155
George, William S. P230
George, Denise P230
George, Susan P361
George, Libby P367
George, Jessica P403
George, Richard P444
George, Amanda P522
George, Thomas F. (Tom) P647
George, Roger E. E10
George, Thomas A. E106
George, Tina E237
George, Dan E252
George, Michael E253
Georges, Laura P176

Georges, Angelo P688
Georgiadis, Margaret H. (Margo) A539
Georgine, Lamvu P198
Gephart, George W. P165
Gephart, Beth P233
Geppert, Michael P229
Ger, Kevin A28
Gera, Chris A536
Geraci, Greg A173
Geraci, Gavin A659
Geraghty, Joanna A474
Geraghty, Timothy A599
Geraghty, Paul D. A907
Geraghty, Paul D. E445
Gerakos, Michael P254
Gerard, Jeff A775
Gerard, Jeff P548
Gerarde, Roberta P296
Gerardi, Marlene A375
Gerardot, Jennie S A738
Gerarve, Robin A234
Gerarve, Robin A917
Gerarve, Robin P139
Gerarve, Robin P701
Gerba, Margaret P170
Gerber, Steve P473
Gerberding, Julie L. A550
Gerbracht, Cheryl P565
Gerdes, Jürgen W125
Gerding, Duncan A481
Geren, Betty P216
Gergen, Mark J. E186
Gerguis, Steven P126
Gerhart, John A247
Gerhart, Bobbie P340
Gerhart, John E102
Gericke, Johan A163
Gering, William A902
Gering, William P693
Geringer, Leonard P324
Gerjets, Sven A539
Gerken, Marc P35
Gerken, Mark P125
Germain, Jackie A438
Germain, Cheryl St P173
Germain, Donald P303
Germain, John P559
German, Scott A341
German, Scott E153
German, Robert D. E214
Germann, Jim A13
Germano, Don A264
Germanson, Christine A700
Germaschewski, Yin P243
Gernandt, Karl W212
Gernath, Eric W343
Gernay, Brenda A272
Gernhart, Diana P410
Gero, James F. E240
Gerrard, Dave P669
Gerratt, Eric L. E420
Gerrell, Matthew P230
Gerrick, Candra P424
Gerron, Daniel E286
Gerry, Janelle L P648
Gers, Alison E A151
Gers, Alison E. E48
Gersema, George H P183
Gersema, Douglas W P183
Gersema, Mary D P183
Gershenhorn, Alan A849
Gershenson, Dennis E. E359
Gershkowitz, Todd A766
Gershon, Peter W255
Gershowitz, Diane E257
Gerson, Jaclyn P626
Gerspach, John C. A203
Gerst, Christopher A711
Gerstenkorn, Petra W376
Gerster, Brennan A449
Gerstle, Douglas A671
Gerstner, Louis A461
Gertz, Morie A540
Gertz, Morie P316
Gerula, Christine A109

Gerula, Christine E36
Gervais, Renee M A484
Gervais, Laurie L A740
Gervasi, Martha (Marty) A406
Gerwert, Bernhard W16
Geselius, Todd P515
Gesing, Stefan W365
Gestrin, Bruce P268
Getchell, Shawn A913
Getman, George J. A225
Getman, George J. E88
Gettinger, Tom P674
Getz, James F. (Jim) A830
Getz, James F. (Jim) E403
Getzfrid, Lisa P230
Geurts, Chuck P51
Gevondyan, Hilary A354
Gewirtz, Henry A537
Geyer, Krista A523
Geyer, Debi A761
Geyer, Deb A762
Geyzel, David Van A30
Gezalyan, Sofia P108
Ghaffarian, Kam P495
Ghaffary, Mike E447
Ghai, Rahul A405
Ghali, Johanne A49
Ghan, P Mark P370
Ghanayem, Steve A71
Ghanayem, Darren A885
Ghanem, Salma P155
Ghartey-Tagoe, Kodwo A281
Ghasemi, Seifi A24
Ghassemian, Vahid A725
Ghazi, Leili A214
Ghazi, Leili P128
Ghia, Filippo A108
Ghia, Filippo E36
Ghilarducci, Dave E52
Ghion, Christopher P8
Ghislier, Andres Carlos Ferrero A753
Ghose, Mohit A565
Ghose, Amit P249
Ghosh, Anirvan A129
Ghosh, Reevu A204
Ghosh, Sourav A434
Ghosh, Bhaskar W5
Ghosh, Asim W176
Ghosn, Carlos W265
Giaccio, Tony E268
Giacobbe, Scott A7
Giacobbe, Ken A76
Giacomin, Jon A165
Giacomini, Thomas W. E227
Giacomo, Cara P220
Giamalis, John A406
Giambrone, Janel A522
Giametta, Lauren A131
Giammatteo, Robb A79
Giamouridis, Kostas A648
Gianarkis, Dean A649
Giancarlo, Charles H P52
Giandinoto, Nicole A707
Gianelli, Arthur A P362
Gianelli, Arthur P362
Gianetti, Dave A676
Gianfortune, Tammy A829
Giang, Daniel W. P294
Giangola, Louis A517
Giangola, Gary P390
Giannantoni, Leslie A109
Giannantoni, Leslie E36
Gianneschi, Stephanie P52
Giannetta, Mario A729
Gianni, Christian A898
Giannone, Gregory A865
Gianoni, Michael P. (Mike) E44
Gianopulos, James N. (Jim) A871
Giaquinto, Corrado A218
Giard, Diane W252
Giarrusso, Rachel A639
Giarrusso, Rachel E326
Gibb, Randall P74
Gibb, Matthew P568
Gibbons, Thomas P. (Todd) A105

Gibbons, Mike A136
Gibbons, James A140
Gibbons, Daniel A532
Gibbons, Peter D. A539
Gibbons, Terry A759
Gibbons, Dale M. A891
Gibbons, Thomas F. P398
Gibbons, Dale M. E434
Gibbs, Lisa A541
Gibbs, Robert A545
Gibbs, Michael A693
Gibbs, Michael A836
Gibbs, David A917
Gibbs, Kenneth P302
Gibbs, Lisa E266
Gibellini, Yasmine E121
Gibilterra, Jennifer A322
Gibler, Bryan P640
Giblin, Mike P620
Giblon, Andrew A461
Gibney, Ronald A201
Gibson, Wes A185
Gibson, Don A327
Gibson, Gregory L A346
Gibson, Andrew A354
Gibson, Kim A399
Gibson, Sandra A560
Gibson, John W. A622
Gibson, Amy A701
Gibson, Lee R. A754
Gibson, Belinda P60
Gibson, Cathy P139
Gibson, Teri P192
Gibson, Monty P305
Gibson, Sandra P342
Gibson, Eric P370
Gibson, Elizabeth C. P372
Gibson, James J. (Jim) P458
Gibson, Susan P472
Gibson, Cynthia L. P489
Gibson, Jeff P681
Gibson, Donald E. E183
Gibson, Mark D. E197
Gibson, Lee R. E380
Giddens, Thomas A18
Gideon, Richard A. (Rick) A263
Gideon, Rick A263
Gido, Jeffrey A390
Giedlin, Tom A565
Gieseman, Greg P73
Giesige, Steve A344
Giesige, Steve E154
Giezendanner, Esther A630
Giffard, Susan A160
Giffard, Susan E55
Gifford, Jenny A98
Gifford, Charlie A175
Gifford, Gerard H (Jerry) A242
Gifford, Bill A388
Gifford, David A718
Gifford, Rose P6
Gifford, Jenny E33
Gift, Deborah P247
Gigg, Paul A461
Giglio, Amy Sheperd A19
Giglio, Gaby A49
Giglio, Gabriella A49
Gigliotti, Anthony A890
Gigliotti, Steven J. (Steve) P488
Gigliotti, Ron P535
Gigliotti, Anthony P684
Giguere, Jillian P450
Gil, Eduardo A514
Gilbane, William J. (Bill) A385
Gilbane, Thomas F. (Tom) A385
Gilbane, William J. (Bill) P212
Gilbane, Thomas F. (Tom) P212
Gilberd, Susan A647
Gilbert, Dana A15
Gilbert, James A122
Gilbert, Matthew A160
Gilbert, Don A402
Gilbert, James A453
Gilbert, Michael A493
Gilbert, E A532

Gilbert, Scott E A533
Gilbert, Bob A548
Gilbert, Andrew A685
Gilbert, Irene A729
Gilbert, Mikel A788
Gilbert, Samantha A808
Gilbert, William M. (Bill) A844
Gilbert, Dana P9
Gilbert, Janet P157
Gilbert, Ozzie P217
Gilbert, Denis P P228
Gilbert, David P232
Gilbert, Vicky P257
Gilbert, Deanne P275
Gilbert, Lisa P300
Gilbert, Bob P321
Gilbert, Linda P441
Gilbert, Joanne T P459
Gilbert, Christopher B P474
Gilbert, Jorge P481
Gilbert, Samantha P581
Gilbert, Peter N. P631
Gilbert, Susan P651
Gilbert, John W125
Gilbert, Matthew E55
Gilbert, Durral R. E337
Gilbert, William M. (Bill) E412
Gilbertson, Gene W217
Gilburne, Miles R. E264
Gilcher, Richard P516
Gilchrist, David A180
Gilchrist, Toby A387
Gilchrist, Grant A417
Gilchrist, Richard I P521
Gilchrist, Toby E177
Gilcrease, Buck P30
Gilcrease, Beck P30
Gildea, Pat A173
Gildea, Edward J. (Ed) E149
Gilder, Sandy A371
Gileadi, Ido A330
Giles, William T. (Bill) A90
Giles, Daniel A105
Giles, Chantal A131
Giles, Brian A493
Giles, Scott A563
Giles, David A872
Giles, Scott P246
Giles, Bobbi P537
Giles, Scott P666
Giles, Jay P. E278
Gilio, Teresa A183
Gilio, Teresa E66
Gilkey, Steven P188
Gill, Sukhbir A131
Gill, Brandon A327
Gill, Phupinder A351
Gill, Chuck A407
Gill, Eric A481
Gill, Bryan K. A659
Gill, Vijay A723
Gill, G. Andrew (Andy) A728
Gill, Charles D. A854
Gill, Joanna A874
Gill, Nicole P12
Gill, James F P63
Gill, Laura D. P172
Gill, Bhupinder P216
Gill, Margaret P324
Gill, Magaret P484
Gill, Alan H P565
Gill, Phupinder E159
Gill, Darla R. E273
Gillan-Myer, Maureen A. A437
Gillani, Aleem A774
Gillean, John A. P119
Gilleland, Diane A575
Gillen, Chip A564
Gillen, David E428
Gillern, Jeffry H. (Jeff) von A865
Gilles, Jean H. A260
Gillespie, Rob A223
Gillespie, Peter K. A440
Gillespie, Phillip S. A766
Gillespie, Jeffrey P531

Gillespie, Michael P570
Gillespie, Ed P594
Gillett, Bob A758
Gillett, Aracely P163
Gillett, Bob P519
Gillett, Nancy A. E69
Gillette, Melissa P500
Gilley, William A100
Gilley, Bryan P200
Gillham, Simon W388
Gilliam, Dabney T. P. (Dexter) A52
Gilliam, Kyle A99
Gilliam, Scott A196
Gilliam, Derek P134
Gilliam, Chris P277
Gilliam, Lisa P663
Gillies, Iris A54
Gilligan, Tommy A193
Gilligan, Matt A695
Gilligan, Terrence A908
Gilligan, Tommy P112

Gilliland, M. Amy A374
Gilliland, Terry A736
Gilliland, Lake P308
Gilliland, Terry P492
Gilliland, Brian P511
Gillin, Greg A517
Gillis, Kathy A13
Gillis, Michelle A. (Shelly) A51
Gillis, Jim A762
Gillis, Robert P38
Gillis, Edwin J E394
Gillman, Heike A782
Gillman, John P61
Gillming, Mark R P334
Gillmon, Brett A532
Gillmore, Ron A555
Gillmore, John A556
Gillrie, Dave P. P76
Gillund, Chris P125
Gilman, Scott A109
Gilman, Fred P96
Gilman, Scott E36
Gilmartin, Thomas N. A830
Gilmartin, Rich P281
Gilmartin, Thomas N. E403
Gilmore, Elizabeth A175
Gilmore, Greg A246
Gilmore, Charissa A272
Gilmore, Deanna A272
Gilmore, Dennis J. A335
Gilmore, Rob A685
Gilmore, Bob A685
Gilmore, Grover C. (Cleve) P98
Gilroy, Ailsa A593
Gilstrap, Carol A865
Gilstrap, Mike P591
Gilstrap, Jamie K P666
Giltner, Dave A173
Gilyard, Scott P599
Gim, Mark K. W. A880
Gimas, Constadine A478
Gimbel, Thomas A703
Gina, Kuehn A3
Ginder, Chelsey E426
Gine, Jaime A292
Gingell, Daryl A141
Gingerich, Bradley A173
Gingras, France M. A721
Gingras, Mercy P613
Gini, Becky P347
Ginn, Porter A729
Ginn, Cheryl A919
Ginn, William (Bill) P596
Ginsberg, Harold P564
Ginsburg, Alan H. E47
Ginter, Matt A2
Ginter, John P6
Ginter, Tom P51
Ginty, Mike A744
Gintzburger, Emmanuel W204
Gintzig, Donald R. P674
Gionfriddo, Robert P. (Bob) A414
Gionfriddo, Robert P. (Bob) E194

A = AMERICAN BUSINESS
E = EMERGING COMPANIES
P = PRIVATE COMPANIES
W = WORLD BUSINESS

Giordanella, Kim A539
Giordano, Karen A583
Giordano, Doug A649
Giordano, Laura A828
Giordano, Joseph P321
Giordano, Karen P374
Giordano, Craig S. E375
Giorelli, Michela A269
Giorgianni, Kathryn A38
Giornelli, Lillian C. E98
Giovanelli, Gabriele E212
Giovani, John Di' P531
Giovanni, Lisa P525
Giovanni, Lisa P533
Giovinazzi, Brian A675
Giovinazzo, Kathy P461
Gipe, David E253
Gipple, Todd A. A683
Gipple, Todd A. E341
GIRALDO, CARLOS MARIO W23
Girard, Jon D P340
Girardot, Jennifer P425
Girguis, Mark P479
Girion, Woody A328
Girlich, Anna P610
Giromonte, Ron A105
Girouard, Denis W252
Giroux, Marc A238
Girre, Xavier W136
Girten, Damian P634
Girton, Tani A103
Gise, James A907
Gise, James E446
Gisler, Jacob P415
Gisler, Mona E110
Gitles, Chuck A542
Gitles, Chuck E267
Gitlin, David L. A854
Gitlitz, Edward A92
Gittleman, Kelly A449
Giudice, William (Bill) P554
Giust, Flavio A489
Giustino, Gerard E277
Given, Christopher P189
Given, Barbara P518
Givens, Carla P13
Givens, Gregg W. P167
Givens, Donna P563
Givler, Sean A196
Gjervik, Staale A313
Gladden, Brian T. A567
Glade, Doug A252
Glade, Doug P150
Gladman, Ian W275
Gladney, Karen A221
Gladney, Tony A558
Gladson, Richard A513
Gladstone, David J. E178
Gladys, Taylor P99
Glandt, Eduardo D. A812
Glandt, Eduardo D. P607
Glant, Tibor P467
Glanvill, Derek W. P318
Glanzer, Joshua D P196
Glarner, Brian A302
Glarner, Brian E128
Glaros, Dean A475
Glaros, Dean P266
Glasco, Judd A101
Glasenberg, Ivan W159
Glaser, Robert A334
Glaser, Daniel S. (Dan) A532
Glaser, Jeff A729
Glaser, Sandy A770
Glaser, Tom P1
Glasgow, Mark A559
Glasgow, Mary Ellen Smith P169
Glasheen, Ken A592
Glasheen, Ken E304

Glasman, Zvi E168
Glasner, Greg P249
Glaspie, John P410
Glass, Lynda A9
Glass, William A115
Glass, Steven A359
Glass, Dennis R. A512
Glass, Shannon A593
Glass, Robert W. A711
Glass, Gene A801
Glass, Steven C. A807
Glass, Ms Sheronda P272
Glass, Thomas P386
Glass, Gene P561
Glass, Steven C. P574
Glass, Kevin W80
Glass, William R. E135
Glassberg, Helene L A812
Glassberg, Helene L P607
Glasscock, Dave A171
Glasscock, James S. A626
Glasscock, Larry C. A918
Glasscock, Dave P100
Glasscock, Melbern G P559
Glasser, Kristin A614
Glastra, Matthijs E308
Glaun, Braeme P290
Glaunert, Curtis P677
Glavey, Patrick P360
Glay, Garry P157
Glaze, Brian A769
Glazer, Victor A130
Glazier, Tony A149
Glazier, Paula P20
Glazier, Alysha P122
Gleason, George G. A107
GLEASON, SUSAN A413
Gleason, Thomas R A535
Gleason, Patrick A578
Gleason, John J. A718
Gleason, Leona A. A904
GLEASON, SUSAN P234
Gleason, Thomas R P312
Gleason, George G. E34
Gleason, Matt E96
Gleason, Leona A. E442
Glebe, Dawn A769
Gledhill, Matt P368
Gledhill, David W119
Gleeson, Suzie E107
Gleissle, Karin A912
Glendinning, Stewart F. A834
Glenn, R Alexander A282
Glenn, T. Michael A327
Glenn, Staci A441
Glenn, Frank A700
Glenn, Rebecca A827
Glenn, Linda P115
Glenn, Richard P620
Glenn, David E251
Glenney, Chris P120
Glesby, James W O P96
Glew, James P. E61
Glick, Andrew A599
Glick, Alvin P27
Glick, Randy P27
Glick, Barry P27
Glickman, Paul A479
Glidden, Craig B. A378
Glied, Sherry A. A585
Glied, Sherry A. P377
Glimcher, Laurie H. P153
Glisic, Kessa A644
Glisson, Britton L. (Britt) A528
Glitch, Keri P342
Glockner, Jacqueline A56
Glodowski, Jonah P48
Glooch, Karen A784
Gloor, Michelle P511
Gloria, Ana P635
Glorioso, Jeanne A244
Gloss, Rodney D. E319
Glover, Andy A214
Glover, Smokey A369
Glover, William A369

Glover, Ric A532
Glover, Kate A549
Glover, Marcus A558
Glover, Amy A649
Glover, Lisa A865
Glover, Ron P6
Glover, Connie P52
Glover, Andy P128
Glover, Jason P285
Glover, Walter P636
Glover, Joseph (Joe) P642
Glover, Kate E270
Glover, Tyler E396
Glovier, Cliff P663
Glowasky, Bob A537
Glubka, Terry P175
Gluck, Stefan A178
Gluck, Mitch A335
Gluck, Melanie A537
Gluckman, Michael Mike A583
Gluckman, Larry A584
Gluski, Andres R A17
Gluzsak, Tim A377
Glyar, David P135
Glykofridis, Minos E117
Glynn, Ted P518
Glynn, Hilton P666
Gmelch, Walter H. P654
Gmelich, Justin G. A389
Gmuer, Stefan A766
Gnetz, Patricia A865
Gnodde, Richard J. A389
Gnoinski, Jeffrey A677
Go, Stanley A132
Goar, Michael P345
Goare, Douglas M. (Doug) A545
Goas, Thomas A513
Gobbel, Liz A781
Goben, Randy A190
Goble, Kathleen E303
Goceljak, John A648
Gockel, Douglas A822
Goday, Swapna P685
Goddard, Jesse P700
Godden, Phil A493
Gode, Pierre W226
Godenzi, Alberto P625
Godfrey, Red A596
Godfrey, Brian A729
Godin, Barbara (Barb) A700
Godin, Barb A700
Godina, Susie P508
Godla, Brian E117
Godridge, Leslie V. A865
Godsey, Jim A384
Godsey, Tracy P60
Godsey, Jim E176
Godshaw, Gary A390
Godsil, Patrick P664
Godsill, Jack A195
Godsted, Matt A890
Godsted, Matt P684
Godusky, Brenda P634
Godwin, Jim D. A115
Godwin, Hank A330
Godwin, Cristina A520
Godwin, Cliff A624
Godwin, Charles A685
Godwin, Benjamin A792
Godwin, Janet E. P5
Godwin, Robin P42
Godwin, John T. P104
Godwin, David P417
Godwin, Donald P653
Godwin, Dwayne P673
Goeb-Burkett, Michelle P323
Goebel, Maryann A732
Goebel, Maryann E365
Goedecke, Nancy Collat P315
Goedecke, Glenn P315
Goedhart, Saskia W26
Goedken, Dennis A637
Goedken, Thomas J. P5
Goeke, George A84
Goel, Vikas A766

Goel, Ashutosh P324
Goel, Anita P640
Goelkel, Chris A596
Goeller, Andy A784
Goemaat, Bruce A84
Goeppinger, Kathleen H P343
Goeschel, Burkhard W229
Goette, Roland A119
Goetz, William W. (Bill) A782
Goetz, Bill A782
Goetz, William P386
Goetz, John P. E341
Goetz-Krummel, Melissa A477
Goetz-Krummel, Melissa P268
Goff, Corinne Le A61
Goff, Stacey W. A185
Goff, Kevin A406
Goff, Robert A693
Goffaux, Denis W379
Goffney, Dr Latonya P20
Goffredi, Paul W. E430
Goforth, Patricia A140
Goggin, Patrick (Pat) A136
Gogswell, Josh E402
Gogue, Jay P51
Goh, Martin A532
Goh, Eng Lim P502
Goh, Francis P510
Goh, Linus T. L. W280
Gohlke, Henry J. E57
Gohsman, Judy A387
Gohsman, Judy E177
Goins, Randy A375
Goins, John A659
Golan, Ela W150
Golanowski, Marie P51
Golato, Andrea P563
Golbasarians, Albert E116
Golbey, Anita R A584
Golbey, Anita R P376
Gold, Andre A79
Gold, Stephen J. A250
Gold, Richard S. A522
Gold, Scott A531
Gold, Jeffrey P. P78
Gold, Barbara P646
Goldbeck, John P331
Goldberg, Scott L. A213
Goldberg, Linda A232
Goldberg, Wendy A448
Goldberg, Bruce A480
Goldberg, Richard A548
Goldberg, Gary J. A588
Goldberg, Larry A741
Goldberg, Howard A865
Goldberg, Jonathan P27
Goldberg, Dror P32
Goldberg, Alexander P107
Goldberg, Neal B P241
Goldberg, Richard P321
Goldberg, Mark A. P417
Goldberg, Dori P632
Goldberg, Steven E268
Goldberg, Larry E370
Goldberger, Mayer A406
Goldblatt, Steve A878
Golden, Andrew A406
Golden, Gail A447
Golden, Elizabeth A648
Golden, Beth P321
Golden, Jed P381
Golden, John P541
Golden, Andrew K. P606
Golden, Andrew P640
Golden, Robert P659
Goldenberg, Scott A817
Goldenberg, Neil P264
Goldenberg, Rodney P670
Goldenberg, Jack E272
Goldenstein, Ihno W235
Golder, George E8
Goldey, Donna A226
Goldfarb, Amy A131
Goldfarb, Michael P321

Goldfarb, Timothy M. P497
Goldfeld, Robert A585
Goldfeld, Robert P377
Goldgut, Harry A. W75
Goldhaber, Jeanne P658
Goldhahn, Laura P68
Goldin, Adam A480
Golding, Stephen D. A812
Golding, Stephen D. P607
Goldman, Nathan D. A243
Goldman, David A390
Goldman, Howard A810
Goldman, Phil P184
Goldman, Howard P597
Goldner, Brian D. A408
Goldsbury, Richard P125
Goldschmidt, Guy A449
Goldschmidt, Lawrence E P223
Goldschmidt, Nancy P410
Goldsmith, Spencer A865
Goldsmith, Ilyse A865
Goldsmith, David L. P263
Goldsmith, Jennifer E426
Goldstein, Jeff A84
Goldstein, Lawrence A. (Larry) A125
Goldstein, Rob L. A130
Goldstein, Brian A214
Goldstein, Marc A449
Goldstein, Robert G. (Rob) A502
Goldstein, Michael A537
Goldstein, Brian P128
Goldstein, Stacy A P204
Goldstein, Lisa A P376
Goldstein, Eliot P565
Goldstein, Allan Moises P590
Goldstein, Brian P P649
Goldstein, Barry B. E233
Goldstein, Arnie E346
Goldstien, Gerald P685
Goldstine, Abner A46
Goldstine, Abner P32
Goldstone, Steven F. (Steve) A231
Goldszer, Robert C. P355
Goldwater, John K. A122
Goldwin, Richard P638
Goler, Michael R. P280
Golestani, Clark A550
Golia, Kanak R P424
Golia, Prebha P424
Golitko, Dave P8
Goliyad, Yuriy E130
Golkiewicz, Tamara P613
Goll, Harold P219
Golladay, Catherine A729
Gollisz, Gustav A204
Golson, Kelly Jo A15
Golson, Kelly Jo P9
Golston, Jeremiah A685
Golub, Bennett W. A130
Golub, Scott A131
Golub, Todd P567
Golwas, Brooke A3
Golz, Judy Briscoe P136
Goman, Elizabeth J P598
Gombac, Jocelyn A481
Gombar, Greg A A806
Gombar, Greg A P569
Gomberg, Mark A869
Gomel, Rick A246
Gomer, Jay A441
Gomes, Maria P296
Gomes, Carlos W286
Gomes, Fernando Jorge Buso W385
Gomez, Jorge M. A165
Gomez, Jaime A219
Gomez, Maribeth A221
Gomez, Henry A418
Gomez, Evelyn A592
Gomez, Rick H. A788
Gomez, Miguel A904
Gomez, Teresa P123
Gomez, Edwin P127
Gomez, Jaime P131
Gomez, Olegario P142
Gomez, Rick P163

Gomez, Jennifer P250
Gomez, Julie P456
Gomez, Clarisa P550
Gomez, Jacqueline P564
Gomez, Fabian E437
Gomez, Miguel E442
Gomez-sanchez, Juan A508
Gomez-urquiza, Jose P610
Gomi, Hideki A559
Gomric, Matt A223
Goncalves, Armando F. A644
Gongxun, Lv W283
Gonick, Lev S. P44
Gonick, Lev P98
Gonick, Denise V. P360
Gonnella, Thomas A201
Gonos, Caroline A904
Gonos, Caroline E442
Gonsior, Tim A371
Gonsman, Shana P53
Gonyea, Paula P614
Gonyea, Dave P672
Gonzales, Chad A49
Gonzales, Phil A175
Gonzales, Maralessa A244
Gonzales, Yolanda A244
Gonzales, Bob A260
Gonzales, Robert A461
Gonzales, Doc P136
Gonzales, Anita P141
Gonzales, Frank P305
Gonzales, Elizabeth P517
Gonzales, Erika P550
Gonzales, Gil P648
Gonzalez, Richard A. (Rick) A6
Gonzalez, Ricardo A122
Gonzalez, Ralph A204
Gonzalez, Alex A221
Gonzalez, Adan A222
Gonzalez, Jaime A240
Gonzalez, Melissa A270
Gonzalez, Dan A323
Gonzalez, Mayra A323
Gonzalez, Richard A398
Gonzalez, Shari A449
Gonzalez, Eliza A459
Gonzalez, Lauren A478
Gonzalez, Jose A478
Gonzalez, Carlos A508
Gonzalez, Carlos R A677
Gonzalez, Edward A. (Eddie) A730
Gonzalez, Eva A734
Gonzalez, Elizabeth A809
Gonzalez, Tracy A823
Gonzalez, Hector A835
Gonzalez, Charles A838
Gonzalez, Alfonso A865
Gonzalez, Beatrice A868
Gonzalez, Sandra P30
Gonzalez, Arthur A. P160
Gonzalez, Michael P225
Gonzalez, Manny P239
Gonzalez, Dolores P245
Gonzalez, Roberto P249
Gonzalez, Kathy P292
Gonzalez, Elizabeth P397
Gonzalez, Carmen P478
Gonzalez, Tina P569
Gonzalez, Elizabeth P586
Gonzalez, Fernando P631
Gonzalez, Jacqueline L P665
Gonzalez, Dena P670
Gonzalez, Linda P688
Gonzalez, Iliana E123
Gonzalez, Tony E219
Gonz--lez, Mario H. P--ez W18
Gooch, Mark A. A227
Gooch, Mark A. A228
Goocher, Robert P514
Good, Jim A96
Good, Lynn J. A281
Good, Lynn J. A282
Good, Lynn J A282
Good, Michael P642
Good, Glenn E. P642

Good, Jennifer E445
Goodall, Laura A122
Goodarzi, Sasan K. A466
Goode, Wilson S P668
Goodell, Denise A316
Goodell, Denise E141
Goodfellow, Kathy P218
Goodfriend, Jim A332
Goodger, Simon A649
Goodhew, Ian A861
Goodhew, Ian P658
Gooding, Marie C. A322
Goodman, Sean D. A78
Goodman, Bennett J. A132
Goodman, Scott R. A302
Goodman, Kim Crawford A355
Goodman, Stacey A366
Goodman, Randy A384
Goodman, Adam A537
Goodman, Gregg M. A744
Goodman, Stacy P32
Goodman, Phyllis Goodman P115
Goodman, Jay S P329
Goodman, Larry J P467
Goodman, Wayne H. P564
Goodman, Andrew E110
Goodman, Scott R. E128
Goodman, Randy E176
Goodman, Jeffrey M. (Jeff) E431
Goodnow, John P68
Goodpaster, Keith A332
Goodreau, Nicole P146
Goodrich, Donna C. A115
Goodrich, Loren P664
Goodrich, Michael F. E361
Goodrion, Sean A234
Goodrion, Sean P139
Goodrow, Carolyn A241
Goodrum, Ryan P563
Goodsaid, Federico E428
Goodsir, Michelle A201
Goodspeed, Randy A260
Goodspeed, Dennis P281
Goodwim, Terry W P450
Goodwin, Annie A387
Goodwin, Dustin A447
Goodwin, Eric A522
Goodwin, Linda P292
Goodwin, Kiani P305
Goodwin, Barry P344
Goodwin, Annie E177
Goodwyn, Bill A269
Goody, James A351
Goody, James E158
Goold, Alex P27
Goon, Julie A67
Goone, David S A457
Goorevich, Charlie P495
Gopalakrishnan, Raja A330
Gopalakrishnan, Venkat E290
Gopalratnam, Vc A199
Gopstein, Etan A530
Goranson, Mark A620
Gorbunov, Igor N. W350
Gord, Dave P482
Gordeon, Tom P102
Gorder, Joseph W. (Joe) A867
Gorder, Christopher D. Van P488
Gordon, Marc D. A48
Gordon, Murdo A147
Gordon, Derek A. A218
Gordon, Ilene S. A453
Gordon, Ben A565
Gordon, Barbara A667
Gordon, Larry A691
Gordon, Russell L. A716
Gordon, Cima A784
Gordon, Bryson A871
Gordon, Michelle A872
Gordon, Howard A902
Gordon, Scott R. P45
Gordon, Tom P102
Gordon, Abram P115
Gordon, Pam P121
Gordon, Eric P126

Gordon, Bernard P279
Gordon, Andrew P406
Gordon, Victor P410
Gordon, Jean P461
Gordon, Jeffrey P685
Gordon, Howard P693
Gordon, Drew B. E208
Gordon, Barbara E336
Gordon-Scott, J P420
Gore, Clark A173
Gore, Steve P432
Gorecki, Teresa A476
Goree, Dr T Lamar P89
Gorham, Roger B. A30
Gorham, Doug P586
Gori, Roy W232
Gorillo, Rodrigo Echenique W45
Gorin, Ariane A311
Gorin, Joanna P175
Goris, Patrick A712
Gorlewski, Todd P528
Gorman, Norma A33
Gorman, Mark A199
Gorman, Patrick A225
Gorman, Christopher M. (Chris) A489
Gorman, James P. A568
Gorman, Mark J. A657
Gorman, Mark J A658
Gorman, Robert M. (Rob) A841
Gorman, Cheryl A854
Gorman, Eric P104
Gorman, Galen P108
Gorman, Maureen J P270
Gorman, Timothy P425
Gorman, Patrick E88
Gorman, Robert M. (Rob) E410
Gormley, Bill A158
Gormley, Ken P169
Gormley, Alice P309
Gormley, Kathleen K. P674
Gornall, Susan P391
Gorney, Len A484
Gorney, David J. P564
Gorno, Mary Louise P610
Gorodetzer, Kristen A195
Gorostiza, Georg A763
Gorrie, Thomas M. P168
Gorriz, Michael W340
Gorska, Anna A184
Gorski, Jim A330
Gorski, Mark A614
Gorski, Bill P550
Gorsky, Alex A476
Gorti, Bhaskar M. W266
Gortney, Jennifer A674
Gorzak, John A616
Gosavi, Sanjeev A461
Gosch, Kenneth L A251
Gosdin, James L A769
Gosebruch, Henry O. A6
Gosevitz, Bernie P61
Goshay, Allison P332
Gosmak, Peter D P640
Gosnell, Jack A173
Goss, David A670
Goss, Karl A865
Goss, Andreas J. W365
Gosselin, Gene A683
Gosselink, Robert A122
Gosser, James P109
Gosser, Alex P542
Gossett, Cindy P272
GOSTOUT, BOBBIE S A540
GOSTOUT, BOBBIE S P316
Goswami, Chitra A255
Gotanda, John Y. P667
Gotelli, Robert A103
Gothard, Joe P247
Gothard, Butch E216
Gotlib, Ian A507
Gotlib, Ian P288
Goto, Noriaki W46
Goto, Katsuhiro W324
Goto, Masao W336
Gott, Sharon P124

A = AMERICAN BUSINESS
E = EMERGING COMPANIES
P = PRIVATE COMPANIES
W = WORLD BUSINESS

Gottardy, Brian G P386
Gottesfeld, Stephen P. A588
Gottfried, John E4
Gottlieb, Katherine P511
Gottlieb, Kevin P511
Gottschalk, Marla A127
Gottschalk, Adrian A129
Gottschling, Andreas W145
Gottscho, Richard A. (Rick) A501
Gottsegen, Jonathan M A851
Gottstein, Thomas P. W111
Gottwals, Bill A349
Gottwals, Bill E156
Gotwals, Janet W A98
Gotwals, Janet W E33
Gotwalt, Darryl E405
Gou, Terry T.M. W171
Goudreau, Christopher A460
Gough, Mitzy A136
Gough, Lisa A782
Gough, Fredric P391
Gough, Michael W P398
Gouin, Kevin A330
Goulart, Steven J. A555
Gould, R Marcia A46
Gould, Jason A248
Gould, Mark A. A324
Gould, Dan A589
Gould, Vicky A670
Gould, Karen A813
Gould, R Marcia P32
Gould, Rod P123
Gould, Karen P608
Gould, Andrea P666
Gould, Matthew J. E47
Gould, Jeffrey A. E47
Gould, Fredric H. E47
Gould, Mitchell K. E47
Gould, Jeffrey A. E47
Gould, Gerard H. (Gerry) E149
Gould, Sharon E248
Gould, Matthew J. E317
Gould, Fredric H. E317
Gouldie, Nichole P342
Goulding, Philip L P350
Goulet, Beverly K. A43
Goulet, Ken A67
Goulet, Nicole A329
Goulet, Alisa A878
Goulopoulos, Paul A767
Goumans, Marcus W167
Gourlay, Alexander W. (Alex) A877
Gouveia, Jeffrey P545
Govan, Christopher A. (Chris) W277
Gove, Matt P428
Govier, George A P330
Govil, Sanjay P248
Govreau, Sharon P19
Gow, Jeff D A232
Gowen, Kevin P. A781
Gower, Greg E52
Goyal, Rahul A456
Goyea, David A767
Gozon, Richard C. P619
GP, Energy T A298
Graaf, Bill Van de A218
Graass, James H. (Jim) E112
Grab, Edward L P227
Grabavoy, Steve A541
Grabavoy, Steven A542
Grabavoy, Steve E266
Grabavoy, Steven E267
Grabowski, Robert A314
Grabowski, John P99
Grabowski, Robert P189
Graca, Amy A158
Grace, Jacqueline A158
Grace, Chris P14
Grace, Richard P316

Grace, William M P668
Grace, Adrian W10
Gracheck, Jack A541
Gracheck, Jack E267
Graddick-Weir, Mirian M. A550
Graddy, Steven P206
Grade, Joel T. A782
Gradert, Scott A738
Gradnik, Amy A874
Grady, Gerry A328
Grady, Melissa A556
Grady, James P529
Graeber, Ann P528
Graebner, Clark P333
Graeff, Scott A. E251
Graf, R Mark A268
Graf, Alan B. A327
Graf, Stacy A886
Graf, Jane P331
Graf, Stacy E433
Graff, Michael J. (Mike) A25
Graff, Michael J. (Mike) P15
Graffy, George P505
Grafman, Laura R. P487
Grafmyre, Richard A. A640
Grafton, Lee P415
Graham, Jonathan P. A61
Graham, Robert M. (Bob) A66
Graham, Jon A69
Graham, John A199
Graham, Kristin A311
Graham, Molly A513
Graham, Derek A591
Graham, John A682
Graham, Melissa A739
Graham, Stephen P A763
Graham, Christopher A. (Chris) A768
Graham, Carolyn A769
Graham, James A782
Graham, Dan A844
Graham, Ned A851
Graham, Mark A A901
Graham, Richard H P51
Graham, John P118
Graham, Amy P148
Graham, Michelle P190
Graham, Teena P214
Graham, John C P217
Graham, Eugene W P217
Graham, Matthew X P217
Graham, Patrick T P217
Graham, Mary P330
Graham, Ed P340
Graham, Paul P379
Graham, Judy P465
Graham, Franklin P478
Graham, Stephen A. P494
Graham, Melissa P501
Graham, Larry P517
Graham, Peter P518
Graham, Tonya P525
Graham, Dale P681
Graham, Mark A P692
Graham, Linda H E258
Graham, John E398
Graham, Dan E412
Grahe, Raymond P333
Grainger, Guy A478
Grainger, Jo P583
Grajeda, Jessica A635
Grajeda, Jessica P419
Graley, David P88
Gramer, John E101
Gramlich, Tom A465
Granado, Alejandro A202
Granado, Alejandro P122
Granata, Thomas A54
Granchi, Annie A391
Grand, Hillary A131
Grande, William P231
Grandidier, Karen Jones P482
Graney, Kevin M. A374
Graney, Thomas (Tom) E428
Grange, Kim A502
Granger, Harvey P421

Granger, Harvey P512
Granger, Carolyn P632
Granger, Clarence L. E408
Granger, Bill E431
Graninger, Clark D. W28
Granndsart, Tom P200
Grannis, Dick A685
Grant, Tim A73
Grant, Marilee A144
Grant, Melanie A155
Grant, Shane A215
Grant, Aja A282
Grant, Joan A284
Grant, Jeffrey A602
Grant, Jasmine A774
Grant, Thomas P8
Grant, Susan P66
Grant, Bryan P108
Grant, Travis P154
Grant, Brenda P613
Grant, Alan P669
Grant, Joan E111
Grant-anderson, Belinda A84
Grantham, Deborah A19
Grantham, Connee A750
Grantham, Michael P126
Grantham, Keith P146
Grantham, Shelton P630
Granzyk, Steve A180
Grasela, Wayne T P603
Grass, Stephanie A702
Grasse, Lisa E107
Grasshoff, Michaela A532
Grassi, Louis C. (Lou) E47
Grassman, Joanne P301
Grasso, Sebastian A133
Grasso, Maria A. A359
Grasso, Davide A592
Grasty, Kevin P37
Grate, Gail P226
Grau, Dominique A22
Grauer, Scott B. A137
Graugnard, Milton P89
Graumlich, Lisa A861
Graumlich, Lisa P658
Graunke, Carrie A540
Graunke, Carrie P316
Grauze, Sarah A2
Gravanis, Georges A91
Gravel, Karine A649
Gravel, Monique W80
Gravel, Louis E172
Gravelle, Michael L. (Mike) A328
Gravelle, Michael L. (Mike) A329
Graves, William W. A90
Graves, Victoria A260
Graves, Christopher A551
Graves, Gerry P6
Graves, Steven P38
Graves, Carmon P213
Graves, Marti P240
Graves, Gina P363
Graves, Cynthia P425
Graves, Michael (Mike) E113
Graves, Gregory B. (Greg) E126
Graves, Jeffrey A. (Jeff) E288
Graves, Scott L. E312
Gravino, Ronald P371
Graviss, Jonathan A448
Gravr--k, Jon W360
Grawe, George A34
Gray, Sean A A124
Gray, Jonathan D. A132
Gray, Harry W A136
Gray, Jonathan D. A421
Gray, William A423
Gray, Robert D A428
Gray, James D. (Jim) A453
Gray, Diedre A663
Gray, James W. A704
Gray, Tom A769
Gray, David J. A811
Gray, Myron A. A850
Gray, M Joel A895
Gray, David L. P58

Gray, Larry W. P58
Gray, Chip P126
Gray, Gregory W P139
Gray, Patrick P159
Gray, Lee P163
Gray, Sarah P172
Gray, Cynthia P179
Gray, Jeffrey P200
Gray, Nancy Ryan P217
Gray, Tracy P262
Gray, Thomas L P271
Gray, Jake P315
Gray, Anna Maria P321
Gray, Nancy P334
Gray, Jim P448
Gray, Geoff P501
Gray, John P506
Gray, Emily P584
Gray, David J. P600
Gray, Dudley P623
Gray, Pamela P653
Gray, Sean A. E41
Gray, James W. E350
Gray, Christopher E355
Gray, Charles J. (Charlie) E394
Graybill, Greg A292
Grayer, Loren E175
Grayfer, Valery I. W290
Graziano, Steven M. A890
Graziano, Steven M. P684
Graziosi, Erin P462
Greasheimer, Sharon A165
Greathouse, Steven R. E92
Grebenc, Jane A342
Grebert, Carl A593
Grebow, Peter E. E113
Grebstein, Marci A640
Grech, Joe A607
Greck, Sonya B P345
Greco, Thomas R. (Tom) A13
Greco, Julie A541
Greco, Joseph D A607
Greco, John R. A634
Greco, Joe A734
Greco, Mario W405
Greco, Julie E266
Greek, Matt P62
Greeley, John A885
Greeley, Donna P231
Greelish, James P97
Green, Keith A33
Green, Anthony C. A66
Green, Joseph A85
Green, Tsahai A109
Green, Phil A131
Green, Gerry A158
Green, Saryia A201
Green, Phillip D. A244
Green, Frederec A260
Green, Allen R. A277
Green, Logan A288
Green, Joe A402
Green, Markham A420
Green, David A422
Green, Steve A422
Green, Mart A425
Green, Andy A442
Green, Elle A476
Green, Mark A. A487
Green, Darryl A525
Green, Bryan A578
Green, Allyson A585
Green, Mark A683
Green, Harold A693
Green, Howard A741
Green, Joyce A743
Green, Ryan A755
Green, Tammy A763
Green, Sheron A770
Green, Barbara A782
Green, Niki A784
Green, Nancy A809
Green, Warren A837
Green, Miguale A838
Green, Paul S. A848

Green, Monique A866
Green, Brian A874
Green, Tara A878
Green, Dee P6
Green, Valerie P8
Green, Peter P25
Green, Jon P29
Green, Louis P69
Green, Robert P92
Green, Teresa P102
Green, Greg P121
Green, Thomas B P125
Green, Mike P144
Green, Judy P145
Green, Jeffrey R P223
Green, David P239
Green, Steve P239
Green, Mart P239
Green, Barbara P242
Green, Susan P298
Green, Allyson P377
Green, James P381
Green, Mark P396
Green, A Hugh P421
Green, Gene E P511
Green, Karen P516
Green, Teressia P518
Green, Rick P522
Green, Beth P576
Green, Stephen D. P588
Green, Danielle P599
Green, Cathy P674
Green, Mary P677
Green, Gary R. W107
Green, John M. W297
Green, William E22
Green, Tsahai E36
Green, Ben E96
Green, Markham E198
Green, William H. E289
Green, Howard E370
Green, Joyce E372
Green, Yulia E428
Green-Lett, Darsee A422
Green-Lett, Darsee P239
Greenan, Joe A16
Greenawalt, Richard A. P165
Greenberg, Jamie A390
Greenberg, Raymond S. A860
Greenberg, Andrew A872
Greenberg, Alan A872
Greenberg, Richard P20
Greenberg, Adam P399
Greenberg, Lawrence P564
Greenberg, Allen P606
Greenberg, Lon R P631
Greenberg, Raymond S. P656
Greenberg, Evan G. W98
Greenberg, Jordan E29
Greenberg, Randi E320
Greenberger, Sharon P381
Greenblatt, David A. E61
Greene, Alexander A40
Greene, Mike A56
Greene, Jason K. A125
Greene, Thomas (Tom) A218
Greene, Matt A287
Greene, Yoonhi A323
Greene, Jeff A354
Greene, Jesse J A460
Greene, Deirdre A635
Greene, Douglas A724
Greene, Aaron A741
Greene, Candy A751
Greene, Ezra A872
Greene, A. Hugh P58
Greene, Tim P93
Greene, Mary Jane P135
Greene, Michael P155
GREENE, CYNTHIA P163
Greene, Matt P174
Greene, Joseph J. P267
Greene, Lance P298
Greene, Deirdre P419
Greene, Amy L P478

Greene, Hugh P512
Greene, David P609
Greene, Michael J P632
Greene, Maureen P687
Greene, Moya M. W314
Greene, Steve E163
Greene, Aaron E370
Greene, Candy E377
Greener, Todd A13
Greener, Geoffrey S. A100
Greenfeig, Sid A558
Greenfield, Karen P440
Greenfield, Andrew J. E3
Greenhaw, Mark A107
Greenhaw, Mark E34
Greenland, Frank P392
Greenlaw, David A607
Greenlee, Stephen A313
Greenlee, Karen P292
Greenlees, Jim P682
Greenspan, Robert P375
Greenspon, Tom A140
Greenstan, Robert P375
Greenstein, Scott A. A745
Greenstein, Sara A. A852
Greenstreet, Michelle M A759
Greenstreet, Michelle M P521
Greensweig, Gary P482
Greenwald, Vicki P94
Greenwald, Judy P554
Greenwalt, Rodgers K. A125
Greenway, Mark A439
Greenway, Suzanne A806
Greenway, Suzanne P569
Greenwell, Melissa P579
Greenwood, John A244
Greenya, Cyril J. A276
Greer, K. Gordon A98
Greer, Emily A372
Greer, Mike A751
Greer, Pam A763
Greer, Greg A774
Greer, Steven K. A822
Greer, Butch A823
Greer, Louis E. A832
Greer, Emily S P34
Greer, James P40
Creer, Rachel P261
Greer, Jeanne P576
Greer, K. Gordon E33
Greer, Mike E377
Greeson, Audrey P642
Greeter, Gerald A631
Gref, Herman W321
Grefe, Roger A693
Greff, Brian A471
Grefstad, Odd Arild W342
Grega, Jocelyn A863
Gregg, Lisa A49
Gregg, Paul A272
Gregg, Hall A649
Gregoire, Christopher J A519
Gregoire, Daniel N. (Dan) A524
Gregoire, Andrew J. E245
Gregor, Carol A195
Gregory, Ryan A180
Gregory, William A196
Gregory, Elisabeth A221
Gregory, Lentz A350
Gregory, Kevin A371
Gregory, Paul A484
Gregory, Sherman A685
Gregory, Paul C. A687
Gregory, Audrey A795
Gregory, Jonathan A800
Gregory, Kay A838
Gregory, Randy P51
Gregory, James P P536
Gregory, Jennie P537
Gregory, Linsey P612
Gregory, Williams P680
Gregory, Lentz E156
Gregory, Julie E364
Gregory, Jonathan E396
Greiff, David E116

Greig, Thomas G. (Tom) E361
Greindl, Jean-Marie A664
Greiner, Phillip A351
Greiner, James (Jim) P14
Greiner, Phillip E158
Grele, Kathy A541
Grele, Kathy E266
Grelle, John K. E39
Grenfell, Alistair A469
Grensteiner, Ronald J. (Ron) A47
Grenz, Dianne M. A868
Grenzig, Gail A P470
Grescovich, Mark J. A110
Grescovich, Mark J. E37
Grese, Frank A396
Gresham, James P687
Greslick, Richard L A212
Greslick, Richard L E79
Gress, William J. A150
Grether, James A920
Gretz, Jayne P35
Greuel, Norm A508
Greulich, Michael P236
Greve, Norman de A250
Grew, Melissa K P146
Grewal, Harjinder P64
Grewal, Harpreet S P237
Grewal, Kanny P405
Grewe, Jerry P455
Grexa, Karen A489
Grey, Noel A175
Grey, Robert A665
Greyber, Rob A311
Gribbin, Patrick A423
Gribbin, John T. P107
Gribble, Dwayne P52
Gribble, Robert P309
Grieco, Chrysanthy M. P494
Grieco, Patrizia W141
Grieder, Daniel A682
Griego, Linda M A175
Griego, Kathleen A782
Griesbaum, Robert P528
Griesemer, David A P629
Grieshaber, Joe A496
Griesheimer, Amy E127
Griesser, Gerard F. E108
Griffeth, Jack T P391
Griffin, Jayson A58
Griffin, Brian T. A67
Griffin, Ronald B. (Ron) A90
Griffin, Jeremy A136
Griffin, Corey A. A143
Griffin, Kevin A155
Griffin, Matthew A221
Griffin, Anthony H A314
Griffin, Gretchen A340
Griffin, Leland A423
Griffin, Robyn A441
Griffin, Alyson A456
Griffin, Janis A541
Griffin, Monty J. A738
Griffin, John A766
Griffin, Nelson A814
Griffin, Sean F. A848
Griffin, Darragh A904
Griffin, Michael P7
Griffin, Amy P42
Griffin, James D. P153
Griffin, Anthony H P189
Griffin, Mike P234
Griffin, April P237
Griffin, Justin P256
Griffin, Charles P271
Griffin, Marcus P441
Griffin, B R P441
Griffin, Dayle P528
Griffin, Nelson P616
Griffin, Wayne J. P678
Griffin, Jayson E16
Griffin, William F. (Bill) E23
Griffin, Gretchen E151
Griffin, Janis E267
Griffin, Darragh E442
Griffith, John B. A1

Griffith, Gia A49
Griffith, Bettyann A323
Griffith, Michelle A332
Griffith, Timothy T. A527
Griffith, Jill A647
Griffith, S. Patricia (Tricia) A672
Griffith, Derek A709
Griffith, G. Sanders A823
Griffith, Jerry A235
Griffith, Darrell P273
Griffith, Donna H P310
Griffith, J. Brian P339
Griffith, Brian P339
Griffith, Lawrence S C P548
Griffith, Bob P631
Griffith, Doreen E236
Griffiths, Diana P526
Griffiths, Guy W40
Griffiths, Peter L. W193
Griffiths, William C. (Bill) E343
Griffo, Michael A360
Griffo, Michael E164
Grigaux, Paul J. A752
Griger, David T P590
Grigg, Robert A480
Grigg, Richard R P37
Grigg, William P206
Grigg, Richard P574
Griggs, Malcolm D. A205
Griggs, Ron P52
Griggs, Judy P118
Griggs, Johnny P250
Griggs, Kathleen M. (Kathy) E226
Grignon, Perianne A733
Grigsby, Todd W P89
Grigsby, L Lane P89
Grigsby, Todd P89
Grill, Neil A105
Grill, Laura D. P172
Grill, Donald L. E147
Grilli, Francesco A685
Grillo, Anthony P525
Grima, Crocefissa A583
Grima, Edward P66
Griman, Emilio A460
Grimes, Jennifer A244
Grimes, Joseph P. (Joe) A797
Grimes, Joe A798
Grimes, Cynda A802
Grimes, Sally A834
Grimes, Dana P140
Grimes, Chuck P141
Grimes, Robert R. P200
Grimes, Leslie P242
Grimes, Brent P357
Grimes, Cynda P562
Grimes, Vicki P584
Grimes, Patricia E98
Grimes, Thomas L. (Tom) E276
Grimet, Howard P271
Grimm, Susan P99
Grimm, Douglas P335
Grimminger, Kurt A907
Grimminger, Kurt P696
Grimshaw, Matt A171
Grimshaw, Matt P100
Grimstone, Gerry W52
Grimstone, Gerry W54
Grimstone, Gerry W341
Grinberg, Paul J. A95
Grinberg, Paul J. E28
Grinberg, Paul J. E123
Grindberg, Guy A855
Grindle, W Harold P207
Griner, Patricia A737
Griner, Lucinda P170
Griner, Patricia E367
Grinnell, Kelly P147
Gripenstraw, Kirk A149
Gripshover, Mark P578
Griscti, Rhonda E268
Grisham, Jon E4
Grismer, Patrick J. (Pat) A445
Grissen, David J. A530
Grissom, Richard A868

A = AMERICAN BUSINESS
E = EMERGING COMPANIES
P = PRIVATE COMPANIES
W = WORLD BUSINESS

Griswold, Venus A838
Griswold, Jimmy P620
Grizzard, Maynard A814
Grizzard, Maynard P616
Grizzle, Kristy P225
Grob, Matthew S. (Matt) A685
Grobe, Tina A807
Grobe, Tina P574
Grobman, Richard P275
Groch, James R. (Jim) A172
Grochocki, Manju A583
Grodin, Joshua A718
Grodowski, Jenie P541
Groebel, Robert E426
Groeber, Robert P670
Groendyke, John E70
Groetken, Doug A894
Groff, Jim A814
Groff, Michael R. (Mike) A824
Groff, Mike A838
Groff, Jeffrey A862
Groff, Jim P616
Groff, Jeffrey E419
Grogan, Edwin A502
Grogan, Sherry P239
Grogin, Scott A175
Grogin, Jeffrey P. A642
Grogin, Jeffrey P. E328
Groh, Kelly L. A382
Groisser, Debra A677
Gronda, Mark P146
Groneman, Joseph L P155
Groner, P Campbell P477
Gronewold, Russell P87
Groom, Scott P590
Groot, René de W14
Gros, Richard R. A539
Gros-Pietro, Gian Maria W189
Grosby, Karen P399
Gross, John A189
Gross, Bob A478
Gross, Bruce E. A508
Gross, Ray A823
Gross, Roger A865
Gross, Anne P153
Gross, Roy P333
Gross, Vaughn P460
Gross, Daniel L. (Dan) P498
Gross, Kathy P522
Grossberg, Michael A659
Grossenbacher, John A528
Grosser, Joy M. P252
Grosshauser, Dan A881
Grossi, Stephen D. A137
Grossi, Therese A165
Grossi, Richard A522
Grossman, Robert I. A585
Grossman, Jeff A594
Grossman, Andrea A677
Grossman, Robert I. P377
Grossman, Divina P645
Grossman, Aaron E242
Grossman, David E404
Grosso, Steve A175
Grosso, Richard A583
Grosvenor, John C. A97
Grosvenor, John C. E32
Grote, Kathleen E146
Groth, Kelly P697
Grottenthaler, Bob P61
Grotzinger, John P. P91
Groux, Charlie A441
Grove, Robin A187
Grove, Hannah A766
Grove, Robin E71
Grover, Michael A180
Grover, Rajeev A199
Grover, Purva A807
Grover, Rishi A854

Grover, Purva P574
Groves, Mary A449
Groves, Tina M. A742
Groves, Taryn P217
Groves, Ned P325
Groves, Lori P369
Groves, Jennifer P567
Groves, Pamela DE P622
Groves, Tina M. E372
Grow, Erin H A100
Grow, Bradford A912
Grow, Heidi P51
Grow, David R P685
Grubber, Karen A434
Grubbs, Cole P273
Grubbs, William J. E101
Grube, Pat A701
Grube, Rüdiger W121
Gruber, William A648
Gruber, Julie A809
Gruber, Scott L. A820
Gruber, Karen N P576
Grubic, Robert C. E276
Grudier, Dale P145
Grudzien, Jeffrey M. E359
Grudzinski, Bill P331
Gruell, Kate A530
Gruenberg, Bruce A729
Gruenthal, Michael P18
Gruner, Dean P618
Grunig, Jared A901
Grunig, Jared P692
Grunin, Josh A407
Grunley, Kenneth M P222
Grunley, Virginia P222
Gruntz, Cory P185
Grunwald, Stefan A165
Grunwald, Gerald B. P618
Gruseke, Christopher A109
Grynberg, Marc W379
Grynspan, Devora P398
Gryparis, Rechelle P481
Gryzbek, Thomas P203
Grzeskowiak, Marc E1
Grzeszczak, Connie P527
Gr-ober, Jürgen W164
Gsoell, Karin P480
Gu, Yaobin (Richard) A62
Gu, Hanson A682
Guadagnoli, Donald A. P92
Guadalupe, Jan A769
Guagliardo, Paul (Guyardo) A269
Guajardo, Dante Contreras W108
Gualino, Guillermo A22
Guan, Chew A461
Guangyu, Yuan W102
Guardino, Lenny A531
Guardiola, Charlie A155
Guardiola, Eva P284
Guardiola, Irene P451
Guarino, Alan E70
Guarisco, Pete P204
Guarriello, Nicholas P P198
Guatero, Montha A328
Guay, Martin A762
Gubala, Jeffrey E437
Gubitosi, David A204
Guckian, Paul A685
Gude, David A433
Gude, Atish A580
Gudgel, Jane A729
Gudgell, Kay E125
Gudibande, Aroon A725
Guedry, John A891
Guedry, John E434
Guelcher, Jeff P175
Guell, Miguel Montes W42
Guenault, Karl A469
Guenther, Greg A175
Guenther, Stephen A439
Guenther, Chris A589
Guenthner, Kevin J. A349
Guenthner, Steven P27
Guenthner, Kevin J. E156
Guerci, Alan P529

Guericke, Keith R. E133
Guerlain, Eric W97
Guernsey, Gina P648
Guerra, Michael A309
Guerra, Joe A422
Guerra, R. David A459
Guerra, Aida A548
Guerra, Marquita A583
Guerra, Robert A744
Guerra, Andrea A786
Guerra, Amy A231
Guerra, Joe P239
Guerra, Aida P324
Guerrazzi, Mark A199
Guerreri, John E125
Guerrero, David A100
Guerrero, Francisco A115
Guerrero, Juan O. A661
Guerrero, Olivia P120
Guerrero, Yolanda P132
Guerrero, Ana P635
Guerrero, --ngel Alija W25
Guerrero, Pedro Guerrero W51
Guerrieri, Gary A360
Guerrieri, Gary E164
Guerry, Cile P465
Guertin, Timothy E394
Guertler, Walter A87
Guest, John P226
Guest, Kevin G. E422
Guettabi, Mouhcine P640
Guevara, Alfredo P665
Guez, Havid N Rodr P641
Guggemos, Michael A454
Guggemos, Julie A788
Guggenheim, Paul A. A636
Guggenheimer, Ron A204
Guggina, William H. W29
Gugino, Ann B. A636
Guglielmi, Joseph M A570
Guglielmi, Michael A342
Guglielmo, Joseph A833
Guha, Krishna A323
Guhe, Joachim A634
Guice, Keisha A475
Guice, Keisha P266
Guichard, Kent B. E15
Guido, James A871
Guidotti, Michael A449
Guidotti, Robert A461
Guidry, Darren A424
Guidry, Darren E200
Guigan, Elizabeth Mc P500
Guilbaud, Jean-Jacques W372
Guilfoile, Peter W. A221
Guilfoyle, John P361
Guiliano, Michelle P283
Guillaume, Steve E381
Guillen, Luz P306
Guillory, Cory A700
Guillotte, Gwen E244
Guillouard, Catherine W303
Guillén, Federico W266
Guinan, Thomas A624
Guinan, Mark J. A687
Guindo, Chirfi A129
Guiniling, Brittney P259
Guinn, Max A. A260
Guinn, Tricia A702
Guinn, Lindsey A777
Guinn, Lindsey E393
Guinta, Caryn A351
Guinta, Caryn E158
Guiony, Jean-Jacques W225
Guire, Valerie Mc P220
Guisinger, Debra L A332
Gula, Mike A728
Gula, Allen J. A781
Gulati, Sanjeev P248
Gulati, Neeraj E286
Gulbin, Michael A175
Gulbrandsen, Carl A905
Gulbrandsen, Carl P693
Gulden, Bj-¶rn W204
Guliano, James V P331

Gullapalli, Raghunath A204
Gulley, Janet A807
Gulley, Janet P574
Gullickson, Cade P663
Gulling, Douglas R. (Doug) A889
Gulliver, Stuart T. W175
Gullo, Samuel A334
Gullo, Erika A774
Gullo, Chris A800
Gullo, Chris E396
Gulmon, Gary A779
Gulotta, Amy A904
Gulotta, Amy E442
Gulrajani, Linda E257
Gum, JC P11
Gumaer, Andy E28
Gumbar, Gitika A390
Gumbert, Jack A505
Gumera, Elly P170
Gumeringer, Bert P560
Gumerson, John A744
Gumm, Gary P676
Gumpert, Phil P620
Gunalan, K A16
Gunasekaran, Deepak P335
Gunderman, Robert E. (Bob) A903
Gunderman, Bob P171
Gundermann, Peter J. E25
Gundimeda, Ravi A599
Gundotra, Vic A36
Gunkel, Damon A449
Gunn, Laurie P614
Gunn, William B P626
Gunning, Jim A173
Gunning, Pat A727
Gunnison, Kyle P693
Gunter, Thomas A489
Gunter, C. Scott W98
Gunther, Guy A185
Gunther, Conrad J. A267
Gunther, Jeffery A423
Gunthner, Richard A537
Guo, Helen A204
Guo, Peng (Patrick) A796
Guo, Lin P659
Guohua, Zhang W102
Guoxiong, Wei W186
Gupta, Sanjay A33
Gupta, Suren A33
Gupta, Vineet A130
Gupta, Arham A204
Gupta, Sanjiv A379
Gupta, Rohit A382
Gupta, Hirdey A542
Gupta, Anu A788
Gupta, Sunil P298
Gupta, Subhash P518
Gupta, Mahendra R. P616
Gupta, Rajiv L. (Raj) W29
Gupta, Piyush W119
Gupta, Sanjeev W329
Gur, Sharon W46
Gurgovits, Stephen J. (Steve) A360
Gurgovits, Stephen J. (Steve) E164
Gurin, Patricia B P34
Gurk, Kevin Mc P67
Gurnani, Roger A870
Gurne, Tanya P531
Gurvitz, Howard A34
Guse, Brad A905
Guse, Brad P694
Gushie, Steve A13
Gusler, Tim P334
Gustafson, Paul A221
Gustafson, Dan A586
Gustafson, Jennifer P577
Gustavson, Timothy B A696
Gutch, Barbara P355
Gutenberger, Thomas P653
Guterman, Neil B. P610
Guth, Amy P170
Gutholc, Robert P508
Guthrie, Jeremy A165
Guthrie, Linda P398
Guthrie, Kevin P398

Guthrie, Chris P615
Gutiahr, Glenn A677
Gutierrez, Jose A85
Gutierrez, Harvey A244
Gutierrez, Carlos A244
Gutierrez, Wanda A474
Gutierrez, Becky A565
Gutierrez, Mauricio A604
Gutierrez, John A729
Gutierrez, Richard P154
Gutierrez, Wanda P262
Gutierrez, Angela P444
Gutierrez, Brian G. P560
Gutierrez, Albert E303
Gutmann, Bernard A620
Gutmann, Amy A812
Gutmann, Amy P607
Gutnick, Michael P. P325
Gutowski, Paul P292
Gutsch, James L. (Jim) A730
Gutter, Ellen P107
Gutteridge, Thomas G. (Tom) P613
Guttery, John A289
Gutting, Gregory J. (Greg) A306
Guttman, Tim G. A59
Guva, Lorie P670
Guy, Doug A484
Guyett, Gregory L. A285
Guyett, Gregory L. E114
Guynn, Kevin P599
Guyot, Pierre A260
Guyot, Hervé W148
Guyse, Clyde A99
Guyton, Jeffrey H. W235
Guzick, David S. P497
Guzick, David S. P642
Guziewicz, Andrew E22
Guzik, Bill A9
Guzik, Bill P4
Guzman, Jennifer A614
Guzman, Andrew T. A860
Guzman, Tanya A872
Guzman, Ramon De P6
Guzman, Andrew T. P656
Guzman, Rafael W133
Guzman, Jorge Andres Saieh W191
Guzman, Douglas A. W310
Guzman-Petter, Teresa P482
Guzy, Edward A532
Guzzardo, Marc P211
Guzzi, Anthony J. (Tony) A294
Gwin, Robert G. (Bob) A63
Gwin, Robert G. E436
Gwinn, Nancy E. P506
Gwithen, Kaye P378
Gwizdala, Lori A. A187
Gwizdala, Lori A. E71
Gwyneth, Jorda A272
Gyland, Kevin P207
Gyles, Jackie P207
Gyurci, John P333
Gyurisin, Margie P546
G--lvez, José Dami--n Bogas W141
G--mez, Eugenio Llorente W6
G-¶nensin, Turgay W377
G-¶rg, Werner W160
G-¶-§men, Mehmet W163
Gélard, Yves Le W143
Généreux, Claude W294
Gérardin, Yann W66
Güney, Turgut W18
Gür, Kaan W18

H

Haack, Michael E112
Haag, Natalie A164
Haag, Donald A631
Haagenson, Deb A171
Haagenson, Deb P100
Haahr, J. Tyler A554
Haahr, J. Tyler E275
Haake, Anne P464
Haake, Dawn E355

Haakenstad, Stein P301
Haaland, Corey L A788
Haan, Taco De A358
Haan, Patti A522
Haan, Luci De P2
Haan, Warren de E385
Haaraoja, Brian A756
Haas, Leo A51
Haas, John A96
Haas, Bernhard A260
Haas, Nancy A575
Haas, Shelly A774
Haas, Mark P. P341
Haas, Jeffrey P439
Haas, Gerard P510
Haas, Herbert K. W164
Haas, Herbert K. W356
Haas-Kogan, Daphne P153
Haase, Joseph A410
Habbit, Anthony A886
Habbit, Anthony E433
Haber, Jack A218
Haber, Rebecca P109
Haber, Daniel A. P590
Haberern, Andrew A214
Haberern, Andrew P128
Haberfield, Patrick A720
Haberfield, Patrick E362
Haberman, Shelley P12
Habermehl, William P408
Habgood, Debbie P157
Habib, Reham A592
Habib, Helen A614
Habib, Hadi P206
Habicht, Kevin B. E293
Habingreither, Robert P563
Hablitzel, Thomas C. A738
Hachigo, Takahiro W172
Hachten, Richard P147
Hacikamiloglu, Mehmet W163
Hackenberg, Amy L. A344
Hackenberg, Amy L. E154
Hacker, Mark S. A570
Hacker, Howard A795
Hacker, Ted P528
Hackerman, Nancy P505
Hackett, William F. (Bill) A235
Hackett, Jim A362
Hackett, Ann A364
Hackett, Steven G. (Steve) A666
Hackett, John A738
Hackett, Steven G. (Steve) P438
Hackett, Sylvia P459
Hackman, Steve A614
Hackman, Jeff E121
Hackney, Candace A146
Hackney, Carol P458
Hackstadt, Kent A339
Hackstadt, Kent E150
Hadad, Henry A147
Hadavi, Judith A649
Haddad, Michael A59
Haddad, Fadi A775
Haddad, Gabriel G. P452
Haddad, Nick P481
Haddad, Ghassan P510
Haddad, Fadi P548
Hadden, Brian A647
Haddock, Ron A173
Haddy, Gary E252
Hadel, Lorie P134
Haden, James E P310
Hader, Jillian A809
Hader, Jillian P584
Hadid, Keith A383
Hadjiliadis, Dennis P241
Hadjisotiriou, Paula N. W253
Hadley, Andrea A857
Hadley, Todd A920
Hadley, David P250
Hadley, Philip A. E140
Hadlock, Harmony P241
Hadsell, Charlie A294
Haeberlein, Samantha A129
Haefele, Alan A655

Haefele, Alan E333
Haefner, Larry A. A211
Haefner, Francis J A276
Haefner, Jeremy A. P464
Haenni, Chris P307
Haessler, Laura A270
Haeussler, Mark A93
Hafeez, Tariq A907
Hafeez, Tariq P696
Hafer, Greg P469
Hafertepen, Eric A489
Haffner, Jon E A221
Haffner, Paul A691
Hafner, Steve A139
Haft, Steven A175
Hafter, Jeffrey M. (Jeff) A122
Hagan, Michael A426
Hagan, Benjamin A628
Hagan, Kevin P216
Hagan, Anna P396
Hagan, Julie P466
Hagan, Michael J. E309
Hagans, Robert R. P1
Hagberg, Robert P227
Hageboeck, Charles R. (Skip) A207
Hagedorn, Michael D. (Mike) A837
Hagel, Shawn R. A666
Hagel, Shawn R. P438
Hagelin, Carl A105
Hagelin, Keith E109
Hagen, Jonathan Hirt A306
Hagen, Thomas B. A306
Hagen, Matt A318
Hagen, Terence D. A472
Hagen, Mary A553
Hagen, Thomas B A641
Hagen, Russell S. A896
Hagen, Kelly P29
Hagen, Mary E P252
Hagen, Bruce P405
Hagen, Thomas B P422
Hagen, Mary E272
Hagens, William P514
Hager, David A. (Dave) A263
Hager, George V. A380
Hager, Tim A448
Hagerman, Douglas M. (Doug) A712
Hagerty, James A880
Hagerty, Thomas E163
Haggard, Keith A474
Haggard, Keith P265
Hagger, Andrew W251
Haggerty, Stephen G. (Steve) A445
Haggerty, Paul A834
Haggerty, Shannon P501
Haghighat, Dennis P535
Hagio, Keiji W260
Hagler, Dan A73
Hagler, Mendel A582
Hagler, Mendel P373
Haglund, Matt A56
Hagner, Nancy A902
Hagner, Nancy P692
Hahey, Joanne P645
Hahl, William A731
Hahl, William E365
Hahn, Heidi A81
Hahn, Gregory A332
Hahn, Terrence S. A429
Hahn, William C. P153
Hahn, Cheri P526
Hahn, Michelle E261
Hai, Zhu W322
Haidamus, Ramzi W266
Haight, Mark A A703
Haijun, Wu W332
Haile, Annette A461
Haile, Kempton C. A813
Haile, Elizabeth P606
Haile, Kempton C. P616
Hailey, Bill A674
Hailey, Fernanda A700
Hailey, Clint A794
Haines, Michelle A115
Haines, Gary A879

Haines, Diana P78
Haines, Kathy P408
Haines, Gerald M. (Gerry) E271
Haines, Michael B. (Mike) E355
Hainey, Chris A616
Hair, Liz P96
Hair, Ken P243
Haire, Gary E219
Hairston, John M. A399
Haise, Olivier A866
Haitaian, Pete E117
Haith, Rosalind W A693
Hajek, Douglas A554
Hajek, Douglas E275
Hak, Seo Kang W180
Hake, Kevin E253
Haken, Jean P137
Hakim, Shazmah A531
Hakim, Dorith A634
Hakim, Veronique P371
Hakim, Hossein P695
Hakimzada, Ahmad P381
Hakso, Chelsea A777
Hakso, Chelsea E393
Halal, Ilan A133
Halamka, John D. D71
Halarnkar, Yuvaraj A478
Halberg, Stuart P196
Halberstadt, Geoffrey L. A151
Halberstadt, Geoffrey L. A152
Halberstadt, Geoffrey L. E48
Halbur, Rita A865
Haldeman, Charles E. (Ed) A721
Hale, Karen A6
Hale, Bernie A59
Hale, Edward A85
Hale, James A103
Hale, Jean R. A227
Hale, Jean R. A228
Hale, Betty A327
Hale, Jordan A765
Hale, Donna P146
Hale, Dana P157
Hale, Philip P299
Hale, Glen P307
Hale, Vicki P361
Hale, Sharon P446
Hale, David F. P452
Hale, Mark S. P488
Hale, Jordan P540
Halepete, Sameer A607
Hales, Kim A604
Hales, Vicky A838
Hales, Randall L. E448
Haley, Jeffrey V. A52
Haley, Chris A322
Haley, Bryan A556
Haley, Timothy A581
Haley, Sarah A644
Haley, Kathleen E119
Halfman, Mark A685
Halford, Philip E P444
Halford, Andy W340
Haliti, Ardian A204
Halkins, Jim A532
Hall, Tom A34
Hall, William (Bill) A35
Hall, Jason A49
Hall, Justin A133
Hall, Jill A137
Hall, Adam A145
Hall, Stephanie A180
Hall, Laura A272
Hall, Michael A335
Hall, Tammy A350
Hall, Charles J. (Chuck) A410
Hall, Veronica M. A413
Hall, Sarah A A441
Hall, Kathleen A461
Hall, Patricia Hemingway A525
Hall, Charlie A537
Hall, John A555
Hall, Ladd R. A605
Hall, William M. (Bill) A620
Hall, Bill A620

A = AMERICAN BUSINESS
E = EMERGING COMPANIES
P = PRIVATE COMPANIES
W = WORLD BUSINESS

Hall, Jodi A641
Hall, J. D. A657
Hall, J D A657
Hall, Leslie (Les) A682
Hall, J. Franklin (Frank) A690
Hall, Andy A693
Hall, O. B. Grayson A700
Hall, Tom A731
Hall, Cynthia A744
Hall, R. Wayne A751
Hall, Paul A759
Hall, Brian A772
Hall, Jack A796
Hall, Kerry L. A800
Hall, Cynthia A811
Hall, Bradley C. A836
Hall, Reggie A851
Hall, Jonathan A878
Hall, Keri A879
Hall, Denise A883
Hall, Justin M. A916
Hall, Steve P21
Hall, Jim P73
Hall, Peggy P109
Hall, Tony P144
Hall, Christopher P182
Hall, Veronica M. P234
Hall, Claudia P242
Hall, Tammy P246
Hall, Mark J P351
Hall, Robert P401
Hall, Jodi P422
Hall, Claude P504
Hall, Spencer P538
Hall, Cynthia P600
Hall, Susan P602
Hall, Kathryn A. P606
Hall, Donna A622
Hall, Ruth P630
Hall, Bryan H. W222
Hall, Adam E46
Hall, Brian E104
Hall, Catherine H. E108
Hall, Tammy E157
Hall, Brian M. E240
Hall, J. Franklin (Frank) E345
Hall, Kari E355
Hall, Tom E365
Hall, R. Wayne E377
Hall, Kerry L. E395
Hallada, Tony P127
Halladay, Tim A390
Halladay, Chris P286
Hallahan, Molly P627
Hallam, Cynthia A885
Hallauer, Paul A904
Hallauer, Paul E442
Hallberg, Joe A34
Hallberg, Cindy A866
Hallberg, Jacqueline P216
Hallberlin, Cindy P216
Halleck, Steve E44
Hallenbeck, Josh A588
Halley, Lisa P239
Hallford, Brad P427
Halliday, Sarah A. A577
Halligan, Sean A593
Halligan, Donald A P312
Halligan, Denise P323
Hallinan, Patrick D. A364
Hallinan, Brian A741
Hallinan, Brian E370
Halliwell, Stephen W217
Hallman, Dwayne D. A430
Hallmark, Michael A446
Hallmark, Jeff P140
Hallmark, Michael E210
Hallock, Kevin F. P143
Halloran, Chris A677

Halloran, Janice P163
Hallworth, Scott A163
Halmy, Christopher A. A35
Halnon, Bill A707
Halnon, William G. (Bill) E101
Halper, Julie A122
Halper, John A464
Halperin, Kenneth J P617
Halpern, Lonnie E47
Halpert, Karen E426
Halpin, Edward D. (Ed) A650
Halpin, Kevin A903
Halpin, Jean P405
Halseth, Donald P305
Halsey, Drew P182
Halsey, Casey S. P256
Halsey, Casey S. P257
Halstead, Mark A175
Halstead, Candace P200
Halstrom, Danielle A147
Halt, Lynn P416
Halter, Patrick G. (Pat) A668
Halter, Michael P. (Mike) A794
Halverson, Thomas A214
Halverson, Bradley A782
Halverson, John P51
Halverson, Thomas A128
Halvin, Fred A432
Halvorson, Bob P344
Haly, Gregg A173
Ham, Ning A480
Hamamoto, Misao W330
Hamano, Wayne Y. A102
Hamano, Wayne Y. A103
Hamaoka, Eiji A664
Hambrecht, Jürgen W55
Hamburg, Marc D. A123
Hamburg, Erin P577
Hamburgh, Rita P85
Hamby, Leigh S. P428
Hamdy, Walid A685
Hamel, Cathy P208
Hameren, Dirk-Jan V A592
Hameren, Dirk-jan Van A593
Hamers, Ralph A. J. G. W187
Hames, Danette R A221
Hamid, Asad A628
Hamill, Laura A61
Hamill, Michael A113
Hamill, Geoffrey S P346
Hamilton, Charles S A140
Hamilton, Booz A A140
Hamilton, Julie A215
Hamilton, Amanda A273
Hamilton, Shelli A407
Hamilton, Joanne G. A434
Hamilton, Scott A449
Hamilton, Jeff A513
Hamilton, Andrew A585
Hamilton, Robin A800
Hamilton, Sam A874
Hamilton, Patrick J A878
Hamilton, Jason A885
Hamilton, Gregg P75
Hamilton, Dennie P284
Hamilton, Andrew P377
Hamilton, Shaya P391
Hamilton, Nikki P460
Hamilton, Theresa P461
Hamilton, Leann P515
Hamilton, Pat P528
Hamilton, Katie P560
Hamilton, Jennifer P620
Hamilton, Mark P664
Hamilton, Scott E213
Hamilton, Robin E396
Hamilton-Chehab, Anne A272
Hamli, Abdulla Ali Obaid Al W130
Hamlin, Phil A452
Hamlin, Scott J. P115
Hamline, Steve P256
Hamline, Steve P257
Hamm, Bradley P398
Hammack, Jeff A775
Hammer, Bonnie A288

Hammer, Doug A458
Hammer, Holly A901
Hammer, Doug P251
Hammer, David P286
Hammer, Holly P692
Hammergren, John H. A546
Hammergren, John H. W235
Hammerstone, Jim P99
Hammes, Eric A2
Hammes, Katherine A530
Hammes, Chris P249
Hammes, Chris P250
Hammock, Gary A101
Hammond, Carol A108
Hammond, Mike A221
Hammond, Jeff A354
Hammond, Harlan A458
Hammond, Marlene A512
Hammond, Scott P105
Hammond, Patti P180
Hammond, Harlan P251
Hammond, Ulysses B. P283
Hammond, James Q P407
Hammond, Michael P412
Hammond, Sally P595
Hammond, Carol E35
Hammond, Jake E216
Hammonds, Kim W123
Hammons, John P1
Hamner, Grace P511
Hamner, R. Steven E268
Hamory, Bruce H. A372
Hamory, Bruce H. P208
Hampson, Chad P261
Hampton, Eve A395
Hampton, Jerry A655
Hampton, Barbara P211
Hampton, Claudia P249
Hampton, Jason P307
Hampton, Philip W158
Hampton, Jerry E333
Hamre, Lasse A449
Hamri, Abdel A683
Hamrock, Joseph (Joe) A594
Han, Bernard L. (Bernie) A270
Han, Grace A565
Han, Marjorie A727
Han, Jenny P3
Han, Joseph P116
Han, John P306
Han, Yunsung P495
Han, Kevin P544
Han, Yoon Gap W179
Han, Sang-Beom W220
Han, J E389
Hanafin, Mark W87
Hanagarth, Heike W121
Hanback, Patricia A140
Hanbury, George L. P398
Hance, James H. (Jim) P267
Hance, Michael L. E167
Hanchett, Edward P213
Hanchey, William A185
Hancock, C. Wayne A228
Hancock, Debbie A408
Hancock, K. Kelly A807
Hancock, Sue A832
Hancock, William P28
Hancock, Todd P119
Hancock, Michele P272
Hancock, Lynne P570
Hancock, K. Kelly P574
Hancox, Steven E390
Hand, Fred A155
Hand, Jason A480
Hand, Tyler A894
Hand, Jack P436
Handanyan, Lynne A648
Handel, Maggie A241
Handler, Jonathan A113
Handlesman, Ralph P695
Handley, Mark A16
Handley, Terry W. A168
Handley, Thomas W. (Tom) A289
Handley, Bill W A481

Handley, Thomas A707
Handley, Teresa A904
Handley, Jack P275
Handley, Teresa E442
Handlon, Carolyn B. A530
Handren, Scott A129
Handt, Scott A508
Handy, Edward O. (Ned) A880
Handy, Christopher E445
Hanes, Tom P281
Hanes, Lesley P471
Haney, Paul R A244
Haney, Matthew A260
Haney, Joe A723
Haney, Annette P134
Haney, Kevin P157
Haney, Susan P435
Haney, Mark P680
Hang, Edward A796
Hangen, Charles A306
Haniel, Franz M. W85
Hanif, Farina A163
Hanigan, Kevin J. A504
Hanigan, Kevin J. E241
Hanighen, John A13
Hanke-baier, Petra A671
Hankey, Brandon P535
Hankins, Anthony P. A443
Hankins, Robert A704
Hankins, Tad P133
Hankins, Deb P627
Hankins, Robert E350
Hankinson, Beverly A244
Hanko, Edward A73
Hanks, W. Bruce A185
Hanks, Jonathan A866
Hanks, Joe P1
Hanks, Lynn P129
Hanks, Jonathan P661
Hanks, Chris E94
Hanley, Doug A120
Hanley, Walter P. A518
Hanley, Joseph R. A794
Hanley, Richard J P146
Hanlon, Crystal A426
Hanlon, Robin P496
Hanlon, Philip J P626
Hanlon, Matt E127
Hanlon, Deborah E132
Hanly, Donna P405
Hann, Michael P334
Hanna, Wade A340
Hanna, Bill A417
Hanna, Nader B P319
Hanna, Jack E61
Hanna, Wade E151
Hannaford, Thomas A441
Hannah, D. Jay A98
Hannah, Joe P297
Hannah, D. Jay E33
Hannah, Robert E51
Hannan, Beth A185
Hannasch, Luann P531
Hannasch, Brian P. W20
Hannay, Robert P172
Hannegan, David A913
Hanneman, Kathryn P469
Hannigan, Anne A507
Hannigan, Anne P288
Hannon, Mary A105
Hannon, Timothy A199
Hannon, Michael J. A659
Hannon, Rita P314
Hanrahan, Ann M A2
Hanrahan, Ann Marie A3
Hanrahan, Tom A449
Hanrahan, Johnathan P402
Hans, Bill P383
Hansberry, Kristin P329
Hansel, Elizabeth A607
Hansel, Henry E193
Hansel, Gary E208
Hanselman, Lisa P682
Hansen, Mike A17
Hansen, John A74

Hansen, J. Michael (Mike) A198
Hansen, Michael A198
Hansen, Russell A201
Hansen, Terry A480
Hansen, Scott A484
Hansen, Janet A645
Hansen, Tim A693
Hansen, Corey A866
Hansen, Craig A885
Hansen, Dennis R. A889
Hansen, Jeffery A920
Hansen, Mike P10
Hansen, John P22
Hansen, James P27
Hansen, Mark P40
Hansen, Jan P92
Hansen, Sherry P94
Hansen, Lynn L P148
Hansen, Darel P233
Hansen, Amanda P268
Hansen, Don P409
Hansen, William P436
Hansen, Dr David P462
Hansen, Jenifer P508
Hansen, Jesper W360
Hansen, Jorgen B. E56
Hansen, Daniel P. E388
Hansford, Lisa P479
Hanson, Breck F. A81
Hanson, Jackson A210
Hanson, Jim A223
Hanson, Rodney D A292
Hanson, Bryan C. A308
Hanson, Bryan A310
Hanson, Victoria A540
Hanson, Bradley C. (Brad) A554
Hanson, Ronald A744
Hanson, Milagros A788
Hanson, Stephen C. P58
Hanson, Victoria P316
Hanson, Gary A. P423
Hanson, Vicki P464
Hanson, Bradley C. (Brad) E275
Hantman, Perla Tabares P602
Hantzinikolaou, George Petros W288
Hanzel, Kevin A304
Happe, Michael J. E441
Happel, Charles T. A319
Haq, Aftab P637
Haque, Nawal P575
Hara, Susumu W200
Hara, Toshiki W301
Hara, Takashi W336
Harada, Craig A201
Harada, Masaaki W28
Harada, Ken W116
Harada, Yuji W235
Harada, Shozo W273
Harada, Hiroya W366
Haran, Edward A721
Harari, Olivier A698
Harayama, Yasuhito W351
Harbarger, Claude W P529
Harbaugh, Todd W392
Harbour, Shawn A838
Harbour, Ron E381
Harchuck, Amanda E140
Harcum, Angie A369
Hardacre, Marilyn A644
Hardeman, Michele A767
Hardeman, Kasonya P23
Harden, Robert A802
Harden, Tim P51
Harden, Billy P141
Harden, Diane P158
Harden, James P325
Harden, Kelly P391
Harden, M C P512
Harden, Robert P562
Harder, Veronica P109
Harder, Andrew J P627
Hardgrove, Ian A2
Hardie, James R. A820
Hardie, Jennifer P306
Hardie, David E185

Hardig, John J. A913
Hardigree, Morris A751
Hardigree, Morris E377
Hardiman, Nathan A513
Hardiman, Kevin A741
Hardiman, Kevin E370
Hardin, Brad A449
Hardin, Marie A811
Hardin, Scott P51
Hardin, Kathrine P482
Hardin, Marie P600
Harding, Bobbi A317
Harding, John D A369
Harding, John A369
Harding, P Russell A509
Harding, James A. (Jim) A727
Harding, Debra A850
Harding, Joe A903
Harding, Lori A920
Harding, Douglas J P53
Harding, Scott P95
Harding, Joe P171
Harding, P Russell P288
Harding, John P339
Harding, Bobbi E142
Hardison, Ann A115
Hardister, Wanda P194
Hardman, Renee A729
Hardman, Scott P396
Hardman, Susan J. P458
Hardnock, Ronald A586
Hardof, Tamir E166
Hardwick, Mark K. A349
Hardwick, Cheryl A441
Hardwick, M Susan P514
Hardwick, Mark K. E156
Hardy, Rhett A101
Hardy, Greg A199
Hardy, Stephen G. A225
Hardy, Karen A446
Hardy, Russ A644
Hardy, James A766
Hardy, Jody A841
Hardy, Marie P71
Hardy, Cody P111
Hardy, Chavonne P181
Hardy, Dana P516
Hardy, Stephen G. E88
Hardy, Karen E210
Hardy, Viann E265
Hardy, Jody E410
Hare, Joshua A201
Hare, Trisha A489
Hare, Diane A702
Hare, Douglas A837
Harford, Simon N. R. P417
Hargadon, Donald A902
Hargadon, Donald P693
Hargenes, Donna P260
Hargens, Donna P260
Hargett, Carla A693
Hargis, Michael A532
Hargis, Jaron A614
Hargraves, Gordon P244
Hargrove, Robin S. (Rob) A567
Hargrove, Sirena P181
Hargrove, Karen P375
Harhai, Brian A774
Harik, Mario A. A913
Harika, Michelle A133
Haring, Don P550
Harion, Jean Marc W278
Hariri, Abdi A501
Harker, Patrick T. A325
Harker, Victoria A442
Harker, Timothy A729
Harker, Patrick T P641
Harkey, Jean A412
Harkey, Jean E192
Harkins, Joseph A328
Harkins, Michael A461
Harkins, Tara A513
Harkins, Elaine A537
Harkins, Bonnie P135
Harkins, Charles F. E209

Harkness, David C. A910
Harkness, Charles L. P242
Harlacher, Donna A522
Harless, Lisa A700
Harless, Donna P97
Harley, April A282
Harlovic, Michael P23
Harlow, David R. A98
Harlow, Bryce A175
Harlow, Tracy A878
Harlow, Susan P214
Harlow, Angela P231
Harlow, David R. E33
Harm, Neal A115
Harman, David A195
Harman, Phil A762
Harman, Jill A878
Harmeling, John T A19
Harmening, Jeffrey L. A377
Harmeson, Dan P549
Harmon, Gordon A287
Harmon, Torrey A685
Harmon, Scott A866
Harmon, Georgann P108
Harmon, Gordon P174
Harmon, Alexandra P428
Harmon, Brad P478
Harmon, Lori P500
Harmon, Scott P661
Harms, Timothy W A261
Harms, Brian K A685
Harms, Albert P528
Harms, Ole W390
Harn, Jerry W154
Harned, Chrystine P464
Harness, Carl P144
Harnett, James A489
Harney, Michael A200
Harney, Earl Reginald P592
Haro, Dianeysis A795
Haroutunian, Karen P624
Harp, Mohamed A526
Harp, Sarah A872
Harpenau, Keith A A712
Harper, Sean E. A61
Harper, Hamilton A246
Harper, Chad A324
Harper, Gant A350
Harper, Craig A439
Harper, Lori A442
Harper, Tom A508
Harper, Ryan A585
Harper, Gregory P183
Harper, David P361
Harper, Ryan P377
Harper, Erin P422
Harper, Raymond P469
Harper, C. Gregory (Greg) W138
Harper, Jane E144
Harper, Gant E157
Harpham, Deena E101
Harpole, Eileen P60
Harra, Robert A901
Harra, Robert P692
Harralson, Jefferson L. A844
Harralson, Beverly P528
Harralson, Jefferson L. E412
Harreld, J. Bruce P611
Harrell, John A108
Harrell, Randy A199
Harrell, James A. A750
Harrell, Robert A894
Harrell, Colleen P329
Harrelson, Ryland L. A823
Harrelson, Katie P84
Harrelson, Gary P108
Harriman, Sherry A878
Harriman, Bob P59
Harriman, Morril P640
Harring, Jeff A693
Harrington, Ben A98
Harrington, Michael W. (Mike) A151
Harrington, Michael W. (Mike) A152
Harrington, Dennis A307
Harrington, Barbara J. A339

Harrington, Michael J. A353
Harrington, Michael J. A511
Harrington, Jeffrey A677
Harrington, Jeff A677
Harrington, Michael A700
Harrington, Parker A774
Harrington, Liam A913
Harrington, John P57
Harrington, Jeff P114
Harrington, John P200
Harrington, Darrell P226
Harrington, Ben E33
Harrington, Michael W. (Mike) E48
Harrington, Barbara J. E150
Harrington, Tony E312
Harris, Scott A33
Harris, David A40
Harris, Stephen A55
Harris, Angelee J. A97
Harris, Mitchell E. A105
Harris, Michael A122
Harris, Timothy A129
Harris, Michael A190
Harris, Isaiah (Ike) A195
Harris, Diane A201
Harris, Kurt A214
Harris, Crystal A218
Harris, Benjamin A247
Harris, David G. A263
Harris, Timothy K. (Tim) A344
Harris, Julie A344
Harris, Tim A344
Harris, Nigel A362
Harris, Jeffrey A478
Harris, Paul N. A489
Harris, Jeff A508
Harris, Jennifer A549
Harris, Yvette A558
Harris, Stephen A565
Harris, Brenda A611
Harris, Jeff A631
Harris, James A643
Harris, Michael A673
Harris, Mike A673
Harris, Timothy P. A676
Harris, John D. A694
Harris, Todd A700
Harris, Randy A704
Harris, Paul V A710
Harris, Henry (Sandy) A736
Harris, Rick A742
Harris, Mark A777
Harris, C. Martin A807
Harris, Charles J. (Chuck) A823
Harris, Jenna A837
Harris, Donald A844
Harris, Jeff M. A881
Harris, Daniel W. A890
Harris, Todd A920
Harris, Chelene P3
Harris, Bill P26
Harris, Brianne P28
Harris, Joan P39
Harris, Holly P41
Harris, Kurt P128
Harris, Gene T P133
Harris, Glenna G P159
Harris, Matthew P168
Harris, David P173
Harris, Sally P237
Harris, Delora P262
Harris, Lisa P285
Harris, Mark A. P303
Harris, Tracy P344
Harris, Phil P398
Harris, Kimberly P410
Harris, Ron P453
Harris, Cheryl P461
Harris, Richard P. (Rick) P489
Harris, Henry (Sandy) P492
Harris, John P493
Harris, Nancy P498
Harris, William P529
Harris, C. Martin P574
Harris, Jeff P617

A = AMERICAN BUSINESS
E = EMERGING COMPANIES
P = PRIVATE COMPANIES
W = WORLD BUSINESS

Harris, Ila P646
Harris, James T. P653
Harris, Ann P663
Harris, Daniel W. P684
Harris, Frederick E26
Harris, Angelee J. E32
Harris, Matthew E70
Harris, Benjamin E103
Harris, Timothy K. (Tim) E154
Harris, Julie E154
Harris, Tim E154
Harris, John E219
Harris, Michael W. E226
Harris, Jennifer E270
Harris, Randy E351
Harris, Rick E372
Harris, Mark E393
Harris, Donald E412
Harris-johnson, Ann A902
Harris-johnson, Ann P692
Harrision, Jimmy A423
Harrison, Andrew R. A28
Harrison, Christopher A117
Harrison, Miranda A131
Harrison, Gregory A140
Harrison, Suzan F. A218
Harrison, Olga A244
Harrison, Leslie A360
Harrison, Gator A449
Harrison, A. Marc A458
Harrison, Winifred A520
Harrison, Nico A593
Harrison, Peter A616
Harrison, Dan A622
Harrison, Matthew A644
Harrison, Larry A659
Harrison, Kelton A743
Harrison, Jason A769
Harrison, Robert A788
Harrison, A. Marc A807
Harrison, Jason A838
Harrison, Bo A839
Harrison, Linda A912
Harrison, John P35
Harrison, Robert S. P143
Harrison, William P149
Harrison, Fonda P201
Harrison, Kimberly P227
Harrison, A. Marc P251
Harrison, William P324
Harrison, Dean P397
Harrison, A. Marc P574
Harrison, John C P584
Harrison, Marianne W232
Harrison, Leslie E164
Harrison, Steven B. E288
Harrison, Kelton E372
Harrison, Bo E409
Harrison, M. Ponder E11
Harrod, Tricia A465
Harrod, Lawrence A857
Harrod, Laurence A857
Harrod, James P469
Harrsch, Cherrayl P446
Harry, Ellen P189
Harry, Roger P376
Harsch, Pamela A524
Harshaw, Andy W30
Harshbarger, Catherine A111
Harshbarger, Mark A725
Harshbarger, Catherine P56
HARSHBARGER, RUTH P536
Hart, Tom A51
Hart, Shannon A101
Hart, Craig A127
Hart, Kris A157
Hart, Randolph A234
Hart, Angela A351
Hart, Kevin A375

Hart, Philip A382
Hart, Michele A611
Hart, Kevin A631
Hart, Mark J. A634
Hart, Laura A685
Hart, R. Rick A704
Hart, Sharon E. Donovan A766
Hart, Craig A835
Hart, Brett J. A846
Hart, Gregory L. (Greg) A846
Hart, Michael P45
Hart, Harold Sam Ray P111
Hart, Randolph P139
Hart, Kay P218
Hart, Carolyn P269
Hart, Richard H. P294
Hart, Joy P385
Hart, Charles P453
Hart, Charles E P456
Hart, Sharon Y. P464
Hart, Trellis P538
Hart, Brent P623
Hart, Tonya P694
Hart, Stephen P. W50
Hart, Eric H. E29
Hart, Jennifer E127
Hart, Angela E158
Hart, Renee E269
Hart, Michele E313
Hart, Charles E. E336
Hart, Charles E. E337
Hart, R. Rick E350
Hart, Brett E445
Harte, Regina P2
Hartenback, Ms Jaime P133
Harter, Scott A29
Harter, Scott E9
Hartert, Daniel W56
Hartery, Nicky W112
Hartford, James M P676
Harti, Mohamed A649
Hartigan, Stephen A108
Hartigan, Matthew D A709
Hartigan, Eric P554
Hartigan, Stephen E36
Hartill, Caroline A. E360
Hartin, Curtis A165
Hartings, Benjamin J A350
Hartings, Benjamin A350
Hartings, Justin P674
Hartings, Benjamin J E157
Hartings, Benjamin E157
Hartl, Thomas A568
Hartley, Karen A56
Hartley, Jerry A332
Hartley, Cynthia A751
Hartley, Lisa A862
Hartley, Sarah P416
Hartley, Cynthia E378
Hartley, Lisa E419
Hartlieb, Jim A340
Hartlieb, Jim E151
Hartling, Earle P145
Hartman, Bret A199
Hartman, Art A772
Hartman, Richard T. (Rick) A819
Hartman, Michael A912
Hartman, Diane P64
Hartman, Matt P207
Hartman, Scott V P279
Hartman, Lynda P290
Hartman, Donna P295
Hartman, Matt P393
Hartman, Susan P526
Hartman, Philip S. (Phil) P560
Hartmann, Ronald A359
Hartmann, William L. (Bill) A489
Hartmann, Margot A635
Hartmann, Eric J P102
Hartmann, Margot P419
Hartmann, Peter P700
Hartmann, Judith W143
Hartmann, Richard E4
Hartmann, Nancy E199
Hartnett, John R. A450

Hartnett, Chad P228
Hartnett, W.J. (Bill) W184
Hartnett, Thomas G. E1
Hartnett, Michael J. E347
Hartog, Byran Den P453
Harton, H. Lynn A844
Harton, H. Lynn E412
Hartong, Hendrik A10
Hartpence, Melissa P629
Hartsell, Kelly A744
Hartsfield, Keith A436
Hartsfield, Russell A800
Hartsfield, Russell E396
Hartshorn, Michael J. A715
Hartshorne, Toinette P18
Hartung, John R. (Jack) A193
Hartung, Maggie A530
Hartung, Stefan W70
Hartwick, George P P144
Harty, Harriet K. A33
Harty, Thomas H. (Tom) E272
Hartz, Gregory J. A820
Hartz, Scott S. W232
Hartz, Jan E161
Hartzel, Cynthia E46
Hartzell, Robert A29
Hartzell, Steve A784
Hartzell, Robert E9
Hartzer, Brian C. W395
Haruki, Warren H. E264
Harvell, Glen A530
Harvey, J Dale A46
Harvey, Staci A163
Harvey, David C. A248
Harvey, Steven A468
Harvey, Thomas H. A542
Harvey, Anna L. A585
Harvey, Gene A599
Harvey, Zelton A754
Harvey, Justin A784
Harvey, J Dale P32
Harvey, Deborah P35
Harvey, Peter P192
Harvey, Steven P252
Harvey, Anna L. P377
Harvey, Len P554
Harvey, Gayla P631
Harvey, Thomas H. E267
Harvey, Zelton E380
Harvill, Beth P157
Harvill, Howard P204
Harvill, Terry P340
Harwell, David A704
Harwell, David E351
Harwood, Randall R. A394
Harwood, Darrell W. A833
Hasan, Muhammad A480
Hasan, Ben A878
Hasanovic, Adnan P290
Hasbrouck, Margaret P26
Hascall, Cynthia P663
Hasegawa, Lise A534
Hasegawa, Takuro W237
Hasegawa, Koji W241
Hasegawa, Yoshisuke W326
Hasegawa, Yasuchika W355
Hasenkamp, Michael A302
Hasenkamp, Michael E128
Haser, H. William A796
Hashimoto, Takeshi W246
Hashimoto, Takashi W250
Hashimoto, Masahiro W344
Hashmoto, Eiji W263
Haskew, Kevin A620
Haskins, James P650
Hasner, Adam E175
Hasold-Schilter, Marianne W50
Hasper, Greg A663
Hassan, Alegra P572
Hasse, William A P359
Hasselbarth, William C. P17
Hasselbarth, William P18
Hassell, Gerald L. A105
Hassett, Joseph (John) A65
Hassett, Tom A264

Hassett, Gerry W161
Hassfurther, Thomas A. (Tom) A631
Hassim, Sharkila A398
Hassing, Ben A878
Hassler, Gregg A881
Hassler, Robert P688
Hassler, Paul E. E324
Hasson, Marsha P682
Hast, Marty A730
Haste, Jeffrey T P144
Hastey, Robin P378
Hasting, Reed A581
Hastings, Scott A107
Hastings, Warren A165
Hastings, Lee A266
Hastings, Reed A580
Hastings, Brian P648
Hastings, Scott E34
Hastings, Mark E172
Hasty, Greg A902
Hasty, Greg P692
Haswell, Mike A710
Hatch, Steven A406
Hatch, Jessica A532
Hatch, Sean P101
Hatch, Nathan O. P673
Hatcher, Doreen P269
Hatcher, Michael E76
Hatfield, Josh E208
Hathaisattayapong, Rewat W88
Hathaway, Scot C. A275
Hathaway, Stephen J P235
Hathaway, William R P345
Hathi, Neesha A728
Hattem, Marita P48
Hattori, Atsushi W201
Hatzmann, Dirk A204
Hau, Robert W A355
Haubenstock, Michael E123
Haudrich, John A628
Hauenstein, Glen W. A261
Hauersperger, Joe A384
Hauersperger, Joe E176
Haug, Laural P146
Haug, Jon E. W360
Haugen, Robert W. A249
Haugen, John A377
Haugen, Juliemarie A788
Haugh, Samantha A97
Haugh, Tom P199
Haugh, Samantha E32
Haught, Deanna A561
Haught, Jim A891
Haught, Deanna E278
Haught, Jim E434
Haugli, Brian A402
Hauk, Jeff E121
Haulle, Susie P699
Haulman, Jean A861
Haulman, Jean P658
Haun, Michael A135
Haun, Michael P78
Haun, Dennis M P125
Haupert, Sue A847
Haupert, John M P217
Haupt, Charlotte P343
Haupt, Helen P576
Hauser, Betsy A160
Hauser, Debbie P20
Hauser, Mark J P59
Hauser, Kevin P462
Hauser, Betsy E55
Haushalter, Todd A558
Hausmann, Jena P114
Hautman, Milla A855
Havalad, Suresh P8
Havard, Robert A476
Havard, Sheila A770
Havelock, Kevin W381
Havelock, Kevin W383
Havemann, David P486
Havener, Wendy A105
Haverkamp, Michael F P72
Haverlock, Scott A73
Havern, Lindsay A649

Haversang, Ed A514
Haverstick, Donald A901
Haverstick, Donald P692
Haverty-Stacke, Dylan A49
Havey, Adam R. E121
Havill, Kathy A614
Havrilak, Sharon A406
Haw, Kate P506
Hawes, Adrienne A907
Hawes, Adrienne E446
Hawk, Patty P444
Hawken, Jeffrey C. E232
Hawkins, Jennifer A49
Hawkins, James jay A190
Hawkins, Jay james A190
Hawkins, Tobin A195
Hawkins, Steve J. A348
Hawkins, Jay A559
Hawkins, Scott A676
Hawkins, Randall A693
Hawkins, Mark J. A723
Hawkins, Duane A758
Hawkins, Randy A857
Hawkins, Jeff A865
Hawkins, J. Michael A873
Hawkins, Rodney A903
Hawkins, Darren D. A916
Hawkins, Phil P2
Hawkins, Robert P136
Hawkins, Linda P143
Hawkins, Lisa P247
Hawkins, Ronald E P290
Hawkins, Sheri P499
Hawkins, J. Michael P668
Hawkins, Barbara P677
Hawkins, John E280
Hawks, Howard L. P78
Hawksley, Lee A723
Hawley, Chad P566
Hawley, Austin E106
Haworth, Joanne A408
Haworth, Steve P439
Haworth, Albert E336
Haws, Dr Lolli P451
Hawthorne, Jon A841
Hawthorne, Jon P633
Hay, Lewis (Lew) A357
Hay, Niall A643
Hayakawa, Shigeru W374
Hayashi, Madelyn A667
Hayashi, Toshihiro W156
Hayashi, Takeshi W261
Hayashi, Takuji W324
Hayashi, Madelyn E336
Hayashida, Eiji W197
Hayden, John A701
Hayden, Don P441
Hayden, Michael W363
Hayden, Jeff E59
Hayden, Gerard M. (Gerry) E190
Hayden, James E268
Hayden-Cook, Melissa P498
Hayden-Pugh, Beverly P663
Haydon, John B. A687
Haydon, Emily P398
Hayek, Aron A493
Hayek, Andrew P. P485
Hayes, John A. A96
Hayes, Rejji P. A210
Hayes, Traci A264
Hayes, James A324
Hayes, Maria Reeves A460
Hayes, Robin A474
Hayes, Deborah A513
Hayes, Stephen A518
Hayes, Joseph A584
Hayes, Bennie A624
Hayes, Holly A693
Hayes, Christina A788
Hayes, Thomas P. (Tom) A834
Hayes, Todd M. A851
Hayes, Gregory J. A854
Hayes, Janet M. A901
Hayes, Ricky P43
Hayes, Heidi P282

Hayes, Stephen P293
Hayes, George P321
Hayes, Lara P329
Hayes, Rejji P340
Hayes, Joseph P376
Hayes, William (Billy) P395
Hayes, Paul P446
Hayes, Sharon P525
Hayes, Margaret P526
Hayes, Deborah (Debbie) P572
Hayes, Michael P610
Hayes, Adrienne P665
Hayes, Marcia P672
Hayes, John E349
Hayford, Michael D A578
Haygood, Vanessa P594
Hayhurst, James B. A843
Hayhurst, Tabatha P635
Hayhurst, James B. E411
Hayles, Carol A201
Hayley, Kathryn A351
Hayley, Kathryn E159
Haymond, Sherri A537
Hayne, Bill P575
Haynes, Brian A701
Haynes, Jim P436
Haynes, Jenna P498
Haynes, Terry E432
Haynie, Tammy A201
Haynie, Mary P700
Hayon, Jack P175
Haye, Carolyn A207
Hays, Ed A215
Hays, Von A221
Hays, Paul A235
Hays, Andrew A654
Hays, Jerry P154
Hays, Chuck P303
Hays, Charles P303
Hays, Sara L. E19
Hays, Anthony E357
Haytaian, Peter D. A67
Haythornthwaite, Richard (Rick) W87
Hayton, Fred A166
Hayward, Jeffery R. A315
Hayward, Michelle A767
Hayward, Lani A839
Hayward, Brent P357
Hayward, Pierre P641
Hayward, Anthony B. (Tony) W159
Hayward, Lani E409
Haywood, Jonathan A898
Hazard, Sharon A817
Hazelip, Rex P275
Hazelton, Brian E441
Hazelwood, Lauris N P486
Hazen, Samuel N. (Sam) A410
Hazen, Samuel N P207
Hazen, Terezia P285
Hazen, Dave P451
Hazen, Andrea P451
Hazen, Verna P464
Hazinski, Michael P173
Hazlin, John A218
He, Dennis A777
He, Yong W175
He, Dennis E393
Heacock, David A. A275
Head, Greg A272
Head, Patricia P211
Head, Julie P627
Headley, Todd E342
Heady, Christopher (Chris) A132
Heafner, Steve E15
Heagler, Brian A489
Heald, Heather A56
Healey, Tracey A67
Healton, Cheryl G. A585
Healton, Cheryl G. P377
Healy, Luke A244
Healy, Denis A359
Healy, Russell A443
Healy, Peter P71
Healy, Dan P188
Healy, Anthony J. W251

Healy, Christine E46
Heaney, Joe A555
Heaney, Dan P445
Heap, Adam A866
Heap, Adam P661
Heard, Mike A213
Hearne, Simon A3
Heart, Cherri A166
Hearty, Stephen A600
Heasley, Teena A489
Heater, Nicole A703
Heath, Don A81
Heather, Roach A744
Heatherington, Jeff P191
Heatley, Robert S P362
Heaton, Gregory L. (Greg) A360
Heaton, Tracey A874
Heaton, Keith P512
Heaton, Gregory L. (Greg) E164
Hebard, Barbara P626
Hebard, George E116
Hebda, Bernard A. P494
Hebel, Daniel A34
Heberle, Mr Ron P293
Hebert, Amy A177
Hebert, Thomas A192
Hebert, Curtis A300
Hebert, Jason A832
Hebert, Kevin P343
Hebert, Darla P630
Hecht, William F. P287
Hechtner, Mike A214
Hechtner, Mike P128
Heck, Christopher B. (Chris) A281
Heck, John P604
Heckenkemper, Carol P126
Hecker, John A489
Hecker, Rob A863
Hecker, Cynthia P396
Heckler, Mark A. A541
Heckler, Mark A. E266
Heckman, Michael P639
Heckman, Dave P641
Hedad, Don P538
Hedblom, Helena W36
Hedgebeth, Reggie A526
Hedgebeth, Reginald D A526
Hedgebeth, Reginald D. (Reggie) A758
Hedgebeth, Reginald D. (Reggie) P519
Hedges, Kathleen P525
Hedgespeth, Dave A552
Hedgespeth, Dave P328
Hedin, Maria W352
Hedman, Britt A507
Hedman, Britt P288
Hedrick, Jerry P183
Hedstrom, Jeff A919
Hee, Lee Won W179
Heeg, Amy P531
Heenan, Regina A292
Heenan, Palmer T. A356
Heenan, David A. E264
Heer, John P388
Heersink, Ewout R. (Eve) W277
Hees, Bernardo V. A494
Heeter, David A572
Heeter, David P359
Hefel, Victoria A847
Hefferen, Dresdyn A659
Heffernan, Edward J. (Ed) A32
Heffernan, Rick A827
Heffernan, John H P53
Heffler, Mava K. A294
Hefflinger, Jeff A85
Heffner, Art A40
Heffner, Steve A173
Hefford, Rod A96
Heft, Adam A390
Hefter, Marcia Z. A145
Hefter, Marcia Z. E46
Hegarty, Kevin P. A698
Hegarty, Barry A725
Hegarty, Kevin P. P456
Hegarty, David J. E366
Hegde, Sunil P420

Hegde, Ashok W274
Hegde, Sharath S. E216
Hegele, Steve A332
Heger, Mary P. A42
Heggen, Elmar W62
Hegi, Maria A741
Hegi, Maria E370
Hegwood, Neil A564
Hehn, Gunther P422
Heidel, Cindy A328
Heidenreich, Julia A423
Heider, John P51
Heidrich, Kevin E290
Heidrick, Richard A225
Heidrick, Richard E88
Heidt, Alex A405
Heidtbrink, Scott P271
Heier, Timothy C. A728
Heijden, R. L. P. J. van der W199
Heijmen, Jos A906
Heikes, Parker A223
Heil, Tim A258
Heil, Stephen E298
Heilbrunn, Greg E209
Heilman, Todd E P414
Heilman, Chandra P. P506
Heim, Chris W780
Heim, Michael A. A787
Heim, Deborah P110
Heiman, Scott A500
Heiman, Scott E237
Heimburg, Sue Von A712
Heimes, Terry J. A579
Hein, Jon A81
Hein, Leland J. (Lee) A318
Hein, Mike P631
Heine, Robert A511
Heine, Chris E273
Heineke, Emily A P213
Heineke, Wendy E326
Heinemann, S Blake A773
Heinen, James A693
Heinrich, Daniel A96
Heinrich, Robert A603
Heinrich, Bonnie P184
Heinrich, Matt P207
Heinrich, Kerry P294
Heinrich, Robert P399
Heinrich, Beth A P410
Heinsen, Kerstin A767
Heinson, Christopher D. E364
Heintz, Elizabeth B P476
Heintzman, David P. A772
Heinz, Greg A493
Heinz, Michael W55
Heinze, Bradley A677
Heinzelmann, Nick A513
Heinzmann, David W. E247
Heise, Arthur G. (Art) A81
Heise, John M A342
Heise, Angela L. A505
Heise, Rus P160
Heisel, David A806
Heiser, Aaron A593
Heisey, John L. P104
Heishman, Dennis P. A614
Heisler, Tom A251
Heismeyer, Cindy A204
Heit, Mark P318
Heitin, Mark A818
Heitzman, Greg E129
Heizer, Gabriela P196
Heizmann, Jochem W390
Hejl, Jeremy A333
Helber, Andreas W60
Held, Michael A323
Helderman, Jessica A502
Helding, Erik M. A213
Heldman, Susan P486
Hele, John C. R. A555
Heleen, Mark L. A575
Heleen, Mark L A575
Helf, Pete E257
Helfrich, Jackie A915
Helgerson, Bryce P285

A = AMERICAN BUSINESS
E = EMERGING COMPANIES
P = PRIVATE COMPANIES
W = WORLD BUSINESS

Hell, Barbara P255
Hellebust, Solveig W129
Heller, Gary A175
Heller, Stephanie A323
Heller, Joseph A332
Heller, Richard A400
Heller, Paul G. A440
Heller, Marc A589
Heller, Jeffrey A597
Heller, David A752
Heller, Robert A P207
Heller, Donald E. P341
Heller, Ellen P565
Heller, Andra P628
Heller, Donald E P654
Helleyer, Nancy P473
Hellige, Joseph P299
Hellighausen, John P553
Helling, Larry J. A683
Helling, Larry J. E341
Hellman, Peter A113
Hellman, Lisa A493
Hellman, Thomas A526
Hellman, Melissa P481
Hellmann, Cindy A115
Hellmann, John C. (Jack) E171
Helm, Robert A374
Helm, James A532
Helm, Lucy Lee A762
Helm, Larry L. A800
Helm, Scott P158
Helm, Cathy P506
Helm, Larry L. E396
Helman, Mark A769
Helman, Karen P503
Helmandollar, Carole P113
Helmer, Rob P356
Helmerick, Shelley A728
Helmers, David A196
Helmers, Maik D. E242
Helmick, Teresa E139
Helminiak, Deanna A81
Helmreich, Anne P560
Helmreich, William E22
Helmrich, Klaus W331
Helms, Lloyd W. (Bill) A304
Helms, Heather A700
Helms, Tabitha A844
Helms, Tabitha E412
Helsel, Christopher A391
Helt, Peter A105
Helton, Marianna A97
Helton, Cary A243
Helton, Marianna E32
Heltzel, Andrew P418
Hemade, Sagar A796
Hemani, Sul A109
Hemani, Sul E36
Hembree, Sean P78
Hembry, Daryl A489
Hemelryck, Tom Van A879
Heminger, Gary R. A527
Heminger, Mark P107
Hemink, David C. E56
Hemker, David J. (Dave) A501
Hemker, Bradd P519
Hemler, Alan J A648
Hemmer, Vince P636
Hemmingsen, Claus V. W1
Hempen, Rande A165
Hemphill, Stuart R. A752
Hemphill, Kirk A814
Hemphill, Norine P114
Hemphill, Kirk P616
Hemphill, J. Bruce W275
Hempton, Sue A353
Hempton, Sue E159
Hemsley, Stephen J. A855
Hemsley, Mark E62

Henak, William S. A789
Henbest, Robert P183
Henchke, Colleen A818
Henck, Dan P472
Henderschedt, Robert A14
Henderschedt, Robert P7
Hendershot, Janeth A500
Hendershot, Janeth E238
Hendershot, Dawn E359
Henderson, Brantley A162
Henderson, Rebecca A182
Henderson, Terrance A221
Henderson, Theodore A270
Henderson, Douglas A333
Henderson, Richie A439
Henderson, Dexter A461
Henderson, Paula A522
Henderson, Frederick A531
Henderson, Howard A583
Henderson, Leah A674
Henderson, Scott A885
Henderson, David T. A890
Henderson, Roger P21
Henderson, Michael W P45
Henderson, Carolina P81
Henderson, Bruce A P157
Henderson, Cecilia P199
Henderson, Jim P218
Henderson, Rosoloc P243
Henderson, Jane P385
Henderson, Carol P487
Henderson, Joe P497
Henderson, Vennie P498
Henderson, Harry P498
Henderson, Phillip P548
Henderson, David T. P684
Henderson, Ralph S. E17
Henderson, Graeme W. E57
Henderson, Rebecca E63
Henderson, Joe E77
Henderson, Marsha S. E135
Henderson, Rebecca E213
Henderson, James P. (Jimmy) E382
Henderson, Michael E408
Hendon, Terry A227
Hendren, Mike A655
Hendren, Mike E333
Hendrick, Bryan A705
Hendrick, Bryan E352
Hendricks, Tracy A49
Hendricks, Melissa A339
Hendricks, Thomas A463
Hendricks, Steve A720
Hendricks, Martin A796
Hendricks, Joan C. A812
Hendricks, William A. (Andy) P495
Hendricks, Joan C. P607
Hendricks, Melissa E150
Hendricks, Steve E362
Hendricksen, Matthew A296
Hendricksen, Theresa P138
Hendrickson, Nancy A818
Hendrickson, Karen P511
Hendrie, Scott P568
Hendrikse, Pieter A478
Hendrikse, Danny A649
Hendrix, Ron A331
Hendrix, Heidi A602
Hendrix, Dean P344
Hendrix, Ron E148
Hendry, Andrew A218
Heneberry, Richard A34
Heneghan, Daniel A405
Heneghan, Steven P590
Heng, Ming W160
Henigin, Susan A342
Henk, Michael A651
Henk, Michael P426
Henke, Dean G P247
Henkel, Herbert A3
Henkel, Robert J A80
Henkel, Robert J P47
Henkel, Lisa P281
Henkes, Scott A835
Henley, Robert W. A608

Henley, Jeffrey O A624
Henley, Tim A770
Henley, Kyle P651
Henley, Joel E281
Henn, Anthony A196
Henn, Vicki C. A659
Henneberger, Mark A878
Henneberry, Alanna P632
Hennegan, Neal P476
Hennelly, Patricia P296
Hennessey, Ruth P529
Hennessy, John L. A507
Hennessy, Ray A683
Hennessy, James J. P200
Hennessy, John L. P288
Hennessy, Michael J. P563
Hennessy, Michael P563
Hennessy, Leslie P653
Hennessy, Neil J E193
Henney, Cheryl P190
Hennigan, Mike A527
Henning, Paul A81
Henning, James P. (Jim) A281
Henning, Brian A614
Henning, Donna P134
Henninger, Tadd J A665
Henrich, David A862
Henrich, David E419
Henrichsen, Kim A458
Henrichsen, Kim P251
Henrickson, Pamela Q. P647
Henrie, Michelle P2
Henriksson, Mats W154
Henrot, Fran-§ois W303
Henry, Maurice A82
Henry, Mildred A115
Henry, Jeff A175
Henry, Lori A327
Henry, Maria A377
Henry, Gene A408
Henry, Brian A459
Henry, Maria G. A490
Henry, Christopher A558
Henry, Peter B. A585
Henry, Jerome A614
Henry, Tong A685
Henry, Colin A691
Henry, Dan A823
Henry, Maurice P49
Henry, Mark P149
Henry, Dane P157
Henry, Philip P233
Henry, Richard A. (Rich) P318
Henry, Peter B. P377
Henry, Jake P472
Henry, April P511
Henry, Brent L. P606
Henry, Stephanie P619
Henry, Lisa P674
Henry, Mike W50
Henry, Mike W63
Henry, Mike W64
Henry, Kenneth R. (Ken) W251
Henry, Pierre W334
Henry, Michael E107
Henry, Faye E147
Henry, Todd E415
Henry, David E426
Henseler, Glenn D A695
Henshall, David E248
Henshaw, Carrie A316
Henshaw, Vern P27
Henshaw, Carrie E141
Hensing, John A111
Hensing, John P56
Henslee, Gregory L. (Greg) A609
Hensley, Robin T A417
Hensley, Scott A599
Hensley, Jennifer A726
Hensley, Roger P47
Hensley, Bruce P332
Hensley, Richard A. P334
Hensley, Harvey P469
Henson, Curtis A25
Henson, Christopher L. (Chris) A115

Henson, Mark A591
Henson, Erica A878
Henson, Meghan A. A913
Henson, Mark A920
Henson, Curtis P15
Henson, Thomas O P602
Henson, Glenda P673
Henstock, Mariko P80
Hentzen, Peter P638
Henzel, Alexandra P292
Hepburn, Cc A496
Hepburn, Christopher P. (Chris) E404
Heperi, Vernon L. P83
Hepner, Adrian E113
Heppenstall, C. Talbot A859
Heppenstall, C. Talbot P652
Hepworth, Simon W78
Herbeck, Tracy P348
Herbek, Gene N P369
Herbel, Vern D. A822
Herbel, Susie P167
Herber, Christie P478
Herberg, James P408
Herbert, Dennis A222
Herbert, Toni A269
Herbert, James H. A353
Herbert, James H. A354
Herbert, Courtney A522
Herbert, Greg P50
Herbert, James P165
Herbert, William NP P181
Herbert, Peter N. P698
Herbert, Clayton W348
Herbert, James L. E299
Herbes, William F. (Bill) E29
Herbes, Bill E29
Herbst, Jeff A607
Herbst, Gary P271
Herbst, Lawrence P578
Herbst-brady, Elizabeth A872
Herd, Robin P435
Herd, Dietrich W140
Herde, Patrick A175
Herde, Carl G. P58
Herdener, Anthony M P391
Herder, Karla A454
Herdiech, Edward K. (Ed) E248
Herdina, Joe P579
Heredia, Beatriz P241
Hereford, James P538
Herena, Monique R. A105
Herencia, Roberto R. A336
Hereng, Patrick W372
Heritage, Brad E306
Herlehy, Ann Harie P22
Herlin, Robert S. E137
Herling, Alfred W123
Hermacinski, Mark A547
Hermacinski, Mark P319
Herman, Mark I. A211
Herman, James A519
Herman, Robert A. (Bob) A653
Herman, Matthew A654
Herman, Linda P144
Herman, JoAnne P211
Herman, Jeff P343
Herman, Amy P505
Herman, Jay P619
Herman, Lisa P630
Hermance, Frank A836
Hermandev-Lichto, Javier P510
Hermann, Christopher A330
Hermann, Valérie A691
Hermann, Steve P49
Hermann, Sandy P343
Hermann, Alex W326
Hermel, Oren A855
Hermiz, Laith M. E7
Hermon, Christopher J. A816
Hermonat, Karl A855
Hermosillo-Alca, Karla P550
Hern, John F O P371
Hernandez, John A108
Hernandez, Cynthia A201
Hernandez, Abdon A235

Hernandez, Carlos M A358
Hernandez, Patrice A414
Hernandez, Teresita A438
Hernandez, Dolores A446
Hernandez, Ean A449
Hernandez, Patricio A538
Hernandez, Enrique (Rick) A545
Hernandez, Emmanuel A620
Hernandez, Jeff A650
Hernandez, Anthony A700
Hernandez, Louis A752
Hernandez, Oscar A869
Hernandez, Victor A878
Hernandez, Mark P47
Hernandez, George B. P73
Hernandez, Zoyla P111
Hernandez, Guadalupe P249
Hernandez, Mary P249
Hernandez, Ty P255
Hernandez, Carol P359
Hernandez, Linda P464
Hernandez, Frank P466
Hernandez, Olga M P478
Hernandez, Blanca P550
Hernandez, Joseph P662
Hernandez, Tom--s W133
Hernandez, John E36
Hernandez, Patrice E195
Hernandez, Elva E208
Hernandez, Dolores E210
Hernandez, Roland E424
Hernas, Carl A786
Herndon, Tomilynn P239
Herndon, Shayla P673
Hernquist, Thomas A416
Herold, Rich A588
Heron, W. David P398
Herr, Daniel A512
Herr-Wilczek, Teri P309
Herrema, Gregory J. (Greg) A815
Herrema, Donald J. E231
Herrenbruck, David W A333
Herrera, Milciades A109
Herrera, Tammy A244
Herrera, Ramiro A459
Herrera, Ailisa A542
Herrera, Manny A770
Herrera, Ana P415
Herrera, Ana P602
Herrera, Milciades E36
Herrera, Ailisa E267
Herrick, Brian A489
Herrick, Glen W. A554
Herrick, Jimmie A770
Herrick, Doug P618
Herrick, James E41
Herrick, Glen W. E275
Herring, Jim A76
Herring, Lori A115
Herring, Terry A531
Herring, Steve A800
Herring, Thomas A901
Herring, Martha J P79
Herring, Tammi P224
Herring, Steve P559
Herring, David J. P648
Herring, Thomas P692
Herring, Darin B E123
Herrington, Richard E A364
Herrman, Ernie A817
Herrman, Eddie P250
Herrmann, Gunnar A362
Herrmann, Steven A584
Herrmann, Bernie J. A703
Herrmann, Mindy P247
Herrmann, Steven P376
Herron, John A282
Herron, Steve A308
Herron, Dallas I. A387
Herron, Michael A512
Herron, C. Keith A700
Herron, Cherry P128
Herron, Dallas I. E177
Herron, J. Brendan E188
Herschel, Tom A175

Hershberger, Carlo P245
Hershberger, Rodney (Rod) E331
Hershey, Dale R. A21
Hershey, Dale R. P12
Hershey, Milton P344
Herskovitz, Rachel A449
Herteg, Diane A764
Herteg, Diane P540
Herthel, Kevin A705
Herthel, Kevin E352
Herting, Joshua A762
Hertogh, Mark De P431
Hertz, Sally A478
Hertz, Claire P67
Hertzberg, George P211
Hervey, Michael D P296
Herweck, Peter W322
Herwig, Chris A838
Herz, Jennifer A195
Herzberg, Victoria A885
Herzberg, Caspar W322
Herzel, David P254
Herzmark, Paula P160
Herzog, Katie A131
Heseltine, Cathy A763
Heskin, John A201
Heslop, Steve A780
Heslop, James R. E278
Hess, William H. (Hal) A55
Hess, Rick D. A65
Hess, John B. A417
Hess, Jennifer P106
Hess, Steven P311
Hess, Jim P334
Hess, Marybeth P487
Hess, Pam P620
Hess, Marc W125
Hess, Beat W. W214
Hess, David Peter F. (Pete) E383
Hesse, Heather P296
Hesse, Thomas W62
Hessekiel, Jeffrey J. E138
Hesselgren, Timothy P211
Hesser, Gregory T P18
Hession, Eric A157
Hession, Michael A406
Hessler, Matthew A740
Hessler, Kathleen P537
Hessler, Matthew E369
Hest, Bruce P520
Hester, Travis A379
Hester, Kevin D. A425
Hester, David A443
Hester, Randy D. A673
Hester, Darin A752
Hester, Joyce P353
Hester, Kevin D. E201
Hester, Debbie E426
Hesterberg, Earl J. A396
Hesterbrink, Christoph A175
Hestin, Ed A659
Heston, Mary A723
Hete, Joseph C. (Joe) E8
Hetherington, Tracy P244
Hetrick, Teresa M. E278
Hett, Gary A611
Hett, Ed P666
Hett, Gary E313
Hetterich, F. Paul A235
Hettler, Charlie M A774
Hetzer, Ben A532
Hetzler, Dustin A701
Heutink, Chris W299
Heutmaker, Lisa P26
Heuvelen, John E185
Hevrony, Nathan P53
Hewatt, Russell A107
Hewatt, Russell E34
Hewett, Mark A. P394
Hewett, Charles E. P587
Hewitson, Amanda A133
Hewitt, Robert C. A122
Hewitt, Dennis E. A619
Hewitt, Kathryn P144
Hewitt, Paul J P631

Hey-Hadavi, Judith A649
HEYA, TOSHIO W169
Heyde, Charles Von Der A654
Heydlauff, Dale E. A46
Heydlauff, Dale E P32
Heyman, William H. (Bill) A828
Heyrich, George P535
Heyrman, Tracie P32
Heyrmann, Heidi A557
Hiatt, Kathy P273
Hibbard, Richard A676
Hibbert, Paul E65
Hickerson, Marcus A423
Hickey, Scott S. A81
Hickey, Dennis J. A218
Hickey, Adam R A224
Hickey, Michael A. (Mike) A289
Hickey, Brian E. A522
Hickey, JP A700
Hickey, Renee A767
Hickey, Lori P28
Hickey, Tim P142
Hickey, Wayne P545
Hickey, Paul R. P570
Hickey, John P. E77
Hickman, Phillip A81
Hickman, Angie A619
Hickman, George T. P17
Hickman, Cynthia P105
Hickman, Kristina U P148
Hickman, Thomas E219
Hickok, Christopher A902
Hickok, Lori A. P488
Hickok, Christopher P693
Hickox, Michelle S. A452
Hickox, Michelle S. E215
Hicks, Weston M. A30
Hicks, Malcolm A107
Hicks, George T. A148
Hicks, George T. A149
Hicks, JO A223
Hicks, Bradley A439
Hicks, Andrew A442
Hicks, Lucas A442
Hicks, Kirkland L. A512
Hicks, Chris A541
Hicks, Jeff A549
Hicks, Jason A773
Hicks, Bridget A788
Hicks, R. Steven (Steve) A860
Hicks, Roland A870
Hicks, Charles A901
Hicks, Ellis P40
Hicks, John D P60
Hicks, Dolores P89
Hicks, Allyson P137
Hicks, Leiser P283
Hicks, Ashley P507
Hicks, Tammy P635
Hicks, R. Steven (Steve) P656
Hicks, Charles P692
Hicks, Malcolm E34
Hicks, Randy E147
Hicks, Chris E266
Hicks, Jeff E270
Hicks, Jason E387
Hicok, Gary A607
Hidalgo, Melissa A513
Hideshima, Nobuya W399
Hieb, William J. E108
Hiel, Kim P247
Hieminger, Steve P338
Hier, Lars A305
Hier, Lars P185
Hiesinger, Heinrich W365
Hiffa, Michael P258
Higa, Marie A199
Higase, Edward T. (Ted) E107
Higashi, Kazuhiro W301
Higginbotham, Herbert A16
Higginbotham, John A137
Higginbotham, Lesley B A221
Higginbotham, Cole A223
Higginbotham, Robert A783
Higginbotham, Nancy A835

Higginbottom, Thomas A221
Higgins, Martha T. A143
Higgins, Christopher A390
Higgins, Jeanne A480
Higgins, Sam A522
Higgins, Kevin A532
Higgins, Kerri A562
Higgins, Keith A644
Higgins, Chip A655
Higgins, Amy A733
Higgins, Kevin A814
Higgins, Scott F. A827
Higgins, Hugh P308
Higgins, Julie P329
Higgins, Vanessa P507
Higgins, Kevin P616
Higgins, Patricia E. E86
Higgins, Tricia E86
Higgins, John L. E246
Higgins, Kerri E279
Higgins, Chip E333
Higginson, Andrew T. W249
High, Joseph C. A393
Highet, David A119
Highland, Mary Anne P529
Highley, Duane D P45
Highley, Duane P46
Highley, Ian E247
Hightman, Carrie J. A594
Hightower, Charles P42
Hightower, Skip P262
Higley, Ralph A744
Higuchi, Takeo W116
Hikim, Amiya P226
Hilado, Maria Teresa (Tessa) W22
Hilaire, Syndie Saint P101
Hilboldt, Susanna A729
Hilburn, Charles P639
Hildebrand, J. Bruce A345
Hildebrand, Mark A441
Hildebrand, J. Bruce E154
Hildebrandt, Michael P487
Hileman, Donald P. A344
Hileman, Donald P. E154
Hilfiker, Amy A436
Hilgart, Bret A528
Hilger, Andy A31
Hilger, James K. (Jim) A255
Hilger, Andy P24
Hill, W. Guy A33
Hill, Guy W A34
Hill, Anne A91
Hill, Jim A115
Hill, J. Tomilson A132
Hill, J. Tomilson A133
Hill, Daniel A136
Hill, Edwin J. (Ed) A166
Hill, ED A166
Hill, Bob A173
Hill, Kathryn A177
Hill, Tim A193
Hill, Curtis A200
Hill, Pam A223
Hill, Frank A223
Hill, Kimberly A262
Hill, Craig D. A319
Hill, Cathy A383
Hill, Maureen A390
Hill, Gregory P. (Greg) A417
Hill, Greg A417
Hill, Tom A433
Hill, Jared A441
Hill, Herbert A448
Hill, Scott A A457
Hill, Peter A475
Hill, Judy A541
Hill, Brian A575
Hill, Robert A578
Hill, Elliott J. A592
Hill, David R. A604
Hill, Robin A616
Hill, Charles H. (Chuck) A648
Hill, Nina A649
Hill, Edward A712
Hill, Robert R. A751

A = AMERICAN BUSINESS
E = EMERGING COMPANIES
P = PRIVATE COMPANIES
W = WORLD BUSINESS

Hill, Allen A850
Hill, Deryl A850
Hill, Stephanie A857
Hill, Becky A865
Hill, John A868
Hill, Lisa P65
Hill, Jason P88
Hill, Phillip C P90
Hill, Tim P112
Hill, Christopher R. P132
Hill, Thomas D P184
Hill, Scott P198
Hill, Christopher P217
Hill, Carolyn P259
Hill, Peter P266
Hill, Allison P281
Hill, Steve P282
Hill, Tim P291
Hill, Dennis P295
Hill, Melissa P315
Hill, Mark P334
Hill, Frederick W P372
Hill, Dan P378
Hill, Sam P430
Hill, Tom P531
Hill, Laurence P610
Hill, Tony P666
Hill, James P675
Hill, Christina P676
Hill, Susan M. E41
Hill, Tim E44
Hill, George E162
Hill, Judy E266
Hill, Brad E276
Hill, Howard F. E357
Hill, Robert R. E377
Hillary, Stanley A140
Hillary, Caitlin P413
Hille, James R. P560
Hilleary, Shawn A537
Hillebrand, Lana L. A46
Hillebrand, James A. (Ja) A772
Hillebrecht, Chris A648
Hillemeier, A. Craig A811
Hillemeier, A. Craig P600
Hiller, Todd A784
Hiller, Sharon A904
Hiller, Sharon E442
Hilliard, Robert P353
Hillier, Scott A. A515
Hilligoss, Ken A484
Hillman, Todd P342
Hillman, John P561
Hillman, Randy E245
Hills, John A904
Hills, Malina M P564
Hills, John E442
Hillson, Jan E72
Hillyer, Christopher D. P372
Hilton, Calvin A32
Hilty, Martha A151
Hilty, Martha E48
Hilzinger, Kurt A59
Hilzinger, Kurt J. A438
Hilzinger, Jeffrey A. E261
Himelfarb, Richard J. A771
Himes, Michael P425
Himes, Vicki P425
Himes, Vicky P425
Himler, Bob A709
Himmelberger, Don P415
Himpe, Robrecht W30
Hinago, Takashi W201
Hincapie, Maria P291
Hinchey, Paul P P92
Hinck, Michael P587
Hinckle, Veronica A166
Hinckley, Gregory K. (Greg) P326
Hinde, Jason A308

Hindel, Joanne A333
Hindoian-Brewster, Marlene A920
Hinds, Tom A912
Hinds, Rick P631
Hinds, Steven E432
Hinduja, Anil A366
Hine, Mark P290
Hine, Chad P482
Hine, Chris E256
Hineman, Mark P622
Hiner, Patrick A2
Hiner, Troy A725
Hines, Michael A173
Hines, Grace A736
Hines, William H P403
Hines, Grace P492
Hines, Anson (Tuck) P506
Hines, Frances P521
Hines, Linda P669
Hines, Neill E65
Hines, Jonathon E185
Hing, Rebecca A906
Hingesbach, Alan P694
Hingsbergen, Michael A196
Hingston, Alex A599
Hingtgen, Tim L. A227
Hinkel, Cynthia P117
Hinkel, Robert W176
Hinkle, Michael A336
Hinkle, James G A425
Hinkle, Michael P194
Hinkle, Craig M P277
Hinkle, Allen J. P360
Hinkle, James G E201
Hinkley, Richard A199
Hinkley, Leo E39
Hinnenkamp, Paul D. A300
Hinojosa, Conrado E230
Hinrichs, Joseph R. (Joe) A362
Hinrichs, Jon P87
Hinsch, Ronda P481
Hinsdale, Bill A885
Hinshaw, Ken A175
Hinshaw, Janice A508
Hinshaw, Bill A603
Hinshaw, Bill P399
Hinshaw, Will P622
Hinson, W. Ron A383
Hinson, Donald J. A414
Hinson, Jeffrey T. A903
Hinson, Craig P406
Hinson, Donald J. E195
Hinterschied, Regina P133
Hinton, Patricia A371
Hinton, Walter A519
Hinton, Shirley P26
Hinton, Phillip P206
Hinton, James H. (Jim) E337
Hinton-Johnson, Kaavonia P406
Hintz, Donald A300
Hintz, Brian A339
Hintz, Brian E150
Hintze, Paul P331
Hintzen, Daniel A599
Hinz, Susan P247
Hippe, Patricia A219
Hippe, Patricia P131
Hippe, Alan W307
Hippen, Lyle A185
Hipskind, Jennifer A640
Hipwell, Todd A264
Hirai, Kenji W156
Hirai, Kazuo (Kaz) W337
Hirakawa, Masaatsu W336
Hiraki, Justin A782
Hirako, Yuji W27
Hirami, Nancy E445
Hirano, Nobuyuki W245
Hiras, Joanne E65
Hirashima, Takayuki W349
Hirata, Vernon A798
Hire, W. Jeffrey E218
Hirji, Rahim W232
Hiroe, Mutsuo W241
Hiromori, Takaya A19

Hirono, Yutaka W326
Hirose, Naomi W369
Hiroshige, Cliff P47
Hirsch, Didier A22
Hirsch, Larry A119
Hirsch, Noah A158
Hirsch, Roderick A659
Hirsch, Karen P80
Hirsch, Constance P144
Hirsch, Bonnie P155
Hirsch, Jim P431
Hirsch, Peter E119
Hirschberg, Alan A555
Hirschfield, Larry P87
Hirsh, Peter A131
Hirshberg, Eric A10
Hirshberg, Gary W117
Hirst, Daniel A59
Hirst, William A247
Hirst, Alistair D. A485
Hirst, William E102
Hirt, Michael E86
Hise, Bill A441
Hisey, David C. A769
Hishikawa, Maki A19
Hislop, Steve E76
Hita, Margarita P508
Hitch, Jordan A155
Hitchcock, Andy A173
Hitchings, Stephen A718
Hitchner, Kenneth W. A389
Hite, Carolyn A316
Hite, Carolyn P191
Hitt, David A662
Hitt, Greg A878
Hitt, Charles A913
Hitt, Kathy P46
Hitter, E. Paul P334
Hitter, Paul P334
Hitz, Travis P685
Hivkumar, Satya S P695
Hiwatari, Kenji W261
Hixson, Richard A480
Hizak, Steve A843
Hizak, Steve E411
Hizkiaho, Rony W150
Hizuka, Shinichiro W349
Hjelm, Christopher T. (Chris) A496
Hjelmstad, Terry P386
Hjelvik, Emily P439
Hladik, David A481
Hnat, Jim A474
Hnat, James G. (Jim) A474
HO, Duong A7
Ho, Peter S. A102
Ho, Peter S. A103
Ho, Emily A133
Ho, Karen A390
Ho, Stephen A530
HO, Kar A774
Ho, Tien A899
Ho, Chaney P7
Ho, Clifton P458
Ho, Tien P690
Ho, Lora W354
Ho, Shih-Yin E268
Ho-Young, Jeong W219
Hoag, Erik A330
Hoagland, Harold R P75
Hoang, Minh-Ha P653
Hobart, Lauren R. A264
Hobart, Brian E. A452
Hobart, Robert P35
Hobart, Brian E. E215
Hobbs, Franklin W. (Fritz) A35
Hobbs, Nicholas (Nick) A439
Hobbs, Beth A655
Hobbs, Rodney A762
Hobbs, David A A851
Hobbs, Lee P40
Hobbs, Stephanie P126
Hobbs, Richard P134
Hobbs, Daisy P418
Hobbs, Richard F P626
Hobbs, Connie P694

Hobbs, Beth E333
Hobby, Paul A604
Hobby, Thomas W P240
Hobert, Christine A331
Hobert, Christine E148
Hobin, Peggy L. A879
Hobson, Christopher K. (Chris) A237
Hobson, James M P323
Hobson, James P323
Hobson, Spencer P372
Hocevar, Christopher A195
Hoch, Erich A471
Hoch, Russell A914
Hochberg, Stanley P80
Hochgesang, Mark A105
Hochman, Rod A674
Hochman, Rod P444
Hochschild, Roger C A268
Hochstein, Craig P64
Hocken, Natalie L. A630
Hockey, Timothy D. (Tim) A791
Hockfield, Susan P313
Hocking, Chris P642
Hockman, Alexander A. E311
Hodes, Jack A375
Hodes, Harold L P371
Hodge, Terry A819
Hodge, Karen P472
Hodges, James R. A99
Hodges, Kristina A115
Hodges, Arthur A214
Hodges, Simon A275
Hodges, Eloy A541
Hodges, James A546
Hodges, Timothy B A644
Hodges, Bob P101
Hodges, Arthur P128
Hodges, Jeff P330
Hodges, Sheila P398
Hodges, Joe P523
Hodges, Bruce M. W32
Hodges, Patrick E44
Hodges, Eloy E266
Hodgin, Dana P226
Hodgkins, Beverly P525
Hodgkinson, Andrew E242
Hodgkiss, Lisa P453
Hodgson, Robert A693
Hodiwalla, Zubin A729
Hodkin, Deborah A316
Hodkin, Deborah E141
Hodnett, David W. P. W4
Hodnett, Larry E216
Hodnik, Alan R. E13
Hodous, Brian A10
Hodson, John W352
Hoechner, Bruce D. E359
Hoeck, Michael A173
Hoedl, Dean P371
Hoefler, Brenda P249
Hoeh, Kristian A391
Hoeing, Antoinette P533
Hoeksema, Brad P30
Hoellein, Ken P20
Hoencamp, Jeroen W389
Hoene, William A. (Bill) Von A308
Hoereth, Anthony A913
Hoerth, Scott A81
Hoesch, Josh A340
Hoesch, Josh E151
Hoesen, Peter Van P24
Hoetzinger, Peter E66
Hoey, Bob A460
Hoey, Cheryl P138
Hoey, Donald P233
Hoey, Amy P298
Hof, Thomas A838
Hofbauer, Patrik W360
Hofelich, Kurt A736
Hofelich, Kurt P492
Hofer, Nicholas A.R. A143
Hofer, SIS Kathleen P536
Hofer, Kathleen P536
Hoff, Linda P285

Hoff, Jeremy E203
Hoffler, Valerie A162
Hoffman, Roger A74
Hoffman, Steve A93
Hoffman, Julie A131
Hoffman, Peter A136
Hoffman, Mark A140
Hoffman, Nate A163
Hoffman, Geoffrey A273
Hoffman, Francis A328
Hoffman, Tammy A366
Hoffman, John A476
Hoffman, Kathleen A677
Hoffman, James D. A703
Hoffman, Jim A703
Hoffman, Susan A864
Hoffman, James E. (Jim) A916
Hoffman, William P38
Hoffman, Angela L P75
Hoffman, Angela L P88
Hoffman, Nancy P101
Hoffman, Geoffrey P162
Hoffman, Thomas P248
Hoffman, Chris P303
Hoffman, Mary J P317
Hoffman, Rany P352
Hoffman, Randy P352
Hoffman, Carole P418
Hoffman, Mark P467
Hoffman, Joe P522
Hoffman, André W307
Hoffman-Day, Denise A522
Hoffmann, Daryl A244
Hoffmann, Marc W131
Hoffmeister, Bruce A530
Hoffmeister, Jan A675
Hoffmeyer, Stig W1
Hofheimer, Andy E349
Hofheins, Todd A674
Hofheins, Todd P444
Hofmann, Kevin A426
Hofmann, Herb E. A520
Hofmann, Herbert A520
Hofmann, Richard A550
Hofmann, Catherine P575
Hofmeister, Brian A663
Hofstadler, Paul P326
Hogan, Cynthia A70
Hogan, Mark D A116
Hogan, James D. A247
Hogan, Patrick A330
Hogan, Michael P. (Mike) A372
Hogan, Rob A442
Hogan, Margaret A532
Hogan, Kathleen T A560
Hogan, David P. A621
Hogan, Jim A788
Hogan, Noel P18
Hogan, Gail P383
Hogan, Gillian P560
Hogan, Joseph M. (Joe) E10
Hogan, Mark D. E39
Hogan, James D. E102
Hogan, George W. E438
Hogarty, Lisa P570
Hoge, Geof A850
Hogenmiller, Mike A426
Hogg, Charlotte M. A874
Hogg, Chris W255
Hogg, John E122
Hogge, Cindy P462
Hoghaug, Paul A56
Hogle, Scott A449
Hoglund, Robert N. A232
Hoglund, Robert N. A233
Hogue, John A441
Hogue, Herbert L P296
Hoheisel, Dirk W70
Hohenadel, Jim A141
Hohentanner, Teri P174
Hohmeister, Harry W124
Hohn, Diedrich P123
Hohndorf, Mike E51
Hoien, Todd A408
Hoisman, Danny A833

Hoke, Margaret A350
Hoke, Margaret E156
Holacka, Karin P460
Holani, Kimberly A103
Holbrook, Jenni A425
Holbrook, James A663
Holbrook, Judy P531
Holbrook, Jenni E201
Holburn, Karen P460
Holcman, Alex A685
Holcomb, Michele A165
Holcomb, Curtis P6
Holcomb, George W. P327
Holcomb, David P560
Holcomb, Alexandra W395
Holda, Margaret P511
Holden, Rochelle A272
Holden, Sean A542
Holden, Zachery J A730
Holden, James A751
Holden, Chris P1
Holden, Peter J. P71
Holden, Teresa P125
Holden, E. Wayne P458
Holden, Sean E267
Holden, James E378
Holder, Sonia A583
Holder, Diane P. A859
Holder, William W. A860
Holder, Diane P. A652
Holder, William W. P656
Holder, Robert E45
Holder, Richard D. E305
Holding, Frank B. A341
Holding, Frank B. E153
Holdings, Midcoast P342
Holdorff, Sharon P126
Hole, Joseph A105
Hole, David E179
Holeksa, Jürgen W402
Holeman, David K. E438
Holguin, Lorena A537
Holguin, Rochelle A872
Holiday, Edith A726
Holiday, Bradley J. E448
Holien, Patrick P624
Holifield, Mark Q. A426
Holinsky, Ronald A513
Holladay, Lisa A531
Holladay, Mark G. A781
Hollan, Michael A251
Holland, Peter A105
Holland, Richard A251
Holland, Tom A327
Holland, Ricky T. A341
Holland, Jim A362
Holland, Christine A441
Holland, Clifford A476
Holland, James A492
Holland, Arlene A521
Holland, Ralph A564
Holland, George A914
Holland, Cindy P45
Holland, Cheryl P269
Holland, Daniele P286
Holland, Lynn P508
Holland, Ricky T. E153
Hollander, Rich A649
Hollander, Martin A734
Hollander, Elie P216
Hollas, Dustin A222
Hollaway, David A673
Hollek, Darrell E. A63
Hollen, J--rgen von E394
Hollenbeck, Martin F. A196
Hollenbeck, Jennifer A839
Hollenbeck, Jennifer E409
Holler, Cindy P331
Holleran, Kevin P. A804
Hollett, Bill E98
Holley, Peter A115
Holley, Jeffrey D A621
Holley, Rick R. A896
Holley, Jeffrey D P407
Holliday, Bob A85

Holliday, Brian A429
Holliday, Carl A622
Holliday, Matt A862
Holliday, Charles O. (Chad) W313
Holliday, Matt E419
Hollihan, Walter P65
Hollinger, Dennis A9
Hollingshead, Jim E354
Hollingsworth, Rebecca A38
Hollingsworth, Pamela A463
Hollingsworth, Audrey A781
Hollingsworth, Glenn P239
Hollingsworth, Ronnie H P239
Hollingsworth, Jarvis V. P643
Hollis, Roy P154
Hollister, John C. E371
Holloman, J. Phillip A198
Hollon, Jeffrey A115
Holloway, Duane D. A79
Holloway, Bavan A136
Holloway, Anita A438
Holloway, John B. P94
Holloway, Erin P537
Hollub, Vicki A. A611
Holly, Mignon P51
Holly, Sally P617
Holly, Tim E127
Holman, Alan A34
Holman, Gene A107
Holman, Brian A180
Holman, Sheila A531
Holman, Jeff P301
Holman, Gene E34
Holmen, Hans A232
Holmer, Shekofeh A915
Holmes, Tom A243
Holmes, Donald N A260
Holmes, Bradley A298
Holmes, Richard A383
Holmes, Dane A390
Holmes, Crystal A461
Holmes, Charlie A493
Holmes, William A530
Holmes, James A682
Holmes, Valerie A890
Holmes, Stephen P. A908
Holmes, John P162
Holmes, Diane P189
Holmes, Brad P197
Holmes, Gerald T P228
Holmes, Carol P449
Holmes, Bryan P450
Holmes, Nicholas P451
Holmes, Nicholas P452
Holmes, Jacpb P461
Holmes, Norman G P515
Holmes, Robin P577
Holmes, Chip P614
Holmes, Valerie P684
Holmgren, Thor A56
Holochuk, James A724
Holodak, Stephen A250
Holschbach, Leon J. A561
Holschbach, Leon J. E278
Holscher, Russ A113
Holshouser, Susan A448
Holsten, Joseph M. A518
Holston, Michael J. A550
Holsworth, Patricia P549
Holt, Alan A56
Holt, Jarrod A480
Holt, Adam P103
Holt, Dennis P237
Holt, Michael E P536
Holt, Curtis P630
Holt, Patrick P670
Holt, Dennis W103
Holt, Tim O. W331
Holt, Victoria M. (Vicki) E339
Holthouser, James E. (Jim) A421
Holton, Terry J. A730
Holton, Mathew P108
Holton, Matthew P108
Holton, Micah E276
Holtrup, Kevin E117

Holtz, Dave A261
Holwill, Richard A37
Holwill, Richard P29
Holyfield, Kevin A558
Holyoak, Steven P125
Holz, Vonna P549
Holzapfel, Nelson P222
Holzem, John D A782
Holzer, Damon A84
Holzer, Sunita A696
Holzer, Shawna P27
Holzer, Harold P594
Holzmann, Thomas P111
Holzmann, Oscar J. E39
Holzshu, Christopher (Chris) A515
Hom, Erwin A354
Hom, John A676
Homan, Jan W145
Hombach, Robert J A113
Homenuik, Terry A395
Homer, David P. (Dave) A377
Homer, Ronald A A535
Homer, Ronald A P312
Homma, Koji W400
Homoky, Bill E117
Homsey, Harvey P188
Hon-shing, Tong W47
Honaker, Lynda P97
Honda, Amy A102
Honda, Yoshitaka P405
Honda, Osamu W351
Honda, Shinji W355
Honeycutt, John A269
Honeycutt, Mike A747
Honeycutt, Tonya P115
Honeyman, Eric A867
Honeyman, Joel P125
Hong, Peter A76
Hong, Eleanor E A493
Hong, John A685
Hong, Scott A872
Hong, Chong P243
Hong, Ching Wei W280
Hong, Chen W316
Hongli, Zhang W186
Hongola, Michael A795
Honig, Lyle P14
Honjo, Masaya W344
Honkus, Tina A556
Honold, Doris W340
Honovic, Johnathan A872
Honovic, Jonny A872
Honovic, John A872
Hood, Chris A485
Hood, Amy E A560
Hood, Ron A866
Hooda, Abdul P629
Hoofman, Jorsof P645
Hoogakker, Jason P653
Hoogenboom, Paul G. P. A716
Hoogenkamp, Eric E8
Hoogeveen, Kevin A339
Hoogeveen, Gary W P274
Hoogeveen, Kevin E150
Hooi, Ng Keng W13
Hook, Rich A643
Hook, Thomas J. E219
Hooker, Thomas A199
Hooker, Tracey P329
Hooks, Samuel P348
Hooley, Joseph L. (Jay) A766
Hooley, Stephen C. P167
Hooper, Anthony C. (Tony) A61
Hooper, Tony A61
Hooper, Ana A254
Hooper, Lisa A272
Hooper, Susie A844
Hooper, Brian A878
Hooper, Susie E412
Hoopes, John R. P478
Hoopes, Jeffrey C P551
Hooser, Steve Van A257
Hoover, Stephen (Steve) A912
Hoover, Carolyn P126
Hoover, Cristi P184

A = AMERICAN BUSINESS
E = EMERGING COMPANIES
P = PRIVATE COMPANIES
W = WORLD BUSINESS

Hoover, Eric P277
Hoover, Denise P476
Hoover, G Michael P546
Hoover, Mike P605
Hoover, Linda M P626
Hopcus, Russell B. (Russ) E86
Hope, Walter A59
Hope, Ken A192
Hope, Jim A782
Hope, Ken P112
Hopf, Clarence J. (Joe) P554
Hopfer, Rick A565
Hopfinger, Mark M A701
Hopke, Debra P659
Hopkins, Christopher A101
Hopkins, Diggy A272
Hopkins, Lynn M. A632
Hopkins, Frank A657
Hopkins, Kevin A807
Hopkins, Larry A835
Hopkins, Destina P108
Hopkins, Rochelle P201
Hopkins, Sam P281
Hopkins, Kevin P574
Hopkins, Geoff E51
Hopkins, Roger R. E292
Hopkins, Lynn M. E321
Hopkinson, Lynette E428
Hoplamazian, Mark S. A444
Hopmans, John A517
Hopp, Jason P454
Hopp, Maryann E320
Hoppe, Mark A. A541
Hoppe, Beth P445
Hoppe, Christoph W364
Hoppe, Mark A. E266
Hopper, Sue A556
Hopson, Jeffrey A702
Horan, Theodore A644
Horan, Terry A716
Horan, Craig A852
Horan, William F P408
Horber, Patrick A6
Hore, David T. E288
Horelica, Kevin P491
Horey, Leo S. E26
Horgan, Dan A692
Horgan, Kathryn M. (Kathy) A766
Horgan, Ralph P96
Horgan, Dan P454
Horgan, Neil J. P667
Horger, Robert R. A751
Horger, Robert R. E378
Horikami, Brian K P493
Horn, Charles L. A32
Horn, Jim A204
Horn, Alan F. A271
Horn, Justin A549
Horn, Joe Van A868
Horn, Nancy Van P178
Horn, Walter K. E22
Horn, Justin E270
Horn, Stephen A. E293
Hornbuckle, William J. A558
Hornby, William P. A184
Horne, Lewis A173
Horne, Mike A173
Horne, Betsy P149
Horner, David A145
Horner, Leigh E A416
Horner, Matt A907
Horner, John P40
Horner, David P82
Horner, Bryan P497
Horner, Andy P611
Horner, Andrew P611
Horner, Shaida P673
Horner, Matt P696
Horning, Brian P98

Hornsby, Jimmy E320
Hornung, Bill A908
Hornung, Andrew P514
Hornung, Bill E446
Horowitz, Paul A130
Horowitz, Zane P410
Horseman, Neil A874
Horstman, Gregory A163
Horstman, Douglas A898
Horstmann, Douglas J. A412
Horstmann, David L. A412
Horstmann, Douglas J. E192
Horstmann, David L. E192
Horswell, Bruce P110
Hortman, Edwin W. (Ed) A57
Hortman, Edwin W. (Ed) E16
Horton, Carrie A64
Horton, Rick A433
Horton, Donald R. A433
Horton, Craig A481
Horton, Michael A664
Horton, Kelly A671
Horton, William E. (Bill) A700
Horton, Andrean A916
Horton, Harriet P289
Horton, Swayzine P292
Horton, Rob P356
Horton, David P371
Horton, Lilla P613
Horton, Lynn P662
Hortsch, Ann P465
Horvath, Karen A122
Horvath, Anthony A407
Horvath, Michael A744
Horvath, Jeff P525
Horvath, John P694
Horwedel, Gregory P P144
Horwood, Gail A485
Hosea, Kristina A584
Hosey, Dr Ashley P129
Hoshii, Susumu W327
Hoshino, Yoshihiko W400
Hoskins, Walter A162
Hoskins, Michelle A351
Hoskins, Roni P613
Hoskins, Michelle E158
Hoskinson, James W A136
Hosmer, Philip A522
Hosoi, Susumu W190
Hosono, Katsuya W28
Hosoya, Kazuo W342
Hossack, Michael A333
Hossein, Abby A551
Host, Gerard R. (Jerry) A832
Hostetler, Kurt A738
Hostetter, Margaret P115
Hosticka, Carl P651
Hosty, Neil J. A522
HoTai, Wendy A638
Hotaling, Michael A313
Hotchkiss, James P. A351
Hotchkiss, James P. E158
Hotsuki, Keishi A568
Hottes, Kimberly A902
Hottes, Kimberly P692
Hottges, Timotheus A785
Hottges, Timotheus W126
Hottois, Kathy P218
Houck, Brenda A428
Houck, Kathleen P80
Houck, Charles J P378
Houdayer, Pascal W168
Houde, Edward A408
Houde, Jean W252
Houdeshell, David D. A731
Houdeshell, David D. E365
Hough, Lynn M A221
Hough, Edana A774
Hough, Brenda A902
Hough, Jay C P343
Hough, Brenda P692
Houghton, Nicole A458
Houghton, Nicole P251
Houghton, Mike P293
Houghton, James R P594

Houghton, Andrew E9
Houkom, Brian L P686
Houliang, Dai W93
Houlihan, Robert A551
Houn, Florence A178
Hourigan, Tim A426
Hourihan, Michael A533
Hours, Bernard W117
House, James L. (Jim) A69
House, Dave A669
House, Barbara A818
House, Gerry P175
House, Deb P480
House, Lance P676
House, Andrew W337
House, Todd W. E163
Householder, Mark A668
Householder, Joseph A. (Joe) A735
Householder, Jeffry M. E74
Houser, Tom A214
Houser, Borgia A770
Houser, Denise A863
Houser, Sandy P87
Houser, Tom P128
Houser, Leesa P449
Houser, Jason P461
Houserman, Lynne E89
Houseworth, Meredith A489
Houshmand, Dr Ali P466
Housianitis, Lisa A648
Houssaye, Brian de la A904
Houssaye, Brian de la E442
Houston, Monica A345
Houston, Helga S. A440
Houston, Daniel J. (Dan) A668
Houston, Stacy W A693
Houston, Sally H. P197
Houston, Bronwyn P285
Houston, Don P339
Houston, Matthew D. E31
Houston, Monica E154
Houston, David L. E185
Housum, Virginia A837
Houten, Matthew A A84
Houten, Diana Van P241
Houweling, Tara Van A164
Houweling, Anson Van P639
Hovey, Dan P162
Hovick, Kevin J. A292
Hovious, Bob P81
Hovis, Carol P95
Howard, Linda A10
Howard, Christine A81
Howard, Jason A204
Howard, Gary A375
Howard, John L. A393
Howard, Jeff A449
Howard, Connie A721
Howard, Dennis A728
Howard, Chris A760
Howard, Kevin J. A781
Howard, Terence A784
Howard, Donald A809
Howard, Kim A810
Howard, Claude A827
Howard, J. Kyle A873
Howard, Michael A899
Howard, Martin P80
Howard, Steve P126
Howard, Michael W. P179
Howard, Christine P189
Howard, Neal P271
Howard, Greggory P276
Howard, James P301
Howard, Mark P425
Howard, Chris P523
Howard, Marty P548
Howard, Donald P586
Howard, Kim P586
Howard, J. Kyle P668
Howard, Michael P690
Howard, Stephen R P692
Howarth, Richard P54
Howarth, Joan W. P341
Howat, Dan A480

Howdyshell, Cathy A324
Howe, Stewart M A449
Howe, Matthew P160
Howe, Jeff P171
Howe, Bobbie P305
Howe, Josh P491
Howe, James P539
Howe, Stephen W61
Howe, Kenneth R. E7
Howell, Keith A26
Howell, Peyton R. A59
Howell, Lloyd W. A140
Howell, John A180
Howell, Douglas K. (Doug) A370
Howell, James A. A596
Howell, Eric A742
Howell, Robert A782
Howell, Paul A800
Howell, Kendra P155
Howell, Rosa P170
Howell, Julie P239
Howell, Elizabeth P340
Howell, Lannie P350
Howell, Katherine A. (Kathy) P473
Howell, Eric P502
Howell, Stephen (Steve) P595
Howell, Hilton H. E181
Howell, Robert G. (Bob) E256
Howell, Charles E272
Howell, Paul E396
Howenstine, Debra P646
Howes, Joshua A163
Howes, David P311
Howie, Jon W. E76
Howland, Bill A724
Howle, James E163
Howlett, C. C. W199
Howley, Michael G. E3
Howson, David A201
Howton, Barry P140
Howze, Marc A. A260
Hoy, Thomas L. A78
Hoyer, Amy A489
Hoyle, Kevin P102
Hoysan, Mandy A709
Hoyson, Chris A814
Hoyson, Chris P616
Hoyt, Hubertus A593
Hoyt, Janet A659
Hradsky, Robert P37
Hricak, Judy P196
Hricko, John E349
Hrina, Sharon P118
Hrit, Barb P81
Hrountas, Stacey P498
Hruby, Jerry N P404
Hruska, Colleen P139
Hrybenko, Michael E89
Hsiao, Chiu Bin P186
Hsieh, John A460
Hsieh, Jennifer A530
Hsieh, Jackson A759
Hsieh, Johnny A182
Hsieh, Jackson P520
Hsieh, Johnny P553
Hsing, Shirley P241
Hsing, Michael R. E284
Hsiung, Ken A583
Hsiung, Ming-Ho W84
Hsu, Joyce A390
Hsu, Christopher P. (Chris) A418
Hsu, Michael D. A490
Hsu, Ted A667
Hsu, Clark A667
Hsu, S.Y. W35
Hsu, J. H. W84
Hsu, Larry W113
Hsu, Boshan W113
Hsu, Vivien W154
Hsu, Jen-Shou (Samuel) W154
Hsu, David W195
Hsu, Judy W340
Hsu, Ted E336
Hsu, Clark E336
Hu, Kathryn A163

Hu, Bradford A204
Hu, Eddie A593
Hu, S. Jack A698
Hu, Alex A723
Hu, Mark A898
Hu, Yazhou P306
Hu, Samson W35
Hu, Arthur W218
Hua, Daniel A482
Hua, Zhong W102
Hua, Yang W102
Hua, Hsieh Fu W384
Huang, Joseph A308
Huang, Victor A377
Huang, Efen A476
Huang, Julia A537
Huang, Jen-Hsun A607
Huang, Sofia A667
Huang, Christopher A724
Huang, Eric P7
Huang, Dominic P155
Huang, Janice P606
Huang, Tao W90
Huang, Yung Jen W130
Huang, Peter M.T. W346
Huang, Wen Zhou W399
Huang, Sofia E336
Huat, Peter Seah Lim W119
Huaxiang, Cai W12
Hubbard, Wade A396
Hubbard, Terry A718
Hubbard, Charles A774
Hubbard, Latonya A901
Hubbard, Bill P97
Hubbard, Richard P103
Hubbard, Sonja P170
Hubbard, Bob P170
Hubbard, Maryann P345
Hubbard, Bart P480
Hubbard, Latonya P692
Hubbell, Michael A266
Hubbell, Richard A. E258
Hubbs, Arthur C. E69
Huber, Gary E A127
Huber, Edgar O. A241
Huber, Marie Oh A288
Huber, John A332
Huber, J. Kendall A402
Huber, Thomas A710
Huber, Timothy P147
Hubert, Angela St P86
Huberty, Sean A311
Hubinger, Jim A187
Hubinger, Jim E71
Hubka, Tim E189
Hubr, Gary Null A127
Huch, Jamie A223
Huck, Jack P87
Huckabay, Evan A221
Huckabay, David A517
Huckaby, Kent P41
Huckaby, Hank A135
Huckaby, Hank P78
Huckelberry, Chuck P429
Huckfeldt, Paul A. E203
Huckle, Amanda A131
Hudak, James L. (Jim) A201
Hudak, John A351
Hudak, John E158
Hudak, Terry E407
Huddart, Andrew E235
Huddleston, Namon P293
Hudgens, Charles A58
Hudgens, John D. A800
Hudgens, Liz A901
Hudgens, Liz P692
Hudgens, Charles E16
Hudgens, John D. E396
Hudgins, Jessie P662
Hudgions, Annette W. A614
Hudnall, Brenda A115
Hudon, Isabelle W347
Hudson, Kirk A163
Hudson, David W. A183

Hudson, Jennifer A231
Hudson, Thomas A288
Hudson, Scott R. A371
Hudson, Elizabeth A644
Hudson, Dennis S. (Denny) A731
Hudson, Jamie A839
Hudson, Roz A857
Hudson, Ray A899
Hudson, David T. A910
Hudson, Terry P64
Hudson, Kevin P121
Hudson, Jerry P141
Hudson, Twana P143
Hudson, Jim M P173
Hudson, Lisa P263
Hudson, R. Guy P550
Hudson, Dorothy P637
Hudson, Ray P690
Hudson, Mark E283
Hudson, Scott E306
Hudson, Dennis S. (Denny) E365
Hudson, Jamie E409
Hudson-Martin, Gerry A530
Hudspeth, Jacqueline P109
Huebner, Kyle E385
Huelskamp, Amy A481
Huerta, Veronica A752
Huerta, Miguel A814
Huerta, Tina P294
Huerta, Miguel P616
Huesser, Larry P511
Huestis, Tim A655
Huestis, Tim E333
Huether, Jamie A67
Huey, Cindy A113
Huey, Marc A659
Huff, Jerry A877
Huff, Scott A878
Huff, Justin P529
Huffer, Linda R. A736
Huffer, Linda R. P492
Huffer, Russell E19
Huffines, James R A420
Huffines, James R. E198
Huffman, Nina A218
Huffman, Gary A489
Huffman, Mona A547
Huffman, Janet A904
Huffman, Chad P125
Huffman, Mona P319
Huffman, R Cyrus P350
Huffman, Janet E442
Huffner, William P645
Hufford, Bob A82
Hufford, Bob P49
Hufford, Dustin P576
Hufman, Chris A784
Hug, Michael A908
Huggins, M J A167
Huggins, John A249
Huggins, Deb P289
Huggins, Shannon P336
Huggins, Keith P512
Hughes, Ted A47
Hughes, Tom A85
Hughes, Tony A155
Hughes, Sean A195
Hughes, Brian D A268
Hughes, Gareth A270
Hughes, Rick A353
Hughes, Edmond E A442
Hughes, Johnathan A484
Hughes, Erik A536
Hughes, Karen Karen Hughes A537
Hughes, Peter A540
Hughes, Robert K. A582
Hughes, Jeffrey A. (Jeff) A707
Hughes, Susaan A725
Hughes, Michael A759
Hughes, Mark A774
Hughes, Christine A807
Hughes, Kate A817
Hughes, Sylvia P30
Hughes, Bill P39
Hughes, Ann M P107

Hughes, Stephen P113
Hughes, Joseph P165
Hughes, Frank P183
Hughes, Scott P219
Hughes, Peter P316
Hughes, William P368
Hughes, Robert K. P373
Hughes, Roddy P431
Hughes, Colleen P481
Hughes, Julie P487
Hughes, Michael P521
Hughes, Christine P574
Hughes, James P589
Hughes, John P658
Hughes, Mark W310
Hughes, Robert E40
Hughes, Rick E159
Hughes, Melanie E402
Hughes, Bryan E441
Hughey, Sandy P386
Hugin, Robert J. (Bob) A178
Hugo, Dan A163
Hugvik, Kjell A305
Hugvik, Kjell P185
Hui, Ka Yan W90
Hui, Chng Sok W119
Hui, Richard E50
Hui, Mary E432
Huie, Stephanie Bond A860
Huie, Stephanie Bond P656
Huie, Robert P692
Huillard, Xavier W387
Huiman, Yi W186
Huiskens, Terry A162
Huiyan, Yang W109
Hulaton, Pat A102
Hulburt, Jeff P71
Hulburt, Benjamin W. E118
Hulburt, Christopher K. E118
Hulihee, John A102
Huling, Rebecca A327
Hull, Dahna A85
Hull, Stacey A180
Hull, George A472
Hull, Anthony E A696
Hull, Daniel P8
Hull, Peter P196
Hull, Pamela P462
Hulse, Walter S. A622
Hulse, Walter S A623
Hulse, Lew P230
Hulse, Walter S P407
Hulsebus, Tyler A432
Hult, David W. A78
Hult, Jason P40
Hultman, Jeff A412
Hultman, Jeff E192
Hultquist, Douglas M. (Doug) A683
Hultquist, Douglas M. (Doug) E341
Hum, Robert P326
Humble, Susan P68
Hume, Richard T. (Rich) A792
Huminski, Monica A295
Humler, Herve A530
Humm, David A213
Hummel, Robert A108
Hummel, William A332
Hummel, John M. A848
Hummel, Chris A851
Hummel, Dennis P307
Hummel, Mike P478
Hummel, Mike P509
Hummel, Robert E35
Hummingbird, Ruth P569
Humphrey, John J. A851
Humphrey, Richard P152
Humphreys, James P687
Humphreys, Adam A774
Humphreys, Donald A878
Humphreys, Glenn P664
Humphries, Colin J P591
Humphries, Paul J. W151
Hunckler, Stephen P. A764
Hund, Kenneth A163
Hund, Lawrence G. A403

Hund-Mejean, Martina A537
Hundzinski, Ronald T. (Ron) A141
Hung, Vani A204
Hung, Jerry B P168
Hung, Benjamin P. C. (Ben) W340
Hung-Lun, Chang (Fred) E21
Hunhoff, Darin A194
Hunkler, Bradley J. A890
Hunkler, Bradley J. P684
Hunley, Danny A442
Hunn, L. Neil A714
Hunniford, Michael A599
Hunsaker, Michelle A878
Hunsberger, Scott A670
Hunt, James A158
Hunt, Marsha L A246
Hunt, Neil A580
Hunt, Lisa Kidd A728
Hunt, N. Craig A742
Hunt, Eugene A743
Hunt, Amy A836
Hunt, Sandy A839
Hunt, Brenda P84
Hunt, Doris P140
Hunt, Anita P173
Hunt, David P175
Hunt, Nathan P199
Hunt, Cheri P327
Hunt, Stephen J P376
Hunt, Hunter P499
Hunt, Linda P627
Hunt, Terry P651
Hunt, Joseph P682
Hunt, John E52
Hunt, Dennis B. E170
Hunt, Hal E288
Hunt, Tony J. E351
Hunt, N. Craig E372
Hunt, Eugene E373
Hunt, Sandy E409
Hunter, Kelli A. A56
Hunter, Jesse N. A179
Hunter, Alisa A332
Hunter, Jim A332
Hunter, George A333
Hunter, David A419
Hunter, Christopher H. (Chris) A437
Hunter, Andrew A685
Hunter, Lisa W. A742
Hunter, Mark A744
Hunter, Julie A755
Hunter, Rhonda C. A896
Hunter, Shalonda P32
Hunter, Leslie P96
Hunter, Lesley P97
Hunter, Adam P224
Hunter, Andrew P268
Hunter, Cathy P666
Hunter, Dan E83
Hunter, John E193
Hunter, Gordon B. E247
Hunter, Lisa W. E372
Hunter, Julie E380
Huntington, Brad A678
Huntington, Archer P594
Huntley, David S. A84
Huntsman, Peter R. A443
Huntsman, Jon M. A443
Huntz, John E. E256
Hunwardsen, Dennis P677
Hunziker, Hans E440
Hupp, Billy P187
Huppertz, Julie P247
Hur, Lucy A763
Huran, Gary P624
Hurand, Gary E47
Hurd, Mark V A624
Hurd, John P106
Hurd, Earl E1
Hurlbert, Terry P96
Hurlbut, Angela A698
Hurlbut, Angela P456
Hurley, Gregg A799
Hurley, John M. E175
Hurley, Alfred E301

A = AMERICAN BUSINESS
E = EMERGING COMPANIES
P = PRIVATE COMPANIES
W = WORLD BUSINESS

Hurn, Patricia D. A698
Hurn, Patricia D. P456
Hurr, Martha P439
Hurst, Trent A241
Hurst, David A258
Hurst, George A405
Hurst, Tony A640
Hurst, Beverly P42
Hurst, Colleen P192
Hurst, Gregory A. (Greg) P428
Hurst, Branen P501
Hurst, A. C. W199
Hurt, Lorraine A28
Hurt, George A. P105
Hurtado, Cesar A199
Hurtig, Howard I P599
Hurvitz, Elizabeth A874
Hurwitz, Jerry A119
Hurwitz, Phil A654
Hurwitz, Brad A906
Hurzeler, Robert A. A621
Husain, Bazmi W4
Huse, Mark A492
Huseman, Kim P276
Huseman, Brian E68
Husk, Melanie P58
Huskins, Keith A400
Huskins, Lee P263
Huslin, Kemsha P109
Husoy, Geir A305
Husoy, Geir P185
Huspeni, Jeffrey A588
Hussain, Aamir A185
Hussey, Fsa A890
Hussey, Joanne A912
Hussey, Fsa P684
Huston, Michael A349
Huston, Sam A441
Huston, Michael E156
Hutchenrider, E. Kenneth P336
Hutcheson, Jennifer A719
Hutcheson, David A819
Hutcheson, Jennifer P468
Hutchings, Doug A15
Hutchings, Kelly A187
Hutchings, Doug P9
Hutchings, Kelly E71
Hutchins, Michael A366
Hutchinson, William R. A81
Hutchinson, Randy A300
Hutchinson, Mark A375
Hutchinson, James A576
Hutchinson, Sharon P60
Hutchinson, Cynthia P408
Hutchinson, Roger P541
Hutchinson, Jeff W69
Hutchinson, James E297
Hutchison, John A649
Hutchison, Larry M. A822
Hutchison, Randall P209
Hutchison, G Duane P211
Hutchison, John P406
Huth, R A920
Huth, Liana E127
Hutmacher, Dustin A877
Hutson, Kirby A195
Hutson, Marc P256
Huttenlocher, Daniel P. P143
Huttle, Frank A231
Hutto, Richard A27
Hutto, Curtis P620
Hutton, Peter A269
Hutton, Rob A508
Hutton, William L. A701
Hutzler, Marilyn P429
Huval, Timothy S. (Tim) A437
Huval, Tim A732
Huval, Caroline P279
Huval, Tim E365

Huver, Edmund A649
Huxen, Nancy A221
Huyck, James P28
Huynh, Tien G A221
Huynh, Ann A285
Huynh, Chinh P40
Huynh, Sheila P231
Huynh, Ann E114
Huza, Callie P332
Hu- «t, Jean Marc W381
Hvasta, Barbara P2
Hwang, Cindy A133
Hwang, Angela A648
Hwang, Jack A674
Hwang, Jack P444
Hwang, Yong-Kee W220
Hwang, Robert P. T. W395
Hwang, Donald W395
Hwee, Koh Boon A22
Hwee, Susan W. C. W384
Hyatt, Chas E195
Hyde, Jeff A187
Hyde, Steve A724
Hyde, Andrew A865
Hyde, Pat P425
Hyde, Jeff E71
Hyder, Rima E140
Hygrell, Lars W3
Hyland, Thomas J A136
Hyland, Jason P. A558
Hyland, Michael A681
Hylander, Ken P364
Hylton, Tracy A207
Hyman, Shana A327
Hyman, Edward S. (Ed) E136
Hyman, Linda E235
Hymel, Rachel P403
Hymes, Jacob A838
Hynds, Joe A342
Hynes, Timothy (Tim) A575
Hyslop, Gregory L. (Greg) A136
Hytinen, Barry A. A400
Hyun, John P126
Hyun, Sung Chul W318
Hyun, Heidi E8
Hyun-Ko, You A682
Hyung-jin, Kim W328
Hyung-soon, Kim W163
Hyzy, Maria E447
H- orter, Daniel W402
H- ousler, Gerd W58
H- ¶lz, Martin W365
H- ¶vell-Patrizi, Allegra van W10
H- idahl, Hans-Olav W20
Hébert, Brigitte W252

I

I-Thieme, Silvia A136
Iacolucci, Michael H P484
Iaconi, Thomas Di A744
Iaconi, Krista Di E349
Iacono, Ivy A272
Iacono, George A576
Iacono, George E297
Iacovitti, Andrea P164
Iacovou, Charles L. P673
Iannarone, Thomas A133
Iannelli, Josephine A112
Iannelli, Josephine E38
Ianniciello, Raffaela A585
Ianniciello, Raffaela P377
Ianniello, Joseph R. A175
Iannone, Jamie A878
Iannotti, Thomas J. (Tom) A71
Iantosca, Joseph R. A611
Iantosca, Joseph R. P107
Iantosca, Joseph R. E313
Iasonides, John A879
Ibach, Jason D A369
Ibach, Jason A369
Ibach, Shelly R. E376
Ibarra, Francisco A899
Ibarra, Frank P132

Ibarra, Francisco P690
Ibata, Naoki P245
Ibbotson, Mark A878
Ibbott, Kinte E265
Ibrahim, Marko A612
Ibrahimpasic, Elvir A193
Ibsen, Stewart A273
Ibsen, Stewart P162
Icahn, Carl C. A249
Icahn, Carl C. A447
Ice, Carl R. A134
Ice, Carl R. A154
Ice, Carl R. P77
Ichihashi, Yasuhiko W169
Ichikawa, Masakazu W169
Ichimiya, Tadao W399
Ichinaga, Stephen A779
Ichinaga, Steve A780
Ichino, Atsushi W400
Ichiura, Yoichi W243
Iczaowski, Carol P48
Ide, Nancy P518
Iden, Ron A272
Idiodi, Christian P333
Idzior, Andrew P167
Iellimo, Domenick P205
Ierna, Diane A34
Ierulli, Laura A353
Ierulli, Laura E159
Ifuku, Masahiro W238
Igarashi, Tetsuo W163
Igel, Bill P256
Iger, Robert A. (Bob) A271
Iger, Robert A. (Bob) A272
Iglesias, Lisa G. A863
Iglesias, Javier Iglesias Javier A865
Igli, Kevin A835
Igoe, Joe A898
Igoe, Paul G. E383
Ihamuotila, Timo W4
Ihara, Yasumori W17
Ihm, Steve A34
IHORI, EISHIN W170
Ii, Sheppard Miers A622
Iida, Osamu W242
Iii, Patrick Flanigan A178
Iijima, Yutaka P35
Iinuma, Yoshiaki W245
Iiyama, Toshiyasu W268
Ikbal, Javed E46
Ikeda, Miki A102
Ikeda, Kyle P658
Ikeda, Junichiro W246
Ikeda, Hajime W268
Ikegaya, Mikio W245
Ikeya, Koji W243
Ikoma, Masao W202
Iku, Tetsuo W323
Ilan, Haviv A803
Ilderem, Vida A456
Ilkka, Heikki W269
Illig, Clifford W. (Cliff) A186
Ilovic, Peter A163
Im, Audrey A513
Imamura, Masashi W337
Imanuel, Ofer A390
Imaya, Akihiko W326
Imber, Barry A. E77
Imbriale, Joseph A522
Imhof, Doug P199
Imhoff, Jenny P270
Imig, John P406
Immaneni, Aravind A332
Imparato, Jean Philippe W286
Imperapori, Jay A564
Imperato, Thomas A589
Imperiali, Rebecca P391
Impicciche, Joseph R A80
Impicciche, Joseph R P47
Imundi, Christine A691
Inaba, Nobuo W304
Inagaki, Shiro W323
Inaguchi, Toshinori W116
Inal, Deniz P610
Inamoto, Nobuhide W235

Incarnati, Philip P249
Incorvaia, A.J. P326
Indaravijaya, Kattiya W202
Inderlied, Donald K P660
Indresano, Michael A38
Infeld, Allan A872
Infeld, Michael P593
Ingerslev, Christian M. W1
Ingersoll, Don A913
Ingersoll, Christopher D. P613
Ingham, Raymond P694
Ingle, Abhi A85
Ingle, Von A530
Ingoldsby, David A243
Ingram, Bill A11
Ingram, Mitchell W. (Mitch) A64
Ingram, Robert C. (Bob) A306
Ingram, David A655
Ingram, Beth F. P611
Ingram, James P660
Ingram, David E333
Inlander, Patricia A131
Inlander, Todd L. A291
Inlander, Todd L. A752
Inman, Larry A244
Inman, Tamra A614
Inman, Kent A866
Inman, Angela P275
Innes, Kim W363
Inoue, Yasuhide A723
Inoue, Shin A917
Inoue, Shin P701
Inoue, Noriyuki W113
Inoue, Katsushi W172
Inoue, Tooru W245
Inoue, Makoto W279
Inoue, Yuri W330
Inouye, Glenn K P493
Insalaco, Sue A734
Insall, Gerard A92
Insch, Gary S. P613
Inscho, Bill A352
Inserra, Andrea A140
Inskeep, Lauren A784
Insley, Patricia A513
Insley, Guy P326
Insoft, Robert P695
Insolia, Matthew T. P507
Intemann, Chris A333
Intili, Louis P682
Inzana, Lou P283
Inzana, Lugene P303
Iogman, Alec P124
Ioriatti, Roberto A262
Iorio, Tony A532
Ip, Norman Ka Cheung W160
Ipp, Alan P361
Ippolito, Peter J. A738
Iqbal, Farhan A81
Irani, Ray A909
Iraola, Mark R P361
Ireland, Scott A180
Ireland, Jay W. A375
Ireland, Frieda A794
Ireton, John A481
Irick, Jaime A. A151
Irish, Stephen J. A301
Irish, Stephen J. E127
Irizarry, Laurens A233
Irizarry, George P85
Irlmeier, Jerome A194
Iroha, Simon P333
Irtel, Konrad W250
Irussi, Bruce G. A738
Irvin, Vernon L. A185
Irvin, Nancy A560
Irvin, Stephanie A920
Irvin, Lisa P94
Irvin, Nancy P342
Irvin, James E. E172
Irvine, Jon A97
Irvine, Laura P336
Irvine, Jon E32
Irvine, Jacqui E320
Irwin, John A440

Irwin, Michael A724
Irwin, Larry (Don) A851
Irwin, Derek P250
Irwin, David P662
Irwin, Bradley C. P679
Irwin, Thomas S. E193
Isaac, William A823
Isaac, Jon E247
Isaacs, Howard P352
Isaacs, Eric D. P609
Isaacson, Marcia P398
Isaacson, John P627
Isaacson, Irit W149
Isaacson, Irit W150
Isaacson, Chris E62
Isabella, Paul M. A117
Isais, Geraldine Forbes P648
Isaka, Ryuichi W324
Isakowitz, Steven J. (Steve) P564
Isbell, Ken A223
Ise, Kiyotaka W374
Isely, Kemper E295
Isely, Zephyr E295
Isely, Heather E295
Isely, Elizabeth E295
Iseman, Jay C. A427
Iseman, Andrew J. (Andy) A837
Iseman, Jay C. E202
Iserman, Lance A88
Isham, Mary A655
Isham, Mary E333
Ishibashi, Takuya W116
Ishibashi, Tamio W116
Ishida, Yoshihisa W326
Ishigami, Hiroyuki W245
Ishiguro, Tadashi P86
Ishiguro, Denroku W19
Ishii, Takuya W115
Ishikawa, Brian A102
Ishikawa, Hiroshi A643
ISHIMARU, FUMIO W318
Ishizaki, Yoshiyuki W368
Ishizuka, Hiroaki W240
Ishizuka, Shigeki W337
Ishmael, Omar P568
Ishtiaq, Ahmer P381
Isidro, Judith P124
Iskow, Julie E268
Isla, Pablo W185
Islam, Munib A113
Islam, Nayeem A685
Islan, Anne E369
Isley, Megan P115
Isom, Robert D. A43
Isom, Gary E P449
Ison, Tamara P680
Isono, Denis K. A183
Isono, Tadahisa W374
Israel, Leonard (Len) A356
Israel, Leslie P297
Israel, Michael D P683
Israel, Joseph E322
Israel, Robert J. E348
Isreal, Toni P286
Isserman, Jacob P355
Isturiz, Raul A649
Italiano, Louis A329
Italiano, Deborah P538
Ito, Craig A102
Ito, Val A102
Ito, Tessa A785
Ito, Shinichiro W27
ITO, TOSHIYASU W176
Ito, Kazuhiko W190
Ito, Takashi W238
Ito, Yujiro W345
Itoyama, Masaaki W192
Iturrey, Albert A536
Itzkowitz, Fredric H P193
Iuppenlatz, Mark A396
IV, William H W Crawford A846
IV, W R Sronce P166
IV, Calvin Thomas P217
IV, Guilliaem Aertsen E301
IV, William H. W. Crawford E414

Ivanis, Milena A827
Ivannikov, Alexander A654
Ivannikov, Alexander W289
Ivanoff, Henry P69
Ivanoff, Kevin P69
Ivanov, Penko A109
Ivanova, Detelina A163
Ivas, Michael A62
Ivashkiv, Lionel B P376
Ive, Jonathan A70
Ivers, Lewis P489
Iversen, Lorraine P83
Iversen, JP W3
Iverson, Mark A865
Iverson, Erik A905
Iverson, Kirk P7
Iverson, Erik P693
Ives, Gray A700
Ivey, Craig S. A232
Ivey, Brian A383
Ivey, Jerry P692
Ivie, Warren P255
Ivie, Brandon P255
Ivie, Brian P446
Ivy, Laura P435
Iwane, Shigeki W202
Iwanik, Diana P440
Iwasa, Hiromichi W245
Iwasaki, Toshihiro W268
Iwasaki, Masato W355
Iwata, Kikuo W48
Iwatsuki, Takashi W351
Iyengar, Jayanthi (Jay) A914
Iyer, Sethu A101
Iyer, Chandresh A105
Iyer, Prasad A537
Iyer, Bask A875
Iyer, Kris P238
Iyer, Vijayalakshmi P270
Iyoya, Martin P263
Izadi, Azade P69
Izaguirre, Luis-Angel Gomez A913
Izaguirre, Gladys P475
Izaki, Kazuhiro W213
Izotov, Andre A685
Izurieta, Laura A777
Izurieta, Laura E393
Izutani, Koji W336
Izzo, Ralph A678
Izzo, Angela A741
Izzo, Angela E370

J

J-amie, White P205
Jabbonsky, Larry A647
Jabbour, Anthony M. A330
Jaber, Adeeb P39
Jablin, Burton F. P488
Jablonski, Dale A489
Jabro, Mark P498
Jacangelo, Joseph P361
Jacinto, Mira A533
Jack, Angela A850
Jackiewicz, Thomas E. A860
Jackiewicz, Thomas E. P656
Jackman, Lorraine A221
Jackowiak, Mary A599
Jackowski, Julia L. (Julie) A168
Jackson, James A67
Jackson, Michael J. (Mike) A88
Jackson, Keri A115
Jackson, Peter A153
Jackson, Lydia A163
Jackson, Rick C. A164
Jackson, Robin A204
Jackson, Brett A221
Jackson, Brian A250
Jackson, Michael J. (Mike) A322
Jackson, Dimetria A336
Jackson, Cyndee A380
Jackson, Brian A425
Jackson, Benjamin A457
Jackson, Tom A463

Jackson, Robert A536
Jackson, Larry A552
Jackson, Beverly A558
Jackson, Keith D. A620
Jackson, Don A654
Jackson, Joanne B. A655
Jackson, Marla A676
Jackson, Stuart A691
Jackson, Jennifer A700
Jackson, Doris A701
Jackson, Bill A709
Jackson, Ronald B. (Ron) A742
Jackson, Mel A754
Jackson, Sherita A788
Jackson, David A802
Jackson, Jamere A809
Jackson, Philip C. (Phil) A862
Jackson, Cj A863
Jackson, Debbie A878
Jackson, Fred L A47
Jackson, Paul P88
Jackson, Bobby P144
Jackson, D T P164
Jackson, Rosa P P177
Jackson, Anthony P191
Jackson, Dimetria P194
Jackson, Richard L. P258
Jackson, R. Shane P258
Jackson, Andrea P262
Jackson, Fred P276
Jackson, Ron P291
Jackson, Jolinda P315
Jackson, Drew P318
Jackson, Laurisa P327
Jackson, Larry P328
Jackson, Melissa P331
Jackson, Maureen P427
Jackson, Kimberley P453
Jackson, Steven P462
Jackson, Lisa P464
Jackson, Grace P501
Jackson, Rosa P P515
Jackson, Michael P558
Jackson, David P562
Jackson, Claire P563
Jackson, Jamere P584
Jackson, Susan P680
Jackson, Linda W286
Jackson, Mary Ann E19
Jackson, W. James E121
Jackson, Brian E201
Jackson, Michael E242
Jackson, Jeffrey T. (Jeff) E331
Jackson, Joanne B. E333
Jackson, Ronald B. (Ron) E372
Jackson, Mel E378
Jackson, Philip C. (Phil) E419
Jackson-Elmoore, Cynthia P341
Jacob, Daniel A113
Jacob, Bobby A244
Jacob, Gregg A263
Jacob, Bijesh A532
Jacob, Dianne A659
Jacob, Ken P89
Jacob, Jeffrey P372
Jacob, Richard P699
Jacob, Sitt W149
Jacobfeuerborn, Bruno W126
Jacobi, Jacqueline A565
Jacobi, John A707
Jacobino, Lucy P325
Jacobo, Keyanus A593
Jacobs, Kerry J. A30
Jacobs, Cindy A244
Jacobs, Gregg A263
Jacobs, Stephen D. (Jake) A361
Jacobs, Kevin J. A421
Jacobs, Lawrence A. (Lon) A502
Jacobs, Lynn A543
Jacobs, Todd A593
Jacobs, Doug A751
Jacobs, Kristine A832
Jacobs, Jennifer A864
Jacobs, Bradley S. A913
Jacobs, Richard F. P45

Jacobs, Michael P99
Jacobs, Richard B. P102
Jacobs, Christy P108
Jacobs, Jill P122
Jacobs, Hannah P205
Jacobs, John P256
Jacobs, John P257
Jacobs, Joyce P292
Jacobs, Ellen E107
Jacobs, William I. E182
Jacobs, Thomas W. E253
Jacobs, Robert E357
Jacobs, Doug E377
Jacobsen, Rene A7
Jacobsen, Leland P406
Jacobsen, Lennart W269
Jacobson, Ken A A93
Jacobson, Paul A. A261
Jacobson, Kristin A266
Jacobson, Jeff A. A478
Jacobson, Scott A709
Jacobson, Jack A879
Jacobson, Jeffrey (Jeff) A911
Jacobson, Pam P192
Jacoby, Rebecca J. A199
Jacoby, Christy A647
Jacoby, Phillip E319
Jaconette, Paul P482
Jacques, Karen A912
Jacques, Lori P392
Jacques, Jean-Sebastien W305
Jacques, Jean-Sébastien W306
Jadin, Ronald L. A393
Jadlowski, Mary P149
Jadot, Maxime (Max) W66
Jaeger, Tom A119
Jaeger, Timothy A173
Jaeke, Erik P393
Jaekel, Carl A51
Jafarnia, Korsh P335
Jaffe, David R. A79
Jaffe, Jonathan M. (Jon) A508
Jaffe, Eric D. A733
Jaffe, Victor A795
Jaffe, Kevin A914
Jaffe, Robert E328
Jaffery, Farhan A480
Jaffray, Dawn M. A847
Jaffrey, Jonathan D P671
Jafry, Syed A. A815
Jagger, Hal A739
Jagger, Hal P501
Jaggers, Richard P54
Jagiela, Mark E. E394
Jaglall, Andy A568
Jagoda, Matthew E369
Jahanian, Farnam P96
Jahn, Timothy P58
Jahn, Barb P531
Jahns, Tracy P613
Jaime, Alex A612
Jain, Deepti A67
Jain, Ajit A123
Jain, Nitin A180
Jain, Jinesh A185
Jain, Shweta A204
Jain, Vishal A371
Jain, Nikhil A685
Jain, Sahil P96
Jain, Nitin P282
Jain, Anshu P346
Jain, Ritesh W67
Jain, Vivek E212
Jaiswal, Jyoti P113
Jakeman, Kelly A59
Jakeman, Brad A647
Jakino, Mike P480
Jakobsen, Henning A218
Jakobsen, Mads G. W269
Jakosky, Donn A630
Jakosky, Donn P415
Jakstys, Kristina A599
Jakub, Paula P32
Jalace-vasold, Melissa A902
Jalace-vasold, Melissa P692

A = AMERICAN BUSINESS
E = EMERGING COMPANIES
P = PRIVATE COMPANIES
W = WORLD BUSINESS

Jalil, Mohammed A280
Jallal, Bahija W34
Jalona, Sanjay P282
Jamal, Arshil W161
Jamar, John P36
Jamarik, Marissa P298
Jambor, Joan A84
Jameel, Hasan A631
James, Karen A98
James, Hamilton E. (Tony) A132
James, David A214
James, Fred A287
James, Schlosser A441
James, Donna A497
James, Galeota A550
James, Phyllis A. A558
James, Miriam A644
James, Kay A659
James, Hunt A693
James, Jerry A802
James, Bradley G. A820
James, Dianne R. A919
James, Marianne F. P115
James, David P128
James, Dick P133
James, Fred P174
James, Scott P345
James, Jan P436
James, Rank P463
James, Hal P463
James, Michael P498
James, Andino P528
James, Laura P535
James, Curtis P537
James, Jerry P562
James, Gena P620
James, Penny W295
James, Karen E33
James, Tyrone E172
James-Francis, Ma P384
James-Nielsen, Lori P476
Jameson, Steven E. (Steve) A227
Jameson, Jeremy A302
Jameson, Lisa A441
Jameson, J. Larry A812
Jameson, J. Larry P607
Jameson, Jeremy E128
Jamieson, Dick P98
Jamieson, T J P259
Jamieson, Lee P259
Jamil, Dhiaa M. A281
Jamison, Gary A432
Jamison, David A468
Jamison, Cynthia T. A825
Jamison, David P252
Jammaers, Arnaud A538
Jan, Couturier A440
Jan, Ng A784
Janaillac, Jean-Marc W14
Janas, Jane P296
Janas, Grzegorz W51
Janbeth, Santos E320
Janchar, Jim A158
Janda, Kenneth P134
Jane, Mara A555
Janell, Joseph E P83
Janeway, Dean P275
Jani, Gita P164
Janicek, Russ A173
Janiga, Kathy A254
Janik, James L. E109
Janis, Robert (Bob) P155
Janis, Bob P155
Janise, Carlton P89
Janish, Thomas P40
Janiszewski, Chuck P11
Janke, Kenneth S. (Ken) A18
Janke, Ken A19
Janke, Grant A842

Janke, AnnMarie A865
Jankelowitz, Larry P440
Janki, Daniel A375
Janki, Daniel P210
Jankos, Dianna P349
Jankovich, Richard A223
Jankowski, Simona A607
Jankowski, Edward A888
Jankowski, Joseph P99
Jankowski, Gary P309
Jankowski, Cecelia P586
Jannah, Shekar G. A487
Jannasch, Charlyn P420
Janney, John P448
Janney, Jeremy P516
Janney, Karen P550
Janofsky, Christine A513
Janosick, Kenneth W. (Ken) E438
Jansen, James C. (Cory) A318
Jansen, Corey A318
Jansen, Chad A649
Jansen, Jacqueline A788
Jansen, Robert P680
Jansen, Paul R. E261
Janser, Kevin P508
Janski, Mary P602
Janson, Julie S. A281
Janson, Steven A542
Janson, Steven E267
Janssen, Gwendolyn A5
Janssen, Ann A304
Jansson, Helena A327
Jante, Adam A343
Jantz, Robert A295
Jantz, Tricia P556
Jantzen, Daniel P154
Janus, Tami A815
Janus, Tammy P329
Janutolo, Kristin A440
Janzekovich, Cathleen P107
Japy, Nicholas W334
Jaramillo, Rafael A295
Jaramillo, Richard P312
Jaramillo, David P433
Jardiniano, Janis A532
Jarman, Samuel Y P27
Jarnot, Christopher E. (Chris) E424
Jarocki, Larry P670
Jaroszewski, J Rosow A244
Jarrell, Paul A628
Jarrett, Thomas K A260
Jarrett, Adam P239
Jarrett, Mark P390
Jarrett, Dr Ehren P464
Jarrold, Tom A691
Jarvie, Steve A478
Jarvis, Sam A223
Jarvis, Cathy A704
Jarvis, Guy W138
Jarvis, Cathy E350
Jarvis, Andrew J. E398
Jarvis, AJ E398
Jasey, Yasmeen A333
Jasinski, Joseph P491
Jasinski, Wojciech W291
Jasionowski, James A478
Jaskaniec, Andy A493
Jasko, Brian P392
Jasko, Donna P660
Jaskunas, Jeremy W P333
Jaspal, Puja A874
Jasper, Thomas F. (Tom) A789
Jasper, Bill E172
Jassy, Andrew R. (Andy) A38
Jastrem, Thomas A247
Jastrem, Thomas E102
Jauch, Mike A416
Jaurequi, Pat P480
Javallana, Maria P560
Javersack, Dawn P79
Javidroozi, Mazyar P184
Jawor, Wojciech A517
Jaworowska, Sabina Bigos W51
Jaworski, Peter W. A886

Jaworski, Brandy P697
Jaworski, Peter W. E433
Jay, Dennis A460
Jay, Colleen E. A671
Jay, Carrick A898
Jay, John C. W147
Jay-Young, Chung W333
Jayachandran, Priya P671
Jayaram, Ganesh A259
Jayaraman, Ganesh A204
Jayavant, Rajeev A607
Jaynes, Gregg A137
Jazayeri, Akbar A291
Jazic, Annemarie A266
Jazwinska, Klaudia P286
JD, J Richard Ludgin MD P51
JD, Howard R Grant P279
Jean, Grace A52
Jean, Ronald W. A292
Jean, Grace P33
Jean, Christopher Des P290
Jean-Felix, Eddy P564
Jeanniot, Lynn W252
Jeary, Cathy A724
Jedlicki, Anne P646
Jedrzejczyk, Slawomir R. W291
Jeevan, Siddharth A766
Jeff, Lee A732
Jeff, Galagher A878
Jeff, Lee E365
Jeffers, Linda P135
Jeffers, Lewis P436
Jefferson, Kirby A456
Jefferson, Timothy P217
Jefferson, Larry P560
Jeffrey, Brad Jeffrey Brad A513
Jeffrey, David A723
Jeffrey, Hanks P143
Jeffrey, William P522
Jeffrey, David E P602
Jeffreys, Marc A195
Jeffs, Mike P136
Jehle, Kent L. A562
Jehle, Kent L. E279
Jejdling, Fredrik W360
Jejurikar, Shailesh G. A671
Jelenic, Lee A362
Jelinek, W. Craig A239
Jelks, Dionne P603
Jelle, Lorraine P74
Jellinek, Michael P380
Jellison, Brian D. A714
Jeng-wu, Tai W326
Jenisch, Jan W214
Jenkin, Thomas M. (Tom) A157
Jenkins, Eben A253
Jenkins, Deborah A366
Jenkins, Amanda A468
JENKINS, WORTH A508
Jenkins, Brian A513
Jenkins, Brad A556
Jenkins, Steve A628
Jenkins, Scott A766
Jenkins, Jeff A775
Jenkins, Dustee T A788
Jenkins, Jeff A814
Jenkins, Jo Ann C. P1
Jenkins, Janet P110
Jenkins, Decosta P178
Jenkins, Sheterra P226
Jenkins, Amanda P252
Jenkins, Julia P252
Jenkins, Ladenea P268
Jenkins, Jeff P548
Jenkins, Justin P556
Jenkins, Marjorie P595
Jenkins, Barbara P599
Jenkins, Jeff P616
Jenkins, Jo W233
Jenkins, Brian A. E105
Jenkins, R. Scott E218
Jenkinson, Rachael A537
Jenks, Maria P271
Jenn, Lisa A774
Jenne, Joan P533

Jenner, Philip A872
Jenness, Calvin E. P76
Jennifer, Shade A817
Jennifr, K P387
Jennings, Lisa A34
Jennings, Gary A82
Jennings, Jennifer A158
Jennings, Michael C. A423
Jennings, Dick A718
Jennings, Shawn A729
Jennings, Rebecca A902
Jennings, Dick A912
Jennings, Gary P49
Jennings, William M P83
Jennings, Reynold J P129
Jennings, Lorie P282
Jennings, Lynn A P286
Jennings, Stephen P452
Jennings, Reynold J. P680
Jennings, William M. (Bill) P698
Jennings, Brenda E407
Jenny, Kim A655
Jenny, Kim E333
Jenrette, John P102
Jensen, Christopher W. (Chris) A177
Jensen, Barry A451
Jensen, Carolann A468
Jensen, Mary A530
Jensen, Eric A560
Jensen, Donald A591
Jensen, Don A591
Jensen, Shea A596
Jensen, Eric A607
Jensen, Derrick A. A686
Jensen, Eric A763
Jensen, Susan A839
Jensen, Jaclyn P102
Jensen, Richard P125
Jensen, Linda A P188
Jensen, Thomas J P188
Jensen, Tom P188
Jensen, Carolann P252
Jensen, Eric P342
Jensen, Craig P487
Jensen, Mira E125
Jensen, Palle E375
Jensen, Susan E409
Jensen, Nate E429
Jensik, Emily A219
Jensik, Emily P131
Jenson, Conrad A423
Jenson, James A496
Jentsch, Dieter W. W50
Jentz, Alan P634
Jeong, Kyong-Deuk W220
Jeong, Tak W292
Jeppesen, Jon A A69
Jepson, Helene A354
Jepson, Brian D. P405
Jereb, Denise A183
Jereb, Denise E66
Jermhansa, Noppawan W203
Jernbeck-Baker, Agneta A532
Jernigan, Donald A14
Jernigan, Janet A101
Jernigan, Donald P7
Jernigan, Emily P81
Jernstedt, Tiffin A683
Jerome, Christopher J. (Chris) A863
Jerome, Brian S P277
Jerpe, David P421
Jerry, Ketcham A272
Jervis, Geoffrey G. E226
Jeske, Julie P527
Jesko, Danielle P128
Jesse, Lisa A795
Jesse, Robert J P421
Jester, Clyde A P133
Jesudason, Rob W105
Jesus, Carmencita De P295
Jeter, Daniel B. A58
Jeter, Daniel B. E16
Jetnil, Anthony E140
Jetter, Martin A460
Jetton, Ann Marie A624

Jewell, Sarika A190
Jewell, Joel A446
Jewell, Marcus A482
Jewell, Matthew J. E167
Jewell, Joel E210
Jewett, Joshua R. (Josh) A274
Jewkes, Roger S. A328
Jha, Rakesh W181
Ji, Seo Na P592
Ji, Henry E377
Jia, Xiaotong A105
Jia, Keith A480
Jiaheng, Wang W68
Jiambalvo, James A861
Jiambalvo, James P658
Jiampetti, Brenda P603
Jian, Yu W94
Jian, Liu W102
Jian, Qiao W218
Jiandani, Soni A199
Jiang, Richard A390
Jiang, Tina A507
Jiang, Tina P288
Jiang, Shibo P372
Jiang, Joseph P511
Jianguo, Yan W92
Jianguo, Han W94
Jianheng, Zhang W403
Jianhua, Zhang W283
Jianwen, Shen P664
Jicinsky, Terry P282
Jick, Daniel P71
Jiga, Anthony A585
Jiga, Anthony P377
Jiganti, Jeanine M. A255
Jilg, Robyn P640
Jillson, Rick A614
Jim, Boan A823
Jimenez, Frank R. A695
Jimenez, Ed P497
Jimerson, Linda P480
Jin, Jeoung (A. J.) A359
Jin, Na A441
Jin, Julie A517
Jin, Jeff E320
Jin-soo, Huh W163
Jin-Soo, Park Jin Soo W219
Jingdong, Wang W186
Jinghui, Tian W283
Jinglei, Cheng W316
Jingzhen, Lin W67
Jinin, Jihan A398
Jinks, Mark P122
Jinping, Gao W332
Jiong, Wang W100
Jipping, Jon E P252
Jishi, Mohannad A522
Jishi, Mohannad P526
Jith, Gayathri S P663
Jitjang, Krit W203
Jivrajani, Jayish A390
Jobanputra, Rakesh A589
Jockett, Joan P620
Joe, Stephanie A875
Joe, David E137
Joerres, Jeffrey A. A894
Joffe, Selwyn E286
Jogaib, Julio A108
Jogaib, Julio E35
Jogrenson, Robert A720
Jogrenson, Robert E362
Johannes, Carol P646
Johanns, Michael A260
Johansen, Kurt A56
Johansen, Jakob V P182
Johansen, Breanna P464
Johansson, Leif W35
Johansson, Leif W360
John, Michelle A100
John, Alan A596
John, Gregory St A698
John, Todd St A850
Johnk, Kellee P481
Johnnie, Mark P55
Johns, Jeff A480

Johns, Beth A500
Johns, John D. A674
Johns, Bobbie P170
Johns, Beth E237
Johnsen, Maryellen A49
Johnsen, Tim P250
Johnsen, David C. P611
Johnsgaard, Dag A305
Johnsgaard, Dag P185
Johnshoy, Nancy A340
Johnshoy, Nancy E151
Johnson, Lesli A2
Johnson, Collister (Coddy) A10
Johnson, Deeadrea A19
Johnson, William A27
Johnson, Stephen L. (Steve) A43
Johnson, Ted M. A47
Johnson, Howard A49
Johnson, Matt A59
Johnson, Sue A81
Johnson, Michele A86
Johnson, Carol A108
Johnson, Jared A109
Johnson, Robert J. A115
Johnson, Paul A115
Johnson, Jennifer A123
Johnson, Timothy A. (Tim) A127
Johnson, Lynn A136
Johnson, Thomas A. A159
Johnson, Jeffrey A164
Johnson, Mary A165
Johnson, Cheryl C A169
Johnson, Denise C A169
Johnson, Nancy A173
Johnson, Bennett A173
Johnson, James W. (Jay) A192
Johnson, Cliff A199
Johnson, William A204
Johnson, Beth A205
Johnson, Eric R. A213
Johnson, Heather A219
Johnson, Bill A257
Johnson, William A257
Johnson, Chris B. A266
Johnson, Don A269
Johnson, Chris A273
Johnson, Richard A286
Johnson, Kimberly H. A315
Johnson, Michael A322
Johnson, Gregory A324
Johnson, Tami A351
Johnson, Richard A. (Dick) A361
Johnson, Gregory E. A365
Johnson, Jennifer M. A365
Johnson, Rupert H. A365
Johnson, Daniel A371
Johnson, S. Daniel (Dan) A374
Johnson, Jill A375
Johnson, Brandon A390
Johnson, James A402
Johnson, Coleman A402
Johnson, Brion A406
Johnson, David A406
Johnson, Dolph A408
Johnson, R. Milton A410
Johnson, Kelly J. A412
Johnson, Brian A432
Johnson, Wes A438
Johnson, Kathryn A448
Johnson, B J A461
Johnson, David A. A478
Johnson, Guy A485
Johnson, Lacy A487
Johnson, Kelli A493
Johnson, Gina A497
Johnson, Ginger A505
Johnson, Erik S A509
Johnson, Philip A511
Johnson, Eric A513
Johnson, Robert A521
Johnson, Romaine A522
Johnson, Clifford A522
Johnson, Emily A543
Johnson, Oliver M. A548
Johnson, Robert A556

Johnson, Melonie A558
Johnson, Margaret L A560
Johnson, Bryon A600
Johnson, Gregory D. (Greg) A609
Johnson, Linda A615
Johnson, Steve A622
Johnson, James W A625
Johnson, Jodie A640
Johnson, Dennis A640
Johnson, Brion A641
Johnson, Vickie A641
Johnson, Rady A. A648
Johnson, Paula A. A653
Johnson, Stuart R. A704
Johnson, Sarah A705
Johnson, David E A709
Johnson, Samuel A718
Johnson, Amy W. A742
Johnson, Robert A758
Johnson, Kevin R. A762
Johnson, Aimee A763
Johnson, Julie H A773
Johnson, Julie A773
Johnson, Susan S. A774
Johnson, Charles A774
Johnson, Matthew A784
Johnson, Brion S A785
Johnson, William D. (Bill) A798
Johnson, Mark M. A800
Johnson, Cheryl H. A804
Johnson, Shannon A. A837
Johnson, Debbie A838
Johnson, Patrick A838
Johnson, Kelly A839
Johnson, Lincoln A861
Johnson, Stephen A866
Johnson, Alan A874
Johnson, Clay A878
Johnson, Jason A902
Johnson, Tracy A912
Johnson, Darrin A912
Johnson, Adam R. A918
Johnson, Robert P26
Johnson, Matt P27
Johnson, Kimberly P32
Johnson, Donna P42
Johnson, Charlotte P45
Johnson, Merida P47
Johnson, Michele P52
Johnson, George P52
Johnson, George P53
Johnson, Dennis P58
Johnson, Darron P60
Johnson, Kendal P63
Johnson, Gerald D. (Jerry) P76
Johnson, Paula P86
Johnson, Peter S P87
Johnson, Bret P94
Johnson, Brooke P106
Johnson, Bertica P108
Johnson, Linda P110
Johnson, Kelly M. P114
Johnson, Boyce P120
Johnson, Clinton L P123
Johnson, Heather P131
Johnson, Kathryn P134
Johnson, J D P145
Johnson, Cindy P147
Johnson, Steve P151
Johnson, Vivian P152
Johnson, Bruce E. P153
Johnson, H Keith P161
Johnson, Greg P166
Johnson, David L P170
Johnson, Deborah C P174
Johnson, David P178
Johnson, Mike P183
Johnson, Barbara P184
Johnson, Harry P185
Johnson, Jt P187
Johnson, Earl P200
Johnson, Lynn P225
Johnson, Steven P. P230
Johnson, Patsy P240
Johnson, Ruthenia P240

Johnson, Christina P242
Johnson, Janice P243
Johnson, Michelle R P247
Johnson, Mark P252
Johnson, Patrice P268
Johnson, Neil P275
Johnson, Janice P279
Johnson, Patricia P286
Johnson, Erik S P288
Johnson, Carrie P300
Johnson, Colleen P312
Johnson, Anthony P313
Johnson, Kathleen P320
Johnson, Oliver M. P321
Johnson, Noila P325
Johnson, Rodney D. P333
Johnson, Brad P337
Johnson, Barbara P340
Johnson, Karen D P343
Johnson, Bernadeia P345
Johnson, Steven P345
Johnson, Cleveland P352
Johnson, Mellisa P356
Johnson, Karen P360
Johnson, David D P363
Johnson, Tracy P391
Johnson, Diane P395
Johnson, Darrell P409
Johnson, Lorette P417
Johnson, Brion P422
Johnson, Vickie P422
Johnson, Kelly P429
Johnson, John P430
Johnson, Joey P439
Johnson, Sandra P464
Johnson, Staci P466
Johnson, Jani L. P473
Johnson, Lisa P474
Johnson, Mike P479
Johnson, Ken P486
Johnson, Robert (Rob) P489
Johnson, James P497
Johnson, Linda P498
Johnson, Susan P500
Johnson, Kirk P506
Johnson, Scott P510
Johnson, Jeff P531
Johnson, Cindy P531
Johnson, Roger P535
Johnson, Jenyl P539
Johnson, Donna P542
Johnson, Sara P546
Johnson, Mark L. P561
Johnson, Ray F P564
Johnson, Aaron P583
Johnson, Zada P610
Johnson, M. Eric P615
Johnson, Mary P617
Johnson, Steven P617
Johnson, Amanda P620
Johnson, Kirk P632
Johnson, Renee P640
Johnson, Julie A. P642
Johnson, Dianne P642
Johnson, Sylvia Smith P644
Johnson, Mary P646
Johnson, Elizabeth J. P654
Johnson, Lincoln P658
Johnson, Jerry N. P676
Johnson, Josephine J P677
Johnson, Paul P680
Johnson, Jason P692
Johnson, Jayme P694
Johnson, Patricia P695
Johnson, Ted P700
Johnson, Sidney W29
Johnson, Chris W258
Johnson, Ingrid W275
Johnson, Gary R. E19
Johnson, Jared E36
Johnson, Roger E38
Johnson, William S. (Bill) E50
Johnson, S. P. (Chip) E59
Johnson, Cheryl E117
Johnson, Leonard F E140

A = AMERICAN BUSINESS
E = EMERGING COMPANIES
P = PRIVATE COMPANIES
W = WORLD BUSINESS

Johnson, J. Thomas (Tommy) E153
Johnson, Tami E158
Johnson, Kelly J. E192
Johnson, Carl J. E214
Johnson, Ginger E241
Johnson, David E288
Johnson, Betty R. E289
Johnson, M. Carl E296
Johnson, Mark E. E298
Johnson, Barry L E300
Johnson, Patrick E349
Johnson, Stuart R. E350
Johnson, Sarah E352
Johnson, Amy W. E372
Johnson, Julie H E387
Johnson, Julie E387
Johnson, Mercedes E394
Johnson, Mark M. E395
Johnson, Kelly E409
Johnson, Wallace H. E419
Johnson, Guy K. E431
Johnson, Bradford D. E438
Johnson, Kirk E447
Johnson-Gregory, Sheree P175
Johnson-Sharp, Jillian P408
Johnston, Mark A25
Johnston, Robert A69
Johnston, Mary A98
Johnston, Maribel A100
Johnston, Debbi A101
Johnston, Lori A. A177
Johnston, Steven J. A196
Johnston, Bryan L A221
Johnston, Andy A231
Johnston, Michael F. (Mike) A279
Johnston, Gregory A322
Johnston, Dave A331
Johnston, Kelly A353
Johnston, Hugh F. A647
Johnston, Mac A655
Johnston, David A676
Johnston, Maryann A721
Johnston, Amy A767
Johnston, Brent A800
Johnston, Lynnette A838
Johnston, Richard A868
Johnston, Greg A878
Johnston, Michael F A898
Johnston, Mark P15
Johnston, Kenneth P60
Johnston, Jeff P101
Johnston, Susan P172
Johnston, Jennifer P239
Johnston, Tammie P250
Johnston, John P256
Johnston, Jeffrey P331
Johnston, Diann P349
Johnston, Lisa P395
Johnston, Charles P421
Johnston, James W. P507
Johnston, Amanda P568
Johnston, Lisa P613
Johnston, J. Dave W161
Johnston, Dave W161
Johnston, Russell (Russ) W297
Johnston, Steve W348
Johnston, Colleen M. W370
Johnston, Mary E33
Johnston, Linda A. E41
Johnston, Dave E148
Johnston, Dan S. E316
Johnston, Daniel E316
Johnston, Mac E333
Johnston, Dale E349
Johnston, Brent E396
Johnston, Bill E405
Johnstone, William O. A98
Johnstone, Jeff A185
Johnstone, Rudolph A753

Johnstone, Sally P685
Johnstone, William O. E33
Johnstone, Rudolph E378
Johnstun, Paul A412
Johnstun, Paul E192
Johri, Akhil A854
Johst, David P. E69
Joia, Eduardo A461
Joiner, Brad A322
Jojo, Linda P. A846
Jokela, Aili A866
Jolas, Paul M. E419
Jolkovsky, Richard P602
Jollay, David L. P157
Jolley, Jennifer A919
Jolley, Jo P92
Jolley, Burke P268
Joly, Hubert A126
Jonas, Ron P259
Jones, Greg A17
Jones, Douglas L. (Doug) A25
Jones, Ross A25
Jones, Katie R A34
Jones, Philip A56
Jones, Brian A59
Jones, Wesley A59
Jones, John P A87
Jones, Alicia A101
Jones, Cary A105
Jones, Bradley A105
Jones, Mike A144
Jones, Anthony A171
Jones, Richard M. A175
Jones, Nicole S. A195
Jones, Rosalyn A201
Jones, Thomas A221
Jones, Larry W. A227
Jones, D. Andrew A227
Jones, Trudy A228
Jones, Bill A240
Jones, Clay A244
Jones, Jeff A246
Jones, Tim A258
Jones, Shane A261
Jones, Laurie A262
Jones, Keri A264
Jones, Wendy A288
Jones, Jeffrey A A332
Jones, Alex A350
Jones, Charles E. (Chuck) A355
Jones, Paul J. A403
Jones, Fred A407
Jones, Bruce A419
Jones, Kevin A440
Jones, Carolyn A441
Jones, Buff A461
Jones, Raymond A461
Jones, Marilyn A466
Jones, Hannah A474
Jones, Dave A485
Jones, Stephen A489
Jones, Steve A496
Jones, David A507
Jones, René F. A522
Jones, Linda A522
Jones, Deanna L. A526
Jones, Beth A530
Jones, Erica A532
Jones, Kevin A560
Jones, Amanda A560
Jones, Wendy A565
Jones, Kim A567
Jones, Julie A578
Jones, Jim A585
Jones, Dan A592
Jones, Christopher T. A602
Jones, Neil A602
Jones, Robert G. (Bob) A614
Jones, Wilson R A625
Jones, Jeff C A630
Jones, Douglas E. (Doug) A642
Jones, Kathleen A644
Jones, Laura A647
Jones, Bill A655
Jones, Rex A655

Jones, Diane A655
Jones, Barbara A659
Jones, Ingrid A671
Jones, Randall T. (Todd) A679
Jones, Randall T. (Todd) A680
Jones, Vk A685
Jones, Bob A693
Jones, Ellen A700
Jones, Karen M. A718
Jones, Tom A718
Jones, Amy A725
Jones, Danny A729
Jones, Ginny A750
Jones, George A766
Jones, Hilliary A774
Jones, Andrea A777
Jones, Tracy A782
Jones, Alicia A785
Jones, Michael S. A789
Jones, Elizabeth A803
Jones, Marni A818
Jones, Bruce A823
Jones, Lisa A826
Jones, Bruce R. A827
Jones, Ernest A836
Jones, Brian A861
Jones, Wally A865
Jones, Jeffrey L A868
Jones, Tony A868
Jones, Steve A885
Jones, Theresa P2
Jones, Joanne P2
Jones, Greg P10
Jones, Douglas L. (Doug) P15
Jones, Ross P15
Jones, Sandra S P20
Jones, Lynwood A P22
Jones, Susan P27
Jones, Doug P54
Jones, C. Todd P58
Jones, Stephen P60
Jones, Jansen P69
Jones, Stephen M. P83
Jones, Stanley P86
Jones, Anthony P100
Jones, Melody L P102
Jones, Vanessa P126
Jones, Trudy P136
Jones, Vernon P144
Jones, Dan P201
Jones, Chris P204
Jones, Otis P P211
Jones, Donna P217
Jones, Jim P219
Jones, Kearline P230
Jones, Jeff P231
Jones, Stephanie P233
Jones, Melanie P242
Jones, Trey P243
Jones, Brian P252
Jones, Mark A P261
Jones, Charles E P261
Jones, Hannah P265
Jones, Raleigh P273
Jones, David P288
Jones, Ashley P310
Jones, Kevin M P314
Jones, Robert V P321
Jones, Steve P334
Jones, Charles E P337
Jones, Barbara P339
Jones, Kevin P342
Jones, Amanda P342
Jones, Jim P377
Jones, Georgia P390
Jones, Donna P403
Jones, Debbie P410
Jones, Jeff C P415
Jones, Jacqueline P420
Jones, Charles E P422
Jones, Janel P424
Jones, Randall T. (Todd) P448
Jones, Lavette P457
Jones, Paulette P462
Jones, Amanda P468

Jones, Kayla P476
Jones, Steve P480
Jones, Thomas H P482
Jones, Dylan P. P489
Jones, Harold P530
Jones, Madelyn P537
Jones, Lauren P539
Jones, Chuck P541
Jones, Elizabeth P562
Jones, Debra P563
Jones, Daniel P578
Jones, Marc P581
Jones, Jeff P594
Jones, Nicholas P. P600
Jones, Tammie P609
Jones, Denise P620
Jones, Barbara P625
Jones, Linda P633
Jones, Reed F P639
Jones, Ruth Ann P645
Jones, Brian P658
Jones, Aranthan P672
Jones, Brad P673
Jones, J Thomas P681
Jones, Samantha P685
Jones, Tiffany P693
Jones, Garth W13
Jones, Den W199
Jones, Jeffrey D. E83
Jones, Mark E96
Jones, Steven M. E99
Jones, Alex E156
Jones, Rob E185
Jones, Barclay G. E226
Jones, Barbara E244
Jones, Andrew M. E281
Jones, Brian E303
Jones, Douglas E. (Doug) E328
Jones, Bill E333
Jones, Rex E333
Jones, Diane E333
Jones, J. Thomas E337
Jones, Andrea E393
Jones, Paul A. E422
Jong, Annemieke De P567
Jonker, Coenraad (Coen) W105
Jons, Douglas A383
Jonsson, Thomas A87
Joo, Miok A204
Jooma, Imran P579
Joon, Lee Won W224
Jope, Alan W381
Jope, Alan W383
Joplin, Joe P391
Jordahl, Mark S. P26
Jordan, Michael A56
Jordan, Raymond A61
Jordan, Kevin A81
Jordan, Steve A115
Jordan, Simon A129
Jordan, Deborah A. A160
Jordan, Michelle A163
Jordan, Teresa A195
Jordan, D. Bryan A348
Jordan, Shawn A446
Jordan, Randy A622
Jordan, Gregory B. A659
Jordan, Robert E. (Bob) A755
Jordan, Sheila A778
Jordan, Henry A878
Jordan, Bill A899
Jordan, Darren A902
Jordan, Terri P177
Jordan, Penny P225
Jordan, Javoris P275
Jordan, Marie K. (Kim) P287
Jordan, Sharon Sobol P336
Jordan, Patrick P380
Jordan, Jeffrey P381
Jordan, Carol P511
Jordan, W M P567
Jordan, Will P594
Jordan, David P627
Jordan, Bill P690
Jordan, Darren P693

Jordan, DeSoto S. E23
Jordan, Deborah A. E55
Jordan, Sheila E140
Jordan, Ronald E147
Jordan, Shawn E210
Jordan-smith, Gavin A912
Jordheim, Robert P. (Rob) E360
Jordon, Stacy P490
Jorgensen, David S. A206
Jorgensen, Blake J. A292
Jorgensen, Helen A434
Jorgensen, Jay T. A878
Jorgensen, Jay T A879
Jorgensen, Mark P222
Jorgensen, Jeffrey B P646
Jorgenson, Rob A720
Jorgenson, Rob E362
Jorsz, William P617
Josaphouitch, Patricia P241
Joseph, Gregory A51
Joseph, Loretta A61
Joseph, Jarvis A105
Joseph, Ritesh A131
Joseph, Oliver A264
Joseph, Tommy S. A462
Joseph, George A551
Joseph, Philip A874
Joseph, Cathy P208
Joseph, Simone P325
Joseph, Leslie P353
Joseph, Dennis P417
Joseph, Michele P459
Joseph, Homan P528
Joseph, Erika E235
Josey, Sheronica P237
Joshi, Amit P446
Joshi, Ketan E119
Joshi, Mehul E355
Joslin, Tim P135
Joslin, Tim A P206
Joslyn, Scott P295
Jossie, Tobey P268
Jostrand, Eric P598
Joswick, David A767
Jotivudh, Ajima P431
Jouett, Brandi P192
Joughin, Dan A767
Jover, Angelines A481
Joves, Fernado P304
Jowers, Gaylon M. A823
Joy, Jennifer A195
Joyal, David A241
Joyal, Shirley P479
Joyce, Matthew A105
Joyce, Deborah A182
Joyce, Thomas P. A253
Joyce, David L. A375
Joyce, Elizabeth A419
Joyce, Robert J. (Bob) A487
Joyce, Tyler P218
Joyce, Katherine A P672
Joyce, Deborah E63
Joyner, Dee A223
Joyner, J. David A250
Joyner, Wayne P591
Joyner, Mildred C. E108
Joysizemore, Dian A98
Joysizemore, Dian E33
Joza, David P30
Jr, John B Morse A17
Jr, James C Carter A22
Jr, William F Gifford A37
Jr, W Hildebrandt Surgner A37
Jr, Paul G Haaga A46
Jr, George Pierce A51
Jr, Murray Watson A145
Jr, Domenic Dell'osso A190
Jr, Roby Thompson A314
Jr, Alton B Lewis A347
Jr, W Michael Amick A463
Jr, Ralph Spencer A572
Jr, John M Fields A624
Jr, Thomas R Quinn A625
Jr, Ronald J Nicolas A630
Jr, Robert C Biesterfeld A711

Jr, Phillip D Joseph A759
Jr, Lawrence C Franklin A765
Jr, Eugene A Deladdy A806
Jr, Richard L Smith A813
Jr, Thomas B Gerlach A813
Jr, Robert A Stewart A846
Jr, Hugh Inman P6
Jr, Todd S Werner P8
Jr, James C Carter P13
Jr, Leroy J Stromberg P19
Jr, Richard Kruse P22
Jr, Walter Sullivan P24
Jr, Everett Alvarez P30
Jr, Paul G Haaga P32
Jr, Donald M Clements P32
Jr, Rick Shadyac P34
Jr, Richard K Trowbridge P37
Jr, John A Miller P39
Jr, James F McEncaney P39
Jr, Donald L Large P51
Jr, Paul J Spina P51
Jr, William J Ferguson P53
Jr, J James Pearce P72
Jr, John F George P75
Jr, Joseph Sarpy P75
Jr, Murray Watson P82
Jr, Andrew Hove P87
Jr, James Walker P88
Jr, Floyd Eharlow P88
Jr, George Robert Vaughan P95
Jr, Horacio De Leon P123
Jr, Claudio Trevino P123
Jr, Arthur C Evans P134
Jr, Henry C Waterer P141
Jr, John Kennedy P145
Jr, Joseph P Santucci P149
Jr, Thomas B Crowley P149
Jr, Wilfred Bahl P149
Jr, John A Garcia P164
Jr, John C Fryer P170
Jr, Ashton J Ryan P173
Jr, Theo Bunting P185
Jr, Roby Thompson P190
Jr, Robert P Lally P204
Jr, Glenn D Steele P209
Jr, Albert Bothe P209
Jr, Glenn D Steele P209
Jr, Roy Tollerson P211
Jr, Ewing Werlein P243
Jr, Ernest J Novak P261
Jr, Carlos Cole P275
Jr, Kenneth E Guise P277
Jr, Emery C Etter P277
Jr, Juan Jos Jj Pea P278
Jr, Robert Dunwoody P282
Jr, Jerry Lamon Falwell P290
Jr, Richard Boland P293
Jr, Martin Salinas P294
Jr, Robert L Lord P310
Jr, Charles A Collat P315
Jr, William K Buscaglia P330
Jr, Thomas M Dono P335
Jr, Ed Witt P343
Jr, Norris L Hodgins P352
Jr, Lindsey Bradely P353
Jr, Dr John Phillips P359
Jr, Ralph Spencer P359
Jr, Robert B Arritt P372
Jr, Robert Blount P396
Jr, Theodore T Myre P398
Jr, Charles E Jones P404
Jr, Griffith R Bryan P412
Jr, Charles N Jordan P414
Jr, Ronald J Nicolas P415
Jr, Louis M Pearce P421
Jr, Jesus Vela P426
Jr, William T Phillips P427
Jr, Robert Allen P453
Jr, Thomas J McCraken P456
Jr, Walter W Austin P462
Jr, Charles M Smith P468
Jr, William Delong P474
Jr, Frederick R Ulrich P480
Jr, Edward M West P482
Jr, J Harry Haslam P484

Jr, Jerome A Benkert P514
Jr, Phillip D Joseph P520
Jr, Theodore Townsend P525
Jr, Lawrence C Franklin P540
Jr, Frederick Seeburger P551
Jr, David Dehaemers P555
Jr, Eugene A Deladdy P569
Jr, William Michael Warren P571
Jr, Eugene A Gargaro P577
Jr, Glenn D Steele P582
Jr, Ben F Kelley P584
Jr, Virgil E Cooper P591
Jr, Daniel Debarba P598
Jr, Kenneth O Johnson P602
Jr, William Hite P603
Jr, Ronald H Foster P605
Jr, Richard L Smith P608
Jr, Thomas B Gerlach P608
Jr, Donald Campbell P612
Jr, J Blacklock Wills P617
Jr, Kenneth J Ronk P631
Jr, Burton Gulnic P632
Jr, George B Hernandez P637
Jr, Eugene P Warr P655
Jr, Mack I Whittle P655
Jr, Mark W Buyck P655
Jr, Othniel H Wienges P655
Jr, Walter F Pratt P655
Jr, William W Jones P655
Jr, James W Dean P659
Jr, David C Hardesty P681
Jr, E Linn Draper P688
Jr, David H Williams P688
Jr, John F Di Lorenzo P688
Jubb, Tim A818
Jubie, Nicole A311
Jubouri, Shams P69
Juby, Alyce A489
Juchno, Stacy M. A659
Jucker, Bernhard W4
Juday, Mark A34
Juday, Ryan A816
Juday, Mark P27
Judd, Paul P65
Judd, Liz P109
Jude, Justin L. A518
Judge, Ann A147
Judge, James J. (Jim) A307
Judge, Will A538
Judge, Robert P6
Judge, Liz P236
Judge, Dennis F. P588
Judge, Martin E. P588
Judy, Ryan A67
Judy, Brian P344
Judy, Bascom P400
Juergensen, Colleen A496
Juett, Phillip P333
Jula, Peg A332
Julian, Paul C. A546
Julian, Steve A736
Julian, Kenneth D. A816
Julian, Steve P492
Julian, James R. P645
Julian, Heather San P663
Juliane, Jeffrey A163
Juliano, Mark A502
Julie, Norton P392
Julien, Jeffrey P. (Jeff) A693
Julien, Marc--%otienne W299
Jump, Darrell P399
Jump, Jamie E97
Jun, Albert P266
Jun-Ho, Kim W332
Junck, Mary E. P566
Junco, Kirk P282
Junco, Kirk D P589
Juneau, Jeff A763
Jung, Katie A682
Jung, Lisa A A777
Jung, Dong-chang W292
Jung, Holger R. E236
Jung, Lisa A E393
Jung-ho, Park W333
Jungmann, Dr John P522

Junior, Joseph P145
Junius, Daniel M E213
Junker, Jason A198
Junker, Heinz K. W230
Junkins, Lowell L. A320
Junkins, Lowell L. E143
Junming, Guo W175
Junod, Vincent A727
Juppenlatz, Stuart A369
Jura, Walter P583
Jureta, Madelaine A49
Jurrens, Erika A165
Jurrens, Lisa A540
Jurrens, Lisa P316
Jurs, Peter A332
Juster, Andrew A. (Andy) A744
Justice, Peggy A429
Justice, Lorraine P464
Justice, Ronald L. E147
Justin, Marianne A863
Justinger, Kimberly A252
Jutras, Mary E144
J-okel, Julia W62
J-rgensen, Torsten Hagen W269
J-rgensen, Lars Fruergaard W271
Jégo-Laveissi-"re, Mari-No-«lle W278

K

Kaahanui, Gisele L P202
Kaare, Rae P48
Kaatman, Nancy J A136
Kaatz, Alexander A454
Kaatz, Gary E P66
Kaban, Leonard P590
Kabani, Farhan E257
Kabat, Kevin A594
Kabat, Kevin T. A864
Kabbani, Samer E83
Kablawi, Hani A105
Kabourek, Chris P78
Kacavas, John P154
Kachel, Denise P223
Kachurka, Matt A247
Kachurka, Matt E103
Kaczmarek, Larry A402
Kaczmarek, Walter T. (Walt) A414
Kaczmarek, Paulette A600
Kaczmarek, Jessica A810
Kaczmarek, Jessica P586
Kaczmarek, Walter T. (Walt) E194
Kaczynski, Tom A527
Kadakia, Jigar P214
Kadam, Deepa P445
Kaden, Ellen O A161
Kadhim, Sarah P292
Kadien, Thomas G. (Tom) A462
Kadlec, Tom A788
Kadnar, Julie A51
Kadokami, Ei W241
Kadoori, Bob A173
Kadouchi, Hitoshi W115
Kadre, Manuel A707
Kaduke, David A497
Kadwa, Kaizad P528
Kadyrova, Tatiana A866
Kaelin, Michael H. (Mike) P458
Kaercher, Walter A644
Kaeser, Joe W331
Kaestner, H. Todd A148
Kaestner, Todd A149
Kaewrungruang, Wallaya W330
Kafer, Tim P303
Kafka, Robert A85
Kafka, Donald L. A336
Kagan, Mariel S P227
Kagawa, Jiro W202
Kahan, James A517
Kahan, Rich A728
Kahl, Cathy P312
Kahl, Cindy P551
Kahler, Charles P361
Kahley, Jeanann M P105
Kahn, Cheryl A165

A = AMERICAN BUSINESS
E = EMERGING COMPANIES
P = PRIVATE COMPANIES
W = WORLD BUSINESS

Kahn, Wendy A785
Kahn, Todd A785
Kahn, Sandy P182
Kahne, Michael A350
Kahny, Michael E156
Kahny, Nicole A872
Kai, Keishi W261
Kaider, Mike A173
Kaifu, Kaifu P405
Kaighn, Chris A79
Kail, Marilyn P96
Kain, Peter A577
Kain, Larry A655
Kain, Larry E333
Kain, Rob E429
Kainer, Darrell A303
Kainersdorfer, Franz W389
Kairys, John P618
Kaiser, George B. A137
Kaiser, Allen A260
Kaiser, Chris A272
Kaiser, Laura S. A458
Kaiser, Frances A583
Kaiser, Gregory A729
Kaiser, Jennifer P30
Kaiser, Michael P178
Kaiser, Laura S. P251
Kaiser, Daphne P277
Kaiser, Maile E96
Kaiserman, David J. A508
Kaiwa, Makoto W366
Kaiyala, Andy P589
Kajtoch, Gary A. E135
Kakar, Dee A522
Kakivayi, Sumana P584
Kakiya, Tatsuo W327
Kakkis, Jane P323
Kakogiannis, Efstathios A. W24
Kakuda, Kevin A171
Kakuda, Kevin P100
Kalafos, Paul A602
Kalajainen, Kimberly P283
Kalakkad, Dinesh A501
Kalamaras, Paul A467
Kalamaras, Paul E223
Kalambur, Ganesh P620
Kalanihuia, Janice P601
Kalanovic, Daniel A649
Kalaria, Brij A133
Kalathur, Rajesh (Raj) A260
Kalchik, Mona A107
Kalchik, Mona E35
Kalchuri, Shantanu A607
Kale, Kathy P440
Kaleel, Reza P536
Kalen, Michael A677
Kalfayan, Terry P653
Kali, Thomas A133
Kalin, Katherine A178
Kalin, Robert A565
Kalinowski, Brian E445
Kalisek, Brian A559
Kalish, David W. E47
Kalish, David W. E317
Kall, Sheryl P515
Kallal, William P503
Kalleeny, Monica A250
Kallenbach, Charles P232
Kallio, Jerry A541
Kallio, Jerry E266
Kallsen, Tony E A720
Kallsen, Terri R. A728
Kallsen, Tony E E362
Kallweit, Keith A292
Kalman, Betsy A500
Kalman, Betsy E237
Kalmar, Steven A461
Kalmin, Steven W159
Kaloussis, Evangelos J. W24

Kaloustian, Maral A152
Kaloustian, Maral E48
Kalp, Dirk P686
Kalsbeek, David P155
Kalscheur, Gregory P625
Kalstein, Michele A323
Kaltenbach, Patrick A22
Kalter, Robert P302
Kamachi, Patrick A101
Kamal, Mostafa M. A524
Kamal, Ashfaq A537
Kamal-Bahl, Sachin A649
Kamara, Abdul A165
Kamara, Ernest T P391
Kamath, Sundar A725
Kambe, Shiro W337
Kamber, Martin A133
Kambik, Phillip P462
Kamei, Katsunobu W279
Kamei, Atsushi W324
Kamell, Ralph P297
Kamenakis, Marina E104
Kamenash, Tracey A406
Kamensky, Allan E. A781
Kameoka, Tsuyoshi W330
Kametz, William (Bill) A720
Kametz, William (Bill) E362
Kamford, Peter A122
Kamijo, Masahito W301
Kamiliotis, Daniela A691
Kamin, John R. A614
Kaminski, Jennifer A81
Kaminski, Ken A199
Kaminski, Jeff J. A484
Kaminski, Robert B. A549
Kaminski, Mark V. A703
Kaminski, Monika A920
Kaminski, Scott P213
Kaminski, Paul P535
Kaminski, Robert B. E270
Kaminsky, John A729
Kaminsky, Jody E407
Kamitaki, Wayne A183
Kamke, Trent G. E242
Kamlot, Andreas P263
Kamm, Terry A136
Kammerer, Richard F. P572
Kammerman, Susan P417
Kammerman, Eli E261
Kamminga, Duane A350
Kamminga, Duane E157
Kammonen, Osmo W257
Kamp, W. Taylor E261
Kamphaus, Randy P651
Kampling, Patricia P36
Kamra, Kush A556
Kamrath, Richard P263
Kamsickas, James K A252
Kan, Tetsuya W301
Kanai, Seita W235
Kanai, Makoto W273
Kanakubo, Atsushi W116
Kanamori, Hitoshi W400
Kanani, Karen P482
Kanarian, Steve A659
Kanas, John A. A109
Kanas, John A. E36
Kanaya, Susan M. E72
Kanazawa, Yugo W223
Kanda, Haruo W400
Kandamangalam, SAI P239
Kandarian, Steven A. (Steve) A555
Kandek, Wolfgang E342
Kandt, Debbie P633
Kane, Rachel A101
Kane, Peter A175
Kane, Thomas M. (Tom) A235
Kane, Jessica A317
Kane, Debbie A406
Kane, Brian A. A437
Kane, Edward A440
Kane, Bob A454
Kane, Terri A458
Kane, James A517
Kane, John A575

Kane, Martha A635
Kane, Eileen A775
Kane, Eric A782
Kane, Patrick P92
Kane, Terri P251
Kane, Kenneth P296
Kane, Martha P419
Kane, Allen R. P506
Kane, Deborah E127
Kane, Jessica E142
Kanefsky, Andrea A122
Kaneko, Shin W86
Kaneko, Hiroshi W201
Kang, SungWon A308
Kang, Katelyn A429
Kang, Charlotte A478
Kang, In-Byeong W220
Kang, Yu Sig W220
Kang, Katelyn E204
Kangas, Chris A537
Kanis, Jordan A777
Kanis, Jordan E393
Kanlic, Elvis A489
Kann, Joe A712
Kanneman, Paul D A743
Kanneman, Paul D E373
Kanome, Hiroyuki W19
Kanouff, Yvette A199
Kansler, Michael R A300
Kant, Surya A789
Kant, Surya P555
Kantamneni, Raje A599
Kantaros, Andrea A644
Kantola, Kevin A855
Kantor, Jonathan D. (Jon) A211
Kantor, Lesley A872
Kantor, Ann P408
Kantro, Gayle A478
Kanwal, Ajay W340
Kanwar, Neena P270
Kanwar, Rahul E383
KAO, Kenneth P338
Kao, Roger W113
Kapcheck, Jeff A173
Kaperi, Ari W269
Kapito, Robert S. (Rob) A130
Kapki, Nick Kapki Nick A865
Kaplan, Dean A175
Kaplan, Bob A175
Kaplan, Robert S. (Rob) A325
Kaplan, Grisel A644
Kaplan, Ralph A725
Kaplan, Robert A766
Kaplan, David A818
Kaplan, Betina P642
Kaplan, Alan P659
Kaplan, Jordan L. E110
Kaplan, Steven E327
Kaplan, Ronald W. (Ron) E401
Kaplin, Leo A100
Kaplon, Sari P349
Kapnick, Stewart A541
Kapnick, Stewart E266
Kapoor, Rakesh A478
Kapoor, Sanjay A758
Kapoor, Rohit E138
Kapur, Patricia P631
Kapusinski, Victor A865
Karachalios, Konstantinos P586
Karadere, Nafiz W377
Karafa, Jeffrey L A754
Karageorges, Carolyn P115
Karam, Chris P118
Karam, Saad P510
Karamanoukian, Henry A671
Karamarkovich, Kim A774
Karamouzis, Nikolaos Basil W145
Karanam, Raj A253
Karanga, Ruth A593
Karanjkar, Ashish A647
Karas, Michelle (Shelley) A640
Karas, Gail P138
Karasawa, Yasuyoshi W249
Karatha, Padmanabhan A221

Karatsu, Masanori W240
Karavias, Fokion Christos W145
Karbach, J William P567
Kareiva, Peter P596
Karen, Friedman A912
Karen, Mahoney E3
Kargar, Peyman W265
Karhan, Dean A317
Karhan, Dean E142
Karkaria, Hormuzd A265
Karl, James A16
Karl, Patricia P146
Karl, Walter P582
Karlovich, Robert W. (Trey) A591
Karlsen, Brooke P189
Karlstromer, Peter A200
Karn, Randy A898
Karnes, Willie A115
Karnes, Merle A673
Karnik, Nihar A599
Karns, Steven R. P280
Karolis, George C. A78
Karp, Jill P470
Karp, Stephen R. P570
Karpik, Mike A766
Karpinos, Robert P528
Karpinski, John A449
Karpowicz, Paul E272
Karr, Kathi A430
Karr, Michael A630
Karr, Thomas P224
Karr, Michael P415
Karran, Tony P290
Karras, Athanasios A429
Karrer, Joy P398
Karriker, Karen A461
Karrip, Brian A342
Karros, Kirt A419
Karsh, Bruce A. E312
Karsh, Bill E320
Karsh, Bruce A. E402
Karshmer, Judith F. P654
Karst, Darren W. A708
Karsten, Diederik W222
Karstensen, Steen S. W1
Karten, Bruce E46
Karter, Nicholas A685
Karuppur, Devi Prasad A687
Karwacki, John A682
Karytinos, Aristotelis W253
Kasai, Yoshiyuki W86
Kasai, Masahiro W342
Kasanoff, Howard A244
Kasbar, Michael J. A906
Kase, Yutaka W336
Kaseman, Sheila P114
Kasendorf, Leonard A556
Kasey, Jay P354
Kashian, Alan E207
Kashiwagi, Yasuo W268
Kashkari, Neel T. A325
Kashyap, Nagraj A685
Kasman, Glenn P357
Kasner, Ken A406
Kasparie, Betty P75
Kasper, Michael A34
Kasper, Meghann A100
Kasper, Andrea A676
Kasper, Meghann E34
Kass, Ryan E122
Kassab, Leanne D. A212
Kassab, Leanne D. E79
Kassem, Amin A438
Kassem, Rona P331
Kasser, James P570
Kassis, Chuck P314
Kast, Pete A173
Kast, Steve P556
Kastanis, Maria A644
Kastberg, Crystal A672
Kastberg, Amalia G A724
Kastner, Christopher D. A442
Kastner, Christopher K. A534
Kastner, Janeen B. A716
Kasuya, Tsuyoshi W208

Kaszuba, Marek A898
Katahira, Satoru W279
Katanick, Ron A493
Kataoka, Kazunori W279
Katariya, Sanjeev A288
Katayama, James P245
Katayama, Masanori W190
Katayama, Mikio W259
Katcher, Abbey A101
Katcher, Keith A607
Kate, Debold A105
Kates, Kenneth P P643
Kather, Peter P134
Katherman, William H. (Bill) E168
Kathy, Dunn P255
Katibian, Benny A685
Katie, Cave A724
Katims, Susan A155
Kato, Takeshi W48
Kato, Minoru W172
Kato, Kazuyasu W207
KATO, KIKUO W250
Kato, Hideaki W336
Kato, Toshizumi W399
Katoh, Nobuaki W121
Katseli, Louka T. W253
Katsianis, John P157
Katsikas, Cindy A541
Katsikas, Cindy E266
Katsuno, Satoru W99
Katsura, Yasuo W282
Katt, Faye A113
Kattan, Omar P631
Kattawar, Michael P443
Katte, Hans-Dieter W223
Katterheinrich, Lean P133
Kattos, Andrew N. (Andy) A737
Kattos, Andrew N. (Andy) E367
Katyal, Navin A648
Katz, Marc D. A155
Katz, Robert L. (Bobby) A471
Katz, Jonathan A635
Katz, Ellen P72
Katz, Martin J. (Marty) P132
Katz, Jonathan P419
Katz, Cathie P480
Katz, Robert A. (Rob) E424
Kauffman, Holly C A355
Kauffman, Andy A530
Kauffman, Robert E428
Kaufman, Jules P. A241
Kaufman, Victor A. A311
Kaufman, Richard A635
Kaufman, Dan P256
Kaufman, Dan P257
Kaufman, Charles P341
Kaufman, Richard P419
Kaufman, Irvin A P451
Kaufman, Irvin A. P452
Kaufman, Sam P663
Kaufman, Ivan E22
Kaufman, Brett H. E236
Kaufmann, Michael C. (Mike) A165
Kaufmann, Kevin A583
Kaul, Will P219
Kaune, Teri P79
Kaup, Nicholas P612
Kaupe, Sandra T P548
Kausch, Thomas P464
Kauser, Nicolas E328
Kaushal, Sunil W340
Kautz, David E207
Kautzman, Barbara P486
Kavanagh, Ben A244
Kavanaugh, James J. A460
Kavanaugh, James P. (Jim) A907
Kavanaugh, James P. (Jim) P696
Kavassalis, Tom A912
Kavehrad, Katie P363
Kawa, Mark A774
Kawahara, Makoto W190
Kawai, Shuji W115
Kawai, Katsutomo W116
Kawai, Masanori W260
Kawai, Hideaki W282

Kawai, Fumiyoshi W344
Kawai, Mitsuru W374
Kawakami, Hiroshi W211
Kawale, Nitin E359
Kawamoto, Ryuichi W223
Kawamoto, Shoichiro W245
Kawamura, Yumiko W169
Kawamura, Takashi W368
Kawanami, Mark E398
Kawasaki, Hiroyuki A917
Kawasaki, Hiroyuki P701
Kawasaki, Hiroya W208
Kawasaki, Yasuyuki W345
Kawasaki, Masuo W349
Kawata, Hiro P215
Kay, Linda Sloane A184
Kay, Julie A186
Kay, Robert A729
Kay, David A762
Kay, Steve A. A860
Kay, Stephen B. P82
Kay, Steve A. P656
Kaye, David J. A142
Kaye, Stephen E235
Kayitalire, Louis A147
Kayser, C. Dallas A207
Kayser, Catherine A782
Kayzerman, Alex A480
Kaza, Srini E10
Kazaglis, Laura P263
Kazakevich, Vadim A105
Kazazian, Haig A475
Kazazian, Haig P266
Kazi, Zubair A204
Kazian, Michelle E127
Kazinski, Beth A774
Keables, Michael P132
Keach, Michael A489
Keadey, Matthew P182
Kealey, Katie P302
Kealy, Mary V P297
Kean, Steven J. (Steve) A491
Kean, Steven J P131
Kean, Steve P366
Kean, Darrin P410
Kean, Sue W275
Keane, Daniel A604
Keane, James A712
Keane, Valerie A736
Keane, Conor A767
Keane, John B P32
Keane, Valerie P492
Keane, Kevin T. E25
Keany, James P345
Kear, Scott A13
Kearley, Donna P159
Kearney, Michael S A78
Kearney, Dan A175
Kearney, Daniel A402
Kearney, Sara A445
Kearney, Nancy A774
Kearney, Tim A818
Kearney, Thomas W. A907
Kearney, Thomas W. E445
Kearns, Richard A82
Kearns, John A306
Kearns, Richard P A49
Kearns, Donald B P451
Kearns, Donald P452
Kearns, Brian E179
Kearns, Jeff E432
Kearny, Ric A163
Kearsley, Alan P477
Keat, Cheong Jin W13
Keating, Leslie A13
Keating, Kim A85
Keating, Thomas P A116
Keating, Johnathan A131
Keating, Tim A136
Keating, Michael A295
Keating, Mark R. A766
Keating, Michael P333
Keating, Patricia P349
Keating, Mary P363
Keating, Katie P522

Keating, Patrick J. P625
Keating, Todd P632
Keats, Michael P192
Keaunui, Naalei A103
Keay, Clinton W137
Keblar, Paula P418
Keckeis, Thomas M. (Tom) P334
Kedderis, Pamela J P139
Kedia, Gunjan A766
Kedia, Gunjan A865
Kee, Rob A453
Kee, Timothy A898
Keefauver, David A439
Keefe, Denise M. A15
Keefe, Tom A388
Keefe, Timothy A542
Keefe, Brenda A744
Keefe, Brandt A770
Keefe, Denise M. P9
Keefe, Pamela J. P179
Keefe, Dennis D P695
Keefer, Joseph G. (Joe) A151
Keefer, Elizabeth P99
Keefer, Joseph G. (Joe) E48
Keefer-Hugill, J A151
Keefer-Hugill, J E48
Keegan, Margaret A469
Keegan, Robert J. (Bob) A912
Keegan, Michael P453
Keel, Errol A914
Keeler, Brian P144
Keeler, Tracy P243
Keeler, Scott P580
Keeler, Martha E183
Keeley, Karen A919
Keeley, Brian E. P57
Keeley, Jim E189
Keeling, E F P410
Keeling, Kelli P685
Keen, Sandy A614
Keen, Eric L P228
Keen, Eric L. P229
Keen, Amy P538
Keenan, Steven J. A69
Keenan, David A522
Keenan, Christopher A539
Keenan, David R. (Dave) A700
Keenan, Karen D. A766
Keenan, Joseph (Joe) P595
Keenan, Paul A. E75
Keene, Mark P14
Keener, Kevin P276
Keener, Larry E61
Keenum, Mark E P346
Keeran, Colleen P550
Keesee, Don A107
Keesee, Annikan P482
Keesee, Don E34
Keetch, Chad A. E125
Keeton, Winn A182
Keeton, Tommy P512
Keeton, Winn E63
Kefeli, Hülya W18
Kefer, Volker W121
Keffer, Terry P567
Kegley, Clark P488
Kehle, Shannon E348
Kehler, Grant A158
Kehoe, James A567
Kehoe, James W355
Kehr, Anthony P109
Kehui, Zhang W94
Keidel, Jill A371
Keiffer, Mark A84
Keil, Kristen A644
Keil, Virginia P613
Keilen, Joyce A449
Keilin, Eugene J. P302
Keim, Mark L. A402
Keim, Michael S A862
Keim, Marco W10
Keim, Michael S E419
Keiper, Joel A413
Keiper, Joel P234
Keiser, Kenneth A. A247

Keiser, Kenneth A. E102
Keitel, Judy A234
Keitel, Judy P139
Keith, Perry A277
Keith, R. Alexandra A671
Keith, Kevin P163
Keith, Greg P258
Keith, Giffney P501
Keivani, Beth P395
Keizer, Henry R A809
Keizer, Henry R P584
Keklak, Stephen C P107
Kekoolani, Kaleo A102
Kelej, Rasha A550
Kelemen, Eric A441
Kelfer, Howard P141
Keliher, Lester A800
Keliher, Lester E396
Kelin, Alex P481
Kell, Stephen A801
Kell, Stephen P561
Kellam, Richard A391
Kellan, Jeff A493
Kellar, Brian A111
Kellar, Michael A513
Kellar, Brian P56
Kellas, Steve A886
Kellas, Steve E433
Kelleher, Ann B. A456
Kelleher, Colm A568
Kelleher, Kevin J. A696
Kelleher, Margaret Ann P352
Kelleher, Dennis P P558
Kelleher, Kathleen P658
Keller, Ken A61
Keller, Brett A139
Keller, Shawn A235
Keller, Kevin A407
Keller, Robert A578
Keller, Kurt A. A634
Keller, Stacey L A684
Keller, Stacey A684
Keller, Erika A691
Keller, Steven L. (Steve) A717
Keller, Greg A782
Keller, Kimberly A841
Keller, Jonell P23
Keller, Martin P25
Keller, San P34
Keller, Kevin P229
Keller, Rick P577
Keller, Dennis J. P610
Keller, John C. P611
Keller, Kimberly P633
Keller, Sue P682
Keller, Doreen L E289
Keller, Bob E331
Keller, Stacey L E341
Keller, Stacey E341
Kellett, James A701
Kelley, Patrick M A120
Kelley, Deborah A127
Kelley, Jack A196
Kelley, Daniel T. (Dan) A214
Kelley, Bruce G. A292
Kelley, Thomas M A336
Kelley, Thomas M. (Tom) A527
Kelley, Kristin A628
Kelley, Scot A667
Kelley, Laurie A674
Kelley, Cindy A709
Kelley, Tim A724
Kelley, Nathan A755
Kelley, Desni A775
Kelley, William A829
Kelley, Scott C. A860
Kelley, Rae P34
Kelley, Laura P105
Kelley, Daniel T. (Dan) P128
Kelley, Thomas M P194
Kelley, Kathy P225
Kelley, Randall P298
Kelley, Brian P314
Kelley, Jennifer P343
Kelley, Jim P388

A = AMERICAN BUSINESS
E = EMERGING COMPANIES
P = PRIVATE COMPANIES
W = WORLD BUSINESS

Kelley, Laurie P444
Kelley, Trenton L P559
Kelley, Lawrence (Larry) P613
Kelley, Scott C. P656
Kelley, Franklin P660
Kelley, Jeannine E101
Kelley, Bruce E300
Kelley, Nathan E380
Kelligrew, James B. A865
Kelling, James E426
Kellmer, Matthias E139
Kellner, Bob A865
Kellogg, Peter N. A178
Kelly, Brian G. A10
Kelly, Thomas B. (Tom) A17
Kelly, Shannon A40
Kelly, Kendra A54
Kelly, Michael A. A61
Kelly, Davitt A133
Kelly, Mark A158
Kelly, William A158
Kelly, Keith A205
Kelly, John A207
Kelly, Paul A234
Kelly, Thomas A. A242
Kelly, Edward J. (Ned) A243
Kelly, Cargile A289
Kelly, John A291
Kelly, Eric A292
Kelly, Carl A310
Kelly, Jody A329
Kelly, Theresa A359
Kelly, Catherine T. (Kate) A412
Kelly, Anastasia A442
Kelly, Joel A449
Kelly, Andy A449
Kelly, John E. A460
Kelly, Christie B. A478
Kelly, Gary A513
Kelly, Daniel A548
Kelly, Marcella A555
Kelly, Tom A555
Kelly, Amber A560
Kelly, Scott A594
Kelly, Laura A644
Kelly, Michael (Mike) A682
Kelly, Gary C. A755
Kelly, Carol A764
Kelly, Michele A A770
Kelly, Peter A836
Kelly, Alfred F. (Al) A874
Kelly, Lawana A920
Kelly, John J. P2
Kelly, Thomas B. (Tom) P10
Kelly, Patrick P18
Kelly, Chari P50
Kelly, Kim A. P107
Kelly, Michael P P113
Kelly, Paul P139
Kelly, Carol P225
Kelly, Francina P233
Kelly, Patty P247
Kelly, Eugene P277
Kelly, Linda P277
Kelly, Daniel P324
Kelly, Amber P342
Kelly, Thomas J P351
Kelly, Thompson P387
Kelly, Alan P487
Kelly, Chad P501
Kelly, Dennis P506
Kelly, Patrice P510
Kelly, Carol P540
Kelly, Elizabeth P548
Kelly, Kevin R. P611
Kelly, Katy P623
Kelly, Melvin L P644
Kelly, Robert P650
Kelly, Catherine T. (Kate) E192

Kelner, Karen P157
Kelsey, Paul A478
Kelso, J. Pete A18
Kelso, Bill A434
Kelso, Alan W A782
Kelson, Richard B A659
Keltner, Thomas N E122
Kelty, Matt A777
Kelty, Matt E393
Kelvinton, William C P421
Kely, Jim A460
Kemer, Dan A517
Kemna, Horst Paulmann W85
Kemp, Terri M A45
Kemp, Gerald A331
Kemp, Kristian A458
Kemp, Stephen J. A661
Kemp, Danin P226
Kemp, Kristian P251
Kemp, Nicole P333
Kemp, Matthew P337
Kemp, Chuck P436
Kemp, Anne P525
Kemp, Gerald E148
Kempczinski, Chris (Chris K) A545
Kempen, Wouter T. van A257
Kemper, David W. A223
Kemper, John W. A223
Kemper, Jonathan M. A223
Kemper, Dorothy A272
Kemper, J. Mariner A837
Kemper, David W. P616
Kemper, Talfourd H. E251
Kempic, Mark A594
Kemps, Steven J. (Steve) A721
Kempton, David D A371
Kenagy, John P285
Kenas, Jamie A49
Kendall, Carter A173
Kendall, Jean P449
Kendall, Randolph L. (Randy) P564
Kendall, Shirley P631
Kendall, Angela P665
Kendall, Clifford M. E430
Kendrick, Robin A141
Kendrick, Lynn A655
Kendrick, Andrew W98
Kendrick, Lynn E333
Kendricks, Samuel B. A399
Kendris, Thomas (Tom) A603
Kendris, Thomas (Tom) P399
Kenefick, Jeffrey P. A334
Kenigsztein, Betzalel W222
Kenkman, Brian P275
Kenna, Sheila Mc P86
Kenna, Wade Mc P157
Kenna, Robert J Mc P575
Kennard, Corey P530
Kennedy, Brad A17
Kennedy, Bryan J. A32
Kennedy, Castlen A69
Kennedy, Terry A101
Kennedy, Al A175
Kennedy, Peter A221
Kennedy, Lisa A247
Kennedy, John A250
Kennedy, Paul A257
Kennedy, Greg A262
Kennedy, Michael A335
Kennedy, Parker S. A335
Kennedy, Ken A338
Kennedy, Chris A497
Kennedy, James E. (Jim) A589
Kennedy, Joanne A596
Kennedy, Douglas L. A639
Kennedy, Stacey A652
Kennedy, Thomas A. (Tom) A694
Kennedy, Aniel O A710
Kennedy, Scott A788
Kennedy, Kevin A792
Kennedy, Shaun A800
Kennedy, Beverly A817
Kennedy, Daniel A819
Kennedy, Brad P10
Kennedy, Kevin J P52

Kennedy, Charles A. P96
Kennedy, Pam P118
Kennedy, Paul P151
Kennedy, John P164
Kennedy, Ryan P239
Kennedy, Dr J D P318
Kennedy, Bruce P335
Kennedy, John F. P367
Kennedy, Peter P395
Kennedy, Danny P460
Kennedy, John W128
Kennedy, Brian W256
Kennedy, Melissa J. W347
Kennedy, James J. E90
Kennedy, Lisa E103
Kennedy, Ken E149
Kennedy, Douglas L. E325
Kennedy, Robin E326
Kennedy, Shaun E396
Kennelly, Nancy A555
Kennemer, Derek A439
Kenner, Andrew A895
Kennett, Ron A667
Kenney, Jeanne A300
Kenney, Anthony R. (Tony) A527
Kenney, David A712
Kenney, Tom A879
Kennon, S. Gary A279
Kenny, Katharine A166
Kenny, David W. A460
Kenny, Natalie A532
Kenny, Mark A788
Kenny, John A869
Kenny, Maureen E. P625
Kenny, Joe W274
Kenski, Laurie A204
Kensler, Lisa W P51
Kent, Muhtar A3
Kent, John A130
Kent, Muhtar A215
Kent, Cory A332
Kent, Kenneth R A362
Kent, James L. (Jim) A547
Kent, Shawn A552
Kent, James L. (Jim) P319
Kent, Shawn P328
Kent, Howard E90
Kent-Sheehan, Kate A353
Kenwood, James A258
Kenyon, John A109
Kenyon, Simone A328
Kenyon, Bill A851
Kenyon, Debra P278
Kenyon, John E36
Keogh, Tracy S. A435
Keogh, Dan A696
Keogh, Dawn A869
Keogh, James P283
Keogh, John W. W98
Keohane, Michael A449
Keon, Thomas L P449
Keough, Susan — A738
Keown, James A84
Keown, Karen A855
Kephart, Bob P308
Kephart, Tina P355
Kepler, Mary A322
Keppel, Mary Ann P230
Kepple, Yann P230
Keppner, Judy L. E414
Keqiang, Xu W102
Kerber, Lynn M. A187
Kerber, Lynn M. E71
Kerbeshian, Marie P611
Kereere, Suzan A49
Kerger, Paula A. P445
Kerins, Sean J. A77
Kerkhoff, Guido W365
Kerley, Jay A71
Kern, Howard P. A736
Kern, Howard P. P492
Kern, Howard P493
Kern, Andreas W166
Kern, Peter M. E402
Kernaghan, Paul W23

Kernan, Michael A98
Kernan, William P A807
Kernan, May P94
Kernan, William P P574
Kernan, Michael E33
Kerner, Jürgen W231
Keroack, Mark A. P65
Kerr, Derek J. A43
Kerr, William A105
Kerr, Andrew A333
Kerr, Julie A A432
Kerr, Debbie A505
Kerr, Mary E. P98
Kerr, Howard J P140
Kerr, Robert W P140
Kerr, Bob P140
Kerr, Barbara P527
Kerr, Cathy P663
Kerr, Mario E359
Kerrigan, Robert A298
Kerris, Robert F. (Bob) E116
Kerschbaum, Manfred A71
Kerschner, Barry A532
Kerschner, Joseph E P591
Kersh, Rogan P673
Kershaw, David A820
Kerslake, Kent P211
Kervin, Karen A866
Kerwin, Cornelius M. P37
Kerwin, George P67
Kerwin, George P68
Kesavan, Sudhakar A7
Keskar, Dinesh A. A136
Keskin, Cengizhan P226
Kesler, Shawn A81
Kesler, Andrew A158
Kesler, D. Craig E112
Kess, Avrohom J. A828
Kessel, Steve A38
Kessel, Cindy A313
Kessel, Kathryn A555
Kessel, Donna Van P505
Kesseler, Brian A796
Kesselman, Marc A917
Kessler, Ben A97
Kessler, Bethmara A161
Kessler, Marla A469
Kessler, Steven A556
Kessler, Irvin R. P503
Kessler, Renee P620
Kessler, Bruce L. W98
Kessler, Michael W98
Kessler, Denis W323
Kessler, Ben E32
Kessler-Sanders, Michelle A682
Kester, John A235
Kester, Paige A423
Kester, Dennis A493
Kester, Jenny P164
Keswick, Ben W195
Keswick, Adam W195
Keswick, Henry W195
Keswick, Ben W196
Keswick, Henry W196
Ketchie, Bertha P670
Ketchum, John A590
Ketelaar, Martin P. E343
Keto, Steven P166
Ketola, Todd P61
Ketola, Cindy P337
Ketter-Hanna, Rosanne P498
Ketterer, Chuck A295
Kettler, Tamara P387
Kettmann, Dana P549
Kettner, Patricia A477
Kettner, Patricia P268
Keucher, Stephen P627
Keucher, Steve P627
Keuer, Steve P120
Keung, Yeung Kwok W109
Keup, Gregory P40
Keuten, John P692
Kevin, Liney A651
Kevin, Lay P198
Kevin, Liney P426

Key, Daniel A214
Key, George A397
Key, Daniel P128
Key, George P221
Key, Lester P275
Key, Charles P275
Keyes, Kevin G. A66
Keyes, Kevin G. A67
Keyes, Gregory A782
Keyes, J. Patrick A884
Keyes, Jim A893
Keyes, Cheralee P184
Keyes, Beth P611
Keyler, Joseph A350
Keyler, Joseph E156
Keys, Lisa P622
Keys, Randall D. E137
Keyser, Richard A819
Keyser, Brian E107
Kezbers, Annette P249
Khadka, Pravesh P345
Khafizova, Ariadna A407
Khairallah, Joseph S. E257
Khait-Palant, Olga V P446
Khalaf, Michel A555
Khaleghi, Trisha P498
Khaliq, Fazila P60
Khan, Nadeem G. A19
Khan, Muhammad A49
Khan, Sohail A201
Khan, Suleman A204
Khan, Rona A221
Khan, Saba A327
Khan, Sabrina A390
Khan, Raheel A456
Khan, Fareed A. A485
Khan, Mehmood A647
Khan, Kanwar Nasir A649
Khan, Atif A691
Khan, Adeel A708
Khan, Nabeel P129
Khan, Tanveer A P263
Khan, Maryam P286
Khan, Adeel P459
Khan, S S P508
Khan, M Aness P531
Khan, Samir P610
Khan, Alia P681
Khan, Iqbal W111
Khan, Irfan W. W360
Khan, Adeel E356
Khanchandani, Ashok P410
Khandpur, Ashish K. A2
Khang, Chris A375
Khare, Anupam A625
Khasis, Lev W321
Khatibi, Alex E8
Khator, Renu P643
Khattar, Jack A. E391
Khazanchi, Shal P464
Khelghatian, Raffi A221
Khemka, Vivek A270
Khera, Neha A144
Khesin, Eugene A321
Khesin, Eugene E144
Khiabani, Ross E439
Khillan, Gaurav A537
Khodos, Jane A537
Khongkham, Kon A644
Khordodi, Mehran E9
Khorshid, Hassan A461
Khouri, Jeff A16
Khouri, Lara P571
Khourie, Matt A172
Khoury, Raymond A140
Khoury, Sara A878
Khoury, Aldo P531
Khudainatov, Eduard W310
Khurana, Sanjay P2
Khym, Danny P495
Kiam, Raphael A133
Kian, David P196
Kiani, Joe E. E261
Kibbey, Anthony E291
Kice, Tiffany B. E437

Kick, Richard A352
Kick, Richard E159
Kickbusch, Laura P104
Kidd, Michael A3
Kidd, Herbert A332
Kidd, Milton A562
Kidder, Paul A729
Kido, Tomoyuki W116
Kiefer, Chris A729
Kiefer, Philippe E428
Kiehn, Erik A33
Kiel, Lori P269
Kieli, Kasia A269
Kielma, Kathrine A323
Kiely, Robert A408
Kiely, Ann P621
Kiener, Pascal W52
Kiernan, Jeff A175
Kiernan, Steve A767
Kiernan, Thomas M. E430
Kiffer, Tracy A576
Kiffer, Tracy E297
Kigawa, Makoto W400
Kight, Rob A261
Kii, Hajime W272
Kiida, Mike A497
Kijima, Tatsuo W393
Kiker, William A. (Bill) A851
Kiker, Bill A851
Kikuchi, Marc T A59
Kikumoto, C. David P14
Kil-Seon, Choi W177
Kilbane, Kevin A693
Kilbane, Catherine A738
Kilberg, James A. (Jim) A896
Kilborn, Jim P32
Kilbride, Marc P183
Kildis, Ahmet A774
Kile, Pam K P125
Kile, Pam P125
Kiley, Tom P313
Kilgore, Gene E22
Kilguss, Matt P357
Kilian, Mitchell P337
Kilian, Craig P677
Kilic, Serkan P226
Kilkenny, Brian A308
Kilkenny, Patrick A830
Kilkenny, Rosemary P582
Kilkenny, Patrick E402
Killabrew, Mike A449
Killea, John L. A769
Killebrew, Lester H P548
Killeen, Greg A390
Killeen, Thomas P333
Killeen, Nora P409
Killeen, Edward F. E245
Killefer, Nancy A165
Killian, Shanna A785
Killinger, Elizabeth A604
Killingsworth, Mark A266
Killion, Kathleen P474
Killman, Scott A832
Killmer, Jonathon P238
Kilman, Ginger A844
Kilman, Ginger E412
Kilmer, Raymond J. (Ray) A76
Kilpatrick, David B A16
Kilpatrick, Carole A244
Kilpatrick, Elena A368
Kilpatrick, David P395
Kilpin, Timothy J. (Tim) A10
Kilpin, Tim A539
Kilroy, Jill A430
Kilroy, Thomas M A456
Kilroy, John B. E232
Kilsgaard, Jill P599
Kim, Christina A3
Kim, Kyo Yung (K Y) A24
Kim, Yup A28
Kim, Anna A130
Kim, Philip A164
Kim, Cynthia A201
Kim, Charles G. (Chuck) A223
Kim, John A311

Kim, Haeran A323
Kim, Jin A359
Kim, Choung A386
Kim, Greg D. A401
Kim, Anthony A401
Kim, Oliver A401
Kim, Patti A517
Kim, Joanne Y A548
Kim, Sarah A556
Kim, Thomas A599
Kim, Henry A629
Kim, Annie A631
Kim, Joseph A773
Kim, Mikyoung A802
Kim, Jeff A874
Kim, Yup P17
Kim, Ginny P103
Kim, Miah P107
Kim, Earl P124
Kim, Joanne Y P324
Kim, Dong Eun P368
Kim, Taeeuk P437
Kim, Changyoung P437
Kim, Jinho P437
Kim, James K P495
Kim, Mike P495
Kim, Betty P495
Kim, Robert P496
Kim, Mikyoung P562
Kim, Jung-In P601
Kim, Cheol Ha W100
Kim, Yeon Bae W165
Kim, Kyung Bae W177
Kim, Sang-Don W220
Kim, Jin-Il W292
Kim, Hag-Dong W292
Kim, Jhi-Yong W292
Kim, Hong-Soo W292
Kim, Min Chul W332
Kim, Jun W333
Kim, Greg D. E187
Kim, Anthony E187
Kim, Oliver E187
Kim, Neil E371
Kimata, Masatoshi W211
Kimball, Jenny A260
Kimball, Kenny A496
Kimball, John A562
Kimball, Kathy P321
Kimball, Scott P659
Kimball, John E279
Kimball, Mark A. E376
Kimbell, David C A836
Kimbell, Jimmy P39
Kimble, Jim A69
Kimble, William A257
Kimble, Brandy A302
Kimble, Lewis P. A361
Kimble, Sally P A364
Kimble, Chandra A441
Kimble, Donald R. A489
Kimble, Brandy E128
Kime, Jeffery L. (Jeff) A816
Kimm, David A791
Kimm, Christopher A870
Kimmel, Jon A513
Kimmel, Bradford P133
Kimmerle, David P164
Kimmerle, Sandra Sue P164
Kimmet, Pamela O. (Pam) A165
Kimmins, Mary P425
Kimmitt, Joseph H A625
Kimmons, Herb P452
Kimpton, Jay A691
Kimura, Yoshimasa P35
Kimura, Yasushi W200
Kimura, Shigeru W211
Kimura, Tomohiko W237
Kimura, Kazuaki W241
Kimura, Yoshihiko W242
Kimura, Hikaru W242
Kimura, Kenji W268
Kimura, Takaaki W399
Kimzey, Megan A838
Kin, Lam Kun W280

Kinak, Melissa A784
Kinane, Denis F. A812
Kinane, Denis F. P607
Kinard, John P501
Kinasewich, Rob A143
Kincaid, John A115
Kincannon, Elizabeth P417
Kincheloe, Duncan P347
Kindelan, Brian E41
Kinder, Richard D. (Rich) A492
Kinder, Lauren A683
Kinder, Richard D P366
Kinder, Richard D P495
Kindle, Fred W405
Kindler, Thomas A865
Kindred, Betty A674
Kindred, Bryan N. P577
Kindred, Glenn E426
King, Kathleen A27
King, Steve A33
King, Michael A56
King, Andrew D. (Andy) A77
King, Steve A113
King, Kelly S. A115
King, Benjamin A250
King, Timothy B. A267
King, Sam A296
King, Jason A345
King, Jerry A375
King, Jason A448
King, Adam A456
King, Lisa M A487
King, David P. (Dave) A499
King, Jennifer A500
King, Darren J. A522
King, Marie A522
King, John A537
King, John A560
King, Jeffrey A565
King, Patricia A583
King, Martin G. A652
King, Sam A655
King, Susan A690
King, Jake A729
King, Terry A800
King, Kirk A801
King, Kara A806
King, John A851
King, John A864
King, Jeremy A878
King, Susan P8
King, Tommy P30
King, Randy P60
King, Chris P81
King, Gena P120
King, Adrian P122
King, Winney P141
King, Yolanda P143
King, David P170
King, Corey P196
King, Jerry P210
King, Michele P301
King, Karen P305
King, John P342
King, Tami P365
King, Jack P396
King, Meg P423
King, Daniel P426
King, Jared P474
King, Jeffrey P493
King, Rick P498
King, Vernon J P536
King, Kirk P562
King, Kara P569
King, Charles P575
King, David P591
King, Michelle P595
King, Michael (Mike) P671
King, Mark W8
King, Aaron W113
King, Peter W395
King, Christine E78
King, Stephen M. E105
King, Alan E163
King, Jennifer E238

A = AMERICAN BUSINESS
E = EMERGING COMPANIES
P = PRIVATE COMPANIES
W = WORLD BUSINESS

King, Jon E276
King, Sam E333
King, Susan E345
King, David G. E384
King, Terry E396
King, Donald P. E431
King, Chris E432
King-Shaw, Ruben J. P645
Kingbury, Mike P206
Kingdeski, Michele A56
Kingham, Jennifer A591
Kingman, John W217
Kingsbury, Thomas A. (Tom) A155
Kingsbury, Charles A402
Kingsbury, Tom A493
Kingsley, Scott A. A225
Kingsley, Lawrence A712
Kingsley, Mary P79
Kingsley, Scott P514
Kingsley, Scott A. E88
Kingsmill, Stephani E. W232
Kingsmore, Stephen P452
Kingston, Robert E. P590
Kingston, Brian W75
Kini, Narendra M P665
Kinkade, Jennifer A219
Kinkade, Jennifer E84
Kinkeade, Holly A478
Kinlin, Clark S. A238
Kinman, Thomas P115
Kinnaird, Jeff A426
Kinnaman, Deborah A770
Kinneer, Mike P133
Kinney, Bryant A257
Kinney, Jothen A282
Kinney, John A406
Kinney, Susan A513
Kinney, Ross A655
Kinney, Patrick J. A827
Kinney, Doug P298
Kinney, Julie E140
Kinney, Ross E333
Kinoshita, Yoshio W116
Kinsella, Paul E226
Kinser, Christine A460
Kinsey, Joseph A196
Kinsey, Kenny A903
Kinsey, Jon P178
Kinsley, Bryce A718
Kinslow, Craig A886
Kinslow, Anthony D P99
Kinslow, Craig E433
Kintigh, Denise P474
Kintner, Mike A168
Kintz, Ronald P404
Kinville, Richard A677
Kinyon, Craig C P457
Kinyon, Craig P457
Kinz, Robert A782
Kip, Pinar A766
Kipnis, Aaron A131
Kipp, Melana C A863
Kipp, Cathy P435
Kippenhan, Matthew P398
Kipps, David P163
Kiraly, Robert G. (Bob) A359
Kiranandana, Khunying Suchada W203

Kirby, John A28
Kirby, Jefferson W. A30
Kirby, Brent G. A521
Kirby, Michelle A801
Kirby, Cheryl A841
Kirby, J. Scott A846
Kirby, Phil P61
Kirby, Ed P276
Kirby, Tim B. P336
Kirby, Tracy P387
Kirby, Bob P515

Kirby, James P541
Kirby, Rex B. P545
Kirby, Michelle P562
Kirby, Adrienne P576
Kirby, Cheryl E410
Kirch, Bob A756
Kirchgaessner, Rainer W98
Kirchheimer, David M. E312
Kirchhoefer, Kari A842
Kirchner, Tim A120
Kirchner, Jeffrey P589
Kirchner, James P592
Kirejczyk, Wanda M P241
Kirgan, Danielle A254
Kirihara, Wayne H. A183
Kirikova, Vera W306
Kirk, Debbie A100
Kirk, Richard A247
Kirk, Joan A350
Kirk, Mathew A406
Kirk, Jennifer A707
Kirk, Melvin (Mel) A718
Kirk, Warren J. A794
Kirk, Roger L P72
Kirk, Ron P145
Kirk, Joyce P145
Kirk, Rich Van P161
Kirk, Warren J P163
Kirk, Joseph P206
Kirk, Bruce M P290
Kirk, Norma P353
Kirk, Evelyn P430
Kirk, Peggy P457
Kirk, Paul P695
Kirk, Richard E103
Kirk, Shawn E121
Kirk, Spencer E139
Kirk, Joan E157
Kirkegaard, Ulrika Stolt W352
Kirkemo, Erik A305
Kirkemo, Erik P185
Kirkendall, Eric A780
Kirkendall, Bill P579
Kirkevold, Dee P553
Kirkland, Richard G A519
Kirkland, Craig A537
Kirkland, Christopher A743
Kirkland, Janice A823
Kirkland, Christopher E373
Kirkland, J. Bryant E425
Kirkpatrick, Paul K A224
Kirkpatrick, Kevin A480
Kirkpatrick, R. James P341
Kirkwood, John A460
Kirkwood, Karen A815
Kirouac, Brenda E144
Kirousis, Marni A815
Kirrane, Joseph A93
Kirsch, Eric M. A18
Kirsch, Peter P183
Kirsch, Becky P249
Kirschenbaum, Norman P225
Kirschner, Sid P428
Kirschner, Sidney E391
Kirshner, Alan I. A528
Kirst, Kenneth C. E135
Kirstetter, Axel P333
Kirtley, Timothy H. A645
Kirtley, Timothy H. E329
Kirton, Nancy P281
Kirwan, Jeff A809
Kisber, Michael E. A348
Kiscaden, Bradley J. A528
Kisch, Horst A214
Kisch, Horst P128
Kiser, Carly A777
Kiser, Janice P110
Kiser, Terry P346
Kiser, Christopher P368
Kiser, Carly E393
Kish, Janine P486
Kishan, Neel P96
Kishbach, Tim A640
Kishi, Jamal Al W123
Kishida, Makoto W273

Kishimoto, Sumiyuki W197
Kishore, Ashok P623
Kiskorna, Mark A659
Kissel, Thomas A621
Kissel, Mark A P131
Kissinger, Tom E257
Kissire, Debbie A619
Kissler, Courtney A763
Kissling, Lou A244
Kister, Jarek (January) E165
Kistner, Tim P185
Kitagawa, Allan S. A798
Kitahara, Yoshikazu W245
Kitamura, Sam A328
Kitamura, Takumi W268
KITAMURA, SEISHI W366
Kitazawa, Toshifumi W367
Kitchens, James E153
Kitcher, Ron A318
Kitchin, Mark A837
Kite, John A. E234
Kitrilakis, Periklis M. W24
Kittoe, Michael P158
Kittoe, Michael E. P280
Kittredge, Teri A648
Kitzmann, Jessica A163
Kitzmiller, Kenneth G. A551
Kiwall, Walter J P674
Kiyono, Jolene A183
Kizer, Jay E235
Kjellberg, Henrik V. A310
Klaassens, Michael A40
Klabe, Jim A901
Klabe, Jim P692
Klaeser, Dennis L. A187
Klaeser, Dennis L. E71
Klahre, Robert A555
Klaich, Daniel P370
Klammer, Thoma P A438
Klappa, Gale E. A884
Klasek, Bob P396
Klasek, Robert P396
Klasko, Stephen K. P618
Klat, Michael A600
Klatte, Erika E117
Klaus, Jeffrey A. (Jeff) A883
Klaus, Rusty P166
Klausner, Herbert W331
Klavsons, David A417
Klawiter, Jeffrey P337
Klawitter, Jerry E220
Klebba, Philip A723
Klebba, Michael A729
Klecker, Donna A537
Klee, Evan A351
Klee, Brian A649
Klee, Evan E158
Kleefisch, Brett A405
Kleffel, Julie A731
Kleffel, Julie E365
Klehr, Joan P48
Kleiber, Dan P437
Kleifges, Mark L. E206
Kleifges, Mark L. E314
Klein, Gene A25
Klein, Dorothea A178
Klein, John E. A217
Klein, David A235
Klein, Steven A A244
Klein, Kelly A295
Klein, Christopher J. (Chris) A364
Klein, Mike A375
Klein, Aaron A489
Klein, Susan A784
Klein, Roger D A807
Klein, Gerald J. A820
Klein, Michael F. A827
Klein, Bart A837
Klein, Matthew A857
Klein, David G P64
Klein, David P172
Klein, Martin H P173
Klein, Larry P187
Klein, Ben P196
Klein, Tammy P213

Klein, Irving P244
Klein, Barry P297
Klein, Vickie Barrow P304
Klein, Jason P325
Klein, Cathy P344
Klein, Howard P402
Klein, Kathy P434
Klein, Steve P447
Klein, Roger D P574
Klein, David P632
Klein, John A. E19
Klein, Phyllis S. E90
Klein, Michael R. E97
Klein, Melvyn N. E322
Klein-Magar, Margret W319
Kleinemeier, Michael W319
Kleiner, Rasiel A500
Kleiner, Rasiel E237
Kleinhanzl, Thomas A. P205
Kleinhemple, Ken A898
Kleinman, Kent P143
Kleinman, Ronald Ellis P590
Kleisterlee, Gerard J. W389
Kleman, Keith A878
Klemencic, Joy A218
Klement, Reiner A685
Klemm, Sara P591
Klemt, Les P422
Klenk, Christopher A489
Klenk, Jeffrey P. (Jeff) A827
Klepner, Ron E391
Klerk, Wim de W30
Klesyk, Andrzej Piotr W294
Kletter, David A140
Kleven, Bill A775
Klevitz, Glenn A906
Klevorn, Marcy A362
Kley, Karl-Ludwig W59
Kley, Karl-Ludwig W131
Kleyle, Tom A213
Klia, Steven P A277
Klick, Dave A886
Klick, Dave E433
Kliethermes, Craig W. A710
Kligman, Michelle P446
Klim, Maria P51
Klimchak, Joseph A701
Klimczak, Bob A549
Klimczak, Bob E270
Klimkowski, Ronald A196
Klinck, James A556
Kline, Betsy A73
Kline, Gary J A196
Kline, Kevin A537
Kline, Mark A759
Kline, David A871
Kline, Douglas B. P258
Kline, Mark W. P560
Klinger, Randall L. E276
Klingler, Jeremy A647
Klingner, Mary P583
Klinitchek, Darryl P511
Klinkner, Kim A81
Klinovskaya, Taisiya W350
Klipp, Todd P80
Kloberdanz, Mark P424
Klobnak, Jennifer L. A710
Klocke, Jill A387
Klocke, Jill E177
Klockhaus, Werner W85
Kloehn, Steve P96
Klokkenga, Pinkaj A324
Klonowski, Lisa P158
Klontz, Richard P634
Kloostra, Jim A549
Kloostra, Jim E270
Klopfenstein, Joshua P610
Klopotek, Robert A885
Klosk, Steven M. (Steve) E54
Klosson, Michael P485
Klosterboer, Robert A. (Bob) A620
Klostermeier, Janice P663
Klotz, Jim A734
Klotzbach, Kevin B. A334
Klucevek, Matt A280

Klueg, Steven P P305
Klug, Loren C. A437
Klug, Sue A707
Klug, Janet P281
Klug, Candice P591
Kluge, Debbie A770
Kluger, Joseph E. A640
Klugherz, Greg P602
Klumb, Begonya A838
Klusik, Hartmut W56
Kluth, Doreen P537
Kluyver, Cornelis A. (Kees) de P651
Klyce, Harvey A480
Klym, Nick A481
Kl- ¶--, Susanne W125
Knackstedt, Beth P361
Knapke, Murph A345
Knapp, Tracy W. A483
Knapp, Michael A559
Knapp, Ken Knapp Ken A700
Knapp, Michelle P217
Knapp, Kyra P321
Knauer, Ron A419
Knauer, Brian A851
Knauer, Dallas P568
Knaus, Ron P519
Knauss, Bob A836
Knauss, Robert A836
Knauth, Tanner P501
Knavish, Timothy M. A664
Knee, David A478
Kneeland, Michael J. A851
Kneidinger, Michael (Mike) A254
Kneller, Tracey W103
Knelly, Shirley J P39
Knepp, Brian L. A640
Knepp, Lynn E P207
Knepper, Chris P136
Knesek, Jill A539
Knesek, Michael J P341
Knickrehm, Mark A. W5
Knies, Theresa A644
Kniffin, Ogden A693
Knight, Bobbie A27
Knight, Barbara J A27
Knight, Charles A219
Knight, Mike A300
Knight, Michelle A332
Knight, Jeffrey W. A395
Knight, Jeffrey L. (Jeff) A614
Knight, Phil A814
Knight, Robert M. A842
Knight, Thomas P21
Knight, Charles P131
Knight, Richard P154
Knight, Tim P247
Knight, Keith P256
Knight, Calvin (Cal) P263
Knight, Cal P263
Knight, George P330
Knight, Gordon D Jr P592
Knight, Phil P616
Knight, Alton P631
Knight, Kevin E44
Knightly, Kevin C. A469
Knipfing, Janet A869
Knipp, Ken P700
Knirsch, Charles A648
Knitzer, Peter R. E350
Knobel, Carsten W168
Knoblauch, Kathleen A484
Knoedler, Peter E349
Knoffloch, Richard E87
Knoll, Thomas A259
Knoll, Lisa E140
Knoll-finn, Mj A585
Knoll-finn, Mj P377
Knoller, Karen A790
Knopf, Matthew A262
Knopf, David A494
Knott, Timothy A483
Knott, Irene A814
Knott, Jack H. A860
Knott, Irene P526
Knott, Irene P616

Knott, Jack H. P656
Knotts, Daniel L. (Dan) A278
Knouse, Sabrina A782
Knowles, Debie A54
Knowles, Michelle A204
Knowles, Leo A230
Knowles, Jane P336
Knowling, Doug A701
Knowlton, Timothy P619
Knowlton, Lori E371
Knox, Tanya P134
Knox, Mark P688
Knoy, Shane A493
Knuckles, Beth A497
Knudson, Dennis P276
Knueven, Matthew A700
Knupp, Bridgett A449
Knupp, Catherine A. (Cathy) A921
Knuth, David A886
Knuth, Barbara A. P143
Knuth, David E433
Knutilla, Tom A718
Knutson, Brad P435
Knüpling, Frieder W323
Ko, Al A466
Ko, William A667
Ko, Suk-Bum W292
Ko, William E336
Kobashi, Kozo W327
Kobashigawa, Scot A729
Kobayakawa, Tomoaki W368
Kobayashi, Edison A102
Kobayashi, Shigeyuki A685
KOBAYASHI, HIDEFUMI W1
Kobayashi, Katsuma W115
Kobayashi, Koji W121
Kobayashi, Hirotake W207
Kobayashi, Yoshimitsu W240
Kobayashi, Kazuo W261
Kobayashi, Toshiaki W282
Kobayashi, Masayuki W330
Kobe, Hiroshi W259
Koble, Keith A105
Koc, Yildirim Ali W402
Koch, Stephen P. (Steve) A703
Koch, Steve A703
Koch, Alan P7
Koch, Robert P87
Koch, Cheryl P265
Koch, Olaf W85
Koch, Monte E75
Kochalski, Miroslaw W291
Kochan, Christian A683
Kochard, Lawrence E P658
Kochem, Gary J. P17
Kochem, Gary J P18
Kocher, Angela A641
Kocher, Pat A663
Kocher, Angela P422
Kocher, Isabelle W143
Kocher, Rollin E290
Kocherlakota, Swamy A721
Kochhar, Chanda D. W181
Kochowicz, Jerry A904
Kochowicz, Jerry E442
Kochvar, Mark A720
Kochvar, Mark E362
Kociancic, Mark W323
Kodama, Hugh P357
Kodama, Yukio W241
Koder, Tim P329
Kodish, Jan A807
Kodish, Jan P574
Koebler, Ellen A283
Koegel, James J. E108
Koehler, Mike A308
Koehler, Mary A904
Koehler, Mary E442
Koehly, Hank A223
Koehn, Dwayne A658
Koehnen, Michael W. A830
Koehnen, Michael W. E402
Koellner, Meliss A A438
Koelmel, John R. P375
Koen, Kenneth A175

Koeneke-hernandez, Ludwig P619
Koenig, Ronald A67
Koenig, Jim A173
Koenig, Ron A223
Koenig, Joseph G. (Joe) A907
Koenig, Tracy P151
Koenig, Carol P397
Koenig, Harris F P479
Koenig, Joseph G. (Joe) P696
Koenigs, Margaret K. (Peg) A323
Koening, John A405
Koeper, John P518
Koepke, Diane P67
Koeppel, Holly P32
Koeppel, Carol P693
Koerner, Spencer P103
Koerner, Erich P396
Koerner, Gert P544
Koerschner, Carl P335
Koertner, William A. (Bill) E289
Koestler, Robert J. P506
Koffer, Danielle A218
Koford, Keith E360
Koga, Akira W235
Kogai, Masamichi W235
Koguchi, Masanori W241
Koh, Peter A429
Koh, Peter E204
Kohalmy, Mark E394
Kohava, Avraham W46
Kohl, Gail A769
Kohl, Gary R. E263
Kohler, Kayleen A110
Kohler, Pete A141
Kohler, Lori A837
Kohler, David A919
Kohler, Doug A886
Kohler, Missey P583
Kohler, Kayleen E37
Kohler, Matt E182
Kohls, Steve A173
Kohn, Thomas W. A187
Kohn, Judy A524
Kohn, Emily P60
Kohn, Rachel P269
Kohn, Les E14
Kohn, Thomas W. E71
Kohnen, Rhonda P298
Kohnen, Scott E348
Kohr, Jeff A81
Kohutek, Kevin R. E419
Koil, Thomas P174
Koizumi, Atsushi (Windy) W349
Kojaian, C. Michael E22
Kojak, Cynthia A770
Kojima, Elaine P339
Kojima, Kazuo W279
Kojima, Nobuhiro W337
Kojima, Koji W349
Kojima, Takashi W349
Kojima, Yoichiro W399
Kokaji, Hiroshi W169
Kokate, Santosh A781
Kokubu, Fumiya W234
Kolander, Geoffrey M. A206
Kolb, Amy A81
Kolb, Dianne C. P92
Kolb, Matthew P95
Kolb, Greg P106
Kolb, Kenneth P119
Kolb, Edward (Rocky) P610
Kolbash, Ronald P610
Kolbe, Martin W212
Kolcz, Crystal A333
Koleci, Carolann P695
Koleszar, Andre E349
Koli, Roshni P270
Koliander, Eric A685
Kolker, Dov P355
Koll, Jesper E443
Kollar, Kevin P51
Kollatz, Christoph A76
Koller, Patrick W148

Kolli, Sreelakshmi E10
Kolluri, Rama A19
Kolluri, Pavan P47
Kolniak, Tiffany A P353
Koloski, David A158
Kolpasky, Paul A413
Kolpasky, Paul P234
Kolpin, Linda E125
Kolster, Luis A878
Koltookian, Aram A816
Koltz, MarisaE P218
Kolytiris, Valerie A335
Komar, June P488
Komata, Lillian A207
Komer, Rick A483
Kometani, Hanbei W170
Komidar, John A827
Komiske, Bruce P225
Komoda, Masanobu W245
Komori, Shigetaka W155
Komos, Thomas A826
Komuniecki, Patricia R. P613
Komura, Yoshifumi W190
Konczaty, Michel W66
Kondamareddy, Suresh E344
Kondapalli, Swathi P568
Kondo, Shiro W304
Kondo, Jun W342
Kondrotis, Krisstie A758
Kong, Boon W160
Kong, Ki Young W177
Konganda, Bobby A685
Kongyingyong, Phanporn W330
Konidari, Penelope E. W24
Konik, David A441
Konings, Frank A476
Konkel, Tom A769
Konop, Amanda P465
Konort, Phil A49
Konrad, Jocelyn A709
Konstans, Kristie E437
Konstantinovsky, Irina A113
Kontul, Dean A489
Konyn, Mark W13
Konzelman, Rich A499
Konzelman, Sharon P275
Konzmann, Richard E. (Rich) E24
Koo, Yun P103
Koocher, Gerald P. P155
Kooda-Chizek, Kristi A56
Koogler, Rob A441
Koogler, David P453
Kooiman, Albert A560
Kookesh, Albert M. P489
Koonce, Scott A25
Koonce, Paul D. A275
Koonce, Scott P15
Koontz, Bill P455
Koopman, Ray A915
Koopman, Trish P692
Koopman, Ray P700
Kooy, Donald P319
Kooyman, John A218
Kopchinski, Richard A659
Kopec, Mike P307
Kopelman, Donna A480
Koper, Alex P482
Kopera, Donna A113
Kopf, Chris P213
Kopfensteiner, Thomas R. A171
Kopfensteiner, Thomas R. P100
Kopicki, John P105
Kopil, Edward A120
Kopitsky, Christopher A819
Kopleff, Steven A49
Koplovitz, Jonathan A520
Koplow, Ellen L. S. A791
Kopp, Greg A729
Koppenhoefer, Kathleen P622
Kopper, Carolyn L A406
Kopra, Amanda P285
Kopstain, Eric P615
Koptyra, Kristin A97
Koptyra, Kristin E32

A = AMERICAN BUSINESS
E = EMERGING COMPANIES
P = PRIVATE COMPANIES
W = WORLD BUSINESS

Kopycinski, Gloria A244
Kopyrski, Andrzej W51
Korajkic, Jasko A222
Korb, Brent L. E343
Korczynski, Sherry E113
Kordahi, Rony C. A626
Korecki, Joseph A644
Koremans, Robert W363
Koren, Ofer W46
Korenaga, Kendall P19
Korenberg, Matthew A390
Korenek, Joe A304
Koretzky, Gary P143
Korey, Lowder P304
Korff, Stephen A677
Korff, Steve A677
Koricanac, Nick A904
Koricanac, Nick E442
Korins, Danielle A682
Koritko, Martin A513
Kornberg, Susan A109
Kornberg, Fred V. E89
Kornblum, David A272
Korneffel, Laurie A185
Kornegay, Alexandria A461
Korner, Barbara O. A811
Korner, Barbara O. P600
Kornowski-Bonnet, Sophie W307
Korolog, George A725
Korsapati, Venka A40
Korsch, Marija G. W2
Korsh, Les B. A636
Korsmeyer, Mark A252
Korsmeyer, Mark P150
Kort, Steve A221
Korzekwinski, Francis W. (Frank) A359
Kos, Heather A453
Kosakai, Kenkichi W240
Kosasa, Paul J A183
Koscielniak, Lucy P205
Kosek, Rick A117
Koseoglu, Ata W163
Koshurba, Sherry P354
Kosiek, Patrick A204
Kosiyangkakul, Tai P471
Koski, Philip A865
Koskull, Casper von W269
Koslow, John A49
Koss, Kristen K P543
Kost, Beth P272
Kostantos, Roland W194
Kosteba, Linda P359
Koster, Teresa A371
Koster, Barbara G. A676
Koster, Craig E408
Kostiw, Michael A16
Kostosky, Robert A A709
Kosturko, Maryellen P83
Kosydor, Vicki A322
Kotagiri, Seetarama W229
Kotch, Noah E99
Kothari, Manish P522
Kotick, Robert A. (Bobby) A10
Kotkin, Jeffrey P188
Kotlikoff, Michael I. P143
Kotsenas, Peter A355
Kotsopoulos, Peter W347
Kottapalli, Pushpanjali A101
Kottapalli, Kishore A766
Kottler, Robert M. (Bob) A446
Kottler, Robert M. (Bob) E210
Kottman, Bill P176
Kotwal, Shailesh M. A865
Kotylo, Ken A794
Kotzin, Brian A61
Kouduki, Kazuo W367
Koulouris, Richard R. A663
Koury, Emile A399
Koury, Jeffrey (Jeff) A794

Koushik, Srinivas (Srini) A524
Kousloglou, Tasos A478
Koustareva, Kate P94
Kovacevich, Richard A200
Kovach, Greg A13
Kovack, Kristen P430
Kovacs, James A A456
Kovacs, Greg P522
Koval, Kathy A734
Koval, Erin P386
Koveos, George A691
Koviak, Jeff A796
Kovoch, Dan P61
Kowal, Dave A158
Kowal, Nadine P588
Kowalczyk, Dave P315
Kowaleski, Tim A210
Kowals, Kathy P111
Kowalski, Kevin P. A548
Kowalski, Kevin P. P321
Kowkabany, Rob A58
Kowkabany, Rob E16
Kowler, Kathy A584
Kowlzan, Mark W. A631
Koyama, Tomoyuki W264
Kozak, Mike A351
Kozak, Colleen A733
Kozak, Mike E158
Kozakov, Alex A173
Kozano, Yoshiaki W329
Kozar, Paul Kozar Paul A865
Kozar, Joseph P611
Kozarich, John W. E246
Kozel, David F. (Dave) A682
Kozel, Kenneth P645
Kozicz, Gregory J P18
Kozicz, Gregory J P19
Koziol, Patrick A105
Kozlowski, Damian A805
Kozoman, Robert L. (Bob) P155
Kozusnik, Maryann P688
Kra, Douglas I. (Doug) E327
Kraats, Robert-Jan van de W299
Krabbe, Mark A257
Krabbenhoft, Kelby K P481
Kracov, Eric A584
Kraemer, Theodore A140
Kraetsch, Jeff P41
Kraev, Igor P180
Krafft, Robert P539
Kraft, Robert O. (Rocky) A250
Kraft, Christopher A733
Kraft, Stephanie P417
Kraft, John P642
Krage, David A446
Krage, David E210
Kraich, Rick A873
Kraich, Rick P669
Krajewski, David P290
Krakauer, Lawrence P313
Krakaur, Ken A736
Krakaur, Ken P492
Krakowsky, Philippe A464
Kralian, Edward A101
Kralingen, Bridget A. van A460
Krall, Donna M. A356
Kramar, John P90
Kramer, Lauren A163
Kramer, Kelly A. A199
Kramer, Richard J. (Rich) A391
Kramer, Michael A562
Kramer, Kevin A562
Kramer, Curt A A577
Kramer, Phillip D. (Phil) A657
Kramer, Phil D A658
Kramer, Mark A708
Kramer, Laurie A724
Kramer, Rick A738
Kramer, Robin C A809
Kramer, Steve A865
Kramer, Lorne P122
Kramer, Adam P441
Kramer, Don P462
Kramer, Robin C P584
Kramer, Jennifer P630

Kramer, Markus W55
Kramer, Marcus W58
Kramer, Christina W80
Kramer, James S. (Jim) E25
Kramer, Gary E38
Kramer, Robert G. (Bob) E121
Kramer, Louise C. (Weezie) E127
Kramer, Marty E147
Kramer, Francis J. E214
Kramer, Kevin E279
Kramer, Caleb S. E312
Krane, Spencer A323
Krane, Hilary K. A592
Krane, Jeffrey P567
Krantz, Missy S A446
Krantz, Missy S E210
Krantz, Donald G. E339
Krapek, Karl J P139
Krapels, Marco P559
Krasnoff, Jeffrey P. (Jeff) A508
Krasowski, Janet D. A675
Kraszewski, Andrew P376
Kratky, Kay W124
Kratsberg, Leon A741
Kratsberg, Leon E370
Kratz, Denise A724
Kratz, Karen P115
Kratz, Steven E286
Kratzer, Doug A402
Kraus, Marie A163
Kraus, Frederick A502
Kraus, Kim A671
Krause, Douglas P. A285
Krause, Kim A774
Krause, Brian P72
Krause, Melissa P119
Krause, Alan J. P360
Krause, Roger P415
Krause, Catherine P648
Krause, David P663
Krause, Douglas P. E114
Krauss, Soheir A201
Krauss, Jim A736
Krauss, Marty W. P82
Krauss, Dora P361
Krauss, Jim P492
Kraut, Jeffrey A. P390
Kravchenko, Kirill W157
Krawczyk, Brian A390
Krawczyk, Tammy A902
Krawczyk, Tammy P693
Krawiec, Ronald P186
Krawtschuk, Christopher A649
Kraynak, Bob A173
Kreatsoulas, John A456
Krebber, Markus W315
Krebs, Donald E. (Don) A483
Krebs, Don A483
Krebs, James A872
Krebsbach, Karen P624
Krech, Joyce A122
Kreger, Julie A101
Krehbiel, Bruce A465
Kreips, Christopher A714
Kreis, Melanie W125
Kremer, Donald A192
Kremer, Lisa A532
Kremer, Wesley D. A695
Kremer, Melissa A788
Kremer, Donald P112
Kremer, Thomas W126
Kremidas, Steve H. E383
Kremin, Donald H. (Don) A432
Kremke, Kevin L A260
Krempl, Stephen A763
Krenk, Chris P94
Krenke, Brian P278
Krenkel, David S. A276
Krenz, William C. (Willie) P564
Kreppel, Rick E179
Krepps, John P503
Kresge, Kevin A133
Kresl, Michael A54
Kress, Jean A386
Kress, Colette M. A607

Kress, Kathy A878
Kretzinger, Cut P231
Kretzmer, William B. (Brian) E226
Kreuger, Jennifer A523
Kreutcer, Alva P622
Kreuzer, Barry A246
Krevans, Sarah A775
Krevans, Sarah P548
Krezmien, Dennis A522
Krhovsky, David M P519
Krick, Brian A734
Krick, Gerd W153
Krick, Gerd W154
Kricka, Larry P241
Krider, Holly P478
Kriebel, Jonathan A546
Krieg, Susan A448
Krieger, Sandra C. (Sandy) A323
Krieger, Sarah A639
Krieger, Kenneth F. (Ken) P588
Krieger, Sarah E326
Kriegner, Martin W214
Kriegsmann, Sonja A614
Kriehn, Judy P208
Kriens, Scott G. A482
Krier, Greg P640
Kriesand, Dave A111
Kriesand, Dave P56
Kriesberg, Barry P227
Krikorian, Lazarus A59
Krikorian, Alex A195
Krill, Steven L. E113
Krimbill, H. Michael A591
Kring, Steven C. A431
Kring, Steven C. E205
Kripalu, Anand W128
Krippner, Brian A837
Krish, Bharani A565
Krishen, Ashok W274
Krishna, R. Murali P250
Krishna, Suresh E376
Krishnamoorthy, Gnana P325
Krishnamurthi, Gopal A327
Krishnamurthy, Nikki A311
Krishnamurthy, Srini A406
Krishnan, Ramayya P96
Krishnan, Sridhar W274
Kriskie, Michele P184
Kristensen, Douglas A. (Doug) P78
Kristiansen, Thore E. W156
Kristjanson, Stefan W161
Kristo, Joni A593
Kristoff, David A588
Kristoffersen, Ashley A133
Kristoffersen, Candi A501
Kristofka, Michael P610
Kritskij, Juriy L. W375
Krmpotic, Deb A111
Krmpotic, Deb P56
Krmpotic, Deb P187
Kroboth, Michael A665
Kroehler, Jon A575
Kroeker, Harrald F. A73
Kroeker, Curtis M. E97
Kroenung, Stefan A87
Kroger, Matt A173
Krohn, Shannon A81
Kroiss, Valerie A838
Krol, Wojciech A218
Krolewicz, Randall A522
Kroll, Edmund A180
Kroll, Brannon A244
Kromm, Elizabeth A475
Kromm, Elizabeth P266
Krone, Roger A. A505
Kronfeld, David P182
Kronlage, Dan A273
Kronlage, Dan P162
Kronman, Jeremy A173
Kronmueller, Margaret A770
Kroos, Karsten W365
Kroot, Irwin P597
Kropf, Susan J A786
Kropilak, Mark J P42
Kropiunik, Frank C P18

Krouse, Michael P405
Krow, Reggie P363
Kruchten, Brad W. E115
Kruczlnicki, David A78
Kruczlnicki, David G P213
Krueger, Pam A85
Krueger, Alan A173
Krueger, Melissa A247
Krueger, Steve A446
Krueger, Eric P500
Krueger, Dennis P520
Krueger, Melissa E102
Krueger, Steve E210
Krug, Carey A691
Kruger, James D. (Jim) A579
Kruger, Scott A599
Kruger, Bob A792
Kruger, Bill A850
Kruger, Cynthia V P231
Kruger, R. M. (Rich) W184
Kruger, Ben W339
Kruglov, Lisa A449
Kruis, Tresa P84
Krulewitch, Jerry A545
Krull, Henry P106
Krummen, William A333
Krummenacher, Cornel W258
Krump, Paul J. W98
Krumrey, Elizabeth A904
Krumrey, Elizabeth E442
Krunic, Nancy E250
Krupa, David E. A722
Krupicki, Shawnda P528
Krupinski, Michal Tomasz W51
Krupinski, Dave E57
Krupka, Jacqueline P35
Krupp, Jeff A696
Kruse, Kevin A153
Kruse, Karen A348
Kruse, Shelly A397
Kruse, Brent A651
Kruse, Eric A655
Kruse, Rebecca A724
Kruse, Mark P102
Kruse, Shelly P221
Kruse, Lowell P231
Kruse, Brent P426
Kruse, Stein W81
Kruse, Richard E94
Kruse, Eric E333
Krusinski, Laura A489
Kruszewski, Ronald J. (Ron) A771
Kruthers, Mike E320
Kruythoff, Kees W383
Krych, Ron P614
Kryda, Michael P473
Krynauw, Pieter A429
Krysl, James A685
Krysti, Galvin P379
Krystopolski, Ruth P481
Krzanich, Brian A260
Krzeminski, Robert E A886
Krzeminski, Robert E E433
Krzmarzick, Brent P646
Krüger, Harald W59
Krüger, Roland W265
Ksenak, Stephen M. A40
Kuang, Ooi Sang W280
Kubacki, Michael L. A500
Kubacki, Michael L. E238
Kubacki, Raymond C. E340
Kubacki, Jeff E441
Kubasak, Heather A441
Kubba, Omar A335
Kubick, David E248
Kubiesa, Susan A599
Kubish, Kristine P671
Kubista, Jennifer P553
Kubo, Taizo W19
Kubo, Toshihiro W211
Kubo, Ken W345
Kubota, Hironobu W211
Kubovcik, Sean A826
Kucera, Randall R A397
Kucera, Margaret P610

Kucera, Kevin P613
Kucharski, Joseph A649
Kucia, Mark A A846
Kuczmanski, John D. P320
Kuczora, Deb A493
Kudler, Douglas A555
Kudo, Sumio W86
Kudo, Yasumi W264
Kudravetz, Douglas P37
Kudrna, Casey A837
Kudzman, Susan W217
Kuebel, Christoph W70
Kueber, Ken A213
Kuehl, Kevin A127
Kuehl, Thomas W265
Kuehn, Kurt A850
Kuehne, Will P286
Kuehner, John E. E31
Kuelbs, Brian P. A97
Kuelbs, Brian P. E32
Kugel, Irene A105
Kuhlmann, Lucas P5
Kuhn, Rebecca (Becky) A111
Kuhn, Rebecca (Becky) P56
Kuhnert, Marcus W239
Kuhns, Dewey A207
Kuick, Kenneth A158
Kuida, Elliot P310
Kuiper, Craig A657
Kuiper, Jeremy L. A806
Kuipers, Peter E316
Kujirai, Yoichi W241
Kukelhan, Allison P6
Kukura, Joe P293
Kukura, Sergei P. W290
Kukurin, James A729
Kula, Tom P391
Kularski, Patty A402
Kulaszewicz, Frank C. A712
Kulatham, Sarakorn W296
Kulchitskaya, Yanina A204
Kulczytzky, Chris A721
Kulikowski, Eileen P603
Kulkarni, Sanjeev R. P606
Kulkin, Harvey A738
Kullander, David A351
Kullander, David E158
Kulshreshtha, Anoop A727
Kulwicki, Billy E294
Kum, Chong Guk (C. G.) A401
Kum, Chong Guk (C. G.) E187
KUMAGAI, TOSHIYUKI W204
Kumakiri, Naomi W115
Kumar, Devinder A14
Kumar, Gopa A324
Kumar, Sunil A475
Kumar, Rajesh A709
Kumar, Viji A774
Kumar, Arvind P210
Kumar, Sunil P266
Kumar, Ranjan V P404
Kumar, Arvind K P479
Kumar, Vinod P556
Kumar, Sandeep E371
Kumbier, Michelle A. A403
Kumler, Alan A844
Kumler, Alan E412
Kumm, Wendy A81
Kummeth, Charles R. (Chuck) E42
Kumpas, James A359
Kuna, Mark L. E318
Kunath, Jan W302
Kuncheff, Ivan A16
Kunde, Gerald A782
Kunde, Grace E139
Kundra, Raj P696
Kundurthy, Praveen A456
Kuney, Terry A441
Kunibe, Takeshi W345
Kunii, Yoshihiro W147
Kunk, James E. A440
Kunkel, Ted A109
Kunkel, Jay K. A503
Kunkel, Lisa A657
Kunkel, Thomas M. (Tom) A827

Kunkel, Ted E36
Kunreuther, Susan A537
Kunst, Jeff A238
Kuntschik, David P368
Kuntz, William A173
Kuntz, JT A318
Kuntz, John F. A675
Kuntz, Kyle P173
Kuntz, Kevin P318
Kunz, Jim A16
Kunz, Michael P115
Kunz, Thomas W117
Kunze, Shane A679
Kunze, Shane A680
Kunze, Shane P448
Kuper, Debra A20
Kuper, Jacob P255
Kuperus, Cindy P98
Kupetz, Dan A175
Kupper, Randy A56
Kuppuswamy, Murali A809
Kuppuswamy, Murali P584
Kurahara, Fumiaki W345
Kuraishi, Hideaki W28
Kuraishi, Seiji W172
Kurali, Andreas A652
Kurani, Maheboob E187
Kurapati, Raja A131
Kurapka, David A131
Kurasch, Aaron A56
Kurdas, Meral E. W163
Kurdes, Ted A323
Kurdle, Florence B P39
Kurek, Robert A489
Kures, Peter P413
Kurian, George A580
Kurihara, Miky A871
Kurin, Richard P506
Kurisu, Toshizo W400
Kurita, Nathan A655
Kurita, Nathan E333
Kuritani, Kevin E110
Kuritsky, Nikki E369
Kuritzkes, Andrew A766
Kuriyel, Ralf E351
Kurkowski, John P149
Kurland, Stanford L. A642
Kurland, Stanford L. E329
Kurnick, Robert H. A642
Kuroda, Haruhiko W48
Kuroda, Tadashi W244
Kuropas, Stephen A599
Kurosawa, Seikichi W327
Kurow, Dave A351
Kurow, Dave E158
Kurrasch, Paul A775
Kurth, Keith A889
Kurtov, Ines A583
Kurtz, Aaron A225
Kurtz, Ronald D A565
Kurtz, Ronald A565
Kurtz, Martin A728
Kurtz, Erin A913
Kurtz, Norma P230
Kurtz, Michelle P557
Kurtz, Aaron E88
Kurup, Veenod W222
Kuryea, Kimberly A374
Kurz, Christian A872
Kurzatkowski, Amy P189
Kurzius, Lawrence E. A544
Kus, Julie A670
Kusano, Shigeya W336
Kuselias, Jason A406
Kush, Henry A306
Kushel, J. Richard (Rich) A130
Kushida, Seiji W116
Kushner, Jared A706
Kushner, Jared E353
Kusinski, Denise P430
Kuslits, Thomas R. A356
Kusterer, Thomas W140
Kutac, Mary-Katherine A180
Kutam, Sreeni A87
Kutateladze, Andrei P132

Kutch, John M P624
Kutcher, Gregory R P316
Kutchera, Kris A28
Kutchmark, Mike A659
Kutryk, Terrance P25
Kutz, Tim E117
Kuwabara, Shigehiro W48
Kuwahara, Takao W147
Kuwahara, Masahiro W245
Kuwano, Mitsumasa W399
Kuykendall, Ronald E. A724
Kuypers, Tom A120
Kuzbel, Jeffrey A163
Kuzdal, John L. E298
Kuzmak, Beth A546
Kuznetsov, Stanislav K. W321
Kuzniasz, Stacey A247
Kuzniasz, Stacey E103
Kvadus, Glen A855
Kvamme, John A81
Kvistad, Gregg P132
Kwan, Irene E B A102
Kwan, Sarah A777
Kwan, Sarah E393
Kwawu, Sena M A763
Kwetkowski, Brian G P695
Kwiatkowski, Paul E346
Kwitchoff, Jim E245
Kwok, Andrew A164
Kwon, Mea A354
Kwon, Bong-Suk W221
Kwon, Oh-Joon W292
Kwong, Melsen P102
Kyff, Emilia A555
Kyger, Carolyn P424
Kyle, Rex A107
Kyle, April P511
Kyle, Rex E34
Kyler, Chrisopsher P661
Kyler, Christopher P661
Kymes, Stacy C. A137
Kyriakidis, Alex A530
Kyse, Julie A311
K-öllenius, Ola W114
K-¶hler, Roland W214

L

LA, Mai A133
Laan, Ron Van Der A105
Laan, Sander van der W209
Labarre, Sedar A140
LaBarre, Michael J. E186
Labass, Bob P247
Labat, Misty A446
Labat, Misty E210
Labay, Charles P166
Labell, Mark E122
LaBelle, Jeanne A335
LaBelle, James P488
Laben, Nancy J. A140
Laber, Larry E. E104
Labeyrie, Christian W387
Labi, Abdul A115
Labib, Joseph A675
Laborde, Sarah A806
Laborde, Sarah P569
Laborde, Thierry W66
Labosky, Laura P123
Labovich, Gary D. A140
Labrecque, Andre G P24
Labrique, Steve A67
Labrosse, Derek A107
Labrosse, Derek E35
Labrot, Andy E116
Lacagnina, Frank E354
Lacaille, Rick A766
Lacassagne, Gtraudmarie A241
Lacasse, Paul E P81
LaCerda, Michael A133
Lacerda, Marcos A685
Lacey, Erin A468
Lacey, Diane E. A582
Lacey, Erin P253

A = AMERICAN BUSINESS
E = EMERGING COMPANIES
P = PRIVATE COMPANIES
W = WORLD BUSINESS

Lacey, Diane E. P373
Lacey, Bonita Washington P457
Lacey, David P670
Lachance, Margaret P. (Meg) A682
Lacher, Joseph P. (Joe) A487
Lacker, Jeffrey M. (Jeff) A325
Lackey, Beth P214
Lackhouse, Gary A84
Lackman, Sara J A671
Lacour, Raymond A693
Lacroix, Didier E82
Lacue, Amanda P619
Lacy, James A85
Lacy, Spring Taylor A676
Lacy, Alan J. E105
Lacy, Stephen M. (Steve) E272
Laczi, Chris E245
Ladd, Emma A513
Ladd, Tim A549
Ladd, Edward H. (Ted) P71
Ladd, Ruta P83
Ladd, Kevin P200
Ladd, Steven P221
Ladd, Tim E270
Lade, Herb E82
Lader, Philip W398
Laderman, Gerald (Gerry) A846
Ladouceur, Jacinthe A49
Ladowicz, John A616
Laduke, David A478
Ladurantey, Joseph De E439
Laenger, William A700
Lafferty, Kevin A263
Lafferty, Jack A912
Lafianza, Nancy P380
Lafitte, Michael J. (Mike) A172
Lafitte, David E. E106
Laflamme, Catie A518
Laflamme, Catie P292
Laflamme, Renée W180
LaFollette, Christopher A67
Lafond, Dan A85
Lafond, Debbie P113
Lafont, Bruno W214
Lafontaine, Henri W136
LaForgia, Felicia A865
Lafrankcis, Janine P231
LaFreniere, Kevin A406
Lagano, Roxanne A921
Lagarde, Michel A815
Lagarrigue, Emmanuel W322
LaGatta, Loreen A. A841
LaGatta, Loreen A. E410
Lage, Jose L. P514
Lagenfeld, Michelle P220
Lager, Jeffrey T A46
Lager, Jeffrey T P32
Lagerlef, Brenda P431
Laginess, Meredith A264
Lagioia, Andrea A218
Lagnado, Silvia A545
Lagneaux, Leon A58
Lago, Jim A287
Lago, Virginia Del A532
Lago, Jim P174
Lagos, William H A754
Lagrone, Craig A591
Laguarta, Ramon A647
LaHaise, James A. A57
LaHaise, James A. E16
Lahanas, Nicholas (Niko) E65
LaHatte, Bernard A814
LaHatte, Bernard P616
Lahay, Jeff A770
Lahey, John L P450
Lahrs, Claus-Dietrich W204
Lai, Nathan A201
Lai, Suet A272
Lai, Johnson E310

Laidler, Lisa A332
Laigneau, Marianne W136
Laine, Jim A348
Laine, Jim E155
Laing, Tom P385
Laing, Ann P451
Laing, Melanie W105
Laird, Bruce A199
Laird, David A483
Laixuthai, Adit W202
Lakdawala, Keta E268
Lake, Charles D. A18
Lake, Marianne A480
Lake, Fred A523
Lake, Linda A890
Lake, Linda P684
Lakin, Ronald A173
Lakin, Kenneth S P79
Lakin, Peter D P80
Lakin, Edwin A P80
Lakkis, Miguel El A589
Lakner, Eric A497
Lakshman, Girish A733
Lal, Pradeep W389
Lalama, Kristen A321
Lalama, Kristen E144
Lalanne, Jean-Christophe W14
Lalas, Jose W P143
Lalima, Anthony A105
Lalithakumar, Ananth A180
Lally, Helen A51
Lally, James B. A302
Lally, James B. E128
Lally-Green, Maureen P169
Lalonde, Kenn W. W370
Lalor, Angela S. A253
Lalwani, Ellen A500
Lalwani, Ellen E237
Lam, Margaret A76
Lam, Michael A105
Lam, Josiah A481
Lam, Benson A685
Lam, Barry W297
Lam, Henry E65
Lam, Dale S E368
Lamacchio, Tom A693
Laman, John A187
Laman, John E71
Lamanno, Lori A838
Lamar, William (Bibb) A737
Lamar, Jim P216
Lamar, William (Bibb) E367
Lamarche, Michael Lamarche
    Michael A865
Lamattere, Shelly De P193
Lamb, Matthew A178
Lamb, Brian A332
Lamb, Gerry A374
Lamb, Emily A387
Lamb, Jennifer A408
Lamb, Robert A727
Lamb, Todd A765
Lamb, Jim P105
Lamb, John P309
Lamb, Carolyn P353
Lamb, Todd P540
Lamb, Angy P554
Lamb, Amy P674
Lamb, Peter E138
Lamb, Emily E177
Lamb, Trisha E183
Lamb, Scott E. E212
Lamba, Sanjiv W223
Lambdin, James P660
Lambert, Karen A. A15
Lambert, Joanna A49
Lambert, Brett A602
Lambert, Richard F. A676
Lambert, Cameron A691
Lambert, Matthew A695
Lambert, Anne A751
Lambert, Jay A913
Lambert, Karen A. P9
Lambert, Leo M P181
Lambert, Courtney P310

Lambert, Robert P404
Lambert, Phil P496
Lambert, Nick W389
Lambert, Sandra L. E229
Lambert, Anne E378
Lamberti, Hermann-Josef M. W187
Lambertson, Stephen A814
Lambertson, Stephen P616
Lambeth, Tracy A564
Lambiase, Matthew E75
LAMEY, KRISTEN A596
Laming, Michael S. A382
Lamkin, Bryan A11
Lamm, Kim A115
Lammas, Mark T. E208
Lammers, James A323
Lammers, Kent A395
Lamneck, Kenneth T. (Ken) A454
LaMontagna, Peter A866
Lamonte, Steve P51
Lamoreaux, Roy I A658
LaMorte, Debra A585
LaMorte, Debra P377
Lamotte, Cheri A71
Lamotte, Joseph A394
Lamparski, Jerry A34
Lampe, Gregory A369
Lampen, Richard J. (Dick) E236
Lampen, Richard J. (Dick) E425
Lampert, Edward S. (Eddie) A733
Lampert, Steven P50
Lamphear, Sue A175
Lampier, Carol A244
Lampley, Marcus A51
Lampo, Craig A. A62
Lamprecht, Charlotte A685
Lampropoulos, Fred P. E273
Lampropoulos, Justin E273
Lamsam, Banthoon W202
Lamsam, Krisada W203
Lamstein, Joel H P269
Lamy, David W343
Lancaster, Tim A345
Lancaster, Rick P219
Lancaster, Tim P233
Lancaster, Bonita P584
Lancaster, Tim E154
Lance, Ryan M A232
Lance, Wendy A724
Lance, Phil P250
Lance, Donald W P602
Lance, Garrett P627
Lanci, Gianfranco W218
Lancia, Pete A685
Landa, Jon A517
Landa, Lisa E286
Landau, Glenn R. A462
Landau, Alan P391
Landau, Igor W8
Landau, Steve E2
Lande, Ruth P325
Landen, Udi A685
Lander, Mike A886
Lander, Eric P567
Lander, Mike E433
Landeros, Lorri A769
Landers, Linda K A221
Landers, Allison A677
Landers, Joseph A777
Landers, Peter P629
Landers, Scott E. E286
Landers, Joseph E393
Landes, Barbara L. P445
Landess, C Barton P202
Landewee, Cassy P339
Landi, Robert A19
Landin, Linda P300
Landless, David E216
Landmann, Simon A478
Landmark, Greg A828
Landre, Jay A607
Landrith, Jody A160
Landrith, Jody E55
Landry, David A244
Landry, Mark A A358

Landry, Robert E. A698
Landry, Steve A743
Landry, Stephen A743
Landry, Dustin P347
Landry, Stephen G. P494
Landry, Ronnie P621
Landry, Steve E373
Landry, Stephen E373
Landschulz, Mark A356
Landsman, Liza K. A878
Landy, Sarah A872
Landy, Michael P. E284
Landy, Eugene W. E284
Landy, Samuel A. E408
Landy, Michael E408
Landy, Eugene W. E408
Lane, Andrew H. A5
Lane, Danny A82
Lane, Deanne A179
Lane, Janet A244
Lane, Eric S. A389
Lane, George A532
Lane, Jeffrey H. A557
Lane, Michael A701
Lane, J. Bret A735
Lane, Richard A781
Lane, Anne A919
Lane, Danny P49
Lane, Michael P143
Lane, Conan P232
Lane, Mark P254
Lane, Kevin P395
Lane, Linda P430
Lane, Melissa P480
Lane, Kevin P503
Lane, Charles E. P642
Lane, Timothy W47
Lane, Christine E213
Lane, James A. E258
Lanell, Randle P20
Lanese, Stephen A775
Lanesey, Rob A466
Laney, G. Timothy (Tim) A573
Laney, Mark P231
Laney, Mark P232
Laney, D. Randy P579
Lang, Doug A101
Lang, Nicholas A122
Lang, Robert A255
Lang, Michael (Mike) A269
Lang, Rick A366
Lang, Patrick A502
Lang, J Brad A671
Lang, Edward A A707
Lang, John D A712
Lang, Rebecca A A837
Lang, Rebecca A837
Lang, Karen P446
Lang, Marcina P654
Lang, Andras E248
Langan, Tom A670
Langberg, Michael L. P102
Langberg, Joanna P191
Langdon, Lynn M A746
Langdon, Matt P356
Lange, Wade A44
Lange, Bob De A169
Lange, Chip A292
Lange, Jeffrey A406
Lange, James A599
Lange, Doug A620
Lange, Peter A644
Lange, Wade P31
Lange, Kristin P408
Lange, Kelley E289
Langel, Craig A A387
Langel, Craig A E177
Langella, Steve A165
Langenbahn, Paul A578
Langendonk, David A898
Langeness, Troy A616
Langenus, John A67
Langer, Robert A272
Langer, Dennis P133
Langer, C E283

Langevin, Eric T. E229
Langfitt, Gary B. A169
Langford, Barbara P27
Langford, Stephen P67
Langham, Fern A204
Langham, Charles P64
Langham, Catherine P580
Langhauser, Diana A548
Langhauser, Diana P321
Langhofer, Veronica E432
Langley, W. John P315
Langlois, Melissa P47
Lango, Cynthia P282
Langou, Suzanne A677
Langston, Danny A260
Langston, Lewis A903
Langton, Clara P69
Lanham, Roger M. A890
Lanham, Cindy P503
Lanham, Roger M. P684
Lanier, Lawrence A327
Lanier, Gina P52
Lanier, Andrea P471
Laniewski, Jeffrey E166
Lanis, Nancy A727
Lankford, Wendy P276
Lankler, Douglas M. (Doug) A648
Lankton, Madelyn A827
Lannen, Angela A58
Lannie, P. Anthony A69
Lannie, P A69
Lanning, Justin A912
Lanning, John E P272
Lanning, Shelley P566
Lannon, David A899
Lannon, David P690
Lannuier, Helen A272
Lansbury, Stephen A366
Lansford, Gordon E. P256
Lansford, Gordon E. P257
Lansing, Alexis P202
Lansing, Linda P485
Lansing, William J. (Will) E368
Lant, Stephen P106
Lant, Todd E44
Lantman, Chris A904
Lantman, Chris E442
Lantos, Phyllis R. A810
Lantos, Phyllis R. P597
Lantrip, Reese T. A304
Lantz, Brian A364
Lantz, Brian A659
Lantz, Paul P147
Lantzsch, Thomas P. (Tom) A456
Lanusse, Adrien A581
Lanza, Steve A501
Lanza, Lorie A676
Lanza, Michael H. A734
Lanzetta, James A770
Lanzi, Mario A204
Lanzino, Becky A369
Lanzoni, Nancy A109
Lanzoni, Nancy E36
Laokwansatit, Anucha W330
Lapcevic, Misha A530
Lapczynski, Susan A131
Lapeer, James P519
Lapiana, John K. P506
Lapidas, Gary P632
Lapkin, Robert A P241
Lapkin, Robert P241
Laplant, Michael A838
LaPlante, Frank A888
Laplante, George W. E14
Laplante, Dawn E290
Lapointe, Johanne A112
Lapointe, Kimberly A677
LAPOINTE, BEN A693
Lapointe, Johanne E38
LaPorta, Cosimo A762
Laporte, Jaime A408
LaPorte, Todd P487
LaPrade, Frank G. A163
Laprade, Ken A405
Laprade, Patricia P54

Lapuente, Chris de W225
Lara, Miguel P127
Larabee, Cheryl A. E448
Laratonda, Susan A902
Laratonda, Susan P693
Laraway, Dennis L. A111
Laraway, Dennis A548
Laraway, Dennis L. P56
Laraway, Dennis P324
Larchenesque, Lee A872
Lardi, Marco G P620
Lardy, Dave A636
Lareau, Richard G. E275
Larimore, Jim P5
Lark, Vercie P167
Lark, J Peter P282
Lark, David C P457
Larkin, Deanna A437
Larkin, Gary A449
Larkin, Terrence B. (Terry) A504
Larkin, C. Raymond E10
Larkins, Thomas F. A71
Larkln, Joyce A180
Larky, Steven A685
Larnaudie-Eiffel, Xavier W103
Larobina, Mark P221
LaRocca, Andrew A583
LaRocca, Gregory A602
LaRocca, John E113
LaRocco, Michael E. (Mike) A764
Larochelle, Steven R. A301
Larochelle, Steven R. E127
Larocque, Jim A270
Larocque, Peter A779
Larocque, Lynda P647
LaRosa, Gregory A649
LaRose, Jason A840
Larose, Doug P41
LaRossa, Ralph A. A678
Laroux, Leonard P51
Laroyia, Varun A518
Larrain, Rodrigo W85
Larrimer, Karen L. A659
Larsen, Kenneth A. (Ken) A110
Larsen, Shild A305
Larsen, Christine E A343
Larsen, Michael M. A450
Larsen, Dan A890
Larsen, Rachel P53
Larsen, Christian P179
Larsen, Shild P185
Larsen, Brenda P406
Larsen, Matthew P506
Larsen, David P666
Larsen, Dan P684
Larsen, David P685
Larsen, Hans J-ṛrgen W201
Larsen, Kenneth A. (Ken) E37
Larsen, Jill E269
Larsh, Roger A748
Larsh, Herbert P480
Larson, Gregory A6
Larson, Erik A107
Larson, Margaret A115
Larson, Matt A173
Larson, Tyla A350
Larson, Greg A390
Larson, Gregory J. (Greg) A434
Larson, April A448
Larson, Julie A524
Larson, Timothy M. A660
Larson, Sherrie L A684
Larson, Todd C. A701
Larson, Michael A707
Larson, Michael A744
Larson, Eric A766
Larson, Steve A784
Larson, David L. A904
Larson, Erik A905
Larson, Kent T. A910
Larson, Angela P157
Larson, Elwin P229
Larson, April P246
Larson, Jamie E P346
Larson, Kenneth S P439

Larson, Thomas R P589
Larson, Lynette P677
Larson, Erik P694
Larson, Erik E34
Larson, Tyla E157
Larson, Sherrie L E341
Larson, David L. E442
Larsson, Greg A406
Larsson, Naya A537
Larsson, Randi P498
Larsson, Christian P636
Larter, Will E426
Larue, Tommy E76
LaRussa, Baldo A691
Lasaga, Manuel P59
Lasala, Joseph A P88
Lasane, Karlos A158
Lascko, Tim A522
Lash, James H. (Jim) A355
Lashbrook, Bill G A659
Lasher, Perry M. E183
Lashier, Mark E. A192
Lashier, Mark E A193
Lashier, Mark E. P112
Lashier, Mark E P112
Lashley, Lorretta A818
Lashmet, Craig A723
Lashway, Rich A868
Lasics, Agnes A350
Lasics, Agnes E157
Lasiter, Paul B. P423
Laskey, Sara P593
Lasky, Charles A355
Lasky, Jeff E208
Laspisa, Jerry A522
Laspisa, Esther A912
Lass, John J. A368
Lasser, Cathy A460
Lassiter, Wright L. A413
Lassiter, Lynn A655
Lassiter, Wright L. P234
Lassiter, Lynn E333
Lastoch, Chris A58
Lastrap, Karla A163
Latacki, Nancy P463
Latchford, Robert A850
Latek, Kevin P. E181
Latella, Robert N. A334
Laten, Steve P27
Lathan, Grenita P242
Lathrop, Ann P149
Latifzai, Khoshal P292
Latimer, Elise A446
Latimer, Elise E210
Latoff, William S. E108
Latorre, Sarah P632
Latovin, Alex A599
Lattal, Frank W98
Lattanzio, Nicole P535
Lattimer, Jay A158
Lattmann, Susan E. A120
Laturette, Deborah A780
Latushie, Dick P453
Latz, Greg P138
Lau, Timothy J. A81
Lau, Malcom A102
Lau, Cindy A163
Lau, Stephen A218
Lau, Jacky A471
Lau, Elisa A558
Lau, Paul P470
Lau, Luther P522
Lau, Jannie K. E222
Laubach, Harold E. P399
Laube, Marcus P431
Lauber, Scott J. A884
Lauber, Uwe W231
Laudenslager, Kevin W. E276
Lauder, Est E A503
Lauder, Heather W103
Lauderdale, Dawn A541
Lauderdale, Mark E182
Lauderdale, Dawn E266
Lauer, Trevor F. A280
Lauer, Kelley A838

Lauf, Michael K. (Mike) P92
Lauffer, Marlee P235
Laughlin, Terence P. (Terry) A100
Laughlin, John P. A701
Laughlin, Michael P536
Laughren, Patrici A438
Laughridge, Mason P620
Laughton, Kim P486
Launius, Steve P170
Lauren, Jerry A691
Lauren, Ralph A691
Lauren, David A691
Laurence, Scott A474
Lauria, Kristen A460
Lauria, Lynette A744
Laurin, Michael W180
Laurin, Fran- §ois W217
Lauro, Jeff A609
Lauro, Neil A693
Laursen, Thomas E. A919
Laury, Véronique W206
Lautenbach, Denise K P598
Lauter, Keith P524
Lautmann, Max A777
Lautmann, Max E393
Lauver, Jennifer A369
Laux, Nancy A885
Lavallee, Paul A863
Lavaty, Brad E70
LaVay, Matthew E119
Lavelle, Tom P440
Lavelli, Lucinda P642
Lavely, Patty P224
Lavender, Shelley K. A136
Lavender, Sunee P639
Laver, Michael A585
Laver, Michael P377
Lavers, Jeffrey A3
Laverty, David A461
Lavery, Anna A556
Lavery, Michelle P480
Lavey, Richard W. (Dick) A402
Lavigne, Joe A143
Lavik, Mary E404
Lavin, John A115
Lavin, John A706
Lavin, Marty A904
Lavin, Pablo Granifo W41
Lavin, John E353
Lavin, Marty E442
Lavinay, Gérard W82
Lavine, Bruce E443
Lavoie, Michael A644
Lavoie, Blair P361
Lavrusky, Nancy P160
Lavu, Ratnakar A493
Law, Christina A377
Law, Anne-Marie A445
Law, David P40
Law, Tom P271
Law, Michelle P691
Law, Simon E97
Lawal, Lekan J A565
Lawhead, Casey A446
Lawhead, Casey E210
Lawhorn, Andy A819
Lawicki, Pat A575
Lawit, Jason A A599
Lawler, Robert D. (Doug) A190
Lawler, Keith A407
Lawler, James P167
Lawler, Michael A P232
Lawler, Maria P352
Lawler, Will P605
Lawler, Paul J P672
Lawless, Cari A721
Lawless, Stephen T P22
Lawless, Fiona P34
Lawley, Heather A13
Lawley, Jennifer A844
Lawley, Jennifer E412
Lawlor, Mike A406
Lawlor, Elizabeth A597
Lawlor, Daniel A904
Lawlor, Kevin P244

A = AMERICAN BUSINESS
E = EMERGING COMPANIES
P = PRIVATE COMPANIES
W = WORLD BUSINESS

Lawlor, Edward F. P616
Lawlor, Daniel E442
Lawonn, Ken P147
Lawonn, Ken P498
Lawrence, Kevin A98
Lawrence, Timothy A113
Lawrence, Ralph A140
Lawrence, Tim A140
Lawrence, Charlotte A204
Lawrence, Paul J A224
Lawrence, Larry A295
Lawrence, David A316
Lawrence, Dugan A390
Lawrence, Guy A555
Lawrence, Edward P. A635
Lawrence, Taylor W. A694
Lawrence, Dr Reita P173
Lawrence, David P191
Lawrence, Bruce P250
Lawrence, Heather P295
Lawrence, Sandra A. J. P327
Lawrence, Ursula P348
Lawrence, Melody P363
Lawrence, Edward P. P419
Lawrence, John D P427
Lawrence, Beth P489
Lawrence, William B. P514
Lawrence, Donald P590
Lawrence, Jane P613
Lawrence, Cindy P619
Lawrence, Paul P651
Lawrence, Sabrina P676
Lawrence, Kevin E33
Lawrence, Bryan H. E185
Lawrence, Rob E248
Lawrie, John E426
Laws, John A375
Laws, Dale A898
Laws, Robert P105
Lawshe, Pam A742
Lawshe, Pam E372
Lawson, Linda A82
Lawson, David C. (Dave) A219
Lawson, Rodger A. A283
Lawson, Beth A532
Lawson, Scott P. A588
Lawson, John A820
Lawson, Ally A875
Lawson, Linda P49
Lawson, Ralph E. P57
Lawson, Ralph P59
Lawson, Matt P318
Lawson, Michael P405
Lawson, Marian W50
Lawson, Brian D. W75
Lawson, Stuart W312
Lawson, Douglas A. (Doug) E27
Lawson, David C. (Dave) E84
Lawson, John P. E160
Lawton, Harry A. (Hal) A288
Lawton, Nancy G A372
Lawton, Chuck A868
Lawton, Nancy G P208
Lawton, Matthew D. E197
Lawyer, Christopher A790
Laxer, Richard A. (Rich) A375
Laxton, Gregory A136
Lay, Garry A16
Lay, Jeri A458
Lay, Jeri P251
Laychak, Heather P564
Layman, Mark P54
Layne, Glenn A655
Layne, Beverly A674
Layne, Paul E207
Layne, Glenn E333
Layton, Donald H. (Don) A366
Layton, Erin P372
Lazan, James P660

Lazar, Melvin F. (Mel) E22
Lazaridis, Nick A435
Lazarus, Larry S. A111
Lazarus, Franz E. A239
Lazarus, Larry S. P56
Lazarus, Edward P. (Eddie) E402
Lazenby, Catherine P289
Lazio, Thomas P392
Lazzaris, Diane E. A888
Le, Hung A51
Le, Elizabeth A247
Le, Cuong A607
LE, Tuyen A644
Le, Que A802
Le, Hung P33
Le, Tuyet P318
Le, Que P562
Le, Elizabeth E103
Lea, Doretha F. (DeDe) A871
Lea, Jenny P277
Leach, Cliff A406
Leach, Kathy P81
Leach, Mary Anne P114
Leach, Joy P303
Leach, DOT P318
Leach, Todd P659
Leach, Michael R. (Mike) E13
Leach, Charles N. E41
Leackfeldt, Stephen M. A112
Leackfeldt, Stephen M. E38
Leadbeater, Seth M. A223
Leager, Mary A522
Leahy, Rosanne P96
Leahy, Kevin P203
Leahy, Mary P216
Leahy, William P. P625
Leal, Vangie A244
Leal, Cynthia A729
Leal, Santiago P14
Leal, Manuel P127
Leal, Ramiro P177
Leaman, Andrew A862
Leaman, Andrew E419
LeaMond, Nancy A. P1
Leap, Arnold P. (Arnie) E1
Lear, Mark A827
Lear, Jan P204
Leary, Alison A585
Leary, Warren A677
Leary, Mike A685
Leary, Christopher A777
Leary, Carol A846
Leary, Alison P377
Leary, Angus P545
Leary, Matt P681
Leary, Christopher E393
Leary, Brian E404
Leath, Janet P321
Leatherberry, William J. E304
Leatherberry, Kristie E437
Leathers, Steve A478
Leavell, Christopher M. A335
Leavell, Bill E. A822
Leavens, Brian A13
Leavenworth, Elaine R. A4
Leavitt, Chris E349
Leavy, David C. A269
Leavy, Jack A669
Leb, Michael A878
Lebaron, Dawn P614
Lebda, Douglas R. (Doug) E243
Lebeau, Christina A384
Lebeau, Christina E176
Lebeck, Shelley A165
Lebedev, Vladimir E269
Lebegue, Lo--s E115
Lebel, Joseph J. A611
Lebel, Joseph J. E313
Lebens, Lucia A575
LeBlanc, Claude L. A40
LeBlanc, Robert J. A460
LeBlanc, Myra A770
Leblanc, Stephen P154
Leblanc, Paul A P639
Leblanc, Franky E3

Lebleu, Tom E116
Lebold, Suzanne A6
LeBow, Bennett S. E425
Lebowitz, Michael A131
Lebrun, Robert A127
Lechleiter, John C. A511
Lechler, Bobby E65
Lechmaier, Deb A493
Lechner, Kim A258
Lechner, David E. P78
Leckman, Linda C. A458
Leckman, Linda C. P251
Leclair, Michael D P53
LeClaire, Brian P. A437
Leclaire, Terri A774
LeClaire, Greg A. E247
Lecorgne, R Paker P403
Lecrone, Samantha P430
Lecroy, Jason E189
Lecuyer, Andrew A270
Ledbetter, David H. A372
Ledbetter, Barry K. A742
Ledbetter, David H. P208
Ledbetter, Barry K. P372
Leddon, Ron A737
Leddon, Ron E367
Leddy, Kim A300
Leddy, H Drake P440
Leddy, Stanton P440
Lederman, Ira S. A122
Ledford, Randall D. A295
Ledford, Andrea L A578
Ledford, Doug A774
Ledford, Carolyn P339
Ledien, Randy P669
Ledocq, Tracy P67
Ledoux, Marque A597
Leduc, Robert F. A854
Lee, Bonnie A34
Lee, Anderson A49
Lee, James C A73
Lee, Charles A136
Lee, Ellen A171
Lee, Steve A173
Lee, Eugene I. (Gene) A254
Lee, Shreve A262
Lee, John M. A285
Lee, Jay A288
Lee, Jae A288
Lee, Bruce A315
Lee, Alice A377
Lee, William A. A386
Lee, Kirk L A397
Lee, Kirk A397
Lee, Bonita I. (Bonnie) A401
Lee, Bruce K. A412
Lee, Brandon A429
Lee, Charlotte A483
Lee, Amy A502
Lee, Hana A507
Lee, Melanie A520
Lee, Lara L. A521
Lee, David A522
Lee, Nancy A530
Lee, Natasha A532
Lee, Esther A555
Lee, Rachel A555
Lee, Jeff A583
Lee, Michael A605
Lee, Ming-Ju A607
Lee, Sang Young A629
Lee, Thomas H. A635
Lee, Sean A640
Lee, Julien A644
Lee, Pearl A683
Lee, Chip A693
Lee, Jeffery (Jeff) A731
Lee, Schavrien A735
Lee, Thai A739
Lee, Henry A741
Lee, Yongheon A784
Lee, Sang A786
Lee, William A810
Lee, Michael A840

Lee, David A850
Lee, Debra L. A871
Lee, Sang A874
Lee, Don A908
Lee, Linda P6
Lee, James G. P8
Lee, Esther P37
Lee, Stephen P58
Lee, Francis P67
Lee, Karen P71
Lee, David L. P91
Lee, Judy P98
Lee, Ellen P100
Lee, Allison P110
Lee, Ronald P111
Lee, Irene P136
Lee, Francine P136
Lee, Renee P144
Lee, Micheal P201
Lee, Hosea P243
Lee, Hana P288
Lee, Wook P331
Lee, Mary P343
Lee, Naomi P396
Lee, Angela Y P398
Lee, Thomas H. P419
Lee, Do Hyun P437
Lee, Mou P461
Lee, Thai P501
Lee, Lynn P584
Lee, Charles P587
Lee, William P597
Lee, David S. P606
Lee, Gentry Patrick P627
Lee, Joyce W56
Lee, Chang-Ken W84
Lee, Alan W84
Lee, Albert W113
Lee, Jae Kyung W130
Lee, Raymond W. H. W154
Lee, Cheol Young W178
Lee, Han Gu W179
Lee, Richard W189
Lee, Hyoung-Keun (Hank) W205
Lee, Young-Hoon W292
Lee, Woo-Kyu W292
Lee, Tae-Ju W292
Lee, Francis C. Y. W384
Lee, Gwang Goo W396
Lee, John M. E114
Lee, Bonita I. (Bonnie) E187
Lee, Bruce K. E192
Lee, Brandon E204
Lee, Marvin E256
Lee, Yongsam E261
Lee, Melinda E272
Lee, John T. C. E282
Lee, David E286
Lee, Jeffery (Jeff) E365
Lee, Henry E370
Lee, Lisa F E445
Lee, Don E446
Leebron, Jack A149
Leece, Lynne A332
Leech, Wilson A599
Leech, Tony W334
Leedom, David W. A554
Leedom, David W. E275
Leedy, Lori P546
Leef, Serge P326
Leeming, Rosemary P209
Leenay, Mark A885
Lees, Susan L. A33
Lees, Fred P498
Lefang, Bernar A438
Lefebvre, Jocelyn W294
Lefevre, Gordon W26
Lefferson, C. Douglas (Doug) A344
Leffler, Stephen P614
Lefkin, Mark E1
LeFort, Alan A456
Leftwich, Snowden E349
Lefurge, Raymond H. E414
LeGall, Didier E14
Legault, Richard W75

Legault, Richard W180
Leger, Tamela A446
Leger, Tamela E210
Legere, John J A785
Legerton, Carla P352
Legette, Brenda P664
Legg, Paul P20
Legg, Jackie E46
Legge, Jeffrey D. (Jeff) A207
Leggett, Robert A390
Leggett, Pat A463
Leggett, G Raymond P96
Leggett, Karen W252
Leggette, Sharon A513
Leggio, John A607
Leggio, Joe A871
Legler, Robert C. E293
Lego, Douglas P358
Legorburo, José Ignacio W170
Legrand, Joseph A788
Legrange, Brandon P347
Legris, Monique A441
Lehan, Felicia A583
Lehman, Jeffrey S. A585
Lehman, Jeffrey S. P377
Lehmann, Mary A61
Lehmann, Daniel A194
Lehmann, Holger A550
Lehmann, Leslie P570
Lehmann, Michal Piotr W51
Lehmus, Matti W257
Lehn, Chuck A111
Lehn, Chuck P56
Lehner, Jon A766
Lehner, Ulrich W131
Lehner, Ulrich W365
Lehotsky, Ed A189
Lehoux, Becky P146
Lehr, Paul P160
Lehrer, Ronald A583
Lehrer, Deborah P355
Lei, Saobo P650
Leib, Mallory A390
Leibel, Stephen A196
Leiber, Phil P297
Leibert, Sharon P654
Leibman, Maya A43
Leibman, Chris A129
Leichner, Charles P186
Leiden, Jeffrey M. (Jeff) E428
Leiderman, Roni P399
Leidwinger, Kevin A211
Leigh, Howard A530
Leiken, Jonathan B. A265
Leimgruber, Jeffrey A P190
Leimkuhler, William F. E23
Leinenbach, Keith A. A384
Leinenbach, Keith A. E176
Leinroth, Peter A464
Leins, Darlena D P435
Leipzig, Inna A818
Leissring, Kevin A440
Leitch, Glenn R. A432
Leitch, Andrew M. E44
Leite, Adriana A218
Leith, Andrew P298
Leithauser, Jeffrey A332
Leiting, Jim P73
Leitman, Steven A676
Leitner, Roger A655
Leitner, Manfred W276
Leitner, Roger E333
Leitze, Zachary A448
Leitze, Zachary P246
Leiva, John A585
Leiva, John P377
LeJeune, Amy E100
Lekberg, Roger A913
Lekhraj, Sharda A131
Lekkala, Maneesh P96
Leland, Todd A390
Leland, Tim A685
Leland, Kim A770
Lell, Brian A729
LeMaitre, George W. E242

Lemaitre, Cornelia E242
Lemaitre, Philippe J. E390
Lembke, Wayne P345
Lembo, Philip J. (Phil) A307
Lemchak, Joseph J. A225
Lemchak, Joseph J. E88
Lemelin, Tracey A513
Lemelin, Jon E265
Lemery, Becky A149
Lemierre, Jean W67
Lemieux, Catharine (Cathy) A323
Lemire, Anne A54
Lemkau, Gregg R. A389
Lemly, Chris A153
Lemmens, Lynn P220
Lemmens, Sabrina E7
Lemmer, Teresa P456
Lemmiksoo, Todd P63
Lemmon, David J. A748
Lemoine, Kevin A163
Lemoine, Colleen A446
Lemoine, Colleen E210
Lemon, Paulette A427
Lemon, Paulette E202
Lemonds, Rick P509
Lemonius, John A49
Lemons, Brian A915
Lemons, Steve P460
Lemons, Brian P700
Lemppenau, Joachim W389
Lemson, Steve A49
Lenahan, Anna W105
Lenard, Lori A268
Lencquesaing, Aymar de W218
Lenderman, Richard P199
Lenertz, Renae P624
Lenhardt, Diana P133
Lenhoff, Timothy K. A267
Lenio, Gary P516
Lenna, Robert A525
Lenna, Robert P303
Lenner, Marc A869
Lennie, William G. (Bill) A426
Lennie, Robert M P617
Lennon, Gary W251
Lenseth, Patti A34
Lenson, Celia P307
Lentenbrink, Laura P79
Lenters, Nienke A398
Lenti-Ponsetto, Jean P155
Lentini, Matt P61
Lentz, Mike E. A434
Lentz, Rick A597
Lentz, Bobby A602
Lentz, Darrell P48
Lentz, Robert L. (Bob) E286
Lenz, Matt A364
Lenz, Joseph E300
Lenzen, John A789
Lenzen, Ron P141
Lenzen, John P555
Leo, Alan A73
Leo, Bruno V. Di A460
Leo, Koguan A739
Leo, Koguan P501
Leon, Alfonso A69
Leon, Sonny A82
Leon, Cynthia A171
Leon, Josefina A272
Leon, Mercedes M A584
Leon, Lori De A777
Leon, Regan A866
Leon, Sonny P49
Leon, Laurie P79
Leon, Cynthia P100
Leon, Roosevelt De P109
Leon, Anna P132
Leon, Alfonso P182
Leon, Mercedes M P374
Leon, Andres De P386
Leon, Monica Ponce de P606
Leon, Mercedes P628
Leon, Fredy De P662
Leon, Jorge A. W28
Leon, J.P. E385

Leon, Lori De E393
Leon-Wade, Pat P20
Leonard, David E. (Dave) A30
Leonard, Jim A58
Leonard, Wayne J A300
Leonard, Joeseph A323
Leonard, James C. A332
Leonard, Dennis A375
Leonard, William A647
Leonard, Shanon A803
Leonard, Robert M. A831
Leonard, Mark P66
Leonard, James C. P95
Leonard, Vivian P122
Leonard, Daniel P154
Leonard, Edward P204
Leonard, Randy P243
Leonard, Pat P371
Leonard, Jim P444
Leonard, Jim P471
Leonard, Judith E. P506
Leonard, James C P568
Leonard, Edward F P688
Leonardi, Joshua A390
Leonardi, Mark A644
Leondakis, Mia A875
Leone, Gary A173
Leone, Roger E. A777
Leone, Roger E. E393
Leonedenie, Karen A322
Leonetti, Debbie E220
Leong, Jamie A322
Leong, Warren P19
Leong, Chris W322
Leong, Jamie E146
Leong, Amy E165
Leonhardt, Darrell T. P45
Leonsis, Theodore J A49
Leonti, Joseph R. A634
Leopold, Diane G. A275
Leopold, David A366
Lepage, Mark A P309
Lepak, Kathleen A644
Lepere, Kristopher P249
Lepin, Julie A550
Lepley, John P329
Lepley, John P332
Lepore, Jonathan A784
Leprince, Igor W266
Lequient, Frederic E426
Lequin, Stan A454
Lerner, Arnold S. A301
Lerner, Mark A537
Lerner, Mark A857
Lerner, Scott E. E29
Lerner, Arnold S. E127
Lerner, Neil L. E340
Leroy, Jennifer A823
Leroy, Didier W374
Lesar, David J. (Dave) A398
Lescault, Michelle P221
Lescoeur, Bruno W136
Lescure, John A644
Lesesne, Pam P187
Lesjak, Catherine A. (Cathie) A435
Lesko, Dirk A374
Lesko, Johnathan A493
Lesko, J A493
Lesko, James A912
Lesko, Mark P622
Lesler, Michael A116
Lesley, Melissa A13
Leslie, Claudia A105
Leslie, Paul P152
Leslie, Andy P368
Lesneski, Gary J. P576
Lesniak, Lisa A15
Lesniak, Lisa P9
Lesselyoung, Shanan A493
Lesser, Brian A84
Lesser, Michael E369
Lessler, Becky P391
Lessner, Philip M. (Phil) E230
Lessor, Deborah P666
Lestang, Martin W143

Lester, Mark C. A801
Lester, William P87
Lester, Greg P170
Lester, Mark C. P562
Lesukoski, Paul E41
Leszczyszyn, David P665
Letbetter, Steve P183
Lete, Laura A508
Leten, Ronnie W3
Letendre, Donald E. P611
Letinsky, Daniel P446
Leto, Francis J. A151
Leto, Francis J. E48
Letson, Alicia P235
Lett, Stan A422
Lett, Rosalind K P182
Lett, Stan P239
Letter, Tim A677
Lettice, Fred P510
Lettig, William A489
Lettman, Dennis S. P613
Letts, Shannon A878
Leuhmann, John A441
Leukert, Bernd W319
Leum, Linda L P164
Leung, Sandra A147
Leung, Pak (Steven) A914
Leung, Angela P356
Leung, C.C. W297
Leupold, Mary P227
Leuthner, Steven P591
Lev, Leonid E224
Lev, Lavi A. E408
Levan, Kris A342
Levan, Alan B. E39
Levan, Jarett S. E39
Levander, Carl W. A594
Levasseur, INA P311
Levatich, Matthew S. (Matt) A403
Levatino, Marilyn A175
Levchets, Regina A614
LeVecchio, Anthony J. A505
LeVecchio, Anthony J. E241
Leveille, Tim D. A192
Leveille, Tim D. P112
Levenson, Susan A530
Levenson, Rodger A907
Levenson, Rodger E445
Leverett, Allen L. A884
Leverett, Allen P36
Levesque, Paula P66
Levesque, Paul E445
Levesque, Stephanie E445
Levi, Linda P565
Levin, Krysten A8
Levin, Marc S A252
Levin, Diane A476
Levin, Bob A556
Levin, Alan G A649
Levin, Krysten P3
Levin, Jesse P102
Levin, Roy P368
Levin, Barry F P505
Levin, Justine P567
Levin, Amy P583
Levin, Kerry P682
Levin, Donna E57
Levin, Eugene D. E127
Levine, Kyle A28
Levine, Jonathan M. A122
Levine, Eric A204
Levine, Jeff A390
Levine, Britt A449
Levine, Carole A539
Levine, Jay N. A621
Levine, Alec A693
Levine, Todd A724
Levine, Layne L. A903
Levine, Benjamin P275
Levine, Mel P297
Levine, Alan P564
Levings, Stuart A382
Levingston, Charles D. A284
Levingston, Charles D. E111
Levins, Jessica A532

A = AMERICAN BUSINESS
E = EMERGING COMPANIES
P = PRIVATE COMPANIES
W = WORLD BUSINESS

Levinsky, Nik P601
Levinson, Arthur D. (Art) A70
Levinson, Andrew A459
Levinson, Daniel A. (Dan) E23
Levinson, Jeff E300
Levirne, Jonathan E306
Levitan, Lara A6
Levitsky, John A537
Levitt, Evan A411
Levitt, Brian M. W370
Levitts, Larry A883
Levonowich, Paul P272
Levounis, Petros P525
Levy, Susan Nestor A80
Levy, Paul S. A153
Levy, Adam A175
Levy, Lance A330
Levy, Anthony A402
Levy, Jay A410
Levy, Jeffrey M. A577
Levy, Susan C. A599
Levy, Dana A691
Levy, Stuart A707
Levy, Andrew C. A846
Levy, Robert A912
Levy, Susan Nestor P47
Levy, Ofer P111
Levy, Scott S. P164
Levy, Ann P368
Levy, Judd S P376
Levy, Ofer W46
Levy, Stuart W175
Levy, Avi W190
Levy, Avraham W190
Levy, Grant E7
Levy, Joel E39
Levy, Alan J. E39
Lewan, Len A115
Lewandowski, Joel P133
Lewandowski, Lynn P444
Lewis, Lisa A56
Lewis, Cindi H. A57
Lewis, Jeff A85
Lewis, Scott A98
Lewis, George A175
Lewis, D A180
Lewis, Rodney A238
Lewis, Michael A. A281
Lewis, Holden A318
Lewis, Margaret G. A324
Lewis, Alton A347
Lewis, John D. A356
Lewis, Kenneth A. A365
Lewis, Daniel A406
Lewis, Scott A406
Lewis, Daniel J A407
Lewis, Dan A408
Lewis, Michael A413
Lewis, Lee A420
Lewis, Patricia A460
Lewis, Amber A468
Lewis, Thomas A475
Lewis, Mitch A482
Lewis, Derek A505
Lewis, John A522
Lewis, Glenn A530
Lewis, Cecilia A530
Lewis, Cecelia A531
Lewis, William (Will) A589
Lewis, Jessica E A602
Lewis, Haston A647
Lewis, Sarae Janes A655
Lewis, Stephen A693
Lewis, Rudy A695
Lewis, Karla R. A703
Lewis, Gary A744
Lewis, Greg A800
Lewis, Celine A818
Lewis, Bryant H A827

Lewis, Steve A833
Lewis, Kim A855
Lewis, Carolyn A872
Lewis, Michael A878
Lewis, Linda A901
Lewis, Lisa A902
Lewis, Donald A919
Lewis, Clinton A. (Clint) A921
Lewis, Michael P2
Lewis, Sherry P26
Lewis, Paul P27
Lewis, Ted P63
Lewis, James R P88
Lewis, Roger P117
Lewis, Kimberly P154
Lewis, Eric P184
Lewis, David P188
Lewis, Curtis P217
Lewis, Jonathan P231
Lewis, Michael P234
Lewis, Amanda P244
Lewis, Jake P247
Lewis, Amber P252
Lewis, Thomas P266
Lewis, Larry P276
Lewis, Jay P279
Lewis, Pat P343
Lewis, Suzy P403
Lewis, Dr Kirk P420
Lewis, Lisa P476
Lewis, Veronica Grijalva P480
Lewis, Ky P498
Lewis, Donna P525
Lewis, Kelli P531
Lewis, Diane P592
Lewis, Daniel K. P593
Lewis, Claudette P601
Lewis, Erin P611
Lewis, Lisa P692
Lewis, Stuart W123
Lewis, Michael W131
Lewis, Jonathan W268
Lewis, Stevan W347
Lewis, Cindi H. E16
Lewis, Scott E33
Lewis, Marva E98
Lewis, Scott E166
Lewis, Lee E198
Lewis, Josh E293
Lewis, Sarae Janes E333
Lewis, Greg E396
Lewis-Hall, Freda C. A648
Lewnard, Jack E74
Lewnes, Ann A11
Ley, A. Lily A629
Ley, Fred A878
Leyden, Bob A406
Leyder, Dennis E. E147
Leyendecker, Ernest A. A64
Leyendecker, R. Greg A412
Leyendecker, R. Greg E192
Leygraaf, Greg A819
Leyoub, Caprice P637
Leyrat, Gilles A200
Leysen, Thomas W379
Leyvi, Michele A532
Lez, Richard Gonz P3
Lezon, Stanley A676
Lherault, Greg A340
Lhota, William J P688
LI, Yuliang A40
Li, Daniel A102
Li, Xuemei A147
Li, Haiyan A221
Li, Zhenqin A568
LI, Isabella A667
Li, William A691
Li, Ruohao A698
Li, Bo A780
Li, Justin P254
Li, Ruohao P456
Li, Mehra P498
LI, Heng P567
Li, David K. P. W47
Li, Samson K. C. W47

Li, Adrian David M. K. W47
Li, Brian David M. B. W47
Li, Arthur K. C. W47
Li, Morris W113
Li, Victor T. K. W176
Li, Baomin W197
Li, Weijian W366
Li, David H. E50
LI, Isabella E336
Lian, Eric V. F. W384
Liang, Kai A201
Liang, Jim A461
Liang, George C. A515
Liang, Frank C A793
Liang, MEI-Yun A793
Liang, Jane A793
Liang, Frank C P557
Liang, MEI-Yun P557
Liang, Jane P557
Liang, Feng W89
Liang, Weikang W90
Liang, Luo W92
Liang, Linda E166
Liano, Martha A476
Liao, Junshuo A204
Liao, Samuel A253
Liao, James A449
Liao, Jun P346
Liao, Edward P511
Liar, Miguel P127
Liaw, Jeffrey E94
Libarle, Daniel E193
Libbe, Allan J P467
Libbe, Allan J P602
Libbe, John A P602
Libbing, Mike A485
Libby, Russell T. A782
Liberatore, Paul A56
Liberatore, Andrea A560
Liberatore, Nick A634
Liberatore, Thomas S. E118
Liberman, Jeffrey A. E129
Libertino, John P279
Liberty, Tiffanie De A235
Librandi, Nancy A583
Libretto, Tom E327
Libstag, Gwen R. A389
Licata, Joseph A725
Licata, Gaetano P663
Lich, Brad A. A286
Licht, Cora A741
Licht, Cora E371
Lichtenberger, Gustavo A273
Lichtenberger, Gustavo P162
Lichtenberger, Brian P622
Lichtendahl, Kenneth A196
Lichtenwalner, Thomas P P474
Lichtenwalner, Rthomas P P525
Lichtl, Javier Hernandez P271
Lichtman, David B. A353
Lico, James E300
Liddiad, Imelda A520
Liding, Lawrence (Larry) A175
Liebel, Hartmut A471
Liebendorfer, Debbie P503
Lieber, Rick P457
Lieber, Richard L P457
Lieber, Chris E320
Lieberman, James P231
Lieberman, Jonathan E6
Lieblein, Grace A379
Liebler, William Bill A460
Liebler, Bill A460
Lieblong, Alex A425
Lieblong, Alex E201
Liebow, Elizabeth P153
Liebowitz, Jeremy A586
Liebowitz, Richard S. A810
Liebowitz, Ronald D. P82
Liebowitz, Richard P381
Liebowitz, Richard S. P597
Liedel, Christopher P506
Liedl, Duane W134
Liedtka, Greg P181
Liedtke, Eric W8

Liefer, Michael E432
Liemer, David A677
Lienhard, Jerome T. A774
Liepold, Stephen A728
Lieske, Brenda P87
Lievonen, Matti W257
Liewen, Mike A647
Lifka, David P143
Lifshitz, Lawrence P695
Liggin, Sunita E119
Light, Eric A908
Light, Darla P201
Light, Earl P522
Light, Eric E446
Lightcap, Deb P331
Lightfoot, Kevin A912
Lightfoot, Lance P560
Lighty, Josh A120
Ligon, Samuel B. E57
Liguori, Thomas A93
Liguori, Andrew P393
Lihua, Wang W283
Liimatainen, Sherman P219
Lijun, Zhao W91
Likes, Robert A489
Likins, Steven A813
Likins, Steve A814
Likins, Steven P616
Likins, Steve P616
Lilienfeld, Rosanne P557
Lilja, Mathias A537
Lilja, Agneta W352
Liljehorn, Dustin P256
Liljestrom, Jason E252
Lill, Thorsten A501
Lillemoe, Keith D. P590
Lillis, Charles A270
Lillis, Terrance A668
Lillis, Joe A865
Lillis, Charles M. (Chuck) P651
Lilly, Brian A204
Lilly, E. Stephen (Steve) A343
Lilly, Brian F. A573
Lilly, Randy A614
Lilly, Tim A912
Lilly, Mitch A916
Lilly, Katie P106
Lilly, Daniel J P223
Lilly, John P356
Lilly, Jason E299
Lim, James A119
Lim, Meiyin A295
Lim, Jean A401
Lim, Henry W A413
Lim, Rachel A429
Lim, Hwee A501
Lim, Giselle A677
Lim, Aerin A777
Lim, Henry W P234
Lim, Sim S W119
Lim, Jean E187
Lim, Rachel E204
Lim, Aerin E393
Lim-Johnson, Hannah S A486
Lima, Roland A344
Lima, Candido A634
Limanni, Darcy E193
Limbaugh, Corey A481
Limberg, Joachim W365
Limerick, Thomas S. (Stan) A345
Limerick, Thomas S. (Stan) E154
Limones, Matthew P166
Limr, Mary E P378
Lin, Sandy A177
Lin, Lynn A533
Lin, Benny A691
Lin, Steve A766
Lin, Sarah A780
Lin, Wilson W. P379
Lin, Fan W95
Lin, Amy H.C. W113
Lin, Howard W154
Lin, J.K. W354
Lin, Henry W395
Lin, Simon H. M. W395

Lincoln, Blanche L A300
Lincoln, David R P146
Lind, Sharon A111
Lind, H A333
Lind, Sharon P56
Lindahl, Richard S P102
Lindauer, Jeff P627
Lindbeck, George P51
Lindberg, Bonita A820
Lindberg, Peter P468
Lindblad, Anders W360
Lindblom, Mike P545
Linde, Tamara L. A678
Linde, Brian A693
Linde, Ronald K. P91
Lindekugel, Jon T. A2
Lindell, Andrew A729
Lindeman, B. John E52
Lindemann, James A169
Lindemann, James J. (Jim) A295
Linden, Andrew A814
Linden, Tomas A898
Linden, George Van Der P190
Linden, Kelly P535
Linden, Andrew P616
Lindenmeyr, Adele P667
Linder, James P78
Linder, Charlie P277
Linder, Christy P347
Linderman, LeeAnne B. A919
Lindfors, Lars P. W257
Lindh, Daniel A P439
Lindh, Daniel P439
Lindholm, Wayne S. P235
Lindicy, Joey P376
Lindle, John E94
Lindley, Melissa P123
Lindley, Michael E257
Lindner, S. Craig A51
Lindner, Carl H. A51
Lindner, Bridget A790
Lindo, Michelle P603
Lindsay, Janice A405
Lindsay, Steven A501
Lindsay, Mike P26
Lindsay, Julie P101
Lindsay, Jane P218
Lindsay, Aaron P462
Lindsay, Gail P479
Lindseth, Michael G A655
Lindseth, Alfred A. (Al) A657
Lindseth, Michael G E333
Lindsey, Mary A A224
Lindsey, Scott A655
Lindsey, H. Eugene (Gene) P50
Lindsey, Leslie P439
Lindsey, Steven L P520
Lindsey, John P537
Lindsey, Don P554
Lindsey, Scott E333
Lindstrom, Scott A589
Lindstrom, Merl R. A653
Lindstrom, Donnie P256
Line, Thomas E. (Tom) E106
Linebarge, Thomas A246
Linebarger, N. Thomas (Tom) A245
Linebarger, N. Thomas (Tom) A246
Liner, David A714
Lines, Lisa E65
Linesch, Mark A419
Linesch, William E P439
Linford, D A16
Ling, Christopher A140
Ling, Mei A199
Ling, Hai A537
Ling, Karen W22
Link, Doug A434
Link, Jeff A489
Link, Mike A513
Link, Denise W P126
Link, Dave P481
Link, Matthew W. (Matt) E310
Linkowski, Brian A328
Linn, Joe P252
Linn, Michael P416

Linn, Terry E336
Linnartz, Stephanie C. A530
Linnehan, Frank P165
Linnen, Edward P. (Ned) A92
Linnenbringer, Jean A213
Linnenbrink, John A204
Linnington, Max E97
Linsey, Jay E195
Lintag, Ronald A133
Linton, William A. (Bill) P443
Linville, Jud A203
Linzer, Daniel I. P397
Linzey, Bob A555
Linzner, Joel A292
Lioi, Vittorio Corbo W43
Liollio, Dean A658
Lionello, Gemma A596
Liotine, Joseph T. A898
Liotta, Gary P. A359
Lipani, Laura P333
Lipar, Eric E244
Lipar, Jack E244
Lipasek, Steven A818
Lipic, Brad A701
Lipinski, John J. (Jack) A249
Lipke, Kenneth A108
Lipke, Kenneth E35
Lipker, Stephen A34
Lipkin, Gerald H. A868
Lippert, Martin J. (Marty) A555
Lippert, Cheryl A855
Lippert, Jason D. E240
Lippeveld, Theo P269
Lippincott, Rodney A. E196
Lippke, Eric A272
Lippman, Frederick P398
Lippmann, Patrick A A98
Lippmann, Patrick A E33
Lippold, Tim A818
Lippoldt, Diana P681
Lipps, Randall A. E316
Lipschultz, Tyler P. E310
Lipscomb, Stephanie A667
Lipscombe, Ailsa P610
Lipsey, William L. E341
Lipsky, Matt P566
Lipton, Lisa P505
Lis, Angela A763
Lisboa, Persio V A577
Lisek, Jon E117
Lisenby, Jeffrey P. A670
Lisenby, Michael P172
Lisi, Ben A691
Lisieski, Sharman P484
Liska, Matt A153
Lisle, William W13
Lisman, Michael A885
Lisowski, Sheryl A. A318
Liss, Michael A173
Liss, Samuel P167
Lissalde, Frédéric B. A141
Lissowski, Antoine W103
List-Stoll, Teri L. A809
Listengardt, Joe P431
Listengart, Joseph P366
Lister, Chip A272
Lister, Noel P458
Lister, Anna E276
Liszt, Mark P284
Liszt, Max P284
Litaker, Tom P446
Litavec, Viliam P201
Litchfield, David A281
Litchfield, Debra P448
Litchford, Mike A266
Lithgow, Dennis A657
Litos, Dennis P249
Litt, Eli A872
Littauer, Andrew A857
Littell, Morgan A838
Littell, John A909
Little, Frank R. A2
Little, Garrett A58
Little, Shannon A81
Little, Mark A136

Little, Richard A143
Little, Patricia A. A416
Little, R Parrish A428
Little, Charles A467
Little, T. Mitchell (Mitch) A526
Little, Daniel F. (Dan) A596
Little, Patrick A685
Little, Daniel A698
Little, Paul R A740
Little, Chuck A763
Little, Chase A777
Little, Melissa A898
Little, Bobby P36
Little, George A P228
Little, George P228
Little, George A. P229
Little, Gregory D P289
Little, Darlene P292
Little, Denise P330
Little, Michael D P408
Little, Daniel P456
Little, James H P583
Little, Thomas A P666
Little, Lou P680
Little, Niki P694
Little, Tom W61
Little, Charles E223
Little, Rob E244
Little, Bradley S E298
Little, Chase E393
Littlefair, Andrew A420
Littlefair, Andrew E198
Littlefield, Jerod A327
Littleford, Frankie A474
Littlejohn, Bill P498
Littleton, Nicole A478
Litwin, Barry A865
Litwin, Jim P247
Litz, William P43
Litzinger, Ronald L. A290
Liu, Chang A97
Liu, Stanley A163
Liu, Thomas A177
Liu, Fengming A375
Liu, Jeffrey A648
Liu, Don H. A788
Liu, John A898
Liu, Ke-Cheng P7
Liu, Deborah P90
Liu, Marsha P396
Liu, Edison T. P587
Liu, Yuzhi W90
Liu, I. Cheng W113
Liu, Fei W151
Liu, Guoyue W175
Liu, Mark W354
Liu, Chun W401
Liu, Chang E32
Liutkus, Tom A826
Liuwen, Tian W89
Lively, Scott A868
Lively, David P398
Liverani, Giovanni W32
Livermore, Craig P158
Livesay, Bruce A. A348
Livesay, Cheryl A857
Livingston, John T. A16
Livingston, Robert A. (Bob) A279
Livingston, Randall S. (Randy) A507
Livingston, Lindsey A751
Livingston, Susannah A759
Livingston, Randall S. (Randy) P288
Livingston, Keith P618
Livingston, Reggie E4
Livingston, Lindsey E377
Livingstone, Mary A108
Livingstone, Catherine B. W105
Livne, Omer A456
Lizardi, Rafael R. A803
Lizdenis, Richard R A533
Lize, Franck W151
Lizhong, Yu A585
Lizhong, Yu P377
Lizo, Ralph A810
Lizo, Ralph P597

Ljungqvist, Katarina W352
LLandreth, David A249
Llanes, Raul A109
Llanes, Osvaldo A914
Llanes, Raul E36
LLC, Sunoco GP A773
Lll, Hunt M P310
Lloyd, Gary A14
Lloyd, Robert A. (Rob) A372
Lloyd, Jack A412
Lloyd, Lisa Kay P563
Lloyd, James P642
Lloyd, Jack E192
Lo, Alice A480
Lo, Francis A899
Lo, Elaine A909
Lo, Francis P690
Loach, Jon E140
Lobach, Carmen P480
Lobach, David M E120
Lobatz, Michael A. E201
Lobel, Elie W278
Lobo, Kevin A. A772
Lochen, Richard S. A646
Lochen, Richard S. E330
Locher, Duane A223
Locher, Vince A830
Locher, Vince E403
Lochhead, Jim P159
Lochner, David A440
Lochner, James A835
Lochner, Karl Manfred W215
Lochocki, Sharon A489
Lochow, Gary P686
Locke, Cherie P500
Locken, Dale P13
Lockery, Michael A163
Lockett, Mark A881
Lockett, Traishon E125
Locketti, Kathy A272
Lockhart, Dennis P. A325
Lockhart, Laura S A486
Lockhart, Laura P120
Lockhart, Melanie P242
Lockridge, Matthew E437
Lockwood, Charles J. P197
Loconsolo, Mike A201
Lodes, Terry A893
Lodesani, Eliano Omar W189
Lodge, Terry L. A25
Lodge, Terry L. P15
Lodge, Simon W352
Lodhi, Mujib P676
Loeb, Paul E117
Loeber, Gary A250
Loeber, Jurguen W133
Loebsack, Grita W204
Loeffelholz, Mary A262
Loeffler, Martin H. A62
Loeffler, Arthur A P539
Loeffler, Jay S. P590
Loera, Patricia A861
Loera, Patricia P658
Loessin, Bruce P98
Loethen, Michael P347
Loewald, Thomas W. (Tom) A815
Loewenbaum, G. Walter E250
Loewentheil, Sanford P278
Lofaro, John P179
Loffler, Alicia P398
Loffredo, Joe P464
Lofgren, Diane Gage P498
Lofgren, Richard P. P631
Lofrumento, Michael A831
Lofties, Paul E236
Loftin, Paul J. A703
Loftin, Karen P242
Loftis, William A196
Lofton, Kevin E. A171
Lofton, James P25
Lofton, Kevin E. P100
Lofton, Kevin E P101
Loftus, Maureen A288
Loftus, Mary A541
Loftus, Phillip A760

A = AMERICAN BUSINESS
E = EMERGING COMPANIES
P = PRIVATE COMPANIES
W = WORLD BUSINESS

Loftus, Phillip P523
Loftus, Thomas R. (Tom) E430
Logan, Charlene A101
Logan, Michelle A141
Logan, Jonathan B. A214
Logan, Jason A221
Logan, Erik A269
Logan, Patrick A318
Logan, Donna A360
Logan, Stephen A406
Logan, Paul A478
Logan, John A774
Logan, Jonathan B. P128
Logan, Donna E164
Logan, Malcolm E405
Logatto, Vincent P541
Logeman, Scott A448
Logeman, David P105
Logemann, Cari P48
Logothetis, Peter A34
Logsdon, Brad A2
Logue, Joseph (Joe) A140
Loh, Evan A649
Lohawatanakul, Chingchai W88
Lohmeier, Michelle J A758
Lohr, Dan P227
Lohrer, Bernadette P486
Lohse, John P468
Loiacono, Jim A727
Lok, James E248
Lokay, Jon A723
Lokke, Scott A158
Lokman, Lawrence A811
Lokman, Lawrence P600
Lollar, Donald P410
Lolli, Christopher A49
Lollini, Claudio E230
Lollock, Rita P564
Lomas, Terry A101
Lomas, Todd A564
Lomas, Alisa A868
Lomax, Stephanie P276
Lombard, Eric W32
Lombardi, Laura A10
Lombardi, Todd A264
Lombardi, Leonard V. A342
Lombardi, Michael J. A826
Lombardi, Ronald M. (Ron) E338
Lombardo, Kevin A405
Lombardo, Thomas P425
Lombardo, Steve E277
Lombra, Sherri A272
Lomeli, Bernardo A813
Lomeli, Bernardo P608
Lomel- n, Carlos Salazar W152
Lomeo, Jody L P186
Lon, Lyons A223
London, Adam A175
London, Daniel T. (Dan) W5
Lonegro, Frank A. A243
Lonergan, Robert A. A83
Loney, Andrew A28
Loney, Andrew P17
Long, Ann A5
Long, Christopher A56
Long, Michael J. (Mike) A77
Long, Jodi A108
Long, Jason E A156
Long, Suzette M A169
Long, Tony A172
Long, Rodney A180
Long, Aileen A204
Long, Jeffrey R. A240
Long, Brett V A247
Long, Thomas E. (Tom) A297
Long, Shayla A518
Long, Deborah J. A674
Long, Michael A676
Long, Robert A700

Long, Ellie A700
Long, Mike A705
Long, Tom A723
Long, Ronald R. (Ron) A801
Long, Andy A815
Long, Mike A868
Long, Susan A878
Long, Mark P. A892
Long, Larry A902
Long, Toby P107
LONG, GARY P188
Long, Laura P233
Long, Thomas P237
Long, Gary P255
Long, Shayla P293
Long, Jerry P333
Long, David P343
Long, Thomas D P343
Long, Ronald R. (Ron) P562
Long, Nathan P572
Long, Greg P618
Long, Larry P692
Long, Annabelle Yu W62
Long, Peter W314
Long, Peter W376
Long, Brad E97
Long, Brett V E103
Long, Gary R. E172
Long, James L. (Jim) E278
Long, Gary S. E337
Long, Mike E352
Long, Darrel S. E364
Longacre, David A432
Longe, Thomas A425
Longe, Thomas E201
Longfellow, Michael P323
Longfield, Charles L. (Chuck) E44
Longhi, William G P408
Longhofer, T. Luke A345
Longhofer, T. Luke E154
Longhurst, John A131
Longlais, Brett J P687
Longley, S. Catherine (Katy) P587
Longman, Gary L. E77
Longo, Christie A901
Longo, Christie P692
Longo, Joseph E209
Longo, Michael E426
Longobardi, Joseph A201
Longobardi, Sara M. A644
Longstaff, William P479
Longstreet, Christopher P309
Longsworth, Nora P613
Longton, Kyle P32
Longworth, Ann A869
Lonski, Jeff E447
Loof, Per-Olof E230
Looker, Travis P626
Loomans, Leslie E385
Loomis, Nate A912
Loomis, Anna P357
Loomis, Nancy P479
Looney, John P380
Loos, Duane A71
Loose, Jeffrey P475
Loosmore, Casey P141
Looten, Kathy P522
Loparco, Michael J. A471
Loparrino, Rosemarie A109
Loparrino, Rosemarie E36
Lopatto, Bill P339
Loper, Brett A49
Loper, D. Shane A399
Loperfito, Sandy A720
Loperfito, Sandy E362
Lopes, Brian A724
Lopes, Luiz Ildefonso Sim- ŏes W75
Lopez, Christian A34
Lopez, Haivyl A115
Lopez, Jose A158
Lopez, Emilia A163
Lopez, Albert A163
Lopez, Adrian A199
Lopez, Samuel A244
Lopez, Randolph A481

Lopez, Tom A494
Lopez, Andres A. A628
Lopez, Norma A632
Lopez, Virgilio A644
Lopez, Patrick A693
Lopez, Christina A785
Lopez, Noemi A810
Lopez, Frank A857
Lopez, Ignacio A878
Lopez, Amy P119
Lopez, David S. P152
Lopez, Ann P315
Lopez, Jorge P325
Lopez, Jody P433
Lopez, Nestor A Ramirez P530
Lopez, Noemi P597
Lopez, Mary P635
Lopez, Andreu Plaza W45
Lopez, George A. E212
Lopez, Christopher E320
Lopez, Norma E322
Lopez-Lay, Ginoris A336
Lopezbartoszewicz, Andrea A81
Lopman, Abe P699
Loppatto, Gregory A850
Loran, Jarrod P159
Loranger, Michelle A766
Lorber, Howard M. E237
Lorber, Howard M. E425
Lorberbaum, Jeffrey S. A563
Lord, Pat A501
Lord, Ellen A804
Lord, W. Leighton P509
Lord, Janet E P552
Lord, Kathy P687
Lore, Marc A878
Loree, James M. (Jim) A761
Lorei, Greg P256
Lorei, Greg P257
Lorenson, Katie A. A562
Lorenson, Katie A. E279
Lorent, Patrick A644
Lorentson, Jeffery B. A349
Lorentson, Jeffrey A350
Lorentson, Jeffery B. E156
Lorentson, Jeffrey E157
Lorenz, Kathryn A920
Lorenz, Dan P73
Lorenz, Paul E P482
Lorenzen, Jeffrey D. (Jeff) A47
Lorenzen, Angela A899
Lorenzen, Angela P690
Lorenzo, Alejandro R. A567
Lorenzo, Antonio Alvarez A894
Lorenzo, Heather P333
Lorenzo, Lisa P577
Lores, Enrique A435
Loreto, Sheila P589
Lorge, Timothy J. (Tim) A242
Lori, Michael A865
Lori, Mathew E301
Loring, Eileen P510
Lorino, Lisa P571
Lorio, Renee P637
Lorne, Eric P293
Lorsson, Devin A499
Lorton, Donald E P95
Losch, William C. (BJ) A348
Loscher, Pam A537
Loschiavo, Rod A478
Loschiavo, Lori A480
Losee, Mark D. E288
Losenegger, Michael J. A340
Losenegger, Michael J. E151
Losh, J. Michael (Mike) A534
Loshin, David S. P399
Losntos, Juan De P386
Loth, Melissa A788
Lott, Wayne J. P83
Lott, Tanya P94
Lott, Ken P172
Lott, Douglas P277
Lott, Lori P293
Lott, Charles E61

Lottig, Jim P211
Lottner, Jens W330
Lotvin, Alan M. A250
Lotze, Timothy P560
Loucks, Andrew A485
Loudermilk, Kerry P427
Loudermilk, Beth P680
Louette, Pierre W278
Louge, Michael W. (Mike) P405
Loughin-Vance, Kristy P622
Loughlin, Leanna A532
Loughman, Tim A907
Loughman, Tim P696
Loughrey, Donal A649
Loughry, Ed C. A655
Loughry, Ed C. E333
Loui, Shelley P270
Louidor, Mildred A246
Louie, Joe A101
Louie, David A130
Louie, Bryan A791
Louie, Lindsay A P236
Louis, David A342
Louis, Kathy St A511
Louis, David N. P590
Louis-Robbins, Nicole A838
Loup, Stephen P476
Louras, Peter N. E374
Loureiro, Guilherme W392
Louton, Beth A857
Louttit, Gordon P564
Louvet, Patrice J. L. A690
Louvis, Soterios P223
Louw, Wy E360
Louw, Johannes E360
Lovaglio, Luigi W380
Lovato, Marty P207
Love, Phillip E A22
Love, Kelli A165
Love, Marcella A192
Love, Lisa A196
Love, Judith S. A221
Love, David A509
Love, George A912
Love, Phillip E P13
Love, Debra P27
Love, Ron P119
Love, Karen P134
Love, Tolli P142
Love, Katie P238
Love, Alexandra P431
Lovelady, James P32
Loveless, Steve P537
Lovell, William A419
Lovely, Dave A850
Lovett, Michael A330
Lovett, Robert P623
Lovins, Gregory S. (Greg) A91
Low, Julianne A163
Low, Jim A453
Low, Mark A619
Low, Lewis P285
Low, Robert E. P371
Low, Brian E447
Lowden, Cynthia A83
Lowden, Simon A647
Lowder, Dr Steve P543
Lowe, Heather A6
Lowe, John E. A69
Lowe, Karen A214
Lowe, Meg A269
Lowe, Rich A410
Lowe, Wendy A568
Lowe, Edward A. (Sandy) A611
Lowe, Michael A693
Lowe, Corey H. A717
Lowe, Albert A878
Lowe, Sheila P92
Lowe, Karen P128
Lowe, Terril P135
Lowe, Kenneth W. (Ken) P488
Lowe, Vicky P493
Lowe, William J. P627
Lowe, Ada P692
Lowe, Nick W352

Lowe, William M. E230
Lowe, John E240
Lowenberg, John P310
Lowenfels, Fred P623
Lower, Joseph T. (Joe) A612
Lower, Dennis P75
Lower, William P277
Lowery, Richard M. A122
Lowery, Norman D. A346
Lowery, Dee A355
Lowery, Peter A731
Lowery, Joseph A781
Lowery, Frederick M. (Fred) A815
Lowery, Peter E365
Lowery-Biggers, LoriAnn V. A576
Lowery-Biggers, LoriAnn V. E297
Lowery-Yilmaz, Barbara A417
Lowman, David B. (Dave) A366
Lown, Christian A575
Lown, Wayne E402
Lowney, Peter A340
Lowney, Peter E151
Lowrey, Mark A362
Lowrey, Charles F. (Charlie) A676
Lowrie, Dan A441
Lowrimore, Bonnie A163
Lowry, Abner A115
Lowry, Dennis A175
Lowry, Bard A344
Lowry, Donna P129
Lowth, Simon W76
Lowther, Aaron P111
Lowther, Mike P382
Lowthers, Bruce A330
Loy, Bertrand E126
Loyd, Peggy P537
Lozada, Leonardo J. P473
Lozano, Natividad A459
Lozano, Philip A513
Lozano, Sandra P348
Lu, Eugene Y. C. A24
Lu, Bin A101
LU, Laura A136
Lu, Chris A170
Lu, Hong A649
Lu, Nicholas A649
Lu, Billy P284
Lu, Gary W106
Lubar, Sheldon B. E185
Lubbers, Paul A34
Lubelli, Luigi W32
Luber, Jean E289
Lubert, Ira M. A811
Lubert, Rachel P565
Lubert, Ira M. P600
Lubi, Garry A182
Lubi, Garry E63
Lubian, Patricia A109
Lubian, Patricia E36
Lubinskas, Amy A149
Lubitz, Kevin A331
Lubitz, Allan A551
Lubitz, Kevin E148
Lubow, Stuart H. A267
Luc, Phuong A877
Lucado, Pat A336
Lucado, Pat P194
Lucado, Joseph E253
Lucareli, Michael B. E283
Lucas, John T. A391
Lucas, Thomas J. (Tom) A738
Lucas, Connie A765
Lucas, Philip P243
Lucas, Julie P313
Lucas, John P324
Lucas, Ken P337
Lucas, Bruce P354
Lucas, Darren P437
Lucas, Connie P540
Lucas, Bryan P560
Lucas, Mary P570
Lucas, Alfredo Escobar San W25
Lucas, Patrice W286
Lucas, Roger C. E42
Lucas, Richard M. (Rich) E431

Lucas-Bull, Wendy E. W4
Lucca, Marc P42
Luccasen, Michael E343
Lucciola, Dario E28
Luce, Jason E248
Lucero, Barbara P281
Lucey, Matthew C. A638
Lucey, Morag P52
Lucey, John W. E332
Luchini, Joseph P188
Luchinsky, Michael A537
Luchtel, Pat A196
Lucia, Amy E44
Luciano, Juan R. A74
Luciano, Louis A817
Luciano, Lou A818
Luciano, Melba P603
Lucie, Alexandra A266
Lucien, Kent T. A103
Lucien, Kent T. E264
Lucier, Jake A25
Lucier, Suzy P6
Lucier, Jake P15
Lucier, Christopher P658
Lucier, Gregory T. E310
Luckas, Nancy P134
Luckey, Jeane P670
Luckoff, Jeff A449
Lucks, Cheryl W. P365
Lucore, Charles P530
Lucy, William P. (Bill) A644
Lucy, Susan A774
Ludden, Paul W. P514
Ludden, Michael F. E160
Ludeman, Christopher R. A172
Ludington, Bob P604
Ludvigsen, Jamie A163
Ludwig, Jeffrey G. A561
Ludwig, Dan A663
Ludwig, Todd P677
Ludwig, David R. E31
Ludwig, Michael M. E165
Ludwig, Jeffrey G. E278
Ludwig-Reymer, Patti P176
Lueck, Kim M. E257
Lueckenhoff, Joe A85
Luessenhop, Patty A149
Luffler, Ann Marie P549
Lugar, David A836
Luginbuhl, William E P570
Lugo, Luz P525
Luis, Victor A785
Luisa, Jennifer F A402
Luisi, Michael E445
Luiz, Gerald A607
Luk, Rebecca A649
Luka-Lognoné, Ida W23
Lukacs, Colleen A A369
Lukacs, Colleen A369
Lukasek, Scott A178
Lukasheva, Oksana A402
Lukaszewski, Michael P421
Lukatch, Heath E217
Luken, Lauren A496
Luken, Ellen P168
Lukens, John J. E90
Luker, Bob P443
Lukis, Lawrence J. E339
Lukow, Bradley S. (Brad) A759
Luksik, Roger A333
Luly, Jay R. E122
Lumb, Richard A. W5
Lumban-tobing, Pago A677
Lumbard, Lisa P105
Lumpkins, Robert L. A569
Lumsdaine, Dianne P164
Lumsden, Chris A. A736
Lumsden, Chris A. P492
Luna, Antonio A784
Luna, Bower P14
Luna, James P420
Luna, Rachel P516
Luna, Nallibe P587
Lunak, Leslie N. A108
Lunak, Leslie N. E35

Lund, Ed P25
Lund, Mary P151
Lund, Dennis P300
Lund, John T. E414
Lund-Jurgensen, Kirsten A648
Lundberg, Fredrik W352
Lundequam, Michael P442
Lundgren, David J. A399
LUNDGREN, DAVID P203
Lundin, Douglas P66
Lundquist, Nicholas J. (Nick) A318
Lundquist, Jane L. A451
Lundquist, Stephanie A. A788
Lundquist, Curt A868
Lundrigan, Phil A49
Lundy, Rich P595
Lundy, Mark H. E47
Lungberg, D'Ann E320
Lunka, Patricia A480
Lunn, Eric P29
Luo, Jason A362
Luong, Bruce E70
Lupica, John J. W98
Lupo, Kimberly A593
Lupone, E. Robert A804
Lurie, Lindsey A461
Lurie, Herbert A732
Lurie, Robert F. P375
Lurie, Herbert E365
Lusco, C. Matthew A700
Luscombe, Caroline W214
Luse, Barry F. E100
Lush, Steve E203
Lusignan, Cindy A532
Lusignan, Sara P48
Lusk, John M. A365
Lusk, Sherri A478
Lusk, Liska A800
Lusk, Liska P559
Lustgarten, Joyce P162
Lutek, Ben W. A822
Lutgen, Garrett A914
Luther, Lisa C. A596
Luther, Richelle E86
Luthi, Francesca A83
Lutlow, Shannon P159
Luton, Shan A258
Lutterbach, Dave G A417
Luttig, J. Michael (Mike) A136
Luttinger, Raymond P264
Lutton, Jamie A164
Luty, Thomas A532
Lutz, John A1
Lutz, Ron A521
Lutz, Danielle A644
Lutz, Laurent C. A746
Lutz, Tom P575
Lutz, John M. P615
Lutz, Klaus J. W60
Lutz, Richard W121
Lutz, Rolf W402
Lutzel, Geraldine A105
Luu, Bao Q P488
Luviano, John A513
Lux, Stephen A42
Luxton, Sam A870
Luz, Eduardo A494
Luzar, Jay A489
Lv, Xiangyang W77
Lyash, Jeffrey J. (Jeff) P179
Lybarger, Ray A260
Lycourt, Darryl A441
Lydecker, Charles H. (Charlie) E47
Lyden, Shawn P118
Lydon, Katy A881
Lydstone, Elizabeth P298
Lyford, Robert M P45
Lyga, Joseph E40
Lykins, Gregory B. (Greg) A339
Lykins, Gregory B. (Greg) E150
Lyle, Butch A704
Lyle, John P620
Lyle, Butch E351
Lyles, Diane A115
Lyles, Donna P289

Lyman, Gregory A P672
Lymer, Scott P212
Lymon, Hari A621
Lyn, Sharon E39
Lynam, Ben A565
Lynas, Peter W40
Lynch, Kevin A70
Lynch, Brian E. A79
Lynch, James A81
Lynch, Ann A105
Lynch, Jack A115
Lynch, Thomas J. A147
Lynch, Kevin A178
Lynch, Thomas A246
Lynch, Charles A312
Lynch, R. Dale A320
Lynch, Kevin A348
Lynch, Christopher S. A366
Lynch, Thomas A390
Lynch, Richard A417
Lynch, Michael A541
Lynch, Kevin J A624
Lynch, Jennifer A644
Lynch, Thomas A665
Lynch, Timothy G. A698
Lynch, Tom A707
Lynch, Sean A784
Lynch, Thomas A815
Lynch, Patrick A889
Lynch, Brian P P155
Lynch, Timothy W P203
Lynch, Diane P235
Lynch, Donald M P261
Lynch, Jack P302
Lynch, Katie P371
Lynch, Timothy G. P456
Lynch, Mel P694
Lynch, Christopher W305
Lynch, Christopher J. (Chris) W306
Lynch, Yvonne E46
Lynch, Bill E65
Lynch, R. Dale E143
Lynch, Kevin E155
Lynch, Michael E266
Lynch, James P. E375
Lynch, Kirsten A. E424
Lynd, Brian A333
Lyndaker, Matthew A902
Lyndaker, Matthew P693
Lynde, Sue A187
Lynde, Sue E71
Lyngdoh, Sheppard P248
Lynham, Lisa A593
Lynn, Patricia A195
Lynn, Scott J. A719
Lynn, David A871
Lynn, Mary P218
Lynn, Scott J. P468
Lynn, Christine E75
Lyon, Nancy A599
Lyon, Robert C. P367
Lyon, Glenn S. P579
Lyon, William H. (Bill) E252
Lyons, Martin J. A42
Lyons, Terrence A332
Lyons, Chad A351
Lyons, Sarah A371
Lyons, Robert C. A394
Lyons, Garry A537
Lyons, Michael P. A659
Lyons, Thomas M. A675
Lyons, Daniel A702
Lyons, Brenda A766
Lyons, Bruce A767
Lyons, Shonyel A784
Lyons, Amy P285
Lyons, Mitch P341
Lyons, Althea P391
Lyons, William P648
Lyons, Chad E158
Lyons, Jeanne M. E170
Lysen, Jan P238
Lyski, James (Jim) A166
Lyssy, Samuel L. (Sam) P367
Lyttle, Lance P433

A = AMERICAN BUSINESS
E = EMERGING COMPANIES
P = PRIVATE COMPANIES
W = WORLD BUSINESS

Lytton, Marcia P6
Lytton, Alexander P544
Lyubomirsky, Robert A912
L'archenesque, Lee A871
L'Heureux, Scott P258
L'Homme, Bert P170
L--pez, Humberto Ch--vez W25
L--pez-Pi-±ol, José Mar-a W6
L-¶venholm, Johan A87
L--thi, Pierre A514
Lévy, Jean-Marc W74
Lévy, Jean-Bernard W136

M

Ma, Kenny A131
MA, Harry A683
Ma, Qingyun A860
Ma, Mahau P356
Ma, Qingyun P656
Maakestad, Paul P394
Maas, John P212
Maas-Brunner, Melanie W55
Maass, Brian W. A790
Maass, Paul T. P604
Maaty, Yehia A912
Mabe, Katherine (Kathy) A33
Mabe, Johnny P183
Mabe, David P475
Mabry, Steven A280
Mabry, Jim A751
Mabry, Jim E377
Macadaeg, Reyne A105
Macak, Jeffrey A120
Macaluso, Charles A654
Macaluso, Diane P24
MacArevey, Mike A489
Macau, Carlos L. E193
Macaulay, Caitlin E P279
Maccarone, Connie A890
Maccarone, Diane P440
Maccarone, Connie P684
Macchia, Richard E163
Macchio, Ralph A241
Macciocchi, Vince F. A74
Macculley, Diana A163
Macdonald, Michael A2
Macdonald, Brian A139
MacDonald, W. Timothy A143
Macdonald, Linda A171
MacDonald, Vivian A292
Macdonald, Deborah A492
MacDonald, Kenneth A607
MacDonald, Don A685
Macdonald, Paul A724
MacDonald, Gregg A885
Macdonald, Eileen B P39
Macdonald, Linda P100
MacDonald, Walt P175
Macdonald, Ellen A P226
Macdonald, John P479
Macdonald, Carrie P641
Macdonald, Sally W396
Macdonald, Laura E82
MacDougall, Molly A691
Macdougall, Betty P34
MacDougall, Harriett P398
Mace, Alexander P514
Macechko, Nicholas A902
Macechko, Nicholas P693
Macedo, Omar E231
Macek, Paul A784
Macfadyen, Simon A532
MacFarlane, Taylor A402
MacGowan, William N. (Bill) A588
Mach, Gary P A221
Mach, Kerry A741

Mach, Kerry E370
Macha, Mark P441
Machamer, Virginia A901
Machamer, Virginia P692
Machen, Elizabeth A742
Machen, Robert P34
Machen, Elizabeth E372
Machetti, Claudio W141
Machozzi, Thomas A857
Machtinger, Richard A500
Machtinger, Richard E238
Machuel, Denis W334
Machuk, Paul P79
Macias, Ruben A101
Maciel, Andre A494
Macina, Tom A693
Macina, Robert P. P589
MacInnes, Glenn I. A883
Macinnes, Dennis M P352
Macintosh, Nancy A70
Macintyre, David A334
Macioce, Domenic A888
Macip, Marcus D. E244
Macisaac, Don P406
Mack, Bill A478
Mack, Stephen A483
Mack, Lawrence A489
Mack, Richard L. (Rich) A569
Mack, Robert P. (Bob) A661
Mack, Rick A862
Mack, Kristina A P159
Mack, Jill P179
Mack, Winifred P516
Mack, Judith P652
Mack, Rick E419
Mack-Brooks, Pamela P241
MacKay, Koley X A478
Mackay, Kevin A555
Mackay, Iain J. W175
Mackay, Michelle M. E226
Macke, Christopher A375
Macke, Kevin M. A837
MacKeen, Ray A814
MacKeen, Ray P616
Mackell, Lisa P306
Mackelwich, Mike E334
Mackenzie, Bill A149
MacKenzie, Alexander R. (Rod) A648
Mackenzie, Celia A774
Mackenzie, George A825
MacKenzie, Wayne P99
Mackenzie, Jake P338
Mackenzie, Andrew W63
Mackenzie, Andrew W64
MacKenzie, Jason W277
MacKenzie, Earle A. E368
Mackenzie, Jeffrey E. E373
Mackey, Edward F. A144
Mackey, Melinda A158
Mackey, Helen A254
Mackey, James G. A366
Mackey, Bob A422
Mackey, John P. A899
Mackey, Bob P239
Mackey, John P. P690
Mackie, H. Spurgeon A446
Mackie, H. Spurgeon E210
MacKimm, James I. A117
Mackinnon, Matt P360
Mackler, Mitchell P693
Macko, David P209
Macko, David P582
Macko, Terence P696
Mackovic, Gayle E276
Mackowiak, Edward A814
Mackowiak, Edward P616
Macky, Edward A144
Maclaren, Catherine P174
Maclasco, Robert A733
Maclasco, Robert P491
Maclean, Thomas A513
MacLean, Brian W. A827
Maclean, Dinah W47
Maclean, Malcolm W176
Maclennon, John P442

Macleod, Simantha A817
MacLeod, Robert W199
MacMahon, John P A238
MacMahon, Mike E51
Macmaster, Gregory P404
MacMillan, Michael A817
Macnamara, Brian A434
MacNaughton, Duncan E264
Macnee, Walt W. A537
Macneil, Dennis A624
Macner, Anne P595
MacNicholas, Garry W161
Macnutt, James P535
Macomber, Marina P392
Macomber, Todd E. E346
Macon, Mary A327
Macon, James P380
Macoun, Jeff W161
Macphail, Winborne P485
Macpherson, Donald G. (D.G.) A393
Macpherson, Ross P301
MacQuillan, Sandra J. A490
Macrae, Steve A830
Macrae, Steve E402
Macrillo, Sam A201
MacSween, Mike W348
Macuga, Daniel A. (Dan) E423
MacVane, Jessica P218
Macveigh, Matt P254
Macwilliams, Robert A16
Macyauski, Michael A327
Madabhushi, Venkata A665
Madalena, Ralph J P376
Madalin, Diane A244
Madarieta, Bernadette A631
Maddalone, Dom P509
Madden, John F. A97
Madden, Joe A449
Madden, Nancy P399
Madden, Thomas P611
Madden, Donald P623
Madden, Daryl W23
Madden, John F. E32
Maddison, John E166
Maddock, Dennis A471
Maddock, Ernest E. (Ernie) A559
Maddox, John A157
Maddox, Brian A200
Maddox, Willie A A369
Maddox, Willie A369
Maddox, Tom A521
Maddox, Matt A909
Maddox, Mark P130
Maddux, Susan A855
Madeira, Harry R. A151
Madeira, Harry R. E48
Madel, Denise P12
Madeley, Paul E A114
Madeley, Paul E P64
Maden, Nicholas A305
Maden, Nicholas P185
Madge, Larry R. W346
Madigan, Deborah A659
Madigan, Kevin A738
Madigan, Angie P133
Madill, Justin P68
Madina, Carlos W85
Madison, Dennis P515
Madonia, Frank E280
Madrid, Bonita P433
Madrigal, Calvin P612
Madsen, Kathy A103
Madsen, C. Fred A122
Madsen, C A122
Madsen, Marci A183
Madsen, Mark A453
Madsen, J-,rn W1
Madsen, J-,rn W20
Madsen, Marci E66
Madson, Deborah P238
Maduck, Sean E95
Maduri, John A368
Maeda, Tsuyoshi A651
Maeda, Tsuyoshi P426
Maeda, Eiji W48

Maeder, Jeff A813
Maeder, Jeff P616
Maeglin, William A369
Maehara, Jenny P482
Maes, Betty A223
Maes, Daniel A869
Maestas, Juan P685
Maestri, Luca A70
Maestri, Bruno A597
Maffei, Gregory B. (Greg) A517
Maffei, Gregory B. (Greg) A688
Maffei, Gregory B. (Greg) A745
Maffeo, Vincent A. (Vince) A505
Mafi, Gabriela P208
Mafune, Yukio W324
Magan, Rahul A555
Magazachi, Wissam A49
Magdefrau, Stuart E. E414
Magdziarz, Wayne F P299
Magee, Chris A558
Magee, Deb P416
Magee, Steven P. E226
Mageli, John P26
Magenheimer, Richard C P21
Magennis, Elizabeth A231
Maggelakis, Sophia P464
Maggio, Michael A476
Maggitti, Patrick G. P667
Maggs, Thomas O. A831
Magid, Bruce R. P82
Magill, M. Elizabeth A507
Magill, M. Elizabeth P288
Maglaque, Neal A56
Maglio, Rafelina A103
Magner, Alvin A478
Magner, Johnette P75
Magnini, Aldo E54
Magnus, Keith E136
Mago, Angela G. A489
Magri, Joseph E232
Magrini, Joyce Manning A155
Magruder, Joan P346
Magruder, Joan P525
Magstadt, Brian J. E373
Maguin, Stephen P145
Maguire, William A300
Maguire, Tim A353
Maguire, Kate P247
Maguire, Andy W175
Mahabadi, Hadi A912
Mahaffee, Joseph W. (Joe) A140
Mahaffey, Jenny P225
Mahaffy, Denise A266
Mahajan, Gaurav A131
Mahalingam, S. A789
Mahalingam, S. P555
Mahan, Chip A518
Mahan, James S A518
Mahan, Michelle P205
Mahan, Chip P292
Mahan, James S P292
Mahaney, Sheryl P276
Mahar, Matt A744
Mahar, Derek P91
Mahard, Kaitlin A452
Mahard, Kaitlin E215
Mahase, Kishan P227
Mahe, Isabel A70
Mahe, Eric-Yves E115
Mahendra-Rajah, Prashanth A65
Mahendran, Bagavathy P228
Maher, Dina A323
Maher, Lee A. A381
Maher, Christopher D. A611
Maher, John A707
Maher, Joshua A709
Maher, Steve A835
Maher, John P362
Maher, Carly E236
Maher, Christopher D. E313
Maheshwari, Umesh P382
Maheshwari, Deepak E123
Mahil, Amandip P163
Mahjoub, Ali P381

Mahlan, Deirdre A. W128
Mahler, Simon A133
Mahler, Carl P554
Mahler, Anthony P683
Mahmud, Shahzad A892
Mahon, Kenneth J. A267
Mahon, Jean A532
Mahon, Paul A. W161
Mahon, Paul A. E415
Mahone, Barbara P692
Mahoney, Ryan A16
Mahoney, Michael A113
Mahoney, Michael F. (Mike) A144
Mahoney, Robert M. (Bob) A152
Mahoney, Mike A198
Mahoney, Timothy O. (Tim) A429
Mahoney, Rob A478
Mahoney, Bob A620
Mahoney, Eileen A682
Mahoney, Mark A707
Mahoney, Kathleen M. (Kathy) A756
Mahoney, Kelly A765
Mahoney, Kevin A782
Mahoney, Mike A850
Mahoney, Robert J. P159
Mahoney, Edward J. P325
Mahoney, Joanne M. P375
Mahoney, Kelly P540
Mahoney, Cornelius D. E41
Mahoney, Robert M. (Bob) E49
Mahoney, Dennis E75
Mahony, Susan (Sue) A511
Mahood, Paul A872
Mai, Darin A479
Mai, Shayne P368
Maia, Paulo W175
Maibach, Doug P61
Maibach, Ben C. P61
Maibach, Ryan P61
Maibach, Benjamin C P61
Maibach, Douglas L P61
Maibach, Sheryl B P61
Maida, Robert P. (Rob) E13
Maidlow, Spencer T P146
Maier, Henry J. A327
Maier, Richard A508
Maier, Mike P383
Maier, Stuart A. E184
Maiers, Mary C A395
Mail, Ingrid M P306
Mailand, William P290
Mailloux, Marc A406
Main, Richard W. (Dick) A301
Main, Timothy L. (Tim) A471
Main, Richard W. (Dick) E127
Main, Rebecca R. E183
Maines, Josh P484
Maingot, Lawrence C. E170
Mains, Kenneth G P344
Maio, Mike A105
Maio, Keith D. A919
Maiorino, Brad A788
Mairet, Daniel A260
Mairs, Debra A731
Mairs, Debra E365
Maisel, Bruce A890
Maisel, Bruce P684
Maislin, Stephen P220
Maiuri, Lou A766
Majcher, Marian W51
Majeski, Carl A34
Majon, Judy A904
Majon, Judy E442
Major, Paul A56
Major, Bruce E92
Majors, Charles H. (Charlie) A52
Majors, Michael C. A822
Majumdar, Anurita A511
Majzoub, Saadi A361
Mak, Derek A199
Mak, Janet P325
Makanju, Kay A721
Maki, Mark A P342
Maki, Jennifer W385
Maki, Corinne A. E201

Makin, Brenna A204
Maklan, David P682
Makori-Nelson, Benadette P129
Makowski, John A173
Makris, George A. A742
Makris, George A. E372
Makuen, David E162
Makulec, Jude P464
Malaga, Jim A871
Malakof, Stacey L P376
Malamed, Adam E236
Maland, David P216
Malanga, J. D. W199
Malat, Jeff A544
Malat, Scott B. A913
Malatesta, Keith A324
Malave, Rockwell P293
Malavé, Andrés P399
Malchin, Kobi W150
Malchuk, Daniel W63
Malchuk, Daniel W64
MalchukBE, Daniel W64
Malcolm, Gregory A218
Malcolm, Mark A374
Malcolm, Robert A416
Malcolm, Steve A622
Malcolm, Steven J A900
Malcolm, Georgette P593
Maldonado, Debbie A765
Maldonado, R. Danny A804
Maldonado, Ricardo P163
Maldonado, Raul P415
Maldonado, Debbie P540
Maldonado, Lisa P546
Male, Timothy A243
Malek, Jeffrey A541
Malek, Ryan P354
Malek, Jeffrey E266
Maleno, Christopher A. (Chris) W98
Maley, Michael A25
Maley, David A493
Maley, Michael P15
Maley, Christopher P589
Malhotra, Saket A61
Malhotra, Raghu A537
Malhotra, Kapil A647
Malhotra, Roopali A860
Malhotra, Meena P296
Malhotra, Roopali P656
Malik, Abinta A809
Malik, Kemal W56
Malik, Muhammad Shahbaz (Boz) E92
Malin, Clint B. E249
Malinovitch, Aviv E67
Malinowski, Joe A1
Malinowski, Barbara A599
Malizia, Vince A375
Malladi, Durga A685
Mallakis, Kosta P433
Mallard, Ben A439
Mallard, Dan A693
Mallen, Ben P245
Mallet, Thierry M. W343
Mallett, Chris P392
Mallette, Michael A228
Mallette, Michael P136
Mallison, Nathan P363
Malliwal, Mahendra A456
Mallon, Ed A130
Mallon, Mark W34
Mallory, Jelicia A700
Mallot, Kyle M P167
Mallott, Philip E. A127
Mallott, Anthony P489
Malloy, John P. (Jack) A570
Malloy, Tom P2
Malloy, William P337
Malloy, Thomas E. P654
Mallozzi, Stephen A A73
Malnati, Ronald A308
Malone, Daniel J. (Dan) A210
Malone, Daniel J. (Dan) A236
Malone, Kevin A269
Malone, Margaret A272
Malone, Steve A324

Malone, Karmela A407
Malone, Robert W. A634
Malone, Rob A634
Malone, John C. A688
Malone, Kevin A863
Malone, Mike P13
Malone, Steve P200
Malone, Jacqueline P300
Malone, Dean A343
Malone, Anthony J P396
Malone, Blake P400
Malone, Jan P413
Malone, K K P469
Malone, Marguerite G. P483
Malone, Laura P565
Malone, John T P660
Malone, Nancy P675
Malone, John C. W222
Malone, Mark E185
Malone, Mike E394
Maloney, Robert A101
Maloney, Drew A417
Maloney, Deiken A599
Maloney, Matt A777
Maloney, Michael A795
Maloney, William P186
Maloney, Patrick P203
Maloney, Katie P220
Maloney, Rosario P415
Maloney, James F P631
Maloney, G P P688
Maloney, G P688
Maloney, Skip E300
Maloney, Matt E393
Maloskie, Tom A878
Maloy, June P387
Malte, Bob P275
Maltsbarger, Richard D. A521
Maltz, Richard B. A112
Maltz, David A281
Maltz, Richard B. E38
Malucci, Joseph E386
Malugen, William C A827
Malverdi, Fabrizio W204
Malzahn, Fred A446
Malzahn, Daniel D. A608
Malzahn, Fred E210
Mamet, Michele P331
Mammadov, Emin A494
Mammen, Mathai E216
Mammen, Timothy P. V. E224
Mamon, Harvey P567
Manacchio, Margot P699
Manacher, Justin A558
Manahan-smith, Suzanne A313
Manasia, Anthony P355
Manbeck, Keith A899
Manbeck, Keith P690
Manby, Jeff A493
Manchandra, Anita A677
Mancheste, George P617
Manchester, Paula A254
Manchester, Eric A496
Mancini, Robert A102
Mancini, Lisa A A243
Mancini, Robert A332
Mancini, Wayne E99
Mancl, Dave A460
Mancoridis, Spiros P165
Mancuso, Salvatore A37
Mancuso, Alfred A332
Mancuso, Anthony P197
Mancuso, Anthony P302
Mandable, Terence A140
Mandado, Marissa A533
Mandala, Rocco A173
Mandel, Joseph G. A472
Mandel, Carol A. A585
Mandel, Henry R A644
Mandel, Don P21
Mandel, Lawrence P275
Mandel, Carol A. P377
Mandel, Adrienne A. P676
Mandell, James P570
Mandell, Jon E1

Mandelli, Maela A682
Mander, Gurpreet P530
Manderino, Louis A A624
Mandersson, Magnus W360
Mandeville, Kathy P315
Mandichak, Mark P310
Mandine, Béatrice W278
Mandola, Kim P313
Mandracchia, Stephen P. E209
Mandraccia, Crocifissa A74
Mandrella, Karen P654
Mandt, Ingo M. W215
Manduca, Paul W295
Maneker, Amy P118
Maner, Bobbie P465
Maneri, Phil P184
Maness, Yolanda A244
Manfredonia, Donald L. A352
Manfredonia, Donald L. E159
Mang, Mark A463
Mangalick, Rita A133
Mangan, Kathy A912
Manganaro, Lynn A678
Mangel, Allen W. P458
Mangel, Barry P680
Mangels, Tonya A41
Manget, Christine P508
Mangiaracina, Brian A59
Mangin, Wendy P213
Mango, John A342
Mangold, Ken A439
Mangold, Michael A825
Mangome, Victor A693
Mangoni, John P244
Mangum, Jesse A478
Mangura, Paul P384
Manheimer, Mark L A759
Manheimer, Mark L P520
Mani, Nat A725
Manias, William G P185
Maniates, Zenaida A865
Manica, Virgil P629
Manifold, Albert W112
Manigan, Elizabeth P200
Manigault, Pierre P94
Manis, Jonathan (Jon) A775
Manis, Jonathan (Jon) P548
Maniscalco, Michael A729
Manivannan, Naveen A774
Manjarrez-Williams, Marcela A180
Manke, Riley E432
Mankes, Saul A531
Mankiller, Kristen T P569
Manlapaz, Nicolo A56
Manley, Kathy A821
Manley, Kathy P621
Manley, Gerard A. (Gerry) W274
Mann, James A17
Mann, Jeff A25
Mann, Bill A34
Mann, Aric A64
Mann, John A260
Mann, Leah A403
Mann, Susan A513
Mann, Steve A778
Mann, James P10
Mann, Jeff P15
Mann, Christopher P141
Mann, Robert P160
Mann, Maria A. P167
Mann, Lindsay K P271
Mann, Erica L. W56
Mann, Trevor W243
Manna, Frank P20
Manna, Rebecca P269
Mannarino, Gwen A32
Mannarino, Frank A. A761
Mannello, Louis J. A395
Manners, Jim A819
Mannhardt, Thilo W379
Manning, Joseph (Joe) A5
Manning, Martin F. (Marty) A15
Manning, Ben A115
Manning, Joyce A155
Manning, Fred A441

A	= AMERICAN BUSINESS
E	= EMERGING COMPANIES
P	= PRIVATE COMPANIES
W	= WORLD BUSINESS

Manning, Maura A691
Manning, Anna A701
Manning, Martin F. (Marty) P9
Manning, Robin E. (Rob) P179
Manning, Peggy P247
Manning, Michael P590
Manning, Mike P685
Manning, Robert J. (Rob) W346
Manning, John T. (Terry) E19
Manning, Margo E105
Mannion, David E426
Mannix, Margaret P2
Mannix, Mary N P51
Manno, Deborah A542
Manno, Deborah E267
Mannon, David P430
Mannon, George P621
Manoogian, Lisa P35
Manos, John G. A108
Manos, Roseann A741
Manos, Steven S. P82
Manos, Roseann E370
Manos-Mchenry, Debbie A440
Manrique, Olga P59
Manseau, James J. A145
Manseau, James J. E46
Mansell, Kevin B. A493
Mansfield, Bob A70
Mansfield, William P. A394
Mansfield, Stephen L. (Steve) P336
Mansky, Patrick P205
Manso, Julio A449
Mansolillo, Scott A122
Manson, Dave P482
Mansur, Carla A489
Mantaring, Rizalina G. W347
Mantella, Philomena V. P392
Manthe, Junior P281
Mantia, Linda P. W232
Mantooth, David A835
Mantovani, Massimo W143
Mantua, Philip J. A724
Mantua, Mitch A728
Mantz, Jay A508
Mantzounis, Demetrios P. W23
Manuel, Mark A863
Manuel, Ethan P326
Manuel, Terri P439
Manuel, Bill P501
Manuel, Shasta P523
Manuel, Trevor W275
Manuele, Maria A407
Manville, Ryan K A338
Manville, Ryan K E149
Manwani, Harish A898
Manzagol, L. Jeff E305
Manzano, Mike A763
Manzano, Wilhelmina A810
Manzano, Wilhelmina P597
Manzari, Margie P516
Manzer, Kenneth A828
Manzi, John A. E305
Manzo, Mark A35
Manzo, Paul E P470
Manzon, Wendy P235
Mao, Li A476
Mapes, Michelle A316
Mapes, Chris A915
Mapes, Michelle P191
Maples, Tracy A195
Maples, Rick A446
Maples, John T. P507
Maples, Rick E210
Mapp, Frederick A14
Maquat, Robert A644
Marafioti, Michael A691
Maragos, George A173
Maraka, Ravi A101
MARAMOTTI, LUIGI W111

Marano, Tom A7
Marano, Robert P P630
Marasigan, Glenn A777
Marasigan, Glenn E393
Maratos, Brooke E127
Marbach, Kenneth D. A304
Marcaccio, Mario J P102
MarcAurele, Joseph J. (Joe) A880
Marceau, Dawn A493
Marced, Maria W354
Marcegaglia, Emma W144
Marcell, Frederick A A706
Marcell, Frederick A E353
Marcellin, Michael (Mike) A482
Marcellino, David L P81
Marcelo, Sheila Lirio E57
March, Keith P350
March, Shayn P E175
Marchael, Tom A841
Marchael, Tom P633
Marchbein, Deane P320
Marchese, Sara P452
Marchetti, Paul K A641
Marchetti, Kevin A655
Marchetti, Paul K P422
Marchetti, Kevin E333
Marchick, Jill A73
Marchik, Katie P252
Marchin, George P270
Marchio, Samuel A67
Marchio, Timothy A734
Marchioni, John J. A734
Marchozzi, Tom P227
Marciniak, Richard P628
Marco, Lori A432
Marco, Maria Di A862
Marco, Mario J. San A890
Marco, Bob P238
Marco, Mario J. San P684
Marco, Maria Di E419
Marcoccla, Roberto A482
Marconi, Luis G. A432
Marcotte, James A. (Jim) A301
Marcotte, James A. (Jim) E127
Marcovitz, James A589
Marcroft, Darlene E407
Marcum, R. Alan A263
Marcum, R Alan E263
Marcum, Lanette A387
Marcum, Lanette E177
Marcus, Deborah A34
Marcus, Avi A A615
Marcus, Avi E615
Marcus, Stuart A850
Marcus, Judith P285
Marcus, Philip P472
Marcus, Ruth P508
Marcus, W. Andrew P651
Marcus, Joel S. E9
Marcus, George M. E133
Marcus, Gregory S. E257
Marcus, Stephen H. E257
Marcus, Brandon E339
Marcuz, Lisa A282
Mardikar, Upendra A49
Mareburter, Robert A622
Maredia, Amin N. A759
Marek, Dave A61
Marek, Liz P22
Marella, Punnaiah P187
Marenghi, Matt A581
Marestaing, Alex P430
Margetts, Dane A920
Margetts, Marty P119
Margol, Kanoe P601
Margolin, Eric M. A166
Margolis, Joseph D. (Joe) E139
Margolis, Nancy E430
Maria, Panayiotou A872
Maria, Peter J De P688
Mariani, John A120
Mariani, Martin A830
Mariani, Harry P244
Mariani, Martin E402
Mariano, Rocco A A677

Maridou, Kathy E140
Marien, Philippe W72
Marik, Shane A309
Marinakis, Eric A238
Marine, Jon A539
Marinello, Kathryn V A809
Marinello, Kathryn V P584
Marinello, Tony P639
Marinez, Lauren P341
Maring, Trent P424
Marini, Dick A514
Marinich, Season P84
Marino, Madelyn A49
Marino, Michael A158
Marino, Pete A173
Marino, Thomas A500
Marino, Linda P532
Marino, Ricardo Villela W191
Marino, Thomas E238
Marinow, Nikolai E261
Marins, Rubia A333
Marinsik, Daniel A725
Marinus, Sven W334
Marion, Melissa A902
Marion, Melissa P692
Mariotti, Marco A652
Maris, George A599
Marissa, Morris A449
Maritato, Christopher (Chris) A749
Maritz, W. Stephen (Steve) P307
Mark, Richard J. A42
Mark, Stocksdale A531
Mark, Miller A536
Mark, William P522
Markantonis, George M. A502
Markarian, Gevork A204
Markel, Tony A528
Markel, Anthony F. A528
Markel, Steven A. A528
Markell, Peter K. A635
Markell, Peter K. P419
Markell, Peter K. P626
Markewicz, Jeremy P315
Markham, Stephen A732
Markham, Pat E193
Markham, Kevin E253
Markham, Stephen E365
Markinson, Bryan P355
Markle, Jami P243
Markley, Stephen A489
Markley, Steve P162
Markos, Aaron A351
Markos, Aaron E158
Markovich, Nick A441
Markovitz, Mike A541
Markovitz, Mike E266
Markowski, Steve A109
Markowski, Steve E36
Marks, Alan A288
Marks, Jeff A501
Marks, Judy F. A854
Marks, George P48
Marks, Julia P227
Marks, Cindy P348
Marks, Stanley W. P508
Marks, Chris W255
Marks, Chris W312
Marks, Howard S. E312
Marks, George R. E357
Markson, Larry P71
Markus, Tim P13
Markus, Donna P218
Markwalter, Jack W80
Markwardt, Lynda A669
Marlatt, Geoff T. A626
Marlette, Tim G. A227
Marlin, Morris A332
Marlin, Chris A508
Marlow, Gary P P391
Marlow, Patty P668
Marlowe, Ted E1
Marnick, Samantha J A758
Marold, Paul E251
Marolis, Jessie A844
Marolis, Jessie E412

Maron, Michael P239
Marone, Sal A369
Maroni, Bradley A129
Marotta, Richard M A124
Marotta, Michael A410
Marotta, Richard M. E41
Marotto, Stephen A353
Marottolo, Lucille P450
Maroulis, George A247
Maroulis, George E103
Maroun, Nabih A140
Maroun, George E144
Marovich, Milan P282
Marquardt, Patti P68
Marquardt, R. Scott P304
Marquardt, Robert P304
Marquardt, Jeanne P625
Marquardt, Rolf W352
Marques, Roberto A567
Marques, Miguel Athayde W156
Marquess, Dan E216
Marquez, Raul A101
Marquez, Octavio A265
Marquez, Antonio F. A284
Marquez, Tony A284
Marquez, Merly P192
Marquez, Rose P245
Marquez, Antonio F. E111
Marquez, Tony E111
Marquis, Jeffrey A. P223
Marr, Richard R A262
Marr, David W396
Marr, Christopher P. (Chris) E102
Marr, John S. E404
Marra, Peter A741
Marra, Michele P387
Marra, Michel P387
Marra, Peter E370
Marrache, Gilles A61
Marrano, Steve P42
Marrapodi, Michelle A505
Marrapodi, Michelle E241
Marrero, Cecilia P161
Marriott, Richard E. A434
Marriott, J. W. (Bill) A531
Marrone, Nicholas A108
Marrone, Nicholas E35
Marrs, Anna A49
Marrs, Douglas W. (Doug) A395
Marrs, Rick P423
Marry, Thomas F. (Tom) E283
Mars, Galen P192
Marsch, Jean P220
Marschall, Patrick A113
Marschall, Matt A173
Marschke, Keith E246
Marsden, Noel P83
Marsh, Nancy M A184
Marsh, Laurie M. A289
Marsh, Andrew S. (Drew) A300
Marsh, Allison A390
Marsh, John T. A400
Marsh, Celeste A458
Marsh, Amy A672
Marsh, Mike A728
Marsh, Leslie A800
Marsh, Andrew P185
Marsh, Celeste P251
Marsh, Randy P368
Marsh, Edward P371
Marsh, Allen J P483
Marsh, Beth P522
Marsh, Amy K P651
Marsh, Peter P673
Marsh, Robert E263
Marsh, Leslie E396
Marshal, Jim P368
Marshall, Steven C. A55
Marshall, Kimberly L A107
Marshall, David A323
Marshall, Daryl A538
Marshall, Jim A541
Marshall, Michelle A644
Marshall, Lance A668
Marshall, Russell A673

Marshall, Ryan R. A681
Marshall, Lynne A902
Marshall, Kimberly A. A908
Marshall, Devona P392
Marshall, Era L. P506
Marshall, David P517
Marshall, Cynthia P623
Marshall, Ken P638
Marshall, Lynne P693
Marshall, John L. W7
Marshall, Rick A. E19
Marshall, Kimberly L E34
Marshall, Jim E266
Marsicano, Michael P202
Marsico, Stephen A724
Marsolais, Christian A727
Marsteller, Brent A P88
Martchek, Jeffrey D. A608
Martel, Roland M. A450
Martel, Ron P267
Martel, Amina P482
Martell, Greg A530
Martell, Rita A809
Martello, Wan Ling W258
Martello, Joseph E22
Marter, Kenneth W P321
Marthens, Thomas P293
Marthinsen, Jim A434
Marti, Keren A335
Martin, Cheryl A96
Martin, Paul E. A113
Martin, Greg A148
Martin, Rodney A164
Martin, Karen A184
Martin, R. Brad A190
Martin, Gus A219
Martin, Kim A221
Martin, John A254
Martin, David A316
Martin, Matthew A. A324
Martin, Chris A328
Martin, Cissy A329
Martin, John J. A349
Martin, John C. A386
Martin, John A A420
Martin, Bradley A429
Martin, Kristin A438
Martin, Sabrena A449
Martin, Jeff A474
Martin, Phil A480
Martin, Greg A480
Martin, Thomas A. (Tom) A492
Martin, Maureen A500
Martin, Elizabeth A500
Martin, Antonio A582
Martin, Kenny A609
Martin, Sean A639
Martin, Joseph A668
Martin, Christopher P. A675
Martin, Roger A685
Martin, Andrew D. A698
Martin, Jeffrey W. A735
Martin, Kenneth B A740
Martin, Jim A744
Martin, Ian A766
Martin, Mitchell P. A779
Martin, Robert W. A816
Martin, Wendy A844
Martin, Susan H. A884
Martin, Julia P6
Martin, Cynthia P22
Martin, Michael P46
Martin, Dan P96
Martin, Michelle P96
Martin, Glen P110
Martin, David P123
Martin, Michael P132
Martin, Sandy P141
Martin, Dan P163
Martin, David P191
Martin, Michael M. P200
Martin, David P226
Martin, Colleen P281
Martin, Barbara P303
Martin, Alexa P313

Martin, Kathryn P325
Martin, Beth P361
Martin, Antonio P373
Martin, Alison P383
Martin, Josh P422
Martin, Andrew D. P456
Martin, Daniel B P466
Martin, Thomas P466
Martin, Gina P475
Martin, Julie P482
Martin, Diane P530
Martin, Kip P569
Martin, John P603
Martin, Michelle P603
Martin, Mark P620
Martin, Paula P620
Martin, Roy P628
Martin, Janet P671
Martin, Jeanene R P674
Martin, R. Bradley (Brad) W62
Martin, Eric W66
Martin, Denis W286
Martin, Paolo De W323
Martin, Daniel L. (Dan) E23
Martin, Gary L. E57
Martin, Wes E65
Martin, Gus E84
Martin, Jay E99
Martin, Timothy M. (Tim) E102
Martin, John J. E156
Martin, Jay E179
Martin, Larry E185
Martin, John A E198
Martin, Bradley E204
Martin, Maureen E237
Martin, Elizabeth E237
Martin, Ronald H. E253
Martin, Steven R. (Steve) E286
Martin, Sean E325
Martin, Todd E339
Martin, Wendy E412
Martin, Anthea E432
Martin, Dan E432
Martin-Flickinger, Gerri A762
Martinbianco, Dino A693
Martindale, Edgar A A324
Martindale, Steven L. (Steve) A450
Martinek, Kenneth A. E306
Martinelli, Anne P43
Martinelli, James E214
Martines, Arnold D. A183
Martines, Dean A728
Martinez, Alexandra A49
Martinez, Charles A101
Martinez, Joel A163
Martinez, Lori A257
Martinez, Albert Al A303
Martinez, Ozzie A452
Martinez, Alvaro A459
Martinez, Robert A597
Martinez, Peter A644
Martinez, Octavio A685
Martinez, John A695
Martinez, Brett A697
Martinez, Maria A723
Martinez, Jorge A752
Martinez, John A832
Martinez, Carlos A872
Martinez, Jason P20
Martinez, Fernando P143
Martinez, Valerie P187
Martinez, Graciela P199
Martinez, Agustin P291
Martinez, Elsa P348
Martinez, Trisha P408
Martinez, Rosanna P416
Martinez, Denise P431
Martinez, Richard P433
Martinez, David P441
Martinez, Brett P454
Martinez, Michael P471
Martinez, Pedro P478
Martinez, Eddie P478
Martinez, Jorge P497
Martinez, Orlando L P517

Martinez, Dorothea P517
Martinez, Christopher P535
Martinez, Steve P630
Martinez, Edward P665
Martinez, Michelle P701
Martinez, Ozzie E215
Martinez, Mark E320
Martinez-Davis, Maya A649
Martini, James (Jim) A813
Martini, James (Jim) P616
Martino, McCrae P601
Martino, Tony E158
Martino-Valdes, Emilio A336
Martinovich, Robert F. (Rob) A622
Martinovich, Robert F A623
Martinovich, Robert F P407
Martins, Jennifer P37
Martins, Eduardo E104
Martinson, Chris A813
Martinson, Eric K P601
Martinson, Chris P616
Martiny, Krista A187
Martiny, Krista E71
Martire, Frank R. A330
Martire, Frank R A578
Martocci, Gino A. A522
Martore-Baker, Susan A159
Martrenchar, Yves W66
Martuza, Robert L. P590
Marty, Angela P343
Marty, Michael E57
Martyn, Derek P567
Martyr, Clive A96
Martynenko, Vladimir A691
Martz, Stephen A360
Martz, B. Bradford A847
Martz, Sheila P112
Martz, Stephen E164
Martz, Raymond D. E326
Martz, B. Bradford E414
Mart-n, Miguel Mart-nez San W300
Mart-nez, Enrique R. (Henry) A269
Mart-nez, Armando T--mez W18
Mart-nez, José Formoso W25
Marumoto, Akira W235
Maruna, Karen A441
Maruyama, Yoshinori W27
Maruyama, Haruya W121
Maruyama, Hidetoshi W264
Marvel, Cheryl P404
Marventano, David Dave A282
Marvin, Michael P623
Marvin, James L. E227
Marx, Michael A496
Marx, Felix A537
Marx, Kara P498
Marx, Anthony P598
Marx, John E174
Marx, Oscar B. (Bud) E174
Mary, Young A103
Mary, Michele St A405
Mary, Howard A446
Mary, Mark P436
Mary, Howard E210
Maryles, Matthew J P32
Marzec, Robert J. E19
Marzen, Russ A914
Marzi, Laura A406
Marzilli, Christopher (Chris) A374
Marzulli, Robert D A556
Mas, Alberto A119
Mas, José R. A536
Mas, Jorge A536
Mascarenhas, Rodrigo A51
Mascarenhas, Rodrigo P33
Mascari, Doreen P560
Mascari, Dorine P560
Mascaro, Dan A672
Mascharka, William L P205
Mascher, Christof W23
Mascia, Angelo A582
Mascia, Angelo P373
Mascioli, Stephen R. E18
Mascorro, Whitney V P233
Mase, Dawn A904

Mase, Dawn E442
Maserang, D Deverl A763
Mash, Lisa A59
Masiar, Stephen P516
Masih, Ashish E123
Masilamani, Palani P297
Mask, Laura A708
Mask, Laura P459
Mask, Laura E356
Maskal, Vanessa E. E29
Maslyaev, Ivan W290
Mason, Heather L. A4
Mason, Rafael A49
Mason, Jeanne K. A113
Mason, Jeannie K A113
Mason, Steve A165
Mason, Linda A175
Mason, Mike A295
Mason, Thomas P. A298
Mason, Louise A308
Mason, Robert A344
Mason, Richard J A369
Mason, Richard A369
Mason, Rich A390
Mason, Mark K. A427
Mason, Craig A483
Mason, Margaret A489
Mason, Tiffany A521
Mason, Jenifer L A531
Mason, Simon A602
Mason, Charlie A725
Mason, Andrew A729
Mason, John A729
Mason, Jeannette P149
Mason, Caroline P188
Mason, April P270
Mason, Marion P289
Mason, Brad P307
Mason, Sally F P449
Mason, Michael Atwood P506
Mason, Edward P560
Mason, Sally P590
Mason, Sally P643
Mason, Barry P680
Mason, Mark K. E202
Mason, J. Thomas (Tom) E253
Mason, J T E253
Mason, Randall A. E295
Masoudi, Gerald F. A178
Masrani, Bharat B. W370
Mass, Greg P220
Massa, Mark P625
Massad, Marc A446
Massad, Marc E210
Massanelli, Stephen C. A742
Massanelli, Stephen C. E372
Massarelli, John A117
Massari, Nate A59
Massaro, Michelle P302
Massaro, Joseph R. W29
Massaron, Paul E. P679
Masschelin, Paul J. W184
Masse, Paul A449
Massengill, Scott R A147
Massengill, Matthew E. (Matt) A892
Masser, Keith E. A811
Masser, Keith E. P600
Massey, Edward A97
Massey, David A774
Massey, Edward E32
Massheder, Alfred A336
Massimo, Larry M P154
Massod, Rafeh A264
Masson, Kevin A192
Mastandrea, James C. E438
Mastandrea, Christine J. E438
Masters, Robert E4
Masteller, Dan A729
Masterman, Andrew V. A666
Masterman, Andrew V. P438
Masterson, Sarah A493
Masterson, David J. (Dave) A736
Masterson, Mike A904
Masterson, David J. (Dave) P492
Masterson, Mike E442

A = AMERICAN BUSINESS
E = EMERGING COMPANIES
P = PRIVATE COMPANIES
W = WORLD BUSINESS

Mastiaux, Frank W140
Mastrantonio, Maryann A163
Mastrapa, Hector A530
Mastro, Thomas J A105
Mastro, Mary Lou P181
Mastrolia, Angelo A734
Mastromattei, Mario A199
Mastromihalis, Eleni A877
Mastromonaco, Gina A173
Mastronardi, Steve P272
Mastropaolo, Joan A195
Mastropietro, Vince A892
Mastrototaro, Daniel A402
Masud, Mohammad A767
Masuda, Ko P381
Masuko, Osamu W243
Masumoto, Kimie A558
Masumoto, Yasuo W211
Mata, Amy P162
Matacunas, Michael (Mike) A274
Matarese, Scott A101
Matarese, Andrew A644
Mateo, Alan E426
Mateos, Beatriz C A178
Mater, Derek De La A230
Mathai, John A480
Matheis, Lisa A384
Matheis, Lisa E176
Matheny, Drue A266
Mather, Lisa A218
Mathern, Mary A676
Mathers, David W111
Matheson, Mark A693
Matheson, Jim A746
Matheson, Aj P211
Matheson, Les W312
Mathew, Julie A178
Mathew, Reji P343
Mathew, Meenu P481
Mathew, Stefanie P653
Mathews, Mike A725
Mathews, Rick A913
Mathews, James E65
Mathias, Robert J. A169
Mathias, Ann P96
Mathieu, Philippe A305
Mathieu, Ronald P136
Mathieu, Philippe P185
Mathieu, Cheryl P230
Mathios, Alan D. P143
Mathiowetz, Pamela E195
Mathis, Sam A331
Mathis, Archard A333
Mathis, Richard A751
Mathis, Anthony P54
Mathis, Larry L P335
Mathis, Freda P542
Mathis, Sam E148
Mathis, Patrick L. E304
Mathis, Richard E378
Mathison, Lora P396
Mathur, Nikhil A130
Mathur, Nikhil A131
Mathur, Prabodh A144
Mathwick, Shelley A493
Mathwick, Shelly A493
Matis, Nina B. E226
Matisak, Phil A738
Matkin, Richard P431
Matkin, Todd P435
Matley, Robert P. A225
Matley, Robert P. E88
Matlock, Mark A74
Matlock, Beverly P34
Matlock, Stephanie P242
Matos, Patricia A201
Matousek, James A440
Matovich, Nick A64
Matovina, John M. A47

Matovina, John M. A48
Matraki, Farid A558
Matre, Frances P631
Matros, Richard K. E363
Matschi, Helmut W108
Matschullat, Robert W. A874
Matson, Shane A185
Matson, Richard A196
Matson, Pamela A507

Matson, Timothy (Tim) A701
Matson, Kenneth J. (Ken) A822
Matson, Brian P59
Matson, Pamela P288
Matsubara, Kazuhiro W99
Matsuda, Michael P38
Matsuda, Pegi P663
Matsui, Connie L. E186
Matsumoto, Toshiya A102
Matsumoto, Dayna A183
Matsumoto, Patrick A183
Matsumoto, Yoshiyuki W172
Matsumoto, Yoshihisa W182
Matsumoto, Sachio W223
Matsumoto, Ryu W324
Matsumoto, Masayoshi W344
Matsumoto, Tamiji W353
Matsumura, Harumi W223
Matsumura, Hiroshi W336
Matsuoka, Kelly A865
Matsuoka, Deron P19
Matsushima, Hidekazu W116
Matsushita, Isao W200
Matsushita, Masayuki W282
Matsuura, Masanori W99
Matsuura, Yohzoh W304
Matsuura, Hiroaki W351
Matsuzaki, Takashi W113
Matt, Hohl A350
Matt, Hohl E157
Matta, Juan A204
Matta, Abraham P80
Mattea, Andrea A454
Mattelaer, Alex E116
Matten, Naomi P135
Matteo, Steve A160
Matteo, Steve E55
Matter, Donald (Chad) A851
Matter, Chad A851
Mattera, Vincent D. (Chuck) E214
Mattern, Julie P192
Mattern, Larry P198
Mattes, Andreas W. (Andy) A265
Matteson, Larry A441
Matteson, Timothy J. A500
Matteson, Timothy J. E237
Mattheus, Deven P391
Matthew, Janet A655
Matthew, Mussallem P333
Matthew, McDaniel P694
Matthew, Janet E333
Matthews, Shelly A98
Matthews, Katie A167
Matthews, Terrence D. (Terry) A439
Matthews, Clay A654
Matthews, Jerome A676
Matthews, William A729
Matthews, Gregory A729
Matthews, Kelley A774
Matthews, Marcia A838
Matthews, Douglas R. A852
Matthews, Charles R. A884
Matthews, Tenisha P8
Matthews, Lorin P64
Matthews, Andrew P97
Matthews, Ted P141
Matthews, Caz P160
Matthews, Kim P202
Matthews, Vincent P480
Matthews, Michael P556
Matthews, Shelly E33
Matthews, Darcey E298
Matthys, Joan P22
Matti, Louis A359
Mattia, Tony P363

Mattiace, Michelle P230
Mattice, Laura A225
Mattice, Alicia A332
Mattice, Laura E88
Mattics, Steven C. A596
Mattis, Archie A52
Mattke, Timothy A557
Mattmiller, Michael P573
Matto, Andrew (Drew) Del E166
Mattocks, Naketha A272
Matton, Jeffrey A P583
Mattos, Cristhy P392
Mattox, Michael A56
Mattox, David A729
Mattox, Cheryl P231
Mattson, Gayle P387
Matturri, Alexander J. (Alex) A721
Matuga, Ed A766
Matulis, Marc P411
Matuschka, Nikolaus Graf von W6
Matuschka, Nikolaus Graf von W170
Matusicky, Cheryl P63
Matuszewski, Karen P158
Matviak, Ivan A766
Matyas, Carole A885
Matyja, Tina P284
Matytsyn, Alexander K. W290
Matz, Glen A187
Matz, R. Kevin A294
Matz, Glen E71
Matzat, James A214
Matzat, James P128
Mau, Jeanne A175
Mauch, Robert P. A59
Mauch, Anneliese P654
Mauck, Jan P483
Maudal, Vaughn P141
Maude, Brian P134
Maughan, Phil A599
Maul, Glenn A148
Mauldin, Vance P580
Mauler, Michael K. (Mike) A372
Maultsby, Chris A655
Maultsby, Chris E333
Maun, Marc C. A137
Maurana, Cheryl P591
Maurel, Laurent W372
Maurer, Mark A465
Maurer, Doug A746
Maurer, Ann A838
Maurer, Marsha P71
Maurer, Robert P533
Maurer, Monika W266
Maurice, Allen R A208
Maurice, Jean R P292
Maurici, Vito A547
Maurici, Vito P319
Mauriello, Elaine A323
Mauriello, Keith P680
Maurno, Frank A693
Mauro, Augie A782
Mauro, Lila A860
Mauro, Lila P656
Maury, Kent A530
Mauvais, Arnaud A875
Mavis, Alan A113
Mavra, Joanne A131
Maw, Scott H. A763
Maxey, Dr Rick P240
Maxfield, Casey A244
Maxfield, Cindy P81
Maxsiimc, David E438
Maxsimic, David D. E163
Maxson, Patricia (Trish) A478
Maxsted, Lindsay P. W395
Maxwell, Emanuel A73
Maxwell, Mike A115
Maxwell, Gary A. A274
Maxwell, David G. A394
Maxwell, Jai A556
Maxwell, Barbara A565
Maxwell, M. Craig A634
Maxwell, Sheron P102
Maxwell, Mark P126
Maxwell, Edwin P210

Maxwell, Crissette P372
Maxwell, Todd P479
Maxwell, Paul E349
May, Christopher J. (Chris) A45
May, Stephen A246
May, John C. A260
May, Greg A262
May, John A265
May, Ron A280
May, Phillip R. A300
May, Thomas J. (Tom) A307
May, Alan A418
May, William A461
May, Gary A505
May, Karen J. A567
May, Ed A583
May, J. Phillip (Phill) A622
May, J Philip A622
May, Philip A622
May, Jerry A. A698
May, Ron A782
May, Thomas J. (Tom) A872
May, Sally P115
May, Lee P144
May, Eric P149
May, Nancy P392
May, Ronald P404
May, John P442
May, Jerry A. P456
May, Lisa P458
May, Grace M. P494
May, Serena P610
May, Laurie P682
May, Nicki E83
Mayadag, Ed E310
Maybee, Stacie A821
Maybee, Stacie P621
Mayberry, Michael C. (Mike) A456
Mayberry, Robert A461
Mayberry, Katherine A464
Maybury, Mark T A761
Maybury, John P115
Maycott, Cathy S P170
Mayer, Gregory A40
Mayer, Jessica L. A165
Mayer, Kevin A. A272
Mayer, Michael G. A337
Mayer, Michael A441
Mayer, Paul A575
Mayer, Bethany A735
Mayer, John A748
Mayer, Raoul P157
Mayer, Dennis P332
Mayer, Chris P545
Mayer, Laurel P596
Mayer, Max E327
Mayer, William E. E337
Mayers, James A101
Mayes, Cindy P652
Mayeux, Lee P89
Mayfield, Jeff A655
Mayfield, Richard A878
Mayfield, Thomas P378
Mayfield, Bill P680
Mayfield, Jeff E333
Mayger, Douglas W. E281
Mayhew, William A282
Mayhew, Brian P338
Maynard, Donna A160
Maynard, Ghen A175
Maynard, Monique W161
Maynard, Donna E55
Mayne, Katie A691
Mayne, Julia P22
Mayo, Marc A330
Mayo, Michael A. P58
Mayo, Stephen L. P91
Mayo, Michelle P174
Mayo, Mark P356
Mayo, C Russell P486
Mayo, Christina E426
Mayopoulos, Timothy J. (Tim) A315
Mayor, Randy E. A425
Mayor, Randy E. E201
Mayor-Mora, Enrique A166

Mayrose, Deetta P87
Mayrs, Paul E86
Mays, Lisa A164
Mays, Denise P145
Mays, Ramona P569
Mayse, Tracy P404
Mazanec, Mark A738
Mazany, Lucy A741
Mazany, Lucy E370
Mazarakis, S. James (Jim) A907
Mazarakis, James A907
Mazarakis, S. James (Jim) E445
Mazarakis, James E446
Mazelsky, Jay E213
Mazey, Mary Ellen P51
Mazhar, Mir A122
Mazile, Yolette A204
Mazman, Mark A693
Mazouch, Nick P342
Mazur-Hofsaess, Katarzyna A918
Mazzanti, Fernando A465
Mazzara, Phil P142
Mazzarella, Kathleen M. A394
Mazzeffi, Bob P1
Mazzella, Christina P486
Mazzeo, Anthony A160
Mazzeo, Anthony E55
Mazzocco, Lisa A860
Mazzocco, Lisa P656
Mazzotta, Brian A741
Mazzotta, Brian E370
Mazzu, Dianne P639
MBA, Gretchen Long P340
Mbah, Ndubuisi P505
Mbanda, Laurent P136
McAdam, Lowell C. A870
Mcadams, Bob A878
McAdams, Robin P243
Mcadoo, Duncan A674
McAfee, Jason A277
McAfee, Lawrance W. (Larry) E405
McAleenan, Donald F. A153
McAleenan, Don A153
McAlindon, Timothy P629
Mcalister, Kay A655
Mcalister, Kay E333
McAllister, Barbara A115
McAllister, Kevin G. A136
McAllister, Gene A685
McAllister, Dan P357
McAloon, Jane F. W64
McAluey, Daniel P510
McAnally, David P258
McAnder, Michael P428
McAndrews, James J. A323
McAnn, Michael T P423
McArdle, William P267
McArthur, John A281
McArthur, John E172
McArtor, Allan W16
McAssey, Gary A813
McAssey, Gary P608
McAtee, David R. A84
McAuslan, Robert R. (Bob) A891
McAuslan, Robert R. (Bob) E434
McAvoy, John T. A232
McAvoy, John T. A233
McAvoy, John P408
McBeath, Mark A196
McBee, Bill A234
McBee, Bill P139
Mcbee, Jacquelyn P613
McBrayer, Preston P620
McBride, Mary E. A214
McBride, R. Perley A368
Mcbride, Douglas A387
McBride, Dennis A844
McBride, Kate A857
Mcbride, Karla A878
Mcbride, Roger L P38
McBride, Mary E. P128
McBride, Maureen P218
McBride, Beverly J P329
McBride, Dwight A. P398
Mcbride, Douglas E177

McBride, Kenneth (Ken) E385
McBride, Dennis E412
McBryan, Michael E. E189
Mcburnie, Karen A808
Mcburnie, Karen P581
Mccabe, Michael A34
Mccabe, Brian A56
Mccabe, Mike A141
McCabe, Alan A244
Mccabe, Natalie A244
Mccabe, James A260
McCabe, Pete A375
McCabe, Robert A. (Rob) A655
McCabe, Kari A709
McCabe, Brian K. A754
McCabe, Catherine A763
Mccabe, Angeline A885
Mccabe, Michael P165
McCabe, Robert A. (Rob) E333
McCabe, Brian K. E380
McCafferty, Donna A204
McCafferty, Marty A235
McCaffery, Karin E31
Mccaffrey, Mary A602
Mccaffrey, Bobbie P335
McCain, Linda P207
McCall, Michael W. A401
Mccall, Michael A693
Mccall, Kim A770
McCall, Dennis P14
McCall, Anne E. P132
McCall, Shannon P158
McCall, Brian P563
McCall, Sandy P621
McCall, Bron E139
McCall, Michael W. E187
McCallin, Nancy P539
McCallion, Anne D. A642
McCallion, Anne D. E328
McCallister, Michael B. A921
McCallister, Terry D. P687
McCallum, Kevan E265
McCallum, John H. E286
McCambridge, Thomas P105
McCampbell, Dan A691
McCandless, Derek S. E96
McCann, Michael V A480
McCann, Peter A833
Mccann, Elle Donovan A863
Mccann, Ellen A863
McCann, Brenda P92
McCann, Bart P612
McCann, James W209
McCann, Christopher G. (Chris) E1
McCann, James F. (Jim) E1
McCann, Brian P. E300
McCanna, Peter P397
McCardle, Linda P359
McCarrie, Michael A247
McCarrie, Michael E102
McCarroll, Lisa P366
Mccarten, Steve A105
McCarter, Kathy A863
McCarter, Cathy A867
McCarter, Cathy P661
McCarthy, Gloria M. A67
McCarthy, J. Kevin A105
McCarthy, Jeff A105
McCarthy, Marie A130
McCarthy, Christine M. A271
McCarthy, Daniel J. A368
Mccarthy, Donald A387
McCarthy, Brian A412
Mccarthy, Eileen A474
Mccarthy, Ayse A726
McCarthy, Peter A727
McCarthy, Kevin A740
McCarthy, Richard A865
McCarthy, Deborah A893
McCarthy, Terence A914
McCarthy, Jennifer P21
McCarthy, Ryan P43
Mccarthy, Patrick P43
McCarthy, Teresa P346
McCarthy, Ellen P383

McCarthy, John P392
McCarthy, Jodi P416
Mccarthy, Sean E107
Mccarthy, Donald E177
McCarthy, Brian E192
McCarthy, Deborah E436
McCartney, David A13
McCartney, John A872
McCartney, William G. (Gerry) P449
McCartney, Joseph E189
McCartney, Bryan D. E189
McCartney, Daniel P. E189
McCarty, Patrick A103
Mccarty, Jeremy A270
McCarty, Mary A388
Mccarty, Jeanette A718
McCarty, Mollie A788
Mccarty, Jan A912
McCarty, Diane P672
McCarty, Geoffrey E251
Mccasland, Fatima E265
Mccaslin, Barbara A223
McCaslin, David E195
McCaughan, James P. (Jim) A668
McCaughey, Ryan A204
McCauley, Dawn A52
McCauley, Cliff A244
McCauley, Laurie A698
McCauley, Charles P30
McCauley, Matt P187
McCauley, Laurie P456
McCausland, Maureen P. A548
McCausland, Maureen P. P321
McCaw, Sue A532
McCaw, Craig O. E328
McCellon-Allen, Venita A46
McChesney, Lee B. A761
McChrystal, William L A166
McClain, Mary A223
McClain, Ronald G. (Ron) A492
Mcclain, Wayne A513
Mcclain, Kenny A693
McClain, Ashley P635
McClamrock, Grady P148
McClanahan, Marsha P124
McClanahan, David P183
McClaskey, Michael A270
Mcclatchey, BE Skip P679
McClaughlin, Don A199
Mccleery, Sam A840
McClellan, Lisa A180
McClellan, John W. A227
McClellan, Stephen R. (Steve) A391
McClellan, Lawson A791
McClellan, Makana P601
McClelland, David A362
McClelland, Miccau A441
McClelland, Dixie P440
McClenahan, Tom E261
McClimans, Jason A704
McClimans, Jason E351
Mcclimon, Timothy A49
McClincy, Christopher J. A312
Mcclintock, Dana A175
McClinton, Donald G P27
McClinton, Stephanie P639
McCloskey, Sharon P152
McCloskey, Brian E17
McCloud, Kimball W242
McCloy, Fiona A552
McCloy, Fiona P328
McClung, Brett S. A801
McClung, Linda P119
McClung, Brett S. P562
McClure, Kathy A238
McClure, Matt A390
McClure, Marc A792
McClure, Patricia P170
McClure, Robert P224
McClure, Carolyn P247
McClure, Sammy P421
McClure, Brenda P457
McClure, Dave W5
McCluskey, Erik A318
McCoige, Maureen P149

Mccolgan, Jack A324
McColl, John S. E98
McCollem, Lauren E248
McColley, Dave P305
McCollum, Keith P170
McCollum, Robert P451
McComas, David P517
McComb, Scott G E191
McCombe, Mark S. A130
McCombs, Gillian M. P514
Mcconkey, Linda A865
McConnell, Scott A3
McConnell, Kelly A221
McConnell, Rob A454
McConnell, Pamela A593
McConnell, Patricia M A674
McConnell, Sarah Hlavinka A912
McConnell, Amy P244
McConnell, Donald P. P365
McConnell, John D P385
McConnell, John P. P405
McConnell, Patricia M P444
McConnell, John D. P673
McConville, Cliff A54
McConville, Dan P361
McConville, Jim W287
McCool, Robert A388
McCool, James D. A728
McCool, Rod P331
McCord, Trey A244
McCormack, Steven A522
McCormack, Lori P148
McCormack, Michael P177
Mccormick, Patrick A40
Mccormick, Phyllis A49
McCormick, Denny A175
McCormick, Stanley A244
Mccormick, Tim A244
McCormick, Michael C. A289
McCormick, Terry A693
Mccormick, William A712
McCormick, Robert J. A831
McCormick, Jenna P134
Mccormick, Bob P155
McCormick, Susan P415
Mccormick, Bob P455
Mccormick, Jonathan P572
McCormick, C. Clair P589
McCormick, Timothy P609
McCormick, Peter M (Pete) E86
McCormick, Robert E109
McCormick, Dan E369
Mccorriston, Michael A780
McCorvey, Michelle A331
McCorvey, Michelle E148
McCourt, MaryFrances P627
McCowan, Debra A580
McCowan, Jon P676
McCoy, Pam A115
McCoy, Melanie A195
McCoy, Mark A500
Mccoy, Lyle A528
McCoy, Tim P254
McCoy, Nancy P440
Mccoy, David P653
McCoy, Thomas A. (Tom) W194
McCoy, Mark E237
McCoy, Dean A. E291
Mccracken, Kathy A502
McCrary, Charles D A383
McCrary, Jim P443
McCray, Ronald A593
McCrea, Marshall S. (Mackie) A298
McCrea, Marshall S P294
McCready, Phyllis P390
McCreary, Lynn S A355
McCreary, Sierra P88
Mccreary, Jim P458
McCreary, William P613
McCree, Donald H. (Don) A205
Mccreery, Sean A502
Mccreery, Susan P449
McCreery, Patrick E272
McCreesh, Michael A390

A = AMERICAN BUSINESS
E = EMERGING COMPANIES
P = PRIVATE COMPANIES
W = WORLD BUSINESS

McCright, Flora P64
MCCRINK, GERALD A323
McCrory, Carol P172
McCrory, Martin P627
McCrossen, Ed A199
McCrum, Chris P216
Mccue, Betsy A549
Mccue, Kristie A685
Mccue, Betsy E270
McCulloch, Tina P74
McCullock, Eva P168
McCullough, Mark C. A46
McCullough, Theodore J. (Ted) A383
McCullough, Mark A A438
McCullough, Howell D. (Mac) A440
McCullough, Steven W A468
McCullough, Bruce A. A526
Mccullough, Kevin A772
McCullough, Joann P198
McCullough, Steven W P253
McCullough, Sandra P498
McCullough, Michael P666
McCullough, A. J. W199
McCune, Lorri S P415
Mccune, William P589
McCurdy, Michael W. A149
McCurdy, Chris A323
McCurdy, Lisa A781
Mccurrie, Brad A71
McCurry, Matt A693
McCurry, Michael P330
Mccusker, Joseph A382
McCutcheon, S. Craig A258
McCutcheon, Stewart H. A289
Mcdade, Brian A744
McDaniel, Cara A800
McDaniel, Marvin E. A910
McDaniel, Cindy P160
McDaniel, Brad P162
McDaniel, Kris P204
McDaniel, John P242
McDaniel, Jane P385
Mcdaniel, Traci P613
McDaniel, Anna P642
McDaniel, Chad A. E251
Mcdaniel, Lynn E276
McDaniel, Cara E396
McDaris, Dewayne P276
McDavid, William H. (Bill) A366
McDearis, Kevin E44
Mcdermod, Matthew E144
McDermott, Christopher A16
McDermott, Mark A173
McDermott, Samantha A446
McDermott, Michael P. A521
Mcdermott, John A537
McDermott, John P. A712
McDermott, Jim P52
McDermott, Mary P223
McDermott, Steve P237
McDermott, Meghan P356
McDermott, William R. (Bill) W319
McDermott, Samantha E210
McDermott, Lee E407
McDevitt, Charles B. A395
McDevitt, Mike P571
McDonald, Mark A. A41
McDonald, John D. A41
McDonald, Byron A64
McDonald, Andrew L. (Andy) A219
McDonald, Michael A336
McDonald, David W. A355
McDonald, Bryan D. A414
McDonald, Angus A518
McDonald, Scott A532
McDonald, Tim A728
McDonald, Andy A766
McDonald, Bobbie A782
McDonald, Jody C P135

McDonald, Kris P148
McDonald, Cindy P194
McDonald, Judy P247
McDonald, David P276
McDonald, Angus P293
McDonald, Michael P297
McDonald, Lori P435
McDonald, Clarke P531
McDonald, William A P531
McDonald, Dr Susan P532
McDonald, Terri P554
McDonald, Thomas M. P593
McDonald, Cindy P697
McDonald, Don W347
McDonald, Andrew L. (Andy) E84
McDonald, Bryan D. E195
McDonald, Robert E207
McDonie, Patrick J. (Pat) A787
McDonnell, Joe A161
McDonnell, Michael R. (Mike) A469
McDonnell, Nancy A480
McDonnell, Robert F A872
McDonnell, Cathy P115
McDonnell, Eileen P441
McDonnell, Matthew P474
McDonnell, John F. P616
McDonnell, Robert F P667
McDonough, Thomas A85
McDonough, Karissa A644
McDonough, Robert J. (Bob) A854
McDonough, Scott P38
McDonough, Robert P454
McDonough, Kevin P545
McDonough, Rachele E144
Mcdougal, Patrick A600
McDougal, Bruce A667
McDougal, Bruce P440
Mcdougall, Douglas A22
McDowell, Ronda M. A724
McDowell, Nina A806
Mcdowell, Magnus Mcdowell
    Magnus A865
McDowell, Paul P47
McDowell, Dennis P101
McDowell, Denise P323
McDowell, Nina P569
McDowell, Robert E75
McDowell, Glenn E405
McDuff, Phillip A129
McDunn, David A513
Mceachern, Archie A593
Mcelderry, John P579
McElhenny, John A890

McElhenny, John P684
McElhinney, Paul A. A375
McElligott, Kathleen D. (Kathy) A546
McElligott, Eileen P338
McElmurry, Julie A594
McElroy, Paul P260
McElroy, Richard P434
McElroy, Wayne P577
Mcelveen, Edward A332
Mcelveen, Beth A792
McElwee, Dave A300
McElya, James S P305
McElyea, Dawn P133
McEniry, James A54
McEntee, Charles E183
McEvoy, Ashley A. A476
McEvoy, John R. A683
McEvoy, Robert A703
Mcevoy, Jim A844
McEvoy, John R. E341
Mcevoy, Jim E412
McEwan, Ross W312
McFadden, David P433
McFaddin, Dena P579
McFall, Thomas G. (Tom) A609
McFall, Keith P188
McFarlan, Susan A105
McFarland, Joseph M. (Joe) A640
McFarland, Casey P688
McFarland, Barry E322
McFarlane, John W52

McFarlane, John W54
McFarlane, James G. E83
Mcfarlin, Willie A814
McFarlin, Dean P169
Mcfarlin, Willie P616
McFarlin, Diane H. P642
McFarling, Harry M. P428
McFatter, Dan P346
McGann, Randy A115
McGann, Tom P680
Mcgarey, Jennifer A602
McGarrity, Andy P256
McGarry, Michael H. A664
McGarry, Steven J. A746
McGarry, John F. (Jack) A863
McGarvey, John A115
Mcgarvey, Lisa A784
McGarvey, Megan P97
Mcgarvie, Blythe A872
McGarvin, Gary A268
McGary, Skip A826
McGaughey, Kathy A168
McGaw, Steve A84
McGeary, Roderick A200
McGee, Susan A223
McGee, Richard K. A657
McGee, Callery A691
McGee, Karen A705
McGee, Genemarie A736
McGee, Thomas P167
McGee, Genemarie A492
McGee, John P P575
Mcgee, Brian E1
McGee, Karen E352
McGettrick, Mark F. A275
McGettrick, Sara P578
McGhee, Craig P118
Mcgill, Dean A56
McGill, Tom A142
Mcgill, Steve A149
McGill, Donald A332
McGill, Bradley A478
McGill, Daniel K. (Dan) A645
McGill, Brian P51
McGill, Lisa E166
McGill, William H. E259
McGill, William Brett E259
McGill, Daniel K. (Dan) E329
McGinley, Paula A406
McGinn, John P507
McGinn, Meghan P530
McGinnis, John T A525
McGinnis, Tim A725
Mcginnis, Vikki A795
McGinnis, David A814
McGinnis, Jeffrey S. (Jeff) A851
McGinnis, Mike P42
McGinnis, David P616
McGinty, Mark A591
McGinty, Daniel P26
McGinty-polito, Janice A461
McGivney, Mark C. A532
McGlynn, Brian E426
McGlenon, Andrew A865
Mcglynn, Patrick A533
McGlynn, Michael A907
McGlynn, Michael P696
McGoff, Sandra P461
McGoldrick, Margaret M. (Meg) P2
McGonagill, Michael P25
McGonigle, James E140
McGookey, James E A208
McGough, Thomas M. (Tom) A230
McGough, W. Thomas (Tom) A859
Mcgough, Marlon P596
McGough, W. Thomas (Tom) P652
McGovern, Lawrence D. A414
McGovern, Cynthia A513
McGovern, Shawn A611
McGovern, Lawrence D. E194
McGowan, Patrick A152
McGowan, David A342
McGowan, Veronica A541
McGowan, Chris A626
McGowan, Marion A. P588

McGowan, Tim P606
McGowan, Patrick E48
McGowan, Thomas K. E234
McGowan, Veronica E266
McGowan, Mike E343
McGowen, Lonnie A738
Mcgrade, Nancy E432
McGrail, Martin P41
McGranaghan, Mark F. P179
McGranahan, Devin B A355
McGrath, Marlene A3
McGrath, Helen A85
McGrath, Garth A178
McGrath, Robert L. (Bob) A357
McGrath, Kathy A546
Mcgrath, Mark A591
McGrath, Elizabeth A635
McGrath, Mike A817
McGrath, George P2
McGrath, Michael P25
McGrath, Robert P211
McGrath, Elizabeth P419
McGraw, Deirdre D. A56
Mcgraw, Ryan A165
McGraw, E. Robinson (Robin) A704
McGraw, Donald F. (Don) A805
McGraw, Virginia P110
Mcgraw, Kari P307
McGraw, E. Robinson (Robin) E350
McGregor, Marcus A105
McGregor, Gaylyn A223
Mcgregor, Mark E A402
McGregor, Sharon A612
McGregor, Robert P118
McGregor, A. Douglas W310
McGrew, Robert D P552
McGrory, Lorna P498
McGrover, Michael A231
McGruder, Jill T. A890
McGruder, Jill T. P684
McGuckin, Sean W50
McGuckin, John W258
McGuff, Greg A508
McGuffey, Steve P199
McGuffin, Colleen A165
McGuigan, Gary A74
McGuigan, Charles C. (Charlie) A497
McGuigan, Peter S A648
McGuinness, Richard A723
McGuire, Jim A85
McGuire, Toretha A131
McGuire, Lake A221
McGuire, Michael A250
McGuire, Mark A287
Mcguire, David A635
Mcguire, Don A685
McGuire, Jim A728
McGuire, Tom A784
Mcguire, Paul A870
Mcguire, David A902
McGuire, Mark P174
McGuire, Anne L. P406
Mcguire, David P419
McGuire, Laura P477
McGuire, Jeremy R. P554
Mcguire, David P693
Mcguire, Brendan E424
McGuirk, Ronald C P644
McGurk, Monica A834
McGurk, Kevin J P68
McGurk, William J. (Bill) E414
McGurn, David A370
McHale, James E P672
McHargue, Lester A461
McHenry, David P135
McHenry, Sharon P573
McHugh, Philip R. A332
McHugh, Joe A379
Mchugh, Kimberly A478
Mchugh, Mark A693
McHugh, Philip A823
McHugh, Lawrence D P139
McHugh, Lawrence P139
McHutchison, John G. A386
Mcilwain, Pinckney P110

McInelly, Chelsie P176
McInerney, Thomas J. (Tom) A382
McInerney, Joseph A599
McInerney, Ryan A874
McInerney, Patrick S. P507
McInnes, Dean P676
McInnis, Joanne A864
McIntosh, John L. A618
McIntosh, Rebecca P619
McIntosh, Keith P653
McIntosh, Stephen W305
McIntosh, Stephen W306
Mcintyre, Dan A3
McIntyre, Mary A597
Mcintyre, Patrick A774
McIntyre, John T A782
McIntyre, Dr Levy P83
Mcjunkin, Stacey A802
Mcjunkin, Stacey P562
McKasson, Craig S. E337
McKay, Ryan A101
McKay, Erik A221
McKay, John D. A240
McKay, Molly A302
McKay, Scott J. A382
McKay, Susan A703
McKay, David I. (Dave) W310
McKay, Molly E128
McKay, Edward H. E368
McKeag, Bryan R. A412
McKeag, Bryan R. E192
McKeand, Kevin A85
McKee, Lynn B. A73
Mckee, John A221
McKee, Michael A371
McKee, Daniel J A765
McKee, Wayne P529
McKee, Daniel J P540
McKee, Michael V. (Mike) P642
McKee, Marcy E290
McKee, Michael D. E348
McKeehan, Effie P578
Mckellar-Jones, Kearline P230
McKelvy, Michael C. (Mike) A385
McKelvy, Michael C. (Mike) P212
McKemie, Gordon A133
McKemie, Ken P172
McKenna, Judith A878
McKenna, Margaret A. P71
McKenna, Sheila O P86
McKenna, Trent P133
McKenna, Quinn L. P538
McKenna, Bertine P590
McKenna, Tom P683
McKenna, Frank J. W75
McKenna, Frank J. W370
McKenney, Josh A350
McKenney, Richard P. (Rick) A863
McKenney, Thomas J. E147
McKenney, Josh E157
McKenney, Michael J. E229
Mckenzie, Renee A78
McKenzie, Paul A129
McKenzie, Isabelle A142
McKenzie, Barbara A. (Barb) A668
McKenzie, Robin A697
McKenzie, A Kirk A764
McKenzie, Maryjo P81
McKenzie, Robin P454
McKenzie, A Kirk P540
McKenzie, Jonathan W176
McKenzie, William G. E268
McKeon, Brian M. A140
Mckeon, Michael A724
McKeon, Brian P. E213
McKeown, Colleen A620
McKeown, Ann M. A722
McKeown, Brona W103
Mckernan, Chris A340
Mckernan, Chris E151
McKernon, Bryan E A156
Mckewen, Robert A795
McKibben, Sheryl A508
McKibbin, Karen S. A596
Mckie, Vicki A329

McKiernan, Anthony A542
McKim, Anoopa A332
McKim, Tony C. A338
McKinley, Gordon A221
McKinley, David C. (Dave) A727
McKinley, Brian P243
McKinley, Ernie P639
McKinney, Greg A107
McKinney, David E A196
McKinney, James J. A487
McKinney, Rex D. A737
McKinney, Sue A828
McKinney, Ivy A912
Mckinney, Roderick P167
Mckinney, Mark P310
McKinney, James P370
McKinney, Marcus P472
McKinney, Becky P538
McKinney, Lisa H P639
McKinney, Kim P672
McKinney, Greg E34
McKinney, Rex D. E367
McKinnon, Lee A737
McKinnon, Howard P198
McKinnon, Lee E367
Mckissick, Michelle P365
McKittrick, Stacy P68
McKnight, Brandon A770
McKnight, Jodi A886
McKnight, Jodi E433
McKoy, Margot A137
Mclachlan, Debora P379
McLamb, Winona P218
McLamb, Michael H. (Mike) E259
McLandon, Jerrylane P260
Mclaren, Gregory E146
Mclaren, Greg E146
McLaughlin, Robert M. (Bob) A25
McLaughlin, Jim A73
Mclaughlin, Walter A110
McLaughlin, Robert A152
McLaughlin, Linda A152
Mclaughlin, Lynn A223
Mclaughlin, Carl A A244
McLaughlin, Sean J. A306
McLaughlin, R A334
McLaughlin, Eddy A422
McLaughlin, Edward (Ed) A537
McLaughlin, David W. A585
Mclaughlin, Patrick A647
Mclaughlin, Sean A676
Mclaughlin, Betsy A710
McLaughlin, John J. A716
McLaughlin, Neal T. A839
McLaughlin, Kathleen A878
McLaughlin, Robert M. (Bob) P15
McLaughlin, Edward W. P143
McLaughlin, Eddy P239
McLaughlin, Gary P346
McLaughlin, Rob P366
McLaughlin, David W. P377
McLaughlin, Michael P227
McLaughlin, William M. (Bill) E26
Mclaughlin, Walter E37
McLaughlin, Robert E48
McLaughlin, Linda E48
McLaughlin, Neal T. E409
McLean, James A693
McLean, Graham A. A772
McLean, Scott J. A919
McLean, Sally P192
McLean, William H. (Will) P397
McLean, Dan P501
McLean, David P662
McLean, David W395
McLean, Colin E107
McLean, Tim E226
McLean, Emmett E. E268
McLeland, Allan H. A750
Mclelland, Alistair A20
McLemore, James R A562
McLendon, Rebecca A327
McLendon, Jenna P685
McLennan, Robert P345
Mcleod, Martha A58

McLeod, David G. A395
Mcleod, Doug A434
McLeod, Heidi P536
McLoone, Brian A767
McLoughlin, Karen A217
McMackin, Thomas (Tom) E383
McMahon, John A77
McMahon, Richard C A120
McMahon, Brian A648
McMahon, Johnathan A785
McMahon, Scott A814
Mcmahon, David A864
McMahon, Molly A865
Mcmahon, Heidi Kahly P210
Mcmahon, Diane P483
McMahon, Scott P616
McMahon, Daniel K. E188
McMahon, John E196
McMahon, William B. E296
McMahon, B. Ian E363
McMahon, Vincent K. (Vince) E444
McMahon, Stephanie E445
McMahon, Linda E445
McMains, Reed A813
McMains, Reed P608
McManamon, Peter E68
McMannen, Julie A272
Mcmannus, Connie A308
McManus, Paul A115
Mcmanus, Laura A300
McManus, Jeannie A542
McManus, John M. A558
McManus, David A657
McManus, Gary P26
McManus, Brian M P94
McManus, John P154
McManus, Jeannie E267
Mcmartin, Bill A449
McMasters, Michael P. (Mike) E74
McMenamin, William V A577
McMichael, Sharon A115
McMichael, Guy P697
McMillan, Darren A449
McMillan, Marilyn A. A585
McMillan, Lee P1
McMillan, Nancy P161
McMillan, Michael P232
McMillan, Therese P338
McMillan, Marilyn A. P377
McMillan, James P601
McMillan, David J. E12
McMillan, Edward L. E31
Mcmillen, Ruth Ann A902
McMillen, Steve P625
Mcmillen, Ruth Ann P693
McMillian, Amanda M. E436
McMillin, Nicole P231
McMillon, C. Douglas (Doug) A878
McMinimee, Dan P261
McMonigle, Andy A166
McMorrow, William J. E231
McMullen, Michael R. (Mike) A22
McMullen, Brad A136
McMullen, Eric R A336
McMullen, W. Rodney A495
Mcmullen, Elizabeth P152
McMullen, Eric R P194
McMullen, J Patrick P427
McMullen, Michael J P543
Mcmullen, Greg E407
McMurray, Kurston A591
McMurray, Michael C. A627
McMurray, Eric P25
Mcmurtry, Sev A327
McNab, Paul A199
McNac, Loretta P569
McNally, Brian P. W303
McNamara, Stephen A85
McNamara, Daniel R. (Dan) A456
McNamara, Michael E. (Mike) A788
McNamara, Kevin A835
McNamara, Michael T P294
McNamara, Ed P439
McNamara, Marilyn P516
McNamara, Julia M. P698

McNamara, Julia M. P699
McNamara, Kyle W50
McNamara, Michael M. (Mike) W151
McNamara, Brian W158
McNamee, Brian M. A61
McNamee, Sean A327
Mcnamee, Sean S A327
McNamee, Mark G. P669
McNamee, Paul W98
Mcnamee, Charles E276
McNaney, Michael P454
McNary, Kelli A817
McNeal, Gwyn E139
Mcneil, Kurt A379
McNeil, Caroline A764
McNeil, Chris E. P489
McNeil, Caroline P540
McNeil, Kathy P646
McNeill, Gale A807
McNeill, Gale P574
McNern, Carol P188
McNey, Jim P387
Mcnichols, William A763
McNiel, Jim E300
Mcniff, Mike A266
McNiff, Mike A266
McNulty, Tim P96
McNulty, Mary Ann P285
McNutt, Pamela G. P336
Mcnutt, Robert P618
McParland, Jeffrey J. (Jeff) A787
McPartland, James E. (Bo) A822
McPeak, Blaine E. P689
McPeek, Brian P596
McPhail, Alastair A434
McPhaill, Kevin J. A740
McPhaill, Kevin J. E369
McPhedran, James W50
McPhee, Debra M. P200
McPhee, Michael E P425
McPhee, Marcus W P425
McPhee, Marcus P425
McPherson, Robert A122
Mcpherson, Julie A140
McPherson, Scott E. A237
Mcpherson, Kevin J A327
McPherson, Amy C. A530
McPherson, Heather A784
McPherson, Annamarie P575
McPherson, Kevin E260
McQuade, Daniel P. A16
McQueen, Jason A98
McQueen, Todd P604
McQueen, Jason E33
McQuilkin, Scott A. E222
McQuillan, Barbara (Barb) P518
McQuillan, Kevin E288
McQuillon, Doyle P183
McRae, Lawrence D. (Larry) A238
Mcrae, Ryan A530
Mcrae, Angus A785
McRae, Mark P478
McRaith, William (Bill) A682
McReynolds, John W. A297
McRitchie, John P318
McRobbie, Michael A. P627
McRobbie, Ian M. E216
McRoberts, Michael J. A717
McRoy, Cynthia P110
McRoy, Lynn P417
McShane, Joseph M. P200
McShane, Gerald J P411
McShea, Sean F. W347
McSheffrey, James A402
McSheffrey, Aidan P478
McSherry, Bill A136
McSteen, Jeffrey A105
Mcsteen, Harry A339
Mcsteen, Harry E150
McSzkowski, Marie E257
McTaggart, Alan P539
McTague, Teresa Q. A19
McTarsney-Horne, Sheila A272
McTier, Charles H A509

A = AMERICAN BUSINESS		
E = EMERGING COMPANIES		
P = PRIVATE COMPANIES		
W = WORLD BUSINESS		

McTier, Charles H P288
McTiernan, James A105
McTpavish, Julie A602
McVeigh, Scott A738
McVeigh, Vincent E1
McVey, Mary Jo P210
McVey, Richard M. (Rick) E260
McWatters, Denise C. A423
McWay, Michael J. P318
McWethy, Brett P566
McWherter, Juliana P503
McWhinney, Robert A472
McWhorter, Larry A222
McWhorter, Laura A801
McWhorter, Haden P439
McWhorter, Laura P562
McWilliams, Jelena A332
McWilliams, Stephen A706
McWilliams, Vicki D. A901
McWilliams, Ben P435
Mcwilliams, Ethan P653
McWilliams, Megan P664
McWilliams, Stephen E353
Meabon, David P613
Meacham, Jacky P561
Mead, John A56
Mead, David L. A645
Mead, Arthur F P149
Mead, David L. E329
Meade, Michael A557
Meador, David E. (Dave) A280
Meadows, Karen C A162
Meadows, Ida A238
Meadows, Perry A372
Meadows, Randy A493
Meadows, April A659
Meadows, Darryl A844
Meadows, Cheryl P129
Meadows, William W. (Bill) P152
Meadows, Perry P208
Meadows, Rick W81
Meadows, Darryl E412
Meads, David A200
Meakins, Ian W148
Meakins, Ian K. W303
Mealer-Burke, Vicki A685
Means, Janet P78
Means, William L. E111
Meany, Kathleen P338
Mears, Jim A570
Mears, Dee P13
Mears, Russell E172
Measel, Kevin A521
Measel, Matthew P368
Mecca, Ray P276
Mechaley, Robert G. E328
Mecham, Jim A173
Mecham, Rex P46
Mechlin, Ana P632
Mecke, Stephen C. E384
Mecklenburg, Gary A119
Mecklenburg, John R P550
Meckler, Roy P398
Medbery, Alison A96
Medearis, Alan A489
Medellin, Rich P430
Meden, Scott A. A596
Medenis, Jim A85
Mederos, Ana P291
Medford, Jeffrey S. A561
Medford, Jeffrey S. E278
Mediavilla, Mark A173
Medina, Mark A920
Medina, Denise P598
Medline, Michael B. W137
Medovic, Tom A886
Medovic, Tom E433
Medrano, Randolph A105
Medvedev, Alexander I. W289

Mee, David G. A439
Meehan, Terry A247
Meehan, Sean A406
Meehan, Connie A500
Meehan, Mary J. P494
Meehan, Terry E103
Meehan, Connie E237
Meehling, Bob A173
Meek, Victor A246
Meek, Thomas J. E281
Meeker, Anthony E38
Meeks, Doana A614
Meeks, Charles C. (Chuck) E230
Meeks, Chuck E230
Meelberg, Andrew A523
Meer, Vincent Van Der A131
Meers, Trey A904
Meers, Trey E442
Mees, Matthew A78
Meeteren, Jedd Van A920
Mefford, Jeffrey A561
Mefford, Jeffrey E278
Megally, Michael P381
Megalou, Christos John W288
Megargee, Scott R. A805
Megias, Michael A204
Megibben, John P334
Meglio, Ron A871
Meh, Césaire W47
Mehaffey, Elizabeth P58
Mehler, Phillip S. P160
Mehmood, Bilal E229
Mehnert, Dana A. A405
Meholic, Anthony A806
Mehra, Asit A619
Mehra, Pankaj A892
Mehra, Arpana A912
Mehran, Alexander R. (Alex) A324
Mehringer, Melinda A539
Mehrle, David A441
Mehrotra, Manu A218
Mehrotra, Sanjay A559
Mehrotra, Sharad W360
Mehrtens, Anne E208
Mehta, Sachin A56
Mehta, Rajeev (Raj) A217
Mehta, Manan A599
Mehta, Sanjay A685
Mehta, Preeti P424
Mehta, Shreeketa M P446
Mehta, Darshan P590
Mehta, Tarak W4
Meidt, Greg A187
Meidt, Greg E71
Meier, Jessica A340
Meier, Richard A. (Randy) A626
Meier, Jessica E151
Meighan, Dori P162
Meignié, Yves W387
Meijers, Neville A685
Meikle, Scott A501
Meiklejohn, Mark J. A149
Meilahn, Jamie A3
Meilahn, Jill R P309
Meinert, Todd A558
Meinhardt, Erika A328
Meiresonne, Mike P151
Meister, Doris P. A522
Meister, Rudi von W402
Meister, Adam E207
Meixner, Willi W331
Meiyun, Zhou W332
Mejia, Maria F. A485
Mejuto, Claudia P415
Mejzak, Richard A131
Mekesa, Kathleen A332
Mekler, Mark K A693
Melandri, Claudio W43
Melanson, Steven A408
Melby, Tom E355
Melchior, Eric L P208
Mele, Jennifer P38
Meleis, Afaf I. A812
Meleis, Afaf I. P607
Melendez, Thelma P433

Melendez, Eduardo P549
Melendreras, Ed A300
Meletiou, Andreas W340
Melfi, Mitch H. A171
Melfi, Joe A683
Melfi, Mitch H. P100
Melfi, Albert J. (Al) E108
Melia, Mark P101
Melichar, Jamie P282
Melillo, Alfred A807
Melillo, Alfred P574
Melim, Marylene A676
Melina, Tom A872
Meline, David W. A61
Melini, Jeffrey N P570
Mella, Chas A244
Mella, Joe A390
Mellado, Santiago P136
Mellander, Carl W360
Melleky, Neil A555
Mellen, Eric E. E170
Mellencamp, Charlene P257
Meller, Craig W26
Mellet, Claudia A408
Mellett, Paul J. E122
Melletz, Steven A342
Mello, Kevin A535
Mello, Kevin P312
Melloh, Heather A56
Melman, Linda A619
Melmed, Shlomo P102
Melnick, Paul E77
Melnick, Jackie E276
Melnyczenko, Andrew P66
Melnyk, Raymond A140
Melotte, Hans A763
Meloy, Mark J. A340
Meloy, Mattthew J. (Matt) A787
Meloy, Mark J. E151
Melrose, Bob W251
Melsen, Gregory J. (Greg) E42
Melshenker, George P441
Melson, Benjamin (Ben) P560
Melton, Stephen A. A57
Melton, Farryn A147
Melton, Steve A A190
Melton, Debbie P410
Melton, Laurie P630
Melton, Stephen A. E16
Meltzer, Neil M P290
Meltzer, Neil P505
Melville, Traci A796
Melville, Laurie P653
Melvin, Vincent P. (Vin) A77
Memis, Adnan W377
Men, Simon A593
Mena, Fernando V P204
Menard, Yvonne P279
Menard, Satya-Christophe W334
Menchaca, Ricardo A438
Menchaca, Hector P670
Mendelsohn, Karen R. A563
Mendelsohn, D. Eric E292
Mendelson, Robert P587
Mendelson, Victor H. E193
Mendelson, Eric A. E193
Mendelson, Laurans A. E193
Mendenhall, Tom A691
Mendenhall, Amy A838
Mendenhall, Dave A886
Mendenhall, Robert W P685
Mendenhall, Dave E433
Menders, Chuck P110
Mendes, Mark S A73
Mendes, Rhys R. W47
Mendez, Roberto D. (Bobby) A289
Mendez, Greg A446
Mendez, Carlos A555
Mendez, Martiza A662
Mendez, Alex P355
Mendez, Lincoln S P510
Mendez, Greg E210
Mendez, W. Rand E281
Mendez-Cartaya, Administrativ I P603
Mendicino, Thomas P302

Mendieta, Adrian A333
Mendillo, Jane P228
Mendiratta, Abhishek P228
Mendis, Nancy A818
Mendis, Paul P369
Mendonca, Hubert A835
Mendoza, Tish A17
Mendoza, Edy A175
Mendoza, Roberto A525
Mendoza, Elizabeth A P404
Menear, Craig A. A426
Menelly, Denise M. A201
Menendez, Oscar A201
Menez, Michael P493
Menezes, Eduardo F. A514
Menezes, Ivan M A786
Menezes, Ivan M. W128
Meng, Francis L Boon A906
Meng, Amanda P666
Mengebier, David G. A210
Mengel, Lee P512
Menges, Kathrin W168
Menke, Julie A565
Menken, Dennis A668
Menne, Simone W124
Menneto, Steven D. A661
Mennihan, Peter A838
Menning, Jeremy A441
Menon, Anil A199
Menon, Geeta A585
Menon, Jyoti A872
Menon, Akash K P99
Menon, Geeta P377
Menon, Satish E368
Mensack, Andrew A204
Mensah, Paul A648
Menschik, Thomas A648
Mense, D. Craig A211
Mensing, Stan J A382
Mentis, Angela W251
Mento, Andrew A568
Mentzer, Patrick A204
Mentzer, Kevin P602
Menzel, Susan L. (Sue) A213
Menzel, David B. (Dave) E117
Meo, Francesco De W154
Meoli, Marc A724
Meotti, Tom A62
Meppiel, Bob P337
Mercado, Kenneth M. A181
Merced, Alexis P413
Mercer, Michelle A541
Mercer, Megan A838
Mercer, Karen P2
Mercer, Dale P26
Mercer, John E117
Mercer, Michelle E266
Merchant, Manisha K. A97
Merchant, Tracey P2
Merchant, Manisha K. E32
Mercier, Dianne M. A644
Mercier, Bruno R. W346
Mercogliano, Kathleen P446
Merdian, Charles E244
Meredith, Ian A144
Meredith, Eric A659
Meredith, Bobbie A835
Meredith, Michael A838
Merejo, Robert P278
Mereness, Scott T. E240
Merfeld, Janet P331
Mergeay, Maurice E288
Mergelmeyer, Gene E. A83
Mergenthaler, Frank A464
Mergin, Murat W377
Mergudich, Ivan A73
Mergy, John P162
Merilli, Philip A597
Merino, John A327
Merkadeau, Stuart L. E165
Merkel, Deborah A481
Merkel, Christophe A593
Merkel, Greg P309
Merkel, Frederick P634
Merkel, B.G. W184

Merkens, Hermann J. W2
Merkl, Laura P357
Merkle, Thomas A332
Merkle, Claudia J. E304
Merkley, Brendon P559
Merkow, David P619
Merle, Denise M. A896
Merling, Laura A84
Merlino, John A508
Merlino, Darryl P284
Merlis, Larry P618
Merlo, Matt A180
Merlo, Larry J. A250
Merlo, Michael A741
Merlo, Michael E370
Merola, Jason P360
Merredith, Eric P101
Merrell, Keaton E432
Merrick, Caren E178
Merril, Donald A. E421
Merrill, Allen A478
Merrill, Ray P36
Merrill, Rick W P141
Merrill, Mike P144
Merriman, Tom A564
Merritt, Lynn A593
Merritt, Chip A721
Merritt, Tim A913
Merritt, Norman A919
Merritt, Jill P41
Merritt, Edee P594
Merritt, William J. E222
Mersky, Seth M. W277
Merten, Joseph (J.) A211
Mertens, George A252
Mertens, George P150
Mertens, Blake A. P579
Mertes, Jim E174
Mertz, Valerie A28
Mertz, Valerie P17
Mertz, Len P497
Merwe, Martin Van Der A235
Meryash, Michael P505
Merz, Stefan E. A265
Mesa, Susan P258
Mesaros, Cindy E447
Mescon, Jed P226
Mesdag, T. Willem (Will) E123
Meshechek, Gene A131
Meskiewicz, Paul A105
Mesnik, Denyse E40
Mesquita, Jorge S. A476
Messer, Angela M. (Angie) A140
Messer, Jason P305
Messer, Rick P480
Messerich, John P604
Messett, Todd P282
Messina, Debbie A583
Messina, Stacy P306
Messina, Daniel J P461
Messina, Carlo W189
Messman, Cathy P676
Messmann, Boyd A759
Messmann, Boyd P520
Messmer, Harold M. A711
Messmer, Heather P125
Messner, Barbara P546
Mestas, Terri A16
Mester, Loretta J. A325
Mestrallet, Gérard W143
Mestrallet, Gérard W343
Mestrio, Karen De E347
Metallic, John A729
Metayer, Sylvia W334
Metcalf, Kim A175
Metcalf, Sue A289
Metcalf, Rob A511
Metcalf, Carole P238
Metcalfe, Gavin A872
Metcalfe, Tom A884
Metcalfe, Bonnie A902
Metcalfe, Jude C. P167
Metcalfe, Bonnie P692
Meter, Rex Van P250
Metheny, Mike A155

Metivier, Elizabeth P666
Metoyer, Regan P30
Metre, Chris Van P6
Metrose, Laurie A175
Metsger, Gary E. A742
Metsger, Gary E. E372
Mettel, Kenneth A851
Mettler, Miles P345
Mettling, Bruno W278
Metts, Jimmy B A22
Metts, Jimmy B P13
Metz, John A151
Metz, Gregory A366
Metz, Randy A369
Metz, Karen A559
Metz, Don P42
Metz, John P575
Metz, Gunnar W60
Metz, John E48
Metzger, William L. A150
Metzger, John A461
Metzger, Thomas M. (Tom) A573
Metzger, Doug A855
Metzger, Mark P32
Metzinger, Adam A105
Metzler, Thomas A555
Metzler, George A599
Metzloff, Kurt A246
Meuchner, Gerard A727
Meulder, Jan De W41
Meunier, Tom E432
Meurer, Paul M. E348
Meury, William (Bill) W22
Meves, Scott C. A883
Mexia, Ant--nio Lu-s Guerra
   Nunes W134
Meyaard, Daniel E213
Meyer, Barry A10
Meyer, Jim A25
Meyer, Janis A129
Meyer, Eric A133
Meyer, Jeffrey A175
Meyer, Darren A180
Meyer, John A223
Meyer, David A252
Meyer, Erling A305
Meyer, Kevin S A314
Meyer, Michele S. A377
Meyer, David A394
Meyer, Dan A710
Meyer, James E. (Jim) A745
Meyer, Robert A868
Meyer, Kenneth (Ken) A899
Meyer, Kenny A899
Meyer, Jim P15
Meyer, Daniel P51
Meyer, Dave P130
Meyer, David P150
Meyer, Erling P185
Meyer, Kevin S P190
Meyer, Mark P217
Meyer, Gary A P257
Meyer, Christian F P266
Meyer, Christopher P346
Meyer, Mark T P439
Meyer, Sarah P659
Meyer, Kenneth (Ken) P690
Meyer, Kenny P690
Meyer, Hans Ola W36
Meyer, Karl E129
Meyer, W. Stan E180
Meyer, Maurice E396
Meyer, Maria E399
Meyer-Davis, Pamela P176
Meyercord, F. Duffield (Duff) A639
Meyercord, F. Duffield (Duff) E326
Meyerrose, Sarah L A364
Meyers, Bill A457
Meyers, Lynn A807
Meyers, Bill A819
Meyers, Tony W P38
Meyers, Nancy P109
Meyers, Dorothea P332
Meyers, Lynn P574
Meyers, Mike E171

Meyerson, Bernard A460
Meyerson, Steve P21
Meynard, Craig A261
Meyrowitz, Carol M. A818
Meyyappan, Chandra A767
Mezeul, Patricia A359
Mezger, Jeffrey T. (Jeff) A484
Mffiorilli, Matt A120
Mha, Jennifer A802
Mha, Jennifer P562
Mhatre, Nitin J. A883
Miagro, Gabriela A909
Mialaret, David A163
Miale, Mark A759
Miano, John A165
Micale, Paul P462
Micali, Enzo A817
Micallef, Frank A903
Micciche, Gaetano W189
Micek, Tomasz A408
Miceli, Matilda P587
Miceli, Charles P614
Micetic, Thomas A529
Michael, Margulis A56
Michael, Marroy A163
Michael, Jonathan E. A710
Michael, Amanya P251
Michael, Kelly P331
Michaelis, Dennis P444
Michaels, Paul A241
Michaels, Charles A390
Michaels, Rich A599
Michaels, Judy P252
Michaelson, DK P170
Michaelson, Dr Steve P598
Michalak, Michael H. A221
Michalerya, William P286
Michales, Kevin A683
Michaleski, Katie A706
Michaleski, Katie E353
Michalik, Christian P. A885
Michalopoulos, Georgios V. W24
Michalski, Gene P692
Michalsky, Bryan P271
Michas, Alexis P. A142
Michaud, Tracie A382
Michaud, Thomas B. (Tom) A771
Michaud, Christopher P501
Michaud, Peter L. P507
Michel, Todd A A208
Michel, Euclid P89
Michel, Howard E. P586
Michele, Barnett A195
Micheletti, Andrew A94
Micheletti, Andrew J. A95
Micheletti, Andrew P53
Micheletti, Andrew J. E28
Michelle, Martin E47
Michels, David P P131
Michels, Becky P248
Michels, Hartwig W55
Michels, Douglas A. E318
Michelucci, Aaron J P65
Michitsch, Sharon A583
Micinski, Gary P254
Mick, Darla Mick Darla A221
Mickelson, Sharon A261
Mickey, Aileen P275
Micklewright, Scott E276
Mickus, Steven P329
Middendorf, Tom P580
Middlebrooks, Dan C. A787
Middleton, Alan P382
Middleton, Debra P613
Middleton, Mike P647
Middleton, Seth E191
Midgett, Alex P183
Midgley, Clare P567
Midkiff, Scott F. P669
Midler, Laurence H. A172
Midlo, Luke P535
Midteide, Thomas W129
Midyett, Ron P41
Miebach, Michael A537
Miedema, Susan A328

Miedema, Andrew A549
Miedema, Andrew E270
Mielak, Gary P176
Miele, Laura A292
Miels, Luke W35
Miels, Luke A158
Mielsch, Christian W302
Mier, Scott A541
Mier, Scott E266
Mieszczanski, Chris A818
Miglani, Nalin E138
Migliore, Michael A746
Migliori, Richard A855
Migliozzi, John A553
Migliozzi, John E272
Mignagna, Gary P660
Mignemi, Caryn A49
Mignini, Luca A161
Mignot, Anna A133
Migoya, Carlos A. P446
Miguel, Josu Jon Imaz San W300
Mihaljcic, Jennifer A25
Mihelich, Bob A173
Mihran, Robin P517
Mijares, Al P408
Mika, Teresa P353
Mikells, Kathryn A. W128
Mikels, Lawrence A493
Mikesell, Kelly A744
Miketa, George A829
Mikkilineni, Krishna A429
Mikl, Mark E133
Miklaszewski, Elana P60
Mikoshiba, Toshiaki W172
Miks, Wai A677
Miksch, Ronnie A244
Milam, Sabrina P664
Milam, Hof P673
Milam, Steve W121
Milando, Tony A915
Milanes, Doug A254
Milani, Lorenzo W3
Milby, Ron A397
Milby, Ron P221
Milcoff, Joe A327
Mildner, Martin W280
Milefchik, Edward F. A541
Milefchik, Edward F. E266
Milem, Anne A746
Miles, Kevin A105
Miles, Mark W. A125
Miles, John A649
Miles, Christopher A835
Miles, Steven P24
Miles, Larry P149
Miles, John P192
Miles, Amy E. P455
Miles, Samantha P601
Miles, Thomas J. P610
Miles, Keith P648
Miles, Larry K. E170
Miles, Patrick (Pat) E310
Miletti, John A828
Milewski, Frank Null A820
Milford, Gregory A109
Milford, Gregory E36
Milhiser, Jim P479
Miliband, David P251
Milina, Tracy A53
Militello, Mary Catherine E135
Mill, Jim A720
Mill, Jack De P450
Mill, Georgia P466
Mill, Jim E362
Millane, Martin B. A159
Millard, Robert B. P313
Millard, Jayne P629
Millard, Suzanne Turtle P629
Millburn, Tom E146
Miller, Rosa M A3
Miller, Paul A15
Miller, Virgil A19
Miller, Chris A27
Miller, Melisa A. A32
Miller, Steve A34

| A = AMERICAN BUSINESS |
| E = EMERGING COMPANIES |
| P = PRIVATE COMPANIES |
| W = WORLD BUSINESS |

Miller, Matthew A56
Miller, Jason A56
Miller, Barbara A59
Miller, Judy A85
Miller, Cheryl A88
Miller, Maryann G A93
Miller, Bill A98
Miller, Craig A110
Miller, Guy A120
Miller, Grace A136
Miller, Gregory A157
Miller, John A165
Miller, Sherry A165
Miller, Debbie A175
Miller, Jacqueline A175
Miller, Terrica A180
Miller, Lisa A185
Miller, Todd A185
Miller, Kip A187
Miller, Kenneth A196
Miller, James O A208
Miller, Margaret A219
Miller, David A221
Miller, Christopher M. (Chris) A237
Miller, Russ A240
Miller, Barry A241
Miller, Michael A246
Miller, Ashlie A250
Miller, Jeffrey D. A276
Miller, Rob A282
Miller, Deb A295
Miller, Sara A304
Miller, Evelyn A313
Miller, Charles S. A318
Miller, Donald J A327
Miller, Grant A328
Miller, James B. A331
Miller, Kevin A338
Miller, David W. A348
Miller, Ty A366
Miller, Lynn A372
Miller, Jamie S. A375
Miller, Heidi A377
Miller, James H A383
Miller, Steve A390
Miller, Jeffrey A. (Jeff) A398
Miller, Chad A408
Miller, Ashlee A420
Miller, Deloris A422
Miller, Archie A436
Miller, Robert A461
Miller, Timothy A470
Miller, Gragg A472
Miller, Ken A482
Miller, Brian A493
Miller, Stuart A. A508
Miller, Linda A530
Miller, Greg A533
MILLER, VALERIE A537
Miller, David A539
Miller, Dave A549
Miller, Stephanie A555
Miller, Lorraine A562
Miller, Michael A589
Miller, Ann A593
Miller, Cassandra A599
Miller, David A607
Miller, Sara L. A614
Miller, Kevin A654
Miller, Craig A659
Miller, Linda A665
Miller, Craig A667
Miller, John M A685
Miller, William A685
Miller, Brian A693
Miller, Doug A707
Miller, Lorraine A734
Miller, Josh A758
Miller, Dan A762

Miller, Thomas R A773
Miller, Mary A777
Miller, David A A785
Miller, Kevin A790
Miller, Alan L. A800
Miller, Guy A800
Miller, Bradley J. (Brad) A844
Miller, Alan B. A857
Miller, Marc D. A857
Miller, Jeffrey A860
Miller, Katherine M. (Kate) A863
Miller, Scott A865
Miller, Kevin A866
Miller, Amanda A869
Miller, Julie A874
Miller, J. J. A890
Miller, Dean A. A901
Miller, Al A902
Miller, Erin A902
Miller, Martin A906
Miller, Travis A908
Miller, Paul P9
Miller, Bill P42
Miller, Dale P53
Miller, Toni P79
Miller, Keith P87
Miller, Leo P89
Miller, Alex P115
Miller, Margaret P131
Miller, Jonathan P135
Miller, Michael P140
Miller, David P155
Miller, Bob P155
Miller, Timothy (Tim) P162
Miller, Mark P170
Miller, Nathan P184
Miller, Adam P190
Miller, Jennifer P201
Miller, Clark P207
Miller, Lynn P208
Miller, Lynn P209
Miller, Deborah P209
Miller, Lorie P212
Miller, Don P216
Miller, Dan P231
Miller, Cathy P231
Miller, Edwin (Glen) P235
Miller, Deloris P239
Miller, Derek P242
Miller, Vickie P247
Miller, Wentz J P249
Miller, Robert P255
Miller, Diane P256
Miller, Gragg P259
Miller, Mary Kay P274
Miller, Kyle P294
Miller, Bob P301
Miller, Andrew P302
Miller, Henry P323
Miller, Matthew P326
Miller, Melissa P327
Miller, Peter C P339
Miller, Brian P357
Miller, Rick P365
Miller, Frank R P372
Miller, H. Gilbert P383
Miller, Darlene P399
Miller, Susi P405
Miller, Linda P412
Miller, Thomas P431
Miller, James P464
Miller, John P483
Miller, Alex P483
Miller, Janice P487
Miller, Jan P487
Miller, Tim P487
Miller, Scott P506
Miller, Rob P507
Miller, Barbara P511
Miller, Glenn P514
Miller, Marge P516
Miller, Karen P516
Miller, Josh P519
Miller, Jon P534
Miller, Betsy P538

Miller, David R P552
Miller, Kurt P553
Miller, Jim P557
Miller, Randy P563
Miller, Logan P566
Miller, Wes P567
Miller, Franklin C. (Frank) P568
Miller, Pamela P589
Miller, Ceil P602
Miller, Ezra P603
Miller, Patrice P619
Miller, Amy P635
Miller, Trevor P636
Miller, Phillip P648
Miller, Jeffrey P656
Miller, Fletcher P666
Miller, J. J. P684
Miller, Al P692
Miller, Erin P693
Miller, Klaus W164
Miller, Alexei B. W289
Miller, Todd E9
Miller, Bill E33
Miller, Craig E37
Miller, Catherine B. E41
Miller, Kip E71
Miller, Jim E94
Miller, Robert G. E135
Miller, Scott G E140
Miller, James B. E148
Miller, Kevin E149
Miller, Megan E158
Miller, Ashlee E198
Miller, Michael T. E218
Miller, Andrew E225
Miller, Todd E253
Miller, Dave E270
Miller, William G. E280
Miller, Kevin S. E284
Miller, Craig E336
Miller, Tom E355
Miller, Thomas E355
Miller, David E374
Miller, Matthew E382
Miller, Mary E393
Miller, Alan L. E396
Miller, Guy E396
Miller, Leonard E398
Miller, Brian K. E404
Miller, Bradley J. (Brad) E412
Miller, Ronnie D. E415
Millet, Shawn A115
Millett, Mark D. A768
Millett, David P439
Millican, Anthony P120
Milligan, John F. A386
Milligan, Jay A769
Milligan, David R. A889
Milligan, Stephen D. (Steve) A892
Milligan, Paul T P102
Milligan, Gretchen P482
Millikan, J. Scott P74
Millington, Manuela A818
Millinor, Payton P164
Millis, Matt A919
Millman, Robert L P344
Millman, Richard G P344
Millman, Robert E162
Millones, Peter J. A139
Mills, Martin A20
Mills, Linda A136
Mills, Ken A140
Mills, William J. (Bill) A203
Mills, Catherine A223
Mills, Joe D A246
Mills, Gary R. A343
Mills, Steve A448
Mills, Linda A575
Mills, Justin A644
Mills, Jennifer A693
Mills, Tracey A782
Mills, Robert D. A825
Mills, Scott M. A871
Mills, Brandon P19
Mills, Dawn P52

Mills, Stephanie P54
Mills, Curt P155
Mills, Kathy P201
Mills, Don P339
Mills, Stephen S P381
Mills, Jane P415
Mills, Angel P496
Mills, Cindy E263
Millum, Deborah A A406
Milne, Tim A788
Milner, Mary A105
Milner, Patrick J. A576
Milner, John A607
Milner, Sheila P158
Milner, Eve P172
Milner, Patrick J. E297
Milnes, Susan P239
Milone-Nuzzo, Paula A811
Milone-Nuzzo, Paula P600
Milosevic, Milos A163
Milotich, Michael A874
Milovich, Steven A272
Milovich, David P90
Milroy, James A187
Milroy, James E71
Milspaugh, Glenn A109
Milspaugh, Glenn E36
Milstein, Jed A78
Milstein, Stephen A155
Milton, Aaron A144
Milton, Patricia A163
Milton, B. W. A313
Milton, Mark A. A483
Milton, Marisa A530
Milton, Robert A. A846
Milton, Jerrod P114
Mimicopoulos, Louise A691
Mims, Verett A136
Min, Sharon A401
Min, Chris A456
Min, Kyung-Zoon W292
Min, Sharon E187
Minaai, Cheryl A102
Minai, Hooman E166
Minaka, Masatsugu W113
Minaki, Kenji W400
Minami, Brad P38
Minami, Hikaru W234
Minard, Timothy A669
Minardi, Christina A899
Minardi, Christina P690
Minarovic, Michael J P42
Minarovic, Rosanne P486
Minasian, Brenda P356
Minato, Norihiko A469
Mincin, Wes P624
Mindak, Maxwell A487
Minden, Michael A872
Mineer, Mike A667
Minehan, Cathy E. P590
Miner, Jim P344
Miner, James D. P588
Miner, Ana E193
Miner, Todd E447
Mines, Michael A. (Mick) P406
Ming, Wong Wai W218
Ming, Tan Wing W280
Mingsheng, Yang W91
Mingzhe, Ma W287
Minhas, Hamza P568
Minicozzi, Rob A888
Minicucci, Benito (Ben) A28
Minicucci, Robert A. A32
Miniger, Bob E31
Mink, Susan W. A323
Minkel, Scott A. A847
Minnehan, Mike P677
Minnich, Brandt N. A551
Minnick, Daniel A270
Minnick, Mike A674
Minnick, Mike P444
Minns, Marla A817
Mino, Warren K. A882
Minogue, Keenan A531
Minogue, Michael R. E3

Minoia, Nicholas E90
Minor, Lloyd A507
Minor, Kirt A780
Minor, Lloyd P288
Minotti, Anthony J P193
Minowitz, Robert (Bob) A727
Minsk, Helayna A877
Minteer, Bob A324
Minter, Doris A300
Minter, Cindy P348
Mintz, Karly P60
Mintz, Alan P297
Minutoli, Robert A813
Minutoli, Robert P616
Minutolo, Joe A513
Minyard, Nelson P174
Mion, Anna P359
Mione, Kelly L A221
Mir, Idris A685
Mirabal, Emanuel P552
Mirabelli, Mary A419
Miralles, Albert J. (Al) A211
Miranda, Edgar A195
Miree, David D. A883
Mireles, Kelli P40
Mires, Charles D. E77
Mirkopoulos, Nicholas S P72
Mirochnick, Ira E286
Mirock, Chad A406
Miron, Robert J. (Bob) A269
Mirviss, Jeff A144
Misawa, Victor A586
Mischner, Sam E243
Misencik, Peg A489
Misencik, Mark P104
Mish, Jonathan A718
Mish, J. Vincent E280
Mishler, Isaac A223
Mishoe, Scott M A718
Mishra, Rajat A200
Mishra, Rakesh A788
Misiak, Dave A636
Misich, Michael T A886
Misich, Michael T E433
Misiewicz, Jack A837
Misita, Bill A651
Misita, Bill P426
Mislan, Tim P346
Misra, Sanghamitra P560
Missil, Kristin A599
Mistler, Thomas E. E214
Mistovich, Michael A886
Mistovich, Michael E433
Mistretta, Fred A201
Mistretta, John J. E44
Mistry, Dinyar B. A650
Mistry, Nilesh A907
Mistry, Nilesh P696
Mistysyn, Allen J. A738
Misuraca, Tami H P624
Miszewski, Matthew E107
Mita, Toshio W99
Mitchell, Peter A56
Mitchell, Steve A85
Mitchell, Brenda A102
Mitchell, Andrea A135
Mitchell, Anthony (Tony) A140
Mitchell, Robert W A166
Mitchell, Jeff A185
Mitchell, Duncan A199
Mitchell, Harvey A325
Mitchell, Joey A328
Mitchell, Duncan A330
Mitchell, Dave A384
Mitchell, Carolyn A433
Mitchell, Joe A513
Mitchell, Edward A532
Mitchell, Ed A577
Mitchell, Paul A593
Mitchell, James A599
Mitchell, Jackie A622
Mitchell, Kevin J. A653
Mitchell, Dennis A655
Mitchell, Robbin A691
Mitchell, Robert A734

Mitchell, Adam A743
Mitchell, Rhett A750
Mitchell, Doug A773
Mitchell, Robert (Rob) A813
Mitchell, R. Brian A822
Mitchell, Betty A912
Mitchell, Andrea P78
Mitchell, Laura P121
Mitchell, Susan P176
Mitchell, J. Stuart P230
Mitchell, Jim P248
Mitchell, Christopher P259
Mitchell, Sheena P279
Mitchell, Michael R P290
Mitchell, Harmon P464
Mitchell, Jenny P529
Mitchell, Robert (Rob) P616
Mitchell, Stephanie P630
Mitchell, Larry P681
Mitchell, Amy P694
Mitchell, Stephen C. E19
Mitchell, W.G. Champion (Champ) E23
Mitchell, Dave E176
Mitchell, Dennis E333
Mitchell, Adam E372
Mitchell, Doug E387
Mitchem, Steven G. A395
Mithipati, Kumar A100
Mitra, Sajal A648
Mitra, Subhro P386
Mitrick, Joseph M. (Joe) P58
Mitrovich, Mark P361
Mitry, Norman F P663
Mitschke, Gina P284
Mitsuya, Makoto W17
Mittal, Gaurav A537
Mittal, Samir A560
Mittal, Lalita P617
Mittal, Aditya W30
Mittal, Lakshmi N. W30
Mittelman, Monty P441
Mittendorfer, Gernot W145
Mittermaier, Pascal P596
Mittl, Cheryl P20
Mittmann, Paul A136
Mitz, Vincent W. E94
Mitzner, Jennifer P238
Miura, Zenji W304
Miwa, Akihisa W273
Mix, Heidi P463
Miyabe, Toshihiko W259
Miyabe, Yoshiyuki W282
Miyake, Shunichi W19
Miyake, Senji W207
Miyaki, Masahiko W121
Miyamoto, Melba A915
Miyamoto, Patti P242
Miyamoto, Gene P538
Miyamoto, Melba P700
Miyamoto, Tsuneo W261
Miyamoto, Ikuo W282
Miyamoto, Yoichi W327
MIYANAGA, MASATO W99
Miyanaga, Shunichi W241
Miyanoya, Atsushi W48
Miyata, Koichi W345
Miyazaki, Shigeki P35
Miyazaki, Higeki P35
Miyazawa, Katsumi W86
Mizelle, C A446
Mizelle, C E210
Mizener, Kathy A489
Mizerak, Ted A377
Mizrahi, Ricardo A574
Mizui, Satoshi W336
Mizuki, Gizo W192
Mizuno, Masayuki W48
Mizuno, Akihisa W99
Mizushima, Kenji W264
Mizushima, Shigeaki W326
Mizutani, Ryosuke W99
Mizutani, Hisakazu W241
Mizutani, Tetsu W349
Mjelde, Bradley A896
Mladenovic, Jeanette P410

Mleczko, Dan P575
Mlotek, Mark E. A727
Mlynek, Chris A6
Mnning, Carol P695
MO, Weiwei P659
Moag, Tony A814
Moag, Tony P616
Moats, Andy A655
Moats, Dan P36
Moats, Andy E333
Mober, Cara E276
Moberg, Kirk P95
Mobley, Stacey A463
Mobley, Michael A693
Mocanu, Michael A513
Mochida, Masanori A389
Mochizuki, Robert M. E415
Mock, Jeff A536
Mock, Kathy P238
Mock, Fred P244
Mock, Robert C. P267
Mock, Angie P440
Mockridge, Tom W222
Mockus, Steve A850
Modde, Margaret Mary P146
Modi, Keyur A390
Modini, Aravind A40
Modjeska, Alicia P134
Modlin, Ryan A628
Modoff, Brian T. A685
Modruson, Frank A351
Modruson, Frank E159
Mody-Baily, Priti P73
Moe, Jeanan A905
Moe, Jeanan P693
Moe, Jonas E119
Moehlenbrock, Todd A263
Moehling, John P576
Moehlman, Stephen A677
Moehn, Michael L. A42
Moelis, Ron P278
Moeller, Kyle A204
Moeller, Jon R. A671
Moeller, Sharon A904
Moeller, Mark P223
Moeller, Clair J. P342
Moeller, Sharon E442
Moen, Timothy A599
Moen, Kayla P481
Moen, Kari Olrud W129
Moenaert, Patricia A178
Moersch, Brian P174
Moesgaard, Lars W352
Moffat, Bob A460
Moffat, Bob A725
Moffet, Brian L P505
Moffett, Randy P637
Moffic-Silver, Joanne E62
Moffitt, Mary A247
Moffitt, Kevin L. A351
Moffitt, Tivon A478
Moffitt, Kevin A612
Moffitt, John P339
Moffitt, Jamie P651
Moffitt, Michael P651
Moffitt, Justin Raoul W227
Moffitt, Mary E102
Moffitt, Kevin L. E158
Mofor, Lapah P96
Mogan, Tom P625
Mogan, Thomas P626
Mogg, Denise P474
Moghadam, Shams P603
Mogi, Yoshio W336
Moglia, Joseph H. (Joe) A791
Moglia, Peter M. E9
Mohammad, Shamim A166
Mohammed, Pasha A185
Mohammed, Khundnir A201
Mohammed, Hafeza A500
Mohammed, Hafeza E237
Mohan, R. Michael (Mike) A126
Mohan, Vamsi A215
Mohan, Rajan A530
Mohan, Stephen A707

Mohanty, Paresh A101
Mohanty, Devi A406
Moharir, Prahlad E165
Mohiuddin, Ashfaq A723
Mohler, Justin A173
Mohler, Orv A555
Mohlman, Kurt P609
Mohn, Mike A200
Mohn, Ross P613
Mohr, Todd M. A17
Mohr, John R A105
Mohr, Doug A270
Mohr, Edward L A727
Mohr, David A736
Mohr, Matthew A912
Mohr, Todd M. P10
Mohr, Steven P294
Mohr, David P492
Mohrman, Michael P467
Mohs, Brad A85
Moilien, Phillip P151
Moisan, Jerome E44
Moise, Mark A542
Moison, Franck J. A218
Moison, Franck A850
Moitoso, Bob E383
Moje, Elizabeth Birr A698
Moje, Elizabeth Birr P456
Mok, Wilbur W. A24
Mokel, Mk A644
Mokma, William A441
Molek, Noreen P516
Molen, Matt P552
Molho, Davide E69
Molina, Oscar A244
Molina, Hope S A244
Molina, Gladys A905
Molina, Mauricio A885
Molina, Dolores P90
Molina, Luis P160
Molina, Claudia P243
Molina, Jennifer P293
Molina, Natalie P372
Molina, Rita P390
Molina, Alvaro G. (Al) de E350
Molinaro, Christopher A417
Molinaro, Vince A482
Molinaro, Frank A795
Molinaro, James P461
Moline, Kathy P329
Molinelli, Gayla A416
Molinie, Bernard P379
Molino, John A68
Moliterno, David P273
Molko, Cindy P474
Moll, Julie A530
Moll, Bud E234
Molle, Josephine A413
Molle, Josephine P234
Mollenkopf, Steven M. (Steve) A685
Mollet, Chris P176
Mollica, Jim A65
Mollica, Anthony A149
Mollica, Paul F. A883
Mollins, Gregg J. A703
Mollins, Sean A703
Mollon, Fernando A875
Molloy, Melinda P113
Molmen, David P29
Molnar, David A. A830
Molnar, Jacqueline A893
Molnar, Cindy P104
Molnar, Richard P313
Molnar, Carol P694
Molnar, David A. E403
Moloney, Ellen P380
Moloney, Jacquie P645
Moloney, John J. W120
Moltrup, Doreen P532
Momper, Matthew J. E218
Monacelli, Fred A85
Monaco, Anthony A87
Monaco, Mark A336
Monaco, Mark P194
Monaco, Donna P302

A = AMERICAN BUSINESS
E = EMERGING COMPANIES
P = PRIVATE COMPANIES
W = WORLD BUSINESS

Monaco, Al W138
Monaghan, Craig T. A78
Monaghan, Virg A872
Monagle, D. J. E281
Monahan, Jay A288
Monahan, Thomas L P102
Monahan, Mike Null P398
Monahan, Michael P. (Mike) E309
Monan, J. Donald P625
Moncau, Ursula A904
Moncau, Ursula E442
Moncher, Daniel P193
Moncla, Jean A163
Moncrief, Jimmy A655
Moncrief, Kit Tennison P561
Moncrief, Jimmy E333
Mondazzi, Massimo W143
Mondello, Mark T. A471
Mondragon, Brian P123
Monery, Dave E166
Mones, Donald A872
Monetta, Dominic J. E209
Monette, Todd A192
Monette, Todd P112
Monette, Perry P685
Money, Celista P668
Mong-Koo, Chung W179
Mong-Koo, Chung W205
Monge, Cathie P675
Mongeau, Luc W394
Mongeon, Kelli A272
Mongillo, Stephen A249
Mongrain, Joe A64
Monhart, James A599
Monhaut, Michelle A478
Monich, Allan R A45
Monighetti, Daniel P441
Moninski, Stacey A101
Moniuskzo, Richard P461
Moniz, Henry A871
Monk, Don A377
Monk, David H. A811
Monk, David H. P600
Monley, Dominic A441
Monlezun, Mike P170
Monroe, Michael A163
Monroe, Marvin A258
Monroe, Charles Chuck A442
Monroe, Sheila P525
Monroe, Alex P572
Monsen, Brian A565
Monser, Edward L. A295
Monserrate, Grace A634
Monson, Jon A144
Monson, Sally A407
Monson, Brian A541
Monson, Kevin W. A562
Monson, Thomas S. P83
Monson, Dale D. P130
Monson, Jeffrey P681
Monson, Brian E266
Monson, Kevin W. E279
Montag, Thomas K. (Tom) A100
Montag, Bernd W331
Montague, Adrian A. W38
Montague, Mark K. E227
Montague, Paul E360
Montana, Gregory G. (Greg) A330
Montana, Peter A780
Montanaro, Tom P230
Montano, Jesus L A555
Montano, Satin A556
Montano, Laz A556
Montano, Cathy P537
Monte, Dave A594
Montebello, Philippe De P594
Monteferrante, Chris A85
Monteforte, Jason A532
Monteiro, Lalit A592

Monteiro, Ken A808
Monteiro, Ken P581
Monteiro, Ivan de Souza W284
Monteith, Stu A443
Monteleone, William (Will) E322
Montellione, Robert A677
Montemurro, Michael P282
Montenegro, Sara P560
Montero, Edward A204
Montero, Juan M A823
Montero, Alejandro P456
Monterosso, Becky A352
Monterosso, Frank S. E108
Montes, John A558
Montes, Myrtho A676
Montesdeoca, Carmella A777
Montesdeoca, Carmella E393
Monteverde, Bryan A105
Montezemolo, Luca Cordero di W380
Montgomery, Erin A49
Montgomery, William A69
Montgomery, Jennifer A101
Montgomery, Norman J. A342
Montgomery, Sheila A446
Montgomery, Richard P198
Montgomery, Toni-Marie P398
Montgomery, James P461
Montgomery, Robert P471
Montgomery, Gregory P493
Montgomery, Lisa P. P591
Montgomery, James P621
Montgomery, Darren E101
Montgomery, Sheila E210
Montgomery-Talley, La June P672
Monti, Philip P501
Montini, Enio A. (Tony) A708
Montjane, Funeka W339
Montminy, Matthew A406
Montminy, Pierre A780
Montminy, Sandy P434
Montoni, Richard A. (Rich) E265
Montonye, Brian P141
Montoya, Nancy A322
Montoya, Isabel A345
Montoya, Luis A647
Montoya, Victoria P189
Montoya, Jessica P410
Montoya, Lillian P537
Montoya, Isabel E154
Montpetit, David A782
Montrond, Deborah P148
Montry, Mindy P460
Montz, Renee D. A47
Montz, Renee D. A48
Montz, Lawrence A163
Monz--n, Gilberto F. A661
Moo, Jason A390
Moochhala, Zenobia E57
Mood, Shawn P101
Moodey, J. Tucker A310
Moody, Allison P6
Moody, Felice P39
Moody, Michael P170
Moody, Russell P391
Moody, Lori P497
Moody, Sharmin P537
Moody, Nathaniel E316
Mooijman, Yannick A850
Mookherjee, Disha P535
Mookini, Debbie A272
Moomey, Sarah P613
Moon, Tina A484
Moon, Dallas A493
Moon, Kimberly P166
Moon, Don P290
Moon, Bob P537
Moon, Frederick P548
Moonen, Glenn P425
Mooney, Niall A223
Mooney, Randy A252
Mooney, Howard F. A339
Mooney, Kathleen A348
Mooney, Beth E. A489
Mooney, William A741
Mooney, Stephen M. (Steve) A794

Mooney, Daniel A886
Mooney, John P145
Mooney, Randy P150
Mooney, Keith P628
Mooney, Kevin W. E44
Mooney, Howard F. E150
Mooney, William E371
Mooney, Daniel E433
Moonves, Leslie (Les) A175
Moor, Bill A162
Mooradian, Anne A624
Mooradian, Arshag P642
Mooradian, John E220
Moore, Ken A13
Moore, Pennie A14
Moore, Karen A15
Moore, Colin A56
Moore, Kevin A85
Moore, John A105
Moore, Bob A107
Moore, Doug A115
Moore, Michael A115
Moore, Beth A130
Moore, Steve A140
Moore, Colleen A158
Moore, Danny A163
Moore, Kevin A164
Moore, Stephen L A171
Moore, Christine A221
Moore, Elizabeth D. A233
Moore, Barbara A282
Moore, Johnnie A324
Moore, Paul A332
Moore, Richard H. A337
Moore, A. Bruce A410
Moore, Amy A446
Moore, Brad A476
Moore, Mary A477
Moore, Andrew A540
Moore, Andrew A546
Moore, Vance A552
Moore, Troy A554
Moore, Frederick V. (Fred) A554
Moore, Daryl D. A614
Moore, Gary L A629
Moore, Chris A630
Moore, Greg A647
Moore, Edward W. A716
Moore, Jeffrey A790
Moore, Scott A792
Moore, Christine A799
Moore, Bob A814
Moore, Heather A820
Moore, Terrell A823
Moore, Alex A834
Moore, Jason A843
Moore, Chad A866
Moore, Michael S. (Mike) A878
Moore, Mike A886
Moore, Craig A899
Moore, Karen A912
Moore, Ken A912
Moore, Pennie P7
Moore, Karen P9
Moore, Kendall P14
Moore, Bud P67
Moore, Andrew P96
Moore, Stephen L P100
Moore, Dana P114
Moore, Maricela S. P119
Moore, Sherie P125
Moore, Dan P200
Moore, Kimberly P203
Moore, Kay P208
Moore, Anne P218
Moore, James D. P250
Moore, Jeanette P263
Moore, Mary P268
Moore, William L P271
Moore, Tamara P307
Moore, Robert P311
Moore, Andrew P316
Moore, Debra L P323
Moore, Vance P328
Moore, David P339

Moore, T P343
Moore, Eric P345
Moore, Bruce P379
Moore, Dana P429
Moore, Rachel P436
Moore, Stephanie P437
Moore, Kim P447
Moore, William M. P458
Moore, Lori P498
Moore, Liz P538
Moore, Kevin P546
Moore, Jason P554
Moore, Barry P567
Moore, Lora P572
Moore, Kelly P582
Moore, Lashonda P599
Moore, Kelly P613
Moore, Jackson W. P615
Moore, Bob P616
Moore, Terrell P622
Moore, Joy P625
Moore, Madeleine G P625
Moore, Joi P646
Moore, Gayle P654
Moore, William T P655
Moore, Chad P661
Moore, Craig P690
Moore, Cindy P699
Moore, Robert J. W217
Moore, Nicholas W. W227
Moore, Bob E34
Moore, James E74
Moore, Sean D. E161
Moore, Michael G. (Mike) E184
Moore, Amy E210
Moore, Troy E275
Moore, Frederick V. (Fred) E275
Moore, Todd R. E298
Moore, James E357
Moore, H. Lynn E404
Moore, Jason E411
Moore, Mike E433
Moore-Hardy, Cynthia P280

Moorhead, Keith P160
Moorjani, Shail A163
Moorman, Charles A282
Moquist, Darren C A855
Mora, Elfa A182
Mora, Elizabeth P568
Mora, Elfa E63
Morabito, Carl S. E252
Moraci, Pj A857
Moraci, Philip J A857
Morain, Anthony P162
Morais, Diane E A34
Morais, Diane A35
Morais, Diane E P27
Moral-Niles, Christopher J. Del A81
Morales, Michael PE A127
Morales, Raquel A182
Morales, Amber A272
Morales, Keith A322
Morales, Elisa A375
Morales, Jimmy A547
Morales, Vincent J. A664
Morales, Mark A801
Morales, Rafael A810
Morales, David P 2
Morales, Martha P72
Morales, Alia P143
Morales, Jimmy P319
Morales, Ralph J P469
Morales, Mark P562
Morales, Rafael P586
Morales, David P685
Morales, Raquel E63
Morales-jaffe, Marcia A906
Moran, Rob A19
Moran, Edward A56
Moran, Mickey A81
Moran, Thomas A287
Moran, Karina A322
Moran, Steve Us A478
Moran, Brian A537

Moran, Thomas A541
Moran, Jennifer A836
Moran, Audrey P58
Moran, Thomas P174
Moran, Jim P184
Moran, Taryn G P217
Moran, Tom P682
Moran, Karina E204
Moran, Edmund J. E216
Moran, Thomas E266
Morant, Felicia A21
Morant, Felicia P12
Morar, August A585
Morar, August P377
Morasutti, Joseph A250
Morathi, Raisibe K. W256
Morazzani, Christina A671
Morch, Otto C. E209
Morche, Ed A185
More, Debrah A115
Morea, Joseph A826
Moreau, Maxine L. A185
Moreau, Gary P295
Morehead, Bruce A219
Morehead, Jere P642
Morehead, Bruce E84
Morel, Hugo W379
Moreland, Kenneth V. A783
Moreland, David A912
Moreland, Jeffrey R P364
Morell, Randy J P408
Morelli, Tony A199
Morelli, Salvatore A406
Morelli, Mark D. E86
Morena, Mike A599
Moreno, Marie A741
Moreno, Claudia P543
Moreno, Oscar Landerretche W108
Moreno, Raul E. E6
Moreno, Marie E370
Moret, Blake D. A712
Moretti, Marty E232
Moretti, Darlene P508
Moretz, Tom P405
Morey, Debra A782
Morfin, Lindsey A390
Morford, Craig S. A165
Morgado, James A482
Morgan, Donna A34
Morgan, David A192
Morgan, Kip A292
Morgan, Lisa A406
Morgan, William A426
Morgan, Mary A446
Morgan, Mary A492
Morgan, Karen A508
Morgan, Bruce A518
Morgan, James A553
Morgan, Rodney A559
Morgan, Emily A583
Morgan, Rose A644
Morgan, Henry A674
Morgan, Jason A772
Morgan, Daniel A781
Morgan, Hugh G A782
Morgan, John A888
Morgan, Lori P67
Morgan, Ada P92
Morgan, David P112
Morgan, Kenneth P136
Morgan, Dennis P147
Morgan, Kristin P147
Morgan, Donna P213
Morgan, Dusty P254
Morgan, Aaron P281
Morgan, Amanda P318
Morgan, Bill P325
Morgan, Shana P331
Morgan, Emily P374
Morgan, Vickie P420
Morgan, Henry P444
Morgan, Merry P521
Morgan, Jennifer P635
Morgan, Renea P669
Morgan, James P673

Morgan, John P683
Morgan, Mark P685
Morgan, Flemming W117
Morgan, Jennifer W319
Morgan, Duane E57
Morgan, Mary E210
Morgan, James E272
Morganflash, Jeff P537
Morgano, Scott A328
Morgano, Scott A330
Morganstein, David P682
Morgante, Elizabeth P221
Morganthall, Frederick J. (Fred) A496
Morge, Kenneth A261
Morgenlender, Mark A204
Morgenstern, Mitch A541
Morgenstern, Mitch E266
Morgenthal, Margie P224
Morgioni, Mike A73
Morgison, Kevin A164
Morgo, Joseph A204
Morhaime, Michael (Mike) A10
Mori, Yoshiki W11
Mori, Chitoshi W242
Moriarty, Linda A56
Moriarty, Lorie A187
Moriarty, Thomas M. A250
Moriarty, Michael A327
Moriarty, Selina A489
Moriarty, Daniel P50
Moriarty, Kristen P482
Moriarty, Lorie E71
Moriarty, J.D. E243
Moriarty, Rowland T. (Row) E438
Morici, John F. E10
Moriconi, Susan E316
Moriguchi, Jaime P103
Morikawa, Jon P270
Morikawa, Taku W147
Morikis, John G. A738
Morimoto, David S. A183
Morimoto, Kathy P601
Morimoto, Hiromichi W241
Morimura, Tsutomu W86
Morin, Thomas A390
Morin, Jeff A508
Morin, Jamie P564
Morishita, Kenichi W330
Morita, Shunsaku W116
Morita, Toshio W268
Moritani, Kazuhiro W326
Moritz, Terry P299
Moriwaki, Lee Y. A183
Moriyama, Toru W243
Mork, John A860
Mork, Lee P26
Mork, John P656
Morken, CeCe A466
Morland, Natalie P439
Morley, Kelly A329
Morley, Debra A477
Morley, Jeffrey A707
Morley, Debra P268
Morlock, David R. P613
Morningstar, Ashley A334
Morningstar, Ashley P193
Moro, Sonya A108
Moro, Masahiro W235
Moro, Sonya E35
Moroney, Bruce E. E108
Morosov, Anatoly A480
Moroye-Young, Jennifer P417
Morozov, Alexander W321
Morrell, Kelley A201
Morrical, Terri A. E299
Morris, Donna A11
Morris, Leslie A49
Morris, Jared A. A58
Morris, Gregory A. (Greg) A74
Morris, M. Catherine (Cathy) A77
Morris, Uri A131
Morris, Jim A136
Morris, Bob A155
Morris, Joe A223
Morris, Jerry A377

Morris, Ken A379
Morris, Chris A537
Morris, Maria R. A555
Morris, Pamela A585
Morris, Jesse E. A686
Morris, Florence A700
Morris, B. Harrison A737
Morris, Pete A761
Morris, Gene A767
Morris, John A768
Morris, Matthew W. (Matt) A769
Morris, Tina A782
Morris, Edna A825
Morris, Fran A870
Morris, John J. A881
Morris, Dawn C. A883
Morris, Megen A901
Morris, William A901
Morris, Michael J. A919
Morris, Diane P28
Morris, Paul P122
Morris, Kenneth C. P168
Morris, Traci P186
Morris, Nath P225
Morris, Granville P283
Morris, Walker P352
Morris, Pamela P377
Morris, Paul P435
Morris, Doug P489
Morris, Gary R. P588
Morris, Rick P636
Morris, Jon P680
Morris, Megen P692
Morris, William P692
Morris, Phil W314
Morris, Tracy L. E57
Morris, Michael J. E167
Morris, G. Ronald E305
Morris, B. Harrison E367
Morris-gettings, Juanita A513
Morris-Hipkins, Stuart A626
Morrisett, J. Gregory P143
Morrison, Christina A73
Morrison, Scott C. A96
Morrison, Victoria A120
Morrison, Denise M. A161
Morrison, Patricia B. (Patty) A165
Morrison, Jim A175
Morrison, Richard A307
Morrison, Millard A446
Morrison, Elizabeth A517
Morrison, Deb A537
Morrison, Trevor A585
Morrison, Jeffrey A644
Morrison, Erin A647
Morrison, Geri A670
Morrison, Kevin A698
Morrison, Ron A737
Morrison, Tim A746
Morrison, Joe A772
Morrison, Julia P22
Morrison, Allen P44
Morrison, Dr Bob P208
Morrison, John P361
Morrison, Trevor P377
Morrison, Karen P405
Morrison, Kevin P456
Morrison, Tom P456
Morrison, Curtis P477
Morrison, Tom P627
Morrison, Millard E210
Morrison, Lana J. E364
Morrison, Ron E367
Morrison, Dave E393
Morriss, Steve A16
Morrissey, Art A96
Morrissey, Mary Carol P167
Morrissey, Joseph P205
Morrissey, Michael M. E138
Morro, Robert H. P667
Morrow, David L A167
Morrow, Richard A229
Morrow, Duncan A244
Morrow, William A446
Morrow, Jerry A546

Morrow, Brian R. A715
Morrow, Sherry P18
Morrow, W. Robert P45
Morrow, Randy M P79
Morrow, W. Robert (Bob) P116
Morrow, Richard P137
Morrow, Kent P234
Morrow, Jennifer P279
Morrow, Shawn P323
Morrow, Joseph P359
Morrow, Grant P365
Morrow, Kirk P469
Morrow, Ron W47
Morrow, Martha E77
Morrow, William E210
Mors, Bernhard A537
Morse, Sherry A85
Morse, Robert J. (Bob) A157
Morse, David L. A238
Morse, Cheryl A300
Morse, Colby A782
Morse, Candace A910
Morse, Alan R P223
Morse, Alan R P292
Morse, Edward J P352
Morse, Virginia P384
Morse, Douglas H. (Doug) E86
Morsi, Deborah S. P50
Morstadt, Mary A351
Morstadt, Mary E158
MORSTOFOLINI, ERNESTINA W111
Morsy, Hany A904
Morsy, Hany E442
Mortensen, Pam A640
Mortensen, Brian P481
Morthland, Lee A693
Morton, David A58
Morton, ED A188
Morton, Susan A532
Morton, Michael J. A541
Morton, George A857
Morton, Jeff A920
Morton, Robyn P354
Morton, Leo E. P647
Morton, Gerry E59
Morton, Michael J. E266
Morton-rowe, Laura A517
Morway, Joe P495
Morzaria, Tushar W52
Morzaria, Tushar W54
Mosakowski, William S P445
Mosca, Andrew P247
Moscaritolo, Daniel A393
Moscho, Harold P357
Moseley, Stephen A28
Moseley, Stephen P17
Moseley, T Hank P240
Mosemann, Russell P207
Moser, Chris A604
Moser, Joseph D P39
Moser, Len P61
Moser, Caitlin P92
Moser, Kathy P643
Moser, Linda E162
Moses, James M A124
Moses, Sharon A449
Moses, Christopher A487
Mosher, Allison A225
Mosher, Almon P368
Mosher, Allison E88
Mosich, Nicholas A. A95
Mosich, Nicholas A. E28
Mosier, Preston A788
Moskal, Joseph T P95
Moskowitz, Ken A366
Moskowitz, Samuel E. A548
Moskowitz, Paul T. A782
Moskowitz, Amy P144
Moskowitz, Samuel E P204
Moskowitz, Samuel E. P321
Moskowitz, Sam E428
Mosley, Christopher R P217
Mosley, Jeanette P440
Moss, Craig A115
Moss, Michelle A163

A = AMERICAN BUSINESS
E = EMERGING COMPANIES
P = PRIVATE COMPANIES
W = WORLD BUSINESS

Moss, Aaron A291
Moss, Kenneth (Ken) A292
Moss, Barbara A324
Moss, Linda L. A355
Moss, Judith A475
Moss, Danielle A691
Moss, Nalann A844
Moss, Regina S P136
Moss, Katrinia P188
Moss, Judith P266
Moss, Beth P301
Moss, R. Lawrence P365
Moss, Ray P663
Moss, Jacqueline C. W80
Moss, Robbie E189
Moss, Nalann E412
Moss-Higham, Sharron A485
Mossel, Mark P582
Mosses, Cheryl P479
Mosshart, Roger E65
Mostow, William P57
Mota, Lorena A158
Mota-Velasco, German Larrea A753
Motakef, Shahin P486
Motes, Joseph A32
Motl, Christopher J. (Chris) A883
Motley, J. Keith P645
Motonaga, Greg P106
Mott, Randall D. (Randy) A378
Mott, Carrie A496
Mott, Vernagene P425
Motta, Stephen A375
Motta, Edgar P160
Motta, Jorge da W194
Motte, Anne-Marie A218
Motty, Diana P279
Moua, Chuck P155
Mouadeb, Daniel A163
Mouli, Chandra A685
Moullemaaz, Karim A328
Moulton, Paul G. A239
Moulton, Don P368
Mounger, Clayton P624
Mounir, Ihssane A136
Mount, Alyson A300
Mount, Carl A763
Mount, James P431
Mountan, Mike A476
Mountjoy, Michelle A838
Mourino, Art P668
Moury, Susan A823
Moury, Susan P622
Moustakakis, John P683
Moutenot, Michael A537
Movassaghi, Eric A446
Movassaghi, Eric P210
Mower, Brian A101
Mowery, Eric A380
Mowery, Geoffrey A440
Moy, Steve A158
Moy, Greg E123
Moyano, Grace A489
Moyer, Priscilla A365
Moyer, Eileen A369
Moyer, Steve A559
Moyer, David A564
Moyer, Glenn A862
Moyer, Kathy P385
Moyer, Angel P669
Moyer, A.J. (Bert) E52
Moyer, Glenn E419
Moyers, Andrew P498
Moyette, Zirley A204
Moylan, Brian P462
Moynihan, Brian T. A100
Moyo, Peter W275
Mozrall, Jacqueline P464
Mrosik, Jan W331
Mrowczynski, Jeff A240

Msays, Joseph A461
MskolfieldpewtrustsO, Melissa P601
Mubing, Zhou W12
Mucha, Zenia A271
Mucha, Joseph A377
Mucha, John A413
Mucha, Bob P64
Mucha, John P234
Muchane, Mur P673
Muchane, Mary P673
Mucic, Luka W319
Mudd, Charles P664
Mudgett, Daniel E268
Mudichintala, Kiran A480
Mudrick, Christopher A309
Muehlen, Constance Von A28
Mueller, Roni A175
Mueller, Meg R. A369
Mueller, Dan A493
Mueller, Paul A540
Mueller, William A552
Mueller, Karl W. A615
Mueller, Perry A674
Mueller, Jochen A850
Mueller, Bernadette M. A868
Mueller, Jeff P40
Mueller, Mary P68
Mueller, Phillip Doc P246
Mueller, Paul P316
Mueller, William P328
Mueller, Lori P410
Mueller, Michael W41
Mueller, Brian E. E180
Mueller, Craig E432
Mueller-Hickler, Tim A38
Muenster, Gary E. E132
Muenzenberger, Susan P630
Mugavero, Jennifer A462
Mugg, Jason P2
Mugnier, Denis W145
Muhammad, Marfiza A417
Muhart, Matthew J. P508
Muhl, Erica A860
Muhl, Erica P656
Muhlenkamp, Janice P6
Muhlfelder, Teddy P186
Muhlhauser, Jurgen A676
Muilenburg, Dennis A. A136
Muina, Tomas Varela W42
Muir, William D. (Bill) A471
Muir, William A726
Mukai, Kazushi W326
Mukhamedov, Leonid W322
Mulcahey, Terri A643
Mulcahy, Nora P283
Mulder, Tim P154
Muldoon, Christine P271
Mulenga, Makumba P342
Mulford, Michael D. A344
Mulford, Michael D. E154
Mulhere, Timothy P. A289
Mulherin, Matthew J. (Matt) A442
Mulhern, Ben P345
Mulholland, Ginny P361
Mulholland, Katie S. P612
Mulka, David S A758
Mulka, David S P519
Mull, Rohit A734
Mullally, Dan A327
Mullaney, Tom A764
Mullaney, Teri L. P167
Mullaney, Eileen P283
Mullaney, Janet P638
Mullarkey, Pat A852
Mullen, Bryan A180
Mullen, Frank A718
Mullen, Frederick L A817
Mullen, Tom P99
Mullen, David P111
Mullen, Kem P129
Mullen, Thomas P329
Mullen, Thomas R P331
Mullen, Paddy C P372
Mullen, John R P372
Mullen, Dennis P412

Mullenix, Matthew (Matt) E430
Muller, John A288
Muller, Bart A761
Muller, Ralph W. A812
Muller, Chris A883
Muller, Denise P207
Muller, David P355
Muller, Garrick P523
Muller, Ralph W. P607
Muller, Brook P651
Mullery, Stephen P. A320
Mullery, Stephen P. E143
Mulligan, Paul A215
Mulligan, Donal L. (Don) A377
Mulligan, Jennifer A781
Mulligan, John J. A788
Mulligan, William C A805
Mulligan, Andrea P283
Mullin, Thomas J. (Tom) A235
Mullin, Lauren A817
Mullin, Shelly P357
Mullin, William W. W10
Mullinix, Mark L. A324
Mullins, Kevin A459
Mullins, Dan A857
Mullins, Anne P140
Mullins, Fred P163
Mullins, Larry P214
Mullins, Karyn P258
Mullins, James P462
Mullins, Miki P475
Mullins, Larry P478
Mullins, Kem M. P680
Mullis, Michael P666
Mullokandov, Izabella R P381
Mullooly, Pat P577
Mulpas, Joe A594
Mulready, Pat A173
Mulrooney, Byrne K. E235
Mulroy, Thomas P. P771
Mulroy, Molly A884
Multon, Hervé W364
Mulva, J J A232
Mulvaney, Kimberly P522
Mulvena, John Mark A901
Mulvena, John Mark P692
Mulvihill, Lenise P462
Mumford, Mark D. P115
Muminovic, Alem A649
Mumm, Jason P361
Mumma, Steven R. E302
Mumme, Alex A919
Munari, Andrea W66
Mundt-Blum, Walter A607
Mundy, Karen A332
Mundy, Robert P. (Bob) A631
Muneoka, Shoji W263
Muney, Alan M. A194
Munger, Charles T. (Charlie) A123
Mungovan, Sandy P226
Muni, Amit E443
Munic-Miller, Donna A807
Munic-Miller, Donna P574
Munie, Sara P619
Muniz, Sean M. A636
Muniz, Charles P105
Muniz, Arturo P291
Muniz, Rafael E349
Munjal, Leena A733
Munk, Anthony W277
Munley, Keith A247
Munley, Keith E103
Munn, Charles A782
Munn, Chuck P782
Munn, Rico P52
Munn, Irving E77
Munneke, Rich A728
Munnelly, Joseph M. (Joe) A73
Munnelly, Kevin P200
Munoz, Oscar A846
Munoz, Alex P514
Munoz, Jose W265
Munro, Euan W38
Munson, Brian A133
Munson, Kelly A. A885

Munson, James A912
Munson, Kenneth P134
Murabito, John M. A194
Murad, Richard A901
Murad, Richard P692
Murai, Kevin M. A779
Murai, Shouhei W11
Murakami, Stephen P553
Murakami, Nobuhiko W342
Murakami, Nobuhiko W374
Muramatsu, Iwao W1
Muraro, Robert A787
MURASE, YUKIO W200
Murashko, Mike P339
Murasko, Donna P165
Muratore, Emiliano W43
Murcek, Bob P209
Murcio, Daniela P216
Murdoch, Britton H. A152
Murdoch, Lachlan K. A589
Murdoch, K. Rupert A589
Murdoch, Tim A723
Murdoch, James R A834
Murdoch, K Rupert A834
Murdoch, Lachlan K A834
Murdoch, Britton H. E48
Murdock, Robert A178
Murdock, Daniel C A220
Murdock, Brett A920
Murdock, Barbara Hein P413
Murdock, Robert O. (Rob) E296
Murdy, James P688
Mureddu, Adriano A898
Murfin, Ross P514
Murgado, Mario P665
Murgalo, Joanne A644
Muri, Scott R P521
Murillo, Lucia A79
Murillo, Jorge P510
Murillo, Armando P550
Murillo, Catalina E265
MURLEY, MARY E410
Muro, David A84
Murota, Trudy P521
Murphy, Christopher J. (Chris) A1
Murphy, John A67
Murphy, Siobhan A70
Murphy, Thomas J. (Tom) A78
Murphy, Sean A84
Murphy, Thomas A123
Murphy, William A132
Murphy, John A215
Murphy, James P. (Jim) A240
Murphy, Drew A291
Murphy, Edward F. A323
Murphy, Steve A345
Murphy, Gwenn A354
Murphy, James H. (Jim) A377
Murphy, Christopher A387
Murphy, Edmund F. A395
Murphy, Tara A441
Murphy, Erica A446
Murphy, Mark A449
Murphy, Noel A456
Murphy, Mary A461
Murphy, Michael T A463
Murphy, Gerry A480
Murphy, Pat A484
Murphy, Lauren A524
Murphy, Michael A532
Murphy, Christopher A533
Murphy, Timothy H. (Tim) A537
Murphy, Brenda A555
Murphy, Stacey A557
Murphy, R. Madison A571
Murphy, Michael M A578
Murphy, Sharon A583
Murphy, Nancy A639
Murphy, Ryan A655
Murphy, John A672
Murphy, Diane A695
Murphy, Chris A701
Murphy, George M. A722
Murphy, Gregory E. A734
Murphy, Lauren L A740

Murphy, Daniel A765
Murphy, Thomas H. (Tom) A812
Murphy, Sean A815
Murphy, Cecil A828
Murphy, Michael A830
Murphy, Neil A836
Murphy, Jack A848
Murphy, Sean A868
Murphy, John A869
Murphy, Luke A872
Murphy, Ken A877
Murphy, Julie A878
Murphy, David A881
Murphy, Richard B. A904
Murphy, Robert A904
Murphy, Joseph A907
Murphy, Michael A912
Murphy, Courtney P2
Murphy, Glenn P18
Murphy, Terry P64
Murphy, Edward P95
Murphy, Bob P103
Murphy, Tyler P159
Murphy, Karen P209
Murphy, Erin P300
Murphy, Mike P304
Murphy, Michael P346
Murphy, Kitty P361
Murphy, Kathryn P480
Murphy, Michael P498
Murphy, Richard J P510
Murphy, Daniel P540
Murphy, Thomas H. (Tom) P607
Murphy, J Pat P612
Murphy, Teresa P614
Murphy, Jeff P686
Murphy, Carolyn P693
Murphy, Donal W120
Murphy, Christopher E177
Murphy, A. Brett E178
Murphy, Erica E210
Murphy, Edward G. E251
Murphy, Nancy E325
Murphy, Ryan E333
Murphy, Michael E402
Murphy, Richard B. E442
Murphy, Robert E442
Murphy, Joseph E446
Murray, Jason A38
Murray, Jay A56
Murray, Harry A169
Murray, Patricia A180
Murray, Richard A244
Murray, Aaron A268
Murray, Brigitte A272
Murray, Craig A303
Murray, Carol A316
Murray, David A330
Murray, Dawn A330
Murray, Michael A433
Murray, Ron A442
Murray, Lisa A452
Murray, Pam A452
Murray, Cathleen A543
Murray, Brian A589
Murray, Janice A603
Murray, Andrea A683
Murray, Dane H A751
Murray, Theodore A782
Murray, Donna A857
Murray, Oliver A863
Murray, Darren P69
Murray, Dwayne P86
Murray, Stephen P120
Murray, Michael P140
Murray, Jeanette P252
Murray, Barry S P372
Murray, Janice P399
Murray, Brian J P415
Murray, Gerry P436
Murray, Ann P486
Murray, Jerry P660
Murray, Carol E141
Murray, John G. E206
Murray, Lisa E215

Murray, Pam E215
Murray, Scott E. E234
Murray, John E E257
Murray, Dane H E377
Murrell, Anita A743
Murrell, Jim P440
Murrell, Anita E373
Murren, James J. A558
Murrer, B. A. W199
Murry, Jerry A A61
Murry, Stefan J. E21
Mursuli, Vivian P559
Murtagh, Nigel J. A728
Murter, Jeffrey A505
Murtha, Mark G. A412
Murtha, Claire P140
Murtha, Jay P379
Murtha, Mark G. E192
Murthy, Ramesh A408
Murto, Risto W386
Murty, Albern W360
Murungi, David M P204
Musacchia, Shanti A204
Musacchia, Jacqueline P99
Musayev, Igor A474
Musayev, Igor P262
Musca, Robert A850
Musen, Robert M. A701
Musgrave, Kendra A441
Musheno, Donise P217
Mushosho, Jonas W275
Musi, Diane E57
Musich, Michelle P195
Musick, Tom P509
Musil, Kevin P483
Musile, Antonio A671
Musk, Elon A799
Musk, Elon P559
Musselman, Barry A700
Musselman, Bennett E191
Musser, Eric S. A238
Musser, Jeffrey S. A312
Musser, Reilly P462
Musso, Chris A661
Mustafa, Aman A912
Mustafa, Shahid W360
Muster, Alan P680
Mustian, J Perry P42
Mustian, Perry P262
Mustier, Jean-Pierre W380
Mustos, Carl W180
Mutch, Marcy D. A349
Mutch, Cecile A485
Mutch, Marcy D. E156
Muthler, Craig A360
Muthler, Craig E164
Muto, Gary P. A79
Muto, Koichi W246
Muto, Naoto W342
Muzaffar, Farooq A911
Muzzillo, Karen P584
Muzzy, Doug A407
Mwangi, John A537
Myagkikh, Maria A61
Myat, Kaung P286
Mychalowych, Jerome A550
Myer, John W176
Myers, Bill A3
Myers, Tim D. A76
Myers, Doug A81
Myers, Timothy D. (Tim) A103
Myers, Timothy A136
Myers, Lindsay A157
Myers, Christopher D. (Chris) A248
Myers, Dan A295
Myers, Carol A346
Myers, Cynthia M. A356
Myers, Curtis J. A369
Myers, Hallie A461
Myers, Ben A475
Myers, Thomas D. A487
Myers, Jodi A558
Myers, Daniel A567
Myers, Fred A585
Myers, Kendall A751

Myers, Daniel P. (Dan) A891
Myers, Jeff A908
Myers, Joseph P29
Myers, David P34
Myers, Donald P37
Myers, Isaac J. P58
Myers, Lora P85
Myers, Marcy P110
Myers, Ben P154
Myers, Ben P266
Myers, Richard B P270
Myers, Mike P318
Myers, Adam L. P336
Myers, Ana P352
Myers, Seth P372
Myers, Fred P377
Myers, Michelle R P422
Myers, H Carter P424
Myers, Kevin P425
Myers, John J. P494
Myers, Catherine V P638
Myers, Jessica P653
Myers, Amy P660
Myers, Russ P697
Myers, Larry W. E160
Myers, Byron E217
Myers, Keith G. E244
Myers, Randy E250
Myers, Kendall E378
Myers, Daniel P. (Dan) E434
Mylonas, Paul W253
Mynatt, John P254
Myochin, Toru W329
Myron, Paul A76
Myron, Thomas R A127
Myszewski, Denice A542
Myszewski, Denice E267
Myszka, Kenneth F. E245
Myszka, Jeffrey E245
M-oki-Kala, Jyrki W257
M-rch, Lars Stensgaard W118
M-ller, Luis A. E83
Müller, Ralph W125
Müller, Matthias W390

N

Nabel, Elizabeth G. (Betsy) A635
Nabel, Elizabeth G. (Betsy) P419
Nabel, Elizabeth G P567
Naber, Andrew A3
Naber, Mike P115
Naber, Stephen P629
Nacey, Sean A888
Nachman, Joseph R. (Jed) E447
Nachmann, Marc A389
Nachtigal, Amy P474
Nackers, Gary P162
Nacpil, Catherine A541
Nacpil, Catherine E266
Nadar, Shiv P228
Nadarajan, Gunalan A698
Nadarajan, Gunalan P456
Naddeo, Eric A836
Nadeau, Renee A158
Nadeau, Gerard F. A451
Nadeau, Sherri P A792
Nadeau, David P43
Nadeau, Richard J. E265
Nadel, Hiyam P590
Nadella, Satya A560
Nader, Elizabeth A109
Nader, Elizabeth E36
Nadig, David A33
Nadimpalli, Aditya P321
Nadkarni, Pranay A40
Nadkarni, Rajeev E300
Nadolny, Stephanie P93
Nagae, Shusaku W282
Nagai, Michael A667
Nagai, Shigeto W48
Nagai, Koji W268
Nagai, Michael E336
Nagamatsu, Shoichi W268

Nagamori, Shigenobu W259
Nagamoto, Toshio P214
Naganathan, Nagi P613
Nagano, Hisashi W342
Nagano, Tsuyoshi W367
Nagao, Tatsunosuke W192
Nagao, Narumi W213
Nagao, Masahiko W351
Nagao, Yutaka W400
NAGAOKA, SUSUMU W39
Nagaoka, Takashi W245
Nagarajan, Rajesh A177
Nagarajan, Sundaram (Naga) A450
Nagarkar, Niranjan A131
Nagasawa, Hitoshi W264
Nagata, Ron A410
Nagata, Paul A532
Nagata, Kenichi W246
Nagata, Osamu (Simon) W374
Nagayama, Osamu W307
Nagel, Paul A260
Nagel, Troy A406
Nagel, Brian A502
Nagel, Brian A851
Nagel, John A905
Nagel, Debra P233
Nagel, Joanne P356
Nagel, Wendy P406
Nagel, John P693
Nagel, Alberto N. W237
Nagelberg, Allison E284
Nagelkerk, Jean P218
Nager, Thomas A51
Nager, Jeff A806
Nagesh, Reddivalen P671
Naggar, Lela A800
Naggar, Lela E396
Nagji, Bansi A546
Nagorsky, Brian A541
Nagorsky, Brian E266
Nagpaul, Ravinder P587
Nagy, Richard A247
Nagy, Kate A333
Nagy, Shayne A572
Nagy, Tom A729
Nagy, Kim P396
Nagy, Richard E102
Nagy-todd, Salit A693
Nahdi, Mohamed Abdulla Al W130
Nahhas, Kamal A865
Naidoo, Shirley P399
Naidoo, Vassi W256
Naidu, Harsh P282
Naidu, Tulsi R. W405
Naik, Piyush A130
Naik, Harshad A443
Nair, Vas A76
Nair, Hari A311
Nair, Raj A362
Nair, Aswathy A513
Nair, Roopa A683
Nair, Auro P587
Nair, Balan W222
Nair, Ajai E102
Naito, Tomo P546
Naito, Tadaaki W264
Naito, Shunichi W349
Naja, Khaled P152
Najima, Hirotaka W116
Najimi, Parnaz A877
Najjar, Ted A390
Nakagawa, Hiroshi W190
Nakagawa, Kuniharu W190
Nakagawa, Junko W268
Nakagome, Kenji W353
Nakahara, Tina A102
Nakahara, Sean E51
Nakai, Shogo W245
Nakai, Takuji W264
Nakajima, Shuichi W147
Nakajima, Shigehiro W155
Nakajima, Yuji W200
Nakajima, Hajime W207
Nakajima, Yutaka W268
Nakamae, Koji W301

A = AMERICAN BUSINESS
E = EMERGING COMPANIES
P = PRIVATE COMPANIES
W = WORLD BUSINESS

Nakamine, Yuji W235
Nakamoto, David P123
Nakamura, Michael P172
Nakamura, Takeshi W48
Nakamura, Mitsuyoshi W201
Nakamura, Akira W213
Nakamura, Jiro W260
Nakamura, Kimiyasu W265
Nakamura, Kunio W282
Nakamura, Yukio W329
Nakamura, Tomomi W342
Nakao, Seiya W374
Nakasato, Davin A102
Nakaso, Hiroshi W48
Nakasone, Norman A183
Nakasone, Robert A432
Nakasuji, Jody P226
Nakata, Toru W190
Nakata, Yuji W268
Nakatsuka, Ralph Y. A798
Nakayama, Masaaki W116
Nakayama, Toshiki W272
Nakazawa, Kazuo A272
Nakis, Dominic J. A15
Nakis, Dominic J. P9
Nalamasu, Omkaram (Om) A71
Nalbandian, Ed P52
Naldi, Robert P302
Nalitt, Craig A34
Nalitt, Craig P27
Nallen, John P A834
Nally, Thomas A (Tom) A791
Nam, Sik W292
Nama, Veeresh A413
Nama, Veeresh P234
Naman, Ananth E50
Namana, Vinod P568
Nambiar, Vinod A218
Nan, Feng Hua W95
Nanavaty, Maulik A144
Nanberg, Joshua A127
Nance, William A P563
Nance, Mark E1
Nancy, Gordon P538
Nanda, Ann A677
Nanda, Sanjiv A685
Nanda, Nihar P402
Nandakumar, Anita A390
Nansen, Erik A537
Nanterme, Pierre W5
Nanthawithaya, Arthid W330
Nanty, Jer-´me W14
Naouri, Jean-Charles W83
Naouri, Jean-Charles W298
Naples, Richard J. A119
Napol, Marcello A3
Napoleon, Rexann E399
Napoli, Gus A434
Napolitan, Raymond S. A605
Napolitan, Ray A605
Napolitano, Glen A333
Napolitano, Kenneth (Ken) A914
Napolitano, Jason A. E196
Napper, Terry P152
Nappi, David A912
Nappi, Ralph A. P390
Naqvi, Syed P103
Naraki, Kazuhide W208
Narang, Manu A49
Narang, Steve A111
Narang, Steve P56
Narang, Vic P508
Narasimhan, Laxman A647
Narayan, Kumar A204
Narayanan, Lakshmi A217
Narayanan, Krishnan A390
Narayanan, Gowri A537
Narayanan, Ramanathan P11
Narayen, Shantanu A11

Narciso, Paul J. A722
Nardecchia, Chris A712
Nardizzi, Steven P697
Nardone, Mary Kaye A500
Nardone, Michael A555
Nardone, Robert A869
Nardone, Joseph R P678
Nardone, Mary Kaye E237
Narendran, T. V. W358
Narev, Ian W105
Nario, Kristine R. E302
Narisety, Chalapathy P261
Narla, Mohandas P372
Narosky, Mary A188
Narowitz, Randy P621
Naruszewicz, Nina P653
Narwani, Gaurav A759
Nasca, David J. E135
Nash, Kevin A13
Nash, William D. (Bill) A166
Nash, Joseph A553
Nash, Michael A837
Nash, Jeffrey L P158
Nash, Felicia P387
Nash, Anita P526
Nash, Donna P535
Nash, David P618
Nash, Joseph E272
Nashar, Raniya Mahmood
   Abdulwahab W316
Nasir, L Paul A782
Naslund, Chuck A42
Nasser, Husna A40
Nasser, Jacques A. (Jac) W63
Nasser, Jac W64
Nassetta, Christopher J. (Chris) A421
Nastasi, Richard P32
Nasuovska, Biljana A481
Nasuti, Joanne A359
Natale, J A119
Natale, Lisa A611
Natale, Peter P339
Natale, Marina W380
Natale, Lisa E313
Natarajan, Venkata A676
Natarajan, Murali A710
Natell, Brian A871
Natelli, Thomas A. E73
Nath, Deepak A5
Nath, Karthik A105
Nath, Munindra A201
Nath, Debby P508
Nath, Pravene P538
Nathan, Scott A108
Nathan, Mike A904
Nathan, Scott E35
Nathan, Mike E442
Nathanson, Jonathan A520
Nathenson, Michael (Mike) P77
Natoli, Joe P57
Natt, Susan A576
Natt, Alec P183
Natt, Susan E297
Natten, Gary Van A246
Naughton, Marc G. A186
Naughton, Duncan C. Mac A274
Naughton, W Terrance A886
Naughton, Des W74
Naughton, Timothy J. (Tim) E26
Naughton, W Terrance E433
Naughton-Gerdes, Joan A34
Naugle, Bob P282
Naugle, Gary R P660
Naugler, Scott P410
Naumann, Peter A855
Nava, Carmen P A85
Nava, Mario A221
Nava, Mr Joe P293
Nava, Peter P435
Navarre, Christophe W225
Navarro, Jen A374
Navarro, Mary W. A440
Navarro, Imelda A459
Navarro, Lisa P278
Navy, David A489

Nawab, Hamid P80
Nawrocki, Alyce P134
Nayak, Vinayak A17
Nayak, Vinayak P10
Nayama, Michisuke W241
Nayar, Deepak E247
Nayar, Sid E296
Naylor, Jeffrey A817
Nazareno, Jeffrey P338
Nazarian, Jeanette A475
Nazarian, Marita Q P45
Nazarian, Jeanette P266
Nazarian, Arthur P527
Nazemetz, Patricia A916
Nazza, Larry A572
Nazza, Larry E288
Nazzaro, Stephen F. (Steve) A766
Ndego, John W389
Neagle, Kelly A620
Neal, Michelle M. A105
Neal, Darcee A115
Neal, Krista A201
Neal, Stephen C. A509
Neal, Gary F. A839
Neal, Joel A877
Neal, Lavone P65
Neal, Theron P120
Neal, Charles P148
Neal, Mikele P174
Neal, Brian P467
Neal, Jake P561
Neal, John W297
Neal, Gary F. E409
Neal, James R. (Jim) E447
Neale, George A. A734
Neale, Gary L. E283
Nealon, Kathleen A740
Nealon, Thomas M. (Tom) A755
Nearhood, William A333
Neary, Ke P482
Neary, Tom E328
Neate, James W50
Neblett, Glenn M. E57
Necas, Kevin P646
Necastro, Butch A33
NeCastro, Timothy G. A306
Nedd, Paul P473
Nedder, Michael A359
Nedl, Katie A130
Nedungadi, Shreenath P99
Neeb, Marc J. W229
Needel, Jerry E44
Needham, Sabine P18
Needham, Judy P201
Needham, John P250
Needham, Floyd E. E288
Neel, Michael A818
Neel, Monty P404
Neeley, Paige A298
Neely, Eric A487
Neely, Emily A614
Neely, Scott A676
Neely, Cathy P284
Neely, Jodi P685
Neemeh, Alain A701
Neemuchwala, Abidali P693
Neese, Jane P612
Neff, Clay A192
Neff, Lorraine A244
Nefsky, Phyllis P697
Negishi, Akio W238
Negron, Felipe E445
Negr--n, Eduardo J. A661
Neher, Terry A865
Neibart, Lee E355
Neice, Keith Mc P97
Neidenbach, Joseph J P537
Neidlein, Paul P256
Neidorff, Michael F. A179
Neidorff, Michael F. A180
Neifert, Kevin T. A695
Neighbors, Bobby G P260
Neighbors, Elizabeth E77
Neighbours, John A345
Neike, Cedrik W331

Neill, James R. (Jim) A381
Neill, Thomas P618
Neilon, Jay A706
Neilon, Jay E353
Neilson, Steve P173
Neilson, Duncan P285
Neilson, Eric G. P398
Neilson, Geoff E354
Neis, Douglas A. E257
Nekrasov, Vladimir I. W290
Nell, Steven E. A137
Nelms, David W A268
Nelms, Cary T A782
Nelsen, Keith J. A126
Nelsen, Denise A763
Nelsen, Mark A874
Nelsen, Suzanne P514
Nelsen, Colleen E383
Nelson, Lawrence A13
Nelson, Ronald L. (Ron) A93
Nelson, Roy A96
Nelson, Robert A105
Nelson, Shelby A111
Nelson, Christopher (Chris) A117
Nelson, Chris A117
Nelson, Kevin A164
Nelson, Rosemary A218
Nelson, Doug A223
Nelson, Brent A246
Nelson, David A260
Nelson, Faye A. A280
Nelson, Lisa A295
Nelson, Ann W. A296
Nelson, John P. A296
Nelson, Zac A345
Nelson, Paul A371
Nelson, Kimberly A. (Kim) A377
Nelson, Rick A397
Nelson, William A448
Nelson, Mike A463
Nelson, Philip B A528
Nelson, Philip A528
Nelson, Susan K. A548
Nelson, Linda A A562
Nelson, Jonathan B. A619
Nelson, Mike A622
Nelson, Rick A655
Nelson, Deanna A744
Nelson, Rick A746
Nelson, Scott A788
Nelson, Jon A817
Nelson, Michael S. A857
Nelson, George A872
Nelson, David D. (Dave) A889
Nelson, Mary A912
Nelson, Zac A920
Nelson, Bryan L P42
Nelson, Bryan P42
Nelson, Wendell P46
Nelson, Shelby P56
Nelson, Maria P60
Nelson, Steven P88
Nelson, Kristin P93
Nelson, Jerrie P94
Nelson, Carrie P96
Nelson, Jeff A P108
Nelson, David P133
Nelson, W Britt P141
Nelson, Mark W. P143
Nelson, Scott P175
Nelson, Neil W P184
Nelson, Deana L. P197
Nelson, Jennifer P216
Nelson, Rick P221
Nelson, Gregory V P243
Nelson, William P246
Nelson, Kathy P257
Nelson, Doug P269
Nelson, Donnita P270
Nelson, Suzy P313
Nelson, Marilyn Carlson P317
Nelson, Keith P323
Nelson, Kevin P369
Nelson, Jeff P433
Nelson, Don P441

Nelson, Marie P445
Nelson, Becky P481
Nelson, Nika P503
Nelson, Peter P653
Nelson, Scott M. P670
Nelson, Ted E1
Nelson, Joyce E44
Nelson, Pierre E122
Nelson, Stephen E. E183
Nelson, Brad E253
Nelson, Linda A E279
Nelson, Rick E333
Nelson, Bradford T E394
Nelson, Sarah E426
Nemat, Claudia W126
Nemec, Mark R. P610
Nemecek, Eneida P410
Nemeroff, Wendy E119
Nemerov, Jacki A691
Nemeth, Kathy A109
Nemeth, Matt A323
Nemeth, Jeffery A362
Nemeth, Julio A671
Nemeth, Rudolph A675
Nemeth, Joseph P329
Nemeth, Kathy E36
Nemeth, Andy L. E324
Nemoto, Masaaki W246
Nemphos, Ann A406
Nemser, Earl H. E221
Nenaber, Donna P72
Nenadal, Cody A777
Nenadal, Cody E393
Nenninger, Clyde P202
Nenow, Mark E86
Nentchev, Nentcho A133
Nentwig, Robert J. A143
Nepveux, Kevin A648
Nerbonne, Daniel A658
Nerbonne, Dan A658
Nerenhausen, Frank R A625
Neri, Antonio A418
Neri, Marc A777
Neri, Christine A901
Neri, Leticia P134
Neri, Christine P692
Neri, Marc E393
Nerino, Alfred P337
NESBIT, JONATHAN A767
Nesbit, Kirk A780
Nesbit, Jeff A817
Nesbit, Dennis P456
Nesbitt, Stephen R. A437
Nesbitt, Douglas A703
Nesbitt, John W348
Nesci, James D. A675
Nesi, Victor J. A771
Neske, Rainer W215
Ness, Laura A855
Ness, Steve A881
Ness, Glenn P184
Ness, Jon P277
Ness, Edwin A P359
Ness, W. Denman Van E447
Nesselbush, Robert P463
Nesta, Cheryl A402
Nestadt, Paul P266
Nestegard, Susan K A432
Nester, Brian A. P287
Nesti, Sarah P392
Nestlerode, R. Edward A640
Nestor, Adrienne A56
Netherton, Linda A330
Neto, Jo-- o Manuel Manso W134
Nette, Claus-Georg W234
Nettesheim, Susan A476
Nettleton, Joe E54
Netto, Armando L. E163
Neu, Laurel A599
Neu, Robert P192
Neu, Erica P697
Neubauer, Joseph P610
Neubaur, D Ick A314
Neubaur, D Ick P190
Neubert, Hanswerner A199

Neugarten, Lisa A449
Neugent, Christopher J. A663
Neuhaus, Joan P21
Neuhaus, Joan P148
Neujahr, Fred P521
Neuman, Susan B A585
Neuman, Jennifer A585
Neuman, Susan B P377
Neuman, Jennifer P377
Neumann, Spencer A10
Neumann, Karl-Thomas A378
Neumann, Dan A655
Neumann, Amy Elliott P348
Neumann, Paul W194
Neumann, Dan E333
Neumeister, Irene P477
Neumeyer, Daniel J. A440
Neupaver, Albert E172
Neuts, Amanda A160
Neuts, Amanda E55
Nevarez, Pedro P291
Neve, Douglas C P183
Neveling, Lisa P391
Nevens, T Michael A580
Nevers, Rick L. P48
Neville, Robert M. A98
Neville, Robert M. E33
Nevins, Steven P211
Nevo-Hacohen, Talya E363
New, Wayne P144
New, John P543
Newan, Karla A446
Newan, Karla E210
Newberg, William A878
Newbern, Thomas B. A90
Newberry, Stephen G. (Steve) A501
Newberry, Peter P81
Newberry, Gary A. E53
Newbery, Michelle M. A521
Newbigging, Alexander W195
Newbower, Ronald S P590
Newbrough, James P. P405
Newbry, Bill P415
Newcomb, Matthew A846
Newcomb, Matthew A872
Newcomb, Mike P285
Newcomer, Mark A309
Newcomer, John A384
Newcomer, Patti A466
Newcomer, John E176
Newell, Scott A729
Newell, Eric R A846
Newell, Michele A881
Newell, John D P643
Newfield, Richard U. A573
Newhall, Charles W. (Chuck) E391
Newhouse, Greg A489
Newhouse, Martin P281
Newkirk, Christopher T. A163
Newlands, William A. (Bill) A235
Newman, Randy A29
Newman, Tracy A101
Newman, Kenneth Kenneth
  Newman A105
Newman, Rebecca A105
Newman, Drew A204
Newman, Sallie A244
Newman, Dennis A270
Newman, Jenifer A310
Newman, Margaret A411
Newman, Michael A449
Newman, Amy A449
Newman, Rainer A476
Newman, Gerald A545
Newman, Brian A647
Newman, Robert A655
Newman, Kurt P113
Newman, Nicholas P115
Newman, Ricardo P143
Newman, Mark F. P168
Newman, David P386
Newman, Gina P498
Newman, Randy E9
Newman, Giles R. E97
Newman, Jeffrey B. (Jeff) E134

Newman, Robert E333
Newmiller, Wayne A681
Newmyer, Joyce P7
Newpol, Jon P628
Newport, Roger K. A26
Newschaffer, Craig P165
Newsom, Richard W. (Rick) A227
Newsom, Gavin A764
Newsom, Terri P167
Newsom, Gavin P540
Newsome, Earl A514
Newsome, Jana P385
Newson, Stephanie P428
Newton, Mike A49
Newton, Debra A201
Newton, Todd A575
Newton, Carl A731
Newton, Steve P64
Newton, Harold P90
Newton, Michael P311
Newton, Gayle P425
Newton, Julianne P651
Newton, Dee D P699
Newton, Mark E173
Newton, Carl E365
Ney, John F P372
Neyland, Stephen J P342
Neylon, Brian V. A270
Neylon, Tom E158
Neymon, Denys W343
Nezhat, Ceana P395
Ng, John A40
Ng, Melanie A131
Ng, Dominic A285
Ng, Stella A480
Ng, Yee A533
Ng, Regina A537
Ng, Chaki A871
Ng, Bee A874
Ng, Lily P440
NG, Larry P699
Ng, Kenneth L. W3
Ng, Dominic E114
Ng, Chong E235
Ngau, Jonathan W. E242
Ngo, A. Catherine A183
Ngo, Michelle E232
Ngo, Nhat H. E316
Nguyen, Thong M. A100
Nguyen, Kim A250
Nguyen, Duc A343
Nguyen, Michael A406
Nguyen, Xuong A465
Nguyen, Tony A555
Nguyen, Trung A698
Nguyen, Tricia A801
Nguyen, Jeff P28
Nguyen, Andy H P145
Nguyen, Lan Quoc P208
Nguyen, Steven P208
Nguyen, Trung P456
Nguyen, Mong Thi P543
Nguyen, Tricia P562
Nguyen, Mai P619
Nguyen, Linh P672
Nguyen, Thi Mai Thanh W195
Nguyen, Van E253
Nguyen-Duy, Jonathan E166
Niall, Oconnor A70
Niblock, Robert A. A520
Nicandrou, Nic W295
Nicart, Maureen P471
Nicastro, Vincent P. P667
Niccolucci, Dani A813
Niccolucci, Dani P616
Nicdao, Nicole A721
Niceberg, Michael A175
Nicely, Jerald A797
Nicely, Jerald P557
Niceswanger, Glenna P30
Nicfaralnd, Kenn P345
Nichitean, Florin P164
Nichol, Janett A593
Nichol, Cynthia P433
Nicholas, Heidi A360

Nicholas, Georgette C. A382
Nicholas, George A478
Nicholas, Jim A480
Nicholas, Brad A681
Nicholas, Marc P234
Nicholas, Richard P609
Nicholas, Terry P669
Nicholas, Heidi E164
Nicholls, Timothy S. (Tim) A462
Nichols, Todd A129
Nichols, Lee A162
Nichols, Ronald O. A291
Nichols, Jim A346
Nichols, Rodney P. A527
Nichols, Dana L. A683
Nichols, Ronald O. (R.O.) A752
Nichols, Donald A827
Nichols, Todd A865
Nichols, Bryan P65
Nichols, Deborah P143
Nichols, Greg P172
Nichols, Lonnie P238
Nichols, Brenda P273
Nichols, Gretchen P285
Nichols, Connie H P427
Nichols, Dana L. E341
Nicholson, Glenn A196
Nicholson, E. Allen A248
Nicholson, Darryl A476
Nicholson, Robert A500
Nicholson, Marla A532
Nicholson, Lyle A835
Nicholson, Matt P154
Nicholson, Jan P260
Nicholson, Brenda P435
Nicholson, James B P441
Nicholson, James M P441
Nicholson, David A P441
Nicholson, Jennifer P466
Nicholson, William R. E39
Nicholson, Robert E238
Nicholson, Steve E248
Nick, Barbara P151
Nickel, Kenneth A869
Nickel, Jackie P3
Nickel-Schindewolf, Sue P99
Nickele, Christopher J. (Chris) A213
Nickele, Gary E228
Nickels, Jeff A346
Nickens, A J P47
Nickerson, Richard A160
Nickerson, Grace P521
Nickerson, Richard E55
Nickles, Jenny A441
Nicklin, Emily P611
Nickman, Gene A165
Nickol, Christopher A734
Nickol, Thomas P277
Nickoles, Cheryl P644
Nicksa, Gary P80
Nicola, Cindy A799
Nicola, Steven F. E263
Nicolai, Jason P79
Nicolais, Michael R. E112
Nicolas, Charles A795
Nicolelli, Maurizio E140
Nicoletti, Laurie A537
Nicoletti, Ralph J. A586
Nicolino, Lynda P296
Nicolosi, Michael A741
Nicolosi, Michael E370
Nicosia, Santo V P225
Nicotra, Christy P205
Nides, Thomas R. (Tom) A568
Niebur, Hana P117
Niedbalski, Dave A517
Nieden, Paul zur A330
Niedziejko, John P51
Niedzielski, Vincent P. (Vince) E226
Niedzielski, Vince E226
Niehaus, James A51
Niehaus, Brenda W339
Niehaus, Sheila E46
Niekamp, Cynthia A96
Niekamp, Frank A564

A = AMERICAN BUSINESS	
E = EMERGING COMPANIES	
P = PRIVATE COMPANIES	
W = WORLD BUSINESS	

Nielsen, Chris A109
Nielsen, Josh A273
Nielsen, Mark D. A368
Nielsen, Rob A478
Nielsen, Jane H. A691
Nielsen, Mark D A695
Nielsen, James L. (Jim) A759
Nielsen, Paul D. P96
Nielsen, Josh P162
Nielsen, James M P319
Nielsen, Rick P368
Nielsen, Gloria P422
Nielsen, Milt P563
Nielsen, Bjorn P628
Nielsen, Peter W312
Nielsen, Chris W374
Nielsen, Chris E36
Nielson, Marlin A519
Niem, Eddie A218
Nieman, Rich A108
NIEMAN, ROGER P2
Niemann, Angela A311
Niemeyer, Bruce A192
Niemi, Albert W. P514
Niemoeller, John Arthur A348
Nienaber, Lisa A500
Nienaber, Margaret W339
Nienaber, Lisa E237
Nierenberg, Gregg A93
Niermann, Nils W58
Nietert, William P48
Nieto, Alejandra A648
Nieto, Luis A718
Nieto, Lourdes P109
Nieto, Enrique Pena W285
Nieuwenhuys, Gerard A642
Nieves, Antonio De Jesus P70
Nieves, Frankie P609
Nigg, Dan P141
Nightingale, Timothy P. A160
Nightingale, Timothy P. E55
Nigon, Thomas A886
Nigon, Thomas E433
Nigrin, Daniel P570
Nigro, Joseph (Joe) A308
Nigro, Stephen (Steve) A435
Nigro, James M. A500
Nigro, James M. E237
Nihei, Ryo W223
Niimura, Ken A102
Niinami, Takeshi W349
Niitani, Brian P19
Nijenhuis, Wouter A142
Nikias, Chrysostomos L. (Max) A860
Nikias, Chrysostomos L. (Max) P656
Nikolaus, Donald H. A277
Nikolov, Anita A599
Nikstad, Timothy P48
Niland, Mark A785
Niles, Thomas A568
Niles, D Michael P213
Niles, Amy P420
Nill, Michael R. (Mike) A186
Nilsson, Ted P264
Nilsson, Ola W3
Nilsson, Stefan W352
Nilsson, Sven-Christer E68
Nimah, Sam P196
Nimbley, Thomas J. A638
Nimer, Richard A2
Nimsgern, Kristi A333
Ning, Wilson A502
Ninneman, Tom E381
Nino, Vicki A183
Nino, Vicki E66
Niper, Chrissy A724
Nipper, Matthew A489
Nirenberg, David P610
Nisbeth, G. Richard E76

Nisbett, Mark A883
Nishi, Masao A782
Nishi, Motohide E268
Nishida, Mitsuo W344
Nishigori, Yuichi W279
Nishihara, Shigeru W336
Nishikata, Masaaki W249
Nishimura, Karen S A740
Nishimura, Christine P236
Nishimura, Tatsushi W116
Nishimura, Karen S E369
Nishitani, Hideto W279
Nishizawa, Keiji W336
Nissen, Mitch P318
Nissen, Tim P406
Nissen, James A P422
Nissen, J. Ted E153
Nissenson, Allen R. A255
Nist, Tom A441
Nitecki, Danuta P165
Nitzan, Nachman W150
Niu, Wen P7
Niubo, Antonio Brufau W300
Niven, Mary M A272
Niver, Clair A647
Nix, Rudy A303
Nix, Craig L. A341
Nix, D Mark P248
Nix, Sarah P428
Nix, Craig L. E153
Nixon, Ken A115
Nixon, Dennis E. A459
Nixon, Barbara A724
Nixon, Bill A727
Nixon, George P319
Nixon, Bruce P676
Nizza, Arthur P252
Nizzari-Mcclain, Cynthia P659
Njonjo, Peter A215
Nkongho, Andrew A691
Nkuhlu, Mfundo W256
Noack, Daniel A658
Noack, David P491
Noakes, Jackie W217
Nober, Roger A134
Nober, Roger A154
Nober, Roger P77
Nobile, Paul A67
Noble, Quintin A5
Noble, Jeff A343
Noble, Jen A460
Noble, Craig A644
Noble, Siba A774
Noble, Anthony A871
Noble, Steve P127
Noble, David P217
Noble, Kim P511
Nobles, Melissa P313
Nobles, Sharon P388
Nobles, Herbert P401
Noblett, Monique A599
Nocchiero, Tony E53
Nocella, Andrew P. A846
Nodiff, Eric W. E56
Noe, Alan A700
Noeker, Jeffrey A332
Noel, Tom A302
Noel, Tom E128
Noelke, Virginia P497
Noelle, Boudler A768
Noga, James W. (Jim) A635
Noga, James W. (Jim) P419
Nogalski, John A483
Nogles, Thomas A407
Noguchi, Tadahiko W273
Nohra, Jude J. A845
Nohra, Jude J. E413
Nolan, Joe A71
Nolan, Patrick A142
Nolan, Joseph R. (Joe) A307
Nolan, Michael J. (Mike) A328
Nolan, James A390
Nolan, Bill A546
Nolan, Elizabeth A766
Nolan, David A. A918

Nolan, Mary Anne P97
Nolan, Greg P105
Nolan, Carrie P307
Nolan, Kevin P400
Nolan, James J P470
Nolan, John P512
Nolan, James J. (Jim) E222
Nolan, Conor E273
Noland, Matt A832
Noland, Curt R. E201
Noll, Kelly A33
Noll, Richard A. (Rich) A400
Noll, Chuck P629
Nollett, Jessica A302
Nollett, Jessica E128
Nolte, Jo A640
Nolting, John A489
Nomoto, Michael P547
Nomura, Mitsuru W48
Nomura, Katsuaki W326
Nomura, Tetsuya W327
Nonaka, Toshihiko W172
Nonog, Elvira P497
Nonomura, Rikiya W268
Nooijer, Marcel de W14
Nook, Greg P256
Nook, Gregory E. (Greg) P257
Noon, Sandy P6
Noonan, Mike A201
Noonan, James R. A500
Noonan, Karla P352
Noonan, James R. E237
Noone, Alyssa A697
Noone, Alyssa P454
Noordende, Alexander M. (Sander) van't W5
Noordhoek, Jeffrey R. (Jeff) A579
Noorzad, Omar P623

Noot, Walter E423
Nooyi, Indra K. A647
Nopar, Bob P623
Norblom, Joan P254
Norby, Stephanie L. P506
Norcia, Gerardo (Jerry) A280
Norcross, Gary A. A330
Norcross, Anna A489
Norcross, Jeanne A757
Norcross, George E. P576
Nordby, Hans G. E97
Nordenberg, Mark P651
Nordgren, Robert P698
Nordli, Lars Johannes W144
Nordlie, Elizabeth M. A377
Nordmeyer, Greg A56
Nordstrom, Blake W. A596
Nordstrom, Peter E. (Pete) A596
Nordstrom, Erik B. A596
Nordstrom, James F. (Jamie) A596
Nordyke, Gloria P214
Norenberg, John A15
Norenberg, John P9
Norfleet, Edward A324
Norfolk, John P644
Norick, Ronald A98
Norick, Ronald E33
Noriega, Erica A244
Noritz, Garey P365
Nork, Rick P679
Norkus, Hans E172
Norling, Lars-- ...ke W360
Norman, Gail A98
Norman, Todd A313
Norman, Paul T. A485
Norman, Jim P27
Norman, Tonia P52
Norman, Bert P249
Norman, Karen Van P494
Norman, Linda P615
Norman, Archie W233
Norman, Gail E33
Norman, David E65
Norman, Vickie E234
Normand, Joe P140
Normile, Robert (Bob) A539

Normington, Debbie A199
Noro, Yukio W344
Noronha, Wilbert A823
Norring, David A738
Norris, Derek J. A102
Norris, Derek J. A103
Norris, Josephine A480
Norris, Patricia A769
Norris, Helen P109
Norris, Carlos W P148
Norris, Robin P685
Norris, Rick E172
Norrman, Helena W360
Norrod, Forrest E. A14
North, Paul A405
North, John F. A515
North, Scott A759
North, Christopher (Chris) E368
Northam, Thadd A532
Northam, Jaime E189
Northcutt, Carla A402
Northcutt, Martha A438
Northcutt, Kevin A446
Northcutt, Kendria A655
Northcutt, Kevin E210
Northcutt, Kendria E333
Northern, Donna A774
Northrop, Ann A354
Norton, Ted A260
Norton, Susan A. A338
Norton, Rick A397
Norton, Ellen A526
Norton, Robert G. (Bob) A635
Norton, David K. A644
Norton, W.D. (Joe) A755
Norton, Noah A920
Norton, Gale P36
Norton, Sidney P115
Norton, Rick P221
Norton, Robert G. (Bob) P419
Norton, Margareta E P451
Norton, Margareta E. (Meg) P452
Norton, W.D. (Joe) E380
Norwitt, Richard A. (Adam) A62
Norwood, Eric P158
Nosal, Edward A323
Nosca-lay, Paula A136
Noseworthy, Darren A649
Noskov, Mikhail W376
Nosler, John S. A703
Nossick, Charles A823
Nossick, Charles P622
Nota, Pieter W59
Notaristefani, Carlo de W363
Noteboom, Diana A232
Noth, Thomas W356
Noto, Lucio A643
Nottingham, Scott P116
Nourot, Mary P549
Nourse, Hal P273
Novack, Elizabeth I P38
Novaes, Djalma A242
Novaes, Lucas P37
Novak, Dan A685
Novak, Scott A725
Novak, Christopher P22
Novak, Ernest P404
Novakovic, Phebe N. A374
Novakovich, Mark E93
Novielli, Jack A675
Noviello, Nicholas R. (Nick) A778
Novo, Guillermo A24
Novy, Benjamin E424
Nowaczyk, Barbara A22
Nowak, Mark P572
Nowell, Memory P389
Nowicki, Joseph M. A117
Nowicki, Edward A649
Nowicki, Paul P196
Nowlin, Bill A693
Noyes, Mark A233
Nuchims, Fran A163
Nuckols, Jeff A419
Nudi, Jonathon J. (Jon) A377
Nugent, Patrick A478

Nugent, Judy A A635
Nugent, Judy A P419
Nuki, Masayoshi W213
Nulter, Steven A645
Nulter, Steven E329
Numata, Shigeru W116
Numata, Kaoru W268
Nunez, Armando A173
Nunez, Ricardo J A411
Nunez, Frank P162
Nunez, Milton P292
Nunez-Mejia, Bibi P420
Nunis, Annette A84
Nunley, Debbie P324
Nunn, Lucy P628
Nunn, Trudy P677
Nuon, Leslie A919
Nurmi, Kathleen P444
Nusbaum, Nathan R P90
Nusbaum, Barbara P525
Nuss, Robert P642
Nussbaum, Craig A537
Nussbaum, Mark P501
Nusterer, Norbert A246
Nusum, Jeremy P431
Nutheti, Guru A607
Nutt, Pam P234
Nutt, Raymond P455
Nutt, William V P594
Nutter, Gary A169
Nutter, Michael A244
Nutton, Debra A909
Nuzzolo, Marc A869
Nu- ±ez, Juan A899
Nu- ±ez, Juan P690
Nye, Catherine A449
Nyenhuis, Michael P37
Nyhuis, Bev P218
Nykoluk, Tim P41
Nylund, Arne A305
Nylund, Arne P185
Nyman, Robert P107
Nysschen, Carel Johannes de A378
Nyul, Renata P392
N-·oger, Lorenz W166
N-·¦ss, Bj-·rn Erik W129
Néemeh, Álain P. A701

O

Oachs, Bradley W. E13
Oahaver, Cort A839
Oahaver, Cort E409
Oakes, John A61
Oakes, Greg A168
Oakes, Stephanie A A640
Oakland, Steven T. A748
Oakley, Chris A322
Oaks, Patrick P256
Oasan, Ann E P21
Oates, Joseph P. A233
Oates, Michael P. A330
Oates, Gary P635
Oba, Masashi W367
Obana, William G P601
Obando, Glenn A105
Obayashi, Takeo W273
Obeid, Sam P275
Obeidat, Mario E328
Ober, Tammy P589
Oberg, Kathleen K. (Leeny) A530
Oberg, Leeny A531
Obergefell, David E92
Obering, Henry A. (Trey) A140
Oberlander, Ricardo W74
Obermeyer, Frank A196
Obermeyer, Paul R. A221
Oberosler, Bob A709
Oberting, Paul P296
Oberton, Willard D. (Will) A318
Oberweger, Timothy A770
Obey, Christopher J. W151
Obleton, Carolynn A781
Oblisk, Sonya Gafsi A899

Oblisk, Sonya Gafsi P690
Obrien, James J A56
OBrien, Laura A172
Obrien, Kevin M. A851
Obrien, Barbara A902
Obrien, Lisa P122
Obrien, Terrence J P338
Obrien, Gary P454
Obrien, John P632
Obrien, Barbara P692
OBrien, John E135
Obrist, Sister Mary P532
Obryan, Megan P126
Obryant, John P392
Obsitnik, Paul A482
Obstfeld, Isaac A325
Ocain, Timothy D. E122
Ocana, Aida A775
Ocarroll, Liz A478
Ocasio-Velez, Anabel A649
Occhiello, Ernesto W320
Ochi, Hitoshi W240
Ochniak, Michael P103
Ochoa, Vanessa A221
Ochoa, Arthur P103
Ochoa, S. Hector P648
Ochs, Amy P397
Ochsner, Brian P70
Ochsner, Lisa Cloud P433
Ochsner, Peter W52
Oconnell, Daniel A407
Oconnell, Michael P353
OConnell, Rick P471
Oconnell, Jaye P666
Oconnor, Debra A15
Oconnor, Michael A19
OConnor, Jim A120
OConnor, Kevin A145
Oconnor, Kimberly A784
OConnor, John A921
Oconnor, Debra P9
Oconnor, Betty P148
Oconnor, Mark P154
Oconnor, Timothy P P279
Oconnor, Samantha P462
OConnor, Christopher J P511
OConnor, Christopher P698
OConnor, Kevin E46
Oconnor, Michele E426
Oda, Calla A103
Oda, Chad P293
Oda, Syuji W116
Odak, Dina A448
Oddleifson, Christopher (Chris) A451
Oddone, Pier P193
Odea, James F P617
Odegaard, Justin P125
Odegaard, Richard P221
Odegaard, Janice W348
Odell, Lawrence A336
Odell, David A489
Odell, Darrel P479
Oden, Barrett A658
Oden, Jtinsley P656
Odiet, Jeff P71
Odinet, Bertrand (Bert) A367
Odipo, Benjamin P143
Odisho, Walter A136
Odjemski, Jan P158
Odom, Ronald A67
Odom, Raymond A600
Odom, Kellie P262
Odoms, Brittany P583
Odonnell, Jim A480
Odonnell, Michelle A683
Odonnell, Joseph A902
Odonnell, Scott P345
Odonnell, Joseph P692
ODowd, Frank E70
Odriozola, Jose Maria (Chema) A850
Oechslin, Joachim W111
Oehling, James P P421
Oehring, Caty P640
Oelsner, Yoav A478
Oeser, Scott E432

Oestreich, Rebecca P521
Oetgen, William J. A548
Oetgen, William J. P321
Oettgen, Hans C P570
Oexmann, Gaven A384
Oexmann, Gaven E176
Offenberger, Eric J. A703
Offensent, Davi P598
Offer, D. Scott W151
Offutt, Ken P81
Ofman, Joshua A61
Oganes, Luis A480
Ogata, Isamu W116
Ogata, Masaki W132
Ogawa, Tetsuji W116
Ogawa, Tetsuo W374
Ogbonda, Sunny A195
Ogburn, Adam A115
Ogden, Kylie A212
Ogden, Bob A395
Ogden, Kurt A443
Ogden, Sandra P255
Ogden, Kylie E79
Ogens, David E301
Ogg, Tom P118
Ogilvy, Allison E86
Oginsky, Daniel J P252
Ogles, Benjamin M. P83
Oglesby, Rodney A243
Oglesby, Larry A484
Ognall, Andrew H. A839
Ognall, Andrew H. E409
Ogoshi, Tatsuo W238
Ogrady, Anne A175
Ogrady, John P204
Ogrady, Steven P408
Ogren, Dan P144
Ogren, Tamera P417
Ogrinc, Mary L. P280
Ogrosky, Kori L. A632
Ogrosky, Kori L. E322
Oguekwe, Chinyere A480
Ogunrinde, Carla A556
Oguz, Orkun W18
Oguz, Bülent W18
Oh, Irene H. A285
Oh, Kyuli A292
Oh, Christopher A558
Oh, James A898
Oh, In-Hwan W292
Oh, Irene H. E114
Oh-gab, Kwon W177
Ohana, Issachar E67
Ohanian, David A221
OHara, Brooks A396
Ohara, Michele A635
Ohara, Yoshinori A917
Ohara, Jason P19
Ohara, Michele P419
Ohara, Mitchell P637
Ohara, Yoshinori P701
Ohara, Kenichiro W99
Ohare, Mike A774
Ohemeng-Dapaah, Michael P290
Oheron, Dennis A449
Ohira, Noriyoshi W240
Ohler, Curt P660
Ohlgart, Christiane E166
Ohlinger, Brian P668
Ohlsson-Leijon, Anna W3
Ohmpornnuwat, Pisit W88
Ohno, Tomohiko W99
Ohno, Naotake W116
Oho, Yoshihiro W116
Ohrn, John E268
Ohta, Jun W345
Ohtsubo, Fumio W282
Oi, Terence A912
Oji, Chukwuemeka P57
Ojima, Koichi W169
Ojok, Alfred P431
Okabe, Hitoshi W17
Okabe, Nobuhiro E242
Okada, Dave A539
Okada, Motoya W11

Okada, Yutaka W48
Okada, Kenji W192
Okada, Shinichi W197
Okada, Tomonori W330
Okamoto, Ron A70
Okamoto, Janis A102
Okamoto, Gary A P601
Okamoto, Kunie W261
Okamura, Cindy A102
Okano, Garett A580
Okano, Michiyuki W329
Okano, Kinosuke W350
Okanobu, Shinichi W366
Okawara, Masaki W342
Okazaki, Soichi W11
Okazaki, Takeshi W147
Okazoe, Kiyoshi W241
Okeeffe, Ellen A537
Okelley, Paige A605
Okello, Christine P431
Okerstrom, Mark D. A311
Okeson, Russell P345
Oketani, Taimi W326
Okochi, Koichi P405
Okonewski, James A774
Okray, Thomas B. (Tom) A13
Oku, Masayuki W345
Okubo, Tsuneo W324
Okuda, Kentaro W268
Okun, Robert B P223
Okun, Sherry P389
Olafson, Harlee N. A889
Olafsson, Sigurdur O. (Siggi) W363
Olander, Anastasia P429
Olczak, Jacek A652
Old, Tim P507
Oldenburg, Camille A706
Oldenburg, Camille E353
Oldfield, Cheryl A818
Oldham, Jon A163
Oldorff, Frithjof E174
Oldroyd, Robert A920
Oldroyd, Rod P368
Oldsberg, Carl E75
Olear, Kathleen A528
OLeary, Robert A651
OLeary, Robert P426
Oleck, Larry A434
Olejer, Leigh A244
Olejniczak, Dave P530
Oleksak, Michael J. (Mike) E41
Oleksiak, Peter B A280
Oleksiuk, Mary A. A834
Oleon, John A330
Oler, Carol A196
Olesen, Debra P269
Olin, John A. A403
Olinsky, Michael A333
Oliphant, Richard P160
Oliphant, Gerald P215
Oliphant, Michael P497
Oliphant, Grant P601
Oliva, Philippe A461
Oliva, Cynthia A655
Oliva, Harvey P61
Oliva, Cynthia E333
Olivares, David A390
Olivarez, Michelle P163
Olive, Stephen R. A626
Olive, Larry A802
Olive, Larry P562
Oliveira, Rafael A494
Oliveira, Victor P92
Oliveira, Eulila P199
Oliveira, Tina P441
Oliver, Jason A100
Oliver, Joel A164
Oliver, Bryan A303
Oliver, George R A477
Oliver, Kirk R. A836
Oliver, Kerry A906
Oliver, Jonathan P45
Oliver, Andrea P196
Oliver, William C P201
Oliver, Carlos P205

A = AMERICAN BUSINESS
E = EMERGING COMPANIES
P = PRIVATE COMPANIES
W = WORLD BUSINESS

Oliver, George P267
Oliver, George R P268
Oliver, Cindy P293
Oliver, Julie P316
Oliver, Mike P343
Oliver, Kris P460
Olivera, Michelle A449
Oliveras, Noel P399
Oliverio, Dale P50
Oliverio, Michael E4
Olivett, John E183
Olivier, Leon J. (Lee) A307
Olivier, Grégoire W286
Olivo, Maria A827
Olivola, Ken P269
Ollagnier, Jean-Marc W5
Oller, Jeanne A901
Oller, Robert S. P399
Oller, Jeanne P692
Olli, Amy Fliegelman P52
Olmos, Martha P433
Olmstead, Traci A295
Olmstead, Roger A685
Olmstead, Cpcu A764
Olmstead, Thomas J P675
Olmstead, Tom P676
Olmsted, Matthew A28
Olmsted, Matthew P17
Olsavsky, Brian T. A38
Olscamp, Karen P644
Olsen, Ron A168
Olsen, Jason A221
Olsen, Neil A316
Olsen, Sonja A466
Olsen, Kristin A535
Olsen, Todd A659
Olsen, Ken A888
Olsen, John A907
Olsen, Dorothy P40
Olsen, Morgan R. P44
Olsen, Kris P109
Olsen, Neil P191
Olsen, Kristin P312
Olsen, Tracy P368
Olsen, Michael P461
Olsen, Steve P664
Olsen, Grant E355
Olsen, John E446
Olson, Lisa A6
Olson, W. Kregg A69
Olson, Knute A A85
Olson, John A96
Olson, Amy A108
Olson, Tiffany P. A165
Olson, Andy A185
Olson, Robert A261
Olson, John D A272
Olson, Karl A319
Olson, Eric A371
Olson, Arik A565
Olson, Laurie J. A648
Olson, Aaron A729
Olson, Scott A865
Olson, Kirsten A920
Olson, Beth P30
Olson, Robert P157
Olson, Brian P167
Olson, Gerald P295
Olson, Dawn P368
Olson, Toni P447
Olson, Lee P511
Olson, Tim P618
Olson, Paul L. H. E126
Olson, Doug E272
Olson, Heather E432
Olson-Wilk, Jennifer E10
Olsson, Jimmy A878
Olszewski, Paul A489
Olthuis, Cameron A175

Omahony, Carol P440
Omalley, William P393
Omalley, Kimberly P458
Omalley, Daniel E253
Omatsuzawa, Kiyohiro W272
Omell, Gary H P533
Omiya, Hideaki W241
Omlor, Joseph G P353
Ommen, Shari P343
Omoss, Mario A240
Omtvedt, Craig P A625
Onai, Tetsuya P35
Onders, Mike A489
Ondieki, Irene P261
ONeal, Patrick P393
Oneil, Ranae A644
Oneill, Kevin A413
ONeill, Heidi A592
Oneill, Kevin P234
Ong, Bernard A513
Ong, Peter P515
Ong, Terence S. E. W384
Ong, Laureen E E445
Onishi, Tadashi W238
Onishi, Akira W373
Ono, Naoki W242
Onoda, Satoshi W99
Onodera, Makoto W354
Onoe, Seizo W272
Onofrey, Debbie A857
Onomura, Brad P249
Onorato, Andrea A868
Onozawa, Yasuo W245
Onuma, Susan J P405
Onumonu, Ngozi A709
Onzuka, Chris A102
Ooi, Boon A718
Oonnoonny, Abel A729
Oorschot, Rich van W121
Oos, Bryan A819
Oostendorp, Kellie A904
Oostendorp, Kellie E442
Oosterman, Linnea P613
Oosterman, Wade W61
Opdyke, Steve A158
Opedal, Tor A537
Opel, Richard P233
Opel, Rick P233
Opembe, Patrick P101
Openshaw, Brian A729
Ophaug, Courtney A111
Ophaug, Courtney P56
Opilio, Giuseppe R. W359
Oppenhuis, Liz A34
Opperman, Carl P70
Opstedahl, Deeanna A171
Opstedahl, Deeanna P100
Oram, Thomas E P293
Oran, Baris W163
Oratis, Michael W253
Oravec, Jon A475
Oravec, Jon P266
Oravitz, Jeffrey J. A664
Orbe, John A482
Orbuch, Liz Sorota A218
Orchard, Bill A304
Orchard, Kenneth R. A830
Orchard, Arlen P470
Orchard, Kenneth R. E403
Orcutt, Kim D A166
Ordan, Daniel A481
Ordan, Mark E426
Ordemann, William (Bill) A303
Ordlock, Cherise A493
Orduna, Arthur A92
Ordway-Teck, Lori P557
Orebaugh, Lisa A426
Orecchio, Maria A734
Orellana, Charles P599
Oren, Gadi A456
Orenstein, Fern A175
Oresick, Mark A342
Orf, David A717
Orf, Harry P590
Orfan, Kevin A649

Orie, James G. A360
Orie, James G. E164
Oringer, Jonathan (Jon) E369
Oriol, Albert P452
Oriti, Anthony A839
Oriti, Anthony E409
Orlando, John A175
Orlando, Dave A178
Orlando, David A784
Orlando, Jeff P125
Orlando, Anthony T P184
Orlando, Adolph M P602
Orleans, Andrea A565
Orlik, Grzegorz P4
Orlob, Alan A530
Orloff, Harvey A201
Orlovsky, David A86
Orlovsky, David P52
Orman, Chris P477
Ormond, Tommy P26
Ormsby, Lenard T. A296
Ornauer, Christina A178
Orndorff, Robert L. A724
Ornelas, José Gonz--lez W152
Orner, John P238
Orner, John P678
Ornstein, Roberta D. E301
Ornstein, Josh E426
Ornt, Daniel B. P464
Orona, Mario P212
Orona, Angelo P653
Oronzio, Lisa P283
Orourke, Kevin M A350
Orourke, Evelyn A766
Orourke, Melanie A795
Orourke, Terry P101
Orourke, Kevin M E157
Oroz, Sylvia P510
Orozco, Javier A61
Orozco, Tomas A67
Orozco, Jean-Marc A725
Orozco, Ruben P482
Orr, Stanley A A136
Orr, Mark A307
Orr, Shenjin A877
Orr, Lydia A878
Orr, Natassia P87
Orr, Mary R P172
Orr, Mark P221
Orr, James P310
Orr, R. Jeffrey W161
Orr, R. Jeffrey W294
Orr, R. Douglas (Doug) E161
Orscheln, Joseph A173
Orsini, Frank C. A504
Orstad, Gary P231
Ort, Gary A800
Ort, Gary E396
Orta, Juanita P22
Ortega, David A350
Ortega, Cindy A558
Ortega, Annette P30
Ortega, Juan Luis W98
Ortega, David E156
Ortegon, Liisa P620
Orth, Matthew A221
Orth, Linda A583
Orth, Douglas A584
Orthwein, Peter B. A816
Ortiz, Yolanda A40
Ortiz, Hidy A302
Ortiz, Luis P221
Ortiz, Miguel P226
Ortiz, Marnique P275
Ortiz, Christine P313
Ortiz, Rafael P525
Ortiz, Dionisio E52
Ortiz, Hidy E128
Ortizlugo, Lydia P375
Ortkiese, Nancy A115
Ortmanns, Thomas W2
Orton, Bryan A542
Orton, Bryan E267
Orwick, William E151
Oryshchyn, Stacy P261

Osada, Yutaka W86
Osada, Hiroshi W116
Osako, Mary A10
Osako, Takashi A19
Osakwe, Franklyn A877
Osano, Hidenori W11
Osawa, Hidetoshi W282
Osawa, Toshiyuki W326
Osbeck, Mary Beth A862
Osbeck, Mary Beth E419
Osberg, Carl A348
Osberg, Carl E155
Osborn, Ryan A196
Osborn, Kevin A541
Osborn, Jo A829
Osborn, Richard S P268
Osborn, William A. P398
Osborn, Jason P557
Osborn, Kelly P630
Osborn, Kevin E266
Osborn, Brian E447
Osborne, Roberta A133

Osborne, Chris A647
Osborne, Roger A655
Osborne, Melanie P120
Osborne, Deann P463
Osborne, David W P564
Osborne, Roger E333
Osbourn, Kay E. A206
Osbourn, William F. (Bill) A912
Osburn, Mark P135
Oschmann, Stefan W239
Osganian, Stavroula P570
Oshea, Daniel A406
Oshea, Luann E62
Oshiro, Don A813
Oshiro, Don P608
Oshman, Michele A511
Oskey, Jesse A87
Osmanzai, John A40
OSMINKINA-JONES, Olga A647
OSMOND, SANDY P394
Osorio, Maryluz P87
Ossip, Alon W229
Osswald, Oliver W214
Ostalé, Enrique A878
Ostalé, Enrique W392
Ostby, Jeremy P141
Osteen, Jamie A737
Osteen, Debra K. A857
Osteen, Jamie E367
Ostendorf, Todd P387
Oster, Mike P318
Osterman, Vincent J. A591
Ostermeier, Timothy P436
Ostler, Gordon A489
Ostrach, Adam A163
Ostrander, Mark P135
Ostrander, R P155
Ostroff, Craig A476
Ostroski, Phil A351
Ostroski, Phil E158
Ostrowsky, Barry P60
Oswald, Robert W55
Oswalt, David A730
Otero, Arnold A302
Otero, Arnold E128
Otis, Alan A556
Otis, Nat A770
Otjen, Renee A35
Otner, Michael I. (Mike) E268
Otoya, Luis A163
Otsuji, Nobuyuki W116
OTSUKA, IWAO W192
Ott, Jennifer A81
Ott, Susan A533
Ott, Jeri A616
Ott, Michael P186
Ott, Nicky P442
Ottaviano, Lori P516
Ottaviano, Gianni E22
Otte, Chad A81
Ottel, Robert P389
Ottenbruch, Peter W402

Ottens, Adrian P400
Otterman, G. P. W199
Ottinger, Eric H. A500
Ottinger, Eric H. E238
Ottino, Julio M. P398
Otto, Shawn A101
Otto, Christopher A102
Otto, Jeff A857
Otto, Greg E253
Ottolenghi, Les A157
Ottolino, Domenica P361
Ottum, Steve P435
Otwell, Shannon P333
Ouartarone, Jim A784
Ouchida, Michael P246
Ouellette, Amy A108
Ouellette, Glenn P692
Ouellette, Amy E35
Ounesavath, John P206
Ousley, Peter P113
Outland, Gail A655
Outland, Gail E333
Outlaw, Annie A850
Outten, Glen A907
Outten, Glen E446
Outwater, John A248
Ovel, Jack P327
Oven, Thomas J P412
Overbeck, Jim E166
Overcast, Judy A387
Overcast, Judy E177
Overman, Steven E115
Overmyer, David A480
Overson, Chris A505
Overton, Camie P701
Overturf, James E139
Oveson, John A192
Ovitt, J. Bradley E172
Ovokaitys, Daniel S. A340
Ovokaitys, Daniel S. E151
Ovtchinnikov, Alexander (Alex) E224
Ovwigho, Godfrey P613
Owen, Douglas A105
Owen, Paul A305
Owen, Terry M. A318
Owen, Catherine A476
Owen, John B. A700
Owen, Jennifer A724
Owen, Julie P60
Owen, Carey P172
Owen, Paul P185
Owen, Terry P198
Owen, Marc E. W235
Owen, B. Carl E47
Owen, John W E385
Owens, Bob A158
Owens, Bill A422
Owens, Tom A693
Owens, Tony A723
Owens, Don G. A737
Owens, Patty A773
Owens, Robert W A773
Owens, Tim P109
Owens, Thomas A. P168
Owens, Bill P239
Owens, William P440
Owens, Betsy P457
Owens, Ben E P528
Owens, Craig P680
Owens, Patricia E65
Owens, Greg E268
Owens, Don G. E367
Owens, Patty E387
Owenson, Steven A260
Ownby, David H. P455
Oyadomari, David A102
Oyamada, Takashi W244
Oyer, Randall P589
Oyewole, Shola E415
Oyler, Clinton P456
Oz, Ran W46
Ozaki, Ernie A685
Ozaki, Masatoshi W245
Ozaki, Norimichi W250
Ozaki, Tetsu W268

Ozan, Kevin M. A545
Ozcelik, Taner A620
Ozeki, Masatatsu W28
Ozene, Brett P42
Ozer, Lynn A369
Ozimek, Michael M. A831
Ozment, Richard P97
Ozuah, Philip O. P351
Ozzie, Ray A419
O'Brien, Shane A34
O'brien, Deirdre A70
O'Brien, Tim A85
O'Brien, Dermot J A87
O'brien, Deborah A101
O'Brien, Michael A158
O'Brien, Ken A278
O'Brien, Richard E. A437
O'Brien, Gregory P. (Greg) A478
O'Brien, Beth A512
O'Brien, Tom A535
O'Brien, Gail A560
O'Brien, Lawrence A565
O'Brien, Michael J. A619
O'Brien, Christopher J A711
O'Brien, Joseph A724
O'brien, Kevin M A851
O'Brien, Lindsay P37
O'Brien, Robert P. (Bob) P90
O'Brien, Keith P104
O'Brien, Charles T P185
O'Brien, Tom P312
O'Brien, Gail P342
O'Brien, Kristine P398
O'Brien, April P632
O'Brien, Frances D. W98
O'Brien, Eddie W120
O'Brien, Sean W180
O'Brien, Patrick D. W282
O'Brien, John R. E135
O'Brien, Thomas (Tom) E303
O'Brien, Mary Jo E311
O'brien, Jenette E348
O'Byrne, Kevin W193
O'connell, Judy A49
O'Connell, Pat A56
O'connell, Tom A221
O'Connell, Alfred A321
O'Connell, Maureen A371
O'Connell, John A678
O'connell, Ian P515
O'Connell, Timothy A E98
O'Connell, Alfred E144
O'Connor, Mark A105
O'Connor, Stephen A133
O'Connor, Kevin M. A145
O'Connor, Mary A173
O'connor, Jacqueline A221
O'Connor, Daniel A244
O'Connor, Jim A281
O'Connor, Sean M. A465
O'Connor, Tom A478
O'Connor, Christopher A513
O'Connor, Thomas L. A638
O'Connor, Rory A649
O'Connor, Richard A749
O'Connor, Leo A872
O'Connor, Michael L. (Mike) A883
O'Connor, Timothy (Tim) A910
O'Connor, Thomas J. (T.J.) A916
O'Connor, Thomas (Tom) P26
O'Connor, Gina P298
O'Connor, John P541
O'Connor, Debra W31
O'Connor, Kevin M. E46
O'Connor, Michael E53
O'Conor, Raymond F. (Ray) A78
O'Day, Terence L. A416
O'Day, Gail R. P673
O'Day, Daniel W307
O'Dea, Edward P287
O'Dell, John A622
O'Dell, Melanie P406
O'Donald, Lewis W268
O'Donnell, Robert G A46
O'Donnell, William A195

O'donnell, Nancy A586
O'Donnell, Robert F A675
O'Donnell, Peter G. A863
O'Donnell, Julie A902
O'Donnell, Robert G P32
O'Donnell, Randall L. P327
O'Donnell, Patrick P546
O'donnell, Meg P614
O'Donnell, Julie P692
O'Donnell, Andrea E106
O'Donnell, Jeffrey E245
O'Donnell, James C. E424
O'Donoghue, Mary Jo P566
O'Donohoe, Karen A105
O'Dowd, Sarah A. A501
O'Dowd, William E108
O'Dwyer, Philip A568
O'Dwyer, Fergal W120
O'Dwyer, Barry W341
O'Farrell, Ray A875
O'Flaherty, Lori L. A214
O'Flaherty, Lori L. P128
O'Flynn, Thomas M A17
O'grady, Anne A175
O'Grady, Shawn P. A377
O'grady, Becky A377
O'grady, Jim A419
O'Grady, Michael G. A599
O'Grady, Steve P408
O'Grady, John E115
O'Hagen, William E47
O'Halla, Mark P354
O'Hanley, Ronald P. (Ron) A766
O'Hanley, Ronald P. (Ron) P71
O'hara, Brooks A396
O'Hara, Gene P368
O'Hara, Brian P544
O'Haver, Cort A839
O'Haver, Cort E409
O'Herlihy, Christopher (Chris) A450
O'Hern, Jim A530
O'Keefe, Laura A767
O'keefe, Peggy P111
O'Keefe, Barbara J. P397
O'Keefe, Sharon P611
O'Keeffe, John W128
O'Leary, Christopher D. (Chris) A377
O'Leary, Glenn A446
O'Leary, Ray P183
O'Leary, Megan P434
O'Leary, Thomas M P600
O'leary, Brian E50
O'Leary, Glenn E210
O'Mahoney, Sean A705
O'Mahoney, Sean E352
O'Malley, Kevin A449
O'Malley, Diana Carloni - P535
O'Malley, Terrence P590
O'Meara, Robert P. (Bob) A351
O'Meara, Robert P. (Bob) E159
O'Neal, Clu Jon A54
O'neal, Ryan A735
O'Neal, Steve A902
O'Neal, Steve P692
O'Neil, Daniel A729
O'Neil, Kristin A775
O'Neil, John A855
O'Neil, William E P401
O'Neil, Cheri P659
O'Neil, Dick E126
O'Neil, Ellen P. E149
O'neill, Michael J A49
O'Neill, Marie A56
O'neill, Angela A81
O'Neill, Michael J A93
O'Neill, Thomas A108
O'Neill, Thomas S A310
O'Neill, Timothy J. A389
O'Neill, Paul A480
O'Neill, Lisa M. A500
O'Neill, Liz A509
O'Neill, Myles A511
O'Neill, Jerry A576
O'Neill, John P. A666
O'Neill, Thomas E. A829

O'Neill, Michael A872
O'Neill, John P. P438
O'Neill, Michael J. (Mike) P667
O'Neill, Thomas C. (Tom) W7
O'Neill, Lisa M. E238
O'Neill, Jerry E297
O'ray, Patrick A835
O'Reagan, Richard A534
O'rear, David A781
O'Reilly, Lawrence P. (Larry) A609
O'Reilly, Charles H. A609
O'Reilly, David E. A609
O'Reilly, Brian A651
O'reilly, Sarah A691
O'Reilly, Charles P229
O'Reilly, Brian P426
O'Riley, Mark A461
O'Riordain, Shane W314
O'Rourke, Joan A521
O'Rourke, James (Joc) A569
O'Rourke, Michael G. A741
O'Rourke, Claudia A869
O'Rourke, Sean P239
O'Rourke, Thomas F P382
O'Rourke, Tracy P543
O'Rourke, Elizabeth P552
O'Rourke, Michael G. E370
O'Shaughnessy, Robert T. (Bob) A681
O'Shea, Daniel A406
O'Shea, John A792
O'Shea, Kevin P. E26
O'Shea, Timothy E104
O'Sullivan, Juliann A133
O'Sullivan, Michael B. A715
O'Sullivan, Richard B. A830
O'Sullivan, James W50
O'Sullivan, Patrick H. W275
O'Sullivan, Richard B. E402
O'Tero, Ilene A163
OÂ'Brien, Raymond V. A248
OÂ'Brien, Sean P. A257
OÂ'Brien, Denis P. A309
OÂ'Brien, Anthony F. A695
OÂ'Brien, Martin P326
OÂ'Bryant, G. Mark P554
OÂ'Connell, Brian A205
OÂ'Connell, Paul W98
OÂ'Hara, Ryan A589
OÂ'Keefe, Thomas J. A618
OÂ'Leary, David A382
OÂ'Neill, Michael J A49
OÂ'Neill, Heidi A592
OÂ'Sullivan, James P. A761

P

P, Kern Howard P493
Pabalate, Donna P584
Pabis, Michelle P487
Paccioretti, Steven A406
Paccura, Lori P504
Pace, Timothy A332
Pace, Paul A489
Pace, Ericka A508
Pace, Sonia P20
Pace, Gerald P344
Pace, Peter E342
Pace, Gary E355
Pace-Burke, Susan A583
Pacelli, Anthony E29
Pacey, John E51
Pacheco, Josie A351
Pacheco, Stacie E65
Pacheco, Josie E158
Pacheco, Peter E320
Pachman, Louis P228
Paciero, Karen P611
Pacilio, Michael J. A308
Pacino, John A175
Pacious, Patrick S. E75
Pacis, Joe A248
Pack, Mike A13
Packard, John A P511
Packard, Julie P576

A = AMERICAN BUSINESS
E = EMERGING COMPANIES
P = PRIVATE COMPANIES
W = WORLD BUSINESS

Packer, Ginny A567
Packer, Robert J. E396
Packwood, Erin A782
Paczkowski, Linda A537
Padbury, Guy A550
Padden, Brian A738
Paddock, Robert W P220
Paddock, Elain P223
Paddock, Ezra P261
Paden, Brent P254
Padfield, Larry E216
Padgett, Pamela A405
Padgett, Francine P343
Padgitt, Laura A165
Padierna, Pedro A647
Padilla, Patricia A204
Padilla, Jose P155
Padilla, Anthony P160
Padilla, Kim P428
Padmanabhan, Srikanth A246
Padmaperuma, Rasika P191
Padon, Leslie P567
Padula, Rich A351
Padula, Rich E158
Paelinck, Charley A158
Paez, Rene A P510
Paez, Pablo E175
Pagano, Christopher J. A83
Pagano, William A101
Pagano, Dawn A250
Pagano, Shelly P40
Page, Gregory A3
Page, Jack A439
Page, Miriah A691
Page, Michael A741
Page, Crystal P94
Page, Joy P300
Page, Roger P330
Page, Elaine P390
Page, Michael P451
Page, Michael P522
Page, Bob P612
Page, Darryl W98
Page, Timothy E51
Page, Michael E370
Pagels, George A P474
Pagliari, Cristina A260
Pagliaro, Renato W237
Pagnanelli, Jodi A886
Pagnanelli, Jodi E433
Pagni, Marco A877
Pagura, Frank P421
Pai, Kathleen E407
Paich, Keith A369
Paich, Brian A683
Paige, Michele A195
Paik, Elaine A218
Paillassot, Laurent W278
Paine, Andrew J. (Randy) A489
Paine, John P123
Painter, Corning F. A24
Painter, Jonathan W. (Jon) E229
Pais, Paula A247
Pais, Paula E103
Paisley, James A. (Andy) A13
Paja, David W29
Pak, Lynda A120
Pak, Chong A183
Pak, Nancy A218
Pak, Gene A430
Pak, Chris A585
Pak, Ian A878
Pak, Chris P377
Pak, Gene E204
Pakula, Krzysztof P248
Palace, Mike A784
Paladino, Steven A727
Palagiano, Vincent F. A267
Palan, Martha P682

Palasek, Andrea A583
Palasthy, Kristen A857
Palatnik, Kevin S. E83
Palazzo, Frank A185
Palazzo, Mark A441
Palazzolo, Joseph A351
Palazzolo, Joseph E158
Palczuk, Linda E319
Palenik, Rudy A764
Palenzona, Fabrizio W380
Paleos, Mike A555
Palermo, Robert J A109
Palermo, Tom A332
Paletta, Nilton A469
Paley, Liz A691
Palfi, Sandor A476
Palfy, Sandor E248
Palincsar, James J A800
Palincsar, James J P559
Palis, Jack A532
Palis, Adar P227
Palkovich, Mary A210
Pall, Christine A56
Palla, Wayne A252
Palla, Wayne P150
Pallas, Tony E75
Pallasch, John A532
Pallier, Patricia A178
Pallin, Angel P355
Pallotta, Jim A774
Palm, Gregory K. A389
Palma, Bryan A199
Palma, Dan De A478
Palma, Dino Di P52
Palmberg, Rob P151
Palmberg, Kent P543
Palmer, John A108
Palmer, Johnathan A129
Palmer, Paul A160
Palmer, Eric P. A195
Palmer, Thomas A306
Palmer, Sheryl A441
Palmer, Anthony J. (Tony) A490
Palmer, C. Michael A527
Palmer, Brian A560
Palmer, Thomas (Tom) A588
Palmer, Adam A647
Palmer, Gary A675
Palmer, Mark A782
Palmer, Frank A814
Palmer, Marcia A865
Palmer, Keith P25
Palmer, Ann P83
Palmer, Mark P101
Palmer, J. Marc P167
Palmer, Mike P187
Palmer, Alice P239
Palmer, Brian P342
Palmer, Christopher P379
Palmer, Mark P402
Palmer, Kelly P455
Palmer, Harvey P464
Palmer, Bart P489
Palmer, Edna P531
Palmer, Frank P616
Palmer, Lauren P617
Palmer, Paul E55
Palmer, Ben M. E258
Palmer, Lisa E349
Palmer, Michael E432
Palmerino, Debbie A475
Palmerino, Debbie P266
Palmieri, Tom A691
Palmieri, Paul A914
Palmisano, Maria A178
Palmisano, Thomas J. (Tom) A752
Palmore, Kysten P204
Palmore, Tammy P239
Palomares, Alfred E1
Palombo, Grace M. W161
Palombo, Grace W161
Palozzola, Joseph A765
Palozzola, Joseph P540
Paltridge, Robert D. E220
Paluck, Eric A56

Palus, Jean Fran-§ois W204
Pamiljans, Janis G. A602
Pamulo, Pj A354
Pan, Qiuting A131
Pan, Pattie A537
Pan, Darong W90
Pan, Ning W147
Panagoplos, Janae P304
Panagos, Costa A469
Panarella, Betty A871
Pancham, Cassan A336
Panchanathan, Sethuraman (Panch) P44
Pancino, Matt W348
Pancoast, James R P439
Panda, Lalitendu P313
Pande, Siddharth A537
Pande, Sunil P282
Pandey, Sangeeta A131
Pandey, Sanjay A276
Pandl, Treasie P133
Pane, Camillo A241
Panek, Ray A484
Panetta, Nancy A480
Pang, Laurinda Y. A185
Pang, Y.K. W195
Pang, Y. K. W196
Pangalos, Menelas (Mene) W34
Pangborn, Robert N. A811
Pangborn, Robert N. P600
Pangia, Bob A129
Panhans, Chet E163
Panikar, John M. A514
Panizza, Sandro W32
Panizza, Florencia E260
Pankaj, Rajesh A685
Panky, Bill P233
Pann, Stuart C. A435
Panno, Enrico A163
Pantaleoni, Anthony P636
Pantel, Lori A539
Panthawangkun, Wirawat W203
Panuccio, Susan A589
Panyarachun, Anand W330
Panyard, Dave A155
Panyard, William A513
Panzarella, Michael E182
Panzer, Kenneth M. (Ken) E110
Panzino, Jodi P137
Paoletti, Rich P589
Paoli, Alberto De W141
Paolicelli, Missy P283
Paolini, Nonce W72
Paolucci, Steve P129
Papa, William A416
Papa, Henry P260
Papa, Gianni Franco W380
Papa, Rosemarie Novello E414
Papac, Michael P184
Papadopoulos, Stelios A129
Papadopoulos, Stelios E138
Papagaryfallou, Lazaros A. W24
Papahristos, Tanya A8
Papahristos, Tanya P3
Papalini, Darlene A272
Papar, Riyaz E209
Paparello, John A724
Pape, Giovanna A480
Pape, Kathy P282
Papermaster, Mark D. A14
Papes, Daniel E107
Papesh, Kristin A649
Papiasse, Alain W66
Papich, Diane A724
Papillo, Carol A16
Papineau, Scott A685
Pappas, Natalie P559
Pappas, Debbie P599
Pappas, John E70
Pappu, Bhoga E116
Papuzek, Stephen A481
Paquette, Michael S. A296
Parada, Ed A81
Paradis, Jim P302
Paradiso, Timothy J P404

Paradowski, Mark E87
Parag, Prakash J A759
Parag, Prakash J P521
Param, Melina A235
Parameswaran, Prabha A218
Parameswaran, Raj E265
Paranji, Sanjay A64
Paranjpe, Nitin W381
Paranjpe, Nitin W383
Parasnis, Abhay A11
Parasuraman, Bhash A649
Paratte, A. Robert E232
Parayno, Marie P498
Parazynski, Gail M P560
Parcel, Jim P314
Parcell, Jordan A777
Parcell, Jordan E393
Parcella, Mike A71
Parcher, Dave A161
Parcher, Charles A A208
Parchisanu, Georgeta A671
Pardee, Charles G. (Chip) A798
Parden, Diana P234
Pardes, Herbert A810
Pardes, Herbert P597
Pardo, Xavier A204
Pardo, Tara A390
Pardo, Emilio P1
Pardo, Felipe Bay--n W133
Pardos, Miguel A. E104
Pardue, Wendel A700
Pare, Mark A864
Pare, Jean-Philippe W117
Paredes, Alfredo A691
Paredes, Jose A902
Paredes, Jose P693
Paredes, Sebastian W119
Pareek, Mayank W357
Pareigat, Thomas G. A806
Pareja, Alvena A781
Parekh, Sireen A478
Parekh, Kam P524
Parent, June B. A160
Parent, Ghislain W252
Parent, June B. E55
Parente, Michael Null A362
Parente, Pedro Pullen W284
Parente, Katherine E140
Paret, Jason P106
Paretsky, Daniel A175
Parfet, Donald R A486
Parham, Joe A78
Paridy, Nancy P457
Parihar, Jagdish W274
Parikh, Chintan A204
Parikh, Rima A250
Parikh, Shamin E140
Parillo, John A461
Parimbelli, Alessandro A471
Parini, Michael E428
Paris, Marty A163
Paris, Fredelyne A585
Paris, Glen A657
Paris, Fredelyne P377
Parise, Joe P282
Parish, Poppie A489
Parish, Glenda P126
Parish, Rebecca A P263
Parisi, Joseph A231
Parisi, Mike A450
Parisi, Janet A584
Parisi, Jeannine P187
Parisi, Janet P376
Parisi, Arianne P579
Park, Ernie A3
Park, Sun A59
Park, David A97
Park, Anthony J. (Tony) A328
Park, Yong A401
Park, Kevin C A565
Park, Matt A593
Park, Peter A648
Park, David P207
Park, Hyun P350
Park, Gary P649

Park, In Gyu W127
Park, Jeongwon W130
Park, Geewon W130
Park, Chang Jong W178
Park, Han-Woo W205
Park, Sung-Ho W292
Park, Yong E187
Parker, Jerome G A22
Parker, Debbie A34
Parker, W. Douglas (Doug) A43
Parker, Alex A84
Parker, Donald T. A137
Parker, Mike A173
Parker, Phil A235
Parker, Greg A244
Parker, Mary Jayne A272
Parker, Jayne A272
Parker, Michael A407
Parker, Brandon A439
Parker, Jefferson G. (Jeff) A446
Parker, Randy P A492
Parker, Mark G. A592
Parker, Kurt A592
Parker, Scott T. A621
Parker, Bruce A837
Parker, Michael A863
Parker, P. William (Bill) A865
Parker, Rob A870
Parker, Carolyn A872
Parker, Brenda A902
Parker, Jerome G P13
Parker, Brian P88
Parker, Doug P101
Parker, Kimberly P108
Parker, Karen P204
Parker, Shirley P243
Parker, Bessant P249
Parker, Beck P339
Parker, Linda P361
Parker, Terra P363
Parker, Scott P366
Parker, Robert P370
Parker, Cindy A P397
Parker, Elizabeth P408
Parker, Cindy P493
Parker, Kim P521
Parker, Carol P522
Parker, Deanna P584
Parker, Lynz P613
Parker, Brenda P692
Parker, John W352
Parker, Jefferson G. (Jeff) E210
Parker, David E253
Parkhill, Rik W80
Parkinson, Alan R. P83
Parkinson, Robert L. P299
Parkinson, John F. E338
Parkman, Barbara P220
Parkman, David P548
Parks, Patrick A3
Parks, Trenton A120
Parks, Lisa A399
Parks, Kathaleen A446
Parks, Karen A821
Parks, Joel P160
Parks, R M P450
Parks, Karen P621
Parks, Kathaleen E210
Parks, Robert E320
Parlapiano, Donna A88
Parlee, Joan P164
Parman, Stacey P57
Parmar, Rishabh E101
Parmenter, Darren E. A420
Parmenter, Brian P91
Parmenter, Darren E. E198
Parmentier, Jennifer A. A634
Parmett, Simon P356
Parnell, Winfred P152
Parnell, Christopher E P193
Parnell, Mary P255
Parnell, Rob P563
Parnes, Marvin A698
Parnes, Marvin P456
Parolin, Jo--o Benjamin W379

Parolisi, John P54
Parr, Gregory L A402
Parra, Jose L P254
Parran, Ted P99
Parrelli, Barbara A846
Parrent, Craig A841
Parrent, Craig E410
Parrish, Karen A461
Parrish, Benjamin F. (Ben) A825
Parrish, David K. P76
Parrish, Mike P387
Parrish, Kim P538
Parrish, Chris P566
Parrott, William A729
Parrott, Keith A795
Parrs, Shari P538
Parry, Michael J. (Mike) A294
Parry, Heather A517
Parsley, Billy A98
Parsley, E. William (Bill) A659
Parsley, Shawn D. A801
Parsley, Shawn D. P562
Parsley, Elizabeth P603
Parsley, Billy E33
Parson, Susan A682
Parsonnet, Abby A883
Parsons, Christopher G A85
Parsons, Romelle K A101
Parsons, Charlene A195
Parsons, Jim A313
Parsons, Jennifer P260
Parsons, Adriana P422
Parsons, Roger P479
Parsons, Blake P523
Parsons, John P564
Partain, Jack P391
Partanapat, Pakorn W202
Partch, Karen P28
Partington, Wayne A364
Partrea, Robert A343
Partridge, John A195
Partridge, Jack P133
Partridge, Ronald K. (Ron) P416
Parvin, Gazala P343
Parvor, Mike A718
Paré, Jean-Philippe W117
Pasalich, John P6
Pasanen, Zachary A E431
Pascal, Maryann A909
Pascarella, Christine A163
Pascaud, Raphael S. E10
Pasch, Coni A865
Pascoe, Ricardo W252
Pascoe, Kevin C. E292
Pascu, Adrian W117
Pascual, Francisco A336
Pascucci, Drew A480
Pasek, Ronald J A580
Pasiechnik, Alexander E40
Paslawsky, William P474
Pasley, Debi P471
Paslick, P. Martin (Marty) A410
Pasma, Diane A698
Pasma, Diane P456
Pasquale, Maria E A178
Pasquale, David P425
Pasqualicchio, Roderick A555
Pasqualone, Frank E217
Pasquarelli, Amy A644
Pasquier, Caroline A786
Pasquino, Jennifer A153
Pass, Sherry A616
Pass, Chris P263
Passafiume, Ralph A869
Passaro, Karen P494
Passas, Isidore S. W24
Passey, BO A671
Passey, Bret A919
Passman, Marj P301
Pasternak, Asaf W190
Pastides, Harris P655
Pastiu, Alina A108
Pastiu, Alina E35
Pastor, Steve W63
Pastore, Martin J P185

Pastorek, Greg A537
Pastorelli, Nicholas P605
Pastorius, John P688
Patak, David P412
Pataki, David A836
Patanella, Richard P175
Patchen, Jason A180
Patchen, Michael E385
Patchett, Mary Sue A148
Patchett, Richard B P309
Patchke, Carl A533
Pate, Joanne A85
Pate, R. Hewitt (Hew) A192
Pate, Robert A505
Pate, David C. P534
Pate, William C. (Bill) E322
Pate, Carter E339
Patel, Harsh A101
Patel, Ketul J. A171
Patel, Sunit S. A185
Patel, Badal A185
Patel, Pankaj S. A199
Patel, Vijay A250
Patel, Harsh A250
Patel, Himanshu A A343
Patel, Mayank A385
Patel, Suresh C A413
Patel, Naimish A487
Patel, Ken A671
Patel, Kirt A709
Patel, Manesh A725
Patel, Shefali A774
Patel, Ben A796
Patel, Raj A855
Patel, Samir A914
Patel, Ketul J. P100
Patel, Kirtan P233
Patel, Suresh C P234
Patel, Sagar P296
Patel, Dhruv P318
Patel, Mahendrabhai P319
Patel, Nikunj P364
Patel, Jay P430
Patel, Bipin P474
Patel, Rajiv J P526
Patel, Bhavana P612
Patel, Nikul E243
Patel, Rajesh E269
Patel, Raj E416
Patel-Yadav, AMI P637
Pater, Krystian W291
Paterno, Andrew J. A440
Paterson, Chris E448
Patick, Kenneth E P329
Patil, Sandeep A733
Patilis, Joanna A328
Patin, Al P279
Patino, Elizabeth P157
Patnaik, Rekha A837
Patnala, Sai A131
Patnaude, Jude A187
Patnaude, Jude E71
Patonai, Nicolas P612
Patout, Frank W P300
Patout, J Jared P301
Patout, Robert B P301
Patric, Sharon P188
Patrick, Erin A87
Patrick, Paul A163
Patrick, Denit A395
Patrick, Connor A556
Patrick, Tony A614
Patrick, Cory A865
Patrick, Brenda P433
Patrick, Barbara P627
Patrick, Gregory S. E391
Patricoff, Tracey C P510
Patridge, Denise A729
Patrissi, Peter A537
Patruno, Joseph P287
Patry, Dean P40
Pattee, Steve A366
Patten, Charlene A671
Patten, Mark E. E92
Pattengill, Wayne P473

Patterson, Ronald A27
Patterson, Frank A64
Patterson, Frank J. A190
Patterson, Ian A221
Patterson, Ryan A391
Patterson, Vernon L A489
Patterson, Eric A513
Patterson, James A727
Patterson, Warren A836
Patterson, Pat P46
Patterson, Dean P99
Patterson, Ashley P143
Patterson, Philip P216
Patterson, James P310
Patterson, Michael P401
Patterson, Scott P528
Patterson, Al P570
Patterson, Lynn K. W47
Patterson, Gavin W76
Patterson, Kevin J. W80
Patterson, Giles E252
Patterson-Randles, Sandra R. P627
Pattijn, Elbert W119
Pattis, Lisa J. A904
Pattis, Lisa J. E442
Pattishall, Jan A886
Pattishall, Jan E433
Patton, Charles R. A46
Patton, Rodman A69
Patton, Jeffrey M A149
Patton, Mary A342
Patton, Gary A460
Patton, Robert A484
Patton, Ross P88
Patton, Chris P210
Patton, Alex P261
Patullo, Rita A532
Patusky, Christopher E415
Patz, Melanie P58
Patz, Dtephen M P685
Paul, Ronald D. A284
Paul, Vivek A292
Paul, Shannon A333
Paul, Barbara A413
Paul, Santa A493
Paul, Andrew A532
Paul, Kevin A549
Paul, Cynthia A729
Paul, Nick A780
Paul, James P78
Paul, Jacqueline P132
Paul, Zohorsky P188
Paul, Barbara P234
Paul, Chausse P303
Paul, Christiana P498
Paul, Janelle P499
Paul, Valerie J. P506
Paul, Stefan W212
Paul, Michael W402
Paul, Ronald D. E111
Paul, David C. E179
Paul, Kevin E270
Paula, Jefferson de W30
Paulakos, Kimberly P241
Pauley, Lisa A. A96
Pauley, Matthew A375
Pauley, Marty A390
Pauley, Jeff P308
Paulk, Steve A115
Paulk, Clint P13
Paulk, Jennifer P101
Paulk, Renee P554
Paulson, Donavon A889
Paulson, Dana P284
Paulson, Mary P476
Paulus, Ronald A P345
Paulus, Ronald A P346
Pauly, Tyler P465
Pauly, Jeremy P465
Pauzer, Stanley A589
Pavel, Shannon P248
Pavia, Rick A826
Pavlakis, Peter A729
Pavlic, Jeanne A898
Pawelzik, Thomas P587

A = AMERICAN BUSINESS
E = EMERGING COMPANIES
P = PRIVATE COMPANIES
W = WORLD BUSINESS

Pawlak, Renard A165
Pawlak, Paul P503
Pawley, Barbara P638
Pawsat, Karen P334
Pawson, Greg P501
Paxton, Drew A913
Paxton, Ken P50
Paxton, Pat E127
Paydarfar, David P695
Payette, Traci A173
Paylor, Vern A52
Paylor, Vern P33
Payne, Amanda A56
Payne, Jon A82
Payne, David A207
Payne, Ileana A244
Payne, Kevin M. A291
Payne, Clifton A A397
Payne, Ulice A525
Payne, Chris A669
Payne, Lisa A712
Payne, Kevin M. A752
Payne, Leslie A810
Payne, Jennifer M. A837
Payne, David L. A889
Payne, Jon P49
Payne, Phyllis P478
Payne, Penelope (Nell) P506
Payne, Leslie P586
Payne, Valerie P701
Paynter, Leslie A152
Paynter, Ken P688
Paynter, Leslie E48
Paysse, Stephanie A741
Paysse, Stephanie E370
Paz, Gustavo Calvo A490
Paz, Jeffery A644
Paziora, Debra A734
Pbuchren, Qnne P320
Peabody, Eric A532
Peabody, Robert A693
Peabody, Robert J. W176
Peabody, Mark E25
Peabody, Mark E419
Peacher, Stephen C. W347
Peacock, Philip A64
Peacock, Dan A330
Peacock, Stephen A478
Peacock, Jeff A727
Peacock, John A737
Peacock, William (Bill) A807
Peacock, Rolland P409
Peacock, William (Bill) P574
Peacock, John E367
Peacock, Philip E436
Peak, Linda A439
Peak, Craig A446
Peak, Craig E210
Pearce, Christopher A115
Pearce, David A332
Pearce, Ed A903
Pearce, Charles T P269
Pearce, Gary M P421
Pearce, Louis P421
Pearce, Stephen R P421
Pearce, David P481
Pearce, Louis M. P678
Pearce, Warren W. E218
Pearison, Megan P603
Pearl, Mike A64
Pearlberg, Jay A413
Pearlberg, Jay P234
Pearlmutter, David A487
Pearre, Austin A522
Pearson, Bryan A. A32
Pearson, Todd A288
Pearson, Lynne A333
Pearson, James F. (Jim) A355
Pearson, Gregory R. (Greg) A456

Pearson, Kevin J. A522
Pearson, Wes A591
Pearson, John A865
Pearson, Jeffrey T P34
Pearson, Kermit P62
Pearson, Joe P233
Pearson, John P290
Pearson, James F P337
Pearson, John P391
Pearson, James F P404
Pearson, James F P422
Pearson, David P430
Pearson, Bruce P487
Pearson, David P554
Pearson, J F P574
Pearson, Shelli P685
Pearson, Lori W75
Pearson, Simon W323
Pearson, Jonathan E104
Pearson, J. Edward E190
Pease, Christopher A532
Pease, William L P466
Pease, Alexander W. P507
Peaslee, Jay A105
Peaslee, Gregory A859
Peaslee, Gregory P652
Peay, D. Anthony (Tony) A841
Peay, D. Anthony (Tony) E410
Pecaric, John P. A278
Peceny, Mark P648
Peck, Patrick F. A140
Peck, Ann A774
Peck, John A777
Peck, Will A788
Peck, Arthur (Art) A809
Peck, Raphael A840
Peck, Kristin C. A921
Peck, Chris P256
Peck, Ty E185
Peck, John E393
Peckham, John P. A891
Peckham, Michael P. (Mike) P452
Peckham, John P. E434
Peckinpaugh, David P307
Pecora, Anthony P A81
Pedaline, Susan P595
Pedersen, Brandon S. A28
Pedersen, Chris E. A218
Pedersen, John P304
Pedigo, Amanda A311
Pedley, Matthew A133
Pedlow, Bernadette P17
Pedlow, Frank P590
Pedone, Joe A480
Pedone, Peter P588
Pedonti, Patrick J. E383
Pedraza, Hector A218
Pedruczny, Jayna J P627
Peebles, Eddie A300
Peel, Matthew P166
Peeples, Andrew A173
Peeples, Trip A180
Peeples, Todd A784
Peeples, Jean P92
Pefanis, Harry N. A657
Pefanis, Harry N A658
Pefanis, Harry N P431
Peffer, Neil A782
Peffly, Chris A344
Peglar, Robert A559
Pehrson, Timothy T. A458
Pehrson, Eric A920
Pehrson, Timothy T. P251
Peigh, Terry D. A464
Peignet, Victor W323
Peirce, Dean P293
Peitz, Chelsea A328
Pekhazis, Fadoul W194
Pelaez, Marc Y. E. E214
Pelan, Dana A120
Pelatowski, Keith E360
Pelch, Steve J. A295
Pelcher, Richard A741
Pelcher, Richard E370
Pelham, Peter A103

Pelissero, John P299
Pelka, Deb P22
Pell, Martyn A. A343
Pell, Gary A873
Pell, Gary P669
Pellakuru, Gurunatham A406
Pellegrino, Alice A406
Pellegrino, Joseph P. E242
Pelleissone, Eduardo A494
Peller, Holger P436
Pellerin, Jon A19
Pellerin, Jodie E262
Pelletier, Mike A446
Pelletier, Stephen (Steve) A676
Pelletier, Mike E210
Pelletiere, Christopher V P8
Pellette, Thomas A A169
Pellicano, Anthony P239
Pellicci, Suzanne A774
Pelliccia, Joe A883
Pelligra, Nicole A105
Pellissier, Gervais W278
Pellon, Brian A443
Peloquin, Thomas A406
Pelster, Michael P398
Pelt, Megan Van A733
Pelt, Debra Van P359
Pelt, Kristi Van P363
Peltier, Dwayne A693
Peltier, Wayne P62
Pelton, Steve P473
Peltz, Nelson A782
Peltz, Marlene A286
Peltzie, Kenneth P72
Peluso, Piergiorgio W359
Pelzer, Susan A441
Pember, Marvin G. A857
Pemberton, Shannon A446
Pemberton, Shannon E210
Pembleton, S. Gillian A599
Pembleton, Sandy P120
Pempek, Kalynn P48
Pena, Lisa A818
Pena, Juan P278
Pena, Rodrigo F. Troni P507
Penake, David E95
Penberthy, Shannon A250
Pence, Beth A244
Pence, Ed A245
Pendergast, Lisa A557
Pendergast, Jim P2
Pendergast, Michael P73
Pendergraft, Shelia P250
Pendergrass, Mike A243
Pendergrass, Tom A725
Pendergrass, Kelly P343
Pendergrass, Patricia P490
Pendergrass, Lynn S. E10
Penders, Kevin A865
Pendery, Lud P140
Pendolino, Sophie A902
Pendolino, Sophie P693
Pendse, Raj P685
Penfield, Susan L. A140
Peng, Shane A760
Peng, Shi K P226
Peng, Shane P523
Peng, Zhaofeng W166
Peng, Liu W403
Pengeroth, Phil A766
Penk, Werner E235
Penn, Ronda A52
Penn, Jayson A654
Penn, Douglas A847
Penn, Kevin P335
Pennacchio, Stephen A648
Pennacchio, Steve A649
Pennebaker, Lori A508
Pennella, William A P149
Penner, Peter Pete P546
Penney, Robert T. P104
Penney, Curtis W P249
Penning, Bruce A305
Pennington, Bob A202
Pennington, Bob P122

Pennington, Angie P542
Pennington, Kelli P677
Pennino, John P337
Penny, J. Scott E47
Pennycuff, Toby A420
Pennycuff, Toby E198
Penrose, Chris A84
Penrose, Sheila A. A479
Penrose, Jill A748
Penry, Chuck A835
Pensak, Myles P631
Penshorn, John A855
Penske, Roger S. A642
Pentz, Mark von A260
Pentz, Larry C. W199
Penvillo, Jim A393
Peoples, Rasheda P440
Peoples, Chanda P486
Pepenelli, Vince A242
Pepinski, Tom A3
Pepito, Christine A149
Peppard, Denise A602
Peppe, Joseph A56
Pepper, Randy A327
Pepper, Nancy A667
Pepper, J David P422
Pepper, J David P423
Pepper, Dave P423
Pepper, H L Perry P570
Pepper, J Stanley P600
Pepper, Richard S P600
Pepper, David A. E75
Pepper, Nancy E336
Pequeno, Norma P127
Peraino, Vito C. A51
Peralta, Pennie P94
Percarpio, Michael F A678
Percefull, Mr Gary P247
Perch, Jeanmarie P439
Perche, Patrice E166
Perchinske, Terese P99
Percy, Harriet P204
Perdomo, Katie A589
Perdue, Rob A223
Perdue, Richard A446
Perdue, Russell A823
Perdue, Richard E210
Perea, Jennifer Rosato P155
Perego, Robert A105
Pereira, Jose A202
Pereira, Sam A254
Pereira, Jose P122
Pereira, Justine P161
Pereira, Sunita P629
Pereira, Ivan de S-- W284
Perera, Jaime P318
Peretz, Richard N. A850
Pereyra, Gerardo A3
Perez, Ventura A100
Perez, Vincent A102
Perez, Cliff A244
Perez, Patricio A244
Perez, Alexa A272
Perez, Rafael A336
Perez, Steven A446
Perez, Javier A537
Perez, Mario A537
Perez, Jose M A678
Perez, Juan R. A850
Perez, Karla A857
Perez, William D A898
Perez, Marta P8
Perez, Gloria P142
Perez, Dave P256
Perez, Victor P426
Perez, Dan P428
Perez, Linda P443
Perez, Dr Sylvester Syl P478
Perez, Steven E210
Perez, Francisco J. (Frank) E337
Perez-Cuevas, Rosa P440
Peri, Gil P138
Perica, Adrian A70
Perikly, Jaime A565
Perille, Thomas P531

Perini, Joe A833
Periquet, Pepper A532
Perkins, Raymond A84
Perkins, Thomas B. A237
Perkins, Jan A485
Perkins, Meleah A572
Perkins, Joe Bob A787
Perkins, Kenneth A851
Perkins, Michael L. A886
Perkins, Gary A. P117
Perkins, Rhonda P118
Perkins, Troy P227
Perkins, Paul P271
Perkins, Meleah P359
Perkins, Collin P379
Perkins, James P381
Perkins, Judy P490
Perkins, Danielle P678
Perkins, Kevin A276
Perkins, Jana E277
Perkins, Michael L. E433
Perkovich, Joseph P361
Perlin, Jonathan B. (Jon) A410
Perlman, Harvey S. P78
Perlman, Joel A. P351
Perlman, Lori P384
Perlman, Lee E337
Perlmutter, Robert J. A71
Perlmutter, Roger M. A550
Permet, Robert P231
Perna, Jeannette A751
Perna, Jeannette E377
Perng, Danny P326
Perno, Joseph A475
Perno, Joseph P266
Pero, Lisa Del P461
Peroceschi, Jacob A729
Perold, Jacques A34
Perotti, Pierce A533
Perotti, Daniel S. A642
Perotti, Daniel S. E329
Perr, Julius A246
Perra, Tim A762
Perrault, Erika A56
Perrault, Paul A. A149
Perrault, Ryan A866
Perreault, Michel G A19
Perreault, Roger A836
Perrell, Kim E432
Perrella, Michael E193
Perren, Katharine P399
Perretta, Christopher E300
Perrette, Jean-Briac (JB) A269
Perrette, Anita P654
Perretti, Leslie A685
Perrey, Dennis P183
Perri, Michael G. P642
Perricone, Jennifer A784
Perrilliat, Javara D. A626
Perrin, Jamie P685
Perrine, Gerry E97
Perrone, Lauren A522
Perrone, Paula P441
Perroots, Stephen A530
Perrotti, Richard P362
Perry, Harvey P. A185
Perry, Lance A199
Perry, Jennifer A221
Perry, Jim A269
Perry, Glynn A278
Perry, Egbert L. J. A315
Perry, David A371
Perry, Marie A423
Perry, Nick A489
Perry, Shannon A614
Perry, Sean A711
Perry, Stephen A767
Perry, Lawrence A774
Perry, Curtis J. A781
Perry, Jim A871
Perry, Doug A890
Perry, Doni P14
Perry, Judy P22
Perry, Jason P67
Perry, James P161

Perry, Tia P275
Perry, Glenn P326
Perry, Amy P355
Perry, Kenneth C P421
Perry, Thirsty P476
Perry, Carol P543
Perry, Sue P579
Perry, Rhonda S P591
Perry, Nancy P603
Perry, Duke P682
Perry, Doug P684
Perry, Jonathan E102
Perry, Robyn E268
Persante, Patricia E175
Persaud, Gloria A109
Persaud, Gloria E36
Pershing, John A79
Pershing, Dennis A560
Pershing, Dennis P342
Persico, Charlie A685
Person, Peter P249
Person, Peter P505
Persondek, Leighann M P666
Pert, Bob P636
Pertl, Kathy A866
Pertoldova, Magdalena P413
Pesce, Alex A829
Pesci, Nello-John (NJ) P489
Pessina, Stefano A877
Pestana, Tiago C- - mara W156
Pestikas, Jennifer A5
Petee, Sandra A698
Petee, Sandra P456
Peter, Coates A159
Peter, John St P12
Peter, Nicolas W59
Peter, Joseph G. (Joe) W265
Peterffy, Thomas E221
Peterman, Thomas A A558
Peterman, Patrick A744
Peters, Chris A300
Peters, Lauren B. A361
Peters, William E. (Bill) A471
Peters, Jill A484
Peters, Greg A581
Peters, Scott M. A700
Peters, Harld A850
Peters, James W. (Jim) A898
Peters, Brian F A898
Peters, Angie P21
Peters, Michael P36
Peters, Mary E P228
Peters, Jerry P280
Peters, Vidya P357
Peters, Alexandra P561
Peters, Chris P642
Peters, Ian W87
Peters, Scott D E189
Peterschick, Shannon P521
Petersen, Christopher A56
Petersen, Andy Kramer A111
Petersen, Nicholas A838
Petersen, Andy Kramer P56
Petersen, Richard W. (Rich) P303
Petersen, David P402
Petersen, Laurel P441
Petersen, Mark P673
Peterson, James N. A96
Peterson, Frances A98
Peterson, John A140
Peterson, Chuck A223
Peterson, Jeffrey A260
Peterson, Terry D. A278
Peterson, Erika A292
Peterson, Jay A340
Peterson, Joseph A350
Peterson, Lloyd A393
Peterson, Mary B A410
Peterson, Dean A449
Peterson, Wes A468
Peterson, Joel C. A474
Peterson, Ronald R A474
Peterson, Sandra E. A476
Peterson, Carl A591
Peterson, David J A599

Peterson, Robert L. A611
Peterson, Doug A676
Peterson, Michael A684
Peterson, Douglas L. (Doug) A721
Peterson, James A729
Peterson, Jeff A729
Peterson, Sheila A767
Peterson, Kelly A866
Peterson, Cherie A872
Peterson, Martha A877
Peterson, Barbara P39
Peterson, Jeannette P74
Peterson, Margaret R P90
Peterson, Terry P113
Peterson, Steve P140
Peterson, Barbara P192
Peterson, David P226
Peterson, Tim P238
Peterson, Wes P252
Peterson, Eric P256
Peterson, Ronald R P265
Peterson, Ronald P266
Peterson, Denise P275
Peterson, Dan P281
Peterson, Phil P331
Peterson, David B P355
Peterson, Penelope L. P398
Peterson, Denise M. P472
Peterson, Larry P512
Peterson, Randall P543
Peterson, Randy P543
Peterson, Glenn E P564
Peterson, Julie P609
Peterson, Karen P641
Peterson, Kelly P661
Peterson, Fross P662
Peterson, Matthew W29
Peterson, Frances E33
Peterson, Jeffrey G. (Jeff) E57
Peterson, Carl E65
Peterson, Scott E65
Peterson, Scott E. E107
Peterson, Mike E127
Peterson, Jason E130
Peterson, Mark A. E131
Peterson, Jay E151
Peterson, Joseph E157
Peterson, Alexander E213
Peterson, Joel E248
Peterson, Michael D. E341
Peterson, Michael E342
Peterson, Lynn A. E382
Petinaux, Bruno P582
Petit, Courtney A478
Petitgas, Franck A568
Petkov, Boris A158
Petkun, William A147
Petkus, Ed A136
Petmecky, William (Tres) A752
Petno, Douglas B. (Doug) A480
Petouhoff, Natalie A723
Petracchini, Marco W143
Petrassi, Fiore A481
Petrasso, Mark A920
Petrick, Teresa G P660
Petrides, Mike P184
Petrie, Michael J. A223
Petro, Nancy A241
Petro, Rosalee A572
Petro, Rosalee P359
Petro, Dan P622
Petromelis, Ted A105
Petrone, Andrew A3
Petropoulos, Michael A406
Petrosino, John P134
Petrossian, John A782
Petru, Margie C A221
Petruccelli, Jennifer A513
Petrulak, Michael P409
Petruleas, Harry A542
Petruleas, Harry E267
Petrunoff, Andre B A648
Petruzillo, Kelli Hunter A56
Petruzzella, Franco P345
Petry, Paul A152

Petry, Paul E49
Petrzelka, Jamie E117
Petters, C. Michael (Mike) A442
Pettigrew, James (Jim) W101
Pettigrew, John W255
Pettis, Allen A823
Pettit, Brenda A700
Pettit, Tom A718
Pettit, Richard A781
Pettit, Dirk P125
Pettoni, Matthew K A78
Pettus, Janice P346
Petty, Trent P555
Petty, Brian P. E147
Petznek, Erwin A235
Petzold, Robert A483
Peugeot-Roncoroni, Marie-
  Hél- ne W286
Peverly, Francis P408
Pewonka, Della P661
Peyton, John A696
Peyton, Joe A697
Peyton, Joe P454
Pezzulo, Paolo A334
Pezzulo, Paolo P193
Pezzuto, Sara P8
Pe- ±alver, Eduardo M. P143
Pfannes, Cheri P191
Pfeifer, John C. A151
Pfeifer, Mark P638
Pfeiffer, Michael R. E348
Pfieffer, James P627
Pfirrman, John A659
Pfirrman, Christopher A726
Pfitzenreiter, Axel A727
Pfitzer, Steven A700
Pflederer, Kent A. A631
Pflugradt, Matt A223
Phadnis, Amit S A199
Phalen, Michael P. (Mike) A144
Phalen, James S. P80
Pham, Dung A802
Pham, Bich P135
Pham, Hai P237
Pham, Dung P562
Pham, James P639
Pham, Hien P654
Pham, Diane E20
Phangaraj, Immanuel P305
Phares, Bob P78
Pharmd, Geoffrey Lawton P101
Phatipat, Michael P207
PHD, Robert Sloan P64
PHD, Elaine Joyce Simpkins P75
PHD, Bruce Messinger P81
PHD, Donde Plowman P87
PHD, Steven Daeschner P260
PHD, J B Silvers P336
PHD, Susan Andrews P359
PHD, C Randal Mills P363
PHD, Charles L Beaty P462
Phebus, Linnie A244
Phelan, Jean A332
Phelan, David C. A766
Phelps, Bob A397
Phelps, Boyd A456
Phelps, Ronald A568
Phelps, Kimberlee A644
Phelps, Julia A871
Phelps, David E P69
Phelps, Jennifer P134
Phelps, Bob P221
Phelps, David P360
Phelps, David E. E41
Phenicie, John E407
Phifer, Anthony A406
Phifer, Lynn P538
Philbert, Martin A698
Philbert, Martin P456
Philbin, Gary M. A274
Philip, Anil A461
Philipoom, Bruce A693
Philippe, Marc W323
Philippe, Hervé W388
Philippin, Charles J A836

A = AMERICAN BUSINESS
E = EMERGING COMPANIES
P = PRIVATE COMPANIES
W = WORLD BUSINESS

Philippopoulos, Evan A19
Philipps, Kate W148
Philips, Peggy A166
Philips, Gail A481
Philips, Christopher A869
Philips, J Michael P480
Philips, Michael P480
Phillip, Thomas C A565
Phillippy, Robert J. P379
Phillips, Charles A13
Phillips, Kara A54
Phillips, Daniel A58
Phillips, Judy A84
Phillips, Eric A269
Phillips, Twila A316
Phillips, Brett A323
Phillips, Paul A369
Phillips, Jeanne A380
Phillips, Shelley A412
Phillips, Eric A443
Phillips, Susan A490
Phillips, Jeremy A589
Phillips, John A647
Phillips, David P. A679
Phillips, David P. A680
Phillips, Ann A683
Phillips, Lynn A702
Phillips, Raakhi A704
Phillips, John A780
Phillips, Don A784
Phillips, Glenn A819
Phillips, Mark D P39
Phillips, Rosemary P60
Phillips, Brent P64
Phillips, Bill P73
Phillips, Debbie P86
Phillips, Robyn P93
Phillips, Joan P110
Phillips, Jannice P118
Phillips, Betty P130
Phillips, Sharon P152
Phillips, Suzie P174
Phillips, Twila P191
Phillips, Anita P202
Phillips, Annette S P235
Phillips, Ross P298
Phillips, John E. P336
Phillips, Andrea P354
Phillips, David P. P448
Phillips, Mark T P472
Phillips, Roland P484
Phillips, John P521
Phillips, Robert P573
Phillips, Robert P575
Phillips, Tammy M P583
Phillips, Neil Foster P587
Phillips, Kelly P613
Phillips, Catherine A P632
Phillips, Aaron E47
Phillips, Kevin E172
Phillips, Kenneth J. (Ken) E174
Phillips, Shelley E192
Phillips, Randall E265
Phillips, Raakhi E351
Phillips, Scott E438
Phillips-Gadley, Terica A522
Philo, Kim A175
Philo, James P467
Phinney, Allen A115
Phipps, Janet A468
Phipps, P. Cody A626
Phipps, Chad F. A918
Phipps, Janet P252
Phipps, Karen P493
Phong, Sam P96
Phy, Jennifer P40
Phyfer, Cheri M. A738
Piacenza, Bruno W168
Piani, Carlos A494

Pianka, Stephanie A585
Pianka, Stephanie P377
Piasecki, Jon A295
Piatkowski, John S. P674
Piazza, Patsy A855
Picard, Steve A115
Picarelli, Sergio W7
Picat, Maxime W286
Picca, Bruno W189
Picchione, Shannon A270
Picciano, Robert J. (Bob) A460
Piccini, Gabriele W380
Piccioni, Alysia A517
Piccioni, Lawrence P64
Picco, Gary A294
Piccolomini, Flavio A532
Piccone, Steve P333
Pichai, Sundar A36
Pichla, Joseph A481
Pick, Ted A568
Pickel, Michael W164
Pickelmann, Gary P539
Pickens, Randi A5
Pickens, Bob A707
Pickens, Robert P113
Pickens, Ann E46
Pickerall, Brian A140
Pickering, Sammy G. A304
Pickering, Steven W103
Pickert, Valerie A869
Pickett, Denise A49
Pickett, Miko A513
Pickett, C. Taylor E315
Pickle, Trevor O A262
Picone, Frank A726
Picone, Joe A850
Pieczynski, James J. (Jim) A632
Pieczynski, James J. (Jim) E321
Piedra, Pedro A489
Pieper, Stephanie P533
Pieper, Rick E289
Piepho, Lindsay A835
Pieragowski, Steve A705
Pieragowski, Steve E352
Pierangeli, Dan P7
Pierce, Will A115
Pierce, Christopher A140
Pierce, Chris A140
Pierce, David A. (Dave) A144
Pierce, Cathy A149
Pierce, Chas A195
Pierce, David A196
Pierce, Teri A336
Pierce, Sandra E. A440
Pierce, Sandra A643
Pierce, Charles E. A671
Pierce, Susan A683
Pierce, Todd A723
Pierce, Larry A756
Pierce, Tom A902
Pierce, Barbara P40
Pierce, Phil P52
Pierce, Phil P53
Pierce, Kevin P171
Pierce, Maryhelen P188
Pierce, Teri P194
Pierce, Ken P563
Pierce, Jason P611
Pierce, Tom P692
Pierce, Karen E139
Pierce, Joseph E273
Pierdon, Steven B P210
Pierfederici, Paolo A649
Pieri, Melody A387
Pieri, Melody E177
Pierluisi, Guillermo P680
Pierog, Michael A133
Pierog, James P531
Pieron, James R. A666
Pieron, James R. P438
Pierre-Louis, Stanley A872
Pierrepont, R S A532
Pierron, Chip A56
Pierson, Ken A201
Pierson, Michael A331

Pierson, Johnathan A478
Pierson, Christine A837
Pierson, Michael E148
Pierz, Brian A407
Pierzchalski, Lawrence J. A557
Piestrack, Nancy A110
Piestrack, Nancy E37
Pieters, Marten W389
Pietragallo, William P301
Pietranton, Anthony F. A886
Pietranton, Anthony F. E433
Pietrantoni, Carlos Power A336
Pietro, Roberto Di A685
Pietrunti, Michael A912
Pietrykowski, Robert P399
Pietsch, Alfred P644
Piette, Daniel W225
Pifer, Nic A56
Pigg, Charles P528
Piggott, Julie A. A134
Piggott, Julie A. A154
Piggott, Julie A. P77
Pignata, Kate E369
Pignuolo, Chuck A99
Pigott, M. Jason A190
Pigott, Mark C. A629
Piha, Isaac P182
Pikuleva, Irina P99
Pilgreen, Brian P22
Pilgrim, Trip A794
Pilgrim, Jerome P254
Pilkington, Kevin A611
Pilla, John A758
Pilla, Rocco A894
Pillai, Smita A677
Pillai, Gopal A877
Pilling, Charles A782
Pilnick, Gary H. A485
Piloti, Akbar E265
Pilotte, Niki A108
Pilwallis, Mark P196
Pimentel, Armando A590
Pimentel, August P494
Pina, Carlos Costa W156
Pinault, Fran-§ois-Henri W204
Pinchera, Matt A235
Pinckney, Tom A288
Pinckney, Nancy A332
Pindak, Mike A541
Pindak, Mike E266
Pinder, Kymberly P648
Pineda, Karen A546
Pinegar, Stan A282
Pinegar, Deak P231
Pinet, Steve De P393
Pinevich, Anthony J P332
Ping, David P230
Ping, Andrew C P332
Pingatore, Holly J. E147
Pingel, Spencer A218
Pingolt, Cindy P310
Pinkerton, Jerry A423
Pinkerton, Jake P664
Pinkerton, Stuart E428
Pinkes, Andrew J. A211
Pinkham, Justin A537
Pinkham, Elizabeth A723
Pinkham, Stan A869
Pinkus, Murray A901
Pinkus, Murray P692
Pinnaro, Catherina P643
Pinnavaia, Ian A131
Pinne, Linda C. E256
Pinnell, Jennifer P356
Pinner, Ian A74
Pinner, Ernest S. (Ernie) A182
Pinner, Ernest S. (Ernie) E63
Pinney, Monique A445
Pinnix-ragland, Hilda A282
Pinnolis, Michael P50
Pinnow, Cole C A649
Pino, Joseph R P620
Pinover, Eugene E426
Pins, George D P695
Pinson, Brad A332

Pint, Daryl E68
Pintek, Michael F. E250
Pinter, John A147
Pinto, Claudia A474
Pinto, Daniel E. A480
Pinto, John J. A583
Pinto, Mark A693
Pinto, Claudia P262
Pinto, Raymond P291
Pinto, Rich P609
Pinto, Arik W46
Pintoff, Craig A. A851
Pio, Ruth P639
Piotrowski, Agnieszka P8
Piou, Olivier W266
Piovaccari, Alessandro E371
Piper, Patrick E. A137
Piper, John A314
Piper, Greg A591
Piper, John P189
Piper, Darren E364
Pipkin, Paul P183
Pipp, Steve A81
Pippin, Jeff P423
Pippins, Dakota A432
Pirard, Eddy W194
Pires, Luciano Siani W385
Pirog, Christine A120
Piroli, Brad A681
Pirozzi, Chris P425
Pirrotta, Rich P293
Pirtle, William L. (Willy) E368
Pisano, Adam A744
Pisarczyk, Karen A437
Pisarenkov, Irina P182
Pisetsky, Bill E207
Pisieczko, Alex A330
Piskura, Mary P83
Pistelli, Lapo W144
Pita, George L. A536
Pitaro, James A. (Jimmy) A272
Pitasky, Scott A763
Pitcher, Terri A125
Pitcher, Daniel D. A319
Pitchford, Gail P110
Pitchford, Earl W P166
Piterans, Marianne A805
Pitesa, John W. (Bill) A281
Pititto, Joseph E1
Pitkethly, Graeme W383
Pitkin, Dale P218
Pitman, Charles A69
Pitman, Martha A635
Pitman, Martha P419
Pitofsky, David B. A589
Pitre, Kathleen E A96
Pitrelli, Jessi A511
Pitt, Douglas A395
Pittard, Joel P172
Pittel, Kimberly A362
Pittenger, David P329
Pittillo, Chad A742
Pittillo, Joe A780
Pittillo, Chad E372
Pittler, Nicholas E440
Pittman, Kim A175
Pittman, Raymond J. (R.J.) A288
Pittman, Carolyn A442
Pittman, Robert W. (Bob) A448
Pittman, Todd A557
Pitton, Kathy A221
Pitts, Jack A133
Pitts, Susan A781
Pitts, Dana P694
Pitts, David L. E59
Pitts, Keith E337
Pitzer, Cheryl A441
Pitzer, Kevin P249
Pizarek, Jenna P218
Pizarro, Pedro J. A291
Pizzi, Michael A. A283
Pizzi, Vince A833
Pizzi, Christopher E101
Pizzini, Ruby A105
Pizzuti, Linda A105

Pizzuto, Frank A857
Pla, Thomas A109
Pla, Angela A364
Pla, Thomas E36
Plaat, Mitch A913
Place, Nick P642
Plaehn, Mark P333
Plaehn, Martin H. E93
Plamondon, William N P166
Planitzer, Warren E19
Plank, Robert A163
Plank, Kevin A. A840
Plankinton, Christine A101
Planos, Robert A532
Plansky, John A766
Plant, John C. A76
Plante, Francis A51
Plante, David A85
Plante, David A330
Plante, James A406
Plante, Robert A. (Bob) A639
Plante, Robert A. (Bob) E325
Plants, J. Daniel E104
Plass, Mary Ellen P18
Platanias, Leon P398
Platchek, Terry A507
Platchek, Terry P288
Plate, William A120
Plater, Alejandro W25
Plater, Alonzo E86
Platford, Giles W355
Plath, Thomas A163
Platsis, Maria E220
Platt, Louise A266
Platt, Jim A589
Platt, Daniel B. A632
Platt, Daniel B. E321
Platteeuw, Filip W379
Plattenberger, Kate A599
Plattner, Hasso W319
Plaza, Robert A489
Pleasant, Kevin A562
Pleasant, Shannon P458
Pleasant, Kevin E279
Plecki, Robert F. (Bob) A339
Plecki, Robert F. (Bob) E150
Pledger, Joe A851
Pleininger, Johann W276
Plemmons, Elizabeth P235
Plessis, Esme A377
Plessis, Jan P. du W76
Plessis, Jan P. du W305
Plessis, Jan P. du W306
Plessis-Bélair, Michel W293
Plessis-Bélair, Michel W294
Pletcher, Brett A386
Pleuhs, Gerhard (Gerd) A567
Plevritis, Peter A204
Plew, Daniel P. Van A698
Plew, Susan Van P176
Plew, Michael P291
Pley, Matthew E166
Plisinski, Michael P. E361
Plodzeen, Tom A333
Plonk, Timothy M P168
Ploszek, Michael P8
Ploszek, Judy P197
Plotkin, Ben A. A771
Plourde, Robert A855
Plousi, Andrew A407
Ploutz-Snyder, Lori A698
Ploutz-Snyder, Lori P456
Plowinske, Sandra A901
Plowinske, Sandra Besso A902
Plowinske, Sandra P692
Pluard, Tim P473
Plumart, Marc W334
Plumb, Steven P164
Plumeri, Joseph J A343
Plummer, Ken A97
Plummer, Ed A264
Plummer, Tammy L. A338
Plummer, Wade A537
Plummer, Cheryl A655
Plummer, William B. A851

Plummer, Shane P184
Plummer, Beth P386
Plummer, Scott P400
Plummer, Ken E32
Plummer, Michelle M. E183
Plummer, Cheryl E333
Plump, Andrew S. W355
Plunkett, Davis P544
Plunkett, J. Michael (Mike) E105
Pluta, Chris A738
Plymell, Shane P497
Poag, Chris A28
Poag, Chris P17
Poch, Andi A175
Pocino, Raymond M P371
Poczekaj, Ken A295
Podesta, Charles (Chuck) P614
Podges, Christopher P359
Podliska, Peggy P330
Podoll, Andrew P513
Podsadecki, Thomas A5
Poe, Shawn K. P432
Poenitske, Jason P P400
Poerschke, John E7
Poetz, Gregg E234
Pofahl, Quinn A691
Poferl, Jeff A246
Poff, Brian W. E5
Pofsky, Robert A323
Pogue, Danielle A25
Pogue, Danielle P15
Pohlman, Kevin A636
Pohlman, Steve A796
Pohly, Glenn E261
Poindexter, Philip S. A772
Poinsatte, Richard A768
Poinsatte, Christopher A. P152
Poirier, Michel W194
Poisson, Keith P208
Poisson, Patrick E415
Pojero, April P323
Poklar, Eric A180
Pokoly, Thomas P632
Pokorny, Deb P434
Pol, Sanjay A199
Polacco, Lorenzo A913
Polanchyck, Mike P254
Polanchyck, Michael P254
Polanski, John J. A413
Polanski, John J. P234
Polatnick, Adam E265
Polek, Wayne V P158
Polen, Thomas E. A119
Polen, Michael R. (Mike) A885
Polep, Lori P140
Poletaev, Maxim W321
Poli, Massimo A218
Policarpio, Ariene A246
Polier, Bruce P526
Polignac, Fran-çois Melchior de W82
Poling, Richard P509
Polipnick, Gary A. A318
Polishook, Debra A. W5
Polisknowski, John P512
Politi, Gary A478
Politopoulou, Marianna W253
Polizzotto, Lawrence A429
Polizzotto, Len P568
Polk, James C. (Jim) A103
Polk, Jonathan A323
Polk, Michael B A472
Polk, Michael B. (Mike) A586
Polk, Dennis A779
Polk, Robert P188
Polk, Michael B P259
Pollack, Michael A175
Pollack, Dave A198
Pollack, Dennis A740
Pollack, Martha E. P143
Pollack, Mike P186
Pollack, Jane P363
Pollak, Matthew A764
Pollard, Victoria A449
Pollard, Gary S. P679
Pollei, Mike A56

Polley, Malcolm E. A720
Polley, Greg P199
Polley, Malcolm E. E362
Polli, Edward A886
Polli, Edward E433
Pollidore, Diana A774
Pollock, Melissa Schwartz A49
Pollock, Carl A677
Pollock, Cynthia A758
Pollock, Cynthia P519
Pollock, Samuel J. B. (Sam) W75
Pollok, John C. A751
Pollok, John C. E377
Poll-'s, Jeanne A652
Polman, Paul W381
Polman, Paul W383
Polohakul, Ampol W202
Poloni, Lara A16
Polonsky, Kenneth S. P609
Polonsky, Kenneth S. P611
Poloz, Stephen S. W47
Polvoriza, Melanie A270
Polzella, Stephanie A407
Poma, Pam P410
Pomaranski, Joseph A. (Joe) A796
Pombar, Xavier P467
Pomer, David A408
Pomerantz, Laura E355
Pomeroy, Claire A119
Pomeroy, John A811
Pomeroy, John P600
Pomilia, Susan E193
Pommellet, Pierre-Eric W364
Pompa, Mark A. A294
Pomplon, Carl A175
Pomponio, Gina P651
Ponczoch, John A826
Pond, Peter B. E265
Ponicki, Charles J. E76
Pons, Jaume A648
Ponte, Andy E65
Pontious, Jane A187
Pontious, Jane E71
Pontis, Ed P501
Ponturo, Allison P556
Pooi, Eric W323
Pool, Devin A436
Pool, Dr Dennis P406
Pool, Taylor E198
Poole, Thomas A219
Poole, Tim A705
Poole, Dawn P139
Poole, Mark A P247
Poole, Nigeria P687
Poole, Thomas E84
Poole, Tim E352
Poonen, Sanjay A875
Poongkumarn, Prasert W88
Poonia, Mohinder P135
Poor, H. Vincent P606
Poore, Mike P292
Pootanasap, Vitit W88
Pope, Gene A38
Pope, John C. (Jack) A278
Pope, Lawrence J. A398
Pope, Jeffrey A723
Pope, David A800
Pope, Leslie P157
Pope, Erin P176
Pope, Robyn P228
Pope, Michael W. (Mike) E368
Pope, David E396
Popeck, Charles A784
Popham, Holly A446
Popham, Matthew A505
Popham, Holly E210
Popielarczyk, Marie P425
Popieski, Tom A731
Popieski, Tom E365
Poplawski, John P297
Poplin, Janice P620
Popovich, John A413
Popovich, John P234

Popovici, Silviu A647
Popowycz, Alex P230
Popp, Jack A408
Poppe, Patricia K. (Patti) A210
Poppe, Patricia K. (Patti) A236
Popper, Jozsi A693
Poppinga, Peter W385
Popwell, David T. A348
Porat, Ruth M. A36
Porath, Ben P151
Porcari, John P312
Porceddu, Barbara Ann P414
Porcelain, Michael D. E89
Porch, Jessica P101
Pordon, Anthony R. (Tony) A642
Pordon, Tony A643
Poremba, Steve P315
Poroch, David A383
Porporino, Dominic A850
Porras, Edward A244
Porras, Julio Carlos W25
Porsa, Esmaeil P152
Port, Stephen A742
Port, Stephen P502
Port, Barry R. E125
Porta, Matt A461
Portacci, Michael T. A227
Portalatin, Julio A. A532
Portalatin, Frances A731
Portalatin, Frances E365
Portantino, Philip A639
Portantino, Philip E325
Porter, Darlene A19
Porter, Cynthia V A221
Porter, Pamela G A221
Porter, Tracy L A224
Porter, David E. A414
Porter, Todd A417
Porter, Roger A631
Porter, Clint A655
Porter, Jonathan A701
Porter, Brian A704
Porter, Stephen D. A736
Porter, R Roderick A754
Porter, Brian A784
Porter, Andrew C. (Andy) A812
Porter, Melvin A837
Porter, Ann A837
Porter, Charlyn Jarrells A878
Porter, Robert P13
Porter, Robert G P154
Porter, Jessica P161
Porter, Paul P176
Porter, Jody P208
Porter, Emily P252
Porter, J Gregory P274
Porter, James R. P423
Porter, Stephen D. P492
Porter, Andy P567
Porter, Joylene P587
Porter, William P595
Porter, Andrew C. (Andy) P607
Porter, Brian J. W50
Porter, John W222
Porter, James S. E19
Porter, Jessie E57
Porter, James E140
Porter, David E. E194
Porter, Terry E263
Porter, Clint E333
Porter, Susan E336
Porter, Brian E351
Portera, Joseph P. (Joe) A239
Porth, Wilfried W114
Portillo, Marilyn A558
Portnoy, Barry M. A826
Portnoy, Barry M. E366
Portnoy, Adam D. E366
Porwal, Hemant A888
Posa, Nicola A912
Posada, Juan F. A671
Posch, Danny P341
Posch, Guillaume de W62
Posey, Robert A878
Posey, Andrea P106

A = AMERICAN BUSINESS
E = EMERGING COMPANIES
P = PRIVATE COMPANIES
W = WORLD BUSINESS

Posey, Bruce K. E342
Poshyanonda, Pipatpong W203
Posniak, Fred E122
Post, Glen F. A185
Post, Barbara P484
Post, Kim P487
Postell, Ann A449
Postema, Bradley G. A306
Postma, Sidney W P446
Postma, Gene P686
Potashner, Kenneth F. P379
Potgieter, Dirk A649
Pothier, Robert A101
Potter, Kevin A149
Potter, Steve A243
Potter, Simon M. A323
Potter, Mary A513
Potter, Stephen N. A599
Potter, Ashton P22
Potthoff, Laura P481
Potts, David L. A703
Potts, Linda A751
Potts, Janna A. A788
Potts, Robert C P164
Potts, Henry P326
Potts, David T. W249
Potts, Robert E274
Potts, Linda E378
Potvin, Brent A711
Pou, Bill P672
Poulakos, Greg A67
Poulos, Ray A780
Poulsen, Greg A458
Poulsen, Greg P251
Poulsen, Niel L. E419
Pouncey, Clarence C. A737
Pouncey, Clarence C. E367
Pound, Greg A591
Pound, Steve P92
Pouyanné, Patrick W372
Pouyanné, Patrick W372
Povenmire, Rex A270
Povolny, Denise A489
Powell, Sarah A13
Powell, Cindy A115
Powell, Heather A263
Powell, Bradley S. (Brad) A312
Powell, Jane A329
Powell, Jon A333
Powell, Kendall J. (Ken) A377
Powell, Ira A390
Powell, Teresa A414
Powell, Ty A446
Powell, Heather A530
Powell, Jonathan A537
Powell, Rebecca A578
Powell, Tyane A655
Powell, Christy A724
Powell, Scott A726
Powell, Deana A742
Powell, Cynthia A. A764
Powell, Terry A814
Powell, Vincent A832
Powell, Wayne A850
Powell, Wm. Eugene (Gene) A860
Powell, Brian A920
Powell, Joan P51
Powell, Sylvia P264
Powell, Chris P315
Powell, Andrew P379
Powell, Jason P415
Powell, Wendy P415
Powell, Paul P466
Powell, Larry E P515
Powell, Courtney P542
Powell, John P614
Powell, Terry P616
Powell, Jeremy P630
Powell, Wm. Eugene (Gene) P656

Powell, Scott E. W45
Powell, William W75
Powell, Rice W153
Powell, Rice W154
Powell, Lisa E126
Powell, Micah E172
Powell, Teresa E194
Powell, Ty E210
Powell, Jeffrey L. E229
Powell, Paul T. E245
Powell, Tyane E333
Powell, Deana E372
Power, Doug A377
Power, Nancy A555
Power, Alan J. (Al) A666
Power, Jamila A698
Power, Gary A898
Power, Michael J P392
Power, Alan J. (Al) P438
Power, Jamila P456
Power, Andrew P. E107
Power, Robert E320
Powers, Robert P. (Bob) A46
Powers, Robert P. (Bob) A47
Powers, James W A136
Powers, John J. A339
Powers, Matthew A478
Powers, Lance A693
Powers, Brenda A700
Powers, Marsha A795
Powers, John A862
Powers, Gary A901
Powers, John J. P70
Powers, Kurt P147
Powers, James P149
Powers, Donald S P359
Powers, Aaron J P397
Powers, Chad P505
Powers, Jamie P541
Powers, William C. (Bill) P656
Powers, Gary P692
Powers, Dave E106
Powers, David B. (Dave) E112
Powers, John J. E150
Powers, Johnny D. E213
Powers, John E230
Powers, Kathleen T E283
Powers, Russell E310
Powers, John E419
Powes, Hammond R P144
Powlus, Lee C. A644
Poynor, Patrick A115
Pozniak, Kim P101
Pozotrigo, Albert A472
Pozzi, James E. A53
Pozzi, James E. A54
Pozzi, Joseph A390
Pozzi, Steven R. W98
Prabhu, Arjun A607
Prabhu, Vasant M. A874
Prabhu, John C. E231
Prada, Ariel De P637
Pradelle, Yann E166
Pragada, Robert V. (Bob) A472
Prager, Richard L. (Richie) A130
Prahlad, Anand A580
Prakasam, Haripriya A456
Pramaggiore, Anne R. A308
Pramaggiore, Anne R. A323
Pramanik, Sharmila P482
Prange, Karen A727
Prasad, Keshav P107
Prashaud, Satie A133
Prasodjo, Bambang A417
Prater, Shawna P341
Prather, Steve A749
Prather, Sharon P146
Prather, David P202
Prather, Jody P584
Pratico, Lisa A817
Pratico, Joseph A863
Prato, Patrick A441
Pratt, Timothy A. (Tim) A144
Pratt, Paul A364
Pratt, Teresa A441

Pratt, William C. (Bill) A745
Pratt, Bill A769
Pratt, John P164
Pratt, Angela M P270
Pratt, Robin P476
Pratt, Daniel P479
Pratt, Scott P651
Pratt, Carol E144
Pratt, Gregory P E212
Pratt, Jim E438
Praw, Albert Z. A484
Pray, Kevin D A402
Pray, Michael E268
Preble, Mark A449
Prebola, Don A703
Precourt, Walter F. (Walt) A569
Predmore, Blaine A493
Preiser, Craig A584
Preising, Weston P653
Preisinger, Bradley A724
Prejean, Joshua A163
Prejean, Jerry A446
Prejean, Jerry E210
Premdas, Perry W. E31
Prendergast, David A33
Prendergast, Ed A95
Prendergast, Neil A351
Prendergast, Thomas F A583
Prendergast, Ed P55
Prendergast, Thomas F P374
Prendergast, E. James (Jim) P586
Prendergast, Neil E158
Prener, Anne A113
Prengler, Irving D P65
Prentice, Bill A257
Prentice, F. Sheldon A577
Prentice, Deborah A. P606
Pres, Thomas J La P243
Presa, Jessica A649
Prescott, Leonard A335
Present, Randall C. (Randy) A433
Preska, Robert P281
Preskenis, Donald A341
Preskenis, Ashley A655
Preskenis, Donald E153
Preskenis, Ashley E333
Presnell, Nancy A705
Presnell, Nancy E352
Presser, Michael E432
Pressey, Matthew A775
Pressley, W. Michael A822
Presson, Jeff A178
Presswood, Russ A280
Presti, Linda A49
Prestipino, Ann P590
Prestipino, Anthony P618
Presto, Michael E28
Preston, James A221
Preston, Susan A308
Preston, Trish A537
Preston, Carolyn A744
Preston, Simeon W13
Prestopine, Hillarie A456
Presutto, Bruno P19
Pretorius, Alwyn A588
Pretorius, Sy P417
Preuss, Cristina P387
Preuss, J. Christopher (Chris) W29
Previn, Fletcher A460
Prewitt, Connie F. P74
Prezelj, Irene A355
Price, Zoila A97
Price, Milton A109
Price, Deb A235
Price, Thomas Michael (Mike) A342
Price, Billy A399
Price, Todd M A548
Price, Michael H. A549
Price, Angela A552
Price, Lisa V A596
Price, Matthew S. A671
Price, Vincent A812
Price, Scott A878
Price, Gerald P4
Price, Shannon P4

Price, David P61
Price, Mia P159
Price, Nicholas P161
Price, Sam P172
Price, David P200
Price, Ryan P256
Price, Scott P296
Price, Todd M P324
Price, Jay P327
Price, Angela P328
Price, Michael O. (Mickey) P336
Price, Walter P356
Price, Ken P442
Price, Troy P486
Price, Audra P546
Price, Stuart P575
Price, Byron P583
Price, Vincent P607
Price, Barbara P677
Price, Greg E29
Price, Zoila E32
Price, Milton E36
Price, Michael H. E270
Price, Kelli E337
Price, Andrew E355
Prichard, Georgia P204
Pricket, Glenn P596
Prickett, Charles (Charlie) P1
Prickett, Glenn T. P595
Pride, Steve P183
Prieb, Kandee P342
Priebe, Nancy P49
Pries, Mike P144
Priest, Stephen J. (Steve) A474
Priest, Steve A474
Priest, Dede A878
Priest, Colleen P12
Priest, Geoffrey P333
Priester, William A332
Prieto, Robert Bob A282
Priewe, Kelly P207
Prill, Gina A244
Primeaux, Mimi P403
Primmer, Jan A556
Prince, William A34
Prince, Scott A101
Prince, Mike A155
Prince, Ryan A806
Prince, Brandon A903
Prince, Kathleen P296
Prince, Don P550
Prince, Ryan P569
Princen, Marc W355
Principato, Giuseppe P451
Prins, Darrell P478
Prinster, Dan P536
Prinz, Corey A108
Prinz, Corey E35
Prior, Jenni A407
Prior, Michael T. E26
Prior, Cornelius B. E26
Prior, Graham E116
Prioux, No- «l W82
Priscak, Dave A620
Prisco, Dale A196
Priselac, Thomas M. (Tom) P102
Prising, Jonas A493
Prising, Jonas A525
Pritchard, Deborah A729
Pritchard, Daryl P120
Pritchard, Cheryl P233
Pritchard, Sarah M. P397
Pritchett, Wanda A513
Pritchett, Osye P255
Pritchett, Julie P255
Pritchett, Patricia P639
Priti, Desai A335
Pritt, Jonathon P88
Pritts, Jim E59
Pritzker, Thomas J. (Tom) A445
Privette, Karen A770
Probst, Lawrence F. (Larry) A292
Probst, Marc A458
Probst, Marc P251
Procaccino, Andrea A810

Procaccino, Andrea P597
Prochazka, Scott M A180
Prochazka, Scott M. A181
Procida, Thomas A133
Procter, Kerrigan W217
Proctor, Donald R A199
Proctor, H. Palmer A331
Proctor, Jason P120
Proctor, H. Palmer E148
Proctor, David K. E153
Prodoehl, Mark P51
Proell, Clor P561
Profancik, Brian E252
Proffitt, Joshua L. E244
Progar, Tom A113
Proia, Gina M. A201
Prokop, Heidi A919
Prokopyschyn, Eugene P292
Promo, Joe A550
Promutico, Alessandro W67
Pronger, Derk P359
Propst, Beverly L. A394
Prosenick, Kevin P543
Prosera, Sharon P535
Proske, Donna P541
Prothro, Caren P514
Proto, Nicholas A323
Proudman, Susi A593
Proudman, Deirdre P298
Proulx, Kevin A782
Proust, Elisabeth W372
Prout, Megan A658
Prout, John P72
Prout, John S P215
Provance, Aaron P114
Provaznik, Mary A532
Provelcher, Catherine P659
Provenza, Frank A487
Provera, Marco Tronchetti W237
Provost, Stephanie A73
Provost, David T. A187
Provost, Paula P617
Provost, David T. E71
Prows, Mark A558
Prowse, Christopher P292
Prozorov, Sergey W289
Pruch, Dan P P406
Pruden, Gary A476
PrudÂ'homme, Sylvain A521
Pruett, William A A823
Pruett, Patti P348
Pruett, Julie P517
Pruett, Julie E303
Pruette, Bill A823
Pruger, Robert P602
Pruitt, Diana A137
Pruitt, Kristin L. A500
Pruitt, Tracy A564
Pruitt, Joey P507
Pruitt, Gary B. P566
Pruitt, Lauren P627
Pruitt, Charlotte E231
Pruitt, Kristin L. E238
Pruitt, Ronnie E419
Prunchunas, Edward M. P102
Pruniaux, Patrick W205
Pruss-Jones, Catherine J A136
Pruzan, Jonathan A568
Pryce, Richard W297
Pryor, David B A80
Pryor, D. Scott A787
Pryor, David B P47
Pryor, Vince P176
Pryor, Robert P486
Psaltis, Vassillios E. W24
Psihas, Julian Jorge Lazalde A753
Pszybylski, Michael A56
Ptak, Joanne P589
Pu, Jian W100
Puapong, Devin P270
Puay, Ky A620
Pucci, David A838
Puccio, Frank A108
Puccio, Mary P621
Puccio, Frank E35

Pucel, Kenneth J. (Ken) A661
Pucel, Scott P503
Pucillo, Anthony L P283
Puckett, Karen A300
Puckett, Sonia P68
Puckett, Pam P98
Puckett, Jeffrey M. (Jeff) P119
Puckett, Rick P507
Puckett, Jeff E404
Puco, Christopher C. E10
Puddy, Mike A249
Puder, William P226
Pudlo, Joe A113
Puechl, Robert L. A750
Puente, Gabriel P245
Puffenberger, Jim P457
Pugel, Callie P268
Pugh, Karen P115
Pugh, Randall P258
Pugh, Mike E226
Pugliese, Nate A56
Puglisi, Jeanmarie A366
Pugni, Carl P683
Puhacz, Wasyl P401
Puhy, Dorothy E. P153
Puishys, Joseph E19
Pujol, Patrice B P47
Pukylo, Brian A342
Pulcinella, Dionne A644
Puleo, Dominic J P665
Pulfer, Kari P659
Pulgini, Margaret A901
Pulgini, Margaret P692
Puliafito, Carmen A. A860
Puliafito, Carmen A. P656
Pulie, Jim A644
Pullan, Rowena A649
Pullen, Donna A751
Pullen, Donna E377
Pulley-Hayes, Erika P143
Pulliam, Ryan A328
Pulliam, Elizebeth P60
Pullin, Ericka A244
Pullins, Jerald L. E405
Pullizzi, Amanda A639
Pullizzi, Amanda E326
Pullman, Roger A136
Pullola, Kristian W266
Pulsifer, Keith A323
Pulsifer, Lindsay P433
Pulsipher, Susan P268
Pultz, Stephen P653
Puma, Grace A647
Puma, Mary G. E27
Pumiglia, Kevin P18
Pumilia, Claude A714
Pumphrey, Lori P636
Punahele, Chris A272
Pundarika, Vasanta B A693
Punta, Stefano Del W189
Punthong, Chavalit W296
Puntney, Jeff A131
Pupillo, Mary A901
Pupillo, Mary P692
Puranik, Gautam A166
Puranik, Shirish A874
Purcell, Cynthia D. (Cindy) A110
Purcell, Stacey A158
Purcell, Eugene A273
Purcell, Kathleen A416
Purcell, Kreg A519
Purcell, David A874
Purcell, Eugene P162
Purcell, Robert P199
Purcell, Alfred L P231
Purcell, Alfred L P232
Purcell, Keith P320
Purcell, Cynthia D. (Cindy) E37
Purdon, Luke A454
Purdy, Rick A490
Purdy, Kim P617
Puri, Ajay K. (Jay) A607
Puri, Jay A607
Puri, Deepak E248
Purington, Joseph A307

Purnell, Carissa P477
Purrier, Paul P86
Pursch, Jonathan A244
Purser, Terrie P563
Purugganan, Michael D. A585
Purugganan, Michael D. P377
Purvis, Edgar A295
Purvis, Shawn N. A602
Purvis, Bill A868
Purvis, Robert P372
Purvis, Peggy P480
Purwin, Dave A238
Pushis, Glenn A. A768
Puskar, Joseph P589
Pustejovsky, Peggy P444
Pusztay, Melentina P139
Put, Dirk Van de A567
Putch, Denise P521
Puthussery, Joseph A199
Putkonen, Kurt A659
Putman, Jim A865
Putnam, Lori A58
Putnam, Chris A439
Putnam, Natalie A718
Putnam, Eric A838
Putnam, Cheryl P139
Putnam, Robert P395
Putnam, Skip P395
Putnam, Lori E16
Putnam, Dana E31
Putur, Christine (Chris) A785
Puyau, Susan P695
Puyfontaine, Arnaud Roy de W359
Puyfontaine, Arnaud Roy de W388
Puzausky, Michael A886
Puzausky, Michael E433
Puzio, Marty A500
Puzio, Marty E238
Puzycki, Ryan P594
Pyatt, Donald C. E19
Pye, Donna A446
Pye, Donna E210
Pyle, Kent P275
Pyle, Clint P605
Pyle, Michael R. (Mike) E327
Pyles, Jonna P108
Pyles, Carolyn P334
Pynchon, Bryan N A163
Pyne, Ryan A103
Pyne, David A682
Pyne, Joseph E172
Pzena, Richard S. E341
P-¶tsch, Hans D. W390
Pécresse, Jér-´me A375
Pépin, Normand W180

Q

Qarni, Adil P640
Qassem, Darla P117
Qian, Liu W95
Qiang, Guo Zhi W95
Qin, Huofa W90
Qingfeng, Fan W403
Qingping, Li W100
Qingsong, Lan W316
Quach, Michael A810
Quach, Michael P586
Quackenbush, Scott A371
Quadri, Mir P187
Quadri, Nuzhath P482
Quadros, Nishant De P591
Quaglia, Joseph H. A792
Quagliana, Steve A836
Quagliata, Joseph A49
Qualey, Marjorie A354
Quam, Bethany C. A377
Quam, Aaron P134
Quam, Lois E. P595
Quan, Patrick F A46
Quan, Patrick F P32
Quandahl, Mr John E435
Quandt, Fred A878
Quandt, Stefan W59

Quant, Fred A878
Quaranta, Francesco A20
Quarantello, Kevin A461
Quarfoot, Bob P90
Quarles, Christa A139
Quarles, Patrick D. (Pat) A177
Quartarone, Lisa A729
Quartuccio, James A677
Quatrano, Ralph S. P616
Quatrocky, Fred P167
Quattrochi, Denise A517
Quay, Martha James P692
Qucab, Robert P96
Queenan, Daniel (Danny) A172
Queener, Hugh M. A655
Queener, Hugh M. E333
Quehl, Richard W A710
Quenell, Eileen A532
Quennessen, Bernard A241
Quenneville, Cathy L A34
Quenneville, Cathy L P27
Quenzer, Ronald P368
Querner, Immo W356
Querrey, Dale L. A686
Quesenberry, Scott A382
Quesenberry, Jeff A754
Quesenberry, Jeff E380
Quesnoy, Dru P271
Quest, Katelin A583
Quiachon, Ernesto P319
Quick, Paul A368
Quick, Janet M. A412
Quick, Michael A860
Quick, Michael P192
Quick, Jonathan P304
Quick, James E. P514
Quick, Michael P656
Quick, Janet M. E192
Quigley, James H. (Jim) A417
Quigley, Peter W A486
Quigley, Janet A635
Quigley, Dan A683
Quigley, Matt A693
Quigley, Janet P419
Quigley, Alicia P434
Quigley, Timothy P511
Quigley, David P625
Quigley, Michelle P663
Quijano, Anna A221
Quijano-Lerma, Mariselle P420
Quillin, M. Kirk A110
Quillin, Sue A835
Quillin, Susan A835
Quillin, M. Kirk E37
Quincey, James R. A215
Quine, Allen A422
Quine, Allen P239
Quiniones, Gil C. P375
Quinlan, Thomas A218
Quinlan, Ruth A693
Quinlan, Raymond J. A746
Quinlan, Catherine A860
Quinlan, Catherine P656
Quinlan, Francis E123
Quinlan, Steven J. (Steve) E299
Quinlivan, Jim E82
Quinn, Robert W. (Bob) A84
Quinn, Rebecca A131
Quinn, Stephen D. A396
Quinn, Jeff A478
Quinn, Jane A500
Quinn, John S. A518
Quinn, R. Patrick A583
Quinn, T. Kyle A629
Quinn, Becky A682
Quinn, Amy A705
Quinn, Lisa A815
Quinn, Katherine B. A865
Quinn, Cody A868
Quinn, Christopher A868
Quinn, Corey P105
Quinn, Robert P163
Quinn, Paula P164
Quinn, Michelle D P183
Quinn, Edward P583

A = AMERICAN BUSINESS
E = EMERGING COMPANIES
P = PRIVATE COMPANIES
W = WORLD BUSINESS

Quinn, Teresa P620
Quinn, Jason W4
Quinn, Peter W120
Quinn, Noel W175
Quinn, George W405
Quinn, James W. (Jim) E23
Quinn, Jane E237
Quinn, Gearoid E273
Quinn, Amy E352
Quinn, John C. E359
Quinnan-Hostein, Laura P396
Quinones, Miguel P514
Quinones, Patty P538
Quinonez, Tanya A314
Quinonez, Tanya P189
Quint, Jason A120
Quintana, Lupe A667
Quintana, Andrew P653
Quintana, Lupe E336
Quintanilla, Abel Coello A242
Quintanilla, Omar A244
Quintanilla, Alejandra P123
Quinter, Mark P570
Quintero, Kaye P249
Quinto, Marcos de A215
Quinton, Scott A66
Quirin, Tina A164
Quirin, Julie L. P473
Quirin, Julie P474
Quirk, Raymond R. (Randy) A328
Quirk, Kathleen L. A367
Quirk, Maureen A782
Quirk, Steven (Steve) A791
Quirk, Sherry A. A798
Quirk, Kim P460
Quirk, Kevin M P688
Quirk, Brian C. E282
Quirke, David P205
Quish, Susan A195
Quitilen, Ligaya P550
Quito, Remy A105
Quizon, David E320
Qureshy, Nafees P326
Quémard, Jean-Christophe W286

R

R, Cynthia P145
Raack, Brian A774
Raad, Mark P. de E261
Raadt, Suzanne Van De A76
Raba, Beth A204
Rabe, Ron A758
Rabel, Fernando A913
Raber, Robin A398
Rabiller, Olivier A429
Rabinoff, Richard P418
Rabinowitz, Terry P614
Rabjohn, Richard A460
Rabkin, David A49
Rable, Brad A769
Rabovsky, Jon P247
Rabun, Daniel A69
Raby, Kaye A919
Raby, Julian P506
Racanelli, Joe A850
Race, Mary Jo P651
Rachide, Mary A681
Rachlin, Ann P416
Rachman, Sherry P145
Rachmeler, Kim A38
Rachunek, Jana A674
Racila, Edward P642
Racine, Andrew D. P351
Racioppi, Michael A727
Rack, Sarah A241
Rack, Karen A611

Rack, Karen E313
Rackley, Chad P554
Racut, Kimberly P99
Racz, Francesca A280
Raczkowski, Carl P250
Rada, Mary A2
Radcliffe, Charles A439
Radda, Hank E180
Radde, Donald E. (Don) A431
Radde, Donald E. (Don) E205
Radding, Rebecca P610
Rade, Arnoud de E172
Radecki, Brian J. E97
Radeloff, Brent A407
Rademacher, Dennis P11
Rademacher, Jeanne M P173
Rader, Rodney P371
Rader, Michael P393
Radford, Karen L. W138
Radhakrishnan, Rupkumar A131
Radhakrishnan, Narayanan A390
Radich, Paula P476
Radick, James A369
Radicy, Wendy P32
Radis, Barbara J. A845
Radis, Barbara J. E413
Radley, Steven A449
Radley, Mary P570
Radloff, Sue A350
Radloff, Sue E157
Radner, Alex P218
Radney, Theresa A781
Radocaj, Mijo P405
Radocaj, Matt P405
Radu, Michael R. (Mike) A885
Rady, Ernest S. A44
Rady, Ernest S. P31
Radziwill, John A465
Rae, John A. W293
Rae, Gary E253
Raess, Daniel E3
Raffa, George A693
Raffensperger, Nick A562
Raffensperger, Nick E279
Rafferty, Emily K. A323
Rafferty, Steven A611
Rafferty, Jim A809
Rafferty, Noreen A872
Rafferty, Dan A878
Rafferty, Gary J P551
Rafferty, Jim P584
Rafferty, Emily Kernan P594
Raffile, Sheryl P699
Rafii, Bejan P556
Raftery, Kelli A175
Raftery, Michael A553
Raftery, Michael E272
Ragalie, Glenn A86
Ragalie, Glenn P52
Ragel, Larry P530
Rager, Tom A246
Rager, R. Scott A615
Raghavan, Vis A480
Raghib, Timur P518
Raghumandala, Harikrishna A734
Raghunathan, Vijay A49
Raghuram, Rangarajan (Raghu) A875
Ragni, Margaret V P301
Ragsdale, John P46
Ragusa, Elysia A800
Ragusa, Elysia E396
Rahe, Maribeth S. A890
Rahe, Maribeth S. P684
Rahill, Edward P252
Rahill, Paul F. E263
Rahim, Rami A482
Rahimi, Morteza Null P398
Rahimyar, Rahim P598
Rahl, Gary A140
Rahman, Sobia A893
Rahman, Asif P110
Rahman, Uzma E294
Rahmstr- ¶m, Mats W36
Rahn, Pete K P312
Rahnamay-Azar, Amir P96

Rahne, Renee P107
Rai, Chetan P382
Raia, Kathy A244
Raikes, Donald A275
Raimonde, Michael A. A675
Raimondi, Peter J. A143
Raimondi, Robert A600
Raimondo, Leslie A140
Raimondo, Gina M A765
Raimondo, Gina M P540
Raina, Sunita A247
Raina, Sunita E103
Raina, Robin E116
Rainbolt, David E. A98
Rainbolt, John A108
Rainbolt, David E. E33
Rainbow, Harris P400
Raine, Robbi P521
Rainer, Sallie A300
Rainer, William A726
Rainer, Thom S. P291
Raines, John A263
Raines, J. Paul A372
Raines, Diane S. P58
Rainey, Joseph D. (Joe) A398
Rainford, Annmarie P191
Rainone, Anthony P408
Rains, Darin A249
Rainville, William A. (Bill) E229
Rainwater, Meghan P50
Rainwater, Tom P171
Rainwater, Marvin P275
Raish, Ann P410
Raj, Atul P422
Raja, Prabu G. A71
Rajagopalan, Sri A476
Rajan, Mickey A186
Rajappa, Aswin E261
Rajasekar, Sunil A288
Rajcevich, Linda P369
Rajendra, Suchitra A647
Rajewski, Josh A693
Rajkowski, E. Mark A914
Rajput, Uzair P291
Rajsingh, Peter A585
Rajsingh, Peter P377
Rakes, Kellie A34
Rakes, Wade A180
Rakestraw, Tyre P421
Rakotci, George A691
Rakove, Roberta P504
Rakowitz, Genny A244
Rakshys, James A115
Ralenkotter, Rossi P282
Rales, Steven M. A253
Raley, Zachary W. A62
Raley, Claire A108
Raley, Anthony R A777
Raley, Claire E35
Raley, Anthony R E393
Ralhan, Dushyant A767
Ralli, Georges W82
Ralph, Ginevra P651
Ralston, Alexander A691
Rama, Michael P. E311
Ramachandran, Sampath A413
Ramachandran, Sampath P234
Ramachandran, Venkataraman P647
Ramadoss, Balaji P197
Ramagano, Cheryl A857
Ramaker, David A187
Ramaker, David E71
Ramalho, Sean A827
Ramamurthy, Sundar A71
Raman, J.V. W381
Ramapriya, Jeevan A767
Ramaswami, Rajiv A875
Ramaswamy, Nandini A723
Ramawy, Dennis A480
Rambo, Jamie A114
Rambo, Jamie P64
Rambole, Bob P157
Ramenda, James (Jim) E383
Ramenofsky, David P396
Ramer, Ginger P243

Rames, Jared E117
Ramey, Eric A235
Ramey, Todd P342
Ramey, H. Craig E349
Ramey, Craig E349
Ramicone, Arthur P651
Ramil, Filip A644
Ramirez, Joe A11
Ramirez, Francisco Munoz A218
Ramirez, Terrie A244
Ramirez, Rene A244
Ramirez, Renato A459
Ramirez, Ricardo A459
Ramirez, Rosie A459
Ramirez, Ryan A490
Ramirez, Bonita A572
Ramirez, German A729
Ramirez, Karlee A740
Ramirez, Jaime A. A761
Ramirez, Josephine A810
Ramirez, Martin P53
Ramirez, Eduardo P126
Ramirez, Megan C P127
Ramirez, Everardo P161
Ramirez, Daniel D P164
Ramirez, Lisa P466
Ramirez, Josephine P586
Ramirez, Ana P603
Ramirez, Juan Roberto P635
Ramirez, Gabriel P635
Ramirez, J M J P644
Ramirez, Raul P681
Ramirez, Karlee E369
Ramkumar, Krishnaswamy W181
Ramlo, Randy A. A847
Ramonat, R. Whitfield A642
Ramonet, Alfonso J. A374
Ramos, Clarissa C A56
Ramos, Carlos X A109
Ramos, David A115
Ramos, Ricardo (Ricky) A218
Ramos, Pilar S A537
RAMOS, REINA A731
Ramos, Aida A785
Ramos, Vic A897
Ramos, Jose P34
Ramos, Harold P182
Ramos, Amy P241
Ramos, Rick P307
Ramos, Hector P471
Ramos, Aurelio P596
Ramos, Vic P687
Ramos, Maria W4
Ramos, Carlos X E36
Ramos, Raul R. E161
RAMOS, REINA E365
Ramos-Desimone, Noemi P652
Ramoutar, Roxanne A255
Rampton, Rhett A919
Rampulla, Marc A478
Ramsay, Omar A441
Ramsay, Paul D. A521
Ramsay, Timothy A906
Ramsay, Royce P394
Ramsay, Brian P401
Ramsay, Nancy P561
Ramsbottom, Scott A66
Ramsden, Derek A904
Ramsden, Derek E442
Ramsey, Craig R. A41
Ramsey, Dean A85
Ramsey, Matthew S A298
Ramsey, Chris A384
Ramsey, Tom A552
Ramsey, Robin A770
Ramsey, Matthew S A773
Ramsey, Doug A834
Ramsey, Paul G. A861
Ramsey, Tom P328
Ramsey, Paul G. P658
Ramsey, Charles T P681
Ramsey, Chris E176
Ramundo, Kate A76
Ramza, Timothy W. W232
Ramzan, Muhammad P632

Ranck, Bruce E. A687
Rancour, Joseph A877
Rand, Allison A667
Rand, Edward L. (Ned) A670
Randal, Randy P254
Randall, Anne L. A142
Randall, Markis A439
Randall, Sarah A532
Randall, Joellen P75
Randall, Marc P273
Randall, Dazarene P318
Randall, Bryan P357
Randall, Dennis E86
Randazzo, Salvatore E306
Randich, David M. A364
Randle, Thomas P281
Randlett, Brad A204
Randolph, Lanny L A137
Randolph, Marjorie A272
Randolph, Diane A836
Randolph, Adrian W. B. P398
Randolph, Karsten P499
Randono, Peggy P68
Randt, Thomas A782
Ranells, Mary Ann P268
Raner, Bonnie P324
Raney, Steven M. (Steve) A693
Raney, Tom P256
Raney, Thomas P256
Raney, Tom P257
Rangarajan, Bharath A875
Rangdale, Arjendra P556
Rangel, Rosa A327
Rangel, Andrea P143
Rangel, Enrique Ortiz de Montellano W25
Ranicar, Jamie A513
Ranjan, Gaurav P282
Rankin, Lisa L A49
Rankin, Chay A441
Rankin, Cindy A782
Rankin, Devina A. A881
Rankin, Denise P331
Ranney, Mark A693
Ranney, Timothy P346
Rannila, Scott A81
Ranque, Cyril A310
Ranque, Denis W16
Ransohoff, Kurt P482
Ransom, Mark A332
Ransom, Elizabeth A801
Ransom, Cheryl P524
Ransom, Elizabeth P562
Ranta, Curtis A406
Rantz, Regina A649
Ranzino, Kirk A163
Rao, Sunil A40
Rao, Venkat A210
Rao, Naveen G. A456
Rao, Anita A456
Rao, Anil A456
Rao, Anu A478
Rao, Jyothi A809
Rao, Mrutyunjaya A898
RAO, Deepak P184
RAO, K S P248
RAO, Lokesh P248
RAO, Anjali S P397
Rao, Vijay M P619
RAO, Michael P665
RAO, Chalapathi E316
Raoult, Frédérique W343
Rapaccioli, Donna P200
Rapanos, Vasileios T. W24
Rapaport, Marc H. P103
Rapelye, Janet L. P606
Raper, Keri P674
Raphael, Carol P2
Raphael, Donna P531
Raphael, Heidi E40
Rapier, Jared A158
Rapino, Brian A390
Rapino, Michael (Mike) A517
Rapkin, Hilary A. E438

Rapoza, Dean P138
Rapp, Valerie Vona A329
Rapp, J D A898
Rapp, John D A898
Rapp, James P120
Rapp, Peter F. P410
Rappa, Victor A871
Rappe, Kristine A884
Rappoport, Adam P284
Rapport, Nicole C A201
Raptis, Beth P296
Rasalam, Livingstone P240
Rasband, James R. P83
Rasberry, Charles P296
Rasche, Steven P P520
Raschke, Uwe W70
Rasco, Jane P639
Rasell, Alan A432
Rasgado, Jesus A260
Rash, John E334
Rashid, Mamoon A620
Rasilainen, Jan A828
Raskin, David P335
Rasmuson, Craig D. E382
Rasmussen, Bart A3
Rasmussen, Steve P405
Rasmussen, Michele P609
Rasmussen, Raquel P630
Rasmussen, Daniel J. E76
Rastetter, Bruce L. P612
Rasula, Jay A56
Raszinski, Andre P666
Ratajczak, Kari A406
Ratanabanchuen, Virachai W88
Ratay, Andrea A105
Ratcliff, Margaret P671
Ratcliff, David G P675
Rater, John P433
Rath, John A500
Rath, John E238
Rathbum, Jim A702
Rathbun, Robert S. A187
Rathbun, Robert S. E71
Rather, Ken P455
Rathke, Tom W129
Rathsack, Dirk E82
Ratinoff, Edward A95
Ratinoff, Edward E28
Ratkovich, Jason A441
Ratliff, John D. A499
Ratnayake, Nish P452
Ratner, Richard A173
Ratner, Joel P83
Rattanapian, Chongrak W202
Ratzan, Scott A476
Ratzi, Robert A171
Ratzi, Robert P100
Rau, John P. A906
Rauch, Scott L. A635
Rauch, Scott L. P419
Rauh, Pattysue E47
Raus, Gregg A478
Rausch, Erin K A59
Rausch, Timothy S. P554
Rausch, Chris P629
Rauscher, Robert J. A223
Rauscher, Eric A223
Rauscher, Nina P570
Rauschl, Christopher A377
Rauske, Jill A478
Rautenstrauch, J-¶rg A804
Rauw, Brendan P410
Ravala, Satheesh E119
Raven, Gary A153
Ravichandran, Guruswami P91
Ravita, John A328
Rawas, Mark A213
Rawlings, Rhonda A350
Rawlings, Rick A433
Rawlings, Sharon Renee P255
Rawlings, Rhonda E157
Rawlins, Rylan A165
Rawot, Billie A287
Rawot, Billie P174
Ray, Terrance A33

Ray, Jim A115
Ray, Erika A163
Ray, Jacqueline A193
Ray, Bobbie A273
Ray, Scott A327
Ray, Neville R A785
Ray, Michael C. A892
Ray, Nancy P73
Ray, Amy G. P105
Ray, Jacqueline P112
Ray, Monica P231
Ray, Jim P256
Ray, Denise P428
Ray, Joel P459
Rayas, Bertha P663
Raybon, Gary P511
Rayburn, Ryan A513
Rayburn, Patricia P570
Rayford, Greg W. A189
Raygani, Mehrasa A865
Raygoza, Jeanette P225
Rayhil, Edward P340
Raykis, Alex A568
Raymon, David A729
Raymond, Philip A27
Raymond, Johnson A95
Raymond, Christopher A136
Raymond, Arthur A282
Raymond, Hans A729
Raymond, Michelle A733
Raymond, Mindy P79
Raymond, Ashley P283
Raymond, Michelle P491
Raymond, Johnson E28
Raymond, Amy E364
Raymoure, Sue A165
Rayner, Craig A814
Rayner, Craig P616
Raynes, Zoya A474
Raynes, Scott P59
Raynes, Zoya P262
Raza, Adnan P381
Razo, Heather A532
Rea, Doug P464
Rea, Danny J. E436
Reach, Shannon A630
Read, Colin A78
Read, Paul A525
Read, Harold T A585
Read, Ian C. A648
Read, Christina A775
Read, Harold T P377
Read, Anthony P583
Read, Nicholas J. (Nick) W389
Reade, Jeff A727
Reading, Christopher J. (Chris) E405
Reado, Dr George P89
Ready, John P567
Reagan, James C. (Jim) A505
Real, Peter A65
Reali, Joseph A556
Reardon, Timothy J. A505
Reasoner, Rod A795
Reaves, Duane A452
Reaves, Larry P64
Reaves, Duane E215
Reavis, Mack P280
Reazin, Jonathan P342
Rebber, Kristine A593
Rebecchini, Clemente W32
Rebellius, Matthias W331
Reber, Jay P183
Rebholz, Andrew J. A826
Rebsch, Gary P144
Rebuck, Gail W62
Rec, Bank A311
Reca, Thomas P541
ReCasino, Maria A201
Recchi, Giuseppe A375
Recchi, Giuseppe P210
Recchi, Giuseppe W359
Recer, James D. (Jim) A800
Recer, James D. (Jim) E396
Rechin, Michael C. (Mike) A349
Rechin, Michael C. (Mike) E156

Rechkemmer, Ben A489
Recht, Evan A390
Recile, Shane P89
Reck, Peter A447
Reck, Una Mae P627
Reckers, Bob P399
Recon, Chris A857
Rector, Jennifer A131
Rector, Christopher A218
Rector, Drew P230
Rector, Allen P233
Rector, Sharon P439
Recupero, Patricia R P695
Reda, Eva A49
Redabaugh, Blake P601
Redd, Mike P411
Redd, Ellis S P514
Redd, Glen P598
Redden, Robert L A734
Reddick, Sheila A162
Reddick, Veder A247
Reddick, Margaret A364
Reddick, Veder E103
Redding, Ron A410
Redding, Richard E248
Reddington, Brian J. P445
Reddish, Thomas J. (Tom) A830
Reddish, Thomas J. (Tom) E402
Reddivari, Darshini A784
Reddrick-Maull, Terrie P538
Reddy, Sriram A131
Reddy, Lata A677
Reddy, Srinivas A677
Reddy, J. Patrick (Pat) A758
Reddy, J. Patrick (Pat) P519
Reddy, Sivakumar P549
Reder, Chris A484
Redfield, Charles A878
Redi, Jason A695
Reding, Douglas P309
Redinger, Shelley P521
Redka, James P617
Redman, Bill A500
Redman, Charleeda P619
Redman, Bill E238
Redmon, Angie A348
Redmon, Angie E155
Redmond, Brian A76
Redmond, Richard L. A280
Redmond, Velma A P421
Redmond, John T. E11
Redmond, Greg E300
Redoutey, Joseph M. A356
Redpath, J. Douglas A761
Redpath, Tammy A788
Redpath, Stuart P161
Redstone, Shari E. A175
Redstone, Shari E. A872
Redwine, Dru P480
Redwitz, Thomas (Tom) E398
Reeber, Carianne A500
Reeber, Carianne E238
Reed, Maurice A. A26
Reed, Pamela A34
Reed, LaDonna A81
Reed, Holly A85
Reed, James T. (Jim) A110
Reed, Rachel A158
Reed, Julie A166
Reed, Eric A195
Reed, Jerry A249
Reed, Cory J. A260
Reed, John A348
Reed, Jane A353
Reed, Lee A459
Reed, Stu A461
Reed, Diana A480
Reed, Chris A513
Reed, Tyrone A535
Reed, James M A695
Reed, Colin V. A719
Reed, Debra L. (Debbie) A735
Reed, Cris A774
Reed, Robert D. (Bob) A775
Reed, Sam K. A829

A = AMERICAN BUSINESS
E = EMERGING COMPANIES
P = PRIVATE COMPANIES
W = WORLD BUSINESS

Reed, Marc C. A870
Reed, Candice A877
Reed, Richard A913
Reed, Margaret P29
Reed, Cheryl P30
Reed, Glenn P242
Reed, Kelly P282
Reed, Daniel C P305
Reed, Connie P306
Reed, Tyrone P312
Reed, Dan P352
Reed, Katie N P396
Reed, Carolyn P435
Reed, Colin V. P468
Reed, Robert D. (Bob) P548
Reed, Laura P618
Reed, David P649
Reed, Kevin P651
Reed, John C. W307
Reed, James T. (Jim) E37
Reed, Michael A. E65
Reed, Mike E65
Reed, John E155
Reed, Jane E159
Reed, John A. E163
Reed, David E240
Reed, Michael E318
Reed, David E424
Reed-harper, Shana A339
Reed-harper, Shana E150
Reeder, Philip P169
Reedy, Thomas W. (Tom) A166
Reedy, Tom A166
Reedy, Bob A185
Reedy, Raquel Martinez P20
Reel, Stephanie L. A475
Reel, Stephanie L. P266
Reemst, Mary W227
Rees, Mary P415
Rees, Dan W50
Reesby, Patrick C. P367
Reese, Jay A2
Reese, David A61
Reese, Kristin A151
Reese, Mark E. A292
Reese, Bruce T. A458
Reese, Craig A481
Reese, Ron A502
Reese, Denyse A599
Reese, Deb A705
Reese, Bertram S. (Bert) A736
Reese, Ken A878
Reese, Steven P27
Reese, Kirk P46
Reese, Mary Ann P202
Reese, Bruce T. P251
Reese, Karin P307
Reese, Roger P410
Reese, Bertram S. (Bert) P492
Reese, Nancy P603
Reese, Amanda P659
Reese, Kristin E48
Reese, Kevin E125
Reese, Nathan R. E302
Reese, F. Timothy (Tim) E343
Reese, Deb E352
Reesing, Jeffrey E97
Reeve, Michael A345
Reeve, Pamela D. A. A368
Reeves, Robert K. (Bobby) A63
Reeves, Cindy A244
Reeves, Rob A685
Reeves, Sandy A802
Reeves, Michael P47
Reeves, Mark P294
Reeves, Sandy P562
Reeves, Brenda P628
Reeves, Greg P672
Reeves, Jim E190

Refermat, Mike A685
Reffler, Rick P629
Reffner, Robert A355
Regan, Sheryl A674
Regan, Timothy J. A814
Regan, Tim A814
Regan, Meg P313
Regan, Sheryl P444
Regan, Timothy J. P616
Regan, Tim P616
Regan, Jack W26
Regan, Patrick C. (Pat) W297
Regele, Michael B P254
Regester, Joyce P627
Regier, Philip P44
Regis, Christine (Chris) P514
Register, Mark A460
Register, Mike A774
Rego, Vagner W36
Rehkopf, Mark D P468
Rehm, Doug A737
Rehm, Wilhelm W402
Rehm, Doug E367
Rehmke, Bruce C. A412
Rehmke, Bruce C. E192
Rehner, Scott E308
Reic, Iskra W35
Reich, Kirk W. A26
Reich, Joel D A580
Reich, Daniel A871
Reich, Bret W P274
Reich, David P298
Reich, Alexandra W360
Reichers, Troy A196
Reichert, Ryan P108
Reichert, Leo E P129
Reichert, Donald P593
Reichert, Joshua S P601
Reichert, Leo P680
Reichfield, Mike P405
Reichle, Paula P518
Reichmann, Randall (Randy) A614
Reichstetter, Arthur A492
Reid, Bill A294
Reid, Bruce A446
Reid, John A517
Reid, Tony A530
Reid, Jack A532
Reid, Chris A538
Reid, Michele A583
Reid, John A658
Reid, Patricia A704
Reid, Alan M. A725
Reid, Charles R. P469
Reid, Michael P642
Reid, Bruce E210
Reid, Patricia E351
Reid, David N. (Dave) E383
Reid, Stephen E407
Reid, Steve E407
Reid-ponte, Patricia P153
Reidy, Christopher R. (Chris) A119
Reidy, M. Bridget A309
Reidy, Kevin P114
Reiersen, John E233
Reierson, Jason A655
Reierson, Jason E333
Reif, David P. A716
Reif, L. Rafael P313
Reifer, Lisa A474
Reifsnyder, JoAnne A380
Reifsteck, John A397
Reifsteck, John P221
Reiley, Peggy J. P487
Reiling, Jason A56
Reilley, James A607
Reilly, Michael A40
Reilly, Mary A49
Reilly, Dan A260
Reilly, Mary A481
Reilly, Daniel A644
Reilly, Robert Q. (Rob) A659
Reilly, Dawn A677
Reilly, Paul C. A693
Reilly, Cathy A781

Reilly, Sally A818
Reilly, Joe A919
Reilly, Bob P39
Reilly, Annemarie P101
Reilly, Jeff P216
Reilly, Ashlee P376
Reilly, Doug P446
Reilly, Joseph R. P494
Reilly, John E75
Reilly, J. Timothy (Tim) E383
Reily, Terry A173
Reiman, Eric (Bill) A111
Reiman, Eric (Bill) P56
Reimer, Seth A489
Reimer, Ashley A502
Reimer, Raymond A828
Reimer, Daniel E P348
Reimer, Elizabeth P439
Reimer, Matt P640
Reinard, Shannon A183
Reinard, Shannon E66
Reinartz, Ronald A532
Reinauer, Greg P620
Reinders, Robert A530
Reiner, Scott P7
Reiner, Carol A243
Reiner, Scott P434
Reiners, Derek S. A622
Reinert, Jim A484
Reingardt, John A446
Reingardt, John E210
Reinhard, Stephan A204
Reinhard, Colette A513
Reinhard, Clark P403
Reinhard, Walter E415
Reinhart, Diane P672
Reinke, Ryan P145
Reinsch, E. James P205
Reinshagen, Dirk A874
Reinstein, James E68
Reinstein, James A. E104
Reis, Mario A241
Reis, Mischa A253
Reis, Jorge A366
Reis, Peter P14
Reis, Kim E127
Reisenbach, Amy A175
Reiser, Trista A589
Reiser, Anne E354
Reisner, John R. A344
Reisner, John R. E154
Reiss, Rena Hozore A445
Reiss, Andrew A890
Reiss, Andrew P684
Reiten, R. Patrick (Pat) A630
Reithofer, Norbert W59
Reitz, David A81
Reitzle, Wolfgang H. W108
Reitzle, Wolfgang W223
Reizman, Elizabeth A103
Rejcek, Leonard J. A833
Rejtig, Mark A272
Relic, Zelko E10
Remark, Christopher E P566
Rembde, Martin W62
Rembert, Deena A487
Remeniuk, Irene A541
Remeniuk, Irene E266
Rementeria, Margarita A272
Remiker, Richard (Rich) A440
Remiker, Rick A441
Remondi, John F. (Jack) A575
Rempe, Melanie A103
Rempe, Thomas A538
Rempe, John P55
Rempel, Steve A709
Remsing, Tiffany P637
Remy, Todd A489
Ren, Yi A796
Renaudie, Jean-Michel W148
Rench, Jerry P458
Rencher, Bradley (Brad) A11
RENDA, BENEDETTO GIOVANNI
  MARIA W111
Rendall, Don P220

Rendeiro, Martha A460
Rendleman, Linda A792
Rendon, Martin S P636
Renduchintala, Venkata M.
  (Murthy) A456
Renetzky, Lisa A701
Reney, Michael L. P153
Renfro, Larry C. A855
Renfroe, Tammy P630
Rengifo, Andres P583
Rengstorff, Jim A764
Rengstorff, Jim P540
Renier, Hugh P P536
Renjel, Louis A243
Renna, Joanne A883
Rennard, Marc W278
Renner, John P329
Renner, John P631
Rennich, Craig P176
Rennick, Mike P410
Rennie, Beth A328
Renninger, Heidi P346
Renschler, Andreas W231
Renschler, Andreas W390
Rensel, Eric E P196
Renspie, William A235
Rentch, Sean A784
Renth, George P7
Rentler, Barbara A715
Renton, Brad E104
Renwick, Glenn M A355
Renwick, Glenn M. A672
Renz, Trish A85
Renz, Brian A98
Renz, John T P348
Renz, Brian E33
Repac, Kimberly S P685
Repas, Karen A446
Repas, Karen E210
Repetti, Barbara A667
Repetz, Brian P525
Repik, Jennifer A201
Repique, R. John P446
Repo, Susan J A799
Reppert, Joe P388
Reppy, Glen A323
Repsher, Brett A696
Rerkpibook, Auttapol W296
Resch, Richard J. (Dick) P278
Resendez, Cindy P420
Resinger, James E A423
Reske, James R. A342
Resneder, Norma P663
Resnick, Jon A469
Resnick, Andrea Shaw P785
Respler, Bruce P308
Resseguie, Dick A599
Ressel, Teresa A620
Ressel, Dawn P647
Resslar, Melissa E123
Ressler, Richard S. E226
Restel, Anthony J. A446
Restel, Anthony J. E210
Restiano, Larry A49
Restrepo, Robert P. (Bob) A764
Resyapov, Alexander F. W350
Reto, Joyce P21
Retter, Donna P523
Retton, Allen A886
Retton, Allen E433
Retz, Jocelyn A616
Retzer, Ingrid P50
Reuland, Charles P265
Reuss, Mark L. A378
Reusswig, Michael A898
Reuter, Deborah K. (Debbie) A414
Reuter, Lawrence G A583
Reuter, John A693
Reuter, Lawrence G P374
Reuter, Deborah K. (Debbie) E194
Reuter, Martin E351
Reuterskiold, Christina A585
Reuterskiold, Christina P377
Reuvers, Dan E220
Revelle, George A61

Revilla, Lisa A102
Reville, Peter A537
Revington, George E203
Rew, Michael P104
Rew, Richard E250
Rex, John A855
Rex, Cindy P430
Rexroad, Jerold L A167
Rey, Juan P326
Rey, Virginia P700
Reyes, Shirley A168
Reyes, Laura A221
Reyes, Jen A329
Reyes, Tisha A452
Reyes, Tarik A602
Reyes, Franklin A700
Reyes, Pedro A860
Reyes, Peggy P160
Reyes, Angel P184
Reyes, Donna P295
Reyes, Pedro P656
Reyes, Marcelo W85
Reyes, Cecilia W405
Reyes, Tisha E215
Reyher, Laura P60
Reyman, Cory P211
Reymondet, Pascal W379
Reynes, Julia E P420
Reynish, Steve W348
Reynolds, Stephen R. (Steve) A73
Reynolds, Brent A163
Reynolds, Eric A208
Reynolds, Catherine M. A210
Reynolds, Tamra A214
Reynolds, Donald A223
Reynolds, Emily A334
Reynolds, Wendy A342
Reynolds, Marshall T A347
Reynolds, Dennis A355
Reynolds, Linda A375
Reynolds, Robert L. A395
Reynolds, Ed A419
Reynolds, Alyssa A438
Reynolds, Matthew A480
Reynolds, Jo A532
Reynolds, Charles A537
Reynolds, Lynn A584
Reynolds, Jim A592
Reynolds, Andrew A602
Reynolds, Sean A683
Reynolds, Mary Ann A769
Reynolds, Robert L. A873
Reynolds, Dave A885
Reynolds, Peter A912
Reynolds, George P117
Reynolds, Tamra P128
Reynolds, Randy P170
Reynolds, Ronald P296
Reynolds, Scott P352
Reynolds, Julie P366
Reynolds, Lynn P376
Reynolds, Sean B. P397
Reynolds, Dudley C. P520
Reynolds, Courtney P559
Reynolds, William P582
Reynolds, April P639
Reynolds, Robert L. P669
Reynolds, Suzanne P673
Reynolds, Robert L. W161
Reynolds, Christopher P. (Chris) W374
Reynolds, Richard V. E19
Reynolds, William H. E257
Reynolds, William L. E357
Reza, Ali P485
Reza, Tony P508
Rezendes, Kelsey P93
Reznikova, Irina A766
Rheaume, Lindsey S. A284
Rheaume, Lindsey S. E111
Rhine, Bruce C. E290
Rhines, Walden C. (Wally) P326
Rho, Joseph K. A401
Rho, Joseph K. E187
Rhoades, Cory P140
Rhoades, Ronald E. E77

Rhoads, Rebecca B. A694
Rhodarmer, Frank A333
Rhode, Bryan A243
Rhode, Ginger P92
Rhode, Jason P. E78
Rhodebeck, Lyle D. A764
Rhoden, Patti P187
Rhodes, Sage A84
Rhodes, William C. (Bill) A90
Rhodes, Michael A193
Rhodes, James A317
Rhodes, Jeff A655
Rhodes, Chandra A802
Rhodes, Michael P112
Rhodes, Barbara P126
Rhodes, Mike P245
Rhodes, Ronald P260
Rhodes, David P284
Rhodes, Steve P483
Rhodes, Chandra P562
Rhodes, Edwardo P627
Rhodes, James E142
Rhodes, Jeff E333
Rhodewalt, Stacey P310
Rhodin, Michael D. (Mike) A460
Rhoman, Cindy P289
Rhone, Denise A877
Rhoten, Marilyn P147
Rhymer, John A816
Rhynalds, Christian A231
Rhyne, Tommy A115
Rhyne, Jerry P291
Rial, Francis A568
Rial, Sergio W45
Riano, Jewell P344
Ribe, Raquel A441
Ribe, Ken P70
Ribeiro, Monica A109
Ribeiro, Ana A639
Ribeiro, Greg A671
Ribeiro, Monica E36
Ribeiro, Ana E326
Ribieras, Jean-Michel A462
Ribiéras, Jean-Michel A462
Riboud, Franck W117
Ricard, Denis W180
Ricardo, Pedro Carmona de
   Oliveira W156
Riccardi, John A3
Ricchezza, John A741
Ricchezza, John E370
Ricchio, Wesley A340
Ricchio, Wesley E151
Ricci, Riccardo A218
Ricciardelli, Kelly A818
Ricciardi, Joe A619
Riccio, Daniel (Dan) A70
Riccio, Anthony A132
Riccio, Louis A583
Riccio, Janet A619
Riccioni, Mich P482
Rice, Amy A109
Rice, Kristin K A262
Rice, Charles A300
Rice, Mary A446
Rice, Brian S. A485
Rice, Mark A599
Rice, Linda Johnson A619
Rice, Ronald A. A716
Rice, Jacqueline Hourigan A788
Rice, Peter A834
Rice, Andrea A872
Rice, Patricia M P22
Rice, William P112
Rice, Steve P182
Rice, Larry P267
Rice, John L P277
Rice, Will P439
Rice, Bret P509
Rice, Jennifer P537
Rice, Ling P598
Rice, Amy E36
Rice, Mary E210
Rice, Jennifer E299
Rich, Michael A158

Rich, Brian F. A210
Rich, Brian F. A236
Rich, Robert A430
Rich, Sarah A774
Rich, Robert E. (Bob) A807
Rich, Robert E. (Bob) P574
Richard, Laino A3
Richard, Henri A580
Richard, Michelle P69
Richard, John P82
Richard, Sylvia P279
Richard, Andy P483
Richard, Harrington P521
Richard, Stéphane W278
Richard, Sheri E74
Richard, Chad E447
Richards, Mark A160
Richards, Todd A269
Richards, Thomas A277
Richards, Ramon A315
Richards, Christine P. A327
Richards, Patricia R. A458
Richards, Jeff A562
Richards, Stephanie A615
Richards, Stacey A655
Richards, Lisa A671
Richards, David A720
Richards, Jeff A724
Richards, Rachel M. A749
Richards, Michael A766
Richards, Barry A. A826
Richards, Alison A855
Richards, Geoff A908
Richards, David P68
Richards, James J P134
Richards, Nicole P176
Richards, Patricia R. P251
Richards, Jeanne P311
Richards, James J P359
Richards, Michael P480
Richards, Larry P627
Richards, Thomas P647
Richards, Anne W295
Richards, Mark E55
Richards, Laura E224
Richards, Jeff E279
Richards, Stacey E333
Richards, David E362
Richardson, Bryan D. A148
Richardson, Cindy A162
Richardson, David A164
Richardson, Michael R. (Mike) A168
Richardson, Jannie A262
Richardson, Cara A371
Richardson, Matt A421
Richardson, Sean P. A440
Richardson, Wendy A537
Richardson, Elizabeth A565
Richardson, Beth A565
Richardson, Levi A583
Richardson, Marty A614
Richardson, Matthew A838
Richardson, Todd P48
Richardson, Trena P106
Richardson, Fred P123
Richardson, Lisa P126
Richardson, Thomas C. P138
Richardson, Danielle G P168
Richardson, Dee P197
Richardson, Kathy P238
Richardson, David P286
Richardson, Christy P331
Richardson, Mark P410
Richardson, Hunter P412
Richardson, Cliff P539
Richardson, David E. P642
Richardson, Stephen A. E9
Richardson, Paul H. E31
Richardson, Chad E163
Richardson, Brent D. E180
Richardson, Frank E203
Richardson, Nina E371
Richardson, Julie E426
Richburg, Joseph A175
Richels, John A263

Richendollar, Deborah A115
Richenhagen, Martin H. A20
Richer, Alvin P46
Richers, Henry A101
Riches, Greg A558
Richey, Bernadina A802
Richey, Ellen A874
Richey, Linda P115
Richey, Mike P542
Richey, Bernadina P562
Richey, Victor L. (Vic) E132
Richland, Scott P91
Richman, David A375
Richmond, Michael A438
Richmond, Brent E. A886
Richmond, Estelle P134
Richmond, Craig P336
Richmond, Craig P593
Richmond, Brent E. E433
Richter, Brandon A34
Richter, Phil A837
Richter, Brian A865
Richter, John A885
Richter, Karen P118
Richter, Alfred P292
Richter, Michael F P550
Richtsmeier, William P590
Richvalsky, James P107
Richway, Terri A620
Ricia, Catherine A532
Rick, Frederick A201
Rickard, Candice J. A614
Ricke, David P556
Rickel, John C. A396
Rickel, Todd A. P613
Ricken, Chris P660
Rickenbach, Josef H. von P417
Ricker, Bob P459
Rickert, Luann A260
Rickett, Tyler P19
Ricketts, Carlton A A164
Ricketts, Carl A164
Ricketts, Lawrence G. E317
Rickley, Brian P21
Ricks, David A. A511
Ricks, Ron A755
Ricks, Michael P238
Ricks, Mary L. E231
Rico, Jean P663
Ricotta, Eduardo W360
Riddell, Carol A232
Riddle, Joe A16
Riddle, Doug A332
Ridenour, Nancy P648
Rider, James A476
Rider, Matthew J. (Matt) W10
Ridgeway, Charlene A406
Ridgeway, Alan A517
Ridinger, James H P308
Ridinger, Loren P308
Ridlen, Debbie P257
Ridley, Kevin P113
Ridolfi, Kaye P99
Riebel, William A807
Riebel, William P574
Rieck, Lewis A480
Riecken, Regina P368
Riecker, Robert A. A733
Ried, Greg E127
Riedel, Norbert A113
Riedel, Judy P473
Riedel, Paul E376
Riedl, Ingo E290
Rief, Lisa A537
Riegel, Matthew A599
Riegelhaupt, Kathleen P598
Rieger, Michael P332
Rieger, Ralf W356
Riehl, Bill E172
Rieker, Karen P525
Riel, Pierre A240
Riel, Susan G. A284
Riel, Susan G. E111
Rieley, John F. E226
Rielly, John P. A417

A = AMERICAN BUSINESS
E = EMERGING COMPANIES
P = PRIVATE COMPANIES
W = WORLD BUSINESS

Rieman, Brooke P617
Rieman, Kendall W. E100
Riemer, Danny A131
Riemer, Hans P144
Riendeau, Nicole P451
Riepe, James S. (Jim) A382
Riepenhoff, Patrick A441
Riera, Shelly A149
Riesche, Elizabeth A542
Riesche, Elizabeth E267
Riese, Werner De P299
Riesterer, Jamie A676
Rieves, JT A426
Rife, John A. A847
Rigales, Luis P537
Rigatti, Maria A291
Rigg, Timothy A163
Riggan, Gisela A673
Riggieri, Rose A817
Riggin, William A201
Riggle, Carrie A342
Riggs, Lane A867
Riggs, Mel G. P367
Riggs, Daniel P429
Riggs, Kirsten P459
Riggs, Jean P603
Riggs, David E. E113
Riggs, Steven C. (Steve) E212
Rights, Nancy A368
Rigler, Mark L P163
Rigsby, Rhonda A863
Rigsby, Dione E303
Riis, Jakob W271
Riis, Kenneth E302
Rijswijk, S.J.A. (Steven) van W187
Rikhye, Manu E123
Riles, Anne M. A640
Riley, Rick D. A206
Riley, Karla A244
Riley, Rick A300
Riley, William O A324
Riley, Kevin P. A349
Riley, Brian A354
Riley, Eric A390
Riley, Shawn A489
Riley, Paul A652
Riley, Scott A700
Riley, Anne A701
Riley, James A901
Riley, Donna P40
Riley, Judith P88
Riley, Shane P200
Riley, Brian P254
Riley, Cheryl P275
Riley, Trent P439
Riley, Denise P449
Riley, Charles P567
Riley, Anne P613
Riley, James P692
Riley, Gillian W50
Riley, Kevin P. E41
Riley, Kevin P. E156
Riley, Sharon L. E196
Riley, Donald R. (Don) E298
Riley-Brown, Michelle P560
Rilloraza, Francisco P412
Rim, Heather A16
Rimar, Stephen P381
Rimel, Rebecca A119
Rimel, Brian A693
Rimmereid, Paul A325
Rimmereid, Tore Olaf W129
Rimon, Karen P228
Rinaldi, Joe A359
Rinaldi, John A478
Rincon, Francisco Del P103
Rincon, Luis P375
Rine, Mary P109
Rinehart, Karen A180

Rinehart, Suzanne A317
Rinehart, Charles R. A543
Rinehart, Lucy P155
Rinehart, Doug P589
Rinehart, Suzanne E142
Rinere, Monique P597
Riney, Stephen J. A69
Riney, Robert G. (Bob) A413
Riney, Robert G. (Bob) P234
Ring, Kenneth R. E275
Ringenberg, Kevin A489
Ringgenberg, Jason T. A916
Ringold, Kim A912
Ringsted, Sean W98
Ringwald, Brad A344
Rini, Anthony A489
Rink, Matthew A446
Rink, Matthew E210
Rinker, Jackie A448
Rinker, Franklin M P224
Rinn, Russell B. (Russ) A768
Rinne, Susan E95
Rinshed, Rick P432
Rion, Deborah P522
Riopel, Daniel W180
Riordan, Jeremiah A478
Riordan, Mark A802
Riordan, Keith P343
Riordan, Mark P562
Riordan, Kimberly E432
Riordan-Pacheco, Ella A741
Riordan-Pacheco, Ella E370
Rios, Roberto A478
Rios, Gerardo A671
Riphagen, Derek P25
Ripoly, Josie P352
Ripper, Karen P310
Ripperda, Amanda P246
Rippey, Loryssa L A47
Ripplinger, Greg A920
Rippy, Richard A109
Rippy, Richard E36
Risan, Michael P62
Risch, Therace M. A640
Rischall, Richard A351
Rischall, Richard E158
Rischar, Kent A59
Risio, Derek M. Di A678
Risio, Gary De P53
Risk, Robert A512
Risley, Hank B A452
Rislow, Deb P223
Risoleo, James F. A434
Rispoli, Michael A644
Rispone, Rodi F P347
Risse, Thomas P444
Rissi, Daniel P283
Rissman, Michael A707
Ritch, Jill A Alexander P649
Ritchey, Jimmy E324
Ritchie, Chris A101
Ritchie, Kevin A195
Ritchie, Michael T. A221
Ritchie, Robert A238
Ritchie, Ken A614
Ritchie, Keely A655
Ritchie, Mike A700
Ritchie, Kevin J. A803
Ritchie, Chris A855
Ritchie, Garth W123
Ritchie, Lisa W347
Ritchie, Keely E333
Ritenour, Jeff L. A263
Rito, Shane A441
Ritrievi, Rory G. E276
Rittelmeyer, Chris A743
Rittelmeyer, Chris E373
Rittenhouse, Gee A200
Rittenmeyer, Ronald A. (Ron) A794
Rittenmeyer, Ronald P52
Ritter, Thomas A9
Ritter, Mark A244
Ritter, Bob A517
Ritter, William D. (Bill) A700
Ritter, Gretchen P143

Ritter, David P159
Ritter, Michael P345
Ritter, Thad P536
Ritter, Tim P557
Ritter, Teresa P573
Ritter, Jane P636
Ritterson, Christoph A122
Ritz, Charle A438
Ritz, Michael D. E315
Rivas, Hiram A336
Rivas, Saul P105
Rivas, Ray P127
Rivas, Isadore P233
Rivas, Manual P391
Rivas, Patricio W85
Rivaz, Vincent de W136
Rivenbark, Eric A844
Rivenbark, Eric E412
Rivera, Dora A102
Rivera, Bonnie A163
Rivera, Alfredo A215
Rivera, Aydin A272
Rivera, Efrain A280
Rivera, Yadira A369
Rivera, Néstor O. A661
Rivera, Christina A855
Rivera, Rosa P152
Rivera, Andrea P362
Rivera, Maria P381
Rivera, Anna P430
Rivera, Mario P648
Rivera, Luisa Fernanda Lafaurie W133
Rivera, Angel E1
Rivera-Batista, Nayda A336
Rivero, Mario A874
Rivero, Diana P630
Rivers, Lori A165
Rivers, Rita A644
Rivers, Bill P441
Rivest, Jeffrey A. P644
Rivet, Jeannine M. A855
Rivett, Paul C. W146
Rivkin, Natalya A214
Rivkin, Natalya P128
Rivkin, Michael P570
Rizk, Norman W. P538
Rizza, Franco W43
Rizzardi, Russell A889
Rizzo, Jamie A19
Rizzo, Mario A33
Rizzo, John A213
Rizzo, James L. A267
Rizzo, Gregory A758
Rizzo, Gregory P519
Rizzo, Richard J P630
Rizzuto, Greg A446
Rizzuto, Greg E210
Rn, Joan P315
Rn, Laura Espinosa PHD P335
Rn, Ann Cella P529
Rnian-bivona, Gail A105
Roach, Jill P620
Roach, Frank W148
Roaldsen, Liz A766
Roback, Sarah A774
Robaina, Ashley P637
Roballo, Marta A671
Robatel, Nicolas A729
Robb, Stephen M. (Steve) A208
Robb, John A244
Robb, Gregory A360
Robb, Walter E. A899
Robb, Gary P333
Robb, Chuck P473
Robb, Walter E. P690
Robb, G. Charles E95
Robb, Gregory E164
Robben, John A643
Robbin, Jeff A70
Robbins, Charles H. (Chuck) A199
Robbins, Charles H. (Chuck) A200
Robbins, Hadley S. A219
Robbins, Paige K. A393

Robbins, Michael (Mike) A640
Robbins, Cindy A723
Robbins, Ira A868
Robbins, Mike A886
Robbins, Tracy P168
Robbins, Sheldon P283
Robbins, Spencer E40
Robbins, Hadley S. E84
Robbins, Rick E360
Robbins, Bradford B. (Brad) E394
Robbins, Mike E433
Robel, Susan M. A372
Robel, Susan M. P208
Robel, Lauren P627
Robelia, Lance P295
Roberge, Michael W. W347
Roberson, Brian A131
Roberson, Laura A837
Robert, Angela A446
Robert, Carrie P108
Robert, Lucas P145
Robert, Debbie P398
Robert, Angela E210
Roberto, Joseph (Joe) A108
Roberto, Joseph (Joe) E35
Roberts, Oz A19
Roberts, Stan A56
Roberts, Matthew A131
Roberts, Vera Rand A160
Roberts, Brian L A220
Roberts, Jonathan C. A250
Roberts, John N. A439
Roberts, Bart A478
Roberts, David A478
Roberts, Kenneth A515
Roberts, William R. A548
Roberts, R Don A572
Roberts, Brian A596
Roberts, Timothy D. (Tim) A653
Roberts, Roderick A677
Roberts, Stewart A685
Roberts, Cathy A732
Roberts, Chris A754
Roberts, Lori A829
Roberts, Sheila A830
Roberts, Jeanie A844
Roberts, Karen A878
Roberts, Clay A894
Roberts, Samuel P67
Roberts, Carrie P108
Roberts, Peter W. P116
Roberts, Angie P143
Roberts, Phyllis P204
Roberts, Kevin V P209
Roberts, Dale P218
Roberts, M. Parker P303
Roberts, William R. P321
Roberts, R Don P359
Roberts, Kristine P361
Roberts, Fred P420
Roberts, Janet P477
Roberts, John G. P506
Roberts, James P578
Roberts, Rebecca P587
Roberts, David N. E6
Roberts, Vera Rand E55
Roberts, Tina E70
Roberts, Justin E75
Roberts, Brett A. E99
Roberts, David B. (Dave) E242
Roberts, Christopher J. (Chris) E286
Roberts, Joe E286
Roberts, Cathy E365
Roberts, Chris E378
Roberts, Sheila E403
Roberts, Jeanie E412
Roberts, Jeffrey W. E419
Robertson, Michael A49
Robertson, Jenifer A85
Robertson, Laura A111
Robertson, Cliff A. A171
Robertson, John A322
Robertson, William A350
Robertson, Bill A350
Robertson, Ben A537

Robertson, Timothy A683
Robertson, Elizabeth Aulick A693
Robertson, Bill A700
Robertson, Bruce A736
Robertson, Lisa A770
Robertson, Thomas S. A812
Robertson, Craig A913
Robertson, Cliff P21
Robertson, Laura P56
Robertson, Cliff A. P100
Robertson, Cliff P148
Robertson, Jessica P209
Robertson, Pamela P269
Robertson, William G. (Bill) P357
Robertson, Euan P372
Robertson, A E P408
Robertson, Joseph (Joe) P410
Robertson, Bruce P492
Robertson, Debbie P501
Robertson, Carla P517
Robertson, Pat P572
Robertson, Gordon P572
Robertson, Thomas S. P607
Robertson, Anne Walters P610
Robertson, Rick M. E100
Robertson, William E157
Robertson, Bill E157
Robertson, Jon W. E252
Robertson-Keck, Karen P204
Robeson, Ziggy P630
Robichaud, Michael A537
Robichaud, Mary A883
Robie, Robert E140
Robillard, Barbara P521
Robillard, Jean P643
Robinett, Jesse A599
Robinett, Pam P363
Robinette, Gary E. P432
Robino, Diana A537
Robins, Rocky A127
Robins, Doug P183
Robins, Alan E46
Robins, Kevin E407
Robinson, Breanna A51
Robinson, Harvey G. A98
Robinson, Bill A105
Robinson, Lester A158
Robinson, Jon A185
Robinson, Charles A196
Robinson, Tori A335
Robinson, Vicki A357
Robinson, Kiersten A362
Robinson, David A375
Robinson, David C. A406
Robinson, Becky A422
Robinson, Rebecca A422
Robinson, Marnetta A519
Robinson, Patricia A532
Robinson, Sharon A574
Robinson, Timothy A577
Robinson, Don A591
Robinson, Kenny A602
Robinson, Guilford A683
Robinson, Robert L. A742
Robinson, Larry A784
Robinson, Albert A793
Robinson, David A802
Robinson, Randy A863
Robinson, Carole A871
Robinson, Deborah A871
Robinson, David L. A889
Robinson, Carl A902
Robinson, Barry A908
Robinson, Rebecca K. A919
Robinson, Breanna P33
Robinson, Ron P58
Robinson, Jeffrey P79
Robinson, Daniel P96
Robinson, Chase P140
Robinson, Debra P173
Robinson, Patricia P187
Robinson, Donna P193
Robinson, Vicki P198
Robinson, John R P215
Robinson, Aaron P230

Robinson, Nina B P238
Robinson, Becky P239
Robinson, Rebecca P239
Robinson, Warren P314
Robinson, Jason P332
Robinson, Lisa P359
Robinson, Edward P359
Robinson, Timothy C. P365
Robinson, Myron P378
Robinson, John P422
Robinson, Thomas L P462
Robinson, Risa P464
Robinson, Phil P471
Robinson, Larry A. P494
Robinson, William J. (Bill) P497
Robinson, Raymond E P510
Robinson, Dave P512
Robinson, Jack P531
Robinson, Susan P536
Robinson, Dick P550
Robinson, Albert P557
Robinson, David P562
Robinson, Wt P566
Robinson, Shirley P630
Robinson, Linda P641
Robinson, Boyd P642
Robinson, Samara P649
Robinson, Douglas P649
Robinson, Lester P678
Robinson, Carl P692
Robinson, Randy P695
Robinson, Harvey G. E33
Robinson, Robert L. E372
Robison, Keela A311
Robison, Mark P81
Robison, Kenneth L P148
Robitaille, Robert P124
Robitaille, Mark E P310
Robitaille, Mark P310
Robitshek, Adam A100
Roble, John A195
Robledo, Neneth A131
Robledo, Becky A614
Robledo, Raymond P587
Robles, Claudia A168
Robles, Norberto (Bert) A582
Robles, Javier A589
Robles, Monica P125
Robles, Norberto (Bert) P373
Robles, Wilma P399
Robles, Janet C P426
Robo, James L. (Jim) A590
Robottom, David T. W138
Robson, Ted A784
Robson, Jeremy W348
Robusto, Dino E. A211
Roby, Darrel A136
Roby, Anne K. A514
Robyn, Lewis A555
Robyn, Betts P68
ROC, Pierre P381
Roca, Marco A. A157
Roccasalvo, Andrea P589
Rocco, David A105
Rocco, Michael Del A109
Rocco, Scott A382
Rocco, Michael Del E36
Roces, Santiago A878
Rocha, Charles P. A746
Rocha, Oscar Gonzalez A753
Rocha, Julie P284
Roche, Michael A33
Roche, Vincent T. A65
Roche, Dan A85
Roche, Kimberly De A314
Roche, John C. (Jack) A402
Roche, Marianne A522
Roche, Jules A912
Roche, Joe P91
Roche, Kimberly De P190
Roche, Brian P260
Roche, Max W135
Roche-Carter, Noreen P470
Rochedieu, Patricia P283
Rocheleau, Duane A599

Rochin, Gerardo P521
Rochon, Sue E213
Rock, Jesse A375
Rock, Jessica P169
Rock, Bernard P623
Rockett, Kathryn P296
Rockey, Joseph E. A659
Rockholt, Tracy A788
Rocks, Eric R. E383
Rockwood, John D. A548
Rockwood, Renee A818
Rockwood, John D. P321
Roco, Ninna A555
Roda, Craig A. A369
Rodarte, Robert P433
Rodato, Vadis A. E288
Roddey, Kevin A655
Roddey, Kevin E333
Rodean, Jennifer A93
Rodell, Angela A28
Rodell, Angela P17
Rodeno, Michaela A103
Roder, Stephen B. (Steve) W232
Roderick, Ryan P458
Rodewald, Chris A865
Rodewald, Renee P40
Rodgers, Jodi A204
Rodgers, Steven R. (Steve) A456
Rodgers, Douglas A565
Rodgers, Debbie A752
Rodgers, Jim A773
Rodgers, Clark A774
Rodgers, Randall A838
Rodgers, Susan L P149
Rodgers, Karri P488
Rodgers, Ron P659
Rodgers, Courtney P700
Rodgers, Jerry E97
Rodgers, Jim E387
Rodi, Lynn P175
Rodie, Robert A351
Rodie, Robert E158
Rodino, Jeffrey M. E324
Rodis, John P472
Rodman, Cheryl P339
Rodrig, Tzahi W151
Rodrigue, Perry A300
Rodrigues, Edison F A456
Rodrigues, Rodolfo A56
Rodriguez, Michael A85
Rodriguez, Carlos A A87
Rodriguez, Aida A97
Rodriguez, Kathy A102
Rodriguez, Carlos A127
Rodriguez, Maro A243
Rodriguez, Javier J. A255
Rodriguez, Deanna A300
Rodriguez, Ryan A311
Rodriguez, Juan A313
Rodriguez, Vicki A316
Rodriguez, Mandy A422
Rodriguez, Linda A446
Rodriguez, Gerry A508
Rodriguez, David A. A530
Rodriguez, Priscilla A541
Rodriguez, James A541
Rodriguez, Rita E. A619
Rodriguez, Leticia A630
Rodriguez, Liesl A A661
Rodriguez, John A. A683
Rodriguez, Abigail A690
Rodriguez, Armando G. A730
Rodriguez, Enrique A745
Rodriguez, Damarie A777
Rodriguez, Rudy P159
Rodriguez, Vicki P191
Rodriguez, Jackie P199
Rodriguez, Camille P201
Rodriguez, Rick P208
Rodriguez, Mandy P239
Rodriguez, Manuel P242
Rodriguez, Richard P271
Rodriguez, Zina P273
Rodriguez, Deb P294
Rodriguez, Angela P387

Rodriguez, Daniel B. P398
Rodriguez, Leticia P415
Rodriguez, Michelle P415
Rodriguez, Barbara P478
Rodriguez, Domingo C P510
Rodriguez, Carlos A623
Rodriguez, Ricardo P635
Rodriguez, Jose Luis Negro W42
Rodriguez, David E4
Rodriguez, Aida E32
Rodriguez, Linda E210
Rodriguez, Rolando B. E257
Rodriguez, Priscilla E266
Rodriguez, Jaime E297
Rodriguez, Mario E307
Rodriguez, John A. E341
Rodriguez, Abigail E345
Rodriguez, Damarie E393
Rodriguez-Borjas, Carlos A703
Rodriguez-Mackintosh, Pat P22
Rodr- guez, Florentino Pérez W6
Roe, Jeffrey A105
Roe, Bob A120
Roe, Jonathan A332
Roe, John E. A359
Roe, Amy A901
Roe, Deanna P97
Roe, Amy P692
Roebuck, Mark P516
Roedel, Richard W. (Rich) E251
Roeder, Craig P443
Roeder, Dieter E247
Roederer, Nick A693
Roegner, Eric V. A76
Roehm, John A489
Roemer, Jeff A327
Roemer, Dennis R. P589
Roesel, Larry M. A90
Roeser, Christopher A526
Roeser, William P518
Roeske, Richard A487
Roesler, Jodi P151
Roesner, Daniel A221
Ruesser, Matthew A56
Roessle, Randy P629
Roesslein, Dennis A541
Roesslein, Dennis E266
Roessner, Karl A. A283
Roeth, George C. E65
Roewe, Gordon A223
Roewe, Randy A345
Roewe, Randy E154
Roffler, Michael J. (Mike) A353
Rofstad, Scott A904
Rofstad, Scott E442
Rogalski, Robert J P686
Rogan, Randall G. (Randy) P673
Roger, Fran- §ois-Xavier W258
Rogers, Patrick A34
Rogers, J. Michael A98
Rogers, Carol A100
Rogers, William D. (Bill) A181
Rogers, Heather A260
Rogers, Lawrence S. (Larry) A296
Rogers, John F.W. A389
Rogers, R. Scott A391
Rogers, Brian A401
Rogers, John A406
Rogers, Steve A439
Rogers, Jay A459
Rogers, Nancy A513
Rogers, John C. A645
Rogers, Bill A663
Rogers, Alexander H. (Alex) A685
Rogers, Alex A685
Rogers, Tom A741
Rogers, William H. (Bill) A774
Rogers, Bradon A778
Rogers, Ann A784
Rogers, Brian C. A784
Rogers, Tony A878
Rogers, Rebecca A902
Rogers, Sandy P59
Rogers, Deb P97
Rogers, Don P103

A = AMERICAN BUSINESS
E = EMERGING COMPANIES
P = PRIVATE COMPANIES
W = WORLD BUSINESS

Rogers, Harlan P141
Rogers, David P231
Rogers, Greg P343
Rogers, Joseph P384
Rogers, Ralph P399
Rogers, Bobby P450
Rogers, Mark P557
Rogers, James E. (Jim) P596
Rogers, Amy P681
Rogers, Rebecca P692
Rogers, John W193
Rogers, J. Michael E33
Rogers, Brian E187
Rogers, Steven E225
Rogers, Michael E245
Rogers, David L. E245
Rogers, John C. E329
Rogers, Kristi E342
Rogers, Tom E370
Rogers, Adam E407
Rogerson, Craig A665
Rogerson, Garry W. E83
Rogge, Matt P19
Roggekamp, Ruud A136
Rogness, Jonathan A865
Rogoff, Richard B. E361
Rogos, Aaron P154
Rogstad, W. David A833
Rogula, Ann A599
Rohan, Mary A143
Rohane, Patricia A178
Rohani, Leila E320
Rohde, William M. A122
Roheim, John P368
Rohit, Mehra A698
Rohit, Mehra P456
Rohkamm, Eckhard W356
Rohlfing, Ron P631
Rohman, Cindy P289
Rohner, Urs W111
Rohr, Mark C. A177
Rohr, James E. (Jim) P96
Rohrbacher, Tim A101
Rohrbaugh, Philmer H. (Phil) A369
Rohrer, Daniel A607
Roig, Ismael A74
Roig, Jorge A661
Rojahn, Benjamin A173
Rojas, Jose A432
Rojas, Daysi A874
Rojas, Manuel F P70
Rojas, Lili P144
Rojas, Eddy P611
Rojas, Héctor Manosalva W133
Rojas, Rigoberto Rojo W137
Rojas, Jorge E125
Rojek, Kenneth J P384
Rokicki, Mike P602
Rolak, Loren A P309
Roland, Barbara A275
Roland, Thierry A437
Rolfes, Francis A162
Rolfes, Kim P387
Rolheiser, Eric J. A237
Roll-Wallace, Kim A113
Rolland, Martial C. W258
Rolland, Marc W334
Roller, Mark A621
Roller, Mark P407
Rollin, Wilber P395
Rollins, James D. (Dan) A99
Rollins, Ceseley A180
Rollins, Lisa A644
Rollins, Barrett J. P153
Rollins, Anne-Herbert P205
Rollins, David P280
Rollins, Greg P361
Rollins, R. Randall E258
Rollison, Marvin L P271

Rollo, Cathy P300
Rolls, Paul E. A620
Rolon, Gil A115
Rolston, Richard P148
Romain, Peter A585
Romain, Peter P377
Romaine, Mark A. A388
Romaine, Stephen S. A820
Roman, Michael F. A2
Roman, Juan A40
Roman, David H A113
Roman, John A151
Roman, James A223
Roman, Edwin A247
Roman, Oraida A255
Roman, Lawrence (Larry) A833
Roman, Elizabeth P22
Roman, Ray P83
Roman, Nancy P273
Roman, Anthony P332
Roman, David A. W218
Roman, John E48
Roman, Edwin E103
Romaneiro, Marcos A494
Romanelli, Christopher A204
Romanko, Michael F. E162
Romano, Frank A553
Romano, Michael A556
Romano, Gregory A870
Romano, Debbie P255
Romano, B P605
Romano, Michael B. W373
Romano, Frank E272
Romanowski, Mike A214
Romanowski, Paul A433
Romanowski, Mike P128
Romay, Connie A58
Romay, Connie E16
Rome, Melanie A611
Romeo, Steven A330
Romer, Paul A585
Romer, Paul P377
Romero, David A73
Romero, Adriana A160
Romero, Javier P297
Romero, Randall K P301
Romero, Daisy P302
Romero, Lujean P408
Romero, Jorge P545
Romero, Nitza P550
Romero, Laura P621
Rometty, Virginia M. (Ginni) A460
Romick, Steven P103
Romig, Timothy D. A247
Romig, Timothy D. E102
Romine, Jeremy A109
Romine, Krisden A699
Romine, Bill A708
Romine, Krisden P456
Romine, Donnie P538
Romine, Jeremy E36
Romito, Joyce A324
Romm, Elisa A537
Romo, Tammy A755
Romo, Ana P670
Romoff, Jeffrey A. A859
Romoff, Jeffrey A. P652
Romojaro, Jaime Guardiola W42
Romstad, Michael A744
Ron, Klimkowski A196
Rona, Michael A175
Ronald, Alan A56
Ronan, Debbie P537
Ronan, Barry P685
Ronchetto, Dan E298
Roney, Gary A244
Rongbin, Zhu W109
Ronn, Jeffrey P57
Ronning, Bruce A796
Ronnow, Jesse Ronnow Jesse A920
Rood, Carol P133
Roode, Tom P159
Roode, Jeanne P519
Roodman, Richard D P446
Rooke, Brian A762

Rooks, Marsha A736
Rooks, Marsha P492
Rooney, Mary A328
Rooney, Jack A555
Rooney, David A555
Rooney, Robert A568
Rooney, James A628
Rooney, Jerome A703
Rooney, John P556
Roop, Kimberly L A67
Roorda, Marten P5
Roos, Jeff A508
Roos, Tom A855
Roosa, Mark S. P423
Root, Chris A257
Root, Julie A522
Root, Carole P32
Root, R Mark R P53
Root, Bob P348
Root, Randall L. E437
Roper, Craig A303
Roper, Jay A844
Roper, Bret P630
Roper, Jay E412
Ropp, Stephen E (Steve) A483
Ropp, Holly A483
Rorabaugh, David A369
Rorsted, Kasper B. W8
Rosa, Dan De La A496
Rosa, Luis A585
Rosa, Enrica De P243
Rosa, Luis P377
Rosa, Cynthia P610
Rosadino, Eugene E162
Rosado, Louis A163
Rosado, Robert A765
Rosado, Oscar P88
Rosado, Robert P540
Rosak-Aminah, Rakefet W46
Rosamilia, Thomas W. (Tom) A460
Rosanova, Don A496
Rosario, Angela P223
Rosati, Bob A558
Rosato, R. David A644
Rosato, Albert P685
Rosborough, Mark N. A338
Rosbrough, Martha A334
Rosbrough, Martha P193
Rosch, Francis C. (Fran) A778
Roscoe, Fred A869
Rose, Matthew K. (Matt) A123
Rose, Matthew K. (Matt) A134
Rose, M. Robert A149
Rose, Matthew K. (Matt) A154
Rose, Sheryl A171
Rose, Timothy L. A239
Rose, Marya M. A245
Rose, Anthony J. A267
Rose, Jim A332
Rose, Dennis E. A344
Rose, Michael A423
Rose, David G. A431
Rose, Mike A476
Rose, Christopher A530
Rose, Ken A556
Rose, Greg A685
Rose, Virginia A802
Rose, George A860
Rose, Marie P30
Rose, Matthew K. (Matt) P77
Rose, Sheryl P100
Rose, Becky P214
Rose, Darcie P422
Rose, Bryan P450
Rose, Stanley P482
Rose, Michael S P515
Rose, Virginia P562
Rose, George P656
Rose, Shawn W50
Rose, Deborah W217
Rose, Alison W312
Rose, Richard E52
Rose, Dennis E. E154
Rose, Nathaniel J. E188
Rose, David G. E205

Rose, Tyler H. E232
Rose, Bill E257
Rose, Roger W. E360
Roseborough, Teresa W. A426
Rosello, Mike A32
Roseman, Jeffrey P379
Rosemore, Lance B. E77
Rosen, Elaine D. A83
Rosen, Sheri A244
Rosen, Rebecca A263
Rosen, Rae A322
Rosen, Mitch A382
Rosen, Mark A461
Rosen, Marc A509
Rosen, Harry P214
Rosen, Deane P456
Rosen, David E56
Rosena, Robens P159
Rosenbach, Lynn A111
Rosenbach, Lynn P56
Rosenbaum, Eileen A727
Rosenbaum, Thomas F. P91
Rosenbaum, Stephen P370
Rosenbaum, Jerrold Frank P590
Rosenberg, Joshua A323
Rosenberg, Paul A480
Rosenberg, Brian A482
Rosenberg, Jennifer A541
Rosenberg, Ken A667
Rosenberg, Donald J. A685
Rosenberg, Stuart P71
Rosenberg, John R. P83
Rosenberg, Stuart A P227
Rosenberg, Michael P237
Rosenberg, Jennifer E266
Rosenberger, T P213
Rosenberger, Thad P650
Rosenberger, H. Wayne E374
Rosenblatt, Sidney D. E417
Rosenblum, Heather A877
Rosenblum, Don P399
Rosencrans, Dean A81
Rosendahl, Tom P151
Rosenfeld, Paul A56
Rosenfeld, Irene B. A567
Rosenfeld, Phyllis A741
Rosenfeld, Phyllis E370
Rosenfeld, Aaron E432
Rosenfield, Eliot M. A155
Rosenfield, Donald P313
Rosengarten, Richard P610
Rosengren, Eric S. A325
Rosenhauer, Joan P101
Rosenstein, Robert A139
Rosenstein, Beryl A474
Rosenstein, Beryl P265
Rosenthal, David A313
Rosenthal, Louis A478
Rosenthal, Gary A530
Rosenthal, Mark A677
Rosenthal, Stacy A744
Rosenthal, Jean-Laurent P91
Rosenthal, Bruce P292
Rosenthal, Andrew P505
Rosenthal, Nadia P587
Rosenthal, Daniel P590
Rosenthaler, Albert E. A688
Rosenzweig, Andrew P20
Rosenzweig, Israel E47
Rosenzweig, Jody E432
Rosetta, Gladys A555
Roshardt, Christoph A530
Roshek, Sonya A536
Roshko, Michael P618
Rosier, W. Grady A547
Rosier, W. Grady P319
Roskelly, Jim P595
Roslin, Eddie A103
Rosman, Adam L A343
Rosmarin, Kelly Bayer W105
Rosner, Judy A706
Rosner, Judy E353
Rosowsky, David P657
Rospond, Nicole A741
Rospond, Nikki A741

Rospond, Nicole E370
Rospond, Nikki E370
Ross, Wayne A105
Ross, Kim A166
Ross, Joyce M. A171
Ross, Cheyenne A180
Ross, Rich A269
Ross, Renee A441
Ross, Heather A446
Ross, John A474
Ross, Brendan A530
Ross, Andrew D. A634
Ross, Thomas J. A639
Ross, Tom A693
Ross, Stephen M. A698
Ross, Bridget A. A727
Ross, Lisa A744
Ross, Sheryl A751
Ross, Dennis E. A766
Ross, James E. (Jim) A766
Ross, Dan A786
Ross, Sara A788
Ross, Kevin A846
Ross, Jeannette P20
Ross, William P42
Ross, Joyce M. P100
Ross, James P258
Ross, Trisha P259
Ross, Alexis P330
Ross, Joseph P333
Ross, Marianne P387
Ross, Tony P402
Ross, Jim P432
Ross, Stephen M. P456
Ross, Susan P503
Ross, Barry P533
Ross, Goldberg P590
Ross, Amy P642
Ross, James E. P644
Ross, Robert S. P675
Ross, Bruce W310
Ross, Heather E210
Ross, Stephen E226
Ross, Brian T. E288
Ross, Thomas J. E325
Ross, Sheryl E377
Rossbauer, Pauline A676
Rosser, Carrene G P306
Rossero, Daniel A355
Rossetta, Melanie A865
Rossetti, Nick A270
Rossetti, Barbara A696
Rossetti, Eugenio W189
Rossetto, Ronald B. A738
Rossi, Mark A. A102
Rossi, Mark A. A103
Rossi, James A207
Rossi, Todd A709
Rossi, Hugo A730
Rossi, Jack A773
Rossi, John P355
Rossi, Roberto Angelini W27
Rossi, Simone W133
Rossi, Roberto Angelini W137
Rossi, Luca W218
Rossi, Jean W387
Rossi, Dino A. E31
Rossi, Alex E117
Rossi, Jack E387
Rossini, Lynn P472
Rossmann, Barbara W. A413
Rossmann, Barbara W. P234
Rossmccalib, Laureen P219
Rosso, Paul A2
Rosswurm, Gretchen A177
Rostan, Richard H. A312
Rosten, James A. (Jim) E231
Rostrup, J-_rgen C. Arentz W360
Roszak, Dave A273
Roszak, Dave P162
Roszczewski, Loretta A493
Roszko, Danielle P437
Roszman, Chris P81
Rota, Kerim W18
Rotaeche, Gonzalo Gort--zar W300

Rotenberg, Lesli P445
Roth, Jay A270
Roth, Julie A441
Roth, Michael I. A464
Roth, Renee S. A781
Roth, Corina A817
Roth, Robert A872
Roth, Cindi A873
Roth, Kevin P40
Roth, Norman P83
Roth, Greg P119
Roth, Doug P162
Roth, Lawrence P183
Roth, Theodore D. (Ted) P452
Roth, Elliot P457
Roth, Ben P466
Roth, Adam P466
Roth, Brett P466
Roth, W Richard P480
Roth, Richard P490
Roth, Merianne P555
Roth, Edward J P566
Roth, Paul B. P648
Roth, Cindi P669
Roth, Irit W46
Roth, Heidi R. E232
Roth, Alan T. E349
Roth, Steven R. E361
Roth, W. Richard (Rich) E375
Rothberg, Michael P352
Rothberger, Richard K. P488
Rothblatt, Martine A. E415
Rothchild, Ellen P99
Rothenberg, David A390
Rothenberg, Craig A476
Rother, Joe A496
Rotherham, Ross A339
Rotherham, Ross E150
Rothfuss, Andre A141
Rothkin, Gregg A173
Rothman, Fred A508
Rothstein, Diahann A321
Rothstein, Sharon A762
Rothstein, Stuart A. E19
Rothstein, Diahann E144
Rotman, Joe P248
Rotner, Phil P570
Rotolo, Jill A103
Rotondi, Steve E117
Rotondo, John A555
Rotter, Franz W389
Rottman, Monica A141
Rottmuller, Lori A541
Rottmuller, Lori E266
Roty, Christopher M. (Chris) P58
Roualet, Mark C. A374
Rouan, Adrienne P565
Rouanne, Marc W266
Roubos, Hind E426
Rougeau, Vincent P625
Roughton, Paul A908
Roughton, Paul E446
Roulot, Antoine Axel A767
Rounds, Mary D P89
Rounds, Jason P118
Roundtree, Barbara P324
Rourk, Kevin A751
Rourk, Kevin E377
Rouse, Mary Ann A806
Rouse, Anthony A868
Rouse, Brad A913
Rouse, Matt P101
Rouse, Mary Ann P569
Rouse, Cecilia E. P606
Rousey, Melody A272
Roush, Phil A199
Roush, Robin S A387
Roush, Richard A811
Roush, Richard P600
Roush, Robin S E177
Roussat, Olivier W72
Rousse, Troy A A303
Rousse, Jonathan A390
Rousseau, Michael T. (Mike) A5
Rousseau, Paul A301

Rousseau, David P478
Rousseau, Thomas P480
Rousseau, Henri-Paul W293
Rousseau, Henri-Paul W294
Rousseau, Paul E127
Roussel, Serge A649
Roussel, Pierre-Yves W225
Roussel, Stéphane W388
Roussos, Michael P126
Routs, Robert J. W10
Roux, Bob A517
Roux, Sommer A788
Roux, Ana Diez P165
Roux, Roger G P451
Roux, David J. P587
Roverato, Jean-Fran-§ois W135
Rowan, Tim A528
Rowan, Dionne P591
Rowan, Barry L. E328
Rowberry, Mike P452
Rowe, Robert C. A201
Rowe, Sharon A207
Rowe, John W A310
Rowe, David A866
Rowe, Zane C. A875
Rowe, Chris A883
Rowe, Mike P36
Rowe, Amy P512
Rowe, James P619
Rowe, Steve W233
Rowe, Dennis E65
Rowell, Christine A266
Rowell, Jim A634
Rowinsky, Eric A129
Rowland, Gerald A448
Rowland, Kevin A537
Rowland, G. Joyce A735
Rowland, Rick A844
Rowland, Gerald P246
Rowland, David P. W5
Rowland, Rick E412
Rowles, Michael G. A517
Rowles, Brandon P32
Rowley, Andrea A300
Rowley, David A449
Rowley, Dean P368
Rowley, Gilbert R P566
Rowly, Cade P546
Roy, Robert A581
Roy, Steve P1
Roy, Donald P34
Roy, Travis P43
Roy, Bharati P66
Roy, Sumit E348
Royal, Debbie A173
Roybal, Tony A620
Royer, Patricia A369
Royer, Lori P108
Rozanski, Horacio D. A140
Rozansky, Kristen P587
Rozario, Peter A204
Rozario, Datuk Mark A375
Rozek, Charles P98
Rozek, Robert P. E235
Rozelle, Matt P315
Rozen, Phil P390
Rozenfeld, Jon A760
Rozenfeld, Jon P523
Rozich, Bill A165
Rozier, Tom P126
Rozmus, Amy P220
Roznowski, Elizabeth P619
Rozow, Stephen E310
Rozwadowski, Jeanne P160
Rozzi, Ted P143
Ro--, Heinz-Peter W356
Rubanenko, Yoram A240
Rubash, Harry E. P590
Rubenstein, Sam A158
Rubenstein, Ira P445
Rubenstein, Jonathan P467
Ruberg, Tony A441
Rubien, Ira P286
Rubin, Karen A49
Rubin, Bob A51

Rubin, Shelley A127
Rubin, Zach A160
Rubin, Bryon A175
Rubin, Amir Dan A507
Rubin, Jonathan N. (Jon) A524
Rubin, Patricia Lee A585
Rubin, Rosalind A644
Rubin, David P145
Rubin, Gail P159
Rubin, Amir Dan P288
Rubin, Patricia Lee P377
Rubin, Donna P464
Rubin, Dick P610
Rubin, Bruce P620
Rubin, Jeffrey G. E47
Rubin, Zach E55
Rubin, Aaron E254
Rubin, Andrea E447
Rubinfeld, Arthur A762
Rubinich, Joshua M A819
Rubinov, Emma E445
Rubinstein, David A723
Rubinstein, Pablo P372
Rubinstein, Jordan E231
Rubio, Laura P482
Rubish, Sue P385
Ruble, Anne A475
Ruble, Anne P266
Ruble, Chris C. E167
Rubocki, Cheri A351
Rubocki, Cheri E158
Rubritz, Timothy G. A360
Rubritz, Timothy G. E164
Ruby, Dave A743
Ruby, Lisa P293
Ruby, Dave E372
Rucker, Nitra A489
Rucker, Paul A861
Rucker, Craig P72
Rucker, Craig P215
Rucker, Michael P485
Rucker, Paul P658
Rucker, James N.B. (Jim) E260
Rucks, Charles C A22
Rucks, Charles C P13
Rudas, Andreas W62
Rudd, W. Troy A16
Rudd, Paul A316
Rudd, Henry A536
Rudd, David A599
Rudd, Paul P191
Ruddick, Lloyd P185
Ruddock, David P. A720
Ruddock, David P. E362
Ruddy, Joseph P P668
Rude, Tom A340
Rude, Tom E151
Rudeck, Al E13
Rudecki, Walter A54
Rudeen, Christian A2
Ruder, Anna A649
Rudinsky, Charles A. (Chuck) A388
Rudisill, Pamela T. A227
Rudman, Robert H. (Bob) A274
Rudman, Amanda P321
Rudoe, Jon W193
Rudolph, John A706
Rudolph, Sandra P261
Rudolph, Elaine P331
Rudolph, Philip J P467
Rudolph, William P467
Rudolph, Bill P602
Rudolph, Frederick W P602
Rudolph, Philip J P602
Rudolph, John E353
Rudy, John A17
Rudy, Sue A49
Rudy, Viscomi A635
Rudy, John P10
Rudy, Viscomi P419
Rudy, Cheryl N P457
Rudys, Karen P20
Rudzik, Robert J. P104
Rudzik, John P104
Rudzinski, John P66

A = AMERICAN BUSINESS
E = EMERGING COMPANIES
P = PRIVATE COMPANIES
W = WORLD BUSINESS

Rue, Lisa La P141
Rueben, Lenny P278
Rueber, Joel P48
Ruegg, Jason A173
Ruegg, Alex P501
Ruehl, Alison A760
Ruehl, Alison P523
Ruehle, Corey J. A847
Ruello, Warren A530
Rueter, Jens P174
Ruff, Tracey A871
Ruffin, Kat A795
Ruffner, Jeff P183
Ruffolo, Carmel P309
Rufo, Gloria P626
Rufolo, Rick A850
Rugani, Gina A780
Ruge, Dawn P225
Ruggieri, Debra P315
Ruggiero, David A199
Ruh, William (Bill) A375
Ruh, Richard J P330
Ruhe, Mark A784
Ruhe, Laura E140
Ruhe, Erin N. E201
Ruhl, Kerry A34
Ruhmann, Don A136
Ruhnke, Atalie P253
Rui, Yong W218
Ruisanchez, Raul Jacob A753
Ruiz, Gisel A878
Ruiz, Colette P19
Ruiz, Marco P87
Ruiz, Beatriz P140
Ruiz, Pablo P222
Ruiz, Israel P313
Ruland, Lisa A691
Ruland, Sharla E298
Rulli, John A744
Ruman, Deborah P295
Rumans, Mark C. P74
Rumbaugh, Rob A685
Rumbaugh, Christine A720
Rumbaugh, Christine E362
Rumbelow, Kevin A836
Rumbolz, Michael D. (Mike) A296
Rumler, John P27
Rummel, Gary P539
Rumple, Belinda A521
Rumsey, Jennifer A246
Runcie, Robert W P86
Runck, Cathy P26
Runckel, Christopher E245
Rundall, Thomas P263
Runde, Christine A486
Rundle, Lisa E445
Runey, Mim L. P267
Runge, Marschall S. A698
Runge, Marschall S. P456
Runge, Terence E44
Rungkasiri, Sarun W295
Runion, Scott P543
Runkel, Mark G. A865
Runne, Amanda P233
Runnels, Chad A693
Runyon, Kevin B. A639
Runyon, Kevin B. E325
Ruocco, Jennifer P410
Ruos, Brian A351
Ruos, Brian E158
Rupert, Teresa A549
Rupert, Beverly A640
Rupert, Dennis P98
Rupert, Nora P486
Rupert, Teresa E270
Rupp, Robert R. A406
Rupp, Eddie A449
Rupp, William C P317
Rupp, Cassie E166

Ruppert, Paul F. A275
Rupprecht, Gerhard W154
Ruquist, Lynn P450
Rusch, Robin P567
Rusch, Susan P687
Rusche, James R. E351
Ruscitto, Kathryn Howe P532
Rusckowski, Stephen H. (Steve) A687
Rush, Dave A153
Rush, Daniel A558
Rush, David G A691
Rush, W. M. (Rusty) A717
Rush, Tim A780
Rush, Steven A898
Rush, Mark P194
Rush, Keith P249
Rushing, Rodney E. A737
Rushing, David A743
Rushing, Rodney E. E367
Rushing, David E372
Rushing, Greg E431
Rushmore, John A105
Rushnak, Jeff A201
Rusk, Mike A318
Rusk, George P222
Rusnak, Patrick J. (Pat) A632
Rusnak, Patrick J. (Pat) E321
Russ, Ioana A649
Russ, Mark A703
Russeau, Chris A505
Russel, Kristin A438
Russel, Kimberly P87
Russel, Kim P87
Russell, Ronnie A54
Russell, Darrel A107
Russell, John G. A210
Russell, Saira A219
Russell, Nicholas S. (Nick) A225
Russell, John G. A236
Russell, David A241
Russell, Monya A339
Russell, Rusty A371
Russell, John A505
Russell, Thomas A555
Russell, Craig A640
Russell, Sandy A693
Russell, Carlos A700
Russell, Rick A725
Russell, Keith A753
Russell, Craig A763
Russell, Rod A838
Russell, David A917
Russell, Barbara P13
Russell, Dorothy P196
Russell, Michael P207
Russell, Caroline P230
Russell, Jon P263
Russell, Bob P440
Russell, Lynn P443
Russell, Judith C. P642
Russell, Sarah A. C. W10
Russell, Darrel E34
Russell, Saira E84
Russell, Nicholas S. (Nick) E88
Russell, Monya E150
Russell, Keith E379
Russeth, Scott A707
Russi, Timothy M. (Tim) A35
Russo, Madeleine A133
Russo, Paul M. A390
Russo, Patricia F. (Pat) A419
Russo, Alejandra A877
Russo, Peter M M P410
Russo, Kimberly D P582
Rust, Steven W. (Steve) A110
Rust, Bradley M. A384
Rust, Melissa P640
Rust, Steven W. (Steve) E37
Rust, Bradley M. E176
Rustad, Shawn P109
Rustand, Kay A703
Rustowicz, Gregory P. E86
Ruth, Michael J. A703
Ruth, James P408
Rutherford, William B. (Bill) A410

Rutherford, John R. A658
Rutherford, Linda B. A755
Rutherford, Peter P107
Rutherford, Shelly P353
Rutherford, Clyde P401
Rutkowski, Claire P361
Rutkowski, James C P635
Rutland, James B P347
Rutland, Thomas B P347
Rutland, James B P347
Rutledge, Elizabeth A49
Rutledge, Reynie A266
Rutledge, Debra A754
Rutledge, Cheryl P537
Rutledge, Debra E380
Rutschman, Cody A449
Rutstein, Mark A61
Rutt, Sheila M. A265
Ruttanaporn, Sarut W330
Rutter, Kenneth S. P62
Rutz, Anne P223
Rutz, Michael P. E247
Ruud, David A280
Ruud, Yngve W212
Ruvolo, Susan A371
Ruzicka, Laura P522
Rwanczyk, Luke P135
Ryan, William J A124
Ryan, Kevin A165
Ryan, Cindy A195
Ryan, Eileen A212
Ryan, Maria A218
Ryan, Jim A235
Ryan, Samantha A292
Ryan, Marc A369
Ryan, Timothy A413
Ryan, Tom A438
Ryan, Kevin A449
Ryan, Collin A454
Ryan, Linda A461
Ryan, Courtney J. A471
Ryan, Sherry A482
Ryan, Edward A. (Ed) A530
Ryan, Lawrence G. A541
Ryan, Robert A576
Ryan, D A605
Ryan, James C. A614
Ryan, Ann A628
Ryan, Paula A635
Ryan, Maryanne A677
Ryan, Dan A711
Ryan, Richard J A717
Ryan, Carol A734
Ryan, Matthew A763
Ryan, Lynn A883
Ryan, Marty P194
Ryan, Barbara P231
Ryan, Timothy P234
Ryan, Philip J. P255
Ryan, Kristen P395
Ryan, Paula P419
Ryan, Jackie P427
Ryan, Tim P470
Ryan, Doug O' P532
Ryan, Pat P625
Ryan, John P627
Ryan, John M P668
Ryan, Fred M P674
Ryan, Kim P680
Ryan, Timothy (Tim) W32
Ryan, Michael W69
Ryan, Leonie W123
Ryan, Daniel J. E9
Ryan, Eileen E79
Ryan, James C. (Jim) E181
Ryan, Lawrence G. E266
Ryan, Robert E297
Ryan, Sister Mary Jean E337
Ryan, Don E405
Ryan-Macie, Sheila A746
Ryans, Tomya P325
Rybar, Ronald E147
Rybczynski, Andrea A902
Rybczynski, Andrea P692
Rychlik, Garrett A232

Rychlik, Wendell P318
Rycyna, Kevin P391
Rydell, David R P550
Ryder, Thomas A105
Ryder, Mark P281
Ryder, Ellen P654
Rye, Curtis P248
Ryea, Alan P658
Ryerson, Lisa M. P2
Ryerson, Lisa Marsh P2
Ryge, Svend A775
Ryge, Svend P548
Ryks, Brian P337
Rylander, Stephen P64
Ryman, Craig W26
Ryn, Janice Van P41
Rynd, John T P382
Rynearson, Debra A350
Rynearson, Debra E156
Ryoo, Young P495
Ryors, Alfred P627
Rysz, David P564
Ryu, Hyungon A607
Rzepecki, Annie P282
Rzepka, Alan M E324
Rzucidlo, Ryan A101
R'bibo, Daniel A371
R--DLER, Friedrich W145
Rémont, Luc W322
Rüdiger, Michael W120

S

S.Gragg, Gary A345
S.Gragg, Gary E154
Sa, Francisco A494
Saad, Moizah P263
Saadoun, Serge P375
Saag, John A269
Saar, Janet A123
Saari, Carolyn P299
Saarony, Gadi P417
Saavedra, Norma A103
Saavedra, Ed A695
Sabag, Mark W363
Sabanci, Erol W163
Sabanci, Guler W163
Sabanovic, Ruza W360
Sabatella, Linda P516
Sabatini, Dominic P544
Sabatini, Mary P590
Sabatowski, Karen A. A356
Sabbag, Russ A906
Sabharwal, Rajiv W181
Sabin, Sam P630
Sabinson, Allen P165
Sabio, Robert A122
Sabnani, Janisha A353
Sabo, Elias J. E168
Sabol, Colin R. A914
Saborio, Bernal A218
Sabourin, David P543
Sabry, Ismail A647
Sabutis, Mike P333
Saccamano, Bob P490
Saccaro, James K. A113
Saccaro, Jay A113
Sacchetti, Courtney A109
Sacco, Austin A173
Sacco, Frank V. P508
Sacco, Christine (Chris) E338
Sach, Derek S. W312
Sachdev, Arvind A218
Sachdev, Punit P568
Sachdev, Amit K. E428
Sacher, Dan A871
Sacher, Elizabeth P451
Sachin, Alexis A133
Sachtleben, Michael C. A548
Sachtleben, Michael C. P321
Sack, Brian P. A323
Sackett, John P8
Sackett, Neil P98
Sacks, Lee B. A15

Sacks, Lee B. P9
Sacks, Rodney C P351
Sacrist--n, Carlos Ruiz A735
Sada, Armando Garza W18
Sadan, Avishai A860
Sadan, Avishai P656
Sadau, Ernie W. P119
Sadek, Hossam A469
Sadi, Eric A744
Sadigh, Mandana A539
Sadler, Jason D. A195
Sadler, Kimberly A330
Sadler, Michael A559
Sadosty, Annie A540
Sadosty, Annie P316
Sadowski, Peter T. A328
Sadowski, John D. A724
Sadro, Cheryl A P323
Sadro, Cheryl P323
Sadvary, Thomas J. (Tom) P487
Sae-hong, Hur W163
Saegusa, Tomihiro W324
Saeki, Yasumitsu W263
Saenz, Alexanders A109
Saenz, Luis A765
Saenz, Pete P123
Saenz, Luis P540
Saenz, Alexanders E36
Saenz, Kari E437
Safa, Aziz A456
Safady, Edward Z. (Eddie) A673
Safady, Randolph W. P119
Saferian, Candee M P441
Saffarian-Toosi, Mitra A907
Saffarian-Toosi, Mitra E446
Safriel, Yair P353
Safyer, Steven M. P351
Sagar, Bijoy A772
Sagara, Kevin A735
Sage, Anya A565
Sage, James A648
Sage, Rudger P168
Sagehorn, David M A625
Sagers, David A480
Sagert, Sharon E442
Saggau, David P219
Sagheer, Omer P604
Sagita, Lisa A204
Saglimbeni, Philip E257
Sagona, Jordan E448
Sagritanti, Mary A567
Saha, Tamal A898
Sahenk, Ferit Faik W377
Sahin, Meltem W389
Sahota, Kamal A685
Said, Riyad A105
Saik, Barry A466
Saikawa, Hiroto W265
Sain, Jeff A521
Sainsbury, Paul W26
Sainz, Marcia P225
Saito, Yoshitaka P248
Saito, Takeo W28
SAITO, KAZUO W163
Saito, Hitoshi W245
Saiyawan, Wasin W330
Sajet, Kim P506
Saji, Nobutada W349
Sakae, Toshiharu W263
Sakaguchi, Masatoshi W99
Sakai, Hitoshi W156
Sakai, Akio W238
Sakai, Yoshikiyo W272
Sakamoto, Satoru W211
Sakamoto, Ryuji W250
Sakamoto, Fukashi W264
Sakamoto, Mitsuhiro W366
Sakhrani, Monesh A906
Saklad, J. Hunter J. E376
Sakuma, Soichiro W263
Sakurada, Kengo W336
Sala, Marcello W189
Saladonis, Melissa P115
Saladrigas, Carlos A282
Salah, Joseph A241

Salah, Jamil A584
Salamacha, Mark P660
Salame, Pablo J. A389
Salamida, Shawn P281
Salamone, Denis A522
Salansky, Karla A272
Salazar, Juan C. P138
Salazar, Crystal P244
Salazar, Cynthia P259
Salazar, Esther P396
Salbod, Stephen P414
Salcedo, Mirta A459
Salcito, Tom A647
Saldarelli, John A447
Saldivar, Ricardo E. A426
Saleem, Amer E39
Salehpour, Ali A71
Saleki-Gerhardt, Azita A6
Salem, Charbel P276
Salem, Laura P345
Salem, Deeb P628
Salemme, R. Gerard (Gerry) E328
Salerno, Robert A93
Salerno, Antonella R P8
Salerno, Todd P172
Sales, William K. A703
Saletnik, Laurie A475
Saletnik, Laurie P266
Salimbene, Nick P125
Salinas, Jerry A244
Salinas, Andres P293
Salinas, Erwin Kaufmann W137
Saline, Chris A647
Salisbury, Julian A390
Salisbury, Dale P378
Salisbury, Chris W305
Salisbury, Chris W306
Salit, Jan F. E77
Salka, Susan R. E17
Salkic, Edin A837
Salla, Francis J. (Frank) La A105
Sallaffie, Moriah P69
Salle, Andrew Bon A315
Saller, Richard P. A507
Saller, Richard P. P288
Salles, Pedro Moreira W191
Sally, William E303
Salmans, Todd L. A420
Salmans, Todd L. E198
Salmirs, Scott A7
Salmon, Thomas E. (Tom) A125
Salmon, Kimberly A847
Salmon, Duane P74
Salmon, Kimberly E414
Salnas, Todd P482
Saloner, Garth A507
Saloner, Garth P288
SALOW, KAREN P518
Salsberry, David P555
Salter, April P54
Saltiel, Albert (Al) A90
Saltzberg, Edward E439
Saltzman, Robert A38
Saltzman, Nancy E138
Salvador, Michael A541
Salvador, Scot R. A831
Salvador, Michael E266
Salvadori, Daniel A5
Salvadori, Rossana A855
Salvage, Neil E243
Salvatore, Bryan J. A402
Salway, Roberta A350
Salway, Roberta E157
Salyers, Sandy A700
Salzman, Mike A158
Sam, Pearl A785
Samaan, Muhannad P566
Samalapa, Patchara W202
Samaniego, David A647
Samant, Rahul A261
Samartsev, Igor E224
Sambar, Christopher A85
Sambrook, David E97
Samet, Kenneth A. A548
Samet, Kenneth A. P321

Sameth, David A272
Samia, Dori J A766
Samir, Mohamed A671
Samitsu, Masahiro W264
Samitt, Craig E. A67
Sammarco, Michael J P186
Sammon, Alison A489
Sammon, Pat E355
Sammons, Lisa A333
Samora, Jessica P446
Sampath, Anand E261
Sample, Marilyn P343
Sample, Vilona P549
Sample, Mike P627
Samples, Jeff A459
Samples, Dustin P22
Samples, Rhonda P225
Samples, Jim P488
Samples, John P572
Sampson, Trent A221
Sampson, Kristin M A371
Sampson, Ley P126
Samreny, Jason E234
Sams, Thomas A171
Sams, Michael A333
Sams, Thomas P100
Sams, Karen P165
Sams, Robert E305
Samson, Brian A58
Samson, Denise A693
Samson, Brian E16
Samsonov, Anastasia P413
Samstein, Ivan P610
Samu, Sriram A878
Samuel, Tonya A369
Samuels, Deborah Addo P333
Samuelson, Jonas W3
Samworth, Martin A173
Samz, Jeff P244
Sanborn, Angela A452
Sances, James P22
Sanchez, Yesenia A195
Sanchez, Danny A221
Sanchez, Anna A244
Sanchez, Marie A244
Sanchez, Lou A288
Sanchez, Pablo A437
Sanchez, Calline A460
Sanchez, Maria A635
Sanchez, Beatriz A649
Sanchez, Tammi A700
Sanchez, Robert E. A718
Sanchez, Victor P81
Sanchez, Debra P143
Sanchez, Dan P145
Sanchez, Linda P211
Sanchez, Fernando P225
Sanchez, Charlie P227
Sanchez, Alex P241
Sanchez, Maria P419
Sanchez, Juan J P516
Sanchez, Gina P538
Sanchez, Robert P546
Sanchez, Ht P628
Sanchez, Saul P681
Sanchez, Enrique W7
Sanchez, Jeanette E17
Sanchez, Becky E147
Sanchez, Antonio R. (Tony) E364
Sanchez, Eduardo A. E364
Sanchez, A. R. (Tony) E364
Sanchirico, Paul A199
Sanda, Robert P91
Sandall, Emily A811
Sandall, Emily P600
Sandberg, Jon A195
Sandberg, Christopher A253
Sandberg, Sheryl K. A314
Sandberg, Louise T. A644
Sandborn, Cindy A243
Sandbrook, William J. (Bill) E419
Sande, Marc van W379
Sandeen, Ashley P643
Sandeno, Greg P130
Sander, Mark G. A351

Sander, Ed P429
Sander, Louise W352
Sander, Mark G. E158
Sandercock, Brett E354
Sanders, Todd A13
Sanders, Carla A41
Sanders, Jay D. A97
Sanders, Marge A101
Sanders, Jeff A137
Sanders, Jeff A244
Sanders, Robert A303
Sanders, William A413
Sanders, Barbara A426
Sanders, Ashley A441
Sanders, Wayne R A487
Sanders, Dax A492
Sanders, Stacy A508
Sanders, Kelly A532
Sanders, Corey I. A558
Sanders, Scott A727
Sanders, M. Jack A750
Sanders, Dan A759
Sanders, Laurence A769
Sanders, Joann P141
Sanders, William P234
Sanders, Greg P280
Sanders, Jeffrey D. (Jeff) P303
Sanders, Mary P330
Sanders, David P334
Sanders, Morgan P363
Sanders, Brenda P368
Sanders, Timothy P449
Sanders, Nancy P472
Sanders, Ashley P521
Sanders, Stephanie P613
Sanders, Jay D. E32
Sanders, John E140
Sanders, Steve E221
Sanderson, Scott A532
Sanderson, Travee P115
Sanderson, La Verne P164
Sandford, W. F. (Bill) W199
Sandfort, Gregory A. (Greg) A825
Sandgren, James A614
Sandgren, Jim A614
Sandh, David A885
Sandhu, Jagveer P57
Sandhu, Dalpinder P135
Sandhu, Sukhjit P290
Sandifer, Craig P132
Sandin, Leslie P518
Sandler, Jane A546
Sandman, James P286
Sandoval, Andres A474
Sandoval, Norma P467
Sandoval, Karla P521
Sandra, Drummond A369
Sandri, Fabio A654
Sandring, Rebecca E95
Sandrock, Alfred W. A129
Sandrock, Al A129
Sands, Robert S. (Rob) A235
Sands, Richard A235
Sands, John A244
Sands, Rodney E P188
Sands, Timothy D. (Tim) P669
Sandstead, David A669
Sandy, Lewis A855
Saner, Deborah P477
Sanfiel, Joaqu-n Cruz W137
Sanford, Marcus A10
Sanford, Kathleen D. A171
Sanford, Linda A461
Sanford, Tom A476
Sanford, Robert M A658
Sanford, Kathleen D. P100
Sanford, Deborah P174
Sanford, Jeffery P174
Sanford, William R. (Bill) E219
Sanford, Mike L. E232
Sanford, Morris E244
Sang-bong, Lee W221
Sang-Young, Kim W293
Sanger, Steve P410
Sanger, Bryna P597

A = AMERICAN BUSINESS
E = EMERGING COMPANIES
P = PRIVATE COMPANIES
W = WORLD BUSINESS

Sangkanarubordee, Sathit W88
Sanglard, Paul André W52
Sangster, Denise A134
Sangster, Denise P78
Sani, Shawn A558
Sanibelli, --zlen W18
Sanjurjo, Katie P630
Sankar, Nandini E383
Sankaran, Vivek A647
Sankaran, Vijay A791
Sankarlingam, Velchamy A875
Sankey, Greg P605
Sankey, Lora P687
Sankovitch, Mark P184
Sanna, Albert A644
Sannizzaro, Peter F A785
SanPhillip, Cynthia A500
SanPhillip, Cynthia E237
Sansalone, Giovanni A390
Sansone, Thomas A. A471
Sansosti, Gerard E197
Sant, Gursharan A532
Santacroce, Kevin L. A145
Santacroce, Kevin L. E46
Santamaria, Joseph A678
Santamaria, Christopher P185
Santana, Megan A862
Santana, Megan E419
Santangelo, Vicky A85
Santangelo, Lillian A388
Santangelo, Charles P617
Santarelli, Denton P422
Santarone, Michael S P605
Santelli, Jonathan N. A693
Santi, E. Scott A450
Santiago, Michael A401
Santiago, Michael E187
Santillan, Laura A32
Santillan, Alfredo A P225
Santillana, Alex A691
Santillanes, Sharon Y A136
Santini, Noel P152
Santirocco, Laura A406
Santis, Rosa P517
Santivisat, Srilawat W203
Santo, Ronald D. A541
Santo, Ronald D. E266
Santomassimo, Michael P. A105
Santor, Eric W47
Santorno, Carla J P553
Santoro, Leonard A173
Santoro, Sandy P508
Santoro, Frank P588
Santos, Bernerd Da A17
Santos, Esteban A61
Santos, Jess Pascual P222
Santos, Roberto J P635
Santos, Carlos Hern--n Zenteno de
  los W25
Santry, Edward A594
Santucci, Debranne A541
Santucci, Debranne E266
Sanz, Erick A405
Sanz, Francisco J. Garc-a W390
Sanzone, Virginia E212
Sapere, Matt A13
Saperstein, Andy A568
Saperstein, Arnold A582
Saperstein, Karen A733
Saperstein, Arnold P373
Saperstein, Karen P490
Sapia, Jolynn P83
Saple, Gaurav A199
Sapnar, Michael C. (Mike) A30
Saporito, Andrea A49
Sapozhnikov, Galina A729
Sapp, William P483
Sapperstein, Sandy A741
Sapperstein, Sandy E370

Sappington, Jim A545
Sapyta, Tim P95
Saraceni, Paul A593
Saracheck, Liz A449
Saradhi, Vijay A582
Saradhi, Vijay P373
Saraf, Tal A763
Saragosa, Rafael P416
Saraiva, Ana A644
Sarandos, Ted A580
Saravi, Maximo A555
Sardinha, Jeffrey A767
Sargen, Gregory P. (Greg) E54
Sargen, Greg E54
Sargent, Angela M. A369
Sargent, Matthew A865
Sargent, Annie P420
Sargent, Darryl P568
Sargent, Jeannine P. W151
Sari, Robert B. A596
Sarid, Uri P356
Sarker, Ari A537
Sarkis, Hashim P313
Sarma, Sanjay P313
Sarner, David A107
Sarner, David E35
Sarratt, Karin A621
Sarratt, Karin P407
Sarrett, David P668
Sarrow, Jonathan A175
Sarsfield, Luke A390
Sarstedt, Armin A456
Sarubbi, Allison A101
Sarvadi, John C. A800
Sarvadi, John C. E396
Sarver, Robert G. A891
Sarver, Theresa P686
Sarver, Robert G. E434
Sarvis, Bill A117
Sasagawa, Toshiro W366
Sasaki, David P236
Sasaki, Eliot P286
Sasaki, Yuuzou W213
Sasaki, Shiro W304
Sasaki, Kazue W373
Sasaoka, Hiroshi W326
Sasashita, Shigeru W116
Sasfai, Beth A870
Sass, Forrest P586
Sass, Kevin P591
Sass, Steven P625
Sassani, Manzar P587
Sassenfeld, Peter W170
Sasser, Bob A274
Sasser, Gary D P52
Sasser, Gary D. P53
Sasser, Sarah P148
Sassoon, Debby A401
Sassoon, Debby E187
Satcher, Richard H P282
Satele, Evelyn P295
Sathe, Kedar A201
Satin, Joel E444
Satina, Elizabeth A659
Satine, Alberto L. A45
Satkewich, Charles A434
Sato, Michael A596
Sato, Margaret A866
Sato, Lisa P413
Sato, Samuel M. (Sam) P579
Sato, Hiroshi W208
Sato, Akira W259
Sato, Hirotaka W272
Sato, Hitomi W329
Sato, Yoji W336
Sato, Yoshio W345
Sato, Kazuhiro W374
Satoh, Kunihiko W304
Satou, Naofumi W213
Satou, Masatoshi W245
Satou, Hironobu W329
Satterfield, Donna A460
Satterfield, William E364
Satterthwaite, Jennifer A100
Satterthwaite, Tony A245

Satterthwaite, Livingston L.
  (Tony) A246
Satterwhite, Matthew J. A47
Satterwhite, Celia A272
Sattora, Gerald E172
Saturnelli, Annette P378
Satyanarayan, Arvind P57
Saucedo, Rosie A803
Sauer, Jon A69
Sauer, David A316
Sauer, Brad A835
Sauer, Dave P62
Sauer, David P151
Sauer, David P191
Sauer, Konstantin W402
Saueressig, Thomas W319
Sauerland, John P. A672
Sauers, Jeff A546
Sauers, Kyle L. E117
Sauerwalt, Craig A784
Sauey, William R P383
Sauey, Eric W P383
Sauey, Todd L P383
Saul, J. Philip P365
Sauls, Randy P240
Saulsberry, Scott A899
Saun, Bruce Van A205
Saun, Bruce W. Van W312
Saunders, Suzanne A445
Saunders, David A449
Saunders, James A492
Saunders, Jeff L. A576
Saunders, Barry L. A750
Saunders, Gilbert A812
Saunders, Jim P366
Saunders, Jane P563
Saunders, Ninfa M P591
Saunders, Gilbert P607
Saunders, Debbie P647
Saunders, Candice P680
Saunders, Brenton L. (Brent) W22
Saunders, Rick W123
Saunders, Mark S. W347
Saunders, Jeff L. E297
Saundrs, Brent P239
Sauquet, Philippe W372
Sausen, Julie A599
Sautter, Allen A322
Sautter, Bruce A440
Sauvigne, Don A478
Savage, Josh A331
Savage, Dave A449
Savage, Douglas A480
Savage, Joseph J. (Joe) A883
Savage, Stanley D. A919
Savage, Mike P460
Savage, Luke W341
Savage, Josh E148
Savage, Thomas E172
Savaiano, Helen A402
Savajols, Jean-Francois A141
Savarese, Lawrence A584
Savell, Melanie A446
Savell, Jason P353
Savell, Melanie E210
Savich, Susan R P329
Savidge, Roderick P196
Saville, Paul C. A608
Saville, Robert A833
Savina, James A908
Savio, Kathleen W405
Savko, Brad A705
Savko, Brad E352
Savoff, Mark T P185
Savoie, Debbie A122
Savoy, Brian D A282
Savoy, Wayne P89
Savu, Andreea A19
Saw, Choon Seong A24
Sawa, Yoshihiro W374
Sawanoi, Makoto P245
Sawant, Dinesh P556
Saward, Laura E161
Sawasky, Joseph F. P679
Sawdey, Mike A53

Sawhney, Ash E116
Sawicki, Michael A781
Sawicki, Joseph P145
Sawicki, Joseph D. (Joe) P326
Sawicki, Robert P411
Sawka, Gary E51
Sawyer, Scott A166
Sawyer, Christina A292
Sawyer, Chris A351
Sawyer, Stephen A781
Sawyer, Kelly P282
Sawyer, Don C P450
Sawyer, Frank P531
Sawyer, Joseph G. E153
Sawyer, Chris E158
Sawyer, Jack E339
Sawyerr, Wraymond P662
Sax, Ward P458
Saxena, Sorabh A84
Saxena, Pallavi A204
Saxena, Anubhav P228
Saxon, Michael A27
Saxon, Matthew A438
Sayavedra, Laura P342
Sayers, Andrew A863
Sayiner, Necip P458
Sayles, Michelle P421
Saylor, Kurt M. A412
Saylor, Keith A878
Saylor, Chad P144
Saylor, Kurt M. E192
Sayre, Rich A593
Sayre, David L. A886
Sayre, David L. E433
Sazekas, Jacqueline A878
Sboui, Silveras A644
Sbraccia, Denise A902
Sbraccia, Denise P692
Sbuttoni, Julie E445
Scaccia, Tiziana A328
Scaer, Robert P207
Scaggiante, Michele P372
Scaggs, Thomas P95
Scaglione, D. Anthony A7
Scaglione, Isela A539
Scaglione, Jan P115
Scala, Luciano A655
Scala, Douglas E. (Doug) A883
Scala, Luciano E333
Scales, Arniga A529
Scales, John P560
Scalese, Vinny A640
Scalise, Anthony A294
Scamihorn, Randy P128
Scaminace, Joseph M. (Joe) A807
Scaminace, Joseph M. (Joe) P574
Scanlan, Patrick A272
Scanlan, John P126
Scanlon, Meghan A144
Scanlon, Suzy A701
Scanlon, John P. P104
Scannell, Timothy J. A772
Scannon, Patrick J. (Pat) E447
Scarano, Dean A693
Scarboro, Jim A162
Scarboro, Lynne P299
Scarboro, Evelynne P299
Scarborough, Dean A. A91
Scarborough, Randy A327
Scarborough, Fred P45
Scarborough, Leslie P238
Scarborough, William P406
Scardina, Barrie A682
Scardino, Diane M P560
Scardullo, John A542
Scardullo, John E267
Scarimbolo, Carmen P440
Scarlett, Catherine M. A577
Scarlett, Dale P235
Scarlett, Lynn P596
Scarpinato, Karin P196
Scarsella, Michael A541
Scarsella, Michael E266
Scarth, Susan E119

Scaturo, Michael A133
Scavella, Steadman P144
Scavilla, Daniel T. E179
Scavone, April A93
Scebold, Alexandra A691
Scenti, Louis A323
Scerch, Andrea A537
Schaack, Greg P92
Schaad, Jeff P381
Schaafsma, Doug E44
Schaal, Barbara A. P616
Schabacker, Marcus A113
Schabacker, Michael P537
Schaber, Carolina P452
Schaberl, Michael E407
Schach, Eric J P514
Schacht, David A744
Schacht, Horst Joachim W212
Schachtel, Bill A500
Schachtel, Bill E237
Schachtel, John D. E350
Schachter, Robert A449
Schachtner, Janet P355
Schacter, Adam A201
Schadt, Angela A369
Schaeberle, Steve A402
Schaefer, Rich A5
Schaefer, Kelly A230
Schaefer, Steven A251
Schaefer, Tammy A333
Schaefer, Aaron A419
Schaefer, Michael A446
Schaefer, Lindsey A744
Schaefer, Terence P308
Schaefer, Michael J. P336
Schaefer, John P516
Schaefer, Linda P663
Schaefer, Michael E210
Schaeffer, Leonard A877
Schaeffer, Joel P155
Schaeffer, Tammi P303
Schaeffer, Erica P582
Schaeffer, David (Dave) E81
Schaeffer, Don E407
Schaeublin, JoAnn A489
Schafer, Todd A185
Schafer, Carol A489
Schafer, Lori A549
Schafer, John A607
Schafer, Dirk P256
Schafer, Dirk P257
Schafer, Dana Lee P603
Schafer, Cathy P646
Schafer, Lori E270
Schaffer, Steve A136
Schaffer, W A195
Schaffer, Barbara M P155
Schaffer, Michael I. E340
Schaffmeyer, Maryjeanne P618
Schaffner, Jerry L. A420
Schaffner, Jerry L. E198
Schager, Marty A17
Schager, Marty P10
Schaible, Jeff A113
Schaidle, Scott A429
Schaidle, Scott E204
Schalk, David A644
Schall, Martha E. P138
Schall, Thomas J. E72
Schall, Michael J. (Mike) E133
Schaller, Heinrich W389
Schalliol, Charles E. A350
Schalliol, Charles E. E157
Schamer, David A441
Schamus, Neil A93
Schandler, Jon B P688
Schanel, Judy P594
Schaper, Katie P18
Schapiro, Sara P445
Schapiro, Howard P614
Schapker, Melanie P183
Schapper, Brian P335
Schappert, Rich A168
Schappert, Lisa P412
Schar, Dwight C. A608

Scharbauer, Clarence P561
Scharf, David A218
Scharf, Michael P. P98
Scharf, Katelyn P619
Scharf, Mark J P632
Scharf, Elizabeth P650
Scharmer, Neal R. A847
Scharnberg, Mark P579
Scharphorn, Douglas A441
Schasel, Brian P74
Schatz, Jacob (Jake) A292
Schau, Duane P627
Schaub, Lauren M P637
Schaubert, Sharon A561
Schaubert, Sharon E279
Schauer, Robert A85
Schauer, Andrew A101
Schauer, Darleen A244
Schauer, Denise P109
Schaufelberger, John A861
Schaufelberger, John P658
Schaumburg, Anne A604
Schaus, Philippe W226
Schechter, Harold A231
Schechter, Lori A. A546
Schechter, Adam H. A550
Schechter, Dave A593
Schechter, Chris P125
Schechter, Harold A. E90
Schechter, David E391
Schechtman, Natalie Rothman A13
Scheder, Valerie A85
Scheel, Lori Y P249
Scheeler, Jeanne P660
Scheet, Brian A355
Scheetz, Dave A677
Schefer, Catherine P361
Scheffler, Brian A258
Scheffler, David J P474
Schefft, Bob A54
Scheib, Barbera P385
Scheid, Tom A196
Scheid, Lisa A774
Scheider, Wolf-Henning W70
Scheidmeir, Thomas A6
Scheifele, Bernd W166
Scheines, Richard P96
Scheinkman, Daniel A366
Scheker, Maria R. E39
Schelanko, Alex A868
Schell, Andrea A67
Schell, Christoph A435
Schell, Jennifer A724
Schell, Daren P214
Schell, Kenneth P498
Schell, Lynn Null E252
Schellenger, Robert P662
Scheller, Robert E276
Schem, Debby P381
Schembri, Lawrence L. W47
Schemm, Dennis E92
Schemmel, Massie A207
Schempf, Duff P598
Schenck, A. William (Bill) A830
Schenck, Marcus W123
Schenck, A. William (Bill) E403
Schenk, Robert A322
Schenk, June A772
Schenk, Norm A850
Schenk, Dieter W153
Schenkel, Scott F. A288
Schenkel, Kendra A402
Scheper, Patrick A777
Scheper, Patrick E393
Schepp, Richard D. (Rick) A493
Scherbakov, Eugene E224
Scherer, Jf A196
Scherer, Ivan P505
Scherer, Jeff P565
Scherler, Lynn A214
Scherler, Lynn P128
Schermeier, Olaf W153
Schermer, Carol A113
Scherpbier, Harm P302
Scherr, Stephen M. A389

Scherr, Scott E407
Scherr, Marc D. E407
Scheschuk, Peter A721
Schettini, Marcio W191
Scheu, Greg W3
Scheuble, Larry A140
Scheuer, Mark P603
Scheuer, Albert W166
Scheuerman, Paul A838
Scheuermann, Rob A291
Scheuren, Jeffrey J. A369
Scheuring, Steve A25
Scheuring, Steve P15
Schewel, Michael A528
Schexnayder, Stephen P45
Schiavo, John Lo P654
Schiavone, Drew A341
Schiavone, Drew E153
Schick, Art A647
Schick, Brian A710
Schick, Jeffrey A770
Schickler, Renee P384
Schidlow, Daniel V. P165
Schiefelbein, Gregory A204
Schieffer, Margaret A423
Schienthal, Lawrence P306
Schierenbeck, Andreas W365
Schiesl, Troy P68
Schievelbein, Thomas A442
Schiffer, Meredith E140
Schiffer, Michael E140
Schillaci, Daniele W265
Schiller, Philip W. A70
Schiller, Steven C. A416
Schiller, Guy P417
Schiller, Lisa P459
Schilling, Grant A81
Schilling, Kathy P79
Schilling, Don P205
Schiltz, Christine A95
Schiltz, Christine P55
Schiltz, Richard P462
Schimkaitis, John R. E74
Schimmelmann, Wulf von W125
Schimmelpfennig, Katie P534
Schimmenti, Kathleen A532
Schindler, Peter A702
Schindler, David E276
Schinski, James E. (Jim) P554
Schipfer, John A659
Schipper, Heiko W258
Schippers, Harrie C.A.M. A629
Schiraldi, Richard J. A845
Schiraldi, Richard J. E413
Schiralli, Nicholas A108
Schiralli, Nicholas E35
Schireson, Kern A871
Schirf, Bill A115
Schirling, Kathleen A644
Schirm, Carla A827
Schissler, Corey A101
Schissler, Steve E613
Schiurba, John P688
Schjetnan, Chris A345
Schjetnan, Chris E154
Schlachter, Chris P566
Schlaegel, Les A507
Schlaegel, Les P288
Schlaff, Raymond C P363
Schlager, Debbie A81
Schlanger, Marvin O. A836
Schlapia, Jennifer P406
Schlappig, Michael A133
Schlarb, Ann M. E175
Schlebusch, Peter W339
Schlegel, John A568
Schleicher, David P183
Schleicher, Donald P284
Schleifer, Michaela A332
Schleifer, Leonard S. A698
Schleiff, Henry S. A269
Schlemmer, David P508
Schlemmer, Thomas P525
Schleper, Denny P127
Schlesinger, Ed A238

Schlesinger, Barry S. E231
Schleyer, Lorenzo Gazmuri W137
Schlicht, Monica A340
Schlicht, Monica E151
Schlichting, Warren W. A270
Schlichting, Nancy M. A413
Schlichting, Nancy M. P234
Schlichting, Nancy M P235
Schlieder, Debbie P687
Schlifske, John A493
Schlise, Sally M P537
Schlissel, Mark S. A698
Schlissel, Mark S. P456
Schlitz, Lei Zhang A450
Schloemer, Elizabeth A131
Schlonsky, Michael A. (Mike) A127
Schlosberg, Hilton H P351
Schloss, Eileen M. E268
Schlossberg, Therese A204
Schlosser, John W. A492
Schlosser, Mark A862
Schlosser, Rocky P345
Schlosser, Mark E419
Schlosstein, Ralph L. E136
Schlotman, J. Michael A496
Schlotterback, Ed A814
Schlotterback, Ed P616
Schlueter, Rick A295
Schlumberger, Allan P441
Schmaeling, Richard J. E127
Schmechel, Daniel J. (Dan) A289
Schmeltekopf, Mark A868
Schmeltz, Andy A649
Schmid, Larry A219
Schmid, Mark A. P609
Schmid, Richard J. P618
Schmid, Stefan W59
Schmid, Hans-Peter W125
Schmid, Justin E51
Schmidt, Franki A49
Schmidt, Paul A81
Schmidt, Darryl A98
Schmidt, Chris A126
Schmidt, Sonya A173
Schmidt, Dany A218
Schmidt, Benea A316
Schmidt, Derek A459
Schmidt, Jason A478
Schmidt, Greg A480
Schmidt, Dave A493
Schmidt, Steven A613
Schmidt, Lisa A677
Schmidt, Brian A838
Schmidt, Craig A851
Schmidt, David P27
Schmidt, Beth P141
Schmidt, Martin A. P313
Schmidt, Donald P396
Schmidt, Todd P399
Schmidt, Michael A P473
Schmidt, Mary P621
Schmidt, Darryl E33
Schmidt, Benea E141
Schmidt, Howard E342
Schmiegel, Brenda P237
Schmiegelow, Brent A835
Schmit, Jim A185
Schmitt, Paul A813
Schmitt, Michael P92
Schmitt, Peggy P387
Schmitt, Paul P616
Schmitt, Christophe W148
Schmittlein, David C. P313
Schmitz, Jackie A541
Schmitz, Bonnie R P12
Schmitz, Tina P272
Schmitz, Kurt P437
Schmitz, Rolf Martin W315
Schmitz, Jackie E266
Schmoll, Brooke D P158
Schmoll, David N. P432
Schmotzer, Mark P296
Schmoyer, Ben A718
Schmucker, Clint E348
Schmukler, Louis S. (Lou) A147

A = AMERICAN BUSINESS
E = EMERGING COMPANIES
P = PRIVATE COMPANIES
W = WORLD BUSINESS

Schnabolk, Maureen A533
Schnall, Mitchell P599
Schnalzer, Michael A131
Schnatz, Rebecca P685
Schnautz, Tom A597
Schneck-Last, Vivian A746
Schneeberger, Carol A. A645
Schneeberger, Carol A. E329
Schneider, Richard E. (Rick) A62
Schneider, Neal C. A213
Schneider, Janelle A223
Schneider, Glenn P A268
Schneider, Donald R. (Donny) A355
Schneider, Kevin D. A382
Schneider, Ryan A478
Schneider, Michael A489
Schneider, Mark K. A548
Schneider, Allen A562
Schneider, Robert A631
Schneider, Elise A691
Schneider, Steve A722
Schneider, Rachel A736
Schneider, Barry T. A768
Schneider, Ken A778
Schneider, Mike A796
Schneider, Richard P A796
Schneider, Amy A855
Schneider, Martin P107
Schneider, Bruce P207
Schneider, Cole P207
Schneider, Robert P273
Schneider, Mark K. P321
Schneider, Debra P338
Schneider, Bill P396
Schneider, Jennifer S. P472
Schneider, Steve P474
Schneider, James P481
Schneider, Donna P481
Schneider, Rachel P492
Schneider, Trena P541
Schneider, Chris P628
Schneider, Roger E P660
Schneider, Michael W58
Schneider, Sven W223
Schneider, Ulf M. (Mark) W258
Schneider, Bernie E104
Schneider, Kathryn E268
Schneider, Allen E279
Schnel, Jonah A97
Schnel, Jonah E32
Schnell, Karen P631
Schnettler, Gary A332
Schneyer, Mark A649
Schnider, Maureen P590
Schnieders, Kurt J. A264
Schnieders, Kurt A497
Schnirring, Greg P143
Schnitz, Chad A13
Schnitzer, Alan D. A827
Schnorr, Joseph A105
Schnorr, Roger A616
Schnuck, Craig D. P616
Schnupp, Craig M A867
Schnur, Frank A49
Schnurbusch, Shawnda A878
Schnurr, Russ A332
Schoch, Dave L. (Dave) A362
Schoch, Manfred W59
Schock, Dan A489
Schock, Larry P126
Schodde, Joseph P243
Schoebel, Richard K. E355
Schoelen, Karen P546
Schoellkopf, Leah A131
Schoemer, Richard P8
Schoen, Michelle A412
Schoen, Colin P218
Schoen, Thomas E78
Schoen, Anthony A. (Tony) E160

Schoen, Michelle E192
Schoen, Jeffrey S. E319
Schoenecker, Melissa A865
Schoenfeld, Lynnette A20
Schoening, Lisa P533
Schoening, Bill E40
Schoepp, Jan Rune P185
Schoessow, Jean P134
Schoettle, Ryan A68
Schoettlin, Kathy A. A614
Schoetz, Nathan A886
Schoetz, Nathan E433
Scholefield, Jim A592
Scholefield, Michael W120
Scholes, John A490
Scholhamer, James P. (Jim) E408
Scholl, Jonathan W. A505
Scholl, Barbara P93
Scholten, Gary P. A668
Scholten, Danielle E P290
Scholz, James E397
Schomburg, Rick A480
Schonacher, Bill A459
Schooler, Richard D P206
Schoolmaster, F. Andrew P560
Schooner, Doug E286
Schoonmaker, Jonathan A461
Schoonman, Gerbert A417
Schoonover, Mark A. A879
Schott, Brian A724
Schott, Stevan R. P90
Schott, Greg P356
Schottenstein, Robert H. E253
Schowalter, Linda G P551
Schoy, Deborah P576
Schrader, Jon A316
Schrader, Bill A417
Schrader, Tom A905
Schrader, Cheryl B. P647
Schrader, Tom P694
Schrader, Jon E141
Schram, Jacob W20
Schramm, Bernie A330
Schramm, James A351
Schramm, Christine M P611
Schramm, James E158
Schranz, Joe P630
Schreck, Eric W. A831
Schreck, Edward E20
SCHRECK, TED E20
Schreiber, Steve Schreiber Steve A369
Schreiber, Michelle A413
Schreiber, Steven A528
Schreiber, Pam A861
Schreiber, Edward P. (Ed) A919
Schreiber, Michelle P234
Schreiber, Nicolette P446
Schreiber, Pam P658
Schreiner, Steve Deb A3
Schreiner, Mark A693
Schreiner, Teri P114
Schreiner, Jeff P604
Schrenker, Jessica A288
Schreuder, Jana R. A599
Schriber, David A593
Schriber, Alan P36
Schrider, Daniel J. (Dan) A724
Schrimpf, Chris A408
Schriner, Ann P147
Schrobilgen, Steve A878
Schroder, Rod P30
Schroeder, Frank A263
Schroeder, Linda A369
Schroeder, Mark A. A384
Schroeder, John A384
Schroeder, F A513
Schroeder, Tracey A531
Schroeder, John A557
Schroeder, Bob A599
Schroeder, Ann A600
Schroeder, Lisa A780
Schroeder, Mary A861
Schroeder, Sam A917
Schroeder, Heather P51
Schroeder, Tammy P109

Schroeder, Glenn P175
Schroeder, Scott P462
Schroeder, Arthur P473
Schroeder, Mary P658
Schroeder, Mark A. E176
Schroeder, John E176
Schroepfer, Michael (Mike) A314
Schroeter, Martin J. A460
Schromm, William A. (Bill) A620
Schu, George A140
SCHUBE, JARRETT A390
Schubert, Julann A788
Schubert, Gail P69
Schubert, Fred E298
Schuchter, Douglas A332
Schuckman, Matthew P213
Schuele, Alan R. E78
Schueler, Kevin P580
Schueller, Gayle A3
Schuemann, Hollyn A871
Schuerman, Janice P339
Schuessler, Gregory P666
Schuette, Matt A676
Schuette, Matthew A677
Schug, Wayne P342
Schuh, Michele A352
Schuh, Jeffrey A701
Schuitema, Kurt A377
Schukar, Shawn E. A42
Schuler, Al A295
Schuler, Tatum A729
Schuler, David R P622
Schuler, Roland W60
Schulhof, Michael P. E226
Schull, Thomas E A262
Schuller, Jeffrey E140
Schulman, Melissa A250
Schulman, Irv A272
Schulman, Daniel H. (Dan) A778
Schulman, Edward M. (Ted) E26
Schulte, Ted A25
Schulte, Ted P15
Schulte, David J. E95
Schulte-Bockum, Jens W389
Schultes, Alex P398
Schultz, Steve A258
Schultz, Kent A295
Schultz, Rob A351
Schultz, Kevin J A355
Schultz, John F. A418
Schultz, Anthony A429
Schultz, Jeff A432
Schultz, John A460
Schultz, Katie A522
Schultz, John M. A561
Schultz, Linda A576
Schultz, Teri A674
Schultz, Howard A. A763
Schultz, David A855
Schultz, Tatiana P298
Schultz, Joshua P417
Schultz, Jason P473
Schultz, Ted P556
Schultz, Gus P567
Schultz, Danielle P603
Schultz, Diane P620
Schultz, Michael P637
Schultz, Michael P644
Schultz, K-- re W363
Schultz, Rob E158
Schultz, Thomas E190
Schultz, John M. E279
Schultz, Linda E297
Schultz, Alan E421
Schultze, Lisa A827
Schulz, Mitch A213
Schulz, Eric A318
Schulz, Lance A512
Schulz, David S (Dave) A888
Schulz, Ekkehard D. W231
Schulze, Gregory A311
Schulze, Trevor A559
Schulzke, Mario P647
Schumacher, Laura J. A6
Schumacher, Michael A82

Schumacher, Hans A101
Schumacher, Larry A171
Schumacher, Laura A374
Schumacher, John A422
Schumacher, Jermoe A786
Schumacher, Michael P49
Schumacher, Larry P100
Schumacher, John P239
Schumacher, Sue Ellen P440
Schumacher, Darren A. E174
Schuman, Theresa A108
Schuman, Scott A175
Schuman, Theresa E35
Schumann, Robert E1
Schumer, Matthew P202
Schuneman, Damen P395
Schupp, Rudy E. A868
Schur, Adam A568
Schur, Thomas P A647
Schurmeier, L Jon P516
Schurr, Daniel A194
Schuster, Andre A538
Schuster, Chris A917
Schuster, Mark P118
Schuster, Francis B. (Frank) P507
Schuster, Chris P701
Schutt, Paul A33
Schutt, Douglas W. (Doug) A240
Schutt, Cherie P577
Schutts, William A85
Schutze, Heinrich A131
Schutzer, Michael A. A500
Schutzer, Michael A. E237
Schuur, Hendrik P671
Schuyler, Matthew W. (Matt) A421
Schuyler, Joe A761
Schvartsman, Fabio W385
Schwab, Susan A531
Schwab, Stefanie A584
Schwab, Jessica P511
Schwab, Joe P667
Schwab, Peter W389
Schwab, Gisela M. E138
Schwab, Holger E283
Schwab-Pomerantz, Carrie P486
Schwabe, Stefan K. F. E391
Schwabero, Mark D. A151
Schwager, Charles A492
Schwager, Charles P366
Schwager, Harald W55
Schwalje, Linda A767
Schwallier, Jerry L. A412
Schwallier, Jerry L. E192
Schwalm, Laura P208
Schwan, Cindy A589
Schwan, Severin W307
Schwandt, Stephanie A247
Schwandt, Stephanie E103
Schwaneke, Jeffrey A A179
Schwaneke, Jeffrey A A180
Schwar, Bill A916
Schwartz, Carol A49
Schwartz, Bart R. A83
Schwartz, George G. A142
Schwartz, Gil A175
Schwartz, Eugene A201
Schwartz, Joel A213
Schwartz, David A368
Schwartz, Harvey M. A389
Schwartz, Mitchell A448
Schwartz, Jay A469
Schwartz, Jill A640
Schwartz, Kathy A700
Schwartz, David A736
Schwartz, Melinda A774
Schwartz, Steven A818
Schwartz, Joel A866
Schwartz, Raymond P20
Schwartz, Jordana P372
Schwartz, Marvin H P399
Schwartz, James K P400
Schwartz, Brian P467
Schwartz, David P586
Schwartz, George P586
Schwartz, Vernon B. E226

Schwartz, Bob E383
Schwartzwald, Karen P622
Schwarz, Konrad A163
Schwarz, Douglas A480
Schwarz, Ronald E. (Ron) A499
Schwarz, David A658
Schwarz, Anthony A685
Schwarz, Tony A685
Schwarz, Diane K. A804
Schwarz, Barbara P117
Schwarz, Amy P333
Schwarz, Ronald E. (Ron) E237
Schwarzbach, Fred A585
Schwarzbach, Fred P377
Schwarzenbach, Jamie A920
Schwarzman, Stephen A. A132
Schwarzman, Stephen A. A133
Schwarzman, Randy A332
Schwebel, Gerardo (Gerald) A459
Schwedler, David A2
Schweer, Kevin P677
Schweiger, Werner J. A307
Schweinfurth, Ralph A456
Schweinhart, Martin G. (Marty) A227
Schweitzer, Jeffrey M A862
Schweitzer, Ashley P30
Schweitzer, Jeffrey M E419
Schwender, Jim E256
Schwerdtle, Willi W8
Schwertner, Raymond D. E57
Schwertner, Ray E57
Schwimmer, Howard A708
Schwimmer, Howard P459
Schwimmer, Howard E356
Schwind, Bill A729
Schwinn, Debra P611
SCHWIZER, PAOLA GINA
    MARIA W111
Schwoyer, Alyse P364
Sch-ofer, Wolfgang W108
Sch-oferkordt, Anke W62
Schüler, Lutz W222
Schürmann, Franz-Josef W7
Schütz, Roland W124
Sciame-Giesecke, Susan P627
Sciammas, Maurice E284
Sciara, Craig A412
Sciara, Craig E192
Scibienski, Sean A838
Scicchitano, Edward P306
Sciortino, Cathy L P143
Sciortino, John E P381
Sclama, Anthony P204
Scobie, Alistair A502
Scofield, Melissa A868
Scoglio, Dave P544
Scogna, Stephen O. P396
Sconzo, Guy M P243
Scopelliti, Joseph A P602
Scotch, Peter A644
Scott, Walter A13
Scott, Benson A25
Scott, Dina A101
Scott, Dwight A132
Scott, Andrew A132
Scott, Jim A165
Scott, Cheryl A173
Scott, Abigal A207
Scott, Phil A321
Scott, James R. A349
Scott, Matthew A407
Scott, Stuart L. A439
Scott, David A449
Scott, Raymond E. (Ray) A503
Scott, Richard W. A520
Scott, Curtis A550
Scott, William A558
Scott, Wesley A611
Scott, Dan A649
Scott, Gina A655
Scott, Steve A655
Scott, Dennis A720
Scott, Randy A738
Scott, Vernon A743
Scott, Julie A750

Scott, Godwin A762
Scott, Cameron A. A842
Scott, Frank A844
Scott, David C. A851
Scott, Anthony A904
Scott, Steve A914
Scott, Benson P15
Scott, Thomas W. P107
Scott, Yvonne P149
Scott, Bh P222
Scott, Anne P261
Scott, Christine P279
Scott, Nancy P284
Scott, Currie P343
Scott, Douglas P450
Scott, Peter M. P458
Scott, Dee P573
Scott, David P628
Scott, Steven M. P642
Scott, Stephanie P662
Scott, Jeralynn P680
Scott, Brian M. E17
Scott, Nancy E47
Scott, David E75
Scott, Brandon E117
Scott, Phil E144
Scott, James R. E156
Scott, Gina E333
Scott, Steve E333
Scott, Dennis E362
Scott, Vernon E373
Scott, Frank E412
Scott, Anthony E442
Scott-Morgan, Peggy A645
Scott-Morgan, Peggy E329
Scottberg, Paul A815
Scotti, Laurie Ann A513
Scozzafava, Ralph P. A258
Scranton, Alec B. P611
Screnar, Ryan T A387
Screnar, Ryan T E177
Scribner, Kent P201
Scribner, Dr Kent P P428
Scribner, Scott P545
Scribner, Matt E217
Scripter, Jay E401
Scrivner, Dana P578
Scroggins, Judy P154
Scudder, Michael L. A351
Scudder, Daniel P23
Scudder, Michael L. E158
Scullans, Greg A764
Scullin, Liza A49
Scullin, Matt A866
Scully, Timothy A407
Scully, Tom A582
Scully, Jodi A758
Scully, Diane P211
Scully, Tom P373
Scully, Jodi P519
Scyphers, Mike A528
Sczygelski, Sidney P48
Seabaugh, Greg A58
Seabaugh, Greg E16
Seabold, Jeffrey T. A97
Seabold, Jeffrey T. E32
Seabright, Jefferson A215
Seabrooks, Nettie P577
Seabury, Bryan A175
Seade, Héctor Slim W25
Seagle, Brenda P490
Seago, Leigh A446
Seago, Leigh E210
Seagraves, Rhonda A219
Seagraves, Rhonda E84
Seale, Willie A591
Sealey, Stephanie A222
Seals, Paul A56
Sealy, Rawle A481
Sealy, James P525
Seaman, John A A156
Seaman, Oliver A671
Seamons, Jennifer A489
Sear, Steve A261
Searle, Nigel A313

Searle, Mark P44
Searles, Sean P361
Sears, Steven A353
Sears, James A. A355
Sears, Peter J. (Pete) A445
Sears, Kathy A572
Sears, Mark A676
Sears, Melissa P518
Seasock, Scott A646
Seasock, Scott E330
Seastone, Bj A56
Seat, David M. A98
Seat, David M. E33
Seaton, Timothy A204
Seaton, Mark E. A335
Seaton, Charlee A339
Seaton, David T A358
Seaton, Doris P343
Seaton, Scott P522
Seaton, Charlee E150
Seaver, Michael L. A644
Seaver, David P567
Seavers, Dean S. W255
Seavey, Darryl A693
Seavey, Thomas E193
Seawell, Katie A763
Sebade, Steve A223
Sebastian, Joe A25
Sebastian, Lesley A478
Sebastian, Kathy P2
Sebastian, Joe P15
Sebastian, Kellie P560
Sebastian, Greg E404
Sebbar, Sa--d W214
Sebring, Jason E368
Secchia, Rick A195
Secchia, Richard A195
Sechin, Igor Ivanovich W187
Sechrist, Paul W. E83
Seck, Wai Kwong A766
Seckinger, Mark P405
Secofsky, Martin P308
Secor, Mark E. A431
Secor, Mark E. E205
Secord, Greg L. E163
Secrest, Brent A303
Sedey, Ray P318
Sedgwick, Alexander A784
Sedgwick, David E125
Sedicino, Dominic A639
Sedicino, Dominic E325
Sedigh, Massoud A906
Sedlacek, Lanie A838
Sedlak, Andrea P682
See, Jonathan P423
Seeberger, Mark A244
Seedig, Landry E17
Seedorf, Herman A638
Seeger, Laureen E. A49
Seeger, Michael A87
Seeger, Rick A155
Seeger, Brian P467
Seeger, Britta W114
Seekely, Martin S P404
Seelbach, Hugh P620
Seele, Rainer W276
Seeley, William A150
Seeley, Connie P410
Seese, Matthew E47
Sefcik, Deborah A446
Sefcik, Deborah E210
Sefzik, Peter L. A221
Segal, Daniel P744
Segal, Nancy A175
Segal, David P369
Segal, Julian W78
Segal, Jeremy E248
Segall, Peter P355
Segrave, Frank A878
Sehgal, Vikas E123
Sehi, John P230
Sehring, Robert P411
Seianna, Apollonia P487
Seibel, Douglas A9
Seibel, Donald J. (Don) A319

Seibert, Jim A277
Seibly, Stephen P495
Seidel, Dave A671
Seidel, Andrew P474
Seiden, Michael A546
Seiden, William P390
Seidl, Jane P537
Seidler, Rick P252
Seidman, Phyllis P145
Seidman, Lawrence B. E90
Seifert, James J. (Jim) A289
Seikaly, Myra P148
Seike, Kouichi W353
Seiler, David R. A340
Seiler, Dawn A671
Seiler, David R. E151
Seim, Robin G. (Rob) E316
Seino, Satoshi W132
Seip, Jan P2
Seitz, James R. A1
Seitze, David A244
Seivold, Stephen A902
Seivold, Stephen P693
Seiwell, Kevin P64
Sejas, Cynthia A721
Sejling, Klaus R. W1
Sekely, Larry E253
Sekerka, Robert P96
Sekhri, Vishal P316
Seki, Masaki W86
Seki, Daisuke W182
Seki, Hiroshi W182
Seki, Jun W265
SEKI, MITSUYOSHI W400
Sekine, Toshitaka W48
Sekizawa, Yukio W28
Sekkaki, Nicolas A461
Sekmakas, Viktoras R. A664
Selden, Thomas A P516
Selders, Sean A857
Seldon, Eric B. A18
Sele, Tim A136
Seleznev, Kirill Gennadievich W289
Selfa, Joan A449
Selfridge, Michael D. (Mike) A353
Selian, Paul J. A766
Seligman, Garry A P333
Seligman, Heather L P392
Seligsohn, Sherwin I. E417
Sell, Bernhard A456
Sell, David P342
Sell, Robert E. (Bob) W5
Sellers, Nicholas A27
Sellers, Mary E. A102
Sellers, Mary E. A103
Sellers, Ronnie A316
Sellers, Ronnie P191
Selley, Clive W76
Selling, Greg A872
Sellinger, Howard L A428
Sellitto, Gayle A101
Sellmger, James P526
Selman, Mark E426
Selmo, Pete P567
Selosse, Eric P326
Selquist, Curtis M. (Curt) E360
Selsor, Darlene A244
Seltz, Peter A669
Selvaraj, Shelly A355
Selwood, Robert C. A558
Selwood, Jim A912
Seman, Gerald A640
Semaneza, Peter P353
Semba, Sho W349
Semeniuk, Nicholas P420
Semet, Gardner A109
Semet, Gardner E36
Semik, Edward A904
Semik, Edward E442
Semke, Audrey P161
Semmens, Mark A387
Semmens, Mark E177
Semmes, Ben E286
Semmler, Carl A512
Semrad, Carrie E59

A = AMERICAN BUSINESS
E = EMERGING COMPANIES
P = PRIVATE BUSINESS
W = WORLD BUSINESS

Sen, Peder C P695
Sen, Michael W331
Sen-Gupta, Prabir A113
Sence, John A371
Sencel, Michael P207
Senecal, Craig P598
Senel, Aydin W377
Senevy, Steven P201
Seng, Hock W160
Senge, James (Jim) E116
Senger, Joe A251
Sengul, Oguz A773
Sengul, Oguz E387
Senker, T. J. A548
Senker, T. J. P321
Senna, Joseph A184
Senner, Christopher J. (Chris) E138
Sennott, John L. (Jack) A30
Senroy, Sid A129
Sensibaugh, Barbara A A345
Sensing, J. Steven (Steve) A718
Senske, Thomas A97
Seo, Kate M P101
Seok-Hui, Lee W332
Seong, Chan W384
Sepulveda, Kirk P361
Sepulveda, Juan P445
Sepulveda, Liliana P700
Sep--lveda, Eli S. A661
Sequeira, Ramona W355
Sequin, Donny P486
Serafino, Joseph A417
Serbun, Joseph A225
Serbun, Joe A225
Serbun, Joseph E88
Serbun, Joe E88
Serck-Hanssen, Harald W129
Sereda, Peter L. A794
Sereni, Judy A158
Serge, Adrian A533
Sergesketter, Randy A260
Serianni, Charles F. (Chuck) A707
Serio, Catherine P231
Serivano, Kenneth P464
Serkes, Jeffrey A461
Serkes, Jeffrey David P350
Sermersheim, Meagan A621
Serna, Michelle A904
Serna, Michelle E442
Serniak, Jay A105
Seroka, Gene P433
Seroux, Henri E256
Serpico, Robert M P63
Serpico, Robert P63
Serpico, Donna P498
Serracin, Linda A272
SERRANO, SHERRY A103
Serrano, Jose Fernando Fernando A218
Serrano, Angela P391
Serrantino, John P188
Serrato, Michael A324
Serrato, Pedro P177
Serricchio, Michael A532
Serros, Joanne A869
Serth, Mike E167
Servello, Aldo P121
Serven, Neal A405
Servodidio, Mark J. A92
Sesana, Marco W32
Seshadri, Raj A537
Seshadri, Sridhar P538
Session, Tracy A81
Seth, Ajay A423
Sethi, Naresh W74
Sethna, Meenal A. E247
Setiawan, Rico W195
Setliff, William A493
Setliff, Will A493
Setlock, Brandon A729

Setnik, Gary P353
Seto, Kinya W223
Seto, Shinichirou W329
Seto, Henry E428
Settembri, Marco W258
Settersten, Scott M A836
Settin, John A115
Settle, Peggy A635
Settle, Judy P398
Settle, Peggy P419
Settle, Diane P483
Setubal, Alfredo Egydio W191
Setzer, Nikolai W108
Seu, Patty P172
Seuferer, Kevin A47
Seung-won, Kang W265
Seurynck, Michael A796
Severance, Matthew P94
Severance, Janna R P439
Severance, Matthew P465
Severance, William E339
Severiano, Gilda P201
Severino, Michael E. A6
Severino, Vittorio M. A437
Severn, Colin T. E252
Severson, Suzanne P223
Severson, Shawn M P316
Sevier, Vincent P592
Sevil, Murat A647
Sevilla, Gene A718
Sevilla-Sacasa, Eugenio A718
Sevimli, Ahmet P358
Seward, Andrew A729
Seward, Robert P334
Sewell, D. Bruce A70
Sewell, Michael J. (Mike) A196
Sewell, David B. A738
Sewell, Mike P222
Sewell, Denise P672
Sewll, Glenn A897
Sewll, Glenn P687
Sexauer, Pam P466
Sexton, Ellen A855
Sexton, Scott A917
Seymour, Chris A273
Seymour, Chris P162
Seze, Amaury de W294
Sfeir, David P516
Sferrazza, Bob A163
Sferrazza, Jillian P283
Sformo, Todd P640
Sgaglione, Lucille T. A122
Sgro, Gianfranco W212
Shaari, Bahren W280
Shabalala, Sandile W256
Shabshab, Nabil A119
Shaby, Dave E46
Shackelford, Larry P675
Shackelford, Lary P676
Shackell, Daniel A242
Shackelton, David E339
Shackelton, Christopher S. (Chris) E339
Shaddix, Mike A878
Shade, Michael A537
Shade, Darren A881
Shadel, Brooke P331
Shadid, Sean A98
Shadid, Sean E33
Shadix, Michelle A693
Shadle, Roger P546
Shadmani, Mike A537
Shae, Kate A313
Shaeffer, Carrie P61
Shaevsky, Mark P692
Shafer, Jennifer A51
Shafer, Thomas C. (Tom) A187
Shafer, Walter F. A654
Shafer, Walt A654
Shafer, Michael A815
Shafer, Joan M. A884
Shafer, Jennifer P33
Shafer, Michael P72
Shafer, Thomas C. (Tom) E71
Shaff, Karen E. A668

Shaffer, Dennis G A208
Shaffer, Richard A348
Shaffer, Michael A. (Mike) A682
Shaffer, Charles M. (Chuck) A731
Shaffer, Kellie P99
Shaffer, Stephen P152
Shaffer, Jeff E322
Shaffer, Doug E349
Shaffer, Charles M. (Chuck) E365
Shagoury, Antoine A766
Shah, Manan A67
Shah, Ken A163
Shah, Manish A227
Shah, Tejas A445
Shah, Sanjiv A456
Shah, Raheel A A456
Shah, Asin A478
Shah, Aarti A511
Shah, Sejal A539
Shah, Ashish A649
Shah, Neal H A657
Shah, Rajen A766
Shah, Pratik A877
Shah, Chethan P126
Shah, Mayank P236
Shah, Hemant P274
Shah, Veeral P479
Shah, Neil H. E195
Shah, Jay H. E195
Shah, Hasu P. E195
Shahane, Dinesh E119
Shaheen, Gabriel L. A430
Shaheen, George T. E235
Shahid, Mohammad P496
Shahin, Gus W151
Shahna, Reilly A655
Shahna, Reilly E333
Shahrestani, Navid A777
Shahrestani, Navid E393
Shahzad, Ali P568
Shaibani, H E Mohammad Ibrahim Abdulrahman Al W130
Shaibel, Ruvi W151
Shaik, Khaja A767
Shaik, Shalina P643
Shaker, Mark P340
Shaker, Mark P439
Shaker, Elizabeth P531
Shaker, Marcus S P626
Shakman, Alice P632
Shala, Chet P269
Shalin, Dmitri P370
Shalowitz, Richard E383
Shamber, Mark E. A756
Shamberger, Rick A865
Shamblin, Annette A115
Shamburger, Julie N. A754
Shamburger, Mike A784
Shamburger, Julie N. E380
Shames, David M P599
Shamilov, Sarah P414
Shamir, Nachum E250
Shamloo, Brenda A115
Shammo, Brian A25
Shammo, Brian P15
Shamseddine, Adel A877
Shamsuarov, Azat W290
Shan, Tan Su W119
Shanahan, Patrick M. (Pat) A136
Shanbhag, Santosh E428
Shang, Mark A143
Shank, Melissa A784
Shankar, Ram A313
Shanks, Robert L. (Bob) A362
Shanks, Alan A835
Shanks, Karen P292
Shannon, John A198
Shannon, Albert A244
Shannon, Sean C A311
Shannon, Johnathan A487
Shannon, Robert E P123
Shannon, Nicole P466
Shannon, Daniel (Dan) E268
Shanteau, Kelly A244
Shaoyong, Liu W89

Shapard, Robert A505
Shaper, Park P431
Shaper, Park P495
Shapira, Adrianne A493
Shapira, Freida P601
Shapiro, Glenn T. A33
Shapiro, Marc A520
Shapiro, Jodi A570
Shapiro, Steve A693
Shapiro, Loretta A737
Shapiro, Steven D. A859
Shapiro, Steven P94
Shapiro, Louis P376
Shapiro, Robert S. (Bob) P390
Shapiro, Morton O. P397
Shapiro, Lawrence B. P503
Shapiro, Larry J. P616
Shapiro, Steven D. P652
Shapiro, Ronald M. E90
Shapiro, Eric E250
Shapiro, Loretta E367
Shapiro, David T. E424
Shara, Thomas J. A499
Shara, Thomas J. E237
Sharan, Nitesh A593
Share, Christopher J. P116
Share, Douglas G. P116
Sharff, Rich P485
Sharieff, Ghazala P488
Sharkawi, Mohamed A200
Sharkey, Michael D. A541
Sharkey, Andrew A703
Sharkey, Allan P456
Sharkey, Michael D. E266
Sharma, Amit A55
Sharma, Ashish A131
Sharma, Vishal A289
Sharma, Roger P122
Sharma, Anupindi P279
Sharma, Madan M P297
Sharma, Harwinder P314
Sharma, Hirsh P619
Sharma, Annette K P675
Sharma, Mahendra Kumar W181
Sharma, Ritesh E10
Sharma, Manu E123
Sharman, Sandy W80
Sharman, James A. (Jim) E381
Sharng, Chris T. E295
Sharon, Bodi S P620
Sharp, Bruce A115
Sharp, M. S. (Scott) A192
Sharp, Robert T. (Bob) A295
Sharp, John A333
Sharp, Erin S. A496
Sharp, Ken A505
Sharp, Rob A676
Sharp, Garland A729
Sharp, John F P75
Sharp, M. S. (Scott) P112
Sharp, Ashlee P191
Sharp, Mike P210
Sharp, Scott P256
Sharp, Linda P424
Sharp, Larry P460
Sharp, Christopher (Topher) P538
Sharp, Chris E107
Sharp, James P. E171
Sharp, Ed E371
Sharpe, Stacy A33
Sharpe, Jeff A187
Sharpe, Matthew P. A430
Sharpe, Mikel A869
Sharpe, Eric P151
Sharpe, Rebakah P172
Sharpe, Ben W8
Sharpe, Jeff E71
Sharpless, Walt A782
Sharr, Michael A402
Shashoua, Stanley A744
Shattock, Matthew J. (Matt) W349
Shattuck, Mayo A. A309
Shattuck, Mayo A A310
Shattuck, Carol P220
Shatzer, Warren A13

Shaughnessy, Amy A247
Shaughnessy, Diane A541
Shaughnessy, Michael A695
Shaughnessy, Gary W405
Shaughnessy, Amy E103
Shaughnessy, Diane E266
Shaughnessy, Michael E290
Shaukat, Tariq M. A36
Shaukat, Tariq M A157
Shaul, Tom P344
Shaver, David A844
Shaver, Jessica P433
Shaver, David E412
Shaviv, Elad A200
Shaw, Anthony A28
Shaw, G W A84
Shaw, Paula A107
Shaw, Jennifer A135
Shaw, Kenneth A136
Shaw, Keri-Lynne A241
Shaw, Amy A262
Shaw, Angela A314
Shaw, Chris A346
Shaw, Robert K. A395
Shaw, Bruce A423
Shaw, William A489
Shaw, Christi A511
Shaw, Alan H. A597
Shaw, Jeff M. A609
Shaw, Lynn T A693
Shaw, Craig W. A833
Shaw, Marliese L A846
Shaw, Anthony P17
Shaw, Jennifer P78
Shaw, Angela P189
Shaw, Jim P451
Shaw, Keeasha P563
Shaw, Craig W P630
Shaw, Jen Day P642
Shaw, Rebecca P696
Shaw, Gene P701
Shaw, G. Alan W3
Shaw, Nicola W255
Shaw, Paula E34
Shaw, Joanne E147
Shaw, Byron E174
Shaw, Douglas E286
Shaw, Marliese E414
Shawah, Paul E426
Shawver, Deborah P444
Shay, Troy A364
Shay, Kaaren De P187
Shay, Lawrence F. E222
Shaye, Gary P485
Shayegi, Cameron A840
Shea, Kevin A122
Shea, Phil A328
Shea, E. Stewart A446
Shea, Brian A644
Shea, David A819
Shea, Molly A893
Shea, William P88
Shea, Cheryl P145
Shea, Dennis P155
Shea, Agnes A P339
Shea, William E. E1
Shea, Bill E1
Shea, Jonathan E140
Shea, John E189
Shea, E. Stewart E210
Sheaffer, Paul A133
Sheahan, Denis K. A159
Sheahan, Jim A330
Shear, Neal A. A189
Shearan, Kevin W98
Sheard, Paul A721
Sheard, Janeen P575
Shearer, Alan P681
Shearer, Mark E298
Shearrow, Brian E81
Shears, Mark A406
Shebik, Steven E. (Steve) A33
Shebik, Steven E. (Steve) A34
Sheckley, Chris A676
Shedd, Scott E57

Shedlin, Gary S. A130
Sheedy, William M. (Bill) A874
Sheedy, Linda L P400
Sheehan, John F. A25
Sheehan, John A83
Sheehan, Paul A101
Sheehan, Meghan A109
Sheehan, Bill A133
Sheehan, Tom A295
Sheehan, Daniel J. (Dan) A382
Sheehan, James N. A432
Sheehan, Richard A584
Sheehan, Rosemary R A635
Sheehan, John F. P15
Sheehan, Dennis P91
Sheehan, Arlene P300
Sheehan, Nancy P330
Sheehan, Rosemary R P419
Sheehan, Diane Dudas P457
Sheehan, Meghan E36
Sheeley, Michael J. A847
Sheely, Lori P101
Sheeran, Nathan P269
Sheers, Matthew A270
Sheets, Brian P233
Sheets, Roger P505
Sheets, John W. E18
Sheets, Brett E426
Shefcik, James A175
Sheffield, Kenneth H. A657
Sheffield, Scott D. A657
Sheftel, Edward A448
Shehadi, Ramez A140
Shehee, Virginia K P75
Sheinbaum, Gary A682
Sheinheit, Alvin A555
Sheinkin, Ari A461
Shekar, A. W274
Shekarabi, Bonnie E336
Shelby, Bryan A133
Sheldon, Tim A530
Sheldon, Matthew A575
Sheldon, Todd N. A681
Sheldon, Donald P428
Sheldon, Nicole P478
Sheldon, Lyle E P645
Sheldon, Lyle E P660
Sheldon, D. Scott E11
Sheline, Steve P149
Shell, Yvonne A438
Shell, Ellen P80
Shell, Jonathan D P183
Shell, Susan P626
Shell-Lamore, Gina P440
Shelley, Bill A862
Shelley, Art A869
Shelley, Alexa P478
Shelley, Bill E419
Shelley-Kessler, Pamela J. (Pam) E249
Shelowitz, Rachel A241
Shelter, Rolando Zubir--n W18
Shelton, Doug A484
Shelton, Roland A614
Shelton, Afton A658
Shelton, Roy A863
Shelton, Jean P106
Shelton, John A P158
Shelton, Mary P480
Shelton, M. Dwight P669
Shelton, Suzanne P669
Shelton, Todd P696
Shelton, Russell E293
Shen, Sam A507
Shen, Sam P288
Shen, Kyle P610
Shen, Jerry W35
Shen, Heting W240
Shen, David W395
Shendell-Falik, Nancy P65
Sheneman, Gary A835
Shengdong, Zhang W401
Shenk, Robert G. A276
Shenkar, Alex A774
Shenkin, Kerri A105
Shenoy, Navin A456

Shepard, Gerald A163
Shepard, Ann A171
Shepard, Sean A195
Shepard, Andrew A218
Shepard, Donald A243
Shepard, Randall A614
Shepard, Ann P100
Shepard, Janet P109
Shepard, Ken P293
Shepardson, Andrew P68
Sheperd, David A905
Sheperd, David P694
Shepheard, Hillary P561
Shepherd, Michael A382
Shepherd, Alison A486
Shepherd, Julie P233
Shepherd, Richard P275
Shepherd, Mary P395
Shepherd, Rick P430
Shepherd, Jane P682
Shepler, Jody A342
Sheppard, Valarie A671
Sheppard, Ben A729
Sheppard, Brooke P359
Sheppard, Dennis P522
Sheppard, William D P522
Sheppard, Ben P611
Sher, Susan S. P611
Shera, Gina A481
Sherbin, Robert A607
Sherer, Matt P554
Sheridan, Tom A25
Sheridan, William A201
Sheridan, Jean E A599
Sheridan, Rachel A644
Sheridan, Jerry E. A836
Sheridan, Philip A904
Sheridan, Tom P15
Sheridan, Chris P98
Sheridan, Richard P488
Sheridan, John P. P576
Sheridan, Patrick P671
Sheridan, Philip E442
Sherif, Tarek A. E268
Sherin, Jonathan P671
Sherlock, Lori P682
Sherman, Ronald A85
Sherman, Jeffrey S. A119
Sherman, Catherine A162
Sherman, Patrick A350
Sherman, Michael (Mike) A380
Sherman, Peter A619
Sherman, Debbie P81
Sherman, Karen P284
Sherman, Mark P488
Sherman, Diane P538
Sherman, Gail P603
Sherman, Malcolm L P628
Sherman, William E78
Sherman, Patrick E157
Sherman, Larry E175
Sherr, Richard A637
Sherrard, Roger S. A634
Sherras, Brian E23
Sherrill, Gregg M. A796
Sherrill, Stephen C. E29
Sherron, Tammy P96
Sherry, Bernie P619
Shertzer, Teresa P277
Sherwin, R Lawrence P520
Sherwood, Ben A272
Sherwood, Charles H. E18
Sherwood-Wetherwax, Joan A522
Shetty, Prajwal Shetty Prajwal A101
Shetye, Rajesh (Raj) E244
Shevchik, Joan A196
Shevsky, David A35
Sheynblat, Len A685
Shi, Carl A685
Shi, Patricia P372
Shi, Chengzhong W401
Shibano, Nobuo W242
Shibasaki, Kenichi W400
Shibata, Kenichi W273
Shibayama, Yoshinari W116

Shibrowski, Michael P40
Shieh, Brian A71
Shiel, James G. A122
Shiel, Dennis A556
Shields, John A133
Shields, Mike A266
Shields, Terence A406
Shields, Joe A449
Shields, Genny A493
Shields, Jason A501
Shields, Kathleen M A744
Shields, Kevin A813
Shields, Christine P121
Shields, Kevin P616
Shiffman, Steven B. (Steve) A682
Shifke, Mark E182
Shifman, Edward A730
Shiga, Toshiyuki W265
Shigemura, Dean Y. A102
Shigenaga, Dean A. E9
Shih, Jonney W35
Shih, Frank W113
Shih, Ming-Hsiung W152
Shikiar, Mindy P79
Shilling, Judy A223
Shillingford, Iwona A369
Shillman, Robert J. (Bob) E82
Shiltz, LauraA A699
Shiltz, LauraA P456
Shima, Masato W116
Shimada, Michael P505
Shimaitis, Jennifer A770
Shimala, Chris A441
Shimamoto, Kevin P662
Shimizu, Shaun P19
Shimizu, Seiichi W48
Shimizu, Hiroshi W261
Shimoda, Dale E208
Shimoe, Kazuo W116
Shimonishi, Yasuhara A796
Shimotori, Etsuo W261
Shimozawa, Scott E320
Shin, Hak Cheol (H.C.) A2
Shin, Hak Cheol (H.C.) A3
Shin, Angie A328
Shin, Jin A401
Shin, Joonhyok A430
Shin, Raphael A542
Shin, Nam A631
Shin, Jung-tak A649
Shin, Hak A678
Shin, Sang-Mun W220
Shin, Jin E187
Shin, Joonhyok E204
Shin, Raphael E267
Shinde, Yogesh A898
Shindler, John A630
Shindler, John P415
Shindo, Kosei W263
Shindome, Katsuaki W330
Shine, Daniel P. (Dan) A815
Shingles, Stan P106
Shinn, Tom A163
Shinn, David A459
Shinn, Bryan A. E421
Shinobe, Osamu W27
Shinohara, Minoru W268
Shinohara, Masashi W336
Shinohara, Hidenori W345
Shinozaki, Kozo W399
Shinsky, Nate A738
Shiokawa, Yorihisa W282
Shiomi, Takao W190
Shipe, Andy A707
Shipley, Susan (Susie) Baker A440
Shipley, Joshua A676
Shipley, Kathy P663
Shipp, Crystal A101
Shippey, Mike A903
Shippey, Mike P171
Shippy, Jared P293
Shirai, Haruo W223
Shiraishi, Toru W273
Shiraji, Kozo W243
Shirakuni, Noriyuki W86

A = AMERICAN BUSINESS
E = EMERGING COMPANIES
P = PRIVATE COMPANIES
W = WORLD BUSINESS

Shirar, Steven J. (Steve) E91
Shiratsuka, Shigenori W48
Shireman, Mark D E151
Shirey, Lonnie A85
Shirk, Amber A731
Shirk, Amber E365
Shirley, Ray A631
Shirley, Edward A782
Shirley, Douglas E. P576
Shirvani, Hamid Augustine P386
Shisheng, Gu W401
Shishman, Scott A614
Shivanandan, Monique W38
Shively, Kari P361
Shivers, William C. A440
Shivery, Toni P645
Shiyou, He W403
Shlomo, Michael Goldfarb W46
Shmerling, James E. P114
Shmerling, James E. P138
Shmulik, Arbel W46
Shnayder, Boris E130
Shoaf, Kirby P134
Shoaf, Donnie P183
Shoback, Jacqueline S. A143
Shobuda, Kiyotaka W235
Shockey, Elizabeth G P612
Shockley, Harold A459
Shockley, Carolyn R. P179
Shockman, Robert A246
Shoemake, James P318
Shoemaker, Laura A340
Shoemaker, Christopher A851
Shoemaker, Laura E151
Shofe, Allen E121
Sholar, Shondra P86
Shome, Surojit W119
Shon, Larry D. De A92
Shono, Hiroshi W261
Shook, Douglas A860
Shook, Douglas P656
Shoop, Bill E355
Shope, Darwin G P676
Shopper, Glenn P20
Shoquist, Debora C. A607
Shoquist, Debbie A607
Shor, David P398
Shore, Angie A521
Shore, Michael A539
Shore, Barbara A693
Shore, Melissa P153
Shore, Lynn P192
Shores, Hoppy A56
Shores, Carolyn A769
Shorey, Yolanda A101
Shorey, Leisha A872
Shori, Yaakov W150
Shoro, Amna A73
Short, Andrea G. A1
Short, Sandra A141
Short, Johnathan H A457
Short, Christa A489
Short, Edward T A663
Short, Marianne D. A855
Short, Steve P197
Short, Andrew K P318
Short, Jeffrey B P581
Shorten, Dermot A687
Shortridge, John P81
Shortt, Thomas A426
Shortt, Tom A426
Shortt, Vittoria W105
Shosh, James A83
Shotwell, David F. (Dave) A839
Shotwell, David F. (Dave) E409
Shoulders, Patrick A. P627
Shoup, Scot P311
Shouping, Chai W283
Shouse, Cory A59

Showers, Mark E. A701
Shows, Susan A509
Shows, W T P141
Shows, Susan P288
Shpits, Samuil A204
Shrader, Ralph W. A140
Shrauger, Sam A874
Shrewsbury, Amber P225
Shriber, Ryan A131
Shriner, Kimberly P244
Shriram, Ram A36
Shrivastava, Siddharth A390
Shrivastava, Manish M. A681
Shrout, Steve A555
Shroyer, Christopher M. (Chris) A339
Shroyer, Christopher M. (Chris) E150
Shu, Gu W186
Shu, Michael E447
Shu-Hua, Yeh (Joshua) E21
Shuck, Theresa P537
Shudtz, Peter A243
Shue, Russell E A136
Shue, Diane A709
Shuey, Joanne E410
Shuffield, Teresa A837
Shufflebarger, Thomas G P571
Shugarts, Marty A49
Shugrue, Vincent A374
Shugrue, Dianne P213
Shui, Conway A175
Shukis, Mariela P699
Shukla, Naveen A131
Shukla, Anand A180
Shuler, Kathryn A25
Shuler, Ken A817
Shuler, Kathryn P15
Shuler, Tomma P239
Shulevich, Gary A741
Shulevich, Gary E370
Shulick, Brett A109
Shulick, Brett E36
Shull, Greg A166
Shulman, Doug A105
Shulman, Brian B. P494
Shultz, Jeff A175
Shultz, Patti A480
Shultz, Cindy P435
Shum, Jenny A49
Shum, Jennifer P589
Shuma, Douglas D. A794
Shumacker, Jake A693
Shumaker, Dan A16
Shumann, C R P231
Shumar, Brenda P686
Shumate, Michael A54
Shumate, Steve A838
Shumate, Carla E243
Shunck, Marybeth A344
Shunck, Marybeth E154
Shupe, Rachel P560
Shupe, Richard E415
Shurniak, William W176
Shurts, Wayne A782
Shuster, Mike A96
Shuster, Sandra L P361
Shuster, Keith P564
Shuster, Bradley M. (Brad) E304
Shute, Stephen E. W319
Shutt, Cheryl P639
Shuttleworth, Edward L. A355
Shutty, Jessica P392
Shyr, Jing A461
Shytle, Debbie A34
Si, Stephanie L P144
Siao, Susan A218
Siarkowski, Tracey A332
Sias, Evelyn A872
Sibalic, Tammy A247
Sibalic, Tammy E103
Sibbald, Andrew E136
Sibergleid, Steven P25
Siberio, John A869
Sibert, Leslie R P211
Sibley, James M A509
Sibley, James M P288

Sica, Frank V. A474
Sicca, Darlene P290
Sicchitano, Joe A774
Sichak, Stephen (Steve) A119
Sichel, Hobart (Bart) A155
Siciliano, Edward J. (Ed) E261
Sickles, Jenny P584
Sicola, Tom A547
Sicola, Tom P319
Sicotte, Luc A890
Sicotte, Luc P684
Sidar, Avinash P531
Siddall, Brenda P282
Siddiqi, Sajid A221
Sideras, John F. P98
Sideris, Harry K. A281
Sidhu, Jay S. A247
Sidhu, Jay S. E102
Sidiqi, Khalid A685
Sidrys, Paul P113
Siebenborn, Bill A252
Siebenborn, Bill P150
Sieber, Thomas W41
Siebers, Dan P190
Siebert, Eric A144
Siebert, Eric E124
Siede, Richard W. E366
Siedlecki, Sandy A523
Sieg, Andy A100
Sieg, John A332
Siegel, Kenneth I. A520
Siegel, Michael A565
Siegel, Deana P553
Siegel, Allen P660
Siegel, Laurie E140
Sieger, Michael D. (Mike) A672
Siegert, Thomas P586
Siegfried, Scott P474
Siegismund, Lee P517
Siegle, Candy P664
Siegmund, Jan A87
Siegrist, Robert N. A159
Siegrist, Joie P538
Siemer, Calvin A502
Siemer, Kristine A P359
Sienkiewicz, Mark A476
Siepman, Milton P63
Siereveld, Ryan P A671
Sierra, Joseph A105
Siersdorfer, Dietmar W331
Siess, Thorsten E3
Sietman, Milton P63
Sievers, Glen P424
Sievert, Frederick J A702
Sievert, G Michael A785
Sieving, Charles E. A357
Sieving, Charles E. A590
Siewertsen, Jim P3
Sifer, Joseph F. (Joe) A140
Sifer, Joe A140
Sifford, Jessica A774
Sigal, Jonathan A693
Sigal, Jonathan E336
Sigler, Maggie A333
Sigler, Lisa P45
Sigman, Brian C. E6
Sigmon, William P53
Signorello, Tom A265
Signorino, Charles A180
Sigrist, Thomas E432
Sih, Gil A685
Siilasmaa, Risto W266
Siino, Joseph E328
Siira, Tyler A863
Sikand, Sarika A855
Sikand, Sarika A416
Sikela, Jozef W145
Siko, Carol P686
Sikorski, Fred J. E253
Silagy, Eric E. A357
Silagy, Eric E. A590
Silander, David A865
Silbaugh, Jason A480
Silber, Jeff A449
Silberberg, Allison P122

Silberman, Jennifer A788
Silberman, Robert S. E322
Silbiger, Martin P129
Silcock, Chris A421
Silfa, Betty A204
Silfen, David M. A812
Silfen, David M. P607
Silfversparre, Gustav E351
Silins, Andris J A535
Silins, Andris J P312
Silitch, Nicholas C. (Nick) A676
Silk, Bert A235
Sill, Scott A658
Sill, Tammy P148
Silliman, Craig L. A870
Sillman, Michael P307
Sills, Stephen J. A30
Sills-Memorial, Clay A614
Siltzer, Jody P324
Silva, Lauren A56
Silva, Nicole A136
Silva, Stephen A199
Silva, Francisco A. Aristeguieta A204
Silva, Judith A635
Silva, Elif A649
Silva, Christopher A676
Silva, Anthony A877
Silva, Judith P419
Silva, Pamela P515
Silva, Eduardo Padilla W152
Silva, Carlos Nuno Gomes da W156
Silva, Filipe Cris--stomo W156
Silva, Nishan E246
Silvagni, Anthony J. P399
Silveira, Fernando P549
Silveira, Elvino da E361
Silver, Richard F A487
Silver, Christopher P642
Silver, Rebecca E426
Silveria, Richard P A80
Silveria, Cheri P159
Silverman, Rob A140
Silverman, Bob A478
Silverman, Barry J. P399
Silverman, Caleb P400
Silverman, Daniel C P505
Silvers, Gary A3
Silvers, J. B. P593
Silvers, Gregory K. (Greg) E131
Silverstein, Martin B. A386
Silverstein, Ray A763
Silversten, Scott P196
Silvey, Brent J P675
Silvey, Jerome C. (Jerry) E385
Silvia, Phil A777
Silvia, Clarence J P241
Silvia, Phil E393
Silvino, Ant-´nio Rubens Silva W284
Silwa, Robert A907
Silwa, Robert E446
Sim, Sugin A219
Sim, Chris A489
Sim, Edward P58
Sim, Sugin P131
Simancas, Jose de Jes--s V--ldez W18
Simard, Curtis C. A112
Simard, Curtis C. E38
Simberg, Bruce F. E147
Simco, Lori A835
Simcoe, Suma A565
Simeck, Shirley P412
Simeone, Giovanni A101
Simerly, Rick P255
Simermeyer, Elizabeth A. (Beth) A289
Simers, Kim P107
Siminski, Mike A549
Siminski, Mike E270
Simio, Frank P200
Simione, Jay A532
Simione, Mark A. P383
Simitian, Vahe E9
Simitz, Robert A453
Simko, Bill P491
Simkowitz, Daniel A. (Dan) A568
Simler, Jordan A869

Simmons, Al A87
Simmons, Paul A97
Simmons, Patrick A377
Simmons, Jodi A458
Simmons, Jeffrey N. (Jeff) A511
Simmons, Gary A867
Simmons, Harris H. A919
Simmons, Randall P42
Simmons, Shelly M P47
Simmons, Sharon P86
Simmons, Adele P112
Simmons, Jodi P251
Simmons, Jay P295
Simmons, Tj P301
Simmons, Eileen P332
Simmons, Elizabeth H. P341
Simmons, Rob P428
Simmons, Corrine P465
Simmons, Brad P474
Simmons, Paul E32
Simmons, James E236
Simmons, Lisa E265
Simmons-Oliver, Cheryl P292
Simms, Tony A408
Simms, David A460
Simms, Susan P421
Simner, Tina E51
Simoes, Antonio W175
Simon, John A3
Simon, Jon A218
Simon, Lynn T. A227
Simon, Mindy A230
Simon, Laura A247
Simon, Aaron A272
Simon, Grigore A588
Simon, John R. A650
Simon, Steve A703
Simon, David A744
Simon, Shari A744
Simon, Deborah A744
Simon, Larry A745
Simon, Marianne A807
Simon, Linda A878
Simon, Dennis P6
Simon, Mary P197
Simon, Carrie P251
Simon, Debbie P252
Simon, John D P286
Simon, Lou Anna K. P341
Simon, Don P390
Simon, Darryl P521
Simon, Linda P531
Simon, Marianne P574
Simon, Alex P602
Simon, Angel W343
Simon, Marc E29
Simon, Jonathan H. (Jon) E47
Simon, Laura E103
Simon, David E232
Simon, Michael K. E248
Simon, Roberto R. E438
Simonds, John A523
Simonds, Michael Q. A863
Simone, Alan Del P681
Simonelli, Lorenzo A375
Simonelli, Richard E97
Simonetti, Beth E. A792
Simonian, T Michael P660
Simons, Brenda A857
Simons, Doyle R. A896
Simons, Pat P166
Simonsen, Carolyn P333
Simonte, Michael K. A45
Simonton, Pamela A E138
Simowitz, Rebecca A277
Simpkins, Cpm A774
Simpson, Doug A67
Simpson, Austin A107
Simpson, Barry N. A215
Simpson, Shelley A439
Simpson, Kelley A480
Simpson, Kristina A489
Simpson, Michael A555
Simpson, Jay A558
Simpson, Kathryn A602

Simpson, David A657
Simpson, David L. A703
Simpson, Mary A752
Simpson, Ryan P231
Simpson, Glenn P320
Simpson, Karen P497
Simpson, Stuart W314
Simpson, Austin E34
Simpson, Melanie E119
Simpson, Wendy L. E249
Sims, Adrienne A264
Sims, C. Randall (Randy) A425
Sims, John V. A462
Sims, Robert H A625
Sims, Scott A724
Sims, Damon A811
SIMS, SUZANNE P152
Sims, Demarlo P297
Sims, Dominique P514
Sims, Damon P600
Sims, Stefanie P621
Sims, C. Randall (Randy) E201
Simson, Thomas H. A145
Simson, Thomas H. E46
Simuro, Frank E97
Sinagra, Jack P629
Sinatra, Kim A909
Sinclair, Jeffrey A478
Sinclair, Christopher A. A539
Sinclair, Donald A700
Sinclair, Donald R. E436
Sindel, Mehmet W18
Sinden, Jessie A390
Sinden, Shaun A792
Sindhu, Pradeep S. A482
Sine, Jeffrey A. P37
Sinek, Jim P79
Singelais, B. C. W199
Singer, David A119
Singer, Lori A241
Singer, Amy A871
Singer, Steven R P153
Singer, Neil P293
Singer, Peter P395
Singer, Bruce H P470
Singer, Samantha P567
Singer, Ethan P627
Singh, Rajinder P. (Raj) A108
Singh, Bobby A131
Singh, Jennifer A133
Singh, Munjeet A140
Singh, Anand A185
Singh, Zorawar Biri A199
Singh, Manjit A208
Singh, Mala A292
Singh, Rajesh A327
Singh, Rakhee A480
Singh, Harmit J. A509
Singh, Jasraj A530
Singh, Kirti A671
Singh, Manvinder A685
Singh, Sanjay A718
Singh, Sangharsh A766
Singh, Maneet A913
Singh, Sanchita A917
Singh, Nonihal P57
Singh, Bhupi P162
Singh, Pooja P292
Singh, Anup V. P382
Singh, Vijayeta P392
Singh, Jasvinder P535
Singh, Premjith L P609
Singh, Sabi P643
Singh, Rajinder P. (Raj) E35
Singh, Rajinder E72
Singhal, Raj A698
Singhal, Aparna P189
Singhal, Raj P456
Singhal, Anil K. E300
Singhal, Ashwani E300
Singhania, Shishir A163
Singleton, J. Barton A781
Singleton, J Knox P21
Singleton, Joanna P197
Singleton, Kali P277

Singleton, J Knox P298
Singleton, Palmer C P359
Singleton, H. Wells P399
Singleton, Arnold R. P509
Singleton, Dennis F. E107
Sinha, Dharmendra Kumar A217
Sinhabahu, Charuka A429
Sinhabahu, Charuka E204
Sinicropi, Steve E127
Sink, Daniel R. E234
Sinko, Jim A738
Sinks, Patrick A557
Sinnard, Pat A51
Sinnott, John A685
Sinnott, Justin A729
Sinnott, Carrie E166
Sinnott, Robert (Rob) E423
Siotia, Sanjeev E256
Sipe, Barb A665
Sipes, Robert A282
Sipes, Kevin A705
Sipes, Kevin E352
Sipilovic, Bridget P276
Sipple, Lanette P685
Sipser, Michael P313
Siqing, Chen W67
Siracusano, Luciano E443
Siragusa, Paul A651
Siragusa, Paul P426
Sirakos, Bill A244
Sireyjol, Nicolas A49
Sirianni, Frank P200

Sirico, William A677
Sirkin, Clive A485
Sirkin, David A682
Sirmon, Gary L. A110
Sirmon, Gary L. E37
Sirois, Charles W80
Sirstins, Max P164
Sisam, Allison P477
Sisemore, Martin B. A833
Sisisky, Richard L P512
Sisitsky, Todd B. P485
Sisler, Andrew P125
Sismondo, Peter R A30
Sisney, Brett P161
Sison, Rob A292
Sissel, Anne A113
Sissman, Terry A599
Sisson, William G. P58
Sistovaris, Violet G. A594
Sitherwood, Suzanne P520
Sitohang, Helman W111
Sitterding, Mary P115
Sitzmann, Edith W215
Siu, Albert P355
Siu, Shawn W90
Siva, Chokkalingam P646
Sivagnanam, Kalyana W265
Sivakumar, Balasubramaniam P532
Sivamurthy, Krupa A649
Sivaram, Siva A892
Sivewright, Bob A302
Sivewright, Bob E128
Sivie, Neal A479
Sivignon, Pierre-Jean W82
Siwek, Janusz A423
Six, Beth A475
Six, Beth P266
Sizemore, Vicki A95
Sizemore, Mark A674
Sizemore, Vicki P55
Sizemore, Thomas P307
Sizemore, Mark P444
Sizer, Paul A73
Sjonell, Peter A691
Sjoqvist, Nikolaj A881
Sjulin, Susie A257
Sjulin, Renee P87
Sjulstad, Ole Bj-̦rn W360
Skabelund, Hoyt A111
Skabelund, Hoyt P56
Skadin, John P473
Skagen, Randy A605

Skaggs, Michael D. (Mike) A798
Skaggs, Robert P207
Skaine, Theresa M P484
Skains, Tom A282
Skala, P. Justin A218
Skaloot, Ed P548
Skar, Alden A701
Skarda, Ed A913
Skare, Todd A. A514
Skarka, Kathy P362
Skarulis, Patricia C. P325
Skaruppa, Cindy P435
Skaugen, Kirk B. W218
Skeans, Tracy A917
Skeans, John P528
Skeats, Lawrence N. A621
Skehan, Michael P310
Skeie, Elisabeth A398
Skelley, Sean A733
Skelsey, Maral P322
Skelton, Bryndon A221
Skelton, Bryce P544
Skeoch, Keith W341
Skibba, Chris E229
Skidmore, Timothy A194
Skidmore, Richard A390
Skiendzielewski, John P209
Skill, Thomas D. (Tom) P611
Skillin, Chris A449
Skinner, Landon A484
Skinner, Paul C A624
Skinner, James A. (Jim) A877
Skinner, Anne P346
Skinner, Mary L P431
Skinner, Stephen P445
Skinner, Stephen P545
Skinner, Douglas J. P610
Skinner, A. Chester E92
Skinner, Dean E397
Skipper, John A271
Skipper, Monica A327
Skivington, Stephanie A886
Skivington, Stephanie E433
Skjodt, Jennifer E127
Sklar, Michelle P654
Skluth, Nancy P333
Skoda, Sophia P172
Skoglund, William B. A616
Skolits, Adele M. E368
Skolny, Bryan A659
Skolrood, Kent P59
Skonieczny, Michael P390
Skopick, Richard A182
Skopick, Richard E63
Skordinski, Matt A748
Skorecki, Adam A782
Skorik, Konstantin E172
Skorkowsky, Patrick P125
Skorton, David J. P506
Skory, John E. A355
Skory, John E P574
Skou, Soren W1
Skoufalos, Yannis A671
Skovran, Patrick A143
Skovronsky, Daniel (Dan) A511
Skowronski, Robert A81
Skrivanos, Stephen F P75
Skrobalak, Matt A175
Skrocki, Denise P632
Skudutis, Tom W229
Skyler, Edward A203
Slabosz, Larry A677
Slack, Charlene P220
Slade, Charlyn A15
Slade, Charlyn P9
Slader, Salene P187
Slager, Chris A649
Slager, Donald W. (Don) A707
Slatas, Brian P102
Slate, Larry A136
Slater, Blake D A196
Slater, David A280
Slater, Catherine I. A462
Slater, Catherine I A463
Slater, Todd A. A618

A = AMERICAN BUSINESS
E = EMERGING COMPANIES
P = PRIVATE COMPANIES
W = WORLD BUSINESS

Slater, Jana Kay P214
Slater, Dave P446
Slater, Mark P487
Slatin, Mark A724
Slatkin, Diane A163
Slatky, Larry I P362
Slaton, Libby A115
Slaton, Christie A774
Slaton, Shawn P111
Slattery, William (Willie) P167
Slattery, Kerrie P421
Slaughter, Roy A835
Slaughter, James G. P469
Slaughter, Veronica P635
Slavick, Amy P535
Slavik, Jerry A500
Slavik, Jerry E237
Slavin, Peter L. A635
Slavin, Peter L. P419
Slavin, Peter L. P590
Slawson, John W. E381
Slaybaugh, Chris A902
Slaybaugh, Chris P692
Slee, Steven A332
Sleece, Kelly A109
Sleece, Kelly E36
Sleight, Barbara A649
Sleiman, Adham A140
Slentz, Andrew A417
Slessor, Michael (Mikie) E165
Sleyster, Scott G. A676
Slezak, Ed E1
Slifka, Eric A388
Slifka, Andrew A388
Slifka, Richard A388
Sliney, David A771
Slingsby, Tim A593
Slinkard, John P546
Slipy, Scott D A471
Sloan, Brian A51
Sloan, Roger W A85
Sloan, Jacob A114
Sloan, Elizabeth A272
Sloan, Rodney L. A412
Sloan, Scott A417
Sloan, Joshua A478
Sloan, Garrett A729
Sloan, Jacob P64
Sloan, Gayle P476
Sloan, Jeffrey E163
Sloan, Rodney L. E192
Sloan, Stuart M. E328
Sloane, Barry R. A184
Sloane, Marshall M. A184
Sloane, Edward G. (Ed) A340
Sloane, Edward G. (Ed) E151
Sloat, Julie A46
Sloat, Jean P96
Slockwell, Paul A173
Slocum, Michael C. A163
Slocumb, Travis A695
Slominski, Donald D. (Don) P320
Slomsky, David P545
Slon, Dennis P299
Slonim, Sheryl P239
Slootskiy, Alex A644
Slotkin, Bryan A390
Slotnik, Joseph J. A149
Sloup, Michael A136
Sloves, Evan A199
Sluka, Joseph P456
Slusher, John F. A592
Slusher, Martin P262
Slutsky, Lorie A A584
Slutsky, Lorie A P374
Sly, Patrick J. (Pat) A295
Slyconish, John A766
Slyter, Mark F P63
Smaglick, Dorothy A865

Small, Richard A115
Small, William J. (Bill) A344
Small, Carolyn A406
Small, Chip A417
Small, Gary M. A845
Small, David A870
Small, Jeff A903
Small, Alliant P6
Small, Jeff P171
Small, Andrew P431
Small, David R. P446
Small, J. Radford P559
Small, Deborah A P606
Small, William J. (Bill) E154
Small, Gary M. E413
Smallens, Sandy E127
Smalley, Gary G. A833
Smalley, James P227
Smalls, Marva A872
Smalls, Kenyell P372
Smarandoiu, George A620
Smart, George M. A355
Smart, Lawrence A885
Smart, James P306
Smart, Denise T. P563
Smart, Justin W. E232
Smeaton, Paul W348
Smedes, Tina P105
Smedt, Mark De W7
Smedt, Rodney E290
Smeenk, Sharon P198
Smeltzer, David P P42
Smet, John H A46
Smet, John H P32
Smethurst, Evan A478
Smiddy, Craig R. A615
Smilde, Renee P488
Smiley, Josh A511
Smilie, Karen A599
Smit, Charl P61
Smith, Jeffrey C. A13
Smith, Rob A20
Smith, Lucinda A20
Smith, Elizabeth A34
Smith, Stephan A51
Smith, Olivia A54
Smith, Ernie A56
Smith, Rodney A. A66
Smith, Denise A70
Smith, Donna N. A81
Smith, Jason A81
Smith, David A82
Smith, Michele A84
Smith, Arthur A86
Smith, Debra A86
Smith, Martyn R. A92
Smith, Julie A101
Smith, Deborah A103
Smith, Joann A107
Smith, Ryan A111
Smith, Doug A115
Smith, John C. (Jack) A117
Smith, Jeffrey A. A130
Smith, Rob A130
Smith, Justin A133
Smith, Taylor A135
Smith, Gregory D. (Greg) A136
Smith, T. Andrew (Andy) A148
Smith, Drew A151
Smith, William G. (Bill) A162
Smith, Darla A163
Smith, Scott A. A178
Smith, Tiffany A180
Smith, Jim A184
Smith, Chris A189
Smith, D. S. (Dave) A192
Smith, Brian A195
Smith, Peter F. A212
Smith, Brian J. A215
Smith, Douglas A221
Smith, Barbara R A224
Smith, Stuart A225
Smith, Wayne T. A227
Smith, P. Paul A227
Smith, Allen A238

Smith, Derrick A243
Smith, Susie A244
Smith, Sam A247
Smith, Kevin F A250
Smith, Richard P. (Rick) A252
Smith, Sherry A260
Smith, Joanne A261
Smith, Anne A261
Smith, Glen A270
Smith, Raiford A300
Smith, Robert C. A304
Smith, Doug A306
Smith, Ken A316
Smith, Edward C. A323
Smith, Frederick W. (Fred) A327
Smith, Graham A327
Smith, Jerome R. (Jerry) A340
Smith, Christy A348
Smith, Rita K A350
Smith, Dale A. A353
Smith, Lee M. A356
Smith, Robert E. (Rob) A374
Smith, William A383
Smith, Sarah E. A389
Smith, Bryan R A406
Smith, James E A408
Smith, Dolois A422
Smith, Bradford A431
Smith, Sally A432
Smith, Denise A438
Smith, Joyce A441
Smith, Donna A441
Smith, Michael S. A442
Smith, Stacy J. A456
Smith, Gregory A461
Smith, Philip A. A465
Smith, Ryan A465
Smith, Brad D. A466
Smith, Mark A478
Smith, Gordon A. A480
Smith, Sara A489
Smith, Benton A489
Smith, Mark A492
Smith, Steve A497
Smith, Elizabeth A A509
Smith, Mark A515
Smith, Jared A517
Smith, Jay A520
Smith, Barry M. A524
Smith, Craig S. A530
Smith, Michael R. A544
Smith, Paul A A546
Smith, Deborah A546
Smith, Allen A549
Smith, Martin A549
Smith, Christopher A556
Smith, Joshua A558
Smith, Bradford L A560
Smith, Carol A565
Smith, Donnie A571
Smith, Susan A572
Smith, Tricia D. A596
Smith, Herbert A597
Smith, Thomas A599
Smith, Carl A602
Smith, Gerry P. A612
Smith, David A621
Smith, Daniel T. (Dan) A627
Smith, Kent A630
Smith, Allen L. A635
Smith, Rhonda A655
Smith, Maureen A659
Smith, Harmon D. A681
Smith, Beth A693
Smith, Eugene A695
Smith, Richard A A696
Smith, Ronald G. (Ronnie) A700
Smith, Michael A700
Smith, Scott A. A703
Smith, Matthew L. (Matt) A703
Smith, Phil A704
Smith, Follin E A718
Smith, Susan F. A742
Smith, B. Scott A749
Smith, O. Bruton A749

Smith, David B. A749
Smith, Janet A751
Smith, Zeta A763
Smith, Maria A763
Smith, Ryan A767
Smith, Mark A774
Smith, Todd A775
Smith, Brian A782
Smith, Rodger A782
Smith, Kristin A782
Smith, Craig A784
Smith, Catherine R. (Cathy) A788
Smith, Ray A801
Smith, Dennis A803
Smith, Eric A811
Smith, Roger C. A822
Smith, Kevin C. A827
Smith, Richard L A827
Smith, Richard P. A830
Smith, Bethany L A832
Smith, Dustin A837
Smith, L. Duane A841
Smith, Craige L. A843
Smith, Orin C. A861
Smith, David A865
Smith, Troy A866
Smith, S. Dawn A875
Smith, Gregory L. (Greg) A878
Smith, Eileen A878
Smith, Catherine A878
Smith, Linda S A880
Smith, James C. (Jim) A882
Smith, Anna A902
Smith, Drew A903
Smith, Jeff S. A906
Smith, Paul V. A913
Smith, Jennifer A. A919
Smith, Wade P10
Smith, Scott P10
Smith, Lisa P26
Smith, Robert P27
Smith, Stephan P33
Smith, Jenni P38
Smith, Rosi P45
Smith, David P49
Smith, Lamont P50
Smith, James P51
Smith, Arthur P52
Smith, Debra P52
Smith, Ryan P56
Smith, Tyler P61
Smith, Gerald P67
Smith, Lloyd V P68
Smith, Hal E P75
Smith, Taylor P78
Smith, Connie D P81
Smith, Catherine P83
Smith, Eli P95
Smith, Ryan P106
Smith, D. S. (Dave) P112
Smith, Rebecca L P122
Smith, Carolyn P133
Smith, Henry P149
Smith, Richard P. (Rick) P150
Smith, Richard P155
Smith, Gary P158
Smith, Lauren P163
Smith, Les P170
Smith, Darrell P171
Smith, Drew P182
Smith, Deron P182
Smith, Kevin P184
Smith, Stephanie P197
Smith, Jen P207
Smith, Terry P225
Smith, Rick P227
Smith, Diane R P232
Smith, Dolois P239
Smith, Jason P242
Smith, Raven P243
Smith, David P248
Smith, Nicola P251
Smith, Douglas P258
Smith, Teresa P260
Smith, Martha P270

Smith, Robert P274
Smith, Steven E P276
Smith, Xan P281
Smith, Rodney P282
Smith, Tommie P282
Smith, Elizabeth A P288
Smith, Randy Smith Randy P290
Smith, Sarah P292
Smith, Quiara P300
Smith, Candace P304
Smith, Wes P315
Smith, Amy M P329
Smith, David A. P361
Smith, Becky P387
Smith, Lawrence G. P390
Smith, Melissa P396
Smith, Charles V P409
Smith, Stanley P410
Smith, Kent P415
Smith, Nancy P415
Smith, Rob P418
Smith, Allen L. P419
Smith, David M. P423
Smith, Dennis P430
Smith, Eddie P430
Smith, Carole P434
Smith, Martha P442
Smith, Andrew O P446
Smith, Thomas P451
Smith, Joanne C P457
Smith, Kitty P462
Smith, Michael G P468
Smith, Jacquelin P477
Smith, Kenneth P479
Smith, Suzanne P480
Smith, Brenda P493
Smith, Tim P498
Smith, Audra P501
Smith, Wayne P511
Smith, Michael P514
Smith, Kenneth A. (Ken) P520
Smith, Roger P522
Smith, Rosemary P531
Smith, Vivian P533
Smith, Cathy P537
Smith, Gretchen P539
Smith, Marilyn P539
Smith, Vincent P539
Smith, Todd P548
Smith, Breck P557
Smith, Dillon P561
Smith, Ray P561
Smith, Joanne P563
Smith, Chad P569
Smith, Larry T P569
Smith, Greg P573
Smith, Eric P580
Smith, Chip P583
Smith, Eric P600
Smith, Neil P602
Smith, Julia P603
Smith, Jennifer R. P616
Smith, Richard J. P616
Smith, Sean P617
Smith, Chris P619
Smith, Elizabeth P619
Smith, Michael P620
Smith, Chris P631
Smith, Roger P640
Smith, Charles H. P654
Smith, John P654
Smith, Barrett P657
Smith, Orin C. P658
Smith, Keith P666
Smith, Dan P681
Smith, James E. P682
Smith, Erica B P685
Smith, Deanna P686
Smith, Sharon P P686
Smith, Herman P691
Smith, Anna P693
Smith, Charles V P694
Smith, Greg P695
Smith, Wayne T. W55
Smith, Gary W78

Smith, Ian W101
Smith, Keith J. W320
Smith, Mark W340
Smith, Kris W348
Smith, Martin W396
Smith, Mark E17
Smith, Joann E35
Smith, Drew E48
Smith, Richard H. E59
Smith, David R. E69
Smith, Peter F. E79
Smith, Stuart E88
Smith, Daniel E. E92
Smith, Daniel E94
Smith, Steven J. E96
Smith, Sam E103
Smith, Ken E141
Smith, Jerome R. (Jerry) E151
Smith, Christy E155
Smith, Rita K E157
Smith, Hunter E172
Smith, Bob E181
Smith, Martin C. E183
Smith, Bradford E205
Smith, Steven R. (Steve) E227
Smith, Dan F. E236
Smith, Kevin R. E239
Smith, Marsha E244
Smith, Beverly E265
Smith, Allen E270
Smith, Martin E270
Smith, Shane E290
Smith, Brian E318
Smith, Rhonda E333
Smith, Greg E348
Smith, Phil E351
Smith, Susan F. E372
Smith, Janet E377
Smith, Gregory E394
Smith, Richard P. E402
Smith, L. Duane E410
Smith, Craige L. E411
Smith, Billy Ray E421
Smith, Ian F. E428
Smith, Howard W. E431
Smith, Melissa D. E438
Smith, Chell E439
Smith, Larry E445
Smith-Acuna, Shelly P132
Smith-anoa'i, Tiffany A175
Smithers, Westwood P143
Smithson, Nate P47
Smithwick, Michael P486
Smithy, M Deron A700
Smitley, Russ E172
Smits, Lynn A81
Smits, Robert P210
Smoak, Shannon A753
Smoak, Shannon E378
Smoke, Tony A27
Smokler, Dr Irving A P565
Smookler, Eric A902
Smookler, Eric P693
Smoot, Steve A458
Smoot, Raymond D. (Ray) A841
Smoot, Steve P251
Smoot, Raymond D. (Ray) E410
Smotrys, Ken E231
Smucker, Darrell A317
Smucker, Mark T. A748
Smucker, Richard K. A748
Smucker, Darrell E142
Smuland, Brad P333
Smullen, F W P101
Smullen-Volz, Lynn A185
Smyers, Debra A180
Smyklo, Mike A175
Smylie, John P249
Smylie, John P505
Smyth, Gerard A56
Smyth, Cameron A565
Smyth, Declan E219
Snabe, Jim Hagemann W1
Snapper, Suzanne D. E125
Snead, Ron A282

Snedaker, Dianne A353
Snedeker, Scott A115
Snee, James P. A432
Snel, Michael A34
Snel, Michael P27
Snell, Barbara P511
Snelling, Dawn A522
Sng, Yih A796
Snider, Maureen A5
Snider, Kami P231
Snider, Michael E244
Sniffen, John A47
Sniffin, Ted A140
Snipe, Alexander E153
Snipes, James P525
Snir, Ran E67
Snitchler, Dave P305
Snively, Melissa P237
Snodgrass, Mark A546
Snodgrass, Tammie P554
Snodgres, Jon K. E351
Snoke, Tim P337
Snook, Pete P155
Snow, Tracey A108
Snow, Scott A115
Snow, Kristine A. (Kris) A199
Snow, Stuart P149
Snow, Terry P196
Snow, Wayne W287
Snow, Tracey E35
Snow, F. Philip E140
Snow, Brad E261
Snowden, Ed A73
Snowden, Joseph I. A666
Snowden, Beau A693
Snowden, Clint P104
Snowden, Joseph I. P438
Snustad, John P30
Snyder, Mary A105
Snyder, Brian A151
Snyder, James A163
Snyder, Tammy A369
Snyder, William A432
Snyder, Bill A432
Snyder, Tamar A474
Snyder, Lori A513
Snyder, Denise A578
Snyder, Rob A614
Snyder, Stephanie A A774
Snyder, Jay A792
Snyder, Mitch A804
Snyder, Vicky A807
Snyder, Michael A819
Snyder, Rod A890
Snyder, Jane A901
Snyder, Chandra P39
Snyder, Barbara R. P98
Snyder, Tamar P262
Snyder, Alan P286
Snyder, Peter P333
Snyder, Tammy P441
Snyder, Debbie P446
Snyder, John P568
Snyder, Vicky P574
Snyder, Linda P628
Snyder, Meredith P641
Snyder, Robert P651
Snyder, Rod P684
Snyder, Jane P692
Snyder, Brian E48
Soab, Alan P276
Soares, Denise C. A582
Soares, Habiba A912
Soares, Denise C. P373
Soave, John S. E99
Sobanet, Henry P132
Sobeck, Ryan A390
Sobecki, Lisa P620
Sobel, Brian M. A103
Sobey, Mark E83
Sobic, Dan A629
Soble, Dan E426
Soby, Barbara P393
Socarras, Aleida E74
Soccorsi, Mark A441

Soch, Susan A801
Soch, Susan P562
Sochacki, Thomas L P686
Socia, Robert E A379
Sock, Shannon P330
Socotch, Jayne A446
Socotch, Jayne E210
Soderberg, John L. A318
Soderblom, Len A599
Soderburg, John L. A318
Soderholm, Glenn W118
Soderstrom, Jeff A56
Sodhi, Raj E355
Sodo, Michael E178
Soehnlen, Leo P368
Soffer, Patricia G P531
Sofish, Greg A738
Sofko, Gary A537
Sogge, Todd A214
Sogge, Todd P128
Sognefest, Peter W. E214
Sohm, Frederick (Rick) E381
Sohn, Mike K. A459
Sohn, Stephanie P672
Soifer, B. Thomas P91
Soiffer, Robert J. P153
Soike, Dave P433
Soirat, Arnaud W305
Soirat, Arnaud W306
Soisson, Tom A827
Sokol, Brandon A589
Sokolov, Richard S. (Rick) A744
Sola, Jure A725
Solanski, David P231
Solarez, Barbara P348
Solazzo, Mark J. P390
Solberg, Jeff A397
Solberg, Jeff P221
Soldatova, Ingrida A677
Soldi, Marinella A269
Soldo, Stephen P471
Solecki, Gregory A413
Solecki, Gregory P234
Solenberger, Scott A599
Soler, Leslie A785
Soles, Darren P209
Solheim, Leif A74
Solheim, Anita A305
Solheim, Anita P185
Soliman, Fady A709
Solis, Andrea A614
Solis, Jose P620
Solis, Robert P645
Solk, Steven (Steve) A201
Solley, Charlie P118
Sollie, Andreas A305
Sollie, Andreas P185
Solma, Martin A. P611
Solochek, Evan P133
Solognier, Ken A476
Soloman, Jeffrey P695
Solomon, Darlene J. S. A22
Solomon, J. Stuart A46
Solomon, John A70
Solomon, Michael A247
Solomon, David M. A389
Solomon, Victor A546
Solomon, Malou A709
Solomon, Michael A729
Solomon, Jay S. P107
Solomon, Howard J P329
Solomon, Michael E103
Solomonson, Angela P368
Solomonson, Susan P430
Solon, Kenneth S. A512
Solotar, Joan A132
Soltis, Diana A677
Solymossy, Matt P281
Sol-s, Oscar Von Hauske W25
Somanchi, Subba P326
Somashekar, Vinay A480
Somasundaram, Sivasankaran (Soma) A279
Somavilla-castro, Ivan A85
Somefun, Ayodeji P205

A = AMERICAN BUSINESS
E = EMERGING COMPANIES
P = PRIVATE COMPANIES
W = WORLD BUSINESS

Somerfeld, Jessica A122
Somerhalder, John W. P131
Somers, Bob A261
Somers, Chuck A265
Somerville, Susan P390
Sommer, Christina A537
Sommer, Stefan W402
Sommerfeldt, Rose P51
Sommerfeldt, Scott D. P83
Sommers, Andy A913
Sommers, Jimmy F P605
Sommers, Sarah W P605
Sommers, Wynelle P605
Sommers, Randy P605
Sommerville, Ross E355
Somphanh, Boun E207
Son, Jamie A912
Son, Chang Hwan W292
Sonderman, Thomas E361
Sondhi, Samrat E139
Sondreal, Sean A493
Sonecha, Sonia A333
Sonego, Michael J. (Mike) A731
Sonego, Michael J. (Mike) E365
Sonenreich, Steven D. P355
Song, J. Jonathan A312
Song, Brian P228
Song, Daniel P266
Song, Zhiyong W13
Song, Zhiping W91
Song, Lin W96
Song, Guangju W291
Song, Se-Bin W292
Songer, Terri P45
Songer, Nancy Butler P165
Soni, Amit A131
Soni, Paul J. A714
Sonnemaker, Scott A. A782
Sonnenberg, Steven A. (Steve) A295
Sonnenfeld, Gerald P652
Sono, Kiyoshi W245
Sonora, Lynn P573
Sonora, Brandi P573
Sonsteby, Charles M. (Chuck) A254
Sonsteng, Chimene A830
Sonsteng, Chimene E402
Sonthalia, Ashok P282
Soo, Huh Chang W163
Sooch, Navdeep S. (Nav) E371
Sood, Anjla A6
Sood, Joyce A810
Sood, Sneha P270
Sood, Joyce P586
Sood, Vivek W360
Sook, Perry A. E303
Soon-ky, Hong W163
Soordelu, Ravi A685
Soper, Martha A869
Soper, Aaron A902
Soper, Aaron P692
Sopp, Karen P621
Sopp, Gerald F. E108
Sorbara, Nicole W227
Sordillo, Emilia P525
Sordo, Michael P107
Sorel, Carolle A201
Soren, Laurie A187
Soren, Laurie E71
Sorendo, Darlene P532
Sorensen, Rosemary A503
Sorensen, Jeralyn A532
Sorensen, Bryan A631
Sorensen, Terrie A677
Sorensen, Deborah P758
Sorensen, Christopher M P270
Sorensen, Rosemary P284
Sorensen, Chris S P368
Sorensen, Jim P453
Sorensen, Deborah P519

Sorensen, Bonny P545
Sorensen, Carl K P653
Sorensen, Norman E123
Sorenson, Steven P. A33
Sorenson, John B. (Brad) A144
Sorenson, Rob A166
Sorenson, Charles A448
Sorenson, Arne M. A530
Sorenson, Charles P246
Sorenson, Chris P256
Sorenson, Roger P661
Soreq, Avigal A260
Sorey, Corinne A221
Sorfleet, Diana A243
Sorge, James E90
Sorgi, Vincent (Vince) A665
Sorgiovanni, Frank A478
Soria, Anthony P630
Soriano, Lidio V. A661
Soriot, Pascal W34
Sorkey, Alan J P692
Sornberger, Andrea P174
Sorrell, Martin W398
Sorrentino, Vincent A201
Sorrentino, Frank A231
Sorrentino, Rob W62
Sortino, Cecilia A457
Sortino, Jean A522
Sorvillo, Domenico A334
Sorvillo, Domenico P193
Sosa, Branden P376
Sosebee, Jane A84
Sosebee, Tim P129
Sosland, Matthew A83
Soso, Gary P688
Sossen, Andrew J. E385
Sotelo, Lisa P305
Soterakis, Jack P529
Sotorp, Kai R. W232
Sotos, Michelle P215
Sottong, Suzy A348
Sottong, Suzy E155
Soucy, Alicia A785
Souders, Michael P293
Souhrada, Kathleen A669
Soukup, Beth P256
Soukup, Beth P257
Soule, David B. A338
Soules, Steve A140
Sounart, Gwen P441
Soung, Nisha A877
Sounillac, Jean-Pierre W148
Soupene, John C. (Jay) A168
Souque, Lionel W302
Sourisse, Pascale W364
Sourisseau, Didier A242
Sourry, Amanda W383
Sousa, Joseph (Joe) A712
Sousa, Chris E166
Sousa, Michael J. E190
South, Ronald A727
South, John R P232
Southam, Arthur M. P119
Southard, Bill P350
Southwick, Michael J P602
Soutomaior, Luiz A728
Soutter, Jim E208
Souza, Michael A528
Sova, Colleen R. A847
Sovereign, Marla A149
Sovine, Robert A526
Sowa, Ashley A401
Sowa, Mark P268
Sowa, Ashley E187
Sowell, Ronald P81
Sowell, Chester P242
Sowinski, Mark A865
Sowmarpet, Mandasmitha P329
Spaashelm, Ernie A408
Space, Jordan A720
Space, Jordan E362
Spada, Gerald A767
Spada, Andrew E54
Spadaro, Mike A782
Spade, Douglas P560

Spadea, Vincent A115
Spagnuolo, Andrea A549
Spagnuolo, John C A741
Spagnuolo, Andrea E270
Spagnuolo, John C E370
Spahr, Tom A426
Spaid, John L. E292
Spain, Wynn A308
Spain, Wade A344
Spain, Wade A345
Spain, Timothy A847
Spain, Wayne P53
Spain, Jeffrey R P149
Spain, Wade E154
Spain-Remy, Claire P357
Spair, Ronald H. E318
Spalding, Jennifer A165
Spalding, Susan P152
Spalding, Shawn P188
Spalding, Donald W P663
Spampinato, Gregory W. E183
Span, David P318
Spangler, Ken A327
Spanier, Mike A579
Spanos, Mike A647
Spanswick, Paul W268
Sparacino, Giuseppe A353
Sparacino, Michael A725
Sparacino, Giuseppe E159
Sparcino, Michael A725
Sparer, Cynthia N. P699
Sparger, Rob P344
Sparke, Andrea P333
Sparkman, Ricky D. A227
Sparkman, Julie A698
Sparkman, Julie P456
Sparks, Tim A210
Sparks, David A214
Sparks, Kevin P. A855
Sparks, Kenneth A868
Sparks, Tracy A915
Sparks, David P128
Sparks, Danny P400
Sparks, William B P630
Sparks, Tracy P700
Sparolini, Sonia A785
Sparrow, Victor A811
Sparrow, Deborah P18
Sparrow, Randy P442
Sparrow, Victor P600
Spatoulis, Dino A223
Spear, Lorna P521
Spears, Winsford A622
Spears, Tara P109
Spears, L Steven P331
Spears, Joe E316
Speas, Dawn A107
Speas, Theodore W A782
Speas, Dawn E35
Specht, Tonja A332
Specht, Bill A693
Specht, William A. E276
Speciale, Rick P A572
Specter, Eric M. E162
Spector, Rick A478
Spector, David A. A642
Spector, David A. E328
Spedding, Martin P167
Speed, Tanya A724
Speer, Stephen A109
Speer, Terry A643
Speer, Kevin P P233
Speer, Stephen E36
Speers, Jodie A351
Speers, Jodie E158
Spees, Shane P388
Speetzen, Michael T. (Mike) A661
Spehar, Danielle E7
Speicher, Charles A. E271
Speidell, Paul A736
Speidell, Paul P492
Speirn, Sterling K P672
Spellicy, Stephen A419
Spellings, James A313
Spellins, Randy A659

Spellman, Brian A390
Spellman, Stephen P363
Spellman, Lynn P621
Spence, Timothy N. A332
Spence, Karis A441
Spence, William H. A665
Spence, Kenneth F. (Ken) A827
Spence, Nick A. E382
Spence, Mitchell E404
Spencer, Steve A27
Spencer, James F. A159
Spencer, Erica A244
Spencer, Robert A350
Spencer, Harry A474
Spencer, Barbara A583
Spencer, Terry K. A622
Spencer, Terry K A623
Spencer, Malcolm A685
Spencer, Christine A693
Spencer, Ruth A877
Spencer, Lorraine A878
Spencer, Larry A898
Spencer, Dennis A919
Spencer, Ian A920
Spencer, Kipp P69
Spencer, Craig P172
Spencer, Lorraine P182
Spencer, Linda P260
Spencer, Jeffrey P330
Spencer, Barbara P374
Spencer, Terry K P407
Spencer, Justin P407
Spencer, Lawrence P475
Spencer, Marjorie P591
Spencer, Ivy P681
Spencer, Geoff E127
Spencer, Robert E156
Spengler, Richard S. A467
Spengler, Richard S. E223
Spera, Richard P584
Speranza, James A583
Speranzo, Anthony J A80
Speranzo, Anthony J P47
Sperber, Loryn A131
Sperber, Julie A557
Spero, Vincent A. A639
Spero, Vincent A. E325
Sperry, Scott P402
Sperry, Diane P413
Speth, Ralf W357
Speyer, Sharon S. A440
Speyer, Sharon S. P613
Sphr, Jean P383
Spicer, Heather A670
Spicer, Randy A855
Spicer, Michael G. E56
Spiegel, Isabella A79
Spiegel, Joan A532
Spiegelman, Donald A763
Spiegelman, Kathy P392
Spiegler, Eric E65
Spieker, Marc W131
Spieler, Robert A85
Spier, Scott P329
Spier, Dr Scott P331
Spiers, Robert H. A21
Spiers, Robert H. P12
Spiesshofer, Ulrich W4
Spiewak, Brian A3
Spigelmyer, Toni A782
Spikes, Noelle A272
Spillane, Michael A592
Spillane, Ciaran E437
Spiller, Elizabeth P669
Spillers, David P244
Spillers, Brian P533
Spillers, David P584
Spillum, Andy P176
Spilman, Jeff A530
Spina, Suzana A420
Spina, Eric F. P611
Spinelli, Luis E83
Spinieo, Bob A417
Spinnato, Joseph E P375
Spinner, Steven L. (Steve) A848

Spiroff, Paul A557
Spitulnik, Aric P290
Spitzer, Allison A103
Spitzer, Dan A539
Spitzer, John A607
Spitzer, Anna A P325
Spitzfaden, Thomas A260
Splaine, Thomas F. A500
Splaine, Bruce P167
Splaine, Kevin R P519
Splaine, Thomas F. E237
Splichal, Tricia P87
Spoelder, Eelco W148
Spoerry, Jon A542
Spoerry, Jon E267
Spohr, Carsten W124
Sponsler, Brian A295
Spoon, Alan A253
Spooner, Patty A101
Spooner, Dave A818
Sporing, Eileen P570
Sposito, Thomas J. A720
Sposito, Thomas J. E362
Spracher, John A343
Spradley, Scott A834
Spradlin, Diane A599
Spradlin, Shane M. A642
Sprague, Joseph A. (Joe) A28
Sprague, Raymond J. (Ray) A406
Sprague, Tim A484
Sprague, Brittney P204
Sprague, Tina P663
Sprague, Neil E. E131
Sprague, Norman F. E275
Spranger, Melissa A187
Spranger, Melissa E71
Spratlen, Susan A657
Spraus, Joyan P208
Spray, Shane A115
Sprecher, Jeffrey C A457
Spreen, Paul A469
Spriggs, Ted A872
Spring, Terry P532
Spring, Doug P639
Spring, Annabel F. W105
Springer, Brian A621
Springer, Jon W. A858
Springer, Brian A407
Springer, Jon W. E418
Springfield, Susan L. A348
Springfield, Claude A704
Springfield, Claude E350
Springmeyer, Douglas A565
Springuel, Myriam P506
Sprinkel, George P582
Sproat, Dan P259
Sprouls, Joe A555
Sprouse, Stephanie P361
Sprunk, Eric A377
Sprunk, Eric D. A592
Sprunk, Robert P358
Spurgeon, William W. (Bill) A279
Spurgeon, Thomas E. P449
Spurlin, Sharon A658
Spurlin, Cindy A823
Spurlin, Cindy P622
Spurling, David A. A414
Spurling, David A. E195
Spyridakos, Vangelis A218
Squadere, Bonnie A489
Squeri, Stephen J. (Steve) A48
Squeri, Stephen J. (Steve) A49
Squier, Jenny A218
Squier, Linda A902
Squier, Linda P693
Squilla, Candy P466
Squire, David A334
Squire, Brandon P452
Squires, James A. (Jim) A597
Squires, Paul A730
Squires, Eric A871
Squires, Gina P416
Sr, Ernest J Verrico A109
Sr, Lee R Anderson P40
Sr, Carlos De La Cruz P88

Sr, Reggie Copeland P123
Sr, Linda Reedy P247
Sr, Jesse T Williams P261
Sr, Dexter Suggs P292
Sr, John R Raymond P591
Sr, Robert Curran P603
Sr, Lee R Anderson P686
Sr, David Totemoff P694
Sr., Jerome L. Davis E19
Sr., Robert K. (Bobby) Reeves E436
Sr., Charles A. (Chuck) Meloy E436
Srbu, Mary A141
Sreenivasan, Katepalli R. (Sreeni) A585
Sreenivasan, Katepalli R. (Sreeni) P377
Srichukrin, Narong W330
Srihong, Teeranun W202
Srikantan, St A199
Srikrishna, Ramakarthikeyan P236
Srimahunt, Pikun W330
Sriniasan, Venkat A600
Srinivasan, Mira A49
Srinivasan, Mukund A71
Srinivasan, Veena A204
Srinivasan, Paddy E248
Sripratak, Adirek W88
Srirongmuang, Songphol W88
Srivastava, Raj A458
Srivastava, Sam K. A524
Srivastava, Raj P251
Srivastava, Isha P392
Srivastava, Gautam E368
Srivathsan, Venkataramani W274
Srivatsan, Nagaraja A217
Sroka, Kenneth P. A122
Sronce, Cindy P166
Sroufe, Daniel P414
Srouji, Johny A70
Srsen, Terrence A878
Staats, Sarah P236
Stabile, Steve P597
Stabio, Victor P. E185
Stabnow, Mark P439
Stacey, Rulon F A314
Stacey, Robert A861
Stacey, Rulon F P190
Stacey, Rulon P435
Stacey, Robert P658
Stack, Edward W. (Ed) A264
Stack, Susan Jane P298
Stack, Edward P319
Stack, John P P522
Stackalis, Jack A813
Stackalis, Jack P616
Stackhouse, Julie A322
Stacy, Jill A244
Stacy, Neel A446
Stacy, Neel E210
Stacy, Donald L. E278
Staczek, Eric A541
Staczek, Eric E266
Stadelmann, Tim P500
Stadler, Rupert W390
Staehle, Robert A151
Staelens, Kurt C. A733
Staffieri, Victor A. A665
Stafford, Connell A215
Stafford, William P. A343
Stafford, Vernon H. A348
Stafford, Nicole P160
Stafford, Deborah P210
Stafford, Ingrid S. P397
Stafford, Ryan K. E247
Stafstrom, Christine A644
Staggs, Lynn A165
Stagliano, Joseph R. A577
Staglin, Garen K. E138
Stagnitti, David A382
Stahl, Neil A698
Stahl, Stephanie A786
Stahl, Kent P227
Stahl, Jim P361
Stahl, Murray E169
Stahler, David A912
Stahlman, Ed A743
Stahlman, Ed E372

Stajduhar, Tony P258
Staley, Nina A599
Staley, Sally J. P98
Staley, David P575
Staley, James E. (Jes) W54
Stalick, Theodore R. A551
Stalker, Rebecca A105
Stalker, Robin J. W8
Stall, Michelle A246
Stall, Hank P511
Stallings, Terri A101
Stallings, Jay A111
Stallings, James B A836
Stallings, John G. A841
Stallings, Jay P56
Stallings, Kim P407
Stallings, John G. E410
Stallings, Norfleet E410
Stalnaker, Jeffrey C. P230
Staly, Amy P515
Stam, Thomas E281
Stamey, Russell H A599
Stamm, Jeffrey J P75
Stamm, Jeffrey J P88
Stamps, Winifred A446
Stamps, Winifred E210
Stanard, Patricia P297
Stanbrough, John A709
Standaart, Linda A770
Standard, John E263
Standeffer, Luke P577
Standish, William A. (Bill) A66
Standish, Dr Liz P406
Standlee, Carrie A446
Standlee, Carrie E210
Standley, John T. A708
Standley, Bonnie P95
Standridge, Brant J. A115
Standring, John A49
Stanek, Janet P543
Stanford, Beth P77
Stanford, Paul P382
Stanford, Barbara P415
Stang, Jeff A637
Stang, Kyle P602
Stanger, Dave A823
Stanic, Linda P87
Staniszewski, Sara A904
Staniszewski, Sara E442
Stankard, Beth A786
Stankey, John T. A84
Stankey, John A850
Stanley, Karen W. A160
Stanley, Jenny A223
Stanley, Gina A328
Stanley, Michael A493
Stanley, Susan D A644
Stanley, Gladys A806
Stanley, Miranda P164
Stanley, Linda P239
Stanley, John D. P287
Stanley, Raied P338
Stanley, David M P346
Stanley, Nicole P521
Stanley, Gladys P569
Stanley, James E. (Jes) W52
Stanley, Karen W. E55
Stanners, Russell W389
Stansberry, Liberty A149
Stansberry, James E371
Stansbury, Christopher D. (Chris) A77
Stansbury, Tracy A81
Stansbury, H. Tayloe A466
Stansbury, Tayloe A466
Stansbury, Tayloe E368
Stansell, Lisa P224
Stanski, Bruce A A358
Stanski, Matthew E P603
Stanton, Jill A. A344
Stanton, Kevin A A537
Stanton, Cheri A549
Stanton, Tim A865
Stanton, Tammie P459
Stanton, Oliver K. P623
Stanton, Cheri E270

Stanush, Dan A868
Stanutz, Nicholas G. (Nick) A440
Stanwood, Christl P269
Stanworth, Paul W217
Stanzione, Dominick P216
Stanzione, Dominick P302
Stapler, Richard P274
Staples, David M. (Dave) A756
Staples, Susan P368
Staples, William A. P643
Stapleton, Jack A223
Stapleton, Rebecca A720
Stapleton, Rebecca E362
Stapley, Gregory K E125
Stapp, Scott A602
Stapp, Ronnie E65
Starace, Francesco W141
Starcher, Jeff A724
Starchvill, Kevin P149
Stark, Ronald J. (Ron) A25
Stark, Arthur (Art) A120
Stark, Paul J A208
Stark, Doug A316
Stark, Ronald J. (Ron) P15
Stark, Lou P99
Stark, Doug P191
Stark, Larry P470
Stark, Kellie E437
Starke, James A640
Starkey, Linda P197
Starkovich, John E8
Starling, Curtis P111
Starmer, Samantha A691
Starnes, Clarke A. A115
Starnes, Karen A115
Starnes, Lee A238
Starnes, Will A330
Starnes, W. Stancil (Stan) A670
Starnes, Dave A751
Starnes, Dave E377
Starr, Vennesa A244
Starr, G. Gabrielle A585
Starr, Ken P64
Starr, Daniel B. (Dan) P162
Starr, Maureen P363
Starr, G. Gabrielle P377
Starsiak, Michael P352
Stashower, Susan A49
Stasior, Bill A70
Staskowski, Thomas A40
Stassi, Phillip J. A472
Stata, Ray A65
Staten, James M. A860
Staten, James M. P656
Staten, James M. P698
States, Lauren A883
Statton, Timothy P53
Statuto, Richard J. (Rich) E336
Staub, Steve A355
Staub, W. Richard A469
Staub, Pam A807
Staub, Lon A913
Staub, Pam P574
Staublin, Valerie A513
Staudt, Donald A678
Staudt, Tom P339
Stauffer, Charlotte A135
Stauffer, Larry A187
Stauffer, Tom A272
Stauffer, Charlotte P78
Stauffer, Larry E71
Stauffer, John E407
Staunton, Mark A541
Staunton, Henry E. W287
Staunton, Mark E266
Staupe, Ase A305
Staupe, Ase P185
Stausberg, Bertram W62
Stausholm, Jakob W1
Stavely, Peggy A823
Stavely, Peggy P622
Stavriotis, Eric A173
Stavropoulos, Nickolas (Nick) A650
Stavros, John P330
Steadman, Dan E193

A = AMERICAN BUSINESS
E = EMERGING COMPANIES
P = PRIVATE COMPANIES
W = WORLD BUSINESS

Stearn, David A508
Stearns, Leah C. A55
Stearns, Caitlin A335
Stearns, Deborah A478
Stearns, David P311
Stearns, Diane P393
Stebbins, Michael P170
Stech, Brian E448
Stecher, Kenneth W. (Ken) A196
Stecher, Esta E. A389
Steck, David A727
Steck, Mark P491
Stedem, Edwin P361
Stedfast, Sarah B. A873
Stedfast, Sarah B. P668
Steeber, Mark A115
Steel, Richard A131
Steele, John A196
Steele, Sally A. A225
Steele, Kelly A366
Steele, Paul Edward P115
Steele, Kevin B. P230
Steele, Athornia P398
Steele, Catherine J. P564
Steele, Sally A. E88
Steele, Barry G. E174
Steele, Glenn D. E337
Steele, Sarah E447
Steelman, Jenny A452
Steelman, Kecia A836
Steelman, Jenny E215
Steenbergen, Phil A332
Steenbergen, Ewout L. A721
Steenrod, Mitchell A166
Steenstra, Jack A685
Steer, Robert L. A730
Stefan, Nikki P628
Stefanac, John A685
Stefani, Tony A221
Stefani, Matt A541
Stefani, Diane P331
Stefani, Matt E266
Stefanini, Pierluigi W383
Stefansic, Robert J. (Bob) A453
Stefanski, Mike A870
Steffe, Greg A676
Steffen, Julie A478
Steffen, Mark A P142
Steffen, Mark P621
Steffens, Mikenzie P398
Steffensen, Mark A437
Steffensen, Dwight A780
Stegall, Larry P275
Stegeman, John A411
Stegeman, Jeff A489
Stegen, Andrew A520
Steger, Pete A541
Steger, David P554
Steger, Pete E266
Stegmann, Stefan Von A260
Stegmayer, Joseph H. (Joe) E61
Stegner, Robert L. (Bob) A779
Stehman, Marge P83
Steidel, Michael P96
Steigelman, Jeffrey A904
Steigelman, Jeffrey E442
Steiger, Peter P417
Steiger, John P541
Steigerwalt, Eric T A146
Steigman, Liz A406
Steimer, Richard A333
Stein, Jeffrey S. A40
Stein, David L. A81
Stein, Derek K. A130
Stein, Laura A208
Stein, Clint E. A219
Stein, William G. A237
Stein, Rona A323
Stein, Richard A332

Stein, Stephanie A449
Stein, Trudy A469
Stein, Anna A863
Stein, Keith L. P58
Stein, Kimberly P161
Stein, Barry P227
Stein, Paul P303
Stein, Lisa P449
Stein, Ronen W46
Stein, Clint E. E84
Stein, A. William (Bill) E107
Stein, Martin E. (Hap) E349
Stein, Sherry E407
Steinbach, Justin A244
Steinbeck, Daryl A813
Steinbeck, Daryl P616
Steinberg, Stephen A478
Steinberg, Kevin A812
Steinberg, Harold A869
Steinberg, Kevin P607
Steinberg, Michael P639
Steinberg, Doug E107
Steinberg, Joseph S. E201
Steinberg, Jonathan L. (Jono) E443
Steinborn, Birgit W331
Steinbronn, Kristi P101
Steiner, Judy A110
Steiner, Tim A149
Steiner, Jeffrey A355
Steiner, Melanie A682
Steiner, Curt A866
Steiner, Judy E37
Steines, Brian P487
Steinhafel, Arthur W. (Art) P432
Steinhardt, Michael H. E443
Steinhauser, Barbara P295
Steinke, Connie A351
Steinke, Lauren A493
Steinke, Angela P399
Steinke, Connie E158
Steinkopf, Gregory E429
Steinlauf, Jon P489
Steinmetz, Bill A820
Steinour, Stephen D. (Steve) A440
Steinwert, Kent A A316
Steinwert, Kent A E141
Stellar, Tom E320
Stelling, Kessel D. A781
Stellmaker, Michael P535
Stellmaker, Donald E13
Stellpflug, Morgan P101
Stelly, Donald D. (Don) E244
Stelman, Randee A5
Stelter, Mari P579
Stelzer, Laurie D. E186
Stemmer, Ralf W125
Stemmler, Matt A693
Stenberg, Melissa P178
Stende, Dave P176
Stenger, Michael J. P203
Stenhouse, John A710
Stenman, Eric P54
Stennis, Todd P364
Stenzel, Christopher (Chris) A235
Stepanova, Ekaterina A475
Stepanova, Ekaterina P266
Stepanski, Robert A480
Stephan, William B P627
Stephanie, Maher-dickerson A886
Stephanie, Maher-dickerson E433
Stephanouk, Alex A19
Stephen, Jim A574
Stephen, Buschmeyer A833
Stephen, Robert P2
Stephen, Antonia P590
Stephens, John J. A84
Stephens, Elizabeth A196
Stephens, Pamela A364
Stephens, Garrett A699
Stephens, Steven D. A919
Stephens, Brian P157
Stephens, Destiny P301
Stephens, Chad P348
Stephens, Linda P425
Stephens, Garrett P456

Stephens, Anthony P535
Stephens, Terry L P542
Stephens, Marty E273
Stephens, John M. E398
Stephenson, Randall L. A84
Stephenson, Jacqueline A136
STEPHENSON, JEAN A422
Stephenson, Sue A531
Stephenson, Pamela A770
Stephenson, Jennifer A802
Stephenson, Stephanie A857
Stephenson, David P27
Stephenson, Harry D P130
Stephenson, Don P130
Stephenson, Paul P148
STEPHENSON, JEAN P239
Stephenson, Patty P243
Stephenson, Steve P252
Stephenson, Roger P361
Stephenson, Mark P417
Stephenson, Karen P479
Stephenson, Anne P498
Stephenson, Jennifer P562
Stephenson, Brandon P649
Stephenson, Robert O. E315
Sterbenz, Isaac A724
Sterenski, Maria P60
Sterghos, Nick A564
Sterin, Steven A177
Sterling, Michelle A685
Sterling, Kira A819
Sterling, Gehane P603
Sterling, Mary P699
Sterling, Neil E39
Stern, Brian A105
Stern, Jonathan A359
Stern, Chris A556
Stern, Jim A909
Stern, James A909
Stern, Philip P168
Stern, Chris P593
Stern, Caryl M P636
Stern, Rachel R. E140
Stern, Paul D E253
Sternberg, Brent A384
Sternberg, Brent E176
Sternlicht, Barry S. E385
Sternthal, Benjamin P356
Stesal, Gennady A744
Stetson, John P658
Stetz, Gary E40
Stetzer, Ed P291
Steuterman, Chris A223
Steve, Harman A185
Steve, Enos A912
Steve, Osterman P333
Steven, Dan P295
Steven, Kukuk P694
Stevens, Jim A2
Stevens, Timothy (Chip) A19
Stevens, Kelly A49
Stevens, Christian A101
Stevens, Mark A108
Stevens, Mark A182
Stevens, Craig A225
Stevens, Dominique A330
Stevens, Charles K. (Chuck) A379
Stevens, Ed A477
Stevens, Chris A513
Stevens, Maureen A522
Stevens, William H A754
Stevens, Doug A770
Stevens, W. Arthur A832
Stevens, Simon A855
Stevens, Shelli A878
Stevens, David M P35
Stevens, Gary P53
Stevens, Chris P74
STEVENS, DEBBIE P213
Stevens, Ronald S P214
Stevens, Ed P248
Stevens, Velinda P269
Stevens, Rebecca P272
Stevens, Eddie P348
Stevens, Terri P361

Stevens, George P387
Stevens, Cheryl P620
Stevens, Kevin P639
Stevens, Ben W74
Stevens, Mark E35
Stevens, Mark E63
Stevens, Craig E88
Stevenson, Mark A350
Stevenson, David A576
Stevenson, Mark P. A815
Stevenson, Mark A902
Stevenson, Tom A907
Stevenson, Rich A920
Stevenson, Cindy P261
Stevenson, Mark P692
Stevenson, Tim E. P. W199
Stevenson, Mark E157
Stevenson, David E297
Stevenson, Tom E445
Steves, Sonya P285
Steward, David L. A907
Steward, Matt P339
Steward, David L. P696
Stewart, Lisa A69
Stewart, Will A115
Stewart, William (Bill) A140
Stewart, Janie A162
Stewart, Greg A166
Stewart, Brett A212
Stewart, Suzanne A266
Stewart, Jamie B A323
Stewart, Michael J. (Mike) A349
Stewart, John F. A359
Stewart, Jennifer A481
Stewart, Carol A485
Stewart, Marlene A496
Stewart, Derrick A614
Stewart, Don A649
Stewart, Stephanie D. A657
Stewart, Cheryl A676
Stewart, Chad P34
Stewart, Donald P148
Stewart, Lydia P149
Stewart, Amanda P243
Stewart, Anna P297
Stewart, Christie P300
Stewart, C Todd P309
Stewart, J P325
Stewart, Donna P333
Stewart, Richard P350
Stewart, Robert P388
Stewart, Austin P400
Stewart, Cindy P482
Stewart, Rick P491
Stewart, Kendall P516
Stewart, George P554
Stewart, Inez P570
Stewart, Thomas P591
Stewart, Deborah P603
Stewart, Lee P657
Stewart, Robert A. (Bob) W22
Stewart, Brett E79
Stewart, Robert S. (Bob) E112
Stewart, Richard R. E112
Stewart, Matt E144
Stewart, Michael J. (Mike) E156
Stgeorge, Marty A474
Stibal, John A864
Stiber, Barri P285
Stich, Mark P58
Stichnoth, Roseann A323
Stickel-Diehl, Valerie P101
Stickland, Davina A131
Stickney, Michael L. W180
Stidham, Cathy A614
Stidham, Mark W148
Stief, Brian A477
Stief, John P158
Stief, Brian P268
Stiefel, Lester A102
Stiegler, James A277
Stiers, Mark W. A280
Stiff, Cory A649
Stifferclaus, Vanessa A260
Stika, Martina P95

Still, Kevin A. A214
Still, Jay A657
Still, Kevin A. P128
Stilla, John A328
Stillar, Melissa A725
Stille, G-¶ran W352
Stills, David A878
Stillwell, Kathy P224
Stillwell, Ken E327
Stilman, Tony P482
Stilp, Erik P133
Stiltz, Bryan P198
Stilwell, Craig G. A207
Stimac, Scott P630
Stimmel, Glen L. A860
Stimmel, Glen L. P656
Stimpson, Sandy P123
Stinger, Harold P495
Stingily, Karl A327
Stinnett, Clay A772
Stinnett, Joseph A852
Stinnett, Donald W P207
Stinsman, Kathleen P618
Stinson, Deirdre A634
Stinson, Ron A655
Stinson, Ron E333
Stipa, John P186
Stipanov, John C A667
Stipanov, John C E336
Stipanovich, Sasha A693
Stipek, Deborah A507
Stipek, Deborah P288
Stipes, Larry P254
Stipp, Keith D. W29
Stipp, Janice E. E359
Stippig, Julian A204
Stiritz, William P. (Bill) A663
Stirling, Wynn C. P83
Stirling, Steve P305
Stites, Mark A185
Stites, Jill D P115
Stith, Melanie P94
Stitt, Kevin A765
Stitt, Livona P171
Stitt, David P360
Stitt, Kevin P540
Stivers, Betsy A863
Stiveson, Karen P25
Stjames, Joanne A407
Stjernholm, Helena W360
Stobak, Michael (Mike) P61
Stober, Renee L A136
Stockdale, Barry A56
Stocke, Sandra A916
Stocker, Michael A. A582
Stocker, Michael A. P373
Stockert, David E276
Stockmal, David A25
Stockmal, David P15
Stockmann, Bill P456
Stockmeister, Aaron A332
Stocksdale, Thomas A317
Stocksdale, Thomas E142
Stockton, Charles A244
Stockton, Dmitri L. A375
Stockton, Don P139
Stockton, Jennifer P271
Stockton, Lyndon P349
Stockton, Kevin P397
Stockwell, Paul A173
Stoddard, Lorilee A920
Stoddard, Thomas D. (Tom) W38
Stodghill, Sheila P157
Stoeckel, Daniel P525
Stoeckert, Michael A670
Stoehr, David L. A904
Stoehr, David L. E442
Stoeptelwerth, Joe P247
Stoering, Mark E. A910
Stoffel, Dawn A729
Stoffel, Jill P188
Stoffel, Timothy P333
Stoffels, Paulus (Paul) A476
Stoffels, Paul A476
Stoffers, Brian F. A172

Stoffregen, Lynn A412
Stoffregen, Lynn E192
Stogsdill, Son P106
Stokes, Russell A375
Stokes, Bobby A410
Stokes, Kristen A532
Stokes, Charles A548

Stokes, Melvina P121
Stokes, Charles P324
Stokey, Keith P135
Stokke, Doug P168
Stolarczyk, Mark A558
Stolarsky, Daniel A904
Stolarsky, Daniel E442
Stolhanske, Ruth A328
Stoll, Jennifer A542
Stoll, Anne P176
Stoll, Jennifer E267
Stolle, Russ A443
Stoller, Debra P52
Stoller, William H. (Bill) P188
Stollings, Anthony M. (Tony) A344
Stolorena, Sheila A844
Stolorena, Sheila E412
Stolpe, Albert K. E298
Stolper, Edward M. P90
Stoltman, Gary A493
Stoltmann, Gary A493
Stone, Peg A15
Stone, Brenda A105
Stone, Robert D. A122
Stone, Natalie A241
Stone, Carolyn A303
Stone, Neil A390
Stone, Denise A440
Stone, Wayne A446
Stone, Beth A486
Stone, Steven M. A497
Stone, Kaelin A518
Stone, Samuel G. A549
Stone, Sam A549
Stone, Claire A647
Stone, Scott A701
Stone, Woodrow A744
Stone, Mike A844
Stone, Kent V. A865
Stone, Bob A916
Stone, Peg P9
Stone, Todd L P42
Stone, Robert W P123
Stone, Jeff P145
Stone, Mildred P173
Stone, David P192
Stone, Terry P235
Stone, Mike P252
Stone, Derrick P283
Stone, Kaelin P293
Stone, Susan P498
Stone, David P530
Stone, Kelly P590
Stone, Christina P590
Stone, Wayne E210
Stone, Rya E216
Stone, Samuel G. E270
Stone, Sam E270
Stone, Sheldon M. E312
Stone, William C. (Bill) E383
Stone, Mike E412
Stoneburner, Charles A196
Stonehill, Robyn Price A83
Stoner, Colin P400
Stonesifer, Timothy C. (Tim) A418
Stoness, Scott A492
Stonestreet, Dana L A428
Stooksbury, Spencer A51
Stopczynski, Pawel W51
Stoppelman, Jeremy E447
Storer, Carrie A269
Storey, Jeffrey K. (Jeff) A185
Storfjell, Judith P294
Stork, Ryan D. A130
Stork, Hans A620
Storm, David P511
Stormo, Taylor A168

Storms, Donna A711
Storr, Hanns-Peter W125
Storset, Snorre W269
Storto, David E. A635
Storto, David E. P419
Storvick, Jim A839
Storvick, Jim E409
Story, Leo A58
Story, Jeryl A754
Story, Edward P458
Story, Leo E16
Story, Jeryl E380
Stoskopf, Tom P437
Stotts, Cheryl A890
Stotts, Cheryl P684
Stouffer, Steve A744
Stough, Joe P348
Stout, Neil A218
Stout, Luanne A802
Stout, Bob A878
Stout, William P207
Stout, Luanne P562
Stout, Deana P583
Stovall, Charles A303
Stover, Jeremy A496
Stoverock, Linda P365
Stowe, Jay C. A798
Stowe, Brandi P157
Stowe, Roy P258
Stowe, Barry L. W295
Stowell, John A282
Stoyanoff, Pamela (Pam) P336
Stoyanovich, Slavica P473
Stpierre, Michael A158
Strabala, Gwen P224
Strabele, Michael A441
Strable-Soethout, Deanna D. A668
Strachan-smith, Genie A866
Strachota, Jenny A81
Strack, Denise P216
Strader, H. Gregg A52
Strader, Gregg A52
Strader, Mark P458
Strader, Christopher E182
Straffi, Glenn R. A639
Straffi, Glenn R. E325
Strah, Steven E. (Steve) A355
Strahlman, Ellen R. A119
Strahlman, John P337
Straight, Sharra A591
Straight, Derek E252
Strain, Robert D. (Rob) A96
Strain, John F. A901
Strain, Charles P155
Strain, Trevor W249
Strain, Kevin D. W347
Strait, Kelli A770
Straker, Gary A620
Stram, Randy A555
Stramel, Joan P181
Strampel, William D. P341
Stranathan, Brent A175
Strange, Mallor A438
Strange, Nicholas (Nick) A682
Strange, John P535
Strangeway, Christine P531
Strangfeld, John R. A676
Stranghoener, V. Raymond (Ray) A223
Strasheim, Alicia P261
Strasser, Michael P314
Strassner, Larry P204
Strathmann, Bill P370
Stratman, R. Joseph A605
Stratton, Ed A125
Stratton, Mike A158
Stratton, Sarah A221
Stratton, John G. A870
STRATTON, MARTHA P163
Straub, Karl P258
Straubel, Jeffrey B. (JB) A799
Straus, David H. A427
Straus, Moshel P32
Straus, David H. E202
Strauss, Sarah A163
Strauss, Cindy P444

Strauss, Andrew L. P611
Strauss, Frank W125
Strauss, Allan H. E90
Strauss, Rick E207
Strauss, Thomas J. E337
Stravitz, Mitchell A173
Straw, Mona A342
Strawser, Joyce P494
Strayer, Joe P255
Straz, David A. P197
Stream, Christopher A100
Stream, Kevin A508
Stream, Christopher E34
Strecker, Jenna P692
Streed, Ben A693
Street, Jim A677
Streeter, Robert P314
Streeter, Bill P339
Streeter, Debra P517
Streit, Steven W. E182
Streletzky, Donna P67
Strength, Brent P256
Strey, Jean P145
Strianese, Anthony T. (Tony) E47
Stribley, Lucy A140
Strickland, Hoyt J. A53
Strickland, Samuel R A140
Strickland, Sam A140
Strickland, Mark A162
Strickland, Robert A171
Strickland, Kristen A446
Strickland, Eric A599
Strickland, Robert P100
Strickland, Greg P320
Strickland, Kristen E210
Strickler, Gayla A440
Strickler, Benjamin E24
Stricklin, Leslie G A700
Stricklin, Mark S A845
Stricklin, Mark S E413
Strike, George L. P640
Strimmenos, Sarah A614
Strinden, Steven P249
Stringer, David A352
Stringer, Peter A800
Stringer, Ruth M P144
Stringer, Peter E396
Stringfellow, West A788
Stringfellow, Ryan P536
Stritikus, Tom A861
Stritikus, Tom P658
Strochak, Scott A105
Stroeh, Brad A344
Stroh, Rosa A416
Stroh, Elizabeth P249
Strohaver, Deborah P671
Strohl, Kingman P98
Strohl, Brenda P694
Strohmaier, Walter W58
Stromberg, Stephanie A458
Stromberg, William J. (Bil) A783
Stromberg, Leroy P18
Stromberg, Stephanie P251
Strong, Brendan A795
Strong, Eric P366
Strongin, Steven H. A389
Stropp, John R A800
Stropp, John R P559
Stroud, Scott A408
Stroud, Andrea A659
Stroud, J. Mark P264
Stroud, Andrew E124
Strout, Matt A677
Stroz, Edward M. P200
Strozzi, Mary A387
Strozzi, Gianluca A648
Strozzi, Mary E177
Strubell, Taylor A230
Strubert, John P206
Struck, Richard A865
Strunk, Thomas W. (Tom) A907
Strunk, Thomas W. (Tom) P696
Strunk, Ed E139
Strup, Richard E57
Struth, Werner W70

A = AMERICAN BUSINESS
E = EMERGING COMPANIES
P = PRIVATE COMPANIES
W = WORLD BUSINESS

Strycker, Samara A A577
Stryker, David M. A443
Str--berg, Hans W36
Stuart, Al A52
Stuart, Christian A157
Stuart, Nicholas A489
Stuart, Susan A597
Stuart, Jack A704
Stuart, Tim A707
Stuart, Cindy P237
Stuart, Travis P268
Stuart, Tim P410
Stuart, Wilma P497
Stuart, Michael P666
Stuart, Nancy E89
Stuart, Jack E351
Stubblefield, Alfred G P59
Stubbs, Don P92
Stubbs, P. Scott E139
Stuck, Nancy P630
STUCKART, ERIC P163
Stucky, Duane P513
Studer, Jackie E213
Stueve, Jo P327
Stuewe, Michael A826
Stuff, Ronald P546
Stuff, Ronald P605
Stuhr, Kim A407
Stukalin, Felix E224
Stukenborg, John A816
Stull, John P160
Stull, Steven E163
Stulpin, Anne A152
Stulpin, Anne E48
Stultz, Liz A105
Stultz, Timothy J. E290
Stumbo, Kevin J. A227
Stumbo, Kevin J. A228
Stump, James M. A423
Sturany, Klaus W164
Sturdivant, Lisa A131
Sturges, Anthony P52
Sturgess, David E P305
Sturgess, Dave P305
Sturm, Stephan W154
Sturycz, Robert A780
Sturz, Jonathan A419
Sturza, Scott G A413
Sturza, Scott G P234
Stutts, Garry A343
Stutts, William A863
Stuver, Douglas K. (Doug) A630
Styles, Maurice A84
Styles, Tracy A912
Styles, Kelly R. P138
Styons, Connie P554
Stys, Richard P227
Su, Lisa A14
Su, Lily A558
Su, David A685
Su, Meihsun W113
Suarez, Jennifer A175
Suarez, Linda A369
Suarez, Jaime A652
Suarez, Zoraya A659
Suarez, JP A878
Suarez, John A878
Suarez, Mar- a Fernanda W133
Suarez-Davis, Annemarie A485
Suasin, Winlove B P544
Subbaswamy, Kumble R.
   (Swamy) P645
Subia, Mario A102
Subilia, Sam A777
Subilia, Sam E393
Subler, Leo A746
Subramaniam, Chandra A620
Subramanian, Bala A878
Subramanian, V A P290

Subramanyan, Raju P333
Sucher, Steve A539
Suchman, Edward A2
Suchora, ED E253
Suchy, Frederick J. P114
Suckale, Margret W55
Sucke, Rebecca P109
Sucy, Michele A525
Sucy, Michele P303
Sud, James (Jim) A899
Sud, James (Jim) P690
Suddeth, Stacy B A737
Suddeth, Stacy A737
Suddeth, Stacy B E367
Suddeth, Stacy E367
Suderman, Julie P566
Suek, Mark P141
Suek, Sheana E437
Suer, Bernard P334
Suetens, David A766
Suever, Catherine A. (Cathy) A634
Suffridge, Guy P469
Sugar, Robert J. A703
Sugarman, Sarah A49
Sugarman, Eli P236
Sugarman, Jay E226
Sugawa, Clyde P19
Sugden, John A273
Sugden, John P162
Sughayer, Manal A541
Sughayer, Manal E266
Sughrue, Timothy P456
Sugiarto, Prijono W195
Sugiura, Junichi W116
Sugiyama, Yoshihiro A917
Sugiyama, Deborah P391
Sugiyama, Yoshihiro P701
Sugiyama, Nao W273
Sugrue, John P482
Suhm, Tom A480
Suit, John M P39
Sukeno, Kenji W155
Sukola, Joe A550
Sukut, Paul P62
Sukut, Paul M P151
Sukys, Dan A489
Sulentic, Robert E. (Bob) A172
Sulerzyski, Charles W. A645
Sulerzyski, Charles W. E329
Sulik, Ronald D P392
Sulkis, Michael A109
Sullivan, Robert A16
Sullivan, Steven R A42
Sullivan, Chris A44
Sullivan, Timothy J. A69
Sullivan, Andrew A85
Sullivan, Darin A95
Sullivan, Gene A108
Sullivan, Bryan A133
Sullivan, Dave A221
Sullivan, William P. (Bill) A291
Sullivan, William A308
Sullivan, Daniel G. A323
Sullivan, Melody A364
Sullivan, Briana A408
Sullivan, Gary A449
Sullivan, Jason A454
Sullivan, John A548
Sullivan, Bonnie A555
Sullivan, Owen J A578
Sullivan, Anne Marie A582
Sullivan, Nicole A584
Sullivan, David A599
Sullivan, Brian A619
Sullivan, Linda A647
Sullivan, Kevin A648
Sullivan, Teresa A698
Sullivan, Frank C. A716
Sullivan, Lynne A725
Sullivan, Charles A750
Sullivan, George E. A766
Sullivan, Martin A766
Sullivan, Michael A767
Sullivan, Roy A770
Sullivan, Bill A770

Sullivan, Thais A774
Sullivan, Steve A784
Sullivan, Mark L. A830
Sullivan, Patrick A878
Sullivan, Burt P4
Sullivan, Chris P31
Sullivan, Pam P36
Sullivan, Sean P58
Sullivan, John P94
Sullivan, Gerald M P113
Sullivan, Kate P122
Sullivan, Thomas P123
Sullivan, Jacqueline P152
Sullivan, Dennis P154
Sullivan, Ken P161
Sullivan, Karen P247
Sullivan, John P321
Sullivan, Robert A P329
Sullivan, Mark A P330
Sullivan, Anne Marie P373
Sullivan, Brian P392
Sullivan, Margaret P398
Sullivan, Timothy F P423
Sullivan, William E. (Bill) P449
Sullivan, Teresa P456
Sullivan, Michael P465
Sullivan, Steve P486
Sullivan, John P527
Sullivan, Kevin P584
Sullivan, George P603
Sullivan, Leo P625
Sullivan, Julie H. P653
Sullivan, John P675
Sullivan, Elizabeth P699
Sullivan, Chris W312
Sullivan, Darin E28
Sullivan, Gene E35
Sullivan, Patrick E41
Sullivan, Joanne E144
Sullivan, Philip E282
Sullivan, Jeffrey M. E384
Sullivan, Mark L. E403
Sullivan, Greg E424
Sullivan, Denis E445
Sullivan-Marx, Eileen A585
Sullivan-Marx, Eileen P377
Sullivan-Yelko, Teri A677
Sulpizio, Don A677
Sulpizio, Richard E355
Sulston, Patrick A537
Sult, John R P177
Sult, John R P515
Sumi, Chrissy A272
Sumi, Shuzo W367
Sumichrast, Robert T. P669
Summerford, Dan A115
Summerford, R. Michael A832
Summers, Kevin V A93
Summers, Diane M. A97
Summers, Laura A175
Summers, Markus A324
Summers, Michael A707
Summers, Vic P152
Summers, Steve P157
Summers, Ashley P289
Summers, Angela M P591
Summers, Diane M. E32
SUMMERSON, NEIL W50
Sumner, Kirstin Baum A149
Sumner, Christopher A517
Sumner, Randee A618
Sumner, Mike P649
Sumoski, David A. A605
Sumpter, Tammy A647
Sumpter, Marlin P348
Sumpter, Nikki P555
Sun, Albert A285
Sun, Benjamin A390
Sun, David P. W84
Sun, Jack W354
Sun, Albert E114
Sunada, Masako A133
Sund, Charlotta W360
Sundaram, Eash A474
Sundell, Daniel A866

Sunderland, Matthew E293
Sunderuaus, Dan P399
Sunderwirth, David A105
Sung, Devin A530
Sung, Keehyuk P243
Sung, Vivian P695
Sung, Se Hwan W65
Sung-joong, Huh W265
Sung-Wook, Park W332
Sunterapak, Todd P662
Suntichok, Pimolpa W330
Suntrapak, Todd P662
Sunvold, Keri P192
Sunywcc, Instructor A476
Suojanen, Tina A120
Supakarapongkul, Viboon W88
Supornpaibul, Jirawat W203
Sur, Moushumi P304
Sura, Catherine P6
Surace, Dennis A578
Suraci, Armond A85
Suranjan, Magesvaran A671
Suranye, Monique A333
Suratos, Arnold A607
Surbaugh, Michael P81
Sureda, Rob A201
Suresh, Subra P96
Suresh, K.C. W274
Surette, Jahn A406
Surette, Stanley P P632
Surface, Suzanne A594
Surface, Michael E146
Suri, Rajeev W266
Suri- ±ach, Ignacio Segura W6
Surjaudaja, Parwati W280
Surls, Courtney P37
Surman, Mark P356
Surovi, Beverly P525
Surovich, Robert A500
Surovich, Robert E237
Surplus, Scott A423
Surplus, Scott E199
Surratt, Jeanette P672
Surridge, Sally B P327
Susca, Vito A741
Susca, Vito E370
Susik, Daniel A718
Susik, Dan A718
Suske, Lori A532
Suskind, Dennis A. A145
Suskind, Dennis A. E46
Susko, Colleen P180
Susman, Sally A648
Susman, Lynn P570
Susor, Mark A850
Sussman, Andrew J. (Andy) A250
Sustana, Mark A508
Sutandar, Laurie A640
Sutaris, Joseph E. A225
Sutaris, Joseph E. E88
Sutcliff, Michael R. (Mike) W5
Suter, Cynthia L P606
Sutera, AJ P579
Sutherland, Kenneth A795
Sutherland, Ken A795
Sutherland, David S. (Dave) A852
Sutherland, Mark A865
Sutherland, Nicol E383
Sutisna, Paulus W119
Sutivong, Arak W330
Sutko, Sally P309
Sutley, Nancy P297
Sutter, David A327
Sutter, Victor A517
Sutter, David A657
Suttle, Tara A754
Suttle, Tara E380
Sutton, Mark A3
Sutton, Richard A51
Sutton, Dave A82
Sutton, Scott M. A177
Sutton, Mark S. A462
Sutton, Patricia A P8
Sutton, Dave P49
Sutton, Brent P108

Sutton, Richard O. P242
Sutton, Ellen P396
Sutton, Jaqueline P576
Sutton, Lynn P673
Sutton, Wendy P678
Sutton, Matt E432
Suvalic, Adnan P251
Suyash, Ashu A721
Suzuki, Kazi A919
Suzuki, Yoshihiro P24
Suzuki, Kenji W169
Suzuki, Masahito W207
Suzuki, Toru W207
Suzuki, Nobuya W238
Suzuki, Yasunobu W242
Suzuki, Daiichiro W243
Suzuki, Hisahito W249
Suzuki, Tomoyuki W337
Suzuki, Toshihiro W351
Suzuki, Osamu W351
Suzuki, Masaharu W373
Svanstrom, Johan A310
Svendsen, Heidi A855
Svendsen, Berit W360
Svendsgaard, Vicki A101
Svenkerud, Doug A51
Svinjar, Djenita A329
Svoboda, Frank M. A822
Svoboda, Dan B. A907
Svoboda, Dan B. P696
Svogun, Joanne P564
Svp, Bernard A54
Swaan, Tom de W209
Swaan, Tom de W405
Swaby, Jonathan P125
Swafford, Jermaine A243
Swafford, C Matt A456
Swafford, Alan A693
Swaha, Charles P669
Swain, Kathy A34
Swain, Steven E. (Steve) A270
Swain, Skip A844
Swain, Debra P86
Swain, Stacy P345
Swain, Nan P399
Swain, Jayme P445
Swain, Skip E412
Swais, Ala A351
Swais, Ala E158
Swallow, Edward M. (Ed) P564
Swallow, Ed P564
Swaminathan, Gnanasekaran
   Sekar A185
Swaminathan, Sekar A185
Swamy, Venkatesh A644
Swan, Bob A288
Swan, Robert H. (Bob) A456
Swan, Mara E A525
Swan, Joshua P243
Swan, Quito P243
Swan, Dennis P518
Swan, Beth A. P618
Swandby, Janet P442
Swanepoel, Pieter P181
Swanepoel, Fred W256
Swango, Gary A397
Swango, Gary P221
Swank, C. Eric A117
Swank, Eric A117
Swank, Colleen P29
Swann, Don A878
Swanner, Angela A640
Swanson, Paulyn A28
Swanson, Brian A94
Swanson, Brian A95
Swanson, Steven A133
Swanson, Duane A196
Swanson, Roxann A199
Swanson, Marc A334
Swanson, Kelly A414
Swanson, Erika A466
Swanson, Brett A489
Swanson, Jerry A540
Swanson, Al A657
Swanson, Al A658

Swanson, Wendy A701
Swanson, Celia A878
Swanson, Jon A904
Swanson, Paulyn P17
Swanson, Brian P53
Swanson, Kim P92
Swanson, Heather P125
Swanson, Malcolm P129
Swanson, Scott J. P153
Swanson, Jerry P316
Swanson, Glenn P348
Swanson, Al P431
Swanson, Brian E28
Swanson, Jim E86
Swanson, Kelly E194
Swanson, Jon E442
Swantek, Kevin A513
Swart, Mackenzie A698
Swart, Mackenzie P456
Swarts, David A481
Swartz, Debbie A8
Swartz, Tim A898
Swartz, Debbie P3
Swartz, David G. P37
Swartz, Jimmy P680
Swartz, Richard S. (Rick) E289
Swarup, Vijay A313
Swaya, Matthew A763
Swayne, Tashaan P125
Swearengin, Mike A609
Swearingen, John S. A527
Sweat, Marcia A772
Sweatt, Clint P239
Swedberg, Greg A449
Swedish, Joseph R. A68
Sweedler, Jonathan A607
Sweeney, Jean A3
Sweeney, Joseph E. (Joe) A56
Sweeney, Richard S. A355
Sweeney, Eileen A388
Sweeney, Sue A406
Sweeney, Anne A581
Sweeney, Sean A651
Sweeney, Tim A718
Sweeney, Brian P376
Sweeney, Ken P409
Sweeney, Chris P425
Sweeney, Sean P426
Sweeney, Ronald M P461
Sweeney, Nathan P550
Sweeney, Allison P655
SWEENEY, MICHAEL W48
Sweeney, Christopher E360
Sweers, Kim A565
Sweet, Joy A34
Sweet, Lindsay S A350
Sweet, Lindsay A350
Sweet, Rob A861
Sweet, Brett P615
Sweet, Rob P658
Sweet, Julie W5
Sweet, Lindsay S E157
Sweet, Lindsay E157
Sweet, John W. E332
Sweetenham, Paul A818
Sweid, Noor P313
Sweney, Elizabeth A640
Swensen, Mark A867
Swenson, Lynn A143
Swenson, Mark A718
Swenson, Peter A838
Swenson, Andrew D. (Andy) A847
Swenson, John P107
Swenson, Beau J P579
Swenson, Andrew D. (Andy) E414
Swepston, Sharon P569
Swerdlow, Steven A. (Steve) A172
Swestka, Jason A562
Swestka, Jason E279
Swett, Christian R. (Chris) A837
Swiader, Josten A817
Swick, Greg E406
Swierenga, Brian E54
Swieringa, John W. A270
Swift, Christopher J. A406

Swift, Christine A513
Swift, Malcolm A544
Swift, Robert A725
Swift, Nick P314
Swift, Brian G P618
Swiger, Andrew P. (Andy) A313
Swiley, Thomas S. A504
Swiley, Thomas S. E241
Swilley, Lori P224
Swim, John E P372
Swindal, James P169
Swindall, Dewayne E172
Swinden, Lauren A390
Swindle, J. Dean A171
Swindle, J. Dean P100
Swinehart, Alice P334
Swinkey, Linda A446
Swinkey, Linda E210
Swinney, Brad A316
Swinney, Brad P191
Swiryn, Steven P390
Swissman, Josh A558
Swistak, Emily P60
Switalski, Pamela A5
Switalski, Brian E350
Switkowski, Zygmunt W348
Switz, Robert E. (Bob) A560
Switzer, Julie P683
Swize, Dr Michael P415
Swonder, Joy P457
Swope, John P330
Swords, Sheridan C. A622
Sy, Alland A390
Sy, Teresita W61
Syal, Rajeev (Raj) A440
Sydnor, Walker P. P105
Syed, Khalid A140
Syiek, Mary A565
Sykes, John A448
Sykes, Rebecca A552
Sykes, Rebecca P328
Sykes, John P545
Syler-Jones, Tracy P560
Sylstra, Michael A375
Sylvain, Nadine A584
Sylvain, Nadine P376
Sylvester, Maryrose T. A375
Sylvester, Ileen P511
Sylvia-Reardon, Mary A635
Sylvia-Reardon, Mary P419
Symonds, Chris A309
Symonds, Jonathan W173
Symonds, Rob W. P. W176
Symons, Robert A. A665
Synek, Christopher R. A913
Syngal, Sonia A809
Synnamon, Bill A879
Syper, John A100
Syran, Jim E123
Syth, David P553
Sytsma, Dan P293
Syverud, Kent D. P616
Szabados, Michael E300
Szablak, Chester J. (Chet) A301
Szablak, Chester J. (Chet) E127
Szablowski, Paul A801
Szablowski, Paul P562
Szabo, Susan P183
Szalla, Todd A10
Szallar, Lori A879
Szambelan, Jill A669
Szaraburak, Deb A406
Szatkiewicz, Cory P629
Szczechowski, Michael A906
Szczepanek, Michael P398
Szczepanski, Chester J. A276
Szczupak, David T. (Dave) A898
Szebenyi, Steven E. P230
Szemborski, Anne A602
Szerlong, Timothy J. (Tim) A211
Szeto, Rita P480
Szewczyk, Michael P79
Szlosek, Thomas A. (Tom) A429
Sznewajs, Robert D. A97
Sznewajs, John G. A534

Sznewajs, Robert D. E32
Szostek, Jeanie A644
Szucs, Theresa P531
Szuldman, Diego A204
Szurek, Paul E. E96
Szwankowski, Anthony A195
Szygiel, Annette A862
Szygiel, Annette E419
Szymanowski, Joe A333
Szymczak, Luke A368
Szymczak, Stephen J P276
S-¶derlund, Patrick A292
S-¶zen, Süleyman W377
S-,rby, Morten K. W360
S-,rensen, Mikael W352

T

T, Holly P639
Taal, Renzo A723
Taaveniku, Arja W206
Taavola, Daryl A16
Tabaka, William A437
Tabaridunn, Neda A331
Tabaridunn, Neda E148
Tabb, Kevin P71
Taber, Gregory A862
Taber, Abram P603
Taber, Terry R. E115
Taber, Gregory E419
Taborga, Jorge R. E316
Tabrizi, Ali A778
Tacella, Micheal P378
Tacha, Deanell Reese P423
Tachasirinugune, Sommai W88
Tachimori, Takeshi W342
Tachna, Jeremiah A272
Tacka, David A416
Tacke, Markus W331
Tackett, Willie A441
Tackett, Garland P301
Tackitt, Susan A143
Tackoor, Gary A97
Tackoor, Gary E32
Tacoma, Ray A460
Tad-Y, Darlene B P641
Tadda, Christopher A599
Tadeo, James A54
Tadiello, Larissa A489
Tadros, Abdullah A351
Tadros, Abdullah E158
Taets, Joseph D. (Joe) A74
Taffe, Pat P387
Tafoya, Lynne A897
Tafoya, Lynne P687
Taft, Matthias W60
Tagaras, Neil A693
Tagert, Steven P42
Tagg, Sherri P34
Tagg, Robin P243
Taggart, Richard G. A766
Taggart, Daniel J. E350
Tagliareni, John P310
TAGUCHI, YUKIO W48
Taha, Ayman A93
Taheri, Paul P614
Tahvonen, Greg A262
Tai, Pin A170
Taiclet, James D. (Jim) A55
Taiclet, David L. (Dave) E1
Taik-Keun, Jung W163
Taillac, Paul P418
Taira, John A183
Taisey, Mark Taisey A61
Tait, Richard A763
Tait, Bryan P601
Tait, Joseph M. (Joe) E251
Takac, Kevin A489
Takagi, Yoshiyuki W116
Takagi, Kazuhiro W272
Takagi, Ichiro W337
Takahama, Satoru W336
Takahashi, Koichi W113
Takahashi, Tetsu W208

A = AMERICAN BUSINESS
E = EMERGING COMPANIES
P = PRIVATE COMPANIES
W = WORLD BUSINESS

Takahashi, Shizuo W246
Takahashi, Kenji W263
Takahashi, Toyonori W279
Takahashi, Kunio W324
TAKAHASHI, SHOJIRO W326
Takahashi, Mitsuru W342
Takami, Kazunori W282
Takara, Kurt P326
Takasaka, Masahiko W192
Takashima, Denise A798
Takayama, Yasushi W268
Takeda, Becky P132
Takeda, Tomohisa W48
Takei, Masato W336
Takemura, Shigeyuki W27
Takemura, Hideaki W237
Takemura, Tsutomu W268
Takeshige, Matsuko P292
Taketa, Richard P238
Takeuchi, Kohei W172
Takeuchi, Akira W242
Takillapati, Rama P632
Takizawa, Soichiro W172
Takizawa, Masahiro W399
Takla, Magdy P576
Takushi, Dana A103
Talada, Dana A350
Talaga, Dana E156
Talati, Vijay A482
Talaulicar, Anant A246
Talavera, Judith A47
Talavera, Alvaro P241
Talbert-chandler, Melanie A565
Talbot, Pat A421
Talbot, Brian A549
Talbot, Chris A685
Talbot, Angela P256
Talbot, Pat E199
Talbot, Brian E270
Talcott, Patrick A644
Talhouet, Patrice de A241
Taliento, Anthony A87
Tallamraju, Raman A784
Tallent, Jimmy C. A844
Tallent, William P542
Tallent, Jimmy C. E412
Tallet, Eric A685
Talley, Cyndi A410
Talley, Doug A784
Talley, Davena P13
Talley, Wanda H P172
Talley, Mike P181
Talley, Verlinda P647
Talley-Smith, Christy A135
Talley-Smith, Christy P78
Tallis, Heather P596
Tallman, Brad A482
Talmontas, Kirk A318
Talonpoika, Nikolas W205
Tam, Eric A133
Tam, Cherry A204
Tam, Jamie A390
Tamagawa, Akio W261
Tamai, Takaaki W367
Tamaka, Hideo A51
Tamaka, Hideo P33
Tamanaha, Nona P601
Tamargo, Rafael P266
Tamasi, Tony A607
Tamayo, Jonathan P112
Tamayo, Kelvin Tamayo E407
Tambakeras, Markos I. A915
Tambe, Ninad E426
Tambling, Dave A22
Tamburi, Carlo W141
Tamez, Cesar P635
Tamir, Tal A685
Tamkin, Gary P314
Tammaro, Vincent P699

Tammy, Miller A382
Tams, Darrin P538
Tan, Alex A24
Tan, Jenny A671
Tan, Nestor W61
Tan, Zhaohui W90
Tan, Darren S. P. W280
Tanabe, Masaki W28
Tanabe, Masahiro W246
Tanaka, Stanley A798
Tanaka, Bryan P643
Tanaka, Masayasu W192
Tanaka, Jun W208
Tanaka, Seiichi W336
Tanaka, Junichi W337
Tanaka, Takaaki E310
Tanasijevich, George A502
Tancredi, Lucy E140
Tande, Gunnar P331
Tandon, Saurabh A67
Tandon, Ashish A163
Tandon, Manu P71
Tandy, Sonya A223
Taneja, Rajat A874
Tang, Michael A22
Tang, Karen A136
Tang, Stephen S. E318
Tangney, Eugene A718
Tango, Yasutake W194
Tangpong, Annie X P386
Tangredi, Edward P688
Tanguay, Bob P179
Taniguchi, Arthur K A102
Taniguchi, Michihiro W243
Taniguchi, Shinichi W336
Tanikawa, Kei W28
Tanimoto, Dale A102
Tanis, Jason P64
Tanishige, Haruyasu W190
Tankala, Ashoka P248
Tankesley, Mark A223
Tanksley, Rob A835
Tannehill, Tom A327
Tannehill, Martha A387
Tannehill, Martha E177
Tannenbaum, Carl A323
Tannenbaum, Mark P101
Tanner, Anthony A105
Tanner, Ryan A107
Tanner, Teresa J. A332
Tanner, Steve A344
Tanner, Kirk A647
Tanner, Edward P266
Tanner, Ryan E35
Tannert, Silvio P96
Tannian, Michael A850
Tanory, Todd A591
Tanoue, Donna A. A103
Tans, Gillian A139
Tantikulanan, Thiti W202
Tantivess, Vittavat W88
Tanum, Anne Carine W129
Tanz, Stuart A. E355
Tanzawa, Hideo W400
Tanzer, David A133
Taohai, Xue W91
Taormina, Jo A A129
Taormina, Jo A129
Taparausky, Kevin A817
Tapler, Howard A727
Taplin, Mary-Ellen P153
Taplits, Steven A120
Tappan, Skip A161
Tappan, Hugh P681
Tappeiner, Max A502
Tarafa, Denise A182
Tarafa, Denise E63
Tarakji, Ahmad P612
Tarango, Rachel P508
Tarantino, Steve A546
Tarantino, Frank P200
Taraporevala, Cyrus A766
Taras, Jennifer A683
Tarasova, Natasha A533
Tarbell, Mike A592

Tarbutton, Audrey P218
Tarby, Todd P374
Tarchetti, Mark S. A586
Tardella, Michael A644
Taride, Michel A809
Taride, Michel P584
Tarim, Soner P226
Tarin, Tatum P332
Taris, Tom A49
Tarleton, Kevin A446
Tarleton, Kevin E210
Tarling, Neil P186
Tarlton, Dudley A591
Tarnowski, Dennis A844
Tarnowski, Dennis E412
Tarpey, John P54
Tarpley, Dan A257
Tarpley, Gary P443
Tarr, Jeffrey A244
Tarriff, Scott L. E113
Tartaglia, Michael A582
Tartaglia, Michael P373
Tartaglione, Paul A140
Tartanella, Michael A109
Tartanella, Michael E36
Tarter, Christopher M P81
Tarvainen, William P118
Tarvestad, Katherine P26
Tarvin, Julie A459
Tarwater, Michael C P97
Tashiro, Tamiharu W201
Taske, Jim A67
Tassada, Inna P256
Tasselli, Stephen M. A640
Tassin, Bruce P537
Tastad, Carolyn A671
Tate, Howard M A787
Tate, Charles P105
Tate, Allyson P140
Tate, Bonnie P284
Tate, Mike P395
Tate, Creston P700
Tatelbaumm, Ron P230
Tateosian, David A353
Tatera, Robert A218
Tateyama, Len A97
Tateyama, Len E32
Tatterson, W. Mark A843
Tatterson, W. Mark E411
Tatum, Mary P75
Tatum, William P317
Taub, Jonathan S P441
Taube, Carl A700
Taube, Jo Ann P272
Taubeneck, Paul A489
Taubeneck, Brian A861
Taubeneck, Brian P658
Taubert, Jennifer A476
Taubman, Ross E. A670
Taunton, Michael A77
Tavaglinoe, John P145
Tavakkolizadeh, Ali P567
Tavakoli, Nader A40
Tavalsky, Gregory A460
Tavares, Chris A136
Tavares, Luis P227
Tavares, Carlos W286
Tavernier, Jacques W387
Tavlarides, Toula A105
Tawasha, Nelson A438
Tawney, Jeff A818
Tawyea, Edward P618
Tay, Talal A244
Tay, Julie E10
Tay, Kee C E394
Tayano, Ken W113
Taylor, J A54
Taylor, Ryan A81
Taylor, David L A96
Taylor, Shawna A101
Taylor, Joyce A101
Taylor, Frank J A101
Taylor, Pam A115
Taylor, Steven W A122

Taylor, Jacque A164
Taylor, Eric A196
Taylor, Gregory A199
Taylor, Warren A247
Taylor, Lyndon C. A263
Taylor, Judy A272
Taylor, Rhonda M A273
Taylor, Stephen M. (Steve) A289
Taylor, Karen A303
Taylor, Robert A387
Taylor, Robert A420
Taylor, Pamela J. (Pam) A427
Taylor, Jim A442
Taylor, Anna A446
Taylor, Todd J A462
Taylor, Jeff A489
Taylor, Patti L A496
Taylor, Bruce A542
Taylor, Daniel A558
Taylor, Scott A572
Taylor, David A593
Taylor, James A600
Taylor, Howard A604
Taylor, Tim G. A653
Taylor, Donna A655
Taylor, David S. A671
Taylor, Julie A671
Taylor, Sharon C. A676
Taylor, Moira A691
Taylor, Zachary A693
Taylor, Bob A693
Taylor, Redmond A700
Taylor, Bret A723
Taylor, Shirley A727
Taylor, Carter A729
Taylor, Michael A736
Taylor, Kenneth R. (Ken) A740
Taylor, Scott C. A778
Taylor, Malcolm A811
Taylor, Marilyn Jordan A812
Taylor, Steve A835
Taylor, Renee A837
Taylor, Ed A861
Taylor, Stacey A874
Taylor, Patricia A. A891
Taylor, Melissa A897
Taylor, Jeffrey A902
Taylor, Mike P. A905
Taylor, Michael A907
Taylor, Rebecca A912
Taylor, Russ A920
Taylor, Kevin P42
Taylor, Robert P72
Taylor, Mike P94
Taylor, Cyrus P98
Taylor, Breann P115
Taylor, Michelle P121
Taylor, Irene P126
Taylor, Ann P138
Taylor, Louise P145
TAYLOR, ANGELA P163
Taylor, Seth P166
Taylor, Shana P259
Taylor, Heather P273
Taylor, Joyce P280
Taylor, Mark P297
Taylor, Jerry P300
Taylor, Dana P301
Taylor, Scott P333
Taylor, Charles P361
Taylor, Stephen P361
Taylor, Nikki P385
Taylor, Michael P416
Taylor, Amanda P422
Taylor, Mimi P466
Taylor, Starla P466
Taylor, David P469
Taylor, Kim P476
Taylor, R. Stephen P483
Taylor, Michael P492
Taylor, Alice P529
Taylor, Mark P530
Taylor, Winna P535
Taylor, J P538
Taylor, Tangula P560

Taylor, Tanjula P560
Taylor, Malcolm P600
Taylor, Marilyn Jordan P607
Taylor, Kyle P631
Taylor, James P638
Taylor, Ed P658
Taylor, Arika P665
Taylor, Gregory B P672
Taylor, Curtis E P672
Taylor, Melissa P687
Taylor, Jeffrey P693
Taylor, Mike P. P696
Taylor, Michael P696
Taylor, Kevin W40
Taylor, Joseph M. (Joe) W282
Taylor, Kathleen P. W310
Taylor, Warren E102
Taylor, W M E140
Taylor, Robert E177
Taylor, Robert E198
Taylor, Pamela J. (Pam) E202
Taylor, Anna E210
Taylor, Brenton E217
Taylor, Bruce E267
Taylor, Les E268
Taylor, D. Deeni E332
Taylor, Donna E333
Taylor, Ronald E355
Taylor, Kenneth R. (Ken) E369
Taylor, W. Kent E397
Taylor, Jason E432
Taylor, Patricia A. E434
Taylor-Gerken, Polly P620
Tazawa, Naoya W264
Tchao, Michael A70
Teagle, Walter C. A353
Teagle, Walter C. E159
Teague, Eric A107
Teague, R. Keith A189
Teague, A. James (Jim) A303
Teague, Sarah A655
Teague, Jeff P183
Teague, Bart P259
Teague, Justin P422
Teague, Eric E35
Teague, Sarah E333
Teal, Travis A774
Teasdale, Chris W352
Tech, Georgia P96
Tedeschi, Anthony A795
Tedesco, Michael P588
Tedjarati, Shane A429
Teed, Fred A661
Teed, Andrew D. E404
Teel, Jordan A555
Teel, Lawrence E. (Skip) A895
Teel, Kerry P258
Teele, Cindy A175
Teepsuwan, Veraphan W195
Teerasoontornwong, Thawee W203
Teeter, Jennifer P205
Teets, Richard T A768
Teetz, Robert P363
Teeven, Jeff E95
Tegel, Bill P202
Tehan, Kerry E251
Tehrani, Sean P459
Teixeira, Miguel A583
Teixeira, Kay P305
Teixeira, Miguel P374
Teja, Sandeep S P310
Tejeda, Ray A449
Telesz, Todd E. A214
Telesz, Scott E. A514
Telesz, Todd E. P128
Televantos, John Y. E31
Telfer, Pamela A513
Tellechea, Julio W234
Telles, Mark A332
Tellez-Gagliano, Laura P22
Tellkamp, Scott A244
Tellmann, Lars E. W360
Temares, Steven H. (Steve) A120
Temmen, Diane P647
Tempchin, Stanley P321

Tempel, Trent A588
Temperley, Donald A432
Temple, Mike A371
Temple, Michael G. (Mike) A674
Templeton, Deborah A372
Templeton, Richard K. (Rich) A803
Templeton, Deborah P208
Templeton, D. Jeffrey E41
Templeton, Gary E175
Templin, Donald C. (Don) A527
Tena, Andrea P478
Tendler, Craig A476
Tenenbaum, Brian M. A703
Tenery, Joanne P418
Teng, Adrian W195
Teng, Ooi Say W347
Tengel, Jeffrey J. (Jeff) A644
Tengelin, Michael A375
Tengler, Nancy A412
Tengler, Nancy E192
Tennant, Nancy A898
Tenney, Traci A160
Tenney, Traci E55
Tennis, Karen P26
Tennison, Lynden L. A842
Tennity, Jennifer Villa A201
Tennyson, Jeff A690
Tennyson, Jeff E345
Tenorio, Orlando A218
Tenpas, Kevin S. A412
Tenpas, Kevin S. E192
Tenuto, Craig A542
Tenuto, Craig E267
Teo, Yvonne A71
Teo, Jean W89
Teodosio, Tammy P444
Tepartimargorn, Pitipan W296
Teper, Steven P133
Teplinsky, Nellie A741
Teplinsky, Nellie E371
Tepper, Robyn A507
Tepper, Robyn P288
Terabatake, Masamichi W194
Teraguchi, Tomoyuki W268
Terajima, Yoshinori W261
Teran, Tim A204
Terasaki, Akira W272
Terashi, Shigeki W374
Tercek, Mark R. P595
Teresi, Todd A70
Terifay, Robert J. A698
Terisse, Pierre-Andre W117
Terner, Franck W14
Terpsma, Daniel W. A187
Terpsma, Daniel W. E71
Terra, Patricia P193
TERRACHINI, FRANCO W111
Terranova, Peter A836
Terranova, Carleen A902
Terranova, Carleen P692
Terrasi, Francesco M P102
Terrazas, Miguel P443
Terrell, Karenann A113
Terrell, Mike A196
Terrell, Ransom P125
Terrell, Michael P207
Terrell, Helen P449
Terrell, Carla P694
Terri, Klopfenstine P255
Terribile, Adriana A201
Terrill, Mark P681
Terry, Rick O. A412
Terry, Cheryl A446
Terry, Jim A578
Terry, Thomas S. (Tom) A837
Terry, Monte P101
Terry, Rick O. E192
Terry, Cheryl E210
Terryn, Kristof W405
Tersigni, Anthony R A80
Tersigni, Anthony R P47
Tertete, Uiopio A200
Teruel, Javier A763
Terwiesch, Peter W4
Terwilliger, Jerry P405

Terzian, John E415
Teska, Rich A599
Teson, Nicholas A221
Tessier, Pamela P227
Tessier, Claude W20
Tessitore, Christopher P. (Chris) E293
Tessler, Hervé A911
Testa, Christopher P. A848
Testa, Steve P365
Testor, Joseph A33
Testy, Kellye A861
Testy, Kellye E658
Tetali, Ashish A537
Tetreault, Kristin A406
Teufel, Sharon P132
Tewatia, Vikram A204
Tewes, Timothy A. (Tim) A579
Teyssen, Johannes W131
Tezel, Tatiana A131
Thacker, Dan A772
Thacker, Lynda P584
Thadani, Sharmila P182
Thai, Emily A770
Thakar, Todd A677
Thakar, Sumedh S. E342
Thaker, Ashish A38
Thakur, Anita P133
Thakur, Netra P204
Tham, Russell A71
Thaman, Michael H. (Mike) A627
Thames, Thomas B. P492
Thames, Bruce A P552
Thamm, Michael W81
Thammasart, DVM Sujint W88
Thandri, Ananthan P326
Thanh, Mai Trang A429
Thani, Jassim bin Hamad Jassim bin
 Jabor Al- W296
Thanopoulos, George P335
Thao, MAI P91
Thapar, Atul E355
Tharby, Linda M. A119
Tharmaratnam, Anand A469
Tharp, Morris A. A740
Tharp, Randall A838
Tharp, William W P197
Tharp, Jeffrey P680
Tharp, Morris A. E369
Thatavakorn, Amy P637
Thatcher, Linda P666
Thaus, Kurt B. A794
Thaw, James P87
Thayer, Tom A222
Thayer, Jonathan W. (Jack) A308
Thaysen, Jacob A22
Theiler, Kris A272
Theiler, Jeff E332
Theiller, George J. E90
Theine, Mark D. E332
Theis, Axel W23
Theisen, Linda A539
Theisen, Randall S. A891
Theisen, Randall S. E434
Theiss, Paul A599
Theissing, Jennifer A56
Theleman, David A577
Themelis, Nicholas E260
Thengvall, Kelly A84
Theobald, Stephen P. E431
Theobalds, Kenneth A300
Theodoredis, Roger E. P689
Theodoridis, Artemios Ch. W24
Theodorou, Tasos A749
Theofilaktidis, Maria W50
Thepaut, Eric A144
Theriault, Jennifer A481
Theriault, Ryan A920
Therrien, Stephane W217
Thiam, Tidjane C. W111
Thibaud, Didier M.C. E271
Thibault, Olivier A691
Thibeault, Robert A119
Thibodaux, Vincent P624
Thibodeau, Johnathan A647
Thibodeaux, Faron J. A69

Thibodeaux, Wayne P561
Thiel, John A100
Thiele, Ron P255
Thieme, Dennis P370
Thien-Ngern, Orapong W330
Thienachariya, Thana W330
Thieneman, Timothy A659
Thiers, Bernard P. A563
Thiesing, James A472
Thiessen, Eric A734
Thiessen, Allen P661
Thigpen, Carl S. A674
Thill, Howard A263
Thill, Howard J. E364
Thillart, Leo van den W75
Thille, Dorcas E52
Thilmany, Andrea P410
Thimmesch, Timothy P218
Thimmesch, Tim P218
Thirot, Olivier G A486
Thiry, Kent J. A255
Thissen, Karen Wilson A56
Thistle, William R. E340
Thiyagarajan, Sakthivel A131
Thoeny, Lysa A905
Thoeny, Lysa P693
Thoke, Steve A718
Thom, Patrick P5
Thom, Jonathan P188
Thoma, Ronald A242
Thoma, Jane A384
Thoma, Joy A537
Thoma, Jane E176
Thomaes, Marc A583
Thoman, Thomas S. A25
Thoman, Thomas S. P15
Thomas, Shantelle A34
Thomas, Toby L. A47
Thomas, LeAnn M A56
Thomas, Dan A107
Thomas, Michael A110
Thomas, Bryan A115
Thomas, Robin A115
Thomas, Michael M. (Mike) A140
Thomas, Mary H. A157
Thomas, Carolyn A180
Thomas, William A196
Thomas, Anthony A204
Thomas, Glenn A244
Thomas, Richard C A248
Thomas, David A280
Thomas, William R. A304
Thomas, Gary L. A304
Thomas, Lee A322
Thomas, Stephanie A328
Thomas, Sue A329
Thomas, Pamela A334
Thomas, Michael A342
Thomas, David M. A364
Thomas, Jim A384
Thomas, Suzanne C. A399
Thomas, Deborah M. (Deb) A408
Thomas, Andy A441
Thomas, Heather A456
Thomas, Michelle A468
Thomas, David J A487
Thomas, Bradley A489
Thomas, Michael A489
Thomas, Rob A505
Thomas, Roni A522
Thomas, Nixon A532
Thomas, Kurt A557
Thomas, Betty A565
Thomas, Paul A572
Thomas, Geevy S.K. A596
Thomas, Paige L. A596
Thomas, Walton A631
Thomas, Brande A655
Thomas, Martin (Marty) A712
Thomas, Kelly A720
Thomas, Jeffrey A725
Thomas, Benjamin A790
Thomas, John M. A797
Thomas, Christy A838
Thomas, Karen A865

A = AMERICAN BUSINESS
E = EMERGING COMPANIES
P = PRIVATE BUSINESS
W = WORLD BUSINESS

Thomas, Cheryl A867
Thomas, Anne A878
Thomas, Anthony W. (Tony) A903
Thomas, Marshall P3
Thomas, Savageau P68
Thomas, Mary P89
Thomas, Jake P92
Thomas, Jacob P125
Thomas, Robin P125
Thomas, Michael J P142
Thomas, Larry P144
Thomas, Stephanie P160
Thomas, Jess P160
Thomas, Tony P171
Thomas, Elaine P172
Thomas, Ryan P173
Thomas, Kenneth P179
Thomas, Pamela P193
Thomas, Dana P248
Thomas, Michelle P252
Thomas, Michael S. P263
Thomas, Rony P291
Thomas, Michael P292
Thomas, Ramona P310
Thomas, Debbie P323
Thomas, Beverly P339
Thomas, Donna P359
Thomas, Olivia P365
Thomas, Jill P422
Thomas, Dan P433
Thomas, Becky P435
Thomas, Tim P436
Thomas, Bill P446
Thomas, Jeff P530
Thomas, Sarah P613
Thomas, Rebecca S. P673
Thomas, Roger P694
Thomas, Anthony (Tony) W265
Thomas, Ralf P. W331
Thomas, Dan E34
Thomas, Michael E37
Thomas, William R. (Will) E57
Thomas, Gregory S E78
Thomas, M. Andrew E97
Thomas, Bruce E123
Thomas, Ed E163
Thomas, Jim E176
Thomas, Bennett E195
Thomas, Jeffrey E213
Thomas, John T. E332
Thomas, Brande E333
Thomas, Donald E. (Don) E350
Thomas, Ian E355
Thomas, Kelly E362
Thomasjr, William A838
Thomason, Troy A136
Thomason, Linton J. (Lin) A395
Thomason, David S. A650
Thomason, Chad A737
Thomason, Jaime P271
Thomason, Alesia P422
Thomason, Keith P594
Thomason, Chad E367
Thome, James A850
Thomford, Mark E140
Thompsen, Kelvin P515
Thompson, Matthew A. (Matt) A11
Thompson, Matt A11
Thompson, Denton A25
Thompson, Ian A61
Thompson, Tommy A117
Thompson, Jeffrey D. (Jeff) A125
Thompson, Elizabeth M. (Betty) A140
Thompson, Terry A140
Thompson, Dale A. A162
Thompson, Dana A163
Thompson, Mike A198
Thompson, Cathy A226
Thompson, Lori A246

Thompson, Christopher A291
Thompson, Mike A318
Thompson, Christine A341
Thompson, Kent T. A344
Thompson, Michael A369
Thompson, Leslie A387
Thompson, Laura K. A391
Thompson, Steve A405
Thompson, Steve A406
Thompson, Kirk A439
Thompson, Mark E. A440
Thompson, Jeff A441
Thompson, Angel A460
Thompson, Mark A468
Thompson, Brenda A493
Thompson, Amy A539
Thompson, Jean A542
Thompson, Robert A542
Thompson, Steve A557
Thompson, John W A560
Thompson, Kevin L. A561
Thompson, Jane A575
Thompson, Timothy A583
Thompson, Richard L. (Rich) A594
Thompson, Geoff A614
Thompson, Judith A621
Thompson, Deanna A630
Thompson, Amy A644
Thompson, Julian A649
Thompson, Maria A659
Thompson, Peter A659
Thompson, Paul W. A665
Thompson, Bryan A671
Thompson, Sarah A677
Thompson, James H. (Jim) A685
Thompson, Marcy J. A750
Thompson, William P. A760
Thompson, Kathy C. A772
Thompson, Sean A777
Thompson, Hugh A778
Thompson, Robert A788
Thompson, Doyle A800
Thompson, Beryl A870
Thompson, John D. (David) A893
Thompson, Joseph F. A904
Thompson, Eric A914
Thompson, Denton P15
Thompson, Dwight P29
Thompson, Jolene P36
Thompson, Arthur P75
Thompson, Arthur P136
Thompson, Linda Valdez P152
Thompson, Jerry E P185
Thompson, Jeffrey E P223
Thompson, Katherine P231
Thompson, Bryan P232
Thompson, Matt P243
Thompson, Gloria P247
Thompson, Dale P249
Thompson, Gigi P249
Thompson, Owen P249
Thompson, Mark P252
Thompson, Susan K. P252
Thompson, Steve P271
Thompson, Julie P281
Thompson, Patrick P291
Thompson, Craig B. P325
Thompson, Dale P345
Thompson, Brittany P346
Thompson, Ray P353
Thompson, Doug P369
Thompson, Timothy P374
Thompson, Barbara P416
Thompson, Steve P427
Thompson, Vicki P435
Thompson, Todd P460
Thompson, Charles P461
Thompson, Lisa P465
Thompson, Richard P476
Thompson, Glynn P480
Thompson, Donna P498
Thompson, William P. P523
Thompson, Aida P537
Thompson, David P554
Thompson, Doyle P559

Thompson, Ryker P561
Thompson, James L P598
Thompson, Staci P602
Thompson, Greg A P620
Thompson, Lewis E P620
Thompson, Kim P636
Thompson, Ken P647
Thompson, Thomas J P660
Thompson, Audrey P669
Thompson, M Keith P672
Thompson, Nell P681
Thompson, Beverly Brooks P695
Thompson, Johnny W107
Thompson, Stephen C. (Steve) E74
Thompson, Steve E74
Thompson, William A. E90
Thompson, Christine E153
Thompson, Kent T. E154
Thompson, Leslie E177
Thompson, Andrew E248
Thompson, Jean E267
Thompson, Robert E267
Thompson, Alfred F. E278
Thompson, Kevin L. E278
Thompson, Dennis L. E291
Thompson, Jill E318
Thompson, H. Brian E328
Thompson, Tommy G. E332
Thompson, James D. (Jim) E349
Thompson, Mark E371
Thompson, Sean E393
Thompson, Joseph F. E442
Thomsen, Simone A511
Thomsen, Mads Krogsgaard W271
Thomson, James A. A26
Thomson, Brooke A84
Thomson, Robert A589
Thomson, Ross A741
Thomson, Michael R A780
Thomson, Andrew J. (Andy) A815
Thomson, Leslie A838
Thomson, Laura P356
Thomson, Greg P634
Thomson, Joanne P645
Thomson, Phil W158
Thomson, Warren A. W232
Thomson, Ross E370
Thorburn, Andrew W251
Thornberry, Richard G. (Rick) A690
Thornberry, Richard G. (Rick) E345
Thornburgh, Richard E. W111
Thorne, Chris A292
Thorne, Sherri A324
Thorne, James A496
Thorne, James P137
Thornhill, Joelle A255
Thornhill, Hugh P405
Thornton, Randolph I. A237
Thornton, Alvin A242
Thornton, Bob A353
Thornton, Janis A532
Thornton, Daniel P. (Dan) A644
Thornton, Curt A685
Thornton, Rhonda P45
Thornton, Brian P96
Thornton, Connie P308
Thornton, Lether P389
Thornton, Glenda P554
Thornton, Ann P573
Thornton, Leslie P687
Thornton, James H. E108
Thornton, Joe B. (Jody) E197
Thorp, Gorman M P233
Thorp, H. Holden P616
Thorp, Madeleine E9
Thorpe, Linda A111
Thorpe, Todd A589
Thorpe, Ruth A603
Thorpe, Linda P56
Thorpe, Ruth P399
Thorpe, Edith D P548
Thorpe, Wendy W26
Thorslund, Katarina W18
Thorson, Robert A. A889
Thorson, Dave P13

Thorson, Michael P219
Thorson, Peter E426
Thorup, Schuyler P101
Thottikamath, Sethu A330
Thouin, Stéphane W82
Thoven, Glenn P308
Thrasher, Kelsey P299
Thrasher, Terrell P299
Thren, Joseph A247
Thren, Joseph E103
Throsby, Tim W54
Thuillier, Larry A591
Thulin, Inge G. A2
Thull, Tom E146
Thullbery, Joan P537
Thunell, Adam P135
Thuning, Elizabeth A865
Thurber, Robert A835
Thurm, Patrick A727
Thurman, William A332
Thurman, Susan A774
Thurman, Ramona P143
Thurman, Lindsay P601
Thurman, Greg E355
Thurow, Rick A439
Thurston, Corydon L. E41
Thurston, John E175
Thuss, Charles A16
Thway, Myint P496
Thyberg, Gordon P563
Thygesen, Mikael A744
Thygesen, Henriette H. W1
Thépaut, Eric A144
Tian, Guoli W67
Tian, Simon E428
Tibbits, Nate A685
Tibbitts, Mark P46
Tibbitts, Betsy P210
Tibbs, E. W. P105
Tibke, Kathy A513
Tice, Casandra P99
Tichenor, Stuart P148
Ticker, Jay P376
Tickles, Chuck P271
Tiddettes, Shawn P668
Tidwell, Kay L. E208
Tieanworn, Min W88
Tiede, Robert C. (Rob) A750
Tiedemann, Ed A685
Tiedemann, Peter P28
Tiedemann, Meredith E364
Tiegs, Randy A800
Tiegs, Randy E396
Tielinen, Roberta A512
Tiemeier, Greg A710
Tiencken, John P105
Tierney, Brian X. A46
Tierney, Kathleen M. A122
Tierney, John A133
Tierney, Thomas J. (Tom) A288
Tierney, Tim A332
Tierney, Steve A484
Tierney, James A513
Tierney, Scott A537
Tierney, Timothy A869
Tierney, Thomas J. P596
Tiesi, Jeffrey P688
Tietjen, Deb P208
Tighe, Thomas P162
Tight, Steven M. A157
Tignor, Chris A324
Tihal, Andrea A693
Tiitinen, Pekka W4
Tiitola, Antti W257
Tilden, Bradley D. (Brad) A28
Tilds, Eric P293
Tilford, Tim P310
Tilghman, Lee A223
Tilghman, Richard A782
Till, Frank P149
Tillemans, Todd W. A416
Tillett, Doug A322
Tilley, Luke A901
Tilley, Martha P109
Tilley, Luke P692

Tilley, James E135
Tillman, Audrey Boone A18
Tillman, Lee M. A526
Tillman, Joseph A850
Tillman, Linda P418
Tillman, Michael C P635
Tilly, Edward T. E62
Tilton, Glenn F A192
Tilton, Stephen A500
Tilton, David P379
Tilton, Jesse C P385
Tilton, Stephen E238
Tim, Snyder P673
Timanus, H. E. (Tim) A673
Timanus, Timothy A733
Timanus, Timothy P490
Timberlake, Rebecca P538
Timcoe, Michael A767
Timm, Bryan L. A839
Timm, Mark P699
Timm, Craig E236
Timm, Bryan L. E409
Timmel, Kurt A532
Timmer, Kristin A523
Timmerman, Douglas A35
Timmerman, Gail A480
Timmerman, Greg P254
Timmerman, Timothy T. P298
Timmermans, Michelle A439
Timmermans, Koos W187
Timmers, Martha P442
Timmins, Lawrence A105
Timmons, Brian A162
Timmons, James T. (Jimmy) A508
Timmons, Tom A886
Timmons, Darla P486
Timmons, Tom E433
Timol, Tarek A533
Tin, Judy A P184
Tin, Kng Hwee W280
Tindal, Carrie A782
Tindall, Michael A677
Tindall, Adam W26
Tindell, Roberta A770
Ting, Henry A810
Ting, Henry P597
Tinga, Wiebe A408
Tingley, Stephen E351
Tingstrom, Ulf A676
Tingue, David A59
Tinkey, James A572
Tinney, Stephen A575
Tinns, Holly P164
Tiplady, Martyn A3
Tippl, Thomas A10
Tipton, John (Stephen) A425
Tipton, Richard P450
Tipton, John (Stephen) E201
Tirador, Gabriel A551
Tirman, Kerry R P86
Tirrell, Matthew P610
Tirumala, Usha E256
Tisch, Jonathan M. A520
Tisch, James S. A520
Tisch, Alex A520
Tisch, Ben A520
Tisch, Andrew H. A520
Tischler, Mary A175
Tischner, Kl P368
Tishman, Daniel R. (Dan) A16
Tison, Jack P416
Tisone, Bob A912
Tistinic, Wendy A262
Titinger, Jorge L. P502
Titov, Debbee P430
Titova, Zornitsa A904
Titova, Zornitsa E442
Titus, James A729
Titzman, Donna A868
Tizzio, Vincent C. A576
Tizzio, Vincent C. E297
Tjernsmo, Dag W352
Tkach, Dennis P457
Tkacz, Richard M. E414
Tkaczyk, Greg P393

Tng, Gillian A131
Toadvine, Stephen P584
Tobi, Kathleen A683
Tobias, Hugh A877
Tobiassen, Marge E183
Tobin, Paul A537
Tobin, Jim P283
Tobin, Philip T P565
Tobin, Thomas J P565
Tobin, James J. (Jim) W229
Tobin, Dominic M. E96
Tocher, Catherine S. A395
Toczydlowski, Greg C A827
Toczydlowski, Gregory A828
Todai, Parul A204
Todaro, Michael J. A522
Todd, Craig A140
Todd, Brian A204
Todd, Paul A288
Todd, Amy A509
Todd, Treadway A614
Todd, Ron A720
Todd, Brian A782
Todd, Paul M. A823
Todd, Diane A886
Todd, Aaron D. P14
Todd, Amy P288
Todd, Irene P300
Todd, Timothy J P343
Todd, Brenda P406
Todd, Andrew N P418
Todd, Andrew P697
Todd, Roderick M. E153
Todd, Ron E362
Todd, Diane E433
Todhanakasem, Kittiya W330
Todhunter, Jeff A427
Todhunter, Jeff E202
Todman, Michael A898
Toellner, Ann P646
Toeniskoetter, Charles P480
Toerpe, William A718
Toerpe, Bill A718
Toffey, Bryan A17
Toffey, Bryan P10
Togami, Kai A878
Togashi, Norio W116
Togawa, Masanori W113
Tognoli, John A513
Toh, Ryugo A676
Tohrnan, Kathy P532
Toivola, Sakari W257
Tokarev, Nikolai P. W375
Tokarski, Chris E385
Tokin, Arthur E264
Tokish, Tim A594
Tokunaga, Christine P245
Tokunari, Muneaki W245
Tol, Daryl P323
Tolan, Matthew A93
Tolany, Brandon E371
Toledano, Udi A30
Toledano, Gaby A799
Toledano, Sidney W97
Tolentino, Ingrid A556
Toler, Patricia A600
Toll, Robert I. A819
Toll, Bruce A819
Tollefsrud, Mike A677
Tolley, Howard A867
Tolley, Howard P661
Tollison, Eddie A258
Tolliver, Michael A7
Tolliver, Paula C. A456
Tolman, Sarah A338
Tolman, Ruth P168
Tolot, Jér-'me W143
Tolson, Glenda A743
Tolson, Glenda E372
Tom, Teresa A744
Tom, Melissa P511
Tom, Crystal P570
Toma, Shigeki W329
Toma, Mike E138
Tomak, Scott A489

Tomas, Jose A67
Tomas, Ron A565
Tomasevic, Josip A20
Tomasi, Peter A869
Tomasik, Andy P341
Tomasky, Susan P32
Tomaszewski, Jeffrey A750
Tomb, Matthew C. (Matt) A342
Tombesi, Paolo A603
Tombesi, Paolo P399
Tomczik, Pam A788
Tomczyk, James E. A187
Tomczyk, James E. E71
Tomek, Michael A163
Tomenson, Walter S. E340
Tomey, Alexander A264
Tomic, Brano A345
Tomita, Jiro W113
Tomita, Tetsuro W132
Tomita, Tetsuji (Mike) W211
Tomiyama, Hideaki W116
Tomlin, Randy A84
Tomlin, Bob P284
Tomlin, Dervla M. W161
Tomlinson, Scott A487
Tomlinson, Eric P385
Tomlinson, Monica P566
Tomlinson, Kevin W194
Tomlinson, D. J. W199
Tomo, Ronald P362
Tompkins, Randy A180
Tompkins, Cathlyn L. (Cathy) A190
Tompkins, Cathy A190
Tompkins, Patrick A318
Tompkins, Michael A328
Toms, Shannon P628
Toms, Paul B. E203
Tomsicek, Michael E3
Tomsovic, Robert A478
Tomuro, Stacy A352
Tomé, Carol B. A424
Toncray, Debby P183
Toner, Richard A676
Toner, John A676
Toner, Renee P160
Toney, Pam A107
Toney, Frederiek A362
Toney, Charles A551
Toney, Pam E35
Tong, Ming A213
Tong, Lim Khiang W280
Tong, Richard E311
Toni, Christine P189
Tonkel, J. Rock E24
Tonkinson, Robert P568
Tonn, Barbara P247
Tonner, Paul P318
Tonnison, John A792
Tonno, Jim A676
Tonomoto, Kiyoshi W27
Toogood, Rosie W217
Toohey, Sean A289
Tooke, David P431
Tooker, A. Morris (Mo) A406
Tooley, Russell A835
Toombs, Ross P182
Toomey, Kimberly A696
Toomey, John A794
Toomey, April P179
Topalian, Leon A605
Topkins, Alex A390
Topor, Martin A555
Toporek, Jill A390
Toporek, Dan A878
Topp, Jonathan A163
Topper, Joan A372
Topper, Joan P208
Topper, John E P331
Topper, Joseph V. (Joe) P667
Toppin, Bruce P388
Toppin, Bruce P389
Torbakhov, Alexander W321
Torbert, Ronald J P61
Torchiana, David F. A635
Torchiana, David A635

Torchiana, David F. P419
Torchiana, David P419
Torello, William A. (Bill) E149
Toresdahl, Brett P376
Torette, Debra A780
Toretti, Christine J. A720
Toretti, Christine J. E362
Torgerson, James P P609
Torgow, Gary H. A187
Torgow, Gary H. E71
Torii, Nobuhiro W349
Torii, Shingo W349
Torino, Christopher P484
Toriumi, Chie W268
Torkelson, Thomas E P245
Torley, Helen I. E186
Tornek, Scott P439
Tornes, James A620
Tornga, Mark A133
Torno, Vitaliano A628
Tornquist, Alice A685
Torok, Ken A136
Torok, Ken A850
Torossian, Lynn M. A413
Torossian, Lynn M. P234
Torrance, Jeffery A685
Torrance, Kelly P235
Torre, Bonnie P480
Torreano, Gail A85
Torres, Jeff A180
Torres, Mark A508
Torres, Russ A586
Torres, Ana A616
Torres, Debra A647
Torres, Edgardo A894
Torres, Donna A902
Torres, Chris P302
Torres, Marilyn P338
Torres, Ceci P393
Torres, Estella P572
Torres, Eddie P632
Torres, Daniel P642
Torres, Donna P693
Torres, Roberto Mendez W43
Torres, Max W133
Torres, Kerry E101
Torres-Springer, Maria P372
Torrey, William P68
Torreyson, Denise A537
Torrion, Philippe W136
Tortorello, Tracy A855
Tortorello, Tracy E416
Tory, Jennifer W310
Toshikuni, Nobuyuki W211
Tosi-Renna, Barbara Ann A583
Toso, Greg A879
Tossava, Kendra P243
Toste, Guen A784
Toth, Scott A258
Totherow, Bill A759
Totherow, Bill P521
Totoki, Hiroki W337
Totten, Elizabeth P606
Touchet, Jennifer P220
Toulme, Patrick P395
Touma-Bruno, Rima E342
Tourangeau, Roger P682
Tournadre, David W364
Tournier, Philippe W104
Tournillon, Toby P475
Tournoy, Patrick A265
Tousignant, Michael A214
Tousignant, Michael P128
Toussaint, Donald R. A248
Toussaint, Claudia S. A914
Touza, Carlos A351
Touza, Carlos E158
Tovin, Hal R. A152
Tovin, Hal R. E49
Towarak, Tim P69
Tower, Erika A818
Towers, Kelly P584
Towler, Fred A463
Townes, Chad A85
Townes, Wlliam P188

A = AMERICAN BUSINESS
E = EMERGING COMPANIES
P = PRIVATE COMPANIES
W = WORLD BUSINESS

Townes, Emilie M. P615
Towns, Fred A779
Townsel, Beadie H P490
Townsend, Kent G. A164
Townsend, Adam A175
Townsend, Jeffrey A. (Jeff) A186
Townsend, Richard A260
Townsend, Drew A412
Townsend, Margaret A439
Townsend, Justin A441
Townsend, Gayle A496
Townsend, Dianne A693
Townsend, Ted P252
Townsend, Drew E192
Towson, Jeff A199
Toy, David A494
Toy, Henry E383
Toyoda, Kanshiro W17
Toyoda, Tetsuro W373
Toyoda, Akio W374
Toyomatsu, Hideki W202
Toyoshima, Masaaki W11
Toyoshima, Masanori W192
Tozzi, Vincent E90
Trabbia, Michael W278
Trabold, Tina P330
Trabulsi, Ann P69
Tracey, Scott A125
Trach, Natalie P384
Trachimowicz, Richard J. E414
Tracy, Nancy A160
Tracy, Erin A329
Tracy, Christina A441
Tracy, Diane A698
Tracy, Diane P456
Tracy, James A. (Jim) P470
Tracy, Jan P549
Tracy, Nancy E55
Traficanti, Joseph J. (Joe) A848
Trafton, Gail A881
Trager, A. Scott A705
Trager, Steven E. (Steve) A705
Trager, Bernard M. A705
Trager, A. Scott E352
Trager, Steven E. (Steve) E352
Trager, Bernard M. E352
Tragl, Karl A76
Tragni, Lauren M P573
Trahan, Claude A233
Trahey-Romanuk, Gina P218
Traicoff, Todd A707
Train, Michael H. A295
Trainer, Michael P118
Trakimas, Ann A214
Trakimas, Ann A128
Trammell, Kenneth R. (Ken) A796
Trammell, Shelly P685
Tramontana, Nick A803
Tramontana, Anthony P261
Tramontana, Nick P562
Tramontin, Shannon A549
Tramontin, Shannon E270
Tramontozzi, Domenick P123
Tran, Long A131
Tran, Henry A221
Tran, Brian A232
Tran, Allen A685
Tran, Michael A729
Tran, Hung A877
Tran, Peter P96
Tran, Chris T P109
Tran, Thomas P145
Tran, Phat P208
Tran, Dana P275
Tran, Lan A458
Tran, Vicki P631
Transon, Robert A34
Transue, Bill A763
Transue, Darren P198

Trant, David E144
Trapani, Stephen P215
Trapp, Megan A221
Traquina, Perry A34
Traquina, Perry A288
Traquina, Perry M. P82
Trasatt, Andrew A351
Trasatt, Andrew E158
Trask, Ethan A120
Trask, Amanda A171
Trask, Amanda P100
Trask, David P435
Tratt, Noah A311
Traut, Mark A56
Trauth, Denise M. P563
Trautman, David L. A633
Trautmann, Robert E. A644
Travaille, Tim A368
Traverso, Robert A204
Traviolia, Brad P566
Travis, Troy P339
Travisano, Jacqueline A. P399
Trawick, John G. A753
Trawick, John G. E379
Trawicki, Roman A921
Traymore, Anthony A691
Traynham, William W. A52
Treadway, Jeff A221
Treadway, Todd A614
Treadway, Brandy A640
Treadway, Carol P563
Treadwell, Melinda P659
Treanor, John A62
Treanor, Jim A105
Trease, Richard A838
Treasure, Jeffrey P213
Treasure, Jeff P276
Trebesch, Butch P38
Trebilcock, James R A487
Trebus, Marilyne A786
Trecker, Kristin E. E219
Treenuchagron, Chansin W296
Trefethen, Angela A621
Trefethen, Angela P407
Trefler, Alan E327
Trefzger, Detlef W212
Treibic, Adam A350
Treibic, Adam E157
Treichel, Gus A869
Treichl, Andreas W145
Trelease, Mark A593
Trella, Ronald A217
Trella, Chris A374
Tremblay, Michel W180
Tremblay, Stephen E. E236
Trembley, Michael A377
Trembulak, Frank A372
Trembulak, Frank P208
Trembulak, Frank J P209
Trembulak, Frank J P582
Tremone, Carl P627
Tremoulis, John A441
Tremper, Glendora P120
Trenary, Ty A785
Trend, Jonathan A555
Trendel, Jennifer P301
Trent, Robert A102
Trento, Mark A69
Trentsch, Brian A728
Trepa, Kevin M. P76
Trepczyk, Aretina A839
Trepczyk, Aretina E409
Trepel, Christopher E123
Tresch, Richard P625
Treschow, Michael W381
Tretiak, Gregory D. W293
Tretiak, Gregory D. W294
Trevallion, Emily A402
Trevathan, James E. A881
Trevett, Denny A199
Trevino, Alyssa P162
Trevisan, Jadran W144
Trevisani, Valter W32
Trevi-±o, Mar-a D. Dancausa W51
Trevorah, Danielle P486

Treworgy, Samantha A134
Treworgy, Samantha P78
Treynor, Elizabeth P676
Trezise, Scott A. A185
Trezza, Steve P363
Triano, Charles A649
Tribble, J Lee A509
Tribble, Agnes A832
Tribble, J Lee P288
Trice, David W. A304
Trice, Barry G. P223
Trick, David A40
Tricoire, Jean-Pascal W322
Trier, Clayton K E405
Triesenberg, Ryan P575
Trigg, Donald D. A186
Triggs, Susan P524
Trikha, Esha A379
Trilling, Stephen A778
Trimble, Fred P479
Trimmer, Kim A500
Trimmer, Kim E237
Trinh, Roger A5
Trinita, Sister Mary P529
Tripathi, Vivek A49
Tripeny, R. Tony A238
Tripi, John P38
Triplett, Michael W. A195
Triplett, Robin A440
Triplett, Rob A614
Triplett, Timothy W P75
Triplett, Timothy W P88
Triplett, Charley P430
Triplitt, Jennifer P482
Tripoli, Domenic A460
Tripp, Mark A81
Tripp, Ann K. A402
Tripp, Steven P170
Trippe, Robert W P36
Trippe, Rai P358
Tritsis, Mary A108
Tritt, Gary A258
Tritton, Mark J. A788
Tritz, Stephane A295
Trivedi, Prithi P236
Trivette, Theresa P637
Troberman, Gayle A448
Troccoli, Alejandro A607
Trocin, Jeffrey E. (Jeff) A693
Trodden, Timothy A885
Trogdon, Sara A221
Troger, Laurent W69
Troia, Maria A877
Troicuk, Brian P25
Trojanowski, Matthew A474
Trojanowski, Matthew P265
Trok, Benjamin M P535
Trolli, Michele D. A522
Trollope, Rowan M. A199
Trombetta, Ian A10
Tropeano, Teresa P422
Tropf, Peter A746
Tropp, Tom A371
Tropp, Emily P464
Troska, Hubertus W114
Trost, Peter A677
Trosvig, Kelli A698
Trosvig, Kelli A861
Trosvig, Kelli P456
Trosvig, Kelli P658
Trott, Richard A173
Trotta, James A500
Trotta, James A238
Trotter, Fred E. E264
Troulis, Maria J. P590
Trout, Christopher A439
Trout, John D P626
Trovato, Joseph A555
Trovillion, Raleigh A837
Troxler, Margie P385
Troy, Thomas M. A33
Troy, Patricia P39
Trubeck, William A885
Trubiano, Steve A449
Truby, Beth A219

Truby, Beth P131
Truckermiller, Debbie A369
Trudeau, Michel C. W217
TRUDEL, SYLVIE A390
Trudel, Arthur F. E23
Trudell, Cynthia M. A647
True, Douglas K. P611
True, Simon W287
Trueblood, Jim A246
Truelove, Brian D. A417
Truesdale, Kellyanne A577
Truesdale, Ken E226
Truglio, Carol P470
Truitt, Jim A746
Trujillo, Becky P329
Trull, Ron P507
Trumble, Clay A345
Trumble, Clay E154
Trump, Christine A585
Trump, Christine P377
Trumpower, Melissa P216
Truong, Alice P338
Trupiano, Anthony P680
Trupiano, Tony P680
Truscheit, Wyatt P245
Truscott, William F. (Ted) A56
Truscott, Tricia P95
Trusty, Steven W. (Steve) A742
Trusty, Mike A878
Trusty, Steven W. (Steve) E372
Trybom, Laura A838
Tryhuss, Gregg P166
Tryniski, Mark E. A225
Tryniski, Mark E. E88
Tryon, Geoffrey P503
Tryon, Bonnie P519
Trytten, Jennifer P135
Tsacalis, Norman A871
Tsacalis, William A P72
Tsadick, Kristy P236
Tsafaridis, George A56
Tsai, Sheng-ta A285
Tsai, Hong-Tu W84
Tsai, Cheng-Ta W84
Tsai, Cheng-Chiu W84
Tsai, Richard M. W154
Tsai, Daniel M. W154
Tsai, Sheng-ta E114
Tsang, Jonathan W35
Tsao, Andy A777
Tsao, Andy E393
Tschakert, Carol P386
Tschetter, Chad E253
Tse, Cindy A691
Tse, Cindy P538
Tse, Edmund S.W. W13
Tse-Gonzalez, Mildred A321
Tse-Gonzalez, Mildred E144
Tseng, F. C. W354
Tseng, Charles E235
Tseng, Saria E284
Tshabalala, Simpiwe (Sim) W339
Tsien, Matthew (Matt) A378
Tsien, Samuel N. (Sam) W280
Tsimbinos, John A584
Tsimbinos, Steven J. A611
Tsimbinos, Steven J. E313
Tso, Stephen T. (Steve) W354
Tsoi, Tracy A558
Tsonis, George D P66
Tsoshima, Naoti P245
Tsoukalas, Arianna P515
Tsourapas, Panagiotis A218
Tsourapas, George A671
Tsuchida, Yukio P326
Tsuchikane, Takuji W163
TSUCHIYA, TAKASHI W274
Tsuga, Kazuhiro W282
Tsuge, Koei W86
Tsuji, Shinji W336
Tsujimura, Hideo W349
Tsukamoto, Shigeru W329
Tsukioka, Nobuo P405
Tsukioka, Takashi W182
Tsurumaki, Fumio W242

Tsurumi, Seiichi W48
Tsutsui, William M. P514
Tsutsui, Yoshinobu W261
Tsvayberg, Leonid A390
Tsymbalyuk, Michael P510
Tsyrkunova, Katsiaryna P69
Tu, Lawrence P. (Larry) A175
Tu, George P545
Tu, L.C. W354
Tubaugh, Jill A441
Tubb, Marga P368
Tubb, Joe P430
Tubbs, Curt E300
Tucker, Michael K. A92
Tucker, Mark A182
Tucker, Jason A350
Tucker, Liz A478
Tucker, Amy A644
Tucker, Jeff A655
Tucker, Scott A889
Tucker, Jerry P108
Tucker, Bryan P154
Tucker, Josh P154
Tucker, Ed P201
Tucker, Richard G. P235
Tucker, Joanne P238
Tucker, Pamela P262
Tucker, Tom P306
Tucker, Kenneth P530
Tucker, Mark E. W175
Tucker, Mark E63
Tucker, Jason E157
Tucker, Matt E178
Tucker, Jeff E333
Tudanger, Rich P243
Tudor, Sorin A130
Tudor, David J. E436
Tueckes, Amy A328
Tufano, Paul A. P667
Tufaro, Paul A201
Tufekci, Suleyman P642
Tuffaha, Sam A84
Tuffin, Mark A496
Tuffy, Gerry A558
Tuftee, Debbie A221
Tufts, Robert P391
Tuggle, Charles T. A348
Tuggle, Deloris Simpson P208
Tugwell, Robert P385
Tuka, Laurie P321
Tulin, Stanley A702
Tuller, Jane P164
Tulliam, Elizabeth P120
Tullier, Kelly M. A874
Tullo, John A537
Tulloch, Maurice W38
Tully, William T P144
Tully, Randy E290
Tulsky, James P153
Tulsyan, Ravi A913
Tulyani, Sonia A854
Tumelty, John B. E339
Tummillo, Michael A521
Tun, David E169
Tunez, Roland A84
Tung, Chao Chin W113
Tung, Tzu Hsien W282
Tung, Roger D. E89
Tunis, Judy A489
Tunnell, Jenne P316
Tunnicliffe, Peter W P102
Tunstall, Peggy P408
Tupa, Mike P151
Tupman, David E78
Turcke, Mary Ann W61
Turco, Cindy P96
Turcotte, Melanie P242
Turek, Dave A461
Turetsky, Larisa A105
Turfe, A. Alan P255
Turi, Carol A105
Turiano, Vincent C A212
Turiano, Gary A P186
Turiano, Vincent C E79
Turicchi, R. Scott E226

Turits, Mark A175
Turits, Michael A693
Turkal, Nick A86
Turkal, Nick P52
Turkal, Nick W. E337
Turley, Susan P162
Turman, Ricky A145
Turman, Ricky P82
Turnage, Sue A244
Turnage, Sharese P544
Turnas, Jeff A899
Turnas, Jeff P690
Turnbull, Robert A244
Turnbull, Thomas P671
Turner, George A25
Turner, Dustin J A122
Turner, Dustin A122
Turner, Jill A185
Turner, Aprile A193
Turner, Gregory A213
Turner, Jeffrey A223
Turner, Jim L. A258
Turner, John A295
Turner, Keene S. A302
Turner, Greg A318
Turner, Mark A362
Turner, Joseph W. (Joe) A395
Turner, William V. A395
Turner, Michael R. (Mike) A417
Turner, Simon A443
Turner, Ethan A449
Turner, Juel A542
Turner, Kit A558
Turner, John C. A563
Turner, Vince A572
Turner, Debra A578
Turner, Kevin A596
Turner, M. Terry A655
Turner, Lance A693
Turner, John M. A700
Turner, David J. A700
Turner, Michele A709
Turner, Chris A765
Turner, Wesley R. A802
Turner, Steve A877
Turner, Jody A898
Turner, Mark A. A907
Turner, David A908
Turner, George P15
Turner, Aprile P112
Turner, Jeffrey P143
Turner, Jeff P200
Turner, Lynn P233
Turner, Aaron P269
Turner, Dinia P291
Turner, Christopher P314
Turner, Thomas P332
Turner, Ana P396
Turner, Dave P512
Turner, R. Gerald P514
Turner, Chris P540
Turner, Wesley R. P562
Turner, Harold P620
Turner, Elaine P642
Turner, Linda P664
Turner, Quint O. E8
Turner, Keene S. E128
Turner, Kathy E213
Turner, John D. E263
Turner, M. Terry E333
Turner, Mark A. E445
Turner, David E446
Turnes, Terje W129
Turney, Brian P276
Turngren, Robert P333
Turocy, Paula P169
Turowski, Steven A806
Turpan, Natalie A683
Turpin, Valerie P213
Turpin, Kevin P575
Turpin, Jennifer E. P654
Turrens, Julio P654
Turrentine, Rebecca J P296
Tursky, Martin E P193
Turton, Daniel A300

Tushman, Earl P410
Tushman, Lawrence P410
Tushman, Larry P410
Tushman, Reed P410
Tushman, Marc P410
Tustin, Sondra A115
Tuten, Chris A575
Tuthill, Allen A83
Tuthill, Debra A774
Tutkovics, Julie C. A440
Tutor, Ronald N. (Ron) A833
Tutson, Tracy A67
Tutt, James A614
Tutt, Jame A614
Tutt, Richard D P676
Tuttle, Mark A560
Tuttle, Russ A744
Tuttle, James A838
Tuttle, Douglas A920
Tuttle, G. Tyson E371
Tuzun, Tayfun A332
Tuzzolo, Karen P264
Tveter, Brian A728
Tveter, Eric J. W222
Twellman, Beverly P300
Twembeke, Willem van W143
Twitty, Tim A. E390
Twohig, Paul A763
Twohy, John A351
Twohy, John E158
Twombly, Daniel P425
Twombly, Dan P425
Twombly, Pat P425
Twomey, Mike A300
Twomey, William A872
Twum, Angela A659
Twumasi, Akua P20
Twyman, Rob A899
Twyman, Rob P690
Tye, Marc R. P509
Tye, David E208
Tygielski, Jonelle P528
Tykocinski, Richard J. P618
Tyksinski, Deborah J. P667
Tyle, Craig S. A365
Tyler, Michele A485
Tyler, Breck W. A832
Tyler, Ollie P89
Tyler, David A. W193
Tymms, Jason A537
Tynan, Michelle P477
Tyndall, William A282
Tyner, Bill A282
Tyner, Melissa A659
Tyner, Judith P222
Tyner, Russell P584
Tyree, Lisa A13
Tyree, Sarah A214
Tyree, Sarah P128
Tyrell, Chris P501
Tyrholm, Laura A130
Tyroller, Peter W70
Tyrrell, Joseph A158
Tyrrell, Nathan S. A434
Tyrrell, Edward L P620
Tyrrell, Joseph E119
Tyson, Dylan A676
Tyson, John H. A835
Tyson, Barbara A835
Tywater, TY A730
Tzakou-Lambropoulou, Nelly W253
T'hart, Marc A113
T-¶zge, A. Galip W18

U

Uanarumit, Wirat W295
Ubagai, Takumi W240
Ubell, Elizabeth A393
Ubrov, Lucie A578
Uchida, Kathryn A59
Uchida, Satoru W200
Uchin, Robert A. P399
Uchioke, Fumikiyo W344

Uchiyamada, Takeshi W374
Udell, David A445
Udell, C. Robert (Bob) E91
Udnoon, Prajit W88
Udovic, Edward P155
Udpa, Satish P341
Udy, Brad A441
Uebber, Bodo W114
Uebelhor, Steve A655
Uebelhor, Steve E333
Ueda, Takuji W116
Ueda, Takashi W245
Ueda, Masahiro W353
Uehara, Daizo A408
Uehara, Edwina (Eddie) A861
Uehara, Edwina (Eddie) P658
Uei, Takashi W211
Ueunten, Paul E284
Ufland, Bob A744
Ugalde, Philip A700
Ugarte, Alfonso J A221
Uhl, Jessica W313
Uhlir, Jason P345
Uhlmann, Paul A838
Uhrig, Christi A185
Ui, Seon Jung W180
Ulbrich, Christian A478
Ulett, John W. P107
Ulibarri, Connie A857
Ulissi, Roberto W143
Ullmann, Michael H. A476
Ulloa, Walter F. E129
Ulmer, David E402
Ulrey, Sharissa A350
Ulrey, Sharissa E157
Ulrich, Catherine E369
Ulveseth, Karl A305
Ulveseth, Karl P185
Umaki, Tamio W279
Umanoff, Adam S. A291
Umansky, Michael M. E286
Umaoka, Seishu W116
Umbel, Eric P404
Umpleby, D James A169
Umscheid, Matthew K. E339
Unciano, Gina A697
Unciano, Gina P454
Underhill, Kim A490
Underhill, Richard P421
Underwood, Michelle A280
Underwood, Todd A456
Underwood, Neil L A518
Underwood, Jennifer A683
Underwood, Clark P90
Underwood, Neil L P292
Ung, Brenda A647
Ungard, Wendy P115
Ungashick, Pam A837
Unger, Laura A575
Unger, Keving P435
Unger, Mark P556
Unroe, Larry P306
Unsworth, John P82
Upadek, Kristen A869
Upchurch, John A282
Upchurch, W. Howard A400
Upfold, Patrick W227
Uppugonduri, Krishna E212
Upton, Ray A803
Uranga, Roberto P123
Urban, Greg A541
Urban, Kevin J. A682
Urban, Greg E266
Urbanovsky, Lamar P563
Urdapilleta, Eduardo A95
Urdapilleta, Eduardo E28
Ure, Michael A611
Ure, Christopher P384
Urech, Greg A508
Urena-Raso, Domingo W16
Uresti, Marybel P278
Ureta, Antonio W85
Uribe, Elias A201
Uribe, Jorge A377
URIBE, JUAN CARLOS MORA W45

A = AMERICAN BUSINESS	
E = EMERGING COMPANIES	
P = PRIVATE COMPANIES	
W = WORLD BUSINESS	

Uriu, Michiaki W213
Urland, Taisha A530
Urlaub, Charles J P330
Urness, Daniel L. E61
Urrabazo, Ignacio A459
Ursat, Xavier W136
Ursini, John A770
Urso, Kristen P210
Urso, Joanne E46
Urso-Rio, Kristen A375
Urso-Rio, Kristen P210
Urtheil, Robert H. E260
Urtin, Charles G. A720
Urtin, Charles G. E362
Urunanon, Teerasak W88
Urwiler, Robert N. E424
Uselton, Jimmy P141
Ushijima, Arthur A P601
Ushijima, Takeo W274
Ushio, Osamu W374
Ushioda, Yoichiro W223
Usiak, Ryan P278
Usmani, Farukh A458
Usmani, Farukh P251
Ussery, Richard A823
Usui, Sonosuke W353
Utermark, D. Chad A605
Utermark, Chad A605
Utley, Mark P442
Utrup, Brian A489
Utsude, Tomoya A19
Utterback, Marty A193
Utterback, Marty P112
Uttermark, Anne P26
Utz, John A. A81
Uy, Maria E75
Uyeda, Dean A102
Uzan, Eric W82

V

Vaccari, Kim P372
Vaccaro, Frank A49
VACCARO, SPHR E297
Vacheron, Terry A774
Vachon, Alain W235
Vachon, Louis W252
Vadaketh, Tom E54
Vadakian, Gary P457
Vadell, Tomeu A202
Vadell, Tomeu P122
Vadell, Pablo Vallbona W6
Vaden, Bob P32
Vadlamannati, Ramaparasad
  (Ram) A664
Vaezazizi, Reza A857
Vagelos, P. Roy A698
Vaglio, Lisa P318
Vagt, Robert A492
Vahabzadeh, Parinaz A691
Vahey, Walter G. E394
Vaidyanathan, Krishnamurthy A390
Vaidyanathan, Ramkumar A574
Vail, Bob A375
Vail, Angela A635
Vail, Angela P419
Vail, Sheree P602
Vaillancourt, Alex P572
Vaillant, Frederic A142
Vainisi, William A33
Vajda, Devit P133
Vakacherla, Ravi A644
Valadez, Ruth P164
Valderrama, Ernesto A13
Valdes, Jose A109
Valdes, Anthony A885
Valdes, Susan L P237

Valdes, Jose E36
Valdespino, Gustavo P663
Valdez, James A244
Valdez, Hernan A648
Valdez, Ernesto P59
Valdez, Robert P254
Valdez, Arthur V P478
Valdez, Alex P537
Valdivia, Angelica P451
Valdés, Luis A668
Vale, Michael G. A2
Vale, MaryAnn A683
Vale, Brenda J. P333
Valenca, Alan A784
Valencia, Jennifer P630
Valente, Donna A726
Valenti, Natalia A109
Valenti, Alessandro A691
Valenti, Brian A729
Valenti, Susan M. A820
Valenti, Joe A912
Valenti, Natalia E36
Valenti, Douglas (Doug) E344
Valentim, Justin P91
Valentin, Raul A241
Valentine, Melinda A105
Valentine, Ken A332
Valentine, Jerry A438
Valentine, Raymond A749
Valentine, Veronica A869
Valentine, Mark P562
Valentine, Annette P647
Valentino, Christina P652
Valenzona, Francis P184
Valenzuela, Joseph A369
Valenzuela, Alejandro W162
Valera, Fernando A202
Valera, Fernando P122
Valeri, Mike A441
Valerio, Chuck A844
Valerio, Chuck E412
Valerius, Barbara P115
Valero, Pastora A200
Valette, Jean-Michel E376
Valeva, Sanya A489
VALGIURATA, LUCIO IGINO ZANON
  DI W111
Valin, Jim Van A438
Valine, Yousef A. A348
Valitutto, Richard A914
Valiveti, Srihari A766
Valkenburg, Tina Van A549
Valkenburg, Tina Van E270
Vallance, Patrick W158
Valle, Dean Della W63
Valle, Dean Della W64
Valle, William (Bill) W153
Vallee, Roy A. A324
Vallee, Roy A. E394
Vallejo, Anthony A244
Vallely, Myrna P670
Vallera, Dino P8
Vallesillo, John P160
Valley, Brian P434
Valley, Kimberly E320
Vallillo, Anthony J P609
Vallin, Jean-Michel W148
Valls, Juan A450
Vallury, Saroja A204
Valluzzo, Charles P412
Valosky, Kenneth G. (Ken) P667
Valtier, Bruno A649
Valukas, Cynthia P396
Vamvalis, Laura A78
Van, David A467
Van, Mike P276
Van, David E223
Van-praag, Mary A241
Vanalebeek, Hans A593
Vanalstyne, Nicole P404
Vanamali, Abhishek P228
Vanaria, Raymond E90
Vanaselja, Siim A. W61
Vance, Tyler A107
Vance, Linda A221

Vance, Brian L. A414
Vance, Quonta A426
Vance, Nichole A765
Vance, Nichole P540
Vance, June P639
Vance, Tyler E34
Vance, Brian L. E195
Vancheeswaran, Pradeep A875
VanCleef, Alan A384
VanCleef, Alan E176
Vande, Sarah A223
Vandekreke, Michael P456
Vandeman, Robert T. P8
Vandenbergh, Robert A. A499
Vandenbergh, Robert A. E237
Vandenbush, Maja A105
Vanderford, Bob P478
Vandergriff, Jody E369
Vanderhelm, Mark A878
Vanderhoff, Bruce P405
Vanderhoof, Ashley A696
Vanderlaan, Meg P361
Vanderlind, Gary A391
Vandermeulen, Thomas A221
Vandermeulen, Johan W74
Vanderslice, Doug P570
Vanderver, Glenn P109
Vandervinne, Jeri A684
Vandervinne, Jeri E341
VanderWeele, Mike A222
Vandeveer, Mary P449
VanDeVelde, Doug A485
VandeVenter, Debra A863
Vandover, Darren A158
Vanella, Gerard A480
Vanella, David E316
Vaness, Craig A333
VanEssendelft, Ed P3
Vang, May A775
Vang, Mao P480
Vang, May P548
VanGelder, Kim E. E115
Vangilder, Grant A591
Vangrevenhof, Heather A34
Vanhandel, Steven E343
Vanhorsen, Debra P41
Vanichvoranun, Vasin W203
Vankirk, Trudy A85
Vanlander, Jean-Pierre W145
Vanloon, Ryan P572
Vanmol, Rik E426
Vanneste, Jeffrey H. A504
Vanni, Mark A538
Vannorman, Steven A448
Vannorman, Raymond A704
Vannorman, Steven P246
Vannorman, Raymond E351
Vanommen, Mike A523
Vanore, Paul P570
Vanoy, Beverly P108
Vanroekel, Lisa A726
Vansickle, Frank P637
Vanstraten, Randy P67
Vantrieste, Martin A61
Vantubergen, Brian P183
Vanwyk, Lisa P479
Vanzo, Kendra L. A614
Varadhan, Ashok A389
VARBERO, BLAKE P629
Vardas, Michael A599
Vardeleon, Christian A133
Vardeman, Tracy P391
Vardon, Heather P51
Varela, Jorge A340
Varela, Javier A480
Varela, Raul P333
Varela, Jorge E151
Varela, John N. E360
Varenne, Fran-çois De W323
Varet, Michael A. E363
Varga, Stephen A. A722
Varga, Daniel W. A801
Varga, Daniel W. P562
Vargas, Gilberto A456
Vargas, Carlota A532

Vargas, Carlos P8
Vargas, Michelle P40
Vargas, Diana P201
Vargas, Carmen P421
Vargas, Joseph P451
Vargas, Roberto P463
Vargas, Nancy P532
Vargas, Esequiel P623
Vargas, Michael M P662
Vargo, Alla A548
Vargo, Alla P324
Varilek, James A. A618
Varma, Ravi A49
Varma, Anu A712
Varma, Vivek A763
Varma, Prasad A800
Varma, Amit P228
Varma, Prasad E396
Varner, Carol A49
Varney, Al A912
Varney, Michael D. W307
Varo, Susan A175
Varughese, Raj A683
Varvaro, Charles A461
Varvel, Victor P233
Varvel, Chris P233
Varvel, Eric W111
Varwig, Chris P620
Vascocu, Norman A446
Vascocu, Norman E210
Vasconcellos, F--bio A682
Vashist, Naveen A712
Vasilatos-Younken, Regina A811
Vasilatos-Younken, Regina P600
Vaske, Brian P688
Vasos, Todd J A273
Vasquez, Jaime A26
Vasquez, Janice A61
Vasquez, Gaddi A291
Vasquez, Christann P73
Vasquez, Gregory P273
Vasquez, Peter P439
Vasquez, Bob P620
Vasquez, Sarah E207
Vassallo, Ralph R. P670
Vassalluzzo, Joseph S. (Joe) A613
Vassem, Timothy Van P463
Vassilidze, Teimouraz V P624
Vassimon, Eduardo W191
Vasudevan, Suresh P382
Vats, Geetika A204
Vaughan, Matthew A314
Vaughan, Richard A543
Vaughan, Rob P95
Vaughan, Matthew P189
Vaughan, Rick P249
Vaughan, Ann P327
Vaughan, Ben W75
Vaughan, Tony D. A263
Vaughn, Taylor A348
Vaughn, Nooshin A443
Vaughn, Karen A770
Vaughn, Sandy P64
Vaughn, David P91
Vaughn, Tiffany M P122
Vaughn, D Blayne P400
Vaughn, Kathleen (Kathy) P447
Vaughn, Gregory R. (Greg) E38
Vaughn, James Matthew (Matt) E322
Vaughn, Victor E391
Vaught, Jamey A446
Vaught, Jamey E210
Vaupel, Mark D. A432
Vawter, Barrett A700
Vazquez, Javier A390
Vazquez, Raul A466
Vazquez, John A870
Vazquez, Javier A874
Vazquez, Frank P539
Vazquez, Damaris P599
Vazquez, Carmen M P653
Veach, Ben A81
Veach, Steve A441
Veacock, Gary P466

Veale, Chris A729
Veall, James A871
Vecchi, Mario P445
Vecchio, Jennifer A155
Vedovotto, Roberto W204
Veer, Jeroen van der W187
Veeraghavachary, Srinivasan A217
Veeramani, Venkat A904
Veeramani, Venkat E442
Vega, Olga De La A85
Vega, David A213
Vega, Venus A223
Vega, Lorenzo De La A461
Vega, Omar A524
Vega, Alma A782
Vega, Elizabeth A810
Vega, Mike P525
Vega, Elizabeth P597
Vega, Anthony P622
Vega, Kristine P696
Vegas, Pablo A. A594
Veglia, Anthony P. P287
Vegliante, Paul C. P70
Veiel, Eric L. A783
Veitenheimer, James R P157
Vekaria, Bhavesh E195
Veksler, Galina A541
Veksler, Angela D. A879
Veksler, Galina E266
Vela, Manuel R. (Manny) A795
Vela, Anna P284
Velasco, Maria Fernanda A649
Velasco, Romeo P108
Velasco, Elizabeth De P636
Velasquez, Margaret A244
Velasquez, Angelica P247
Velazquez, David M. (Dave) A308
Velazquez, Rachel P149
Velde, Tamara Vande A164
Veldhuizen, Norbert Van A130
Velez, Eric A272
Velez, Rafy P237
Velez, Pablo P498
Velez, Ismael P564
Velin, Tom P130
Velkey, Karen A442
Vella, Susan A122
Vella, James G. (Jim) A362
Vella, Antonio W144
Vellequette, David P52
Vellinga, David H. A171
Vellinga, David H. P100
Vellinga, David P101
Vellios, Thomas G. (Tom) E162
Vels, Michael H. W137
Veltmaat, Hans-Bernd A20
Veltman, Warren E305
Vel--squez, Gustavo A202
Vel--squez, Gustavo P122
Vemana, Prat A426
Ven, Michael G. (Mike) Van de A755
Venable, Cheryl L. A322
Venable, Bryan A784
Venanzio, Debbie A115
Venarchick, Paul P209
Vendemo, Shelly P101
Venditti, Denise A372
Venditti, Denise P208
Veneziano, Giuseppe E158
Venghaus, Jarret A478
Venhoek, Mark W343
Venhoff, Chris A865
Venhuizen, John S. A9
Venhuizen, John S. P4
Venkat, Sam P297
Venkat, Geralyn P297
Venkatacharya, Patanjali E407
Venkatakrishnan, C.S. W54
Venkatesh, Kim A215
Venkayya, Rajeev W355
Venn, Richard E. W80
Venner, David A476
Venti, Jane P570
Vento, John A536
Ventola, Tony P629

Ventola, Anthony P629
Ventresca, Dino A912
Ventsam, Steve A505
Ventura, Lillian A327
Ventura, Tom A916
Ventura, Marc P105
Venturella, David E175
Venturini, Francesco W141
Venturino, Philip T P594
Venuto, Ken P620
Veraldi, Veronica E432
Veras, Harry P375
Veraska, Brad P567
Verde, Edward P163
Verdecchia, Emmett P660
Verdes, Marcelino Fern--ndez W6
Verdes, Marcelino Fern--ndez W170
Verdesca, Justin A105
Verdier, Damien W334
Verdile, Vincent P18
Verdoorn, Ronald D. P502
Verduin, Patricia A218
Verebelyi, Ernest R. (Ernie) E87
Vereen, Don P53
Verenna, Robin A705
Verenna, Robin E352
Vergara, Yanira A40
Verghese, Sunny G. W274
Vergine, Stephen A85
Verhoff, Gary A344
Verhoff, Gary E154
Veri, Clive A223
Verinder, David P483
Verity, John R. A313
Verity, Susannah A872
Verma, Pawan A361
Verma, Anuraag A390
Verma, Arun A912
Verma, Anil P228
Verma, Vivek W274
Vermeer, Mark P191
Vermeer, Kevin P252
Vermeer, Koen A P406
Vermeer, Jennifer P611
Vermillion, Tony A295
Vermillion, Scott A350
Vermillion, Kerry P59
Vermillion, Scott E157
Vermilye, David A187
Vermilye, David E71
Verna, Jonathan A912
Vernachio, Joe E86
Vernick, Marc A869
Vernon, Zana A522
Vernon, Bruce P176
Vernon, James P380
Veronneau, Marcel E42
Verostek, Elizabeth P372
Verrier, James R. A141
Verschelden, Katie A730
Verslues, Ernie P339
Verst, Cynthia L. A469
Verst, Robert P334
Vertner, Arthur E439
Verutes, Thomas A49
Vervalin, Paul P391
Vervlied, Michele A247
Vervlied, Michele E103
Verzella, James E E127
Verzera-Fair, Staci A449
Vesey, Joseph P. (Joe) A914
Vespoli, Leila L. A355
Vespoli, James A659
Vespoli, Leila L P337
Vespoli, Leila L P422
Vespoli, L L P574
Vespoli, Leila P574
Vessa, Michael A500
Vessa, Michael E237
Vessells, Carmen A272
Vessey, S.J. Rupert A178
Vestberg, Hans A870
Vester, Thomas A655
Vester, Thomas E333
Vetere, Jayne A647

Vetta, David J. (Dave) A340
Vetta, David J. (Dave) E151
Vetter, David R. (Dave) A792
Vetter, Hans-J-¶rg W215
Vetter, Robert E407
Vetto, Irene P410
Veziris, Christina A644
Vial, Arnaud W293
Viale, Enrico W141
Vialle, Karen P553
Vian, Kathy A335
Viater, Charles A572
Viater, Charles P359
Viater, Charles P473
Vibert, Paul A113
Vicari, Douglas W. E73
Vice, Aresi
Vice, Charles A457
Vice, Aresi
Vicente, Oscar P291
Vick, Paul P168
Vick, Alfie P642
Vick, Tracy E349
Vickers, Tonya A115
Vickers, Andy A596
Vickers, Gordon A599
Vickers, Keeley P19
Vickers, Monique P242
Vickers, Brandi P541
Vickory, David A774
Victor, Stan E78
Victor, Paul E171
Victoria, Ana A295
Victoria, Farah P368
Victorino, Chris A532
Videka, Lynn A585
Videka, Lynn A698
Videka, Lynn P377
Videka, Lynn P456
Vido, Eileen A857
Vidovich, Chad A729
Vidrine, Andre A819
Vieau, Nikki P537
Vieira, Cory A49
Viel, Leo A885
Viele, Dave A13
Vielehr, Byron A355
Viens, Dan E140
Viergutz, Jason A762
Vieron, Leonidas P60
Viers, Christopher P627
Vierula, Carmen P. W47
Vierzba, Christy P333
VIESTI, FRAN A272
Vietor, Barbara E220
Vifquain, Scott A493
Vig, Ravi P24
Vigar, Jill P449
Vigesaa, Claire P661
Viggiano, David A204
Vigil, Celia A70
Vigil, Ana P348
Vigil, Gabe P435
Vigil, Czar E8
Vigilante, Kevin A140
Vigue, Peter G. (Pete) P121
Vigue, Andi P121
Vihn, Daniel A530
Vijayvargiya, Jugal K. W29
Vikara, Jerry A671
Vikram, Ashish A522
Vilarin, Luis A147
Vilca, Lina Vingerhoets A753
Villa, Rudy A94
Villa, Rudy P53
Villa, Rembert de E138
Villafane, Jose M. E129
Villagran, Christopher P201
Villaneda, Robert A97
Villaneda, Robert E32
Villanueva, Maritza A202
Villanueva, Kelly A402
Villanueva, Maritza P122
Villanueva, Gustavo Blanco W25
Villareal, Al A459

Villareal, Kenneth P149
Villareal, David P149
Villareal, Roger E426
Villarreal, Kate P81
Villarreal, Sandra P278
Villarreal, Anselmo P517
Villavincencio, Julio A478
Villeger, Nicolas A785
Villont, Lisa P697
Vimard, Fran-§ois W137
Vincent, Lucie Claire Claire A218
Vincent, Anton A377
Vincent, Simon A421
Vincent, Suzanne M A477
Vincent, Deb A481
Vincent, Sherri P22
Vincent, Kelly P228
Vincent, Suzanne M P268
Vincent, Blane P469
Vincent, Tracy P491
Vincent, Mary Ann P531
Vincent, Jacques W117
Vincent, Yann W286
Vinci, Don A300
Vinci, Francesco Saverio W237
Vinciczky, Alexander S A712
Vinczeller, Shiela P A463
Vinecombe, Nigel A. E288
Vinet, Pascal A25
Vinet, Pascal P15
Vineyard, Tim P291
Vingerhoets, Cindy P163
Vining, Alexis A724
Vinitsky, Mark E432
Vinkler, David A565
Vinluan, Cynthia P643
Vinney, Les C. A161
Viola, Joseph A480
Viola, Carol A675
Viola, Mark A727
Viola, Ronald P688
Violagis, Dean Dean L Violagis E97
Violi, Anthony A800
Violi, Anthony E396
Viotty, Michelle A532
Viozzi, V. Anthony A277
Vipperman, Joseph P688
Virago, Beverly P87
Virchaux, Dominique E235
Virella, Jose A474
Virella, Jose P262
Virgil, Marcia P333
Virta, Ronald F A878
Visch, Matthijs A592
Visedpaitoon, Pong W88
Viselli, Michael A729
Vishakhadatta, Diwakar P458
Viswanathan, Ramesh A71
Viswanathan, Kusum P568
Vita, Giuseppe W380
Vitale, Domenick A369
Vitale, Robert V. A663
Vitale, Steven A869
Vitalie, John A723
Vitellas, Yianni A441
Vitelle, Richard K. (Rick) E51
Vitner, Stephanie P423
Vitto, Vincent E271
Vittorio, Michael N. A353
Vittorio, Michael N. E159
Vitulli, Jennifer P395
Vivaldi, Carlo W380
Vivaldi, Carlo W402
Vivas, Francisco J A729
Viviano, Jeffery A412
Viviano, Anthony A729
Vivier, Laurent W372
Vivoda, Rob P610
Vizag, Akw E140
Vizza, Mark A659
Vi- ±als, José W340
Vlahos, Jim E426
Vlassis, Christine P589
Vlastelica, Pete A10
Vleet, Robert Van A677

A = AMERICAN BUSINESS
E = EMERGING COMPANIES
P = PRIVATE COMPANIES
W = WORLD BUSINESS

Vlies, Paul P67
Vnenchak, David A701
Vnuck, Steve A555
Vo, Phillip A69
Vodicka, Devin P670
Vodopivec, Larry A133
Voelkel, Tyson A800
Voelkel, Tyson P559
Voge, Jan A775
Voge, Jan P548
Vogel, Michael A649
Vogel, Richard L. A813
Vogel, Delia P102
Vogel, Richard L. P616
Vogel, Tracey P685
Vogel, Roland W164
Vogel, Andy E402
Vogelpohl, Joe A784
Vogelsang, Harold A. (Jay) P550
Vogt, Dana A246
Vogt, Guy A678
Vogt, Debra A857
Vogt, Peter R. W258
Vohs, Erik A489
Voigt, Gary P45
Voisin, Jean-Baptiste W225
Voland, Scott A673
Volino, Robert S. A267
Voliva, Richard L. A423
Volk, Christopher H. (Chris) A111
Volk, Timothy M A295
Volk, Jackie A851
Volk, Christopher H. (Chris) P56
Volk, Emily P73
Volkert, Michael A502
Volkmer, Mark A837
Voll, Staci P559
Vollenweider, Emmett A480
Vollmer, Greg A332
Vollmer, Barbara J P192
Vollmer, John E. P495
Vollmer, Benjamin P544
Voloch, Bill P231
Voloch, Bill P681
Volpe, Jane A871
Volpe, Lorraine V P184
Volpe, Michele P439
Volpe, Rocco E82
Volpetti, Stefano A671
Voltaire, Marie P121
Volz, Sheilagh P535
Von, Susan A712
VonBerg, John A658
Vonderfecht, Dennis P356
Vonderfecht, Dennis E337
Vongbunyong, Sumeth W88
Vongjitvuttikrai, Vallop W203
Vongvanich, Tevin W295
Vonnes, Kristin A390
Vonwiller, Brett P371
Voorhies, Leah P268
Vopni, Scott K. A258
Vora, Sanjeev P111
Vorel, Mark A81
Vorobyev, Vadim W290
Vorpahl, Larry L. A432
Vorpahl, Roberto Hetz W137
Vorspel-Rueter, Christian P161
Vortherms, Joseph J. (Joe) A181
Vos, Jelmer J P406
Vos, Glen De W29
Vosburg, Craig A537
Vosburgh, Andrew P444
Voser, Peter R. W4
Voshell, Shane P7
Vosilla, James P292
Voskresensky, George E440
Vosper, Donna A744
Voss, Ryan A158

Voss, David A539
Voss, Thomas P647
Vossoughi, John A456
Votek, Glenn A. A66
Votek, Glenn Alan A201
Voter, Eric P224
Votta, Kate P619
Vounatsos, Michel A129
Vouvalides, Alexander (Alex) E208
Vovos, Vassilis W194
Voyles, Robb L. A398
Voyles, Brent A. A813
Voyles, David P506
Voyles, Brent A. P616
Voytovich, Anna M A323
Vrcelj, Stevan W227
Vries, Sabine A574
Vries, Glen de E268
Vroman, Danita P694
Vroonland, David P334
Vrzak, Jim E216
Vu, John A565
Vuich, Richard A683
Vuich, Chris A703
Vukelich, Ty A296
Vuncannon, Tony J A428
Vyas, Veena P323
V--zquez, Carlos J. A661
V--zquez, Mauricio Escobedo W25

W

W, Tim P323
Waccard, John A101
Wachel-Florczyk, Magda A644
Wachs, Gary A729
Wachsstock, Daniel P533
Wachtel, Jeffrey A507
Wachtel, Andrew G A575
Wachtel, Jeffrey P288
Wackerhagen, George P361
Wada, Isami W323
Waddell, Michael K. A348
Waddell, M. Keith A711
Waddington, Cliff A242
Waddle, Rick A772
Wade, Scott A117
Wade, Ralph A140
Wade, Patrick A173
Wade, Susan A351
Wade, Robyn A390
Wade, Tracy A407
Wade, Heather A446
Wade, Don A769
Wade, Anne A844
Wade, Joanne E P209
Wade, Benjamin P226
Wade, Brenda P440
Wade, Melissa P542
Wade, Susan E158
Wade, Heather P210
Wade, Anne E412
Wadhwa, Shyam A721
Wadhwa, Amit P628
Wadleigh, Martha P153
Wadsworth, Philip A685
Wadsworth, Con P452
Wadsworth, Tod P452
Wadsworth, Cole P452
Wadsworth, Kade P452
Waerum, Jesper A682
Wagers, Gary W. A110
Wagers, Gary W. E37
Wagester, Ray A214
Wagester, Ray P128
Waggoner, Matt A478
Waggoner, Brad P291
Waggoner, Gabe E91
Waggoner, Douglas R. (Doug) E117
Waggoner, Marla E209
Waghray, Ajay A83
Wagler, Theresa E. A768
Wagman, Marc A371
Wagner, Jason A67

Wagner, Elizabeth A105
Wagner, Karl A141
Wagner, Jeff A158
Wagner, Janette A162
Wagner, Theresa A188
Wagner, Greg A192
Wagner, Scott A227
Wagner, Robert F A521
Wagner, Eric R. A548
Wagner, David A620
Wagner, Matthew P. (Matt) A632
Wagner, Patricia K. (Patti) A735
Wagner, Jack W. P7
Wagner, Greg P112
Wagner, Frederick P123
Wagner, Kevin P246
Wagner, Richard P259
Wagner, Mary K P286
Wagner, Eric R. P321
Wagner, Harvey L P337
Wagner, Richard P337
Wagner, Callie P345
Wagner, Harvey L P404
Wagner, Harvey L P422
Wagner, Judy P535
Wagner, Harvey L P574
Wagner, Michael P628
Wagner, Scott P697
Wagner, Gerhard W402
Wagner, Donald S. (Don) E111
Wagner, William R. E248
Wagner, Kevin E272
Wagner, Matthew P. (Matt) E321
Wagnon, Teri A770
Wagnon, John E424
Wagoner, Ryan P500
Wagoner, Greg P672
Wagonlander, John C P316
Wagstaff, Craig C. A275
Wagstaff, Nathan V P530
Waguespack, Robert L P53
Wahl, Jeffrey A693
Wahl, Theodore E189
Wahlman, Robert A247
Wahlman, Robert E102
Wahlroos, Bj-¶rn W269
Wahlstrom, Pelle A676
Wahr, Bradley A549
Wahr, Bradley E270
Waidmann, Olivia P514
Waind, Mark P29
Wainwright, Robbie A547
Wainwright, Robbie P319
Wais, Marc A585
Wais, Marc P377
Wait, Mark P615
Wait, Dan E212
Waite, Jonathan A539
Waite, Stacey A555
Waits, Charles V P252
Waitz, Ian A. P313
Wajner, Matthew F. A335
Wajnrajch, Michael A648
Wajsgras, David C. A694
Wakabayashi, Takahiro W147
Wakabayashi, Tatsuo W245
Wakamura, Keith A183
Wake, Art A73
Wakeen, Suzanne A644
Wakefiel, Peter D P144
Wakerly, John A199
Wakita, Takeshi W116
Wakulchik, Grace P118
Wal, Eric Van De P507
Walb, Terry P101
Walchirk, Mark S. A636
Wald, Karen A32
Waldburger, Daniel A685
Walde, Van Der P32
Waldeck, Phil A676
Walden, Theodore A369
Walden, Joshua M. (Josh) A456
Walden, Richard A678
Walden, Marni M. A870
Walden, Susan A P343

Waldermann, Richard E83
Waldman, Mitchell B. (Mitch) A442
Waldman, Mitch A442
Waldman, David A555
Waldmann, Daniel R A794
Waldo, Peggy E445
Waldred, Linda P560
Waldrin, Michele A662
Waldrip, Mark P640
Waldron, Jennifer A49
Waldron, Gregory A364
Waldron, John A389
Waldron, John A429
Waldron, Blain P133
Waldron, Jay P410
Waldrum, Michael P638
Walerstein, Steven J P362
Walesiewicz, Patricia A119
Waleski, Anne G. A528
Walia, Ash A763
Walke, Barbara A422
Walke, Barbara P239
Walker, Mark A54
Walker, R. A. (Al) A63
Walker, R. A. (Al) A64
Walker, Sara A81
Walker, Marvonia A85
Walker, Jeanne A110
Walker, Trish A126
Walker, John A163
Walker, Chad A165
Walker, Brian A167
Walker, Debra A183
Walker, Robert A183
Walker, Karen A199
Walker, Terry A350
Walker, Sean N. A377
Walker, Steve A384
Walker, Kathryn A423
Walker, Kellye L. A442
Walker, Cody A446
Walker, Amy A522
Walker, Myron A530
Walker, William A532
Walker, Geoffrey H. A539
Walker, Thomas A592
Walker, Cynthia L. A611
Walker, David M. (Dave) A642
Walker, Darren A647
Walker, Roberto A668
Walker, Steven G. A674
Walker, Sky A697
Walker, John A724
Walker, Robin A725
Walker, Kevin A751
Walker, Kevin A752
Walker, Jill A763
Walker, Rob A777
Walker, Scott A792
Walker, Virginia A830
Walker, Bryan A837
Walker, Ben A844
Walker, Steven A862
Walker, Stephen William A863
Walker, Joseph C A907
Walker, Larry P40
Walker, Karen P113
Walker, Aaron P136
Walker, Cindy P169
Walker, Darcy P188
Walker, Robert L P215
Walker, Kristina P221
Walker, Tom P222
Walker, Carlene P225
Walker, Jeremy P233
Walker, Randall H P240
Walker, Terry P254
Walker, Doug P258
Walker, Dale P284
Walker, DK P289
Walker, Kristen P310
Walker, Steve P329
Walker, Jesse P343
Walker, James P355
Walker, Marsha P363

Walker, Sky P454
Walker, H. Fred P464
Walker, Rhonda P468
Walker, Judy P468
Walker, Brooks P486
Walker, Grace P633
Walker, James R P644
Walker, Andrew W36
Walker, J. F. W199
Walker, Donald J. W229
Walker, Jeanne E37
Walker, Chris E47
Walker, Debra E66
Walker, Robert E66
Walker, Daniel H. (Danny) E125
Walker, Terry E157
Walker, Steve E176
Walker, Cody E210
Walker, Mathew E253
Walker, Nico E273
Walker, David M. (Dave) E328
Walker, Kevin E378
Walker, Rob E393
Walker, Virginia E402
Walker, Ben E412
Walker, Steven E419
Walker, Joseph E424
Walker, William M. (Willy) E431
Walker, R. A. (Al) E436
Walker, Joseph C E446
Walkup, Kevin A725
Wall, Marya A159
Wall, Michael P A173
Wall, Daniel R. A312
Wall, Peter A374
Wall, Shane D. A435
Wall, Pam A781
Wall, Michael P40
Wall, Pat P78
Wall, Timothy B P102
Wall, Amanda P207
Wall, Tom P334
Wall, John P505
Wall, Richard W47
Wall, Kevin W54
Wall, Adam E117
Wallace, Molly A3
Wallace, Steve A136
Wallace, Jeff A163
Wallace, Marcus A180
Wallace, Noel R. A218
Wallace, Mark K. A243
Wallace, Shirley A266
Wallace, John A332
Wallace, Pauline A407
Wallace, Brent E. A458
Wallace, Henry D. G. A504
Wallace, Leslie A522
Wallace, Tricia Primrose A530
Wallace, Benjamin W A625
Wallace, Michael A685
Wallace, William A692
Wallace, Ann A769
Wallace, Bruce E. A777
Wallace, Antoinette A818
Wallace, Melissa A840
Wallace, Mark R. A850
Wallace, Bobby P64
Wallace, Nancy P148
Wallace, Victoria P220
Wallace, Brent E. P251
Wallace, Phillip O P281
Wallace, Paul P281
Wallace, Mark P302
Wallace, Tot P334
Wallace, Gail P391
Wallace, Erin P398
Wallace, William P454
Wallace, Rick P480
Wallace, Mark A. P560
Wallace, Cari P611
Wallace, Linda P674
Wallace, Bruce E. E392
Wallach, Russell A517
Wallen, Kathleen P220

Wallenberg, Jacob W4
Wallenberg, Jacob W360
Wallenfelsz, Don A25
Wallenfelsz, Don P15
Waller, Kathy N. A215
Waller, William A246
Waller, Cathy A674
Waller, Tom A706
Waller, Billy P148
Waller, Gregg P211
Waller, Nina P300
Waller, Deborah A P406
Waller, Robert R P474
Waller, Nick E181
Waller, Tom E353
Wallerstedt, Mike P382
Wallerstein, Barry R P510
Walles, Rob A173
Wallin, Joshua A133
Wallin, Ulrich W164
Wallin, Ulrich W356
Wallis, Julie A101
Walljasper, William J. (Bill) A168
Wallquist, Dianna A827
Walls, Robert H. A448
Walls, Brandon P13
Walls-Honeycutt, Julie P196
Walmsley, Emma W158
Walno, Vicki A196
Walsdorf, John A. (Jack) E149
Walsh, Jim A3
Walsh, Lambert A11
Walsh, Brian A34
Walsh, David A52
Walsh, Timothy A. A53
Walsh, Timothy A. A54
Walsh, Tim A84
Walsh, Steven A122
Walsh, Joseph A122
Walsh, Catherine A241
Walsh, Caitlin A390
Walsh, Matt A413
Walsh, Joe A458
Walsh, Nancy A537
Walsh, William P. A582
Walsh, Timothy J. A635
Walsh, Amanda A724
Walsh, Marguerite A727
Walsh, Michael A741
Walsh, Martin A749
Walsh, Karen Bianchi A764
Walsh, Ian K. A804
Walsh, Laurie A810
Walsh, John L. A836
Walsh, Michael P2
Walsh, Kate E. P80
Walsh, Stephen J. P107
Walsh, Katie P109
Walsh, Martin J P122
Walsh, Kate P143
Walsh, Joann P179
Walsh, Matt P234
Walsh, Susan P249
Walsh, Joe P251
Walsh, Steve P315
Walsh, William P. P373
Walsh, Timothy J. P419
Walsh, Matt P424
Walsh, Marshall T P490
Walsh, Leonard P528
Walsh, Karen Bianchi P540
Walsh, Laurie P597
Walsh, Kathleen P622
Walsh, Paul S. W107
Walsh, Robert B. E136
Walsh, Keith E144
Walsh, Matthew O. E171
Walsh, Daniel E229
Walsh, Michael E371
Walsh, Kevin E432
walshe, siobhan A528
Walshe, Christine P636
Walter, Luc A62
Walter, Stephanie A73
Walter, Tim A204

Walter, Kade A204
Walter, John A249
Walter, Pati A328
Walter, Frank E. A412
Walter, Randall R A413
Walter, Brian A522
Walter, Glen A567
Walter, Lawrence A599
Walter, Richard A670
Walter, Stephen P206
Walter, Randall R P234
Walter, Ashley P291
Walter, Steve P329
Walter, Kevin P329
Walter, Scott P339
Walter, Larry P519
Walter, Susan P521
Walter, Todd P538
Walter, Kenneth E39
Walter, Frank E. E192
Walters, Thomas A313
Walters, Kirk W. A644
Walters, Joey A743
Walters, David A838
Walters, Matt P19
Walters, H Patrick P21
Walters, David P81
Walters, Kayon P284
Walters, Sherry P289
Walters, Leigh P424
Walters, John F P465
Walters, John P465
Walters, Jerry P487
Walters, Kelly S. P579
Walters, Laura M P592
Walters, Tyler O. P669
Walters, Joey E373
Walters, Andrew F. E375
Walther, Leanna A6
Waltman, Naomi A175
Walton, Demetra A327
Walton, Karen A505
Walton, Lynell A614
Walton, Thomas W. H. (Tom) A631
Walton, Dan A819
Walton, Jarrod P50
Walton, Keith P308
Walton, Edward P655
Walton, Don P664
Walton, Debbie P665
Walton, Louis E298
Waltz, Mike A81
Waltz-Jaskolski, Donna M A208
Walz, John E265
Walzer, Eric A890
Walzer, Eric P684
Wambold, Richard A796
Wamboldt, John A109
Wamboldt, John E36
Wampler, Kevin S. A274
Wampler, Dan P424
Wamser, Chris A300
Wanchik, Marry A101
Wanchun, Zheng W186
Wancowicz, Jason A659
Wandeler, Roland A61
Wandell, Keith E A252
Wander, John A133
Wandke, Simon W30
Wandling, Janet A614
Wandschneider, Robin A223
Waner, Leo A796
Wang, Kai A49
Wang, Bill A355
Wang, Jiahong A375
Wang, Xia A413
Wang, Kai A456
Wang, Li A511
Wang, Ed A537
Wang, Didi A556
Wang, Yao A649
Wang, Richard A741
Wang, Jonathan A775
Wang, Min A874
Wang, Ernest P109

Wang, George P114
Wang, WEI P154
Wang, Xia P234
Wang, Su P378
Wang, Leon W35
Wang, Chuanfu W77
Wang, Gregory K.H. W84
Wang, Chuan W90
Wang, Shi W96
Wang, Wilfred W152
Wang, J.K. W354
Wang, Ling E294
Wang, Richard E370
Wangsness, Erik P8
Wanli, Lin W89
Wanly, Bahaa P476
Wann, Robert A583
Wanta, Gregory T. A462
Wanzek, Kent W153
Wappel, Paul A430
Waravdekar, Neil P205
Warbinton, Craig A84
Warburton, Christopher A693
Warburton, Kerry P324
Warburton, Suzette P375
Ward, Victor A100
Ward, Michelle A167
Ward, Paul J. A225
Ward, Patrick J. (Pat) A246
Ward, F. Stephen A338
Ward, David A348
Ward, Bill A353
Ward, Steven E. A412
Ward, Vicki A449
Ward, John M A519
Ward, Geoffrey A691
Ward, Thomas A744
Ward, Ron A781
Ward, Jacquelyn M. (Jackie) A782
Ward, Laysha L. A788
Ward, Peter P. A826
Ward, Susan A850
Ward, Lori P154
Ward, Cynthia S P194
Ward, Kevin P303
Ward, Ronnie P319
Ward, John P320
Ward, Marilyn P331
Ward, Kristi P345
Ward, Robert T P352
Ward, Peter P375
Ward, Brian P376
Ward, Kevin P381
Ward, Karyn P430
Ward, Jennifer P432
Ward, Jim P451
Ward, Jennifer P537
Ward, Debra P560
Ward, Keith P665
Ward, Pat P682
Ward, Greg C. W227
Ward, Paul J. E88
Ward, Steven E. E192
Ward, Adrian E320
Ward, Stew E385
Ward-Callan, Mary P586
Wardell, Carol P448
Warden, Kathy J. A324
Warden, Kathy J. A602
Warden, Rachel P11
Wardlaw, Van M. A798
Wardwell, Myra A100
Wardynski, Paula A589
Ware, Timothy A537
Ware, Hilary A581
Ware, Daniel A667
Ware, Scott D. A916
Ware, Pam P383
Ware, Brandon P420
Ware, Nancy W. E135
Ware, Demetrius E432
Waring, Michael A183
Waring, Pat P218
Waring, Stephen P505
Waring, Wendy P632

A = AMERICAN BUSINESS
E = EMERGING COMPANIES
P = PRIVATE COMPANIES
W = WORLD BUSINESS

Waring, Thomas H. E135
Warlow, Thomas P. E92
Warman, D. Scott N. A522
Warman, D Scott N A522
Warman, Scott A522
Warmbier, Kimberly (Kim) A258
Warmbier, Kim A258
Warminsky, Jeff A644
Warne, Jen A513
Warne, Peter H. W227
Warner, Richard A101
Warner, Joe A369
Warner, Jane A450
Warner, Jason A546
Warner, Mark A599
Warner, Richard P147
Warner, Dan P149
Warner, Casey P193
Warner, Laura P449
Warner, Craig P515
Warner, Alexa P665
Warner, Richard C. E431
Warner, Michelle E432
Warnick, Lorin D. P143
Warnock, Greg A487
Warren, Armida A101
Warren, Karmon A129
Warren, Kelcy L A298
Warren, Thomas A330
Warren, Brandy A390
Warren, Dennis A402
Warren, Cindy A476
Warren, Carmen A532
Warren, Burney A573
Warren, Tiffany R A619
Warren, Ken A655
Warren, Travis A785
Warren, V'Ella A861
Warren, Alice A865
Warren, Kristin A903
Warren, Kevin M. A911
Warren, Doug P81
Warren, Daryl P108
Warren, Robert M P205
Warren, Brenda P220
Warren, Kelcy L P294
Warren, Eric P359
Warren, Allyson P427
Warren, Richard P435
Warren, Robert P440
Warren, Joni P521
Warren, Dave P536
Warren, Demarcus P567
Warren, Steve P613
Warren, V'Ella P658
Warren, Brian P. E96
Warren, Paul E117
Warren, Donnie E189
Warren, Ken E333
Warren, Galen E363
Warren, Miriam E447
Warrick, Paula P37
Warring, Wendy P570
Warsh, Kevin A850
Wartenbergh, Marcela A682
Warthen, Wayne B. E97
Warwick, John J. E51
Warzala, Richard S. (Dick) E13
Warzman, Yaron A481
Warzyniak, Bob P602
Wascom, D. G. A313
Wasden, Mitch P646
Wasdovich, Andrea P280
Wasechek, Wayne E424
Waser, Eric H. A639
Waser, Eric H. E325
Waserman, Alan P321
Washam, Daniel A866
Washburn, Dana P417

Washburne, Tom A614
Washer, Dr Cathy P293
Washington, Justina A135
Washington, Mike A173
Washington, Roderick A244
Washington, Ken A362
Washington, Robin L. A386
Washington, Herbert A522
Washington, Justina P78
Washington, A. Eugene P168
Washington, Ladosha P249
Washington, Adrienne P286
Washington, Lorraine P332
Wasiak, Xavier A478
Wasielczyk, Michael A784
Wasilewski, Raymond W. A319
Wasilewski, Jennifer P353
Wasko, John P392
Wasniski, Laurie P180
Wasser, Marilyn J A696
Wasserman, Robert A34
Wasserman, Bruce P266
Wassersug, Mark A457
Wassmer, Michael J. A163
Wasson, Malia E86
Wasti, Rashid W394
Wastler, Ernst W154
Wasyliw, Rob A484
Watanabe, Shelly P261
Watanabe, Yutaka W99
Watanabe, Yoshinori W116
Watanabe, Dai W211
Watanabe, Yoshiro W213
Watanabe, Shuichi W237
Watanabe, Shinjiro W237
Watanabe, Kenji W260
Watanabe, Kunio W268
Watanabe, Hiroshi W330
Watanabe, Takao W366
Waterbury, Todd A788
Waterfall, Marcy A532
Waterfield, John E357
Waterhouse, Danielle P281
Waterhouse, Deborah W158
Waterman, Robert T P207
Waters, Eddie A54
Waters, Stephen M. A143
Waters, Andy D. A228
Waters, Simon A408
Waters, Jim A564
Waters, Ron A724
Waters, Stephanie A751
Waters, Robin A838
Waters, Robyn P25
Waters, Michael J P154
Waters, Stephanie E377
Waterson, Blake A260
Watkin, Jared L. A5
Watkins, Roger A163
Watkins, John A246
Watkins, Charles E A300
Watkins, James A700
Watkins, James A743
Watkins, Brad A801
Watkins, W Juan P75
Watkins, Jesse P177
Watkins, Glissandia P460
Watkins, Brad P561
Watkins, Anthony P675
Watkins, Gretchen H. W1
Watkins, Kameshia E65
Watkins, James E373
Watne, Zachariah A377
Watriss, Whitney P506
Watsa, V.Prem W146
Watson, Jimmy A54
Watson, Tim A81
Watson, Beth A101
Watson, Pamela A115
Watson, Joseph A158
Watson, Melvin A195
Watson, David N A220
Watson, David A238
Watson, Devon R. A265
Watson, Lois A328

Watson, Randi A371
Watson, Katie L. A386
Watson, Ian A460
Watson, Lucas A466
Watson, Greg A545
Watson, Brandon A622
Watson, Tom A631
Watson, Brian A727
Watson, Bob A767
Watson, Patricia A. A823
Watson, Scott P300
Watson, Alan P314
Watson, George E P359
Watson, Christopher P398
Watson, Mike P422
Watson, Brad P452
Watson, Leslyn P482
Watson, Bud P486
Watson, Amy E. P520
Watson, Aaron P529
Watson, Dean P554
Watson, James M. P611
Watson, Gordon W13
Watson, John W61
Watson, J. Howard W76
Watson, Peter H. E161
Watson, Bob E432
Watt, John H. A577
Watt, Kelley A P298
Watt, Abby P370
Watt, Andrew P515
Watt, Robert M P694
Watt, Brian R. E216
Watt, Wylie E398
Watters, Lyle A362
Watters, Jack A649
Watters, James H. P464
Watterson, Andrew A755
Watteville, Jacques de W52
Watts, Mike A127
Watts, Phillip R. A266
Watts, Jeffery M. A318
Watts, Myles J. A320
Watts, Gary A330
Watts, Michael A390
Watts, Alan A421
Watts, James A791
Watts, Karen P152
Watts, Dr Calvin J P273
Watts, Richard P421
Watts, Charles P550
Watts, R. Andrew E47
Watts, Myles J. E143
Waty, Elin W347
Waugh, Scott A635
Waugh, Alex P30
Waugh, Scott P419
Waugh, Wendi P516
Wax, Meri A537
Way, Chrisanne P40
Way, John A. E339
Waycaster, Billy A257
Waycaster, C. Mitchell (Mitch) A704
Waycaster, C. Mitchell (Mitch) E350
Waye, Janice A34
Waye, Janice P27
Wayland, Joseph F. W98
Wayling, Brian A458
Wayling, Brian P251
Wayne, John C. P432
Wayne, Rodney P541
Wayson, Amy P410
Wayton, Kathleen A755
Weadock, Suzanne A770
Weagley, Anthony C. (Tony) E90
Weakland, Darrell A591
Weant, Paula A744
Weant, Jerry A. E53
Weatherhead, Craig A318
Weatherhead, Jim A599
Weathers, Hugh E A22
Weathers, Hugh E P13
Weaver, Bob A27
Weaver, Jason A54
Weaver, David H. A115

Weaver, Jennifer A115
Weaver, Gary A250
Weaver, Robert A332
Weaver, Matthew A420
Weaver, Ken A513
Weaver, Casey A541
Weaver, Susan A583
Weaver, Janine M A596
Weaver, Derrek A717
Weaver, Amy E. A723
Weaver, Dorenda A823
Weaver, Keith A913
Weaver, Michael P108
Weaver, George P175
Weaver, Carl P417
Weaver, Jeremy P453
Weaver, Jennifer P567
Weaver, Donald P658
Weaver, Gail P697
Weaver, Matthew E198
Weaver, John E224
Weaver, Casey E267
Webb, David A25
Webb, Randy A71
Webb, Patricia G. (Pat) A171
Webb, James R. A190
Webb, Thomas J. (Tom) A210
Webb, Thomas J. (Tom) A236
Webb, Mark O. A275
Webb, Cody A318
Webb, Sarah A328
Webb, Marva A359
Webb, Brian A439
Webb, Jan C. A452
Webb, Charles A508
Webb, Jan A513
Webb, Ian A537
Webb, Sandy A693
Webb, Scott A730
Webb, Mike A781
Webb, Martin A912
Webb, David P15
Webb, Sandra P30
Webb, David P64
Webb, Sandra P81
Webb, Donna P95
Webb, Patricia G. (Pat) P100
Webb, Marie P178
Webb, Christopher P201
Webb, Kim P277
Webb, Steven P378
Webb, Maryjo P498
Webb, Kathleen M. P611
Webb, Steven T P664
Webb, Jan C. E215
Webb, H. Lawrence (Larry) E398
Webber, Jerome A84
Webber, Patrick A434
Webber, Diane A767
Webber, Henry S. P615
Webber, Rhonda P637
Webber, Michael J. P654
Weber, Roger A25
Weber, Susan A160
Weber, Todd A244
Weber, Tom A324
Weber, Christopher T. (Chris) A398
Weber, David F A432
Weber, Hubert A567
Weber, Lisa A677
Weber, Roger P15
Weber, Amy P261
Weber, Lance P301
Weber, Emily P321
Weber, Jeff P338
Weber, Scott P441
Weber, Rhonada P525
Weber, Keith P539
Weber, Emily P641
Weber, Stephen P691
Weber, Ulrich W121
Weber, Christophe W355
Weber, David M. E3
Weber, Fred E22
Weber, Susan E55

Weber, Richard E108
Weber, Michael E290
Weber, Kathleen E318
Weber, Thomas E322
Weberling, Matt A542
Weberling, Matt E267
Webster, Allyson A101
Webster, Jill A539
Webster, Marshall W. A859
Webster, Ted A885
Webster, Keith P96
Webster, Rick P619
Webster, Marshall W. P652
Webster, Steven A. E59
Wechsler, Ron A806
Weddington, Brian A105
Wedepohl, Eric A377
Wedin, Robert J. (Rob) E52
Wedral, Elaine R. E31
Weed, Thaddeus G. (Tad) E81
Weekes, Cristina E65
Weekley, Daniel A275
Weekly, Julia Willett P174
Weeks, Wendell P. A238
Weeks, Felicia A446
Weeks, Andrew M. A634
Weeks, Albert P60
Weeks, Susan P560
Weeks, Felicia E210
Weel, Pascal A204
Weel, Allan A904
Weel, Allan E442
Weems, Mac A369
Wegehaupt, Olga A15
Wegehaupt, Olga P9
Wegel, Michael P8
Wegener, Paul A549
Wegener, Mildred P613
Wegener, Paul E270
Weger, Larry A73
Weglarz, Liliam P603
Wegman, Jill P141
Wegman, Thomas I. E43
Wegmann, Tom A161
Wegner, Christoph W55
Wegner, Jeremy E69
Wegrzyn, Daniel A762
Wehe, Brad P29
Wehmer, Edward J. A904
Wehmer, Edward J. E442
Wehner, David M. (Dave) A314
Wehner, Dominik W153
Wehr, Van A173
Wehrly, Donald W. A527
Wehrman, Susan A702
Wei, Wang W12
Wei, Chris W38
Wei, Chen W102
Wei, Peter W113
Wei, C.C. W354
Weibel, Kurt A111
Weibel, Kurt P56
Weibelt, Daniel P605
Weideling, Peter A875
Weidman-Grunewald, Elaine W360
Weigley, David E. P8
Weigman, Mark A784
Weih, Lori P252
Weihe, Huang W283
Weil, Robert J. A171
Weil, Robert J. A372
Weil, Robert J. P100
Weil, Robert J. P208
Weil, Edward M E426
Weiland, John A920
Weiland, Ed P481
Weiler, Nathan P48
Weiliang, Xie W403
Weilinghoff, Andreas A289
Weimer, Robert A246
Weimer, Gail A555
Weimer, Loren Karp P106
Weimer, Theodor W380
Weimerskirch, Kevin A372
Wein, Arthur E90

Weinand, Dieter W57
Weinberg, Meryl A582
Weinberg, Meryl P373
Weinberg, Ido P590
Weinberg, John S. E136
Weiner, Jeffrey M P306
Weiner, Toby P414
Weiner, Jack P531
Weiner, Edward G. P623
Weiner, Scott E19
Weinert, Robert S A100
Weinert, Michael A260
Weinert, Robert S E34
Weinert, Fred J. E340
Weingarden, Craig A221
Weingart, Saul N P628
Weingartner, Jeffrey A344
Weinheimer, Don D. E421
Weinkle, Brian A568
Weinraub, Michelle P683
Weinstein, Laura A241
Weinstein, Larry A744
Weinstein, Michael Arthur P14
Weinstein, James P154
Weinstein, Susan P223
Weinstein, James P371
Weinstein, Debra P590
Weinstein, Daniel E140
Weinstein, Glen D. E225
Weinstein, Scott E305
Weinstock, Craig L A574
Weinstock, Richard P278
Weintraub, Herschel A461
Weintraub, Jonathan P144
Weir, Cecile A A1
Weir, David A584
Weir, Walter P78
Weir, George P257
Weir, David P376
Weir, Helen A. W233
Weir, Amanda E311
Weirick, Cecilia P204
Weis-Smith, Linda P473
Weisberg, James P182
Weise, Stuart A704
Weise, Lori P103
Weise, Stuart E351
Weisel, Thomas W. (Thom) A771
Weisenberger, Mike A34
Weisenhorn, John A105
Weisensel, Bill P281
Weiser, Anna P571
Weishaar, Annette A158
Weisickle, John A51
Weisickle, John P33

Weisler, Dion J. A435
Weismann, Marty P308
Weiss, Mark A51
Weiss, Justin A180
Weiss, Jerry A366
Weiss, Barry A419
Weiss, Steve A497
Weiss, Mark A520
Weiss, Gregory A537
Weiss, Richard A599
Weiss, George P59
Weiss, Tamara P264
Weiss, Howard P290
Weiss, Aaron P303
Weiss, Allen S P361
Weiss, David E. E19
Weiss, Elie E47
Weiss, Richard R. E374
Weissbaum, Martha A710
Weisser, Christian A265
Weisser, Marc A568
Weisser, Hellmuth W234
Weissert, J A693
Weissman, Gabriel A59
Weissman, Neil J. A548
Weissman, Martin P308
Weissman, Neil J. P321
Weissman, Seth R. P559
Weissman, Paul P688

Weisz, Terry A530
Weisz, Karen A593
WEITGENANT, DAVID A354
Weitzel, David P105
Weitzman, Debbie A165
Weitzner, Michael A855
Weizhao, Qiu W403
Welage, Lynda S. P648
Welborn, Jamie A564
Welborn, Sally S A878
Welborn, Tom P347
Welborn, Thomas O P347
Welborn, Gregory S. (Greg) P367
Welborn, Ruth B. P563
Welborn, Gant E146
Welborne, Martha A272
Welch, Marty A73
Welch, John A442
Welch, Shawn P A628
Welch, Matt A677
Welch, Richard A677
Welch, Susan A811
Welch, Jerry A815
Welch, Zachary A844
Welch, James L. A916
Welch, Debi P145
Welch, Kevin P208
Welch, Carrie P251
Welch, Joseph L P252
Welch, Kevin P255
Welch, Patrick J P268
Welch, Joseph L P340
Welch, Michael F P418
Welch, Susan P600
Welch, Michael F P697
Welch, Christopher A. (Chris) E106
Welch, Zachary E412
Welcome, Dorothy P249
Welday, Rick A85
Weldon, Cece A16
Weldon, Alex A49
Weldon, Mary A332
Weldon, Michael A912
Weldon, Terry P188
Weldon, Aaron P197
Weldon, Marcus W266
Weldy, John P670
Welke, Katherine A. (Katy) A458
Welkie, Katherine A. (Katy) P251
Welkley, Steve A912
Wellborn, W. Christopher (Chris) A563
Welle, Patricia P486
Welleck, George A461
Wellendorf, Don P301
Weller, Matthew P269
Weller, Simcha P628
Weller, Rick L. E134
Welles, Scott A140
Welling, Brandon A221
Welling, Steven D. (Steve) E420
Wellington, Gavin C A639
Wellington, Gavin C E326
Wellman, Arnold A850
Wellman, Michael A885
Wellman, Laura Meyer P202
Wells, Brooks A17
Wells, Martha K A85
Wells, Stephen G A221
Wells, Scott R. A448
Wells, Ryan A484
Wells, David A581
Wells, Larry A599
Wells, Michael K A667
Wells, Robert A738
Wells, Gregory D. (Greg) A755
Wells, Samuel A814
Wells, Tim A881
Wells, Brooks P10
Wells, Kelly P108
Wells, Beverly P243
Wells, Alex P268
Wells, David A P346
Wells, John P359
Wells, Karla P407
Wells, Samuel P616

Wells, Mike W295
Wells, Charles C. (Chris) E447
Wells, Chris E447
Welsh, Bill A835
Welsh, Wesley A917
Welsh, James P211
Welsh, Gary P281
Welsh, Jon P343
Welsh, Richard P391
Welsh, Peter P545
Welsh, Jeff P567
Welsh, Craig E440
Welt, Philip S. A122
Welton, Isabelle W405
Welty, Bonnie P500
Welu, Todd P149
Welz, Edward A. (Ed) P375
Welzen, James van A607
Welzenbach, Mark A402
Wemmer, Dieter W23
Wen, Pauline A871
Wen, Ling W94
Wenaas, Jeffrey K. (Jeff) P235
Wendelboe, Steven A522
Wendell, Michael E269
Wender, Herbert A690
Wender, Herbert E345
Wendland, Andy P548
Wendler, Kenneth A201
Wendler, John A825
Wendt, Stephen C P164
Wendy, Warring P570
Wenerstrom, Stewart A127
Weng, Kirsti A507
Weng, Kirsti P288
Wenger, E. Philip (Phil) A369
Wenger, Philip R. P589
Wenguo, Tian W403
Wenhui, Qian W186
Wenig, Devin N. A288
Wenk, Martin W41
Wenkoff, Carman R A273
Wenlong, Lou W12
Wennerstrom, Tiffany P30
Wenning, Werner W57
Wenning, Werner W331
Wenta, Ted P188
Wente, James W P511
Wente, Susan P615
Wente, Heinz-Gerhard W108
Wentling, Robert A195
Wentworth, Brian A5
Wentworth, Peter A221
Wentworth, Harold M. (Harry) A225
Wentworth, Steven D. A304
Wentworth, Carlos P252
Wentworth, Harold M. (Harry) E88
Wentz, Deanna P22
Wentz, Robert J P410
Wentz, Myron W. E423
Wenzel, Gregory G. (Greg) A140
Wenzel, Patricia P340
Wenzell, Jeffrey A P188
Werbeckes, Jim A296
Werdegar, Stefan E404
Werft, Ronald C P482
Werle, Haley A201
Wermers, Michael P621
Wermes, Eric A198
Werneck, Melissa A494
Werner, Frederick W. (Fred) A16
Werner, Todd S. A111
Werner, Tom A230
Werner, Melissa A489
Werner, Lisa A886
Werner, Todd S. P56
Werner, Patrick P352
Werner, Lisa E433
Wernick, Mark P22
Wernick, Joel P427
Wernikoff, Daniel A. (Dan) A466
Werpy, Todd A. A74
Werrbach, John P22
Wersal, Ann P301
Wersch, Wouter Van A375

| A = AMERICAN BUSINESS |
| E = EMERGING COMPANIES |
| P = PRIVATE COMPANIES |
| W = WORLD BUSINESS |

Wert, Lawrence (Larry) E402
Werth, Dennis L. P379
Wertheim, Ram D. A542
Wertheizer, Gideon E67
Werther, Jon E272
Werthman, Ronald J A474
Werthman, Ronald J P265
Werthman, Ronald P266
Wertman, Linda P588
Wescoe, Nicole A899
Wescoe, Nicole P690
Wescombe, Gary E189
Weslager, Jim A659
Wesley, Carla A45
Wesley, Mary Lou P680
Weslock, Kathleen A368
Wesolek, Lisa M. E106
Wesolowski, Karen P136
Wesp, Clyde P663
Wessel, Tyler P257
Wessel, Rick L. E161
Wessells, Chris P653
Wessels, Philip W256
Wessely, Boris A724
Wessler, Alan P339
Wessman, Cal A173
West, Joseph A16
West, Judy A37
West, Pam A101
West, Nora A158
West, Ed A162
West, Steven A200
West, Robert F. (Rob) A214
West, Wayne G. (Gil) A261
West, Roderick K. (Rod) A300
West, Joanne A343
West, Cliff A478
West, Mindy K. A571
West, Jerret A581
West, Jeffrey A600
West, William Corey A624
West, Richard A631
West, Tony A647
West, Mark D. A698
West, Melissa A832
West, Eric A912
West, Judy P29
West, Patrick H P123
West, Robert F. (Rob) P128
West, George P208
West, David P341
West, Tom P399
West, Mark D. P456
West, Karen P460
West, Sarah P510
West, Lashonda P599
West, Bradley (Brad) E331
West, Josh E432
West, Chris E441
Westad, Erik A305
Westad, Erik P185
Westapher, Bernard P416
Westbrook, C Hunter A428
Westbrook, Bennett D. A719
Westbrook, Bennett D. P468
Westby, Ross P151
Westcott, Brian A115
Wester, K Scott P412
Westerfield, Blake A213
Westering, Karen Van P598
Westermann, Marit P565
Western, Keith A. A110
Western, Keith A. E37
Westervelt, Karen S A810
Westervelt, Karen S P597
Westfall, Toni A101
Westfield, Mike A520
Westle, Marc B P345
Westlie, Trond -- . W118

Westlin, William A178
Westlund, M. Randolph (Rand) A684
Westlund, M. Randolph (Rand) E341
Westman, David A98
Westman, Shelley A460
Westman, Carl E P361
Westman, David E33
Westmoreland, Rick A136
Westmoreland, Mary Beth E44
Weston, Mike A199
Weston, Kathleen A364
Weston, Karl A703
Weston, Ivy P123
Weston, Andrew P499
Weston, George G. W33
Weston, Galen G. W394
Weston, Alannah W394
Westphal, Kenneth P164
Westphal, Dan P384
Westra, Richard A251
Westrick, Thomas A375
Westrick, Karl J P305
Westrick, Karl P305
Westwood, Melanie Maurer A659
Wet, Misty de A755
Wet, Misty de E380
Wetherington, Suzzane A93
Wetherly, Mark P129
Wetmore, Griffin P. P503
Wetselaar, Maarten W313
Wetter, Phil A489
Wetterer, Diana P398
Wetzel, Kurt A105
Wetzel, Todd P449
Wetzel, Laura P474
Wetzel, Leslie P654
Wetzel, Cindy L. E276
Wever, Karen A195
Wexler, Ronnie A390
Wexler, Samantha A815
Wexler, Barrie A871
Wexner, Leslie H. A497
Wexner, Abigail S. P365
Weyerhaeuser, William T. A219
Weyerhaeuser, William T. E84
Weyker, Debbie A100
Weyker, Debbie E34
Weymouth, Carma A769
Weymouth, Tara P149
Whalen, Ellie A105
Whalen, Douglas A151
Whalen, Phil A164
Whalen, Angie A164
Whalen, Kim A341
Whalen, Edward A519
Whalen, Dan A723
Whalen, James W. A787
Whalen, Julie P. A901
Whalen, Chad P90
Whalen, Anna P273
Whalen, Thomas V. P287
Whalen, Anna P296
Whalen, Douglas E48
Whalen, Kim E153
Whalen, Chad E166
Whaley, Kristi A163
Whaley, Justin P101
Whaley, Ron P101
Whaley, Alan P248
Whalley, Ken A388
Whalley, Sue W314
Wharton, Charles A886
Wharton, Junaye P571
Wharton, Charles E433
Wheat, William W. (Bill) A433
Wheat, Douglas D. (Doug) E17
Wheatlake, Franklin C. A187
Wheatlake, Franklin C. E71
Wheatley, Charles A685
Wheatley, Chuck A685
Wheatley, Tim A705
Wheatley, Sandra E166
Wheatley, Tim E352
Wheaton, Guy A589
Wheaton, Pam P528

Wheaton, Craig P670
Wheeler, Al A13
Wheeler, Monte A115
Wheeler, Hanley A250
Wheeler, Deborah A541
Wheeler, William J A556
Wheeler, Michael J. A597
Wheeler, Scott A767
Wheeler, Robert H. A816
Wheeler, David A870
Wheeler, Dane P6
Wheeler, Penny Ann P26
Wheeler, Zach P42
Wheeler, Debi P251
Wheeler, Brett P319
Wheeler, Steven M. (Steve) P487
Wheeler, Melanie P567
Wheeler, James R P591
Wheeler, Peter P595
Wheeler, Kelsey P626
Wheeler, Bradley C. (Brad) P627
Wheeler, Brad P627
Wheeler, Paul P660
Wheeler, Scott E97
Wheeler, Deborah E266
Wheeler, Chad E430
Wheeler-Fair, Martha P344
Whelan, Christopher A195
Whelan, John P627
Whelan, Lyndsey E117
Whelan, John K. W138
Whelpley, Rodd P246
Whichard, Betty M P649
Whiddon, Georgia P563
Whigham, Teresa P110
Whiitely, B Glen P145
Whipple, Andrew A478
Whipple, John P444
Whisenhunt, Dan A70
Whistle, Kristi A532
Whitaker, Charles N A37
Whitaker, Douglas A328
Whitaker, Maureen A691
Whitaker, Grant A866
Whitaker, Sandy P281
Whitaker, Erin P332
Whitaker, Hal P444
Whitaker, John P473
Whitaker, Candace P501
Whitaker, Grant P661
Whitaker, Ralph P700
Whitaker, Thomas A. (Tom) E368
Whitbread, Mary A413
Whitbread, Mary P234
Whitcomb, Lisa P329
White, Miles D. A4
White, Brad A16
White, Teresa L. A18
White, Steve A20
White, John A54
White, Amy A91
White, Ed A115
White, Laura A133
White, Keith P A136
White, Sylvia A162
White, Gina A164
White, Dayl A185
White, Cris A A219
White, Antoine A219
White, Anthony A244
White, J T A246
White, Robert A. A247
White, Bill A249
White, Jim A253
White, John A258
White, Tim A282
White, Andrew A295
White, Elijah A313
White, Mary A350
White, Brett A377
White, Matthew A390
White, Duane A412
White, Alan B. A420
White, Teresa A428
White, James C. (Jim) A452

White, Katharyn A460
White, Andrew A478
White, Barbara A496
White, Matthew J. (Matt) A514
White, Jeff A537
White, Joseph W. A565
White, Robert A585
White, Doug A591
White, Elizabeth V A599
White, Linda A614
White, J. Edward (Ed) A655
White, J. Harvey A655
White, Edward A655
White, Debbie A667
White, Megan A720
White, Joshua A744
White, Stephanie A774
White, Lynn A781
White, Melissa A782
White, Clark A787
White, James A800
White, Douglas A802
White, Mark A815
White, Noel A834
White, Diana A844
White, Wayne A855
White, Lou Ann A863
White, Michelle A864
White, Amy A867
White, Brendan M. A890
White, Charles A890
White, Wendy A901
White, Patrick A912
White, Matthew P12
White, Allen P42
White, Doug P46
White, Rev. William W. P57
White, William W P59
White, Cooper P118
White, Joseph P121
White, Terry P123
White, Keith A. P125
White, Paul P125
White, Cris A P131
White, Jennifer P134
White, Jeffery P149
White, Erika P149
White, James M P158
White, Bob P158
White, Andrew P161
White, Paul P175
White, Andrea P181
White, Steven T P191
White, Greg P220
White, Joseph E P232
White, James P250
White, Christine P266
White, Marietta R P270
White, Joseph P298
White, Kevin P303
White, David P327
White, Eric P339
White, Don P345
White, Judy D P352
White, Rita P369
White, Robert P377
White, Jacob P400
White, Thomas D P400
White, Sam P415
White, Christine P433
White, Stephen F P462
White, Curt P500
White, Lori P514
White, Douglas P562
White, Michael P618
White, Winona P627
White, Raymond E P639
White, Owen C P641
White, Craig G. P648
White, Amy P661
White, Brendan M. P684
White, Charles P684
White, Wendy P692
White, Dan E17
White, Antoine E84

White, Tom E91
WHITE, BUFFY E101
White, Robert A. E102
White, Mary E157
White, Andrew E178
White, Duane E192
White, Alan B. E198
White, James C. (Jim) E214
White, J. Edward (Ed) E333
White, J. Harvey E333
White, Edward E333
White, Debbie E336
White, Megan E362
White, James E396
White, Diana E412
White, Omar E428
White-Coleman, Debra P243
Whited, Amanda A273
Whited, Gary L. A374
Whited, Elizabeth F. (Beth) A842
Whitefield, Adam A919
Whiteford, Grace Puma A647
Whitehair, Kevin P342
Whitehall, Ellen A86
Whitehall, Ellen P52
Whitehead, Dane E. A526
Whitehead, Craig A649
Whitehead, Roy M. A879
Whitehead, Angela P63
Whitehead, Benjamin P75
Whitehead, David P617
Whitehead, Dave P617
Whitehead, Nigel W40
Whitehead, Linda E46
Whitehead, Loretta R. E153
Whitehouse, Kirk A832
Whitehurst, Bradford D. (Brad) A298
Whitehurst, Jay F. E89
Whitehurst, Julian E. (Jay) E293
Whiteing, David W105
Whitelaw, Kelly A273
Whitelaw, Kelly P162
Whitelaw, Gary W346
Whiteley, Dudley A377
Whiteley, Sherry A466
Whitely, B Glen P145
Whiteman, Keith A585
Whiteman, Charles H. A811
Whiteman, Keith P377
Whiteman, Charles H. P600
Whitemyer, Jennifer A101
Whiten, Torivia A101
Whitenack, Kimberly A321
Whitenack, Kimberly E144
Whitener, Pam P297
Whiteside, Hayes V. A670
Whiteside, Cathie A683
Whiteside, S A684
Whiteside, Tom P73
Whiteside, Darwin P391
Whiteside, Cathie E341
Whiteside, S E341
Whitfield, Rob W395
Whitham, Rande A151
Whitham, Rande E48
Whiting, Jennifer A16
Whiting, Ted A558
Whitlatch, Christopher P601
Whitley, J C A417
Whitley, David A765
Whitley, Keva A838
Whitley, Russell A902
Whitley, David P540
Whitley, Russell P693
Whitlock, Matthew A173
Whitlock, Melanie P584
Whitlow, Betsy A600
Whitman, Reed H A149
Whitman, Margaret C. (Meg) A418
Whitman, Terri A441
Whitman, Debra P2
Whitman, Bill P555
Whitmer, Jeff A607
Whitmer, George A659
Whitmer, Tom A682

Whitmer, Thomas A683
Whitmire, Larry P26
Whitmore, Martin A818
Whitmore, Justin A835
Whitney, Randy P66
Whitney, Carolyn A467
Whitney, Cindy P644
Whitson, Linda A548
Whitson, Linda P324
Whitt, Richard R. A528
Whitt, Don A559
Whitt, Karen P176
Whittaker, Thomas F. (Tom) P256
Whittaker, Tom P257
Whittemore, John A152
Whittemore, John E49
Whittemore, Joe E252
Whittingham, Andrew J P598
Whittington, Lisa A434
Whittington, John A461
Whittington, Ray P155
Whittington, Gerald P181
Whittle, Scott A458
Whittle, Scott P251
Whittle, John E166
Whitton, R A733
Whitton, James A820
Whitty, Patricia A329
Whitwer, Derek A284
Whitwer, Derek E111
Whorley, John F. (Jeff) A575
Whynot, Lori A864
Whyte, Mike A868
Wiatrowski, Jacob P646
Wibbenmeyer, Nick E349
Wible, Brad A183
Wible, Brad E66
Wichert, Burkhard A113
Wichmann, David S. A855
Wicinski, Tom A327
Wick, Chad P. P5
Wicker, Cary A800
Wicker, Cary E396
Wickham, Gregory I. (Greg) A252
Wickham, Robert A723
Wickham, Gregory I. (Greg) P150
Wickland, David E P134
Wickland, David E P359
Wicklander, Jeff P387
Wickline, Heath P236
Wickman, Paul A691
Wickman, Jaala P135
Wicks, Franklin A169
Wicks, Tonja L P36
Wickus, Jared P223
Wickwar, Dean A762
Widders, James R. (J.R.) E305
Widdicombe, Mark A561
Widdicombe, Mark E279
Widener, Jason A784
Wider, John J. P1
Widerlite, Paula P39
Widing, Robert E. P98
Widmer, Judy A572
Widmer, Kathleen P697
Widuch, Paul A163
Wiedemann, Herbert A807
Wiedemann, Herbert P574
Wiedemann, Clay E29
Wiedenfels, Gunnar A269
Wiederspan, Jon P395
Wiedman, Mark K. A130
Wiegand, Kathleen A85
Wiegand, Robert A620
Wiegert, Cory A460
Wiehe, Robert P631
Wiehoff, John P A711
Wieland, Robert A. P26
Wiemann, Michael C P530
Wiemer, Frank W302
Wiener, James S. (Jim) A105
Wiener, David A520
Wiener, Jeanne P79
Wiener, Joseph S P296
Wiener-Kronish, Jeanine P. P590

Wier, Jeff A A153
Wiercinski, Katy A. P588
Wierdsma, Thomas E175
Wierschke, Janice A180
Wiese, Jeremy A622
Wiese, Edward A. A784
Wiese, Cary A835
Wiesinger, Kathleen E320
Wiesner, Paula A163
Wiesner, Hagen W148
Wiessing, Theodore E. A794
Wiessmann, Robin A641
Wiessmann, Robin P422
Wietmarschen, Mark A196
Wiggershaus, Tom A886
Wiggershaus, Tom E433
Wiggs, David H. P297
Wight-Tally, Nancy A709
Wiglesworth, Janet A873
Wiglesworth, Janet P668
Wignall, Douglas P228
Wignall, Doug S. P229
Wijers, Hans W313
Wik, Jennifer P228
Wike, Kevin A641
Wike, Kevin P422
Wiker, Darren P437
Wikert, Lisa A328
Wiklund, Christian A914
Wiklund, Jens W352
Wikramanayake, Shemara W227
Wilbanks, Cynthia H. A698
Wilbanks, John F. P58
Wilbanks, John F P421
Wilbanks, Cynthia H. A456
Wilbanks, John P512
Wilbanks, John P512
Wilburn, Tyree G P27
Wilburn, Gary P79
Wilburn, James R. P423
Wilch, Peter P654
Wilcox, Mike A133
Wilcox, Lee F. A277
Wilcox, James A390
Wilcox, Kevin A417
Wilcox, Jim A483
Wilcox, Mark A. A734
Wilcox, William H. (Bill) A795
Wilcox, Frank C A858
Wilcox, Ella P334
Wilcox, Laura P345
Wilcox, Scott P408
Wilcox, Greg P579
Wilcox, Brian P620
Wilcox, Frank C E418
Wilcoxson, Kristin P565
Wild, Sandra A412
Wild, Sandra E192
Wilda, Christine P645
Wildberger, Karsten W131
Wilde, Constance A173
Wilde, Dominic A419
Wilde, Malcolm A465
Wilde, Frederic de A652
Wilde, Gary P135
Wildebrandt, David P59
Wildenthal, Kern P116
Wilder, Terry P141
Wildes, Kevin A564
Wildfong, Kelly A158
Wildman, Brian J. A541
Wildman, Laura A641
Wildman, Laura P422
Wildman, Mary P449
Wildman, Brian J. E266
Wildrick, Edward A693
Wile, Jeff A763
Wileman, Linda A244
Wiles, Sandy A599
Wiles, Lynn P2
Wiley, Robert A323
Wiley, James (Rusty) P333
Wiley, Donald J P532
Wiley, Ronette P590
Wiley, Karl E368

Wilfong, Philip E245
Wilgenbusch, Scott A56
Wilhelm, Melissa A350
Wilhelm, Ryan A406
Wilhelm, Johnathan P391
Wilhelm, Markus P544
Wilhelm, Cathy P544
Wilhelm, Edward W. (Ed) P579
Wilhelm, Ed P579
Wilhelm, Harald W16
Wilhelm, Melissa E157
Wilhoite, Charles A. P410
Wilk, Len P526
Wilke, Jeffrey A. (Jeff) A38
Wilke, Brent A412
Wilke, Beth P12
Wilke, Brent E192
Wilken, Shane A344
Wilkerson, Terrie A101
Wilkerson, Lee A419
Wilkerson, Drew A913
Wilkerson, Neal P126
Wilkerson, Scott P518
Wilkerson, Bob P630
Wilkes, Kathy A223
Wilkes, Mitzi P277
Wilkin, Janine M. P596
Wilkins, Robyn A101
Wilkins, Cliff A218
Wilkins, David A844
Wilkins, Michael T. A847
Wilkins, Charles L. (Chad) A883
Wilkins, David P92
Wilkins, H Wayne P183
Wilkins, Bridgette P220
Wilkins, Jim P371
Wilkins, Carolyn W47
Wilkins, David E412
Wilkinski, Barbara P184
Wilkinson, Marty A260
Wilkinson, Brent A457
Wilkinson, Jason A460
Wilkinson, Jonathan A784
Wilkinson, Vince A877
Wilkinson, Mark A913
Wilkinson, Christine K. P44
Wilkinson, Bruce P101
Wilkinson, Scott E217
Wilkowski, Eric A21
Wilkowski, Eric P12
Will, Jerry A2
Will, Kristin A532
Will, W Anthony P558
Will-kaess, Lisa A691
Willard, Roger A16
Willard, Howard A A37
Willard, Veronika A51
Willard, Joel A164
Willard, Kathy A517
Willbanks, Brad P319
Willborn, Steven P648
Willcoxon, Jennifer A673
Willemse, Norman A45
Willemsen, Marie A390
Willemsen, Eugene A647
Willemsen, Jane A. P263
Willensky, Scott M. A910
Willett, Samuel A101
Willett, Sarah A542
Willett, Steve W206
Willett, Robert E82
Willett, Sarah E267
Willey, Stan A734
Willhoite, Nila P692
William, Aston A61
William, Bass A113
William, Hart A243
Williams, Anré A49
Williams, Bill A56
Williams, Jeffrey E. (Jeff) A70
Williams, Gene A81
Williams, Xavier A84
Williams, Steve A84
Williams, Thomas A87
Williams, Valerie A101

A = AMERICAN BUSINESS
E = EMERGING COMPANIES
P = PRIVATE COMPANIES
W = WORLD BUSINESS

Williams, Facheryl A101
Williams, Leilani A102
Williams, Bill A108
Williams, John A112
Williams, Shawn A152
Williams, Marian A180
Williams, Lexie A182
Williams, Glynn A185
Williams, Mike A187
Williams, Donna L A198
Williams, Carol A204
Williams, Andi A204
Williams, Craig A215
Williams, Hyla G A221
Williams, Michael A244
Williams, Kevin A257
Williams, Ben A263
Williams, E Michael A282
Williams, Janice L. A284
Williams, Weston A291
Williams, Richard A292
Williams, Randa D. A303
Williams, Jack A313
Williams, Alicia A323
Williams, John C. A324
Williams, John C. A325
Williams, Denise A330
Williams, Jason A337
Williams, James R. A344
Williams, Karen A359
Williams, John C. A360
Williams, Barbara A390
Williams, Gary A438
Williams, Meredit A438
Williams, Travis A476
Williams, Phil A483
Williams, Alan A489
Williams, R A496
Williams, Noel A505
Williams, Dave A508
Williams, Adam A513
Williams, Aaron A513
Williams, Christine A533
Williams, Donna A572
Williams, Clay C A574
Williams, Jeffrey A583
Williams, Dale A594
Williams, Peter A599
Williams, Carol A. A628
Williams, Thomas L. (Tom) A634
Williams, Michael A644
Williams, Geisha J. A650
Williams, Rick A667
Williams, Mark A693
Williams, Stephanie A701
Williams, W. Mark A704
Williams, Maureen A707
Williams, Rae A712
Williams, Daniel A723
Williams, Bob A743
Williams, Grant A755
Williams, Rossann A763
Williams, R Bradley A773
Williams, David A800
Williams, Darren K. A843
Williams, Debbie A844
Williams, Dyfan A868
Williams, Daniel A878
Williams, Charles A881
Williams, Richard L. A893
Williams, Mark A898
Williams, Joseph A900
Williams, Marlene A912
Williams, John D A917
Williams, Rebecca P7
Williams, Mario P20
Williams, Dewayne P52
Williams, Robert D P60
Williams, Ken P75

Williams, Mark P97
Williams, Melissa P98
Williams, Steve P111
Williams, Katherine P129
Williams, Michael D. (Mike) P152
Williams, David A. P153
Williams, Peggy P161
Williams, Blair S P167
Williams, Jack P170
Williams, Jenell P204
Williams, Scott P213
Williams, Claude P243
Williams, Avilla P250
Williams, Spenser P252
Williams, David P252
Williams, Mike P252
Williams, Jack P258
Williams, Tra P281
Williams, Lauren P283
Williams, Eric P297
Williams, Claire P301
Williams, Rita P314
Williams, Kirk P330
Williams, James P332
Williams, Mark P333
Williams, Robert P334
Williams, Gary P347
Williams, Amy P356
Williams, Cathy P359
Williams, Clayton W. P367
Williams, Sabrina P369
Williams, Michaelle P381
Williams, David W P382
Williams, William D P384
Williams, Betsy P386
Williams, Mary Ellen C P393
Williams, Steven A P398
Williams, Brad P398
Williams, David P403
Williams, Amy P406
Williams, Helen E. P423
Williams, Mike P441
Williams, Pat P457
Williams, Aaron S. P458
Williams, Tom P459
Williams, Rosie P459
Williams, A Greg P490
Williams, Freenae P496
Williams, Brittany P525
Williams, Bonnie P530
Williams, Dewayne P548
Williams, Christopher P553
Williams, Lacy H P563
Williams, Treby P606
Williams, Jovita P613
Williams, Janna P619
Williams, Kirk P630
Williams, Bruce P630
Williams, Brent P630
Williams, Gordon P643
Williams, Alison P646
Williams, Lance R P660
Williams, Jason P681
Williams, Katina P694
Williams, John D P701
Williams, Steve W348
Williams, Bill E35
Williams, John E38
Williams, Stacy E44
Williams, Shawn E48
Williams, Lexie E63
Williams, Mike E71
Williams, Janice L. E111
Williams, Dustin E117
Williams, Andrea E140
Williams, James R. E154
Williams, Wes E163
Williams, John C. E164
Williams, Michael J. E213
Williams, Patrick S. E216
Williams, Edward P. E276
Williams, Matt E293
Williams, Grayson E342
Williams, M. Dewayne E343
Williams, W. Mark E350

Williams, Bob E373
Williams, Grant E380
Williams, David E396
Williams, Darren K. E411
Williams, Debbie E412
Williams-Roll, Jacqueline A377
Williamson, Jen A32
Williamson, Jennifer A37
Williamson, Joe A59
Williamson, Graeme A144
Williamson, Keith H. A179
Williamson, Keith H. A180
Williamson, Rich A196
Williamson, Jim A406
Williamson, Tracey A589
Williamson, James A765
Williamson, Scott H. A794
Williamson, Stephen A815
Williamson, Daniel E. (Dan) A918
Williamson, Jennifer P29
Williamson, Steve P116
Williamson, Sharon N P211
Williamson, Pete P223
Williamson, Anthony P391
Williamson, Robert P400
Williamson, James P540
Williamson, Stephen P552
Williamson, Ann P643
Williamson, J. David W80
Williamson, James W98
Williamson, Randall S. E218
Williamson, John B. E251
Willie, David P701
Williford, Joy P148
Williman, Glenn A85
Willingham, Edward L. (Ed) A341
Willingham, Phil A711
Willingham, Miranda P201
Willingham, Edward L. (Ed) E152
Willis, Jeff A117
Willis, Jonathan A143
Willis, George A282
Willis, Lee A313
Willis, Mark A659
Willis, Troy A782
Willis, Velina P145
Willis, Martin P407
Willis, Peter M. E69
Willman, Richard A774
Willman, Jerry P36
Willmott, David A. P76
Willoughby, Dawn A208
Willoughby, Michele B. A264
Willoughby, Scott A602
Willoughby, Mitchell M. E153
Willoughby, Bob E230
Willow, Michelle P53
Wills, Kevin G. A785
Wills, Melissa P124
Wills, Julian B P617
Wills, Joseph M P617
Wills, Bess E357
Wilmer, Susan P165
Wilmot, Edward A51
Wilmoth, Floyd A869
Wilmshurst, Neil P179
Wilshaw, Robert K A643
Wilsher, Barbara A674
Wilson, Wayne A25
Wilson, Thomas J. A33
Wilson, Thomas J. A34
Wilson, Stacey A49
Wilson, Jason A56
Wilson, Brian A69
Wilson, James A71
Wilson, Dont-- L. A115
Wilson, Ron A126
Wilson, Sharon D A136
Wilson, Michelle A151
Wilson, David J. A165
Wilson, Pam A168
Wilson, Michael A173
Wilson, Julia M. (Julie) A186
Wilson, Michael A204
Wilson, J. Michael A225

Wilson, James A225
Wilson, James D. (Jim) A242
Wilson, Floyd A244
Wilson, Christine A262
Wilson, Carolyn A272
Wilson, Kimberly A272
Wilson, Jenene A291
Wilson, Andrew A292
Wilson, Mike A300
Wilson, Carolyn A314
Wilson, Wendy A372
Wilson, Ralph Martin A438
Wilson, Timothy A446
Wilson, Kevin A453
Wilson, Chris A478
Wilson, Lynn A489
Wilson, Samuel A500
Wilson, Melissa A502
Wilson, Debbie A530
Wilson, Thomas A542
Wilson, Charles A546
Wilson, Ross A582
Wilson, Billy A591
Wilson, Judith A599
Wilson, Brent A620
Wilson, Kelly A641
Wilson, Ted A725
Wilson, Bob A733
Wilson, Zilpha A743
Wilson, Wayne A743
Wilson, Debbie A769
Wilson, Bill A800
Wilson, Rebecca A801
Wilson, John A801
Wilson, Bill A836
Wilson, Rachel A843
Wilson, D. Ellen A855
Wilson, Tyner A855
Wilson, Ernest J. A860
Wilson, Lizabeth A. (Betsy) A861
Wilson, Ward A865
Wilson, Jake A865
Wilson, Malcolm A913
Wilson, Wayne P15
Wilson, Ann P22
Wilson, Nancy P38
Wilson, Preshie M P64
Wilson, R Lynn P87
Wilson, Tiana P99
Wilson, Matthew P102
Wilson, Dennis P109
Wilson, Pamela P134
Wilson, Kevin P154
Wilson, Robert P157
Wilson, Robert P158
Wilson, Jamie P159
Wilson, Amy P161
Wilson, Eleanor P164
Wilson, Carolyn P190
Wilson, Terrance E. P203
Wilson, Wendy P208
Wilson, John P231
Wilson, John P232
Wilson, Eric L. P235
Wilson, Fred P242
Wilson, Phil P298
Wilson, Wade P302
Wilson, Keith A P305
Wilson, Ross P373
Wilson, Russell P402
Wilson, Kelly P422
Wilson, Wayne P470
Wilson, Mike P472
Wilson, Debbie P474
Wilson, Bob P491
Wilson, Nancy P521
Wilson, Terry P524
Wilson, Alice P533
Wilson, Rebecca P562
Wilson, John P562
Wilson, Bridget P584
Wilson, Dan P599
Wilson, Mary P601
Wilson, Carolyn S. P611
Wilson, Keith P640

Wilson, Michael P640
Wilson, Ernest J. P656
Wilson, Lizabeth A. (Betsy) P658
Wilson, Ed P673
Wilson, M. Roy P679
Wilson, Monte P680
Wilson, Mark A. W38
Wilson, Jimmy W64
Wilson, Nigel W217
Wilson, Stephen W. (Steve) E26
Wilson, Michelle E48
Wilson, John H. E57
Wilson, J. Michael E88
Wilson, James E88
Wilson, James N. E95
Wilson, Jean E172
Wilson, Kevin S. E196
Wilson, Timothy E210
Wilson, Samuel E238
Wilson, Thomas E267
Wilson, George E343
Wilson, Scott E349
Wilson, Zilpha E372
Wilson, Wayne E372
Wilson, Bill E396
Wilson, Rachel E411
Wilson, Laurence E447
Wilson-thissen, Karen A56
Wilson-Thompson, Kathleen A877
Wilton, Keith A. A414
Wilton, Keith A. E194
Wiltshire, John A555
Wilwerding, Nicholas E437
Wimmer, Kelly A40
Winbush, Brandon P566
Winchar, Brian A599
Winchell, Richard Rhett E231
Winchester, Jeffrey D A158
Winckler, Georg W145
Wind, Edward S P390
Windele, Hanns P326
Winder, Mike A919
Windisch, Matt E231
Windle, Keith A275
Windle, Alexandra P621
Windley, John F. A751
Windley, John F. E377
Windram, Elizabeth A474
Windrow, Kimberly G. A888
Windsor, Bryan A166
Windsor, Kathy P30
Wine, Scott W. A660
Wineberger, Bruce P368
Winebrake, James J. P464
Winek, Chris A316
Winek, Chris E141
Wineman, Scott A221
Wineman, Matthew A508
Winesett, Steve P114
Winestock, James A916
Winfield, Donna A583
Winfree, Kersey P523
Winfrey, John P577
Wing, Scott A811
Wing, Bill P7
Wing, Bill P434
Wing, Scott P600
Wing, Nip Yun W92
Wingard, Brian W. A212
Wingard, Brian W. E79
Wingate, Darryl A268
Wingate-Jones, Phyllis P97
Wingenroth, Sharon A369
Wingfield, Gena G. P45
Wingfield, Bill E316
Wingo, Pat A85
Winham, Elizabeth P391
Winick, Joseph P225
Winistorfer, Paul M. P669
Winkates, Scott A599
Winkel, Mike A29
Winkel, Alma A481
Winkel, Mike E9
Winkelmeier, Stephan W58
Winkelried, John P615

Winker, Mark A837
Winkle, Claudia A818
Winkler, Barry A85
Winkler, Beth A817
Winkler, Brenda P213
Winkler, Mike E421
WinklerPrins, Vince P583
Winlove-smith, Shannon A375
Winn, Cathy A34
Winn, Kenneth V. A334
Winnebald, Skip Winnebald Skip A101
Winnekens, Laura P68
Winnie, Brad A86
Winnie, Brad P52
Winningham, Rick E. E217
Winokur, Barton J. P143
Winskill, Debbie P553
Winslow, Alex A599
Winslow, Alisa A659
Winstead, Kim A327
Winston, Wyman B A905
Winston, Wyman A905
Winston, Wyman B P694
Winston, Wyman P694
Wintemute, Mike P563
Winter, Kevin A140
Winter, Amy A223
Winter, James A591
Winter, Terra A844
Winter, Gert De W41
Winter, Jaap W299
Winter, Terra E412
Winterbottom, Brad L. A889
Winterer, Ed P123
Winters, Robert P178
Winters, Lonnie P430
Winters, Margaret E. P679
Winters, William T. (Bill) W340
Winters, Eric E251
Wintrob, Jay S. E312
Wipf, Todd V. A738
Wirahadiraksa, Ron H. W214
Wireman, Rich A668
Wirkman, Alan A828
Wirt, Ken A199
Wirth, Michael K. (Mike) A191
Wirth, Mike A192
Wirth, Michael K. (Mike) A192
Wirth, Joel P109
Wirth, Volker W215
Wirtz, Monika A34
Wirtz, Rolf W365
Wisadkosin, Yukontorn (Vickie) A362
Wisbar, Beverly A784
Wischmeier, Holly P257
Wisdom, Kimberlydawn A413
Wisdom, Kimberlydawn P234
Wisdom, Betty P334
Wise, Heather A81
Wise, Brad A349
Wise, Steve A423
Wise, Angela A502
Wise, Roberta P110
Wise, Bonnie P144
Wise, Elizabeth P287
Wise, Desiree P293
Wise, Claude P545
Wise, Allen P548
Wise, John P673
Wise, Seth M. E39
Wise, Brad E156
Wise, Stephen E199
Wise, Michael E251
Wisecup, Reyne K. A318
Wiseman, Mark A130
Wiseman, Ken A685
Wiseman, Kim P94
Wiseman, John W. E140
Wisenbaker, Randall C. A686
Wishart, Emily P463
Wishon, Gordon P44
Wisnewski, Nancy E196
Wisniewski, Alex Wisniewski Alex A101
Wisniewski, Mark A339
Wisniewski, Richard P355

Wisniewski, Tony E116
Wisniewski, Mark E150
Wisnoski, Kenneth (Ken) A76
Wisnoski, Mark A782
WISSEL, STEVE P213
Wiswell, Sherri A709
Wit, Leigh A872
Wit, Harry de W153
Witcombe, David A649
Witham, John A38
Witherspoon, Marisa A101
Withrow, Randy A655
Withrow, Sarah A904
Withrow, Randy E333
Withrow, Sarah E442
Witkowski, Bob A272
Witmer, Kendall A698
Witmer, Kendall P456
Witt, Tom A333
Witt, Mary J. A704
Witt, Marshall A779
Witt, Kathryn P355
Witt, Suann P406
Witt, Rebecca P509
Witt, Scott V P605
Witt, Becky De P682
Witt, John W195
Witt, John R. W196
Witt, Mary J. E350
Witte, Blair A135
Witte, Ryan A904
Witte, Blair P78
Witte, Ryan E442
Wittekind, Beverly B. E125
Wittenberg, Joel R A485
Wittenkeller, Emily P176
Wittenstein, Robin P541
Witter, Jonathan W. A163
Witter, Gene A244
Witter, Marcia A359
Witter, Frank W390
Wittgrove, Alan P332
Wittkop, Scott P318
Wittmann, George A478
Witts, Karen W206
Witwicki, Witold A3
Witynski, Michael A274
Witzel, Leslie D A886
Witzel, Leslie D E433
Wixtead, James E. W98
Wlaz, Meghan A322
Wlazlo, Rebecca A818
WO, ROBERT A103
Woehrle, Tom A144
Woelfer, W. Todd A816
Woelfer, Todd A816
Woeltjen, William P483
Woerner, Sangita A28
Woerner, John R. A56
Wofford, Martha A255
Wofford, Susanne L. A585
Wofford, Susanne L. P377
Wogel, Jeffrey A729
Wohl, Richard H. A248
Wohland, William A241
Wohlberg, Christopher A648
Wohlgelernter, Beth A474
Wohlgelernter, Beth P262
Wohlgemuth, Jay G. A687
Wojciechowicz, Michelle A901
Wojciechowicz, Michelle P692
Wojcik, Frank A333
Wojcik, Paul A784
Wojdula, Diana P260
Wojdyla, David A115
Wojnar, T. J. A313
Wojtalewicz, Nikki A235
Wojtalewicz, Jeanette P21
Wojtalewicz, Jeanette P148
Wolak, Joel A883
Wolbach, Richard A163
Wolbach, Cindy A446
Wolbach, Cindy E210
Wolcott, Tom A644
Wolcowitz, Jeffrey P98

Wold, Lynn P252
Wolden, Thomas M P372
Woldt, Sheldon A599
Wolf, Dave A173
Wolf, Dale B. A565
Wolf, Christopher G. A661
Wolf, John A677
Wolf, Joseph B. A703
Wolf, Joseph P. A703
Wolf, Daniel A812
Wolf, Kevin P43
Wolf, John P73
Wolf, Kelly P89
Wolf, Jeanne M P358
Wolf, Dan P401
Wolf, Melissa P464
Wolf, Daniel P607
Wolf, Reinhard W60
Wolf, Gary E15
Wolfe, Blake A71
Wolfe, Bernie A642
Wolfe, John A665
Wolfe, Harriet M. A882
Wolfe, Jacy P110
Wolfe, Philip R P224
Wolfe, Micaela P310
Wolfe, Ron P489
Wolfe, Bethany P658
Wolff, Zachary A81
Wolff, Denis P192
Wolff, Benjamin G. (Ben) E328
Wolffis, Janet A333
Wolfgruber, Kurt E301
Wolfle, Joan A140
Wolfram, Katie A496
Wolfrom, Jennifer A42
Wolfson, Richard P658
Wolgemuth, Jen A323
Wolgemuth, Elizabeth A537
Wolin, Edward P103
Wolinski, Jeffery A904
Wolinski, Jeffery E442
Wolitzer, Joel A201
Wolking, Christopher A. (Chris) A614
Woll, Nicole A372
Woll, Nicole P208
Wollberg, Johnny A305
Wollberg, Johnny P185
Wollbrinck, Jim P480
Wolle, Harold P677
Wolle, Joerg W. W212
Wollenberg, Scott D. E283
Wolljung, Greg P507
Wollman, Eric A225
Wollman, Eric E88
Wolney, Juliann P480
Woloschuk, Eric P354
Wolpin, Harriet Harriet Wolpin E1
Wolt, Dave P495
Woltanski, Laura E432
Wolter, Gary P36
Woltersdorf, Ken A175
Wolterstorff, Duane P348
Woltosz, Walter S. (Walt) E374
Woltosz, Virginia E. E374
Womack, David H A22
Womack, Chris A383
Womack, Daniel A765
Womack, David H P13
Womack, Robert R P476
Womack, Daniel P540
Womack, Mark P605
Womble, Aaron P363
Womble, Dustin R. E404
Wondafrash, Worku P319
Wong, Robert A36
Wong, Gordon A105
Wong, Danny A105
Wong, Irwin A170
Wong, Rebecca A201
Wong, Wilfred A502
Wong, Stephen A507
Wong, Cindy A558
Wong, Richard A568
Wong, Philip A667

A = AMERICAN BUSINESS
E = EMERGING COMPANIES
P = PRIVATE COMPANIES
W = WORLD BUSINESS

Wong, John A667
Wong, Annie A682
Wong, Francis A757
Wong, Belinda A763
Wong, Wah A785
Wong, Marissa P99
Wong, Stephen P288
Wong, Christina P292
Wong, Michael P299
Wong, Colleen P627
Wong, Allan C. Y. W47
Wong, Jeanette W119
Wong, Peter T. S. W175
Wong, Philip E336
Wong, John E336
Wong, Gregory E344
Wong, Stanley E426
Wonnacott, David E121
Woo, Carolyn A594
Woo, Tracy P601
Woo, Melissa P651
Woo, Deborah E422
Woo-Jong, Lee W221
Wood, Warren A42
Wood, Jonathan A163
Wood, William C. (Cliff) A166
Wood, Dorothy A244
Wood, Andrea A291
Wood, Denise A327
Wood, Laura A475
Wood, Michael A484
Wood, Brian A532
Wood, Lee A555
Wood, Carolyn A585
Wood, Sarah A589
Wood, Ben A714
Wood, Grant A723
Wood, Michael A737
Wood, Jonathan S A740
Wood, Adam A750
Wood, Daniel A752
Wood, Brian A874
Wood, Patrick A902
Wood, Jo P60
Wood, Kevin P105
Wood, William P161
Wood, Bill P161
Wood, Kurt P166
Wood, Laura P266
Wood, Carolyn P377
Wood, Carl P449
Wood, Rhonda P518
Wood, Nancy P550
Wood, Steve P640
Wood, Patrick P693
Wood, Adrian W331
Wood, Michael E367
Woodall, James W. (Woody) A330
Woodall, Doyle P174
Woodall, Niki P639
Woodard, R. Bryan A766
Woodard, Beth P436
Woodard, Elizabeth P436
Woodard, Eric P506
Woodburn, Charles W40
Woodbury, Brooke A160
Woodbury, Eileen A448
Woodbury, Roy A489
Woodbury, Chip A869
Woodbury, Brooke E55
Woodcock, Arthur A260
Woodcock, John P54
Woodcock, Tim E158
Wooden, Maurice A909
Woodford, Philip A173
Woodford, Brent A. A271
Woodford, Buckner E231
Woodhouse, Loraine W219
Woodley, Leni A252

Woodlin, Kenneth A878
Woodman, Doug A446
Woodman, Clare A568
Woodman, Doug E210
Woodring, Joseph E175
Woodruff, Steve A107
Woodruff, Bob A593
Woodruff, Seth A649
Woodruff, David P313
Woodruff, Steve E34
Woods, Stevens A19
Woods, Don A82
Woods, Jeremy A173
Woods, John F. A205
Woods, J. Pat A304
Woods, J Pat A304
Woods, Darren W. A313
Woods, Mike A397
Woods, Marie A727
Woods, Eugene A A806
Woods, Chris A814
Woods, M. Troy A823
Woods, Carla T A835
Woods, Don P49
Woods, Joseph P144
Woods, Clyde P218
Woods, Mike P221
Woods, Brian T P396
Woods, Randall P416
Woods, Andrea P527
Woods, Christopher P545
Woods, Eugene A P569
Woods, Chris P616
Woods, Tiffany P621
Woods, Dan P680
Woods, Dennis R. E415
Woods-Moss, Julie P556
Woodside, David B. A112
Woodside, David B. E38
Woodside, Stephen P. (Steve) E86
Woodson, Bart A838
Woodson, Nathaniel D P609
Woodson, Jonathan P697
Woodson, Bret A E441
Woodward, Daniel A173
Woodward, Brett A729
Woodward, Joan Kois A827
Woodward, James L P333
Woodworth, Leigh A784
Woody, Bill A422
Woody, Craig W. P132
Woody, Bill P239
Wool, Julius A582
Wool, Julius P373
Wool, Norman P467
Woolard, Randy A136
Wooldridge, Sherry P443
Wooley, Mylowe P398
Woolf, Michael T. (Mike) E415
Woolfolk, James W P89
Woolfork, Carolyn A272
Woolley, Hunter A537
Woolley, Kenneth M. E139
Woolridge, Anthony P255
Woolridge, Diane P345
Woolridge, Victor P645
Woolsey, Danielle A406
Woolston, Kristina P111
Woolway, Paul V. A728
Woolworth, William E255
Woonton, David B. A184
Wooten, Scott P58
Wooten, Michelle P462
Wooten, M. Rhem E188
Wootten, Graham J. E73
Wootton, Charles A. A338
Wootton, Ken A906
Woram, Brian J. A484
Worboys, Philip E217
Worcester, Hilary P342
Wordell, Doug P521
Worhatch, Kathleen A489
Work, Victor P632
Work, Rick E161
Workman, Vince A207

Workman, Glenn A235
Workman, Sue B. P98
Workman, Donald W312
Worl, Rosita F. P489
Worland, Peter A178
Worley, Andrew A113
Worley, Robert B. A446
Worley, Robert B. E210
Worman, Karen A158
Worman, Douglas M. (Doug) A211
Worner, John R A709
Worrall, Judy A371
Worrall, Robert (Bob) A482
Worrell, Robert G A842
Worsham, Todd A165
Worsham, Sharon A857
Worsham, Richard P491
Worth, Denny A397
Worth, Jeff A533
Worth, Read A691
Worth, Denny P221
Worth, Greg P676
Worth, John W103
Wortham, E Dale P226
Wortham, Lee C. E135
Worthen, Kevin J. P83
Worthey, Tracy P612
Worthington, Alice A137
Worthington, John A332
Worthington, John A493
Worthington, Joel A511
Worthington, Bob A549
Worthington, Bill P482
Worthington, Randall T P660
Worthington, Bob E270
Wortley, Michael J. A189
Wortman, Mandy P107
Wortman, Mandi P107
Wortmann-Kool, Corien M. W10
Worzel, Kenneth J. (Ken) A596
Woschenko, Christian J. E75
Wotring, Randall A. (Randy) A16
Wotring, Debora P154
Wotton-Gantner, Kelley P66
Wouda, Tito A377
Wozniak, David A512
Wozniak, Debbie P81
Wozniak, Greg P535
Wozniak, Kurt F. E87
Wrabetz, Joan A892
Wrang, William E. A883
Wranovix, Tim A693
Wray, Christine R. A548
Wray, Christine R. P321
Wren, John D. A619
Wrenn, Reece A751
Wrenn, Reece E378
Wright, Will A16
Wright, Grady A49
Wright, Wesley A49
Wright, Andrew A56
Wright, Winston A73
Wright, Tim A131
Wright, Cooper A133
Wright, Clay A163
Wright, Frank H. A164
Wright, Chris A182
Wright, Jack A195
Wright, Lance A223
Wright, Robert R. A312
Wright, Scott A331
Wright, James A382
Wright, Christopher A390
Wright, Scott J. A443
Wright, Jeff A480
Wright, Ken A515
Wright, James A532
Wright, Greg A543
Wright, Dale A584
Wright, Lori A648
Wright, Andy A655
Wright, David A658
Wright, Deanna A727
Wright, Dennis A838
Wright, Catherine A857

Wright, Clarice A902
Wright, Richard M. (Rick) A907
Wright, Rodney L P14
Wright, Craig P46
Wright, Tom P158
Wright, Mike P184
Wright, Robert P184
Wright, Michaella P228
Wright, W Cameron P240
Wright, Alexander P241
Wright, Lori A P271
Wright, Jamal P275
Wright, David H. (Dave) P297
Wright, Rachel P354
Wright, Kenneth P354
Wright, Dale P376
Wright, Adam P394
Wright, Lori P415
Wright, John P461
Wright, Anika P464
Wright, Robert S P482
Wright, Victor P528
Wright, Mark P566
Wright, Daniel P634
Wright, Steve P659
Wright, Daniel P667
Wright, Clarice P692
Wright, A. W199
Wright, Timothy R. W363
Wright, Emory M. E10
Wright, William H. (Bill) E29
Wright, Chris E63
Wright, Scott E148
Wright, Joseph (Joe) E273
Wright, Dickerson E311
Wright, Andy E333
Wright, Richard M. (Rick) E445
Wright-Jones, Angela A223
Wrighton, Mark S. P615
Writt, Mark A173
Wroblewski, Jo P57
Wroblowski, Peter W168
Wrubel, Harvey P182
Wu, Ben A131
Wu, Ernest A158
WU, Iris A456
Wu, Tracy A480
Wu, Feng A648
Wu, Shengpo (Samuel) A898
Wu, Chwan Hwa P51
Wu, Ye P196
Wu, Jiang P215
Wu, Wendy P482
Wu, Ming P559
Wu, Nick W35
Wu, Simone E75
Wuellner, James P535
Wuerffel, Nathaniel A323
Wujek, Ed A173
Wukitch, Carolyn A546
Wulf, Clark A489
Wulff, John A177
Wulff, Henrik W271
Wunder, Lori A. E90
Wunderlich, Daniel P343
Wunram, J--rgen A265
Wurtz, Steven A644
Wurtzel, Douglas A530
Wussow, Luanne A540
Wussow, Luanne P316
Wustefeld, Ed A555
Wutke, Steve P371
Wyant, Jill S. A289
Wyant, Ashley A332
Wyatt, E. Lee A364
Wyatt, Mark A758
Wyatt, John H. A. A761
Wyatt, David A356
Wyatt, Bill P433
Wyatt, Mark P519
Wyckoff, Sandra A282
Wye, John Van P346
Wyffels, Michael J. A683
Wyffels, Chad P521
Wyffels, Michael J. E341

Wyk, Steven C. (Steve) Van A659
Wyks, Philip M A624
Wylie, Sean A871
Wylie, Kevin P141
Wyllie, Robert A807
Wyllie, Robert P574
WyllieAndrews, Victoria P395
Wyman, Scott R A355
Wyman, Kenneth R. E13
Wymore, Kelle P533
Wynaendts, Alexander R. (Alex) W10
Wynd, Colin A322
Wyness, Tom A235
Wynia, Eric A611
Wynia, Marvin P191
Wynn, Elaine A10
Wynn, Stephen A. A909
Wynn, Barry P509
Wynne, Laura A769
Wynne, Susan P588
Wynne, Kaye P604
Wynter, Rudolph L P371
Wyrick, Cynthia A102
Wyrsch, Martha B. A735
Wyrsch, Martha B P561
Wyse, Kenneth L. (Ken) A682
Wysong, Toni A262
W-¦rsted, Gunn W360

X

Xi, Chuyu A426
Xia, Haijun W90
Xia, Howard E214
Xiang, Ester A793
Xiang, Ester P557
Xiangjun, Yao W68
Xiangqun, Zhong W67
Xianming, Zhao W403
Xiao, Harry A555
Xiao, Dana P613
Xiao, Deming E284
Xiaobing, Chang W95
Xiaodong, Liu W68
Xiaoqiu, Wang W316
Xiaoxuan, Lin W186
Xie, Bing A803
Xie, Andrew P116
Xie, Ken E166
Xie, Michael E166
Xin, Xiao Li W95
Xiong, Yan A885
Xiquan, Wang W186
Xiyong, Li W401
Xu, Xiaoya A649
Xu, Anqing A767
Xu, Lily P390
Xudong, Chen W218
Xue, Wang Zhi W95
Xuezhong, Zeng W403
Xulun, Ma W89
Xun, H A192

Y

Yabannavar, Vijay A550
Yabe, Nobuhiro W234
Yabuki, Jeffery W A355
Yacob, Ezra Y. A304
Yacob, Desalegn P365
Yadley, Sloan A693
Yaeger, Jackie P224
Yager, Jennifer A869
Yagi, Sakurako A532
Yagi, Makoto W202
Yagishita, Naomichi W132
Yagita, Masamichi W116
Yahn-urlaub, Patty A235
Yajima, Tsutomu W197
Yajnik, Sanjiv A163
Yake, Kim A252
Yakovlev, Vadim W157

Yakushinji, Hideomi W213
Yale, Craig P14
Yale, Neha P66
Yalof, Stephen J. A744
Yam, Brendan A871
Yamada, Donna P270
Yamada, Yasuhiro W48
Yamada, Yoshiomi W86
Yamada, Ryosuke W99
Yamada, Shoji W115
Yamada, Yuji W116
Yamada, Takashi W116
Yamada, Yoshihiko (Yoshi) W282
Yamada, Noboru W399
Yamadi, Asghar P168
Yamaguchi, Sasha A195
Yamaguchi, Ikuhiro W208
Yamaguchi, Eiichiro W268
Yamaguchi, Hiroshi W368
Yamakawa, Mark P601
Yamakoshi, Koji W28
Yamamoto, Lisa P276
Yamamoto, Kazuo W176
Yamamoto, Ichiro W200
Yamamoto, Takashi W245
Yamamoto, Takeru E268
Yamanaka, Yasushi W121
Yamane, Yoshi W172
Yamane, Kenji W282
Yamaoka, Hiromi W48
Yamasaki, Takashi W213
Yamashina, Hiroko W279
Yamashita, Akinori W11
Yamashita, Tadaie W39
Yamashita, Toshihiko W238
Yamashita, Mitsuhiko (Mike) W243
Yamashita, Yoshinori W304
Yamashita, Masashi W329
Yamauchi, Tim P441
Yamauchi, Yasuhiro W265
Yamauchi, Masaki W400
Yamazaki, Yuji W349
Yamazoe, Shigeru W234
Yammout, Saleh P464
Yamynn, Angelis A248
Yan, Lucy A61
Yan, Kelly A133
Yan, Yingli (Christine) A761
Yanagi, Hiroyuki W399
Yanagi, Jeff E327
Yanagihara, Jason A131
Yanagisawa, David S. A500

Yanagisawa, David S. E237
Yanai, Tadashi W147
Yancey, Carol B. A381
Yancey, Bryan P224
Yancopoulos, George D. A698
Yandrofski, Nancy A478
Yanehiro, Jan A103
Yanfeng, Zhu W286
Yang, Bonnie A199
Yang, Irene A201
Yang, Alice A221
Yang, Taiyin A386
Yang, Peter A401
Yang, Kristie A667
Yang, Mary P339
Yang, Honggang P399
Yang, Daniel P405
Yang, Jenny P495
Yang, Sui W67
Yang, Amy W113
Yang, Elton W297
Yang, Shen W316
Yang, Wendy E106
Yang, Peter E187
Yang, Eric E284
Yang, Kristie E336
Yanisch, Stephen P36
Yanjun, Wang W68
Yankevich, Alexei W157
Yankowski, Daniel H. (Dan) A514
Yano, James A. (Jay) A764
Yanshun, Chen W68

Yantis, Debbie A186
Yao, Felix A140
Yao, Benjamin A793
Yao, Benjamin P557
Yao, Dong W90
Yao, Hiroshi W242
Yao, Howard E9
Yap, Stella A131
Yapp, John A725
Yarbrough, Todd A572
Yarbrough, Mary A870
Yarbrough, Todd P359
Yarbrough, Shelly P662
Yarde, Terence E140
Yardley, William T. (Bill) A758
Yardley, William T P22
Yardley, Bill P22
Yardley, William T. (Bill) P519
Yarimizu, Hiroshi W237
Yarobough, Martin P201
Yaros, Joseph A212
Yaros, Joseph E79
Yarrington, Patricia E. (Pat) A191
Yasaki, Glen A889
Yasuda, Masamichi (Mitch) W245
Yasui, Shinichi W374
Yatch, Emily A280
Yates, W. Rufus A115
Yates, Lloyd M. A281
Yates, Pat A446
Yates, Beth A489
Yates, Stacy P170
Yates, Faellen P170
Yates, Vinson M. P405
Yates, Deirdre P494
Yates, Catherine E71
Yates, Pat E210
Yates, Jim E322
Yates, A. David E443
Yau, Benjamin A417
Ybarra, Paco A203
Ybarra, Leticia P560
Ye, Xiangdong W175
Yeager, David A551
Yeager, Rande K. A615
Yeakley, Rourke P534
Yealy, Dana E145
Yeap, Geoffrey A685
Yearley, Douglas C. (Doug) A819
Yearous, Timothy A257
Yeater, Pat A189
Yedla, Anupama P584
Yee, James A81
Yee, Michael A809
Yee, Aynna P482
Yeghyayan, Silva A703
Yegneswaran, PK A550
Yeh, David P510
Yeh, Openmind W113
Yehiely, Fruma P398
Yeigh, Bjong Wolf A861
Yeigh, Bjong Wolf P658
Yeilding, Dan A173
Yelamchili, Balaji A778
Yelicanin, Nicholas A862
Yelicanin, Nicholas E419
Yellen, Janet L. A325
Yellin, Jason P566
Yelverton, Greg A449
Yemin, Ezra Uzi A260
Yen, David A199
Yen, Andy A285
Yen, Terry A685
Yen, Andy E114
Yenor, Douglas A265
Yeo, Sang-Deog (Eddie) W220
Yeomans, Tim P450
Yepes, Maria P296
Yerbury, Jon E355
Yergeau, Edgar A175
Yerigan, Marna A345
Yerigan, Marna E154
Yerkes, John B E255
Yeroshek, David P630
Yesho, LaDawn D. A720

Yesho, LaDawn D. E362
Yeshoalul, Melon P617
Yeskie, Andrew P312
Yetto, Kristin A288
Yetton, Jason W395
Yetzer, Geri A487
Yezhkov, Sergey E130
YI, June A558
Yi, Sang A918
Yi, Yue W67
Yi, Byung K. E222
Yi-bin, Chien W171
Yieh, Ellie A71
Yilin, Wang W283
Yim, Chang-Hee W292
Yimin, Lu W95
Yimin, Yin W403
Yin, Deryu P7
Ying, Song W68
Yinger, Scott E97
Yingling, Nathaniel A328
Yip, Byron P22
Yip, Angela P480
Ylonen, Paul A865
Yochum, Alice P96
Yocum, Deb P543
Yocum, Patricia R P550
Yoder, Lamont A111
Yoder, Lamont P56
Yoh, Caren A359
Yohe, Erik A420
Yohe, Erik E198
Yoho, Franklin H. A281
Yoho, Quentin P556
Yoho, Ryan P567
Yokoo, Hiroshi W11
Yokouchi, Ryuzo W270
Yokoyama, Terunori W353
Yokum, Dan A127
Yoldas, Erol P87
Yona, Ilan E68
Yoney, Dennis A709
Yoneyama, Yoshiteru W156
YONEYAMA, AKIHIRO W350
Yong, Tang W94
Yong, Li W102
Yong, Wei W316
Yong-Byoung, Cho W328
Yong-soo, Huh W163
Yongliang, Wu W89
Yoo, Alicia A51
Yoo, Christie A429
Yoo, Charles A429
Yoo, Peter P479
Yoo, Scott P480
Yoo, Cheol Woo W180
Yoo, David E123
Yoo, Christie E204
Yoo, Charles E204
Yoon, Steve A153
Yoon, Sei Seung A685
Yoon, Michael S P2
Yoon, Jong Kyoo W203
Yoon, Dong-Jun W292
Yoor, Brian B. A5
Yordy, Matt A546
Yordy, Alan R. E337
York, Max A375
York, Greg A390
York, Jill E. A541
York, Amy A644
York, Douglas A. E160
York, Jill E. E266
Yorks, Andrew A513
Yortsos, Yannis C. A860
Yortsos, Yannis C. P656
Yosef, Erez W46
Yoshida, Yoshiyuki W264
Yoshida, Mamoru W282
Yoshida, Kazuo W327
Yoshida, Kenichiro W337
Yoshihara, Scott A102
Yoshikawa, Naotoshi W86
Yoshikawa, Masato W211
Yoshikawa, Tetsuya W249

A = AMERICAN BUSINESS
E = EMERGING COMPANIES
P = PRIVATE COMPANIES
W = WORLD BUSINESS

Yoshimatsu, Masuo W259
Yoshimoto, Haruyuki W116
Yoshimura, Toshiharu W336
Yoshinaga, Yasuyuki W342
Yoshino, Takashi W337
Yoshioka, Nobuyasu W48
Yoshizawa, Dirk A102
Yoshizawa, Kazuhiro W272
Yost, Jerold A244
Yost, Jerry A244
Yost, Kevin C. P689
You, Peter A204
Youatt, June P341
Youcis, Stacey P589
Youdeem, Gilda A97
Youdeem, Gilda E32
Youel, Lisa A311
Youmei, Dong W68
Younes, George E320
Younessi, Ramin A169
Young, Robert H. A25
Young, James N A34
Young, Dennis A47
Young, Ray G. A74
Young, Diane A85
Young, Robin A85
Young, Michael A100
Young, Teri A102
Young, Jackson A109
Young, Stephen A182
Young, Mary A182
Young, Brenda A192
Young, Ruben A218
Young, Jim A221
Young, Dave A223
Young, Steven K. A281
Young, Steven K A282
Young, John A310
Young, Mark A314
Young, Chris A330
Young, Matt A382
Young, Kevin A386
Young, Christopher D. (Chris) A405
Young, Marlon A437
Young, Lesli C A438
Young, Jeremy A446
Young, Mark A446
Young, Pete A472
Young, Larry D A487
Young, Maureen A530
Young, Yvette A530
Young, Bonny A540
Young, Steve A570
Young, Trish A592
Young, C. Erik A638
Young, John D. A648
Young, Dennis R. A725
Young, Mark R. A826
Young, Douglas A845
Young, Joby A878
Young, Robert H. A886
Young, Mark R. A919
Young, Kevin P8
Young, Robert H. P15
Young, Russell P19
Young, James N P27
Young, Kerry P72
Young, K. Richard P83
Young, Lynn P96
Young, Jason P103
Young, Stephen P103
Young, Christopher P125
Young, Brittney P136
Young, Wayne P187
Young, Mark P189
Young, Christine P192
Young, Tammy P231
Young, Blaine P247
Young, Tom P249

Young, Carol P271
Young, Eric P307
Young, Bonny P316
Young, Carmen P340
Young, Joanna P341
Young, Sandra P346
Young, Theresa P370
Young, Cassie P441
Young, Alan P493
Young, Gary S. P576
Young, Randy P581
Young, Fred P603
Young, Ann P613
Young, Theresay P672
Young, William L. W229
Young, Jackson E36
Young, Stephen E63
Young, Mary E63
Young, Christopher T. E129
Young, Steve E147
Young, Craig E203
Young, Jeremy E210
Young, Mark E210
Young, Douglas E413
Young, Richard E426
Young, Robert H. E433
Young, Jeff E438
Young-bong, Ha W163
Young-deuk, Lim W179
Young-ki, Son W163
Young-woong, Woo W328
Youngblood, Mike A547
Youngblood, Dave A803
Youngblood, Mike P319
Youngdahl, Lyle P207
Younger, Rob A163
Younger, Jon P550
Youngerman, Chuck A700
Younggren, Craig A489
Youngquist, Gene P73
Youngs, June A250
Youngs, Michael P152
Younkle, Kim P220
Yount, Michael C. A885
Youso, Steven R. A372
Youso, Steven R. P208
Youssef, Tarek A649
Yovich, Mark A517
Yu, Angel A585
Yu, Li A667
Yu, Gladys A682
Yu, Nick A685
Yu, Teb A729
Yu, Sue A793
Yu, Daniel A865
Yu, Nancy P333
Yu, Angel P377
Yu, Sue P557
Yu, Yong W166
Yu, Seong W292
Yu, Li E336
Yuan, Chao A49
Yuanqing, Yang W218
Yue, Li W91
Yuejia, Sha W91
Yuen, Alex A767
Yuen, Wang Kai W89
Yuen, Loretta W280
Yuhas, George A. E65
Yuhong, Xie W102
Yultyev, Aleksandr P215
Yun, William Y. A365
Yun, Sun W68
Yunck, Kara P67
Yung, Stanley A893
Yunker, Jean A86
Yunker, Jean P52
Yunoki, Osamu W147
Yupu, Wang W93
Yurek, Dianne E268
Yurgens, Igor W312
Yurich, Steve P. W240
Yurovitsky, Alyssa P290
Yuse, Richard R. (Rick) A694
Yusuf, Kareem A460

Yuza, Chad A231
Yuzhuo, Zhang W94
Yvonne, Luttschwager P543
Yüce, Burcu Civelek W18
Yüksel, Alper Hakan W18

Z

Zaas, David P167
Zaas, David P168
Zabaneh, Samir P232
Zabarina, Svetlana A767
Zabel, Matt A788
Zabetakis, Paul P290
Zablo, Allison P361

Zacconi, Riccardo A10
Zachan, Michael P. (Mike) E51
Zacharias, Rhonda P281
Zacharius, Sherrie P564
Zachary, Beth D. P7
Zachary, Jayton P299
Zachensky, Michele A555
Zack, Linda A441
Zack, Michael P A727
Zadoks, Jeff A. A663
Zadrazil, Robert W380
Zaeske, Mark A. A437
Zafft, Wayne P269
Zafirau, William A807
Zafirau, William P574
Zafonte, Ross D. P590
Zagar, Frank A496
Zahner, Rick E175
Zahour, Paul A81
Zaic, Daniel A144
Zaisheng, Wei W403
Zaist, Matthew R. E252
Zajicek, Randall C. (Randy) A703
Zak, Jenal A221
Zakhour, Lutfi A140
Zakian, Aram A107
Zakian, Aram E35
Zako, Tracy A904
Zako, Tracy E442
Zakrzewski, Lorrie A513
Zaky, Nicholas A201
Zalar, William A489
Zale, Kathleen A51
Zale, Hisashima P270
Zaleski, Ronald J. A734
Zalisk, Jonathan R A460
Zallaps, Jeff A893
Zallie, James P. A453
Zalman, David A673
Zaluzney, Michelle A165
Zaluzney, Joseph B. A626
Zalzman, Gabriel A539
Zaman, Bill A877
Zamansky, Steve A493
Zambanini, Adam D. E401
Zambas, Becky A823
Zamis, Darienne A418
Zammer, William P92
Zammit, Patrick A792
Zammit, Wade P489
Zamora, Lynn A103
Zamora, Julius A838
Zamora, Abel P278
Zamorano, Juan Pablo A218
Zamost, Michael E117
Zampi, Jason A597
Zamudio, Jaime A869
Zanardo, Fabrizio A683
Zanata, Alberto W3
Zanavich, W Marie P609
Zanayed, Juwana A616
Zand, Pooja A272
Zander, Winfried W168
Zanen, Nicolas A189
Zanetich, Thomas N. P689
Zanetton, Fausto A568
Zang, David P664
Zanghellini, Luigi A538

Zangrilli, Janine A706
Zangrilli, Janine E353
Zank, Dennis W. A693
Zanolini, Annalena A102
Zanon, Craig A593
Zantello, Frederick A. (Fred) E359
Zanten, Walter van A658
Zapalac, Richard A. (Rick) A181
Zaparanick, Melissa A406
Zapata, Ray A244
Zapien, Melissa A795
Zapletal, Robert A558
Zapotocky, John A641
Zapotocky, John P422
Zapp, Ted E76
Zappa, James A194
Zara, Antonio A379
Zarcone, Dominick P. (Nick) A518
Zaren, Howard P92
Zarghami, Cyma A871
Zarhoun, Jalal A671
Zarouk, Jesse A173
Zarraga, Manny De E197
Zarubi, Kathy P487
Zaslav, David M. A269
Zatta, Jayson M. A886
Zatta, Jayson M. E433
Zauk, Adel M P531
Zauner, Alois P482
Zavala, Tony A244
Zavala, Elsa I. A248
Zavala, Veronica A877
Zavala, Donna P145
Zavarella, Andrew A350
Zavarella, Andrew E157
Zaveduk, Mitchell A541
Zaveduk, Mitchell E266
Zayas, Ricardo A147
Zazon, Sue E. A440
Zbell, Jennifer A883
Zebot, Cy P183
Zebula, Charles E. (Chuck) A46
Zech, Kurt E231
Zechmeister, Michael P. A848
Zeev, Eti Ben W46
Zeevi, Gary P493
Zegal, Chris E432
Zehnder, William A P539
Zehnder, Drew P539
Zei, Christopher P A712
Zeidel, Mark L. P71
Zeiger, Richard A489
Zeigler, Shelly A71
Zeigler, Denise A204
Zeigler, Erika A272
Zeigler, Michael A559
Zeile, Arthur A573
Zeiler, Karen A565
Zeiler, Ann A599
Zeilor, Eric A782
Zeiner, Melanie A774
Zeinert, Bonnie A318
Zeitchick, Mark E236
Zeitler, Denise P662
Zeitlin, Jide J. A786
Zekoski, Joseph (Joe) A391
Zekraus, Edward A359
Zelanko, Marc A871
Zeldin, Marian A555
Zeleszko, Tony A869
Zelinske, John A556
Zell, Samuel A66
Zell, Kristin A616
Zeller, Pat P478
Zellner, Mary A81
Zellner, Jon A449
Zelnick, Strauss E385
Zember, Dennis J. A57
Zember, Dennis J. E16
Zemkoski, Alex A244
Zemlyak, James M. A771
Zemore, Pamela A699
Zemore, Pamela P456
Zen-Ruffinen, Bernard S. E235
Zepeda, Curt A701

Zepeda, Carl P119
Zeppos, Nicholas S. P615
Zerbo, Joann A247
Zerbo, Joann E103
Zerbs, Michael W50
Zerhouni, Elias A A253
Zernicke, Paul P392
Zeske, Terry A81
Zetsche, Dieter W114
Zetter, Bruce P570
Zettinger, Daniel A81
Zettler, Casey A327
Zetwick, James (Jim) A588
Zeumer, Jim A681
Zezzo, Anthony (Tony) E318
Zgonc, Kevin A332
Zhang, Lin A41
Zhang, Peter A115
Zhang, Gene A122
Zhang, Cherry A135
Zhang, Frank A204
Zhang, Stella A204
Zhang, Chet A480
Zhang, Stephen A556
Zhang, Jizhi A607
Zhang, Nan A767
Zhang, Rick A784
Zhang, Cherry P78
Zhang, Harry P249
Zhang, Jin P392
Zhang, MEI P466
Zhang, Marianna P610
Zhang, Daisy P619
Zhang, Jianwei W69
Zhang, Xiaohua W90
Zhang, Yingchao E300
Zhang, Helen E359
Zhao, Wenbiao A49
Zhao, Fay A130
Zhao, Dorothy A285
Zhao, Susan X P482
Zhao, Huan W12
Zhao, Qingchun W401
Zhao, Honggang W401
Zhao, Dorothy E114
Zheng, Ru A144
Zhengzhang, Zhao W283
Zhenjiang, Li W12
Zhenming, Chang W100
Zhi, Lin E246
Zhiqiang, He (George) W218
Zhiqing, Wang W332
Zhixin, Chen W316
Zhong, XJ E166
Zhongdong, Xie W68
Zhou, Jason P610
Zhou, Hui W175
Zhou, Dayong E166
Zhu, Haizhen P147
ZHU, JANE E166
Zibrov, Andre P149
Zick, Kenneth P673
Zickefoose, John Z P143
Zidar, Thomas P. (Tom) A904
Zidar, Thomas P. (Tom) E442
Ziebell, William F. A371
Ziecheck, Hal P352
Ziegler, Kristine A180
Ziegler, Marie Z A684
Ziegler, Gregg A819
Ziegler, Richard A P37
Ziegler, Michael P441
Ziegler, Brandon E268
Ziegler, Marie Z E341
ZIELINSKI, MIKE A3
Zielinski, Thomas C. A67
Zielinski, Richard A493
Zielinski, Miroslaw A652
Zielinski, Trudy P133
Zielinski, Marybeth P361
Ziemba, Lawrence M. (Larry) A653
Ziemba, Peter M. E443
Ziemianski, Karen P186
Zier, Dawn M. E309
Zierden, Ann P602

Zieser, John S. E272
Zietlow, Paul A223
Ziffer, Jack A. P57
Zijderveld, Jan W381
Zijderveld, Jan W383
Zik, Eran W46
Zike, Nancy A350
Zike, Nancy E157
Zilbering, Roman A659
Zilbermann, Mark P567
Zilewicz, Eric A158
Zilieris, Nick P59
Zillmer, Eric P165
Ziman, Richard S. A708
Ziman, Anthony A865
Ziman, Richard S. P459
Ziman, Philip E290
Ziman, Richard S. E356
Zimmer, Kris A. A760
Zimmer, Mark P399
Zimmer, Kris A. P523
Zimmer, Robert J. (Bob) P609
Zimmer, Ing. Hans-Josef W140
Zimmer, Dana E402
Zimmerer, Maximilian W23
Zimmerli, Bert A448
Zimmerli, Bert R. A458
Zimmerli, Bert P246
Zimmerli, Bert R. P251
Zimmerly, Debra A500
Zimmerly, Debra E237
Zimmerman, Andrew A3
Zimmerman, Michael R. A450
Zimmerman, Mike A450
Zimmerman, Shawn A485
Zimmerman, Geoff A496
Zimmerman, Stanley A532
Zimmerman, Steven A655
Zimmerman, Matthew T. A816
Zimmerman, Jennifer P72
Zimmerman, Trinity P207
Zimmerman, Linda K P418
Zimmerman, Gail P451
Zimmerman, Doris P451
Zimmerman, Mark P493
Zimmerman, James P564
Zimmerman, Craig K. E133
Zimmerman, Steven E333
Zimmermann, Michael P591
Zimpfer, Matthew J. (Matt) A213
Zingaretti, Michael P218
Zingoni, Maria Victoria W300
Zink, Eric A165
Zink, Daniel A549
Zink, Daniel E270
Zinkan, Lynn P571
Zinkan, Rob P627
Zinkin, Peter A95
Zinkin, Peter P55
Zinkula, Mark W217
Zinner, Michael J. P57
Ziolo, Mykel A417
Zionts, Paul P155
Zipf, Bruce G. A696
Zipparro, Vincent P361
Zirbser, Glenn P298
Zirkle, Matthew A671
Zitkus, Lester E185
Zito, Peter A583
Zito, Joseph A850
Zitterkopf, Brian A480
Zivelonghi, G. Larry A248
Zizzi, Michele A375
Zizzo, Larry A26
Zlatkis, Bella W321
Zmich, Kenneth W. P104
Zmrhal, Gary P230
Zobair, Talha A602
Zobrist, Sandra A158
Zoccoli, James G. (Zeke) E5
Zock, George J A430
Zoe, Benjamin A678
Zoeller, Kathrin A589
Zogg, Jack A371
Zoghlin, Alex D. A444

Zohn, Patrick P126
Zoilo, John P118
Zoiss, Edward J. (Ed) A405
Zola, S. Robert (Bob) E74
Zolenas, Joseph A475
Zolenas, Joseph P266
Zoley, George C. E175
Zolfo, Suzanne P549
Zoller, Clifford A718
Zoller, Jeff A784
Zoller, Richard P334
Zoller, Edgar W58
Zollinger, Wendy P163
Zollmann, Mary Ann P299
Zollotuchen, Mandi A615
Zoltick, Steve A408
Zongyan, Zhang W94
Zontos, Donna A288
Zook, Dennis R. A240
Zorger, Charles R P660
Zorn, Russ A56
Zou, Peter E78
Zuanich, Mark A13
Zubairi, Ahmad P671
Zuber, Steven P369
Zuberi, Faheem A438
Zubkov, Victor A. W289
Zubretsky, Joseph M. A565
Zubrickas, J. V. W199
Zucaro, Aldo C. (Al) A615
Zucker, Nehemia (Hemi) E226
Zuckerberg, Mark A314
Zuckerbrow, Michael A556
Zuckerman, David A685
Zuehlke, Vonnie A788
Zuengler, Hugh A877
Zuercher, David P299
Zufall, David A270
Zugibe, Kevin J. E209
Zuhl, Colleen A. A816
Zuhlke, Dan A458
Zuhlke, Dan P251
Zuhone, Laura A350
Zuhone, Laura E157
Zuk, Donna P66
Zukis, Katy A443
Zulberti, Andrea A780
Zulli, Mark A175
Zullinger, Joel R A625
Zuluaga, Patricia W133
Zulueta, Alfonso G. (Chito) A511
Zumpano, Judy A15
Zumpano, Judy P9
Zumwalt, LeAnne M. A255
Zuniga, Carla A34
Zuniga, Andrew A40
Zuniga, Gaspar A476
Zuniga, Aamsa A692
Zuniga, Aamsa P454
Zunker, Arthur R E112
Zupan, Leon W138
Zurack, Marlene A582
Zurack, Marlene P373
Zuraitis, Marita A430
Zurek, Thomas M A621
Zurek, Thomas M P407
Zuro, Matthew A342
Zuschke, Stefan W72
Zuschneid, Carol P480
Zutshi, Upinder P248
Zwan, Joan P60
Zwang, Jonathan A691
Zwany, Abe A140
Zweier, George E. E47
Zweifach, Gerson A834
Zwischenberger, Joseph N P273
Zydel, Brian A20
Zygiel, Kenneth A406
Zygocki, Rhonda A192
Zyl, Adriaan Van A94
Zyl, Adriaan Van P53
Zywicz, Margaret AE A353
Zühlke, Oliver W57

This Page left intentionally blank